Organic Electronic Spectral Data
Volume XXII 1980

Organic Electronic Spectral Data

Volume XXII   1980

JOHN P. PHILLIPS, DALLAS BATES
HENRY FEUER & B. S. THYAGARAJAN

EDITORS

CONTRIBUTORS

Dallas Bates

H. Feuer

L. D. Freedman

C. M. Martini

F. C. Nachod

J. P. Phillips

AN INTERSCIENCE ® PUBLICATION
JOHN WILEY & SONS
New York • Chichester • Brisbane • Toronto • Singapore

INTRODUCTION TO THE SERIES

In 1956 a cooperative effort to abstract and publish in formula order all the ultraviolet-visible spectra of organic compounds presented in the journal literature was organized through the enterprise and leadership of M.J. Kamlet and H.E. Ungnade. Organic Electronic Spectral Data was incorporated in 1957 to create a formal structure for the venture, and coverage of the literature from 1946 onward was then carried out by chemists with special interests in spectrophotometry through a page by page search of the major chemical journals. After the first two volumes (covering the literature from 1946 through 1955) were produced, a regular schedule of one volume for each subsequent period of two years was introduced. In 1966 an annual schedule was inaugurated.

Altogether, more than fifty chemists have searched a group of journals totalling more than a hundred titles during the course of this sustained project. Additions and subtractions from both the lists of contributors and of journals have occurred from time to time, and it is estimated that the effort to cover all the literature containing spectra may not be more than 95% successful. However, the total collection is by far the largest ever assembled, amounting to about half a million spectra in the twenty-two volumes so far.

Volume XXIII is in preparation.

PREFACE

Processing of the data provided by the contributors to Volume XXII as to the last several volumes was performed at the University of Louisville.

John P. Phillips
Dallas Bates
Henry Feuer
B.S. Thyagarajan

ORGANIZATION AND USE OF THE DATA

The data in this volume were abstracted from the journals listed in the reference section at the end. Although a few exceptions were made, the data generally had to satisfy the following requirements: the compound had to be pure enough for satisfactory elemental analysis and for a definite empirical formula; solvent and phase had to be given; and sufficient data to calculate molar absorptivities had to be available. Later it was decided to include spectra even if solvent was not mentioned. Experience has shown that the most probable single solvent in such circumstances is ethanol.

All entries in the compilation are organized according to the molecular formula index system used by Chemical Abstracts. Most of the compound names have been made to conform with the Chemical Abstracts system of nomenclature.

Solvent or phase appears in the second column of the data lists, often abbreviated according to standard practice; there is a key to less obvious abbreviations on the next page. Anion and cation are used in this column if the spectra are run in relatively basic or acidic conditions respectively but exact specifications cannot be ascertained.

The numerical data in the third column present wavelength values in nanometers (millimicrons) for all maxima, shoulders and inflections, with the logarithms of the corresponding molar absorptivities in parentheses. Shoulders and inflections are marked with a letter s. In spectra with considerable fine structure in the bands a main maximum is listed and labelled with a letter f. Numerical values are given to the nearest nanometer for wavelength and nearest 0.01 unit for the logarithm of the molar absorptivity. Spectra that change with time or other common conditions are labelled "anom." or "changing", and temperatures are indicated if unusual.

The reference column contains the code number of the journal, the initial page number of the paper, and in the last two digits the year (1980). A letter is added for journals with more than one volume or section in a year. The complete list of all articles and authors thereof appears in the References at the end of the book.

Several journals that were abstracted for previous volumes in this series have been omitted, usually for lack of useful data, and several new ones have been added. Most Russian journals have been abstracted in the form of the English translation editions.

ABBREVIATIONS

s	shoulder or inflection
f	fine structure
n.s.g.	no solvent given in original reference
$C_6H_{11}Me$	methylcyclohexane
C_6H_{12}	cyclohexane
DMF	dimethylformamide
DMSO	dimethylsulfoxide
THF	tetrahydrofuran

Other solvent abbreviations generally follow the practice of Chemical Abstracts.

Underlined data were estimated from graphs.

JOURNALS ABSTRACTED

Journal	No.	Journal	No.
Acta Chem. Scand.	1	Talanta	86
Indian J. Chem.	2	J. Med. Chem.	87
Anal. Chem.	3	Tetrahedron Letters	88
J. Heterocyclic Chem.	4	Angew. Chem., Intl. Ed.	89
Ann. Chem. Liebigs	5	J. Inorg. Nucl. Chem.	90
Ann. chim.(Rome)	7	J. Applied. Chem. U.S.S.R.	93
Chemica Scripta	11	Chem. Pharm. Bull. Japan	94
Australian J. Chem.	12	J. Pharm. Soc. Japan	95
Steroids	13	The Analyst	96
Bull. Chem. Soc. Japan	18	Z. Chemie	97
Bull. Acad. Polon. Sci.	19	J. Agr. Food Chem.	98
Bull. soc. chim. Belges	20	J. Natural Products	100
Bull. soc. chim. France	22	J. Organometallic Chem.	101
Can. J. Chem.	23	Phytochemistry	102
Chem. Ber.	24	Khim. Geterosikl. Soedin.	103
Chem. and Ind.(London)	25	Zhur. Organ. Khim.	104
Chimia	27	Khim. Prirodn. Soedin.	105
Compt. rend.	28	Die Pharmazie	106
Doklady Akad. Nauk S.S.S.R.	30	Synthetic Comm.	107
Experientia	31	Israel J. Chem.	108
Gazz. chim. ital.	32	Doklady Phys. Chem.	109
Helv. Chim. Acta	33	Russian J. Phys. Chem.	110
J. Chem. Eng. Data	34	Spectroscopy Letters	112
J. Am. Chem. Soc.	35	Acta Chim. Acad. Sci. Hung.	114
J. Pharm. Sci.	36	Egyptian J. Chem.	115
J. Chem. Soc., Perkin Trans. II	39B	Macromolecules	116
J. Chem. Soc., Perkin Trans. I	39C	Org. Preps. and Procedures	117
Nippon Kagaku Kaishi	40	Synthesis	118
J. Chim. Phys.	41	S. African J. Chem.	119
J. Indian Chem. Soc.	42	Pakistan J. Sci. Ind. Research	120
J. Org. Chem.	44	J. Macromol. Sci.	121
J. Phys. Chem.	46	Ukrain. Khim. Zhur.	124
J. Polymer Sci., Polymer Chem. Ed.	47	Inorg. Chem.	125
J. prakt. Chem.	48	Makromol. Chem.	126
Monatsh. Chem.	49	Croatica Chem. Acta	128
Rec. trav. chim.	54	Bioorg. Chem.	130
Polish J. Chem.	56	J. Mol. Structure	131
Spectrochim. Acta	59	J. Appl. Spectroscopy S.S.S.R.	135
J. Chem. Soc., Faraday Trans. I	60	Carbohydrate Research	136
Ber. Bunsen Gesell. Phys. Chem.	61	Chemistry Letters	138
Z. phys. Chem.	62	P, S and Related Elements	139
Z. physiol. Chem.	63	J. Anal. Chem. S.S.S.R.	140
Z. Naturforsch.	64	Heterocycles	142
Zhur. Obshchei Khim.	65	Arzneimittel. Forsch.	145
Biochemistry	69	J. Appl. Chem. Biotech.	146
Izvest. Akad. Nauk S.S.S.R.	70	J. Luminescence	147
Coll. Czech. Chem. Comm.	73	Photochem. Photobiol.	149
J. Chem. Soc., Chem. Comm.	77	J. Chem. Research	150
Tetrahedron	78	J. Photochem.	151
Revue Roumaine Chim.	80	Nouveau J. Chim.	152
Arch. Pharm.	83		

Organic Electronic Spectral Data
Volume XXII 1980

Compound	Solvent	$\lambda_{max}(\log \epsilon)$	Ref.
CHO			
Formyl radical	gas	230(3.95)	46-0231-80
CH₃BrClN			
Methanamine, N-bromo-N-chloro-	H₂O	223(3.44),328(2.54)	90-1123-80
	CCl₄	344(2.64)	90-1123-80
CH₃CdI			
Cadmium, iodomethyl-	ether	294(3.57),360(3.34)	30-0105-80
CH₃Cl₂N			
Methanamine, N,N-dichloro-	H₂O	303(2.42)	90-1123-80
	CCl₄	307(--)	90-1123-80
CH₃MgI			
Magnesium, iodomethyl-	ether	294(3.20),360(3.00)	30-0105-80
CH₃N₃O₃			
Urea, nitro-	acid	225.0(4.23)	104-0407-80
	base	259.0(4.27)	104-0407-80
CH₄N₂O₂			
Methanamine, N-nitro-	acid	232.5(3.86)	104-0407-80
	base	228.0(3.91)	104-0407-80
C₂HN₅S			
1,3,4-Thiadiazole, 2-azido-	n.s.g.	242(3.6721)	103-0721-80
C₂H₂N₄O₃			
3H-1,2,4-Triazol-3-one, 1,2-dihydro- 5-nitro-	neutral	315(3.68)	104-0375-80
	anion	345(3.50)	104-0375-80
	dianion	410(3.82)	104-0375-80
C₂H₂N₄O₈			
Ethane, 1,1,2,2-tetranitro-, bis(4-chlorobenzenediazonium) salt	H₂O	219(--),282(4.16), 364(4.41)	104-2059-80
C₂H₂N₆O₃S			
2H-1,2,4,6-Thiatriazin-3(4H)-one, 5-azido-, 1,1-dioxide	H₂O	217(4.06)	44-1662-80
C₂H₃CsS₂			
Ethane(dithioic) acid, cesium salt	EtOH	336(4.08),453(1.53)	64-0458-80B
C₂H₃F₃N₂O			
Acetic acid, trifluoro-, hydrazide	EtOH	217(3.6)	70-1915-80
(C₂H₃NO)ₙ			
Acetonitrile N-oxide, hexamer	EtOH	217(4.71)	32-0341-80
heptamer	EtOH	217(4.72)	32-0341-80
C₂H₃N₃O₂			
Acetonitrile, (nitroamino)-	acid	220.0(3.93)	104-0407-80
	anion	232.0(4.01)	104-0407-80
C₂H₃RbS₂			
Ethane(dithioic) acid, rubidium salt	EtOH	336(4.28),454(1.67)	64-0458-80B
C₂H₄N₄			
Guanidine, cyano-	MeOH	216(4.18)	32-0287-80

Compound	Solvent	λ_{max}(log ϵ)	Ref.
$C_2H_4N_4O_2$			
Diazenedicarboxaldehyde, dioxime	H_2O	293(4.29),399(2.26)	150-3853-80
	MeOH	294(4.35),400(2.28)	150-3853-80
	ether	289(4.36),404(2.26)	150-3853-80
	pH 5	293(4.29)	150-3853-80
	pH 12	356(4.55)	150-3853-80
$C_2H_4OS_2$			
Carbonodithioic acid, O-methyl ester, sodium salt	H_2O	228(3.97),304(4.31), 383(1.71)	139-0171-80A
$C_2H_4S_2$			
Ethane(dithioic) acid, cesium salt	EtOH	336(4.08),453(1.53)	64-0458-80B
potassium salt	EtOH	338(4.16),451(1.64)	64-0458-80B
rubidium salt	EtOH	336(4.28),454(1.67)	64-0458-80B
$C_2H_4S_3$			
Carbonotrithioic acid, monomethyl ester, potassium salt	H_2O	235(3.72),303(4.13), 333(4.22)	139-0171-80A
$C_2H_5ClN_2O_2$			
Ethanamine, 2-chloro-N-nitro-	H_2O	230(3.70)	104-1006-80
C_2H_5NOS			
Carbamothioic acid, methyl-, mono-potassium salt	H_2O	c.229(c.4)	97-0100-80
$C_2H_6Cl_4HgSi_2$			
Mercury, bis[(dichloromethyl)silyl]-	C_6H_{12}	218(4.34),287(2.57), 331(0.92)	101-0169-80N
	THF	216(4.26),255(2.85), 295(0.70)	101-0169-80N
$C_2H_6N_2O$			
Acetic acid hydrazide	EtOH	200(3.73)	70-1915-80
$C_2H_6N_2O_2$			
Ethanamine, N-nitro-	acid	233.5(3.90)	104-0407-80
	anion	229.0(3.94)	104-0407-80
$C_2H_6N_2O_3$			
Ethanol, 2-(nitroamino)-	acid	232.0(3.87)	104-0407-80
	anion	229.0(3.94)	104-0407-80
Hydroperoxide, (methylnitrosoamino)-methyl	EtOH	227(3.85),362(1.90)	88-1761-80

Compound	Solvent	$\lambda_{max}(\log \epsilon)$	Ref.
$C_3H_3N_3O_2S$ 2-Thiazolamine, 5-nitro-	H_2O	380(4.09)	39-1156-80B
$C_3H_3N_5O$ Carbonazidimic acid, cyano-, methyl ester	n.s.g.	240(4.03)	4-0187-80
$C_3H_3N_5S$ 1,3,4-Thiadiazole, 2-azido-5-methyl-	n.s.g.	247(3.722)	103-0721-80
$C_3H_4Cl_2N_2O_2$ Cyclopropanamine, 2,2-dichloro-N-nitro-	H_2O	245(3.73)	104-0858-80
$C_3H_4N_2O$ 1,3,4-Oxadiazole, 2-methyl-	MeOH	206(2.62)	33-0588-80
$C_3H_4N_4O$ 2H-Tetrazole, 2-acetyl-	THF	218(3.72)	33-0588-80
$C_3H_4N_4O_3$ 1H-1,2,4-Triazole, 3-methoxy-5-nitro-	neutral anion	285(3.48) 330(3.50)	104-0375-80 104-0375-80
3H-1,2,4-Triazol-3-one, 2,4-dihydro- 2-methyl-5-nitro-	neutral anion	325(3.71) 355(3.56)	104-0375-80 104-0375-80
3H-1,2,4-Triazol-3-one, 2,4-dihydro- 4-methyl-5-nitro-	neutral anion	315(3.62) 375(3.76)	104-0375-80 104-0375-80
$C_3H_4O_2$ Propanedial	pH 1 pH 7	243(<u>4.0</u>) 267(<u>4.5</u>)	94-3323-80 94-3323-80
$C_3H_4SSe_2$ 1,3-Diselenolane-2-thione	C_6H_{12}	210(--),220(3.82), 270(--),290(3.22), 330(4.10)	44-2632-80
$C_3H_5CsS_2$ Propane(dithioic) acid, cesium salt	EtOH	338(4.17),450s(--), 515s(--)	64-0458-80B
$C_3H_5N_3O_2$ Propanenitrile, 3-(nitroamino)-	acid anion	228.5(3.81) 230.0(3.91)	104-0407-80 104-0407-80
$C_3H_5N_3S$ Carbamimidothioic acid, cyano-, methyl ester	MeOH	240(4.11)	32-0287-80
$C_3H_5N_5O_8$ 1-Propanamine, N,3,3,3-tetranitro-	acid anion	226s(4.02) 230s(4.06)	104-0407-80 104-0407-80
$C_3H_5RbS_2$ Propane(dithioic) acid, rubidium salt	EtOH	338(4.26),440s(1.79)	64-0458-80B
$C_3H_6Cl_2N_2O_2$ Ethanamine, 2-chloro-N-(chloromethyl)- N-nitro-	H_2O	234(3.81)	104-1006-80
$C_3H_6N_2O_2$ 2-Propen-1-amine, N-nitro-	acid	233.0(3.88)	104-0407-80

Compound	Solvent	$\lambda_{max}(\log \epsilon)$	Ref.
2-Propen-1-amine, N-nitro- (cont.)	anion	231.0(3.97)	104-0407-80
$C_3H_6N_2O_4$			
Carbamic acid, nitro-, ethyl ester	acid	219.5(3.99)	104-0407-80
	anion	258.5(4.08)	104-0407-80
Glycine, N-nitro-, methyl ester	acid	226.5(3.84)	104-0407-80
	anion	230.5(3.93)	104-0407-80
$C_3H_6N_4$			
Guanidine, N-cyano-N'-methyl-	MeOH	218(4.21)	32-0287-80
$C_3H_6N_4O_2$			
Diazenecarboxaldehyde, [1-(hydroxy-imino)ethyl]-, oxime	pH 5	293(4.30)	150-3853-80
	H_2O	293(4.30),413(2.23)	150-3853-80
	pH 12	354(4.53)	150-3853-80
	ion	346(4.41)	150-3853-80
	MeOH	294(4.36),413(2.26)	150-3853-80
	ether	289(4.36),416(2.26)	150-3853-80
$C_3H_6N_4O_3S$			
Carbonazidimidic acid, (methylsulfon-yl)-, methyl ester	n.s.g.	231(4.00)	4-0187-80
$C_3H_6S_2$			
Propane(dithioic) acid, potassium salt	EtOH	337(4.26),454(1.68)	64-0458-80B
C_3H_7NOS			
Carbamothioic acid, ethyl-, monopotass-ium salt	H_2O	229(4)(approx.)	97-0100-80
$C_3H_7NO_3S_3$			
Ethanesulfonic acid, 2-[(dithiocarb-oxy)amino]-, diammonium salt	H_2O	252(4.09),286(4.14)	90-0775-80
$C_3H_7NS_2$			
Carbamodithioic acid, dimethyl-, sodium salt	EtOH	253(4.12),287(4.18), 356(1.79)	139-0171-80A
$C_3H_8N_2O_2$			
2-Propanamine, N-nitro-	acid	233.5(3.90)	104-0407-80
	anion	229.0(3.93)	104-0407-80
$C_3H_8N_2O_3$			
Hydroperoxide, (ethylnitrosoamino)-methyl	EtOH	230(3.81),366(1.86)	88-1761-80
$C_3H_8N_2S_2$			
Carbamodithioic acid, (2-aminoethyl)-	H_2O	253(4.05),287(4.14)	90-0775-80
C_3H_9ClSn			
Stannane, chlorotrimethyl-	isooctane	none above 220 nm	35-7892-80

Compound	Solvent	$\lambda_{max}(\log \epsilon)$	Ref.
$C_4Cl_2O_2S$ 2,5-Thiophenedione, 3,4-dichloro-	CCl_4	<u>265f(4.3)</u>,325(2.6)	49-0177-80
$C_4Cl_4O_2S$ Thiophene, tetrachloro-, 1,1-dioxide	n.s.g.	234(3.6ℓ),325(3.36)	44-0856-80
$C_4F_4O_3$ 2,5-Furandione, 3,3,4,4-tetrafluoro- dihydro-	gas	234(1.71)	60-0503-80
$C_4F_6O_3$ Acetic acid, trifluoro-, anhydride	gas	245(1.77)	60-0503-80
$C_4H_2N_6O_3$ [1,2,4]Triazolo[5,1-c][1,2,4]triazin- 4(1H)-one, 3-nitro-, sodium salt	n.s.g.	204(4.15),283(3.79), 358(4.00)	103-0974-80
$C_4H_2N_8O$ 1H-Imidazole-4-carbonyl azide, 5-azido-	EtOH	207(3.79),225s(3.75), 298(3.95)	103-1171-80
$C_4H_3ClN_2O_2$ 1H-Imidazole-4-carboxylic acid, 5-chloro-	EtOH	238(4.05)	103-1171-80
$C_4H_3ClS_2$ 2-Thiophenethiol, 5-chloro-	EtOH	206(3.61),258(3.80), 310(3.68)	103-0991-80
$C_4H_3NO_2$ 6H-1,3-Oxazin-6-one	$MeOCH_2CH_2OMe$	263(3.6)	5-0798-80
C_4H_4 1,3-Cyclobutadiene (at -180°)	2-MeTHF	<u>300(2.0)</u>	78-0343-80
$C_4H_4N_2S$ 2(1H)-Pyrimidinethione	pH 1	215(3.763),285(4.364), 360(3.154)	112-0001-80
	pH 13	212(4.011),234(3.602), 270(4.177)	112-0001-80
	EtOH	211(3.813),290(4.236), 373(3.234)	112-0001-80
	CH_2Cl_2	236(4.436),294(4.364), 384(3.366)	112-0001-80
1,2,5-Thiadiazole, 3-ethenyl-	isooctane	218f(3.85),276(4.03), 281(4.03)	78-1245-80
$C_4H_4N_2S_2$ Cyanamide, 1,3-dithiolan-2-ylidene-	MeOH	272(4.21)	32-0287-80
$C_4H_4N_4O_3S$ Imidazo[4,5-e]-1,2,4-thiadiazin-3(2H)- one, 4,5-dihydro-, 1,1-dioxide	pH 0 pH 7 pH 10 pH 13	230(3.62) 226(3.65) 228(3.65) 229(3.64)	87-0575-80 87-0575-80 87-0575-80 87-0575-80
$C_4H_4N_6$ 8-Azapurine, 2-amino-	pH 0 pH 4.5	235s(3.98),326(2.53) 237s(3.68),311(3.84)	39-2918-80C 39-2918-80C

Compound	Solvent	$\lambda_{max}(\log \epsilon)$	Ref.
$C_4H_4S_2$			
2-Thiophenethiol	EtOH	219(3.52),255(3.88), 295(3.71),305(3.62), 317(3.56)	103-0991-80
3-Thiophenethiol	EtOH	218(3.72),256(4.06), 296(3.78),305(3.74), 317(3.76)	103-0991-80
$C_4H_5BrN_4$			
4,6-Pyrimidinediamine, 5-bromo-	MeOH	280(3.87)	4-1587-80
$C_4H_5BrN_4O$			
4(1H)-Pyrimidinone, 2,6-diamino-5-bromo-	MeOH	278(4.21)	4-1587-80
$C_4H_5Cl_3N_2O_2$			
Cyclopropanamine, 2,2-dichloro-N-(chloromethyl)-N-nitro-	H_2O	238(3.74)	104-0858-80
$C_4H_5N_3O_2$			
Acetamide, 2-cyano-2-(methoxyimino)-	EtOH	238(3.93)	5-1623-80
$C_4H_5N_3S$			
Cyanamide, 2-thiazolidinylidene-	MeOH	237(4.21)	32-0287-80
$C_4H_5N_5O$			
Carbonazidimidic acid, cyano-, ethyl ester	n.s.g.	241(4.03)	4-0187-80
$C_4H_5N_5O_2$			
4,6-Pyrimidinediamine, 5-nitro-	pH -2.3	233(4.38),325(3.92)	12-0131-80
	pH 7.0	206(4.50),225s(4.18), 330(4.02)	12-0131-80
$C_4H_5N_5O_2S$			
Imidazo[4,5-e]-1,2,4-thiadiazin-3-amine, 2,5-dihydro-, 1,1-dioxide	pH 1	228(3.53)	87-0575-80
	pH 9	242s(3.49),255(3.56)	87-0575-80
	pH 14	240(3.45),257s(3.43)	87-0575-80
$C_4H_5N_5O_3$			
2(1H)-Pyrimidinone, 4,6-diamino-5-nitro-	pH -2.3	228(4.55),250s(4.33), 310(4.37)	12-0131-80
	pH 5.5	200(4.31),231s(4.03), 325(3.90)	12-0131-80
$C_4H_5N_5O_4$			
4,6-Pyrimidinediamine, 5-nitro-, 1,3-dioxide	pH -2.3	231s(4.40),254s(3.83), 312(4.16)	12-0131-80
	pH 7.0	203s(4.39),230s(4.09), 327s(4.06)	12-0131-80
$C_4H_5N_5S$			
1,3,4-Thiadiazole, 2-azido-5-ethyl-	n.s.g.	247(3.793)	103-0721-80
$C_4H_5N_7O$			
1H-Imidazole-4-carboxylic acid, 5-azido-, hydrazide	H_2O or EtOH	212(4.00),270(4.16)	103-1171-80
$C_4H_6Br_2N_2O_2$			
Cyclopropanamine, 2,2-dibromo-N-methyl-N-nitro-	H_2O	251(3.72)	104-0858-80

Compound	Solvent	$\lambda_{max}(\log \epsilon)$	Ref.
C_4H_6ClNS 4H-1,3-Thiazine, 2-chloro-5,6-dihydro-	EtOH	233(3.57)	39-0665-80C
$C_4H_6Cl_2N_2O_2$ Cyclopropanamine, 2,2-dichloro-N-methyl-N-nitro-	H_2O	247(3.72)	104-0858-80
$C_4H_6Cl_4O_4S_4$ Methane, dithiobis[dichloro(methylsulfonyl)-	n.s.g.	end absorption	23-1106-80
$C_4H_6N_2S_2$ Carbonimidodithioic acid, cyano-, dimethyl ester	MeOH	263(4.24)	32-0287-80
$C_4H_6N_4$ Cyanamide, 2-imidazolidinylidene-	MeOH	215(4.26)	32-0287-80
$C_4H_6N_4OS$ 4(1H)-Pyrimidinone, 2,6-diamino-5-mercapto-	MeOH	213(4.08),274(3.74), 330(3.33)	4-1587-80
$C_4H_6N_4O_3$ 1H-1,2,4-Triazole, 5-methoxy-1-methyl-3-nitro-	neutral	288(3.64)	104-0375-80
3H-1,2,4-Triazol-3-one, 2,4-dihydro-2,4-dimethyl-5-nitro-	neutral	325(3.50)	104-0375-80
$C_4H_6N_4O_3S$ 1H-Imidazole-4-sulfonamide, 5-(formylamino)-	pH 1 pH 7 pH 13	237(4.07) 246(4.00) 223(3.88),252s(3.82)	87-0575-80 87-0575-80 87-0575-80
$C_4H_6N_4S$ 5-Pyrimidinethiol, 4,6-diamino-	MeOH	213(4.09),241(4.06), 283(3.37),330(3.42)	4-1587-80
C_4H_7ClS Ethene, 1-chloro-2-(ethylthio)-, cis	n.s.g.	235(3.93),246s(3.76)	65-2185-80
$C_4H_7CsS_2$ Butane(dithioic) acid, cesium salt	EtOH	338(3.94),440s(--)	64-0458-80B
Propane(dithioic) acid, 2-methyl-, cesium salt	EtOH	338(4.19),455(1.69)	64-0458-80B
$(C_4H_7NO)_n$ Butanenitrile, N-oxide, homopolymer (hexamer)	EtOH	212(4.66)	32-0341-80
$C_4H_7NS_2$ 2-Thiazolidinethione, 4-methyl-, (-)-	CH_2Cl_2	246(--),280(4.23), 340(2.05)	28-0161-80B
$C_4H_7N_3O$ 1,2,4-Triazine, 2,5-dihydro-3-methoxy-	EtOH	247(3.04)	44-4594-80
$C_4H_7N_3S$ Carbamimidothioic acid, N-cyano-N'-methyl-, methyl ester	MeOH	227(4.17)	32-0287-80
1,2,4-Triazine, 2,5-dihydro-3-(methylthio)-	EtOH	270s(3.00)	44-4594-80

Compound	Solvent	$\lambda_{max}(\log \epsilon)$	Ref.
$C_4H_7RbS_2$			
Butane(dithioic) acid, rubidium salt	EtOH	338(3.96),450s(--)	64-0458-80B
$C_4H_8N_2O_3$			
Ethenamine, N-(methoxymethyl)-N-nitro-	H_2O	273(3.74)	104-1006-80
$C_4H_8N_2S$			
2(1H)-Pyrimidinethione, tetrahydro-	EtOH	206(4.10),246(4.12)	104-1124-80
$C_4H_8N_4$			
Guanidine, N-cyano-N',N''-dimethyl-	MeOH	220(4.17)	32-0287-80
$C_4H_8N_4O_2$			
Diazene, bis[1-(hydroxyimino)ethyl]-	pH 5	293(4.29)	150-3853-80
	H_2O	293(4.29),424(2.22)	150-3853-80
	pH 12	350(4.49)	150-3853-80
	MeOH	293(4.31),424(2.20)	150-3853-80
	ether	288(4.32),427(2.23)	150-3853-80
$C_4H_8N_4O_3S$			
Carbonazidimidic acid, (methylsulfon-yl)-, ethyl ester	n.s.g.	231(3.98)	4-0187-80
C_4H_8OSe			
Ethaneselenoic acid, O-ethyl ester	EtOH	272(3.86),443(1.70)	39-1627-80C
$C_4H_8S_2$			
Butane(dithioic) acid, cesium salt	EtOH	338(3.94),440s(--)	64-0458-80B
potassium salt	EtOH	339(4.31),453(1.72)	64-0458-80B
Propane(dithioic) acid, 2-methyl-, cesium salt	EtOH	338(4.19),455(1.69)	64-0458-80B
potassium salt	EtOH	339(4.25),445s(1.70)	64-0458-80B
$C_4H_9ClN_2O_3$			
Ethanamine, 2-chloro-N-(methoxymethyl)-N-nitro-	H_2O	235(3.80)	104-1006-80
C_4H_9NOS			
Carbamothioic acid, propyl-, mono-potassium salt	H_2O	229(4)(approx.)	97-0100-80
Thionitrous acid, S-(1,1-dimethyl-ethyl) ester	hexane	198(3.70),228(3.93), 342(2.80)	18-0775-80
$C_4H_9NO_2$			
Nitrous acid, 1,1-dimethylethyl ester	hexane	196(3.83),219(3.52), 339(1.45),351(1.68), 397(1.76)	18-0775-80
$C_4H_9NO_2S$			
Thionitric acid, S-(1,1-dimethylethyl) ester	hexane	201(3.76),268(3.53)	18-0775-80
$C_4H_9NO_3$			
Nitric acid, 1,1-dimethylethyl ester	hexane	201(3.72),380(1.94), 397(1.76)	18-0775-80
$C_4H_9N_3$			
Ethanimidic acid, ethylidenehydrazide	MeOH	239(3.96)	104-0822-80
$C_4H_{10}N_2O_2$			
1-Butanamine, N-nitro-	acid	234.5(3.93)	104-0407-80

Compound	Solvent	λ_{max}(log ϵ)	Ref.
1-Butanamine, N-nitro- (cont.)	anion	229.0(3.99)	104-0407-80
2-Propanamine, 2-methyl-N-nitro-	acid	233.5(3.91)	104-0407-80
	anion	228.5(3.98)	104-0407-80
$C_4H_{10}N_2O_3$			
Hydroperoxide, 1-(ethylnitrosoamino)-ethyl	EtOH	229(3.83),357(1.83)	88-1765-80
Hydroperoxide, (nitrosopropylamino)-methyl	EtOH	230(3.80),366(1.87)	88-1761-80
$C_4H_{10}O_4S_4$			
Methane, dithiobis[(methylsulfonyl)-	MeCN	243(2.86)	23-1106-80
$C_4H_{10}S_2Si$			
1,3-Dithia-2-silacyclopentane, 2,2-di-methyl-	hexane	198(3.58),233(2.38)	101-0147-80A
	hexane	233(2.38)	131-0099-80C
$C_4H_{12}Cl_2HgSi_2$			
Mercury, bis(chlorodimethylsilyl)-	C_6H_{12}	212(4.74),310(2.79), 356(2.20)	101-0169-80N
	THF	214(4.34),274(2.64), 320(2.20)	101-0169-80N
$C_4H_{12}Si$			
Silane, tetramethyl-	gas	164(3.8)	61-0056-80

Compound	Solvent	$\lambda_{max}(\log \epsilon)$	Ref.
C_5HCl_3OS 2H-Pyran-2-thione, 3,4,5-trichloro-	MeCN	241(4.49),292(4.23), 384(4.20),400(4.19)	5-1960-80
$C_5H_2Cl_3NO_2$ 4-Cyclopentene-1,3-dione, 4-amino- 2,2,5-trichloro-	EtOH	265(4.17),333(4.11)	104-1404-80
$C_5H_2Cl_5NO$ 2-Cyclopenten-1-one, 3-amino- 2,4,4,5,5-pentachloro-	EtOH	310(4.05)	104-1404-80
2,4-Pentadienamide, 2,3,4,5,5-penta- chloro-	EtOH	225(4.30)	104-1404-80
$C_5H_2F_3N_3$ Propanedinitrile, (1-amino-2,2,2-tri- fluoroethylidene)-	EtOH	210(3.57),284(4.21)	104-1441-80
$C_5H_2N_6O_5$ [1,2,4]Triazolo[5,1-c][1,2,4]triazine- 7-carboxylic acid, 1,4-dihydro-3-ni- tro-4-oxo-, disodium salt	n.s.g.	209(4.29),295(3.69), 359(4.06)	103-0974-80
$C_5H_3ClN_2O_3$ Pyrazinecarboxylic acid, 5-chloro-, 1-oxide	pH 1	234(4.28),268(3.97), 303(3.49)	94-3057-80
	H_2O	233(4.13),270(3.98), 303(3.52)	94-3057-80
	pH 13	269(4.00),303(3.53)	94-3057-80
$C_5H_3ClO_2$ 3-Cyclobutene-1,2-dione, 3-chloro- 4-methyl-	MeCN	224(4.16),270(2.41)	33-1130-80
$C_5H_3Cl_3S_2$ 2-Cyclobutene-1-thione, 2,4,4-tri- chloro-3-(methylthio)-	CH_2Cl_2	286(2.71),353(3.3), 513(0.8)	83-0959-80
$C_5H_3Cl_4NO_2$ 2-Pentenamide, 2,3,5,5-tetrachloro- 4-oxo-	EtOH	219(4.15),225(4.12)	104-1404-80
$C_5H_3NO_4S$ Acetic acid, (2,4-dioxo-5-thiazolidin- ylidene)-	H_2O	230(3.33),292(3.48)	80-1097-80
C_5H_3NSSe Thieno[2,3-d]isoselenazole	EtOH	203(3.68),227(3.46), 263(3.90),303(3.95)	20-0773-80
Thieno[3,2-d]isoselenazole	EtOH	225(4.20),291(3.50)	20-0773-80
Thieno[3,4-d]isoselenazole	EtOH	206(4.05),234(4.04), 324(3.20)	20-0773-80
$C_5H_3NS_2$ Thieno[2,3-d]isothiazole	EtOH	202(3.06),217(3.08), 252(3.56),280(3.61), 284(3.61),288(3.60)	20-0773-80
Thieno[3,2-d]isothiazole	EtOH	220(3.96),274(3.13)	20-0773-80

Compound	Solvent	$\lambda_{max}(\log \epsilon)$	Ref.
$C_5H_3NSe_2$ Selenolo[3,2-d]isoselenazole	EtOH	225(4.20),266(3.66), 295(3.61)	20-0773-80
$C_5H_3N_3OS$ 7H-[1,2,4]Triazolo[5,1-b][1,3]thiazin- 7-one	EtOH	214(4.05),248(3.59), 288(3.85)	39-1352-80C
$C_5H_3N_5O_3$ Pyrazolo[5,1-c][1,2,4]triazin-4(1H)- one, 3-nitro-, sodium salt	n.s.g.	210(4.35),316(2.47), 391(4.09)	103-0974-80
$C_5H_4Cl_2N_4O_4$ Ethanol, 2-[(4,6-dichloro-1,3,5-tria- zin-2-yl)oxy]-, nitrate	MeCN	214(3.534),240(3.329)	104-1150-80
$C_5H_4Cl_2N_6O$ 1,3,5-Triazine, 2-(2-azidoethoxy)- 4,6-dichloro-	MeCN	214(3.506),238(3.336)	104-1150-80
$C_5H_4Cl_3N_3O$ 1,3,5-Triazine, 2,4-dichloro-6-(2-chlo- roethoxy)-	MeCN	214(3.363),238(3.354)	104-1150-80
$C_5H_4N_2O_3$ 2(1H)-Pyridinone, 3-nitro-	EtOH	248(3.43),361(3.83)	36-1074-80
$C_5H_4N_2O_4$ Pyrazinecarboxylic acid, 1,4,5,6- tetrahydro-5,6-dioxo-	pH 1 H_2O pH 13	267(4.02),302(4.01), 318s(3.91),338s(3.51) 258(3.94),305(3.98), 323s(3.89),341s(3.54) 276(4.00),313(4.12), 327s(4.09),342s(3.80)	94-3057-80 94-3057-80 94-3057-80
$C_5H_4N_4O_2$ Acetamide, 2-cyano-2-[(cyanomethoxy)- imino]-	EtOH	230(3.98)	5-1623-80
$C_5H_4N_4O_4$ 1,3,6,8-Tetraazaspiro[4.4]nonane- 2,4,7,9-tetrone	H_2O	205s(3.78)	44-0065-80
$C_5H_4N_6O_3$ · [1,2,4]Triazolo[5,1-c][1,2,4]triazin- 4(1H)-one, 7-methyl-3-nitro-, sodium salt	n.s.g.	204(4.27),282(3.48), 362(4.04)	103-0974-80
$C_5H_4OS_4$ 1,3-Dithiolo[4,5-b][1,4]dithiin-2-one, 5,6-dihydro-	C_6H_{12}	292.5(3.47)	24-1898-80
$C_5H_4O_2$ 2-Furancarboxaldehyde	EtOH	225(3.53),273(4.21)	59-0349-80
$C_5H_5BrN_2O_2$ 3(2H)-Pyridazinone, 4-bromo-5-hydroxy- 2-methyl- 3(2H)-Pyridazinone, 5-bromo-4-hydroxy- 2-methyl-	MeOH MeOH	214(4.38),291(3.68) 218(4.22),284(3.71)	73-0127-80 73-0127-80

Compound	Solvent	$\lambda_{max}(\log \epsilon)$	Ref.
$C_5H_5BrN_2O_4$			
4-Imidazolidineacetic acid, α-bromo-2,5-dioxo-	H_2O	210s(3.67),294(3.42)	103-1115-80
$C_5H_5Br_2N_3$			
2,4-Pyridinediamine, 3,5-dibromo-	pH 1	227(4.63),274(3.76), 285s(3.74)	87-0384-80
	pH 12	222(4.60),290(3.32)	87-0384-80
$C_5H_5ClN_2O_2$			
3(2H)-Pyridazinone, 4-chloro-5-hydroxy-2-methyl-	MeOH	214(4.18),287(3.61)	73-0127-80
3(2H)-Pyridazinone, 5-chloro-4-hydroxy-2-methyl-	MeOH	205s(--),217(4.35), 288(3.95)	73-0127-80
C_5H_5ClOS			
2H-Thiopyran-3(6H)-one, 5-chloro-	EtOH	243(3.84)	4-0289-80
C_5H_5N			
2,4-Pentadienenitrile	hexane	242(4.42)	47-0477-80
Pyridine	H_2O	200(3.75),252(3.45)	70-0740-80
protonated	H_2O	258(3.76)	70-0740-80
C_5H_5NOS			
3-Thiophenecarboxamide	EtOH	242(3.98),275s(3.40)	59-0349-80
$C_5H_5NO_2$			
2-Furancarboxamide	EtOH	214(3.74),248(4.06)	59-0349-80
3-Furancarboxamide	EtOH	234s(3.37)	59-0349-80
1H-Pyrrole-2,5-dione, 1-methyl-	C_6H_{12}	288(3.0)	41-0161-80
	benzene	295s(2.9)	41-0161-80
	THF	295(2.9)	41-0161-80
$C_5H_5NO_4S$			
3-Oxazolidineacetic acid, 4-oxo-2-thioxo-	H_2O	203(3.64),231(3.53)	80-1097-80
$C_5H_5N_2O_2$			
Pyridinium, 1-nitro-, tetrafluoroborate	n.s.g.	273(3.51)	35-3507-80
$C_5H_5N_5$			
2H-Pyrazolo[3,4-d]pyrimidin-4-amine	0.01N H_2SO_4	260(3.9)	64-0878-80C
$C_5H_5N_5O$			
1H-1,2,3-Triazole-4-carboxamide, 5-(cyanomethyl)-	pH 1	207(3.91),217s(3.88)	4-0159-80
	pH 7	217s(3.79),233(3.89)	4-0159-80
	pH 11	234(3.93)	4-0159-80
4H-1,2,3-Triazolo[4,5-c]pyridin-4-one, 6-amino-1,5-dihydro-	pH 1	211(4.27),275(3.94), 298s(3.66)	4-0159-80
	pH 7	212(4.27),274(3.99), 299s(3.66)	4-0159-80
	pH 11	222(4.27),263(3.81), 304(3.64)	4-0159-80
$C_5H_5N_5OS$			
Thiocyanic acid, 2,6-diamino-1,4-dihydro-4-oxo-5-pyrimidinyl ester	MeOH	222(4.19),267(3.77)	4-1587-80
$C_5H_5N_5S$			
Thiocyanic acid, 4,6-diamino-5-pyrimidinyl ester	MeOH	223(4.13),270(2.97)	4-1587-80

Compound	Solvent	λ_{max}(log ϵ)	Ref.
$C_5H_6BrN_3$ 2,4-Pyridinediamine, 3-bromo-	pH 2	221(4.54),266s(3.86), 277(3.90)	87-0384-80
	pH 12	217(4.58),237s(3.96), 279(3.34)	87-0384-80
$C_5H_6BrN_3O$ 4(1H)-Pyrimidinone, 6-amino-5-bromo-2-methyl-	MeOH	227(4.18),288(3.94)	4-1587-80
$C_5H_6BrN_3O_2$ 1H-Pyrazole, 5-bromo-1,3-dimethyl-4-nitro-	EtOH	271(3.97)	65-1714-80
$C_5H_6Br_2N_2O_2$ 4H-Pyrazole, 4,4-dibromo-3,5-dimethyl-, 1,2-dioxide	CHCl$_3$	274(3.96)	44-0076-80
$C_5H_6Br_2N_2O_4$ Butanoic acid, 4-[(aminocarbonyl)amino]-2,3-dibromo-4-oxo-	H$_2$O	210s(4.05),240s(3.28)	103-1115-80
C_5H_6ClNOS 1,4-Thiazepin-5(2H)-one, 6-chloro-3,4-dihydro-	MeOH	230(3.67),283(3.86)	24-0995-80
1,4-Thiazepin-5(2H)-one, 7-chloro-3,4-dihydro-	MeOH	262(3.88)	24-0995-80
$C_5H_6ClN_3O$ 1H-Pyrazole-3-carboxamide, 5-(chloromethyl)-	EtOH	233(3.60)	87-0657-80
$C_5H_6Cl_2N_2O$ 4H-Pyrazole, 4,4-dichloro-3,5-dimethyl-, 1-oxide	CHCl$_3$	251(3.89),300s(3.00)	44-0076-80
$C_5H_6IN_3O$ 1H-Pyrazole-3-carboxamide, 5-(iodomethyl)-	EtOH	238(4.06),290(3.50), 360(3.22)	87-0657-80
$C_5H_6N_2$ 3-Pyridinamine	MeOH	230(3.96),290(3.45)	33-0456-80
4-Pyridinamine (Beer's law not obeyed)	MeOH	240(4.2),270s(3.6)	142-1195-80B
$C_5H_6N_2O$ 2(1H)-Pyridinone, 3-amino-	EtOH	254(3.75),309(3.94)	36-1074-80
$C_5H_6N_2O_2$ 3(2H)-Pyridazinone, 5-hydroxy-2-methyl-	MeOH	252(4.02),282(3.93)	73-0127-80
4(1H)-Pyrimidinone, 2-methoxy-	H$_2$O	218(3.76),259(3.77)	47-2959-80
$C_5H_6N_2O_3$ 2(1H)-Pyrazinone, 6-(hydroxymethyl)-, 4-oxide	pH 1	220(4.29),270(3.90), 330(3.76)	94-2720-80
	H$_2$O	222(4.27),270(3.88), 330(3.76)	94-2720-80
	pH 13	230(4.38),254(3.86), 330(3.81)	94-2720-80
3(2H)-Pyridazinone, 4,5-dihydroxy-2-methyl-	MeOH	215(4.31),286(3.71)	73-0127-80

Compound	Solvent	$\lambda_{max}(\log \epsilon)$	Ref.
$C_5H_6N_2O_3S$			
5-Thiazoleacetic acid, 2-amino-4,5-di-hydro-4-oxo-	H_2O	224(3.89),252(3.83)	80-1097-80
5-Thiazolecarboxylic acid, 2-amino-4,5-dihydro-4-oxo-, methyl ester	MeOH	214(4.33),249(3.94), 309(3.20)	78-2675-80
$C_5H_6N_2O_4$			
2,3,4(5H)-Furantrione, 5-methyl-, 3,4-dioxime	EtOH	226(3.74),267(3.69), 308(3.57)	78-2955-80
after 100 hr.	EtOH	230(3.93),267s(3.57)	78-2955-80
$C_5H_6N_2S$			
Pyrimidine, 2-(methylthio)-	pH 1	214(3.48),255(4.10), 313(3.51)	112-0001-80
	EtOH	220(3.414),251(4.021), 287s(3.163)	112-0001-80
	CH_2Cl_2	250(4.079),286(3.113)	112-0001-80
2(1H)-Pyrimidinethione, 1-methyl-	pH 1	283(4.34),378(3.14)	112-0001-80
	EtOH	279(4.26),344(3.45)	112-0001-80
$C_5H_6N_4O_2S$			
4(1H)-Pyrimidinone, 6-amino-2-(methyl-thio)-5-nitroso-, cobalt(II) chelate	$CHCl_3$	402(4.73)	95-0515-80
iron(II) chelate	$CHCl_3$	364(4.64),667(4.26)	95-0515-80
$C_5H_6N_4O_4$			
1H-Pyrazole, 1,5-dimethyl-3,4-dinitro-	EtOH	270(3.85)	65-1705-80
$C_5H_6N_4O_5$			
4-Imidazolidinecarboxamide, N-(amino-carbonyl)-4-hydroxy-2,5-dioxo-	H_2O	205(3.92),240s(2.70)	44-0065-80
$C_5H_6N_6$			
8-Azapurine, 2-amino-8-methyl-	pH 0	245(4.09),322(1.79)	39-2918-80C
	pH 4.5	255(3.58),332(3.76)	39-2918-80C
1H-1,2,3-Triazolo[4,5-d]pyrimidin-5-amine, 1-methyl-	pH 4.5 or 90% EtOH	256(3.57),338(3.64)	39-2918-80C
	pH 0	229(4.96),326(2.06)	39-2918-80C
$C_5H_6N_6O$			
1H-Imidazole-4-carboxamide, 5-azido-N-methyl-	H_2O or EtOH	212(4.07),267(4.18)	103-1171-80
C_5H_6O			
2,4-Pentadienal, (E)-	EtOH	257(4.35)	35-6114-80
Cyclobutanone, 2-methylene-	MeCN	226(3.88),233s(--)	44-2874-80
$C_5H_6OS_4$			
1,3-Dithiol-2-one, 4,5-bis(methylthio)-	C_6H_{12}	281(3.48)	24-1898-80
$C_5H_6O_2$			
2(3H)-Furanone, dihydro-3-methylene- (tulipalin)	C_6H_{12}	210.5(3.90)(end abs.)	33-1204-80
	MeOH	214.5(3.97)(end abs.)	33-1204-80
C_5H_6Si			
Silabenzene	A at 10^oK	212(--),272(--), 305(--),313(--), 320(--)	89-0052-80
$C_5H_7BrN_2S$			
2-Thiazolamine, 5-bromo-N,N-dimethyl-	H_2O	273(3.93)	39-1156-80B

Compound	Solvent	$\lambda_{max}(\log \epsilon)$	Ref.
2-Thiazolamine, 5-bromo-N,N-dimethyl-, protonated (cont.)	H_2O	265(3.95)	39-1156-80B
$C_5H_7Br_2ClN_2O_2$ Cyclopropanamine, 2,2-dibromo-N-(2-chloroethyl)-N-nitro-	H_2O	250(3.68)	104-0858-80
C_5H_7ClO 3-Penten-2-one, 4-chloro-, (Z)-	EtOH	233(3.95)	39-2272-80C
$C_5H_7Cl_3$ 2-Pentene, 2,4,4-trichloro-	EtOH	222(3.73)	39-2272-80C
$C_5H_7Cl_3N_2O_2$ Cyclopropanamine, 2,2-dichloro-N-(2-chloroethyl)-N-nitro-	H_2O	246(3.72)	104-0858-80
C_5H_7N Pyrrole, 2-methyl-	hexane	217(3.91)	103-0488-80
C_5H_7NOS 1,4-Thiazepin-5(2H)-one, 3,4-dihydro- 1,4-Thiazepin-5(4H)-one, 6,7-dihydro-	MeOH MeOH	235(3.71),275(3.96) 238(3.55),277(3.70)	24-0995-80 24-0995-80
$C_5H_7NO_3$ Cyclopentanone, 2-nitro-	EtOH	210(3.09),234(2.80), 343(3.14)	107-0929-80
$C_5H_7NO_4S_2$ Glycine, N-(carboxymethyl)-N-(dithio-carboxy)-, triammonium salt	H_2O	259(4.09),287(4.09)	90-0775-80
$C_5H_7NO_7$ Butanedioic acid, 2-hydroxy-2-(nitro-methyl)-	pH 13	239(3.98)	69-2358-80
$C_5H_7N_3$ 2,4-Pyridinediamine	pH 2 pH 12	261(3.95) 241s(3.85),275(3.30)	87-0384-80 87-0384-80
$C_5H_7N_3OS$ 4-Imidazolidinone, 5-imino-1,3-dimethyl-2-thioxo-	EtOH	309(4.06)	18-0442-80
$C_5H_7N_3O_2$ 1H-Pyrazole, 1,3-dimethyl-4-nitro- 1,3,5-Triazine-2,4(1H,3H)-dione, 3,6-dimethyl-	EtOH EtOH-NaOH	275(3.97) 250(3.92)	65-1705-80 4-0673-80
$C_5H_7N_3O_2S$ 1,2,3-Thiadiazolium, 5-[(methoxycarbonyl)amino]-3-methyl-, hydroxide, inner salt 2-Thiazolamine, N,N-dimethyl-5-nitro- protonated 1,3,5-Triazine-2,4(1H,3H)-dione, 3-methyl-6-(methylthio)-	MeOH H_2O H_2O EtOH-NaOH	218(4.1),244(4.02), 342(4.2) 397(4.33) 333(4.03) 243(4.27)	88-2101-80 39-1156-80B 39-1156-80B 4-0673-80
$C_5H_7N_3O_3$ 1H-Pyrazol-5-ol, 1,3-dimethyl-4-nitro-	EtOH	285(3.97),356(3.79)	65-1714-80

Compound	Solvent	$\lambda_{max}(\log \epsilon)$	Ref.
1,3,5-Triazine-2,4(1H,3H)-dione, 6-methoxy-3-methyl-	EtOH-NaOH	231(3.89)	4-0673-80
$C_5H_7N_5O_2$			
1H-1,2,3-Triazole-4-acetamide, 5-(aminocarbonyl)-	pH 1	210(3.98)	4-0159-80
	pH 7	212(3.88),230(3.88)	4-0159-80
	pH 11	238(3.94)	4-0159-80
$C_5H_7N_5O_3$			
4,6-Pyrimidinediamine, 2-methyl-5-nitro-, 1-oxide	pH -0.22	234(4.25),319(3.85)	12-0131-80
	pH 6.0	212(4.34),325(3.90)	12-0131-80
$C_5H_7N_5S$			
1,3,4-Thiadiazole, 2-azido-5-propyl-	n.s.g.	245(3.7093)	103-0721-80
C_5H_8			
1,3-Butadiene, 2-methyl-	heptane	223.5(4.37)	24-1663-80
1,3-Pentadiene, cis ?	heptane	277(4.34)	24-1663-80
$C_5H_8Cl_2N_2O_3$			
Cyclopropanamine, 2,2-dichloro-N-(methoxymethyl)-N-nitro-	H_2O	241(3.81)	104-0858-80
$C_5H_8N_2O_4S$			
Thiophenium, tetrahydro-, dinitromethylide	H_2O	333(4.02)	70-0123-80
$C_5H_8N_2O_4Se$			
Selenophenium, tetrahydro-, dinitromethylide	MeCN	347(3.97)	70-0123-80
$C_5H_8N_2S$			
Imidazo[2,1-b]thiazole, 2,3,5,6-tetrahydro-	EtOH	205(4.11),227(3.81)	4-0393-80
$C_5H_8N_4O_2$			
1H-Pyrazol-5-amine, 1,3-dimethyl-4-nitro-	EtOH	280(3.71),335(3.69)	65-1714-80
C_5H_8O			
1,3-Butadiene, 1-methoxy-, cis	CH_2Cl_2	248(4.31)	24-1663-80
trans	CH_2Cl_2	238(4.29)	24-1663-80
1,3-Butadiene, 2-methoxy-	CH_2Cl_2	236(3.99)	24-1663-80
Cyclopentanone	hexane	300(1.26)	39-0453-80B
	MeOH	287(1.26)	39-0453-80B
C_5H_8OS			
Cyclopentanone, 2-mercapto-	hexane	237(2.43),304(2.02)	39-0453-80B
	MeOH	237(2.49),301(2.13)	39-0453-80B
	KOH	255(2.97),313(3.10)	39-0453-80B
C_5H_9NO			
2-Propenal, 3-(dimethylamino)-	pH 1	272(4.5)	94-3323-80
	pH 2	279(4.5)	94-3323-80
	pH 3	285(4.6)	94-3323-80
	pH 4.5-12	288(4.6)	94-3323-80
$C_5H_9NS_2$			
2-Thiazolidinethione, 4-ethyl-, (-)-	CH_2Cl_2	246(--),280(4.22), 340(2.03)	28-0161-80B

Compound	Solvent	$\lambda_{max}(\log \epsilon)$	Ref.
$C_5H_9N_3O$			
1,2,4-Triazine, 2,5-dihydro-3-methoxy-5-methyl-	EtOH	247(3.15)	44-4594-80
1,2,4-Triazine, 4,5-dihydro-3-methoxy-5-methyl-	EtOH	221(4.07),255(3.89)	44-4594-80
$C_5H_9N_3S$			
Carbamimidothioic acid, N'-cyano-N,N-dimethyl-, methyl ester	MeOH	253(4.19)	32-0287-80
1,2,4-Triazine, 2,5-dihydro-5-methyl-3-(methylthio)-	EtOH	270s(3.04)	44-4594-80
1,2,4-Triazine, 4,5-dihydro-5-methyl-3-(methylthio)-	EtOH	221(3.77),265s(3.18), 326s(2.30)	44-4594-80
$C_5H_{10}N_2OS$			
2H-1,4,6-Oxadiazocine-5(6H)-thione, tetrahydro-	H_2O	209(4.09),246(4.09)	88-0313-80
	H_2O	208(4.09),246(4.10)	104-1124-80
	MeOH	209(4.08),251(4.10)	104-1124-80
$C_5H_{10}N_2O_3$			
Ethenamine, N-(ethoxymethyl)-N-nitro-	H_2O	274(3.72)	104-1006-80
$C_5H_{10}N_2S$			
2H-1,3-Diazepine-2-thione, hexahydro-	EtOH	210(4.03),254(4.21)	104-1124-80
$C_5H_{10}N_4$			
Guanidine, N'-cyano-N,N,N''-trimethyl-	MeOH	225(4.22)	32-0287-80
$C_5H_{10}N_4O$			
1H-Tetrazole, 1(or 2)-(1-ethoxyethyl)-	pentane	203(3.64)	33-0588-80
$C_5H_{10}O$			
Furan, tetrahydro-2-methyl-	gas	188s(2.9)	23-2819-80
Pentanal	heptane	294(1.29)	41-0497-80
Propanal, 2,2-dimethyl-	heptane	295(1.10)	41-0217-80
$C_5H_{10}OSe$			
Propaneselenoic acid, 2-methyl-, O-methyl ester	EtOH	271(3.86),443(1.70)	39-1627-80C
$C_5H_{11}ClN_2O_3$			
Ethanamine, 2-chloro-N-(ethoxymethyl)-N-nitro-	EtOH	235(3.76)	104-1006-80
$C_5H_{11}NO_2S_2$			
Carbamodithioic acid, bis(2-hydroxyethyl)-, monoammonium salt	H_2O	259(4.10),288(4.11)	90-0775-80
$C_5H_{11}N_3$			
Ethanimidic acid, (1-methylethylidene)-hydrazide	MeOH	237(3.90)	104-0822-80
$C_5H_{12}N_2O_3$			
Hydroperoxide, (butylnitrosoamino)-methyl	EtOH	231(3.83),366(1.90)	88-1761-80
Hydroperoxide, [(1,1-dimethylethyl)-nitrosoamino]methyl	EtOH	237(3.72),384(1.79)	88-1761-80
Hydroperoxide, 1-(methylnitrosoamino)-butyl	EtOH	228(3.88),353(1.86)	88-1761-80

Compound	Solvent	$\lambda_{max}(\log \epsilon)$	Ref.
$C_5H_{12}S_2Si$			
1,3-Dithia-2-silacyclohexane, 2,2-di-methyl-	hexane	195(3.58),228(2.82)	101-0147-80A
1,4-Dithia-2-silacyclohexane, 2,2-di-methyl-	hexane	200(3.70),238s(2.46)	101-0147-80A
1,3-Dithia-2-silacyclopentane, 2,2,4-trimethyl-	hexane	198(3.54),233(2.33)	101-0147-80A
	hexane	233(2.33)	131-0099-80C
$C_5H_{14}B_9CoSe_2$			
Cobalt, $(\eta^5$-2,4-cyclopentadien-1-yl)-[(7,8,9,10,11-η)nonahydro-7,8-di-selenaundecaborato(2-)]-	MeCN	257s(4.29),279(4.35), 450(3.11)	125-0458-80
$C_5H_{14}OSi$			
Silane, ethoxytrimethyl-	heptane	186.7(2.54)	65-1280-80
	MeCN	187.7(2.40)	65-1280-80
$C_5H_{14}SSi$			
Silane, (ethylthio)trimethyl-	hexane	223(2.49)	101-0147-80A
	hexane	223(2.49)	131-0099-80C
$C_5H_{16}N_4O_4S_2$			
Glycine, N-(carboxymethyl)-N-(dithio-carboxy)-, triammonium salt (hydrate)	H_2O	259(4.09),287(4.09)	90-0775-80

Compound	Solvent	$\lambda_{max}(\log \epsilon)$	Ref.
$C_6Cl_2F_5NO_2S$ Benzenesulfonamide, N,N-dichloro- 2,3,4,5,6-pentafluoro-	heptane	220(3.88),273(3.23)	104-0347-80
$C_6Cl_2N_4S_2Se$ Amidosulfenyl chloride, (3,4-dicyano- 2,5-selenophenediylidene)bis-	CH_2Cl_2	296(3.80),400(3.83), 427(4.01),454(4.18), 511(4.04)	44-3211-80
$C_6Cl_2N_4S_3$ Amidosulfenyl chloride, (3,4-dicyano- 2,5-thiophenediylidene)bis-	CH_2Cl_2	282s(3.77),297(3.89), 400(3.67),507(4.36)	44-3211-80
$C_6Cl_4O_2$ 2,5-Cyclohexadiene-1,4-dione, 2,3,5,6-tetrachloro-, sodium salt of radical ion	DMSO	320f(3.8),420(3.8), 450(3.8)	65-0916-80
hydrogenation product	DMSO dianion	290(3.88),355(3.71) 393(3.46)	65-0916-80 65-0916-80
C_6Cl_6O 2H-Pyran, 3,4,5,6-tetrachloro-2-(di- chloromethylene)-	heptane	209(4.51),252(3.78), 347(4.45),362(4.48)	24-0806-80
C_6Cl_8O 3,5-Hexadien-2-one, 1,1,1,3,4,5,6,6- octachloro-, (Z)-	heptane	220(4.03),240s(3.91)	5-0403-80
C_6HCl_4NO 2,5-Cyclohexadien-1-one, 2,3,6-tri- chloro-4-(chloroimino)-	C_6H_{12}	300(4.38),312(4.38), 352(3.14),461(1.00)	59-0103-80
$C_6HN_3O_2$ 1H-Pyrrole-3,4-dicarbonitrile, 2,5-di- hydro-2,5-dioxo-	CH_2Cl_2 dioxan	252(4.16),262s(3.98) 246(4.11),320(3.06)	24-1663-80 24-1663-80
$C_6H_2Cl_3NO$ 2,5-Cyclohexadien-1-one, 2,6-dichloro- 4-(chloroimino)-	C_6H_{12}	210(3.80),300(4.42), 316(4.42),345(3.31), 460(1.02)	59-0103-80
$C_6H_2Cl_4N_2$ 2,5-Cyclohexadiene-1,4-diimine, 2,3,5,6-tetrachloro-	C_6H_{12}	271(4.35),283(4.48), 318(3.10)	88-4119-80
$C_6H_2N_2S_4$ [1,4]Dithiino[2,3-c:5,6-c']diisothia- zole	MeCN	211(4.25),295(4.06)	44-5122-80
$C_6H_3ClN_4O_2S$ Benzenesulfenyl chloride, 4-azido- 2-nitro-	HOAc HOAc	261(4.43),425(3.49) 420(3.47)	69-3280-80 69-4539-80
$C_6H_3Cl_2NO$ 2,5-Cyclohexadien-1-one, 2-chloro- 4-(chloroimino)-	C_6H_{12}	218(3.88),296(4.29), 335(3.56),440(1.26)	59-0103-80
$C_6H_3I_2NO_3$ Phenol, 2,6-diiodo-4-nitro-	EtOH	280(4.0),325(3.9), 380(3.6)	70-1597-80

Compound	Solvent	$\lambda_{max}(\log \epsilon)$	Ref.
$C_6H_3N_3O_3$ Benzofurazan, 4-nitro-	MeOH	320(<u>3.9</u>)	44-2666-80
$C_6H_3N_3O_3S$ 7H-[1,2,4]Triazolo[5,1-b][1,3]thiazine- 6-carboxylic acid, 7-oxo-	0.3% NaHCO$_3$	274(3.96)	39-1352-80C
C_6H_4ClNO 2,5-Cyclohexadien-1-one, 4-(chloro- imino)-	C_6H_{12}	236(3.63),282(4.32), 330(3.04),430(1.08)	59-0103-80
$C_6H_4ClNO_2$ Benzene, 1-chloro-4-nitro- AlBr$_3$ complex GaCl$_3$ complex	C_6H_{12} C_6H_{12} benzene	<u>270(4.0)</u> <u>355(4.1)</u> <u>340(4.0)</u>	65-1297-80 65-1297-80 65-1297-80
$C_6H_4ClNO_2S$ Benzenesulfenyl chloride, 2-nitro-	HOAc	391(3.51)	69-4539-80
$C_6H_4ClN_3$ Pyridine, 4-(3-chloro-3H-diazirin-3- yl)-	MeOH	215(3.96),266(3.28), 273s(--),354(2.06), 372(2.06)	24-2040-80
$C_6H_4Cl_2FOP$ Phosphonic dichloride, (4-fluoro- phenyl)-	C_6H_{12} MeCN	224(4.06),253(2.30), 260(2.36),265(2.26), 270(2.15) 198(4.17),224(4.06), 254(2.34),260(2.42), 264(2.32),270(2.26)	65-1578-80 65-1578-80
$C_6H_4Cl_2N_2$ 2,5-Cyclohexadiene-1,4-diimine, N,N'-dichloro-	C_6H_{12}	216(4.01),260(3.93), 238(3.93),322(4.20), 365(2.96)	59-0106-80
$C_6H_4Cl_2N_4O$ Propanenitrile, 3-[(4,6-dichloro- 1,3,5-triazin-2-yl)oxy]-	MeCN	214(3.775),237(3.322)	104-1150-80
$C_6H_4Cl_3FP$ Phosphorus(1+), trichloro(4-fluoro- phenyl)-, hexachlorophosphate tetrachloroaluminate	$C_2H_4Cl_2$ MeCN MeCN	247(4.12),267(3.88), 345(2.04) 243(4.16),267(3.88), 344(2.08) 243(4.10),270s(3.28)	65-1578-80 65-1578-80 65-1578-80
$C_6H_4Cl_3NO_2$ 4-Cyclopentene-1,3-dione, 2,2,4-tri- chloro-5-(methylamino)-	EtOH	275(4.18),347(4.09)	104-1404-80
$C_6H_4Cl_3OP$ Phosphonic dichloride, (4-chloro- phenyl)-	C_6H_{12} $C_2H_4Cl_2$ MeCN	202(4.34),235(4.26), 260(2.78),266(2.86), 270(2.86),278(2.80) 236(4.23),261(2.84), 270(2.90),278(2.78) 200(4.48),235(4.26), 261(2.83),270(2.91), 278(2.79)	65-1578-80 65-1578-80 65-1578-80

Compound	Solvent	$\lambda_{max}(\log \epsilon)$	Ref.

$C_6H_4Cl_4FP$
  Phosphorane, tetrachloro(4-fluoro-
  phenyl)-
	C_6H_{12}	231(4.00),267s(2.99)	65-1578-80

$C_6H_4Cl_4OS$
  2,4-Pentadienethioic acid, 2,3,4,5-
  tetrachloro-, S-methyl ester, (Z,Z)-
	heptane	208(4.07),251(3.99)	5-1960-80

$C_6H_4Cl_4P$
  Phosphorus(1+), trichloro(4-chloro-
  phenyl)-, hexachlorophosphate
  tetrachloroaluminate
	$C_2H_4Cl_2$
	MeCN
	MeCN
		262(4.33),344(2.04)
		256(4.31),344(2.04)
		202(4.24),256(4.27),
		  278s(3.28)
			65-1578-80
			65-1578-80
			65-1578-80

$C_6H_4Cl_5NO$
  2-Cyclopenten-1-one, 2,4,4,5,5-penta-
  chloro-3-(methylamino)-
  2,4-Pentadienamide, 2,3,4,5,5-penta-
  chloro-N-methyl-
	EtOH
	
	EtOH
		328(4.24)
		
		225(4.18)
			104-1404-80
			
			104-1404-80

$C_6H_4Cl_5P$
  Phosphorane, tetrachloro(4-chloro-
  phenyl)-
	C_6H_{12}	239(4.22),267s(3.23)	65-1578-80

$C_6H_4I_2O$ Phenol, 2,6-diiodo-	EtOH	270(3.7)	70-1597-80

$C_6H_4N_2OS$
  5H-Imidazo[2,1-b][1,3]thiazin-5-one
	EtOH	227(4.22),256(3.56),
		  320(3.65)
			39-1352-80C

$C_6H_4N_2O_5$ Phenol, 2,4-dinitro-, anion	pH 7.5	360(4.06)	44-0906-80

$C_6H_4N_4O_2$
  2,4(1H,3H)-Pteridinedione (lumazine)
	pH -4.9
	
	pH 0.0
		240(4.11),280s(2.92),
		  343(3.88)
		226(4.02),240s(3.87),
		  323(3.84)
			142-0437-80B
			
			142-0437-80B

$C_6H_4N_4O_3$
  [1,2,4]Triazolo[1,5-a]pyrimidine-
  6-carboxylic acid, 7-hydroxy-
	NaHCO$_3$	264(4.04),293(4.17)	39-1347-80C

$C_6H_4N_6$
  Bis[1,2,4]triazolo[1,5-a:1',5'-c]-
  pyrimidine
	EtOH	214(4.42),230s(3.86),
		  256(3.91),262(3.92),
		  275s(3.68)
			12-1147-80

$C_6H_4O_2$
  2,5-Cyclohexadiene-1,4-dione
	C_6H_{12}	240(4.23),285(2.57),
		  450(1.24)
			59-0103-80

$C_6H_4O_3$ 3,4-Furandicarboxaldehyde	EtOH	261(3.62)	39-0643-80C

$C_6H_4O_4$
  2,5-Cyclohexadiene-1,4-dione, 2,5-di-
  hydroxy-
	dianion	313(4.4),325(4.4)	150-0908-80

Compound	Solvent	λ_{max}(log ϵ)	Ref.
C₆H₄S₂Se₂			
1,3-Thiaselenole, 2-(1,3-thiaselenol-2-ylidene)-	hexane	210(3.95),235s(3.57), 282(3.96),297(3.99), 325(3.77),?s(2.99), 470(2.30)	44-2632-80
C₆H₄S₄			
1,3-Dithiole, 2-(1,3-dithiol-2-ylidene)-	hexane	303(4.11),316(4.06), 368(3.30)	11-0196-80A
3:2 bromide hydrate	MeCN	302(4.24),315(4.23), 350s(--),400s(--), 438(4.19),500s(--), 583(3.67)	11-0196-80A
3:2 chloride hydrate	MeCN	305s(--),317(4.23), 340(4.11),400s(--), 436(4.51),500s(--), 580(3.97)	11-0196-80A
7:5 iodide	MeCN	293(4.23),315s(--), 335s(--),433(3.90), 510s(--),580(3.34)	11-0196-80A
3:2 tetrafluoroborate	MeCN	250s(--),290s(--), 305s(--),316(4.30), 335s(--),375s(--), 397s(--),432(4.53), 576(3.98)	11-0196-80A
C₆H₅BrO			
Phenol, 2-bromo-	hexane	215(3.51),270(3.23), 275(3.43),282(3.43)	65-2236-80
	pentane-EtOH-ether	217(3.93),279(3.41), 286(3.36)	65-2236-80
Phenol, 4-bromo-	hexane	225(3.86),276(3.15), 283(3.20),292(3.18)	65-2236-80
	pentane-EtOH-ether	229(4.11),279(3.04), 286(3.18),292(3.08)	65-2236-80
C₆H₅BrSe			
Benzeneselenenyl bromide	n.s.g.	468(2.38)	23-2745-80
C₆H₅ClN₂O₂			
Pyrazinecarboxylic acid, 5-chloro-, methyl ester	pH 1 H₂O pH 13	224(4.05),279(4.00) 224(4.05),279(4.00) 279(3.93)	94-3057-80 94-3057-80 94-3057-80
C₆H₅ClN₂O₃			
Pyrazinecarboxylic acid, 5-chloro-6-methyl-, 1-oxide	pH 1	230(4.30),266(3.85), 308(3.61)	94-3057-80
	H₂O	230(4.17),269(3.91), 305(3.61)	94-3057-80
	pH 13	270(3.92),305(3.61)	94-3057-80
C₆H₅ClO			
Phenol, 4-chloro-	hexane	228(3.54),277(3.15), 283(3.26),285(3.26), 289(3.11),291(3.23)	65-2236-80
	pentane-EtOH-ether	230(4.08),286(3.28), 292(3.23)	65-2236-80
C₆H₅ClSe			
Benzeneselenenyl chloride	n.s.g.	433(2.42)	23-2745-80

Compound	Solvent	$\lambda_{max}(\log \epsilon)$	Ref.
$C_6H_5Cl_2N_5O_7$ 1,3-Propanediol, 2-[(4,6-dichloro- 1,3,5-triazin-2-yl)oxy]-, dinitrate	MeCN	· 214(3.621),234(3.128)	104-1150-80
$C_6H_5Cl_2N_9O$ 1,3,5-Triazine, 2-[2-azido-1-(azido- methyl)ethoxy]-4,6-dichloro-	MeCN	214(3.459),239(3.335)	104-1150-80
$C_6H_5Cl_2OP$ Phosphonic dichloride, phenyl-	C_6H_{12}	194(4.48),252(4.03), 262(2.88),267(3.04), 275(2.93)	65-1578-80
	$C_2H_4Cl_2$	224(4.08),262(2.94), 268(3.08),274(3.04)	65-1578-80
	MeCN	223(4.08),261(2.91), 267(3.08),274(3.00)	65-1578-80
$C_6H_5Cl_3P$ Phosphorus(1+), trichlorophenyl-, hexa- chlorophosphate	$C_2H_4Cl_2$	244(4.13),271(3.81), 345(2.00)	65-1578-80
	MeCN	240(4.11),270(3.81), 345(2.00) ⁀	65-1578-80
	$MeNO_2$	242(4.12),270(3.81), 345(2.00)	65-1578-80
tetrachloroaluminate	MeCN	244(4.11),277(3.26)	65-1578-80
$C_6H_5Cl_4NO_2$ 2-Pentenamide, 2,3,5,5-tetrachloro- N-methyl-4-oxo-	EtOH	220(4.14),226(4.12)	104-1404-80
$C_6H_5Cl_4N_3O$ 1,3,5-Triazine, 2,4-dichloro-6-[2- chloro-1-(chloromethyl)ethoxy]-	MeCN	214(3.401);238(3.337)	104-1150-80
$C_6H_5Cl_4P$ Phosphorane, tetrachlorophenyl-	C_6H_{12}	197(4.48),228(4.03), 267s(3.08)	65-1578-80
C_6H_5FO Phenol, 4-fluoro-	hexane	216(3.49),275(3.32), 278(3.36),282(3.43), 286(3.34),288(3.34)	65-2236-80
	pentane- EtOH-ether	213(3.81),220(3.81), 284(3.18),290(3.08)	65-2236-80
$C_6H_5F_3OS$ 2-Cyclobuten-1-one, 3-(ethylthio)- 2,4,4-trifluoro-	isooctane	221(3.23),270(4.37), 310(2.93)	44-4429-80
C_6H_5IO Phenol, 2-iodo-	hexane	219(3.40),225(3.36), 230(3.28),270(2.78), 276(2.93),284(2.90)	65-2236-80
	pentane- EtOH-ether	230(3.98),282(3.51), 290(3.48)	65-2236-80
Phenol, 4-iodo-	hexane	232(4.10),236(4.01), 276(3.04),283(3.08), 292(2.95)	65-2236-80
	pentane- EtOH-ether	235(4.09),279(3.08), 286(3.11),292(3.04)	65-2236-80

Compound	Solvent	$\lambda_{max}(\log \epsilon)$	Ref.
$C_6H_5I_2NO$			
Phenol, 4-amino-2,6-diiodo-	EtOH	275(4.2),380s(2.6)	70-1597-80
$C_6H_5NO_3$			
Phenol, 4-nitro-	isooctane	280(4.2),380(3.4)	70-1597-80
	pentane-	231(3.75),313(3.65),	65-2236-80
	EtOH-ether	396(3.96)	
$C_6H_5N_3OS$			
Thieno[2,3-d]pyrimidin-2(1H)-one,	pH 1	235(4.49),303(3.72)	39-1853-80C
4-amino-	pH 11	226(4.39),274(4.00)	39-1853-80C
	MeOH	228(4.46),264(3.85),	39-1853-80C
		276(3.60)	
3H-1,2,4-Triazole-3-thione, 5-(2-furan-	MeOH	255(3.97),313(4.20)	73-2804-80
yl)-1,2-dihydro-			
$C_6H_5N_3O_4$			
Pyrazinecarboxylic acid, 3-(aminocarbo-	pH 1	263(4.08),308(3.76)	94-3057-80
nyl)-1,6-dihydro-6-oxo-	H_2O	256(4.09),315(3.84)	94-3057-80
	pH 13	268(4.18),310(3.93)	94-3057-80
$C_6H_5N_3Se$			
Selenocyanic acid, 6-amino-3-pyridinyl	MeOH	253(4.19),303(3.65)	104-1963-80
ester			
$C_6H_5N_5S$			
3-Pyridinamine, N-1,2,3,4-thiatriazol-	n.s.g.	241(3.96),297(4.20)	73-2329-80
5-yl-			
4-Pyridinamine, N-1,2,3,4-thiatriazol-	n.s.g.	241(3.82),291(4.29)	73-2329-80
5-yl-			
$C_6H_6ClN_3$			
Pyridine, 4-(3-chloro-3-diaziridinyl)-	MeCN	263(3.73)	24-2040-80
$C_6H_6Cl_3NS$			
2-Cyclobutene-1-thione, 2,4,4-tri-	CH_2Cl_2	344(4.7),410(2.1)	83-0959-80
chloro-3-(dimethylamino)-			
$C_6H_6F_2OS_2$			
2-Cyclobuten-1-one, 4,4-difluoro-	isooctane	229(3.97),299(4.21)	44-4429-80
2,3-bis(methylthio)-			
$C_6H_6IN_3O_3$			
2H-Pyran-3(6H)-one, 5-azido-4-iodo-	n.s.g.	314(4.11)	56-1319-80
6-methoxy-			
$C_6H_6N_2O$			
2-Pyridinecarboxaldehyde, oxime, (E)-	pH 8	240(4.0),278(3.9)	104-1252-80
	pH 13	291(4.18)	104-1252-80
2-Pyridinecarboxaldehyde, oxime, (Z)-	pH 8	236(4.0),278(3.8)	104-1252-80
	pH 13	291(4.00)	104-1252-80
$C_6H_6N_2O_2$			
Benzenamine, N-hydroxy-N-nitroso-,	MeOH	225(4.06),293(4.03)	90-0851-80
ammonium salt (cupferron)			
7H-Oxazolo[3,2-a]pyrimidin-7-one,	H_2O	226(3.82),259(3.84)	47-2959-80
2,3-dihydro-			
2-Propenoic acid, 3-(1H-imidazol-	pH 5.55	265(4.2+)	149-0711-80B
4-yl)-, (E)-			
2-Propenoic acid, 3-(1H-imidazol-	pH 5.55	260(4.2-)	149-0711-80B
4-yl)-, (Z)- (urocanic acid)			

Compound	Solvent	$\lambda_{max}(\log \epsilon)$	Ref.
$C_6H_6N_2O_3$			
Pyrazinecarboxylic acid, 1,6-dihydro-6-oxo-, methyl ester	pH 1	237(3.72),315(3.81)	94-3057-80
	H_2O	238(3.72),316(3.81)	94-3057-80
	pH 13	239(3.88),325(3.81)	94-3057-80
Pyrazinecarboxylic acid, 4,5-dihydro-5-oxo-, methyl ester	pH 1	256(4.20),305(3.74)	94-3057-80
	H_2O	256(4.19),305(3.75)	94-3057-80
	pH 13	263(4.16),311(3.89)	94-3057-80
$C_6H_6N_2O_4$			
Pyrazinecarboxylic acid, 4,5-dihydro-6-methyl-5-oxo-, 1-oxide	pH 1	238(4.39),315(3.77)	94-3057-80
	H_2O	233(4.28),270(3.68), 323(3.78)	94-3057-80
	pH 13	240(4.37),330(3.88)	94-3057-80
1H-Pyrrole-2-carboxylic acid, 1-methyl-5-nitro-	EtOH	225(4.04),392(4.19)	36-1334-80
$C_6H_6N_2S_3$			
5-Isothiazolecarbonitrile, 3,4-bis-(methylthio)-	MeCN	337(3.80)	44-5122-80
$C_6H_6N_4$			
7H-Pyrrolo[2,3-d]pyrimidin-4-amine	MeOH	271(4.05)	24-2069-80
$C_6H_6N_4OS$			
Thiocyanic acid, 6-amino-1,4-dihydro-2-methyl-4-oxo-5-pyrimidinyl ester	MeOH	224(4.21),237(4.23)	4-1587-80
$C_6H_6N_4OS_2$			
Thiocyanic acid, 6-amino-1,4-dihydro-2-(methylthio)-4-oxo-5-pyrimidinyl ester	MeOH	227(4.11),280(3.82)	4-1587-80
$C_6H_6N_4O_2$			
1H-1,2,3-Triazole-4-carboxylic acid, 5-(cyanomethyl)-, methyl ester	pH 1	211s(3.78),222(3.85)	4-0159-80
	pH 7	233(3.96)	4-0159-80
	pH 11	235(3.98)	4-0159-80
$C_6H_6N_6$			
2-Pyridinamine, N-1H-tetrazol-5-yl-	n.s.g.	254(3.99),271(3.99)	73-2329-80
1H-Tetrazol-5-amine, 1-(2-pyridinyl)-	n.s.g.	248(4.28),290(3.75)	73-2329-80
$C_6H_6N_6O$			
Pyrimido[5,4-e]-1,2,4-triazin-5(6H)-one, 7-amino-3-methyl-, monosodium salt	pH 13	215(3.87),259(4.30), 390(3.61)	150-3630-80
$C_6H_6N_6O_2$			
Xanthopterin, 7-amino- (hydrate)	M HCl	241(4.24),286s(3.93), 291(3.49),333(4.12), 348(4.16),361s(3.97)	33-1805-80
	M NaOH	245(4.21),282(3.80), 355(4.0)	33-1805-80
C_6H_6O			
7-Oxabicyclo[4.1.0]hepta-2,4-diene	isooctane	271(3.15)	142-1569-80B
Oxepin	isooctane	305(2.95)	142-1569-80B
Phenol	C_6H_{12}	278f(3.3)	70-1597-80
	hexane	210(3.77),263(3.18), 270(3.36),277(3.32)	65-2236-80
	hexane	210(3.78)	70-1928-80

Compound	Solvent	$\lambda_{max}(\log \epsilon)$	Ref.
C_6H_6OS			
Ethanone, 1-(2-thienyl)-	benzene	280(4.0)	70-0039-80
	EtBr	263(4.1),291(4.4)	70-0039-80
1:1 AlBr$_3$ complex	benzene	288(3.8),335(3.4)	70-0039-80
	EtBr	260(4.1),282(4.0), 330s(3.3)	70-0039-80
1:2 AlBr$_3$ complex	benzene	306(3.6),340(3.6)	70-0039-80
	EtBr	305(4.4),340(4.4)	70-0039-80
$C_6H_6OS_4$			
5H-1,3-Dithiolo[4,5-b][1,4]dithiepin- 2-one, 6,7-dihydro-	C_6H_{12}	285(3.72)	24-1898-80
$C_6H_6O_2$			
1,3-Benzenediol	pentane- EtOH-ether	222(3.89),278(3.40), 284(3.34)	65-2236-80
1,4-Benzenediol	hexane	223(3.64)	70-1928-80
1-Cyclobutene-1,2-dicarboxaldehyde	ether	255.5(3.85)	118-0543-80
Ethanone, 1-(2-furanyl)-	benzene	300s(3.2)	70-0039-80
	EtOH	225(3.28),270(4.12)	59-0349-80
	EtBr	265(4.3)	70-0039-80
1:1 AlBr$_3$ complex	benzene	307(3.4)	70-0039-80
	EtBr	265(4.3),312(3.6)	70-0039-80
1:2 AlBr$_3$ complex	benzene	322(4.1)	70-0039-80
	EtBr	266(4.0),322(4.2)	70-0039-80
2(3H)-Furanone, 3-ethenylidenedihydro-	EtOH	218.0s(3.84)	33-1204-80
$C_6H_6O_3$			
2H-Pyran-2,4(3H)-dione, 6-methyl-	EtOH	211(4.26),280(3.94)	2-0546-80
$C_6H_7BrN_2O_4$			
5-Oxazoleacetic acid, 2-amino-α-bromo- 4,5-dihydro-4-oxo-, methyl ester, hydrobromide	EtOH	220(4.29)	103-1115-80
hydrochloride	EtOH	220(4.30)	103-1115-80
$C_6H_7ClN_2O_2$			
3(2H)-Pyridazinone, 4-chloro-2-ethyl- 5-hydroxy-	MeOH	216(4.45),227s(--), 286(3.76)	73-0127-80
C_6H_7ClOS			
2H-Thiopyran-3(6H)-one, 5-chloro- 2-methyl-	EtOH	242(4.21)	4-0289-80
2H-Thiopyran-3(6H)-one, 5-chloro- 4-methyl-	EtOH	250(3.90)	4-0289-80
$C_6H_7FN_2O_3$			
2,4(1H,3H)-Pyrimidinedione, 5-fluoro- 1-(methoxymethyl)-	pH 2	269(3.91)	103-1176-80
	pH 7	269(3.90)	103-1176-80
	pH 12	269(3.77)	103-1176-80
C_6H_7N			
Benzenamine	C_6H_{12}	234(--),286(3.19)	44-2195-80
2,4-Pentadienenitrile, 3-methyl-	hexane	248(4.35)	47-0477-80
C_6H_7NO			
Phenol, 3-amino-	C_6H_{12}	234(3.83),284(3.36)	65-2236-80
	pentane- EtOH-ether	240(3.40),286(3.34)	65-2236-80

Compound	Solvent	$\lambda_{max}(\log \epsilon)$	Ref.
C₆H₇NOS			
3-Furancarbothioamide, 2-methyl-	EtOH	208(4.14),269(3.87), 299(3.88)	128-0069-80
3-Thiophenecarboxamide, N-methyl-	EtOH	244(3.98),273s(3.39)	59-0349-80
C₆H₇NO₂			
2-Furancarboxamide, N-methyl-	EtOH	250(4.13)	59-0349-80
3-Furancarboxamide, N-methyl-	EtOH	230s(3.49)	59-0349-80
6H-1,3-Oxazin-6-one, 2,4-dimethyl-	isopentane	265(3.9)	5-0798-80
6H-1,3-Oxazin-6-one, 4,5-dimethyl-	MeOCH₂CH₂OMe	267(3.7)	5-0798-80
4(1H)-Pyridinone, 3-hydroxy-2-methyl-	EtOH	276.5(4.17)	36-1074-80
1H-Pyrrole-2,5-dione, 1-ethyl-	n.s.g.	294(2.76)	116-0826-80
C₆H₇NS₂			
Thiazole, 2-(ethenylthio)-4-methyl-	n.s.g.	220s(3.61),278(3.94)	121-1015-80
C₆H₇N₂O₂			
Pyridinium, 2-methyl-1-nitro-, tetrafluoroborate	n.s.g.	263(3.82)	35-3507-80
C₆H₇N₃O₂			
Acetamide, N-(1,2-dihydro-2-oxo-4-pyrimidinyl)-	EtOH	215(4.32),245(4.15), 293(3.69)	136-0195-80A
C₆H₇N₃O₃			
Acetamide, 2-cyano-2-[(2-oxopropoxy)-imino]-, (E)-	EtOH	241(3.91)	5-1623-80
3-Isoxazolecarboxamide, 5-acetyl-4-amino-	EtOH	263(3.45),342(3.82)	5-1623-80
C₆H₇N₃O₃S			
Acetamide, 2-[(1,2,3,4-tetrahydro-2,4-dioxo-5-pyrimidinyl)thio]-	pH 13	293(3.84)	87-0569-80
C₆H₇N₃O₄			
5-Pyrimidineacetic acid, 2-amino-1,4-dihydro-6-hydroxy-4-oxo-	50% MeOH-HCl	259(4.23)	73-3583-80
	+ NaOH	266(4.12)	73-3583-80
C₆H₇N₅			
2H-Pyrazolo[3,4-d]pyrimidin-4-amine, 2-methyl-	0.01N H₂SO₄	268(4.0)	64-0878-80C
7H-Pyrazolo[3,4-d]pyrimidin-4-amine, 7-methyl-	0.01N H₂SO₄	262s(3.8),289(3.9)	64-0878-80C
	KOH	270(4.0)	64-0878-80C
C₆H₇N₅O			
Pyridazine, 4-azido-3,6-dimethyl-, 1-oxide	EtOH	207(4.01),283(4.21), 342(3.95)	94-0529-80
Pyridazine, 4-azido-3,6-dimethyl-, 2-oxide	EtOH	235(4.07),250(4.21), 323(3.67)	94-0529-80
C₆H₈			
1,3-Cyclohexadiene	CH₂Cl₂	260(3.67)	24-1663-80
1,3,5-Hexatriene, cis	CH₂Cl₂	251(4.46),260(4.57), 270(4.45)	24-1663-80
1,3,5-Hexatriene, trans	CH₂Cl₂	251(4.56),260(4.58), 270(4.45)	24-1663-80
C₆H₈BrNOS			
1,4-Thiazepin-5(2H)-one, 6-bromo-3,4-dihydro-7-methyl-	MeOH	237(3.60),276(3.62)	24-0995-80

Compound	Solvent	$\lambda_{max}(\log \epsilon)$	Ref.

$C_6H_8BrN_3OS$
  4(1H)-Pyrimidinone, 6-amino-5-bromo-
  2-(ethylthio)-
	MeOH	226(3.91),287(3.57)	4-1587-80

$C_6H_8Br_2$ 1,3-Butadiene, 2,3-bis(bromomethyl)-	isooctane	225(4.00)	44-0870-80

C_6H_8ClNOS
  1,4-Thiazepin-5(2H)-one, 6-chloro-
  3,4-dihydro-7-methyl-
	MeOH	230s(3.49),283(3.48)	24-0995-80

$C_6H_8Cl_2O_2$ 2,5-Hexanedione, 1,6-dichloro-	MeOH	206(2.70)	103-0151-80

C_6H_8FNOS
  5-Thiazoleethanol, 2-fluoro-4-methyl-
  conjugate acid
	n.s.g.
	n.s.g.
		242(3.60)
		257(3.51)
			39-2026-80C
			39-2026-80C

$C_6H_8N_2$
  1,4-Diazocine, 1,4-dihydro-
	MeCN	254s(3.77+),263(3.82+),
		  284s(3.41+)(changing)
			24-3161-80

$C_6H_8N_2O_2S$
  3(2H)-Pyridazinone, 4-hydroxy-2-methyl-
  5-(methylthio)-
	MeOH	208s(--),215(4.17),
		  306(3.75)
			73-0127-80

3(2H)-Pyridazinone, 5-hydroxy-2-methyl-
  4-(methylthio)-
	MeOH	215(4.23),228s(--),
		  318(3.72)
			73-0127-80

5-Thiazolecarboxylic acid, 2-amino-, ethyl ester	H_2O	298(4.21)	39-1156-80B
protonated	H_2O	276(4.17)	39-1156-80B

$C_6H_8N_2O_3$
  2(1H)-Pyrazinone, 6-(hydroxymethyl)-
  3-methyl-, 4-oxide
	pH 1	222(4.26),265(3.83),
		  318(3.82)
			94-2720-80

	H_2O	222(4.27),265(3.83), 318(3.83)	94-2720-80
	pH 13	226(4.41),254s(3.77), 325(3.88)	94-2720-80

3(2H)-Pyridazinone, 4-hydroxy-5-meth-
  oxy-2-methyl-
	MeOH	205s(--),218(4.35),
		  288(3.94)
			73-0127-80

3(2H)-Pyridazinone, 5-hydroxy-4-meth-
  oxy-2-methyl-
	MeOH	214(4.50),224s(--),
		  285(3.75)
			73-0127-80

1H-Pyrrole, 2-methoxy-1-methyl-4-nitro-	MeOH	280(3.84),359(3.62)	77-0123-80

$C_6H_8N_2S$
  Pyrimidine, 2-(ethylthio)-
	EtOH	215(3.301),255(4.184),
		  285s(3.276)
			112-0001-80

	CH_2Cl_2	255(4.198),286s(3.285)	112-0001-80

$C_6H_8N_2S_3$
  2-Thiazolidinethione, 3-(4,5-dihydro-
  2-thiazolyl)-
	EtOH	277(4.10),307(4.00)	39-0665-80C

$C_6H_8N_4$
  1H-Imidazole-4-carbonitrile, 1-methyl-
  5-(methylamino)-
	pH 1
	pH 7
	pH 13
	EtOH
		241(4.00),261(3.89)
		251(4.05)
		251(4.05)
		251(4.10)
			94-2819-80
			94-2819-80
			94-2819-80
			94-2819-80

$C_6H_8N_4O_2S$ 4(1H)-Pyrimidinone, 6-amino-2-(ethyl-	$CHCl_3$	402(4.50)	95-0515-80

Compound	Solvent	$\lambda_{max}(\log \epsilon)$	Ref.
thio)-5-nitroso-, cobalt chelate			95-0515-80
iron(II) chelate	CHCl₃	385(4.33),640(4.16)	95-0515-80
$C_6H_8N_4O_3$			
1H-1,2,3-Triazole-4-carboxylic acid,	pH 1	208(3.95),222(3.93)	4-0159-80
5-(2-amino-2-oxoethyl)-, methyl	pH 7	224s(3.88),233(3.92)	4-0159-80
ester	pH 11	238(3.99)	4-0159-80
$C_6H_8N_4O_5$			
2,4(1H,3H)-Pyrimidinedione, 6-[(2-hy-	pH 1	322(4.08)	39-2645-80C
droxyethyl)amino]-5-nitro-	pH 13	337(4.20)	39-2645-80C
$C_6H_8N_4S$			
5-Thiazolecarbonitrile, 4-amino-2,3-di-	MeOH	252s(3.79),292(4.24)	78-2675-80
hydro-3-methyl-2-(methylimino)-,			
monohydrobromide			
$C_6H_8N_6$			
1,3-Butadiene, 2,3-bis(azidomethyl)-	isooctane	220(4.15),282(1.69)	44-0870-80
$C_6H_8N_6O$			
1H-Imidazole-4-carboxamide, 5-azido-	H₂O or EtOH	220(4.05),263(4.14)	103-1171-80
N,N-dimethyl-			
Pyrimido[5,4-e]-1,2,4-triazin-5(1H)-	pH 1	215(4.02),232s(--),	150-3630-80
one, 7-amino-2,6-dihydro-3-methyl-		274(4.12)	
$C_6H_8N_6O_2$			
Pyrimido[5,4-e]-1,2,4-triazin-5(1H)-	pH 1	213(4.08),233s(--),	150-3630-80
one, 7-amino-2,6-dihydro-3-(hydroxy-		274(4.12)	
methyl)-			
$C_6H_8N_6O_4$			
Acetic acid, 2-(2-amino-1,6-dihydro-	pH 1	236(4.17),330(4.18)	150-3630-80
5-nitro-6-oxo-4-pyrimidinyl)hydrazide	pH 13	257(4.39),329(4.14),	150-3630-80
		396(3.91)	
$C_6H_8N_6O_5$			
Acetic acid, hydroxy-, 2-(2-amino-1,6-	pH 1	236(4.14),330(4.15)	150-3630-80
dihydro-5-nitro-6-oxo-4-pyrimidinyl)-	pH 13	258(4.35),328(4.10),	150-3630-80
hydrazide		394(3.86)	
C_6H_8O			
Furan, tetrahydro-3,4-bis(methylene)-	isooctane	245(3.95)	44-0870-80
C_6H_8OS			
Thiophene, tetrahydro-3,4-bis(methyl-	EtOH	244(3.79)	44-0870-80
ene)-, 1-oxide			
2H-Thiopyran-3(4H)-one, 2-methyl-	EtOH	219(3.59),241(3.55)	4-0289-80
2H-Thiopyran-3(6H)-one, 2-methyl-	EtOH	232(3.77)	4-0289-80
$C_6H_8O_2$			
2,3-Butadienoic acid, 2-methyl-,	EtOH	213.5s(3.87)	33-1204-80
methyl ester			
2-Cyclopenten-1-one, 2-hydroxy-	EtOH	258(4.09)	88-1685-80
3-methyl-	EtOH-NaOH	297(3.96)	88-1685-80
7-Oxabicyclo[4.1.0]heptan-2-one, (1S)-	hexane	305(1.3)	44-0158-80
2H-Pyran-2-one, 5,6-dihydro-6-methyl-	EtOH	221(3.91)	102-2199-80
$C_6H_8O_2S$			
Thiophene, tetrahydro-3,4-bis(methyl-	EtOH	244(3.82)	44-0870-80
ene)-, 1,1-dioxide			

Compound	Solvent	$\lambda_{max}(\log \epsilon)$	Ref.
$C_6H_8O_4$ Butanedioic acid, ethylidene-	n.s.g.	235(4.09)	70-0421-80
C_6H_8S Thiophene, tetrahydro-3,4-bis(methyl-ene)-	EtOH	240(3.78)	44-0870-80
$C_6H_9BrN_4S$ 5-Thiazolecarbonitrile, 4-amino-2,3-di-hydro-3-methyl-2-(methylimino)-, monohydrobromide	MeOH	252s(3.79),292(4.24)	78-2675-80
C_6H_9N 1H-Pyrrole, 2,3-dimethyl-	hexane	212(3.89)	103-0488-80
C_6H_9NOS 1,4-Thiazepin-5(4H)-one, 2,3-dihydro-6-methyl-	MeOH	228(3.44),282(3.78)	24-0995-80
1,4-Thiazepin-5(4H)-one, 2,3-dihydro-7-methyl-	MeOH	235(3.55),272(3.81)	24-0995-80
1,4-Thiazepin-5(4H)-one, 6,7-dihydro-6-methyl-	MeOH	233(3.55),272(3.60)	24-0995-80
1,4-Thiazepin-5(4H)-one, 6,7-dihydro-7-methyl-	MeOH	235(3.62),273(3.71)	24-0995-80
5-Thiazoleethanol, 4-methyl-	n.s.g.	249(3.62)	39-2026-80C
conjugate acid	n.s.g.	258(3.65)	39-2026-80C
$C_6H_9NO_3$ 2-Propenoic acid, 3-(formylamino)-, ethyl ester	EtOH	261(4.3)	5-0798-80
$C_6H_9N_3OS_2$ 4(1H)-Pyrimidinone, 6-amino-2-(ethyl-thio)-5-mercapto-	MeOH	240s(4.20),273(3.72), 292(3.71),350(3.50)	4-1587-80
$C_6H_9N_3O_2$ Cupferron	MeOH	225(4.06),293(4.03)	90-0851-80
4(1H)-Pyrimidinone, 2-amino-1-(2-hy-droxyethyl)-	H_2O	261.5(3.74)	117-0275-80
$C_6H_9N_3O_3$ 1,3,5-Triazine-2,4(1H,3H)-dione, 6-ethoxy-3-methyl-	EtOH-NaOH	231(3.89)	4-0673-80
$C_6H_9N_9O_3$ DL-chiro-Inositol, 1,2,4-triazido-1,2,4-trideoxy-	H_2O	210(3.28),281(1.91)	24-3127-80
$C_6H_9S_3$ Cyclopropenylium, tris(methylthio)-, hexabromoantimonate	MeCN	276(4.24)	118-0225-80
hexachloroantimonate	MeCN	276(4.45)	118-0225-80
$C_6H_9Se_3$ Cyclopropenylium, tris(methylseleno)-, hexachloroantimonate	MeCN	290(4.35)	118-0225-80
C_6H_{10} 1,3-Butadiene, 2,3-dimethyl-	dioxan	229(4.31)	24-1663-80
Cyclopentene, 3-methyl-, (R)-	gas	160(3.7),168(3.5), 180(3.8),183(3.8),	35-6972-80

Compound	Solvent	$\lambda_{max}(\log \epsilon)$	Ref.
Cyclopentene, 3-methyl-, (R)- (cont.)		190(3.7)	35-6972-80
2,4-Pentadiene, 2-methyl-	C_6H_{12}	234(4.35)	24-1663-80
$C_6H_{10}Cl_2N_2O_3$			
Cyclopropanamine, 2,2-dichloro-N-(ethoxymethyl)-N-nitro-	EtOH	240(3.75)	104-0858-80
$C_6H_{10}N_2$			
2,3-Diazabicyclo[2.2.1]hept-2-ene, 1-methyl-	pentane	344(2.13)	35-1633-80
6,7-Diazabicyclo[3.2.1]oct-6-ene	pentane	347(2.48)	35-1633-80
	C_6H_{12}	347(2.51)	44-3756-80
$C_6H_{10}N_2OS$			
3(2H)-Thiazoleethanol, 2-imino-4-methyl-, monohydrobromide	MeOH	264(3.80)	39-1773-80C
	MeOH-NaOMe	267(3.85)	39-1773-80C
$C_6H_{10}N_2S$			
2-Thiazolamine, N,N,5-trimethyl-protonated	H_2O	267(3.99)	39-1156-80B
	H_2O	263(4.03)	39-1156-80B
$C_6H_{10}N_4O$			
1H-Imidazole-4-carboxamide, 1-methyl-5-(methylamino)-	pH 1	253(3.85)	94-2819-80
	pH 7	269(3.96)	94-2819-80
	pH 13	269(3.96)	94-2819-80
	EtOH	270(3.99)	94-2819-80
$C_6H_{10}N_6O_3$			
4(1H)-Pyrimidinone, 2-amino-6-(1,2-dimethylhydrazino)-5-nitro-	pH 1	219(4.07),243(4.07), 270s(3.74),348(3.74)	150-3630-80
	pH 13	222(4.28),253(4.04), 366(3.75)	150-3630-80
$C_6H_{10}O$			
Cyclohexanone	hexane	291(1.18)	39-0453-80B
	MeOH	282(1.18)	39-0453-80B
$C_6H_{10}OS$			
3-Buten-2-one, 4-(ethylthio)-, trans	C_6H_{12}	282(4.17)	65-2185-80
	EtOH	292(4.15)	65-2185-80
	dioxan	285(4.15)	65-2185-80
	$C_2H_4Cl_2$	289(4.17)	65-2185-80
	MeCN	288(4.22)	65-2185-80
$C_6H_{10}O_2$			
1,3-Butadiene, 1,4-dimethoxy-, (E,E)-	CH_2Cl_2	241(4.30)	24-1663-80
$C_6H_{10}O_6$			
epi-Inosose	H_2O	275(1.48)	136-0033-80I
$C_6H_{11}NO_2S$			
Sulfonium, dimethyl-, 1-(aminocarbonyl)-2-oxopropylide	EtOH	250(4.20)	94-0795-80
$C_6H_{11}NS_2$			
2-Thiazolidinethione, 4-(1-methylethyl)-, (-)-	CH_2Cl_2	280(4.19),336(2.07)	28-0161-80B
$C_6H_{11}N_3O$			
1,2,4-Triazine, 2,5-dihydro-3-methoxy-5,6-dimethyl-	EtOH	243(3.23)	44-4594-80

Compound	Solvent	$\lambda_{max}(\log \epsilon)$	Ref.
$C_6H_{11}N_3S$			
1,2,4-Triazine, 2,5-dihydro-5,6-dimethyl-3-(methylthio)-	EtOH	260s(3.28)	44-4594-80
1,2,4-Triazine, 4,5-dihydro-5,6-dimethyl-3-(methylthio)-	EtOH	216(3.80),267(3.30)	44-4594-80
$C_6H_{12}N_2$			
1,4-Butanediamine, 2,3-bis(methylene)-	EtOH	224(4.11)	44-0870-80
$C_6H_{12}N_2O_2$			
Cyclohexanamine, N-hydroxy-N-nitroso-	hexane	235(3.64)	140-0949-80
	decane	230(3.71)	140-0949-80
	0.05M H_2SO_4	230(3.72)	140-0949-80
	pH 13	250(3.84)	140-0949-80
	6M HCl	230(3.89)	140-0949-80
	EtOH	210(3.43),237(3.85)	140-0949-80
	$CHCl_3$	246(3.28)	140-0949-80
Cyclohexanamine, N-nitro-	n.s.g.	237.0(3.90)	104-0407-80
anion	n.s.g.	231.0(3.93)	104-0407-80
$C_6H_{12}N_2S_3$			
Carbamodithioic acid, methyl[(methylimino)(methylthio)methyl]-, methyl ester	EtOH	248(3.96),269(3.95)	39-0665-80C
$C_6H_{12}N_4$			
Guanidine, N''-cyano-N,N,N',N'-tetramethyl-	MeOH	233(4.26)	32-0287-80
$C_6H_{12}N_4O_4S$			
Methanaminium, N-[(dimethylamino)[(dinitromethyl)thio]methylene]-N-methyl-, hydroxide, inner salt	MeCN	358(4.00)(changing)	70-0123-80
$C_6H_{12}O$			
Butanal, 2-ethyl-	heptane	300(1.34)	41-0217-80
Furan, tetrahydro-2,5-dimethyl-, cis	gas	187s(3.1)	23-2819-80
trans	gas	190f(3.1)	23-2819-80
Hexanal	heptane	294(1.31)	41-0497-80
$C_6H_{12}S_2$			
1,3-Dithiolane, 2,2,4-trimethyl-	hexane	194(3.65),249(2.20)	101-0147-80A
$C_6H_{12}S_4Si$			
1,4,6,9-Tetrathia-5-silaspiro[4.4]nonane, 2,7-dimethyl-	hexane	235(3.03)	101-0147-80A
$C_6H_{13}N_3$			
Ethanimidic acid, (1-methylpropylidene)hydrazide	MeOH	237(3.91)	104-0822-80
Methanhydrazonamide, N,N-dimethyl-N'-(1-methylethylidene)-, (E)-	MeOH	256(3.93)	104-0822-80
1H-1,2,4-Triazole, 2,5-dihydro-1,3,5,5-tetramethyl-	MeOH	245(3.56)	104-0822-80
$C_6H_{14}N_2O_3$			
Hydroperoxide, 1-(nitrosopropylamino)propyl	EtOH	231(3.85),363(1.82)	88-1765-80

Compound	Solvent	$\lambda_{max}(\log \epsilon)$	Ref.

$C_6H_{14}S_2Si$
  1,4-Dithia-2-silacyclohexane, 2,2,5-
  trimethyl-
	hexane	200(3.56),240s(2.42)	101-0147-80A

$C_6H_{15}P$ Phosphine, triethyl-	EtOH MeCN	260(1.09) 224(3.13)	65-0945-80 65-0945-80
$C_6H_{16}O_2Si$ Silane, diethoxydimethyl-	heptane MeCN	186.7(1.90) 187.4(2.04)	65-1280-80 65-1280-80
$C_6H_{16}S_2Si$ Silane, bis(ethylthio)dimethyl-	hexane hexane	190(--),224(3.14) 224(3.14)	101-0147-80A 131-0099-80C

$C_6H_{18}Ge_2Hg$
  Mercury, bis(trimethylgermyl)-
	C_6H_{12}
	
	THF
	
	Et_3N
		230(4.66),322(2.78),
		  364(2.26)
		228(4.60),296(2.72),
		  255(2.08)
		313(2.74),364(2.28)
			101-0169-80N
			
			101-0169-80N
			
			101-0169-80N

$C_6H_{18}HgSi_2$
  Mercury, bis(trimethylsilyl)-
	C_6H_{12}
	
	THF
	
	Et_3N
		214.2(4.42),328.0(2.57),
		  390.0(2.04)
		212.5(4.43),312.5(2.46),
		  370.0(0.88)
		331(2.45),386(0.94)
			101-0169-80N
			
			101-0169-80N
			
			101-0169-80N

$C_6H_{18}Si_2$ Disilane, hexamethyl-	gas	<u>163(4.3),192(4.2)</u>	61-0056-80
C_6N_4 Ethenetetracarbonitrile	CH_2Cl_2 CH_2Cl_2 dioxan	266(4.16),277(4.11) <u>265(4.2),277(4.1)</u> <u>259(4.11),350(3.15)</u>	24-1663-80 32-0037-80 24-1663-80

Compound	Solvent	λ_{max}(log ϵ)	Ref.
$C_7Cl_2F_5NO$ Benzamide, N,N-dichloro-2,3,4,5,6- pentafluoro-	heptane	218(3.81),267(3.30), 318(2.43)	104-0347-80
C_7F_9N Cyclohexenecarbonitrile, nonafluoro-	n.s.g.	238(4.74),276(4.42)	39-1507-80C
$C_7H_3Br_2NO$ 2,1-Benzisoxazole, 5,7-dibromo-	EtOH	250(2.97),255(3.05), 259(3.17),264(3.22), 270(3.34),275(3.35), 282(3.65),306(3.69)	12-0091-80
$C_7H_4Br_2N_2$ 2H-Cyclopenta[d]pyridazine, 5,7-di- bromo-	ether	248(4.34),265(4.29), 321(3.19),330(3.18), 412(3.09)	44-1695-80
$C_7H_4ClN_3O_2$ 1H-Indazole, 7-chloro-5-nitro-	EtOH	225(--),256(4.20), 298s(--),305(3.72), 325s(--)	5-0908-80
$C_7H_4ClRbS_2$ Benzenecarbodithioic acid, 4-chloro-, rubidium salt	EtOH	298(4.10),507(2.12)	64-0458-80B
$C_7H_4N_2O_3S$ 5H-Imidazo[2,1-b][1,3]thiazine- 6-carboxylic acid, 5-oxo-	0.3% NaHCO$_3$	211(4.17),271(4.16)	39-1352-80C
$C_7H_4OS_3$ 3H-1,2-Benzodithiole-3-thione, S-oxide	MeCN	440(4.01)	138-0619-80
$C_7H_5BrN_2$ 2H-Cyclopenta[d]pyridazine, 7-bromo-	ether	243(4.55),248s(4.53), 262s(4.32),312(3.42), 325(3.42),401(2.95)	44-1695-80
$C_7H_5BrN_4$ 1H-Tetrazole, 5-(2-bromophenyl)- 1H-Tetrazole, 5-(3-bromophenyl)- 1H-Tetrazole, 5-(4-bromophenyl)-	MeOH MeOH MeOH	212.5(4.20),222s(3.98) 215(4.31),245(4.15) 213(4.04),251(4.30), 279s(3.08)	56-0925-80 56-0925-80 56-0925-80
$C_7H_5ClN_2$ 1H-Indazole, 4-chloro- 1H-Indazole, 5-chloro- 1H-Indazole, 6-chloro- 1H-Indazole, 7-chloro-	EtOH EtOH EtOH EtOH	219(--),257(3.76), 264(3.76),283s(--), 288(3.75),293(3.72), 299(3.68) 222(--),262s(--), 266(3.61),288s(--), 295(3.63),299s(--), 308(3.58) 222(--),260s(--), 266(3.67),279s(--), 287(3.64),286s(--), 298(3.63) 218(--),253(3.57), 260(3.53),284s(--), 291(3.62),294s(--),	5-0908-80 5-0908-80 5-0908-80 5-0908-80

Compound	Solvent	$\lambda_{max}(\log \epsilon)$	Ref.
1H-Indazole, 7-chloro- (cont.)		302(3.58)	5-0908-80
C₇H₅ClN₂O₃			
Benzenecarboximidoyl chloride, N-hydroxy-4-nitro-	MeOH	219(4.03),294(4.22)	39-1051-80B
C₇H₅ClN₄			
1H-Tetrazole, 5-(2-chlorophenyl)-	MeOH	213(4.16),234(3.98)	56-0925-80
1H-Tetrazole, 5-(3-chlorophenyl)-	MeOH	214(4.28),245(4.13)	56-0925-80
1H-Tetrazole, 5-(4-chlorophenyl)-	MeOH	209(3.97),248(4.28), 330(2.78)	56-0925-80
C₇H₅ClO₄			
Acetic acid, (4-chloro-3-methyl-5-oxo-2(5H)-furanylidene)-, (Z)-	EtOH	281(4.30)	23-2765-80
C₇H₅ClS₂			
Benzenecarbodithioic acid, 4-chloro-, cesium salt	EtOH	242(3.87),290(3.99), 367(3.80),507(2.18)	64-0458-80B
potassium salt	EtOH	288(4.26),367(4.11), 468s(2.42)	64-0458-80B
C₇H₅Cl₂NO			
Benzenecarboximidoyl chloride, 4-chloro-N-hydroxy-	C₆H₁₂	218s(4.03),256(4.21), 284s(3.15),292(2.72)	39-1051-80B
C₇H₅Cl₂N₃O			
1H-Benzotriazole, 4,5-dichloro-1-methoxy-	EtOH	209(4.52),264(3.98), 272(4.00),294(3.82)	4-1115-80
C₇H₅CsS₂			
Benzenecarbodithioic acid, cesium salt	EtOH	285(3.62),362(3.53)	64-0458-80B
C₇H₅IN₄			
1H-Tetrazole, 5-(2-iodophenyl)-	MeOH	214.5(4.29),225s(--)	56-0925-80
1H-Tetrazole, 5-(3-iodophenyl)-	MeOH	211(4.08),247(4.10), 273s(2.90)	56-0925-80
1H-Tetrazole, 5-(4-iodophenyl)-	MeOH	215(4.08),255(4.37)	56-0925-80
C₇H₅NO			
2,1-Benzisoxazole	EtOH	250(2.97),255(3.05), 259(3.17),264(3.22), 270(3.34),275(3.35), 282(3.65),306(3.69)	12-0091-80
C₇H₅NOSe			
Selenocyanic acid, 4-hydroxyphenyl ester	MeOH	239(3.98)	104-1963-80
C₇H₅NO₂S			
Thieno[3,2-b]pyridin-5(4H)-one, 7-hydroxy-	EtOH	268(4.05),278(4.12), 314(4.01)	150-0113-80
C₇H₅NO₄			
Benzoic acid, 2-nitro-, anion	pH 6.0	268(3.72)	77-0394-80
	15.8M KOH	274(3.67)	77-0394-80
	10M LiCl	275(3.77)	77-0394-80
1,4-Cyclohexadiene-1-carboxylic acid, 6-(hydroxyimino)-3-oxo-	pH 13	404(4.45)	77-0394-80
	15.8M KOH	404(4.42?)	77-0394-80

Compound	Solvent	$\lambda_{max}(\log \epsilon)$	Ref.
$C_7H_5NO_4S$			
Benzoic acid, 5-mercapto-2-nitro-	3M NaOH	412(4.15)	139-0127-80B
$C_7H_5NO_5S$			
Benzenesulfenic acid, 3-carboxy- 4-nitro-, dianion	3M NaOH	492(4.06)(changing)	139-0127-80B
$C_7H_5N_3OS_2$			
Thieno[3,2-d]isothiazole-5-carbonitrile, 4-amino-3-methoxy-	MeOH	221(4.28),248(4.26), 279(3.73),319(3.93)	48-1021-80
$C_7H_5N_3O_2$			
1,2,4-Oxadiazol-5(2H)-one, 3-(2-pyri- dinyl)-	MeOH	220(3.87),272(3.79), 279s(3.66)	39-0959-80C
$C_7H_5N_3O_4$			
Benzofurazan, 4-methoxy-7-nitro-	MeOH	330(<u>4.2</u>)	44-2666-80
$C_7H_5N_3S_3$			
Thieno[2,3-c]isothiazole-5-carbo- nitrile, 4-amino-3-(methylthio)-	MeOH	269(4.32),288(4.03), 375(3.76)	48-1021-80
Thieno[3,2-d]isothiazole-5-carbo- nitrile, 4-amino-3-(methylthio)-	MeOH	238(4.08),259(4.12), 295(3.90),319(3.70)	48-1021-80
$C_7H_5N_5O$			
1H-Pyrrolo[2,3-d]pyrimidine-5-carbo- nitrile, 2-amino-4,7-dihydro-4-oxo-	pH 13	225(4.23),245(4.00), 292(3.86)	138-0559-80
$C_7H_5N_5O_2$			
1H-Tetrazole, 5-(2-nitrophenyl)-	MeOH	220(4.09),248s(3.79), 278s(3.30)	56-0925-80
1H-Tetrazole, 5-(3-nitrophenyl)-	MeOH	208s(3.87),243(4.29), 290s(3.00)	56-0925-80
1H-Tetrazole, 5-(4-nitrophenyl)-	MeOH	212(3.96),301(4.10)	56-0925-80
$C_7H_5RbS_2$			
Benzenecarbodithioic acid, rubidium salt	EtOH	280(4.21),362(3.98), 498(2.22)	64-0458-80B
$C_7H_6BrNO_2$			
Formamide, N-(4-bromophenyl)-N-hydroxy-	EtOH	260(4.21)	44-2834-80
$C_7H_6BrN_3O_4$			
Imidazo[1,2-c]pyrimidine-2-carboxylic acid, 8-bromo-1,2,3,5,6,7-hexahydro- 5,7-dioxo-	pH 1 pH 7	275(3.83) 277(3.94)	103-0418-80 103-0418-80
C_7H_6ClNO			
Benzaldehyde, 4-chloro-, oxime, (E)-	C_6H_{12}	205s(4.36),208(4.40), 214(4.38),219(4.20), 259(4.35),287(3.36), 297(3.20)	39-1051-80B
Benzaldehyde, 4-chloro-, oxime, (Z)-	C_6H_{12}	206(4.39),211(4.34), 217(4.12),250(4.37), 283s(3.43),292(2.75)	39-1051-80B
Benzenecarboximidoyl chloride, N-hy- droxy-	C_6H_{12}	247(4.16),289s(2.54)	39-1051-80B
$C_7H_6ClNO_2$			
Formamide, N-(3-chlorophenyl)-N-hy- droxy-	EtOH	255(4.09)	44-2834-80

Compound	Solvent	$\lambda_{max}(\log \epsilon)$	Ref.
Formamide, N-(4-chlorophenyl)-N-hydroxy-	EtOH	258(4.15)	44-2834-80
C₇H₆Cl₄O			
2-Cyclopenten-1-one, 2,3,5,5-tetrachloro-4,4-dimethyl-	MeOH	260(4.05),320(2.20)	20-0307-80
C₇H₆Cl₅NO			
2-Cyclopenten-1-one, 2,4,4,5,5-pentachloro-3-(dimethylamino)-	EtOH	328(4.26)	104-1404-80
2-Cyclopenten-1-one, 2,4,4,5,5-pentachloro-3-(ethylamino)-	EtOH	311(4.32)	104-1404-80
2,4-Pentadienamide, 2,3,4,5,5-pentachloro-N,N-dimethyl-	EtOH	220(4.30)	104-1404-80
2,4-Pentadienamide, 2,3,4,5,5-pentachloro-N-ethyl-	EtOH	225(4.31)	104-1404-80
C₇H₆FNO₂			
Formamide, N-(4-fluorophenyl)-N-hydroxy-	EtOH	249(3.99)	44-2834-80
C₇H₆N₂			
1H-Indazole	EtOH	215(--),252(3.68), 257s(--),275s(--), 285(3.69),290(3.69), 297(3.65)	5-0908-80
C₇H₆N₂OS			
Pyridine, 5-isothiocyanato-2-methoxy-	hexane	228(4.44),260s(3.98), 274(4.17),285s(4.11), 307s(3.67)	44-4219-80
C₇H₆N₂O₂			
1(2H)-Pyridinecarbonitrile, 3-hydroxy-6-methyl-2-oxo-	EtOH	212(4.07),323(3.89)	39-1587-80C
	EtOH-NaOH	223(4.04),265(3.65), 349(3.92)	39-1587-80C
C₇H₆N₂O₂S			
2,4(1H,3H)-Pyrimidinedione, 5-(2-propynylthio)-	pH 13	292(3.85)	87-0569-80
Thieno[2,3-d]pyrimidine-2,4(1H,3H)-dione, 3-methyl-	pH 1	225(4.49),252(3.84), 277(3.58)	39-1853-80C
	pH 11	226(4.43),265(3.98), 299(3.79)	39-1853-80C
	MeOH	223(4.46),256(3.78), 278(3.58)	39-1853-80C
C₇H₆N₂O₂S₃			
3H-1,2-Dithiolo[3,4-d]pyrimidine-4,6(5H,7H)-dione, 5,7-dimethyl-3-thioxo-	EtOH	235(4.10),291(4.32), 395(3.75)	142-0679-80B
C₇H₆N₂O₃			
Benzaldehyde, 4-nitro-, oxime, (Z)-	MeOH	222(4.02),300(4.13)	39-1051-80B
C₇H₆N₂O₄			
Acetamide, N-(1,2,5,6-tetrahydro-2,5,6-trioxo-3-pyridinyl)-	EtOH	210(4.10),262(4.13), 348(3.76)	39-1788-80C
C₇H₆N₂Se			
Selenocyanic acid, 4-aminophenyl ester	MeOH	260(4.13)	104-1963-80

Compound	Solvent	$\lambda_{max}(\log \epsilon)$	Ref.
C₇H₆N₄			
1H-Tetrazole, 5-phenyl-	MeOH	207(4.01),241(4.20)	56-0925-80
C₇H₆N₄O			
Phenol, 2-(1H-tetrazol-5-yl)-	MeOH	214(4.30),242(4.12), 251(4.04),300(3.72)	56-0925-80
Phenol, 4-(1H-tetrazol-5-yl)-	MeOH	209(3.91),250(4.18), 284s(3.15)	56-0925-80
C₇H₆N₄OS			
4(1H)-Pteridinone, 2-(methylthio)-	pH -3.05	287(3.81),296s(3.77), 379(3.81)	18-2344-80
	pH 3.0	230(3.92),278(4.15), 331(3.83)	18-2344-80
	pH 9.0	240(3.92),268(4.27), 349(3.85)	18-2344-80
C₇H₆N₄O₂			
2,4(1H,3H)-Pteridinedione, 1-methyl-	pH -4.9	245(4.20),295s(2.94), 352(3.80)	142-0437-80B
	pH 0.0	231(4.12),245s(3.94), 329(3.89)	142-0437-80B
2,4(1H,3H)-Pteridinedione, 3-methyl-	pH -4.9	242(4.13),287(3.33), 342(3.86)	142-0437-80B
	pH 0.0	230(4.15),247s(3.73), 323(3.89)	142-0437-80B
2,4(1H,3H)-Pteridinedione, 8-methyl-	pH -3.0	240(4.07),274s(3.12), 344(4.05)	142-0437-80B
C₇H₆N₄O₃			
2,4,7(1H,3H,8H)-Pteridinetrione, 1-methyl-	pH 1.0	264(3.77),285(3.52), 324(4.01)	24-1524-80
	pH 7.0	276(3.99),328(4.20)	24-1524-80
	pH 13.0	249(4.00),272(3.67), 334(4.15)	24-1524-80
2,4,7(1H,3H,8H)-Pteridinetrione, 3-methyl-	pH 1.2	274(3.79),326(4.03)	24-1524-80
	pH 7.0	274(4.01),328(4.20)	24-1524-80
	pH 12.5	225(4.57),259(4.04), 276(3.91),358(4.15)	24-1524-80
2,4,7(1H,3H,8H)-Pteridinetrione, 8-methyl-	pH 1.5	277(4.20),330(4.08)	24-1535-80
	pH 7.8	248(3.73),286(4.00), 348(4.17)	24-1535-80
	pH 14.0	260(3.96),362(4.07)	24-1535-80
C₇H₆N₄O₆			
Benzenamine, N-methyl-2,4,6-trinitro-	DMSO-5%MeOH	350(4.19),410s(3.83)	23-1615-80
C₇H₆N₄S			
2-Pyridinamine, N-1,2,3-thiadiazol-5-yl-	n.s.g.	241(3.89),317(4.27)	73-2329-80
3-Pyridinamine, N-1,2,3-thiadiazol-5-yl-	n.s.g.	246(3.66),322(4.09)	73-2329-80
4-Pyridinamine, N-1,2,3-thiadiazol-5-yl-	n.s.g.	250(3.79),317(4.34)	73-2329-80
C₇H₆N₆			
Bis[1,2,4]triazolo[1,5-a:1',5'-c]pyrimidine, 5-methyl-	EtOH	215(4.45),229(3.96), 257s(4.01),264(4.01), 275s(3.76)	12-1147-80
Bis[1,2,4]triazolo[1,5-a:1',5'-c]pyrimidine, 8-methyl-	EtOH	219(4.41),230s(3.97), 256s(3.92),263(3.95),	12-1147-80

Compound	Solvent	$\lambda_{max}(\log \epsilon)$	Ref.
(cont.)		275s(3.75)	12-1147-80
C₇H₆O₂ 2-Propenal, 3-(2-furanyl)-	n.s.g.	314(4.32)	39-2081-80C
C₇H₆O₃ Benzoic acid, 2-hydroxy-	MeOH	233(4.81),303(4.56)	95-0466-80
C₇H₆O₄ Propanoic acid, 2-(5-oxo-2(5H)-furan- ylidene)-	MeOH	206s(3.51),292(4.22)	48-0559-80
C₇H₆O₄SSe₂ 1,3-Thiaselenone-4,5-dicarboxylic acid, 2-selenoxo-, dimethyl ester	C₆H₁₂	215(4.18),313(3.25), 400(4.09),540(1.32)	44-2632-80
C₇H₆S₂ Benzenecarbodithioic acid, cesium salt	EtOH	285(3.62),362(3.53)	64-0458-80B
potassium salt	EtOH	283(4.03),361(3.91)	64-0458-80B
rubidium salt	EtOH	280(4.21),362(3.98), 498(2.22)	64-0458-80B
C₇H₇BrN₄ 9H-Purine, 6-bromo-9-ethyl-	H₂O	267.5(3.95)	44-3969-80
C₇H₇ClN₂ Diaziridine, 3-chloro-3-phenyl-	MeOH	230(3.71),255s(--)	24-2040-80
C₇H₇ClN₂O₂ Pyrazinecarboxylic acid, 5-chloro- 6-methyl-, methyl ester	pH 1	226(3.97),283(4.01)	94-3057-80
	H₂O	226(3.97),283(4.01)	94-3057-80
	pH 13	220(4.30),283(3.96)	94-3057-80
3(2H)-Pyridazinone, 4-chloro-5-hydroxy- 2-(2-propenyl)-	MeOH	215(4.45),227s(--), 286(3.77)	73-0127-80
C₇H₇ClN₄ 9H-Purine, 6-chloro-9-ethyl-	H₂O	265.5(3.97)	44-3969-80
C₇H₇ClO₄ 2,4-Hexadienedioic acid, 2-chloro- 5-methyl-	EtOH	281(4.31)	23-2765-80
	EtOH-base	272(4.28)	23-2765-80
C₇H₇Cl₂OP Phosphonic dichloride, (4-methyl- phenyl)-	C₆H₁₂	198(4.42),231(4.22), 259(2.76),269(2.88), 277(2.85)	65-1578-80
	C₂H₄Cl₂	234(4.09),260(2.85), 270(2.94),277(2.86)	65-1578-80
	MeCN	199(4.45),233(4.16), 260(2.85),268(2.92), 276(2.83)	65-1578-80
C₇H₇Cl₂O₂P Phosphonic dichloride, (4-methoxy- phenyl)-	C₆H₁₂	203(4.46),245(4.31), 269(3.40),278(2.88)	65-1578-80
	C₂H₄Cl₂	249(4.34),272(3.53), 278(3.04)	65-1578-80
	MeCN	201(4.42),248(4.30), 272(3.48),278(3.04)	65-1578-80

Compound	Solvent	$\lambda_{max}(\log \epsilon)$	Ref.
$C_7H_7Cl_3O$			
2-Cyclopenten-1-one, 2,3,5-trichloro-4,4-dimethyl-	MeOH	248(4.03)	20-0307-80
$C_7H_7Cl_3OP$			
Phosphorus(1+), trichloro(4-methoxy-phenyl)-, hexachlorophosphate tetrachloroaluminate	$C_2H_4Cl_2$	289(4.38),345(2.04)	65-1578-80
	MeCN	282(4.37),345(2.00)	65-1578-80
	MeCN	283.5(4.30)	65-1578-80
	$MeNO_2$	285(4.31)	65-1578-80
$C_7H_7Cl_3P$			
Phosphorus(1+), trichloro(4-methyl-phenyl)-, hexachlorophosphate tetrachloroaluminate	C_6H_{12}	237(4.19),267s(3.34)	65-1578-80
	MeCN	254(4.25),345(2.00)	65-1578-80
	MeCN	252(4.19),278s(3.51)	65-1578-80
	$MeNO_2$	256(4.16),278s(3.60)	65-1578-80
$C_7H_7Cl_4OP$			
Phosphorane, tetrachloro(4-methoxy-phenyl)-	C_6H_{12}	250(4.20),290s(2.92)	65-1578-80
$C_7H_7Cl_4P$			
Phosphorane, tetrachloro(4-methyl-phenyl)-	C_6H_{12}	236.5(4.14),267s(3.18)	65-1578-80
C_7H_7D			
Bicyclo[2.2.1]hepta-2,5-diene-2-d	heptane	202s(3.38),213s(3.19), 220s(2.94),230s(2.30)	35-5749-80
$C_7H_7F_3N_2O_2$			
Pyrimidine, 2,4-dimethoxy-5-(trifluoro-methyl)-	MeOH	257(3.71)	39-2755-80C
	MeOH-acid	256(3.73)	39-2755-80C
	MeOH-base	257(3.74)	39-2755-80C
Pyrimidine, 2,4-dimethoxy-6-(trifluoro-	MeOH	265(3.76)	39-2755-80C
	MeOH-acid	265(3.77)	39-2755-80C
	MeOH-base	265(3.77)	39-2755-80C
$C_7H_7IN_4$			
9H-Purine, 9-ethyl-6-iodo-	H_2O	276.5(4.03)	44-3969-80
C_7H_7N			
1-Cyclobutene-1-carbonitrile, 2-methyl-3-methylene-	hexane	252(4.29)	47-0477-80
C_7H_7NO			
Benzaldehyde, oxime, (E)-	C_6H_{12}	250(4.21),281(3.14), 283s(3.11),291(2.98)	39-1051-80B
Benzaldehyde, oxime, (Z)-	C_6H_{12}	240(4.26),278s(3.02), 288(2.82)	39-1051-80B
C_7H_7NOS			
1,4-Oxathiino[3,2-b]pyridine, 2,3-di-hydro-	EtOH	251(3.65),306(3.86)	1-0619-80
	EtOH-HCl	254(3.52),333(3.95)	1-0619-80
3-Pyridinecarboxaldehyde, 2-(methyl-thio)-	EtOH	224(4.16),253(3.73), 275(3.91),338(3.45)	118-0405-80
$C_7H_7NO_2$			
Anthranilic acid	MeOH	214(4.55),246(3.81), 330(3.62)	94-2428-80
Formamide, N-hydroxy-N-phenyl-	EtOH	250(4.03)	44-2834-80

Compound	Solvent	λ$_{max}$(log ε)	Ref.
C$_7$H$_7$NO$_2$S 2(1H)-Pyridinethione, 3-acetoxy-	EtOH	280(4.05),362(3.89)	36-1074-80
C$_7$H$_7$NO$_3$ 3-Pyridinecarboxylic acid, 1,4-dihydro- 5-methyl-4-oxo-	EtOH	255(3.83),283(3.54)	4-0359-80
C$_7$H$_7$NO$_5$ 2-Furancarboxylic acid, 5-nitro-, ethyl ester	MeOH	213(4.16),293(4.15)	73-0135-80
C$_7$H$_7$N$_3$ Pyrazolo[1,5-a]pyrimidine, 5-methyl-	MeOH	207(4.40),229(4.65), 232(4.66),280(3.23)	39-0481-80C
Pyrazolo[1,5-a]pyrimidine, 7-methyl-	MeOH	228(4.64),278(3.27), 318(3.28)	39-0481-80C
C$_7$H$_7$N$_3$OS$_3$ Thieno[2,3-c]isothiazole-5-carboxamide, 4-amino-3-(methylthio)-	MeOH	264(4.12),299(3.93), 349(3.80)	48-1021-80
C$_7$H$_7$N$_3$O$_2$ Imidazo[1,5-a]pyridine-1,3(2H,8aH)-di- one, 1-oxime, sulfate (2:1)	MeOH	268(3.96),388(3.70)	39-0959-80C
bromide	MeOH	207(3.96),239(3.97), 334s(4.02),347(4.15), 383(4.08)	39-0959-80C
Sydnone, 3-(1,4-dihydro-3-pyridinyl)-	MeOH	233(3.75),315(3.33), 398(3.92)	39-0020-80C
C$_7$H$_7$N$_3$O$_4$ Pyrazinecarboxylic acid, 3-(aminocarbo- nyl)-1,6-dihydro-5-methyl-6-oxo-	pH 1 H$_2$O pH 13	271(3.85),305(3.65) 260(3.94),308(3.81) 273(4.07),308(3.95)	94-3057-80 94-3057-80 94-3057-80
C$_7$H$_7$N$_3$Se Selenocyanic acid, 3,4-diaminophenyl ester	MeOH	220(4.45),257(3.90), 310(3.75)	104-1963-80
C$_7$H$_7$N$_5$ Benzenamine, 2-(1H-tetrazol-5-yl)-	MeOH	220(4.27),248(3.81), 312(3.53)	56-0925-80
Benzenamine, 3-(1H-tetrazol-5-yl)-	MeOH	225(4.32),244s(4.02), 301(3.38)	56-0925-80
Benzenamine, 4-(1H-tetrazol-5-yl)-	MeOH	211(4.14),266(4.33)	56-0925-80
C$_7$H$_7$N$_5$O Pyrimido[4,5-c]pyridazin-5(6H)-one, 7-amino-3-methyl-	pH 13	252(4.33),270s(3.89), 362(3.62)	44-3919-80
C$_7$H$_7$N$_5$O$_2$ 4(1H)-Pteridinone, 2-amino-6-(hydroxy- methyl)-	pH 0.0 pH 5.0 pH 11.0	247(4.03),320(3.93) 235(4.08),273(4.14), 345(3.80) 254(4.35),277s(3.79), 363(3.87)	24-1514-80 24-1514-80 24-1514-80
C$_7$H$_7$N$_5$S Thiazolo[2,3-b]purin-4-amine, 7,8-di- hydro-	pH 1 pH 7 pH 13	247(4.41),292(4.05) 238(4.44),294(4.06) 238(4.44),294(4.06)	4-0583-80 4-0583-80 4-0583-80

Compound	Solvent	$\lambda_{max}(\log \epsilon)$	Ref.
Thiazolo[3,2-a]purin-9-amine, 6,7-di-hydro-	pH 1	224(4.17),271(4.17)	4-0583-80
	pH 13	277(4.17),287s(4.02)	4-0583-80
C_7H_8			
Bicyclo[2.2.1]hepta-2,5-diene	heptane	203s(3.38),214s(3.20), 220s(2.95),230s(2.30)	35-5749-80
Toluene	C_6H_{12}	262.5(2.34)	80-0651-80
	hexane	262.3(2.41)	80-0651-80
	heptane	262.2(2.33)	80-0651-80
	$CHCl_3$	263.0(2.37)	80-0651-80
(also other solvents)	CCl_4	263.9(2.47)	80-0651-80
$C_7H_8BrN_3O_2$			
2H-Pyrimido[1,6-a]pyrimidine-6,8(1H,7H)-dione, 9-bromo-3,4-dihydro-	MeOH	279(4.30)	78-0865-80
$C_7H_8BrN_3O_4$			
1(2H)-Pyrimidinepropanoic acid, α-amino-5-bromo-3,4-dihydro-2,4-dioxo-	$NaHCO_3$	<u>277(3.9)</u>(changing)	103-0418-80
$C_7H_8Br_2Si$			
Silane, dibromomethylphenyl-	hexane	218(3.73),255s(2.39), 260(2.55),266(2.64), 273(2.52)	101-0147-80A
$C_7H_8Cl_2Si$			
Silane, dichloromethylphenyl-	hexane	216(3.88),254s(2.37), 259(2.56),265(2.68), 272(2.58)	101-0147-80A
$C_7H_8F_2Si$			
Silane, difluoromethylphenyl-	hexane	211(3.83),253s(2.39), 258(2.60),264(2.74), 270(2.66)	101-0147-80A
$C_7H_8N_2O_2$			
Acetamide, N-(1,2-dihydro-2-oxo-3-pyridinyl)-	EtOH	248(3.98),256(3.91), 308(4.00)	36-1074-80
1,2-Diazepine-1-carboxylic acid, methyl ester	EtOH	228(4.03),355(2.38)	142-1569-80B
7H-Oxazolo[3,2-a]pyrimidin-7-one, 2,3-dihydro-6-methyl-	H_2O	228(3.74),267(3.88)	47-2959-80
$C_7H_8N_2O_2S$			
2,4(1H,3H)-Pyrimidinedione, 5-(2-propenylthio)-	pH 13	293(3.86)	87-0569-80
2(1H)-Pyrimidinone, 3,4-dihydro-4-(1-mercapto-2-oxopropylidene)-	pH 1-6	265(3.72),320s(3.82), 370(4.01)	44-3651-80
	pH 13	273(3.82),325s(3.74), 376(4.19)	44-3651-80
2(1H)-Pyrimidinone, 4-[(2-oxopropyl)-thio]-	0.6M HCl	220(3.67),268(3.35), 324(4.25)	44-3651-80
	pH 6	206(4.15),223s(3.82), 268(3.86),297(3.99), 333s(2.80)	44-3651-80
	pH 12	223(4.15),244s(3.74), 300(3.96)	44-3651-80
$C_7H_8N_2O_3$			
Pyrazinecarboxylic acid, 4,5-dihydro-6-methyl-5-oxo-, methyl ester	pH 1	259(4.18),300(3.85)	94-3057-80
	H_2O	259(4.18),300(3.87)	94-3057-80

Compound	Solvent	$\lambda_{max}(\log \epsilon)$	Ref.
(cont.)	pH 13	271(4.12),303(4.05)	94-3057-80
$C_7H_8N_2O_4$			
1(2H)-Pyrimidinepropanoic acid, 3,4-di-hydro-2,4-dioxo-	HCl	268.5(3.98)	47-0949-80
	DMSO	268.5(3.96)	47-0949-80
$C_7H_8N_2O_5$			
2-Furancarboxylic acid, 5-amino-4-nitro-, ethyl ester	MeOH	222(3.96),285(4.23), 336(4.23)	73-0135-80
$C_7H_8N_2S$			
Pyrimidine, 2-(2-propenylthio)-	EtOH	251(4.204),285s(3.301)	112-0001-80
	CH_2Cl_2	252(4.204),285s(3.301)	112-0001-80
$C_7H_8N_4$			
9H-Purine, 9-ethyl-	H_2O	264.5(3.90)	44-3969-80
1,2,4-Triazolo[4,3-a]pyridin-3-amine, N-methyl-	MeOH	245(4.12),288(3.84)	142-1125-80
$C_7H_8N_4OS_2$			
Thiocyanic acid, 6-amino-2-(ethylthio)-1,4-dihydro-4-oxo-5-pyrimidinyl ester	MeOH	223(4.25),238(4.22), 284(3.98)	4-1587-80
$C_7H_8N_4S$			
1H-Pyrrolo[2,3-d]pyrimidin-4-amine, 2-(methylthio)-	MeOH	232(4.43),281(4.14)	24-2069-80
$C_7H_8N_6O$			
6-Pteridinemethanol, 2,4-diamino-	pH 2.0	244(4.21),286(3.71), 336(4.02),348s(3.96)	24-1514-80
	pH 8.0	226(4.07),258(4.36), 370(3.87)	24-1514-80
1-Triazene-1-carbonitrile, 3-(3,6-di-methyl-4-pyridazinyl)-, 1-oxide, potassium salt	EtOH	223(3.76),265(3.50), 325(3.97),392(4.33)	94-0529-80
2-oxide	EtOH	272(4.24),356(4.22)	94-0529-80
potassium salt	EtOH	275(4.21),364(4.37)	94-0529-80
$C_7H_8N_6O_3$			
1-Triazene-1-carbonitrile, 3-(3,6-di-methoxy-4-pyridazinyl)-, 1-oxide	EtOH	250(3.69),325(3.63), 415(4.12)	94-0529-80
$C_7H_8N_6S_2$			
1H-Pyrazolo[3,4-d]pyrimidine-3-carbo-thioamide, 4-amino-6-(methylthio)-	EtOH	197(4.31),203(4.25), 248(4.34),250(4.36), 285(4.19)	103-0182-80
C_7H_8O			
Benzene, methoxy- (anisole)	hexane	220(3.882),265(3.108), 271(3.264),277(3.278)	65-0491-80
	hexane	220(3.88),223(3.78)	70-1928-80
	EtOH	222(3.707),265(3.132), 271(3.240),277(3.184)	65-0491-80
Phenol, 2-methyl-	hexane	214(3.79),272(3.28), 279(3.26)	65-2236-80
	pentane-EtOH-ether	217(3.77),275(3.30), 282(3.23)	65-2236-80
Phenol, 3-methyl-	hexane	216(3.78),269(3.11), 274(3.26),280(3.28)	65-2236-80
	pentane-EtOH-ether	220(3.88),276(3.22), 281(3.26)	65-2236-80

Compound	Solvent	$\lambda_{max}(\log \epsilon)$	Ref.
Phenol, 4-methyl-	hexane	222(3.83),264(3.00), 265(3.11),269(3.20), 270(3.32),274(3.36), 277(3.43),280(3.50), 282(3.30)	65-2236-80
	pentane- EtOH-ether	226(3.85),281(3.34), 289(3.15)	65-2236-80
C_7H_8OS Benzene, (methylsulfinyl)-, radical	H_2O	320(3.50)	39-0146-80B
$C_7H_8O_2$ 4-Cyclopentene-1,2-dicarboxaldehyde	ether	261(3.85)	118-0543-80
2(3H)-Furanone, dihydro-5-(2-propen- ylidene)-	C_6H_{12}	216.5(3.76)	33-1204-80
	EtOH	221.0(3.97)	33-1204-80
Phenol, 2-methoxy-	hexane	218(3.73),273(3.43), 276(3.49),282(3.46)	65-2236-80
	pentane- EtOH-ether	223(3.87),279(3.54), 286(3.48)	65-2236-80
Phenol, 4-methoxy-	hexane	225(3.72),287(3.34), 290(3.38),295(3.38)	65-2236-80
	pentane- EtOH-ether	235(4.04),277(3.89)	65-2236-80
4H-Pyran-4-one, 2,6-dimethyl-	MeOH	<u>248(4.1)</u>	18-0469-80
$C_7H_8O_3$ 2H-Pyran-2-one, 4-hydroxy-5,6-dimethyl-	EtOH	380(3.75)	39-2272-80C
$C_7H_8O_5$ 2-Furanacetic acid, 2,5-dihydro-3-hy- droxy-4-methyl-5-oxo-	MeOH-acid MeOH-base	228.3(4.15) 258.4(4.32)	48-0559-80 48-0559-80
$C_7H_9BrClN_3$ 4-Pyrimidinamine, 2-chloro-N-ethyl- N-methyl-	MeOH	267(4.03),305(3.72)	56-1557-80
$C_7H_9ClN_2O_2$ 1H-Pyrazole-3-carboxylic acid, 5-(chloromethyl)-, ethyl ester	EtOH	232(3.76)	87-0657-80
3(2H)-Pyridazinone, 4-chloro-5-hydroxy- 2-(1-methylethyl)-	MeOH	215(4.50),226s(--), 286(3.75)	73-0127-80
3(2H)-Pyridazinone, 4-chloro-5-hydroxy- 2-propyl-	MeOH	215(4.46),227s(--), 286(3.76)	73-0127-80
$C_7H_9ClN_2O_2S$ 3(2H)-Pyridazinone, 4-chloro-2-[(ethyl- thio)methyl]-5-hydroxy-	MeOH	222s(--),287(4.31), 298(4.04)	73-0127-80
$C_7H_9ClN_2O_3$ 3(2H)-Pyridazinone, 4-chloro-2-(ethoxy- methyl)-5-hydroxy-	MeOH	215(4.49),226s(--), 287(3.82)	73-0127-80
C_7H_9DO Bicyclo[2.2.1]heptan-7-one-2-d, (1S- endo)-	heptane	291(1.20)	35-1983-80
(1S-exo)-	heptane MeOH	292f(1.20) 288(--)	35-1983-80 35-1983-80
$C_7H_9FN_2O_3$ 2,4(1H,3H)-Pyrimidinedione, 1-(ethoxy- methyl)-5-fluoro-	pH 2 pH 7	268(3.92) 268(3.92)	103-1176-80 103-1176-80

Compound	Solvent	$\lambda_{max}(\log \epsilon)$	Ref.
(cont.)	pH 12	268(3.78)	103-1176-80
$C_7H_9FN_2O_4$			
2,4(1H,3H)-Pyrimidinedione, 5-fluoro-1-[(2-hydroxyethoxy)methyl]-	pH 2	269(3.92)	103-1176-80
	pH 7	269(3.89)	103-1176-80
	pH 12	270(3.78)	103-1176-80
$C_7H_9IN_2O_2$			
1H-Pyrazole-3-carboxylic acid, 5-(iodomethyl)-, ethyl ester	EtOH	232(4.09)	87-0657-80
2,4(1H,3H)-Pyrimidinedione, 1-(2-iodoethyl)-3-methyl-	H_2O	266.0(4.00)	117-0275-80
C_7H_9N			
Benzenamine, 2-methyl-	C_6H_{12}	234(--),285(3.22)	44-2195-80
Benzenamine, 4-methyl-	C_6H_{12}	238(--),295(3.20)	44-2195-80
2,4-Pentadienenitrile, 2,4-dimethyl-	hexane	249(4.39)	47-0477-80
C_7H_9NO			
Cyclopenta[b]pyrrol-3(2H)-one, 1,4,5,6-tetrahydro-	MeOH	313.5(4.03)	5-0564-80
	MeOH-2M HCl	290.5(--)	5-0564-80
	$CHCl_3$	312(4.70)	5-0564-80
Ethanone, 1-(2-methyl-1H-pyrrol-3-yl)-	EtOH	210(3.92),243(3.90), 282(3.80)	23-0794-80
C_7H_9NOS			
3-Furancarbothioamide, N,2-dimethyl-	EtOH	210(3.94),226s(3.69), 270(3.90)	128-0069-80
3-Thiophenecarboxamide, N,N-dimethyl-	EtOH	239(3.88)	59-0349-80
$C_7H_9NO_2$			
2-Azetidinone, 4-[(1-methylene-2-propenyl)oxy]-	EtOH	228(4.11)	39-2222-80C
2-Furancarboxamide, N,N-dimethyl-	EtOH	224s(3.78),253(4.08)	59-0349-80
2-Furancarboxamide, N,2-dimethyl-	EtOH	213(3.88),237s(3.68)	128-0069-80
3-Furancarboxamide, N,N-dimethyl-	EtOH	220s(3.85)	59-0349-80
6H-1,3-Oxazin-6-one, 2,4,5-trimethyl-	pentane	274(3.9)	5-0798-80
2(1H)-Pyridinone, 4-methoxy-6-methyl-	C_6H_{12}	225(3.42),285(3.72)	44-1354-80
4(1H)-Pyridinone, 3-methoxy-2-methyl-	EtOH	264(4.14)	36-1074-80
$C_7H_9NO_3$			
2-Furancarboxylic acid, 5-amino-, ethyl ester	MeOH	206(3.68),316(4.28)	73-0135-80
5-Isoxazolemethanol, 3-methyl-, acetate	MeOH	211(3.78),252(2.60)	94-3296-80
$C_7H_9NO_3S_2$			
1,2,4-Dithiazine-3-carboxylic acid, tetrahydro-4-methyl-5-oxo-, ethyl ester	MeCN	<u>290s(2.3)</u>	11-0102-80B
$C_7H_9NO_6$			
Propanedioic acid, (2-aci-nitro-ethylidene)-, dimethyl ester, sodium salt	MeOH	238(4.01),423(4.55)	104-2055-80
$C_7H_9N_3O_2$			
2H-Pyrimido[1,6-a]pyrimidine-6,8-dione, 1,3,4,7-tetrahydro-	MeOH	271(4.42)	78-0865-80
Sydnone, 3-(1,4,5,6-tetrahydro-3-pyridinyl)-	MeOH	216(3.80),305(3.90), 359(4.23)	39-0020-80C
Urea, N-(1,2-dihydro-2-oxo-3-pyridinyl)-N'-methyl-	EtOH	251(4.01),305(4.04)	36-1074-80

Compound	Solvent	$\lambda_{max}(\log \epsilon)$	Ref.
$C_7H_9N_3O_4$			
Acetic acid, [[(2-amino-1-cyano-2-oxo-ethylidene)amino]oxy]-, ethyl ester, (E)-	EtOH	236(4.07)	5-1623-80
1-Pyrimidinepropanoic acid, α-amino-3,4-dihydro-2,4-dioxo-	pH 2	261(3.88)	94-2748-80
	pH 12	286(4.02)	94-2748-80
5-Pyrimidinepropanoic acid, 2-amino-1,4-dihydro-6-hydroxy-4-oxo-	50% MeOH-HCl	262(4.20)	73-3583-80
	+ NaOH	267(4.12)	73-3583-80
1H-1,2,3-Triazole-4-acetic acid, 5-(methoxycarbonyl)-, methyl ester	pH 1	223(3.96)	4-0159-80
	pH 7	235(3.95)	4-0159-80
	pH 11	234(3.94)	4-0159-80
$C_7H_9N_5$			
1H-Purin-6-amine, 1-ethyl-, monohydro-bromide	pH 1	259(4.08)	4-0583-80
	pH 7	267(4.05)	4-0583-80
	pH 13	272(4.16)	4-0583-80
3H-Purin-6-amine, 3-ethyl-	pH 1	274(4.18)	4-0583-80
	pH 7	273(4.08)	4-0583-80
	pH 13	273(4.08)	4-0583-80
9H-Purin-6-amine, 9-ethyl-	H_2O	262(4.11)	44-3969-80
$C_7H_9N_5O_2$			
2,4-Pyridinedicarboxylic acid dihydra-zide	pH 7	215s(4.13),271(3.77)	87-0384-80
2,4(1H,3H)-Pyrimidinedione, 1-(3-azido-propyl)-	MeOH	264(3.99)	78-0865-80
C_7H_{10}			
1,3-Cyclopentadiene, 5,5-dimethyl-	C_6H_{12}	248(3.38)	24-1818-80
Cyclopropane, 1,3-butadienyl-, (E)-	hexane	236(4.51)	35-0711-80
(Z)-	hexane	237(4.35)	35-0711-80
$C_7H_{10}N_2$			
4-Pyridinamine, N,N-dimethyl- (Beer's law not followed)	MeOH	258(4.3),280s(3.7)	142-1195-80B
$C_7H_{10}N_2O_2S$			
3(2H)-Pyridazinone, 4-(ethylthio)-5-hydroxy-2-methyl-	MeOH	214(4.24),225s(--),317(3.70)	73-0127-80
3(2H)-Pyridazinone, 5-(ethylthio)-4-hydroxy-2-methyl-	MeOH	215(4.11),303(3.82)	73-0127-80
$C_7H_{10}N_2O_3$			
3(2H)-Pyridazinone, 4-ethoxy-5-hydroxy-2-methyl-	MeOH	214(4.42),286(3.72)	73-0127-80
3(2H)-Pyridazinone, 5-ethoxy-4-hydroxy-2-methyl-	MeOH	218(4.32),287(3.91)	73-0127-80
3(2H)-Pyridazinone, 2-ethyl-5-hydroxy-4-methoxy-	MeOH	220(4.42),285(3.63)	73-0127-80
$C_7H_{10}N_2O_3S$			
2(1H)-Pyrimidinone, 3,4-dihydro-1-[2-hydroxy-1-(hydroxymethyl)ethyl]-4-thioxo-	pH 2	247(3.62),335(4.31)	103-0864-80
	pH 7	247(3.60),335(4.29)	103-0864-80
	pH 11	318(4.23)	103-0864-80
5-Thiazolecarboxylic acid, 2,3-dihydro-4-methoxy-3-methyl-2-(methylimino)-, monohydrobromide (or isomer)	MeOH	217(3.98),253(3.31),260(3.30),311(3.49)	78-2675-80
$C_7H_{10}N_2O_5S$			
1(2H)-Pyrimidinepropanesulfonic acid,	H_2O	266(4.01)	107-0267-80

Compound	Solvent	$\lambda_{max}(\log \epsilon)$	Ref.
3,4-dihydro-2,4-dioxo-, monosodium salt (cont.)			107-0267-80
$C_7H_{10}N_2S$			
Pyrimidine, 2-[(1-methylethyl)thio]-	EtOH	253(4.214),285s(3.278)	112-0001-80
	CH_2Cl_2	254(4.176),285s(3.278)	112-0001-80
$C_7H_{10}N_4$			
1H-Imidazole-4-carbonitrile, 1-ethyl-5-(methylamino)-	pH 1	242(4.03),262(3.92)	94-2819-80
	pH 7	252(4.08)	94-2819-80
	pH 13	252(4.08)	94-2819-80
	EtOH	251(4.13)	94-2819-80
$C_7H_{10}N_4O_2S$			
4(1H)-Pyrimidinone, 6-amino-5-nitroso-2-(propylthio)-, cobalt chelate	$CHCl_3$	406(4.77)	95-0515-80
iron(II) chelate	$CHCl_3$	376(4.52),665(4.21)	95-0515-80
$C_7H_{10}O$			
Bicyclo[2.2.1]heptan-7-one	heptane	292(1.20)	35-1983-80
Bicyclo[2.2.1]hept-5-en-2-ol	n.s.g.	192(3.78)	35-6872-80
Bicyclo[3.1.0]hexan-3-one, endo	gas	280(1.40)	44-1753-80
	pentane	287(1.16)	44-1753-80
Bicyclo[3.1.0]hexan-3-one, exo	gas	280(1.43)	44-1753-80
	pentane	288(1.23)	44-1753-80
Cyclobutanone, 2-(1-methylethylidene)-	MeCN	249(4.03)	44-2874-80
$C_7H_{10}OS$			
2H-Thiopyran-3(6H)-one, 2,4-dimethyl-	EtOH	241(3.97)	4-0289-80
2H-Thiopyran-3(6H)-one, 2,5-dimethyl-	EtOH	240(3.92)	4-0289-80
$C_7H_{10}O_2$			
2(5H)-Furanone, 4,5,5-trimethyl-	EtOH	206(4.21)	138-1521-80
2,3-Pentadienoic acid, 2-methyl-, methyl ester	EtOH	216.5(3.95)	33-1204-80
$C_7H_{10}O_4$			
Hexanoic acid, 3,5-dioxo-, methyl ester	MeOH	272(3.89)	39-2272-80C
	MeOH-NaOH	294(4.26)	39-2272-80C
$C_7H_{11}ClN_2O_2$			
3H-Pyrazole, 4-chloro-3-ethoxy-3,5-di-methyl-, 1-oxide	$CHCl_3$	245(3.89)	44-0076-80
$C_7H_{11}ClN_2O_2S_2$			
Methanesulfonamide, N-[3-(2-chloroeth-yl)-4-methyl-2(3H)-thiazolylidene]-	MeOH	278(3.97)	39-1773-80C
$C_7H_{11}N$			
1H-Pyrrole, 2-ethyl-3-methyl-	hexane	224(3.83)	103-0488-80
1H-Pyrrole, 3-ethyl-2-methyl-	hexane	213(3.95)	103-0488-80
$C_7H_{11}NO$			
2-Cyclopenten-1-one, 2-(ethylamino)-	ether	290(3.66)	78-1585-80
$C_7H_{11}NOS$			
1,4-Thiazepin-5(4H)-one, 6,7-dihydro-7,7-dimethyl-	MeOH	235(3.57),278(3.60)	24-0995-80
$C_7H_{11}NO_2S$			
Acetic acid, [(3,4-dihydro-2H-pyrrol-	MeOH	267(2.85)	5-0168-80

$C_7H_{11}NO_2S-C_7H_{12}N_4O$

Compound	Solvent	λ_{max}(log ϵ)	Ref.
5-yl)thio]-, methyl ester (cont.)			5-0168-80
$C_7H_{11}NO_3$			
Acetic acid, [(3,4-dihydro-2H-pyrrol-5-yl)oxy]-, methyl ester	MeOH	284(2.39)	5-0168-80
3(2H)-Isoxazolone, 2-(methoxymethyl)-4,5-dimethyl-	C_6H_{12}	240(3.83)	39-1826-80C
$C_7H_{11}N_3O_4S$			
3H-1,2,4-Triazole-3-thione, 2,4-dihydro-5-β-D-ribofuranosyl-	H_2O	212s(3.82),247(4.20)	44-0203-80
$C_7H_{11}N_5$			
2H-Purin-6-amine, 3,9-dihydro-3,9-dimethyl-	pH 1	291(3.71)	142-1729-80
	pH 7	289(3.73)	142-1729-80
	pH 13	265s(3.63)	142-1729-80
$C_7H_{11}N_6$			
1H-1,2,3-Triazolo[4,5-d]pyrimidinium, 1,3-dimethyl-7-(methylamino)-, iodide	n.s.g.	289(4.31)	104-1879-80
1H-1,2,3-Triazolo[4,5-d]pyrimidinium, 3,6-dimethyl-7-(methylamino)-, iodide	n.s.g.	269(4.22)	104-1879-80
$C_7H_{11}N_9S$			
1H-Pyrazolo[3,4-d]pyrimidine-3-carboximidic acid, 4-hydrazino-6-(methylthio)-, hydrazide	EtOH	203(4.25),248(4.34), 285(4.19)	103-0182-80
$C_7H_{11}P$			
1H-Phosphole, 1,3,4-trimethyl-, $PdBr_2$ complex (2:1)	$CHCl_3$	249(4.36),261(4.34), 273(4.24),371(3.83)	125-0709-80
$PdCl_2$ complex (2:1)	$CHCl_3$	235(4.50),251(4.40), 262(4.33),343(3.70)	125-0709-80
$C_7H_{12}ClN_2$			
Cyclopropenylium, chlorobis(dimethylamino)-, perchlorate	MeCN	230(3.94)	24-1746-80
$C_7H_{12}N_2$			
2,3-Diazabicyclo[2.2.1]hept-2-ene, 1,4-dimethyl-	pentane	347(2.24)	35-1633-80
6,7-Diazabicyclo[3.2.1]oct-6-ene, 1-methyl-	pentane	349(2.15)	35-1633-80
$C_7H_{12}N_2O$			
2-Cyclopropen-1-one, 2,3-bis(dimethylamino)-	MeCN	230(4.00)	88-3241-80
Methanaminium, N,N-dimethyl-, 1-cyano-2-oxopropylide	EtOH	247(4.19)	73-0092-80
$C_7H_{12}N_2O_2$			
2-Butenamide, 2-acetyl-3-amino-N-methyl-	MeOH	240(3.32),302(4.14)	44-0936-80
$C_7H_{12}N_4O$			
1H-Imidazole-4-carboxamide, 5-(ethylamino)-1-methyl-	pH 1	252(3.83),266(3.79)	94-2819-80
	pH 7	267(3.97)	94-2819-80
	pH 13	267(3.97)	94-2819-80
	EtOH	269(3.98)	94-2819-80

Compound	Solvent	$\lambda_{max}(\log \epsilon)$	Ref.
1H-Imidazole-4-carboxamide, 1-ethyl-5-(methylamino)-	pH 1	254(3.83),267s(3.81)	94-2819-80
	pH 7	268(3.95)	94-2819-80
	pH 13	268(3.95)	94-2819-80
	EtOH	270(3.97)	94-2819-80
$C_7H_{12}OS$			
3-Buten-2-one, 4-[(1-methylethyl)thio]-	C_6H_{12}	285(4.23)	65-2185-80
	EtOH	294(4.21)	65-2185-80
	Pr_2O	285(4.19)	65-2185-80
	dioxan	287(4.18)	65-2185-80
	$C_2H_4Cl_2$	290(4.20)	65-2185-80
	MeCN	290(4.21)	65-2185-80
Cyclopentanone, 2-(ethylthio)-	hexane	249(2.90),310(2.69)	39-0453-80B
	MeOH	250(2.66),308(2.56)	39-0453-80B
$C_7H_{12}OSi$			
1,3-Butadien-1-one, 2-(trimethylsilyl)-	isooctane	233(3.95)	44-4810-80
$C_7H_{12}O_2$			
1-Penten-3-one, 1-methoxy-2-methyl-	EtOH	283(4.04)	101-0367-80K
$C_7H_{12}O_6$			
α-D-ribo-Hexopyranosid-3-ulose, methyl	H_2O	288(2.08)	136-0033-80I
$C_7H_{12}S_2$			
Cyclohexanecarbodithioic acid, potassium salt	EtOH	339(4.16),458(1.53)	64-0458-80B
3-Thietanethione, 2,2,4,4-tetramethyl-	isooctane	206(4.19),211(4.20), 237(3.59),330(2.26), 490(1.00)	24-2255-80
$C_7H_{13}NO$			
3-Buten-2-one, 4-(dimethylamino)-3-methyl-	EtOH	306(4.42)	4-0033-80
1-Penten-3-one, 1-(dimethylamino)-	EtOH	220(4.09),304(4.42)	4-0033-80
$(C_7H_{13}NO)_n$			
Heptanenitrile, N-oxide, polymer	EtOH	211(4.66)	32-0341-80
$C_7H_{13}N_3O$			
1,2,4-Triazine, 2,5-dihydro-3-methoxy-5,5,6-trimethyl-	EtOH	218(3.65),255(3.89), 322(3.42)	44-4594-80
$C_7H_{13}N_3S$			
1,2,4-Triazine, 2,5-dihydro-2,5,6-trimethyl-3-(methylthio)-	EtOH	225s(3.88),256s(3.42)	44-4594-80
$C_7H_{13}N_7OS_2$			
Hydrazinecarbothioamide, 2,2'-[2-(hydroxyimino)-1,3-dimethyl-1,3-propanediylidene]bis-	n.s.g.	246(4.297),316(4.091)	56-2349-80
$C_7H_{14}N_2O_2S$			
1,9-Dioxa-4,6-diazacycloundecane-5-thione	H_2O	209(4.08),240(4.07)	88-0313-80
	H_2O	209(4.15),240(4.10)	104-1124-80
	MeOH	211(4.12),245(4.15)	104-1124-80
$C_7H_{14}OSi$			
3-Buten-2-one, 4-(trimethylsilyl)-, (E)-	C_6H_{12}	225(4.01),406(1.94), 424(1.99),442(1.83)	35-1577-80

Compound	Solvent	$\lambda_{max}(\log \epsilon)$	Ref.
$C_7H_{15}N_3$ Butane, 2-azido-2,3,3-trimethyl-	C_6H_{12}	285(1.23)	35-0735-80
$C_7H_{18}S_3Si$ Silane, tris(ethylthio)methyl-	hexane hexane	190(3.90),225(3.26) 225(3.26)	101-0147-80A 131-0099-80C
$C_7H_{18}Si_2$ Disilane, ethenylpentamethyl-	isooctane	223.2(3.72)	101-0261-80Q
$C_7N_2S_3$ Propanedinitrile, (2,3,4-trithioxo-cyclobutyl)-, ion(2-), dipotassium	H_2O	220(4.1),312(4.4), 399(4.2),444(4.4)	5-1409-80

Compound	Solvent	λ_{max}(log ϵ)	Ref.
$C_8Cl_2N_2O_2S_4$ [1,4]Dithiino[2,3-c:6,5-c']diisothia- zole-3,7-dicarbonyl dichloride	CH_2Cl_2	301(3.97),411(4.04)	44-5122-80
$C_8F_{12}P_2$ 1,4-Diphosphorin, 2,3,5,6-tetrakis- (trifluoromethyl)-	hexane	282(3.60)(changing)	35-0252-80
C_8HN_5 1H-Pyrrole-2,3,4,5-tetracarbonitrile	EtOH	236(4.57),269(4.02)	44-5113-80
$C_8H_2Br_2O_2$ Bicyclo[4.2.0]octa-1,3,5-triene-7,8-di- one, 3,4-dibromo-	EtOH	248(4.51),270s(3.67), 310s(3.64),322(3.88), 332(3.92)	39-1834-80C
$C_8H_2Cl_2O_2$ Bicyclo[4.2.0]octa-1,3,5-triene-7,8-di- one, 2,5-dichloro-	EtOH	247(4.43),258s(3.52), 296(3.80),303(3.85)	39-1834-80C
$C_8H_2Cl_6N_2$ 2H-Cyclopenta[d]pyridazine, 5,6,7-tri- chloro-2-(trichloromethyl)-	ether	256(4.36),259(4.38), 261(4.41),263(4.41), 278(4.33),282(4.32), 320(3.73)	44-1695-80
$C_8H_2N_2O_4S_4$ [1,4]Dithiino[2,3-c:6,5-c']diisothia- zole-3,7-dicarboxylic acid	EtOH	219(4.47),277(3.69), 368(4.07)	44-5122-80
$C_8H_3ClO_2$ Bicyclo[4.2.0]octa-1,3,5-triene-7,8-di- one, 3-chloro-	EtOH	240(4.16),258s(3.54), 296(3.68),303(3.69)	39-1834-80C
$C_8H_3Cl_4NO_2$ Acetamide, N-(2,3,5,6-tetrachloro-4- oxo-2,5-cyclohexadien-1-ylidene)-	$CHCl_3$	298(4.39),400(2.57)	12-2299-80
$C_8H_3Cl_5N_2$ 2H-Cyclopenta[d]pyridazine, 1,5,6,7- tetrachloro-2-(chloromethyl)-	ether	256(4.36),263(4.41), 281(4.34),284(4.35), 289(4.35),325(3.66)	44-1695-80
2H-Cyclopenta[d]pyridazine, 5,6,7-tri- chloro-2-(dichloromethyl)-	ether	252(4.41),260(4.41), 282(4.32),284(4.33), 286(4.33),291(4.36), 300(3.73)	44-1695-80
C_8H_4BrNOS Benzoyl isothiocyanate, 4-bromo-	dioxan	270(4.30),290(3.98)	73-2334-80
$C_8H_4Br_2S_3$ Thiophene, 2,2'-thiobis[3-bromo- Thiophene, 2,2'-thiobis[4-bromo-	heptane heptane	255(4.19),264s(4.15) 238(4.05),256s(3.97), 275(3.86)	20-0353-80 20-0353-80
Thiophene, 3,3'-thiobis[2-bromo-	heptane	206(4.41),241(4.11), 283(3.72)	20-0353-80
Thiophene, 3,3'-thiobis[4-bromo-	heptane	259(3.88),271s(3.84)	20-0353-80
C_8H_4ClNOS Benzoyl isothiocyanate, 4-chloro-	dioxan	268(4.12),286(3.92)	73-2334-80

Compound	Solvent	$\lambda_{max}(\log \epsilon)$	Ref.
$C_8H_4ClNO_2$ 3H-Pyrrolizine-2-carbonyl chloride, 3-oxo-	CH_2Cl_2	232(3.79),264(3.6), 300(3.59),376(3.56), 465(3.08)	150-3090-80
$C_8H_4Cl_4N_2$ 2H-Cyclopenta[d]pyridazine, 5,6,7-tri- chloro-2-(chloromethyl)-	ether	253(4.38),261(4.41), 282(4.26),320(3.57), 416(3.19)	44-1695-80
$C_8H_4F_{11}N_3$ Pentanenitrile, 3-amino-2-(1-amino- 2,2,2-trifluoroethylidene)-4,4,5,5,5- pentafluoro-3-(trifluoromethyl)-, (E)-	$CHCl_3$	260(4.19)	39-1551-80C
$C_8H_4I_2S_3$ Thiophene, 2,2'-thiobis[3-iodo-	heptane	265(4.16)	20-0353-80
$C_8H_4N_2O_2S$ Thieno[3,2-b]pyridine-6-carbonitrile, 4,5-dihydro-7-hydroxy-5-oxo-	EtOH	230(4.28),285(3.98), 295(4.05)	150-0113-80
$C_8H_4N_2O_3S$ Benzoyl isothiocyanate, 4-nitro-	dioxan	263(4.24),295(3.90)	73-2334-80
$C_8H_4N_2S_2$ [1]Benzothieno[3,2-d][1,2,3]thiadiazole	EtOH	255(3.62),293(3.18)	24-0183-80
$C_8H_4N_4S_3$ Thieno[3,2-d]isothiazole-5-carboni- trile, 4-amino-3-[(cyanomethyl)thio]-	MeOH	235(4.21),254(4.18), 296(3.95)	48-1021-80
$C_8H_4O_3$ Bicyclo[4.2.0]octa-1,3,5-triene-7,8-di- one, 3-hydroxy-	pH 1	230s(4.17),244(4.31), 270(3.76),327(3.69)	39-1841-80C
	pH 8.5	260(4.30),302(3.98), 358(3.81)	39-1841-80C
$C_8H_4O_4$ Bicyclo[4.2.0]octa-1,3,5-triene-7,8-di- one, 2,5-dihydroxy-	pH 2.2	248(4.14),330(3.57)	39-1841-80C
	pH 6.3	254(4.07),350(3.15)	39-1841-80C
	pH 11.3	220(4.05),274(3.63), 338(4.16)	39-1841-80C
Bicyclo[4.2.0]octa-1,3,5-triene-7,8-di- one, 3,4-dihydroxy-	pH 1	244(4.86),332(4.40), 345s(4.32)	39-1841-80C
	pH 6	235(4.59),260(4.60), 275(4.43),325s(4.21), 362(4.48)	39-1841-80C
	pH 10	254(4.67),300(4.07), 370(4.63),386(4.66)	39-1841-80C
$C_8H_5BrCl_2N_2O_2$ 1H,7H-Pyrazolo[1,2-a]pyrazole-1,7-di- one, 3-(bromomethyl)-2,6-dichloro- 5-methyl-	dioxan	250(4.09),383(3.85)	35-4983-80
$C_8H_5Br_2ClN_2$ 2H-Cyclopenta[d]pyridazine, 5,7-di- bromo-6-chloro-2-methyl-	ether	262(4.53),273s(4.35), 320(3.29),408(3.06)	44-1695-80

Compound	Solvent	λ_{max} (log ϵ)	Ref.
C$_8$H$_5$Br$_2$N$_3$ 2-Cycloheptimidazolamine, 4,6-dibromo-	MeOH	260(4.58),367(4.32), 425(3.51)	138-0205-80
C$_8$H$_5$NOS Benzoyl isothiocyanate	dioxan	252(4.16),280(3.90)	73-2334-80
C$_8$H$_5$NO$_2$ 1H-Indole-2,3-dione	EtOH	<u>240(4.4)</u>,248(4.3), <u>295(3.6)</u>,405(3.3)	78-2441-80
C$_8$H$_5$NO$_3$ 3H-Pyrrolizine-2-carboxylic acid, 3-oxo-	EtOH	230(3.98),302(3.61), 352(3.52),442(3.06)	150-3090-80
C$_8$H$_5$N$_3$Se Selenocyanic acid, 2-amino-5-cyano- phenyl ester	MeOH	278(4.41),310s(3.64)	104-1963-80
Selenocyanic acid, 4-amino-2-cyano- phenyl ester	MeOH	274(4.17),335(3.65)	104-1963-80
Selenocyanic acid, 4-amino-3-cyano- phenyl ester	MeOH	219(4.44),263(4.11), 333(3.59)	104-1963-80
C$_8$H$_5$N$_5$ Benzonitrile, 2-(1H-tetrazol-5-yl)-	MeOH	218(4.33),244(3.94), 290(3.48)	56-0925-80
Benzonitrile, 3-(1H-tetrazol-5-yl)-	MeOH	220(4.41),248(4.07), 285s(3.15)	56-0925-80
Benzonitrile, 4-(1H-tetrazol-5-yl)-	MeOH	211(3.82),264(4.31)	56-0925-80
C$_8$H$_5$N$_5$S 1,3,4-Thiadiazole, 2-azido-5-phenyl-	n.s.g.	287(4.1903)	103-0721-80
C$_8$H$_6$AsCl$_3$ Arsenous dichloride, (2-chloro-2-phen- ylethenyl)-	EtOH	<u>212(5.4),260(5.5)</u>	4-1341-80
C$_8$H$_6$BrClO$_3$ 1,3-Benzodioxole, 5-bromo-7-chloro- 4-methoxy-	EtOH	217(4.66),290(2.99)	103-0993-80
1,3-Benzodioxole, 7-bromo-5-chloro- 4-methoxy-	EtOH	217(4.59),290(3.03)	103-0993-80
C$_8$H$_6$BrIO$_3$ 1,3-Benzodioxole, 5-bromo-7-iodo- 4-methoxy-	EtOH	223(4.66),239(4.15), 284(3.13)	103-0993-80
C$_8$H$_6$BrN$_3$ 2H-1,2,3-Triazole, 2-(4-bromophenyl)-	MeOH	265(4.21)	39-0744-80C
C$_8$H$_6$Br$_2$N$_2$O$_2$ 1H,5H-Pyrazolo[1,2-a]pyrazole-1,5-di- one, 2,6-dibromo-3,7-dimethyl-	dioxan	325(4.17)	35-4983-80
1H,7H-Pyrazolo[1,2-a]pyrazole-1,7-di- one, 2,6-dibromo-3,7-dimethyl-	dioxan	235(4.15),255s(3.88), 368(3.85)	35-4983-80
C$_8$H$_6$Br$_2$O$_3$ 1,3-Benzodioxole, 5,7-dibromo-4-meth- oxy-	EtOH	217(4.65),232(4.06), 283(3.09)	103-0993-80

Compound	Solvent	$\lambda_{max}(\log \epsilon)$	Ref.
C_8H_6ClNO			
2H-Indol-2-one, 3-chloro-1,2-dihydro-	EtOH	216(4.40),255(3.57), 300(3.06)	78-2459-80
$C_8H_6Cl_2N_2O_2$			
1H,5H-Pyrazolo[1,2-a]pyrazole-1,5-di-one, 2,6-dichloro-3,5-dimethyl-	dioxan	325(4.19)	35-4983-80
1H,7H-Pyrazolo[1,2-a]pyrazole-1,7-di-one, 2,6-dichloro-3,5-dimethyl-	dioxan	235(4.16),255s(3.85), 364(3.85)	35-4983-80
$C_8H_6Cl_2O_3$			
1,3-Benzodioxole, 5,7-dichloro-4-meth-oxy-	EtOH	217(4.62),290(2.96)	103-0993-80
$C_8H_6Cl_3N_3O_4S_2$			
4H-1,2,4-Benzothiadiazine-7-sulfon-amide, 6-chloro-3-(dichlorometh-yl)-, 1,1-dioxide	n.s.g.	213(4.57),305(4.06), 323(4.14)	39-0712-80C
1H-Diazirino[1,2-b][1,2,3]benzothia-diazole-5-sulfonamide, 6-chloro-1-)dichloromethyl)-, 3,3-dioxide	n.s.g.	221(4.56),250(3.91)	39-0712-80C
$C_8H_6I_2N_2O_2$			
1H,7H-Pyrazolo[1,2-a]pyrazole-1,7-di-one, 2,6-diiodo-3,5-dimethyl-	dioxan	232(3.72),265(3.65), 384(3.88)	35-4983-80
$C_8H_6I_2O_3$			
1,3-Benzodioxole, 5,7-diiodo-4-meth-oxy-	EtOH	226(4.66),241(4.06), 279(3.14)	103-0993-80
$C_8H_6N_4O_2$			
Benzoic acid, 2-(1H-tetrazol-5-yl)-	MeOH	212(4.17),230(3.93)	56-0925-80
Benzoic acid, 3-(1H-tetrazol-5-yl)-	MeOH	220(4.36),240s(4.12), 286s(2.60)	56-0925-80
Benzoic acid, 4-(1H-tetrazol-5-yl)-	MeOH	210(3.99),261(4.27)	56-0925-80
$C_8H_6N_4O_2S$			
3H-1,2,4-Triazole-3-thione, 1,2-di-hydro-5-(4-nitrophenyl)-	MeOH	229(4.13),322(4.16)	73-2804-80
$C_8H_6N_4O_3$			
3H,8H-Imidazo[1,2,3-ij]pteridine-3,8,10(9H)-trione	pH 5.0	215(4.19),275(4.06), 325(4.08)	142-0437-80B
	pH 12.0	215(4.15),255(3.99), 274(3.73),338(4.07)	142-0437-80B
$C_8H_6N_8$			
1H-Tetrazole, 5,5'-(1,2-phenylene)bis-	MeOH	219(4.36),238(4.04), 287(3.30)	56-0925-80
1H-Tetrazole, 5,5'-(1,3-phenylene)bis-	MeOH	207s(4.14),233(4.43), 280s(3.08)	56-0925-80
1H-Tetrazole, 5,5'-(1,4-phenylene)bis-	MeOH	211(4.00),268(4.39), 290s(3.97)	56-0925-80
C_8H_6OS			
2-Benzofuranthiol	EtOH	214(3.85),248(3.63), 258(3.42),285(3.39), 305(3.34),325(3.26)	103-0991-80
$C_8H_6O_2$			
1(3H)-Isobenzofuranone (phthalide)	EtOH	227(4.00),273(3.23),	73-1950-80

Compound	Solvent	$\lambda_{max}(\log \epsilon)$	Ref.
Phthalide (cont.)		280(3.23)	73-1950-80
$C_8H_6O_2S$ 2(5H)-Thiophenone, 4-(2-furanyl)-	EtOH	216(3.50),318(4.17)	73-0142-80
$C_8H_6O_3$ 1,3-Benzodioxole-4-carboxaldehyde	EtOH	227(4.2),260(4.0), 340(3.6)	142-1159-80
1,3-Benzodioxole-5-carboxaldehyde	EtOH	210(4.1),230(4.2), 273(3.8),313(4.0)	142-1159-80
$C_8H_6O_4$ 1,2-Benzenedicarboxaldehyde, 4,5-di- hydroxy-	pH 2 pH 8.6 pH 13	256(4.03),304(3.54) 228(3.76),266(4.17) 241(3.58),298(4.22), 449(3.63)	39-1841-80C 39-1841-80C 39-1841-80C
1,2-Benzenedicarboxylic acid (phthalic acid)	ether CF$_3$CHOHCF$_3$	217(3.85),276(3.04), 282(2.99) 240(--),285(3.38)	96-0462-80 96-0470-80
Benzoic acid, 3-formyl-2-hydroxy-	DMSO	333(3.7),385s(3.3)	1-0469-80A
1(3H)-Isobenzofuranone, 5,7-dihydroxy-	EtOH EtOH-base	217(4.37),257(4.05), 292(3.74) 237(4.29),286(4.16), 315(3.88)	2-0927-80 2-0927-80
$C_8H_6S_2$ Benzo[b]thiophene-2-thiol	EtOH	213(4.11),218(4.10), 268(3.95),298(3.90), 318(3.63),290[sic](3.98)	103-0991-80
2,2'-Bithiophene	heptane MeCN	245(3.77),256(3.70), 288s(4.00),301(4.07), 311s(4.02),317s(3.95), 330s(3.61) 245(3.77),284(3.71), 302s(4.09),312s(4.04), 318s(3.96),332s(3.60)	4-0321-80 4-0321-80
3,3'-Bithiophene	heptane MeCN	213(4.41),230s(4.03), 259(4.15),270s(4.02), 283s(3.49) 210(4.42),232s(4.03), 260(4.14),271s(4.01), 285s(3.48)	4-0321-80 4-0321-80
$C_8H_6S_3$ Thiophene, 2,2'-thiobis-	gas heptane	233(--),270(--) 238(4.08),250s(4.00), 268(3.89)	20-0353-80 20-0353-80
Thiophene, 3,3'-thiobis-	gas heptane	246s(--),271(--) 249s(3.71),278(3.79)	20-0353-80 20-0353-80
C_8H_7AsO 1,3-Benzoxarsole, 2-methyl-	MeOH	234(3.76),288(3.23)	101-0039-80C
$C_8H_7BrN_2O$ Ethanedial, mono[(4-bromophenyl)hydra- zone]	hexane EtOH	300(--),333(--) 304(3.92),351(4.39)	65-2072-80 65-2072-80
$C_8H_7BrN_2O_3S$ 2(1H)-Pyrimidinone, 5-bromo-3,4-di- hydro-1-(tetrahydro-2-oxo-3-furan- yl)-4-thioxo-	pH 2 pH 7 pH 11	255(3.79),345(4.39) 250(3.88),340(4.42) 335(4.28)	103-0864-80 103-0864-80 103-0864-80

Compound	Solvent	λ_{max}(log ϵ)	Ref.
C_8H_7BrO Ethanone, 1-(4-bromophenyl)-	EtOH	257(4.25)	44-3651-80
$C_8H_7BrO_2$ Benzaldehyde, 5-bromo-2-methoxy-	EtOH	221(4.40),252(4.05), 332(3.58)	35-3837-80
$C_8H_7ClN_2O$ Ethanedial, mono[(4-chlorophenyl)hydrazone]	EtOH hexane	305(3.87),353(4.33) 301(--),331(--)	65-2072-80 65-2072-80
$C_8H_7ClN_2O_2$ 1H,7H-Pyrazolo[1,2-a]pyrazole-1,7-dione, 2-chloro-3,7-dimethyl-	dioxan	250s(3.63),362(3.82)	35-4983-80
$C_8H_7ClO_3$ 1,3-Benzodioxole, 5-chloro-4-methoxy-	EtOH	212(4.51),240(3.63), 288(3.05)	103-0993-80
$C_8H_7Cl_2NO_2$ Benzoic acid, 3,5-dichloro-4-(methylamino)-	8M HCl pH 13 EtOH	288(4.11),295(4.10) 269(4.04) 292(4.27)	44-0527-80 44-0527-80 44-0527-80
$C_8H_7Cl_2N_3O$ 1H-Benzotriazole, 4,5-dichloro-1-ethoxy-	EtOH	209(4.51),264(3.94), 272(3.95),294(3.81)	4-1115-80
$C_8H_7Cl_3FN_3O_4S_2$ 2H-1,2,4-Benzothiadiazine-7-sulfonamide, 6-chloro-3-(dichloromethyl)-5-fluoro-3,4-dihydro-, 1,1-dioxide	n.s.g.	223(4.65),264(4.15), 310(3.57)	39-0712-80C
$C_8H_7Cl_5O_2$ 1,3-Cyclohexanedione, 2,4,4,6,6-pentachloro-5,5-dimethyl-	MeOH-HCl MeOH-NaOH	280(4.16) 235(3.48),307(4.33)	20-0307-80 20-0307-80
$C_8H_7CsOS_2$ Benzenecarbodithioic acid, 4-methoxy-, cesium salt	EtOH	232(3.92),320(3.93), 503(2.10)	64-0458-80B
$C_8H_7CsS_2$ Benzenecarbodithioic acid, 4-methyl-, cesium salt	EtOH	303(4.10),364(3.93)	64-0458-80B
$C_8H_7FN_2O_3S$ 2(1H)-Pyrimidinone, 5-fluoro-3,4-dihydro-1-(tetrahydro-2-oxo-3-furanyl)-4-thioxo-	pH 2 pH 7 pH 11	287(3.60),342(4.46) 286(3.62),335(4.42) 330(4.42)	103-0864-80 103-0864-80 103-0864-80
$C_8H_7F_6N$ 1,3-Cyclohexadien-1-amine, N,N-bis(trifluoromethyl)- 1,5-Cyclohexadien-1-amine, N,N-bis(trifluoromethyl)-	hexane hexane	257(3.47) 260(3.37)	39-1544-80C 39-1544-80C
$C_8H_7IO_3$ 1,3-Benzodioxole, 4-iodo-7-methoxy- 1,3-Benzodioxole, 5-iodo-4-methoxy-	EtOH EtOH	219(4.66),234(4.10), 274(3.13) 217(4.53),238(3.85), 285(3.09)	103-0993-80 103-0993-80

Compound	Solvent	λ_{max}(log ϵ)	Ref.
C_8H_7NO			
Benzeneacetonitrile, N-oxide, heptamer	EtOH	201(5.05),206s(--), 217s(--)	32-0341-80
C_8H_7NOS			
Azirino[1,2-a]thieno[2,3-d]pyridin-7(4H)-one, 6,6a-dihydro-	EtOH	203(3.78),281(3.99)	138-1389-80
8H-Thieno[3,2-c]azepin-8-one, 4,5-dihydro-	EtOH	242(4.03),277(3.84), 343(3.96)	138-1389-80
$C_8H_7NO_2S$			
Thieno[3,2-b]pyridin-5(4H)-one, 7-hydroxy-6-methyl-	EtOH	216(4.15),245(3.97), 277(3.88),305(3.97)	150-0113-80
$C_8H_7N_3$			
Benzene, 1-azido-3-ethenyl-	MeOH	237(4.39),300s(2.95)	35-2033-80
$C_8H_7N_3O_2$			
Benzimidazole, 2-methyl-4-nitro-	EtOH	227(3.97),320(3.93)	104-1458-80
Imidazo[1,5-a]pyridine, 1-methyl-3-nitro-	MeOH	208(4.07),255(3.85), 261(3.85),332(3.01), 425(4.15)	39-0959-80C
1H-Indazole, 7-methyl-5-nitro-	EtOH	232(--),256(4.04), 296s(--),305(3.65), 325s(--)	5-0908-80
$C_8H_7N_3O_3$			
Ethanedial, mono[(4-nitrophenyl)hydrazone	EtOH	286(3.73),375(4.56)	65-2072-80
$C_8H_7N_3O_3S$			
7H-[1,2,4]Triazolo[5,1-b][1,3]thiazine-6-carboxylic acid, 7-oxo-, ethyl ester	EtOH	211(4.15),255(3.80), 300(3.93)	39-1352-80C
$C_8H_7N_3O_5$			
Acetamide, N-(2,4-dinitrophenyl)-	EtOH	302(4.03)	103-0386-80
$C_8H_7N_3S$			
3H-1,2,4-Triazole-3-thione, 1,2-dihydro-5-phenyl-	MeOH	224(4.26),256(4.34)	73-2804-80
$C_8H_7N_5$			
1H-Imidazo[2,1-i]purine, 5-methyl-, monohydrochloride	pH 1	275(4.10)	35-0770-80
	pH 7.0	264s(3.86),274(3.96), 281s(3.90),296s(3.70)	35-0770-80
	pH 13	224(4.42),232s(4.34), 272(3.85),280(3.95), 297(3.83)	35-0770-80
$C_8H_7ORbS_2$			
Benzenecarbodithioic acid, 4-methoxy-, rubidium salt	EtOH	320(4.25),503(2.33)	64-0458-80B
$C_8H_7RbS_2$			
Benzenecarbodithioic acid, 4-methyl-, rubidium salt	EtOH	300(4.08),503(2.23)	64-0458-80B
C_8H_8			
Bicyclo[4.1.0]hepta-1,3,5-triene, 2-methoxy-	C_6H_{12}	255(3.22),263(3.22), 276(3.13)	35-7076-80

Compound	Solvent	λ_{max}(log ϵ)	Ref.
Bicyclo[4.1.0]hepta-1,3,5-triene, 3-methyl-	C_6H_{12}	270(2.89),277(2.98), 284(2.93)	35-7076-80
$C_8H_8BF_2NO$ Boron. difluoro[2-[(methylimino)methyl]phenolato-N,O]-, (T-4)-	$C_2H_4Cl_2$	271(4.19),348(3.64)	101-0001-80I
$C_8H_8BrFN_2O_2S$ 2(1H)-Pyrimidinone, 1-(3-bromotetrahydro-2-furanyl)-5-fluoro-3,4-dihydro-4-thioxo-	pH 2 pH 7 pH 11	257(3.18),337(4.23) 257(3.18),337(4.23) 328(4.23)	103-0864-80 103-0864-80 103-0864-80
$C_8H_8Br_2O_2$ Phenol, 2,6-dibromo-4-(methoxymethyl)-	EtOH	290(3.46)	18-2020-80
$C_8H_8Br_6$ 2,4-Hexadiene, 1,2,5,6-tetrabromo-3,4-bis(bromomethyl)-, (E,Z)-	EtOH	235(4.18)	5-1786-80
$C_8H_8ClFN_2O_2S$ 2(1H)-Pyrimidinone, 1-(3-chlorotetrahydro-2-furanyl)-5-fluoro-3,4-dihydro-4-thioxo-	pH 2 pH 7 pH 11	256(3.60),340(4.15) 256(3.58),337(4.15) 325(4.11)	103-0864-80 103-0864-80 103-0864-80
$C_8H_8ClNO_2$ Acetamide, 2-chloro-N-(2-hydroxyphenyl)-	C_6H_{12}-$CHCl_3$	285(3.48)	44-1715-80
Benzenecarboximidoyl chloride, N-hydroxy-4-methoxy-	C_6H_{12}	211s(4.25),265(4.32), 296(3.30)	39-1051-80B
Benzoic acid, 3-chloro-4-(methylamino)-	EtOH	293(4.27)	44-0527-80
$C_8H_8Cl_2N_2O_3$ 2-Butenoic acid, 2-chloro-3-(4-chloro-2,3-dihydro-5-methyl-3-oxo-1H-pyrazol-1-yl)-	pH 6.6 pH 10.8 MeCN	222(3.78),260(3.76) 242(3.79),294(3.70) 224(3.89),286(3.57)	35-4983-80 35-4983-80 35-4983-80
$C_8H_8Cl_3NOS$ 2-Cyclobutene-1-thione, 2,4,4-trichloro-3-morpholino-	CH_2Cl_2	345(4.7),422(2.1)	83-0959-80
$C_8H_8Cl_3NS$ 2-Cyclobutene-1-thione, 2,4,4-trichloro-3-pyrrolidino-	CH_2Cl_2	349(4.7),416(2.1)	83-0959-80
$C_8H_8Cl_3N_3O_4S_2$ 2H-1,2,4-Benzothiadiazine-7-sulfonamide, 6-chloro-3-(dichloromethyl)-3,4-dihydro-, 1,1-dioxide	n.s.g.	225(4.68),267(4.35), 313(3.45)	39-0712-80C
$C_8H_8FeO_2$ Iron, dicarbonyl(η^5-2,4-cyclopentadien-1-yl)methyl-	MeCN	353(2.91)	35-6887-80
$C_8H_8N_2$ 1H-Benzimidazole, 1-methyl-	CCl_4	266(4.3),274(4.34), 281(4.3)	44-2518-80
2,2'-Bi-1H-pyrrole	benzene	281(4.24)	33-1190-80
5,6-Diazatricyclo[5.3.0.0^{4,8}]deca-2,5,9-triene	heptane	352(2.08)	24-2154-80
1H-Indazole, 3-methyl-	EtOH	216(--),254(3.61), 262s(--),284s(--),	5-0908-80

Compound	Solvent	$\lambda_{max}(\log \epsilon)$	Ref.
1H-Indazole, 3-methyl- (cont.)		289(3.72),293(3.71), 301(3.66)	5-0908-80
1H-Indazole, 5-methyl-	EtOH	220(--),251(3.63), 258s(--),287s(--), 292(3.64),297(3.63), 304(3.58)	5-0908-80
1H-Indazole, 6-methyl-	EtOH	220(--),261(3.61), 265s(--),278s(--), 285(3.59),287s(--), 295(3.53)	5-0908-80
1H-Indazole, 7-methyl-	EtOH	218(--),252(3.67), 258(3.66),281s(--), 287(3.86),291s(--), 297(3.60)	5-0908-80
$C_8H_8N_2O$			
Ethanedial, mono(phenylhydrazone)	hexane	293(3.93),331(4.36)	65-2072-80
	EtOH	296(3.73),347(4.35)	65-2072-80
1H-Indazole, 3-methoxy-	EtOH	250(3.26),257s(--), 300(3.66),311s(--)	5-0908-80
1H-Indazole, 6-methoxy-	EtOH	226(--),267(3.72), 273s(--),279(3.75), 283(3.75),291(3.75)	5-0908-80
$C_8H_8N_2OS_3$			
Ethanone, 1-[4-amino-3-(methylthio)- thieno[3,2-d]isothiazol-5-yl]-	MeOH	238s(4.09),264(4.24), 352(4.10)	48-1021-80
$C_8H_8N_2O_2$			
1H,5H-Pyrazolo[1,2-a]pyrazole-1,5-di- one, 3,7-dimethyl-	dioxan	325(4.16)	35-4983-80
1H,7H-Pyrazolo[1,2-a]pyrazole-1,7-di- one, 3,5-dimethyl-	dioxan	354(3.93)	35-4983-80
1H-Pyrazolo[1,2-a]pyrazol-4-ium-3-ol- ate, 2-ethyl-1-oxo-	MeCN	210(4.284),238(3.882), 244(3.891),250(3.826), 257s(3.578),400(3.812)	64-1002-80B
$C_8H_8N_2O_2S$			
Thieno[2,3-d]pyrimidine-2,4(1H,3H)-di- one, 1,5-dimethyl-	pH 1	231(4.41),260(3.79), 292(3.65)	39-1853-80C
	pH 11	230(4.41),261(3.83), 290s(3.46)	39-1853-80C
	MeOH	228(4.09),259s(3.42), 290(3.32)	39-1853-80C
$C_8H_8N_2O_3$			
Acetamide, N-(2-nitrophenyl)-	hexane	237(4.33),274(3.81), 352(3.79)	103-0386-80
	EtOH	228(4.16),269(3.36), 328(3.28)	103-0386-80
Acetamide, N-(4-nitrophenyl)-	EtOH	315(4.13)	103-0386-80
$C_8H_8N_2O_3S$			
2(1H)-Pyrimidinone, 3,4-dihydro- 1-(tetrahydro-2-oxo-3-furanyl)- 4-thioxo-	pH 2	287(3.85),335(4.34)	103-0864-80
	pH 7	287(3.85),335(4.34)	103-0864-80
	pH 11	320(4.30)	103-0864-80
$C_8H_8N_2O_3S_2$			
Thieno[3,2-d]isothiazole-5-carboxylic acid, 4-amino-3-methoxy-, methyl ester	MeOH	223(4.10),256(4.25), 280(3.74),326(4.12)	48-1021-80

Compound	Solvent	$\lambda_{max}(\log \epsilon)$	Ref.
$C_8H_8N_2Se$ Selenocyanic acid, 4-amino-2-methyl- phenyl ester	MeOH	259(4.03)	104-1963-80
$C_8H_8N_3O_2$ Sydnone, 3-(1-methylpyridinium-3-yl)-, iodide	MeOH	245s(3.97),265s(3.78), 322(3.44)	39-0020-80C
$C_8H_8N_4$ 2,2'-Bi-1H-imidazole, 1-ethenyl-	EtOH	225(4.02),284(4.18)	70-1655-80
1H-Tetrazole, 5-(2-methylphenyl)-	MeOH	209(4.16),232(3.91)	56-0925-80
1H-Tetrazole, 5-(3-methylphenyl)-	MeOH	210(4.24),243(4.11)	56-0925-80
1H-Tetrazole, 5-(4-methylphenyl)-	MeOH	208(4.16),244(4.25)	56-0925-80
$C_8H_8N_4O$ 1H-Tetrazole, 5-(3-methoxyphenyl)-	MeOH	216(4.33),246(4.05), 287(3.48)	56-0925-80
1H-Tetrazole, 5-(4-methoxyphenyl)-	MeOH	209(4.06),251(4.27), 281s(3.30)	56-0925-80
$C_8H_8N_4O_2$ 2,4(1H,3H)-Pteridinedione, 1,3-di- methyl-	pH -6.1	250(4.20),294s(3.18), 356(3.74)	142-0437-80B
	pH 0.0	235(4.21),253s(3.79), 330(3.88)	142-0437-80B
2,4(1H,3H)-Pteridinedione, 6,7-di- methyl-	pH -4.9	236(4.16),347(3.99)	142-0437-80B
	pH 1.0	245(3.90),328(4.01)	142-0437-80B
$C_8H_8N_4O_3$ 3H,8H-Imidazo[1,2,3-ij]pteridine- 8,10(9H)-dione, 5,6-dihydro- 3-hydroxy-	pH -1.0	246(4.10),280s(2.87), 364(3.92)	142-0437-80B
	pH 6.0	220(4.05),269(4.22), 296(3.88)	142-0437-80B
	pH 13.0	232s(4.06),277(4.12), 302s(3.85)	142-0437-80B
2,4(1H,3H)-Pteridinedione, 1-(2-hy- droxyethyl)-	pH 5.0	234(4.10),250s(3.95), 330(3.84)	142-0437-80B
	pH 12.0	211(4.00),243(4.22), 285(3.52),337(3.89)	142-0437-80B
2,4,7(1H,3H,8H)-Pteridinetrione, 1,6- dimethyl-	pH 1.0	267(3.91),283(3.85), 327(4.11)	24-1524-80
	pH 7.0	278(3.97),328(4.24)	24-1524-80
	pH 13.0	249(4.05),272(3.70), 334(4.21)	24-1524-80
2,4,7(1H,3H,8H)-Pteridinetrione, 3,6- dimethyl-	pH 2.0	276(3.98),324(4.09)	24-1524-80
	pH 7.3	275(4.09),328(4.20)	24-1524-80
	pH 12.5	224(4.47),257(4.08), 279(3.95),336(4.11)	24-1524-80
2,4,7(1H,3H,8H)-Pteridinetrione, 6,8- dimethyl-	pH 2.0	282(4.07),327(4.10)	24-1535-80
	pH 6.5	250s(3.69),288(4.06), 344(4.16)	24-1535-80
	2M KOH	259(4.07),280(3.74), 360(4.19)	24-1535-80
7(1H)-Pteridinone, 2,4-dimethoxy-	pH 4.0	237s(3.96),246(4.04), 262(4.01),317s(4.14), 326(4.15)	24-1535-80
	pH 9.0	246(4.02),262s(3.69), 318s(4.14),326(4.19), 340(4.08)	24-1535-80
[1,2,4]Triazolo[1,5-a]pyrimidine-6-car- boxylic acid, 7-hydroxy-, ethyl ester	EtOH	264(3.94),297(4.18)	39-1347-80C

Compound	Solvent	λ_{max}(log ϵ)	Ref.
C₈H₈N₄O₄			
2,4,6,7(1H,3H,5H,8H)-Pteridinetetrone,	pH 1	293(3.95),327(3.88)	39-2645-80C
8-ethyl-	pH 13	308(4.10),345(4.04)	39-2645-80C
2,4,7(1H,3H)-Pteridinetrione, 7,8-di-	pH 0.0	280(3.91),332(3.91)	142-0437-80B
hydro-8-(2-hydroxyethyl)-	pH 7.0	214(4.67),258(3.82),	142-0437-80B
		287(4.11),350(4.27)	
C₈H₈N₄O₅			
2,4,6,7(1H,3H,5H,8H)-Pteridinetetrone,	pH 1	294(3.94),325s(3.84)	39-2645-80C
8-(2-hydroxyethyl)-	pH 13	309(4.04),349(3.94)	39-2645-80C
C₈H₈N₄O₆			
Benzenamine, N,N-dimethyl-2,4,6-tri-	DMSO-5%MeOH	383(4.15)	23-1609-80
nitro-	+ NaOMe	402(--),474(--)	23-1609-80
C₈H₈N₄S			
2-Pyridinamine, N-(4-methyl-1,2,3-thia-	n.s.g.	247(3.94),324(4.30)	73-2329-80
diazol-5-yl)-			
3-Pyridinamine, N-(4-methyl-1,2,3-thia-	n.s.g.	247(3.84),320(4.13)	73-2329-80
diazol-5-yl)-			
4-Pyridinamine, N-(4-methyl-1,2,3-thia-	n.s.g.	249(3.83),326(4.19)	73-2329-80
diazol-5-yl)-			
C₈H₈N₅			
Imidazo[2,1-i]purin-6-ium, 1,9-dihydro-	pH 1	275(4.08)	35-0770-80
9-methyl-, chloride	pH 7	280(4.10)	35-0770-80
	pH 13	285(4.12)	35-0770-80
C₈H₈N₆			
Bis[1,2,4]triazolo[1,5-a:1',5'-c]pyri-	EtOH	216(4.51),228s(4.08),	12-1147-80
midine, 5,8-dimethyl-		256s(3.99),266(4.02),	
		277s(3.82)	
C₈H₈O			
Ethanone, 1-phenyl- (acetophenone)	benzene	280(2.9)	70-0039-80
	EtBr	280(3.2)	70-0039-80
	n.s.g.	241(4.07),278(3.03),	78-0397-80
		313(1.81)	
AlBr₃ complex (1:1)	benzene	285(3.9)	70-0039-80
	EtBr	288(4.0)	70-0039-80
AlBr₃ complex (2:1)	benzene	289(4.1)	70-0039-80
	EtBr	291(4.4)	70-0039-80
C₈H₈OS₂			
Benzenecarbodithioic acid, 4-methoxy-,	EtOH	232(3.92),320(3.93),	64-0458-80B
cesium salt		503(2.10)	
potassium salt	EtOH	321(4.18),360s(4.06),	64-0458-80E
		465s(2.55)	
rubidium salt	EtOH	320(4.25),503(2.33)	64-0458-80B
C₈H₈O₂			
Benzaldehyde, 2-hydroxy-5-methyl-	EtOH	258(4.03),339(3.56)	90-0431-80
Benzoic acid, methyl ester, Cr(CO)	C₆H₁₂	258(3.8),323(4.0),	110-0749-80
complex		395(3.0)	
Ethanone, 1-(2-hydroxyphenyl)-	EtOH	251(4.00),325(3.57)	90-0431-80
Ethanone, 1-(4-hydroxyphenyl)-	n.s.g.	325(4.41)	102-1349-80
C₈H₈O₃			
Benzeneacetic acid, 3-hydroxy-	MeOH	209(3.82),216s(3.76),	98-0071-80
		275(3.24),281s(3.19)	

Compound	Solvent	$\lambda_{max}(\log \epsilon)$	Ref.
Benzoic acid, 2-hydroxy-, methyl ester	hexane	252(3.97),257(3.91), 309(3.70)	65-2236-80
	pentane- EtOH-ether	239(4.00),309(3.67)	65-2236-80
Cyclopenta[b]pyran-2(6H)-one, 7,7a-di- hydro-6-hydroxy-, (Z)-	MeOH	253(3.82)	102-1866-80
$C_8H_8O_4$			
2,5-Cyclohexadiene-1,4-dione, 2,6-di- methoxy-	MeOH	286(3.72)	100-0353-80
Propanoic acid, 2-(5-oxo-2(5H)-furan- ylidene)-, methyl ester, (E)-	MeOH	206s(3.67),216(3.71), 291(4.24)	48-0559-80
(Z)-	MeOH	208s(3.65),215(3.66), 291(4.18)	48-0559-80
4H-Pyran-4-one, 3-acetyl-2-hydroxy- 6-methyl-	EtOH	207(3.91),227(4.08), 307(4.02)	2-0546-80
$C_8H_8S_2$			
Benzenecarbodithioic acid, 4-methyl-, cesium salt	EtOH	303(4.10),364(3.93)	64-0458-80B
potassium salt	EtOH	298(4.05),365(3.84)	64-0458-80B
rubidium salt	EtOH	300(4.08),503(2.23)	64-0458-80B
$C_8H_8S_4$			
1,3-Dithiole, 2-(1,3-dithiol-2-yli- dene)-4,5-dimethyl-	hexane	278s(4.01),290s(4.10), 299(4.16),308s(4.13), 322s(4.09),360s(3.49), 445(2.81)	11-0196-80A
tetrafluoroborate (11:5)	MeCN	298s(--),310s(--), 322(4.19),385s(--), 410s(--),450(4.19), 505s(--),615(3.74)	11-0196-80A
1,3-Dithiole, 4-methyl-2-(4-methyl- 1,3-dithiol-2-ylidene)-	hexane	278s(4.09),290s(4.17), 298(4.20),308(4.17), 321(4.13),355s(3.70), 440s(3.13)	11-0196-80A
tetrafluoroborate (11:5)	MeCN	295s(--),310s(--), 319(4.23),350s(--), 408s(--),447(4.20), 500s(--),610(3.74)	11-0196-80A
$C_8H_8Se_3$			
Carbonotriselenoic acid, mono(phenyl- methyl) ester, potassium salt	80% DMSO	353(3.77),404(3.87), 558(2.30)	78-1451-80
$C_8H_9BrN_2O_2S$			
2(1H)-Pyrimidinone, 1-(3-bromotetra- hydro-2-furanyl)-3,4-dihydro-4-thi- oxo-	pH 2	255(3.61),335(4.38)	103-0864-80
	pH 7	255(3.61),335(4.38)	103-0864-80
	pH 11	317(4.32)	103-0864-80
$C_8H_9ClN_2O_2S$			
2(1H)-Pyrimidinone, 1-(3-chlorotetra- hydro-2-furanyl)-3,4-dihydro-4-thi- oxo-	pH 2	257(3.78),335(4.42)	103-0864-80
	pH 7	257(3.18),332(4.40)	103-0864-80
	pH 11	319(4.34)	103-0864-80
$C_8H_9Cl_3O_2$			
1,3-Cyclohexanedione, 2,4,4-trichloro- 5,5-dimethyl-	MeOH-HCl	280(4.05)	20-0307-80
	MeOH-NaOH	235(3.48),307(4.23)	20-0307-80
C_8H_9D			
Bicyclo[2.2.2]octa-2,5-diene-2-d, (1S)-	heptane	220s(2.40)	35-5749-80

Compound	Solvent	$\lambda_{max}(\log \epsilon)$	Ref.
C_8H_9N			
Methanamine, N-(phenylmethylene)-	C_6H_{12}	243(4.21),248s(4.16), 276(2.98),286(3.86)	39-0849-80B
	MeOH	244(4.18),277s(3.12), 287s(2.94)	39-0849-80B
C_8H_9NOS			
1,4-Oxathiino[3,2-b]pyridine, 2,3-dihydro-2-methyl-	EtOH	250(3.62),307(3.84)	1-0619-80
	EtOH-HCl	253(3.50),332(3.94)	1-0619-80
1,4-Oxathiino[3,2-b]pyridine, 2,3-dihydro-6-methyl-	EtOH	250(3.55),310(3.84)	1-0619-80
	EtOH-HCl	256(3.52),340(4.03)	1-0619-80
8H-Thieno[3,2-c]azepin-8-one, 4,5,6,7-tetrahydro-	EtOH	277(4.01),330(2.72)	138-1389-80
$C_8H_9NO_2$			
Acetamide, N-(2-hydroxyphenyl)-	C_6H_{12}-CHCl$_3$	244(4.02)	44-1715-80
1H-Azepine-1-carboxylic acid, methyl ester	EtOH	205(3.34),266(3.48)	142-1569-80B
Benzaldehyde, 2-hydroxy-5-methyl-, oxime	EtOH	260(4.05),314(3.60)	90-0431-80
Benzaldehyde, 4-methoxy-, oxime, (E)-	C_6H_{12}	215(4.30),221s(4.12), 254s(4.23),264(4.36), 271s(4.32),290(3.68), 301(3.44)	39-1051-80B
Benzaldehyde, 4-methoxy-, oxime, (Z)-	C_6H_{12}	212(4.27),217s(4.13), 261(4.37),282s(3.62), 293(3.19)	39-1051-80B
Ethanone, 1-(2-hydroxyphenyl)-, oxime	EtOH	254(3.97),303(3.60)	90-0431-80
Formamide, N-hydroxy-N-(2-methylphenyl)-	EtOH	238(3.78)	44-2834-80
Formamide, N-hydroxy-N-(4-methylphenyl)-	EtOH	253(4.06)	44-2834-80
2H-Indol-2-one, 1,4,6,7-tetrahydro-3-hydroxy-	MeOH	277(4.14)	5-0564-80
$C_8H_9NO_3$			
Formamide, N-hydroxy-N-(4-methoxyphenyl)-	EtOH	254(4.03)	44-2834-80
3-Pyridinecarboxylic acid, 1,4-dihydro-4-oxo-, ethyl ester	EtOH	250(3.99),256(4.01), 282(3.58)	4-0359-80
3-Pyridinecarboxylic acid, 1-ethyl-1,4-dihydro-4-oxo-	EtOH	254(4.11),280(3.60)	4-0359-80
4(1H)-Pyridinone, 3-acetoxy-2-methyl-	EtOH	260(4.10)	36-1074-80
$C_8H_9NO_3S_2$			
4-Thia-1-azabicyclo[3.2.0]hept-2-ene-2-carboxylic acid, 3-(ethylthio)-7-oxo-	EtOH	253(3.77),325(3.87)	33-1093-80
$C_8H_9NO_4$			
3,7-Dioxatricyclo[4.1.0.0^{2,4}]heptane-5-methanol, 5-hydroxy-1-isocyano-α-methyl- (trichoviridin)	EtOH	220s(3.40)	78-0515-80
$C_8H_9NO_4S$			
4-Thia-1-azabicyclo[3.2.0]hept-2-ene-2-carboxylic acid, 6-(2-hydroxyethyl)-7-oxo-, erythro-trans	EtOH	260(3.56),311(3.80)	35-2039-80
threo	EtOH	260(3.59),311(3.81)	35-2039-80
$C_8H_9N_2$			
Pyridinium, 4-cyano-1-ethyl-, iodide	EtOH	378(2.72)	35-6780-80
	acetone	460(2.91)	35-6780-80

Compound	Solvent	$\lambda_{max}(\log \epsilon)$	Ref.
Pyridinium, 4-cyano-1-ethyl-, iodide (cont.)	HCOOMe	458(3.02)	35-6780-80
	CH_2Cl_2	484(3.13)	35-6780-80
	MeCN	425(2.53)	35-6780-80
$C_8H_9N_3$			
Benzene, (1-azidoethyl)-	C_6H_{12}	257(2.29),283(1.42)	35-0735-80
1H-Benzotriazole, 1-ethyl-	dioxan	260(3.74),285(3.63)	56-0107-80
2H-Benzotriazole, 2-ethyl-	dioxan	280(4.05)	56-0107-80
$C_8H_9N_3O_3$			
Acetamide, N-(2-amino-3-nitrophenyl)-	EtOH	283(3.56),407(3.78)	104-1458-80
2,4-Pyridinedicarboxylic acid, 4-methyl ester 2-hydrazide	pH 7	215s(4.16),281(3.65)	87-0384-80
$C_8H_9N_3O_4$			
Benzenamine, N-ethyl-2,4-dinitro-	hexane	250(3.97),326(4.24), 390(3.73)	103-0386-80
	EtOH	260(3.95),347(4.22), 410s(3.83)	103-0386-80
$C_8H_9N_5O$			
9H-Purin-6-amine, 9-(2-propenyl)-, 1-oxide	pH 1	259(4.09)	94-3443-80
	pH 7	232(4.66),262(3.91), 292(3.32)	94-3443-80
	pH 13	232(4.46),269(3.94), 305(3.61)	94-3443-80
	EtOH	235(4.63),263(3.90), 300(3.32)	94-3443-80
$C_8H_9N_5O_2$			
3H-1,2,4,5a,9a-Pentaazabenz[cd]azulene-3,5(4H)-dione, 6,7,8,9-tetrahydro-	MeOH	238(3.86),255(3.93)	78-0865-80
9H-Purine-9-propanoic acid, 6-amino-	HCl	260.5(4.12)	47-0949-80
	DMSO	266.5(4.12)	47-0949-80
	3:2 DMSO-$HOCH_2CH_2OH$	264.5(4.14)	47-0949-80
Pyrido[2,3-d]pyrimidin-5(1H)-one, 2,4-diamino-6-(hydroxymethyl)-	pH 1	257(4.28),292(3.54)	44-3746-80
	pH 7	254(4.22),287(3.72)	44-3746-80
	pH 11	255(4.20),287(3.63)	44-3746-80
$C_8H_9N_5O_3$			
4H-Pyrimido[6,1-c][1,2,4]triazine-3-carboxylic acid, 6-amino-1,8-dihydro-1-methyl-8-oxo-	pH 13	330(4.21)	44-3919-80
C_8H_{10}			
Bicyclo[2.2.1]hepta-2,5-diene, 2-methyl-	heptane	213s(3.23),220s(2.95), 237(2.40)	35-5749-80
Bicyclo[2.1.1]hexane, 2,3-bis(methylene)-	isooctane	222s(--),231s(--), 239(3.91),247s(--)	33-1176-80
Bicyclo[2.2.2]octa-2,5-diene	heptane	203s(3.36),220s(2.40)	35-5749-80
Bicyclo[4.2.0]octa-1,5-diene	C_6H_{12}	267(3.55)	118-0238-80
1,3-Cyclopentadiene, 5-(1-methylethylidene)-	isooctane	265(3.9)	88-4287-80
$(C_8H_{10})_n$			
1,3-Cyclopentadiene, 5-(1-methylethylidene)-, polymer	dioxan	253(3.99)	126-0031-80
$C_8H_{10}BrN$			
Benzenamine, 4-bromo-N,N-dimethyl-,	aq EtOH	505(4.15)	104-2099-80

Compound	Solvent	$\lambda_{max}(\log \epsilon)$	Ref.
radical ion(1+) (cont.)			104-2099-80
$C_8H_{10}BrN_5O_2$ 2,4(1H,3H)-Pyrimidinedione, 1-(4-azido-butyl)-	MeOH	281(3.96)	78-0865-80
$C_8H_{10}ClN$ Benzenamine, 4-chloro-N,N-dimethyl-, radical ion(1+)	aq EtOH	480(4.40)	104-2099-80
$C_8H_{10}FN$ Benzenamine, 4-fluoro-N,N-dimethyl-, radical ion(1+)	aq EtOH	465(3.81)	104-2099-80
$C_8H_{10}F_2OS_2$ 2-Cyclobuten-1-one, 2,3-bis(ethylthio)-4,4-difluoro-	isooctane	215(3.84),230(3.90), 300(4.19)	44-4429-80
$C_8H_{10}NO$ Methanaminium, N-methyl-N-(4-oxo-2,5-cyclohexadien-1-ylidene)-	H_2O	280(4.27)	39-1601-80B
$C_8H_{10}N_2$ 5,6-Diazatricyclo[5.3.0.0^{4,8}]deca-2,5-diene	heptane	352(2.39)	24-2154-80
$C_8H_{10}N_2O$ Acetamide, N-methyl-N-(2-pyridinyl)-	EtOH	230(3.78),265(3.56)	39-2272-80C
Acetic acid, 2-phenylhydrazide	EtOH	198(4.81),235(4.4), 282(3.5)	70-1915-80
Benzenamine, N,N-dimethyl-4-nitroso-	pH 8.75	440(4.55)	69-0731-80
$C_8H_{10}N_2O_2$ Benzenamine, N,N-dimethyl-2-nitro-	EtOH	245(4.33),416(3.47)	103-0386-80
Benzenamine, N-ethyl-2-nitro-	EtOH	232(4.32),280(3.66), 425(3.79)	103-0386-80
Benzenamine, N-ethyl-4-nitro-	EtOH	390(4.28)	103-0386-80
2(1H)-Pyrimidinone, 3,4-dihydro-5-methyl-4-(2-oxopropylidene)-	6M HCl	235(3.57),297(3.49), 340s(3.98),360s(4.21), 372(4.29)	44-3651-80
	pH 6	260(3.67),338s(4.30), 351(4.39),364(4.28)	44-3651-80
	pH 13	258(3.83),272(3.93), 378(4.53)	44-3651-80
$C_8H_{10}N_2O_2S$ 2-Thiophenecarboxaldehyde, 2-(ethoxy-carbonyl)hydrazone	C_6H_{12} EtOH 50% EtOH	268(3.96) 261(3.62) 264(3.99),276(4.03), 303(4.34)	115-0151-80 115-0151-80 115-0151-80
$C_8H_{10}N_2O_3$ Ethanol, 2-[(2-nitrophenyl)amino]-	base	441(3.79)	35-4848-80
Ethanol, 2-[(4-nitrophenyl)amino]-	base	404(4.12)	35-4848-80
Ethenamine, N,N-dimethyl-2-(5-nitro-2-furanyl)-	MeOH	276(4.15),504(4.31)	73-0155-80
2-Furancarboxaldehyde, 2-(ethoxy-carbonyl)hydrazone	C_6H_{12} EtOH 50% EtOH	289(4.35) 290(4.52) 290(4.44)	115-0151-80 115-0151-80 115-0151-80
2(1H)-Pyrazinone, 1-(tetrahydro-2-fur-anyl)-, 4-oxide, (R)-	pH 1	221(4.34),272(3.96), 330(3.68)	94-2734-80

Compound	Solvent	$\lambda_{max}(\log \epsilon)$	Ref.
2(1H)-Pyrazinone, 1-(tetrahydro-2-fur-anyl)-, 4-oxide, (R)- (cont.)	H_2O	222(4.35),272(3.96), 330(3.70)	94-2734-80
	pH 13	221(4.39),272(3.97), 328(3.72)	94-2734-80
3(2H)-Pyridazinone, 5-hydroxy-4-meth-oxy-2-(2-propenyl)-	MeOH	218(4.31),289(3.88)	73-0127-80
4(1H)-Pyridinone, 2-methyl-3-[[(methyl-amino)carbonyl]oxy]-	EtOH	258.5(4.16)	36-1074-80
$C_8H_{10}N_2O_3S$			
2,4(1H,3H)-Pyrimidinedione, 1-(2-acet-ylthioethyl)-	H_2O	267.5(3.99)	117-0275-80
$C_8H_{10}N_2O_3S_2$			
4-Thia-1-azabicyclo[3.2.0]hept-2-ene-2-carboxylic acid, 3-[(2-aminoeth-yl)thio]-7-oxo-	H_2O	250(3.66),319(3.80)	94-3232-80
$C_8H_{10}N_2O_4$			
2,4(1H,3H)-Pyrimidinedione, 1-[2-(acet-yloxy)ethyl]-	H_2O	267(3.92)	47-2959-80
1(2H)-Pyrimidinepropanoic acid, 3,4-di-hydro-5-methyl-2,4-dioxo-	aq HCl	273.5(3.96)	47-0949-80
	DMSO	273.5(3.96)	47-0949-80
$C_8H_{10}N_4$			
2,2'-Bi-1H-imidazole, 1-ethyl-	EtOH	272(4.21)	70-1655-80
$C_8H_{10}N_4O_2$			
2(3H)-Furanone, dihydro-3-[1-(1H-1,2,4-triazol-3-ylimino)ethyl]-	EtOH	306.3(4.31)	87-0927-80
6H-Purin-6-one, 1,7-dihydro-8-(1-hy-droxy-1-methylethyl)-	pH 7	253(4.10)	149-0195-80A
4H-Pyrazolo[3,4-d]pyrimidin-4-one, 1,5-dihydro-6-(1-hydroxy-1-methyl-ethyl)-	pH 7	251(3.84)	149-0195-80A
[1,2,4]Triazolo[1,5-a]pyrimidin-7(1H)-one, 6-(2-hydroxyethyl)-5-methyl-	EtOH	210(4.35),241(3.66), 279(4.05)	87-0927-80
$C_8H_{10}N_4S$			
2,5,6-Benzothiazoletriamine, N^2-methyl-	acid	308.5(3.91)	78-3087-80
	n.s.g.	276(4.01),319(3.95)	78-3087-80
$C_8H_{10}N_5O$			
Imidazo[2,1-i]purin-6-ium, 1,7,8,9-tetrahydro-8-hydroxy-9-methyl-, chloride	pH 1	212(4.34),262(4.09)	35-0770-80
	pH 7	228(4.31),274(4.03)	35-0770-80
	pH 13	228(4.31),274(4.07)	35-0770-80
$C_8H_{10}N_6OS_2$			
1H-Pyrazolo[3,4-d]pyrimidine-3-carbox-imidamide, N-hydroxy-4,6-bis(methyl-thio)-	EtOH	198(4.18),216(4.12), 246(4.26),258(4.20), 285(4.03),302(3.99)	103-0182-80
$C_8H_{10}N_6O_2$			
Morpholine, 4-[(5-azido-1H-imidazol-4-yl)carbonyl]-	H_2O or EtOH	232(4.05),268(4.10)	103-1171-80
$C_8H_{10}O$			
Benzene, ethoxy-	EtOH	221(3.976),266(3.351), 272(3.435),279(3.81)	65-0491-80
Bicyclo[2.2.1]heptan-2-one, 3-methyl-ene-, (1R)-	$C_6H_{11}Me$	235(3.96),347(1.60)	44-3518-80

Compound	Solvent	$\lambda_{max}(\log \epsilon)$	Ref.
Phenol, 2-ethyl-	hexane	214(3.72),267(3.20), 273(3.36),279(3.34)	65-2236-80
1-Propanol, 2-(2,4-cyclopentadien-1-ylidene)-	pentane	262(4.25),267(4.26), 360(2.52)	34-0184-80
$C_8H_{10}OS$			
Benzene, (ethylsulfinyl)- (radical)	H_2O	320(3.44)	39-0146-80B
$C_8H_{10}O_2$			
Benzene, 1,4-dimethoxy-	hexane	210(3.76),226(3.80)	70-1928-80
2,3-Benzodioxin, 1,4,6,7-tetrahydro-	EtOH	258(3.53)	24-0586-80
2,3-Dioxabicyclo[2.2.2]octane, 5,6-bis(methylene)-	EtOH	238(3.92)	24-0586-80
2(3H)-Furanone, 3-(2-methyl-1-propenylidene)-	C_6H_{12}	216.5(3.91)	33-1204-80
	EtOH	221.5(4.02)	33-1204-80
4-Hexen-2-ynoic acid, 5-methyl-, methyl ester	MeCN	260(4.00)	88-0671-80
2-Oxabicyclo[4.1.0]hept-3-en-5-one, 1,3-dimethyl-	MeOH	260(3.6)	18-0469-80
$C_8H_{10}O_5$			
3-Cyclopentene-1-carboxylic acid, 1-hydroxy-4-methoxy-2-oxo-, methyl ester, (R)- (kjellmanianone)	n.s.g.	242(4.16)	138-1243-80
2-Furanacetic acid, 2,5-dihydro-3-hydroxy-4-methyl-5-oxo-, methyl ester	MeOH-acid	228.3(4.23)	48-0559-80
	MeOH-NaOMe	258.4(4.26)	48-0559-80
$C_8H_{10}S$			
Benzene, (ethylthio)-	hexane	210(--),256(3.90), 270(3.40)	101-0147-80A +131-0099-80C
$C_8H_{10}S_3$			
2H-Thiopyran-2-thione, 3,4-dimethyl-6-(methylthio)-	C_6H_{12}	216(4.15),250(4.31), 328(3.90),464(3.82)	22-0539-80
	EtOH	213(4.15),252(4.36), 319(3.85),467(3.92)	22-0539-80
$C_8H_{11}BrClN_3$			
2-Pyrimidinamine, 5-bromo-4-chloro-N-methyl-N-(1-methylethyl)-	MeOH	258(4.32),300(3.46)	56-1557-80
4-Pyrimidinamine, 5-bromo-2-chloro-N-methyl-N-(1-methylethyl)-	MeOH	270(4.01),300(3.72)	56-1557-80
$C_8H_{11}BrN_2O_3$			
2,4(1H,3H)-Pyrimidinedione, 5-bromo-1-(4-hydroxybutyl)-	MeOH	281(3.98)	78-0865-80
7H-Pyrimido[6,1-b][1,3]oxazepine-7,9(8H)-dione, 10-bromohexahydro-, cis	CHCl_3	238(4.18)	78-0865-80
$C_8H_{11}ClN_2O_2$			
3(2H)-Pyridazinone, 2-butyl-4-chloro-5-hydroxy-	MeOH	216(4.42),227s(--), 287(3.73)	73-0127-80
$C_8H_{11}ClN_4O_2$			
4H-Oxazolo[3,2-a]-1,3,5-triazin-4-one, 7-(chloromethyl)-6,7-dihydro-2-(dimethylamino)-	EtOH	237(4.56)	103-0316-80
$C_8H_{11}ClN_6O_4$			
Acetic acid, chloro-, 2-(2-amino-1,6-	pH 1	251(4.13),271s(4.04),	150-3630-80

Compound	Solvent	$\lambda_{max}(\log \epsilon)$	Ref.
dihydro-5-nitro-6-oxo-4-pyrimidinyl)-1,2-dimethylhydrazide (cont.)	pH 13	362(3.59) 252(3.98),376(3.53)	150-3630-80 150-3630-80
$C_8H_{11}ClO_2$ 2-Cyclopenten-1-one, 2-chloro-3-methoxy-4,4-dimethyl-	MeOH	250(4.15)	20-0307-80
$C_8H_{11}FN_2O_3$ 2,4(1H,3H)-Pyrimidinedione, 1-(1-ethoxyethyl)-5-fluoro-	pH 2 pH 7 pH 12	271(3.93) 271(3.96) 272(3.79)	103-1176-80 103-1176-80 103-1176-80
2,4(1H,3H)-Pyrimidinedione, 5-fluoro-1-(propoxymethyl)-	pH 2 pH 7 pH 12	269(3.79) 269(3.81) 269(3.65)	103-1176-80 103-1176-80 103-1176-80
$C_8H_{11}FN_2O_4$ 2,4(1H,3H)-Pyrimidinedione, 5-fluoro-1-[(2-methoxyethoxy)methyl]-	pH 2 pH 7 pH 12	268(3.88) 268(3.87) 269(3.74)	103-1176-80 103-1176-80 103-1176-80
$C_8H_{11}IN_2O_2$ 2,4(1H,3H)-Pyrimidinedione, 1-(2-iodoethyl)-3,5-dimethyl-	H_2O	271.5(4.01)	117-0275-80
$C_8H_{11}N$ 1H-Indole, 4,5,6,7-tetrahydro-	hexane	222(3.87)	103-0488-80
$C_8H_{11}NO$ 7-Oxabicyclo[4.1.0]hepta-2,4-diene-1-ethanamine	BuOH	290(3.18)	44-3149-80
7-Oxabicyclo[4.1.0]hepta-2,4-diene-2-ethanamine	BuOH	271(3.48)	44-3149-80
7-Oxabicyclo[4.1.0]hepta-2,4-diene-3-ethanamine	BuOH	272.5(3.26)	44-3149-80
$C_8H_{11}NO_6$ 3,5-Isoxazoledicarboxylic acid, 4,5-dihydro-4-methyl-, dimethyl ester, 2-oxide, trans	MeOH	267(3.94)	94-0479-80
$C_8H_{11}NS_2$ 2,1-Benzisothiazole-3(1H)-thione, 4,5,6,7-tetrahydro-1-methyl-	EtOH	260(4.00),365(4.41)	118-0566-80
$C_8H_{11}N_2O_5PS$ 3(2H)-Pyridazinone, 5-(1,3,2-dioxaphospholan-2-yloxy)-4-methoxy-2-methyl-, P-sulfide	MeOH	213(4.29),284(3.60)	73-2343-80
$C_8H_{11}N_3O_2$ Hydrazinecarboxylic acid, (1H-pyrrol-2-ylmethylene)-, ethyl ester	C_6H_{12} EtOH 50% EtOH	304(4.44) 302(4.47) 302(4.42)	115-0151-80 115-0151-80 115-0151-80
$C_8H_{11}N_3O_4$ 5-Pyrimidinebutanoic acid, 2-amino-1,4-dihydro-6-hydroxy-4-oxo-	50% MeOH-HCl + NaOH	263(4.17) 267(4.13)	73-3583-80 73-3583-80
$C_8H_{11}N_5$ 3H-Purin-6-amine, N,N,3-trimethyl-	pH 1	291(4.31)	94-1920-80

Compound	Solvent	$\lambda_{max}(\log \epsilon)$	Ref.
3H-Purin-6-amine, N,N,3-trimethyl- (cont.)	pH 7	294(4.23)	94-1920-80
	pH 13	295(4.21)	94-1920-80
	EtOH	299(4.19)	94-1920-80
9H-Purin-6-amine, N,N,9-trimethyl-	pH 1	270(4.25)	94-1920-80
	pH 7	278(4.26)	94-1920-80
	pH 13	278(4.26)	94-1920-80
	EtOH	277(4.25)	94-1920-80
9H-Purin-6-amine, 9-propyl-	pH 1	261(4.16)	94-3443-80
	pH 7	263(4.16)	94-3443-80
	pH 13	263(4.16)	94-3443-80
	EtOH	262(4.16)	94-3443-80
$C_8H_{11}N_5O$ 8H-Pyrimido[6,1-c][1,2,4]triazin-8-one, 6-amino-1,4-dihydro-1,3-dimethyl-	MeOH	254s(3.67),300(4.14), 313s(3.99)	44-3919-80
$C_8H_{11}N_5OS$ 1,6,8,11,12-Pentaazabicyclo[8.2.1]tri- deca-10(13),11-dien-7-one, 9-thioxo-	MeOH	230(3.88),287(4.16)	78-0865-80
2(1H)-Pyrimidinone, 1-(4-azidobutyl)- 3,4-dihydro-4-thioxo-	MeOH	247(3.77),332(4.28)	78-0865-80
$C_8H_{11}N_5O_2$ 2,4(1H,3H)-Pyrimidinedione, 1-(4-azido- butyl)-	MeOH	265(4.01)	78-0865-80
$C_8H_{11}N_5O_3S$ 3H-Purine-3-propanesulfonic acid, 6-amino-	H_2O	273(4.27)	107-0267-80
9H-Purine-9-propanesulfonic acid, 6-amino-, monosodium salt	H_2O	262(4.11)	107-0267-80
C_8H_{12} 1,3-Cyclohexadiene, 2,3-dimethyl-	C_6H_{12}	261(3.52)	118-0238-80
Cyclohexane, 1,2-bis(exo-methylene)-	dioxan	221(3.81)	24-1663-80
Cyclopropane, (1-methyl-1,3-butadi- enyl)-, (E)-	hexane	243(4.31)	35-0711-80
(Z)-	hexane	241(4.36)	35-0711-80
1,3,5-Octatriene, (E,Z)- (fucoserratene)	hexane	254(4.45),263(4.58), 274(4.48)	35-6114-80
$C_8H_{12}ClN_3O$ 3H-Pyrrol-3-one, 4-chloro-2,5-bis(di- methylamino)-	CH_2Cl_2	307(3.88),482(3.14)	88-2883-80
$C_8H_{12}Cl_2N_3$ Methanaminium, N-[3,4-dichloro-5-(di- methylamino)-2H-pyrrol-2-ylidene]- N-methyl-, chloride	$CHCl_3$	306(3.98),408(3.35)	88-2883-80
$C_8H_{12}N_2$ 5,6-Diazatricyclo[5.3.0.0^{4,8}]dec-5-ene	heptane	348(2.44)	24-2154-80
1,4-Diazocine, 1,4-dihydro-1,4-dimeth- yl-	C_6H_{12}	217(4.53),276(3.99)	24-3161-80
$C_8H_{12}N_2O_2S$ 3(2H)-Pyridazinone, 4-hydroxy-2-methyl- 5-(propylthio)-	MeOH	202s(--),215(4.19), 308(3.75)	73-0127-80
3(2H)-Pyridazinone, 5-hydroxy-2-methyl- 4-[(1-methylethyl)thio]-	MeOH	214(4.21),227s(--), 317(3.70)	73-0127-80

Compound	Solvent	$\lambda_{max}(\log \epsilon)$	Ref.
2,4(1H,3H)-Pyrimidinedione, dihydro-1,3,5,5-tetramethyl-6-thioxo-	benzene	296(4.31),392(1.56)	5-0873-80
2(1H)-Pyrimidinone, 3,4-dihydro-1-(4-hydroxybutyl)-4-thioxo-	MeOH	247(3.70),332(4.30)	78-0865-80
$C_8H_{12}N_2O_2S_2$			
Butanedithioamide, N,N,N',N'-tetramethyl-2,3-dioxo-	EtOH	233(4.20),265(4.20), 325(3.92),381s(3.36), 444(3.38)	97-0436-80
2,4(1H,3H)-Pyrimidinedione, 6-(1,3-dithian-2-yl)dihydro-, (S)-	MeOH	245(2.85)	136-0033-80A
$C_8H_{12}N_2O_3$			
3-Isoxazolidinone, 4-[(1-methyl-3-oxo-1-butenyl)amino]-, (R)-	MeOH MeOH-NaOH	310(4.29) 313(4.32)	87-0006-80 87-0006-80
3(2H)-Pyridazinone, 5-hydroxy-4-methoxy-2-(1-methylethyl)-	MeOH	220(4.40),285(3.63)	73-0127-80
3(2H)-Pyridazinone, 5-hydroxy-4-methoxy-2-propyl-	MeOH	215(4.31),290(3.63)	73-0127-80
3(2H)-Pyridazinone, 4-hydroxy-2-methyl-5-propoxy-	MeOH	205s(--),218(4.32), 288(3.91)	73-0127-80
3(2H)-Pyridazinone, 5-hydroxy-2-methyl-4-(1-methylethoxy)-	MeOH	214(4.37),225s(--), 287(3.71)	73-0127-80
3(2H)-Pyridazinone, 5-hydroxy-2-methyl-4-propoxy-	MeOH	215(4.49),287(3.71)	73-0127-80
2,4(1H,3H)-Pyrimidinedione, 1-(4-hydroxybutyl)-	MeOH	264(3.99)	78-0865-80
2(1H)-Pyrimidinone, 4-ethoxy-1-(2-hydroxyethyl)-	H_2O	276(3.86)	47-2959-80
4(1H)-Pyrimidinone, 1-(2-hydroxyethyl)-2-methoxy-5-methyl-	H_2O	262.0(3.96)	117-0275-80
$C_8H_{12}N_2O_4$			
2,4(1H,3H)-Pyrimidinedione, 1,3-bis(2-hydroxyethyl)-	H_2O	267(3.94)	47-2959-80
$C_8H_{12}N_2O_4S_4$			
Glycine, N,N'-1,2-ethanediylbis[N-(dithiocarboxy)-, tetraammonium salt	H_2O	263(4.33),288(4.37)	90-0775-80
$C_8H_{12}N_2S$			
Pyrimidine, 2-(butylthio)-	EtOH	215(3.255),253(4.170), 285s(3.230)	112-0001-80
	CH_2Cl_2	254(4.198),285s(3.285)	112-0001-80
$C_8H_{12}N_4OS$			
4H,6H-[1,3]Thiazino[3,2-a]-1,3,5-triazin-4-one, 2-(dimethylamino)-7,8-dihydro-	EtOH	217(4.54),236(4.49), 267(4.38)	103-0316-80
$C_8H_{12}N_4O_2$			
Diazene, bis(1-isocyanato-1-methylethyl), (E)-	hexane	337(1.00)	78-1753-80
4H,6H-[1,3]Oxazino[3,2-a]-1,3,5-triazin-4-one, 2-(dimethylamino)-7,8-dihydro-	EtOH	214(4.57),235(4.54)	103-0316-80
$C_8H_{12}N_4S$			
Thiourea, N-(3,4-diaminophenyl)-N'-methyl-	acid n.s.g.	239(4.36),265s(4.10) 241(4.33),303s(3.81)	78-3087-80 78-3087-80

Compound	Solvent	$\lambda_{max}(\log \epsilon)$	Ref.
$C_8H_{12}N_6$			
3H-Purine-3-propanamine, 6-amino-, dihydrochloride	H_2O	274(4.10)	24-2043-80
$C_8H_{12}N_6O$			
Pyrimido[5,4-e]-1,2,4-triazin-5(1H)-one, 7-amino-2,6-dihydro-1,2,3-trimethyl-	pH 1	222(4.03),279(4.10)	150-3630-80
$C_8H_{12}N_6O_2$			
Pyrimido[5,4-e]-1,2,4-triazin-5(1H)-one, 7-amino-2,6-dihydro-3-(hydroxymethyl)-1,2-dimethyl-	pH 1	233(4.02),281(3.98), 310(4.04)	150-3630-80
	pH 13	227(4.04),281(4.02), 301(3.97)	150-3630-80
$C_8H_{12}N_6O_4$			
Acetic acid, 2-(2-amino-1,6-dihydro-5-nitro-6-oxo-4-pyrimidinyl)-1,2-dimethylhydrazide	pH 1	238(3.96),250s(3.95), 271(3.89),364(3.47)	150-3630-80
	pH 13	228(4.03),254(3.92), 378(3.40)	150-3630-80
$C_8H_{12}N_8O_2$			
[3,3'-Bi-1,2,4,5-tetrazine]-2,2'-(1H,1'H)-diyl, 5,5',6,6'-tetrahydro-1,1',5,5'-tetramethyl-6,6'-dioxo-	dioxan	241(4.44),383(3.58), 420(3.34),500(3.02)	89-0724-80
$C_8H_{12}O$			
Bicyclo[3.1.0]hexan-3-one, 2,2-dimethyl-	pentane	297(1.44)	44-1753-80
Bicyclo[2.2.2]oct-5-en-2-ol	n.s.g.	196(3.60)	35-6872-80
2-Cyclohexen-1-one, 3,5-dimethyl-	MeCN	232(4.14),323(1.40)	44-1800-80
2-Cyclohexen-1-one, 6,6-dimethyl-	hexane	235(3.95)	150-1551-80
2-Cycloocten-1-one, (E)-	EtOH	230(4.12),314(1.64)	44-1800-80
2,4-Heptadienal, 6-methyl-, (E,E)-	EtOH	272(4.42)	35-1390-80
$C_8H_{12}OS$			
3(2H)-Thiophenone, dihydro-2-methyl-4-(1-methylethylidene)-	EtOH	253(3.97)	4-0289-80
$C_8H_{12}O_2$			
2,4-Hexadienoic acid, ethyl ester	EtOH	259(4.31)	12-1537-80
7-Oxabicyclo[4.1.0]heptan-2-one, 3,3-dimethyl-, (-)-	hexane	312(1.6)	44-0158-80
7-Oxabicyclo[4.1.0]heptan-2-one, 4,4-dimethyl-, (+)-	hexane	305(1.3)	44-0158-80
2,3-Pentadienoic acid, 2,4-dimethyl-, methyl ester	EtOH	216.5(3.93)	33-1204-80
$C_8H_{12}O_3$			
Cyclopentanecarboxylic acid, 2-oxo-, ethyl ester	C_6H_{12}	255(2.78)	151-0305-80A
2,5-Hexadienoic acid, 3-ethoxy-	EtOH	231(4.16)	78-2291-80
2H-Pyran-2-one, tetrahydro-3-(1-methoxyethylidene)-, (E)-	isooctane	246(4.06)	44-0920-80
	MeOH	260(4.07)	44-0920-80
(Z)-	isooctane	257(4.12)	44-0920-80
	MeOH	272(4.20)	44-0920-80
$C_8H_{12}O_4$			
Hexanoic acid, 3,5-dioxo-, ethyl ester	EtOH	275(3.81)	39-2272-80C
	EtOH-NaOH	295(4.18)	39-2272-80C

Compound	Solvent	λ_{max}(log ϵ)	Ref.
Hexanoic acid, 4-methyl-3,5-dioxo-, methyl ester	EtOH	273(3.42),286(3.00)	39-2272-80C
C₈H₁₂O₆			
2-Cyclohexen-1-one, 3,5,6-trihydroxy-5-(hydroxymethyl)-2-methoxy-(gadusol)	acid base	269(4.09) 296(4.35)	88-4043-80 88-4043-80
C₈H₁₂S₂			
2-Thietanethione, 3,3-dimethyl-4-(1-methylethylidene)-	C₆H₁₂ MeOH	340(3.65),460(1.08) 344(3.76),442(1.20)	77-0243-80 77-0243-80
C₈H₁₃BrO₂			
2-Hexenoic acid, 4-bromo-, ethyl ester	EtOH	219(3.91)	12-1537-80
C₈H₁₃IO			
Bicyclo[2.2.2]octan-1-ol, 4-iodo-	EtOH	260.5(2.92)	44-3933-80
C₈H₁₃N			
1H-Pyrrole, 2-methyl-3-propyl-	hexane	213(3.90)	103-0488-80
C₈H₁₃NO₃			
2-Butenoic acid, 3-(formylamino)-2-methyl-, ethyl ester	EtOH	275(4.2)	5-0798-80
C₈H₁₃NO₃S			
6-Azabicyclo[3.2.0]heptan-4-one, 7-methyl-6-(methylsulfonyl)-	MeOH	215(2.54),270(2.06)	78-1585-80
7-Azabicyclo[4.2.0]octan-5-one, 7-(methylsulfonyl)-	MeOH	214(2.86),254(2.16)	78-1585-80
Methanesulfonamide, N-ethyl-N-(5-oxo-1-cyclopenten-1-yl)-	MeOH	216(3.38),300(2.23)	78-1585-80
Methanesulfonamide, N-methyl-N-(6-oxo-1-cyclohexen-1-yl)-	ether	210(3.75),240(3.30),326(1.93)	78-1585-80
Sulfonium, dimethyl-, 1-[(acetylamino)-carbonyl]-2-oxopropylide	EtOH	271(4.16)	94-0795-80
2H-1,4-Thiazine-6-carboxylic acid, 3,4-dihydro-3-hydroxy-2,2-dimethyl-, methyl ester	EtOH	303(4.02)	39-2322-80C
C₈H₁₃NO₄S			
2H-1,4-Thiazine-6-carboxylic acid, 3,4-dihydro-3-hydroxy-2,2-dimethyl-, methyl ester, 1-oxide	EtOH	275(4.18)	39-2322-80C
more polar isomer	EtOH	274(4.12)	39-2322-80C
C₈H₁₃NO₅			
Butanoic acid, 4-carbomethoxycarbonyl-amino-, methyl ester	EtOH	224(3.63)	78-2735-80
C₈H₁₃NS₂			
Cyclohexanecarbodithioic acid, 2-(methylimino)-	EtOH	305(3.93),393(4.27)	118-0566-80
C₈H₁₃N₃O			
4(1H)-Pyrimidinone, 2-(dimethylamino)-5,6-dimethyl-	pH 1 pH 7 pH 12	270(4.90) 275(3.69),298s(--) 290(3.82)	59-0563-80 59-0563-80 59-0563-80
C₈H₁₃N₃O₂			
1,3,5-Triazine-2,4(1H,3H)-dione, 6-(1,1-dimethylethyl)-3-methyl-	EtOH-NaOH	252(3.89)	4-0673-80

Compound	Solvent	$\lambda_{max}(\log \epsilon)$	Ref.
$C_8H_{14}N_2$			
6,7-Diazabicyclo[3.2.1]oct-6-ene, 1,5-dimethyl-	pentane	351(2.28)	35-1633-80
$C_8H_{14}N_2O_2$			
2-Butenamide, 2-acetyl-3-amino-N-ethyl-	MeOH	240(3.30),302(4.15)	44-0936-80
Pentanamide, 2-(1-aminoethylidene)-N-methyl-3-oxo-	MeOH	240(3.26),302(4.14)	44-0936-80
2-Pentenamide, 2-acetyl-3-amino-N-methyl-	MeOH	240(3.36),302(4.14)	44-0936-80
$C_8H_{14}N_2O_4$			
Carbamic acid, 1,2-ethenediylbis-, diethyl ester	H_2O	235(4.36)	35-6784-80
$C_8H_{14}N_4O$			
1H-Imidazole-4-carboxamide, 1-ethyl-5-(ethylamino)-	pH 1	253(3.82),267s(3.79)	94-2819-80
	pH 7	267(3.96)	94-2819-80
	pH 13	267(3.96)	94-2819-80
	EtOH	269(3.96)	94-2819-80
$C_8H_{14}N_6O_2$			
1H-1,2,3-Triazole-4-carboxamide, 1-[4-[(aminocarbonyl)amino]butyl]-	MeOH	211(4.06)	78-0865-80
$C_8H_{14}O$			
2,4-Heptadienol, 6-methyl-, (E,E)-	hexane	227(4.34)	35-1390-80
3-Hexanone, 5-methyl-4-methylene-	EtOH	220(3.78),320(1.60)	101-0367-80K
4-Hexen-2-one, 3,3-dimethyl-, (E)-	C_6H_{12}	289(1.82)	39-0592-80B
4-Hexen-3-one, 4,5-dimethyl-	EtOH	245(3.73),305(1.95)	101-0367-80K
$C_8H_{14}OS$			
3-Buten-2-one, 4-(butylthio)-, trans	C_6H_{12}	284(4.17)	65-2185-80
	EtOH	293(4.21)	65-2185-80
	Pr_2O	284(4.16)	65-2185-80
	dioxan	286(4.18)	65-2185-80
	$C_2H_4Cl_2$	289(4.21)	65-2185-80
	MeCN	290(4.18)	65-2185-80
3-Buten-2-one, 4-[(1,1-dimethylethyl)-thio]-, trans	C_6H_{12}	290(4.21)	65-2185-80
	EtOH	298(4.21)	65-2185-80
	Pr_2O	289(4.20)	65-2185-80
	dioxan	292(4.21)	65-2185-80
	$C_2H_4Cl_2$	294(4.21)	65-2185-80
	MeCN	294(4.20)	65-2185-80
Cyclohexanone, 2-(ethylthio)-	hexane	248(2.51),309(2.41)	39-0453-80B
	MeOH	250(2.45),306(2.46)	39-0453-80B
3-Penten-2-one, 3-(ethylthio)-4-methyl-	C_6H_{12}	236(3.57),275(3.27)	78-1943-80
$C_8H_{14}OSi$			
2-Cyclopenten-1-one, 2-(trimethyl-silyl)-	pentane	225(4.83),332(1.72)	44-4462-80
$C_8H_{14}O_2$			
1,3-Butadiene, 2,3-bis(methoxymethyl)-	isooctane	224(4.17)	44-0870-80
3,4-Hexanedione, 2,5-dimethyl-	EtOH	274(1.60),434(1.36)	90-0441-80
2-Hexenoic acid, ethyl ester	EtOH	224(3.52)	12-1537-80
$C_8H_{15}NO$			
3-Buten-2-one, 4-(diethylamino)-	C_6H_{12}	290(4.34)	65-2185-80
	EtOH	303(4.52)	65-2185-80
	Pr_2O	292(4.37)	65-2185-80

Compound	Solvent	$\lambda_{max}(\log \epsilon)$	Ref.
3-Buten-2-one, 4-(diethylamino)- (cont.)	dioxan	294(4.38)	65-2185-80
	$C_2H_4Cl_2$	296(4.41)	65-2185-80
	MeCN	300(4.50)	65-2185-80
Cycloheptanone, 3-(methylamino)- (physoperuvine)	MeOH	273(1.09)	44-3265-80
$C_8H_{15}NO_2$			
3,4-Hexanedione, 2,5-dimethyl-, mono-oxime	EtOH	318(1.66)	90-0441-80
$C_8H_{15}NO_4$			
Methanaminium, N,N-dimethyl-, 2-meth-oxy-1-(methoxycarbonyl)-2-oxoethylide	EtOH	254(2.59)	73-0092-80
$C_8H_{15}N_2O_3P$			
Phosphonic acid, (1H-imidazol-1-yl-methyl)-, diethyl ester	EtOH	205(2.2),218(2.2), 233(2.2),276(1.2)	65-1217-80
$C_8H_{15}N_3$			
Ethanimidic acid, cyclohexylidenehydra-zide	MeOH	239(3.97)	104-0822-80
Methanamine, N-(3,5-dihydro-3,3,5,5-tetramethyl-4H-pyrazol-4-ylidene)-	hexane	273(1.926),342(2.308)	89-0049-80
$C_8H_{15}N_3S$			
Carbodiimide, tert-butyl(dimethylthio-carbamoyl)-	dioxan	244(4.17),297(3.81)	24-0079-80
$C_8H_{15}OS$			
Sulfonium, dimethyl(2-oxocyclohexyl)-	EtOH	270(c.3.85)	39-0931-80B
$C_8H_{16}GeO$			
Germane, trimethyl(3-methyl-1-oxo-2-butenyl)-	C_6H_{12}	363s(1.23),389s(1.73), 408s(1.99),432(2.15), 443(2.12),478s(1.79)	35-1577-80
$C_8H_{16}NOS$			
Sulfonium, dimethyl(2-nitrosocyclo-hexyl)-, tetrafluoroborate	MeCN	298(3.89)	39-0931-80B
$C_8H_{16}N_2O_2S$			
1,4,5-Thiadiazepine, 2,3,6,7-tetrahy-dro-3,3,6,6-tetramethyl-, 1,1-di-oxide, (E)-	EtOH	418(2.52)	88-0339-80
(Z)-	EtOH	404(1.98)	88-0339-80
$C_8H_{16}N_4$			
1H-1,2,4-Triazol-3-amine, 5-hexyl-	EtOH	205(3.75)	103-1271-80
$C_8H_{16}N_4O_2$			
Propanamide, 2,2'-azobis[2-methyl-	EtOH	375(1.36)	78-1753-80
$C_8H_{16}O$			
Furan, tetrahydro-2,2,5,5-tetramethyl-	gas	192(2.9),197(2.9)	23-2819-80
3-Hexanone, 2,5-dimethyl-	EtOH	285(1.48)	90-0441-80
$C_8H_{16}O_2$			
3-Hexanone, 4-hydroxy-2,5-dimethyl-	EtOH	286(1.57)	90-0441-80
$C_8H_{16}Si$			
Silane, trimethyl-2,4-pentadienyl-	hexane	234(4.31)	33-0555-80

Compound	Solvent	$\lambda_{max}(\log \epsilon)$	Ref.
Silane, trimethyl-2,4-pentadienyl-(cont.)	n.s.g.	237.5(3.75)	88-3783-80
C$_8$H$_{16}$Sn Stannane, trimethyl-2,4-pentadienyl-	hexane	239.5(4.00)	88-0355-80
C$_8$H$_{17}$N$_3$ 1H-1,2,4-Triazole, 2,5-dihydro-3,5,5-trimethyl-1-propyl-	MeOH	216s(3.45),245(3.55)	104-0822-80
C$_8$H$_{18}$N$_2$O$_3$ Hydroperoxide, 1-(butylnitrosoamino)-butyl	EtOH	231(3.84),358(1.85)	88-1761-80
C$_8$H$_{18}$Si$_2$ Disilane, 1,2-diethenyl-1,1,2,2-tetra-methyl-	isooctane	227.0(3.99)	101-0261-80Q
C$_8$H$_{19}$O$_2$PS$_2$ Phosphorodithioic acid, O,O-dibutyl ester	M acid	225(3.61)	1-0301-80A
C$_8$H$_{20}$O$_4$Si Silicic acid, tetraethyl ester	heptane MeCN	189.5(1.85) 189.8(1.95)	65-1280-80 65-1280-80
C$_8$H$_{20}$S$_4$Si Thiosilicic acid, tetraethyl ester	hexane hexane	190(--),227(3.48) 227(3.48)	101-0147-80A 131-0099-80C
C$_8$H$_{24}$Sn$_4$Te$_2$ 1,4,2,3,5,6-Ditelluratetrastannin, tetrahydro-2,2,3,3,5,5,6,6-octa-methyl-	C$_6$H$_{12}$	245(3.30),315(2.78), 352s(2.48)	101-0037-80K
C$_8$N$_2$O$_2$S$_2$ Propanedinitrile, (2,5-dioxo-3,4-di-thioxocyclopentyl)-, ion(2-), di-potassium	H$_2$O	302(4.1),461(3.9), 571(4.4)	5-1409-80
C$_8$N$_4$O Furantetracarbonitrile	EtOH	220(4.37),258(4.09), 310(4.53)	44-5113-80
C$_8$N$_4$S Thiophenetetracarbonitrile	EtOH	239(4.39),281(4.04)	44-5113-80
C$_8$N$_4$S$_3$ Butanedinitrile, 2,2'-thiobis[3-thioxo-, ion(2-), dipotassium	EtOH	218(4.23),380(4.27)	44-5113-80
C$_8$N$_4$S$_4$ [1,4]Dithiino[2,3-c:6,5-c']diisothia-zole-3,7-dicarbonitrile	MeCN	218(4.40),278(3.69), 338(4.04)	44-5122-80

Compound	Solvent	λ_{max}(log ϵ)	Ref.
C$_9$BrN$_5$S Thieno[2,3-d]pyrimidine-4,5,6-tricarbo- nitrile, 2-bromo-	n.s.g.	253(4.20),315s(3.99), 330(4.12),346(4.08)	44-5113-80
C$_9$H$_3$N$_5$ 1H-Pyrrole-2,3,4,5-tetracarbonitrile, 1-methyl-	EtOH	223(4.55),230(4.54), 283s(3.46),262(4.04)	44-5113-80
C$_9$H$_5$BrO$_2$ 4H-Cyclohepta[b]furan-4-one, 5-bromo-	n.s.g.	228(4.09),257(4.15), 322(3.78),352(3.94), 368(3.95)	39-2081-80C
C$_9$H$_5$ClN$_2$ 1H-Indole-2-carbonitrile, 3-chloro-	MeOH	228(4.51),288(4.24)	94-1157-80
C$_9$H$_5$ClO 1H-Inden-1-one, 3-chloro-	MeOH	232(4.47),239(4.47)	4-1313-80
C$_9$H$_5$Cl$_5$O Benzene, 1,3,5-trichloro-2-[(2,2-di- chlorocyclopropyl)oxy]-	hexane	227s(--),273s(--), 279(3.11),288(3.15)	70-1928-80
C$_9$H$_5$NO$_2$S$_2$ [1]Benzothieno[2,3-d]isothiazole, 4,4- dioxide	n.s.g.	235(4.29),264(3.89), 273(3.92),300(3.79)	150-0833-80
C$_9$H$_5$NO$_4$ 1(3H)-Isobenzofuranone, 3-(nitrometh- ylene)-	EtOH	277s(3.19),282(3.21), 330(2.93)	88-1163-80
C$_9$H$_6$Br$_2$N Quinolizinium, 1,2-dibromo-, bromide	MeOH	222(4.42),238(4.36), 298(3.64),328(4.06), 342(4.25)	142-0213-80B
Quinolizinium, 2,7-dibromo-, bromide	H$_2$O	231(4.57),245(4.50), 289(3.72),296(3.74), 325(4.15),340(--)	142-0213-80B
Quinolizinium, 3,4-dibromo-, bromide	EtOH	249(4.26),305(3.83), 337(3.97),350(4.09)	142-0213-80B
C$_9$H$_6$ClNO$_2$ Benzoic acid, 4-chloro-2-(cyanomethyl)- Benzoic acid, 5-chloro-2-(cyanomethyl)-	EtOH EtOH	239(4.08),227(2.91)[sic] 226(3.95),284(3.15)	95-0819-80 95-0819-80
C$_9$H$_6$ClNS$_3$ 5(2H)-Isothiazolethione, 4-(4-chloro- phenyl)-3-mercapto-	CHCl$_3$	312(4.17),392(3.95)	39-2693-80C
C$_9$H$_6$Cl$_2$O Benzofuran, 5-chloro-2-(chloromethyl)-	EtOH	215(4.29),256(4.14), 288(3.54),298(3.48)	36-0232-80
C$_9$H$_6$Cl$_4$O Benzene, 2,4-dichloro-1-[(2,2-dichloro- cyclopropyl)oxy]-	hexane	228s(--),275s(--), 282(3.34),290(3.32)	70-1928-80
C$_9$H$_6$N$_2$ Pyrazino[2,1,6-cd]pyrrolizine	EtOH	247(4.56),290(3.61), 380s(3.26),388(3.29), 400s(3.22),410(2.99)	39-1319-80C

Compound	Solvent	λ_{max} (log ϵ)	Ref.
Pyrazino[2,1,6-cd]pyrrolizine (cont.)	EtOH-HCl	232(4.74),256(4.41), 278s(3.96),304(3.50), 370(3.11)	39-1319-80C
C₉H₆N₂S₂ Propanedinitrile, [[5-(methylthio)- 2-thienyl]methylene]-	MeOH	206(3.95),244(3.69), 283(3.54),347(4.18)	73-2360-80
C₉H₆N₂S₃ Propanedinitrile, [2,3-bis(methylthio)- 4-thioxo-2-cyclobuten-1-ylidene]-	CH₂Cl₂	292(4.3),382(4.4), 401(4.4),420(4.4)	5-1409-80
C₉H₆N₄O 1H-Pyrazolo[3,4-f]quinazolin-9(8H)-one	pH 7.5	255(4.31),315(3.85), 327(3.86)	88-3029-80
	pH 7.7	252(4.31),304s(3.79), 313(3.89),326(3.89)	142-1053-80B
	pH 7.8	252(4.39),314(3.92), 326(3.92)	44-3072-80
	pH 12.6	253(4.31),260(4.26), 284(3.69),302s(3.78), 312(3.90),325(3.89)	142-1053-80B
Tetrazolo[1,5-a]quinolin-5-ol	EtOH	256(4.0),288(3.9), 298(3.8),311(3.7)	103-1286-80
[1,2,4]Triazolo[1,5-a]quinazolin- 5(4H)-one	n.s.g.	219(4.58),250s(--), 260s(--),302(3.57), 312s(--)	33-0001-80
C₉H₆N₄O₂ 1H-Pyrazolo[4,3-g]quinazoline- 5,7(6H,8H)-dione	pH 7.5	203(4.25),239s(4.66), 245(4.72),307(3.79)	88-3029-80
C₉H₆N₄O₃ 2-Propenoic acid, 3-(5-azido-2-furan- yl)-2-cyano-, methyl ester	MeOH	211(3.96),242(4.14), 391(4.23)	73-1831-80
C₉H₆O₂ 4H-Cyclohepta[b]furan-4-one	n.s.g.	220(4.42),260(3.86), 300(3.88),312(3.93), 342(3.94),356(3.93)	39-2081-80C
C₉H₆O₃ 4H-1-Benzopyran-4-one, 7-hydroxy-	pH 4.5	241(4.18),248(4.26), 298(4.07)	86-0977-80
	pH 10	254(4.35),307s(3.81), 335(4.03)	86-0977-80
Bicyclo[4.2.0]octa-1,3,5-triene-7,8- dione, 3-methoxy-	EtOH	246(4.37),259s(3.87), 273s(3.76),322(3.83), 332(3.81)	39-1841-80C
C₉H₆O₄ Furo[3,4-e]-1,3-benzodioxol-6(8H)-one	EtOH	224(4.45),269(3.79), 294(3.69)	73-1950-80
Furo[3,4-e]-1,3-benzodioxol-8(6H)-one	EtOH	221(4.39),234(3.90), 322(3.66)	73-1950-80
C₉H₇BrCl₂O Benzene, 1-bromo-2-[(2,2-dichloro- cyclopropyl)oxy]-	hexane	220s(--),266s(--), 272(3.46),280(3.45)	70-1928-80
Benzene, 1-bromo-4-[(2,2-dichloro- cyclopropyl)oxy]-	hexane	226(4.33),271s(--), 277(3.26),286(3.23)	70-1928-80

Compound	Solvent	$\lambda_{max}(\log \epsilon)$	Ref.
$C_9H_7Br_3O_2$			
4H-Cyclohepta[b]furan-4-one, 5,5,8-tri-bromo-5,6,7,8-tetrahydro-	n.s.g.	228(4.01),295(3.75)	39-2081-80C
C_9H_7ClN			
Quinolizinium, 2-chloro-, bromide	MeOH	229(4.36),238(3.46), 317(4.10),324(4.03), 331(4.30)	142-0213-80B
Quinolizinium, 4-chloro-, bromide	H_2O	237(4.32),292(3.59), 320(4.00),334(4.20)	142-0213-80B
$C_9H_7ClN_2O$			
1(2H)-Isoquinolinone, 3-amino-6-chloro-	EtOH	240(4.62),310(4.41), 379(3.53)	95-0819-80
1(2H)-Isoquinolinone, 3-amino-7-chloro-	EtOH	225(4.61),308(4.58), 389(3.48)	95-0819-80
$C_9H_7Cl_3O$			
Benzene, 1-chloro-2-[(2,2-dichloro-cyclopropyl)oxy]-	hexane	222s(--),261s(--), 273(3.32),279(3.32)	70-1928-80
Benzene, 1-chloro-4-[(2,2-dichloro-cyclopropyl)oxy]-	hexane	228s(--),271s(--), 279(3.28),286(3.28)	70-1928-80
$C_9H_7Cl_4NO_3$			
Acetamide, N-(2,3,5,6-tetrachloro-1-methoxy-4-oxo-2,5-cyclohexadien-1-yl)-	MeCN	224(3.60),243(3.83), 262(3.78)	12-2299-80
$C_9H_7FN_2O_3$			
2,4(1H,3H)-Pyrimidinedione, 1-(2,5-di-hydro-5-methylene-2-furanyl)-5-flu-oro-	MeOH	263(4.17)	87-0852-80
C_9H_7NOS			
Benzoyl isothiocyanate, 4-methyl-	dioxan	264(4.16),286(3.92)	73-2334-80
$C_9H_7NO_2$			
Benzenepropanenitrile, 2-hydroxy-β-oxo-	EtOH	253(3.94),327(3.66)	114-0271-80A
2H-1-Benzopyran-4-ol, 2-imino-	EtOH	290(4.06)	114-0271-80A
Cyclopropen-1-imine, 2,3-dihydroxy-N-phenyl-	$CHCl_3$	271(4.39)	77-0223-80
1H-Indole-2,3-dione, 4-methyl-	EtOH	237(4.3),310(3.7), 405(3.3)	78-2441-80
Phenol, 2-(5-isoxazolyl)-	EtOH	261(4.26),272(4.14), 306(4.02)	114-0271-80A
$C_9H_7NO_2S$			
4H-1-Benzothiopyran-4-one, 2-amino-, S-oxide	MeOH	308(3.99),415(3.96)	23-0369-80
Benzoyl isothiocyanate, 4-methoxy-	dioxan	251(4.11),283(3.86)	73-2334-80
$C_9H_7NO_3$			
1H-Indole-2,3-dione, 5-methoxy-	EtOH	253(4.4),290s(3.8), 450(3.3)	78-2441-80
$C_9H_7NO_3S$			
1,2-Benzothiazepin-5(2H)-one, 1,1-diox-ide	MeOH	298(3.90)	23-0369-80
Thieno[3,2-b]pyridin-5(4H)-one, 6-acet-yl-7-hydroxy-	EtOH	225(4.04),275(4.08), 297(4.19)	150-0113-80

Compound	Solvent	$\lambda_{max}(\log \epsilon)$	Ref.
$C_9H_7NO_4$			
1H-Indole-2,3-dione, 6-hydroxy-5-methoxy-	MeOH	265(4.40),318(3.90), 470(3.20)	150-4154-80
$C_9H_7NS_3$			
5(2H)-Isothiazolethione, 3-mercapto-4-phenyl-	$CHCl_3$	312(4.17),392(3.95)	39-2693-80C
$C_9H_7N_3$			
1H-Benzimidazole-2-acetonitrile, hydrochloride	MeOH	207(4.11),242(3.72), 248(3.68),265(3.58), 271(3.70),278(3.70), 313(2.90)	94-0567-80
Pyrrolo[3,2-e]benzimidazole, 1,6-dihydro-	EtOH	272(3.97),287(3.98), 297(3.95)	103-0062-80
$C_9H_7N_3O_2$			
1,3-Dioxolo[4,5-g]quinazolin-8-amine	EtOH	210(3.98),223s(3.98), 243(4.26),253s(4.11), 278(3.66),298s(3.60), 320(3.73),333(3.72)	114-0253-80B
$C_9H_7N_3O_2S$			
1,3-Benzenediol, 4-(2-thiazolylazo)-	80% EtOH-pH 7	470(3.72)	140-0314-80
	cation	481(--)	73-1502-80
	anion	480(--)	73-1502-80
	dianion	513(--)	73-1502-80
4H-1-Benzothiopyran-4-one, 2-azido-2,3-dihydro-, 1-oxide, trans	MeOH	244(3.99),298(3.44)	23-0369-80
2-Thiazolamine, 4-(4-nitrophenyl)-	MeOH	216(4.14),239(4.10), 266(4.09),362(4.02)	78-2675-80
$C_9H_7N_3O_3S$			
4H-1-Benzothiopyran-4-one, 2-azido-2,3-dihydro-, 1,1-dioxide	MeOH	247(3.95),287(3.32), 295(3.25)	23-0369-80
$C_9H_7N_3O_5$			
Glycine, N-(5-benzofurazanylcarbonyl)-, N-oxide	EtOH	224(4.42),265s(3.52), 315s(3.32),333s(3.48), 366(3.81)	4-0213-80
	MeCN	222(4.44),265s(3.46), 315s(3.32),331s(3.46), 364(3.81)	4-0213-80
$C_9H_7N_3S$			
Diazene, phenyl(2-thiazolyl)-	EtOH	365(4.23)	62-0158-80
$C_9H_7N_3S_2$			
Triazene, 3-(4-thioxo-1-benzothiopyran-2-yl)-	MeOH	240s(3.65),283(2.91), 390s(2.30)	23-0369-80
C_9H_7O			
Cyclohepta[b]furylium tetrafluoroborate	H_2O	254(4.52),298(3.42), 359(3.71)(changing)	88-3375-80
final spectrum	H_2O	235(4.33),320(3.86)	88-3375-80
	96% H_2SO_4	254(4.68),295(3.44), 359(3.79)	88-3375-80
C_9H_8			
Tricyclo[5.2.0.0^{2,4}]nona-1,4,6-triene	C_6H_{12}	264(3.10),270(3.20),	44-4183-80

Compound	Solvent	λ_{max} (log ϵ)	Ref.
(cont.) Tricyclo[5.2.0.0³,⁵]nona-1,3(5),6-triene	C_6H_{12}	277(3.20) 284(3.00),288(3.00), 294(2.80)	44-4183-80 44-4183-80
$C_9H_8Br_2$ Bicyclo[4.2.0]octa-1,3,5-triene, 3-bromo-2-(bromomethyl)-	C_6H_{12}	236(3.80),275(2.92), 283(2.84)	44-4183-80
Bicyclo[4.2.0]octa-1,3,5-triene, x-bromo-3-(bromomethyl)-	hexane	217(4.18),240s(3.87), 275(3.18),283(3.29), 292(3.18)	44-4183-80
$C_9H_8Br_2O_2$ Benzoic acid, 3,5-dibromo-4-methyl-, methyl ester	EtOH	213(4.63)	118-0409-80
4H-Cyclohepta[b]furan-4-one, 5,5-di- bromo-5,6,7,8-tetrahydro-	n.s.g.	228s(--),290(3.64)	39-2081-80C
Ethanone, 1-(2,3-dibromo-4-methoxy- phenyl)-	EtOH	230(4.11),275(4.07)	39-2405-80C
$C_9H_8ClIO_3$ 1,4-Benzodioxin, 6-chloro-2,3-dihydro- 8-iodo-5-methoxy-	EtOH	220(4.30),237(4.11), 290(3.08)	103-0993-80
C_9H_8ClNO 2-Propenal, 3-[(4-chlorophenyl)amino]-	79.7% H_2SO_4	250(4.0),328(4.4)	94-3401-80
$C_9H_8ClNO_4S$ 1-Propene-2-sulfonic acid, 1-[(4-chlo- rophenyl)amino]-3-oxo-	96% H_2SO_4	251(4.1),332(4.3)	94-3401-80
$C_9H_8ClN_3O$ 1(2H)-Isoquinolinone, 2,3-diamino- 6-chloro-	EtOH	240(4.35),311(4.01), 380(3.30)	95-0819-80
1(2H)-Isoquinolinone, 2,3-diamino- 7-chloro-	EtOH	227(4.35),311(4.23), 390(3.41)	95-0819-80
$C_9H_8Cl_2O$ Benzene, [(2,2-dichlorocyclopropyl)- oxy]-	hexane	220(4.26),261(3.23), 267(3.26),274(3.23)	70-1928-80
$C_9H_8Cl_3NO_3$ 4-Cyclopentene-1,3-dione, 2,2,4-tri- chloro-5-morpholino-	EtOH	289(4.17),360(4.07)	104-1404-80
$C_9H_8Cl_5NO_2$ 2-Cyclopenten-1-one, 2,4,4,5,5-penta- chloro-3-morpholino-	EtOH	330(4.33)	104-1404-80
Morpholine, 4-(2,3,4,5,5-pentachloro- 1-oxo-2,4-pentadienyl)-	EtOH	223(4.29)	104-1404-80
$C_9H_8FIN_2O_3$ 2,5-Methano-5H,7H-pyrimido[2,1-b]- [1,5,3]dioxazepin-7-one, 8-fluoro- 2,3-dihydro-3-(iodomethyl)-	dioxan	281(3.81)	87-0852-80
2,5-Methano-5H,9H-pyrimido[2,1-b]- [1,5,3]dioxazepin-9-one, 8-fluoro- 2,3-dihydro-3-(iodomethyl)-	H_2O	231(3.82),254(3.95)	87-0852-80
$C_9H_8F_3N_3O$ Propanedinitrile, [2,2,2-trifluoro- 1-(4-morpholinyl)ethylidene]-	EtOH	201(3.73),281(3.83), 322(3.95)	104-1441-80

Compound	Solvent	$\lambda_{max}(\log \epsilon)$	Ref.
C₉H₈I₂			
Bicyclo[4.2.0]octa-1,3,5-triene, 3-iodo-2-(iodomethyl)-	hexane	226(4.22),255(3.85), 285(2.42)	44-4183-80
Bicyclo[4.2.0]octa-1,3,5-triene, x-iodo-3-(iodomethyl)-	C₆H₁₂	231(4.23),260(3.77)	44-4183-80
C₉H₈N₂			
5H-Dipyrrolo[1,2-c:2',1'-e]imidazole	EtOH	293(4.21)	33-1190-80
Propanedinitrile, (3-cyclopropyl-2-propenylidene)-, (E)-	EtOH	316(4.47)	35-0711-80
(Z)-	EtOH	320(4.40)	35-0711-80
C₉H₈N₂O			
1H-Indazole, 1-acetyl-	EtOH	230(4.51),241s(--), 249s(--),257(4.01), 283s(--),292(3.96), 301(3.99)	5-0908-80
C₉H₈N₂O₂S₂			
2-Thiazolamine, 5-(phenylsulfonyl)-	H₂O	290(3.79)	39-1156-80B
protonated	H₂O	270(3.91)	39-1156-80B
C₉H₈N₂O₃S			
5H-Imidazo[2,1-b][1,3]thiazine-6-carboxylic acid, 5-oxo-, ethyl ester	EtOH	223(4.16),238(4.15), 333(3.78)	39-1352-80C
C₉H₈N₂O₄			
2H-Benzimidazole-4,7-dione, 2,2-dimethyl-, 1,3-dioxide	EtOH	230(4.06),298(3.73), 390(3.55),435(3.30)	103-0628-80
C₉H₈N₂S			
2-Thiazolamine, 5-phenyl-	H₂O	306(4.16)	39-1156-80B
protonated	H₂O	286(4.17)	39-1156-80B
Thiazolo[3,2-a]benzimidazole, 2,3-dihydro-	EtOH	250(3.92),255s(3.85), 280s(3.88),285(4.05), 293(4.09)	4-0393-80
C₉H₈N₂S₂			
2-Thiazolamine, 5-(phenylthio)-	H₂O	276(4.06)	39-1156-80B
protonated	H₂O	254(4.09)	39-1156-80B
C₉H₈N₄OS			
Benzothiazole, 2-[[1-(hydroxyimino)-ethyl]azo]-	50% EtOH	365(3.28)	103-0857-80
C₉H₈N₄O₂			
Sydnone, 3-(4-cyano-1,4-dihydro-1-methyl-3-pyridinyl)-	MeOH	239(3.82),260s(3.60), 330(3.49),365(3.49)	39-0020-80C
1H-1,2,4-Triazole, 3-methyl-5-(4-nitrophenyl)-	MeOH	295(4.21)	56-1067-80
C₉H₈N₄O₃			
3H,8H-Imidazo[1,2,3-ij]pteridine-3,8,10(9H)-trione, 5,6-dihydro-2-methyl-	pH 5.0	214(4.14),275(4.02), 320(4.06)	142-0437-80B
	pH 12.0	215(4.20),252(4.02), 275(3.76),335(4.11)	142-0437-80B
C₉H₈N₄O₅			
Pyrido[2,3-d]pyrimidine-2,4(3H,8H)-dione, 8-(2-hydroxyethyl)-6-nitro-	pH 1	354(4.15)	39-2645-80C
	pH 13	265s(3.86),463(4.39)	39-2645-80C

Compound	Solvent	λ_{max} (log ϵ)	Ref.
C₉H₈N₆			
1H-Cyclohepta[1,2-d:4,5-d']diimidazole-2,6-diamine	MeOH	284(4.37),296(4.40), 411(4.07)	138-0205-80
C₉H₈O			
1H-Inden-1-one, 2,3-dihydro-	EtOH	244(4.16),286(3.48), 291(3.49)	73-1950-80
C₉H₈O₂			
2,4-Pentadienal, 5-(2-furanyl)-	n.s.g.	350(4.40)	39-2081-80C
2-Propenoic acid, 3-phenyl-, trans	MeOH	216(4.14),221(4.07), 272(4.18)	94-1859-80
C₉H₈O₃			
1,3-Isobenzofurandione, 4,7-dihydro-5-methyl-	EtOH	237(3.26)	24-0531-80
1(3H)-Isobenzofuranone, 4-methoxy-	EtOH	214(4.51),229(3.85), 292(3.46)	73-1950-80
1(3H)-Isobenzofuranone, 5-methoxy-	EtOH	210(4.20),215s(4.11), 256(4.04),276s(3.56), 287(3.20)	73-1950-80
1(3H)-Isobenzofuranone, 6-methoxy-	EtOH	211(4.50),226s(3.86), 298(3.56)	73-1950-80
1(3H)-Isobenzofuranone, 7-methoxy-	EtOH	209(4.52),234(3.91), 296(3.67)	73-1950-80
2-Propenoic acid, 3-(4-hydroxyphenyl)-, trans	MeOH	226(4.02),288(4.28)	94-1859-80
C₉H₈O₄			
Benzoic acid, 2-acetoxy-	pH 9.0	297(3.60)	106-0739-80
1(3H)-Isobenzofuranone, 7-hydroxy-5-methoxy-	EtOH	219(4.53),256(4.37), 292(3.84)	2-0927-80
	EtOH-NaOH	229(4.42),259(3.86), 323(3.75)	2-0927-80
C₉H₈O₅			
Benzoic acid, 2-formyl-3,5-dihydroxy-4-methyl-	MeOH	225(4.314),290(4.302)	120-0016-80
C₉H₈S₂			
Benzo[b]thiophene-2-thiol, 3-methyl-	EtOH	213(4.11),232(4.23), 252(3.94),277(3.77), 297(3.74),308(3.52)	103-0991-80
C₉H₉BrN₂O₄S			
6H-Furo[2',3':4,5]thiazolo[3,2-a]pyrimidin-6-one, 7-bromo-2,3,3a,9a-tetrahydro-3-hydroxy-2-(hydroxymethyl)-, [2R-(2α,3β,3aβ,9aβ)]-	H₂O	233(4.35),270s(3.90)	94-0939-80
C₉H₉BrO₂			
4H-Cyclohepta[b]furan-4-one, 5-bromo-5,6,7,8-tetrahydro-	n.s.g.	282(3.63)	39-2081-80C
C₉H₉BrO₃			
2-Propenoic acid, 2-(bromomethyl)-3-(2-furanyl)-, methyl ester, (Z)-	EtOH	304(4.28)	73-0906-80
C₉H₉Br₃O			
Bicyclo[5.1.0]octa-2,4-diene, 4,8,8-tribromo-3-methoxy-	EtOH	240(4.04),285(3.23)	39-2405-80C

Compound	Solvent	$\lambda_{max}(\log \epsilon)$	Ref.
C₉H₉Cl			
Bicyclo[4.2.0]octa-1,3,5-triene, 3-(chloromethyl)-	hexane	223(4.15),265(3.34), 270(3.45),274(3.47), 279(3.50)	44-4183-80
C₉H₉ClN₂O₂			
1H,5H-Pyrazolo[1,2-a]pyrazole-1,5-dione, 2-chloro-3,6,7-trimethyl-	dioxan	323(4.18)	35-4983-80
1H,7H-Pyrazolo[1,2-a]pyrazole-1,7-dione, 2-chloro-3,5,6-trimethyl-	dioxan	252(3.77),365(3.90)	35-4983-80
C₉H₉ClN₄			
1,2,4-Triazolo[3,4-a]phthalazine, 6-chloro-7,8,9,10-tetrahydro- (spectra in ethanol)	pH 1	270(3.64)	44-2320-80
	pH 7	292(3.58)	44-2320-80
	pH 11	292(3.58)	44-2320-80
C₉H₉ClN₄O			
1(2H)-Isoquinolinone, 2-amino-6-chloro-3-hydrazino-	EtOH	240(4.51),311(4.27), 373(3.60)	95-0819-80
1(2H)-Isoquinolinone, 2-amino-7-chloro-3-hydrazino-	EtOH	228(4.46),311(4.34), 383(3.60)	95-0819-80
C₉H₉ClO₃			
Acetic acid, (4-chlorophenoxy)-, methyl ester	MeCN	225(3.80),280(2.93), 288(2.85)	65-0481-80
1,4-Benzodioxin, 5-chloro-2,3-dihydro-8-methoxy-	EtOH	212(4.64),236(4.09), 285(3.54)	103-0993-80
1,4-Benzodioxin, 6-chloro-2,3-dihydro-5-methoxy-	EtOH	210(4.51),233(3.90), 275(2.74)	103-0993-80
C₉H₉Cl₂NO₂			
Benzoic acid, 3,5-dichloro-4-(dimethylamino)-	EtOH	316(3.89)	44-0527-80
C₉H₉Cl₂N₃O			
1H-Benzotriazole, 4,5-dichloro-1-propoxy-	EtOH	209(4.52),265(3.91), 272(3.92),294(3.84)	4-1115-80
C₉H₉Cl₅O			
4,6-Heptadien-3-one, 4,5,6,7,7-pentachloro-2,2-dimethyl-, (Z)-	heptane	210(4.08),226(4.09), 258s(3.58)	5-0403-80
2,4-Heptadienoyl chloride, 2,3,4,5-tetrachloro-6,6-dimethyl-	heptane	213(4.19),264(4.08)	5-0403-80
C₉H₉FI₂N₂O₃			
2,4(1H,3H)-Pyrimidinedione, 5-fluoro-1-[tetrahydro-4-iodo-5-(iodomethyl)-2-furanyl]-, [2R-(3α,4α,5α)]	MeOH	268(4.00)	87-0852-80
isomer	MeOH	268(3.99)	87-0852-80
2,4(1H,3H)-Pyrimidinedione, 5-fluoro-3-[tetrahydro-4-iodo-5-(iodomethyl)-2-furanyl]-, [2R-(2α,4β,5α)]-	MeOH	269(3.86)	87-0852-80
	pH 12	303(3.89)	87-0852-80
C₉H₉FN₂O₃			
2,3'-Anhydro-1-(2',5'-dideoxy-β-D-threo-pentofuranosyl)-5-fluorouracil	MeOH	232(3.90),251(3.90)	87-0852-80
2,3'-Anhydro-3-(2',5'-dideoxy-β-D-threo-pentofuranosyl)-5-fluorouracil	MeOH	217(3.80),279(3.79)	87-0852-80
C₉H₉FN₂O₃S			
2(1H)-Pyrimidinone, 5-fluoro-3,4-di-	pH 2	245(3.51),340(4.30)	103-0864-80

Compound	Solvent	$\lambda_{max}(\log \epsilon)$	Ref.
hydro-1-(tetrahydro-5-methyl-2-oxo-3-furanyl)-4-thioxo- (cont.)	pH 7	243(3.56),340(4.27)	103-0864-80
	pH 11	328(4.29)	103-0864-80
C_9H_9NO			
2-Propen-1-one, 1-phenyl-, oxime, (Z)-	EtOH	235s(4.10)	150-4726-80
	EtOH-base	281(--)	150-4726-80
$C_9H_9NO_2$			
2-Azetidinone, 3-hydroxy-3-phenyl-	EtOH	256(2.30)	33-1915-80
Formamide, N-(2-oxo-2-phenylethyl)-	EtOH	242(4.11),278(3.08)	33-1915-80
1H-Indole-5,6-diol, 2-methyl-	EtOH	203(4.50),272(3.77),304(3.95)	44-2899-80
$C_9H_9NO_2S$			
Benzene, 1-nitro-4-(2-propenylthio)-	MeOH	337(4.04)	12-1345-80
$C_9H_9NO_3$			
Benzoic acid, 2-hydroxy-3-[(methylimino)methyl]-	DMSO	400(3.8)	1-0469-80A
1,3-Propanedione, 1-(2-hydroxyphenyl)-, 3-oxime	EtOH	243(4.20),299(4.02)	114-0271-80A
$C_9H_9NO_3S$			
Benzene, 1-nitro-4-(2-propenylsulfinyl)-	MeOH	247(3.87),289(3.84)	12-2635-80
$C_9H_9NO_5$			
3,5-Pyridinedicarboxylic acid, 1,4-dihydro-4-oxo-, dimethyl ester	EtOH	250(3.79),256(3.77),303(3.66)	4-0359-80
3,5-Pyridinedicarboxylic acid, 1-ethyl-1,4-dihydro-4-oxo-	EtOH	254(3.89),257s(3.89),307(3.73)	4-0359-80
$C_9H_9NO_5S_2$			
4-Thia-1-azabicyclo[3.2.0]hept-2-ene-2-carboxylic acid, 3-[(2-carboxyethyl)thio]-7-oxo-, (R)-, sodium salt	H_2O	251(3.52),321(3.58)	94-3232-80
$C_9H_9NO_7$			
Isoxazoletricarboxylic acid, trimethyl ester	MeOH	209(3.83),236(3.66)	94-3296-80
C_9H_9NS			
1H-Indole, 3-(methylthio)-	H_2O	277(3.64)	44-0780-80
	dioxan	273(3.74)	44-0780-80
$C_9H_9N_3$			
1H-1,2,4-Triazole, 3-methyl-5-phenyl-	MeOH	240(4.18)	56-1067-80
$C_9H_9N_3O$			
1,6-Naphthyridine-8-carbonitrile, 1,2,3,4,6,7-hexahydro-7-oxo-	pH 13	290(3.72),322(3.81)	103-0873-80
Phenol, 2-(5-methyl-1H-1,2,4-triazol-3-yl)-	MeOH	245(4.09),300(3.75)	56-1067-80
Phenol, 4-(5-methyl-1H-1,2,4-triazol-3-yl)-	MeOH	260(4.28)	56-1067-80
$C_9H_9N_3O_4$			
Quinoline, 1,2,3,4-tetrahydro-6,8-dinitro-	EtOH	270(4.00),360(4.20),420(3.82)	103-0386-80

Compound	Solvent	$\lambda_{max}(\log \epsilon)$	Ref.
$C_9H_9N_3S$ 3H-1,2,4-Triazole-3-thione, 1,2-di-hydro-5-(4-methylphenyl)-	MeOH	263(4.19)	73-2804-80
$C_9H_9N_5O$ Acetamide, N-[3-(1H-tetrazol-5-yl)-phenyl]-	MeOH	214s(4.17),234(4.49), 280s(3.15)	56-0925-80
Acetamide, N-[4-(1H-tetrazol-5-yl)-phenyl]-	MeOH	210(4.01),267(4.32)	56-0925-80
1H-Benzimidazole, 2-[[1-(hydroxyimino)-ethyl]azo]-	50% EtOH	372(4.24)	103-0857-80
$C_9H_9N_5O_3$ 4(1H)-Pteridinone, 6-(acetoxymethyl)-2-amino-	pH 0.0	230s(4.10),246(4.05), 321(3.91),334s(3.83)	24-1514-80
	pH 5.0	234(4.11),275(4.16), 345(3.79)	24-1514-80
	pH 10.0	254(4.34),277s(3.80), 363(3.85)	24-1514-80
C_9H_{10} Benzene, cyclopropyl-	hexane	220(3.92),274(2.45)	70-1928-80
Bicyclo[5.1.0]octa-2,4-diene, 6-methylene-	hexane	215(3.59),299(3.37)	88-0471-80
$C_9H_{10}BrNO_4$ 2-Furancarboxylic acid, 5-(acetyl-amino)-4-bromo-, ethyl ester	MeOH	206(4.00),271(4.07)	73-0135-80
$C_9H_{10}BrN_3O_4$ Furo[3',2':4,5]imidazo[1,2-a]pyrimidin-6(4H)-one, 7-bromo-2,3,3a,9a-tetrahy-dro-3-hydroxy-2-(hydroxymethyl)-, [2R-(2α,3β,3aβ,9aβ)]-	pH 1	227(3.88),283(3.60)	94-0939-80
	H₂O	226(4.17),280(3.62)	94-0939-80
	pH 13	237(4.24),305(3.04)	94-0939-80
$C_9H_{10}Br_2$ Bicyclo[4.1.0]heptane, 7,7-dibromo-2.3-bis(methylene)-	hexane	223(4.00),253(3.54)	44-4183-80
$C_9H_{10}ClNO_2$ Benzoic acid, 3-chloro-4-(dimethyl-amino)-	EtOH	299(4.19)	44-0527-80
$C_9H_{10}ClNO_3S$ Benzene, 1-chloro-4-[(1-methyl-1-nitro-ethyl)sulfinyl]-	EtOH	225(4.26)	39-1407-80C
$C_9H_{10}ClN_3O_2S$ Urea, [6-chloro-2-[(2-oxopropyl)thio]-3-pyridinyl]-	n.s.g.	259(4.005),309(3.84)	103-0607-80
$C_9H_{10}Cl_2$ Bicyclo[4.1.0]heptane, 7,7-dichloro-2,3-bis(methylene)-	hexane	218(4.15),243(3.70)	44-4183-80
Bicyclo[4.1.0]heptane, 7,7-dichloro-3,4-bis(methylene)-	C_6H_{12}	243(3.85)	44-4183-80
$C_9H_{10}Cl_2N_2O_3$ 2-Propenoic acid, 2-chloro-3-(4-chloro-2,3-dihydro-2,5-dimethyl-3-oxo-1H-pyrazol-1-yl)-, methyl ester	MeCN	225(3.70),289(3.48)	35-4983-80

Compound	Solvent	$\lambda_{max}(\log \epsilon)$	Ref.
$C_9H_{10}Cl_3NO_2$			
4-Cyclopentene-1,3-dione, 2,2,4-trichloro-5-(diethylamino)-	EtOH	289(4.19),352(4.10)	104-1404-80
$C_9H_{10}Cl_3NS$			
2-Cyclobutene-1-thione, 2,4,4-trichloro-3-piperidino-	CH_2Cl_2	346(4.7),417(2.1)	83-0959-80
$C_9H_{10}Cl_5NO$			
2-Cyclopenten-1-one, 3-(butylamino)-2,4,4,5,5-pentachloro-	EtOH	313(4.39)	104-1404-80
2,4-Pentadienamide, N-butyl-2,3,4,5,5-pentachloro-	EtOH	223(4.37)	104-1404-80
$C_9H_{10}FIN_2O_4$			
Uridine, 2',5'-dideoxy-5-fluoro-5'-iodo-	H_2O	267(3.96)	87-0852-80
$C_9H_{10}FN_3O_5$			
1(2H)-Pyrimidinepropanoic acid, β-(acetylamino)-5-fluoro-3,4-dihydro-2,4-dioxo-	MeOH	269(3.89)	94-1137-80
$C_9H_{10}N_2$			
1H-Indazole, 3,7-dimethyl-	EtOH	220(--),254(3.60), 261s(--),284s(--), 289(3.67),294s(--), 301(3.65)	5-0908-80
1H-Indazole, 7-ethyl-	EtOH	215(--),252(3.64), 257(3.63),281s(--), 286(3.66),290s(--), 297(3.60)	5-0908-80
1H-Pyrrole, 1,1'-methylenebis-	EtOH	227(3.89)	33-1190-80
$C_9H_{10}N_2O$			
Ethanedial, mono(phenylhydrazone)	hexane	317(4.40)	65-2072-80
	EtOH	332(4.25)	65-2072-80
Propanal, 2-oxo-, 1-(phenylhydrazone)	hexane	292(4.15),327(4.51)	65-2072-80
	EtOH	296(3.85),348(4.56)	65-2072-80
$C_9H_{10}N_2OS$			
4H-Thiazolo[5,4-c]azepine, 6-methoxy-2-methyl-	MeOH	218(4.067)	39-2362-80C
$C_9H_{10}N_2O_2$			
Benzenemethanamine, N-ethenyl-N-nitro-	EtOH	278(3.90)	104-1006-80
Quinoline, 1,2,3,4-tetrahydro-6-nitro-	EtOH	404(4.24)	103-0386-80
Quinoline, 1,2,3,4-tetrahydro-8-nitro-	EtOH	235(4.23),294(3.77), 447(3.83)	103-0386-80
$C_9H_{10}N_2O_2S_3$			
Thieno[2,3-c]isothiazole-5-carboxylic acid, 4-amino-3-(methylthio)-, ethyl ester	MeOH	276(4.34),294s(4.07), 387(3.73)	48-1021-80
Thieno[3,2-d]isothiazole-5-carboxylic acid, 4-amino-3-(methylthio)-, ethyl ester	MeOH	241(4.20),258(4.22), 311s(4.00)	48-1021-80
$C_9H_{10}N_2O_3$			
Acetamide, N-methyl-N-(2-nitrophenyl)-	EtOH	215s(4.00),300s(3.00)	103-0386-80
Acetamide, N-methyl-N-(4-nitrophenyl)-	EtOH	286(3.89)	103-0386-80

Compound	Solvent	$\lambda_{max}(\log \epsilon)$	Ref.
$C_9H_{10}N_2O_3S$			
2(1H)-Pyrimidinone, 3,4-dihydro-5-meth-yl-1-(tetrahydro-2-oxo-3-furanyl)-4-thioxo-	pH 2 pH 7 pH 11	287(3.68),340(4.19) 287(3.68),340(4.16) 320(4.19)	103-0864-80 103-0864-80 103-0864-80
2(1H)-Pyrimidinone, 3,4-dihydro-1-(tet-rahydro-5-methyl-2-oxo-3-furanyl)-4-thioxo-	pH 2 pH 7 pH 11	253(3.60),333(4.29) 253(3.70),333(4.27) 320(4.25)	103-0864-80 103-0864-80 103-0864-80
$C_9H_{10}N_2O_3S_2$			
5-Thia-1-azabicyclo[4.2.0]oct-2-ene-2-carboxylic acid, 3-methyl-7-[(meth-ylthio)imino]-8-oxo-, (R)-	MeOH	244(3.69),318(3.99)	35-1690-80
$C_9H_{10}N_2O_4S_2$			
6H-Furo[2'.3':4,5]thiazolo[3,2-c]pyri-midin-6-one, 2,3,3a,7,8,9a-hexahy-dro-3-hydroxy-2-(hydroxymethyl)-8-thioxo-, [2R-(2α,3β,3aβ,9aβ)]-	H_2O pH 13	212(4.17),231(4.16), 260s(4.04),282(4.29) 228(4.30),248(4.30), 275(4.05),294(4.05)	94-0939-80 94-0939-80
$C_9H_{10}N_2O_5$			
Benzene, 3-methoxy-1,2-dimethyl-4,5-di-nitro-	MeOH	277(3.86)	54-0115-80
$C_9H_{10}N_2O_5S$			
S^6,2'-Cyclouridine	H_2O pH 13	218(3.90),280(4.27) 277(4.17)	94-0939-80 94-0939-80
$C_9H_{10}N_2O_6$			
2-Furancarboxylic acid, 5-(acetylami-no)-4-nitro-, ethyl ester	MeOH	215(4.12),275(14)[sic], 333(3.77)	73-0135-80
$C_9H_{10}N_2Se$			
Selenocyanic acid, 4-(dimethylamino)-phenyl ester	MeOH	273(4.21)	104-1963-80
$C_9H_{10}N_3O_2$			
Sydnone, 3-(1-ethylpyridinium-3-yl)-, iodide	MeOH	245s(3.90),265s(3.73), 322(3.42)	39-0020-80C
$C_9H_{10}N_4$			
1,2,4-Triazolo[3,4-a]phthalazine, 7,8,9,10-tetrahydro- (spectra in ethanol)	pH 1 pH 7 pH 11	264(3.71) 237(3.56),282(3.49) 282(3.51)	44-2320-80 44-2320-80 44-2320-80
$C_9H_{10}N_4O$			
3H-1,2,4-Triazol-3-one, 4-amino-2,4-di-hydro-2-methyl-5-phenyl-	EtOH	263(3.99)	4-1691-80
$C_9H_{10}N_4OS$			
Acetamide, N-[2-(methylthio)-7H-pyrro-lo[2,3-d]pyrimidin-4-yl]-	MeOH	248(4.13),312(3.81)	24-2069-80
$C_9H_{10}N_4O_2$			
2,4(1H,3H)-Pteridinedione, 1,6,7-tri-methyl-	pH -5.0 pH 1.0	246(4.25),265s(3.95), 355(3.93) 228(4.09),250(3.98), 332(3.99)	142-0437-80B 142-0437-80B
2,4(1H,3H)-Pteridinedione, 3,6,7-tri-methyl-	pH -4.9 pH 1.0	243(4.21),286s(3.24), 348(4.02) 232(4.14),248s(3.87), 329(4.02)	142-0437-80B 142-0437-80B

Compound	Solvent	$\lambda_{max}(\log \epsilon)$	Ref.
2,4(3H,8H)-Pteridinedione, 6,7,8-tri-methyl-	pH −3.0	244(4.11),356(4.23)	142-0437-80B
$C_9H_{10}N_4O_2S$ Pyrido[2,3-d]pyrimidin-5(1H)-one, 4-amino-6-(hydroxymethyl)-2-(methylthio)-	pH 1 pH 7 pH 11	268(4.21),295(3.73) 265(4.18),312(3.52) 265(4.16),302(3.52)	44-3746-80 44-3746-80 44-3746-80
$C_9H_{10}N_4O_3$ 4,7(3H,8H)-Pteridinedione, 2-methoxy-3,8-dimethyl-	MeOH	241(3.89),248s(3.84), 278s(3.79),286(3.87), 333(4.04)	24-1535-80
2(1H)-Pteridinone, 4,7-dimethoxy-1-methyl-	MeOH	235s(3.92),258(3.71), 331(4.19),343s(4.12)	24-1535-80
7(1H)-Pteridinone, 2,4-dimethoxy-6-methyl-	pH 5.0	233(3.84),242s(3.78), 276(3.73),312s(4.15), 321(4.16)	24-1535-80
	pH 10.0	245(3.95),260s(3.68), 316s(4.16),324(4.22), 338(4.09)	24-1535-80
3H,5H,9H-Pyrimido[1,2,3-ij]pteridine-9,11(10H)-dione, 6,7-dihydro-3-hydroxy-	pH 0.0 pH 6.0	248(4.11),355(4.01) 217(4.18),277(4.26), 301(3.98)	142-0437-80B 142-0437-80B
	pH 13.0	217(4.23),285(4.22), 308s(3.92)	142-0437-80B
1H-Pyrrole-2-carboxamide, N-(2-cyanoethyl)-1-methyl-5-nitro-	EtOH	271(4.03),345(4.15)	36-1334-80
$C_9H_{10}N_4O_4$ 2,4,7(1H,3H,8H)-Pteridinetrione, 8-(2-hydroxyethyl)-6-methyl-	pH 0.0 pH 7.0	282(4.13),327(4.14) 215(4.50),250s(3.68), 290(4.04),347(4.13)	142-0437-80B 142-0437-80B
$C_9H_{10}N_6O_2$ Cytidine, 5'-azido-2',3'-didehydro-2',3',5'-trideoxy-	MeOH	240(3.89),271(3.89)	136-0067-80A
6-Pteridinemethanol, 2,4-diamino-, acetate	pH 2.0	244(4.21),287(3.74), 335(4.01),348s(3.95)	24-1514-80
	pH 7.0	226(4.07),261(4.37), 372(3.85)	24-1514-80
	MeOH	227(4.03),261(4.35), 371(3.82)	24-1514-80
$C_9H_{10}N_8O_4$ Uridine, 3',5'-diazido-3',5'-dideoxy-	MeOH	260(4.01)	118-0559-80
$C_9H_{10}O$ Benzene, (cyclopropyloxy)-	hexane	220(4.30),264(3.31), 270(3.34),276(3.32)	70-1928-80
2-Cyclopropen-1-one, 2,3-dicyclopropyl-	MeCN	217(3.77),256(2.96)	88-0947-80
1H-Inden-1-one, 2,3,3a,7a-tetrahydro-	MeCN	263(3.54),268(3.52)	88-1165-80
$C_9H_{10}OS$ Benzene, (2-propenylsulfinyl)-	MeOH	246(3.69)	12-2635-80
$C_9H_{10}O_2$ Benzoic acid, 4-methyl-, methyl ester	EtOH	206(4.01),238(4.16), 268(2.92)	80-0701-80
	EtOH	236(4.19)	118-0409-80
4H-Cyclohepta[b]furan-4-one, 5,6,7,8-tetrahydro-	n.s.g.	206(4.11),216s(--), 266(3.72)	39-2081-80C

Compound	Solvent	$\lambda_{max}(\log \epsilon)$	Ref.
Ethanone, 1-(5-ethynyl-4,5-dihydro-2-methyl-3-furanyl)-	EtOH	275(4.04)	103-0678-80
Ethanone, 1-(2-hydroxy-5-methylphenyl)-	EtOH	255(3.98),338(3.56)	90-0431-80
Phenol, 4-(3-hydroxy-1-propenyl)-	n.s.g.	312(3.95)	102-1349-80
$C_9H_{10}O_2S$			
2,5-Cyclohexadiene-1,4-dione, 2,5-dimethyl-3-(methylthio)-	EtOH	246(4.03),257s(3.95),291s(3.34),437(3.19)	39-0289-80C
$C_9H_{10}O_3$			
Benzaldehyde, 2,3-dimethoxy-	EtOH	220(4.3),260(3.9),320(3.4)	142-1159-80
Benzaldehyde, 3,4-dimethoxy-	EtOH	232(4.2),273(4.0),310(3.9)	142-1159-80
Benzeneacetic acid, 3-methoxy-	MeOH	203(3.85),218s(3.56),273(2.96),280s(2.90)	98-0071-80
2,4-Cyclohexadien-1-one, 6-acetoxy-6-methyl-, (±)-	C_6H_{12}	292(3.67),359(2.24),373(2.28)	24-2227-80
	hexane	292(3.68)	24-2227-80
	MeOH	298(3.65)	24-2227-80
	EtOH	238(4.21),299(3.73)	24-2227-80
1,3-Isobenzofurandione, 3a,4,5,6-tetrahydro-3a-methyl-	C_6H_{12}	219(4.04)	2-0601-80
$C_9H_{10}O_3S$			
2-Propanone, 1-(phenylsulfonyl)-	MeOH	272(2.97),293s(2.02)	24-2462-80
$C_9H_{10}O_4$			
2,5-Cyclohexadiene-1,4-dione, 2-ethoxy-5-methoxy-	EtOH	279(4.71),374(2.70)	12-0527-80
2,5-Cyclohexadiene-1,4-dione, 2-hydroxy-6-methoxy-3,5-dimethyl-	EtOH	217(4.00),287(4.14),410(2.61)	64-1497-80B
2H-Pyran-3-carboxylic acid, 4,6-dimethyl-2-oxo-, methyl ester	EtOH	310(3.79)	39-2272-80C
4H-Pyran-3-carboxylic acid, 2,6-dimethyl-4-oxo-, methyl ester	EtOH	216(3.87),244(3.90)	107-0581-80
$C_9H_{10}S$			
Benzene, (2-propenylthio)-	MeOH	256(3.91)	12-1345-80
$C_9H_{11}BrSe$			
Benzeneselenenyl bromide, 2,4,6-trimethyl-	n.s.g.	497(2.26)	23-2745-80
$C_9H_{11}ClN_2O_2$			
Benzenemethanamine, N-(2-chloroethyl)-N-nitro-	MeOH	242(3.87)	104-1006-80
$C_9H_{11}ClO$			
Ethanone, 1-bicyclo[2.2.1]hept-5-en-2-yl-2-chloro-	benzene	289(1.67)	44-1286-80
$C_9H_{11}FN_2O_3$			
Uridine, 2',3',5'-trideoxy-5-fluoro-	MeOH	207(3.95),270(3.94)	87-0852-80
$C_9H_{11}FN_2O_4$			
2,4(1H,3H)-Pyrimidinedione, 1-(2,5-dideoxy-β-D-threo-pentofuranosyl)-5-fluoro-	H_2O	205(3.99),271(3.95)	87-0852-80
Uridine, 2',5'-dideoxy-5-fluoro-	MeOH	269(3.94)	87-0852-80

Compound	Solvent	$\lambda_{max}(\log \epsilon)$	Ref.
$C_9H_{11}FN_2O_5$			
2,4(1H,3H)-Pyrimidinedione, 1-[(2-acet-oxyethoxy)methyl]-5-fluoro-	pH 2	270(3.90)	103-1176-80
	pH 7	270(3.89)	103-1176-80
	pH 12	270(3.76)	103-1176-80
$C_9H_{11}F_3O$			
2-Cyclohexen-1-one, 4,4-dimethyl-2-(trifluoromethyl)-	hexane	221(3.82)	39-1114-80C
$C_9H_{11}N$			
Methanamine, N-[(2-methylphenyl)meth-ylene]-	hexane	206(4.44),244(4.11), 248(4.10),278(3.13), 285(3.14),296s(2.98)	39-0849-80B
	C_6H_{12}	208(4.42),244(4.13), 248s(4.11),279(3.10), 286(3.12),296s(2.96)	39-0849-80B
	MeOH	206(4.37),248(4.09), 286(3.20)	39-0849-80B
	EtOH	216(4.36),248(4.08), 286(3.17)	39-0849-80B
Methanamine, N-[(4-methylphenyl)meth-ylene]-	C_6H_{12}	213(4.21),251(4.24), 257s(4.16),280(3.10), 290(2.94)	39-0849-80B
	MeOH	253(4.27),282s(3.37), 291(3.27)	39-0849-80B
Methanamine, N-(1-phenylethylidene)-	C_6H_{12}	238(4.09),278s(2.74), 285s(2.60)	32-0597-80
	MeOH	236(4.02),278s(2.83)	32-0597-80
$C_9H_{11}NOS$			
1,4-Oxathiino[3,2-b]pyridine, 2,3-di-hydro-2,6-dimethyl-	EtOH	249s(3.61),311(3.89)	1-0619-80
	EtOH-HCl	254(3.57),341(4.05)	1-0619-80
$C_9H_{11}NO_2$			
Benzoic acid, 2-amino-, ethyl ester	C_6H_{12}?	333(3.65)	44-2195-80
Benzoic acid, 4-amino-, ethyl ester	C_6H_{12}?	278(4.32)	44-2195-80
	MeOH	225(3.86),310(4.37)	33-0456-80
Carbamic acid, phenyl-, ethyl ester	C_6H_{12}?	268(--),274(2.93), 287(--)	44-2195-80
Ethanone, 1-(2-hydroxy-5-methylphenyl)-, oxime	EtOH	255(3.95),312(3.59)	90-0431-80
$C_9H_{11}NO_2S$			
Pyridine, 3-(1,3-dioxolan-2-yl)-2-(methylthio)-	EtOH	252(4.05),292(3.60)	118-0405-80
$C_9H_{11}NO_3$			
3-Pyridinecarboxylic acid, 1,4-dihydro-5-methyl-4-oxo-, ethyl ester	EtOH	256s(3.90),260(3.92), 284(3.64)	4-0359-80
3-Pyridinecarboxylic acid, 1-ethyl-1,4-dihydro-5-methyl-4-oxo-	EtOH	260(3.91),285(3.52)	4-0359-80
3H-Pyrrolizine-1-carboxylic acid, 2,5,6,7-tetrahydro-5-oxo-, methyl ester	n.s.g.	279(4.36)	88-4585-80
$C_9H_{11}NO_3S_2$			
4-Thia-1-azabicyclo[3.2.0]hept-2-ene-2-carboxylic acid, 7-oxo-3-(propyl-thio)-, (R)-, sodium salt	H_2O	252(3.73),322(3.87)	94-3232-80

Compound	Solvent	$\lambda_{max}(\log \epsilon)$	Ref.
$C_9H_{11}NO_3S_3$			
4-Thia-1-azabicyclo[3.2.0]hept-2-ene-2-carboxylic acid, 3-[[2-(methylthio)ethyl]thio]-7-oxo-, (R)-, sodium salt	H_2O	253(3.72),320(3.82)	94-3232-80
$C_9H_{11}NO_4$			
2-Furancarboxylic acid, 5-(acetylamino)-, ethyl ester	MeOH	207(3.69),292(4.35)	73-0135-80
1H-Pyrrole-3,4-dicarboxylic acid, 1-methyl-, methyl ester	MeOH	252(3.98)	44-4573-80
$C_9H_{11}NO_6$			
1H-Pyrrole-2,4-dicarboxylic acid, 4,5-dihydro-4-methoxy-5-oxo-, dimethyl ester, (±)- (sargassumlactam)	EtOH	208(3.79),293(3.53)	138-1453-80
1H-Pyrrole-2,5-dione, 3-β-D-ribofuranosyl- (2'epishowdomycin)	EtOH	222(4.36)	23-2024-80
$C_9H_{11}N_3$			
Acetaldehyde, (methylimino)-, phenylhydrazone	hexane	298(3.63),366(4.20)	65-2072-80
	EtOH	299(3.90),339(4.37)	65-2072-80
Benzenecarboximidic acid, ethylidenehydrazide	MeOH	225(4.03),275(4.03)	104-0822-80
Ethanimidic acid, (phenylmethylene)hydrazide, (E)-	MeOH	221(4.12),293(4.23)	104-0822-80
$C_9H_{11}N_3O_2$			
Acetic acid, 1-methyl-2-nitroso-2-phenylhydrazide	CH_2Cl_2	296(3.72)	94-1820-80
2-Pyridinecarboxylic acid, carbethoxyhydrazone	C_6H_{12}	283(4.23)	115-0151-80
	EtOH	283(4.33)	115-0151-80
	50% EtOH	285(4.28)	115-0151-80
$C_9H_{11}N_3O_3$			
Carbamic acid, [2-(aminocarbonyl)-4-pyridinyl]-, ethyl ester	M HCl	221(4.32),270(4.19)	87-0384-80
	pH 7	218(4.46),241(4.10), 273s(3.49)	87-0384-80
$C_9H_{11}N_3O_4S$			
S^6,2'-Cycloisocytidine	pH 1	226(4.00),281(4.21), 290s(4.10)	94-0939-80
	H_2O	219(4.35),277(4.11)	94-0939-80
$C_9H_{11}N_4O_7$			
1,3-Cyclohexadien-1-amine, 5-methoxy-N,N-dimethyl-2,4,6-trinitro-, ion (1-), sodium	DMSO-5% MeOH-NaOMe	402(4.49),474(4.29)	23-1609-80
$C_9H_{11}N_5$			
Benzenamine, N,N-dimethyl-4-(1H-tetrazol-5-yl)-	MeOH	209(3.96),215(4.04), 285(4.35)	56-0925-80
$C_9H_{11}N_5O_2$			
3H-Purine-3-butanoic acid, 6-amino-hydrobromide	pH 7	274(4.12)	24-2043-80
	MeOH	276(4.19)	24-2043-80
$C_9H_{11}N_9O_3$			
Cytidine, 3',5'-diazido-3',5'-dideoxy-	pH 7	270(3.95)	118-0559-80

Compound	Solvent	λ_{max}(log ϵ)	Ref.
C_9H_{12}			
Bicyclo[2.2.2]octa-2,5-diene, 2-methyl-	heptane	228s(2.44)	35-5749-80
1,3,5-Cyclononatriene, cis-cis-cis	EtOH	296(3.00)	44-3377-80
1H-Indene, 2,3,3a,7a-tetrahydro-, cis	pentane	261(3.62)	35-4456-80
trans	EtOH	260(3.60)	44-3377-80
1H-Indene, 2,3,5,6-tetrahydro-	C_6H_{12}	267(3.52)	118-0238-80
$C_9H_{12}BrN_3O_5$			
4(1H)-Pyrimidinone, 2-amino-5-bromo-	pH 1	227(3.97),275(3.91)	94-0939-80
1-β-D-ribofuranosyl-	H_2O	272(3.76)	94-0939-80
$C_9H_{12}BrN_5O_2$			
3H-Purine-3-butanoic acid, 6-amino-,	MeOH	276(4.19)	24-2043-80
monohydrobromide			
$C_9H_{12}Br_2N_2O_2$			
2H-Benzimidazole, 4,7-dibromo-4,5,6,7-	EtOH	270(4.00),365(3.80)	103-0628-80
tetrahydro-2,2-dimethyl-, 1,3-dioxide			
$C_9H_{12}Br_2O_2$			
Cyclopropanecarboxylic acid, 3-(2,2-di-	MeOH	222(4.11),263s(2.76)	39-0728-80C
bromoethenyl)-2,2-dimethyl-, methyl			
ester			
$C_9H_{12}ClN_2O_4PS$			
3(2H)-Pyridazinone, 4-chloro-2-methyl-	MeOH	213(4.32),296(3.68)	73-2343-80
5-[(4-methyl-1,3,2-dioxaphosphorinan-			
2-yl)oxy]-, P-sulfide			
$C_9H_{12}Cl_2O_2$			
Cyclopropanecarboxylic acid, 3-(2,2-di-	MeOH	218(4.01)	39-0728-80C
chloroethenyl)-2,2-dimethyl-, methyl			
ester			
$C_9H_{12}F_2O_3$			
Furo[2,3-d]-1,3-dioxole, 5-(2,2-diflu-	EtOH	207(1.54),211s(1.52),	33-1644-80
oroethenyl)tetrahydro-2,2-dimethyl-,		227(1.18)	
[3aR-(3aα,5α,6aα)]-			
D-ribo-Hex-1-enitol, 3,6-anhydro-1,2-	EtOH	206(1.78),213s(1.70)	33-1644-80
dideoxy-1,1-difluoro-4,5-O-(1-methyl-			
ethylidene)-			
$C_9H_{12}NO$			
Methanaminium, N-methyl-N-(3-methyl-	H_2O	286(4.21)	39-1601-80B
4-oxo-2,5-cyclohexadien-1-ylidene)-			
$C_9H_{12}N_2O_2$			
Benzeneethanamine, α-methyl-4-nitro-,	EtOH	273(4.04)	87-0282-80
(S)-			
1H-1,3-Diazepine-1-carboxylic acid,	EtOH	245(3.76),310(3.18)	77-0444-80
5-methyl-, ethyl ester			
1H-1,3-Diazepine-1-carboxylic acid,	EtOH	243(3.65),293(3.34)	77-0444-80
7-methyl-, ethyl ester			
$C_9H_{12}N_2O_2S$			
Carbamothioic acid, (6-methoxy-3-pyri-	EtOH	223(3.94),273(4.11)	44-4219-80
dinyl)-, O-ethyl ester			
2(1H)-Pyrimidinone, 4-[(1,1-dimethyl-	pH 1	219(3.68),271(3.26),	44-3651-80
2-oxopropyl)thio]-		329(4.27)	
	pH 6	222s(3.82),264s(3.71),	44-3651-80
		300(3.95),308s(3.92),	

Compound	Solvent	$\lambda_{max}(\log \epsilon)$	Ref.
(cont.)		332s(3.65)	44-3651-80
$C_9H_{12}N_2O_3$			
Benzenamine, 2-methoxy-3,4-dimethyl-6-nitro-	MeOH	228(4.29),296(3.86), 417(3.71)	54-0115-80
Benzenamine, 3-methoxy-4,5-dimethyl-2-nitro-	MeOH	234(4.16),288(3.47), 408(3.39)	54-0115-80
1H-1,3-Diazepine-1-carboxylic acid, 5-methoxy-, ethyl ester	EtOH	245(3.74),305(3.26)	77-0444-80
1H-Imidazole-4-carboxylic acid, 5-formyl-, butyl ester	EtOH	276(3.99)	39-0495-80C
Pyrazinecarboxylic acid, 3,4-dihydro-5,6-dimethyl-3-oxo-, ethyl ester	EtOH	235(3.87),323(3.77), 380(3.65)	70-0774-80
$C_9H_{12}N_2O_3S$			
Ethanethioic acid, S-[2-(3,4-dihydro-5-methyl-2,4-dioxo-1(2H)-pyrimidin-yl)ethyl] ester	H_2O	274.0(3.97)	117-0275-80
$C_9H_{12}N_2O_3S_2$			
4-Thia-1-azabicyclo[3.2.0]hept-2-ene-2-carboxylic acid, 3-[(3-aminopropyl)-thio]-7-oxo-	H_2O	251(3.63),320(3.76)	94-3258-80
$C_9H_{12}N_2O_4$			
2-Furancarboxylic acid, 5-(acetylami-no)-4-amino-, ethyl ester	MeOH	229(4.02),313(4.01)	73-0135-80
$C_9H_{12}N_2O_4S$			
5-Pyrimidinepentanoic acid, hexahydro-4,6-dioxo-2-thioxo-	50% MeOH-HCl	212(4.02),287(4.33)	73-3583-80
	+ NaOH	237(4.25),289(4.12)	73-3583-80
$C_9H_{12}N_2O_5$			
Acetic acid, cyano[(2-ethoxy-2-oxoeth-oxy)imino]-, ethyl ester	EtOH	242(3.97)	5-1623-80
5-Pyrimidinepentanoic acid, hexahydro-2,4,6-trioxo-	50% MeOH-HCl	210(3.95),263(3.41)	73-3583-80
	+ NaOH	233(3.76),270(4.23)	73-3583-80
$C_9H_{12}N_4O_4$			
1H-Imidazole-4-carbonitrile, 5-amino-1-β-D-arabinofuranosyl-	MeOH	250(4.04)	39-2304-80C
$C_9H_{12}N_6$			
[1,2,4]Triazolo[5',1':2,3]pyrimido-[4,5-c]pyridazine, 1,2,3,4-tetra-hydro-1,5-dimethyl-	EtOH	222(4.31),309(4.08)	87-0927-80
$C_9H_{12}N_6O$			
Piperidine, 1-[(5-azido-1H-imidazol-4-yl)carbonyl]-	H_2O or EtOH	230(4.02),267(4.03)	103-1171-80
$C_9H_{12}N_6O_2$			
3H-Purine-3-butanoic acid, α,6-di-amino-, monohydrochloride, (S)-	H_2O	275(4.10)	24-2043-80
$C_9H_{12}O$			
Benzene, (1-methylethoxy)-	EtOH	223(3.836),267(3.102), 273(3.129),280(3.102)	65-0491-80

Compound	Solvent	$\lambda_{max}(\log \epsilon)$	Ref.
Benzene, propoxy-	EtOH	221(3.886),265(3.188), 272(3.275),279(3.238)	65-0491-80
Bicyclo[2.2.1]heptan-2-ol, 5,6-bis-(methylene)-, endo	isooctane	239s(3.90),245(3.97), 254s(3.79)	33-1016-80
	MeOH	240s(3.88),245(3.91), 254s(3.72)	33-1016-80
2,4-Cyclohexadien-1-one, 2,6,6-tri-methyl-	hexane	299(3.72),341(2.12), 347(2.13),350(2.15), 355(2.19),364(2.16), 373(2.17)	24-2227-80
	MeOH	308(3.71)	24-2227-80
	CF_3CH_2OH	311(3.71)	24-2227-80
2-Cyclohexen-1-one, 3,5-dimethyl-4-methylene-	EtOH	273(4.21)	23-2460-80
1,3-Cyclopentadiene, 5-(2-methoxy-1-methylethylidene)-	EtOH	262s(4.15),267(4.26), 355(2.37)	34-0184-80
Spiro[bicyclo[2.2.1]heptane-7,1'-cyclo-propan]-2-one	MeCN	295(1.77)	35-6056-80
Tricyclo[2.2.1.0^{2,6}]heptane-1-methanol, 7-methylene-	isooctane	218.5(2.30)	33-1016-80

$C_9H_{12}O_2$

Compound	Solvent	$\lambda_{max}(\log \epsilon)$	Ref.
2-Cyclohexene-1,4-dione, 2,5,5-tri-methyl-	pentane	366(1.72)	33-2370-80
2-Cyclopenten-1-one, 5-(hydroxymeth-ylene)-2,4,4-trimethyl-	n.s.g.	247(3.87),291(3.83)	39-1516-80C
2-Cyclopenten-1-one, 5-(hydroxymeth-ylene)-3,4,4-trimethyl-	n.s.g.	245(4.08),285(3.90)	39-1516-80C
Ethanone, 1-bicyclo[2.2.1]hept-5-en-2-yl-2-hydroxy-, endo	C_6H_{12}	273(1.68)	44-1286-80
	benzene	275(1.70)	44-1286-80
	EtOH	280(1.66)	44-1286-80
Ethanone, 1-(5-ethenyl-4,5-dihydro-2-methyl-3-furanyl)-	EtOH	280(3.96)	103-0678-80
4H-Pyran-4-one, 2,3,5,6-tetramethyl-	MeOH	<u>258(4.1)</u>	18-0469-80

$C_9H_{12}O_3$

Compound	Solvent	$\lambda_{max}(\log \epsilon)$	Ref.
1-Cyclopentene-1-acetic acid, 5-oxo-, ethyl ester	MeOH	224(4.01)	44-4702-80

$C_9H_{12}O_4$

Compound	Solvent	$\lambda_{max}(\log \epsilon)$	Ref.
Genipic acid	n.s.g.	203(3.45)	100-0649-80
2H-Pyran-3-carboxylic acid, 3,4-di-hydro-2,6-dimethyl-4-oxo-, methyl ester	EtOH	269(4.04)	107-0581-80

$C_9H_{12}O_5$

Compound	Solvent	$\lambda_{max}(\log \epsilon)$	Ref.
2-Furanacetic acid, 2,5-dihydro-3-meth-oxy-4-methyl-5-oxo-, methyl ester	MeOH	210(4.30),233s(4.15), 271s(3.39)	48-0559-80
2,4-Hexadienedioic acid, 3-hydroxy-2-methyl-, dimethyl ester, (Z,E)-	$MeOH-H_2SO_4$	211(3.96),233(3.98), 313(4.16)	48-0559-80
	MeOH-MeONa	234(4.27),366(4.00)	48-0559-80

$C_9H_{12}S$

Compound	Solvent	$\lambda_{max}(\log \epsilon)$	Ref.
Benzene, (ethylthio)methyl-	hexane	240(3.90),260s(2.58), 265(2.40)	101-0147-80A +131-0099-80C
Dispiro[2.1.2.2]nonane-4-thione	isooctane	203(3.77),240(3.96), 276(3.92),459(1.18)	24-2255-80
Spiro[2.5]oct-5-ene-4-thione, 6-methyl-	isooctane	547(1.45),581(1.40)	150-3361-80

$C_9H_{12}S_2Si$

Compound	Solvent	$\lambda_{max}(\log \epsilon)$	Ref.
1,3-Dithia-2-silacyclopentane, 2-meth-	hexane	194(4.52),220s(3.86),	101-0147-80A

Compound	Solvent	$\lambda_{max}(\log \epsilon)$	Ref.
yl-2-phenyl- (cont.)		245s(3.13),266(2.61), 274(2.45)	101-0147-80A +131-0099-80C
$C_9H_{12}Si$ 7-Silabicyclo[4.2.0]octa-1,3,5-triene, 7,7-dimethyl-	C_6H_{12}	212(3.99)	65-1621-80
$C_9H_{13}BrClN_3$ 2-Pyrimidinamine, 5-bromo-N-butyl-4-chloro-N-methyl-	MeOH	260(4.42),338(3.38)	56-1557-80
4-Pyrimidinamine, 5-bromo-N-butyl-2-chloro-N-methyl-	MeOH	269(4.09),303(3.74)	56-1557-80
$C_9H_{13}BrN$ Pyridinium, 1-(3-bromophenyl)-2-methyl-, bromide	H_2O	263(4.2)	104-2044-80
Pyridinium, 1-(3-bromophenyl)-3-methyl-, bromide	H_2O	262(4.0)	104-2044-80
Pyridinium, 1-(3-bromophenyl)-4-methyl-, bromide	H_2O	254(4.3)	104-2044-80
$C_9H_{13}BrO$ 2-Cyclohexen-1-one, 4-bromo-2,6,6-trimethyl-	hexane	230(3.07)	24-2227-80
$C_9H_{13}ClFNO$ 2-Cyclobuten-1-one, 4-chloro-3-(diethylamino)-4-fluoro-2-methyl-	EtOH	228(3.72),267(4.44)	33-1130-80
$C_9H_{13}ClN_2O_2$ 3(2H)-Pyridazinone, 4-chloro-5-hydroxy-2-pentyl-	MeOH	216(4.51),227s(--), 287(3.73)	73-0127-80
$C_9H_{13}Cl_2NO$ 2-Cyclobuten-1-one, 2,4-dichloro-3-(diethylamino)-4-methyl-	EtOH	228(3.58),271(3.44)	33-1130-80
$C_9H_{13}FN_2O_3$ 2,4(1H,3H)-Pyrimidinedione, 1-(butoxymethyl)-5-fluoro-	pH 2	270(3.91)	103-1176-80
	pH 7	270(3.91)	103-1176-80
	pH 12	270(3.78)	103-1176-80
2,4(1H,3H)-Pyrimidinedione, 5-fluoro-1-(1-propoxyethyl)-	pH 2	271(3.93)	103-1176-80
	pH 7	271(3.93)	103-1176-80
	pH 12	271(3.83)	103-1176-80
$C_9H_{13}FN_2O_4$ 2,4(1H,3H)-Pyrimidinedione, 1-[(2-ethoxyethoxy)methyl]-5-fluoro-	pH 2	268(3.97)	103-1176-80
	pH 7	268(3.99)	103-1176-80
	pH 12	268(3.86)	103-1176-80
$C_9H_{13}N$ Benzenamine, 2,4,6-trimethyl-	C_6H_{12}	236(--),290(3.23)	44-2195-80
Cyclohepta[b]pyrrole, 1,4,5,6,7,8-hexahydro-	hexane	224(3.89)	103-0488-80
$C_9H_{13}NO$ 3H-Indol-3-one, 1,2,4,5,6,7-hexahydro-1-methyl-	MeOH	332(4.18)	5-0564-80
$C_9H_{13}NO_2$ 3-Cyclobutene-1,2-dione, 3-(diethylami-	EtOH	253(4.43),276s(4.03),	33-1130-80

Compound	Solvent	$\lambda_{max}(\log \epsilon)$	Ref.
no)-4-methyl- (cont.)		337s(2.03)	33-1130-80
2,4-Pentadienal, 5-morpholino-, (E,E)-	EtOH	370.0(4.71)	1-0513-80
$C_9H_{13}NO_2S$			
Pyridine, 3-(dimethoxymethyl)-2-(methylthio)-	EtOH	252(4.05),292(3.60)	118-0405-80
$C_9H_{13}NO_4S$			
2H-1,4-Thiazine-3,6-dicarboxylic acid, 3,4-dihydro-2,2-dimethyl-, 6-methyl ester, (S)-	EtOH	314(4.08)	39-2322-80C
$C_9H_{13}NO_5S$			
2H-1,4-Thiazine-3,6-dicarboxylic acid, 3,4-dihydro-2,2-dimethyl-, 6-methyl ester, 1-oxide, (1S-trans)	EtOH	275(4.10)	39-2322-80C
$C_9H_{13}NO_6$			
3,5-Isoxazoledicarboxylic acid, 4-ethyl-4,5-dihydro-, dimethyl ester, 2-oxide, trans	MeOH	268(3.97)	94-0479-80
$C_9H_{13}NS_2$			
2,1-Benzisothiazole-3(1H)-thione, 1-ethyl-4,5,6,7-tetrahydro-	EtOH	261(3.81),367(4.22)	118-0566-80
$C_9H_{13}N_2O_2$			
Pyridinium, 3-[[(dimethylamino)carbonyl]oxy]-1-methyl-, bromide, complex with iodine	CHCl₃	280(4.56)	106-0030-80
$C_9H_{13}N_2O_3$			
Ethenaminium, N,N,N-trimethyl-2-(5-nitro-2-furanyl)-, bromide, (E)-	MeOH	225(4.09),258(3.70), 340(4.15)	73-0155-80
(Z)-	MeOH	225(4.11),257(3.65), 337(4.10)	73-0155-80
iodide, (E)-	MeOH	255(3.80),340(4.15)	73-0155-80
iodide, (Z?)-	MeOH	257(3.85),342(4.10)	73-0155-80
$C_9H_{13}N_2O_9P$			
1H-Imidazole-4-carboxylic acid, 1-(5-O-phosphono-β-D-ribofuranosyl)-	pH 2	215(4.00)	65-1723-80
	pH 6-7	223(3.90)	65-1723-80
	pH 12	223(3.90)	65-1723-80
$C_9H_{13}N_2O_{10}P$			
Barbituric acid, 1-(5'-phospho-β-D-ribofuranosyl)-, barium salt	pH 6.0	260(4.29)	69-4993-80
$C_9H_{13}N_3$			
1-Triazene, 3,3-dimethyl-1-(2-methylphenyl)-	EtOH	230(4.03),285(4.09), 312(4.03)	80-0701-80
$C_9H_{13}N_3O_4$			
Cytidine, 5'-deoxy-	H₂O	211(4.04),270(3.98)	73-0599-80
5-Pyrimidineacetic acid, 2-amino-1,4-dihydro-6-hydroxy-4-oxo- -propyl-	50% MeOH-HCl	263(4.24)	73-3583-80
	+ NaOH	269(4.18)	73-3583-80
5-Pyrimidinepentanoic acid, 2-amino-1,4-dihydro-6-hydroxy-4-oxo-	50% MeOH-HCl	266(4.22)	73-3583-80
	+ NaOH	270(4.16)	73-3583-80

Compound	Solvent	$\lambda_{max}(\log \epsilon)$	Ref.
monosodium salt (cont.)	HCl	266(4.25)	73-3583-80
(all spectra in 50% MeOH)	NaOH	270(4.16)	73-3583-80
disodium salt	HCl	266(4.03)	73-3583-80
	NaOH	270(4.05)	73-3583-80
$C_9H_{13}N_3O_6$			
1H-Imidazole-4-carboxamide, 5-hydroxy-2-β-D-ribofuranosyl-	H_2O	244(3.83),283(4.20)	44-0203-80
$C_9H_{13}N_4OP$			
1,2,4,5,3-Tetraazaphosphorine, 1,2,3,4-tetrahydro-2,4-dimethyl-3-phenyl-, 3-oxide	dioxan	218(4.02),240s(3.69)	64-0250-80B
$C_9H_{13}N_5$			
3H-Purin-6-amine, 3-ethyl-N,N-dimethyl-	pH 1	291(4.32)	94-1920-80
	pH 7	294(4.23)	94-1920-80
	pH 13	295(4.21)	94-1920-80
	EtOH	299(4.20)	94-1920-80
9H-Purin-6-amine, 9-ethyl-N,N-dimethyl-	pH 1	270(4.26)	94-1920-80
	pH 7	278(4.27)	94-1920-80
	pH 13	278(4.27)	94-1920-80
	EtOH	278(4.27)	94-1920-80
$C_9H_{13}N_5O_2$			
2,4(1H,3H)-Pyrimidinedione, 1-(5-azido-pentyl)-	MeOH	263(4.04)	78-0865-80
$C_9H_{13}N_5O_3$			
1H-Pyrrole-2-carboxamide, N-(3-amino-3-iminopropyl)-1-methyl-5-nitro-, monohydrochloride	EtOH	240(3.91),344(3.99)	36-1334-80
$C_9H_{13}OS$			
Sulfonium, (4-hydroxy-2-methylphenyl)-dimethyl-, hexafluoroarsenate	n.s.g.	252(4.00),275(3.81), 284(3.81)	47-1021-80
Sulfonium, (4-hydroxy-3-methylphenyl)-dimethyl-, hexafluoroarsenate	n.s.g.	250(4.03),275(3.69), 283(3.65),295(3.40)	47-1021-80
C_9H_{14}			
1,3-Cyclohexadiene, 2-ethyl-3-methyl-	C_6H_{12}	258(3.44)	118-0238-80
2,4,6-Octatriene, 3-methyl-, (E,E,E)-	hexane	236s(--),246s(--), 256(4.52),266(4.63), 276(4.53)	39-1045-80C
$C_9H_{14}ClNO_2$			
2-Cyclobuten-1-one, 2-chloro-3-(diethylamino)-4-hydroxy-4-methyl-	EtOH	267(4.35)	33-1130-80
$C_9H_{14}Cl_2N_4OS$			
1,3,5-Triazin-2-amine, 4-[2-chloro-1-(chloromethyl)ethoxy]-N,N-dimethyl-6-(methylthio)-	EtOH	234(4.59)	103-0316-80
1,3,5-Triazin-2(1H)-one, 1-(2,3-dichloropropyl)-4-(dimethylamino)-6-(methylthio)-	EtOH	218(4.38),236(4.47), 257(4.59)	103-0316-80
$C_9H_{14}NO$			
Furo[3,2-c]pyridinium, 4,5,6,7-tetrahydro-5,5-dimethyl-, iodide	MeOH	219(4.31)	83-0805-80

Compound	Solvent	$\lambda_{max}(\log \epsilon)$	Ref.
$C_9H_{14}N_2O$			
1,3,4-Oxadiazole, 2-(cyclohexylmethyl)-	MeOH	209(2.88)	33-0588-80
Piperidine, 2-methyl-1-(5-oxazolyl)-	EtOH	258(3.76)	4-0705-80
$C_9H_{14}N_2O_2$			
2,4(1H,3H)-Azocinedione, 3-(1-aminoeth-ylidene)tetrahydro-	MeOH	244(3.57),300(4.14)	44-0936-80
2H-Benzimidazole, 4,5,6,7-tetrahydro-2,2-dimethyl-, 1,3-dioxide	EtOH	212(3.90),350(3.90)	103-0628-80
2H-Benzimidazole, 4,5,6,7-tetrahydro-2,2-dimethyl-, 1,3-dioxide, HCl salt	EtOH	212(3.90),350(3.90)	103-0628-80
2,4-Pentadienal, 5-morpholino-, oxime	EtOH	215(3.64),332(3.59)	1-0513-80
$C_9H_{14}N_2O_3$			
1H-Pyrazolium, 4-(ethoxycarbonyl)-2,5-dihydro-1,1,3-trimethyl-5-oxo-, hydroxide, inner salt (no change in hydrochloric acid)	EtOH	236(4.20),274(3.76)	88-5059-80
3(2H)-Pyridazinone, 2-butyl-5-hydroxy-4-methoxy-	MeOH	215(4.26),284(3.63)	73-0127-80
2,4(1H,3H)-Pyrimidinedione, 1-(5-hy-droxypentyl)-	MeOH	264(4.00)	78-0865-80
4(1H)-Pyrimidinone, 2-ethoxy-1-(2-hy-droxyethyl)-5-methyl-	H_2O	261.0(3.90)	117-0275-80
$C_9H_{14}N_2O_4$			
2H-Benzimidazole-4,7-diol, 4,5,6,7-tetrahydro-2,2-dimethyl-, 1,3-dioxide	EtOH	222(4.02),355(3.90)	103-0628-80
$C_9H_{14}N_2O_5$			
Carbamic acid, [2-[(ethoxycarbonyl)ami-no]ethenyl]formyl-, ethyl ester	H_2O	215(4.38)	35-6784-80
$C_9H_{14}N_4O$			
2H-Tetrazole, 2-(cyclohexylacetyl)-	THF	213(3.90)	33-0588-80
$C_9H_{14}N_4O_4$			
Uridine, 3',5'-diamino-3',5'-dideoxy-	MeOH	260(4.04)	118-0559-80
$C_9H_{14}N_5$			
3H-Purinium, 6-(dimethylamino)-3,9-di-methyl-, iodide	pH 1	223(4.38),288(4.26)	94-2522-80
	pH 7	223(4.38),288(4.26)	94-2522-80
	EtOH	290(4.26)	94-2522-80
$C_9H_{14}O$			
Bicyclo[2.2.1]heptan-2-one, 7,7-di-methyl-	MeCN	292(1.46)	35-6056-80
2H-Inden-2-one, octahydro-, (3aR-trans)	MeCN	296(1.46),307(1.42), 316(1.08)	33-1158-80
$C_9H_{14}OSi$			
Silane, trimethylphenoxy-	hexane	221(3.840),267(3.036), 270(3.014),272(2.986), 276(2.908)	65-0491-80
$C_9H_{14}O_2$			
Cyclohexanone, 2-acetyl-3-methyl-	EtOH	292(3.74)	88-2337-80
2,4-Heptadienoic acid, 6-methyl-, methyl ester, (E,E)-	EtOH	259(4.36)	35-1390-80

Compound	Solvent	$\lambda_{max}(\log \epsilon)$	Ref.
$C_9H_{14}O_3$			
Bicyclo[3.3.1]nonan-3-one, 1-hydroperoxy-	EtOH	274(1.30)	44-1800-80
Cyclohexanecarboxylic acid, 2-oxo-, ethyl ester	C_6H_{12}	255(2.90)	151-0305-80A
Cyclopentanecarboxylic acid, 1-methyl-2-oxo-, ethyl ester	C_6H_{12}	300(1.60)	151-0305-80A
2-Hexenoic acid, 2-methyl-6-oxo-, ethyl ester, (E)-	C_6H_{12}	215(4.06),290(1.58)	151-0305-80A
(Z)-	C_6H_{12}	217(3.95),290(1.52)	151-0305-80A
$C_9H_{14}Si$			
Silane, trimethylphenyl-	C_6H_{12}	211(4.00),260f(2.4)	65-1615-80
$C_9H_{15}ClN_4OS$			
1,3,5-Triazin-2(1H)-one, 1-(3-chloropropyl)-4-(dimethylamino)-6-(methylthio)-	EtOH	217(4.50),235(4.44), 257(4.30)	103-0316-80
$C_9H_{15}ClN_4O_2$			
1,3,5-Triazin-2-amine, 4-(3-chloropropoxy)-6-methoxy-N,N-dimethyl-	EtOH	227(4.33)	103-0316-80
$C_9H_{15}IO$			
Bicyclo[2.2.2]octane, 1-iodo-4-methoxy-	EtOH	260.3(2.80)	44-3933-80
$C_9H_{15}N$			
1H-Pyrrole, 3-ethyl-2-propyl-	hexane	222(3.87)	103-0488-80
$C_9H_{15}NO$			
3,5-Hexadien-2-one. 6-(dimethylamino)-5-methyl-	EtOH	385(4.46)	70-1643-80
	CHCl$_3$	375(4.43)	70-1643-80
$C_9H_{15}NO_2$			
3-Buten-2-one, 3-methyl-4-morpholino-	EtOH	304(4.47)	4-0033-80
1-Penten-3-one, 1-morpholino-	EtOH	304(4.43)	4-0033-80
$C_9H_{15}NO_3$			
2-Butenoic acid, 3-(acetylamino)-2-methyl-, ethyl ester	EtOH	277(4.3)	5-0798-80
$C_9H_{15}NO_3S$			
7-Azabicyclo[4.2.0]octan-5-one, 8-methyl-7-(methylsulfonyl)-	ether	216(2.97),250(2.52), 295(2.02)	78-1585-80
Methanesulfonamide, N-ethyl-N-(6-oxo-1-cyclohexen-1-yl)-	ether	221(3.86),250(3.27), 320(2.13)	78-1585-80
Sulfonium, dimethyl-, 2-oxo-1-[[(1-oxopropyl)amino]carbonyl]propylide	EtOH	271(4.17)	94-0795-80
2H-1,4-Thiazine-6-carboxylic acid, 3,4-dihydro-3-methoxy-2,2-dimethyl-, methyl ester	EtOH	305(3.91)	39-2322-80C
$C_9H_{15}NO_5$			
Pentanoic acid, 5-[(methoxyoxoacetyl)-amino]-, methyl ester	EtOH	233(3.63)	78-2735-80
$C_9H_{15}NS_2$			
Cyclohexanecarbodithioic acid, 2-(ethylimino)-	EtOH	305(3.73),393(4.06)	118-0566-80

Compound	Solvent	λ_{max} (log ϵ)	Ref.
$C_9H_{15}N_2O_{13}P_3$ 2(1H)-Pyrimidinone, 1-(2-deoxy-β-D-ribofuranosyl)-, 5'-O-triphosphate, sodium salt	H_2O	216(3.70),303(3.48)	33-2488-80
$C_9H_{15}N_3OS$ 4-Imidazolidinone, 1-butyl-3-ethyl-5-imino-2-thioxo-	EtOH	312(4.20)	18-0442-80
$C_9H_{15}N_3O_6$ D-Ribitol, 1-deoxy-1-[(1,2,3,6-tetra-hydro-2,6-dioxo-4-pyrimidinyl)amino]-	pH 1 pH 13	267(4.33) 267(4.23)	39-2645-80C 39-2645-80C
$C_9H_{15}N_3O_6S_3$ 1H-1,4,7-Triazonine, 4,7-dihydro-1,4,7-tris(methylsulfonyl)-, (Z,Z,Z)-	MeCN	244(3.42)	24-3127-80
$C_9H_{15}N_5O$ 4(1H)-Pteridinone, 2-amino-5,6,7,8-tetrahydro-6,7,7-trimethyl-, hydro-chloride	pH 2.5	266(4.13)	150-3911-80
$C_9H_{15}N_5O_3$ Cytidine, 3',5'-diamino-3',5'-dideoxy-1H-1,2,3-Triazole-4-carboxylic acid, 1-[4-[(aminocarbonyl)amino]butyl]-, methyl ester	MeOH MeOH	270(3.95) 213(4.07)	118-0559-80 78-0865-80
C_9H_{16} 1,3-Hexadiene, 4,5,5-trimethyl-, (E)-	n.s.g.	236(4)	39-1756-80C
$C_9H_{16}NO_2$ 1-Piperidinyloxy, 2,2,6,6-tetramethyl-4-oxo-	hexane H_2O EtOH MeCN	236(3.38),457(0.83) 237(3.40),413(0.88) 236(3.36),436(0.82) 236(3.34),442(0.90)	94-3178-80 94-3178-80 94-3178-80 94-3178-80
$C_9H_{16}N_2$ 4H-Pyrazole, 4,4-diethyl-3,5-dimethyl-	EtOH	203(3.8)	24-1507-80
$C_9H_{16}N_2O$ 4H-Pyrazole, 4,4-diethyl-3,5-dimethyl-, 1-oxide	EtOH	198(4.1),269(3.4)	24-1507-80
$C_9H_{16}N_2O_2$ 2-Butenamide, 2-acetyl-3-amino-N-prop-yl- 4-Piperidinone, 2,2,6,6-tetramethyl-1-nitroso-	MeOH MeOH	240(3.30),302(4.12) 232(3.82)	44-0936-80 70-0765-80
$C_9H_{16}N_4O_5$ D-Arabinitol, 1-[5-amino-4-(aminocarbo-nyl)-1H-imidazol-1-yl]-1-deoxy-	H_2O	267(3.98)	39-2304-80C
$C_9H_{16}OS$ 3-Penten-2-one, 4-methyl-3-[(1-methyl-ethyl)thio]-	C_6H_{12}	236(3.62),275(3.57)	78-1943-80
$C_9H_{16}OSi$ 2-Cyclohexen-1-one, 2-(trimethyl-silyl)-	pentane	223(4.00),342(1.72)	44-4462-80

Compound	Solvent	$\lambda_{max}(\log \epsilon)$	Ref.
$C_9H_{16}O_4$ 2-Cyclopentene-1,2-dimethanol, 4-hy- droxy-3-(2-hydroxyethyl)- (eucommiol)	n.s.g.	206(3.8)	100-0649-80
$C_9H_{16}SeSi$ 1,4-Pentadiene-1-selone, 3-methyl- 2-(trimethylsilyl)-	isooctane	222(4.4),291(3.3), 554(1.3)	88-4251-80
$C_9H_{17}NO$ 3-Buten-2-one, 4-(dimethylamino)- 3-methyl- 1-Penten-3-one, 1-(diethylamino)-	EtOH EtOH	306(4.42) 307(4.46)	4-0033-80 4-0033-80
$C_9H_{17}N_3$ 1,2,4-Triazaspiro[4.5]dec-2-ene, 1,3- dimethyl-	MeOH	249(3.53)	104-0822-80
$C_9H_{18}Cl_3O_3P$ Phosphonic acid, (trichloromethyl)-, bis(2-methylpropyl) ester	MeCN	257(1.19),300(0.47)	18-1421-80
$C_9H_{18}CoN_5O$ Cobalt(2+), tetraammine(8-quinolinol- ato-N^1,O^8)-, dichloride, (OC-6-23)-	MeOH	325(3.01),338(3.09), 401(3.40)	138-1555-80
$C_9H_{18}NO$ 1-Piperidinyloxy, 2,2,6,6-tetramethyl-	hexane H_2O EtOH MeCN	243(3.22),470(1.02) 246(3.32) 244(3.33),452(1.11) 244(3.23),462(1.04)	94-3178-80 94-3178-80 94-3178-80 94-3178-80
$C_9H_{18}NOS$ Sulfonium, dimethyl[1-methyl-2-(4-mor- pholinyl)ethenyl]-, fluorosulfate	MeCN	255(4.2)	118-0466-80
$C_9H_{18}N_2O$ Piperidine, 2,2,6,6-tetramethyl-1-ni- troso-	MeOH	237(3.82)	70-0765-80
$C_9H_{18}N_2O_3S$ 1,9,12-Trioxa-4,6-diazacyclotetra- decane-5-thione	H_2O MeOH	208(4.21),239(4.16) 207(4.18),244(4.18)	104-1124-80 104-1124-80
$C_9H_{18}N_2S$ 1,3-Diazacycloundecane-2-thione	MeOH	211(4.22),242(4.09)	104-1124-80
$C_9H_{18}Si$ Silane, (2,4-hexadienyl)trimethyl-	n.s.g.	238.5(4.11)	88-3783-80
$C_9H_{19}N_3O_2$ 1-Triazenium, 3-(ethoxycarbonyl)-1,2- bis(1-methylethyl)-, hydroxide, inner salt isomer 3b Triaziridinecarboxylic acid, bis(1- methylethyl)-, ethyl ester	n.s.g. n.s.g. C_6H_{12}	285(3.86) 289(3.87) 283(2.48)	77-1197-80 77-1197-80 77-1197-80
$C_9H_{20}N_3$ Methanaminium, N-[1,3-bis(dimethyl- amino)-2-propenylidene]-N-methyl-, perchlorate	H_2O MeOH MeCN	328(4.84) 326(4.83) 326(4.82)	2-0146-80 2-0146-80 2-0146-80

Compound	Solvent	λ_{max} (log ϵ)	Ref.
Methanaminium, N-[1,3-bis(dimethyl- amino)-2-propenylidene]-N-methyl-, perchlorate (cont.)	CH_2Cl_2 $CHCl_3$ DMSO	318(4.81) 324(4.81) 320(4.83)	2-0146-80 2-0146-80 2-0146-80
$C_9H_{27}NSi_4$ Azatetrasilacyclopentane, nonamethyl-	isooctane	210(3.95),235(3.60)	101-0159-80N
$C_9H_{27}PSi_4$ Phosphatetrasilacyclopentane, nona- methyl-	isooctane	210(4.08),234(3.78), 277(2.72)	101-0159-80N
$C_9H_{28}OSi_4$ Tetrasilane, 1-methoxy-1,1,2,2,3,3,4,4- octamethyl-	C_6H_{12}	236.0(4.01)	101-0029-80L

Compound	Solvent	$\lambda_{max}(\log \epsilon)$	Ref.
$C_{10}ClF_{15}N_2$ 2,3-Diazabicyclo[3.2.0]hepta-2,6-diene, 4-chloro-1,4,5,6,7-pentakis(trifluoromethyl)-, $(1\alpha,4\beta,5\alpha)$-	C_6H_{12}	236(2.77),345(2.16)	35-6634-80
$C_{10}F_{14}S$ 4H-Thiopyran, 4-(difluoromethylene)-2,3,5,6-tetrakis(trifluoromethyl)-	C_6H_{12}	277(3.88)	35-6634-80
$C_{10}HF_{15}N_2$ 2,3-Diazabicyclo[3.2.0]hepta-3,6-diene, 1,4,5,6,7-pentakis(trifluoromethyl)-	C_6H_{12}	242(3.40),263s(--)	35-6633-80
$C_{10}HF_{15}N_2S$ 3-Thia-6,7-diazatricyclo[3.3.0.0^{2,4}]-oct-6-ene, 1,2,4,5,8-pentakis(trifluoromethyl)-, $(1\alpha,2\beta,4\beta,5\alpha,8\alpha)$-	C_6H_{12}	235(3.09),270(2.13), 330(2.37)	35-6633-80
$C_{10}HF_{15}S$ 3,5-Heptadiene-2-thione, 1,1,1,7,7,7-hexafluoro-3,4,5-tris(trifluoromethyl)-, (E,E)-	C_6H_{12}	239(3.10),266(3.41)	35-6634-80
2H-Thiopyran, 2,3,4,5,6-pentakis(trifluoromethyl)-	C_6H_{12}	227(3.58),313(3.39)	35-6634-80
$C_{10}H_3Cl_4NO_2$ 1,4-Naphthalenedione, 5-amino-2,3,6,8-tetrachloro-	EtOH	288(4.20),520(3.83)	40-1862-80
$C_{10}H_3N_5S_2$ Thieno[2,3-d]pyrimidine-4,5,6-tricarbonitrile, 2-(methylthio)-	n.s.g.	287(3.90),387(4.32), 401(4.30)	44-5113-80
$C_{10}H_4Cl_3NO_3$ 1,4-Naphthalenedione, 5-amino-2,6,8-trichloro-3-hydroxy-	EtOH	248(4.31),500(3.86)	40-1862-80
1,4-Naphthalenedione, 5-amino-3,6,8-trichloro-2-hydroxy-	EtOH	245(4.31),512(3.82)	40-1862-80
$C_{10}H_4F_9NO_8S_3$ Benzene, 2-(nitromethyl)-1,3,5-tris-[(trifluoromethyl)sulfonyl]-, compd. with triethylamine (1:1)	MeCN	226(4.21),277(4.03), 457(4.29)	104-1292-80
$C_{10}H_5Br_2NO_3$ Furan, 3,5-dibromo-2-(4-nitrophenyl)-	EtOH	238(4.00),345(4.27)	103-0334-80
$C_{10}H_5ClN_2O$ 3,1-Benzoxazepine-2-carbonitrile, 5-chloro-	MeOH	242(4.40),325(3.58)	94-1157-80
	MeCN	241(4.37),319(3.53)	94-1157-80
1H-Indole-2-carbonitrile, 4-chloro-3-formyl-	MeOH	220(4.54),246(4.27), 314(4.05)	94-1157-80
1H-Indole-2-carbonitrile, 5-chloro-3-formyl-	MeOH	222(4.55),247(4.23), 314(4.04)	94-1157-80
1H-Indole-2-carbonitrile, 7-chloro-3-formyl-	MeOH	219(4.55),246(4.37), 254(4.30),311(4.10)	94-1157-80
$C_{10}H_5F_9O_6S_3$ Benzene, 2-methyl-1,3,5-tris[(trifluoromethyl)sulfonyl]-, compd. with triethylamine (1:1)	MeCN	230(4.23),304(4.42), 495(3.44)	104-1292-80

Compound	Solvent	$\lambda_{max}(\log \epsilon)$	Ref.
$C_{10}H_5N_3O_4$ Pyrrolo[2,1,5-cd]indolizine, 1,6-dinitro-	EtOH	248(4.30),297(3.95), 365(3.66),425s(3.93), 434(3.99)	39-1319-80C
$C_{10}H_5N_5O_4S$ 1H-Pyrazino[2,3-b][1,4]benzothiazine, 3,7-dinitro-	EtOH	215(4.21),291(4.23), 366(3.76),463(3.97), 607(3.06)	78-2681-80
$C_{10}H_5N_5O_4Se$ 1H-Pyrazino[2,3-b][1,4]benzoselenazine, 3,7-dinitro-	EtOH	211(4.18),295(4.23), 363(3.61),465(4.02)	78-2681-80
$C_{10}H_5N_5O_5S$ 1H-Pyrazino[2,3-b][1,4]benzothiazine, 3,7-dinitro-, 5-oxide	EtOH	209(4.37),240(4.08), 265(4.07),282(4.04), 347(3.99),380(4.10), 463(3.92)	78-2681-80
$C_{10}H_6BrClO$ Furan, 2-bromo-5-(4-chlorophenyl)-	EtOH	222(3.93),293(4.46)	103-0334-80
$C_{10}H_6BrNOS$ 2-Propenoyl isothiocyanate, 3-(4-bromophenyl)-	dioxan	317(4.44)	73-2334-80
$C_{10}H_6BrNO_3$ Furan, 2-bromo-5-(4-nitrophenyl)-	EtOH	242(3.95),352(4.26)	103-0334-80
$C_{10}H_6Br_2O$ Furan, 2-bromo-5-(4-bromophenyl)-	EtOH	223(3.92),295(4.44)	103-0334-80
$C_{10}H_6ClNOS$ 2-Propenoyl isothiocyanate, 3-(4-chlorophenyl)-	dioxan	317(4.44)	73-2334-80
$C_{10}H_6ClN_3O_3$ Pyrrolidinetetrone, 3-[(4-chlorophenyl)hydrazone]	EtOH	252(3.99),325(4.02), 400(4.45)	104-0751-80
$C_{10}H_6N_2$ 1,4-Diazabiphenylene	EtOH	221(4.37),268(4.15), 358(4.04),373(4.08)	150-2941-80
1,8-Diazabiphenylene	EtOH	288(4.41),233(4.36)[sic], 313(3.83),350(4.01)	150-2911-80
2,7-Diazabiphenylene	MeOH	235(4.79),242(4.93), 284(3.25),298(3.26), 312(3.17),327(2.04)	150-2911-80
$C_{10}H_6N_2O_2$ Pyrrolo[2,1,5-cd]indolizine, 6-nitro-	EtOH	224(4.26),265(4.43), 275s(4.37),312(3.53), 392(3.89)	39-1319-80C
$C_{10}H_6N_2O_2S_2$ Propanedinitrile, [3,4-bis(methylthio)-2,5-dioxo-3-cyclopenten-1-ylidene]-	CH_2Cl_2	286(2.5),401(2.4), 503(2.4)	5-1409-80
$C_{10}H_6N_2O_3S$ 2-Propenoyl isothiocyanate, 3-(4-nitro-	dioxan	314(4.37)	73-2334-80

Compound	Solvent	$\lambda_{max}(\log \epsilon)$	Ref.
phenyl)- (cont.)			73-2334-80
$C_{10}H_6N_2O_4S_4$ [1,4]Dithiino[2,3-c:6,5-c']diisothia-zole-3,7-dicarboxylic acid, dimethyl ester	CH_2Cl_2	272(4.08),280(3.79)	44-5122-80
$C_{10}H_6N_2O_6$ 4H,8H-Benzo[1,2-c:4,5-c']diisoxazole-4,8-dione, 3,7-dimethoxy-	MeCN	218(3.70),278(3.98), 295(3.75)	83-0572-80
Furan, 2,2'-(1,2-ethenediyl)bis[5-ni-tro-, (E)-	MeOH	245(4.23),288(3.94), 415(4.54)	73-3347-80
$C_{10}H_6N_4$ Pyrazino[2,3-c]cinnoline	dioxan	267(4.08),304(3.53), 368(3.53)	150-2941-80
Pyrazino[2,3-f]quinoxaline	EtOH	215(4.48),280(4.48)	118-0116-80
$C_{10}H_6N_4O_2$ 1,2,4,5-Tetrazine, 3,6-di-2-furanyl-	MeOH	340(4.46),528(2.57)	24-2566-80
$C_{10}H_6N_4S_2$ 1,2,4,5-Tetrazine, 3,6-di-2-thienyl-	MeOH	334(4.65),520(2.73)	24-2566-80
$C_{10}H_6N_4S_3$ 2-Butenedinitrile, 2,2'-thiobis[3-(methylthio)-	EtOH	200(3.98),339(3.72)	44-5113-80
$C_{10}H_6N_6O_3$ [1,2,4]Triazolo[5,1-c][1,2,4]triazin-4(1H)-one, 3-nitro-7-phenyl-, sodium salt	n.s.g.	205(4.49),256(4.37), 360(4.07)	103-0974-80
$C_{10}H_6O_2$ 1,2-Azulenedione	$CHCl_3$	260(4.3),395(4.0), 600f(2.8),800(2.3)	138-0197-80
$C_{10}H_6O_3$ 1H-2-Benzopyran-3-carboxaldehyde, 1-oxo- (artimidinal)	EtOH	231(4.3),240(4.25), 255(3.95),261(3.95), 272(3.88),321(3.77)	25-0084-80
$C_{10}H_6O_4$ 1,4-Naphthalenedione, 2,5-dihydroxy-	MeOH	242(4.10),284(4.08), 414(3.59)	39-1161-80C
1,4-Naphthalenedione, 2,8-dihydroxy-	MeOH	230(4.32),271(4.21), 292s(3.99),410(3.65)	39-1161-80C
1,4-Naphthalenedione, 5,6-dihydroxy-	EtOH	224(4.2),262(4.0), 460(3.5)	118-0753-80
$C_{10}H_6O_5$ 1,4-Naphthalenedione, 2,3,5-trihydroxy-	MeOH	228(3.90),283(3.87), 403(3.50)	39-1161-80C
$C_{10}H_7BrN_2$ Pyrimidine, 4-(3-bromophenyl)-	$CHCl_3$	250(4.03),270(4.19)	24-2739-80
$C_{10}H_7BrN_2OS$ Phenol, 4-bromo-2-[(2-thiazolylimino)-methyl]-	pH 5	380(4.01)	2-0492-80

Compound	Solvent	$\lambda_{max}(\log \epsilon)$	Ref.
$C_{10}H_7BrOS$			
2H-1-Benzothiopyran-2-one, 6-bromo-4-methyl-	EtOH	248(4.65),287(3.81), 298(3.78),351(3.45)	18-2046-80
4H-1-Benzothiopyran-4-one, 6-bromo-2-methyl-	EtOH	224(4.26),252(4.40), 281(3.48),292(3.48), 342(3.90)	18-2046-80
$C_{10}H_7ClN_2O_2$			
3(2H)-Pyridazinone, 4-chloro-5-hydroxy-2-phenyl-	MeOH	211(4.22),236s(--), 285(4.01)	73-0127-80
3(2H)-Pyridazinone, 5-chloro-4-hydroxy-2-phenyl-	MeOH	247(4.27),300(4.00)	73-0127-80
$C_{10}H_7ClN_2O_2S$			
1,3,4-Thiadiazol-2(3H)-one, 5-acetyl-3-(3-chlorophenyl)-	EtOH	236s(3.88),304(3.98)	4-1713-80
1,3,4-Thiadiazol-2(3H)-one, 5-acetyl-3-(4-chlorophenyl)-	EtOH	229s(4.12),304(4.05)	4-1713-80
$C_{10}H_7ClN_4$			
[1,2,4]Triazolo[1,5-a]quinazoline, 5-chloro-2-methyl-	n.s.g.	231(4.62),290(3.81), 299(3.81),325(3.65), 340s(--)	33-0001-80
$C_{10}H_7ClN_4O_2S$			
Ethanone, 1-[4-(3-chlorophenyl)-4,5-di-hydro-5-(nitrosoimino)-1,3,4-thiadia-zol-2-yl]-	EtOH	275(3.52),347(3.81), 465(1.81)	4-1713-80
Ethanone, 1-[4-(4-chlorophenyl)-4,5-di-hydro-5-(nitrosoimino)-1,3,4-thiadia-zol-2-yl]-	EtOH	278(4.47),347(3.95), 465(1.85)	4-1713-80
$C_{10}H_7ClOS$			
2H-1-Benzothiopyran-2-one, 6-chloro-4-methyl-	EtOH	246(4.65),287(3.81), 298(3.78),350(3.46)	18-2046-80
2H-1-Benzothiopyran-2-one, 7-chloro-4-methyl-	EtOH	233(4.45),241(4.46), 266(4.04),290(4.08), 301(4.00),337(3.48)	18-2046-80
4H-1-Benzothiopyran-4-one, 6-chloro-2-methyl-	EtOH	223(4.23),250(4.38), 280(3.70),291(3.60), 342(3.95)	18-2046-80
$C_{10}H_7Cl_3S$			
Cyclopropene, 1,3,3-trichloro-2-[4-(methylthio)phenyl]-	CH_2Cl_2	239(4.1),317(4.3)	5-1409-80
$C_{10}H_7D_2NO_5$			
1-Benzoxepin-5(2H)-one-4-d, 3,4-dihy-dro-2-(hydroxy-d)-4-nitro-	EtOH	238(3.88),297(3.49)	39-2049-80C
$C_{10}H_7F_3N_2$			
2-Propenenitrile, 3-amino-3-[4-(tri-fluoromethyl)phenyl]-	EtOH	303(4.04)	39-1635-80C
$C_{10}H_7F_3O$			
Ethanone, 1-[4-(trifluoroethenyl)-phenyl]-, homopolymer	$CHCl_3$	325(1.85)	44-2903-80
$C_{10}H_7NOS$			
2-Propenoyl isothiocyanate, 3-phenyl-, (E)-	dioxan	311(4.37)	73-2334-80

Compound	Solvent	$\lambda_{max}(\log \epsilon)$	Ref.
$C_{10}H_7NO_2$			
Naphthalene, 1-nitro-	MeCN	210s(3.51),224(4.30), 250(3.91),340(3.59)	56-2161-80
1,2-Naphthalenedione, 4-amino-	EtOH	235(4.20),273(4.31), 280s(--),330s(--), 456(3.56)	94-1207-80
1H-Pyrrole-2,5-dione, 1-phenyl-	n.s.g.	285(3.72)	116-0826-80
$C_{10}H_7NO_2S$			
4-Quinolinecarboxylic acid, 1,2-di-hydro-2-thioxo-	EtOH	221(4.52),286(4.28), 413(3.95)	94-0049-80
$C_{10}H_7NO_2S_2$			
[1]Benzothieno[2,3-d]isothiazole, 3-methyl-, 4,4-dioxide	n.s.g.	234(4.30),270s(3.88), 280(3.94),300(3.79)	150-0833-80
$C_{10}H_7NO_3$			
4H-1-Benzopyran-3-carboxaldehyde, 2-amino-4-oxo-	EtOH	231(4.28),260(4.16), 264(4.15),292(4.04)	44-1964-80
1,3-Dioxolo[4,5-g]isoquinolin-5(6H)-one	MeOH	268s(3.60),282(3.58), 293(3.59),312s(3.37), 326(3.47),340(3.36)	100-0143-80
2,5-Oxazolidinedione, 4-(phenylmethyl-ene)-, (Z)-	EtOH	228(3.80),235(3.80), 313(4.33)	39-0858-80C
$C_{10}H_7NO_4$			
9H-[1]Benzopyrano[3,2-c]isoxazol-9-one, 3,3a-dihydro-, 1-oxide	EtOH	302(3.86),345(3.45)	39-2049-80C
$C_{10}H_7N_3O_3$			
Pyrrolidinetetrone, 3-(phenylhydrazone)	EtOH	252(4.67),310(3.89), 395(3.27)	104-0751-80
$C_{10}H_7N_3O_3S$			
4(5H)-Thiazolone, 2-amino-5-[(4-nitro-phenyl)methylene]-	EtOH	224(4.05),293(4.12), 354(4.29)	103-0718-80
$C_{10}H_7N_3O_4S$			
1,3,4-Thiadiazol-2(3H)-one, 5-acetyl-3-(3-nitrophenyl)-	EtOH	240(3.92),304(4.02)	4-1713-80
1,3,4-Thiadiazol-2(3H)-one, 5-acetyl-3-(4-nitrophenyl)-	EtOH	238(4.61),304(4.23)	4-1713-80
$C_{10}H_7N_3Se$			
1H-Pyrazino[2,3-b][1,4]benzoselenazine	EtOH	248(4.37)	78-2681-80
$C_{10}H_7N_5O_4S$			
Ethanone, 1-[4,5-dihydro-4-(3-nitro-phenyl)-5-(nitrosoimino)-1,3,4-thiadiazol-2-yl]-	EtOH	275(4.09),347(3.82), 464(1.82)	4-1713-80
Ethanone, 1-[4,5-dihydro-4-(4-nitro-phenyl)-5-(nitrosoimino)-1,3,4-thiadiazol-2-yl]-	EtOH	279(4.39),348(4.27), 466(4.81)	4-1713-80
$C_{10}H_8$			
Bicyclo[6.2.0]deca-1,3,5,7,9-pentaene	C_6H_{12}	275f(4.3),400f(2.5)	88-0107-80
Naphthalene, Cr(CO)$_3$ complex	C_6H_{12}	250s(3.9),300s(3.6), 350(3.8),443(3.3)	110-0749-80
Tricyclo[6.2.0.0^{3,6}]deca-1,4,7,9-tetra-ene	C_6H_{12}	215(4.2),265s(3.3)	88-0107-80

Compound	Solvent	$\lambda_{max}(\log \epsilon)$	Ref.
$C_{10}H_8BrNO_2$			
4H-1,3-Oxazin-5(6H)-one, 2-(4-bromo-phenyl)-	MeOH	208(4.23),250(4.21)	103-1000-80
$C_{10}H_8BrNS$			
2(1H)-Quinolinethione, 6-bromo-4-methyl-	EtOH	226(4.65),287(4.30), 394(4.00)	94-0049-80
2(1H)-Quinolinethione, 7-bromo-4-methyl-	EtOH	227(4.66),280(4.19), 390(3.90)	94-0049-80
$C_{10}H_8BrN_3O_2$			
4,5-Isoxazoledione, 3-methyl-, 4-[(4-bromophenyl)hydrazone]	MeOH MeOH-base?	375(4.32) 365(4.31)	4-0897-80 4-0897-80
$C_{10}H_8Br_2N_2O_2$			
4H-Pyrazole, 4,4-dibromo-3-methyl-5-phenyl-, 1,2-dioxide	$CHCl_3$	248(4.25),278s(3.96), 350(3.49)	44-0076-80
$C_{10}H_8ClNO_2$			
Benzoic acid, 4-chloro-2-(cyanomethyl)-, methyl ester	EtOH	242(4.18),275(2.97)	95-0819-80
Benzoic acid, 5-chloro-2-(cyanomethyl)-, methyl ester	EtOH	228(3.42),286(3.10)	95-0819-80
2H-Indol-2-one, 5-acetyl-3-chloro-1,3-dihydro-	EtOH	217(4.32),246(3.86), 288(4.14)	78-2459-80
4H-1,3-Oxazin-5(6H)-one, 2-(4-chloro-phenyl)-	MeOH	208(4.26),246(4.16)	103-1000-80
$C_{10}H_8ClNO_4$			
Acetic acid, [(benzoyloxy)imino]-chloro-, methyl ester	MeOH	240(4.16)	94-3296-80
$C_{10}H_8ClNS$			
2(1H)-Quinolinethione, 6-chloro-4-methyl-	EtOH	223(4.67),287(4.30), 394(4.04)	94-0049-80
2(1H)-Quinolinethione, 7-chloro-4-methyl-	EtOH	224(4.82),279(4.31), 388(4.10)	94-0049-80
$C_{10}H_8ClN_3O$			
1H-Pyrazole-4-carboxaldehyde, 5-amino-1-(4-chlorophenyl)-	EtOH	253(4.26)	114-0127-80C
$C_{10}H_8ClN_3OS$			
Ethanone, 1-[4-(3-chlorophenyl)-4,5-dihydro-5-imino-1,3,4-thiadiazol-2-yl]-	EtOH	215(4.23),245(4.20), 343(4.03)	4-1713-80
Ethanone, 1-[4-(4-chlorophenyl)-4,5-dihydro-5-imino-1,3,4-thiadiazol-2-yl]-	EtOH	228(4.23),248(4.28), 340(4.03)	4-1713-80
$C_{10}H_8ClN_3O_2$			
Benzoic acid, 5-chloro-2-(3-methyl-4H-1,2,4-triazol-4-yl)-	EtOH	224s(4.07),281(3.06), 287s(3.02)	87-0873-80
$C_{10}H_8Cl_2N_2O$			
4H-Pyrazole, 4,4-dichloro-3-methyl-5-phenyl-, 2-oxide	$CHCl_3$	240(3.91),285(3.91), 354(3.26)	44-0076-80
$C_{10}H_8Cl_2N_2O_2$			
4H-Pyrazole, 4,4-dichloro-3-methyl-5-phenyl-, 1,2-dioxide	$CHCl_3$	256(4.24),337(3.67)	44-0076-80

Compound	Solvent	$\lambda_{max}(\log \epsilon)$	Ref.
$C_{10}H_8Cl_6N_2O_2$			
4H-1,3-Oxazin-4-one, 6-[(1-methyleth-yl)amino]-5-(trichloroethenyl)-2-(trichloromethyl)-	MeCN	203(4.27),261(4.00), 300s(3.4)	24-0811-80
$C_{10}H_8N_2$			
2,2'-Bipyridine	hexane	236(3.96),244(3.93), 282(4.05)	5-0291-80
	H_2O	233(3.43),280(4.05)	70-0740-80
	CH_2Cl_2	237(4.04),244(4.00), 283(4.16)	35-7892-80
protonated	H_2O	240(3.83),301(4.17)	70-0740-80
2,3'-Bipyridine	H_2O	237(4.06),275(4.03)	70-0740-80
protonated	H_2O	275(4.16)	70-0740-80
2,4'-Bipyridine	hexane	242(4.11),272(3.99)	5-0291-80
3,3'-Bipyridine	H_2O	239(4.10),269(3.9)	70-0740-80
protonated	H_2O	230(3.90),269(4.08)	70-0740-80
4,4'-Bipyridine	hexane	236(4.10)	5-0291-80
	H_2O	239(4.19),270s(--)	70-0740-80
protonated	H_2O	250(4.23)	70-0740-80
$C_{10}H_8N_2O$			
2,2'-Bipyridine, 1-oxide	EtOH	205(--),222(--), 243(4.3),270(4.0)	70-0740-80
	H_2SO_4	260(--),300(--)	70-0740-80
2,3'-Bipyridine, 1-oxide	EtOH	202(--),242(4.5), 268(4.55)	70-0740-80
	H_2SO_4	275(--)	70-0740-80
3,3'-Bipyridine, 1-oxide	EtOH	205(--),248(4.3), 270(4.2)	70-0740-80
	H_2SO_4	238(--),265(--)	70-0740-80
4,4'-Bipyridine, 1-oxide	EtOH	205(--),225(4.1), 325(4.32)	70-0740-80
	H_2SO_4	258(--)	70-0740-80
Methanone, 1H-imidazol-2-ylphenyl-	EtOH	298(4.15)	103-0247-80
	EtOH-5N HCl	282(4.18)	103-0247-80
	dioxan	303(4.01)	103-0247-80
2-Naphthalenamine, 1-nitroso-	$CHCl_3$	365(3.78),438(3.86), 700(1.80)	95-0515-80
Co(III) chelate	$CHCl_3$	276(4.57),328(4.77), 384s(4.37),400(4.38)	95-0515-80
$C_{10}H_8N_2OS$			
Phenol, 2-[(2-thiazolylimino)methyl]-	pH 5	365(4.05)	2-0492-80
4(5H)-Thiazolone, 2-amino-5-(phenyl-methylene)-	EtOH	238(4.00),288(4.12), 330(4.34)	103-0718-80
$C_{10}H_8N_2O_2$			
2,2'-Bipyridine, 1,1'-dioxide	EtOH	203(--),238(4.1), 268(4.3),280s(--)	70-0740-80
	H_2SO_4	268(--)	70-0740-80
2,3'-Bipyridine, 1,1'-dioxide	EtOH	203(--),247(4.52), 272(3.8)	70-0740-80
	H_2SO_4	270(--)	70-0740-80
3,3'-Bipyridine, 1,1'-dioxide	EtOH	203(--),243(--), 268(4.3)	70-0740-80
	H_2SO_4	240(--),260(--)	70-0740-80
4,4'-Bipyridine, 1,1'-dioxide	EtOH	207(--),223(4.1), 305(4.22)	70-0740-80
	H_2SO_4	258(--)	70-0740-80

Compound	Solvent	λ_{max}(log ϵ)	Ref.
1,4'-Bipyridinium, 3-hydroxy-, hydroxide, inner salt, 1'-oxide	EtOH	227(4.48),287(4.50)	150-3337-80
2(1H)-Pyrazinone, 1-phenyl-, 4-oxide	pH 1	223(4.39),280(4.05), 333(3.73)	94-2720-80
	H_2O	223(4.39),280(4.04), 335(3.73)	94-2720-80
	pH 13	282(3.92),330(3.72)	94-2720-80
2(1H)-Pyrazinone, 6-phenyl-, 4-oxide	pH 1	244(4.25),348(3.93)	94-2720-80
	H_2O	243(4.28),345(4.02)	94-2720-80
	pH 13	242(4.40),343(4.02)	94-2720-80
$C_{10}H_8N_2O_2S$			
1,3-Dioxolo[4,5-g]quinazoline, 8-(methylthio)-	EtOH	217(4.23),236(4.28), 250s(4.24),282s(3.88), 325(4.08),340(4.15)	114-0253-80B
1,3,4-Thiadiazol-2(3H)-one, 5-acetyl-3-phenyl-	EtOH	240s(3.93),304(3.98)	4-1713-80
$C_{10}H_8N_2O_4$			
4H-1,3-Oxazin-5(6H)-one, 2-(4-nitrophenyl)-	MeOH	206(4.0),216s(3.86), 280(4.02)	103-1000-80
$C_{10}H_8N_4$			
2,2a,4,5-Tetraazabenz[cd]azulene, 1-methyl-	MeOH	348(3.84),365(3.75), 430s(2.77),454(2.82), 484(2.80),516s(2.66), 560s(2.32)	4-1057-80
$C_{10}H_8N_4O$			
4-Isoxazolecarbonitrile, 5-[(2-aminophenyl)amino]-	MeOH	204(3.90),219(4.22), 255(4.05),312(4.33)	94-0567-80
5H-Pyrazolo[3,4-b][1,6]naphthyridin-5-one, 1,6-dihydro-7-methyl-	MeOH	220(4.60),226(4.61), 278(4.23),287(4.25), 310(4.15),344(4.13)	39-0522-80C
	acid	220(4.57),264(4.21), 296(4.06),312(4.02), 390(4.11)	39-0522-80C
Tetrazolo[1,5-a]quinoline, 5-methoxy-	EtOH	257(3.6),293(3.4), 305(3.3),316(3.2)	103-1286-80
[1,2,4]Triazolo[1,5-a]quinazolin-5(1H)-one, 2-methyl-	n.s.g.	220(4.56),253(3.93), 307(3.62)	33-0001-80
$C_{10}H_8N_4O_2S$			
Ethanone, 1-[4,5-dihydro-5-(nitrosoimino)-4-phenyl-1,3,4-thiadiazol-2-yl]-	EtOH	275(4.22),347(4.23), 465(1.72)	4-1713-80
	$CHCl_3$	278(4.25),355(4.36), 485(1.73)	4-1713-80
	HOAc	275(2.98),345(4.09), 460(1.77)	4-1713-80
$C_{10}H_8N_4O_3S$			
Ethanone, 1-[4,5-dihydro-5-imino-4-(3-nitrophenyl)-1,3,4-thiadiazol-2-yl]-	EtOH	218(4.20),252(4.29), 338(3.98)	4-1713-80
Ethanone, 1-[4,5-dihydro-5-imino-4-(4-nitrophenyl)-1,3,4-thiadiazol-2-yl]-	EtOH	230(4.20),247(4.24), 346(4.18)	4-1713-80
$C_{10}H_8N_4O_4$			
4,5-Isoxazoledione, 3-methyl-, 4-[(3-nitrophenyl)hydrazone]	MeOH	368(4.39)	4-0897-80
	MeOH-base?	364(4.44)	4-0897-80
4,5-Isoxazoledione, 3-methyl-, 4-[(4-nitrophenyl)hydrazone]	MeOH	375(4.44)	4-0897-80
	MeOH-base?	405(4.42)	4-0897-80

Compound	Solvent	$\lambda_{max}(\log \epsilon)$	Ref.
$C_{10}H_8OS$			
2H-1-Benzothiopyran-2-one, 4-methyl-	EtOH	235(4.40),241(4.40), 289(3.85),298(3.85), 342(3.46)	18-2046-80
$C_{10}H_8OS_2$			
Dithieno[2,3-c:3',2'-e]oxepin, 4,6-di-hydro-	heptane	205s(4.25),229s(4.33), 238s(4.22),278(3.78), 288s(3.74),294s(3.65)	4-0321-80
	MeCN	207s(4.25),228s(4.34), 240s(4.16),283(3.80)	4-0321-80
Dithieno[3,2-c:2',3'-e]oxepin, 4,6-di-hydro-	heptane	216(3.81),251(3.76), 261(3.75),315(4.11)	4-0321-80
	MeCN	218(3.84),250(3.79), 260(3.78),317(4.13)	4-0321-80
4H,6H-Dithieno[3,4-c:3',4'-e]oxepin	heptane	208(4.35),230s(4.13), 237s(4.05),265(3.90), 288s(3.62)	4-0321-80
	MeCN	209(4.28),229s(4.10), 236s(4.02),267(3.78)	4-0321-80
1,3-Dithiol-2-one, 4-(phenylmethyl)-	EtOH	242(3.60),265(3.52)	44-2959-80
$C_{10}H_8OS_3$			
3H-1,2-Dithiole-3-thione, 5-(4-methoxyphenyl)-	benzene	347(4.27),437(3.95)	94-1067-80
	$C_6H_{11}Me$	238(4.07),280s(3.73), 338(4.31),438(3.87), 540(1.75)	94-1067-80
	MeOH	234(4.05),270s(3.77), 349(4.24),433(3.99)	94-1067-80
	isoBuOH	236(4.11),274s(3.77), 348(4.29),434(4.02)	94-1067-80
3H-1,2-Dithiole-3-thione, 4-(4-methylphenyl)-, S-oxide	MeCN	439(3.80)	138-0619-80
1,2-Dithiol-1-ium, 4-hydroxy-3-(methylthio)-5-phenyl-, hydroxide, inner salt	EtOH dioxan MeCN	478(4.20) 543(4.52) 525(4.48)	139-0079-80A 139-0079-80A 139-0079-80A
$C_{10}H_8O_2$			
Bicyclo[4.2.0]octa-1,3,5-triene-7,8-dione, 3,4-dimethyl-	EtOH	237(4.07),262s(3.20), 306(3.33),316(3.35)	39-1834-80C
8H-Cyclohepta[b]furan-8-one, 3-methyl-	MeOH	227(4.18),273(4.27), 340(3.57)	18-0745-80
Cyclopenta[c]pyran-7-carboxaldehyde, 4-methyl- (viburtinal)	MeOH	228(4.12),243(4.06), 251(3.94),287(4.00), 424(3.85)	100-0649-80
Ethanone, 1-(3-benzofuranyl)-	MeOH	224(4.51),242(3.79), 262(3.84)	118-0236-80
$C_{10}H_8O_3$			
1H-2-Benzopyran-5-carboxaldehyde, 3,4-dihydro-1-oxo- (erythrocentaurine)	n.s.g.	223(4.3),290(3.3)	100-0649-80
2H-1-Benzopyran-2-one, 7-hydroxy-6-methyl-	EtOH	249s(3.58),260s(3.50), 338(4.10)	2-0085-80
	EtOH-NaOEt	237(--),274s(--), 296s(--),392(--)	2-0085-80
	EtOH-NaOAc	229(--),249s(--), 260s(--),338(--), 392(--)	2-0085-80
2H-1-Benzopyran-2-one, 8-methoxy-	MeOH	250(3.94),290(4.21)	102-2494-80
4H-1-Benzopyran-4-one, 7-hydroxy-2-methyl-	pH 4.5	243(4.18),249(4.22), 295(4.11)	86-0977-80

Compound	Solvent	$\lambda_{max}(\log \epsilon)$	Ref.
4H-1-Benzopyran-4-one, 7-hydroxy-2-methyl- (cont.)	pH 10.5	256(4.41),299s(3.76), 336(4.13)	86-0977-80
4H-1-Benzopyran-4-one, 7-hydroxy-3-methyl-	pH 4.5	243(4.12),249(4.16), 298(4.10)	86-0977-80
	pH 10.5	258(4.39),306s(3.87), 336(4.08)	86-0977-80
1H-Inden-1-one, 2,3-dihydro-4,5-(methylenedioxy)-	EtOH	236(4.37),286(--), 307s(3.69)	73-1950-80
1H-Inden-1-one, 2,3-dihydro-5,6-(methylenedioxy)-	EtOH	231(4.20),267(3.85), 316(3.95)	73-1950-80
1H-Inden-1-one, 2,3-dihydro-6,7-(methylenedioxy)-	EtOH	232(4.30),247(4.01), 256(4.02),347(3.55)	73-1950-80
$C_{10}H_8O_3W$			
Tungsten, tricarbonyl[[(1,2,3,4,5-η)-2,4-cyclopentadien-1-ylidene]-1,2-ethanediyl]-	hexane	257s(4.0),305s(3.4), 415(2.6)	24-1033-80
$C_{10}H_8O_4$			
2H-1-Benzopyran-2-one, 7-hydroxy-6-methoxy- (scopoletin)	MeOH	210(4.31),228(4.11), 250(3.43),300(3.45), 350(4.04)	100-0285-80
	EtOH	230(4.16),254(3.71), 263s(3.66),300(3.73), 347(4.11)	94-1847-80
Bicyclo[4.2.0]octa-1,3,5-triene-7,8-dione, 2,5-dimethoxy-	EtOH	248(4.46),254(4.40), 338(3.49)	39-1841-80C
Bicyclo[4.2.0]octa-1,3,5-triene-7,8-dione, 3,4-dimethoxy-	EtOH	245(4.47),258s(4.15), 280(3.63),313s(3.88), 325(4.08),339(4.03)	39-1841-80C
6H-1,3-Dioxolo[4,5-f][2]benzopyran-6-one, 8,9-dihydro-	n.s.g.	226(4.92),268(4.08), 320(4.11)	2-0009-80
4H,5H-Pyrano[4,3-b]pyran-4,5-dione, 2,7-dimethyl-	EtOH	207(4.05),277(3.92), 377(4.06)	2-0546-80
$C_{10}H_8O_7$			
1,2,4-Benzenetricarboxylic acid, 6-methoxy-	pH 1	217(4.47),314(3.63)	94-3601-80
	pH 13	218(4.39),250s(--), 301(3.57)	94-3601-80
$C_{10}H_8S_2$			
2H-1-Benzothiopyran-2-thione, 4-methyl-	EtOH	234(4.59),302(4.23), 420(4.04)	18-2415-80
4H-1-Benzothiopyran-4-thione, 2-methyl-	EtOH	236(4.20),244(4.36), 293(3.88),412(4.32)	18-2415-80
$C_{10}H_8S_3$			
Dithieno[2,3-c:3',2'-e]thiepin, 4,6-dihydro-	heptane	215(4.32),237(4.20), 290(3.43),302s(3.15)	4-0321-80
	MeCN	212(4.29),237(4.23), 289(3.59),301s(3.35)	4-0321-80
Dithieno[3,2-c:2',3'-e]thiepin, 4,6-dihydro-	heptane	218s(3.96),254(3.79), 260s(3.79),281s(3.79), 308(3.89),325s(3.79)	4-0321-80
	MeCN	217s(3.97),255(3.76), 318(3.94),341s(3.67)	4-0321-80
4H,6H-Dithieno[3,4-c:3',4'-e]thiepin	heptane	210(--),257(--)	4-0321-80
	MeCN	210(4.41),255(4.01)	4-0321-80

Compound	Solvent	$\lambda_{max}(\log \epsilon)$	Ref.
$C_{10}H_9BrCl_2O$ Benzene, 2-bromo-1-[(2,2-dichlorocyclo-propyl)oxy]-4-methyl-	hexane	220s(--),265s(--), 270(3.08),276(3.08)	70-1928-80
$C_{10}H_9BrO_2$ 1,2-Naphthalenediol, 5-bromo-1,2-di-hydro-, cis	EtOH	220(4.30),224(4.30); 265(3.91)	39-1920-80C
C H Cl Benzene, 1-(1,3-butadienyl)-3-chloro-, (E)-	C_6H_{12}	217(4.22),224(4.20), 231(4.20),238(4.07), 275(4.42),281(4.43), 314(3.46)	39-0805-80B
Benzene, 1-(1,3-butadienyl)-4-chloro-, (E)-	C_6H_{12}	213(4.18),219(4.10), 226(4.04),233(3.82), 280(4.49),285(4.50), 312(3.82)	39-0805-80B
$C_{10}H_9ClN$ Quinolinium, 4-chloro-1-methyl-, methyl sulfate	EtOH	235(4.49),319(3.85)	22-0316-80
$C_{10}H_9ClN_2O$ 1(2H)-Isoquinolinone, 3-amino-6-chloro-2-methyl-	EtOH	240(4.28),313(4.00), 273(3.44)	95-0819-80
1(2H)-Isoquinolinone, 3-amino-7-chloro-2-methyl-	EtOH	226(4.30),312(4.17), 388(3.31)	95-0819-80
$C_{10}H_9ClN_2OS$ Benzamide, 2-chloro-N-(4,5-dihydro-2-thiazolyl)-	C_6H_{12} EtOH	272(--) 269(4.15)	150-4432-80 150-4432-80
Benzamide, 4-chloro-N-(4,5-dihydro-2-thiazolyl)-	C_6H_{12} EtOH	276(--) 277(4.33),<u>295s(4.2)</u>	150-4432-80 150-4432-80
Ethanone, 1-(6-chloro-2-methyl-1H-pyrido[2,3-b][1,4]thiazin-3-yl)-	n.s.g.	290(3.8),367(3.8)	103-0607-80
$C_{10}H_9ClN_4S$ 2-Thiazolamine, 5-[(4-chlorophenyl)-azo]-4-methyl-	EtOH	248(4.33),413(4.19)	4-1713-80
$C_{10}H_9Cl_2NO_3$ Acetic acid, chloro-, 2-[(chloro-acetyl)amino]phenyl ester	C_6H_{12}-CHCl$_3$	241(4.31)	44-1715-80
$C_{10}H_9F_2NO_5S$ Glycine, N-[4-[(difluoromethyl)sulfon-yl]benzoyl]-	H_2O	230(4.17)	103-0701-80
$C_{10}H_9N$ 1H-Indole, 5-ethenyl-	EtOH	246(4.62)	104-2236-80
1H-Pyrrole, 2-phenyl-	hexane	205(4.32),219(4.06), 222(4.04),237(3.97), 287(4.46),305(4.21)	103-0488-80
Quinoline, 6-methyl-	93.8% H$_2$SO$_4$	<u>241(4.6),315(3.9)</u>	94-3395-80
$C_{10}H_9NO$ Cyclohepta[b]pyrrol-4(1H)-one, 1-meth-yl-	n.s.g.	239(4.48),247(4.48), 312(4.03),373(3.96), 390s(--)	39-2081-80C

Compound	Solvent	$\lambda_{max}(\log \epsilon)$	Ref.
$C_{10}H_9NO_2$			
2H-1-Benzopyran-4-ol, 2-imino-3-methyl-	EtOH	307(4.07)	114-0271-80A
4H-1,3-Oxazin-5(6H)-one, 2-phenyl-	MeOH	207(4.15),238(4.08)	103-1000-80
2-Oxazolidinone, 4-(phenylmethylene)-, (Z)-	EtOH	268(4.39)	39-0858-80C
Phenol, 2-(4-methyl-5-isoxazolyl)-	EtOH	252(4.02),293(3.73)	114-0271-80A
$C_{10}H_9NO_2S$			
Benzoyl isothiocyanate, 4-ethoxy-	$CHCl_3$	305(4.38)	73-2334-80
$C_{10}H_9NO_3$			
Benzoic acid, 2-(cyanomethyl)-4-methoxy-	EtOH	255(4.16)	95-0819-80
Benzoic acid, 2-(cyanomethyl)-5-methoxy-	EtOH	233(3.88),298(3.39)	95-0819-80
1H-Indole-2,3-dione, 7-methoxy-4-methyl-	EtOH	222(4.3),330(3.8), 450(3.3)	78-2441-80
3H-Pyrrolizine-2-carboxylic acid, 3-oxo-, ethyl ester	EtOH	230(4.13),296(3.71), 448(3.16)	150-3090-80
$C_{10}H_9NO_3S$			
2H-Benzo[f][1,2]thiazepin-5-one, 2-methyl-, 1,1-dioxide	MeOH	306(3.83)	23-0369-80
2-Butenoic acid, 3-(2-furanyl)-4-thiocyanato-, methyl ester, (E)-	EtOH	213(4.10),317(4.39)	73-0142-80
$C_{10}H_9NO_4$			
1H-Indole-2,3-dione, 4,5-dimethoxy-	MeOH	250(4.23),320(3.47), 460(3.13)	150-4154-80
1H-Indole-2,3-dione, 4,6-dimethoxy-	EtOH	248(3.9),350(4.0)	78-2441-80
1H-Indole-2,3-dione, 4,7-dimethoxy-	EtOH	350(3.6),455(3.5)	78-2441-80
1H-Indole-2,3-dione, 5,6-dimethoxy-	MeOH	270(4.43),319(3.88), 460(3.20)	150-4154-80
	EtOH	262(4.3),317(3.8), 445(3.3)	78-2441-80
1H-Indole-2,3-dione, 6,7-dimethoxy-	EtOH	255(4.1),340(3.9)	78-2441-80
$C_{10}H_9NO_4S$			
Thieno[3,2-b]pyridine-6-carboxylic acid, 4,5-dihydro-7-hydroxy-5-oxo-, ethyl ester	EtOH	230(4.23),285(4.07), 296(4.12)	150-0113-80
$C_{10}H_9NO_5$			
1-Benzoxepin-5(2H)-one, 3,4-dihydro-2-hydroxy-4-nitro-	EtOH	238(3.71),298(3.22)	39-2049-80C
$C_{10}H_9NS_3$			
5(2H)-Isothiazolethione, 3-mercapto-4-(4-methylphenyl)-	$CHCl_3$	314(4.14),393(3.94)	39-2693-80C
2(3H)-Thiazolethione, 5-(methylthio)-4-phenyl-	EtOH	240(4.14),333(4.12)	150-4133-80
$C_{10}H_9N_2$			
Pyrazino[2,1,6-cd]pyrrolizinium, 2-methyl-, iodide	EtOH	237(4.60),260(4.25), 280s(3.73),288(3.70), 320(3.38),375(2.90)	39-1319-80C
$C_{10}H_9N_3$			
3-Pyridinamine, N-3-pyridinyl-	MeOH	254(3.72),280(4.16)	33-0456-80
2-Pyrimidinamine, N-phenyl-	C_6H_{12}	270(4.41),305s(3.40)	18-0717-80
	EtOH	273(4.33),307s(3.36)	18-0717-80

Compound	Solvent	$\lambda_{max}(\log \epsilon)$	Ref.
2-Pyrimidinamine, N-phenyl- (cont.)	MeCN	270(4.46),313s(3.40)	18-0717-80
$C_{10}H_9N_3O$ 1,2,4-Triazin-3(2H)-one, 2-methyl- 5-phenyl-	MeOH	215s(4.15),293(4.13)	44-4594-80
$C_{10}H_9N_3OS$ Ethanone, 1-(4,5-dihydro-5-imino- 4-phenyl-1,3,4-thiadiazol-2-yl)-	EtOH	216(4.05),245(4.04), 342(3.78)	4-1713-80
4-Imidazolidinone, 5-imino-3-methyl- 1-phenyl-2-thioxo-	EtOH	300(4.16)	18-0442-80
$C_{10}H_9N_3OS_2$ 1H-Thieno[3,4-b][1,4]diazepine-6-carbo- nitrile, 2,3-dihydro-4-methyl-8- (methylthio)-2-oxo-	EtOH	230(4.19),312(4.05)	95-0699-80
1H-Thieno[3,4-b][1,4]diazepine-8-carbo- nitrile, 2,3-dihydro-4-methyl-6- (methylthio)-2-oxo-	EtOH	253(4.11),280(4.17), 338(4.01)	95-0699-80
$C_{10}H_9N_3O_2$ 4,5-Isoxazoledione, 3-methyl-, 4-(phenylhydrazone)	MeOH MeOH-base?	381(4.36) 361(4.30)	4-0897-80 4-0897-80
1,3,5-Triazine-2,4(1H,3H)-dione, 3-methyl-6-phenyl-	EtOH-NaOH	251(4.30)	4-0673-80
1,3,5-Triazine-2,4(1H,3H)-dione, 6-methyl-3-phenyl-	EtOH-NaOH	253(3.95)	4-0673-80
$C_{10}H_9N_3O_2S_3$ Acetic acid, [(4-amino-5-cyanothieno- [2,3-c]isothiazol-3-yl)thio]-, ethyl ester	MeOH	267(4.27),295(3.99), 388(3.58)	48-1021-80
Acetic acid, [(4-amino-5-cyanothieno- [3,2-d]isothiazol-3-yl)thio]-, ethyl ester	MeOH	237(4.25),256(4.23), 298(3.97),317(3.82)	48-1021-80
$C_{10}H_9N_3O_3$ Pyrimido[1,6-a]pyrimidine-3-carboxylic acid, 4-oxo-, ethyl ester	CHCl$_3$	246(3.27),353(4.17), 364s(4.08)	94-2148-80
$C_{10}H_9N_3O_5$ L-Alanine, N-(5-benzofurazanylcarbo- nyl)-, N-oxide	EtOH	223(4.42),265s(3.01), 315s(3.34),332s(3.48), 366(3.82)	4-0213-80
	MeCN	222(4.50),266s(3.49), 315s(3.43),332s(3.59), 365(3.91)	4-0213-80
Glycine, N-(5-benzofurazanylcarbonyl)-, methyl ester, N-oxide	EtOH	222(4.45),265s(3.53), 315s(3.38),334s(3.53), 367(3.86)	4-0213-80
	MeCN	222(4.49),270s(3.46), 315s(3.38),332s(3.54), 364(3.86)	4-0213-80
1(2H)-Quinolinecarboxaldehyde, 3,4-di- hydro-6,8-dinitro-	EtOH	270(3.99),365(4.25), 410(4.03)	103-0386-80
$C_{10}H_9N_5$ [1,2,4]Triazolo[1,5-a]quinazolin- 5-amine, 2-methyl-	n.s.g.	218s(--),225(4.52), 262(3.85),286(3.64), 298(3.68),322(3.75)	33-0001-80

$C_{10}H_9N_5O_2S-C_{10}H_{10}Cl_3NO_2$

Compound	Solvent	$\lambda_{max}(\log \epsilon)$	Ref.
$C_{10}H_9N_5O_2S$			
2-Thiazolamine, 4-methyl-5-[(4-nitro-phenyl)azo]-	EtOH	252(4.31),410(4.38)	4-1713-80
$C_{10}H_{10}$			
Benzene, 1,3-butadienyl-, cis	CH_2Cl_2	270(4.30)	24-1663-80
Benzene, 1,3-butadienyl-, trans	CH_2Cl_2	274s(4.45),283(4.49), 295s(4.32),306s(3.93)	24-1663-80
Benzene, (1-methylene-2-propenyl)-	CH_2Cl_2	235s(4.11)	24-1663-80
Tricyclo[6.2.0.0^{2,5}]deca-1,5,7-triene	n.s.g.	266(3.13),269(3.14), 275(3.19)	44-4183-80
Tricyclo[6.2.0.0^{3,6}]deca-1,3(6),7-triene	n.s.g.	276(3.66),280(3.71), 286(3.59)	44-4183-80
$C_{10}H_{10}BrN$			
3H-Indole, 3-bromo-2,3-dimethyl-	CH_2Cl_2-Et$_3$N	285(3.46),291s(--)	23-0808-80
$C_{10}H_{10}Br_2N_2O_2$			
1H,5H-Pyrazolo[1,2-a]pyrazole-1,5-di-one, 3,7-bis(bromomethyl)-2,6-di-methyl-	dioxan	349(4.06)	35-4983-80
1H,7H-Pyrazolo[1,2-a]pyrazole-1,7-di-one, 3,5-bis(bromomethyl)-2,6-di-methyl-	dioxan	266(4.04),390(3.82)	35-4983-80
$C_{10}H_{10}ClN$			
3H-Indole, 3-chloro-2,3-dimethyl-	CH_2Cl_2	266(c.3.70),292s(--)	142-0867-80
	CH_2Cl_2-Et$_3$N	285(3.45),308s(--)	23-0808-80
$C_{10}H_{10}ClNO_3$			
Acetamide, N-(2-acetoxyphenyl)-2-chloro-	C_6H_{12}-CHCl$_3$	241(4.14)	44-1715-80
Acetic acid, chloro-, 2-(acetylamino)-phenyl ester	C_6H_{12}-CHCl$_3$	239(4.33),280(3.42)	44-1715-80
$C_{10}H_{10}ClN_5O$			
1,2,4-Triazine-3,5(2H,4H)-dione, 6-[(4-chlorophenyl)methyl]-, 3-hydrazone	EtOH	227(4.04),266(3.95)	12-0619-80
$C_{10}H_{10}Cl_2$			
Bicyclo[2.2.2]oct-2-ene, 5,6-bis(chloro-romethylene)-	EtOH	261(4.04)	88-3167-80
$C_{10}H_{10}Cl_2N_2O_2$			
Benzenemethanamine, N-(2,2-dichloro-cyclopropyl)-N-nitro-	EtOH	245(3.72)	104-0858-80
$C_{10}H_{10}Cl_2O$			
Benzene, [(2,2-dichlorocyclopropyl)-methoxy]-	hexane	219(4.11),265s(--), 270(3.26)	70-1928-80
Benzene, 1-[(2,2-dichlorocyclopropyl)-oxy]-2-methyl-	hexane	221(4.23),270(3.18), 276(3.18)	70-1928-80
Benzene, 1-[(2,2-dichlorocyclopropyl)-oxy]-4-methyl-	hexane	223(4.24),275(3.30), 281(3.28)	70-1928-80
3-Oxatricyclo[3.2.2.0^{2,4}]nonane, 6,7-bis(chloromethylene)-, (1α,2β,4β,5α,6E,7E)-	EtOH	260(4.00)	88-3167-80
$C_{10}H_{10}Cl_3NO_2$			
4-Cyclopentene-1,3-dione, 2,2,4-tri-	EtOH	291(4.18),353(4.02)	104-1404-80

$$C_{10}H_{10}Cl_3NO_2-C_{10}H_{10}N_2O_2 \qquad 117$$

Compound	Solvent	$\lambda_{max}(\log \epsilon)$	Ref.
chloro-5-piperidino- (cont.)			104-1404-80
$C_{10}H_{10}Cl_5NO$			
2-Cyclopenten-1-one, 2,4,4,5,5-penta-chloro-3-piperidino-	EtOH	333(4.45)	104-1404-80
Piperidine, 1-(2,3,4,5,5-pentachloro-1-oxo-2,4-pentadienyl)-	EtOH	223(4.29)	104-1404-80
$C_{10}H_{10}Fe$			
Ferrocene	C_6H_{12}	440(1.95)	101-0345-80J
$C_{10}H_{10}FeO_2$			
Iron, dicarbonyl[(η^5-cyclopentadien-1-ylidene)(1-methyl-1,2-ethanediyl)]-	hexane at -13°	269(3.8),360(2.9)	24-2211-80
$C_{10}H_{10}MnNO_3$			
Manganese, [(1,2,3,4,5-η)-1-(1-amino-ethyl)-2,4-cyclopentadien-1-yl]tri-carbonyl-	EtOH	330(3.05)	101-0301-80R
$C_{10}H_{10}N_2$			
7,8-Diazatetracyclo[4.3.3.0^{2,10}.0^{5,9}]-dodeca-3,7,11-triene	ether	342(2.03)	5-1428-80
2,3-Diazatricyclo[5.3.2.0^{4,10}]dodeca-2,5,8,11-tetraene	ether	340(1.93)	5-1428-80
Indeno[1,2-c]pyrazole, 1,3a,4,8b-tetra-hydro-, cis	MeOH	265(3.29),272(3.22)	44-3756-80
Indeno[1,2-c]pyrazole, 3,3a,4,8b-tetra-hydro-	MeOH	226(3.16),266(3.13), 327(2.63)	44-3756-80
1,4-Methano-1H-2,3-benzodiazepine, 4,5-dihydro-	MeOH	267(2.70),276(2.60), 340(2.00)	44-3756-80
1,8-Naphthalenediamine	CHCl$_3$	337(4.02)	104-1890-80
Propanedinitrile, (3-cyclopropyl-2-buten-1-ylidene)-, (E)-	n.s.g.	331(4.59)	35-0711-80
(Z)-	n.s.g.	331(4.51)	35-0711-80
$C_{10}H_{10}N_2O$			
2-Butanone, 1-diazo-4-phenyl-	MeOH	211(3.87),249(4.00), 268(3.95)	4-1081-80
8(1H)-Cycloheptapyrazolone, 1,3-di-methyl-	MeOH	235(4.33),303(3.89), 316(3.89),372(3.80)	18-1461-80
8(2H)-Cycloheptapyrazolone, 2,3-di-methyl-	MeOH	226(4.36),244(4.17), 252(4.04),290(3.72), 303(3.71),377(3.84)	18-1461-80
$C_{10}H_{10}N_2OS$			
Benzamide, N-(4,5-dihydro-2-thiazolyl)-	C_6H_{12}	275(--)	150-4432-80
	EtOH	275(4.20)	150-4432-80
4H-1,3-Thiazin-5(6H)-one, 2-(phenyl-amino)-	MeOH	208(4.18),229s(3.83), 269(3.90)	103-1003-80
$C_{10}H_{10}N_2O_2$			
Benzeneacetic acid, α-diazo-4-methyl-, methyl ester	C_6H_{12}	230(4.21),243s(4.15), 276(3.97),305s(3.69), 440(2.00)	33-0063-80
1(2H)-Isoquinolinone, 3-amino-6-meth-oxy-	EtOH	248(4.60),306(4.14), 354(3.58)	95-0819-80
1(2H)-Isoquinolinone, 3-amino-7-meth-oxy-	EtOH	226(4.29),295(4.18), 389(3.45)	95-0819-80
7H-Pyrrolo[2,3-b]pyridine-7-acetic acid, methyl ester	MeOH	226(4.05),301(3.76), 395(3.08)	48-0517-80

Compound	Solvent	λ_{max}(log ϵ)	Ref.
7H-Pyrrolo[2,3-b]pyridine-7-acetic acid, methyl ester, monohydrobromide	MeOH	226(4.21),299(3.95)	48-0517-80
$C_{10}H_{10}N_2O_2S_3$ 2-Propanone, 1-[(5-acetyl-4-amino-thieno[3,2-d]isothiazol-3-yl)thio]-	MeOH	246(4.09),264(4.19), 287(3.87),352(4.05)	48-1021-80
$C_{10}H_{10}N_2O_3$ 1(2H)-Quinolinecarboxaldehyde, 3,4-di-hydro-6-nitro-	EtOH	335(4.08)	103-0386-80
$C_{10}H_{10}N_2O_3S$ 4-Thiazolecarboxylic acid, 4,5-dihydro-2-(3-hydroxy-2-pyridinyl)-4-methyl-	H_2O	200(4.18),235s(3.73), 308(3.79),382(3.33)	33-1400-80
$C_{10}H_{10}N_2O_4S_3$ Thieno[3,2-d]isothiazole-5-carboxylic acid, 4-amino-3-[(2-methoxy-2-oxo-ethyl)thio]-, methyl ester	MeOH	241(4.22),258(4.25), 311(4.02),324(4.02)	48-1021-80
$C_{10}H_{10}N_2S$ 6-Thia-1,4-diazabicyclo[3.2.0]hept-4-ene, 7-phenyl-	EtOH	245(4.16),290(3.48)	88-0293-80
2H-[1,3]Thiazino[3,2-a]benzimidazole, 3,4-dihydro-	EtOH	218(4.46),255s(3.89), 263s(3.89),280s(3.92), 286(4.10),297(4.17)	4-0393-80
$C_{10}H_{10}N_4$ 2,2'-Bi-1H-imidazole, 1,1'-diethenyl-	EtOH	206(4.35),236(4.11), 286(4.07)	70-1655-80
2,2a,4,5-Tetraazabenzo[cd]azulene, 3,4-dihydro-1-methyl-	MeOH	222(4.37),293(3.58), 372(3.98)	118-0331-80
$C_{10}H_{10}N_4O_2$ Acetamide, N-(1,5-dihydro-5-oxo-3-phen-yl-4H-1,2,4-triazol-4-yl)-	EtOH	254(4.02)	4-1691-80
3H,8H-Imidazo[1,2,3-ij]pteridine-8,10(9H)-dione, 5,6-dihydro-2-methyl-3-methylene-	pH 0.0	246(4.16),370(4.06)	142-0437-80B
	pH 7.0	228(4.08),302(4.41), 355(3.60)	142-0437-80B
	pH 12.0	216(4.32),300(4.27), 363(3.75)	142-0437-80B
Pyrimido[4',5':4,5]pyrrolo[2,3-c]aze-pine-4,6-dione, 1,5,7,8,9,10-hexa-hydro-	pH 13	246(4.25),286(4.13)	103-0853-80
Sydnone, 3-(4-cyano-1-ethyl-1,4-di-hydro-3-pyridinyl)-	MeOH	240(3.81),260s(3.61), 330(3.46),360(3.46)	39-0020-80C
1H-1,2,4-Triazolium, 1-methyl-4-[(4-ni-trophenyl)methylide]	pH 13	524(3.98)	80-0407-80
3H-1,2,4-Triazol-3-one, 2-acetyl-4-ami-no-2,5-dihydro-5-phenyl-	EtOH	224(4.29),263(4.16)	4-1691-80
$C_{10}H_{10}N_4S$ 2-Thiazolamine, 4-methyl-5-(phenylazo)-	EtOH	243(4.32),395(4.47)	4-1713-80
$C_{10}H_{10}N_6$ 1H-Cyclohepta[1,2-d:4,5-d']diimidazole-2,6-diamine, 4-methyl-	MeOH	285(4.50),295(4.57), 405(4.18)	138-0205-80
[1,2,4]Triazolo[1,5-a]quinazolin-5(1H)-one, 2-methyl-, hydrazone	n.s.g.	216(4.53),283(3.59), 295(3.60),325(3.76)	33-0001-80
hydrochloride (2:1)	n.s.g.	216(4.58),283(3.63), 295(3.66),324(3.82)	33-0001-80

Compound	Solvent	$\lambda_{max}(\log \epsilon)$	Ref.
$C_{10}H_{10}N_6O$ 4(1H)-Pyrimidinone, 2,6-diamino-5- [(4-pyridinylmethylene)amino]-	pH 13	253(4.10),284(3.80), 388(4.24)	150-0549-80
$C_{10}H_{10}N_6O_4$ Imidazolidine, 2-[nitro[(4-nitrophenyl)azo]methylene]-	MeCN	241(3.97),330(4.03), 428(4.40)	48-0087-80
$C_{10}H_{10}N_8O_2$ 9H-Purin-6-amine, 9-(5-azido-2,3,5-trideoxy-β-D-glycero-pent-2-enofuranosyl)-	MeOH	260(4.13)	136-0067-80A
$C_{10}H_{10}O$ 1(2H)-Naphthalenone, 3,4-dihydro-	EtOH	248(4.10),291(3.20), 325s(2.78)	73-1950-80
7-Oxabicyclo[2.2.1]heptane, 2,3,5,6-tetrakis(methylene)-	isooctane	221(4.09),228(4.11), 238s(3.84),248s(3.72), 263(3.28)	33-1149-80
11-Oxatricyclo[4.2.2.1^{2,5}]undeca-3,7,9-triene	C_6H_{12}	284(3.08)	39-2174-80C
$C_{10}H_{10}O_2$ Benzoic acid, isopropenyl ester	C_6H_{12}	227(4.26),265(3.18)	39-1659-80B
1H-2-Benzopyran-1-one, 3,4-dihydro-3-methyl-	n.s.g.	225(4.89),255(4.3)	2-0009-80
1H-2-Benzopyran-1-one, 3,4-dihydro-5-methyl-	n.s.g.	225(4.71),255(4.37)	2-0009-80
1H-2-Benzopyran-1-one, 3,4-dihydro-6-methyl-	n.s.g.	226(5.26),261(4.5)	2-0009-80
1H-Inden-1-one, 2,3-dihydro-5-methoxy-	n.s.g.	266(3.32),287(3.19)	73-1950-80
1H-Inden-1-one, 2,3-dihydro-6-methoxy-	EtOH	219(4.29),248(3.95), 320(3.61)	73-1950-80
1,2-Naphthalenediol, 1,2-dihydro-, trans	EtOH	212(4.39),218(4.35), 263(3.88)	39-1920-80C
7-Oxatetracyclo[5.4.0.0^{3,10}.0^{4,8}]undec-5-en-2-one	pentane	287(1.56)	33-2019-80
2-Propenal, 3-(4-methoxyphenyl)-	EtOH	231(4.12),325(4.51)	118-0815-80
$C_{10}H_{10}O_3$ 1,3-Isobenzofurandione, 4,7-dihydro-5,6-dimethyl-	EtOH	244s(3.27)	24-0531-80
2,4-Pentadienoic acid, 5-(2-furanyl)-, methyl ester	n.s.g.	335(4.48)	39-2081-80C
$C_{10}H_{10}O_3W$ Tungsten, tricarbonylmethyl[(1,2,3,4,5-η)-1-methyl-2,4-cyclopentadien-1-yl]-	hexane	259s(3.85),315(3.36), 357s(3.04)	24-1033-80
$C_{10}H_{10}O_4$ 1,3-Benzodioxole-5,6-dione, 2-ethyl-2-methyl-	EtOH	293(4.23),395(3.23)	12-0527-80
1(3H)-Isobenzofuranone, 6,7-dimethoxy-	EtOH	221(4.42),260(4.04), 291s(3.18)	73-1950-80
2-Propenoic acid, 3-(4-hydroxy-3-methoxyphenyl)- (ferulic acid)	n.s.g.	350(4.43)	102-1349-80
Pyrenolide A	MeOH	222(3.83),245(3.86)	88-0301-80
$C_{10}H_{10}O_5$ 2,4-Cyclohexadien-1-one, 6,6-diacetoxy-	hexane	300(3.58),353(1.95), 358(1.99),366(1.98),	24-2227-80

Compound	Solvent	$\lambda_{max}(\log \epsilon)$	Ref.
2,4-Cyclohexadien-1-one, 6,6-diacetoxy- (cont.)	 MeOH CF_3CH_2OH	375(1.97),382(1.94) 306(3.55) 310(3.53)	24-2227-80 24-2227-80 24-2227-80
$C_{10}H_{10}Ru$ Ruthenocene	 hexane $C_2H_4Cl_2$	 218(3.68),238(3.36), 320(2.36) 237(3.58),322(2.37)	 44-2032-80 44-2032-80
dimer	hexane $C_2H_4Cl_2$	247(3.80),262(3.65), 320(2.79) 249(3.81),261(3.72), 322(2.83)	44-2032-80 44-2032-80
trimer	$C_2H_4Cl_2$	252(3.9),265(3.93), 322(3.02)	44-2032-80
tetramer	$C_2H_4Cl_2$	253(3.97),265(3.93), 323(3.11)	44-2032-80
$C_{10}H_{10}S_8$ 1,3-Dithiole-2-thione, 4,4'-dithiobis- [5-ethyl-	 EtOH	 232(4.43),372(4.52), 380(4.52)	 150-4133-80
$C_{10}H_{11}BrN_2O$ Benzamide, 4-bromo-N-[(dimethylamino)- methylene]-	 EtOH	 268(3.88)	 44-4522-80
$C_{10}H_{11}BrN_2O_2$ Hydroperoxide, 5-bromo-2,3-dihydro- 2-imino-1,3-dimethyl-1H-indol-3-yl 1H,5H-Pyrazolo[1,2-a]pyrazole-1,5-di- one, 3-(bromomethyl)-2,6,7-trimethyl- 1H,7H-Pyrazolo[1,2-a]pyrazole-1,7-di- one, 3-(bromomethyl)-2,5,6-trimethyl-	 n.s.g. dioxan dioxan	 262(4.02),297(3.2) 336(4.05) 248(4.13),377(3.85)	 103-0917-80 35-4983-80 35-4983-80
$C_{10}H_{11}BrO$ 2-Butanone, 1-bromo-4-phenyl-	 MeOH	 212(3.78)	 4-1081-80
$C_{10}H_{11}BrO_3$ 2H-1,5-Benzodioxepin, 6-bromo-3,4-di- hydro-9-methoxy- 2-Butenoic acid, 4-bromo-3-(2-furan- yl)-, ethyl ester	 EtOH EtOH	 213(4.20),234(3.91), 280(2.88) 224(3.69),320(4.20)	 103-0993-80 73-0142-80
$C_{10}H_{11}Br_3O$ Bicyclo[5.1.0]octa-2,4-diene, 4,8,8- tribromo-3-ethoxy- Bicyclo[5.1.0]octa-2,4-diene, 4,8,8- tribromo-3-methoxy-1-methyl-	 EtOH EtOH	 240(4.00),285(3.29) 240(3.98),285(3.27)	 39-2405-80C 39-2405-80C
$C_{10}H_{11}ClN_4O_5$ 6H-Purin-6-one, 9-β-D-arabinofuranosyl- 2-chloro-1,9-dihydro- 6H-Purin-6-one, 2-chloro-1,9-dihydro- 9-β-D-ribopyranosyl-	 pH 1 pH 13 pH 1 pH 7 pH 12	 253(4.08) 257(4.13) 247s(4.07),251(4.08) 255(4.12) 254(4.12)	 88-0479-80 88-0479-80 4-0461-80 4-0461-80 4-0461-80
$C_{10}H_{11}ClO_2$ 4H-1,3-Benzodioxin, 6-chloro-2,4-di- methyl- 3,5-Cyclohexadiene-1,2-dione, 3-chloro- 5-(1,1-dimethylethyl)-	 EtOH C_6H_{12}	 228(3.9),283(3.2) 390(c.3.42),408(3.13)	 118-0724-80 44-4210-80

Compound	Solvent	$\lambda_{max}(\log \epsilon)$	Ref.
$C_{10}H_{11}Cl_2NOS$ 2-Propanesulfenamide, N-(3,5-dichloro-4-oxo-2,5-cyclohexadien-1-ylidene)-2-methyl-	hexane	424(4.53)	18-0775-80
$C_{10}H_{11}Cl_2N_3O$ 1H-Benzotriazole, 1-butoxy-4,5-di-chloro-	EtOH	209(4.51),265(3.95), 272(3.98),294(3.87)	4-1115-80
$C_{10}H_{11}Cl_3O$ 7-Oxabicyclo[2.2.1]heptane, 2,3-bis-(chloromethyl)-5-(chloromethylene)-6-methylene-, (E)-	hexane	250(4.00)	88-3167-80
(Z)-	hexane	245(3.95)	88-3167-80
$C_{10}H_{11}F_3N_2O_5$ Thymidine, α,α,α-trifluoro-	MeOH MeOH-acid MeOH-base	262(3.97) 262(3.97) 260(3.81)	39-2755-80C 39-2755-80C 39-2755-80C
$C_{10}H_{11}F_3N_2O_6$ Uridine, 5-(trifluoromethyl)-	MeOH MeOH-acid MeOH-base	262(3.99) 262(4.00) 260(3.83)	39-2755-80C 39-2755-80C 39-2755-80C
$C_{10}H_{11}F_3N_2S$ Thiourea, N-[3-(trifluoromethyl)phen-yl]-N',N'-dimethyl-	HOAc MeCN	<u>280(3.1)</u> <u>284(3.3)</u>	140-1175-80 140-1175-80
$C_{10}H_{11}F_6NO_2$ 2,4-Pentanedione, 3-[(diethylamino)-methylene]-1,1,1,5,5,5-hexafluoro-	n.s.g.	284(4.36)	88-1027-80
$C_{10}H_{11}IO_3$ 2H-1,5-Benzodioxepin, 3,4-dihydro-6-iodo-9-methoxy-	EtOH	216(4.28),238(4.10), 278(3.03)	103-0993-80
$C_{10}H_{11}N$ 1H-Indole, 1,3-dimethyl-	EtOH	282(3.74),292(3.74)	44-0462-80
$C_{10}H_{11}NO$ 3H-Indol-3-ol, 2,3-dimethyl- 2-Propenal, 3-[(4-methylphenyl)amino]-	tert-BuOH 1% dioxan +HOAc-NaOAc	256(3.56),278s(3.45) <u>325(4.6)</u> <u>250(4.0)</u>	35-7559-80 94-2356-80 94-2356-80
$C_{10}H_{11}NO_2$ Acetamide, N-(2,6-dimethyl-4-oxo-2,5-cyclohexadien-1-ylidene)-	hexane	214(3.27),262s(4.41), 268(4.42)	87-1153-80
Acetamide, N-(3,5-dimethyl-4-oxo-2,5-cyclohexadien-1-ylidene)-	hexane	215(3.92),269s(4.40), 275(4.41)	87-1153-80
3-Buten-2-one, 4-[(2-hydroxyphenyl)-amino]-, (Z)-	dioxan	234(3.94),290(3.78), 348(4.37)	48-0099-80
Hydroperoxide, 2,3-dimethyl-3H-indol-3-yl-	tert-BuOH	258(3.57),280s(3.48)	35-7559-80
$C_{10}H_{11}NO_3$ Acetamide, N-(2-acetoxyphenyl)-	C_6H_{12}-CHCl$_3$	240(4.13)	44-1715-80
$C_{10}H_{11}NO_4$ Benzeneacetic acid, 4-nitro-, ethyl ester (enolate anion)	DMSO	548(4.52),580(4.48)	18-1656-80

$C_{10}H_{11}NO_4-C_{10}H_{11}N_3S$

Compound	Solvent	$\lambda_{max}(\log \epsilon)$	Ref.
Benzoic acid, 4-(formylhydroxyamino)-, ethyl ester	EtOH	281(4.25)	44-2834-80
Glycine, N-(4-methoxybenzoyl)-	H_2O	250(4.27)	103-0701-80
$C_{10}H_{11}NO_4S$			
Benzenesulfonic acid, 5-methyl-2-[(3-oxo-1-propenyl)amino]-, monosodium salt	82.3% H_2SO_4	250(3.9),320(4.3)	94-3395-80
1-Propene-2-sulfonic acid, 1-[(4-methylphenyl)amino]-3-oxo-, monosodium salt	99.4% H_2SO_4	250(4.1),325(4.2) (changing)	94-3395-80
$C_{10}H_{11}NO_5$			
2H-1,5-Benzodioxepin, 3,4-dihydro-6-methoxy-8-nitro-	EtOH	206(4.16),223(4.11), 240(3.77),330(3.81)	103-0993-80
1H-Pyrrole-3,4-dicarboxylic acid, 1-acetyl-, dimethyl ester	MeOH	249(3.96)	44-4573-80
$C_{10}H_{11}NO_6$			
2-Oxa-7-azaspiro[4.5]decane-10-carboxylic acid, 1,6,8-trioxo-, methyl ester	MeOH	211(4.34)	118-0698-80
$C_{10}H_{11}NO_7S_2$			
Benzenesulfonic acid, 5-methyl-2-[(3-oxo-2-sulfo-1-propenyl)amino]-	82.3% H_2SO_4	250(3.9),325(4.3) (changing)	94-3395-80
$C_{10}H_{11}NS$			
1H-Indole, 2-methyl-3-(methylthio)-	H_2O	280(3.83),285(3.79)	44-0780-80
	dioxan	272(3.95)	44-0780-80
Sulfonium, 1H-indol-3-yldimethyl-, hydroxide, inner salt	H_2O	261(3.79)	44-0780-80
	dioxan	262(3.86)	44-0780-80
$C_{10}H_{11}N_3O$			
Benzeneacetamide, α-diazo-N,N-dimethyl-	C_6H_{12}	261(4.21),280(4.11), 302(3.59),440(2.04)	33-0063-80
3H-Pyrido[1,2-c]pyrimidine-4-carbonitrile, 5,6,7,8-tetrahydro-1-methyl-3-oxo-	pH 13	292(4.11)	103-0873-80
1,2,4-Triazine, 2,5-dihydro-3-methoxy-5-phenyl-	EtOH	258(3.04)	44-4594-80
1,2,4-Triazine, 4,5-dihydro-3-methoxy-5-phenyl-	EtOH	264(3.90),287(3.72)	44-4594-80
$C_{10}H_{11}N_3O_2$			
1H-Benzimidazole, 1-ethyl-2-methyl-7-nitro-	pH 1	235s(3.66),290(3.77)	104-1458-80
1(2H)-Isoquinolinone, 2,3-diamino-6-methoxy-	EtOH	249(4.44),295(3.94), 350(3.46)	95-0819-80
1(2H)-Isoquinolinone, 2,3-diamino-7-methoxy-	EtOH	229(4.27),295(4.11), 389(3.44)	95-0819-80
$C_{10}H_{11}N_3O_2S$			
1H-Imidazole, 4,5-dihydro-2-[[(4-nitrophenyl)methyl]thio]-	MeOH	270(4.01)	78-2675-80
$C_{10}H_{11}N_3S$			
1,2,4-Triazine, 2,5-dihydro-3-(methylthio)-5-phenyl-	EtOH	240s(3.68)	44-4594-80
1,2,4-Triazine, 4,5-dihydro-3-(methylthio)-5-phenyl-	EtOH	235(3.91),286s(3.78)	44-4594-80

Compound	Solvent	$\lambda_{max}(\log \epsilon)$	Ref.
$C_{10}H_{11}N_4O$			
1,2,4,5-Tetrazin-1(2H)-yl, 3,4-dihydro-2,4-dimethyl-3-oxo-6-phenyl-	dioxan	248(4.46),413(3.21), 492(2.68)	89-0724-80
$C_{10}H_{11}N_4O_2$			
1H-1,2,4-Triazolium, 1-methyl-4-[(4-nitrophenyl)methyl]-, bromide	MeOH	258(4.03)	80-0407-80
$C_{10}H_{11}N_4O_7PS$			
8,2'-S-Cycloinosine 3'-phosphate	pH 2	263.5(4.23)	94-3621-80
	pH 7	264(4.23)	94-3621-80
	pH 12	266(4.24)	94-3621-80
8,2'-S-Cycloinosine 5'-phosphate	pH 2	263.5(4.21)	94-3621-80
	pH 7	264(4.21)	94-3621-80
	pH 12	266(4.22)	94-3621-80
$C_{10}H_{11}N_5O$			
2-Propenenitrile, 3-amino-3-[(2-aminophenyl)amino]-2-[(hydroxyimino)methyl]-	MeOH	211(4.16),220(4.15), 245(4.12),264(4.21), 294(3.79)	94-0567-80
1,2,4-Triazine-3,5(2H,4H)-dione, 6-(phenylmethyl)-, 3-hydrazone	EtOH	220(3.98),264(3.92)	12-0619-80
$C_{10}H_{11}N_5O_2$			
Imidazolidine, 2-[nitro(phenylazo)methylene]-	MeCN	242(4.11),247s(4.05), 335(4.25),378(4.37)	48-0087-80
$C_{10}H_{11}N_5O_3$			
2,5'-Anhydroformycin	pH 1	231(--),260(3.75), 304(4.05)	35-2817-80
	pH 11	234s(3.99),305(4.10)	35-2817-80
4,5'-Anhydroformycin	pH 1	245(3.90),304(4.16)	35-2817-80
	pH 11	253(4.00),272(3.99), 317(3.90)	35-2817-80
5',8-Cycloadenosine, 5'-deoxy-	EtOH	264(4.08)	78-1579-80
$C_{10}H_{11}N_5O_3Se$			
Furo[2'',3'':4',5']selenazolo[2',3':2,3]-imidazo[4,5-c]pyridazine-8-methanol, 4-amino-6a,7,8,9a-tetrahydro-7-hydroxy-, [6aS-(6aα,7α,8β,9aα)]-	pH 1	283(4.33)	142-0345-80B
	H_2O	277(4.34)	142-0345-80B
	pH 11	277(4.34)	142-0345-80B
$C_{10}H_{11}N_5O_4$			
Adenosine, 2',3'-anhydro-, 1-oxide	MeOH	233(4.60),261(3.90), 299(3.36)	44-0788-80
	MeOH-HCl	258(4.10)	44-0788-80
	MeOH-NaOH	231(4.41),267(3.90), 310(3.59)	44-0788-80
$C_{10}H_{11}N_7$			
Pyrimidinetetramine, N^5-(4-pyridinylmethylene)-	EtOH	265(4.16),391(4.21)	150-0549-80
$C_{10}H_{11}N_{11}O_2$			
Adenosine, 3',5'-diazido-3',5'-dideoxy-	pH 7	259(4.17)	118-0559-80
$C_{10}H_{12}$			
1,3,5,7,9-Decapentaene	isooctane	334(5.08)	5-2039-80
$C_{10}H_{12}BrN$			
Benzenamine, 4-(1-bromoethenyl)-N,N-di-	n.s.g.	307(4.18)	88-4241-80

Compound	Solvent	$\lambda_{max}(\log \epsilon)$	Ref.
methyl- (cont.)			88-4241-80
$C_{10}H_{12}BrNO_3$			
α-D-erythro-Hept-5-eno-1,4-furanurono-	EtOH	228(3.96)	136-0187-80H
nitrile, 6-bromo-3,5,6-trideoxy-1,2-			
O-(1-methylethylidene)-, (E)-			
(Z)-	EtOH	223(3.97)	136-0187-80H
$C_{10}H_{12}Br_2O$			
2-Cyclohexen-1-one, 5-bromo-2-(2-bromo-	MeOH	275(3.62)	44-3401-80
ethenyl)-4,4-dimethyl-, (E)-			
$C_{10}H_{12}ClN_5O_2$			
Hydrazinecarboxamide, N-[3-(4-chloro-	EtOH	225(4.11),264(3.93)	12-0619-80
phenyl)-2-hydrazono-1-oxopropyl]-			
$C_{10}H_{12}Cl_2O$			
2,4-Cyclohexadien-1-one, 6-(dichloro-	hexane	314(3.69),364(2.43),	24-2227-80
methyl)-2,4,6-trimethyl-		385(2.21),403(1.73)	
	MeOH	317(3.62)	24-2227-80
	CF_3CH_2OH	323(3.61)	24-2227-80
$C_{10}H_{12}FN_3O_5$			
β-Alanine, N-[(5-fluoro-3,4-dihydro-	MeOH	271(3.92)	94-1137-80
2,4-dioxo-1(2H)-pyrimidinyl)carbo-			
nyl]-, ethyl ester			
$C_{10}H_{12}F_3NO$			
Ethanone, 1-[5-(1,1-dimethylethyl)-1H-	hexane	253(3.63),310(4.36)	103-0488-80
pyrrol-2-yl]-2,2,2-trifluoro-			
$C_{10}H_{12}F_3N_3O_4$			
Cytidine, 2'-deoxy-5-(trifluoromethyl)-	MeOH	270(3.85)	39-2755-80C
	MeOH-acid	283(4.11)	39-2755-80C
	MeOH-base	274(3.87)	39-2755-80C
$C_{10}H_{12}F_3N_3O_5$			
Cytidine, 5-(trifluoromethyl)-	MeOH	270(3.85)	39-2755-80C
	MeOH-acid	283(4.11)	39-2755-80C
	MeOH-base	274(3.87)	39-2755-80C
2(1H)-Pyrimidinone, 4-amino-1-β-D-ara-	MeOH	271(3.86)	39-2755-80C
binofuranosyl-5-(trifluoromethyl)-	MeOH-acid	283(4.11)	39-2755-80C
	MeOH-base	278(3.91)	39-2755-80C
$C_{10}H_{12}NO$			
Furo[3,2-c]pyridinium, 4-ethyl-5-meth-	MeOH	212(4.61),253(3.87),	83-0809-80
yl-, iodide		284(3.73)	
$C_{10}H_{12}NS$			
Sulfonium, 1H-indol-3-yldimethyl-,	H_2O	260(3.74)	44-0780-80
iodide	dioxan	279(3.75)	44-0780-80
$C_{10}H_{12}N_2$			
Benzo[b]-1,4-diazabicyclo[2.2.2]octene	pH 1	210(4.20),256(2.34),	103-0645-80
		264(2.20)	
	0.1M NH_3	204(3.95),258(2.57),	103-0645-80
		265(2.45)	
Pyridine, 3-(2,5-dihydro-1-methyl-1H-	EtOH	212(3.57),243(3.59)	39-0579-80C
pyrrol-2-yl)-			

Compound	Solvent	$\lambda_{max}(\log \epsilon)$	Ref.
$C_{10}H_{12}N_2O$			
2-Pyrrolidinone, 1-methyl-5-(3-pyridinyl)-	MeOH	212(3.77),263(3.60)	39-0579-80C
$C_{10}H_{12}N_2O_2$			
Benzeneacetic acid, α-(methylhydrazono)-, methyl ester, anti	EtOH	217s(3.97),273(3.98)	33-0063-80
syn	EtOH	235(4.08),302(3.95)	33-0063-80
Hydroperoxide, 2,3-dihydro-2-imino-1,3-dimethyl-1H-indol-3-yl	n.s.g.	264(4.1),297(3.4)	103-0917-80
1H,5H-Pyrazolo[1,2-a]pyrazole-1,5-dione, 2,3,6,7-tetramethyl-	dioxan	322(4.18)	35-4983-80
1H,7H-Pyrazolo[1,2-a]pyrazole-1,7-dione, 2,3,5,6-tetramethyl-	dioxan	235(4.16),255s(3.72), 359(3.81)	35-4983-80
1H-Pyrazolo[1,2-a]pyrazol-4-ium, 2-ethyl-3-hydroxy-5,7-dimethyl-1-oxo-, hydroxide, inner salt	MeCN	215(3.999),230s(3.972), 245s(3.95),260s(3.766), 397(3.066)	64-1002-80B
Quinoline, 1,2,3,4-tetrahydro-1-methyl-8-nitro-	EtOH	255(4.20),295(3.60), 433(3.48)	103-0386-80
$C_{10}H_{12}N_2O_3$			
Acetamide, N,N'-(4-hydroxy-1,2-phenylene)bis-	EtOH	220(3.30),245(3.00)	103-0628-80
1-Propanone, 2-amino-2-methyl-1-(3-nitrophenyl)-, monohydrochloride	EtOH	208(4.2),254(3.9)	5-1016-80
$C_{10}H_{12}N_2O_3S$			
2(1H)-Pyrimidinone, 3,4-dihydro-5-methyl-1-(tetrahydro-5-methyl-2-oxo-3-furanyl)-4-thioxo-	pH 2	245(3.60),338(4.28)	103-0864-80
	pH 7	245(3.56),338(4.28)	103-0864-80
	pH 11	324(4.24)	103-0864-80
$C_{10}H_{12}N_2O_3S_4$			
4-Thia-1-azabicyclo[3.2.0]hept-2-ene-2-carboxylic acid, 3-[[3-[(aminothioxomethyl)thio]propyl]thio]-7-oxo-, sodium salt	H_2O	247(3.92),275(4.00), 321(3.87)	94-3258-80
$C_{10}H_{12}N_2O_4$			
1,4-Diazocine-1,4-dicarboxylic acid, dimethyl ester	MeCN	224(4.32),274s(3.25)	24-3161-80
2-Propenoic acid, 2-(3,4-dihydro-5-methyl-2,4-dioxo-1(2H)-pyrimidinyl)ethyl ester	EtOH	270(3.94)	47-0427-80
4H-Pyrazolo[5,1-c][1,4]oxazine-3-carboxylic acid, 6,7-dihydro-2-methyl-6-oxo-, ethyl ester	EtOH	237(3.89)	118-0875-80
$(C_{10}H_{12}N_2O_4)_n$			
2-Propenoic acid, 2-(3,4-dihydro-5-methyl-2,4-dioxo-1(2H)-pyrimidinyl)ethyl ester, polymer	DMF	270.5(3.91)	47-0427-80
$C_{10}H_{12}N_2O_4S_2$			
4-Thia-1-azabicyclo[3.2.0]hept-2-ene-2-carboxylic acid, 3-[[2-(acetylamino)ethyl]thio]-7-oxo-, (R)-, monosodium salt	H_2O	253(3.58),320(3.70)	94-3232-80
	EtOH	254(3.77),328(3.85)	33-1093-80
$C_{10}H_{12}N_2O_5$			
Formamide, N-[2-hydroxy-1-(hydroxymethyl)-2-(4-nitrophenyl)ethyl]-	pH 7	276(3.94)	87-1299-80

Compound	Solvent	$\lambda_{max}(\log \epsilon)$	Ref.
2-Furancarboxylic acid, 5-(acetylamino)-4-(formylamino)-, ethyl ester	MeOH	220(4.26),293(4.07)	73-0135-80
5-Pyrimidinecarboxylic acid, 1,2,3,4-tetrahydro-2,4-dioxo-3-(tetrahydro-2H-pyran-2-yl)-	EtOH	220(3.93),280(3.98)	142-0769-80
$C_{10}H_{12}N_2O_5S$			
$S^6,2'$-Cyclo-2-O-methyluridine	H_2O	215(4.25),273(4.21), 280s(4.17)	94-0939-80
$C_{10}H_{12}N_2S$			
2-Pyrrolidinethione, 1-methyl-5-(3-pyridinyl)-	MeOH	206(3.57),269(4.00)	39-0579-80C
$C_{10}H_{12}N_4O$			
3H-1,2,4-Triazol-3-one, 4-amino-2-ethyl-2,4-dihydro-5-phenyl-	n.s.g.	262?(4.12)	4-1691-80
$C_{10}H_{12}N_4O_2$			
1(2H)-Isoquinolinone, 2-amino-3-hydrazino-6-methoxy-	EtOH	249(4.59),307(4.12), 346(3.61)	95-0819-80
1(2H)-Isoquinolinone, 2-amino-3-hydrazino-7-methoxy-	EtOH	227(4.41),295(4.08), 380(3.50)	95-0819-80
2,4(1H,3H)-Pteridinedione, 1,3,6,7-tetramethyl-	pH -4.0	251(4.28),290s(3.25), 358(3.94)	142-0437-80B
	pH 1.0	235(4.21),253s(3.91), 332(3.98)	142-0437-80B
$C_{10}H_{12}N_4O_3$			
2,4(1H,3H)-Pteridinedione, 1-(2-hydroxyethyl)-6,7-dimethyl-	pH 5.0	228s(4.06),250(3.94), 332(3.94)	142-0437-80B
	pH 12.0	212(4.11),243(4.22), 277(3.40),338(3.97)	142-0437-80B
[1,2,4]Triazolo[1,5-a]pyrimidine-6-carboxylic acid, 3-ethyl-3,7-dihydro-7-oxo-, ethyl ester	EtOH	253(3.83),303(4.19)	39-1347-80C
[1,2,4]Triazolo[1,5-a]pyrimidine-6-carboxylic acid, 4-ethyl-4,7-dihydro-7-oxo-, ethyl ester	EtOH	252(3.95),290(4.11)	39-1347-80C
$C_{10}H_{12}N_4O_3S$			
4(1H)-Pteridinone, 6-(1,2-dihydroxypropyl)-2-(methylthio)-	pH -3.05	280(4.15),300s(4.11), 386(3.81)	18-2344-80
	pH 3.0	231(3.99),282(4.21), 336(3.85)	18-2344-80
	pH 9.0	247(4.03),269(4.32), 353(3.86)	18-2344-80
$C_{10}H_{12}N_4O_4$			
Quinoxaline, 1,2,3,4-tetrahydro-1,4-dimethyl-5,7-dinitro-	DMSO	279(4.12),330(3.93), 448(4.06)	39-2205-80C
D-Ribose, 5-deoxy-5-(9H-purin-9-yl)-	H_2O	264.0(3.84)	130-0423-80
$C_{10}H_{12}N_4O_4S$			
4(1H)-Pteridinone, 2-(methylthio)-6-(1,2,3-trihydroxypropyl)-, [R-(R*,S*)]-	pH -3.05	289(4.17),300s(4.13), 386(3.84)	18-2344-80
	pH 3.0	230(3.96),282(4.24), 336(3.90)	18-2344-80
	pH 9.0	244(4.04),270(4.35), 353(3.39)	18-2344-80

Compound	Solvent	λ_{max}(log ϵ)	Ref.
4(1H)-Pteridinone, 2-(methylthio)-6-(1,2,3-trihydroxypropyl)-, [S-(R*,S*)]-	pH -3.05	289(4.19),300s(4.15), 386(3.87)	18-2344-80
	pH 3.0	230(3.95),282(4.22), 336(3.89)	18-2344-80
	pH 9.0	244(4.04),270(4.36), 353(3.90)	18-2344-80
$C_{10}H_{12}N_4O_5$ 6H-Purin-6-one, 1,9-dihydro-9-β-D-ribopyranosyl-	pH 1	248(4.09)	4-0461-80
	pH 13	252(4.11)	4-0461-80
$C_{10}H_{12}N_4O_6$ 6H-Furo[2',3':4,5]oxazolo[3,2-a]pyrimidine-8-carboxylic acid, 2,3,3a,9a-tetrahydro-3-hydroxy-2-(hydroxymethyl)-6-oxo-, hydrazide, [2R-(2α,3β,3aβ,9aβ)]-	pH 5.6	263(3.99)	145-2087-80
$C_{10}H_{12}N_4S_4$ Carbamodithioic acid, dimethyl-, 1,2-dicyano-1,2-ethenediyl ester	EtOH	236(4.38),277(4.25), 300s(3.80),400(3.31)	44-5113-80
$C_{10}H_{12}N_5O_6PS$ Guanosine, 2-thio-, cyclic 3',5'-(hydrogen phosphate)	pH 1	233(4.16),291(4.32)	94-0115-80
	pH 13	242(4.32),284(4.21)	94-0115-80
$C_{10}H_{12}N_5O_9PS$ 9H-Purine-2-sulfonic acid, 6-amino-9-(3,5-O-phosphinico-β-D-ribofuranosyl)-	pH 1	261.5(4.13)	94-0115-80
	pH 13	262.0(4.13)	94-0115-80
$C_{10}H_{12}N_6O$ 4(1H)-Pyrimidinone, 2,6-diamino-5-[(4-pyridinylmethyl)amino]-	pH 13	266(3.98)	150-0549-80
$C_{10}H_{12}N_8O_4$ Uridine, 5'-azido-5-(azidomethyl)-2',5'-dideoxy-	pH 2	265(4.02)	87-0127-80
$C_{10}H_{12}O$ Benzo[3,4]cyclobuta[1,2-b]furan, 2,3,3a,3b,7a,7b-hexahydro-	C_6H_{12}	277(3.32)	39-0869-80C
1(2H)-Naphthalenone, 4a,5,8,8a-tetrahydro-	C_6H_{12}	276(2.42)	88-2799-80
$C_{10}H_{12}OS$ Benzene, (2-butenylsulfinyl)-(3:1 E:Z)-	MeOH	244(3.70),271s(3.11)	12-2635-80
Benzene, 1-methoxy-4-(2-propenylthio)-	MeOH	234(4.02),259(3.84), 283s(3.18)	12-1345-80
Benzene, [(1-methyl-2-propenyl)sulfinyl]-	MeOH	247(3.66)	12-2635-80
Benzene, 1-methyl-4-(2-propenylsulfinyl)-	MeOH	220s(4.00),243(3.78)	12-2635-80
1-Propene, 2-methyl-3-(phenylsulfinyl)-	MeOH	244(3.63)	12-2635-80
$C_{10}H_{12}O_2$ Acetaldehyde, (5,5-dimethyl-4-oxo-2-cyclohexen-1-ylidene)-, (E)-	MeOH	277(4.03)	44-3401-80
(Z)-	MeOH	282(3.83)	44-3401-80
4H-1,3-Benzodioxin, 2,4-dimethyl-	EtOH	273(3.3),280(3.3)	118-0724-80

Compound	Solvent	$\lambda_{max}(\log \epsilon)$	Ref.
4H-1-Benzopyran-4-one, 5,6,7,8-tetra-hydro-2-methyl-	EtOH	252(3.75)	94-2460-80
1-Propanone, 1-(2-hydroxy-5-methyl-phenyl)-	EtOH	254(3.97),337(3.58)	90-0431-80
$C_{10}H_{12}O_2S$			
Benzene, 1-methoxy-4-(2-propenylsul-finyl)-	MeOH	233s(3.97),249(4.07), 275(3.43),283(3.18)	12-2635-80
$C_{10}H_{12}O_2S_2$			
2,5-Cyclohexadiene-1,4-dione, 2,5-di-methyl-3,6-bis(methylthio)-	EtOH	247(4.17),271s(3.64), 380(3.72)	39-0289-80C
2,5-Cyclohexadiene-1,4-dione, 2,6-di-methyl-3,5-bis(methylthio)-	EtOH	247(3.99),267s(3.61), 375(3.57),456s(3.03)	39-0289-80C
$C_{10}H_{12}O_3$			
Benzeneacetic acid, 3-methoxy-, methyl ester	MeOH	208(3.89),217s(3.84), 274(3.21),281s(3.14)	98-0071-80
2H-1,5-Benzodioxepin, 3,4-dihydro-6-methoxy-	EtOH	207(4.07),224(3.65), 273(2.85)	103-0993-80
1,3-Benzodioxol-5-ol, 2-ethyl-2-methyl-	EtOH	236(3.48),299(3.71)	12-0527-80
2,4-Cyclohexadien-1-one, 6-acetoxy-2,6-dimethyl-	C_6H_{12}	300(3.73),355(2.48), 369(2.49),386(2.32)	24-2227-80
	MeOH	304.5(3.69)	24-2227-80
	EtOH	305(--)	24-2227-80
	CF_3CH_2OH	306(3.66)	24-2227-80
2,4-Cyclohexadien-1-one, 6-acetoxy-3,6-dimethyl-	C_6H_{12}	292(3.70),360(2.30)	24-2227-80
	hexane	290(3.74)	24-2227-80
	MeOH	299(3.69)	24-2227-80
	EtOH	298(3.73)	24-2227-80
	CF_3CH_2OH	300.5(3.69)	24-2227-80
2,4-Cyclohexadien-1-one, 6-acetoxy-4,6-dimethyl-	C_6H_{12}	301(3.62),358(2.50), 373(2.51)	24-2227-80
	MeOH	305.5(3.57)	24-2227-80
	CF_3CH_2OH	309.5(3.55)	24-2227-80
2,4-Cyclohexadien-1-one, 6-acetoxy-5,6-dimethyl-	C_6H_{12}	302(3.77),356(2.65), 373(2.67)	24-2227-80
	MeOH	307.5(3.71)	24-2227-80
	CF_3CH_2OH	311(3.68)	24-2227-80
Ethanone, 1-[4-(2-hydroxyethoxy)phen-yl]-	$CHCl_3$	270(4.48),323(2.48)	73-1826-80
2,7-Oxepindione, 4-(1,1-dimethylethyl)-	C_6H_{12}	260(3.60)	44-1153-80
Phenol, 4-(3-hydroxy-1-propenyl)-2-methoxy-	MeOH	266(4.06)	98-0427-80
	n.s.g.	325(3.85)	102-1349-80
Propanoic acid, 2-methoxy-, phenyl ester	MeCN	200(3.85),254s(2.28), 260(2.34),266(2.15)	108-0142-80
$C_{10}H_{12}O_3S$			
Benzene, 1-methoxy-4-(2-propenylsul-fonyl)-	MeOH	243(4.27),268s(3.20)	12-2635-80
Benzenesulfinic acid, 4-methoxy-, 2-propenyl ester	MeOH	240(4.03),249(4.04)	12-2635-80
$C_{10}H_{12}O_4$			
Benzoic acid, 3,5-dimethoxy-4-methyl-	EtOH	210(4.54),256(3.96), 298(3.36)	118-0409-80
1,5-Epoxy-1H-2,6-dioxacyclopent[cd]-indene-4-methanol, 2a,4a,5,7,7a,7b-hexahydro-	MeOH	204(3.70)	78-1613-80
4H-Pyran-2-acetic acid, 6-methyl-4-oxo-, ethyl ester	EtOH	281(3.73)	39-2272-80C

Compound	Solvent	$\lambda_{max}(\log \epsilon)$	Ref.
1H,3H-Pyrano[3,4-c]pyran-5-carboxalde- hyde, 4,4a,5,6-tetrahydro-6-methyl- 1-oxo- (naucledal)	n.s.g.	246(3),285s(3)	100-0649-80
$C_{10}H_{12}O_5$ 1H,6H-Pyrano[3,4-c]pyran-1,6-dione, 5-ethyl-3,4,5,8-tetrahydro-5-hydroxy- (gentiolactonè)	MeOH	228(3.74)	100-0649-80
$C_{10}H_{12}S$ Benzene, (2-butenylthio)-	MeOH	240(3.86)	12-1345-80
Benzene, [(1-methyl-2-propenyl)thio]-	MeOH	254(3.67)	12-1345-80
Benzene, [(2-methyl-2-propenyl)thio]-	MeOH	253(3.81)	12-1345-80
Benzene, 1-methyl-4-(2-propenylthio)-	MeOH	255(3.90)	12-1345-80
$C_{10}H_{12}S_4$ 1,3-Dithiole, 2-(4,5-dimethyl-1,3-di- thiol-2-ylidene)-4,5-dimethyl-	$C_2H_4Cl_2$	287s(4.08),297s(4.11), 315(4.15),327(4.14), 473(2.40)	11-0196-80A
complex with tetrafluoroborate (17:8)	MeCN	297s(--),310(4.16), 325(4.17),390s(--), 420s(--),459(4.09), 525(3.26),650(3.67)	11-0196-80A
$C_{10}H_{13}BrN_2O_5$ Uridine, 5-bromo-2'-deoxy-6-methyl-	pH 2	280(4.04)	73-2364-80
	pH 7	280(4.04)	73-2364-80
	pH 12	280(3.86)	73-2364-80
$C_{10}H_{13}BrO_2$ 3(2H)-Benzofuranone, 6-bromo-5,6,7,7a- tetrahydro-5,5-dimethyl-, trans-(-)-	MeOH	234(3.92)	44-3401-80
4(2H)-Benzofuranone, 6-bromo-5,6,7,7a- tetrahydro-5,5-dimethyl-, trans-(-)-	MeOH	253(3.72)	44-3401-80
$C_{10}H_{13}Br_2Cl$ Cyclohexene, 4-bromo-1-(2-bromoethen- yl)-6-chloro-5,5-dimethyl-, [1(E),4α,6β]-(+)-	MeOH	242(3.72)	44-3401-80
$C_{10}H_{13}Br_2ClO$ 2-Cyclohexen-1-one, 5-bromo-2-(2-bromo- 1-chloroethyl)-4,4-dimethyl-	MeOH	235(3.94)	44-3401-80
$C_{10}H_{13}ClN_2O_2$ 3(2H)-Pyridazinone, 4-chloro-2-cyclo- hexyl-5-hydroxy-	MeOH	217(4.53),227s(--), 280(3.92)	73-0127-80
$C_{10}H_{13}ClN_6O_3$ 1,2-Cyclopentanediol, 3-(5-amino-7- chloro-3H-1,2,3-triazolo[4,5-d]- pyrimidin-3-yl)-5-(hydroxymethyl)-, (1α,2β,3α,5β)-(±)-	pH 1	223(4.43),314(3.88)	36-1019-80
	H_2O	223(4.36),314(3.88)	36-1019-80
	pH 13	276(4.09)	36-1019-80
$C_{10}H_{13}ClO$ 2,4,6-Octatrienal, 8-chloro-2,7-di- methyl-, (E,E,E)-	EtOH	326(4.67)	33-1473-80
$C_{10}H_{13}ClO_3$ Cyclopenta[c]pyran-4-carboxylic acid, 1-chloro-1,4a,5,6,7,7a-hexahydro-,	MeOH	237(4.06)	78-1231-80

Compound	Solvent	$\lambda_{max}(\log \epsilon)$	Ref.
methyl ester, (1α,4aα,7aα)- (cont.)			78-1231-80
$C_{10}H_{13}FN_2O_6S$			
Uridine, 2',5'-dideoxy-5-fluoro-, 3'-methanesulfonate	MeOH	267(3.94)	87-0852-80
$C_{10}H_{13}IN_2O_5$			
Uridine, 2'-deoxy-5-iodo-6-methyl-	pH 2	284(3.95)	73-2364-80
	pH 7	284(3.94)	73-2364-80
	pH 12	280(3.84)	73-2364-80
$C_{10}H_{13}N$			
Benzenamine, 2-(1-methyl-2-propenyl)-, (-)-	C_6H_{12}	237(3.89),287(3.42)	33-1823-80
	MeOH	236(3.87),285(3.39)	33-1823-80
Methanamine, N-[(2,4-dimethylphenyl)-methylene]-	hexane	209(4.42),212(4.42), 250(4.23),286(3.19), 297(3.02)	39-0849-80B
	C_6H_{12}	209(4.45),212s(4.44), 251(4.25),286(3.22), 297(3.02)	39-0849-80B
	MeOH	208(4.31),256(4.12), 287s(3.36),297s(3.10)	39-0849-80B
	EtOH	209(4.36),256(4.19), 288s(3.39),298s(3.20)	39-0849-80B
Methanamine, N-[1-(2-methylphenyl)eth-ylidene]-	hexane	196(4.41),233(3.76), 245s(3.70),252s(3.56)	32-0597-80
	C_6H_{12}	197(4.37),234(3.84), 248s(3.67),254s(3.60)	32-0597-80
	MeOH	232(3.83)	32-0597-80
	EtOH	233(3.84)	32-0597-80
Methanamine, N-[1-(4-methylphenyl)eth-ylidene]-	C_6H_{12}	204(4.36),246(4.15), 275s(2.98),282s(2.81)	32-0597-80
$C_{10}H_{13}NO$			
Bicyclo[3.3.1]nonan-3-one, 1-cyano-	EtOH	282(1.28)	44-1800-80
Cyclohepta[b]pyrrol-4(1H)-one, 5,6,7,8-tetrahydro-1-methyl-	n.s.g.	212(4.00),257(3.99), 276s(--)	39-2081-80C
Ethanone, 1-[4-(dimethylamino)phenyl]-	n.s.g.	325(4.30)	88-4241-80
Isoquinoline, 1,2,3,4-tetrahydro-7-methoxy-	H_2O	200(4.4),214(3.8), 280(3.4),288(3.4)	102-0673-80
1-Propanone, 2-amino-2-methyl-1-phen-yl-, hydrochloride	EtOH	197(4.1),245(4.0)	5-1016-80
$C_{10}H_{13}NOS$			
2,5-Cyclohexadiene-1,4-dione, mono-[S-(1,1-dimethylethyl)thiooxime]	hexane	401(4.43)	18-0775-80
2,5-Cyclohexadiene-1,4-dione, mono-[S-(1-methylpropyl)thiooxime]	hexane	425(4.34)	18-0775-80
$C_{10}H_{13}NO_2$			
1H-Azepine-1-carboxylic acid, 2,7-di-methyl-, methyl ester	EtOH	215(4.29),230s(3.58), 285(3.32)	142-1569-80B
1-Propanone, 1-(2-hydroxy-5-methyl-phenyl)-, oxime	EtOH	257(3.93),313(3.59)	90-0431-80
2-Propenamide, 3-(2-furanyl)-N-(1-meth-ylethyl)-	MeOH	297(4.42)	2-0815-80
$C_{10}H_{13}NO_2S$			
Benzenethiol, 4-(1-methylpropyl)-2-nitro-	pH 8.8	259(4.24),419(3.20)	44-4216-80
	EtOH	265(4.12),363(3.52)	44-4216-80

Compound	Solvent	$\lambda_{max}(\log \epsilon)$	Ref.
Benzenethiol, 4-(1-methylpropyl)- 2-nitro- (cont.)	EtOH-NaOH 20% EtOH- pH 7	264(4.24),419(3.19) 258(4.23),423(3.20)	44-4216-80 44-4216-80
$C_{10}H_{13}NO_3$ Cyclopenta[b]pyrrole-2-carboxylic acid, 1,4,5,6-tetrahydro-3-hydroxy-, ethyl ester	MeOH CHCl$_3$	281.5(4.29) 283(4.35)	5-0564-80 5-0564-80
$C_{10}H_{13}NO_3$ α-D-erythro-Hept-5-enofuranurononi- trile, 3,5,6-trideoxy-1,2-O-(1- methylethylidene)-, (E)-	EtOH	209(3.92)	136-0187-80H
(Z)-	EtOH	209(3.74)	136-0187-80H
5H-Pyrano[3,2-c]pyridin-5-one, 2,3,4,6- tetrahydro-2-hydroxy-2,7-dimethyl-	MeOH acid	213(4.77),285(4.35) 209(4.66),234(4.16), 269(4.35)	39-0522-80C 39-0522-80C
	base	220(4.89),280(4.37)	39-0522-80C
3-Pyridinecarboxylic acid, 5-butyl- 1,4-dihydro-4-oxo-	EtOH	256(3.79),283(3.55)	4-0359-80
3-Pyridinecarboxylic acid, 1,5-diethyl- 1,4-dihydro-4-oxo-	EtOH	260(3.97),286(3.60)	4-0359-80
3-Pyridinecarboxylic acid, 5-ethyl- 1,4-dihydro-4-oxo-, ethyl ester	EtOH	256s(3.87),261(3.90), 285(3.64)	4-0359-80
3H-Pyrrolizine-1-carboxylic acid, 2,5,6,7-tetrahydro-5-oxo-, ethyl ester	n.s.g.	280(4.29)	88-4585-80
$C_{10}H_{13}NO_4$ 3-Pyridinecarboxylic acid, 5-ethoxy- 1,4-dihydro-4-oxo-, ethyl ester	EtOH	272(3.95),290s(3.82)	4-0359-80
3-Pyridinecarboxylic acid, 5-ethoxy- 1-ethyl-1,4-dihydro-4-oxo-	EtOH	275(4.01)	4-0359-80
1H-Pyrrole-2,3-dicarboxylic acid, 4,5-dimethyl-, dimethyl ester	EtOH	220(4.23),258(3.96), 304(4.32)	44-4587-80
$C_{10}H_{13}NO_4S_2$ 4-Thia-1-azabicyclo[3.2.0]hept-2-ene- 2-carboxylic acid, 3-[(2-ethoxyeth- yl)thio]-7-oxo-, sodium salt	H$_2$O	251(3.73),320(3.86)	94-3232-80
$C_{10}H_{13}NO_5$ DL-Tyrosine, 2,5-dihydroxy-α-methyl-, hydrochloride	pH 4 pH 7.4	292(3.67) 269(3.93)	87-1318-80 87-1318-80
$C_{10}H_{13}N_3$ Benzenecarboximidic acid, (1-methyl- ethylidene)hydrazide	MeOH	224(4.08),272(3.94)	104-0822-80
Ethanimidic acid, (1-phenylethylidene)- hydrazide	MeOH	217(4.11),282(4.12)	104-0822-80
1H-1,2,4-Triazole, 4,5-dihydro-1,3-di- methyl-5-phenyl-	MeOH	215(3.85),233(3.70)	104-0822-80
$C_{10}H_{13}N_3O$ Glyoxylamide, N,N-dimethylphenyl-, hydrazone, syn	EtOH	218(4.14),258s(4.00), 281(4.07)	33-0063-80
$C_{10}H_{13}N_3O_2$ Benzoic acid, 3-(3,3-dimethyl-1-tria- zenyl)-, methyl ester	EtOH	237(4.12),289(4.19), 320(4.01)	80-0701-80

Compound	Solvent	$\lambda_{max}(\log \epsilon)$	Ref.
$C_{10}H_{13}N_3O_3$			
Acetamide, N-[2-(ethylamino)-3-nitro-phenyl]-	EtOH	238(4.23),425(3.52)	104-1458-80
1-Propanone, 2-amino-2-methyl-1-(3-nitrophenyl)-, oxime, (E)-	EtOH	201(4.3),260(3.9)	5-1016-80
$C_{10}H_{13}N_3O_4$			
Benzenamine, N,N-diethyl-2,4-dinitro-	EtOH	375(4.22)	103-0386-80
6,5'-Imino-5-deoxythymidine	H_2O	291(4.26)	44-3274-80
	0.5M HCl	291(4.26)	44-3274-80
	0.5M NaOH	288(4.14)	44-3274-80
6,3'-Imino-1-(2,3-dideoxy-β-D-threo-pentofuranosyl)thymine	H_2O	283(4.39)	44-3274-80
	0.5M HCl	284(4.39)	44-3274-80
	0.5M NaOH	284(4.26)	44-3274-80
$C_{10}H_{13}N_3O_5$			
$N^6,2'$-Cyclo-6-(methylamino)uridine	H_2O	268(4.44)	94-0939-80
	pH 13	272(4.28)	94-0939-80
$N^6,5'$-Cyclo-6-(methylamino)uridine	H_2O	284(4.30)	94-0939-80
	pH 13	283(4.19)	94-0939-80
$C_{10}H_{13}N_3S$			
3(2H)-Benzothiazolepropanamine, 2-imino-	aq MeOH-HCl	203(4.78),212s(4.71), 250(4.24),267s(4.10), 277(4.13),285(4.18)	103-0169-80
1-Pyrazolidinecarbothioamide, 2-phenyl-	EtOH	250(4.28)	103-0169-80
$C_{10}H_{13}N_5$			
1H-Imidazole-2-carboximidic acid, 4,5-dihydro-, 2-phenylhydrazide	EtOH	246(3.85),307s(4.01), 329s(4.08),364s(3.78)	48-0087-80
$C_{10}H_{13}N_5O$			
9H-Purin-6-amine, 9-(3-methyl-2-butenyl)-, 1-oxide	pH 1	260(4.11)	94-3443-80
	pH 7	232(4.68),262(3.93), 290(3.38)	94-3443-80
	pH 13	232(4.51),268(3.96), 303(3.62)	94-3443-80
	EtOH	235(4.67),266(3.89), 300(3.40)	94-3443-80
6H-Purin-6-imine, 1-ethoxy-1,9-dihydro-9-(2-propenyl)-, hydrobromide	pH 1	260(4.11)	94-3443-80
	pH 7	260(4.11)	94-3443-80
	pH 13	258(4.13),265s(4.08)	94-3443-80
	EtOH	259(4.10)	94-3443-80
$C_{10}H_{13}N_5O_2$			
1,1-Ethenediamine, N,N'-dimethyl-2-nitro-2-(phenylazo)-	MeCN	236s(4.06),400(4.34)	48-0087-80
Hydrazinecarboxamide, N-(2-hydrazono-1-oxo-3-phenylpropyl)-	EtOH	217(3.92),262(3.94)	12-0619-80
$C_{10}H_{13}N_5O_3$			
Adenosine, 2'-deoxy-	MeOH	260(4.18)	142-0761-80B
$C_{10}H_{13}N_5O_4$			
Adenosine	MeOH	260(4.19)	142-0761-80B
Formycin	pH 1	233(3.92),295(4.00)	35-2817-80
	pH 11	234(4.25),302(3.90)	35-2817-80
9H-Purin-6-amine, 9-β-D-arabinofuranosyl-	EtOH	258.5(4.14)	39-0563-80C
D-Ribose, 5-(6-amino-9H-purin-9-yl)-5-deoxy-	H_2O	259.7(4.17)	130-0423-80

Compound	Solvent	$\lambda_{max}(\log \epsilon)$	Ref.
$C_{10}H_{13}N_5O_4S$			
6H-Purine-6-thione, 2-amino-1,9-dihydro-9-β-D-arabinofuranosyl-	pH 1	264(3.89),351(4.32)	88-0479-80
	pH 13	252(4.08),270s(3.85), 321(4.25)	88-0479-80
$C_{10}H_{13}N_5O_4Se$			
Adenosine, 7,8-dihydro-8-selenoxo-	H_2O	310(4.47)	142-0345-80B
$C_{10}H_{13}N_5O_5$			
6H-Purin-6-one, 2-amino-9-β-D-arabinofuranosyl-	pH 1	257(4.11),278s(3.94)	88-0479-80
	pH 13	259(4.08),267(4.09)	88-0479-80
2H-1,2,3-Triazole-4-carboxamide, 5-(cyanomethyl)-2-β-D-ribofuranosyl-	pH 1	232(4.05)	4-0159-80
	pH 7	232(4.03)	4-0159-80
	pH 11	232(4.13)	4-0159-80
4H-1,2,3-Triazolo[4,5-c]pyridin-4-one, 6-amino-1,5-dihydro-1-β-D-ribofuranosyl-	pH 1	218(3.94),246s(3.45), 286(4.20)	4-0159-80
	pH 1	286.5(4.17)	23-2550-80
	pH 7	217(4.10),287(4.23)	4-0159-80
	pH 11	227(4.17),285(3.80), 312(3.68)	4-0159-80
	pH 11	230(4.29),286(3.86), 315(3.85)	23-2550-80
	MeOH	287.5(4.22)	23-2550-80
4H-1,2,3-Triazolo[4,5-c]pyridin-4-one, 6-amino-2,5-dihydro-2-β-D-ribofuranosyl-	pH 1	228s(3.91),249(4.12)	4-0159-80
	pH 7	222(4.24),268(3.98), 340s(3.49)	4-0159-80
	pH 11	233(4.30),263s(3.49), 348s(3.45)	4-0159-80
Uridine, 5-(azidomethyl)-2'-deoxy-	pH 2	265(4.04)	87-0127-80
	pH 12	265(3.88)	87-0127-80
Uridine, 5-(hydroxymethyl)-5'-azido-2',5'-dideoxy-	pH 2	264(3.97)	87-0127-80
	pH 12	264(3.85)	87-0127-80
$C_{10}H_{13}N_7$			
Pyrimidinetetramine, N^5-(4-pyridinylmethyl)-	EtOH	244(3.84),273(3.97)	150-0549-80
$C_{10}H_{14}$			
Azulene, 1,4,5,6,7,8-hexahydro-	C_6H_{12}	240(3.89)	150-4601-80
Benzene, (1-methylpropyl)-	MeCN	197(3.88),207(3.86), 254(2.23),258(2.28), 260(2.30),263(2.18), 268(2.20)	108-0142-80
Bicyclo[5.1.0]octa-2,4-diene, 8,8-dimethyl-	hexane	258(3.51)	44-0724-80
1,3-Cycloheptadiene, 1-(1-methylethenyl)-	hexane	283(4.20)	44-0724-80
1,3-Cycloheptadiene, 2-(1-methylethenyl)-	hexane	247(3.94)	44-0724-80
1,3-Cycloheptadiene, 5-(1-methylethenyl)-	hexane	253(3.95)	44-0724-80
1,3-Cycloheptadiene, 6-(1-methylethenyl)-	hexane	249(3.94)	44-0724-80
1H-Indene, 2,3,5,6-tetrahydro-1-methyl-	C_6H_{12}	266(3.47)	118-0238-80
Naphthalene, 1,2,3,4,4a,8a-hexahydro-, cis	EtOH	261(3.61)	35-4456-80
trans	EtOH	262(3.55)	44-3377-80
Naphthalene, 1,2,3,4,5,6-hexahydro-	EtOH	266(3.72)	44-3999-80
Naphthalene, 1,2,3,4,6,7-hexahydro-	C_6H_{12}	263(3.47)	118-0238-80

Compound	Solvent	$\lambda_{max}(\log \epsilon)$	Ref.
$(C_{10}H_{14})_n$			
1,3-Cyclopentadiene, 5-(1-ethylpropyli-dene)-, homopolymer	THF	254(4.03)	126-0031-80
1,3-Cyclopentadiene, 5-(3-methylbutyli-dene)-, homopolymer	dioxan	242(3.93)	126-0031-80
$C_{10}H_{14}Br_2N_2O_2$			
Cycloheptimidazole, 4,8-dibromo-2,4,5,6,7,8-hexahydro-2,2-di-methyl-, 1,3-dioxide	EtOH	260(3.10),365(2.80)	103-0628-80
$C_{10}H_{14}Br_2O$			
2-Cyclohexen-1-ol, 5-bromo-2-(2-bromo-ethenyl)-4,4-dimethyl-	MeOH	240(4.23)	44-3401-80
$C_{10}H_{14}Br_2O_4$			
α-D-ribo-Hex-5-enofuranose, 6,6-dibro-mo-5,6-dideoxy-3-0-methyl-1,2-0-(1-methylethylidene)-	EtOH	214(4.33)	33-1181-80
β-D-ribo-Hex-5-enofuranoside, methyl 6,6-dibromo-5,6-dideoxy-2,3-0-(1-methylethylidene)-	EtOH	212(3.87)	33-1181-80
$C_{10}H_{14}ClFO_4$			
α-D-xylo-Hex-5-enofuranose, 6-chloro-5,6-dideoxy-6-fluoro-3-0-methyl-1,2-0-(1-methylethylidene)-, (E)-	EtOH	208(2.90)	33-1644-80
(Z)-	EtOH	207(2.86)	33-1644-80
$C_{10}H_{14}ClNO$			
Benzenemethanol, α-(1-amino-1-methyl-ethyl)-4-chloro-	EtOH	221(4.08)	4-1563-80
$C_{10}H_{14}ClNO_2$			
2H-Pyran-2-one, 3-chloro-4-(dimethyl-amino)-3,6-dihydro-6-(1-methyleth-ylidene)-	EtOH	230(4.02),264(3.62),305(3.73)	4-0507-80
$C_{10}H_{14}ClN_2O_4PS$			
3(2H)-Pyridazinone, 4-chloro-5-[(5,5-dimethyl-1,3,2-dioxaphosphorinan-2-yl)oxy]-2-methyl-, P-sulfide	MeOH	212(4.29),294(3.56)	73-2343-80
$C_{10}H_{14}ClN_2O_6P$			
Phosphonamidic acid, P-(chloromethyl)-N-[2-hydroxy-1-(hydroxymethyl)-2-(4-nitrophenyl)ethyl]-, monosodium salt, [R-(R*,R*)]-	pH 7	280(4.09)	87-1299-80
$C_{10}H_{14}Cl_2O_4$			
α-D-ribo-Hex-5-enofuranose, 6,6-dichlo-ro-5,6-dideoxy-3-0-methyl-1,2-0-(1-methylethylidene)-	EtOH	209(3.72)	33-1644-80
α-D-xylo-Hex-5-enofuranose, 6,6-dichlo-ro-5,6-dideoxy-3-0-methyl-1,2-0-(1-methylethylidene)-	EtOH	209(3.76)	33-1644-80
α-D-ribo-Hex-5-enofuranoside, methyl 6,6-dichloro-5,6-dideoxy-2,3-0-(1-methylethylidene)-	EtOH	210(3.49)	33-1644-80

Compound	Solvent	$\lambda_{max}(\log \epsilon)$	Ref.
$C_{10}H_{14}Cl_4O$ 7-Oxabicyclo[2.2.1]heptane, 2,3,5,6-tetrakis(chloromethyl)-, (2-endo-3-exo,5-endo,6-exo)	EtOH	210(2.30)(end abs.)[*]	33-1149-80
$C_{10}H_{14}F_2O_4$ α-D-ribo-Hex-5-enofuranoside, methyl 5,6-dideoxy-6,6-difluoro-2,3-0-(1-methylethylidene)-	EtOH	209(1.66),227s(1.30)	33-1644-80
$C_{10}H_{14}FeO_5Si$ Iron, tetracarbonyl[(η^2-ethenyl)ethoxy-dimethylsilane]-	hexane	215(4.43),262s(3.90)	35-6349-80
$C_{10}H_{14}GaNO$ Gallium, methyl[2-[(methylimino)methyl]phenolato-N,0]-	hexane MeCN	282(3.85),387(3.64) 280(3.76),372(3.60)	101-0001-80I 101-0001-80I
$C_{10}H_{14}NO$ Ethanaminium, N-ethyl-N-(4-oxo-2,5-cyclohexadien-1-ylidene)- Methanaminium, N-(3,5-dimethyl-4-oxo-2,5-cyclohexadien-1-ylidene)-N-methyl-	acid H_2O	284(4.30) 294(4.25)	39-1601-80B 39-1601-80B
$C_{10}H_{14}N_2$ 7,8-Diazatetracyclo[4.3.3.0^{2,10}.0^{5,9}]-dodec-7-ene Pyrazole, 4-(3-butenyl)-3-(2-propenyl)-	MeCN EtOH	343(2.46) 222(3.65)	5-1428-80 35-1633-80
$C_{10}H_{14}N_2O$ 6,7-Diazatricyclo[3.3.0.0^{2,4}]oct-7-ene, 6-acetyl-3,3-dimethyl-, (1α,2β,4β,5α)- 1,8-Naphthyridin-4(1H)-one, 5,6,7,8-tetrahydro-2,8-dimethyl- 1-Propanone, 2-amino-2-methyl-1-phenyl-, oxime, (E)-	EtOH EtOH +25% dioxan +50% dioxan +75% dioxan EtOH	244(4.04),292(2.11) 290(<u>4.0</u>) 290(<u>3.9</u>) 262(<u>3.8</u>),290(<u>3.9</u>) 262(<u>3.9</u>),290(<u>3.7</u>) 197(4.2),256(2.7)	88-1223-80 103-0260-80 103-0260-80 103-0260-80 103-0260-80 5-1016-80
$C_{10}H_{14}N_2O_2$ Benzenamine, N,N-diethyl-4-nitro- 1H,7H-Pyrazolo[1,2-a]pyrazole-1,7-dione, 2,3-dihydro-2,3,5,6-tetramethyl-	EtOH MeOH	395(4.34) 306(3.85)	103-0386-80 35-4983-80
$C_{10}H_{14}N_2O_3$ Benzenamine, 2-methoxy-N,3,4-trimethyl-6-nitro- Pyrazinecarboxylic acid, 5-ethyl-3,4-dihydro-6-methyl-3-oxo-, ethyl ester	MeOH EtOH	242(4.29),303(3.77), 438(3.65) 235(3.83),320(3.80), 368(3.57)	54-0115-80 70-0774-80
$C_{10}H_{14}N_2O_5$ Uridine, 2'-deoxy-6-methyl-	pH 7.0	262(4.08)	73-2364-80
$C_{10}H_{14}N_2O_6$ D-Mannitol, 2,5-anhydro-1-deoxy-1-(3,4-dihydro-2,4-dioxo-1(2H)-pyrimidinyl)- 2,4(1H,3H)-Pyrimidinedione, 1-(6-deoxy-α-L-talofuranosyl)- Uridine, 2'-deoxy-5-(hydroxymethyl)-	pH 13 EtOH pH 1 pH 13 pH 2 pH 12	209(4.11),263(3.89) 209(3.91),265(3.92) 263(4.00) 263(3.87) 265(4.01) 265(3.88)	136-0195-80A 136-0195-80A 73-2550-80 73-2550-80 87-0127-80 87-0127-80

Compound	Solvent	λ_{max} (log ϵ)	Ref.
Uridine, 5-methyl-	EtOH	267(3.89)	33-2179-80
$C_{10}H_{14}N_2O_6S$			
Methanesulfonamide, N-[2-hydroxy-1-(hydroxymethyl)-2-(4-nitrophenyl)-ethyl]-, [R-(R*,R*)]-	pH 7	277(3.96)	87-1299-80
2-Thiouracil, 5-[1-(hydroxymethyl)-β-ribofuranosyl]-	pH 13	223(4.11),264(3.93), 289(3.85)	88-2535-80
	MeOH	214(3.94),276(4.06), 293(4.00)	88-2535-80
2-Thiouracil, 5-[4-(hydroxymethyl)-β-ribofuranosyl]-	pH 1	214(4.13),273(4.20), 292s(4.08)	88-2535-80
	pH 13	265(4.14),285(4.11)	88-2535-80
	MeOH	213(4.15),275(4.20), 296s(4.12)	88-2535-80
$C_{10}H_{14}N_2O_7$			
2,4(1H,3H)-Pyrimidinedione, 5-[2-C-(hydroxymethyl)-β-DL-ribofuranosyl]-	pH 1	266(3.71)	142-0321-80B
	pH 13	285(3.58)	142-0321-80B
	MeOH	287(3.76)	142-0321-80B
2,4(1H,3H)-Pyrimidinedione, 5-[4-(hydroxymethyl)-β-ribofuranosyl]-	pH 1	264(3.78)	88-2535-80
	pH 13	287(3.83)	88-2535-80
	MeOH	264(3.82)	88-2535-80
$C_{10}H_{14}N_2S$			
Imidazo[2,1-b]thiazole, 6-(1,1-dimethylethyl)-3-methyl-	EtOH	245(3.80)	18-3308-80
$C_{10}H_{14}N_4$			
2,2'-Bi-1H-imidazole, 1,1'-diethyl-	EtOH	253(4.07)	70-1655-80
Imidazo[5,1-f][1,2,4]triazine, 2,5-dimethyl-7-propyl-	EtOH	228(4.49),361(3.42), 370(3.37)	39-1139-80C
$C_{10}H_{14}N_4O$			
Benzamide, 3-(3,3-dimethyl-1-triazenyl)-N-methyl-	EtOH	238(4.16),290(4.20), 318(4.06)	80-0701-80
Imidazo[5,1-f][1,2,4]triazin-4(1H)-one, 2,5-dimethyl-7-propyl-	EtOH	222(4.38),248(3.94), 263s(3.79),280s(3.38)	39-1139-80C
	EtOH-NaOH	233(--),260(--), 269s(--),297(--)	39-1139-80C
Imidazo[5,1-f][1,2,4]triazin-4(1H)-one, 5-methyl-7-(2-methylpropyl)-	EtOH	224(4.38),247(3.94), 262s(3.74),285s(--)	39-1139-80C
	EtOH-NaOH	258s(--),268s(--)	39-1139-80C
$C_{10}H_{14}N_4O_2$			
Pyrazinecarbonitrile, 3-amino-6-(diethoxymethyl)-	EtOH	250(4.20),353(3.84)	88-3759-80
$C_{10}H_{14}N_4O_4$			
6H-Furo[2',3':4,5]oxazolo[3,2-a]pyrimidine-2-methanol, 6-[(aminomethyl)-imino]-2,3,3a,9a-tetrahydro-3-hydroxy-, dihydrochloride, [2R-(2α,3β,3aβ,9aβ)]-	MeOH	237(3.76),268(3.88)	44-1577-80
$C_{10}H_{14}N_4O_5S$			
7H-Purine-7-propanesulfonic acid, 1,2,3,6-tetrahydro-1,3-dimethyl-2,6-dioxo-	H_2O	272(3.97)	107-0267-80

Compound	Solvent	$\lambda_{max}(\log \epsilon)$	Ref.
$C_{10}H_{14}N_4O_8$ 1-Cyclohexen-1-amine, 3,5-dimethoxy-N,N-dimethyl-2,4,6-trinitro-, ion(2-), disodium	DMSO-5%MeOH-NaOMe	430(4.47)	23-1609-80
$C_{10}H_{14}N_6$ [1,2,4]Triazolo[5',1':2,3]pyrimido[4,5-c]pyridazine, 1,2,3,4-tetrahydro-1,2,5-trimethyl-	EtOH	224(4.29),311(4.09)	87-0927-80
$C_{10}H_{14}N_6O_4$ 7H-1,2,3-Triazolo[4,5-d]pyrimidin-7-one, 5-amino-3-[2,3-dihydroxy-4-(hydroxymethyl)cyclopentyl]-, $(1\alpha,2\beta,3\alpha,5\beta)-(\pm)-$	pH 1 H_2O pH 13	252(4.18),270s(--) 202(4.38),252(4.13), 270s(--) 277(4.11)	36-1019-80 36-1019-80 36-1019-80
$C_{10}H_{14}N_6O_5$ Acetic acid, 2-[2-(acetylamino)-1,6-dihydro-5-nitro-6-oxo-4-pyrimidinyl]-1,2-dimethylhydrazide	pH 1 pH 13	247(3.96),278(3.85), 366(3.23) 233(4.06),250s(3.98), 382(3.29)	150-3630-80 150-3630-80
$C_{10}H_{14}O$ Benzene, butoxy- Benzenemethanol, α-ethyl-α-methyl- Bicyclo[4.3.1]dec-6-en-8-one Bicyclo[2.2.1]heptan-2-one, 7,7-dimethyl-3-methylene-, (1R)- 2,3-Cyclodecadien-1-one, (R)- Phenol, 4-(1,1-dimethylethyl)- 	EtOH MeCN MeCN $C_6H_{11}Me$ EtOH hexane pentane-EtOH-ether	221(3.873),266(3.095), 272(3.250),279(3.153) 251(2.18),257(2.28), 260s(2.18),263(2.18), 267(2.04) 250(3.71),345(1.96) .227(4.09),344(1.60) 224(3.72) 222(3.95),272(3.15), 278(3.28),284(3.28) 225(3.94),273(3.08), 280(3.20),287(3.11)	65-0491-80 108-0142-80 44-1800-80 44-3518-80 35-5370-80 65-2236-80 65-2236-80
$C_{10}H_{14}OS$ 2,4-Cyclohexadien-1-one, 2,6-dimethyl-6-[(methylthio)methyl]- 	hexane MeOH CF_3CH_2OH	299(3.62),369s(2.29), 391s(2.13),426s(1.73) 307(3.58) 312(3.55)	24-2227-80 24-2227-80 24-2227-80
$C_{10}H_{14}O_2$ Bicyclo[2.2.1]heptane-2,3-dione, 1,7,7-trimethyl- (1R)- Bicyclo[4.1.0]heptane-2,5-dione, 1,4,4-trimethyl- Bicyclo[2.1.0]pnetane-1-carboxaldehyde, 5-acetyl-2,2-dimethyl-, $(1\alpha,4\alpha,5\alpha)-$ 1,3-Cyclopentadiene, 5-(2,2-dimethoxy-1-methylethylidene)- Cyclopentaneacetaldehyde, 2-formyl-3-methyl-α-methylene- 1,3-Cyclopentanedione, 2-ethenyl-2,4,4-trimethyl- 2-Cyclopentene-1-acetaldehyde, 2-formyl- ,3-dimethyl- (dehydroiridodial) 2,4,6-Octatrienal, 8-hydroxy-2,6-dimethyl-, (E,E,E)-	CF_3CH_2OH n.s.g. pentane EtOH H_2O n.s.g. EtOH hexane	$\underline{455(2.6)}$ 292(1.73) 286(1.79),300(1.85), 311(1.83),321s(1.72) 262(4.33),354(2.47) 223(3) 274(1.97),287(2.07), 298(2.13) 253(4.08) 299(3.40),313(3.37)	77-0273-80 33-1499-80 33-2212-80 34-0184-80 100-0649-80 33-1499-80 78-3115-80 33-0716-80

Compound	Solvent	$\lambda_{max}(\log \epsilon)$	Ref.
2-Oxabicyclo[4.1.0]hept-3-en-5-one, 1,3,4,6-tetramethyl-	MeOH	<u>269(3.8)</u>	18-0469-80
2-Oxabicyclo[3.3.0]oct-3-en-6-one, 5,8,8-trimethyl-	pentane	305s(2.38),312(2.39), 322s(2.28)	33-2370-80
$C_{10}H_{14}O_3$			
Bicyclo[4.2.0]octan-7-one, 8-acetoxy-, endo	MeOH	290(1.76)	44-0177-80
3-Cyclohexene-1-acetic acid, 3-methyl-5-oxo-, methyl ester	MeOH	234(4.06),305(1.75)	44-0570-80
1-Cyclopentene-1-butanoic acid, 5-oxo-, methyl ester	MeOH	236(4.24)	44-0570-80
2,8-Decadienoic acid, 4,5-epoxy-5,9-di-methyl-	EtOH	223(4.07)	70-0754-80
$C_{10}H_{14}O_4$			
α-D-ribo-Hex-5-ynofuranose, 5,6-dide-oxy-3-O-methyl-1,2-O-(1-methyleth-ylidene)-	EtOH	215(1.81),228s(--)	33-1181-80
α-D-xylo-Hex-5-ynofuranose, 5,6-dide-oxy-3-O-methyl-1,2-O-(1-methyleth-ylidene)-	EtOH	225(1.97)	33-1181-80
β-D-ribo-Hex-5-ynofuranoside, methyl 5,6-dideoxy-2,3-O-(1-methylethylidene)-	EtOH	210(1.81),233s(--)	33-1181-80
Oxiranebutanoic acid, 3-(3-oxo-1-prop-enyl)-, methyl ester	EtOH	228(4.20)	35-1436-80
$C_{10}H_{14}S$			
Benzene, [2-(ethylthio)ethyl]-	hexane	212(3.95),248(2.22), 253(2.28),259(2.35), 265(2.25),268(2.15)	101-0147-80A +131-0099-80C
$C_{10}H_{14}S_2$			
1H,4H-Thieno[3,4-c]thiophene, 1,1,4,4-tetramethyl-	EtOH	270(4.08),330(4.11)	88-3617-80
$C_{10}H_{14}S_2Si$			
1,3-Dithia-2-silacyclohexane, 2-methyl-2-phenyl-	hexane	198(4.51),218(4.14), 236s(3.43),272(2.55)	131-0099-80C
1,3-Dithia-2-silacyclopentane, 2,4-dimethyl-2-phenyl-	hexane	192(4.44),217(3.88), 245s(3.05),266(2.58), 276(2.44)	101-0147-80A +131-0099-80C
$C_{10}H_{14}Si$			
1H-2-Silaindene, 2,3-dihydro-2,2-di-methyl-	C_6H_{12}	218(3.81)	65-1621-80
$C_{10}H_{15}BrO$			
Bicyclo[3.3.1]nonan-3-one, 1-bromo-2-methyl-	EtOH	283(1.76)	44-3545-80
2-Cyclohexen-1-ol, 5-bromo-2-ethenyl-4,4-dimethyl-, cis-(-)-	MeOH	230(4.00)	44-3401-80
$C_{10}H_{15}BrO_4S_2$			
Sulfonium, (2-bromophenyl)dimethyl-, methyl sulfate	H_2O	209(4.1),271(2.83)	124-0957-80
Sulfonium, (3-bromophenyl)dimethyl-, methyl sulfate	H_2O	272(2.78)	124-0957-80
Sulfonium, (4-bromophenyl)dimethyl-, methyl sulfate	H_2O	232(4.19)	124-0957-80

Compound	Solvent	$\lambda_{max}(\log \epsilon)$	Ref.
$C_{10}H_{15}ClN_2O_2$ 3(2H)-Pyridazinone, 4-chloro-2-hexyl-5-hydroxy-	MeOH	216(4.47),227s(--), 286(3.71)	73-0127-80
$C_{10}H_{15}ClN_4O_3$ 1,2-Cyclopentanediol, 3-[(2-amino-6-chloro-4-pyrimidinyl)amino]-5-(hydroxymethyl)-, (1α,2β,3β,5β)-(±)-	pH 1 H$_2$O pH 13	210(4.45),238(4.23), 274(4.06),310(3.95) 210(4.48),239(4.11), 284(4.06) 236(4.12),284(4.05)	36-1019-80 36-1019-80 36-1019-80
$C_{10}H_{15}ClO$ 2-Cyclohexen-1-ol, 4-(2-chloroethylidene)-6,6-dimethyl-	MeOH	238(4.32)	44-3401-80
$C_{10}H_{15}ClO_4S_2$ Sulfonium, (2-chlorophenyl)dimethyl-, methyl sulfate Sulfonium, (3-chlorophenyl)dimethyl-, methyl sulfate Sulfonium, (4-chlorophenyl)dimethyl-, methyl sulfate	H$_2$O H$_2$O H$_2$O	207(4.08),270(2.72) 209(4.21),266(3.6) 220(4.25)	124-0957-80 124-0957-80 124-0957-80
$C_{10}H_{15}FN_2O_3$ 2,4(1H,3H)-Pyrimidinedione, 1-(1-but-oxyethyl)-5-fluoro-	pH 2 pH 7 pH 12	270(3.89) 270(3.88) 270(3.73)	103-1176-80 103-1176-80 103-1176-80
$C_{10}H_{15}IO_2$ Bicyclo[2.2.2]octan-1-ol, 4-iodo-, acetate	EtOH	261(2.91)	44-3933-80
$C_{10}H_{15}N$ Benzenamine, 2-(1-methylpropyl)-, (S)-	C_6H_{12}	236(3.94),286(3.40)	33-1823-80
$C_{10}H_{15}NO$ 2,5,7-Octatrien-4-one, 8-(dimethyl-amino)-, (E,E,E)- 2-Propenal, 3-(2,3-dihydro-5-(1-methyl-ethyl)-1H-pyrrol-1-yl)-, (E)- 2-Propenal, 3-(2,3-dihydro-3,3,5-tri-methyl-1H-pyrrol-1-yl)-, (E)-	EtOH MeOH MeOH	420(4.71) 214(3.64),234(3.59), 319(4.56) 219(3.77),320(4.17)	70-0980-80 83-0858-80 83-0858-80
$C_{10}H_{15}NOS$ Ethanone, 1-(1,3-dimethyl-7-thia-2-aza-bicyclo[3.2.1]oct-3-en-4-yl)- 3-Furancarbothioamide, N,N-diethyl-2-methyl-	EtOH EtOH	273(3.30),325(3.96) 209(3.84),227s(3.53), 283(3.93)	23-0794-80 128-0069-80
$C_{10}H_{15}NO_2$ 3-Furancarboxamide, N,N-diethyl-2-methyl- 2,4-Pentanedione, 3-[3-(dimethylamino)-2-propenylidene]-	EtOH hexane EtOH CHCl$_3$	212(3.93),237s(3.55) 250(3.65),370(4.66) 240(3.56),289(3.84), 400(4.78) 282(3.41),395(4.79)	128-0069-80 70-1643-80 70-1643-80 70-1643-80
$C_{10}H_{15}NO_3$ Butanoic acid, 3-oxo-2-(2-piperidin-ylidene)-, methyl ester	MeOH	248(3.83),304(4.14)	44-0936-80

Compound	Solvent	λ_{max}(log ϵ)	Ref.
2-Propenoic acid, 2-(acetyl-2-propenyl-amino)-, ethyl ester	ether	200(4.22),300(1.83) (end absorption)	88-4577-80
$C_{10}H_{15}NO_5S$			
2H-1,4-Thiazine-3,6-dicarboxylic acid, 3,4-dihydro-2,2-dimethyl-, dimethyl ester, 1-oxide, (1S-trans)-	EtOH	306(4.00)	39-2322-80C
$C_{10}H_{15}NO_6$			
3,5-Isoxazoledicarboxylic acid, 4,5-di-hydro-4-(1-methylethyl)-, methyl ester, 2-oxide, trans	MeOH	269(3.95)	94-0479-80
3,5-Isoxazoledicarboxylic acid, 4,5-di-hydro-4-propyl-, dimethyl ester, 2-oxide, trans	MeOH	268(3.96)	94-0479-80
$C_{10}H_{15}NO_6S$			
2H-1,4-Thiazine-3,6-dicarboxylic acid, 3,4-dihydro-3-hydroxy-2,2-dimethyl-, dimethyl ester, 1-oxide	EtOH	276(4.08)	39-2322-80C
$C_{10}H_{15}N_2O_4PS$			
3(2H)-Pyridazinone, 5-[(5,5-dimethyl-1,3,2-dioxaphosphorinan-2-yl)oxy]-2-methyl-, P-sulfide	MeOH	211(4.30),292(3.49)	73-2343-80
$C_{10}H_{15}N_2O_5PS$			
3(2H)-Pyridazinone, 5-[(4,5-dimethyl-1,3,2-dioxaphospholan-2-yl)oxy]-4-methoxy-2-methyl-, P-sulfide	MeOH	213(4.31),286(3.70)	73-2343-80
3(2H)-Pyridazinone, 4-methoxy-2-methyl-5-[(4-methyl-1,3,2-dioxaphosphorin-an-2-yl)oxy]-, P-sulfide	MeOH	213(4.30),285(3.72)	73-2343-80
$C_{10}H_{15}N_3O$			
1H-1,2,4-Triazole, 1-(cyclohexylacetyl)-	THF	223(3.93)	33-0588-80
$C_{10}H_{15}N_3O_2$			
Piperidine, 1-(1-methyl-4-nitro-1H-pyrrol-2-yl)-	MeOH	281(3.86),358(3.58)	77-0123-80
$C_{10}H_{15}N_3O_3$			
2(1H)-Pyrimidinone, 4-amino-1-[2-hy-droxy-4-(hydroxymethyl)cyclopentyl]-	pH 1	214(4.00),285(4.12)	4-0353-80
	pH 7	275(3.96)	4-0353-80
	pH 13	275(3.95)	4-0353-80
2(1H)-Pyrimidinone, 4-amino-1-[3-hy-droxy-4-(hydroxymethyl)cyclopentyl]-	pH 1	214(4.02),284(4.14)	4-0353-80
	pH 7, 13	275(3.98)	4-0353-80
$C_{10}H_{15}N_3O_4$			
Cytidine, 2'-deoxy-N-methyl-	pH 1	280(4.11)	39-2787-80C
	pH 7	272(3.93)	39-2787-80C
	pH 13	274(3.93)	39-2787-80C
5-Pyrimidinehexanoic acid, 2-amino-1,4-dihydro-6-hydroxy-4-oxo-	50%MeOH-HCl	266(4.22)	73-3583-80
	50%MeOH-NaOH	270(4.17)	73-3583-80
2(1H)-Pyrimidinone, 4-amino-1-[2,3-di-hydroxy-4-(hydroxymethyl)cyclopent-yl]-	pH 1	214(4.00),285(4.13)	4-0353-80
	pH 7	275(3.97)	4-0353-80
	pH 13	275(3.97)	4-0353-80
$C_{10}H_{15}N_3O_5$			
Cytidine, 2'-O-methyl-	pH 7	271(3.95)	44-3865-80
Cytidine, 3'-O-methyl-	pH 7	271(3.92)	44-3865-80

Compound	Solvent	$\lambda_{max}(\log \epsilon)$	Ref.
Cytidine, 3-methyl-	pH 1	278(4.05)	39-2787-80C
	pH 7	278(4.04)	39-2787-80C
	pH 13	265(3.95)	39-2787-80C
D-Mannitol, 1-(4-amino-2-oxo-1(2H)-	pH 13	205(4.09),275(3.80)	136-0195-80A
pyrimidinyl)-2,5-anhydro-1-deoxy-	EtOH	210(3.93),285(3.95)	136-0195-80A
4(1H)-Pyrimidinone, 2-amino-5-(2-C-	pH 1	222(3.76),264(3.63)	88-1971-80
methyl-β-ribofuranosyl)-	pH 13	233(3.96),280(3.83)	88-1971-80
	MeOH	224(4.03),265(3.84)	88-1971-80
Uridine, 5'-amino-2',5'-dideoxy-5-(hy-	pH 2	264(3.99)	87-0127-80
droxymethyl)-	pH 12	264(3.88)	87-0127-80
Uridine, 2'-deoxy-5-(aminomethyl)-	pH 2	265(4.03)	87-0127-80
	pH 12	265(3.87)	87-0127-80
$C_{10}H_{15}N_3O_6$			
4(1H)-Pyrimidinone, 2-amino-5-[4-C-(hy-	pH 1	222(3.98),263(3.88)	88-2535-80
droxymethyl)-β-D-erythro-pentofuran-	pH 13	233(4.04),278(3.93)	88-2535-80
osyl]-, monohydrochloride	MeOH	224(3.97),263(3.90)	88-2535-80
4(1H)-Pyrimidinone, 2-amino-5-[2-C-(hy-	pH 13	232(3.94),280(3.81)	142-0321-80B
droxymethyl)-β-DL-ribofuranosyl]-,	MeOH	224(4.10),265(3.89)	142-0321-80B
monohydrochloride			
Uridine, 6-(methylamino)-	H_2O	274(4.37)	94-0939-80
	pH 13	276(4.23)	94-0939-80
$C_{10}H_{15}N_5$			
Ethanimidic acid, 2-(methylamino)-	EtOH	284(3.93),326(3.75)	48-0087-80
2-(methylimino)-, 2-phenylhydrazide			
3H-Purin-6-amine, N,N-diethyl-3-methyl-	pH 1	294(4.33)	94-1920-80
	pH 7	296(4.25)	94-1920-80
	pH 13	297(4.24)	94-1920-80
	EtOH	300(4.22)	94-1920-80
9H-Purin-6-amine, N,N-diethyl-9-methyl-,	pH 1	271(4.28)	94-1920-80
hydrochloride	pH 7	279(4.29)	94-1920-80
	pH 13	279(4.29)	94-1920-80
	EtOH	279(4.28)	94-1920-80
$C_{10}H_{15}N_5O$			
6H-Purin-6-imine, 1-ethoxy-1,9-dihydro-	pH 1	260(4.10)	94-3443-80
9-propyl-, monohydriodide	pH 7	260(4.10)	94-3443-80
	pH 13	258(4.14),265s(4.09)	94-3443-80
		(changing)	
	EtOH	259(4.10)	94-3443-80
$C_{10}H_{15}N_5O_2$			
1H-Pyrrole-2-carboxamide, N-(3-amino-	EtOH	280(4.32)	36-1334-80
3-iminopropyl)-5-(formylamino)-			
1-methyl-, monohydrochloride			
$C_{10}H_{15}N_7O_2$			
Adenosine, 3',5'-diamino-3',5'-dideoxy-	MeOH	259(4.18)	118-0559-80
$C_{10}H_{15}N_7O_3$			
1,2-Cyclopentanediol, 3-(5,7-diamino-	pH 1	211(4.52),252(4.11),	36-1019-80
3H-1,2,3-triazolo[4,5-d]pyrimidin-		282(3.96)	
3-yl)-5-(hydroxymethyl)-,	H_2O	222(4.43),250s(--),	36-1019-80
(1α,2β,3α,5β)-(±)-		283(4.07)	
	pH 13	254s(--),283(4.10)	36-1019-80
$C_{10}H_{15}OP$			
Phosphinous acid, diethyl-, phenyl	EtOH	274(3.14)	65-0945-80
ester	MeCN	275(2.86)	65-0945-80

Compound	Solvent	$\lambda_{max}(\log \epsilon)$	Ref.
$C_{10}H_{15}OS$			
Sulfonium, (4-hydroxy-3,5-dimethyl-phenyl)dimethyl-, hexafluoroarsenate	n.s.g.	252(3.97),279(3.60), 284(3.61),300(3.48)	47-1021-80
tetrafluoroborate	n.s.g.	252(3.97),279(3.60), 284(3.61),300(3.48)	47-1021-80
$C_{10}H_{15}O_3S$			
Sulfonium, (4-hydroxy-3,5-dimethoxy-phenyl)dimethyl-, hexafluoroarsenate	n.s.g.	220(4.39),275(3.79), 315(3.62)	47-1021-80
$C_{10}H_{16}$			
2,4,7-Nonatriene, 6-methyl-	EtOH	230(4.10)	93-1509-80
2,4,6-Octatriene, 3,6-dimethyl-, (E,E,E)-	hexane	237s(--),246s(--), 257(4.53),267(4.63), 278(4.52)	39-1045-80C
(E,E,Z)-	hexane	262(4.47),271(4.58), 281(4.48)	39-1045-80C
Piperylene dimer	EtOH	230(4.14)	93-1509-80
trimer	EtOH	232(3.92)	93-1509-80
$C_{10}H_{16}ClN_2O_3PS_2$			
Phosphorodithioic acid, O-(5-chloro-1,6-dihydro-1-methyl-6-oxo-4-pyrid-azinyl) O-ethyl S-(1-methylethyl) ester	MeOH	218(4.28),296(3.31)	73-2247-80
Phosphorodithioic acid, O-(5-chloro-1,6-dihydro-1-methyl-6-oxo-4-pyrid-azinyl) O-ethyl S-propyl ester	MeOH	219(4.20),297(3.60)	73-2247-80
$C_{10}H_{16}ClN_5O_3$			
1,2-Cyclopentanediol, 3-[(2,5-diamino-6-chloro-4-pyrimidinyl)amino]-5-(hy-droxymethyl)-, (1α,2β,3β,5β)-(±)-	pH 1	234(4.28),298(3.90)	36-1019-80
	H_2O	202(4.28),226(--), 242(--),302(3.97)	36-1019-80
	pH 13	244(--),302(3.95)	36-1019-80
$C_{10}H_{16}NO_{13}P_3$			
2(1H)-Pyridinone, 1-[2-deoxy-5-O-[hy-droxy[[hydroxy(phosphonooxy)phosph-inyl]-β-D-erythro-pentofuranosyl]-, tetrasodium salt	H_2O	192(4.20),224(3.71), 298(3.77)	33-2488-80
$C_{10}H_{16}N_2O_2$			
1H-Azonine-2,4(3H,5H)-dione, 3-(1-ami-noethylidene)tetrahydro-	MeOH	244(3.23),304(4.09)	44-0936-80
2H-Benzimidazole, 2-ethyl-4,5,6,7-tetra-hydro-2-methyl-, 1,3-dioxide	EtOH	212(3.90),350(3.90)	103-0628-80
Cycloheptimidazole, 2,4,5,6,7,8-hexa-hydro-2,2-dimethyl-, 1,3-dioxide	EtOH	220(4.10),350(4.00)	103-0628-80
$C_{10}H_{16}N_2O_2S$			
4,6(1H,5H)-Pyrimidinedione, 5-ethyldi-hydro-5-(1-methylpropyl)-2-thioxo-	MeOH	234(4.04),284(4.39), 369(1.65)	36-1164-80
	$CHCl_3$	284(4.46),362(1.76)	36-1164-80
$C_{10}H_{16}N_2O_3$			
3(2H)-Pyridazinone, 5-hydroxy-4-meth-oxy-2-pentyl-	MeOH	215(4.39),282(3.58)	73-0127-80
$C_{10}H_{16}N_2O_3S$			
2(1H)-Pyrimidinone, 1-[bis(2-hydroxy-ethyl)methyl]-5-methyl-4-thioxo-	pH 2	240(3.75),342(4.46)	103-0864-80
	pH 7	240(4.11),342(4.53)	103-0864-80

Compound	Solvent	$\lambda_{max}(\log \epsilon)$	Ref.
(cont.)	pH 11	325(4.41)	103-0864-80
$C_{10}H_{16}N_2O_4$			
4,8-Cycloheptimidazolediol, 2,4,5,6,7,8- hexahydro-2,2-dimethyl-1,3-dioxo-	EtOH	228(3.78),355(3.90)	103-0628-80
$C_{10}H_{16}N_4$			
Imidazo[5,1-f][1,2,4]triazine, 1,4-di- hydro-2,5-dimethyl-7-propyl-	EtOH	254(3.96)	39-1139-80C
Imidazo[5,1-f][1,2,4]triazine, 1,4-di- hydro-5-methyl-7-(2-methylpropyl)-	EtOH	253(3.95)	39-1139-80C
$C_{10}H_{16}N_4O_2$			
Butanamide, N-[1-(2,5-dihydro-3-methyl- 5-oxo-1,2,4-triazin-6-yl)ethyl]-	EtOH	235(3.96),265s(3.72)	39-1139-80C
	EtOH-NaOH	233(--),283(--)	39-1139-80C
Butanamide, N-[1-(2,5-dihydro-5-oxo- 1,2,4-triazin-6-yl)ethyl]-3-methyl-, hydrochloride	EtOH	239(3.97),263s(3.72)	39-1139-80C
2,4(1H,3H)-Pteridinedione, 5,6,7,8- tetrahydro-1,3,5,6-tetramethyl-, (±)-	pH 3.0	263(4.22)	18-3385-80
	pH 8.0	235s(3.73),286(4.10)	18-3385-80
(6S)-	pH 3.0	263(4.22)	18-3385-80
	pH 8.0	235s(3.72),286(4.11)	18-3385-80
$C_{10}H_{16}N_4O_4$			
Uridine, 5'-amino-5-(aminomethyl)- 2',5'-dideoxy-	pH 2	265(4.01)	87-0127-80
	pH 12	265(3.86)	87-0127-80
$C_{10}H_{16}N_4O_7$			
Vicine	0.5M HCl	273(4.20)	94-2753-80
	H_2O	210(4.31),275(4.11)	94-2753-80
	pH 13	217(3.93),235(3.75), 268(3.99)	94-2753-80
$C_{10}H_{16}N_5$			
3H-Purinium, 6-(dimethylamino)-3-ethyl- 9-methyl-, iodide	pH 1	223(4.36),288(4.23)	94-2522-80
	pH 7	223(4.36),288(4.23)	94-2522-80
	EtOH	290(4.24)	94-2522-80
3H-Purinium, 6-(dimethylamino)-9-ethyl- 3-methyl-, iodide	pH 1	224(4.36),288(4.25)	94-2522-80
	pH 7	224(4.36),288(4.25)	94-2522-80
	EtOH	290(4.25)	94-2522-80
$C_{10}H_{16}O$			
1-Cyclohexene-1-carboxaldehyde, 2,5,6-trimethyl-, cis	EtOH	251(4.09),323(1.85)	33-0293-80
trans	EtOH	251(4.09),324(1.92)	33-0293-80
4-Hexenal, 5-methyl-2-(1-methylethyli- dene)-	EtOH	247(4.14)	33-0571-80
1(2H)-Naphthalenone, octahydro-, (+)-	hexane	290(1.31),296(1.33), 305(1.26),315(1.00)	39-0950-80C
	MeOH	287(1.40)	39-0950-80C
2,7-Octadienal, 3,7-dimethyl-, (E)-	n.s.g.	232(4.27),324s(1.57), 335(1.66),348(1.67), 365(1.56),380(1.20)	33-0571-80
2,7-Octadienal, 3,7-dimethyl-, (Z)-	n.s.g.	232(4.21),324s(1.51), 335(1.60),348(1.61), 365(1.49),380s(1.18)	33-0571-80
$C_{10}H_{16}OSi$			
Silane, trimethyl(phenoxymethyl)-	hexane	220(4.127),267(3.23), 272(3.315),279(3.225)	65-0491-80

Compound	Solvent	$\lambda_{max}(\log \epsilon)$	Ref.
Silane, trimethyl(phenoxymethyl)- (cont.)	EtOH	222(4.034),266(3.210), 272(3.368),279(3.298)	65-0491-80
$C_{10}H_{16}O_2$			
Bicyclo[3.3.1]nonan-3-one, 1-hydroxy-2-methyl-	EtOH	280(1.66)	44-3545-80
Bicyclo[2.2.1]heptan-2-one, 3-hydroxy-1,7,7-trimethyl-	MeOH	303(1.46)	136-0033-80I
1,4-Cycloheptanedione, 2,6,6-trimethyl-	pentane	298(1.65),305(1.63), 314s(1.53),328s(1.20)	33-1499-80
4-Cyclohexene-1,2-diol, 5-ethenyl-3,3-dimethyl-, (R)-	MeOH	230(4.09)	44-3401-80
(S)-	MeOH	230(4.07)	44-3401-80
2-Cyclohexen-1-ol, 4-(2-hydroxyethylidene)-6,6-dimethyl-, (E)-(+)-	MeOH	238(4.29)	44-3401-80
(Z)-	MeOH	238(4.03)	44-3401-80
$C_{10}H_{16}O_2Se$			
Selenonium, dimethyl-, 4,4-dimethyl-2,6-dioxocyclohexylide?	EtOH	263(4.25)	104-0119-80
$C_{10}H_{16}O_2Si$			
Silane, (2-methoxyphenoxy)trimethyl-	hexane	220(4.153),275(3.816)	65-0491-80
Silane, (4-methoxyphenoxy)trimethyl-	hexane	225(5.153),288(4.663)	65-0491-80
$C_{10}H_{16}O_3$			
Cyclohexanecarboxylic acid, 1-methyl-2-oxo-, ethyl ester	C_6H_{12}	290(1.32)	151-0305-80A
Cyclopentanecarboxylic acid, 1-ethyl-2-oxo-, ethyl ester	C_6H_{12}	303(1.67)	151-0305-80A
2-Heptenoic acid, 2-methyl-7-oxo-, ethyl ester, (E)-	C_6H_{12}	217(3.93),290s(--)	151-0305-80A
(Z)-	C_6H_{12}	217(3.86),290(1.54)	151-0305-80A
$C_{10}H_{16}O_4$			
2-Cyclopenten-1-one, 3-(diethoxymethyl)-4-hydroxy-, (R)-	MeCN	212(4.00)	118-0807-80
2H-Pyran-3(4H)-one, dihydro-2-[(tetrahydro-2H-pyran-2-yl)oxy]-	EtOH	302(3.45)	4-0045-80
$C_{10}H_{16}O_4S$			
2-Cyclohexen-1-one, 4,5-dihydroxy-2-(hydroxymethyl)-6-(propylthio)-, (4α,5β,6α)-(±)-	EtOH	235(4.05)	35-7987-80
$C_{10}H_{16}O_4S_2$			
Sulfonium, dimethyl(phenylmethyl-thio)-, methyl sulfate	H_2O	216(3.88),264(2.67), 294(2.14)	124-0957-80
$C_{10}H_{16}O_4Si$			
Silane, trimethoxy(phenoxymethyl)-	hexane	220(3.896),265(3.127), 271(3.228),277(3.188)	65-0491-80
$C_{10}H_{16}O_5$			
Butanedioic acid, 2-formyl-2-methyl-, diethyl ester	MeOH	237(3.78)	44-2576-80
Butanedioic acid, (methoxymethylene)-, diethyl ester	MeOH	238(3.80)	44-2576-80
$C_{10}H_{16}O_8P_2$			
Acetic acid, 2,2',2'',2'''-(1,2-ethane-	n.s.g.	215(3.94)	73-2049-80

Compound	Solvent	$\lambda_{max}(\log \epsilon)$	Ref.
diyldiphosphinidene)tetrakis-, tetrasodium salt (cont.)			73-2049-80
$C_{10}H_{16}Si$ Silane, trimethyl(2-methylphenyl)-	C_6H_{12}	215(3.81)	65-1621-80
$C_{10}H_{17}ClN_3O$ Methanaminium, N-[3-chloro-5-(dimethyl-amino)-4-ethoxy-2H-pyrrol-2-yli-dene]-N-methyl-, tetrafluoroborate	CHCl	313(4.32),405(3.14)	88-2883-80
$C_{10}H_{17}NO$ 2-Propenal, 3-(2,4,4-trimethyl-1-pyrro-lidinyl)-	MeOH	204(3.22),282(4.32)	83-0858-80
$C_{10}H_{17}NO_2$ 2-Cyclopenten-1-one, 2-(4-hydroxy-butyl)-, O-methyloxime	MeOH	243(4.03)	44-4702-80
1-Penten-3-one, 4-methyl-1-morpholino-	EtOH	307(4.37)	4-0507-80
$C_{10}H_{17}NO_3S$ Methanesulfonamide, N-(1-methylethyl)-N-(6-oxo-1-cyclohexen-1-yl)-	ether	220(3.97),322(1.91)	78-1585-80
$C_{10}H_{17}NS_2$ Cyclohexanecarbodithioic acid, 2-(prop-ylimino)-	EtOH	306(4.08),396(4.41)	118-0566-80
$C_{10}H_{17}N_3O$ 4(1H)-Pyrimidinone, 5-butyl-2-(dimeth-ylamino)-	pH 1	272(4.90)	59-0563-80
	pH 7	277(3.70),300s(--)	59-0563-80
	pH 13	290(3.82)	59-0563-80
4(1H)-Pyrimidinone, 5-butyl-2-(ethyl-amino)-	pH 1	269(4.90)	59-0563-80
	pH 7	276(3.69),296s(--)	59-0563-80
	pH 12.1	283(3.82)	59-0563-80
$C_{10}H_{17}N_3O_2$ 1H-Pyrrol-2-amine, 1-(1,1-dimethyl-ethyl)-N,N-dimethyl-4-nitro-	MeOH	280(3.85),336(3.72)	77-0123-80
1H-Pyrrol-3-amine, 1-(1,1-dimethyl-ethyl)-N,N-dimethyl-4-nitro-	MeOH	310(3.97)	77-0123-80
$C_{10}H_{17}N_5O_3$ 1H-1,2,3-Triazole-4-carboxylic acid, 1-[4-[(aminocatbonyl)amino]butyl]-, ethyl ester	MeOH	212(4.09)	78-0865-80
$C_{10}H_{17}P$ 1H-Phosphole, 1-butyl-3,4-dimethyl-, $PdCl_2$ complex (2:1)	$CHCl_3$	238(4.76),250(4.64), 349(4.04)	125-0709-80
1H-Phosphole, 3,4-dimethyl-1-(1,1-di-methylethyl)-, $PdCl_2$ complex (2:1)	$CHCl_3$	238(4.54),250(4.37), 259(4.35),274(4.25), 353(3.77)	125-0709-80
$C_{10}H_{18}ClN_4$ Methanaminium, N-(3-chloro-4,5-bis(di-methylamino)-2H-pyrrol-2-ylidene]-N-methyl-, chloride	$CHCl_3$	350(4.10),477(3.07)	88-2883-80
$C_{10}H_{18}FeO_3Si_2$ Iron, tricarbonyl[(η^2-ethenyl)dimethyl-	hexane	212(4.31),221s(4.24),	101-0013-80A

Compound	Solvent	$\lambda_{max}(\log \epsilon)$	Ref.
silyl](trimethylsilyl)- (cont.)		236(4.10),270s(3.85)	101-0013-80A
$C_{10}H_{18}N_2O$ 9-Azabicyclo[3.3.1]nonan-3-one, 9-(di- methylamino)-	MeCN	224s(3.2)	35-5482-80
$C_{10}H_{18}N_2O_2$ Acetaldehyde, (3-hydroxy-1,2,2,5,5- pentamethyl-4-imidazolidinylidene)-	EtOH	223(3.70),313(3.90)	70-0956-80
$C_{10}H_{18}N_2O_2Si$ 2,4-Diazabicyclo[4.2.0]octane-3,5-di- one, 8-methyl-6-(trimethylsilyl)-	MeOH	222(3.45)	44-4462-80
$C_{10}H_{18}N_4O_2S$ 2(1H)-Pyrimidinethione, 4,6-diamino- 5-(2,2-diethoxyethyl)-	MeOH	247(4.28),269(4.16), 304(4.15)	24-2069-80
$C_{10}H_{18}N_4S$ 3H-Pyrrole-3-thione, 2,4,5-tris(di- methylamino)-	benzene	347(4.21),563(3.65)	88-2883-80
$C_{10}H_{18}N_4S_2$ 1H-Imidazole, 2,2'-[(2-methylpropyli- dene)bis(thio)]bis[4,5-dihydro-	EtOH	245.5(4.69)	88-0293-80
$C_{10}H_{18}O$ Cyclohexanone, 4-(1,1-dimethylethyl)-	hexane MeOH	290(1.20) 281(1.26)	39-0453-80B 39-0453-80B
3-Hepten-2-one, 5,5,6-trimethyl-, (E)- 4-Hexen-2-one, 5-methyl-3-(1-methyl- ethyl)-	n.s.g. n.s.g.	219(4.10) 289(2.36),297(2.37), 304s(2.28),319s(2.00)	33-1499-80 33-1499-80
p-Menthan-3-one, (1R,4S)-	MeOH	288(1.34)	28-0255-80B
$C_{10}H_{18}SeSi$ 1,4-Pentadiene-1-selone, 3,3-dimethyl- 2-(trimethylsilyl)-	isooctane	229(4.3),291(3.4), 554(1.4)	88-4251-80
$C_{10}H_{19}B_9Co_2Se$ Cobalt, bis(η^5-2,4-cyclopentadien-1- yl)[μ-[η^5:η^5-mercuryselenadecabor- ato[4-)]]di-	MeCN	258(4.12),299(4.47), 423(3.06)	125-0458-80
$C_{10}H_{19}NO_2$ Octanamide, N,N-dimethyl-3-oxo-	EtOH EtOH-NaOH	254(3.54) 279(3.75)	39-2272-80C 39-2272-80C
$C_{10}H_{19}N_2O_4S$ Methanaminium, N-[(dimethylamino[[2- methoxy-1-(methoxycarbonyl)-2-oxo- ethyl]thio]methylene]-N-methyl-, perchlorate	MeOH	253(4.35),312(3.45)	78-2675-80
$C_{10}H_{19}N_3S$ Thiourea, [(1,1-dimethylethyl)carbon- imidoyl]diethyl-	CH_2Cl_2	253(4.0)	24-0079-80
$C_{10}H_{20}NOS$ Sulfonium, dimethyl[1-(4-morpholinyl- methylene)propyl]-, (E)-, fluorosulfate	MeCN	255(4.3)	118-0466-80

Compound	Solvent	$\lambda_{max}(\log \epsilon)$	Ref.
$C_{10}H_{20}N_2$ 9-Azabicyclo[3.3.1]nonan-9-amine, N,N-dimethyl-	MeCN	240(3.0)(end abs.)	35-5482-80
$C_{10}H_{20}N_4O_2S_2$ 1,9-Dioxa-4,6,12,14-tetraazacyclohexa-decane-5,13-dithione	H_2O H_2O MeOH	209(4.40),238(4.33) 209(4.34),238(4.31) 209(4.44),244(4.42)	88-0313-80 104-1124-80 104-1124-80
$C_{10}H_{20}OTe$ Propanetelluroic acid, 2,2-dimethyl-, O-(2,2-dimethylpropyl) ester	C_6H_{12}	243(3.49),265(2.93), 336(3.77),584(2.23)	39-2191-80C
$C_{10}H_{21}NO$ 1-Pyrrolidinepropanol, 2,4,4-trimethyl-	MeOH	204(3.08)	83-0858-80
$C_{10}H_{21}N_2O$ Piperidinium, 1-(methoxyimino)-2,2,6,6-tetramethyl-, perchlorate	MeOH	227(3.94),229(3.66)	70-0765-80
$C_{10}H_{28}Hg_2Si_4$ Mercury, bis[μ-[methylenebis(dimethyl-silylene)]]di-, cyclo	C_6H_{12}	384s(2.80),435(2.11)	101-0169-80N
$C_{10}H_{30}SSi_5$ Thiapentasilacyclohexane, decamethyl-	n.s.g.	202(--),207s(--), 227(4.09)	101-00C1-80P
$C_{10}H_{30}SeSi_5$ Selenapentasilacyclohexane, decamethyl-	n.s.g.	202(--),217s(--), 240(4.01)	101-00C1-80P
$C_{10}H_{30}Si_4$ Tetrasilane, decamethyl-	isooctane	235(4.17)	101-0159-80N
$C_{10}H_{30}Si_5$ Cyclopentasilane, decamethyl-	isooctane	210(4.38),265(2.90), 275(2.85)	101-0159-80N

Compound	Solvent	$\lambda_{max}(\log \epsilon)$	Ref.
$C_{11}H_4N_6O_8$			
1H-Perimidine, 4,6,7,9-tetranitro-	MeOH	280s(3.90),325(3.70), 410(4.19),495(4.42)	103-0071-80
	acid	440(4.33)	103-0071-80
	base	495(4.25)	103-0071-80
$C_{11}H_5BrClNOS$			
Benzothiazole, 2-(5-bromo-2-furanyl)- 6-chloro-	EtOH	201(4.67),216(4.54), 331(4.50)	128-0069-80
$C_{11}H_5Br_2NOS$			
Benzothiazole, 6-bromo-2-(5-bromo- 2-furanyl)-	EtOH	215(4.12),330(4.24)	128-0069-80
$C_{11}H_5F_5O_2$			
2-Cyclopenten-1-one, 2,4,4,5,5-penta- fluoro-3-phenoxy-	isooctane	227(4.03),244(4.15)	44-4429-80
$C_{11}H_5N_5O_6$			
1H-Perimidine, 4,6,7-trinitro-	MeOH	235(4.26),260s(4.05), 425(4.10)	103-0071-80
$C_{11}H_6BrNOS$			
Benzothiazole, 2-(5-bromo-2-furanyl)-	EtOH	209(4.36),223s(4.10), 325(4.42)	128-0069-80
$C_{11}H_6Br_2N_2$			
Propanedinitrile, [2-bromo-1-(4-bromo- phenyl)ethylidene]-	dioxan	315(4.11)	1-0289-80
$C_{11}H_6ClN$			
1-Azulenecarbonitrile, 2-chloro-	CHCl$_3$	290(4.78),303(4.88), 340(3.74),353(3.86), 365(3.47),520(2.72), 550(2.69)	18-1647-80
$C_{11}H_6Cl_2O_2S$			
4H-Pyran-4-one, 3,5-dichloro-2-(phenyl- thio)-	MeOH	215(4.13),225s(4.11), 287(3.97)	5-1960-80
$C_{11}H_6F_3N_3$			
Propanedinitrile, [2,2,2-trifluoro- 1-(phenylamino)ethylidene]-	EtOH	203(4.30),299(4.16)	104-1441-80
$C_{11}H_6F_5NO$			
2-Cyclopenten-1-one, 2,4,4,5,5-penta- fluoro-3-(phenylamino)-	isooctane	219(3.85),292(5.30)	44-4429-80
$C_{11}H_6N_2O_3$			
Pyrrolo[2,1,5-cd]indolizine-1-carbox- aldehyde, 6-nitro-	EtOH	263(4.41),309(3.86), 380s(3.79),414(3.97), 423(3.97)	39-1319-80C
$C_{11}H_6N_4O_4$			
3-Isoxazolecarbonitrile, 4-amino-5-(4- nitrobenzoyl)-	EtOH	264(4.15),299(4.03), 382(3.54)	5-1623-80
1H-Perimidine, 4,9-dinitro-	MeOH	275(4.20),330(3.71), 454(4.16)	103-0071-80
	acid	454(4.03)	103-0071-80
	base	550(4.39)	103-0071-80

Compound	Solvent	$\lambda_{max}(\log \epsilon)$	Ref.
Perimidine, 6,9-dinitro-	HCl	410(3.90)	103-0071-80
	pH 13	543(3.47)	103-0071-80
	MeOH	245(4.27),275(4.21),	103-0071-80
		340s(3.70),440(4.39)	
	HOAc	440(4.28)	103-0071-80
	CF₃COOH	400(4.05)	103-0071-80
Propanedinitrile, [[2-(4-nitrophenyl)-	EtOH	265(4.11),381(3.73)	5-1623-80
2-oxoethoxy]imino]-			
$C_{11}H_6OS_2$			
4H-[1]Benzothieno[3,2-b]pyran-4-thione	MeOH	261(3.50),270(3.51),	83-0385-80
		299(3.87),379(4.22)	
$C_{11}H_6OS_4$			
1,2-Dithiol-1-ium, 4-hydroxy-3,5-di-2-	EtOH	562(4.26)	139-0079-80A
thienyl-, hydroxide, inner salt	dioxan	607(4.48)	139-0079-80A
	MeCN	590(4.50)	139-0079-80A
$C_{11}H_6O_2$			
2H-Naphtho[1,8-bc]furan-2-one	1% MeCN	337(3.80)	35-4815-80
$C_{11}H_6O_2S$			
4H-[1]Benzothieno[3,2-b]pyran-4-one	MeOH	248(4.34),291(4.30),	83-0385-80
		324(3.89)	
4H-Pyrano[3,2-b]benzofuran-4-thione	MeOH	297(4.03),307(4.04),	83-0385-80
		372(4.41)	
$C_{11}H_6O_3$			
4H-Furo[3,2-f]benzopyran-4-one	MeOH	262(4.22),291(4.26),	42-0532-80
		318(4.27)	
7H-Furo[3,2-g][1]benzopyran-7-one	EtOH	242s(4.38),247(4.40),	94-1847-80
(psoralen)		291(4.03),330(3.80)	
4H-Pyrano[3,2-b]benzofuran-4-one	MeOH	206(4.37),289(4.41)	83-0385-80
$C_{11}H_6O_4$			
1-Naphthalenecarboxaldehyde, 5,8-di-	EtOH	248(4.22),278s(3.93),	39-0249-80C
hydro-2-hydroxy-5,8-dioxo-		315s(3.51),379(3.39)	
	EtOH-base	234(--),314(--),	39-0249-80C
		528(--)	
1-Naphthalenecarboxaldehyde, 7,8-di-	CHCl₃	250(3.93),296(4.16),	39-0249-80C
hydro-2-hydroxy-7,8-dioxo-		340s(3.52),478(3.27)	
2H-Naphtho[1,8-bc]furan-2-one, 3,6-di-	MeOH	230(4.04),279(4.15),	39-0249-80C
hydroxy-		342(3.64),390(3.61)	
2H-Naphtho[1,8-bc]furan-2-one, 3,8-di-	MeOH	256(4.00),357(3.61)	39-0249-80C
hydroxy-	MeOH-base	270(--),394(--)	39-0249-80C
Xanthotoxol	EtOH	220(4.49),244s(4.28),	94-1847-80
		251(4.33),263(4.27),	
		269(4.28),309(4.14)	
$C_{11}H_7BrClNOS$			
2-Furancarbothioamide, 5-bromo-N-(4-	EtOH	199(4.29),231s(3.87),	128-0069-80
chlorophenyl)-		304(4.18)	
$C_{11}H_7BrN_2$			
Propanedinitrile, (2-bromo-1-phenyl-	dioxan	305(4.03)	1-0289-80
ethylidene)-			
$C_{11}H_7BrOS_2$			
Ethanone, 1-(4-bromophenyl)-2-(1,3-di-	EtOH	226(4.05),234s(3.99),	18-2281-80
thiol-2-ylidene)-		271(4.06),412(4.49)	

$C_{11}H_7BrO_3-C_{11}H_7NO_3$

Compound	Solvent	$\lambda_{max}(\log \epsilon)$	Ref.
$C_{11}H_7BrO_3$ 2-Furancarboxaldehyde, 5-(4-bromophen-oxy)-	MeOH	218(3.98),300(4.32)	73-0423-80
$C_{11}H_7BrO_4$ 2-Furancarboxylic acid, 5-(4-bromophen-oxy)-	MeOH	222(3.91),265(4.20)	73-0910-80
$C_{11}H_7Br_2NOS$ 2-Furancarbothioamide, 5-bromo-N-(4-bromophenyl)-	EtOH	204(4.16),233(4.04), 318(4.33)	128-0069-80
$C_{11}H_7ClN_2$ 1H-Naphth[1,2-d]imidazole, 8-chloro-	EtOH	219(4.50),243(4.75), 248(4.73)	4-0679-80
$C_{11}H_7ClN_4$ 1H-Pyrazolo[3,4-d]pyrimidine, 1-(4-chlorophenyl)-	EtOH	248(4.48),270(3.97), 304(3.35)	114-0127-80C
$C_{11}H_7ClN_4O$ 1H-Pyrazolo[3,4-d]pyrimidine, 1-(4-chlorophenyl)-, 5-oxide	EtOH	235(3.97),285(4.38), 360(3.43)	114-0127-80C
$C_{11}H_7ClO_3$ 2-Furancarboxaldehyde, 5-(4-chlorophen-oxy)-	MeOH	218(3.96),300(4.33)	73-0423-80
$C_{11}H_7ClO_4$ 2-Furancarboxylic acid, 5-(4-chloro-phenoxy)-	MeOH	223(3.83),265(4.16)	73-0910-80
1,4-Naphthalenedione, 2-chloro-3,5-di-hydroxy-7-methyl-	MeOH	236(3.97),247s(3.95), 294(3.95),410(3.51)	39-1161-80C
$C_{11}H_7CsS_2$ 1-Naphthalenecarbodithioic acid, cesium salt	EtOH	346(3.93),479(2.29)	64-0458-80B
$C_{11}H_7F_3N_4$ 1H-Pyrazole-4-carbonitrile, 5-amino-1-phenyl-3-(trifluoromethyl)-	EtOH	203(4.41),225(4.27)	104-1441-80
$C_{11}H_7N$ 1-Naphthalenecarbonitrile	pentane	293(3.92)	149-0327-80B
	C_6H_{12}	294(3.94)	149-0327-80B
	isooctane	294(3.91)	149-0327-80B
	H_2O	297(3.86)	149-0327-80B
	MeOH	295(3.89)	149-0327-80B
	EtOH	295(3.89)	149-0327-80B
	BuOH	295(3.84)	149-0327-80B
	$HOCH_2CH_2OH$	297(3.88)	149-0327-80B
	ether	294(3.86)	149-0327-80B
	MeCN	294(3.86)	149-0327-80B
$C_{11}H_7NOS$ 2-Azaphenoxathiin	EtOH	240(4.38),285(3.29)	4-0989-80
Benzothiazole, 2-(3-furanyl)-	EtOH	217(4.44),289(4.16)	128-0069-80
$C_{11}H_7NO_3$ 5H-Oxazolo[3,2-a]quinoline-2,5(1H)-di-one	EtOH	215(4.50),284(4.30)	78-1385-80

Compound	Solvent	$\lambda_{max}(\log \epsilon)$	Ref.
$C_{11}H_7NO_5$			
2-Furancarboxaldehyde, 5-(3-nitrophen-oxy)-	MeOH	211(4.23),293(4.42)	73-0423-80
2-Furancarboxaldehyde, 5-(4-nitrophen-oxy)-	MeOH	218(4.10),294(4.45)	73-0423-80
$C_{11}H_7NO_6$			
2-Furancarboxylic acid, 5-(3-nitrophen-oxy)-	MeOH	262(4.42)	73-0910-80
2-Furancarboxylic acid, 5-(4-nitrophen-oxy)-	MeOH	214(4.05),267(4.26)	73-0910-80
$C_{11}H_7N_3$			
3H-1,2a-Diazacyclopent[cd]azulene-4-carbonitrile	EtOH	223(4.16),256s(4.04), 354(3.93),370s(3.85), 424(3.34),452(3.33), 483(3.25),520(3.06), 560s(2.74)	18-1773-80
2-Propenenitrile, 3-(2-quinoxalinyl)-	MeOH	205(4.35),265(4.46), 336(4.03)	73-0150-80
$C_{11}H_7N_3O_2$			
α-Carboline, 3-nitro-	CHCl$_3$	282(4.04),298(3.79), 351(3.56)	103-0926-80
3-Isoxazolecarbonitrile, 4-amino-5-benzoyl-	EtOH	230(4.06),310(3.95), 362s(3.52)	5-1623-80
1H-Perimidine, 6-nitro-	MeOH	265(3.65),325(3.33), 350s(--),365(3.44), 382(3.49),475(3.93)	103-0071-80
	acid	440(3.88)	103-0071-80
	base	525(4.27)	103-0071-80
Perimidine, 9-nitro-	MeOH	285(4.11),315s(3.75), 460(3.99)	103-0071-80
	acid	435(3.86)	103-0071-80
	base	520(4.26)	103-0071-80
Propanedinitrile, [(2-oxo-2-phenyl-ethoxy)imino]-	EtOH	250(4.19),281s(3.83)	5-1623-80
$C_{11}H_7N_3O_4$			
Diazene, (2-furanylcarbonyl)(4-nitro-phenyl)-	CHCl$_3$	287(4.37),466(2.28)	39-1212-80C
$C_{11}H_7N_5O$			
[1,2,4]Triazolo[1,5-a]quinazoline-2-acetonitrile, 1,5-dihydro-5-oxo-	n.s.g.	220(4.59),251(3.95), 260s(--),302(3.62), 312s(--)	33-0001-80
$C_{11}H_7N_5O_2S$			
5-Thiazolecarbonitrile, 4-amino-2-[[(4-nitrophenyl)methylene]amino]-	MeOH	228(4.14),288(4.39), 394(3.93)	78-2675-80
$C_{11}H_7RbS_2$			
1-Naphthalenecarbodithioic acid, rubidium salt	EtOH	348(4.25),481(2.23)	64-0458-80B
$C_{11}H_8BrOS_3$			
1,3-Dithiol-1-ium, 2-[[2-(4-bromophen-yl)-2-oxoethyl]thio]-, bromide	EtOH	229s(4.02),261(4.00), 465(4.19)	18-2281-80
$C_{11}H_8ClNO$			
5H-Benzocyclohepten-5-one, 7-amino-	EtOH	215(4.18),261(4.65),	39-2077-80C

Compound	Solvent	$\lambda_{max}(\log \epsilon)$	Ref.
2-chloro- (cont.)		273(4.59),346(3.86)	39-2077-80C
$C_{11}H_8ClNOS$			
3-Thiophenecarboxamide, N-(3-chloro-phenyl)-	EtOH	265(4.30)	59-0349-80
3-Thiophenecarboxamide, N-(4-chloro-phenyl)-	EtOH	231(4.04),271(4.24)	59-0349-80
$C_{11}H_8ClNOS_2$			
4-Thiazolidinone, 5-[1-(2-chlorophen-yl)methylene]-3-methyl-2-thioxo-	MeOH	249s(3.97),305s(3.97), 361(4.41)	48-0835-80
4-Thiazolidinone, 5-[1-(4-chlorophen-yl)methylene]-3-methyl-2-thioxo-	MeOH	274(3.97),294s(4.97), 376(4.48)	48-0835-80
4(5H)-Thiazolone, 5-[(2-chlorophenyl)-methylene]-2-(methylthio)-	MeOH	263(3.81),308(4.07), 385(4.42)	48-0835-80
4(5H)-Thiazolone, 5-[(4-chlorophenyl)-methylene]-2-(methylthio)-	MeOH	268(3.99),314(4.06), 374(4.47)	48-0835-80
$C_{11}H_8ClNO_2$			
2-Furancarboxamide, N-(3-chlorophenyl)-	EtOH	215(4.15),279(4.30)	59-0349-80
2-Furancarboxamide, N-(4-chlorophenyl)-	EtOH	281(4.31)	59-0349-80
3-Furancarboxamide, N-(3-chlorophenyl)-	EtOH	262(4.18)	59-0349-80
3-Furancarboxamide, N-(4-chlorophenyl)-	EtOH	265(4.21)	59-0349-80
$C_{11}H_8ClNO_3S$			
2,5-Pyrrolidinedione, 1-[(3-chloro-benzoyl)thio]-	CH_2Cl_2	248(4.14)	118-0721-80
2,5-Pyrrolidinedione, 1-[(4-chloro-benzoyl)thio]-	CH_2Cl_2	265(4.26)	118-0721-80
$C_{11}H_8NS_2$			
1,3-Dithiol-1-ium, 2-(1H-indol-3-yl)-, iodide	MeCN	438(3.53)	18-1661-80
$C_{11}H_8N_2$			
1H-Naphth[1,2-d]imidazole	EtOH	219(4.65),238(4.69), 245(4.67)	4-0679-80
$C_{11}H_8N_2OS$			
2-Butenedinitrile, 2-(methylthio)-3-phenoxy-	n.s.g.	220(2.96),317(3.20)	44-5113-80
4-Isoquinolinecarbonitrile, 1,2-di-hydro-3-(methylthio)-1-oxo-	EtOH	235(4.15),252(3.99), 314(4.18)	95-0456-80
$C_{11}H_8N_2O_2$			
Diazene, (2-furanylcarbonyl)phenyl-	$CHCl_3$	301(4.07),494(2.13)	39-1212-80C
$C_{11}H_8N_2O_3S$			
3-Thiophenecarboxamide, N-(3-nitro-phenyl)-	EtOH	215s(4.20),238s(4.14), 263(4.40)	59-0349-80
3-Thiophenecarboxamide, N-(4-nitro-phenyl)-	EtOH	220s(4.15),324(4.29)	59-0349-80
$C_{11}H_8N_2O_4$			
2-Furancarboxamide, N-(3-nitrophenyl)-	EtOH	215(3.96),275(4.43)	59-0349-80
2-Furancarboxamide, N-(4-nitrophenyl)-	EtOH	223(4.04),262(3.84), 325(4.38)	59-0349-80
3-Furancarboxamide, N-(3-nitrophenyl)-	EtOH	258(4.33)	59-0349-80
3-Furancarboxamide, N-(4-nitrophenyl)-	EtOH	221s(4.07),320(4.23)	59-0349-80
3-Isoxazolecarboxylic acid, 4-amino-5-benzoyl-	EtOH	230(3.91),259(3.87), 364(3.90)	5-1623-80

Compound	Solvent	$\lambda_{max}(\log \epsilon)$	Ref.
6H-1,2,4-Oxadiazin-5-one, 4,5-dihydro-6-(carboxymethylene)-3-phenyl-, (E)-	MeOH	237(4.14),264(4.15), 305s(3.87)	4-1101-80
(Z)-	MeOH	237(4.11),263(4.11), 310(3.81)	4-1101-80
$C_{11}H_8N_2Se$			
Selenocyanic acid, 2-amino-1-naphthalenyl ester	MeOH	244(4.68),273(3.77), 284(3.74),296(3.53), 354(3.59)	104-1963-80
Selenocyanic acid, 4-amino-1-naphthalenyl ester	MeOH	218(4.40),248(4.29), 338(4.00)	104-1963-80
$C_{11}H_8N_4S$			
5-Thiazolecarbonitrile, 4-amino-2-[(phenylmethylene)amino]-	MeOH	218(3.84),227(3.83), 273(4.29),356(3.81)	78-2675-80
$C_{11}H_8N_6O$			
4(1H)-Pteridinone, 2-amino-6-(4-pyridinyl)-	pH 1	285(4.20),336(4.27), 378s(3.81)	150-0549-80
	pH 13	276(4.43),307s(4.17), 376(4.15)	150-0549-80
$C_{11}H_8O$			
2-Azulenecarboxaldehyde	C_6H_{12}	244(4.23),275s(4.50), 288(4.69),296(4.70), 335(3.68),346(3.72), 360(3.80),613(2.61), 664(2.19)	18-3696-80
$C_{11}H_8O_2$			
1,4-Naphthalenedione, 2-methyl-	n.s.g.	330(3.45),440(1.70)	18-0757-80
3H-Naphtho[1,8-bc]furan-3-one, 4,5-dihydro-	MeOH	203(4.63),232(4.01), 284(3.69)	118-0236-80
$C_{11}H_8O_3$			
Naphth[2,3-b]oxirene-2,7-dione, 1a,7a-dihydro-1a-methyl-	hexane	227(4.48),269(3.66), 304(3.23)	44-2498-80
(-)-	isooctane	225(4.43),261(3.70), 302(3.20),304(3.15), 341(2.26),356s(2.18), 374s(1.72)	44-4094-80
$C_{11}H_8O_4$			
2H-1-Benzopyran-2-one, 7-acetoxy-	MeOH	280(4.04),310(3.96)	44-1470-80
2H-1-Benzopyran-2-one, 8-acetyl-7-hydroxy-	MeOH	209(4.35),233(3.97), 242(3.97),267(3.94), 316(4.06),340s(3.99)	44-1470-80
Naphtho[2,3-b]oxirene-2,7-dione, 1a,7a-dihydro-3-hydroxy-5-methyl-	MeOH	242(4.19),289(3.69), 365(3.69)	39-1161-80C
$C_{11}H_8O_5$			
2H-1-Benzopyran-4-carboxylic acid, 7-methoxy-2-oxo-	C_6H_{12}	356(3.97)	95-0289-80
$C_{11}H_8S_2$			
1-Naphthalenecarbodithoic acid, cesium salt	EtOH	346(3.93),479(2.29)	64-0458-80B
rubidium salt	EtOH	348(4.25),481(2.23)	64-0458-80B
$C_{11}H_9BrOS_2$			
Ethanone, 1-(4-bromophenyl)-2-(1,3-di-	EtOH	220s(3.89),269(4.00),	18-2281-80

Compound	Solvent	$\lambda_{max}(\log \epsilon)$	Ref.
thiolan-2-ylidene)- (cont.)		349(4.30)	18-2281-80
$C_{11}H_9BrOS_3$ Ethanone, 1-(4-bromophenyl)-2-(1,3-di- thiolan-2-yl)-2-thioxo-	EtOH	260(4.31),350(3.76)	18-2281-80
$C_{11}H_9ClN_2$ 1H-Imidazole, 4-[2-(2-chlorophenyl)- ethenyl]-, cis	EtOH	226(4.03),278(3.82)	4-0679-80
trans	EtOH	232(4.04),301(4.42)	4-0679-80
1H-Imidazole, 4-[2-(3-chlorophenyl)- ethenyl]-, cis	EtOH	230(4.18),292(3.95)	4-0679-80
trans	EtOH	233(4.09),303(4.43)	4-0679-80
1H-Imidazole, 4-[2-(4-chlorophenyl)- ethenyl]-, cis	EtOH	228(4.14),291(3.95)	4-0679-80
trans	EtOH	228(4.03),304(4.46)	4-0679-80
$C_{11}H_9ClN_2O_2$ 3(2H)-Pyridazinone, 4-chloro-5-hydroxy- 2-(phenylmethyl)-	MeOH	216s(--),227s(--), 280(4.05)	73-0127-80
$C_{11}H_9ClN_4O$ 6H-[1,2,4]Triazolo[4,3-a][1,4]benzodi- azepin-6-one, 8-chloro-4,5-dihydro- 1-methyl-	EtOH	212(4.56),236(4.24), 283(3.18),291s(3.13)	87-0873-80
$C_{11}H_9ClN_4S$ 6H-[1,2,4]Triazolo[4,3-a][1,4]benzodi- azepine-6-thione, 8-chloro-4,5-di- hydro-1-methyl-	EtOH	223(4.50),316(3.89)	87-0873-80
$C_{11}H_9ClO$ 2,4-Pentadienal, 5-(4-chlorophenyl)-, (E,E)-	EtOH	237(4.13),324(4.60)	118-0815-80
$C_{11}H_9ClO_2$ 2,4-Pentadienoic acid, 5-(4-chloro- phenyl)-, (E,E)-	EtOH	235(4.03),310(4.34)	118-0815-80
$C_{11}H_9ClO_4$ 1H-2-Benzopyran-1-one, 5-chloro-8-hy- droxy-6-methoxy-3-methyl-	EtOH	248(4.32),265(3.76), 281s(3.33)	102-2003-80
	EtOH-AlCl$_3$	240(4.23),266(3.81), 274(3.83)	102-2003-80
$C_{11}H_9F_3N_2$ Pyrimidine, 1,4-dihydro-4-[4-(tri- fluoromethyl)phenyl]-	EtOH	283(3.12)	4-1617-80
$C_{11}H_9NO$ 5H-Benzocyclohepten-5-one, 7-amino-	EtOH	262(4.41),272(4.51), 280(4.55),332(3.86)	39-2077-80C
1,3-Oxazepine, 2-phenyl-	EtOH	238(4.15),323(3.66)	142-1569-80B
$C_{11}H_9NOS$ 3-Furancarbothioamide, N-phenyl-	EtOH	207(4.35),253(4.09)	128-0069-80
2-Propenoyl isothiocyanate, 3-(4-meth- ylphenyl)-	dioxan	322(4.46)	73-2334-80
3-Thiophenecarboxamide, N-phenyl-	EtOH	224s(4.04),267(4.14)	59-0349-80

Compound	Solvent	$\lambda_{max}(\log \epsilon)$	Ref.
$C_{11}H_9NOS_3$			
Ethanethioic acid, S-(2,5-dihydro-4-phenyl-5-thioxo-3-isothiazolyl) ester	CHCl$_3$	308(4.20),415(4.24)	39-2693-80C
$C_{11}H_9NO_2$			
2-Furancarboxamide, N-phenyl-	EtOH	277(4.25)	59-0349-80
3-Furancarboxamide, N-phenyl-	EtOH	262(4.11)	59-0349-80
5(4H)-Oxazolone, 2-methyl-4-(phenylmethylene)-	dioxan	330(4.37)	70-0576-80
$C_{11}H_9NO_2S$			
2-Propenoyl isothiocyanate, 3-(4-methoxyphenyl)-	dioxan	344(4.48)	73-2334-80
4-Quinolinecarboxylic acid, 1,2-dihydro-5-methyl-2-thioxo-	EtOH	223(4.53),287(4.42), 392(4.01)	94-0049-80
4-Quinolinecarboxylic acid, 1,2-dihydro-6-methyl-2-thioxo-	EtOH	222(4.54),288(4.35), 400(3.98)	94-0049-80
4-Quinolinecarboxylic acid, 1,2-dihydro-7-methyl-2-thioxo-	EtOH	223(4.64),282(4.38), 398(4.10)	94-0049-80
4-Quinolinecarboxylic acid, 1,2-dihydro-8-methyl-2-thioxo-	EtOH	222(4.50),284(4.34), 395(3.98)	94-0049-80
4-Quinolinecarboxylic acid, 1,2-dihydro-2-thioxo-, methyl ester	EtOH	222(4.49),289(4.22), 419(3.97)	94-0049-80
$C_{11}H_9NO_3$			
4-Quinolinecarboxylic acid, 1,2-dihydro-1-methyl-2-oxo-	EtOH	230(4.51),276(3.78), 283(3.78),331(3.76)	94-1157-80
4-Quinolinecarboxylic acid, 1,2-dihydro-3-methyl-2-oxo-	EtOH	221(4.55),273(3.89), 324(3.88)	94-1157-80
$C_{11}H_9NO_3S$			
2,5-Pyrrolidinedione, 1-(benzoylthio)-	CH$_2$Cl$_2$	246(4.09),256(4.06)	118-0721-80
2-Quinolinecarbothioic acid, 8-hydroxy-4-methoxy-	MeOH	218(4.27),268(4.40), 355(3.25),417(3.13)	64-1569-80B
$C_{11}H_9NO_4$			
4H-1-Benzopyran-4-one, 2-ethyl-3-nitro-	EtOH	245(4.06),370(3.78)	39-2049-80C
2H-Isoindole-2-carboxylic acid, 1,3-dihydro-1,3-dioxo-, ethyl ester	MeCN	216(4.68),263(3.15), 292(3.15)	44-0174-80
2-Quinolinecarboxylic acid, 8-hydroxy-4-methoxy-	MeOH	211(4.48),249(4.56), 315(3.45),348(3.57)	64-1569-80B
$C_{11}H_9N_3$			
4-Pyridinamine, N-(4-pyridinylmethylene)-	EtOH	246(4.29),331s(3.31)	12-1397-80
Pyridine, 2-(phenylazo)-	EtOH	320(4.26)	62-0158-80
Pyridine, 3-(phenylazo)-	EtOH	318(4.30)	62-0158-80
Pyridine, 4-(phenylazo)-	EtOH	312(4.28)	62-0158-80
Pyrimidine, 5-[2-(3-pyridinyl)ethenyl]-, cis	MeCN	265(4.00),292(4.05)	44-1557-80
trans	MeCN	267(4.22),317(4.34)	44-1557-80
[1,2,4]Triazolo[4,3-a]quinoline, 1-methyl-	MeOH	290(3.97)	56-0661-80
$C_{11}H_9N_3O$			
2-Pentenenitrile, 4-oxo-5-(phenylhydrazono)-	MeOH	202(4.21),251(4.09), 278(3.78),399(4.29)	73-0150-80
1H-Pyrazole-5-acetonitrile, 4-hydroxy-1-phenyl-	MeOH	204(4.17),220(3.90), 261(3.93)	73-0150-80

Compound	Solvent	λ_{max}(log ϵ)	Ref.
$C_{11}H_9N_3O_2$			
1,3-Benzenediol, 4-(2-pyridinylazo)-	pH 7.5	415(3.51)	140-0314-80
	n.s.g.	385(4.15)	73-1502-80
	anion	415(4.44)	73-1502-80
	dianion	485(4.38)	73-1502-80
	cation	400(4.20)	73-1502-80
lead complex	n.s.g.	515(4.58)	140-0314-80
1H-Imidazole, 4-[2-(2-nitrophenyl)eth-enyl]-, cis	EtOH	239(4.04)	4-0679-80
trans	EtOH	214(4.23),278(4.24), 295(4.27)	4-0679-80
1H-Imidazole, 4-[2-(3-nitrophenyl)eth-enyl]-, cis	EtOH	215(4.48),273(4.32)	4-0679-80
1H-Imidazole, 4-[2-(4-nitrophenyl)eth-enyl]-, cis	EtOH	254(4.16),355(3.99)	4-0679-80
trans	EtOH	245(3.95),366(4.23)	4-0679-80
2-Pyridinamine, 5-nitro-N-phenyl-	C_6H_{12}	247(4.06),348(4.29)	18-0717-80
	EtOH	215(4.17),378(4.29)	18-0717-80
	MeCN	250(4.19),377(4.33)	18-0717-80
$C_{11}H_9N_3O_3$			
Acetamide, 2-cyano-2-[(2-oxo-2-phenyl-ethoxy)imino]-, (E)-	EtOH	244(4.40),312s(3.00)	5-1623-80
Acetamide, N-1,3-dioxolo[4,5-g]quin-azolin-8-yl-	EtOH	204(3.95),227s(4.28), 244(4.48),278s(3.74), 309s(3.81),320(3.99), 333(4.05)	114-0253-80B
3-Isoxazolecarboxamide, 4-amino-5-benz-oyl-	EtOH	265(3.69),360(3.73)	5-1623-80
$C_{11}H_9N_3O_4S$			
4(5H)-Thiazolone, 2-[(hydroxymethyl)-amino]-5-[(4-nitrophenyl)methylene]-	EtOH	223(4.05),299(4.09), 355(4.28)	103-0718-80
$C_{11}H_9N_5O_3$			
2-Pentenenitrile, 5-[(6-amino-1,3-di-methyl-2,4-dioxo-5-pyrimidinyl)imino]-	MeOH	202(4.24),254(4.09), 278(3.94),412(4.09)	73-0150-80
$C_{11}H_9N_5O_4$			
3-Pentenenitrile, 5-[(2,4-dinitrophen-yl)hydrazono]-, (E,E)-	EtOH	360(4.51)	1-0031-80
(Z,E)-	EtOH	360(4.51)	1-0031-80
$C_{11}H_{10}$			
Benzene, 1-ethenyl-2-(1,2-propadienyl)-	hexane	228(4.58),258(4.51)	89-0631-80
Dicycloprop[a,b]indene, 1,2,2a,6b-tet-rahydro-	hexane	209(4.77),230s(3.92), 275(3.46),283(3.51)	89-0631-80
$C_{11}H_{10}BrNO$			
Cyclopent[d]azepine, 1-bromo-2-ethoxy-	C_6H_{12}	280(4.7),330s(3.8), 625(2.9),800(2.4)	77-0974-80
$C_{11}H_{10}BrNOS$			
1,4-Thiazepin-5(2H)-one, 6-bromo-3,4-dihydro-7-phenyl-	MeOH	235(3.77),298(3.62)	24-0995-80
$C_{11}H_{10}BrN_3O$			
1H-1,2,4-Triazolium, 1-methyl-, 4-[2-(4-bromophenyl)-2-oxoethylide]	pH 13	318(4.00)	80-0407-80

Compound	Solvent	$\lambda_{max}(\log \epsilon)$	Ref.
$C_{11}H_{10}BrN_5$			
Pyrazolo[3,4-d]-1,2,3-triazole, 2-(2-bromo-4-methylphenyl)-2,3-dihydro-4-methyl-	CHCl$_3$	430(3.25)	103-1160-80
$C_{11}H_{10}ClN$			
Isoquinoline, 6-chloro-1,3-dimethyl-	MeOH-acid	235(4.73),275(3.46), 343(3.75)	118-0070-80
	MeOH-base	227(4.71),268(3.60), 331(3.54)	118-0070-80
Isoquinoline, 7-chloro-1,3-dimethyl-	MeOH-acid	235(4.78),276(3.57), 353(3.55)	118-0070-80
	MeOH-base	222(4.78),273(3.76), 338(3.51)	118-0070-80
$C_{11}H_{10}ClNO$			
2(1H)-Quinolinone, 3-(2-chloroethyl)-	CHCl$_3$	243(3.83),272(3.83), 281(3.77),320(3.71), 329(3.78),340(3.62)	150-0414-80S
$C_{11}H_{10}ClNOS$			
1,4-Thiazepin-5(2H)-one, 6-chloro-3,4-dihydro-7-phenyl-	MeOH	245(3.89),300(3.66)	24-0995-80
$C_{11}H_{10}ClNO_4$			
Acetic acid, chloro[[(4-methylbenzoyl)-oxy]imino]-, methyl ester	MeOH	251(4.26)	94-3296-80
$C_{11}H_{10}ClN_3OS$			
5H-Pyrimido[4,5-b][1,4]benzothiazin-9(6H)-one, 4-chloro-7,8-dihydro-5-methyl-	EtOH	222(4.16),247(3.89), 300(3.89),356(3.75)	103-0580-80
$C_{11}H_{10}ClN_3O_2$			
Benzoic acid, 5-chloro-2-(3-methyl-4H-1,2,4-triazol-4-yl)-, methyl ester	EtOH	206(4.60),225s(4.04), 283(3.13),291s(3.08)	87-0873-80
$C_{11}H_{10}ClN_3O_2Se$			
1,3,4-Selenadiazole-2-carboxylic acid, 4-(4-chlorophenyl)-4,5-dihydro-5-imino-, ethyl ester	EtOH	258(4.02),330(4.00)	4-1185-80
$C_{11}H_{10}Cl_2O$			
Benzene, 1-[(2,2-dichlorocyclopropyl)-oxy]-4-ethenyl-	hexane	222(4.48),275s(--), 285(3.46)	70-1928-80
$C_{11}H_{10}Cl_2O_2$			
Phenol, 4-chloro-2-(2-chloro-2-propen-yl)-, acetate	EtOH	228(3.50),278(1.74)	36-0232-80
$C_{11}H_{10}Cl_2O_3$			
2-Propanone, 1-(2-acetoxy-5-chloro-phenyl)-3-chloro-	EtOH	226(3.51),270(2.74), 278(1.72)	36-0232-80
$C_{11}H_{10}Cl_6N_2O_2$			
4H-1,3-Oxazin-4-one, 6-[(1,1-dimethyl-ethyl)amino]-5-(trichloroethenyl)-2-(trichloromethyl)-	MeCN	202(4.23),263(4.05), 300s(3.47)	24-0811-80
4H-1,3-Oxazin-4-one, 6-[(1-methylprop-yl)amino]-5-(trichloroethenyl)-2-(trichloromethyl)-	MeCN	203(4.27),260(4.11), 300(3.52)	24-0811-80

Compound	Solvent	$\lambda_{max}(\log \epsilon)$	Ref.
$C_{11}H_{10}F_{11}N_3$			
3-Azetemethanamine, 1,2-dihydro-N,1-dimethyl-2-(methylimino)-α-(pentafluoroethyl)-α,4-bis(trifluoromethyl)-	C_6H_{12}	290(4.13)	39-1551-80C
$C_{11}H_{10}FeO_3$			
Iron, dicarbonyl[(η^5-cyclopentadien-1-ylidene)(1-methyl-3-oxo-1,3-propanediyl)]-	hexane	250s(3.8),327(3.6)	24-2211-80
Iron, dicarbonyl[(η^5-cyclopentadien-1-ylidene)(2-methyl-3-oxo-1,3-propanediyl)]-	hexane	251s(3.8),326(3.6)	24-2211-80
Iron, tricarbonyl[(4,5,6,7-η)-1-methylspiro[2.4]hepta-4,6-diene]-	hexane at -13°	294(3.7)	24-2211-80
$C_{11}H_{10}MoO_3$			
Molybdenum, tricarbonyl[(1,2,3,4,5-η)-propyl-2,4-cyclopentadiene-1,2'-diyl]-	hexane	265s(3.9),304s(3.5), 423(2.5)	24-1033-80
$C_{11}H_{10}N_2$			
1H-Imidazole, 4-(2-phenylethenyl)-, cis	EtOH	223(4.16),285(3.94)	4-0679-80
trans	EtOH	227(4.09),300(4.43)	4-0679-80
$C_{11}H_{10}N_2O$			
[2,4'-Bipyridin]-3'-ol, 2'-methyl-	MeOH	252(4.0),285(3.9), 325(3.8)	103-0951-80
$C_{11}H_{10}N_2OS$			
4-Thiazolidinone, 2-imino-3-methyl-5-(phenylmethylene)-	EtOH	232(3.95),254(3.82), 325(4.35)	103-0718-80
4-Thiazolidinone, 2-(methylimino)-5-(phenylmethylene)-	EtOH	240(3.83),293(4.04), 331(4.28)	103-0718-80
$C_{11}H_{10}N_2O_2$			
Acetonitrile, [[(2-oxo-1-phenylpropylidene)amino]oxy]-	EtOH	229(4.00),288(4.05)	5-1623-80
Ethanone, 1-(4-amino-3-phenyl-5-isoxazolyl)-	EtOH	229(4.10),330(3.81)	5-1623-80
2(1H)-Pyrazinone, 1-(phenylmethyl)-, 4-oxide	pH 1	222(4.40),275(3.99), 330(3.70)	94-2734-80
	H_2O	222(4.39),275(3.99), 330(3.70)	94-2734-80
	pH 13	223(4.42),275(3.99), 330(3.71)	94-2734-80
4(1H)-Pyrimidinone, 5-(4-methoxyphenyl)-	EtOH	223(3.92)	22-0559-80
$C_{11}H_{10}N_2O_2S$			
1,3-Dioxolo[4,5-g]quinazoline, 6-methyl-8-(methylthio)-	EtOH	205s(4.18),213(4.28), 233(4.32),245(4.32), 308s(3.79),314s(3.81), 330(4.07),344(4.13)	114-0253-80B
2-Furanpropanenitrile, α-[1-aziridinyl-(methylthio)methylene]-β-oxo-	MeOH	221(3.90),268(4.02), 351(4.33)	78-1791-80
3(2H)-Pyridazinone, 4-hydroxy-5-(methylthio)-2-phenyl-	MeOH	214(4.28),232s(4.28), 291(3.81)	73-0127-80
3(2H)-Pyridazinone, 5-hydroxy-4-(methylthio)-2-phenyl-	MeOH	212(4.23),232s(--), 310(3.73)	73-0127-80
1,3,4-Thiadiazol-2(3H)-one, 5-acetyl-3-(3-methylphenyl)-	EtOH	235s(3.85),305(3.98)	4-1713-80

Compound	Solvent	$\lambda_{max}(\log \epsilon)$	Ref.
1,3,4-Thiadiazol-2(3H)-one, 5-acetyl-3-(4-methylphenyl)-	EtOH	242s(3.96),310(3.99)	4-1713-80
4(5H)-Thiazolone, 2-amino-5-[(3-methoxyphenyl)methylene]-	MeOH	249(4.08),350(4.47)	48-0835-80
4(5H)-Thiazolone, 2-amino-5-[(4-methoxyphenyl)methylene]-	EtOH	246(4.09),296(3.93), 350(4.39)	103-0718-80
4(5H)-Thiazolone, 2-[(hydroxymethyl)amino]-5-(phenylmethylene)-	EtOH	238(3.96),287(4.08), 331(4.29)	103-0718-80
Thiourea, (4-methyl-2-oxo-2H-1-benzopyran-6-yl)-	EtOH	260(3.90),302(4.29), 329(4.41)	95-0289-80
$C_{11}H_{10}N_2O_2Se$			
1,3,4-Selenadiazol-2(3H)-one, 5-acetyl-3-(4-methylphenyl)-	EtOH	322(4.02)	4-1185-80
$C_{11}H_{10}N_2O_3$			
1H-Indazol-5-ol, 1-acetyl-, acetate	EtOH	232(4.45),257s(--), 295(3.83),304(3.80)	5-0908-80
3(2H)-Pyridazinone, 4-hydroxy-5-methoxy-2-phenyl-	MeOH	222(4.35),285(3.79)	73-0127-80
3(2H)-Pyridazinone, 5-hydroxy-4-methoxy-2-phenyl-	MeOH	210(4.41),223s(--), 283(3.91)	73-0127-80
2-Quinazolinecarboxylic acid, 1,4-dihydro-4-oxo-, ethyl ester	EtOH	229(4.29),298(4.00)	117-0219-80
2-Quinolinecarboxamide, 8-hydroxy-4-methoxy-	MeOH	215(4.33),249(4.24), 269(4.04),349(3.27), 411(3.02)	64-1569-80B
$C_{11}H_{10}N_2O_3S$			
1,3,4-Thiadiazol-2(3H)-one, 5-acetyl-3-(4-methoxyphenyl)-	EtOH	243(4.06),315(3.91)	4-1713-80
$C_{11}H_{10}N_2O_3Se$			
1,3,4-Selenadiazole-2-carboxylic acid, 4,5-dihydro-5-oxo-4-phenyl-, ethyl ester	EtOH	319(3.98)	4-1185-80
$C_{11}H_{10}N_2S$			
Ethanethioamide, N-[2-(2-cyanoethenyl)phenyl]-, (E)-	MeOH	224s(4.09),232s(4.00), 270(4.15)	44-1549-80
Pyrimidine, 2-[(phenylmethyl)thio]-	EtOH	215s(--),254(4.230), 275s(3.857),285s(3.397)	112-0001-80
	CH_2Cl_2	253(4.225),285s(3.301)	112-0001-80
1,3,4-Thiadiazole, 2-methyl-5-(2-phenylethenyl)-	EtOH	225(4.00),308(4.44)	94-2116-80
$C_{11}H_{10}N_2S_2$			
Propanedinitrile, [[5-[(1-methylethyl)thio]-2-thienyl]methylene]-	MeOH	205(4.08),245(3.76), 282(3.60),346(4.25)	73-2360-80
$C_{11}H_{10}N_4$			
2-Pyridinecarboxaldehyde, 2-pyridinylhydrazone, anti	benzene	356.5(4.36)	151-0083-80B
syn	benzene	331(4.47)	151-0083-80B
2,2a,4,5-Tetrazabenz[cd]azulene, 1,3-dimethyl-	MeOH	307s(3.60),318s(3.66), 335s(3.77),347(3.84), 365(3.71),426s(2.66), 448(2.72),477(2.71), 506s(2.59),558s(2.28)	4-1057-80

Compound	Solvent	$\lambda_{max}(\log \epsilon)$	Ref.
$C_{11}H_{10}N_4O$ 1H-Benzimidazole-2-acetonitrile, α-[(methoxyamino)methylene]-	MeOH	207(4.39),223(4.48), 259(4.09),266(4.15), 281(4.28),288(4.29), 318(4.44),327(4.44)	94-0567-80
4-Pyridazinecarboxamide, N-(2-amino-phenyl)-	DMSO	295s(3.5),330(3.4)	39-1339-80B
$C_{11}H_{10}N_4O_2S$ Ethanone, 1-[4,5-dihydro-4-(3-methyl-phenyl)-5-(nitrosoimino)-1,3,4-thiadiazol-2-yl]-	EtOH	276(3.45),347(3.73), 465(1.73)	4-1713-80
Ethanone, 1-[4,5-dihydro-4-(4-methyl-phenyl)-5-(nitrosoimino)-1,3,4-thiadiazol-2-yl]-	EtOH	273(3.96),345(4.01), 465(1.74)	4-1713-80
4(1H)-Pyrimidinone, 6-amino-5-nitroso-2-[(phenylmethyl)thio]-	CHCl$_3$	279(3.83),350(4.25), 646(1.88)	95-0515-80
Co(III) chelate	CHCl$_3$	410(4.85)	95-0515-80
$C_{11}H_{10}N_4O_2Se$ Ethanone, 1-[4,5-dihydro-4-(4-methyl-phenyl)-5-(nitrosoimino)-1,3,4-selenadiazol-2-yl]-	EtOH	253(4.00),281(4.83), 480(1.72)	4-1185-80
$C_{11}H_{10}N_4O_3S$ Ethanone, 1-[4,5-dihydro-4-(4-methoxy-phenyl)-5-(nitrosoimino)-1,3,4-thiadiazol-2-yl]-	EtOH	284(4.33),347(4.35), 465(1.82)	4-1713-80
$C_{11}H_{10}N_4O_3Se$ 1,3,4-Selenadiazole-2-carboxylic acid, 4,5-dihydro-5-(nitrosoimino)-4-phen-yl-, ethyl ester	EtOH	268(3.93),342(4.00), 480(1.75)	4-1185-80
$C_{11}H_{10}N_4O_4S$ 2-Thiazolemethanamine, N-(2,4-dinitro-phenyl)-α-methyl-, (R)-	MeOH	232(4.19),340(4.29)	78-2133-80
$C_{11}H_{10}N_4S$ 2H-1,2,4-Triazino[5,6-b]indole, 3-(ethylthio)-	MeOH-HCl	283(4.61),344(3.65)	83-0108-80
3H-1,2,4-Triazino[5,6-b]indole-3-thi-one, 2,5-dihydro-6,7-dimethyl-	EtOH	236(3.52),260(3.48), 306(4.22)	142-1139-80
	EtOH-HCl	260(3.44),306(4.25)	142-1139-80
	EtOH-KOH	290(4.09),370(3.36)	142-1139-80
$C_{11}H_{10}N_6O$ 4(1H)-Pteridinone, 2-amino-7,8-dihydro-6-(4-pyridinyl)-	pH 1	258(4.17),283(4.12), 448(4.07)	150-0549-80
	pH 13	265(4.28),309(4.09)	150-0549-80
$C_{11}H_{10}N_6O_4$ 4(1H)-Pyrimidinone, 2-amino-5-nitro-6-[[2-oxo-2-(4-pyridinyl)ethyl]-amino]-, monohydrochloride	pH 1	253s(4.04),333(4.19), 404(4.05)	150-0549-80
$C_{11}H_{10}N_8$ 2,4,7-Pteridinetriamine, 6-(4-pyridin-yl)-	pH 1	253s(4.35),311s(4.03), 382(4.32)	150-0549-80

Compound	Solvent	$\lambda_{max}(\log \epsilon)$	Ref.
$C_{11}H_{10}O$			
Cyclobutanone, 2-(phenylmethylene)-	EtOH	303(4.15)	44-4183-80
3a,7a-Etheno-1H-inden-2(3H)-one	EtOH	215(3.40),220(3.41),	88-3583-80
		226s(3.32),267(3.43)	
$C_{11}H_{10}OS$			
2-Benzofuranthiol, 3-(2-propenyl)-	EtOH	213(3.84),237(3.39),	103-0991-90
		248(3.45),255(3.33),	
		285(3.34),305(3.26),	
		320(3.16)	
2H-1-Benzothiopyran-2-one, 4,6-di-methyl-	EtOH	237(4.45),243(4.48),	18-2046-80
		290(3.90),298(3.90),	
		350(3.48)	
2H-1-Benzothiopyran-2-one, 4,7-di-methyl-	EtOH	230(4.38),239(4.38),	18-2046-80
		295(3.90),303(3.95),	
		343(3.60)	
$C_{11}H_{10}OS_2$			
2H-1-Benzothiopyran-2-thione, 7-meth-oxy-4-methyl-	EtOH	245(4.65),272(4.08),	18-2415-80
		278(4.08),309(3.91),	
		432(4.18)	
4H-1-Benzothiopyran-4-thione, 7-meth-oxy-2-methyl-	EtOH	253(4.28),289(4.04),	18-2415-80
		343(3.87),409(4.34)	
Ethanone, 2-(1,3-dithiolan-2-ylidene)-1-phenyl-	EtOH	214s(3.85),221s(3.75),	35-3095-80
		259(3.91),288(3.77),	
		345(4.34)	
$C_{11}H_{10}OS_3$			
1,2-Dithiol-1-ium, 3-(ethylthio)-4-hy-droxy-5-phenyl-, hydroxide, inner	EtOH	482(4.28)	139-0079-80A
	dioxan	545(4.42)	139-0079-80A
salt	MeCN	527(4.28)	139-0079-80A
$C_{11}H_{10}O_2$			
1-Naphthalenol, 4-methoxy-	MeCN	320(3.8),332(3.8)	49-0563-80
2H-Pyran-3(6H)-one, 5-phenyl-	EtOH	215(3.77),285(4.16)	1-0295-80
$C_{11}H_{10}O_2S_3$			
Benzo[b]thiophene-4,7-dione, 5-(methyl-thio)-6-[(methylthio)methyl]-	EtOH	239(4.19),275(3.88),	39-0282-80C
		330(3.80),467(3.29)	
$C_{11}H_{10}O_2Se$			
Selenonium, dimethyl-, 1,3-dihydro-1,3-dioxo-2H-inden-2-ylide	EtOH	217(4.52),255(4.49),	104-0119-80
		265(4.49),300(3.38),	
		374(3.20)	
$C_{11}H_{10}O_3$			
2H-1-Benzopyran-2-one, 7-methoxy-6-methyl-	EtOH	222(4.13),246s(3.62),	2-0085-80
		253s(3.54),298s(3.79),	
		337(4.07)	
4H-1-Benzopyran-4-one, 7-hydroxy-2,3-dimethyl-	pH 4.5	244.8(4.11),250.9(4.10),	86-0977-80
		296.1(4.21)	
	pH 10.5	259.6(4.51),302s(4.17),	86-0977-80
		333.7(4.31)	
2,8-Decadiene-4,6-diynoic acid, 10-hy-droxy-, methyl ester, cis-cis	MeOH	233(4.18),246(4.27),	102-0563-80
		258(4.23),294s(3.94),	
		310(4.06),330(3.98)	
Ethanone, 1-(3-methoxy-2-benzofuranyl)-	MeOH	223(3.91),233(3.87),	83-0385-80
		302(4.33)	
1(3H)-Isobenzofuranone, 6-ethenyl-4-methoxy-	MeOH	216(4.38),268(4.29),	94-3601-80
		313(3.68)	

$C_{11}H_{10}O_4-C_{11}H_{11}ClO_4$

Compound	Solvent	$\lambda_{max}(\log \epsilon)$	Ref.
$C_{11}H_{10}O_4$			
5H-1,3-Dioxolo[4,5-g][2]benzopyran-5-one, 7,8-dihydro-7-methyl-	n.s.g.	225(4.48),266(3.83), 304(3.99)	2-0009-80
6H-1,3-Dioxolo[4,5-f][2]benzopyran-6-one, 8,9-dihydro-8-methyl-, (±)-	n.s.g.	225(4.46),272(3.99), 297(3.95)	2-0009-80
2-Heptene-4,6-diynoic acid, 7-[3-(hydroxymethyl)oxiranyl]-, methyl ester	MeOH	227(3.38),260s(3.72), 273(3.91),288(4.09), 307(4.05)	102-0563-80
2-Propenal, 3-(7-methoxy-1,3-benzodioxol-5-yl)-	MeOH	243(4.03),337(4.04)	100-0407-80
Scoparone	MeOH	232(4.18),254s(3.70), 262s(3.60),296(3.67), 345(3.99)	95-0466-80
Spiro[1,3-benzodioxole-2,1'-cyclopentane]-5,6-dione	EtOH	292(4.17),395(3.16)	12-0527-80
$C_{11}H_{10}O_5$			
1,2-Benzenedicarboxylic acid, 5-ethenyl-3-methoxy-	pH 1	225(4.41),255s(--), 317(3.85)	94-3601-80
	pH 13	223(4.39),260s(--), 309(3.56)	94-3601-80
$C_{11}H_{10}O_6$			
Benzoic acid, 2,4-diacetoxy-	pH 9.0	295(3.93)	106-0739-80
Benzoic acid, 2,5-diacetoxy-	pH 9.0	322(3.67)	106-0739-80
$C_{11}H_{10}S_2$			
Benzo[b]thiophene-2-thiol, 3-(2-propenyl)-	EtOH	212(4.04),233(4.16), 253(3.83),268(3.79), 281(3.80),300(3.66), 309(3.51),338(3.11)	103-0991-80
2H-1-Benzothiopyran-2-thione, 4,7-dimethyl-	EtOH	238(4.43),303(4.04), 425(4.00)	18-2415-80
4H-1-Benzothiopyran-4-thione, 2,7-dimethyl-	EtOH	238(4.11),247(4.38), 296(3.92),412(4.26)	18-2415-80
$C_{11}H_{11}BrN_3O$			
1H-1,2,4-Triazolium, 4-[2-(4-bromophenyl)-2-oxoethyl]-1-methyl-, bromide	MeOH	261(4.24)	80-0407-80
$C_{11}H_{11}BrO_2$			
2-Butenoic acid, 3-(4-bromophenyl)-2-methyl-, (E)-	EtOH	247(3.81)	32-0327-80
(Z)-	EtOH	250(3.65)	32-0327-80
1(2H)-Naphthalenone, 5-bromo-3,4-dihydro-8-methoxy-	EtOH	226(4.40),256(3.80), 327(3.62)	78-2513-80
$C_{11}H_{11}ClN_2O_3$			
Quinoline, 1-(chloroacetyl)-1,2,3,4-tetrahydro-8-nitro-	EtOH	245(4.08),270s(3.53), 325(3.34)	103-0386-80
$C_{11}H_{11}ClO_2$			
2-Butenoic acid, 3-(4-chlorophenyl)-2-methyl-, (E)-	EtOH	242(4.06)	32-0327-80
(Z)-	EtOH	247(3.97)	32-0327-80
$C_{11}H_{11}ClO_4$			
1H-2-Benzopyran-1-one, 5-chloro-3,4-dihydro-8-hydroxy-6-methoxy-3-methyl-	EtOH	220(4.37),267(4.67), 313(3.76)	94-1622-80

Compound	Solvent	$\lambda_{max}(\log \epsilon)$	Ref.
$C_{11}H_{11}Cl_2N_3O$ 1H-Benzotriazole, 4,5-dichloro-1-(cyclopentyloxy)-	EtOH	209(4.49),265(3.90), 272(3.91),294(3.80)	4-1115-80
$C_{11}H_{11}Cl_3N_2O_5$ Acetamide, 2,2,2-trichloro-N-(hydroxymethyl)-N-[2-hydroxy-2-(4-nitrophenyl)ethyl]-	pH 7	279(4.00)	87-1299-80
$C_{11}H_{11}FO_2$ 2-Butenoic acid, 3-(4-fluorophenyl)-2-methyl-, (E)-	EtOH	236(3.93)	32-0327-80
(Z)-	EtOH	240(3.82)	32-0327-80
$C_{11}H_{11}F_3N_4O_4$ 9H-Purine, 9-β-D-ribofuranosyl-6-(trifluoromethyl)-	MeOH	271(4.08)	39-2755-80C
	MeOH-acid	271(4.08)	39-2755-80C
	MeOH-base	258(4.08)	39-2755-80C
$C_{11}H_{11}N$ Isoquinoline, 1,3-dimethyl-	MeOH-acid	228(4.70),274(3.43), 344(3.76)	118-0070-80
	MeOH-base	218(4.82),272(3.64), 330(3.56)	118-0070-80
2-Naphthalenamine, N-methyl-	MeOH	215(4.60),246(4.82), 285(4.00),295(3.97), 347(3.50)	103-0965-80
$C_{11}H_{11}NO$ 2H-1,4-Ethanoquinolin-2-one, 3,4-dihydro-	n.s.g.	271(2.86)	150-3650-80
1(2H)-Isoquinolinone, 2,3-dimethyl-	MeOH	208(4.56),228(4.30), 248s(3.90),283(4.04), 290(4.03),335(3.70)	103-0965-80
2(1H)-Quinolinone, 3,7-dimethyl-	CHCl$_3$	243(3.88),275(3.83), 283(3.81),318s(3.84), 324(3.92),338(3.78)	150-0414-80S
$C_{11}H_{11}NOS$ 1,4-Thiazepin-5(2H)-one, 3,4-dihydro-6-phenyl-	MeOH	228(3.93),296(3.85)	24-0995-80
1,4-Thiazepin-5(2H)-one, 3,4-dihydro-7-phenyl-	MeOH	238(3.99),250s(3.97), 292(3.90)	24-0995-80
1,4-Thiazepin-5(4H)-one, 6,7-dihydro-6-phenyl-	MeOH	236(3.49),275(3.56)	24-0995-80
$C_{11}H_{11}NOS_2$ Benzothiazole, 2-[[2-(ethenyloxy)ethyl]thio]-	THF	225(4.37),247(4.01), 280(4.14),291(4.07), 302(3.96)	121-0853-80
$C_{11}H_{11}NO_2$ Benzeneacetic acid, 4-cyano-, ethyl ester (enolate anion)	DMSO	405(4.34)	18-1656-80
4H-Cyclohepta[b]furan-4-one, 6-(ethylamino)-	n.s.g.	280(4.69),338(3.84)	39-2081-80C
Ethanone, 1-(3-hydroxy-1-methyl-1H-indol-2-yl)-	MeOH	242(4.24),315(4.29), 362(3.82)	83-0405-80
4H-1,3-Oxazin-5(6H)-one, 2-(4-methylphenyl)-	MeOH	208(4.29),245(4.19)	103-1000-80

Compound	Solvent	$\lambda_{max}(\log \epsilon)$	Ref.
4H-1,3-Oxazin-5(6H)-one, 4-methyl-2-phenyl-	MeOH	208(4.23),238(4.22)	103-1000-80
$C_{11}H_{11}NO_2S$			
Benzoxazole, 2-[[2-(ethenyloxy)ethyl]-thio]-	THF	250(4.15),258(4.03), 272(3.96),280(4.12), 287(4.13)	121-0853-80
$C_{11}H_{11}NO_3$			
Benzoic acid, 2-(cyanomethyl)-4-methoxy-	EtOH	258(4.21)	95-0819-80
Benzoic acid, 2-(cyanomethyl)-5-methoxy-	EtOH	234(3.89),300(3.44)	95-0819-80
Glycine, N-(1-oxo-3-phenyl-2-propenyl)-	H_2O	245(4.26)	103-0701-80
1(2H)-Isoquinolinone, 6,7-dimethoxy-	EtOH	246(4.26),253s(4.00), 268(3.45),278(3.48), 290(3.51),310(3.25), 322(3.35),335(3.24)	39-0911-80C
$C_{11}H_{11}NO_3S$			
Thieno[3,4-c]pyridine-7-carboxylic acid, 1,3-dihydro-4,6-dimethyl-3-oxo-, methyl ester	EtOH	215(4.25),239s(3.97), 264s(3.84),285s(3.72)	23-0794-80
$C_{11}H_{11}NO_4$			
Benzoic acid, 2-(cyanomethyl)-4,5-dimethoxy-	EtOH	262(4.02),294(3.66)	95-0819-80
1H-Indole-2,3-dione, 4,6-dimethoxy-1-methyl-	MeOH	250(4.39),350(4.15)	150-4154-80
1H-Indole-2,3-dione, 4,7-dimethoxy-1-methyl-	MeOH	228(4.13),361(3.83), 467(3.79)	150-4154-80
1H-Indole-2,3-dione, 5,6-dimethoxy-1-methyl-	MeOH	269(4.36),320(3.73), 460(3.00)	150-4154-80
1H-Indole-2,3-dione, 5,7-dimethoxy-1-methyl-	MeOH	224(4.28),258(4.16), 324(3.57),490(2.92)	150-4154-80
1H-Indole-2,3-dione, 6,7-dimethoxy-1-methyl-	MeOH	224(4.33),260(4.22), 338(4.02)	150-4154-80
$C_{11}H_{11}NO_4S$			
Pyrrolo[2,1-b]thiazole-6,7-dicarboxylic acid, 3-methyl-, dimethyl ester	EtOH	225(4.28),242(4.29), 290(4.08)	18-3308-80
$C_{11}H_{11}NS_2$			
2(3H)-Thiazolethione, 5-ethyl-4-phenyl-	EtOH	240(4.10),327(4.22)	150-4133-80
$C_{11}H_{11}N_3$			
Benzenamine, N-(1-methyl-2(1H)-pyrimidinylidene)-	C_6H_{12}	271(3.89),361s(3.04)	18-0717-80
	EtOH	275(3.86),367(3.15)	18-0717-80
	MeCN	280(3.95),370(3.18)	18-0717-80
2-Pyrimidinamine, N-methyl-N-phenyl-	C_6H_{12}	227(4.14),265(4.09), 295s(3.45)	18-0717-80
	EtOH	229(4.10),265(4.15), 310s(3.38)	18-0717-80
	MeCN	234(4.06),254(4.09), 269(4.07),303s(3.52)	18-0717-80
Pyrrolo[3,2-e]benzimidazole, 1,6-dihydro-7,8-dimethyl-	EtOH	283(4.03),293(4.07), 303(4.06)	103-0062-80
$C_{11}H_{11}N_3O$			
Benzenamine, 4-(4-methoxy-5-pyrimidinyl)-	EtOH	297(4.13)	22-0559-80

Compound	Solvent	$\lambda_{max}(\log \epsilon)$	Ref.
4(1H)-Pyrimidinone, 5-(4-aminophenyl)-1-methyl-	EtOH	232(4.21),313(4.06)	22-0559-80
4(3H)-Pyrimidinone, 5-(4-aminophenyl)-3-methyl-	EtOH	247(3.95),330(4.05)	22-0559-80
1,2,4-Triazin-3(2H)-one, 2-ethyl-5-phenyl-	MeOH	215s(4.11),293(4.14)	44-4594-80
1H-1,2,4-Triazolium, 1-methyl-, 4-(2-oxo-2-phenylethylide)	pH 13	317(3.94)	80-0407-80
$C_{11}H_{11}N_3OS$			
Acetamide, N-methyl-N-(5-phenyl-1,3,4-thiadiazol-2-yl)-	EtOH	291.5(4.22)	44-1473-80
Acetamide, N-(3-methyl-5-phenyl-1,3,4-thiadiazol-2(3H)-ylidene)-	EtOH	313(4.23)	44-1473-80
Ethanone, 2-(5-amino-3-methyl-1,3,4-thiadiazol-2(3H)-ylidene)-1-phenyl-	EtOH	245(4.08),382(4.35)	94-0447-80
Ethanone, 1-[4,5-dihydro-5-imino-4-(3-methylphenyl)-1,3,4-thiadiazol-2-yl]-	EtOH	215(4.19),245(4.19), 342(4.03)	4-1713-80
Ethanone, 1-[4,5-dihydro-5-imino-4-(4-methylphenyl)-1,3,4-thiadiazol-2-yl]-	EtOH	220(4.12),245(4.16), 344(3.81)	4-1713-80
4-Imidazolidinone, 5-imino-1-methyl-3-(phenylmethyl)-2-thioxo-	EtOH	310(4.20)	18-0442-80
4-Imidazolidinone, 5-imino-3-methyl-1-(phenylmethyl)-2-thioxo-	EtOH	308.5(4.19)	18-0442-80
1,3,4-Thiadiazolium, 5-(benzoylamino)-2,3-dimethyl-, hydroxide, inner salt	EtOH	237(4.02),274(3.88), 315(4.17)	94-0447-80
$C_{11}H_{11}N_3O_2$			
4,5-Isoxazoledione, 3-methyl-, 4-[(4-methylphenyl)hydrazone]	MeOH MeOH-base	396(4.24) 358(4.48)	4-0897-80 4-0897-80
1H-Pyrrole-2,5-dione, 3-amino-1-methyl-4-(phenylamino)-	MeOH	237(4.42),435(3.24)	78-1801-80
$C_{11}H_{11}N_3O_2S$			
Ethanone, 1-[4,5-dihydro-5-imino-4-(4-methoxyphenyl)-1,3,4-thiadiazol-2-yl]-	EtOH	222(4.23),246(4.25), 344(3.92)	4-1713-80
$C_{11}H_{11}N_3O_3$			
2,3,4(5H)-Furantrione, 5-methyl-, 3-(phenylhydrazone) 4-oxime	EtOH	234(4.19),382(4.25)	78-2955-80
2,3,4(5H)-Furantrione, 5-methyl-, 4-(phenylhydrazone) 3-oxime after 100 hr.	EtOH EtOH	244(4.07),396(3.89) 244(4.15),304(3.97), 396(<3)	78-2955-80 78-2955-80
4H-Pyrimido[1,6-a]pyrimidine-3-carboxylic acid, 8-methyl-4-oxo-, ethyl ester	CHCl$_3$	351(4.23),362(4.22)	94-2148-80
1,3,5-Triazine-2,4(1H,3H)-dione, 6-ethoxy-3-phenyl-	EtOH-NaOH	235(3.99)	4-0673-80
$C_{11}H_{11}N_3O_4$			
Butanoic acid, 2,3-dioxo-, 2-methyl-2-nitroso-1-phenylhydrazide	EtOH	370(2.00)	94-1820-80
4H-Pyrimido[1,6-a]pyrimidine-3-carboxylic acid, 8-methoxy-4-oxo-, ethyl ester	CHCl$_3$	356(4.39),364(4.38)	94-2148-80
2(1H)-Quinoxalinone, 3,4-dihydro-6-nitro-3-(2-oxopropyl)-	EtOH	267(4.22),314(3.84), 393(3.67)	104-0938-80

Compound	Solvent	$\lambda_{max}(\log \epsilon)$	Ref.
$C_{11}H_{11}N_3O_4S$			
4H-Furo[2',3':4,5]oxazolo[3,2-a]thieno-[3,2-e]pyrimidine-8-methanol,	pH 1	225(4.47),235s(4.42), 268(3.92),286(3.91)	39-1853-80C
6a,7,8,9a-tetrahydro-7-hydroxy-4-imino-, monohydrochloride,	pH 11	234(4.54),265s(3.86), 295(3.76)	39-1853-80C
[6aS-(6aα,7α,8β,9aα)]-	MeOH	228(4.46),268(3.86), 286(3.88)	39-1853-80C
$C_{11}H_{11}N_3O_5$			
L-Alanine, N-(5-benzofurazanylcarbo-nyl)-, methyl ester, N-oxide	EtOH	223(4.46),265s(3.52), 315s(3.46),333s(3.54), 365(3.85)	4-0213-80
	MeCN	222(4.47),265s(3.49), 315s(3.49),332s(3.58), 364(3.89)	4-0213-80
Quinoline, 1-acetyl-1,2,3,4-tetrahydro-6,8-dinitro-	EtOH	270(3.99),365(4.24), 410(4.01)	103-0386-80
$C_{11}H_{11}N_3S$			
1H-1,2,4-Triazole, 3-(methylthio)-5-(2-phenylethenyl)-	MeOH	294(4.45)	48-0434-80
$C_{11}H_{11}N_5O$			
[1,2,4]Triazolo[1,5-a]quinazolin-5-amine, N-hydroxy-N,2-dimethyl-	n.s.g.	221(4.57),249(4.06), 284(3.58),352(3.88)	33-0001-80
$C_{11}H_{11}N_5O_2$			
Pyrrolo[2,3-c]azepin-8(1H)-one, 4-(2-amino-1,5-dihydro-5-oxo-4H-imidazol-4-ylidene)-4,5,6,7-tetrahydro-, monohydrochloride	MeOH	228(4.07),260(3.98), 348(4.24)	77-0435-80
$C_{11}H_{11}N_5O_3$			
9H-Purine-9-acetaldehyde, 6-amino-2-[(1-formyl-2-propenyl)oxy]-, [R-(R*,R*)]-	pH 7.0	259(4.13)	87-0039-80
isomer	pH 7.0	259(4.14)	87-0039-80
$C_{11}H_{11}N_5O_3S_2$			
Benzamide, N-[[[5-(aminosulfonyl)-1H-imidazol-4-yl]amino]thioxomethyl]-	pH 1	220(3.98),243s(3.72)	87-0575-80
	pH 7	225(4.01)	87-0575-80
	pH 13	227(3.91)	87-0575-80
$C_{11}H_{11}N_5O_4$			
Acetamide, N-[6-(acetoxymethyl)-1,4-di-hydro-4-oxo-2-pteridinyl]-	pH -3.0	252(4.07),294(3.92), 312(3.88),377(3.60)	24-1514-80
	pH 3.0	234(4.20),280(4.21), 336(3.94)	24-1514-80
	pH 9.0	256(4.46),282s(3.78), 346(3.91)	24-1514-80
$C_{11}H_{11}OS$			
1-Benzothiopyrylium, 7-methoxy-4-meth-yl-, perchlorate	acetone	415(3.81)	18-2415-80
$C_{11}H_{12}$			
Benzene, 1-(1,3-butadienyl)-3-methyl-	C_6H_{12}	213(4.18),223(4.12), 229(4.12),236(3.97), 275(4.38),283(4.40), 310(3.60)	39-0805-80B

Compound	Solvent	$\lambda_{max}(\log \epsilon)$	Ref.
Benzene, 1-(1,3-butadienyl)-4-methyl-	C_6H_{12}	209(4.11),213(4.16), 221(4.09),227(4.08), 235(3.92),276(4.42), 283(4.44),310(3.82)	39-0805-80B
5H-Benzocycloheptene, 1,2-dihydro-	EtOH	242(3.79),316(3.85)	35-0643-80
1H-Cyclobut[e]indene, 2,5,6,7-tetra-hydro-	n.s.g.	267(2.99),271(2.94), 276(3.02)	44-4183-80
1H-Cyclobut[f]indene, 2,4,5,6-tetra-hydro-	n.s.g.	276(3.66),280(3.64), 286(3.57)	44-4183-80
Cycloprop[a]indene, 1,1a,6,6a-tetra-hydro-1-methyl-, endo	MeOH	272(3.21),279(3.23)	44-3756-80
$C_{11}H_{12}BrNO$ 2-Propen-1-one, 1-(4-bromophenyl)-3-(dimethylamino)-	EtOH	248(4.11),343(4.34)	44-4522-80
$C_{11}H_{12}BrNO_2S$ 3H-Indole, 3-bromo-2-(ethylsulfonyl)-3-methyl-	EtOH	230(4.25),290(3.71)	142-0867-80
$C_{11}H_{12}BrNS$ 3H-Indole, 3-bromo-2-(ethylthio)-3-methyl-	EtOH	243(4.23),330(3.82)	142-0867-80
$C_{11}H_{12}Br_2N_2O_5$ Acetamide, 2,2-dibromo-N-[2-hydroxy-1-(hydroxymethyl)-2-(4-nitrophenyl)-ethyl]-, [R-(R*,R*)]-	pH 7	278(3.95)	87-1299-80
$C_{11}H_{12}Br_4O_2$ Tricyclo[5.1.0.0^{3,5}]octan-1-ol, 4,4,8,8-tetrabromo-3-methyl-, acetate	EtOH	210(3.54)	80-0559-80
Tricyclo[5.1.0.0^{3,5}]octan-1-ol, 4,4,8,8-tetrabromo-5-methyl-, acetate	EtOH	210(3.54)	80-0559-80
$C_{11}H_{12}Br_4O_3$ Tricyclo[5.1.0.0^{3,5}]octan-1-ol, 4,4,8,8-tetrabromo-3-methoxy-, acetate	EtOH	209(3.51)	80-0559-80
Tricyclo[5.1.0.0^{3,5}]octan-1-ol, 4,4,8,8-tetrabromo-5-methoxy-, acetate	EtOH	209(3.52)	80-0559-80
$C_{11}H_{12}ClN_3O_3S$ Urea, [2-[(1-acetyl-2-hydroxy-1-prop-enyl)thio]-6-chloro-3-propyl]-	n.s.g.	260(4.14)	103-0607-80
$C_{11}H_{12}ClN_5O_2$ Pyrrolo[2,3-c]azepin-8(1H)-one, 4-(2-amino-1,5-dihydro-5-oxo-4H-imidazol-4-ylidene)-4,5,6,7-tetrahydro-, monohydrochloride	MeOH	228(4.07),260(3.98), 348(4.24)	77-0435-80
$C_{11}H_{12}Cl_2O$ Benzene, 2-[(2,2-dichlorocyclopropyl)-oxy]-1,3-dimethyl-	hexane	215s(--),264s(--), 268(2.69),275s(--)	70-1928-80
$C_{11}H_{12}Cl_2O_2S$ 4H-Pyran-4-one, 3,5-dichloro-2-(cyclo-	MeOH	228(4.17),293(4.13)	5-1960-80

$C_{11}H_{12}F_3N_5O_3-C_{11}H_{12}N_2O_2$

Compound	Solvent	$\lambda_{max}(\log \epsilon)$	Ref.
hexylthio)- (cont.)			5-1960-80
$C_{11}H_{12}F_3N_5O_3$			
Adenosine, 2'-deoxy-8-(trifluoromethyl)-	MeOH	266(4.11)	39-2755-80C
	MeOH-acid	263(4.20)	39-2755-80C
	MeOH-base	266(4.11)	39-2755-80C
$C_{11}H_{12}F_3N_5O_4$			
Adenosine, 8-(trifluoromethyl)-	MeOH	264(4.07)	39-2755-80C
	MeOH-acid	262(4.18)	39-2755-80C
	MeOH-base	267(4.08)	39-2755-80C
$C_{11}H_{12}MoO_3$			
Molybdenum, tricarbonyl[(1,2,3,4,5-η)-1-ethyl-2,4-cyclopentadien-1-yl]methyl-	hexane	316(3.30),360s(2.97)	24-1033-80
Molybdenum, tricarbonylethyl[(1,2,3,4-5-η)-1-methyl-2,4-cyclopentadien-1-yl]-	hexane	254(3.92),315(3.30), 359s(2.97)	24-1033-80
$C_{11}H_{12}NO$			
Furo[3,2-c]pyridinium, 5-methyl-4-(2-propenyl)-, perchlorate	MeOH	211(4.54),254(3.82), 285(3.68)	83-1048-80
$C_{11}H_{12}NO_2$			
1,3-Dioxolo4,5-g]isoquinolinium, 7,8-dihydro-6-methyl-	EtOH-HCl	244(4.25),306(4.00), 355(3.93)	73-1950-80
	EtOH-NaOH	234(3.66),293(3.67)	73-1950-80
$C_{11}H_{12}N_2$			
1H-1,5-Benzodiazepine, 2,4-dimethyl-	H_2O	480(3.03)	96-0165-80
Cyclopent[c]azepin-1-amine, N,N-dimethyl-	hexane	221(3.99),267(4.28), 306(4.29),396(3.34), 410(3.31),492(3.16)	89-0199-80
Indeno[1,2-c]pyrazole, 1,3a,4,8b-tetrahydro-3-methyl-	MeOH	265(3.30),272(3.26)	44-3756-80
Indeno[1,2-c]pyrazole, 3,3a,4,8b-tetrahydro-3-methyl-, (3α,3aα,8bβ)-	MeOH	267(3.11),276(3.12), 333(2.42)	44-3756-80
(3α,3aβ,8bβ)-	MeOH	267(3.15),276(3.20), 333(2.45)	44-3756-80
1,8-Naphthalenediamine, N-methyl-	CHCl₃	339(3.95)	104-1890-80
Naphtho[1,2-c]pyrazole, 2,3a,4,5-tetrahydro-	MeOH	247(4.03),292(3.24)	44-3756-80
$C_{11}H_{12}N_2OS$			
Benzamide, N-(4,5-dihydro-2-thiazolyl)-2-methyl-	C_6H_{12}	274(--)	150-4432-80
	EtOH	272(4.15)	150-4432-80
Benzamide, N-(4,5-dihydro-2-thiazolyl)-4-methyl-	C_6H_{12}	275(--)	150-4432-80
	EtOH	276(4.34)	150-4432-80
1H-Benzimidazole, 2-[[2-(ethenyloxy)-ethyl]thio]-	THF	215(4.55),252(3.92), 259(3.87),286(4.15), 294(4.17)	121-0853-80
4H-1,3-Thiazin-5(6H)-one, 4-methyl-2-(phenylamino)-	MeOH	207(4.22),228s(3.91), 272(4.02)	103-1003-80
$C_{11}H_{12}N_2O_2$			
Ethanone, 1-(2-hydroxyphenyl)-2-(2-imidazolidinylidene)-	EtOH	209(4.14),244(3.90), 272(3.62),333(4.11)	44-1964-80
1(2H)-Isoquinolinone, 3-amino-6-methoxy-2-methyl-	EtOH	248(4.53),309(4.02), 352(3.51)	95-0819-80

Compound	Solvent	$\lambda_{max}(\log \epsilon)$	Ref.
1(2H)-Isoquinolinone, 3-amino-7-methoxy-2-methyl-	EtOH	229(4.41),295(4.22), 387(3.58)	95-0819-80
1(2H)-Isoquinolinone, 6-methoxy-3-(methylamino)-	EtOH	249(4.60),305(4.21), 352(3.62)	95-0826-80
1(2H)-Isoquinolinone, 7-methoxy-3-(methylamino)-	EtOH	228(4.36),297(4.25), 387(3.53)	95-0826-80
2(1H)-Quinoxalinone, 8-methoxy-6,7-dimethyl-	MeOH	235(4.34),302(3.84), 357(3.68)	54-0115-80
$C_{11}H_{12}N_2O_3$			
1(2H)-Isoquinolinone, 3-amino-6,7-dimethoxy-	EtOH	246(4.39),300(4.04), 363(3.63)	95-0819-80
2-Propenoic acid, 2-cyano-3-[5-(dimethylamino)-2-furanyl]-, methyl ester	MeOH	235(3.46),466(4.86)	73-1831-80
2-Propen-1-one, 3-(dimethylamino)-1-(4-nitrophenyl)-	EtOH	271(4.23),363(4.08)	44-4522-80
2,4(1H,3H)-Pyrimidinedione, 5-(5-methyl-2-furanyl)-	MeCN	254(4.50),321(4.45)	88-2813-80
Quinoline, 1-acetyl-1,2,3,4-tetrahydro-6-nitro-	EtOH	340(4.08)	103-0386-80
2(1H)-Quinoxalinone, 8-methoxy-6,7-dimethyl-, 4-oxide	MeOH	231(4.39),262(4.11), 304(3.88)	54-0115-80
$C_{11}H_{12}N_2O_3S$			
4-Thiazolecarboxylic acid, 4,5-dihydro-2-(3-hydroxy-2-pyridinyl)-4-methyl-, methyl ester	EtOH	210(4.22),238(3.82), 313(4.01)	33-1400-80
$C_{11}H_{12}N_2O_5S_2$			
5-Thia-1-azabicyclo[4.2.0]oct-2-ene-1-carboxylic acid, 3-(acetoxymethyl)-7-[(methylthio)imino]-8-oxo-, (R)-	MeOH	243(3.66),324(4.01)	35-1690-80
Thieno[2,3-d]pyrimidin-2(1H)-one, 3,4-dihydro-1-β-D-ribofuranosyl-4-thioxo-	pH 1	249(4.23),352(4.28)	39-1853-80C
	pH 11	249(4.20),299(4.07), 331(4.23)	39-1853-80C
	MeOH	249(4.15),280(3.91), 341(4.28)	39-1853-80C
$C_{11}H_{12}N_2O_6S$			
Thieno[2,3-d]pyrimidin-2,4(1H,3H)-dione, 1-β-D-ribofuranosyl-	pH 1	228(4.39),255s(3.78), 287(3.68)	39-1853-80C
	pH 11	229(4.39),245s(3.84), 285(3.65)	39-1853-80C
	MeOH	226(4.38),245s(3.73), 285(3.65)	39-1853-80C
$C_{11}H_{12}N_2S$			
3H-Pyrazole-3-thione, 1,2-dihydro-1,5-dimethyl-2-phenyl-	benzene	278(3.95),344(4.39)	140-0560-80
	H_2O	252(4.10),282(4.07)	140-0560-80
2-Thiazolamine, N,N-dimethyl-5-phenyl-	H_2O	318(3.87)	39-1156-80B
protonated	H_2O	294(3.86)	39-1156-80B
$C_{11}H_{12}N_3O$			
1H-1,2,4-Triazolium, 1-methyl-4-(2-oxo-2-phenylethyl)-, bromide	MeOH	247(4.18)	80-0407-80
$C_{11}H_{12}N_4$			
2,2a,4,5-Tetraazabenz[cd]azulene, 3,4-dihydro-1,3-dimethyl-	MeOH	221(4.44),293(3.65)	118-0331-80

Compound	Solvent	λ_{max}(log ϵ)	Ref.
$C_{11}H_{12}N_4OS$ 2-Thiazolamine, 5-[(4-methoxyphenyl)-azo]-4-methyl-	EtOH	250(4.35),415(4.46)	4-1713-80
$C_{11}H_{12}N_4O_2$ 3H,8H-Imidazo[1,2,3-ij]pteridine-8,10(9H)-dione, 5,6-dihydro-2,9-dimethyl-3-methylene-	pH 0.0 pH 7.0	250(4.20),290s(3.21), 372(4.05) 224(4.11),302(4.31), 355(3.48)	142-0437-80B 142-0437-80B
Methanimidic acid, N-(1,5-dihydro-5-oxo-3-phenyl-4H-1,2,4-triazol-4-yl)-, ethyl ester	EtOH	260(3.97)	4-1691-80
3H,5H,9H-Pyrimido[1,2,3-ij]pteridine-9,11(10H)-dione, 6,7-dihydro-2-methyl-3-methylene-	pH 1.0 pH 7.0 pH 12.0	251(4.08),365(4.10) 230(4.02),286s(3.97), 314(4.32),365s(3.47) 218(4.23),311(4.31), 364(3.68)	142-0437-80B 142-0437-80B 142-0437-80B
$C_{11}H_{12}N_4O_2S$ Cyclohexanone, 2-[5-(methylthio)-[1,2,5]oxadiazolo[3,4-d]pyrimi-din-7(3H)-ylidene]-	MeOH	241(4.17),275(4.06), 387(4.15)	44-3827-80
$C_{11}H_{12}N_4O_3$ 1H-1,2,4-Triazole-1-carboxylic acid, 4-amino-4,5-dihydro-5-oxo-3-phenyl-, ethyl ester	EtOH	254(4.04)	4-1691-80
$C_{11}H_{12}N_4O_4$ 1H-Pyrazole-5-acetic acid, 3,4-dicyano-4,5-dihydro-5-(methoxycarbonyl)-1-methyl-, methyl ester (4R,5S/4S,5R)-(4S,5S/4R,5R)-	MeOH MeOH	300(3.87) 213(4.39),311(3.38)	24-2028-80 24-2028-80
2,4(1H,3H)-Pyrimidinedione, 1-[3-(3,6-dihydro-2,6-dioxo-1(2H)-pyrimidin-yl)propyl]-	pH 2 pH 7 pH 12	233(3.63),265(4.21) 232(3.52),265(4.19) 244(3.70),274(4.11)	56-2357-80 56-2357-80 56-2357-80
$C_{11}H_{12}N_4O_7$ 2,4,7(1H,3H,8H)-Pteridinetrione, 1-β-D-ribofuranosyl-	pH 0 pH 7.0 pH 13.0	230s(3.97),258(3.88), 317(4.09),323s(4.05) 208(4.41),240s(3.76), 276(4.07),325(4.20), 337s(4.08) 249(4.10),272(3.85), 300s(3.75),330(4.23), 342s(4.15)	24-1524-80 24-1524-80 24-1524-80
2,4,7(1H,3H,8H)-Pteridinetrione, 3-β-D-ribofuranosyl-	pH 1.0 pH 6.0 pH 13.0	270s(3.86),277(3.86), 325(4.09) 277(3.99),328(4.19), 341s(4.07) 227(4.60),263(3.99), 283(3.94),339(4.11)	24-1524-80 24-1524-80 24-1524-80
2,4,7(1H,3H,8H)-Pteridinetrione, 8-β-D-ribofuranosyl-, ammonium salt	pH 1.0 pH 7.0 2M KOH	278(4.08),334(4.02) 210(4.50),265s(3.71), 288(4.01),355(4.10) 261(4.05),280s(3.67), 370(4.13)	24-1535-80 24-1535-80 24-1535-80
$C_{11}H_{12}N_4S$ Benzenamine, N,N-dimethyl-4-(2-thiazo-lylazo)-	EtOH	486(4.56)	62-0158-80

Compound	Solvent	λ_{max}(log ϵ)	Ref.
2-Thiazolamine, 4-methyl-5-[(4-methyl-phenyl)azo]-	EtOH	250(4.29),399(4.39)	4-1713-80
$C_{11}H_{12}N_5O_8P$ 9H-Purine-2-carboxylic acid, 6-amino-9-(3,5-0-phosphinico-β-D-ribo-furanosyl)-	pH 1 pH 13	258s(4.00),265(4.03), 290(3.69) 258s(3.93),264(4.11), 290s(3.76)	94-0115-80 94-0115-80
$C_{11}H_{12}N_6$ 3H-1,2,3-Triazolo[4,5-d]pyrimidin-5-amine, 4,7-dihydro-3-(phenylmethyl)- [1,2,4]Triazolo[1,5-a]quinazoline, 2-methyl-5-(1-methylhydrazino)-	pH 0 EtOH n.s.g.	228(4.46),326(3.58) 244s(3.66),317(3.89) 222(4.59),288(3.69), 300(3.74),330(3.91)	39-2918-80C 39-2918-80C 33-0001-80
$C_{11}H_{12}N_6O$ 4(1H)-Pteridinone, 2-amino-5,6,7,8-tetrahydro-6-(4-pyridinyl)-	pH 1 pH 13	260(4.08),296(3.74) 257(3.94),288(3.86)	150-0549-80 150-0549-80
$C_{11}H_{12}N_6O_3$ Acetamide, N-[6-(acetoxymethyl)-4-amino-2-pteridinyl]-	pH 1 pH 7.0 MeOH	214(4.36),249(4.32), 284(3.99),329(4.02), 342s(3.96) 208s(4.23),259(4.49), 284s(3.77),350(3.89) 213(4.17),226s(4.09), 261(4.49),290s(3.74), 355(3.86)	24-1514-80 24-1514-80 24-1514-80
β-D-ribo-Hexofuranurononitrile, 1-(6-amino-9H-purin-9-yl)-1,5-dideoxy-	H_2O	258(4.20)	24-2530-80
$C_{11}H_{12}N_6O_3S_3$ 5-Thia-1-azabicyclo[4.2.0]oct-2-ene-2-carboxylic acid, 3-[[(1-methyl-1H-tetrazol-5-yl)thio]methyl]-7-[(methylthio)imino]-8-oxo-, (R)-	MeOH	332(4.06)	35-1690-80
$C_{11}H_{12}O$ Benzofuran, 2,3-dihydro-2-(1-methyl-ethenyl)- Benzofuran, 2,4,7-trimethyl- 1,3-Butadiene, 1-(3-methoxyphenyl)-, trans 1,3-Butadiene, 1-(4-methoxyphenyl)-, trans 3-Buten-2-one, 3-methyl-4-phenyl- 3,5,7-Decatrien-9-yn-2-one, 8-methyl-, (E,Z,E)- 3-Penten-1-one, 1-phenyl-, (E)-	MeOH EtOH C_6H_{12} hexane EtOH ether C_6H_{12}	216(3.72),226(3.69), 280(3.51),287(3.45) 217(4.30),250(4.22), 274(3.52),285(3.38) 222(4.20),228(4.19), 235(4.13),238(3.97), 279(4.39),280(4.27), 309(3.83),323(3.51) 221(4.12),226(4.05), 234(3.78),288(4.43) 273(4.19) 305(4.27),322(4.41), 334s(4.38),386s(3.41) 241(3.80),325(1.52), 337(1.51)	150-0127-80 12-1817-80 39-0805-80B 39-0805-80B 101-0367-80K 44-3564-80 39-0592-80B
$C_{11}H_{12}OS_2$ 2-Propen-1-one, 3,3-bis(methylthio)-1-phenyl-	EtOH	220s(3.73),263(3.90), 279(3.92),344(4.28)	35-3095-80
$C_{11}H_{12}O_2$ 1H-2-Benzopyran-1-one, 3,4-dihydro-3,5-dimethyl-	n.s.g.	225(4.73),256(4.33)	2-0009-80

$C_{11}H_{12}O_2-C_{11}H_{12}O_4S_2$

Compound	Solvent	$\lambda_{max}(\log \epsilon)$	Ref.
1H-2-Benzopyran-1-one, 3,4-dihydro-3,6-dimethyl-	n.s.g.	225(4.58),260(4.24)	2-0009-80
1H-2-Benzopyran-1-one, 3,4-dihydro-3,7-dimethyl-	n.s.g.	225(4.96),252(4.41)	2-0009-80
1(2H)-Naphthalenone, 3,4-dihydro-5-methoxy-	EtOH	257(4.10)	73-1950-80
1(2H)-Naphthalenone, 3,4-dihydro-6-methoxy-	EtOH	225(4.09),274(4.18)	73-1950-80
1(2H)-Naphthalenone, 3,4-dihydro-7-methoxy-	EtOH	225(4.29),252(4.01),320(3.36)	73-1950-80
1(2H)-Naphthalenone, 3,4-dihydro-8-methoxy-	EtOH	255(3.99),315(3.59)	78-2513-80
Spiro[4.5]deca-6,9-diene-2,8-dione, 1-methyl-	EtOH	242(4.07),242s(--)[sic]	94-1932-80

$C_{11}H_{12}O_3$

Compound	Solvent	$\lambda_{max}(\log \epsilon)$	Ref.
1H-2-Benzopyran-1-one, 3,4-dihydro-8-hydroxy-3,5-dimethyl- (5-methyl-mellein)	EtOH	214(4.34),248(3.83),323(3.63)	102-0445-80
	EtOH-AlCl$_3$	337(3.49)	102-0445-80
Ethanone, 1-(2,3-dihydro-5-methyl-[2,2'-bifuran]-4-yl)-	EtOH	215(3.86),278(3.92)	103-0678-80
1H-Inden-1-one, 2,3-dihydro-4,5-dimethoxy-	EtOH	230(4.36),281(4.14)	73-1950-80
1H-Inden-1-one, 2,3-dihydro-5,6-dimethoxy-	EtOH	210(4.22),229(4.25),268(4.05),312(4.00)	73-1950-80
1H-Inden-1-one, 2,3-dihydro-5,7-dimethoxy-	EtOH	226(4.35),275(4.27),298(3.81)	73-1950-80
1H-Inden-1-one, 2,3-dihydro-6,7-dimethoxy-	EtOH	219(4.36),255(3.98),325(3.55)	73-1950-80
2,4-Pentadienoic acid, 5-(2-furanyl)-, ethyl ester	n.s.g.	337(4.46)	39-2081-80C

$C_{11}H_{12}O_3S$

Compound	Solvent	$\lambda_{max}(\log \epsilon)$	Ref.
2-Butenal, 2-methyl-4-(phenylsulfonyl)-	EtOH	236(4.02)	35-1602-80

$C_{11}H_{12}O_3W$

Compound	Solvent	$\lambda_{max}(\log \epsilon)$	Ref.
Tungsten, tricarbonyl[(1,2,3,4,5-η)-1-ethyl-2,4-cyclopentadien-1-yl]methyl-	hexane	259s(3.40),314(3.37),354s(3.05)	24-1033-80
Tungsten, tricarbonylethyl[(1,2,3,4,5-η)-1-methyl-2,4-cyclopentadien-1-yl]-	hexane	257s(3.99),316(3.36),355s(3.03)	24-1033-80

$C_{11}H_{12}O_4$

Compound	Solvent	$\lambda_{max}(\log \epsilon)$	Ref.
1,3-Benzodioxole-5-carboxylic acid, 2-ethyl-2-methyl-	EtOH	218(4.36),262(3.81),296(3.81)	12-0527-80
4H-1-Benzopyran-3-carboxylic acid, 5,6,7,8-tetrahydro-2-methyl-4-oxo-	EtOH	251(3.60)	94-2460-80
2H-1-Benzopyran-2-one, 3-acetyl-5,6,7,8-tetrahydro-4-hydroxy-	EtOH	315(4.06)	94-2460-80
Ethanone, 1-(2-acetoxy-5-methoxyphenyl)-	n.s.g.	308(3.34)	44-0501-80
Homophthalide, 7,8-dimethoxy-	EtOH	223(4.36),243s(4.04),292(3.84),325(3.64)	73-1950-80
1(3H)-Isobenzofuranone, 5,7-dimethoxy-6-methyl-	EtOH	217(4.537),255(3.834),296(3.449)	120-0016-80
2H-Pyran-2-one, 4-methoxy-6-methyl-5-(1-oxo-2-butenyl)-, (E)-	MeOH	273(3.86)	88-4481-80

$C_{11}H_{12}O_4S_2$

Compound	Solvent	$\lambda_{max}(\log \epsilon)$	Ref.
2-Butenoic acid, 3-(2-furanyl)-4-(methoxythiocarbonylthio)-, methyl ester	EtOH	220(3.84),314(4.24)	73-0142-80

Compound	Solvent	$\lambda_{max}(\log \epsilon)$	Ref.
$C_{11}H_{12}O_5$			
2,4-Cyclohexadien-1-one, 6-acetoxy-6-(1-oxopropoxy)-	EtOH	222(3.57),306(3.65)	12-1553-80
3-Furanpropanoic acid, 4-(1-butenyl)-2,5-dihydro-2,5-dioxo-, (E)-	MeOH	211(4.03),268(4.23)	39-2134-80C
4-Isobenzofurancarboxylic acid,	C_6H_{12}	215(3.74),251(3.51)	2-0601-80
1,3,4,5,6,7-hexahydro-4-methyl-1,3-dioxo-, methyl ester	EtOH	208(3.81),250(3.36)	2-0601-80
after twenty hours	EtOH	212(3.84)	2-0601-80
Propanoic acid, 2-acetoxy-, 2-hydroxyphenyl ester	EtOH	218(3.81),277(3.54)	12-1553-80
$C_{11}H_{12}S_2$			
Spiro[2H-1,5-benzodithiepin-3(4H),1'-cyclopropane]	CHCl₃	268(3.77)	48-0909-80
$C_{11}H_{13}AsO$			
1,3-Benzoxarsole, 2-(1,1-dimethylethyl)-	MeOH	231(4.28),290(3.76)	101-0039-80C
$C_{11}H_{13}BrN_2O_7$			
Uridine, 5-bromo-5'-O-(carboxymethyl)-	pH 7	279(3.97)	73-0606-80
2'-deoxy-	pH 8.5	276(3.82)	73-0606-80
	pH 12	276(3.82)	73-0606-80
$C_{11}H_{13}Br_3O$			
Bicyclo[5.1.0]octa-2,4-diene, 4,8,8-tribromo-3-ethoxy-1-methyl-	EtOH	240(4.00),285(3.28)	39-2405-80C
$C_{11}H_{13}Br_3O_2$			
Bicyclo[5.1.0]octa-2,4-diene, 4,8,8-tribromo-3-(methoxymethoxy)-1-methyl-	EtOH	240(4.00),287(3.28)	39-2405-80C
$C_{11}H_{13}ClN_2O_5$			
Acetamide, 2-chloro-N-[2-hydroxy-1-(hydroxymethyl)-2-(4-nitrophenyl)ethyl]-	pH 7	279(4.01)	87-1299-80
$C_{11}H_{13}ClO$			
Phenol, 2-(2-chloro-2-propenyl)-3,6-dimethyl-	EtOH	224(3.73),279(3.30)	12-1817-80
$C_{11}H_{13}Cl_3N_2O_3S_2$			
4-Thia-1-azabicyclo[3.2.0]heptane-2-carboxylic acid, 3,3-dimethyl-6-[(methylthio)imino]-7-oxo-, 2,2,2-trichloroethyl ester, (2S-cis)	MeOH	247(3.26),313(3.89)	35-1690-80
$C_{11}H_{13}FN_2O_5$			
Acetamide, 2-fluoro-N-[2-hydroxy-1-(hydroxymethyl)-2-(4-nitrophenyl)ethyl]-, [R-(R*,R*)]-	pH 7	278(4.01)	87-1299-80
$C_{11}H_{13}FN_2O_7$			
Uridine, 5'-O-(carboxymethyl)-2'-deoxy-	pH 7	269(3.95)	73-0606-80
5-fluoro-	pH 8.7	267(3.83)	73-0606-80
	pH 12	267(3.83)	73-0606-80
$C_{11}H_{13}IN_2O_7$			
Uridine, 5'-O-(carboxmethyl)-2'-deoxy-	pH 7	288(3.85)	73-0606-80
5-iodo-	pH 8.7	282(3.73)	73-0606-80
	pH 12	280(3.72)	73-0606-80

Compound	Solvent	$\lambda_{max}(\log \epsilon)$	Ref.
$C_{11}H_{13}NO$			
Acetamide, N-[2-(1-propenyl)phenyl]-, cis	MeOH	250(4.03),320(2.95)	44-1549-80
trans	MeOH	219(4.26),251(4.20)	44-1549-80
1H-Indole-2-ethanol, 1-methyl-	EtOH	223(4.38),283(3.77), 292(3.61)	39-1688-80C
2-Propenal, 3-[4-(dimethylamino)phenyl]-	pH 6.83	398(4.49)	35-3062-80
	50% dioxan-KOH	397(4.54)	44-2099-80
	pH 1.45	281(--)	35-3062-80
	pH 5.8	376(--)	35-3062-80
	pH 10.5	396(--)	35-3062-80
$C_{11}H_{13}NOS$			
Methanamine, 1-(methylthio)-N-(1-phenyl-2-propenylidene)-, N-oxide, (E)-	EtOH	299(4.10)	150-4726-80
$C_{11}H_{13}NO_2$			
Isoquinoline, 3,4-dihydro-6,7-dimethoxy-	EtOH-NaOH	230(4.21),272(3.98), 303(3.91)	73-1950-80
4-Quinolineacetic acid, 1,2,3,4-tetrahydro-	pH 7.2	295(3.45)	150-3650-80
sodium salt	MeOH	253(3.92),305(3.45)	150-3650-80
Strobiline	EtOH	213(3.88),253(4.02)	102-0949-80
$C_{11}H_{13}NO_2S$			
Sulfonium, dimethyl-, 2-amino-1-benzoyl-2-oxoethylide	EtOH	259(4.09)	94-0795-80
$C_{11}H_{13}NO_3S$			
Thieno[3,4-c]pyridine-7-carboxylic acid, 1,3,5,7a-tetrahydro-4,6-dimethyl-3-oxo-, methyl ester	EtOH	236(4.08),242s(4.06), 267(4.03),391(3.80)	23-0794-80
$C_{11}H_{13}NO_4$			
1H-Pyrrole-3-propanoic acid, 4-(1-butenyl)-2,5-dihydro-2,5-dioxo-, (E)-	MeOH	230(4.09),335(3.54)	39-2134-80C
$C_{11}H_{13}NO_5$			
3,5-Pyridinedicarboxylic acid, 1,4-dihydro-4-oxo-, diethyl ester	EtOH	250(3.79),256(3.75), 303(3.69)	4-0359-80
$C_{11}H_{13}NO_5S$			
4-Thia-1-azabicyclo[3.2.0]hept-2-ene-2-carboxylic acid, 6-(1-hydroxyethyl)-7-oxo-, 2-oxopropyl ester, erytro-trans	EtOH	253(3.48),320(3.88)	35-2039-80
threo	EtOH	253(3.48),318(3.87)	35-2039-80
$C_{11}H_{13}NO_6$			
2-Oxa-7-azaspiro[4.5]decane-10-carboxylic acid, 7-methyl-1,6,8-trioxo-, methyl ester	MeOH	210(3.78)	118-0698-80
4aH-Pyrano[4,3-c]pyridine-4a-carboxylic acid, octahydro-3-methyl-1,5,7-trioxo-, methyl ester	MeOH	210(4.27)	118-0698-80
4aH-Pyrano[4,3-c]pyridine-4a-carboxylic acid, octahydro-1,5,7-trioxo-, ethyl ester	MeOH	213(3.32)	118-0698-80

Compound	Solvent	$\lambda_{max}(\log \epsilon)$	Ref.
$C_{11}H_{13}NS$			
Ethanethioamide, N-[2-(1-propenyl)-phenyl]-, cis	MeOH	236(4.01),276(3.95)	44-1549-80
trans	MeOH	256(4.23),280s(4.01)	44-1549-80
Sulfonium, dimethyl(2-methyl-1H-indol-3-yl)-, hydroxide, inner salt	dioxan	273(3.84)	44-0780-80
$C_{11}H_{13}N_3O$			
Pyrimido[1,6-a]azepine-4-carbonitrile, 3,5,6,7,8,9-hexahydro-1-methyl-3-oxo-	pH 13	306(4.28)	103-0873-80
$C_{11}H_{13}N_3O_2$			
1H-Benzimidazole, 2-methyl-7-nitro-1-propyl-, hydrochloride	pH 1	240s(3.62),288(3.76)	104-1458-80
$C_{11}H_{13}N_3O_3$			
1(2H)-Isoquinolinone, 2,3-diamino-6,7-dimethoxy-	EtOH	247(4.24),300(3.98), 360(3.49)	95-0819-80
$C_{11}H_{13}N_3O_3S$			
Carbamidothioic acid, N,N'-dimethyl-, 2-(4-nitrophenyl)-2-oxoethyl ester	MeOH	263(4.06)	78-2675-80
$C_{11}H_{13}N_3O_4$			
Quinoline, 1-ethyl-1,2,3,4-tetrahydro-6,8-dinitro-	EtOH	378(4.27)	103-0386-80
$C_{11}H_{13}N_3O_5$			
4H-Pyrrolo[2,3-d]pyrimidin-4-one, 1,7-dihydro-7-β-D-ribofuranosyl-	MeOH	259(3.99)	24-2389-80
$C_{11}H_{13}N_3O_5S$			
Thieno[2,3-d]pyrimidin-2(1H)-one, 4-amino-1-β-D-arabinofuranosyl-	pH 1	243(4.49),315(3.82)	39-1853-80C
	pH 11	234(4.53),267s(3.79), 297(3.71)	39-1853-80C
	MeOH	233(4.54),267s(3.84), 297(3.71)	39-1853-80C
Thieno[2,3-d]pyrimidin-2(1H)-one, 4-amino-1-β-D-ribofuranosyl-	pH 1	238(4.48),260s(3.92), 308(3.84)	39-1853-80C
	pH 11	233(4.53),255s(3.92), 295(3.73)	39-1853-80C
	MeOH	231(4.51),265s(3.83), 295(3.63)	39-1853-80C
$C_{11}H_{13}N_5O_2$			
1,2,4-Triazine-3,5(2H,4H)-dione, 6-[(4-methoxyphenyl)methyl]-, 3-hydrazone	EtOH	229(4.09),267(4.02)	12-0619-80
1H-1,2,4-Triazole-1-carboxamide, 4-amino-4,5-dihydro-N,N-dimethyl-5-oxo-3-phenyl-	EtOH	265(4.04)	4-1691-80
$C_{11}H_{13}N_5O_4$			
8,5'(R)-Cycloadenosine, 5'-deoxy-5'-(hydroxymethyl)-	pH 1	260(4.21)	94-0876-80
	H2O	263(4.21)	94-0876-80
(S)-	pH 1	260.5(4.15)	94-0876-80
	H2O	264.5(4.16)	94-0876-80
9H-Purine-9-acetaldehyde, 6-amino-α-(1-formyl-2-hydroxypropoxy)-	pH 7.0	259(4.16)	87-0039-80
isomer	pH 7.0	259(4.15)	87-0039-80

Compound	Solvent	λ_{max}(log ϵ)	Ref.
$C_{11}H_{13}N_5O_5$			
Acetamide, 2-azido-N-[2-hydroxy-1-(hydroxymethyl)-2-(4-nitrophenyl)ethyl]-, [R-(R*,R*)]-	pH 7	279(3.97)	87-1299-80
Adenosine-5'-carboxylic acid, 5'-deoxy-	pH 7	258(4.19)	24-2530-80
$C_{11}H_{13}N_5O_6$			
9H-Purine, 6-(nitromethyl)-9-β-D-ribofuranosyl-	H_2O	202(4.22),245(3.85), 290(4.55),398(4.54)	94-0150-80
$C_{11}H_{13}N_6O_7P$			
Adenosine, 2-(aminocarbonyl)-, cyclic 3',5'-(hydrogen phosphate)	pH 1	259s(4.10),265(4.10), 295(3.81)	94-0115-80
$C_{11}H_{13}OP$			
1,3-Benzoxaphosphole, 2-(1,1-dimethylethyl)-	n.s.g.	223(4.11),272(3.83)	97-0342-80
$C_{11}H_{14}$			
Bicyclo[2.2.2]octa-2,5-diene, 7,7-dimethyl-3-methylene-	hexane	200(end absorption)	44-0958-80
Tricyclo[3.3.0.0^{2,8}]oct-6-ene, 4,4-dimethyl-3-methylene-	hexane	225s(3.76)	44-0958-80
$(C_{11}H_{14})_n$			
Cyclohexane, 2,4-cyclopentadien-1-ylidene-, homopolymer	CH_2Cl_2	255(3.88)	126-0031-80
$C_{11}H_{14}AsN$			
1H-1,3-Benzazarsole, 2-(1,1-dimethylethyl)-	MeOH	236(4.70),270s(3.74), 284s(3.64),322(3.86)	101-0039-80C
$C_{11}H_{14}BrNO_4$			
α-D-ribo-Hept-5-enofuranurononitrile, 6-bromo-5,6-dideoxy-3-O-methyl-1,2-O-(1-methylethylidene)-, (E)-	EtOH	229(3.91)	136-0187-80H
(Z)-	EtOH	229(3.85)	136-0187-80H
α-D-xylo-Hept-5-enofuranurononitrile, 6-bromo-5,6-dideoxy-3-O-methyl-1,2-O-(1-methylethylidene)-, (E)-	EtOH	228(3.90)	136-0187-80H
(Z)-	EtOH	222(3.81)	136-0187-80H
$C_{11}H_{14}BrN_3O_4$			
Carbamic acid, (5-bromo-2,4-pyridinediyl)bis-, diethyl ester	M HCl	236(4.61),264(4.18), 291(3.95)	87-0384-80
$C_{11}H_{14}ClNO_4$			
α-D-xylo-Hept-5-enofuranurononitrile, 6-chloro-5,6-dideoxy-3-O-methyl-1,2-O-(1-methylethylidene)-, (E)-	EtOH	222(3.93)	136-0187-80H
(Z)-	EtOH	219(3.89)	136-0187-80H
$C_{11}H_{14}ClN_5O_3$			
1,2-Cyclopentanediol, 3-(2-amino-6-chloro-9H-purin-9-yl)-5-(hydroxymethyl)-, (1α,2β,3β,5β)-(±)-	pH 1	218(4.47),242(--), 312(3.85)	36-1019-80
	H_2O	222(4.45),246(--), 306(3.91)	36-1019-80
	pH 13	246(--),306(3.91)	36-1019-80
$C_{11}H_{14}FNO_4$			
α-D-xylo-Hept-5-enofuranurononitrile,	EtOH	210(3.75)	136-0187-80H

Compound	Solvent	$\lambda_{max}(\log \epsilon)$	Ref.
5,6-dideoxy-6-fluoro-3-0-methyl-1,2- O-(1-methylethylidene)-, (E)- (cont.)			136-0187-80H
(Z)-	EtOH	210(3.67)	136-0187-80H
$C_{11}H_{14}FN_3O_5$			
1(2H)-Pyrimidinepropanoic acid, β-(ace- tylamino)-5-fluoro-3,4-dihydro-2,4- dioxo-, ethyl ester	MeOH	268(3.94)	94-1137-80
$C_{11}H_{14}INO_4$			
α-D-xylo-Hept-5-enofuranurononitrile, 5,6-dideoxy-6-iodo-3-0-methyl-1,2- O-(1-methylethylidene)-, (E)-	EtOH	253(3.80)	136-0187-80H
(Z)-	EtOH	230(3.64)	136-0187-80H
$C_{11}H_{14}NS$			
Sulfonium, dimethyl(2-methyl-1H-indol- 3-yl)-, iodide	dioxan	276(3.93)	44-0780-80
$C_{11}H_{14}N_2O_2$			
Quinoline, 1-ethyl-1,2,3,4-tetrahydro- 8-nitro-	EtOH	255(4.16),295s(3.40), 430(3.32)	103-0386-80
2-Quinoxalinol, 1,4-dihydro-8-methoxy- 6,7-dimethyl-	MeOH	231(4.42),262(3.84), 304(3.71)	54-0115-80
$C_{11}H_{14}N_2O_3$			
2,4-Cyclohexadien-1-one, 6-acetoxy- 2,6-dimethyl-, pyrazoline with diazomethane	MeOH	330(2.45)	24-2227-80
Glycine, N-[4-(dimethylamino)benzoyl]-	H_2O	260(4.28)	103-0701-80
$C_{11}H_{14}N_2O_4$			
Cyclopropanecarboxamide, N-(1-methyl- ethyl)-2-(5-nitro-2-furanyl)-	MeOH	280(3.13)	2-0815-80
4H-Pyrazolo[5,1-c][1,4]oxazine-3-carb- oxylic acid, 6,7-dihydro-2,4-dimeth- yl-6-oxo-, ethyl ester	EtOH	233(3.89)	118-0875-80
2-Pyridinecarboxylic acid, 5-[(meth- oxycarbonyl)amino]-, propyl ester	MeOH	255(4.22),282(4.17)	87-1405-80
2,4(1H,3H)-Pyrimidinedione, 5-(1,4-di- oxopentyl)-1,3-dimethyl-	MeCN	225(4.36),286(4.43)	88-2813-80
$(C_{11}H_{14}N_2O_4)_n$			
Poly[1-[[2-(3,4-dihydro-5-methyl-2,4- dioxo-1(2H)-pyrimidinyl)ethoxy]- carbonyl]-1-methyl-1,2-ethanediyl]	DMF	270.5(3.91)	47-0427-80
$C_{11}H_{14}N_2O_4S_2$			
4-Thia-1-azabicyclo[3.2.0]hept-2-ene- 2-carboxylic acid, 3-[[3-(acetylam- ino)propyl]thio]-7-oxo-, (R)-, monosodium salt	H_2O	252(3.61),322s(3.74)	94-3258-80
$C_{11}H_{14}N_2O_5$			
Acetamide, N-[2-hydroxy-1-(hydroxymeth- yl)-2-(4-nitrophenyl)ethyl]-, [R- (R*,R*)]-	pH 7	278(3.97)	87-1299-80
5H-Indazole-5,5-dicarboxylic acid, 2,3,3a,4,6,7-hexahydro-3-oxo-, dimethyl ester	EtOH	249(3.44)	23-1860-80

Compound	Solvent	$\lambda_{max}(\log \epsilon)$	Ref.
$C_{11}H_{14}N_2O_5S$			
Propanedioic acid, (3,4-dihydro-2-oxo-	pH 2	253(3.58),333(4.32)	103-0864-80
4-thioxo-1(2H)-pyrimidinyl)-,	pH 7	253(3.58),332(4.26)	103-0864-80
diethyl ester	pH 11	259(4.38),317(4.18)	103-0864-80
$C_{11}H_{14}N_2O_6$			
Acetamide, 2-hydroxy-N-[2-hydroxy-	pH 7	278(4.16)	87-1299-80
1-(hydroxymethyl)-2-(4-nitro-			
phenyl)ethyl]-, [R-(R*,R*)]-			
2,4(1H,3H)-Pyrimidinedione, 5-acetyl-	pH 1	230(4.01),283(4.11)	78-1269-80
1-(2-deoxy-α-D-erythro-pentofurano-	pH 14	235(4.04),288(3.98)	78-1269-80
syl)-	EtOH	229(4.05),288(4.12)	78-1269-80
$C_{11}H_{14}N_2O_7$			
Uridine, 5'-O-(carboxymethyl)-2'-deoxy-	pH 7	260(4.00)	73-0606-80
	pH 8.7	260(3.94)	73-0606-80
	pH 12	260(3.88)	73-0606-80
$C_{11}H_{14}N_2O_{12}P_2$			
Uridine 5'-(trihydrogen phosphate),	pH 7	288(3.98)	78-0155-80
5-ethynyl-	pH 12	286(3.88)	78-0155-80
$C_{11}H_{14}N_2Se$			
Selenocyanic acid, 4-(diethylamino)-	MeOH	280(4.27)	104-1963-80
phenyl ester			
$C_{11}H_{14}N_4$			
8(1H)-Cycloheptapyrazolone, 1,3-di-	MeOH	260s(3.96),270s(3.92),	18-1461-80
methyl-, methylhydrazone		350(4.10)	
1H-1,2,3-Triazol-5-amine, 1-(1-methyl-	EtOH	213(3.80),239(3.85),	49-0635-80
ethyl)-N-phenyl-		265(4.03)	
$C_{11}H_{14}N_4O$			
1,2,4,5-Tetrazin-3(2H)-one, 1,4-di-	dioxan	260(4.09),317(3.74)	89-0724-80
hydro-1,2,4-trimethyl-6-phenyl-			
3H-1,2,4-Triazol-3-one, 4-amino-2,4-di-	EtOH	262(4.13)	4-1691-80
hydro-5-phenyl-2-propyl-			
$C_{11}H_{14}N_4O_2$			
4(1H)-Pyridinone, 3-butyl-5-(2,5-di-	EtOH	231(4.02),303(3.89)	4-0175-80
hydro-5-oxo-1H-1,2,4-triazol-3-yl)-			
$C_{11}H_{14}N_4O_3$			
1(2H)-Isoquinolinone, 2-amino-3-hydra-	EtOH	246(4.51),301(4.09),	95-0819-80
zino-6,7-dimethoxy-		361(3.64)	
[1,2,4]Triazolo[1,5-a]pyrimidine-	EtOH	231(4.12),285(3.59)	87-0927-80
6-acetic acid, 1,5-dihydro-α,7-			
dimethyl-5-oxo-, ethyl ester			
[1,2,4]Triazolo[1,5-a]pyrimidine-	EtOH	209(4.31),246(3.70),	87-0927-80
6-acetic acid, 1,7-dihydro-α,5-		277(4.01)	
dimethyl-7-oxo-, ethyl ester			
$C_{11}H_{14}N_4O_4$			
7H-Pyrrolo[2,3-d]pyrimidin-4-amine,	MeOH	271(4.08)	24-2069-80
7-β-D-arabinofuranosyl-			
$C_{11}H_{14}N_4O_5$			
7H-Pyrazolo[4,3-d]pyrimidin-7-one,	pH 1	226(3.99),280(3.68)	35-2817-80
1,4-dihydro-1-methyl-3-β-D-ribo-	pH 11	230(3.32),290(3.76),	35-2817-80
furanosyl- (1-methylformycin B)		308s(3.48)	

Compound	Solvent	λ_{max}(log ϵ)	Ref.
7H-Pyrazolo[4,3-d]pyrimidin-7-one,	pH 1	277.5(4.01)	35-2817-80
1,4-dihydro-4-methyl-3-β-D-ribo-	pH 11	240(4.06),264s(3.86),	35-2817-80
furanosyl-		302(3.90)	
7H-Pyrazolo[4,3-d]pyrimidin-7-one,	pH 1	275(3.95)	35-2817-80
1,6-dihydro-6-methyl-3-β-D-ribo-	pH 11	230(4.37),282(3.79)	35-2817-80
furanosyl-			
$C_{11}H_{14}N_6$			
Pyrimidinetetramine, N^5-(phenylmethyl)-	EtOH	246(3.85),277(4.01)	150-0549-80
$C_{11}H_{14}O$			
Benzene, 2-(cyclopropyloxy)-1,3-di-	hexane	215s(--),268(2.78),	70-1928-80
methyl-		274(1.70)	
6H-Benzocyclohepten-6-one, 1,2,3,4,5,7-	EtOH	237(3.68),298(3.34)	44-5088-80
hexahydro-			
Benzofuran, 2,3-dihydro-2-(1-methyl-	MeOH	226(3.51),281(3.37),	150-0127-80
ethyl)-, (-)-		287s(3.30)	
Bicyclo[4.2.0]octa-1,3,5-triene,	hexane	215(4.20),263(2.97),	44-4183-80
3-(ethoxymethyl)-		270(2.98),276(2.98)	
3a,7a-Ethano-1H-inden-1-one,	EtOH	240(3.72),321(1.86)	44-3999-80
3a,4,5,6,7,7a-hexahydro-			
3a,7a-Methano-1H-indene-8-methanol,	C_6H_{12}	248(3.60),254(3.60),	35-0331-80
2,3-dihydro-, anti		272(3.62)	
syn	C_6H_{12}	246(3.51),252(3.61),	35-0331-80
		257(2.51)	
2-Naphthalenol, 5,6,7,8-tetrahydro-	EtOH	286(3.44)	94-2460-80
4-methyl-			
2H-Pyran, 5-(1,3-cyclohexadien-1-yl)-	C_6H_{12}	270(3.28)	39-0869-80C
3,4-dihydro-			
Spiro[4.5]deca-6,9-dien-8-one, 6-methyl-	MeOH	238(4.21),243(4.20)	44-3790-80
Tricyclo[6.2.1.0^{1,6}]undec-6-en-11-one	EtOH	270(1.32)	44-3999-80
$C_{11}H_{14}O_2$			
4H-1,3-Benzodioxin, 2,4,8-trimethyl-	EtOH	273(3.3),280(3.2)	118-0724-80
2-Benzofuranmethanol, 2,3-dihydro-	MeOH	216s(3.63),226(3.66),	150-0127-80
α,α-dimethyl-		281(3.56),288(3.51)	
2-Butene-1,4-diol, 2-methyl-1-phenyl-,	MeOH	252(2.48),257(2.48),	12-2635-80
(E)-(±)-		263(2.30)	
2-Norbornyl acetate, 5,6-bis(methyl-	isooctane	239s(3.90),244(3.94),	33-1016-80
ene)-, endo		253s(3.76)	
	MeOH	239s(3.90),244(3.93),	33-1016-80
		253s(3.75)	
exo	isooctane	238s(3.94),244(3.98),	33-1016-80
		253s(3.78)	
	MeOH	238s(3.90),244(3.96),	33-1016-80
		253s(3.78)	
Tricyclo[2.2.1.0^{2,6}]heptane-1-methanol,	isooctane	216(2.40)	33-1016-80
7-methylene-, acetate			
$C_{11}H_{14}O_2S$			
2,5-Cyclohexadiene-1,4-dione, 2,3,5-	EtOH	265(4.20),350(2.85)	39-0289-80C
trimethyl-6-[(methylthio)methyl]-			
$C_{11}H_{14}O_2S_3$			
2,5-Cyclohexadiene-1,4-dione, 2-methyl-	EtOH	247(4.18),276s(--),	39-0289-80C
3,5-bis(methylthio)-6-[(methylthio)-		341(3.59),380(3.63)?	
methyl]- (3λ,4ε)-			
2,5-Cyclohexadiene-1,4-dione, 2-methyl-	EtOH	248(4.44),274s(3.58),	39-0289-80C
3,6-bis(methylthio)-5-[(methylthio)-		382(3.63)	
methyl]-			

Compound	Solvent	$\lambda_{max}(\log \epsilon)$	Ref.
$C_{11}H_{14}O_3$			
3,5-Cyclohexadiene-1,2-dione, 4-(1,1-dimethylethyl)-5-methoxy-	MeOH	273(3.82),418(3.04)	44-4210-80
2,4-Cyclohexadien-1-one, 6-acetoxy-2,3,6-trimethyl-	hexane	299(3.72)	24-2227-80
	MeOH	307(3.70)	24-2227-80
	CF_3CH_2OH	309(3.69)	24-2227-80
2,4-Cyclohexadien-1-one, 6-acetoxy-2,4,6-trimethyl-	hexane	305(3.73)	24-2227-80
	C_6H_{12}	306(3.64),350s(2.62), 367(2.59),385s(2.43)	24-2227-80
	MeOH	311(3.59)	24-2227-80
	EtOH	311.5(3.56)	24-2227-80
2,4-Cyclohexadien-1-one, 6-acetoxy-2,5,6-trimethyl-	hexane	308(3.78),350s(2.88), 368(2.86),382s(2.72)	24-2227-80
	MeOH	314(3.72),360s(3.22)	24-2227-80
	CF_3CH_2OH	316(3.68),350s(3.42)	24-2227-80
2,4-Cyclohexadien-1-one, 6-acetoxy-3,5,6-trimethyl-	hexane	300(3.74)	24-2227-80
	MeOH	308(3.72)	24-2227-80
	CF_3CH_2OH	310(3.68)	24-2227-80
2,4,7-Nonatrienoic acid, 6-oxo-, ethyl ester	n.s.g.	286(4.48)	70-0425-80
Phenol, 4,5-dimethoxy-2-(2-propenyl)-	MeOH	230(3.63),290(3.44)	102-0285-80
$C_{11}H_{14}O_3S$			
2-Butenoic acid, 3-(2-furanyl)-4-(methylthio)-, ethyl ester, (E)-	EtOH	209(3.96),316(4.26)	73-0142-80
$C_{11}H_{14}O_3S_2$			
2,5-Cyclohexadiene-1,4-dione, 2-(methoxymethyl)-5-methyl-3,6-bis(methylthio)-	EtOH	248(4.00),384(3.61)	39-0289-80C
$C_{11}H_{14}O_4$			
Benzoic acid, 4-(2-hydroxyethoxy)-, ethyl ester	$CHCl_3$	269(4.44),313(2.36)	73-1826-80
2,7-Oxepindione, 5-(1,1-dimethylethyl)-3-methoxy-	C_6H_{12}	257s(--),267s(--), 288(3.37)	44-1153-80
Phenol, 4-(3-hydroxy-1-propenyl)-2,6-dimethoxy-	MeOH	271(4.04)	98-0427-80
	n.s.g.	315(4.05)	102-1349-80
$C_{11}H_{14}O_5$			
2,5-Methano-4H,5H-pyrano[2,3-d]-1,3-dioxin-6-carboxylic acid, 4a,8a-dihydro-4-methyl-, methyl ester (sarracenin)	EtOH	232(3.98)	100-0649-80
$C_{11}H_{14}O_6$			
Genipinic acid	n.s.g.	203(3.5)	100-0649-80
$C_{11}H_{14}O_7$			
Cyclopenta[c]pyran-4-carboxylic acid, 1,4a,5,6,7,7a-hexahydro-5,6,7-trihydroxy-7-methyl-1-oxo-, methyl ester (posoquenin)	MeOH	248(4.04)	100-0571-80
$C_{11}H_{15}N$			
Benzenamine, 2-(3-butenyl)-N-methyl-	C_6H_{12}	245(4.02),293(3.50)	33-1823-80
	MeOH	246(3.97),294(3.45)	33-1823-80
Methanamine, N-[1-(2,4-dimethylphenyl)-ethylidene]-	hexane	195(4.44),235s(3.72), 250s(3.54)	32-0597-80
	C_6H_{12}	196(4.42),238s(3.72), 252s(3.53)	32-0597-80

Compound	Solvent	$\lambda_{max}(\log \epsilon)$	Ref.
Methanamine, N-[1-(2,4-dimethylphenyl)-ethylidene]- (cont.)	MeOH	228s(3.64)	32-0597-80
	EtOH	229s(3.68)	32-0597-80
Methanamine, N-[(2,4,6-trimethylphenyl)methylene]-	hexane	212s(4.45),215(4.48),254(4.17),294s(3.02),301s(2.88)	39-0849-80B
	C_6H_{12}	212s(4.42),216(4.45),254(4.15),294s(3.09),302s(3.02)	39-0849-80B
	MeOH	208(4.31),212(4.30),250(3.98)	39-0849-80B
	EtOH	208(4.30),212(4.29),252(3.94)	39-0849-80B
$C_{11}H_{15}NO$			
2-Butanone, 1-(methylamino)-4-phenyl-, hydrochloride	MeOH	217(3.47)	4-1081-80
1-Propanone, 2-amino-2-methyl-1-(4-methylphenyl)-, hydrochloride	EtOH	200(4.3),257(4.0)	5-1016-80
2-Pyridinol, 6-methyl-3-(1-pentenyl)-, (E)-	CH_2Cl_2	250(3.78),332(2.90)	44-1354-80
$C_{11}H_{15}NOS$			
2-Butanesulfenamide, 2-methyl-N-(4-oxo-2,5-cyclohexadien-1-ylidene)-	hexane	402(4.43)	18-0775-80
Ethanone, 2-(1-methyl-2-pyrrolidinyl)-1-(2-thienyl)-, hydrochloride	n.s.g.	262(4.04),285(3.94)	48-0475-80
	EtOH	262(4.04),285(3.94)	115-0265-80
2-Propanesulfenamide, 2-methyl-N-(2-methyl-4-oxo-2,5-cyclohexadien-1-ylidene)-	hexane	399(4.32)	18-0775-80
$C_{11}H_{15}NO_2$			
Benzoic acid, 2-amino-3-methyl-, propyl ester	C_6H_{12}	245(--),333(3.73)	44-2195-80
Benzoic acid, 2-amino-5-methyl-, propyl ester	C_6H_{12}	250(--),341(3.61)	44-2195-80
Benzoic acid, 4-amino-3-methyl-, propyl ester	C_6H_{12}	271(4.17)	44-2195-80
Carbamic acid, (2-methylphenyl)-, propyl ester	C_6H_{12}	267(--),279(2.88),281(--)	44-2195-80
Carbamic acid, (4-methylphenyl)-, propyl ester	C_6H_{12}	236(--),280(--),287(2.94),273(--)	44-2195-80
Cyclopropanecarboxamide, 2-(2-furanyl)-N-(1-methylethyl)-	MeOH	285(3.80)	2-0815-80
Ethanone, 1-(2-furanyl)-2-(1-methyl-2-pyrrolidinyl)-, hydrochloride	EtOH	225(3.26),272(4.06)	48-0475-80 +115-0265-80
Ethanone, 1-[4-(3-hydroxypropyl)amino]phenyl-	pH 1	240(4.16)	5-1259-80
	pH 11	335(4.34)	5-1259-80
Isoquinoline, 1,2,3,4-tetrahydro-6,7-dimethoxy- (heliamine)	H_2O	203(4.5),220(3.8),284(3.6),288s(3.6)	102-0673-80
Isoquinoline, 1,2,3,4-tetrahydro-7,8-dimethoxy-	H_2O	201(4.5),223s(3.9),278(3.4),286(3.4),293s(3.3)	102-0673-80
Strobiline, dihydro-	EtOH	272(3.85)	102-0949-80
$C_{11}H_{15}NO_3$			
1-Indolizinecarboxylic acid, 2,3,5,6,7,8-hexahydro-5-oxo-, ethyl ester	n.s.g.	283(4.37)	88-4585-80
5H-Pyrano[3,2-c]pyridin-5-one, 2,3,4,6-tetrahydro-2-hydroxy-2,6,7-trimethyl-	MeOH	215(4.70),290(4.22)	39-0522-80C
	MeOH-acid	211(4.65),237(4.07),274(4.16)	39-0522-80C

Compound	Solvent	$\lambda_{max}(\log \epsilon)$	Ref.
(cont.) 3-Pyridinecarboxylic acid, 1,4-dihydro- 4-oxo-5-propyl-, ethyl ester	MeOH-base EtOH	220(4.78),282(4.25) 255s(3.88),260(3.90), 286(3.70)	39-0522-80C 4-0359-80
3-Pyridinecarboxylic acid, 1,4-dihydro- 5-(1-methylethyl)-4-oxo-, ethyl ester	EtOH	260(3.83),285(3.63)	4-0359-80
3-Pyridinecarboxylic acid, 1-ethyl- 1,4-dihydro-5-(1-methylethyl)-4-oxo-	EtOH	261(3.93),288(3.61)	4-0359-80
3-Pyridinecarboxylic acid, 1-ethyl- 1,4-dihydro-4-oxo-5-propyl-	EtOH	260(4.10),287(3.76)	4-0359-80
3H-Pyrrolizine-1-carboxylic acid, 2,5,6,7-tetrahydro-6-methyl-5- oxo-, ethyl ester	n.s.g.	280(4.29)	88-4585-80
$C_{11}H_{15}NO_4$ α-D-xylo-Hept-5-enofuranurononitrile, 5,6-dideoxy-3-O-methyl-1,2-O-(1- methylethylidene)-, (Z)-	EtOH	210(3.65)	136-0187-80H
$C_{11}H_{15}NO_6$ 1,1-Cyclohexanedicarboxylic acid, 3-(aminocarbonyl)-4-oxo-, dimethyl ester	EtOH	254(3.85)	23-1860-80
$C_{11}H_{15}N_3$ Benzenecarboximidic acid, (1-methyl- propylidene)hydrazide	MeOH	224(4.00),273(3.90)	104-0822-80
1H-Benzimidazol-4-amine, 2-methyl- 1-(1-methylethyl)-, hydrochloride	M HCl	238(3.69),267(3.79), 275(3.83)	104-1458-80
1H-Benzimidazol-5-amine, N,N-diethyl-	MeOH	223(4.049),279(3.660)	39-2362-80C
1H-Indole-3-ethanamine, 2-amino- 1-methyl-, dihydrochloride	EtOH	217(4.33),270(3.67)	103-0368-80
1H-1,2,4-Triazole, 2,5-dihydro- 1,5,5-trimethyl-3-phenyl-	MeOH	228(4.17),315(3.73)	104-0822-80
$C_{11}H_{15}N_3O_2$ 3H-Pyrazole-3-carboxamide, 4-(2-furan- yl)-4,5-dihydro-N-(1-methylethyl)-	MeOH	283(4.3)	2-0815-80
$C_{11}H_{15}N_3O_3$ Acetamide, N-[2-[(1-methylethyl)amino]- 3-nitrophenyl]-	EtOH	240(4.21),428(3.53)	104-1458-80
Acetamide, N-[3-nitro-2-(propylamino)- phenyl]-	EtOH	230s(4.17),419(3.37)	104-1458-80
Glycine, N-(4-cyano-2,5,6,7-tetrahydro- 2-oxo-1H-azepin-3-yl)-	EtOH	225(3.62),305(3.95)	103-0853-80
Pyrrolo[2,3-c]azepine-2-carboxylic acid, 3-amino-1,4,5,6,7,8-hexahydro- 8-oxo-, ethyl ester	EtOH	233(4.10),282(4.27)	103-0853-80
$C_{11}H_{15}N_3O_4$ Carbamic acid, 2,4-pyridinediylbis-, diethyl ester	pH 1 pH 8	223(4.62),257(4.29), 278(4.18) 224(4.59),238s(4.31), 273(3.59),280s(3.52)	87-0384-80 87-0384-80
$C_{11}H_{15}N_3O_6S$ Uridine, 5-[(2-amino-2-oxoethyl)thio]- 2'-deoxy-	H_2O	223(3.92),278(3.67)	87-0569-80
$C_{11}H_{15}N_3S$ 1-Pyrazolidinecarbothioamide, 4-methyl-	EtOH	250(4.24)	103-0169-80

Compound	Solvent	$\lambda_{max}(\log \epsilon)$	Ref.
2-phenyl- (cont.)			103-0169-80
1-Pyrazolidinecarbothioamide, 5-methyl-	EtOH	253(4.26)	103-0169-80
2-phenyl-			
$C_{11}H_{15}N_5O_2$			
3H-Purine-3-butanoic acid, 6-amino-,	MeOH	276(4.15)	24-2043-80
ethyl ester, monohydrobromide			
$C_{11}H_{15}N_5O_3$			
Hydrazinecarboxamide, N-[2-hydrazono-	EtOH	227(4.13),265(3.97)	12-0619-80
3-(4-methoxyphenyl)-1-oxopropyl]-			
$C_{11}H_{15}N_5O_4$			
Adenosine, N-methyl-	EtOH	266(4.20)	118-1025-80
Adenosine, 2'-O-methyl-	pH 7	259(4.14)	44-3865-80
Adenosine, 3'-O-methyl-	pH 7	259(4.14)	44-3865-80
Formycin, 1-methyl-	pH 1	236(3.85),302(3.80)	35-2817-80
	pH 11	232(3.81),293s(3.79),	35-2817-80
		301(3.81),314s(3.59)	
Formycin, 2-methyl-	pH 1	231(4.04),260(3.78),	35-2817-80
		270(3.77),305(4.05)	
	pH 11	237(3.75),295s(4.05),	35-2817-80
		305(4.11),317s(3.93)	
Formycin, 4-methyl-	pH 1	242(3.77),300(4.04),	35-2817-80
		307(4.03),325s(3.61)	
	pH 11	246(4.02),270(3.99),	35-2817-80
		314(3.81)	
Formycin, 6-methyl-	pH 1	229(4.16),293(3.89)	35-2817-80
	pH 11	239(4.20),279s(4.01),	35-2817-80
		288(4.05),303s(3.85)	
Formycin, N-7-methyl-	pH 1	241s(4.03),298(4.23),	35-2817-80
		307(4.20),324s(3.76)	
	pH 11	240(4.16),301(4.11),	35-2817-80
		317s(3.88)	
D-Mannitol, 1-(6-amino-9H-purin-9-yl)-	pH 1	209(4.19),260(4.05)	136-0195-80A
2,5-anhydro-1-deoxy-	EtOH	212(4.19),262(4.06)	136-0195-80A
6H-Purin-6-one, 2-amino-9-(2,3-dihy-	pH 1	227s(--),252(4.15)	36-1019-80
droxy-4-(hydroxymethyl)cyclopentyl]-	pH 13	254s(--),267(4.08)	36-1019-80
1,9-dihydro-, (1α,2α,3β,4α)-(±)-			
β-D-Ribofuranoside, methyl 5-(6-amino-	H_2O	261.5(4.11)	130-0423-80
9H-purin-9-yl)-5-deoxy-			
$C_{11}H_{15}N_5O_4S$			
6H-Purine-6-thione, 9-β-D-arabinofuran-	pH 1	270(4.01),356(4.27)	88-0479-80
osyl-1,9-dihydro-2-(methylamino)-	pH 13	258(4.15),277s(3.97),	88-0479-80
		324(4.16)	
$C_{11}H_{15}N_5O_5$			
Guanosine, N-methyl-	H 0	253(4.14),276s(3.79)	118-1025-80
Guanosine, 2'-O-methyl-	pH 7	253(4.15)	44-3865-80
Guanosine, 3'-O-methyl-	pH 7	254(4.13)	44-3865-80
Isoguanosine, 1-methyl-	pH 1.5	237(3.75),283(4.11)	44-4020-80
	pH 6.3	250(3.93),294(4.06)	44-4020-80
	pH 11.5	253(3.92),292(4.05)	44-4020-80
6H-Purin-6-one, 2-amino-9-β-D-arabino-	pH 1	261(4.14),284s(3.87)	88-0479-80
furanosyl-1,9-dihydro-2-(methyl-	pH 13	259(4.06),272(4.02)	88-0479-80
amino)-			
$C_{11}H_{15}N_7$			
Guanidine, [[5-amino-1-(phenylmethyl)-	H_2O	245(3.72)	39-2918-80C
1H-1,2,3-triazol-4-yl]methyl]-	pH 13	246(3.74)	39-2918-80C

Compound	Solvent	$\lambda_{max}(\log \epsilon)$	Ref.
$C_{11}H_{16}$			
5H-Benzocycloheptene, 4a,6,7,8,9,9a-hexahydro-, cis	hexane	262(3.59)	35-4456-80
trans	hexane	264(3.40)	35-4456-80
1,3,5-Cycloundecatriene, cis-cis-trans	hexane	254(3.70)	35-4456-80
Dictyopterene B (1-ethenyl-2-(1,3-hexadienyl)cyclopropane)	hexane	246(4.42)	35-6114-80
$C_{11}H_{16}BrN_5O_2$			
3H-Purine-3-butanoic acid, 6-amino-, ethyl ester, monohydrobromide	MeOH	276(4.15)	24-2043-80
$C_{11}H_{16}ClNO$			
2-Butanone, 1-(methylamino)-4-phenyl-, hydrochloride	MeOH	217(3.47)	4-1081-80
1-Propanone, 2-amino-2-methyl-1-(4-methylphenyl)-, hydrochloride	EtOH	200(4.3),257(4.0)	5-1016-80
$C_{11}H_{16}ClNOS$			
Ethanone, 2-(1-methyl-2-pyrrolidinyl)-1-(2-thienyl)-, hydrochloride	n.s.g.	262(4.04),285(3.94)	48-0475-80
$C_{11}H_{16}ClNO_2$			
Ethanone, 1-(2-furanyl)-2-(1-methyl-2-pyrrolidinyl)-, hydrochloride	n.s.g.	225(3.26),272(4.06)	48-0475-80
2H-Pyran-2-one, 3-chloro-4-(dimethyl-amino)-6-(1,1-dimethylethyl)-	EtOH	236(4.26),270(3.80), 319(4.02)	4-0507-80
$C_{11}H_{16}ClN_2$			
Methanaminium, N-[chloro[5-[(dimethyl-amino)methylene]-1,3-cyclopentadien-1-yl]methylene]-N-methyl-, chloride	MeCN	284(4.18),386(4.66)	89-0199-80
$C_{11}H_{16}ClN_2O_4PS$			
3(2H)-Pyridazinone, 4-chloro-5-[(5,5-dimethyl-1,3,2-dioxaphosphorinan-2-yl)oxy]-2-ethyl-, P-sulfide	MeOH	213(4.34),296(3.61)	73-2343-80
$C_{11}H_{16}ClN_3$			
1H-Benzimidazol-4-amine, 2-methyl-1-(1-methylethyl)-, hydrochloride	M HCl	238(3.69),267(3.79), 275(3.83)	104-1458-80
$C_{11}H_{16}FN_3O_7P$			
Uridine, 2'-deoxy-5-fluoro-, 3'-acetate 5'-phosphorodiamidate	MeOH	269(3.96)	87-1229-80
$C_{11}H_{16}F_2O_4$			
α-D-ribo-Hept-6-enofuranose, 5,6,7-tri-deoxy-7,7-difluoro-3-O-methyl-1,2-O-(1-methylethylidene)-	EtOH	210s(1.48),217(1.48), 254(1.00)	33-1644-80
α-D-xylo-Hept-6-enofuranose, 5,6,7-tri-deoxy-7,7-difluoro-3-O-methyl-1,2-O-(1-methylethylidene)-	EtOH	203(1.88),213s(1.70)	33-1644-80
$C_{11}H_{16}GeO$			
Germane, trimethyl(phenylacetyl)-	hexane	198(4.18),230(3.72), 244s(3.36),258(3.08), 354s(2.00),366(2.09), 381(2.00)	35-1577-80

Compound	Solvent	$\lambda_{max}(\log \epsilon)$	Ref.
$C_{11}H_{16}NO$			
Ethanaminium, N-ethyl-N-(3-methyl-4-oxo-2,5-cyclohexadien-1-ylidene)-	H_2O	291(4.28)	39-1601-80B
$C_{11}H_{16}N_2O$			
1,3-Cyclopentadiene-1-carboxamide, 5-[(dimethylamino)methylene]-N,N-dimethyl-	dioxan	239(3.99),340(4.44)	89-0199-80
1-Propanone, 2-amino-2-methyl-1-(4-methylphenyl)-, oxime, (E)-	EtOH	201(4.2),216(3.9), 258(2.7)	5-1016-80
Pyridine, 3-(4,5-dihydro-4,4-dimethyl-2-oxazolyl)-1,4-dihydro-4-methyl-	EtOH	328(3.967)	39-2070-80C
$C_{11}H_{16}N_2O_2$			
Benzenamine, 3,5-dimethyl-N-(1-methylethyl)-2-nitro-	EtOH	245(4.29),300(3.68), 420(3.68)	103-0962-80
Benzenamine, 3,5-dimethyl-N-(1-methylethyl)-4-nitro-	EtOH	253(3.07),312(2.58), 400(2.96)	103-0962-80
Benzenamine, 3,5-dimethyl-2-nitro-N-propyl-	EtOH	242(4.15),296(3.51), 430(3.48)	103-0962-80
Benzenamine, 3,5-dimethyl-4-nitro-N-propyl-	EtOH	248(3.90),312(3.48), 400(3.76)	103-0962-80
3H-Pyrazole-4-carboxylic acid, 3,3-dimethyl-5-(2-methyl-1-propenyl)-, methyl ester	MeCN	236(4.09),316(3.91), 384(2.42)	88-0671-80
3H-Pyrazole-5-carboxylic acid, 3,3-dimethyl-4-(2-methyl-1-propenyl)-, methyl ester	MeCN	303(3.82),361(2.97)	88-0671-80
2-Pyridinecarboxylic acid, 5-(butylamino)-, methyl ester	MeOH	294(4.26),307(4.24)	87-1405-80
Spiro[2H-benzimidazole-2,1'-cyclopentane], 4,5,6,7-tetrahydro-, 1,3-dioxide	EtOH	212(3.90),350(3.90)	103-0628-80
$C_{11}H_{16}N_2O_3$			
3(2H)-Pyridazinone, 2-cyclohexyl-5-hydroxy-4-methoxy-	MeOH	215(4.45),286(3.66)	73-0127-80
$C_{11}H_{16}N_2O_3S$			
Pyrazinecarboxylic acid, 3,4-dihydro-6-methyl-5-[2-(methylthio)ethyl]-3-oxo-, ethyl ester	EtOH	233(3.84),318(3.90), 363(3.50)	70-0774-80
$C_{11}H_{16}N_2O_5$			
3-Pyridinecarboxamide, 1,4-dihydro-1-β-D-xylopyranosyl-	MeOH	335(3.77)	23-0387-80
$C_{11}H_{16}N_2O_5S$			
Thymine, 1-(2-deoxy-β-D-ribofuranosyl)-α-(methylthio)-	pH 1	267(3.99)	87-0252-80
	pH 11	265.5(3.86)	87-0252-80
$C_{11}H_{16}N_2O_6$			
D-Mannitol, 2,5-anhydro-1-deoxy-1-(3,4-dihydro-5-methyl-2,4-dioxo-1(2H)-pyrimidinyl)-	pH 13	209(4.39),268(3.92)	136-0195-80A
	EtOH	211(3.99),270(3.91)	136-0195-80A
Pseudouridine, 1',4'-dimethyl-	pH 13	287(3.68)	138-0679-80
	MeOH	265(3.79)	138-0679-80
Uridine, 3-methyl-2'-O-methyl-	pH 7	262(3.92)	44-3865-80
Uridine, 3-methyl-3'-O-methyl-	pH 7	262(3.94)	44-3865-80
Uridine, 3'-C-ethyl-	H_2O	260(4.03)	136-0219-80B
	pH 13	260(3.90)	136-0219-80B

Compound	Solvent	$\lambda_{max}(\log \epsilon)$	Ref.
$C_{11}H_{16}N_2O_6S$			
Thymidine, α-(methylsulfinyl)-	pH 1	270(4.18)	87-0252-80
	pH 11	268(4.02)	87-0252-80
Uridine, 2'-deoxy-5-[(2-hydroxyethyl)-thio]-	H_2O	279(3.69)	87-0569-80
$C_{11}H_{16}N_2O_7$			
1H-Imidazole-4-carboxylic acid, 5-hydroxy-2-β-D-ribofuranosyl-, ethyl ester	H_2O	242(3.89),282(4.22)	44-0203-80
$C_{11}H_{16}N_2O_7S$			
Thymidine, α-(methylsulfonyl)-	pH 1	268.5(4.01)	87-0252-80
	pH 11	267(3.86)	87-0252-80
$C_{11}H_{16}N_2S$			
1,3-Cyclopentadiene-1-carbothioamide, 5-[(dimethylamino)methylene]-N,N-dimethyl-	dioxan	265(4.24),304(4.38), 417(3.47)	89-0199-80
$C_{11}H_{16}N_3O_3P$			
Phosphonic acid, (1H-benzotriazol-1-ylmethyl)-, diethyl ester	n.s.g.	<u>207(4.1),261(3.8), 282(3.6)</u>	65-1217-80
$C_{11}H_{16}N_4$			
1H-Benzimidazole-4,5-diamine, N^4,N^4-diethyl-	MeOH	222(4.065),261(3.750), 289(3.530)	39-2362-80C
1H-Benzimidazole-4,5-diamine, N^5,N^5-diethyl-	MeOH	223(4.005),296(3.495)	39-2362-80C
Imidazo[5,1-f][1,2,4]triazine, 2,5-dimethyl-7-(2-methylpropyl)- (maleate)	EtOH	229(4.25),250(3.95), 368(--)	39-1139-80C
1H-Indazole-6,7-diamine, N^6,N^6-diethyl-	MeOH	223(4.151),296(3.953)	39-2362-80C
$C_{11}H_{16}N_4O$			
Imidazo[5,1-f][1,2,4]triazin-4(1H)-one, 2,5-dimethyl-7-(2-methylpropyl)-	EtOH	222(4.38),252(3.95), 265s(3.79),281s(--)	39-1139-80C
	EtOH-NaOH	235(--),261(--), 269s(--),300(--)	39-1139-80C
Imidazo[5,1-f][1,2,4]triazin-4(1H)-one, 2-ethyl-5-methyl-7-propyl-	EtOH	221(4.38),250(3.94), 278s(3.43)	39-1139-80C
$C_{11}H_{16}N_4O_2$			
6H-Purin-6-one, 1,7-dihydro-8-(1-hydroxy-1-methylethyl)-2-(1-methylethyl)-	pH 7	253(4.12)	149-0195-80A
6H-Purin-6-one, 1,7-dihydro-8-(2-hydroxy-1,1,2-trimethylpropyl)-	pH 7	254(4.13)	149-0195-80A
4H-Pyrazolo[3,4-d]pyrimidin-4-one, 1,2-dihydro-2-(2-hydroxy-1,1,2-trimethylpropyl)-	pH 7	260(3.97)	149-0195-80A
$C_{11}H_{16}N_4O_3$			
3-Pyridinecarboxylic acid, 5-butyl-1,4-dihydro-4-oxo-, 2-(aminocarbonyl)hydrazide	EtOH	254(3.93),287(3.79)	4-0175-80
$C_{11}H_{16}N_6O_3$			
1,2-Cyclopentanediol, 3-(2,6-diamino-9H-purin-9-yl)-5-(hydroxymethyl)-, (1α,2β,3β,5β)-($\pm$)-	pH 1	216(4.43),251(4.10), 290(4.04)	36-1019-80
	H_2O	214(4.44),254(3.94), 280(4.02)	36-1019-80

Compound	Solvent	$\lambda_{max}(\log \epsilon)$	Ref.
(cont.)	pH 13	254(3.97),279(4.06)	36-1019-80
$C_{11}H_{16}N_8$			
2,4,7-Pteridinetriamine, 6-piperidino-	pH 1	255(4.02),345(4.15)	150-0549-80
$C_{11}H_{16}O$			
Benzene, (1-methoxy-2-methylpropyl)-	MeCN	247(1.95),251(2.08), 257(2.18),264(2.00), 266s(1.78)	108-0142-80
6H-Benzocyclohepten-6-one, 1,2,3,4,5-	EtOH	293(2.33)	44-5088-80
7,8,9-octahydro-	EtOH	292(2.40)	44-5088-80
Bicyclo[2.2.1]heptan-2-one, 1,7,7-tri-	$C_6H_{11}Me$	227(3.96),344(1.60)	44-3518-80
methyl-3-methylene-, (1R,4S)-			
(1S,4R)-	$C_6H_{11}Me$	227(3.82),346(1.56)	44-3518-80
Bicyclo[3.2.1]oct-3-en-2-one, 6,7,7-	n.s.g.	237(3.80)	39-1516-80C
trimethyl-, exo			
Bicyclo[5.3.1]undec-7-en-9-one	MeCN	240(4.17),335(1.70)	44-1800-80
2-Cyclopenten-1-one, 2,4,4-trimethyl-	n.s.g.	231(3.79)	39-1516-80C
5-(2-propenyl)-			
2-Cyclopenten-1-one, 3,4,4-trimethyl-	n.s.g.	230(4.14)	39-1516-80C
5-(2-propenyl)-			
2-Cyclopenten-1-one, 2,4,4-trimethyl-	n.s.g.	256(3.76)	39-1516-80C
5-propylidene-			
4H-Inden-4-one, 1,2,3,5,6,7-hexahydro-	hexane	242(3.90)	150-1551-80
5,5-dimethyl-			
4H-Inden-4-one, 1,2,3,5,6,7-hexahydro-	EtOH	249(4.07)	35-0409-80
7,7-dimethyl-			
1(2H)-Naphthalenone, 3,4,5,6,7,8-hexa-	hexane	235(3.81)	150-1551-80
hydro-2-methyl-			
Spiro[4.5]decan-1-one, 6-methylene-	EtOH	303(1.83)	44-5088-80
$C_{11}H_{16}OSi$			
Ethanone, 1-phenyl-2-(trimethylsilyl)-	hexane	225s(3.83),259s(3.00), 368s(2.01),377(2.05), 392(1.90)	35-1577-80
$C_{11}H_{16}O_2$			
2-Cyclohexen-1-one, 4-methoxy-3,4,5,6-	EtOH	230(3.96)	44-4337-80
tetramethyl-			
1,3-Cyclopentadiene, 5-(3,3-dimethoxy-	MeOH	268(4.17),348(2.60)	34-0184-80
1-methylpropylidene)-			
1,3-Cyclopentanedione, 2-(3-methyl-	MeOH	254(4.19)	33-1198-80
4-pentenyl)-			
$C_{11}H_{16}O_3$			
Benzene, 1-(1,1-dimethoxyethyl)-	n.s.g.	229(3.49),272(3.29), 278(3.26)	44-0501-80
2-methoxy-			
Cyclopentanecarboxylic acid, 2-oxo-	C_6H_{12}	303(1.75)	151-0305-80A
1-(2-propenyl)-, ethyl ester			
1-Cyclopentene-1-butanoic acid,	MeOH	227(4.00)	44-4702-80
5-oxo-, ethyl ester			
1-Cyclopentene-1-hexanoic acid, 5-oxo-	MeOH	228(4.02)	44-4702-80
2,4,6-Decatrienoic acid, 10-hydroxy-,	n.s.g.	300(4.23)	88-2887-80
methyl ester			
1-Naphthalenecarboxylic acid, deca-	MeOH	284(1.45)	39-0950-80C
hydro-8-oxo-, (+)-			
$C_{11}H_{16}O_7$			
Cyclopenta[c]pyran-4-carboxylic acid,	MeOH	210(2.26)	100-0571-80
octahydro-5,6,7-trihydroxy-7-methyl-			
1-oxo-, methyl ester (latifonin)			

Compound	Solvent	$\lambda_{max}(\log \epsilon)$	Ref.
$C_{11}H_{16}S$			
Ethanethione, 1-(3,3-dimethylbicyclo-[2.2.1]hept-5-en-2-yl)-, endo	C_6H_{12}	510(1.04)	44-2517-80
$C_{11}H_{16}S_2Si$			
1,3-Dithia-2-silacycloheptane, 2-methyl-2-phenyl-	hexane	198(4.51),218(4.14), 236s(3.43),272(2.55)	101-0147-80A
$C_{11}H_{16}Sn$			
Stannane, trimethyl(2-phenylethenyl)-, 90% cis	MeOH	293(2.86)	101-0233-80R
trans	MeOH	293(3.29)	101-0233-80R
$C_{11}H_{17}ClO_4S_2$			
Sulfonium, [2-(2-chlorophenyl)ethyl]di-methyl-, methyl sulfate	H_2O	264(2.82)	124-0957-80
$C_{11}H_{17}Cl_2N_3$			
1H-Indole-3-ethanamine, 2-amino-1-methyl-, dihydrochloride	EtOH	217(4.33),270(3.67)	103-0368-80
$C_{11}H_{17}FN_2O_6S$			
D-Lyxitol, 1-S-ethyl-1-(5-fluoro-uracil-1-yl)-1-thio-, (1R,1S)-	MeOH	272(4.0)	136-0263-80C
D-allo-Pentitol, 1-S-ethyl-1-(5-fluoro-uracil-1-yl)-1-thio-	MeOH	272(4.1)	136-0263-80C
D-gluco-Pentitol, 1-S-ethyl-1-(5-fluoro-uracil-1-yl)-1-thio-	MeOH	272(4.1)	136-0263-80C
D-gulo-Pentitol, 1-S-ethyl-1-(5-fluoro-uracil-1-yl)-1-thio-	MeOH	271(4.0)	136-0263-80C
$C_{11}H_{17}F_3N_2O_2$			
1-Propen-2-ol, 1-(2,5-dihydro-1,2,2,5-5-pentamethyl-1H-imidazol-4-yl)-3,3,3-trifluoro-, N-oxide	EtOH	229(3.48),324(4.10)	70-0956-80
$C_{11}H_{17}NO$			
3-Buten-2-one, 4-(2,3-dihydro-3,3,5-trimethyl-1H-pyrrol-1-yl)-	MeOH	214(3.57),236(3.50), 335(4.41)	83-0858-80
Cyclohexanone, 2-[3-(dimethylamino)-2-propenylidene]-	hexane	360(4.59)	70-1643-80
	EtOH	393(4.53)	70-1643-80
	$CHCl_3$	395(4.67)	70-1643-80
Tricyclo[3.3.1.1^{3,7}]decan-1-amine, N-methylene-, N-oxide	MeCN	253(4.08)	54-0246-80
$C_{11}H_{17}NO_2$			
2,4-Pentanedione, 3-[3-(dimethylamino)-2-methyl-2-propenylidene]-	hexane	213(4.18),238(4.03), 285(3.77)	70-1643-80
	H_2O	305(3.80),410(4.36)	70-1643-80
	EtOH	245(3.92),300(3.96), 395(3.50)	70-1643-80
	MeOH	240(3.83),308(3.86), 400(3.78)	70-1643-80
	67% MeOH	212s(3.85),240s(3.74), 308(4.08),410(4.12)	70-1643-80
	50% MeOH	208s(3.84),240s(3.73), 308(4.14),410(4.35)	70-1643-80
	$CHCl_3$	250(3.83),300(3.73), 390(3.15)	70-1643-80

Compound	Solvent	$\lambda_{max}(\log \epsilon)$	Ref.
$C_{11}H_{17}NO_2S$			
Pyridine, 3-(diethoxymethyl)-2-(methyl-thio)-	EtOH	251(4.01),291(3.58)	118-0405-80
$C_{11}H_{17}NO_3$			
1-Azabicyclo[5.2.0]nonan-9-one, 8-acetyl-7-methoxy-	MeOH	258(3.03),309(3.10)	44-0936-80
Butanoic acid, 2-(hexahydro-2H-azepin-2-ylidene)-3-oxo-, methyl ester	MeOH	251(3.72),309(4.19)	44-0936-80
Butanoic acid, 3-oxo-2-(2-piperidin-ylidene)-, ethyl ester	MeOH	248(3.88),300(4.19)	44-0936-80
2,4-Pentadienoic acid, 2-acetyl-5-(di-methylamino)-4-methyl-, methyl ester (or isomeric pyran)	H_2O 66% MeOH	290(3.52),400(4.69) 203(4.03),235(3.86), 292(3.90),400(4.50)	70-1643-80 70-1643-80
	50% MeOH	290(3.66),400(4.58)	70-1643-80
100% pyran form	hexane	210(3.98),235(3.98), 294(3.68)	70-1643-80
97% pyran form	$CHCl_3$	294(3.81),385(3.19)	70-1643-80
78% pyran form	80% EtOH	300(3.83),405(4.03)	70-1643-80
$C_{11}H_{17}NO_6$			
3,5-Isoxazoledicarboxylic acid, 4-but-yl-4,5-dihydro-, dimethyl ester, 2-oxide, trans	MeOH	268(3.95)	94-0479-80
3,5-Isoxazoledicarboxylic acid, 4,5-dihydro-4-(2-methylpropyl)-, dimethyl ester, 2-oxide, trans	MeOH	268(3.89)	94-0479-80
$C_{11}H_{17}N_2O_5PS$			
3(2H)-Pyridazinone, 5-[(5,5-dimethyl-1,3,2-dioxaphosphorinan-2-yl)oxy]-4-methoxy-2-methyl-, P-sulfide	MeOH	212(4.30),285(3.72)	73-2343-80
$C_{11}H_{17}N_2O_8PS$			
5'-Thymidylic acid, α-(methylthio)-, compd. with Et N (1:2)	pH 1 pH 11	267(3.93) 266(3.80)	87-0252-80 87-0252-80
$C_{11}H_{17}N_2O_9P$			
1H-Imidazole-4-carboxylic acid, 1-(5-O-phosphono-β-D-ribofuranosyl)-, 4-ethyl ester	pH 2 pH 6-7 pH 12	221(4.03) 234(4.00) 234(4.00)	65-1723-80 65-1723-80 65-1723-80
$C_{11}H_{17}N_3OS$			
Thiourea, N-butyl-N'-(6-methoxy-3-pyri-dinyl)-	EtOH	243(4.30),270s(3.00), 300s(3.51)	44-4219-80
$C_{11}H_{17}N_3O_4$			
5-Pyrimidineheptanoic acid, 2-amino-1,4-dihydro-6-hydroxy-4-oxo-	50%MeOH-HCl + NaOH	267(4.20) 270(4.15)	73-3583-80 73-3583-80
5-Pyrimidinepentanoic acid, 2-amino-1,4-dihydro-6-hydroxy-4-oxo-, ethyl ester	50%MeOH-HCl + NaOH	267(4.19) 269(4.11)	73-3583-80 73-3583-80
5-Pyrimidinepentanoic acid, 2-amino-5-ethyl-1,4,5,6-tetrahydro-4,6-dioxo-	50%MeOH-HCl + NaOH	215(4.367) 226(4.35),264(4.04)	73-3583-80 73-3583-80
$C_{11}H_{17}N_3O_5$			
Cytidine, N-ethyl-	pH 7	267(4.2)	44-2704-80
$C_{11}H_{17}N_3O_6$			
1H-Imidazole-4-carboxylic acid, 5-ami-no-1-β-D-arabinofuranosyl-, ethyl ester	H_2O	269(4.05)	39-2304-80C

Compound	Solvent	$\lambda_{max}(\log \epsilon)$	Ref.
$C_{11}H_{17}N_5$			
3H-Purin-6-amine, N,N,3-triethyl-	pH 1	293(4.34)	94-1920-80
	pH 7	295(4.25)	94-1920-80
	pH 13	296(4.24)	94-1920-80
	EtOH	300(4.22)	94-1920-80
7H-Purin-6-amine, N,N,7-triethyl-	pH 1	229(3.89),300(4.25)	94-1920-80
	pH 7	227(4.01),298(4.11)	94-1920-80
	pH 13	298(4.11)	94-1920-80
	EtOH	225(4.03),295(4.09)	94-1920-80
$C_{11}H_{18}ClN_2O_3PS_2$			
Phosphorodithioic acid, O-(5-chloro-1-ethyl-1,6-dihydro-6-oxo-4-pyridazinyl) O-ethyl S-propyl ester	MeOH	213(4.00),296(3.23)	73-2247-80
$C_{11}H_{18}FeO_4Si_2$			
Iron, tetracarbonyl[(η^2-ethenyl)pentamethyldisilane]-	hexane	212(4.37),236s(4.17), 270s(3.94)	35-6349-80
$C_{11}H_{18}NO_4$			
1-Piperidinyloxy, 3-(methoxycarbonyl)-2,2,6,6-tetramethyl-4-oxo-	hexane	252(4.00),455(0.93)	94-3178-80
	H_2O	247(3.58)	94-3178-80
	EtOH	251(3.96),400(1.00)	94-3178-80
	MeCN	250(3.86),452(0.96)	94-3178-80
$C_{11}H_{18}N_2O_2S$			
4,6(1H,5H)-Pyrimidinedione, 5-ethyldihydro-5-(1-methylbutyl)-2-thioxo-	MeOH	238(4.31),287(4.62), 374(1.86)	36-1164-80
	$CHCl_3$	287(4.59),367(1.95)	36-1164-80
$C_{11}H_{18}N_2O_3$			
3(2H)-Pyridazinone, 2-hexyl-5-hydroxy-4-methoxy-	MeOH	221(4.31),285(3.73)	73-0127-80
Thymine, N-2-isobutoxyethyl-	DMF	271.0(3.97)	47-0427-80
$C_{11}H_{18}N_2O_5$			
1H-Imidazole-1,3(2H)-dicarboxylic acid, 2-ethoxy-, diethyl ester	MeCN	240(3.82)	35-6784-80
$C_{11}H_{18}N_2O_6S$			
D-Lyxitol, 1-C-(3,4-dihydro-2,4-dioxo-1(2H)-pyrimidinyl)-1-S-ethyl-1-thio-	H_2O	266(3.99)	136-0364-80C
D-Ribitol, 1-C-(3,4-dihydro-2,4-dioxo-1(2H)-pyrimidinyl)-1-S-ethyl-1-thio-	H_2O	265(4.05)	136-0364-80C
$C_{11}H_{18}N_4$			
Imidazo[5,1-f][1,2,4]triazine, 1,4-dihydro-2,5-dimethyl-7-(2-methylpropyl)- (maleate)	EtOH	253(3.97)	39-1139-80C
Imidazo[5,1-f][1,2,4]triazine, 1,4-dihydro-2,4,5-trimethyl-7-propyl-	EtOH	256(4.03)	39-1139-80C
Imidazo[5,1-f][1,2,4]triazine, 2-ethyl-1,4-dihydro-5-methyl-7-propyl-	EtOH	253(3.97)	39-1139-80C
$C_{11}H_{18}N_4O_2$			
Butanamide, N-[1-(2,5-dihydro-3-methyl-5-oxo-1,2,4-triazin-6-yl)ethyl]-3-methyl-, (S)-	EtOH	235(3.97),261s(3.73)	39-1139-80C
Butanamide, N-[1-(3-ethyl-2,5-dihydro-5-oxo-1,2,4-triazin-6-yl)ethyl]-, (S)-	EtOH	236(3.96),260s(3.74)	39-1139-80C

Compound	Solvent	λ_{max} (log ϵ)	Ref.
$C_{11}H_{18}N_4O_5$			
Cytidine, N-(2-aminoethyl)-	H_2O	270(3.97)	44-2704-80
$C_{11}H_{18}N_5$			
3H-Purinium, 6-(diethylamino)-3,9-di-	pH 1	223(4.39),290(4.28)	94-2522-80
methyl-, iodide	pH 7	223(4.37),291(4.28)	94-2522-80
	EtOH	292(4.28)	94-2522-80
3H-Purinium, 6-(dimethylamino)-3,9-di-	pH 1	223(4.39),289(4.25)	94-2522-80
ethyl-, iodide	pH 7	223(4.39),289(4.25)	94-2522-80
	EtOH	291(4.25)	94-2522-80
$C_{11}H_{18}O$			
1-Decalone, 8-methyl-, (8R,9R,10S)-(-)-	hexane	223(1.00),290(1.29), 298(1.30),307(1.22), 318s(0.97)	39-0950-80C
	MeOH	227s(1.10),288(1.38)	39-0950-80C
(8R,9S,10S)-(+)-	hexane	291s(1.31),297(1.32), 305s(1.26)	39-0950-80C
	MeOH	290(1.42)	39-0950-80C
(8S,9R,10S)-(+)-	hexane	297(1.34),305(1.28), 315s(1.05)	39-0950-80C
	MeOH	290(1.43)	39-0950-80C
5-Hepten-2-one, 6-methyl-3-(1-methyl- ethenyl)-	n.s.g.	295(2.15)	33-0571-80
3,7-Nonadien-2-one, 4,8-dimethyl-, (E)-	n.s.g.	235(4.14),330(1.64)	33-0571-80
(Z)-	n.s.g.	234(3.96),312(2.60), 340(2.60)	33-0571-80
3,8-Nonadien-2-one, 4,8-dimethyl-, (E)-	n.s.g.	235(4.17),330(1.60)	33-0571-80
(Z)-	n.s.g.	235(4.07),310s(1.60), 330(1.62)	33-0571-80
$C_{11}H_{18}OS$			
Bicyclo[2.2.1]heptan-2-one, 1,7,7-tri-	hexane	245(2.31),315(2.18)	39-0453-80B
methyl-3-(methylthio)-	MeOH	247(2.29),310(2.13)	39-0453-80B
2-Cyclohexen-1-one, 2-(ethylthio)- 3,6,6-trimethyl-	C_6H_{12}	223(4.12),315(3.53)	78-1943-80
$C_{11}H_{18}OS_2$			
1,2-Dithiol-1-ium, 3,5-bis(1,1-dimeth-	EtOH	426(4.00)	139-0079-80A
ylethyl)-4-hydroxy-, hydroxide,	dioxan	463(3.77)	139-0079-80A
inner salt	MeCN	453(3.80)	139-0079-80A
$C_{11}H_{18}OSi$			
Silane, (1,1-dimethylethoxy)methyl- phenyl-	C_6H_{12}	247s(2.60),253(2.69), 259(2.78),264(2.77), 270(2.65),275s(2.31)	101-0007-80A
$C_{11}H_{18}O_2$			
2-Furanol, tetrahydro-5-(5-methyl- 1,3-hexadienyl)-	EtOH	230(4.43)	35-1390-80
2,4-Hexanedione, 5-methyl-3-(2-methyl-	EtOH	216(3.73),293(3.93)	33-1499-80
1-propenyl)-	EtOH-KOH	245(3.62),318(4.14)	33-1499-80
1(2H)-Naphthalenone, octahydro-8-(hy- droxymethyl)-, [4aS-(4aα,8β,8aβ)]-	hexane	291(1.29)	39-0950-80C
3-Octene-2,6-dione, 5,5,7-trimethyl-, (E)-	n.s.g.	208(3.92),232(3.94), 300(2.69)	33-1499-80
(Z)-	n.s.g.	225(3.83)	33-1499-80
1-Propanone, 1-(3-acetyl-2,2-dimethyl- cyclopropyl)-2-methyl-	n.s.g.	287(1.92)	33-1499-80
1-Propanone, 1-(4-hydroxy-1,4-dimethyl- 2-cyclopenten-1-yl)-	n.s.g.	298(2.60)	33-1499-80

Compound	Solvent	$\lambda_{max}(\log \epsilon)$	Ref.
$C_{11}H_{18}O_3$			
Cyclohexanecarboxylic acid, 1-ethyl-2-oxo-, ethyl ester	C_6H_{12}	290(1.43)	151-0305-80A
Cyclopentanecarboxylic acid, 2-oxo-1-propyl-, ethyl ester	C_6H_{12}	302(1.67)	151-0305-80A
$C_{11}H_{18}O_4S_2$			
Sulfonium, ethylmethyl(phenylmethyl)-, methyl sulfate	H_2O	218(3.90),264(2.64), 274(2.6)	124-0957-80
$C_{11}H_{18}S_2Si$			
Silane, bis(ethylthio)methylphenyl-	hexane	216s(3.91),238s(3.24), 265(2.59),272(2.44)	101-0147-80A +131-0099-80C
$C_{11}H_{18}Si$			
Silane, dimethyl[(2-methylphenyl)methyl]-	C_6H_{12}	221(3.60)	65-1621-80
$C_{11}H_{18}Si_2$			
1H-1,2-Disilaindene, 2,3-dihydro-1,1,2,2-tetramethyl-	C_6H_{12}	222(3.97)	65-1621-80
$C_{11}H_{19}ClSi_2$			
Disilane, (3-chlorophenyl)pentamethyl-	isooctane	236(3.99)	101-0261-80Q
Disilane, (4-chlorophenyl)pentamethyl-	isooctane	237.5(4.25)	101-0261-80Q
$C_{11}H_{19}N$			
1H-Pyrrole, 2-butyl-3-propyl-	hexane	222(3.89)	103-0488-80
$C_{11}H_{19}NO$			
3-Buten-2-one, 4-(2,4,4-trimethyl-1-pyrrolidinyl)-, (E)-	MeOH	308(4.05)	83-0858-80
$C_{11}H_{19}NO_2$			
2-Cyclopenten-1-one, 2-(5-hydroxypentyl)-, O-methyloxime	MeOH	243(4.07)	44-4702-80
1-Penten-3-one, 4,4-dimethyl-1-morpholino-	EtOH	310(4.31)	4-0507-80
$C_{11}H_{19}NO_2Si_2$			
Disilane, pentamethyl(3-nitrophenyl)-	C_6H_{12}	234(4.19)	101-0261-80Q
Disilane, pentamethyl(4-nitrophenyl)-	C_6H_{12}	287.5(4.08)	101-0261-80Q
$C_{11}H_{19}NO_4S$			
2-Cyclopenten-1-one, 2-[4-[(methylsulfonyl)oxy]butyl]-, O-methyloxime	MeOH	243(4.13)	44-4702-80
$C_{11}H_{19}N_2O_4PS_2$			
Phosphorodithioic acid, O-(1,6-dihydro-5-methoxy-1-methyl-6-oxo-4-pyridazinyl) O-ethyl S-(1-methylethyl) ester	MeOH	212(4.31),287(3.70)	73-2247-80
Phosphorodithioic acid, O-(1,6-dihydro-5-methoxy-1-methyl-6-oxo-4-pyridazinyl) O-ethyl S-propyl ester	MeOH	220(4.13),286(3.68)	73-2247-80
$C_{11}H_{19}N_3O_5S$			
D-Arabinitol, 1-(1-cytosinyl)-1-S-ethyl-1-thio-, (R)-	H_2O	275(4.12)	136-0364-80C
(S)-	H_2O	276(3.96)	136-0364-80C
D-Lyxitol, 1-(1-cytosinyl)-1-S-ethyl-1-thio-	H_2O	278(4.05)	136-0364-80C

Compound	Solvent	$\lambda_{max}(\log \epsilon)$	Ref.
D-Ribitol, 1-(1-cytosinyl)-1-S-ethyl-1-thio-	H_2O	277(4.02)	136-0364-80C
D-Xylitol, 1-(1-cytosinyl)-1-S-ethyl-1-thio-, (R)-(+)-	MeOH	275(4.05)	136-0364-80C
(S)-(-)-	MeOH	277(4.0)	136-0364-80C
$C_{11}H_{20}$			
1,3-Heptadiene, 2,5,5,6-tetramethyl-	n.s.g.	224(4.24),230(4.28),236s(4.10)	33-1499-80
2,4-Octadiene, 2,5,7-trimethyl-	n.s.g.	240s(3.99),246(4.03),253s(3.94)	33-1499-80
$C_{11}H_{20}N_2O$			
2-Cyclopropen-1-one, 2,3-bis(diethylamino)-	MeCN	234(3.99)	88-3241-80
$C_{11}H_{20}N_2O_2Si$			
2,4-Diazabicyclo[4.2.0]octane-3,5-dione, 8,8-dimethyl-6-(trimethylsilyl)-	MeOH	226(3.23)	44-4462-80
$C_{11}H_{20}N_4O_2S$			
4,6-Pyrimidinediamine, 5-(2,2-diethoxyethyl)-2-(methylthio)-	MeOH	219(4.54),258(3.96),271(3.99)	24-2069-80
$C_{11}H_{20}OS$			
Cyclohexanone, 4-(1,1-dimethylethyl)-2-(methylthio)-	hexane	248(2.51),308(2.45)	39-0453-80B
	MeOH	249(2.47),305(2.51)	39-0453-80B
$C_{11}H_{20}OSi$			
2-Cyclopenten-1-one, 2-(trimethylsilyl)-, propene adduct	MeOH	292(1.93)	44-4462-80
$C_{11}H_{20}OSi_2$			
2,4-Cyclopentadien-1-one, 3,5-bis(trimethylsilyl)-	C_6H_{12}	387(2.88),405s(2.83),435s(2.58)	89-1023-80
Disilane, pentamethylphenoxy-	hexane	217(3.921),260(2.986),268(3.036),273(3.022)	65-0491-80
$C_{11}H_{20}Si_2$			
Disilane, pentamethylphenyl-	C_6H_{12}	231(4.41)	65-1615-80
	isooctane	231.0(4.04)	101-0261-80Q
$C_{11}H_{21}N$			
2-Propanamine, N-[(1,1-dimethylethyl)cyclopropylidene]-2-methyl-	C_6H_{12}	275.5(2.002)	5-1814-80
$C_{11}H_{21}NO_2$			
1-Pyrrolidinepropanoic acid, 2,4,4-trimethyl-, methyl ester	MeOH	210(2.98)	83-0858-80
$C_{11}H_{23}NO$			
1-Pyrrolidinepropanol, α,2,4,4-tetramethyl-	MeOH	204(3.18)	83-0858-80
$C_{11}H_{23}NO_2Si$			
Cyclopentane, [[(1,1-dimethylethyl)dimethylsilyl]-aci-nitro]-	hexane	233(4.08)	33-0697-80
$C_{11}H_{23}N_2O$			
Piperidinium, 1-(ethoxyimino)-2,2,6,6-tetramethyl-, tetrafluoroborate	MeOH	229(3.80)	70-0765-80

Compound	Solvent	$\lambda_{max}(\log \epsilon)$	Ref.
$C_{11}H_{30}OSi_4$ 1-Oxa-2,3,4,5-tetrasilacyclooctane, 2,2,3,3,4,4,5,5-octamethyl-	C_6H_{12}	236.0(4.07)	101-0029-80L
$C_{11}H_{33}NSi_5$ Azapentasilacyclohexane, undecamethyl-	isooctane	214(3.94),242(3.28)	101-0159-80N
$C_{11}H_{33}PSi_5$ Phosphapentasilacyclohexane, undeca- methyl-	isooctane	226(3.77),249(3.56)	101-0159-80N

Compound	Solvent	$\lambda_{max}(\log \epsilon)$	Ref.
$C_{12}Cl_2O_{12}Os_3$ Osmium, dodecacarbonyldichlorotri-	CCl₄	348(4.29)	35-3022-80
$C_{12}Cl_8$ Biphenylene, octachloro-	dioxan	229(4.27),244(4.11), 270s(4.30),279(4.68), 291(5.00),340s(2.94), 356(2.96),376(3.35), 394(3.50)	150-2901-80
$C_{12}H_2O_6$ s-Indacene-1,2,3,5,6,7-hexone	MeCN	217(4.14),246(4.31), 265(4.43),620s(1.72)	89-0715-80
$C_{12}H_4Cl_6S_2$ Disulfide, bis(2,4,5-trichlorophenyl)	dioxan	255(4.38),295(3.62), 305(3.59)	142-0955-80
$C_{12}H_4Cl_6S_3$ Trisulfide, bis(2,4,5-trichlorophenyl)	dioxan	249(4.37),308(3.67)	142-0955-80
$C_{12}H_5ClN_2$ 1,3-Azulenedicarbonitrile, 2-chloro-	CHCl₃	297(4.70),310(4.83), 347(3.89),353(3.89), 372(3.71),498(2.86), 520(2.85)	18-1647-80
$C_{12}H_6ClNO_2$ 3H-Phenoxazin-3-one, 2-chloro- 3H-Phenoxazin-3-one, 8-chloro-	EtOH EtOH	364(4.04),455(3.84) 340(4.17),457(4.09)	78-1813-80 78-0529-80
$C_{12}H_6ClN_7O_3S$ 1H-Pyrimido[4',5':5,6][1,4]thiazino- [2,3-b]quinoxalin-4-amine, 9-chloro- 8-nitro-, 5-oxide	MeOH	283(4.30),360(4.11)	4-1587-80
$C_{12}H_6ClN_7O_4S$ 1H-Pyrimido[4',5':5,6][1,4]thiazino- [2,3-b]quinoxalin-4(12H)-one, 2-ami- no-9-chloro-8-nitro-, 5-oxide	MeOH	252(3.98),362(3.89)	4-1587-80
$C_{12}H_6Cl_3NO$ 2,5-Cyclohexadien-1-one, 2,6-dichloro-	hexane + CF₃COOH benzene + CF₃COOH CH₂Cl₂ + CF₃COOH CHCl₃ + CF₃COOH	477(3.66) 461(3.83) 484(3.72) 466(3.85) 484(3.77) 466(3.91) 488(3.77) 475(3.85)	104-2020-80 104-2020-80 104-2020-80 104-2020-80 104-2020-80 104-2020-80 104-2020-80 104-2020-80
$C_{12}H_6F_{12}P_2$ 1,4-Diphosphabicyclo[2.2.2]octa-2,5,7- triene, 2,3-dimethyl-5,6,7,8-tetra- kis(trifluoromethyl)-	MeOH	272(2.96),326(2.79)	35-0252-80
$C_{12}H_6I_4O_2$ [1,1'-Biphenyl]-4,4'-diol, 3,3',5,5'- tetraiodo-	EtOH	285(5.1)	70-1597-80

Compound	Solvent	$\lambda_{max}(\log \epsilon)$	Ref.
$C_{12}H_6O_2$			
Cyclobuta[a]naphthalene-1,2-dione	EtOH	224(4.14),265s(4.53), 312(3.63),330(3.56), 340(3.64)	39-1834-80C
Cyclobuta[b]naphthalene-1,2-dione	EtOH	236(3.92),271(4.97), 340s(4.30),348s(4.42), 359(4.56)	39-1834-80C
$C_{12}H_6O_3$			
Benzo[1,2-c:3,4-c':5,6-c"]trifuran	C_6H_{12}	216(3.69),223(3.72), 237s(3.29),249s(2.92), 259(2.82),278(2.32)	88-3831-80
$C_{12}H_6O_4S$			
4H-[1]Benzothieno[3,2-b]pyran-3-carboxylic acid, 4-oxo-	MeOH	248(4.22),291(4.19), 321(3.89)	83-0385-80
$C_{12}H_7ClN_6OS$			
1H-Pyrimido[4',5':5,6][1,4]thiazino-[2,3-b]quinoxalin-4(12H)-one, 2-amino-9-chloro-	MeOH	212(4.76),275(4.42), 326(3.50),396(3.38)	4-1587-80
$C_{12}H_7ClN_6S$			
1H-Pyrimido[4',5':5,6][1,4]thiazino-[2,3-b]quinoxalin-4-amine, 9-chloro-	MeOH	221(4.73),260(4.29), 334(3.98),358(3.98), 396(3.48)	4-1587-80
$C_{12}H_7ClO_2$			
2,5-Cyclohexadiene-1,4-dione, 2-(2-chlorophenyl)-	PrOH	344(3.1)	70-1087-80
2,5-Cyclohexadiene-1,4-dione, 2-(3-chlorophenyl)-	PrOH	356(3.4)	70-1087-80
2,5-Cyclohexadiene-1,4-dione, 2-(4-chlorophenyl)-	PrOH	370(3.6)	70-1087-80
$C_{12}H_7Cl_3N_2O_7S_2$			
Furan, 2-nitro-5-[2-(5-nitro-2-thienyl)-1-[(trichloromethyl)sulfonyl]-cyclopropyl]-, trans-(±)-	MeOH	207(4.22),312(4.34)	73-1704-80
$C_{12}H_7Cl_3N_2O_8S$			
Furan, 2,2'-[1-[(trichloromethyl)sulfonyl]-1,2-cyclopropanediyl]bis[5-nitro-, trans-(±)-	MeOH	209(4.32),305(4.36)	73-1704-80
$C_{12}H_7Cl_4N$			
[1,1'-Biphenyl]-2-amine, 2',3,4',5-tetrachloro-	MeOH	240(2.78),290(3.28)	33-0456-80
$C_{12}H_7F_4N_3$			
1-Triazene, 1,3-bis(2,5-difluorophenyl)-	MeOH	282(3.72),356(4.34)	73-2688-80
$C_{12}H_7F_9O_7S_3$			
2-Propanone, 1-[2,2,6-tris[(trifluoromethyl)sulfonyl]phenyl]-, compd. with Et_3N	MeCN	226(4.25),282(3.92), 400(4.05)	104-1292-80
$C_{12}H_7NO$			
1-Azulenecarbonitrile, 2-formyl-	MeOH	233(4.25),287(4.57), 298(4.79),345(3.69),	18-3696-80

Compound	Solvent	$\lambda_{max}(\log \epsilon)$	Ref.
1-Azulenecarbonitrile, 2-formyl- (cont.)		362(3.64)	18-3696-80
$C_{12}H_7NOS$ 3H-Phenothiazin-3-one	EtOH	365(4.42),500(4.19)	78-1813-80
$C_{12}H_7NO_2$ 3H-Phenoxazin-3-one	50% EtOH	360(4.10),458(4.00)	86-0349-80
$C_{12}H_7NO_3$ 3H-Phenoxazin-3-one, 2-hydroxy-	EtOH EtOH-base	400(4.14) 414(--),436s(--)	78-0529-80 78-0529-80
$C_{12}H_7NO_3S$ 4H-[1]Benzothieno[3,2-b]pyran-2-carbox- amide, 4-oxo-	MeOH	218(4.40),232(4.36), 248(4.26),298(4.19), 331(3.83)	83-0385-80
$C_{12}H_7NO_4$ 4H-Pyrano[3,2-b]benzofuran-2-carbox- amide, 4-oxo-	MeOH	217(4.32),242(4.02), 300(4.23)	83-0385-80
$C_{12}H_7N_3O$ Imidazo[1,2-b]isoquinoline-10-carbo- nitrile, 1,5-dihydro-5-oxo-	EtOH	236(4.53),266(4.06), 294(4.36),360(3.71)	95-0456-80
$C_{12}H_7N_3OS$ 2,4(1H)-Isoquinolinedicarbonitrile, 3-(methylthio)-1-oxo-	EtOH	240(4.40),315(4.73)	95-0456-80
$C_{12}H_7N_5O_6$ 1H-Perimidine, 2-methyl-4,6,9-trinitro-	MeOH acid base	285(4.27),315s(3.90), 355s(3.45),370s(3.35), 495(4.10) 440(4.33) 512(4.35).	103-0071-80 103-0071-80 103-0071-80
1H-Perimidine, 2-methyl-6,7,9-trinitro-	MeOH acid base	235(4.40),260s(4.18), 325(3.60),425(4.26) 380(4.20) 495(4.12)	103-0071-80 103-0071-80 103-0071-80
$C_{12}H_8BrNO$ 2,5-Cyclohexadien-1-one, 4-[(4-bromo- phenyl)imino]-	hexane + CF$_3$COOH benzene + CF$_3$COOH CH$_2$Cl$_2$ + CF$_3$COOH CHCl$_3$ + CF$_3$COOH	450(3.55) 433(3.87) 458(3.58) 438(3.95) 461(3.63) 439(4.03) 463(3.59) 440(3.82)	104-2020-80 104-2020-80 104-2020-80 104-2020-80 104-2020-80 104-2020-80 104-2020-80 104-2020-80
$C_{12}H_8BrNOS$ Benzenesulfenamide, 4-bromo-N-(4-oxo- 2,5-cyclohexadien-1-ylidene)-	hexane	448(4.32)	18-0775-80
Benzothiazole, 2-(5-bromo-2-furanyl)- 6-methyl-	EtOH	213(4.26),228s(4.02), 331(4.42)	128-0069-80
$C_{12}H_8BrNO_2S$ Thiophene, 2-bromo-3-[2-(2-nitrophen- yl)ethenyl]-, (E)-	EtOH	213(4.24),281(4.25)	142-1227-80B

Compound	Solvent	$\lambda_{max}(\log \epsilon)$	Ref.
$C_{12}H_8BrN_3O_2$ 2,4-Imidazolidinedione, 5-[(6-bromo- 1H-indol-3-yl)methylene]-	MeOH	360(4.13)	44-1435-80
$C_{12}H_8ClNO$ 2,5-Cyclohexadien-1-one, 4-[(4-chloro- phenyl)imino]-	hexane + CF$_3$COOH benzene + CF$_3$COOH CH$_2$Cl$_2$ + CF$_3$COOH CHCl$_3$ + CF$_3$COOH	451(3.53) 427(3.87) 460(3.56) 433(3.94) 462(3.61) 433(4.04) 465(3.61) 437(3.83)	104-2020-80 104-2020-80 104-2020-80 104-2020-80 104-2020-80 104-2020-80 104-2020-80 104-2020-80
$C_{12}H_8ClNOS$ Benzenesulfenamide, 4-chloro-N-(4-oxo- 2,5-cyclohexadien-1-ylidene)-	hexane	447(4.34)	18-0775-80
Benzothiazole, 6-chloro-2-(2-methyl- 3-furanyl)-	EtOH	202(4.28),222(4.42), 296s(4.20),304(4.21), 316(4.18)	128-0069-80
Benzothiazole, 6-chloro-2-(5-methyl- 2-furanyl)-	EtOH	202(4.45),216(4.40), 332(4.36)	128-0069-80
$C_{12}H_8ClN_3OS$ 3H-1,2,4-Triazole-3-thione, 2-(4-chlo- rophenyl)-5-(2-furanyl)-1,2-dihydro-	MeOH	268(4.36),345(4.10)	73-2804-80
$C_{12}H_8Cl_2N_2O_3$ Isoxazole, 5-[2-(2,4-dichlorophenyl)- ethenyl]-3-methyl-4-nitro-	MeOH	252(4.09),262s(4.07), 350(4.31)	4-0621-80
$C_{12}H_8Cl_2O_2S$ 4H-Pyran-4-one, 3,5-dichloro-2-(methyl- thio)-6-phenyl-	heptane	201(4.20),251(4.40)	5-1960-80
$C_{12}H_8Cl_3NO_5S_2$ Furan, 2-nitro-5-[2-(2-thienyl)-1- [(trichloromethyl)sulfonyl]cyclo- propyl]-, trans-(±)-	MeOH	212(4.12),312(4.10)	73-1704-80
$C_{12}H_8Cl_3N_3O_2$ 2,5-Pyrrolidinedione, 1-(5,6,7-tri- chloro-2-methyl-2H-cyclopenta[d]- pyridazin-1-yl)-	ether	247(4.39),254(4.44), 259(4.41),283s(4.27), 287(4.29),295(4.30), 335(4.15),360s(4.12)	44-1695-80
$C_{12}H_8Cl_4OS$ 2,4-Pentadienethioic acid, 2,3,4,5- tetrachloro-5-phenyl-, S-methyl ester, (Z,E)- (Z,Z)-	heptane heptane	215(4.09),260(4.25) 195(4.27),240(4.11)	5-1960-80 5-1960-80
$C_{12}H_8F_3NO$ Ethanone, 2,2,2-trifluoro-1-(5-phenyl- 1H-pyrrol-2-yl)-	hexane	235(4.10),341(4.52)	103-0448-80
$C_{12}H_8F_3NO_3$ Oxazolium, 5-hydroxy-3-methyl-2-phenyl- 4-(trifluoroacetyl)-, hydroxide, inner salt	MeCN CHCl$_3$	235(3.91),274(3.90), 337(4.33) 274(3.88),345(4.19)	5-1836-80 5-1836-80

Compound	Solvent	$\lambda_{max}(\log \epsilon)$	Ref.
$C_{12}H_8F_6$			
3a,6-Methano-3aH-indene, 1,6-dihydro-4,5-bis(trifluoromethyl)-	C_6H_{12}	251s(2.10)	77-0670-80
3a,6-Methano-3aH-indene, 3,6-dihydro-4,5-bis(trifluoromethyl)-	C_6H_{12}	211(4.10),243(3.81), 280s(3.20)	77-0670-80
$C_{12}H_8N_2$			
1,10-Phenanthroline	CH_2Cl_2	263(4.52)	35-7892-80
Propanedinitrile, [(4-ethenylphenyl)-methylene]-	THF	230(4.00),338(4.51)	116-0244-80
Pyridine, 4,4'-(1,2-ethynediyl)bis-	MeOH	227s(--),260s(--), 274(4.45),283s(--), 291(4.34)	27-0023-80
Pyrrolo[1',2':3,4]pyrimido[2,1,6-cd]-pyrrolizine	C_6H_{12}	229(4.29),262(4.41), 268(4.44),288(4.08), 300(3.94),374(3.94), 394(4.12),450(3.71), 470(3.56),480(3.49)	24-0614-80
$C_{12}H_8N_2O$			
1H-Pyrrolo[1,2-a]indole-2-carbonitrile, 2,3-dihydro-1-oxo-	EtOH	242s(4.21),262s(3.58), 282s(3.53),325(4.31)	39-0097-80C
$C_{12}H_8N_2O_2$			
Benzo[1,2-b:3,4-b']dipyrrole-3,8-di-carboxaldehyde	EtOH	204s(4.26),216(4.47), 234s(4.06),292(4.38)	103-0495-80
1H-Indene-3-acetamide, α-cyano-1-oxo-	MeOH	229(4.18),238(4.20), 245(4.22),253(4.16), 292(4.25)	4-1313-80
2H-Pyrimido[6,1-a]isoquinoline-2,4(3H)-dione	EtOH	222(4.51),248s(3.84), 276(4.35),285(4.52), 320s(3.62),338(3.72), 358(3.91),376(4.05), 396(3.91)	95-1261-80
Pyrrolo[3,4-b]quinoline-1,3(2H)-dione, 1,3-dihydro-9-methyl-	EtOH	213(4.35),259(4.66)	94-3457-80
$C_{12}H_8N_2O_2S$			
5H-Imidazo[2,1-b][1,3]thiazine-5,7(6H)-dione, 6-phenyl-	MeOH	208(4.28),227(4.25), 300(3.94)	44-2474-80
$C_{12}H_8N_2O_3S_2$			
4-Thiazolecarboxylic acid, 2-(6-hy-droxy-2-benzothiazolyl)-, methyl ester	MeOH	275(4.02),351(4.34)	35-3199-80
$C_{12}H_8N_2O_4$			
3-Pyridinecarboxylic acid, 4-nitro-phenyl ester	EtOH	216(4.24),269(4.19), 350(2.48)	65-1339-80
$C_{12}H_8N_2O_4S$			
2H-1,4-Benzoxazin-2-ol, 7-nitro-3-(2-thienyl)-	MeOH	232(4.06),290(3.83), 376(4.36)	4-1625-80
2H-1,4-Benzoxazin-2-ol, 7-nitro-3-(3-thienyl)-	MeOH	227(4.23),360(4.30)	4-1625-80
$C_{12}H_8N_2O_5$			
2H-1,4-Benzoxazin-2-ol, 3-(2-furanyl)-7-nitro-	MeOH	234(4.04),372(4.38)	4-1625-80

Compound	Solvent	$\lambda_{max}(\log \epsilon)$	Ref.
$C_{12}H_8N_4O_4$			
Perimidine, 2-methyl-6,7-dinitro-	MeOH	244(4.27),295s(3.48), 425(4.19)	103-0071-80
	acid	395(3.77)	103-0071-80
	base	463(4.53),563(4.05)	103-0071-80
Perimidine, 2-methyl-6,9-dinitro-	MeOH	250(4.00),272(4.22), 325(3.69),350s(3.56), 440(4.28)	103-0071-80
$C_{12}H_8N_6$			
Bis[1,2,4]triazolo[1,5-a:1',5'-c]pyrimidine, 8-phenyl-	EtOH	216(4.47),229(3.92), 256s(3.96),262(3.97), 275s(3.72)	12-1147-80
$C_{12}H_8N_6OS$			
1H-Pyrimido[4',5':5,6][1,4]thiazino-[2,3-b]quinoxalin-4(12H)-one, 2-amino-	MeOH	213(4.57),273(4.18), 329(3.45),396(3.25)	4-1587-80
$C_{12}H_8N_6S$			
1H-Pyrimido[4',5':5,6][1,4]thiazino-[2,3-b]quinoxalin-4-amine	MeOH	222(4.66),261(4.23), 334(3.76),363(3.69), 396(4.24)	4-1587-80
$C_{12}H_8O$			
Cyclopent[cd]azulene-2(1H)-one	hexane	250f(4.3),305f(4.6), 350f(3.9),520f(2.6), 580f(2.7),625(2.5)	151-0309-80B
$C_{12}H_8OS$			
Indeno[1,2-b]pyran-4(5H)-thione	MeOH	221(4.09),227(4.09), 251(3.53),296(4.15), 377(4.42)	83-0429-80
$C_{12}H_8O_2$			
1,2-Azulenedicarboxaldehyde	CHCl₃	290(4.48),315(4.60), 325(4.57),350(4.08), 370(4.08),390(4.04), 540(2.63),600(2.94), 640s(2.75)	18-3696-80
2,5-Cyclohexadiene-1,4-dione, 2-phenyl-	PrOH	363(3.4)	70-1087-80
Indeno[1,2-b]pyran-4(5H)-one	MeOH	286(4.27),297(4.27)	83-0429-80
$C_{12}H_8O_3$			
1-Azulenecarboxylic acid, 2-formyl-	CH₂Cl₂	308(4.54),355(3.98), 610(2.99)	18-3696-80
4H-Furo[3,2-f]benzopyran-4-one, 2-methyl-	MeOH	227(4.64),265(4.28), 294(4.28),328(4.31)	42-0532-80
1,2-Naphthalenedione, 3-acetyl-	CHCl₃	262(4.46),355(3.53), 409(3.65),535(1.90)	39-1414-80C
$C_{12}H_8O_4$			
7H-Furo[3,2-g][1]benzopyran-7-one, 4-methoxy- (bergapten)	EtOH	223(4.35),243s(4.18), 250(4.23),260(4.18), 269(4.22),311(4.14)	94-1847-80
7H-Furo[3,2-g][1]benzopyran-7-one, 9-methoxy- (xanthotoxin)	H₂O	303(3.38)	35-1977-80
	EtOH	219(4.38),245s(4.34), 250(4.37),264s(4.13), 300(4.07)	94-1847-80
	45% H₂SO₄	309(3.54)	35-1977-80
	60% H₂SO₄	316(3.74)	35-1977-80

Compound	Solvent	$\lambda_{max}(\log \epsilon)$	Ref.
(cont.)	65% H_2SO_4	321(3.85)	35-1977-80
	70% H_2SO_4	333(4.02)	35-1977-80
	81% H_2SO_4	344(4.20)	35-1977-80
	95% H_2SO_4	347(4.22)	35-1977-80
2,3-Naphthalenedicarboxaldehyde, 1,4-dihydroxy-	EtOH	249(4.28),278s(3.95), 401(3.75),419(3.75), 450s(3.37)	39-0282-80C
$C_{12}H_8O_5$ 1,4-Naphthalenedione, 5-acetoxy-8-hydroxy-	MeOH	210(4.51),252(4.05), 425(3.56)	24-1575-80
$C_{12}H_8O_5S$ Benzo[b]thiophene-2-butanoic acid, 3-hydroxy-α,γ-dioxo-	MeOH	204(4.36),262(4.16), 304(4.10),346(4.00)	83-0385-80
$C_{12}H_8O_6$ 2-Benzofuranbutanoic acid, 3-hydroxy-α,γ-dioxo-	MeOH	204(4.26),243(3.86), 372(4.32)	83-0385-80
$C_{12}H_8S_4$ 1,3-Dithiole, 2-(1,3-dithiol-2-ylidene)-4-phenyl-	hexane	228(4.06),277(4.14), 302(4.15),322(4.10), 400(3.45)	11-0196-80A
$C_{12}H_9BrCl_5N_2OSb$ Antimony, pentachloro[(4-bromophenyl)-phenyldiazene 1-oxide-O]-, (OC-6-21)-	$CHCl_3$	240(3.95),270(4.01), 327(4.20)	78-3177-80
$C_{12}H_9BrNOS$ Benzothiazolium, 2-(5-bromo-2-furanyl)-3-methyl-, iodide	EtOH	199(4.00),218(4.11), 367(4.05)	128-0069-80
$C_{12}H_9BrN_2$ Propanedinitrile, (2-bromo-1-phenylpropylidene)-	dioxan	297(3.73)	1-0289-80
$C_{12}H_9BrN_2O$ Benzo[f]quinoxalin-6(2H)-one, 5-bromo-3,4-dihydro-	EtOH	232(4.33),278(4.26), 432(3.76)	83-0603-80
Propanedinitrile, [2-bromo-1-(4-methoxyphenyl)ethylidene]-	dioxan	353(4.16)	1-0289-80
$C_{12}H_9BrN_2O_2S$ 2(1H)-Pyrimidinone, 4-[[2-(4-bromophenyl)-2-oxoethyl]thio]-	6M HCl	270(4.04),330(4.25)	44-3651-80
	pH 6	263(4.33),290s(4.16)	44-3651-80
	pH 11.6	261(4.24),295(4.10), 400(4.25)	44-3651-80
	pH 13	305(4.12)	44-3651-80
$C_{12}H_9ClN_2$ Diazene, (4-chlorophenyl)phenyl-	EtOH	325(4.38)	62-0158-80
Perimidine, 2-chloromethyl-	MeOH	231(4.39),330(4.09)	118-0155-80
$C_{12}H_9ClN_2O$ Benzo[f]quinoxalin-6(2H)-one, 5-chloro-3,4-dihydro-	EtOH	237(4.10),273(4.24), 432(3.51)	83-0603-80
$C_{12}H_9ClN_2O_3$ Isoxazole, 5-[2-(2-chlorophenyl)ethenyl]-3-methyl-4-nitro-	MeOH	248(4.04),262s(4.02), 350(4.27)	4-0621-80

Compound	Solvent	$\lambda_{max}(\log \epsilon)$	Ref.
Isoxazole, 5-[2-(3-chlorophenyl)ethen-yl]-3-methyl-4-nitro-	MeOH	247(4.11),262(4.11), 346(4.31)	4-0621-80
Isoxazole, 5-[2-(4-chlorophenyl)ethen-yl]-3-methyl-4-nitro-	MeOH	245(3.96),266(4.04), 360(4.20)	4-0621-80
$C_{12}H_9ClN_4O_4$			
Furo[2,3-c]pyridin-2(6H)-one, 3-chloro-6-(4,6-dimethoxy-1,3,5-triazin-2-yl)-	EtOH	217(3.56),378(4.35), 398(4.36)	39-1176-80C
$C_{12}H_9ClO$			
[1,1'-Biphenyl]-3-ol, 5-chloro-	EtOH	206(4.45),224(4.30), 254(4.13),282(3.40)	104-1298-80
$C_{12}H_9ClO_6S$			
[1]Benzothieno[3,2-b]pyrylium, 4-meth-oxy-, perchlorate	MeOH	229(4.29),250(4.23), 279(4.00),291(4.08), 305(3.98),325(3.98)	83-0385-80
$C_{12}H_9ClO_7$			
Benzofuro[3,2-b]pyrylium, 4-methoxy-, perchlorate	MeOH	226(4.18),286(4.27), 298(4.25),324(3.86)	83-0385-80
$C_{12}H_9Cl_5N_3O_3Sb$			
Antimony, pentachloro[(4-nitrophenyl)-phenyldiazene 1-oxide]-, (OC-6-21)-	CHCl₃	256(4.41),290(3.85)	78-3177-80
$C_{12}H_9Cl_6N_2OSb$			
Antimony, pentachloro[(4-chlorophenyl)-phenyldiazene 1-oxide-O]-, (OC-6-21)-	CHCl₃	242(3.92),261(3.90), 328(3.11)	78-3177-80
$C_{12}H_9F_5N_2O_3S$			
Benzenesulfonic acid, 4-methyl-, 2-(2,4,4,5,5-pentafluoro-3-oxo-1-cyclopenten-1-yl)hydrazide	MeCN	227(4.10),279(4.48)	44-4429-80
$C_{12}H_9NO$			
2,5-Cyclohexadien-1-one, 4-(phenyl-imino)-	hexane	488(3.45)	104-2020-80
	+ CF₃COOH	398(3.83)	104-2020-80
	benzene	456(3.49)	104-2020-80
	+ CF₃COOH	406(3.82)	104-2020-80
	pH 8.75	440(3.6)	69-0731-80
	CH₂Cl₂	456(3.52)	104-2020-80
	+ CF₃COOH	411(3.85)	104-2020-80
	CHCl₃	460(3.53)	104-2020-80
	+ CF₃COOH	418(3.82)	104-2020-80
10H-Phenoxazine	MeCN	234(--),238(4.6), 315(3.9)	39-0291-80B
cation	MeCN	420(c. 4.1)	39-0291-80B
phenoxazinyl radical (approximate absorption data)	MeCN	336(3.6),360(3.9), 368(3.9)	39-0291-80B
radical cation	MeCN	381(3.6),406(3.7), 529(4.2)	30-0291-80B
binuclear cation	MeCN	410(--),530(--), 590(--)	39-0291-80B
$C_{12}H_9NOS$			
2H-1,4-Benzoxazine, 3-(2-thienyl)-	MeOH	240s(--),257(3.97), 275s(--),348(4.14)	4-1625-80
Benzothiazole, 2-(2-methyl-3-furanyl)-, hydrochloride	EtOH	201(4.26),220(4.43), 295s(4.19),303(4.21), 315s(4.14)	128-0069-80

Compound	Solvent	$\lambda_{max}(\log \epsilon)$	Ref.
Benzothiazole, 2-(5-methyl-2-furanyl)-	EtOH	210(4.17),225(3.40), 328(4.41)	128-0069-80
Pyrano[3,2-b]indole-4(5H)-thione, 5-methyl-	MeOH	228(4.29),266(3.60), 310(3.95),364(4.20), 409(4.36)	83-0405-80
10H-Thieno[3,2-b][1]benzazepin-10-one, 4,9-dihydro-	EtOH	245(4.27),275(3.85), 360(3.95)	142-1227-80B
$C_{12}H_9NO_2$			
2,4-Pentadienenitrile, 5-(benzoyloxy)-, (E,E)-	EtOH	240s(4.16),271(4.52)	1-0031-80
Pyrano[3,2-b]indol-4(5H)-one, 5-methyl-	MeOH	240(4.02),300(4.25), 334(3.77)	83-0405-80
$C_{12}H_9NO_2S$			
2H-1,4-Benzoxazin-2-ol, 3-(2-thienyl)-	MeOH	238(3.87),250(3.83), 280(3.89),339(4.23)	4-1625-80
2H-1,4-Benzoxazin-2-ol, 3-(3-thienyl)-	MeOH	238(4.10),292(4.20), 312(4.18)	4-1625-80
$C_{12}H_9NO_3$			
2H-1,4-Benzoxazin-2-ol, 3-(2-furanyl)-	MeOH	239(3.86),333(4.27)	4-1625-80
2H-Naphth[1,2-b]-1,4-oxazine-2,3(4H)-dione, 5,6-dihydro-	EtOH	213(4.16),250(4.15), 289(3.38)	39-2126-80C
$C_{12}H_9NO_5S$			
Acetic acid, [(4-nitro-1-naphthalenyl)-sulfinyl]-, (R)-(+)-	MeCN	204s(3.72),223(4.51), 250(4.06),298s(3.65), 330(3.80)	56-2161-80
$C_{12}H_9NS$			
10H-Phenothiazine	MeCN	254(4.7),317(3.6)	39-0291-80B
cation	MeCN	419(c. 4.0)	39-0291-80B
phenothiazinyl radical	MeCN	344(c. 3.5),380(c. 3.9)	39-0291-80B
radical cation	MeCN	437(3.7),498(3.8), 517(3.9)	39-0291-80B
4H-Thieno[3,2-b][1]benzazepine	EtOH	238(4.13),270(4.34)	142-1227-80B
$C_{12}H_9N_3$			
2H-Benzotriazole, 2-phenyl-	EtOH	310(4.2)	109-0034-80
$C_{12}H_9N_3O$			
4(1H)-Pyrimidinone, 5-(1H-indol-3-yl)-	EtOH	207s(4.25),222(4.35), 278(3.92),340(4.06)	103-0045-80
2H-1,2,3-Triazole, 4-(2-furanyl)-2-phenyl-	EtOH	300(4.38)	2-0975-80
$C_{12}H_9N_3O_2$			
Diazene, (4-nitrophenyl)phenyl-	EtOH	333(4.49)	62-0158-80
1H-Perimidine, 1-methyl-4-nitro-	MeOH	270(3.98),285(3.96), 315(3.81),325(3.82), 445(3.96)	103-0071-80
	acid	430(3.75)	103-0071-80
1H-Perimidine, 1-methyl-6-nitro-	MeOH	235(4.24),260s(3.99), 325(3.90),365s(3.61), 385(3.65),470(4.02)	103-0071-80
1H-Perimidine, 1-methyl-7-nitro-	MeOH	265(4.10),323(3.80), 345(3.52),364(3.63), 380(3.66),480(4.05)	103-0071-80
Perimidine, 2-methyl-6-nitro-	MeOH	265(3.57),325(3.15), 350s(--),362(3.35),	103-0071-80

Compound	Solvent	$\lambda_{max}(\log \epsilon)$	Ref.
Perimidine, 2-methyl-6-nitro- (cont.) (6λ,5ε)		377(3.40),475(4.03)	103-0071-80
	acid	425(3.79)	103-0071-80
	base	525(4.23)	103-0071-80
Perimidine, 2-methyl-9-nitro-	MeOH	285(4.27),315s(3.90), 360s(3.43),370s(3.35), 465(4.10)	103-0071-80
	20% HCl	435(3.49)	103-0071-80
	HOAc	452(4.03)	103-0071-80
Pyridazino[4,5-b]quinoline-1,4-dione, 2,3-dihydro-10-methyl-	EtOH	216(4.28),249(4.71), 283(3.93)	94-3457-80 +142-0267-80
compd. with hydrazine	EtOH	215(4.36),248(4.72), 287(3.94)	142-0267-80
1H-Pyrrolo[3,4-b]quinoline-1,3(2H)-dione, 2-amino-9-methyl-	EtOH	213(4.30),262(4.67)	94-3457-80
$C_{12}H_9N_3O_3$			
4-Pyridazinecarboxylic acid, 5-[(phenylamino)carbonyl]-	DMSO	230s(4.1),262(3.6)	39-1339-80B
Pyrimido[4,5-b]quinoline-2,4(3H,10H)-dione, 8-hydroxy-10-methyl-	M HCl	250(4.40),270s(4.32), 373(4.49)	83-0937-80
	pH 4	250(4.43),263(4.37), 275s(4.28),335s(3.85), 382s(4.30),393(4.31)	83-0937-80
	pH 8	245(4.45),265(4.41), 293(4.13),417(4.64)	83-0937-80
	M NaOH	245(4.50),255s(4.35), 288(4.00),417(4.68)	83-0937-80
$C_{12}H_9N_3O_4$			
4-Pyridazinecarboxylic acid, 5-[[(2-hydroxyphenyl)amino]carbonyl]-	DMSO	281(3.7)	39-1339-80B
Pyridine, 2-[(2,4-dinitrophenyl)methyl]-	EtOH	565(4.08)	104-1856-80
	EtOH-KOH	472(4.53)	104-1856-80
	isoPrOH	567(4.29)	104-1856-80
	anion	472(4.53)	104-1856-80
	cation	565(4.64)	104-1856-80
Pyridine, 4-[(2,4-dinitrophenyl)methyl]-	EtOH	575(4.56)	104-1856-80
	isoPrOH	580(4.38)	104-1856-80
	at -78°	575(4.34)	104-1856-80
$C_{12}H_9N_3O_6$			
Acetic acid, [2,5-dihydro-3-(4-nitrophenyl)-5-oxo-6H-1,2,4-oxadiazin-6-ylidene]-, methyl ester, (E)-	MeOH	215(4.05),225(4.06), 303(4.09)	4-1101-80
$C_{12}H_9N_3S$			
2H-1,2,3-Triazole, 2-phenyl-4-(2-thienyl)-	EtOH	302(4.40)	2-0975-80
$C_{12}H_9O_2S$			
[1]Benzothieno[3,2-b]pyrylium, 4-methoxy-, perchlorate	MeOH	229(4.29),250(4.23), 279(4.00),291(4.08), 305(3.98),325(3.98)	83-0385-80
$C_{12}H_9O_3$			
Benzofuro[3,2-b]pyrylium, 4-methoxy-, perchlorate	MeOH	226(4.18),286(4.27), 298(4.25),324(3.86)	83-0385-80
$C_{12}H_{10}$			
1,1'-Biphenyl-, Cr(CO)$_3$ complex	C_6H_{12}	240s(4.3),327(4.0),	110-0749-80

Compound	Solvent	$\lambda_{max}(\log \epsilon)$	Ref.
(cont.)		400(3.3)	110-0749-80
$C_{12}H_{10}BF_2NO$			
Boron, difluoro[1-[(methylimino)methyl]-2-naphthalenolato-N,O]-, (T-4)-	$C_2H_4Cl_2$	248(4.13),330(3.92), 370(3.84),385(3.77)	101-0001-80I
$C_{12}H_{10}ClNO$			
2-Propenal, 3-chloro-3-(3-methyl-1H-indol-2-yl)-	EtOH	264(3.85),370(4.19)	78-2125-80
$C_{12}H_{10}ClNOS$			
Benzothiazole, 2-(2-methyl-3-furanyl)-, hydrochloride	EtOH	201(4.26),220(4.43), 295s(4.19),303(4.21), 315s(4.14)	128-0069-80
2-Furancarbothioamide, N-(4-chlorophenyl)-5-methyl-	EtOH	199(4.18),231(3.94), 323(4.31)	128-0069-80
3-Furancarbothioamide, N-(4-chlorophenyl)-2-methyl-	EtOH	203(4.30),305(4.11)	128-0069-80
$C_{12}H_{10}ClNO_2$			
2-Furancarboxamide, N-(4-chlorophenyl)-5-methyl-	EtOH	203(4.18),286(4.42)	128-0069-80
2,4-Hexadienal, 6-[(4-chlorophenyl)imino]-, N-oxide	n.s.g.	255(4.20),325(4.02)	5-1630-80
1,4-Naphthalenedione, 2-chloro-3-(dimethylamino)-	heptane isoPrOH	484(3.52) 498(3.63)	70-0897-80 70-0897-80
$C_{12}H_{10}ClNO_4$			
3H-Indole-2,3-dicarboxylic acid, 3-chloro-, dimethyl ester	CH_2Cl_2	240(3.92),300(3.49)	142-0867-80
$C_{12}H_{10}ClN_3O_2S$			
Acetamide, N-[5-acetyl-3-(3-chlorophenyl)-1,3,4-thiadiazol-2(3H)-ylidene]-	EtOH	225s(3.88),285(3.88), 315(3.79)	4-1713-80
Acetamide, N-[5-acetyl-3-(4-chlorophenyl)-1,3,4-thiadiazol-2(3H)-ylidene]-	EtOH	229s(3.99),275(4.31), 308(4.37)	4-1713-80
$C_{12}H_{10}ClN_3O_3$			
Propanoic acid, 3-[(4-chlorophenyl)hydrazono]-3-cyano-2-oxo-, ethyl ester	EtOH	245(4.06),367(4.43)	104-0751-80
$C_{12}H_{10}Cl_5N_2OSb$			
Antimony, pentachloro(diphenyldiazene 1-oxide-O)-, (OC-6-21)-	$CHCl_3$	240(3.94),322(4.04)	78-3177-80
$C_{12}H_{10}FeO_3$			
Iron, dicarbonyl[(η^5-2,4-cyclopentadien-1-ylidene)(2-ethylidene-3-oxopropanediyl)]-	hexane	228s(4.21),278(4.0), 326(3.4)	24-3211-80
$C_{12}H_{10}N_2$			
Benzenamine, N-(4-imino-2,5-cyclohexadien-1-ylidene)-	pH 8.75	<u>420(3.5)</u>	69-0731-80
1,4-Diazabiphenylene, 2,3-dimethyl-	EtOH	223(4.66),276(4.03), 373s(4.16),384(4.22)	150-2941-80
Diazene, diphenyl-	EtOH	318(4.32)	62-0158-80
1H-Naphth[1,2-d]imidazole, 8-methyl-	EtOH	226(4.59),240(4.65), 245(4.62)	4-0679-80
Pyridine, 2,2'-(1,2-ethenediyl)bis-	hexane	220(3.94),226(3.85), 266(4.23),316(4.47), 330(4.34)	5-0291-80

Compound	Solvent	$\lambda_{max}(\log \epsilon)$	Ref.
Pyridine, 4,4'-(1,2-ethenediyl)bis-	hexane	216(4.03),221(4.03), 284(4.41),294(4.39)	5-0291-80
Pyridine, 2-[2-(4-pyridinyl)ethenyl]-	CH_2Cl_2	217(4.17),224s(4.13), 268s(4.25),277s(4.27), 305(4.36)	5-0291-80
Pyrrolo[1',2':3,4]pyrimido[2,1,6-cd]-pyrrolizine	EtOH	219(4.05),251(4.25), 273(3.78),297(3.69), 394(3.18)	24-0614-80
$C_{12}H_{10}N_2O$			
Benzenamine, 4-nitroso-N-phenyl-	pH 8.75	440(4.52)	69-0731-80
Benzo[f]quinoxalin-6(2H)-one, 3,4-di-hydro-	EtOH	238(4.16),270(4.31), 430(3.62)	83-0603-80
Diazene, diphenyl-, 1-oxide	MeOH	233(4.13),238(4.07), 260(4.05),323(4.34)	49-0909-80
Ethanone, 2-(2-pyridinyl)-1-(3-pyridin-yl)- (also other solvents)	H_2O	232(4.3),256f(4.0), 318(3.4),384(3.8)	61-1108-80
Phenol, 4-(phenylazo)-	n.s.g.	347(4.34)	150-2415-80
Phenol, 2-[(2-pyridinylimino)methyl]-	n.s.g.	302(3.94),338(3.79)	90-0349-80
Phenol, 4-[(2-pyridinylimino)methyl]-	n.s.g.	360(3.04)	90-0349-80
$C_{12}H_{10}N_2O_2$			
1,3-Benzenediol, 4-(phenylazo)-	n.s.g.	383(4.28)	150-2415-80
2H-Benz[f]indazole-4,9-dione, 3,3a-di-hydro-3a-methyl-	EtOH	239(4.18),260s(3.88), 306(3.60),342(3.70)	39-1994-80C
Benzoic acid, (2-furanylmethylene)hy-drazide	C_6H_{12}	305(4.47)	115-0013-80
	benzene	307(4.44)	115-0013-80
	EtOH	313(4.53)	115-0013-80
	ether	307(4.32)	115-0013-80
	dioxan	307(4.32)	115-0013-80
	$CHCl_3$	311(4.56)	115-0013-80
	CCl_4	308(4.42)	115-0013-80
α-Carboline, 1,2-dihydro-3-methoxy-2-oxo-	MeOH	242(4.27),280(3.74), 320(3.66),363(3.97)	94-2987-80
2-Pyridinecarboxylic acid, 5-(phenyl-amino)-	MeOH	240(3.79),301(4.25), 320(4.22)	87-1405-80
2(1H)-Pyrimidinone, 3,4-dihydro-4-(2-oxo-2-phenylethylidene)-	pH 2,5,11	262(3.86),375(4.54), 390s(4.49)	44-3651-80
	pH 13	250(3.97),280(3.71), 395(4.60)	44-3651-80
	2M NaOH	245s(3.93),282(3.70), 390(4.47)	44-3651-80
	EtOH	260(3.88),355s(4.39), 371(4.52),386(4.44)	44-3651-80
	ether	257(3.87),353s(4.40), 367(4.50),386(4.38)	44-3651-80
	8M HCl	251(3.99),310(3.91), 388(4.25)	44-3651-80
4(1H)-Pyrimidinone, 2,3-dihydro-2-(2-oxo-2-phenylethylidene)-	pH 3	225(4.14),245(4.06), 350(4.44)	44-3651-80
	pH 10	238(4.12),293s(3.71), 357(4.33)	44-3651-80
	6M HCl	228(4.08),253(4.16), 325(3.83)	44-3651-80
Pyrrolo[3,4-b]indole-1,3(2H,4H)-dione, 2,6-dimethyl-	MeOH	244(4.62),323(4.43)	78-1801-80
$C_{12}H_{10}N_2O_2S$			
5H-Imidazo[2,1-b][1,3]thiazine-5,7(6H)-dione, 2,3-dihydro-6-phenyl-	MeOH	209(4.08),231(4.02), 268(3.66)	44-2474-80

Compound	Solvent	$\lambda_{max}(\log \epsilon)$	Ref.
2(1H)-Pyrimidinone, 4-[(2-oxo-2-phenyl-ethyl)thio]-	4.25M HCl	256(3.89),330(4.24)	44-3651-80
	pH 5.2	252(4.18),295(4.05)	44-3651-80
	pH 9.65	250(4.19),298(4.02)	44-3651-80
	pH 13	250s(4.06),303(4.07)	44-3651-80
	2M NaOH	307(4.16)	44-3651-80
$C_{12}H_{10}N_2O_3$			
Isoxazole, 3-methyl-4-nitro-5-(2-phen-ylethenyl)-	MeOH	244s(4.04),265(4.13), 352(4.36)	4-0621-80
3-Pyridinol, 2-[(4-nitrophenyl)methyl]-	CHCl₃	340(4.12)	39-1176-80C
$C_{12}H_{10}N_2O_3S$			
1H-Perimidine-6-sulfonic acid, 2-methyl-	pH 13	347(3.86)	103-0541-80
	MeOH	324(3.79)	103-0541-80
$C_{12}H_{10}N_2O_3S_2$			
4-Thiazolecarboxylic acid, 4,5-dihydro-2-(6-hydroxy-2-benzothiazolyl)-, methyl ester, (S)-	MeOH	269(3.87),332(4.20)	35-3199-80
$C_{12}H_{10}N_2O_4$			
Acetic acid, (2,5-dihydro-5-oxo-3-phen-yl-6H-1,2,4-oxadiazin-6-ylidene)-, methyl ester, (E)-	MeOH	240(4.15),262(4.13), 310(3.94)	4-1101-80
(Z)-	MeOH	241(4.08),270(4.05), 310(3.80)	4-1101-80
2H-1-Benzopyran-4-carboxylic acid hy-drazide, 7-methoxy-N-methylene-2-oxo-	EtOH	332(4.21)	95-0289-80
$C_{12}H_{10}N_2O_4S$			
4H-Benzothieno[3,2-d][1,3]oxazin-4-one, 2-(dimethylamino)-, 5,5-dioxide	MeOH	245(4.59)	24-2818-80
$C_{12}H_{10}N_2O_4S_2$			
4-Hydroxyluciferin methyl ester	MeOH	269(3.83),337(4.22)	35-3199-80
$C_{12}H_{10}N_3PS_2$			
1,3,2,4,6,5-Dithia(3-S^{IV})triazaphos-phorine, 5,5-dihydro-5,5-diphenyl-	n.s.g.	252(3.78),301(3.48), 550(3.70)	77-1204-80
$C_{12}H_{10}N_4$			
Pyrazino[2,3-f]quinoxaline, 2,3-di-methyl-	EtOH	232(4.62),273(4.25), 304(3.74),356(3.69), 368(3.73)	150-2941-80
1H-Pyrazole, 1,1'-(1,4-phenylene)bis-	EtOH	209(4.23),280(4.42)	24-2749-80
1H-Pyrazolo[3,4-d]pyrimidine, 3-methyl-1-phenyl-	EtOH	245(4.31),265(3.79), 308(3.27)	114-0127-80C
$C_{12}H_{10}N_4O$			
1H-Pyrazolo[3,4-d]pyrimidine, 3-methyl-1-phenyl-, 5-oxide	EtOH	235(3.77),270(3.85), 299(3.94),368(3.44)	114-0127-80C
$C_{12}H_{10}N_4O_2$			
Benzenamine, 4-[(4-nitrophenyl)azo]-	EtOH	438(4.46)	62-0158-80
Pyridazino[4,5-c]pyridazine-5,8-dione, 1,4,6,7-tetrahydro-3-phenyl-	EtOH	240s(3.95),270(4.30), 345(3.70)	4-0529-80
Pyridazino[3,4-b]quinoxaline-4-carbox-ylic acid, 1,2-dihydro-, methyl ester	EtOH	246(4.63),416(3.96), 441(4.01),473s(3.85)	94-3537-80
$C_{12}H_{10}N_4O_3$			
Benzo[g]pteridine-2,4(3H,10H)-dione,	6M HCl	258(4.40),422(4.53)	83-0937-80

Compound	Solvent	$\lambda_{max}(\log \epsilon)$	Ref.
Benzo[g]pteridine-2,4(3H,10H)-dione,	pH 3	262(4.49),435(4.42)	83-0937-80
8-hydroxy-7,10-dimethyl- (cont.)	pH 9	300(4.07),472(4.61)	83-0937-80
	pH 13	283(4.05),472(4.73)	83-0937-80
4-Pyridazinecarboxylic acid, 5-[[(2-	H_2O	313s(3.3)	39-1339-80B
aminophenyl)amino]carbonyl]-	MeOH	308(3.8)	39-1339-80B
	DMSO	313(4.1)	39-1339-80B
$C_{12}H_{10}N_4O_4S$			
Acetamide, N-[5-acetyl-3-(3-nitrophen-	EtOH	224s(3.78),280(3.91),	4-1713-80
yl)-1,3,4-thiadiazol-2(3H)-ylidene]-		314(3.96)	
Acetamide, N-[5-acetyl-3-(4-nitrophen-	EtOH	232s(4.25),270(4.27),	4-1713-80
yl)-1,3,4-thiadiazol-2(3H)-ylidene]-		316(4.42)	
$C_{12}H_{10}N_4O_6$			
4H-1,3-Benzoxazin-4-one, 6,8-dinitro-	MeOH	220(4.56)	24-2818-80
2-pyrrolidino-			
$C_{12}H_{10}N_6$			
1,2,4,5-Tetrazine, 1,2-dihydro-3,6-di-	MeOH	268(4.41),530(2.53)	24-2566-80
4-pyridinyl-			
$C_{12}H_{10}N_6O$			
4(1H)-Pteridinone, 2-amino-7-(4-pyri-	pH 1	252(4.11),321(4.01)	150-0549-80
dinylmethyl)- (2:1 mixture with	pH 13	255(4.40),361(3.96)	150-0549-80
6-pyridinylmethyl isomer)			
$C_{12}H_{10}O$			
Benzene, 1,1'-oxybis-, Cr(CO)$_3$ complex	C_6H_{12}	258(3.9),319(4.0)	110-0749-80
[1,1'-Biphenyl]-4-ol	hexane	220(3.91),264(2.85),	65-2236-80
		268(3.04),271(3.08),	
		274(3.11),276(3.20),	
		283(3.17)	
	pentane-	226(3.94),281(3.26),	65-2236-80
	EtOH-ether	287(3.15)	
4-Hexen-1-yn-3-one, 1-phenyl-	n.s.g.	212(4.16),247(4.09),	70-0418-80
		260(3.97),279(3.99),	
		295(3.91)	
$C_{12}H_{10}OS$			
Benzene, 1,1'-sulfinylbis- (radical)	H_2O	330(3.62)	39-0146-80B
$C_{12}H_{10}O_2$			
1-Azulenecarboxaldehyde, 2-(hydroxy-	CH_2Cl_2	265(4.24),269(4.29),	18-3696-80
methyl)-		315(4.85),365(4.10),	
		380(4.22),514(2.69)	
[1,1'-Biphenyl]-2,4-diol	EtOH	215(4.47),258(4.11),	104-1298-80
		291(3.84)	
Ethanone, 1-(1-hydroxy-2-naphthalenyl)-	THF	284(3.75),294(3.73),	116-1138-80
		306(3.35),364(3.73)	
Ethanone, 1-(2-hydroxy-1-naphthalenyl)-	THF	309(3.69),337(3.55),	116-1138-80
		360(3.50)	
Ethanone, 1-(4-hydroxy-1-naphthalenyl)-	THF	324(4.01)	116-1138-80
Ethanone, 1-(6-hydroxy-2-naphthalenyl)-	THF	312(4.08),332s(3.71)	116-1138-80
1,4-Naphthalenedione, 2,3-dimethyl-	n.s.g.	330(3.44),440(1.78)	18-0757-80
1,4-Naphthalenedione, 2-ethyl-	n.s.g.	330(3.41),440(1.85)	18-0757-80
Tricyclo[4.2.2.0^{1,6}]deca-2,4,7,9-	EtOH	212(3.82),264s(3.35),	88-3583-80
tetraene-7-carboxylic acid, methyl		274s(3.31)	
ester			
$C_{12}H_{10}O_3$			
2H-1-Benzopyran-2-one, 6-ethenyl-	EtOH	221s(4.12),253(4.25),	12-0395-80

Compound	Solvent	λ_{max}(log ϵ)	Ref.
7-methoxy- (cont.)		295s(3.79),305(3.83), 338(3.97)	12-0395-80
2-Furancarboxaldehyde, 5-(4-methylphenoxy)-	MeOH	218s(3.79),304(4.30)	73-0423-80
$C_{12}H_{10}O_3S$			
2-Furancarboxaldehyde, 5-[4-(methylthio)phenoxy]-	MeOH	205(4.30),255(4.02), 304(4.36)	73-0423-80
$C_{12}H_{10}O_4$			
2H-1-Benzopyran-2-one, 7-acetoxy-6-methyl-	EtOH	278(4.02),320(3.90)	2-0085-80
2H-1-Benzopyran-2-one, 8-hydroxy-7-(2-propenyloxy)-	MeOH	204(4.58),277s(3.90), 270(3.94),318(4.13)	44-1470-80
Cyclopenta[c]pyran-7-carboxaldehyde, 4-(acetoxymethyl)- (baldrinal)	n.s.g.	227(4.2),244(4.18), 287(4.08),425(3.87)	100-0649-80
2-Furancarboxaldehyde, 5-(4-methoxyphenoxy)-	MeOH	222(4.43),308(3.38)	73-0423-80
2-Furancarboxylic acid, 5-(4-methylphenoxy)-	MeOH	220(3.84),272(4.22)	73-0910-80
1,4-Naphthalenedione, 2-ethoxy-8-hydroxy-	MeOH	240s(3.96),283(4.06), 416(3.51)	39-1161-80C
1,4-Naphthalenedione, 5-ethoxy-8-hydroxy-	MeOH	202(4.15),260(3.90), 484(3.60)	24-1575-80
$C_{12}H_{10}O_4S$			
2-Furancarboxylic acid, 5-[4-(methylthio)phenoxy]-	MeOH	205(4.25),266(4.34)	73-0910-80
$C_{12}H_{10}O_5$			
2H-1-Benzopyran-4-carboxylic acid, 7-methoxy-1-oxo-, methyl ester	EtOH	345(4.07)	95-0289-80
2H-1-Benzopyran-2-one, 6-acetoxy-7-methoxy-	EtOH	217(4.22),250s(3.6), 323(4.1)	2-0495-80
2H-1-Benzopyran-2-one, 8-acetyl-7-hydroxy-6-methoxy-	MeOH MeOH-NaOH	260(3.87),355(3.87) 310(--),385(--)	102-2494-80 102-2494-80
2-Furancarboxylic acid, 5-(4-methoxyphenoxy)-	MeOH	222(3.81),270(4.10)	73-0910-80
1,4-Naphthalenedione, 2-ethoxy-3,5-dihydroxy-	MeOH	229(4.21),255(4.11), 282(4.14),410(3.66)	39-1161-80C
1,4-Naphthalenedione, 2,5-dihydroxy-3-methoxy-7-methyl- (nepenthone C)	MeOH	235(4.22),271(4.26), 391(3.63),484(3.48)	12-1073-80
$C_{12}H_{10}O_6$			
1,4-Benzenedipropanoic acid, β,β'-dioxo-	MeOH	250(4.29),301(3.87)	47-3029-80
2H-1-Benzopyran-6-acetic acid, 7-hydroxy-8-methoxy-2-oxo-	MeOH	225(4.18),247(3.57), 257(3.58),329(4.15)	44-1470-80
$C_{12}H_{11}BrN_2O_2$			
2(1H)-Pyrimidinone, 4-[2-(4-bromophenyl)-2-oxoethylidene]tetrahydro-	pH 11-12	268(3.94),327(4.41)	44-3651-80
$C_{12}H_{11}Cl$			
Benzene, (2-chloro-3-methyl-1,3-cyclopentadien-1-yl)-	EtOH	217(3.90),297(4.06)	142-1739-80
$C_{12}H_{11}ClN_2O$			
Ethanone, 1-[2-(4-chlorophenyl)-5-methyl-1H-imidazol-4-yl]-	EtOH	291(4.37)	4-1723-80

Compound	Solvent	$\lambda_{max}(\log \epsilon)$	Ref.
$C_{12}H_{11}ClN_2O_2$			
1H-Imidazole-4-carboxylic acid, 1-[(4-chlorophenyl)methyl]-, methyl ester	n.s.g.	223(4.27)	145-1051-80
1H-Imidazole-5-carboxylic acid, 1-[(4-chlorophenyl)methyl]-, methyl ester	n.s.g.	238(4.08)	145-1051-80
$C_{12}H_{11}ClN_2O_3$			
1H-Pyrazole-3-carboxylic acid, 1-(3-chlorophenyl)-4-hydroxy-, ethyl ester	EtOH	246(4.03),298(4.12)	142-0697-80B
1H-Pyrazole-3-carboxylic acid, 1-(4-chlorophenyl)-4-hydroxy-, ethyl ester	EtOH	251(4.06),298(4.17)	142-0697-80B
$C_{12}H_{11}ClN_4S$			
4H-[1,2,4]Triazolo[4,3-a][1,4]benzodiazepine, 8-chloro-1-methyl-6-(methylthio)-	EtOH	218(4.55),220s(4.54), 241(4.10),275(3.55), 286s(3.53),295s(3.46)	87-0873-80
6H-[1,2,4]Triazolo[4,3-a][1,4]benzodiazepine, 8-chloro-1-methyl-4-(methylthio)-	EtOH	223(4.31),243s(4.09), 269s(3.88),277s(3.78), 284s(3.70)	87-0873-80
$C_{12}H_{11}ClO$			
2,4-Pentadienal, 5-(4-chlorophenyl)-3-methyl-, (E,E)-	EtOH	242(4.15),326(4.50)	118-0815-80
$C_{12}H_{11}ClO_2$			
2,4-Pentadienoic acid, 5-(4-chlorophenyl)-3-methyl-	EtOH	238(4.07),316(4.45)	118-0815-80
$C_{12}H_{11}Cl_2N_3O_2$			
Benzoic acid, 5-chloro-2-[3-(chloromethyl)-5-methyl-4H-1,2,4-triazol-4-yl]-, methyl ester	EtOH	206(4.67),227s(4.09), 281(3.11),288(3.06)	87-0873-80
$C_{12}H_{11}F_3O_2S$			
Sulfonium, dimethyl-, 1-benzoyl-3,3,3-trifluoro-2-oxopropylide	50% EtOH	242(3.98),300(3.98)	104-0729-80
$C_{12}H_{11}N$			
Benzenamine, N-phenyl-	H_2O	278(4.16)	152-0615-80
9H-Pyrrolo[1,2-a]indole, 9-methyl-	EtOH	264(4.23),292(3.40)	39-0097-80C
$C_{12}H_{11}NO$			
9H-Benzocyclohepten-5,8-imin-9-one, 6,8-dihydro-10-methyl-	EtOH	218(4.28),262(3.61)	39-2077-80C
picrate	EtOH	356(4.18)	39-2077-80C
5H-Benzocyclohepten-5-one, 7-(methylamino)-	EtOH	274(4.59),282(4.62), 342(3.93)	39-2077-80C
3-Pyridinol, 2-(phenylmethyl)-	CHCl$_3$	282(3.89)	39-1176-80C
$C_{12}H_{11}NOS$			
2-Furancarbothioamide, 5-methyl-N-phenyl-	EtOH	203(4.15),228s(3.95), 322(4.34)	128-0069-80
3-Furancarbothioamide, 2-methyl-N-phenyl-	EtOH	203(4.34),213s(4.30), 296(4.05)	128-0069-80
3-Thiophenecarboxamide, N-(3-methylphenyl)-	EtOH	230s(4.01),268(4.10)	59-0349-80
3-Thiophenecarboxamide, N-(4-methylphenyl)-	EtOH	227(4.06),271(4.12)	59-0349-80
$C_{12}H_{11}NOS_3$			
Ethanethioic acid, O-[5-(methylthio)-	CHCl$_3$	314(3.98),378(4.37)	39-2693-80C

Compound	Solvent	$\lambda_{max}(\log \epsilon)$	Ref.
4-phenyl-3-isothiazolyl] ester (cont.)			39-2693-80C
$C_{12}H_{11}NO_2$			
1,3-Dioxolo[4,5-g]isoquinoline, 5,7-di-methyl-	MeOH-acid	248(4.78),308(3.93), 346(3.72)	118-0070-80
	MeOH-base	235(4.70),278(3.67), 335(3.62)	118-0070-80
2-Furancarboxamide, N-(3-methylphenyl)-	EtOH	279(4.22)	59-0349-80
2-Furancarboxamide, N-(4-methylphenyl)-	EtOH	253s(4.05),275(4.22)	59-0349-80
2-Furancarboxamide, 5-methyl-N-phenyl-	EtOH	192(4.22),285(4.26)	128-0069-80
3-Furancarboxamide, N-(3-methylphenyl)-	EtOH	264(4.11)	59-0349-80
3-Furancarboxamide, N-(4-methylphenyl)-	EtOH	265(4.13)	59-0349-80
1,4-Naphthalenedione, 2-(dimethyl-amino)-	heptane	440(3.51)	70-0897-80
	isoPrOH	466(3.61)	70-0897-80
$C_{12}H_{11}NO_2S$			
Azepine, 1-(phenylsulfonyl)-	EtOH	205(3.34),266(3.48)	142-1569-80B
4-Quinolinecarboxylic acid, 1,2-di-hydro-2-thioxo-, ethyl ester	EtOH	221(4.53),288(4.31), 419(3.95)	94-0049-80
3-Thiophenecarboxamide, N-(3-methoxy-phenyl)-	EtOH	226s(4.22),268(4.10), 282s(4.05)	59-0349-80
3-Thiophenecarboxamide, N-(4-methoxy-phenyl)-	EtOH	231(4.09),281(4.11)	59-0349-80
$C_{12}H_{11}NO_2S_2$			
4-Thiazolidinone, 5-[(2-methoxyphenyl)-methylene]-3-methyl-2-thioxo-	MeOH	276(4.05),285s(3.84), 386(4.43)	48-0835-80
4-Thiazolidinone, 5-[(3-methoxyphenyl)-methylene]-3-methyl-2-thioxo-	MeOH	286(4.01),392(4.43)	48-0835-80
4-Thiazolidinone, 5-[(4-methoxyphenyl)-methylene]-3-methyl-2-thioxo-	MeOH	286(4.01),392(4.43)	48-0835-80
4(5H)-Thiazolone, 5-[(2-methoxyphenyl)-methylene]-2-(methylthio)-	MeOH	262(3.77),310(4.04), 385(4.39)	48-0835-80
4(5H)-Thiazolone, 5-[(3-methoxyphenyl)-methylene]-2-(methylthio)-	MeOH	256s(3.95),307(4.15), 373(4.36)	48-0835-80
4(5H)-Thiazolone, 5-[(4-methoxyphenyl)-methylene]-2-(methylthio)-	MeOH	258s(3.88),280(4.04), 305s(3.95)	48-0835-80
$C_{12}H_{11}NO_3$			
2-Furancarboxamide, N-(3-methoxyphen-yl)-	EtOH	237(3.88),272(3.40), 278(3.40)	59-0349-80
2-Furancarboxamide, N-(4-methoxyphen-yl)-	EtOH	260s(4.03),283(4.20)	59-0349-80
3-Furancarboxamide, N-(3-methoxyphen-yl)-	EtOH	263(4.07),282s(3.93)	59-0349-80
3-Furancarboxamide, N-(4-methoxyphen-yl)-	EtOH	273(4.09)	59-0349-80
1H-Indole-3-acetic acid, α-formyl-, methyl ester	EtOH	205s(4.29),222(4.55), 280(3.93),289(3.88)	103-0045-80
1H-Indole-3-carboxylic acid, 1-formyl-2-methyl-, methyl ester	MeCN	212(4.49),232(4.14), 249(4.07),256(4.07), 283(3.84),300(2.93)	94-1157-80
Oxazolium, 4-acetyl-5-hydroxy-3-methyl-2-phenyl-, hydroxide, inner salt	MeCN	234(4.15),264(4.26), 343(4.36)	5-1836-80
5(4H)-Oxazolone, 4-[(4-methoxyphenyl)-methylene]-2-methyl-	dioxan	320(4.14),362(4.37)	70-0576-80
2,4-Pentadienal, 5-(benzoyloxy)-, 1-oxime, (E,?,E)-	EtOH	236(3.98),268(3.90)	1-0031-80
$C_{12}H_{11}NO_3S$			
2,5-Pyrrolidinedione, 1-[(3-methylbenz-	CH₂Cl₂	249(4.10),258(4.09)	118-0721-80

Compound	Solvent	$\lambda_{max}(\log \epsilon)$	Ref.
oyl)thio]- (cont.)			118-0721-80
2,5-Pyrrolidinedione, 1-[(4-methylbenz-	CH_2Cl_2	266(4.25)	118-0721-80
oyl)thio]-			
2-Quinolinecarbothioic acid, 8-hydroxy-	MeOH	215(4.48),255(4.77),	64-1569-80B
4-methoxy-, S-methyl ester		254(3.36)	
$C_{12}H_{11}NO_4$			
2H-1-Benzopyran-4-carboxamide, 7-meth-	EtOH	332(4.19)	95-0289-80
oxy-N-methyl-2-oxo-			
Cyclopropa[b][1]benzopyran-7(1H)-one,	EtOH	214(4.22),255(3.95),	39-2049-80C
1a,7a-dihydro-1,1-dimethyl-7a-nitro-		328(3.43)	
4-Isoxazolecarboxylic acid, 2,5-dihy-	MeOH	221(4.17),278(4.09)	39-1667-80C
dro-2-methyl-5-oxo-3-phenyl-,			
methyl ester			
1H-Pyrrole-1-carboxylic acid, 2,5-di-	EtOH	218(3.60),231s(3.45)	142-1073-80
hydro-2-hydroxy-5-oxo-, phenylmethyl			
ester			
1(2H)-Quinolineacetic acid, 4-hydroxy-	EtOH	217(4.18),257(3.84)	78-1385-80
3-methyl-2-oxo-			
2-Quinolinecarboxylic acid, 1,4-dihy-	MeOH	229(4.36),239(4.37),	64-1569-80B
dro-8-methoxy-4-oxo-, methyl ester		249(4.39),269(3.67),	
		353(3.89)	
$C_{12}H_{11}NO_4S$			
2,5-Pyrrolidinedione, 1-[(4-methoxy-	CH_2Cl_2	288(4.24)	118-0721-80
benzoyl)thio]-			
$C_{12}H_{11}NO_5$			
1,3,4(2H)-Isoquinolinetrione, 6,7-di-	MeOH	233(3.89),267(4.25),	39-2013-80C
methoxy-2-methyl-		340(3.46),364(3.45)	
$C_{12}H_{11}NO_6S$			
Enol of 3-thio-(3-carboxy-4-nitro-	pH 8	289(4.18),371(4.04)	35-7059-80
phenyl)-2,4-pentanedione			
$C_{12}H_{11}NS$			
4H-Thieno[3,2-b][1]benzazepine,	EtOH	229(4.11),265(3.91),	142-1227-80B
9,10-dihydro-		304(3.91)	
$C_{12}H_{11}N_3$			
Benzaldehyde, 2-pyridinylhydrazone,	benzene	307.5(4.22)	151-0083-80B
anti			
syn	benzene	327.5(4.44)	151-0083-80B
Benzenamine, 4-(phenylazo)-	EtOH	389(4.40)	62-0158-80
1H-Cyclopenta[4,5]pyrrolo[3,2-e]benz-	EtOH	280(4.06),294(4.12),	103-0062-80
imidazole, 6,7,8,9-tetrahydro-		303(4.09)	
Propanedinitrile, [[4-(dimethylamino)-	benzene	425(4.67)	46-2803-80
phenyl]methylene]-	MeOH	427(4.70)	46-2803-80
	EtOAc	421(4.71)	46-2803-80
	BuOAc	421(4.71)	46-2803-80
	THF	425(4.71)	46-2803-80
	2-MeTHF	424(4.69)	46-2803-80
	MeCN	427(4.69)	46-2803-80
$C_{12}H_{11}N_3OS$			
Acetamide, N-[5-(2-phenylethenyl)-	EtOH	317(4.46)	94-2116-80
1,3,4-thiadiazol-2-yl]-			
2-Thiophenepropanenitrile, α-[bis(1-	MeOH	245(4.04),333(4.28)	78-1791-80
aziridinyl)methylene]-β-oxo-			

Compound	Solvent	$\lambda_{max}(\log \epsilon)$	Ref.
$C_{12}H_{11}N_3O_2$			
Benzenamine, N-(1-methyl-5-nitro-2(1H)-pyridinylidene)-	C_6H_{12}	217(4.20),352(4.16), 376s(4.08)	18-0717-80
	EtOH	215(4.16),353(4.11), 394s(4.01)	18-0717-80
	MeCN	216(4.19),359(4.14), 384s(4.11)	18-0717-80
2-Furanpropanenitrile, α-[bis(1-aziridinyl)methylene]-β-oxo-	MeOH	234(3.84),273(3.39), 334(4.17)	78-1791-80
1H-Isoindol-1-one, 2,3-dihydro-3-hydroxy-3-(1H-imidazol-2-yl)-2-methyl-	EtOH-5M HCl	260s(3.48)	103-0247-80
4-Isoquinolinecarbonitrile, 1,2-dihydro-3-[(2-hydroxyethyl)amino]-1-oxo-	EtOH	234(4.41),264(3.95), 304(4.33),362(3.70)	95-0456-80
2-Pyridinamine, N-methyl-5-nitro-N-phenyl-	C_6H_{12}	220(4.13),352(4.33)	18-0717-80
	EtOH	226(4.16),365(4.29)	18-0717-80
	MeCN	223(4.10),373(4.28)	18-0717-80
Pyrrolo[3,2-e]benzimidazole-7-carboxylic acid, 1,6-dihydro-, ethyl ester	EtOH	250(4.22),302(4.37)	103-0062-80
$C_{12}H_{11}N_3O_2S$			
Acetamide, N-(5-acetyl-3-phenyl-1,3,4-thiadiazol-2(3H)-ylidene)-	EtOH	228s(3.96),285(4.23), 315(4.07)	4-1713-80
$C_{12}H_{11}N_3O_2Se$			
Acetamide, N-(5-acetyl-3-phenyl-1,3,4-selenadiazol-2(3H)-ylidene)-	EtOH	258(4.12),320(4.10)	4-1185-80
$C_{12}H_{11}N_3O_3$			
Acetamide, N-(6-methyl-1,3-dioxolo[4,5-g]quinazolin-8-yl)-	EtOH	206(4.12),224s(4.38), 243(4.55),280s(3.65), 323(3.96),337s(3.97), 339(3.99)	114-0253-80B
Ethanone, 1-[5-methyl-2-(4-nitrophenyl)-1H-imidazol-4-yl]-	EtOH	229(4.09),280(3.86), 345(4.32)	4-1723-80
Propanoic acid, 3-cyano-2-oxo-3-(phenylhydrazono)-, ethyl ester	EtOH	245(4.15),365(4.51)	104-0751-80
$C_{12}H_{11}N_3O_3S$			
Benzenesulfonic acid, 4-[(4-aminophenyl)azo]-	anion	217(3.70),350s(3.70), 420(4.00)	59-0279-80
$C_{12}H_{11}N_3O_5$			
1H-Pyrazole-3-carboxylic acid, 4-hydroxy-1-(3-nitrophenyl)-, ethyl ester	EtOH	298(4.14)	142-0697-80B
1H-Pyrazole-3-carboxylic acid, 4-hydroxy-1-(4-nitrophenyl)-, ethyl ester	EtOH	270(3.98),333(4.26)	142-0697-80B
$C_{12}H_{12}$			
Benzene, (1,5-cyclohexadien-1-yl)-	C_6H_{12}	228(4.25),272s(3.58)	118-0238-80
Benzene, (3-methyl-1,3-cyclopentadien-1-yl)-	EtOH	219(3.91),304(4.07)	142-1739-80
$C_{12}H_{12}BrNS$			
Benzenamine, 2-[2-(2-bromo-3-thienyl)ethyl]-	EtOH	236(4.18),286(3.39)	142-1227-80B
$C_{12}H_{12}Br_2N_2O_4$			
1H-Benzimidazole, 1-α-D-arabinofuranosyl-5,6-dibromo-	pH 2	288(3.79),296(3.75)	64-0030-80C
	pH 8	251(3.78),289(3.63), 297(3.60)	64-0030-80C

Compound	Solvent	$\lambda_{max}(\log \epsilon)$	Ref.
1H-Benzimidazole, 5,6-dibromo-1-β-D-ribofuranosyl-	pH 2 pH 8	288(3.83),296(3.81) 255(3.77),288(3.64), 297(3.63)	64-0030-80C 64-0030-80C
$C_{12}H_{12}ClN$ 1H-Carbazole, 4a-chloro-2,3,4,4a-tetra-hydro-	CH$_2$Cl$_2$ + Et$_3$N	235(4.14),264(3.56) 264(c.3.35),290s(--)	142-0867-80 23-0808-80
$C_{12}H_{12}ClNO$ 2(1H)-Quinolinone, 3-(2-chloroethyl)-7-methyl-	CHCl$_3$	243(3.92),277(3.83), 284(3.80),320(3.79), 329(3.88),340(3.73)	150-0414-80S
$C_{12}H_{12}ClN_2O_2S_2$ Imidazo[2,1-b]thiazolium, 7-[(4-chloro-phenyl)sulfonyl]-5,6-dihydro-3-meth-yl-, chloride	MeOH	233(4.13)	39-1773-80C
$C_{12}H_{12}ClN_3OS$ 5H-Pyrimido[4,5-b][1,4]benzothiazin-9(6H)-one, 4-chloro-7,8-dihydro-7,7-dimethyl-	EtOH	218(4.26),249(4.19), 290(3.94),368(3.96), 440s(3.17)	103-0580-80
$C_{12}H_{12}ClN_3O_3$ Benzoic acid, 5-chloro-2-[3-(hydroxy-methyl)-5-methyl-4H-1,2,4-triazol-4-yl]-, methyl ester	EtOH	204(4.63),225s(4.03), 283(3.10)	87-0873-80
$C_{12}H_{12}ClN_3O_4$ Butanoic acid, 4-amino-3-[(4-chloro-phenyl)hydrazono]-2,4-dioxo-, ethyl ester	EtOH	245(4.28),370(4.60)	104-0751-80
$C_{12}H_{12}Cl_2N_2O_2S_2$ Benzenesulfonamide, 4-chloro-N-[3-(2-chloroethyl)-4-methyl-2(3H)-thiazol-ylidene]-	MeOH	228(4.18),292(4.13)	39-1773-80C
$C_{12}H_{12}Cl_2N_2O_4$ 1H-Benzimidazole, 1-α-D-arabinofurano-syl-5,6-dichloro-	pH 2 pH 8	254(3.77),286(3.88), 295(3.87) 255(3.89),287(3.77), 296(3.77)	64-0030-80C 64-0030-80C
1H-Benzimidazole, 5,6-dichloro-1-β-D-ribofuranosyl-	pH 2 pH 8	253(3.55),285(3.78), 294(3.77) 254(3.81),287(3.69), 296(3.70)	64-0030-80C 64-0030-80C
$C_{12}H_{12}MnNO_4$ Manganese, [(1,2,3,4,5-η)-1-[1-(acetyl-amino)ethyl]-2,4-cyclopentadien-1-yl]tricarbonyl-	EtOH	330(3.21)	101-0301-80R
$C_{12}H_{12}NO_3$ 1,3-Dioxolo[4,5-g]isoquinolinium, 4-methoxy-6-methyl-, perchlorate	MeOH	264(4.57),320(3.78)	83-0715-80
$C_{12}H_{12}N_2$ Benzenediamine, N-phenyl- 2,3'-Bipyridine, 5',6'-dimethyl-	H$_2$O MeOH	276(4.10) 262(3.8),268(3.7)	152-0615-80 103-0951-80

Compound	Solvent	$\lambda_{max}(\log \epsilon)$	Ref.
1H-Imidazole, 4-[2-(2-methylphenyl)ethenyl]-, cis	EtOH	224(4.04),263(3.92)	4-0679-80
trans	EtOH	230(4.03),299(4.35)	4-0679-80
1H-Imidazole, 4-[2-(3-methylphenyl)ethenyl]-, cis	EtOH	225(4.16),285(3.93)	4-0679-80
trans	EtOH	226(4.10),301(4.37)	4-0679-80
1H-Imidazole, 4-[2-(4-methylphenyl)ethenyl]-, cis	EtOH	226(4.07),286(3.89)	4-0679-80
trans	EtOH	227(4.11),306(4.48)	4-0679-80
2,4-Pentadienenitrile, 5-(methylphenylamino)-, (E,E)-	EtOH	232(3.74),345(4.33)	1-0031-80
Propanedinitrile, (3,3-dicyclopropyl-2-propen-1-ylidene)-	EtOH	345(4.48)	35-0711-80

$C_{12}H_{12}N_2O$

Compound	Solvent	$\lambda_{max}(\log \epsilon)$	Ref.
Azepino[4,5-b]indol-2(1H)-one, 3,4,5,6-tetrahydro-	EtOH	274(3.84),282(3.86), 292(3.78)	94-0900-80
Azepino[4,5-b]indol-4(1H)-one, 2,3,5,6-tetrahydro-	EtOH	283(3.90),291(3.85)	94-0900-80
Azepino[4,5-g]indol-7(1H)-one, 6,8,9,10-tetrahydro-	EtOH	272(3.80),281(3.80), 292(3.68)	94-0900-80
Azocino[4,5,6-cd]indol-4-one, 1,3,4,5,6,7-hexahydro-	EtOH	283(3.78),294(3.69)	94-0900-80
Azocino[4,5,6-cd]indol-6-one, 1,3,4,5,6,7-hexahydro-	EtOH	285(3.80),292(3.79)	94-0900-80
1H-1,3-Benzodiazepine, 1-acetyl-2-methyl-	EtOH	240(3.97),284(3.73)	94-2602-80
[2,3'-Bipyridin]-5'-ol, 2',6'-dimethyl-	MeOH	297(4.2)	103-0951-80
[2,4'-Bipyridin]-3'-ol, 2',6'-dimethyl-	MeOH	256(4.1),282(3.9), 336(3.8)	103-0951-80
1,3-Diazabicyclo[2.2.0]hex-5-en-2-one, 4,6-dimethyl-3-phenyl-	EtOH	240(4.73),270s(4.20), 280s(4.10)	39-0607-80C
1H-[1,4]Diazocino[6,5,4-hi]indol-2-one, 2,3,4,5-tetrahydro-	EtOH	275(3.94),281(3.95), 291(3.84)	94-0900-80
1H-[1,4]Diazepino[1,7-a]indol-2(3H)-one, 4,5-dihydro-	EtOH	275(3.94),281(3.95), 291(3.84)	94-0900-80
Ethanone, 1-(5-methyl-2-phenyl-1H-imidazol-4-yl)-	EtOH	287(4.47)	4-1723-80
Pyrazineethanol, α-phenyl-	EtOH	208(4.09),256(3.74), 267(3.85),273(3.80), 305(2.93)	44-0999-80
Pyrido[3,4-b]indol-1-one, 2,3,4,9-tetrahydro-2-methyl-	isoPrOH	227(4.17),238s(4.04), 302(4.11)	103-0244-80
2(1H)-Pyrimidinone, 4,6-dimethyl-1-phenyl-	EtOH	210(4.35),304(3.98)	39-0607-80C

$C_{12}H_{12}N_2OS$

Compound	Solvent	$\lambda_{max}(\log \epsilon)$	Ref.
Ethanone, 2-(3,5-dimethyl-1,3,4-thiadiazol-2(3H)-ylidene)-1-phenyl-	EtOH	248(4.04),278s(3.36), 367(4.39)	94-0447-80
Isoquinolinium, 2-[(ethoxythioxomethyl)amino]-, hydroxide, inner salt	EtOH	226(4.54),248(4.45), 277(3.98),327(3.62), 354s(3.35)	114-0259-80A
5(4H)-Oxazolethione, 4-[(dimethylamino)methylene]-2-phenyl-	heptane	245s(3.7),252(3.7), 273(3.9),338(3.7), 357(3.6),425(3.8), 450(3.6)	103-0028-80
	EtOH	234s(4.2),264(4.2), 335(4.1),412(4.3)	103-0028-80
5(4H)-Thiazolone, 4-[(dimethylamino)methylene]-2-phenyl-	heptane	245s(3.7),252(3.7), 273(3.9),338(3.7), 357(3.6),425(3.8),	103-0028-80

Compound	Solvent	λ_{max}(log ϵ)	Ref.
(cont.)	EtOH	450(3.6) 255(3.8),330s(3.7), 374(4.1),384s(4.0)	103-0028-80 103-0028-80
$C_{12}H_{12}N_2O_2$			
6H-Cyclopenta[d]cyclopenta[3,4]pyraz- olo[5,1-b][1,3]oxazin-4(1H)-one, 2,3,7,8-tetrahydro-	dioxan	299(3.74)	35-4983-80
1H-Imidazole-4-carboxylic acid, 1-(phen- ylmethyl)-, methyl ester	n.s.g.	233(4.13)	145-1051-80
1H-Imidazole-4-carboxylic acid, 5-methyl-2-phenyl-, methyl ester	EtOH	278(4.35)	4-1723-80
1H-Imidazole-5-carboxylic acid, 1-(phenylmethyl)-, methyl ester	n.s.g.	239(4.08)	145-1051-80
5(4H)-Oxazolone, 4-[(dimethylamino)- methylene]-2-phenyl-	heptane	235(3.8),245(3.8), 275(3.8),340(4.0), 375(4.1)	103-0028-80
	EtOH	235(4.1),285(3.7), 295(3.7),337s(4.4), 352(3.6),368(4.4)	103-0028-80
2(1H)-Pyrazinone, 1-(1-phenylethyl)-, 4-oxide	pH 1	223(4.40),275(3.98), 330(3.71)	94-2734-80
	H_2O	223(4.39),275(3.98), 333(3.71)	94-2734-80
	pH 13	223(4.40),276(3.98), 333(3.71)	94-2734-80
3H-Pyrazol-3-one, 4-acetyl-2,4-dihydro- 5-methyl-2-phenyl-	n.s.g.	261(4.39)	64-0715-80B
sodium salt	n.s.g.	261(4.29)	64-0715-80B
Pyrimidine, 4-methoxy-5-(4-methoxy- phenyl)-	EtOH	260(4.07),279(4.09)	22-0559-80
4(1H)-Pyrimidinone, 5-(4-ethoxyphenyl)-	EtOH	224(3.97)	22-0559-80
4(1H)-Pyrimidinone, 5-(4-methoxyphen- yl)-1-methyl-	EtOH	224(4.24),297(4.06)	22-0559-80
$C_{12}H_{12}N_2O_2S$			
3(2H)-Pyridazinone, 4-(ethylthio)-5-hy- droxy-2-phenyl-	MeOH	210(4.31),244s(--), 313(3.79)	73-0127-80
3(2H)-Pyridazinone, 5-(ethylthio)-4-hy- droxy-2-phenyl-	MeOH	215(4.32),232s(4.36), 295(3.71)	73-0127-80
Thiourea, N-methyl-N'-(4-methyl-2-oxo- 2H-1-benzopyran-7-yl)-	EtOH	337(4.29)	95-0289-80
$C_{12}H_{12}N_2O_3$			
3H-Indol-3-one, 1-acetyl-1,2-dihydro-, 3-(O-acetyloxime)	EtOH	241(4.41),248(4.39), 268(4.23),330(4.85)	103-0828-80
1H-Pyrazole-3-carboxylic acid, 4-hy- droxy-1-phenyl-, ethyl ester	EtOH	250(4.03),294(4.17)	142-0697-80B
3(2H)-Pyridazinone, 4-ethoxy-5-hydroxy- 2-phenyl-	MeOH	211(4.40),227s(--), 281(3.82)	73-0127-80
3(2H)-Pyridazinone, 5-ethoxy-4-hydroxy- 2-phenyl-	MeOH	222(4.35),285(3.69)	73-0127-80
3(2H)-Pyridazinone, 5-hydroxy-4-meth- oxy-2-(phenylmethyl)-	MeOH	214(4.49),286(3.76)	73-0127-80
$C_{12}H_{12}N_2O_3S$			
4(5H)-Thiazolone, 2-[(hydroxymethyl)- amino]-5-[(4-methoxyphenyl)methyl- ene]-	EtOH	246(3.86),295(3.70), 351(4.13)	103-0718-80

Compound	Solvent	λ_{max} (log ϵ)	Ref.
C₁₂H₁₂N₂O₄			
6-Phthalazinecarboxylic acid, 3,4-di-hydro-1-(hydroxymethyl)-4-oxo-, ethyl ester	EtOH	252(3.83),262(3.83), 306(3.86)	94-2770-80
C₁₂H₁₂N₂S			
Benzo[7,8]cycloocta[1,2-d][1,2,3]thia-diazole, 4,5,6,7-tetrahydro-	EtOH	273(3.02)	24-0183-80
Pyrimidine, 2-[(2-phenylethyl)thio]-	EtOH	207s(4.017),252(4.110), 284(3.200)	112-0001-80
	CH₂Cl₂	253(4.212),285(3.255)	112-0001-80
C₁₂H₁₂N₂S₂			
5(4H)-Thiazolethione, 4-[(dimethyl-amino)methylene]-2-phenyl-	heptane	255(3.6),260(3.6), 304(4.1),312(4.0), 376(3.5),397(3.5), 460s(3.5)	103-0028-80
	EtOH	250(4.1),294(4.3), 374(4.2),444(4.1)	103-0028-80
C₁₂H₁₂N₃O₃			
Pyrimidinium, 1,4-dihydro-1,3-dimethyl-5-(4-nitrophenyl)-4-oxo-, iodide	EtOH	370(4.02)	22-0559-80
C₁₂H₁₂N₄			
3H-Imidazo[4,5-f]quinolin-2-amine, 3,4-dimethyl-	MeOH	219(4.37),265(4.58), 332(3.51)	138-1391-80
3H-Imidazo[4,5-f]quinolin-2-amine, 3,5-dimethyl-	MeOH	213(4.40),265(4.66), 354(3.56)	138-1391-80
Pyrazolo[5,1-c][1,2,4]benzothiazine, 2-ethyl-3-methyl-	MeOH	305s(3.59),335s(3.79), 347(3.86),364(3.75), 424s(2.37),447(2.80), 474(2.78),506s(2.63), 546s(2.29)	4-1057-80
C₁₂H₁₂N₄O₃			
2-Aziridinecarboxylic acid, 1-(1,5-di-hydro-5-oxo-3-phenyl-4H-1,2,4-tria-zol-4-yl)-, methyl ester	EtOH	249(3.87)	4-1691-80
C₁₂H₁₂N₄O₄			
Pyrazolo[1,5-a]pyrimidine-7-carboxylic acid, 6-acetyl-3-(aminocarbonyl)-, ethyl ester	EtOH	257(4.40),312(3.90)	4-0945-80
C₁₂H₁₂N₄S			
2H-1,2,4-Triazino[5,6-b]indole, 3-(propylthio)-	MeOH-HCl	231(3.87),282(4.68), 343(3.66)	83-0108-80
5H-1,2,4-Triazino[5,6-b]indole, 6,7-di-methyl-3-(methylthio)-	EtOH	230(4.17),270(4.47), 352(3.93)	142-1139-80
	EtOH-KOH	230(4.19),282(4.47), 350(3.88)	142-1139-80
2H-1,2,4-Triazino[5,6-b]indole-3(2H)-thione, 3,4-dihydro-4,6,7-trimethyl-	EtOH	247(3.98),259(4.11), 294(4.56),382(3.96)	142-1139-80
	EtOH-HCl	240(4.08),282(4.39)	142-1139-80
5H-1,2,4-Triazino[5,6-b]indole-3(2H)-thione, 5,6,7-trimethyl-	EtOH	236(3.31),264(3.31), 308(3.77)	142-1139-80
	EtOH-HCl	238(3.47),256(3.36), 292(3.73)	142-1139-80

Compound	Solvent	λ_{max} (log ϵ)	Ref.
$C_{12}H_{12}N_5O_9PS$ 3H-Imidazo[2,1-i]purine-5-sulfonic acid, 3-(3,5-O-phosphinico-β-D-ribofuranosyl)-	pH 1	227s(4.44),233(4.46), 273s(3.94),280(3.96)	94-0115-80
$C_{12}H_{12}N_6$ Tetramethylammonium tetracyanopyrrolidide	EtOH	227(4.50),235(4.59), 254(4.02),268(4.03)	44-5113-80
$C_{12}H_{12}N_6O$ Pyrimido[5,4-e]-1,2,4-triazin-5(1H)-one, 7-amino-2,6-dihydro-3-(phenylmethyl)-	pH 1	218(3.93),233s(--), 275(4.09)	150-3630-80
$C_{12}H_{12}N_6O_4$ Benzeneacetic acid, 2-(2-amino-1,6-dihydro-5-nitro-6-oxo-4-pyrimidinyl)-hydrazide	pH 1 pH 13	236(4.04),330(4.04) 260(4.38),329(4.13), 398(3.85)	150-3630-80 150-3630-80
$C_{12}H_{12}O$ Bicyclo[2.2.2]octane, 7,8-epoxy-2,3,5,6-tetrakis(methylene)-	EtOH	229(4.10),237(4.09), 249(4.04),255(4.04), 266s(3.79)	78-0149-80
as-Indacen-1(2H)-one, 3,6,7,8-tetrahydro-	EtOH	250(4.06)	23-1344-80
as-Indacen-3(2H)-one, 1,6,7,8-tetrahydro-	EtOH	261(4.14)	23-1344-80
s-Indacen-1(2H)-one, 3,5,6,7-tetrahydro-	EtOH	255(3.88)	23-1344-80
4-Pentenal, 2-(phenylmethylene)-, (E)-	EtOH	285(4.27)	39-1477-80C
$C_{12}H_{12}OS_2$ Ethanone, 2-(1,3-dithian-2-ylidene)-1-phenyl-	EtOH	215s(3.85),260(3.87), 280s(3.74),353(4.31)	35-3095-80
$C_{12}H_{12}O_2$ 3-Benzofurancarboxaldehyde, 2,4,7-trimethyl-	EtOH	213(4.19),236(4.24), 289(3.76)	12-1817-80
5-Benzofurancarboxaldehyde, 2,3-dihydro-2-(1-methylethenyl)-	MeOH	206(4.43),229s(4.37), 283s(4.35),293(4.37)	150-0127-80
6-Benzofurancarboxaldehyde, 2,4,7-trimethyl-	EtOH	231(4.20),295(4.15), 323s(3.93)	12-1817-80
2,4-Pentadienal, 5-(4-methoxyphenyl)-	EtOH	246(4.14),350(4.59)	118-0815-80
Spiro[cyclopentane-1,1'(3'H)-isobenzofuran]-3'-one	EtOH	277(3.26)	44-1828-80
$C_{12}H_{12}O_3$ 5-Benzofuranacetic acid, 2-ethyl-	MeOH	249(4.129),281(3.514), 288(3.537)	36-0164-80
3-Benzofuranol, 2,6-dimethyl-, acetate	EtOH	207(4.25),213(4.24), 250(3.97),255(3.94), 282(3.42),290(3.39)	1-0177-80
1H-Cyclopenta[b]benzofuran-1-one, 2,3,3a,8b-tetrahydro-3a-hydroxy-8b-methyl-, cis	n.s.g.	284(3.35),296(3.08)	44-0501-80
4,7-Methanoisobenzofuran-1,3-dione, 3a,4,4,7,7a-tetrahydro-8-(1-methylethylidene)-	dioxan	232(4.15)	126-0037-80
1,4-Naphthalenedione, 6-acetyl-5,6,7,8-tetrahydro-	EtOH	257(3.81),336(--)	23-1161-80

Compound	Solvent	$\lambda_{max}(\log \epsilon)$	Ref.
2,4-Pentadienoic acid, 5-(4-methoxy-phenyl)-	EtOH	238(4.03),326(4.32)	118-0815-80
$C_{12}H_{12}O_3W$ Tungsten, [1,4-butanediyl[(1,2,3,4,5-η)-2,4-cyclopentadien-1-ylidene]]-tricarbonyl-	hexane	261s(3.9),312(3.4), 356s(2.9)	24-1033-80
$C_{12}H_{12}O_4$ 4H-1-Benzopyran-4-one, 5-hydroxy-7-methoxy-2,6-dimethyl- (eugenitin)	EtOH	231(4.25),255(4.21), 291(3.98),330s(--)	94-2428-80
Spiro[1,3-benzodioxole-2,1'-cyclohex-ane]-5,6-dione	EtOH	293(4.13),395(3.20)	12-0527-80
Spiro[1,3-benzodioxole-2,1'-cyclopent-ane]-5-carboxylic acid	EtOH	219(4.40),262(3.82), 298(3.85)	12-0527-80
$C_{12}H_{12}O_5$ 4H-1-Benzopyran-4-one, 5-hydroxy-7,8-dimethoxy-2-methyl-	EtOH	242(4.07),259(3.69), 280(3.57)	102-2003-80
	EtOH-AlCl₃	239(4.11),268(3.77), 282(3.55)	102-2003-80
$C_{12}O_{12}Os_3$ Dodecacarbonyltriosmium	2-Mepentane	330(3.93),385s(3.56)	35-3022-80
$C_{12}H_{12}S_4$ 4H-Cyclopenta-1,3-dithiole, 2-(5,6-di-hydro-4H-cyclopenta-1,3-dithiol-2-ylidene)-5,6-dihydro-	$C_2H_4Cl_2$	307(4.02),327(3.97), 462(2.25)	11-0196-80A
$C_{12}H_{13}BrN_2$ 4-Quinolinamine, 7-bromo-N-propyl-	EtOH	260(4.32),330(4.08)	22-0316-80
$C_{12}H_{13}BrN_2O$ 2,4-Pentadienal, 5-[(4-bromophenyl)-methylamino]-, oxime	EtOH	250(3.99),348(4.70)	1-0513-80
$C_{12}H_{13}BrN_2O_3S$ Glycine, N-[[(4-bromobenzoyl)amino]-thioxomethyl]-	CHCl₃	261(4.40)	73-2334-80
$C_{12}H_{13}BrN_2O_4$ 1H-Benzimidazole, 1-α-D-arabinofurano-syl-5(or 6)-bromo-	pH 2	217(4.13),249(3.67), 280(3.77)	64-0030-80C
	pH 8	250(3.80),283(3.59)	64-0030-80C
1H-Benzimidazole, 5(or 6)-bromo-1-β-D-ribofuranosyl-	pH 2	255(3.61),279(3.74), 287(3.71)	64-0030-80C
	pH 8	250(3.76),280(3.56), 287(3.57)	64-0030-80C
$C_{12}H_{13}BrN_2O_4S$ 4,12-Epoxy-5H,8H-1,3-dioxolo[4,5-e]-pyrimido[2,1-b][1,3]thiazocin-8-one, 9-bromo-3a,4,12,12a-tetrahydro-2,2-dimethyl-, [3aS-(3aα,4β,12β,12aα)]-	H₂O	251(4.19),275s(4.02)	94-0939-80
$C_{12}H_{13}BrN_2O_5$ 4,12-Epoxy-5H,8H-1,3-dioxolo[4,5-e]-pyrimido[2,1-b][1,3]oxazocin-8-one, 9-bromo-3a,4,12,12a-tetrahydro-2,2-dimethyl-, [3aR-(3aα,4β,12β,12aα)]-	EtOH	248(3.93),265s(3.89)	94-0939-80

Compound	Solvent	$\lambda_{max}(\log \epsilon)$	Ref.
C₁₂H₁₃BrN₂S			
Imidazo[2,1-b]thiazolium, 5,6-dihydro-7-methyl-3-phenyl-, bromide	MeOH	278(4.12)	39-1773-80C
C₁₂H₁₃ClN₂			
1H-Pyrido[3,4-b]indole, 4a-chloro-2,3,4,4a-tetrahydro-2-methyl-	EtOH	226(3.94),286(3.04)	142-0867-80
C₁₂H₁₃ClN₂O			
Acetamide, 2-chloro-N-[2-(1H-indol-1-yl)ethyl]-	EtOH	273(3.78),280(3.78),293(3.66)	94-0900-80
Acetamide, 2-chloro-N-[2-(1H-indol-2-yl)ethyl]-	EtOH	271(3.89),277(3.85),288(3.78)	94-0900-80
Acetamide, 2-chloro-N-[2-(1H-indol-4-yl)ethyl]-	EtOH	271(3.89),277(3.88),288(3.75)	94-0900-80
Acetamide, 2-chloro-N-[2-(1H-indol-7-yl)ethyl]-	EtOH	270(3.82),279(3.80),289(3.67)	94-0900-80
5-Oxazolamine, 4-chloro-N-(1-methylethyl)-N-phenyl-	EtOH	237(4.16)	4-0705-80
C₁₂H₁₃ClN₂O₂			
3H-Pyrazole, 4-chloro-3-ethoxy-5-methyl-3-phenyl-, 1-oxide	CHCl₃	247(3.90)	44-0076-80
C₁₂H₁₃ClN₂O₃S			
Glycine, N-[[(4-chlorobenzoyl)amino]-thioxomethyl]-, ethyl ester	CHCl₃	255(4.37)	73-2334-80
C₁₂H₁₃ClN₂O₃S₂			
Benzenesulfonamide, 4-chloro-N-[3-(2-hydroxyethyl)-4-methyl-2(3H)-thiazolylidene]-	MeOH	228(4.17),292(4.03)	39-1773-80C
C₁₂H₁₃ClN₄			
Methanimidamide, N'-[1-(4-chlorophenyl)-1H-pyrazol-5-yl]-N,N-dimethyl-	EtOH	255(4.27),290(4.18)	114-0127-80C
C₁₂H₁₃ClO			
2-Oxabicyclo[4.1.0]heptane, 7-chloro-7-phenyl-	C₆H₁₂	211(3.93),218(3.93)	4-1097-80
C₁₂H₁₃Cl₂N₃O			
1H-Benzotriazole, 4,5-dichloro-1-(cyclohexyloxy)-	EtOH	209(4.48),265(3.96),272(3.97),294(3.83)	4-1115-80
C₁₂H₁₃N			
Isoquinoline, 1,3,6-trimethyl-	MeOH-acid	236(4.71),285(3.45),343(3.73)	118-0070-80
	MeOH-base	227(4.83),278(3.63),328(3.55)	118-0070-80
Isoquinoline, 1,3,7-trimethyl-	MeOH-acid	233(4.74),276(3.49),352(3.73)	118-0070-80
	MeOH-base	223(4.83),271(3.73),337(3.61)	118-0070-80
1-Naphthalenamine, N,3-dimethyl-	MeOH	216(4.76),253(4.40),338(3.86)	103-0965-80
2-Naphthalenamine, N,4-dimethyl-	MeOH	215(4.58),246(4.89),288(4.07),297(4.04),350(3.53)	103-0965-80
2-Naphthalenamine, N-ethyl-	MeOH	213(4.52),246(4.73),283(3.93),290s(3.93),	103-0965-80

Compound	Solvent	$\lambda_{max}(\log \epsilon)$	Ref.
(cont.) 1H-Pyrrolo[1,2-a]indole, 2,3-dihydro- 9-methyl-	EtOH	350(3.42) 230(4.49),280s(3.67), 286(3.72),293s(3.69)	103-0965-80 39-0097-80C
$C_{12}H_{13}NO$ Isoquinoline, 1-ethyl-7-methoxy-	MeOH	235(3.68),266(3.41), 271(3.38),328(3.28), 338(3.32)	142-1151-80
Isoquinoline, 6-methoxy-1,3-dimethyl-	MeOH-acid MeOH-base	246(4.62),309(3.82) 235(4.71),284(3.61), 321(3.37)	118-0070-80 118-0070-80
Isoquinoline, 7-methoxy-1,3-dimethyl-	MeOH-acid MeOH-base	241(4.66),277(3.70), 368(3.63) 227(4.70),268(3.77), 349(3.49)	118-0070-80 118-0070-80
Isoquinoline, 8-methoxy-1,3-dimethyl-	MeOH-acid MeOH-base	250(4.20),306(3.40), 371(3.70) 238(4.23),299(3.51), 331(3.61)	118-0070-80 118-0070-80
$C_{12}H_{13}NO_2$ 4H-1-Benzopyran-4-one, 3-[(dimethyl- amino)methylene]-2,3-dihydro-	EtOH	215(4.20),234(4.13), 255s(4.02),317(3.99), 364(4.26)	4-0061-80
4H-Cyclohepta[b]furan-4-one, 6-[(1- methylethyl)amino]-	n.s.g.	282(4.64),340(3.85)	39-2081-80C
Ethanone, 1-(1-ethyl-3-hydroxy-1H- indol-2-yl)-	MeOH	242(4.18),315(4.25), 361(3.79)	83-0405-80
1H-Indole-3-carboxylic acid, 2-ethyl-, methyl ester	MeOH	214(4.55),228(4.25), 255(3.95),283(4.04), 288s(4.07)	94-1157-80
1H-Isoindol-1-one, 2,3-dihydro-2-meth- yl-3-(2-oxopropyl)-	EtOH	222(4.01),229(4.00), 279(3.24)	39-2077-80C
4H-1,3-Oxazin-5(6H)-one, 4-ethyl- 2-phenyl-	MeOH	208(4.24),239(4.20)	103-1000-80
$C_{12}H_{13}NO_2S$ [2]Benzothiopyrano[4,3-b]pyrrole, 2,3,3a,5-tetrahydro-5-methyl-, 4,4-dioxide	MeOH	210(4.3),249(4.1)	94-1131-80
1,4-Thiazepin-5(2H)-one, 3,4-dihydro- 7-(4-methoxyphenyl)-	MeOH	235(3.88),275s(3.79), 328(3.85)	24-0995-80
$C_{12}H_{13}NO_3$ 1(2H)-Isoquinolinone, 6,7-dimethoxy- 2-methyl-	MeOH	270(3.84),281(3.85), 293(3.87),310s(3.59), 321(3.64),335(3.53)	100-0372-80
$C_{12}H_{13}NO_3Se$ Selenophenium, tetrahydro-, 1-nitro- 2-oxo-2-phenylethylide	MeCN	346(3.90)	70-0123-80
$C_{12}H_{13}NO_4$ Benzoic acid, 2-(cyanomethyl)-4,5-di- methoxy-, methyl ester	EtOH	265(4.06),295(3.73)	95-0819-80
1H-Indole-2-carboxylic acid, 2,6-di- hydro-5-hydroxy-2-methyl-6-oxo-, ethyl ester, (S)-	EtOH EtOH-HCl EtOH-NaOEt	312(4.56),322s(4.52), 422(3.56) 318(4.24) 243(4.21),334(4.61), 346(4.60)	87-1318-80 87-1318-80 87-1318-80

Compound	Solvent	λ_{max}(log ϵ)	Ref.
2(3H)-Isoquinolinecarboxylic acid, 4,6-dihydro-7-hydroxy-6-oxo-, ethyl ester	CHCl$_3$	245(3.81),257(3.74), 340s(3.92),404(4.35)	33-0938-80
4H-1,3-Oxazin-5(6H)-one, 2-(3,4-dimethoxyphenyl)-	MeOH	211(4.35),217(4.33), 261(4.11),293(3.79)	103-1000-80
$C_{12}H_{13}NO_5$			
2H-1-Benzopyran, 2-ethoxy-4-methoxy-3-nitro-	EtOH	240(3.66),308(3.80), 350(3.70)	39-2049-80C
1-Benzoxepin-5(2H)-one, 2-ethoxy-3,4-dihydro-4-nitro-	EtOH	250(3.82),302(3.35), 360(3.58)	39-2049-80C
$C_{12}H_{13}NS_2$			
4H-Dithieno[2,3-c:3',2'-e]azepine, 5-ethyl-5,6-dihydro-	heptane	226s(4.39),279s(3.73), 284s(3.75)	4-0321-80
	MeCN	227s(4.41),279s(3.77), 284s(3.79),290(3.80), 296s(3.71),301s(3.65)	4-0321-80
4H-Dithieno[3,2-c:2',3'-e]azepine, 5-ethyl-5,6-dihydro-	heptane	216(3.93),249(3.78), 258(3.78),309s(4.06), 320(4.11),336s(3.96)	4-0321-80
	MeCN	217(3.87),249(3.76), 258(3.76),308s(4.05), 321(4.09),337s(3.94)	4-0321-80
4H-Dithieno[3,4-c:3',4'-e]azepine, 5-ethyl-5,6-dihydro-	heptane	205(--),226s(--), 235s(--),264(--), 290s(--),301s(--)	4-0321-80
	MeCN	206(4.31),225s(4.15), 235s(4.06),264(3.86), 288s(3.58),300s(3.28)	4-0321-80
$C_{12}H_{13}N_2S$			
Imidazo[2,1-b]thiazolium, 5,6-dihydro-7-methyl-3-phenyl-, bromide	MeOH	278(4.12)	39-1773-80C
$C_{12}H_{13}N_3$			
Pyrrolo[3,2-e]benzimidazole, 1,6-dihydro-1,7,8-trimethyl-	EtOH	238(4.55),282(4.06), 294(4.01),305(4.00)	103-1039-80
Pyrrolo[3,2-e]benzimidazole, 1,6-dihydro-2,7,8-trimethyl-	EtOH	279(4.03),293(4.07), 303(4.08)	103-0062-80
Pyrrolo[3,2-e]benzimidazole, 1,6-dihydro-6,7,8-trimethyl-	EtOH	229(4.14),280(4.02), 300s(4.07),310(4.21)	103-1039-80
Pyrrolo[3,2-e]benzimidazole, 3,6-dihydro-3,7,8-trimethyl-	EtOH EtOH	302(4.28) 301(4.29)	103-0062-80 103-1039-80
$C_{12}H_{13}N_3OS$			
4-Imidazolidinone, 3-ethyl-5-imino-1-(phenylmethyl)-2-thioxo-	EtOH	309(4.20)	18-0442-80
$C_{12}H_{13}N_3O_2$			
Hydrazinecarboxylic acid, (1H-indol-2-ylmethylene)-, ethyl ester	C$_6$H$_{12}$ EtOH 50% EtOH	268(4.11),298(4.27) 269(4.20),300(4.35) 269(4.20),302(4.37)	115-0151-80 115-0151-80 115-0151-80
$C_{12}H_{13}N_3O_2S$			
2,4(1H,3H)-Pyrimidinedione, 6-[(2-aminophenyl)thio]-1,3-dimethyl-	MeOH	256s(4.25),285(4.12)	78-2097-80
$C_{12}H_{13}N_3O_4$			
Butanoic acid, 4-amino-2,4-dioxo-3-(phenylhydrazono)-, ethyl ester	EtOH	247(4.27),370(4.59)	104-0751-80

Compound	Solvent	$\lambda_{max}(\log \epsilon)$	Ref.
2-Quinoxalineacetaldehyde, 1,2,3,4-tetrahydro-α,α-dimethyl-7-nitro-3-oxo-	EtOH	269(4.30),314(3.86), 402(3.70)	104-0938-80
$C_{12}H_{13}N_3O_4S$			
4H-Furo[2',3':4,5]oxazolo[3,2-a]thieno-[3,2-e]pyrimidine-8-methanol, 6a,7,8,9a-tetrahydro-7-hydroxy-4-imino-3-methyl-, monohydrochloride, [6aS-(6aα,7α,8β,9aα)]-	pH 1 pH 11 MeOH	243(4.38),293(3.66) 239(4.48),301(3.63) 241(4.38),293(3.70)	39-1853-80C 39-1853-80C 39-1853-80C
$C_{12}H_{13}N_3O_4S_2$			
Acetic acid, [6-(aminocarbonyl)-4,5-dihydro-8-(methylthio)-4-oxo-1H-thieno-[3,4-b][1,4]diazepin-2(3H)-ylidene]-, methyl ester	EtOH	230(4.25),292(4.38), 346(4.21)	95-0699-80
$C_{12}H_{13}N_3O_5$			
Acetamide, 2-cyano-N-[2-hydroxy-1-(hydroxymethyl)-2-(4-nitrophenyl)ethyl]-, [R-(R*,R*)]-	pH 7	278(3.98)	87-1299-80
Butanoic acid, 2-[(4-nitrophenyl)hydrazono]-3-oxo-, ethyl ester	MeOH	373(4.499)	2-0676-80
L-Valine, N-(5-benzofurazanylcarbonyl)-, N-oxide	EtOH	223(4.47),264s(3.59), 315s(3.53),334s(3.60), 365(3.89)	4-0213-80
	MeCN	222(4.46),265s(3.46), 315s(3.46),332s(3.57), 364(3.88)	4-0213-80
$C_{12}H_{13}N_3O_5S$			
Glycine, N-[[(4-nitrobenzoyl)amino]-thioxomethyl]-, ethyl ester	CHCl₃	258(4.39)	73-2334-80
$C_{12}H_{13}N_3S$			
1,3,4-Thiadiazol-2-amine, N,N-dimethyl-5-(2-phenylethenyl)-	EtOH	342(4.46)	94-2116-80
2-Thiophenamine, N,N-dimethyl-5-(phenylazo)-	EtOH	482(4.98)	62-0158-80
$C_{12}H_{13}N_5$			
[1,2,4]Triazolo[1,5-a]quinazolin-5-amine, N,N,2-trimethyl-	n.s.g.	222(4.60),292(3.67), 304(3.75),334(3.92)	33-0001-80
$C_{12}H_{13}N_5O$			
[1,2,4]Triazolo[1,5-a]quinazolin-5-amine, N-methoxy-N,2-dimethyl-	n.s.g.	224(4.57),292(3.74), 304(3.81),330(3.92)	33-0001-80
$C_{12}H_{13}N_5O_2$			
1(2H)-Pyridazino[4,5-b]quinolinone, 4-hydroxy-10-methyl-, hydrazine salt	EtOH	215(4.36),248(4.72), 287(3.94)	94-3457-80
$C_{12}H_{13}N_9O_4$			
Hydrazinecarboxamide, N-(2-amino-1,6-dihydro-5-nitro-6-oxo-4-pyrimidinyl)-2-[2-amino-1-(4-pyridinyl)ethylidene]-	pH 1	235(4.23),289s(4.04), 328(4.24)	150-0549-80
$C_{12}H_{13}OS$			
Sulfonium, (4-hydroxy-1-naphthalenyl)-dimethyl-, tetrafluoroborate	n.s.g.	246(4.21),317(3.89), 326(3.91),353(3.81), 366(3.73)	47-1021-80

Compound	Solvent	$\lambda_{max}(\log \epsilon)$	Ref.
$C_{12}H_{13}P$			
1H-Phosphole, 3,4-dimethyl-1-phenyl-, PdCl$_2$ complex (2:1)	CHCl$_3$	237(4.47),248(4.35), 259(4.26),360(3.58)	125-0709-80
$C_{12}H_{14}$			
Benzene, 1-cyclohexen-1-yl-	pentane	246(4.11)	33-0588-80
Benzene, 2-cyclohexen-1-yl-	pentane	249(2.97)	33-0588-80
1H-Cyclopenta[1,4]cyclobuta[1,2]cyclo-heptene, 2,3,3a,5-tetrahydro-, (3aα,9aR*)-	EtOH	245(4.26),253(4.29), 263(4.12)	35-0643-80
$C_{12}H_{14}BrN_3O_4$			
4,12-Epoxy-8H-1,3-dioxolo[4,5-f]pyrimi-do[1,2-a][1,3]diazocin-8-one, 9-bro-mo-3a,4,5,6,12,12a-hexahydro-2,2-di-methyl-, [3aR-(3aα,4β,12β,12a)]-	H$_2$O	225(4.38),270s(3.70)	94-0939-80
$C_{12}H_{14}Br_2N_2$			
1H-Indole-3-ethanamine, 5,6-dibromo-N,N-dimethyl-	MeOH	230(4.60),285(3.69), 300(3.52)	44-1435-80
$C_{12}H_{14}Br_4O_2$			
Tricyclo[5.1.0.0^{3,5}]octan-1-ol, 4,4,8,8-tetrabromo-5-ethyl-, acetate	EtOH	210(3.58)	80-0559-80
$C_{12}H_{14}ClN_3O_2S_2$			
Benzenesulfonamide, 4-chloro-N-[2-(2-imino-4-methyl-3(2H)-thiazolyl)-ethyl]-	MeOH	233(4.15),265(3.75)	39-1773-80C
$C_{12}H_{14}Cl_2O$			
3-Oxatricyclo[3.2.2.0^{2,4}]nonane, 6,7-bis(chloromethyl)-8,9-bis(methyl-ene)-, (1α,2α,4α,5α,6α,7β)-(±)-	dioxan	242s(3.95),246(3.96), 256s(3.78)	78-0149-80
	EtOH	241s(3.94),245(3.95), 254s(3.78)	78-0149-80
$C_{12}H_{14}Cl_4$			
Benzocyclooctene, 1,2,3,4-tetrachloro-4a,5,6,7,8,9,10,10a-octahydro-	CHCl$_3$	285(3.79),295(3.78)	44-0856-80
$C_{12}H_{14}FeO_4$			
Iron, tetracarbonyl[(1,2-η)-cyclo-octene]	hexane	201(3.76)	33-0738-80
$(C_{12}H_{14}I_2N_2O_2)_n$			
Polymer of 2,2'-diiodobiphenyl-4,4'-di-carbonyl chloride and 2,6-diaminotol-uene	DMSO	280(4.74)	126-0333-80
$C_{12}H_{14}MnNO_3$			
Manganese, tricarbonyl[(1,2,3,4,5-η)-1-[1-(dimethylamino)ethyl]-2,4-cyclo-pentadien-1-yl]-	EtOH	331(3.13)	101-0301-80R
$C_{12}H_{14}MoO_3$			
Molybdenum, tricarbonylethyl[(1,2,3,4,5-η)-1-ethyl-2,4-cyclopentadien-1-yl]-	hexane	256(3.94),312(3.34), 363s(2.99)	24-1033-80
$C_{12}H_{14}NO_2$			
Isoquinolinium, 6,7-dimethoxy-2-methyl-	MeOH	253(4.91),310(3.95)	100-0270-80

Compound	Solvent	$\lambda_{max}(\log \epsilon)$	Ref.
$C_{12}H_{14}NO_3P$			
Phosphonic acid, (2-quinolinylmethyl)-,	H_2O	244(4.40),316(3.87)	4-0685-80
monoethyl ester	$CHCl_3$	244(4.07),317(3.70)	4-0685-80
Phosphonic acid, (8-quinolinylmethyl)-,	H_2O	243(4.51),317(3.74)	4-0685-80
monoethyl ester, hydrochloride			
$C_{12}H_{14}N_2$			
4,4'-Bipyridinium, 1,1'-dimethyl-,	H_2O	254(4.32)	98-1026-80
dichloride			
1,8-Naphthalenediamine, N,N-dimethyl-	$CHCl_3$	341(3.94)	104-1890-80
1,8-Naphthalenediamine, N,N'-dimethyl-	$CHCl_3$	351(3.78)	104-1890-80
1H-Pyrazole, 3-phenyl-4-propyl-	EtOH	247(4.14),269s(3.81)	39-0072-80C
	EtOH-HCl	251(4.26),271s(3.87)	39-0072-80C
4H-Pyrazole, 3,4,4-trimethyl-5-phenyl-	EtOH	208(3.9),275(4.1)	24-1507-80
4-Quinolinamine, N-propyl-	EtOH	242(4.22),320(4.10)	22-0316-80
$C_{12}H_{14}N_2O$			
5-Oxazolamine, N-(1-methylethyl)-	EtOH	238(4.15)	4-0705-80
N-phenyl-			
2,4-Pentadienal, 4-(methylphenylamino)-,	C_6H_{12}	234(3.75),340(4.70),	1-0513-80
oxime		347(4.63)	
4H-Pyrazole, 3,4,4-trimethyl-5-phenyl-,	EtOH	232(3.9),238s(--),	24-1507-80
1-oxide		312(4.0)	
$C_{12}H_{14}N_2OS$			
4H-1,3-Thiazin-5(6H)-one, 4-ethyl-	MeOH	207(4.14),230s(3.91),	103-1003-80
2-(phenylamino)-		272(3.91)	
$C_{12}H_{14}N_2O_2$			
1(2H)-Isoquinolinone, 3-(dimethyl-	EtOH	251(4.59),310(4.18),	95-0826-80
amino)-6-methoxy-		346(3.61)	
1(2H)-Isoquinolinone, 3-(dimethyl-	EtOH	231(4.39),295(4.24),	95-0826-80
amino)-7-methoxy-		373(3.53)	
3H-Pyrrolizine-2-carboxamide, N,N-di-	EtOH	228(3.83),294(3.94),	150-3090-80
ethyl-3-oxo-		434(3.26)	
$C_{12}H_{14}N_2O_2S$			
3H-Thieno[2,3-d]1,3-diazepine-3-carbox-	EtOH	228(4.03),305(3.32)	77-0454-80
ylic acid, 2,5-dimethyl-, ethyl ester			
$C_{12}H_{14}N_2O_3$			
Carbamic acid, [2-(5-hydroxy-1H-indol-	EtOH	224(4.33),279(3.78),	142-0187-80B
3-yl)ethyl]-, methyl ester		301(3.66)	
1(2H)-Isoquinolinone, 3-amino-6,7-di-	EtOH	247(4.41),302(4.04),	95-0819-80
methoxy-2-methyl-		365(3.54)	
1(2H)-Isoquinolinone, 6,7-dimethoxy-	EtOH	246(4.59),301(4.23),	95-0826-80
3-(methylamino)-		367(3.66)	
1,4-Naphthalenedione, 2-hydroxy-,	H_2O	264(4.4),446(3.5)	83-0603-80
2-aminoethylammonium salt			
Pentaleno[2,1-d]pyrimidine-2,4,8(3H)-	MeCN	249(3.27),313(3.82)	35-3948-80
trione, 1,4b,5,6,7,7a-hexahydro-			
1,3-dimethyl-			
2-Propen-1-amine, N-[2-(5-nitro-2-fur-	MeOH	280(4.19),526(4.28)	73-0155-80
anyl)ethenyl]-N-2-propenyl-, (E)-			
$C_{12}H_{14}N_2O_3S$			
Glycine, N-[(benzoylamino)thioxometh-	$CHCl_3$	247(4.40)	73-2334-80
yl]-, ethyl ester			
$C_{12}H_{14}N_2O_3S_2$			
1H-Thieno[3,4-b][1,4]diazepine-6-carb-	EtOH	266(4.06),316(4.20),	95-0699-80

Compound	Solvent	$\lambda_{max}(\log \epsilon)$	Ref.
oxylic acid, 2,5-dihydro-4-methyl-8-(methylthio)-2-oxo-, ethyl ester (cont.)		384(3.67)	95-0699-80
$C_{12}H_{14}N_2O_4$			
Acetamide, N,N'-(4-acetoxy-1,2-phenylene)bis-	EtOH	220(3.30),245(3.15)	103-0628-80
1H-Benzimidazole, 1-α-D-arabinofuranosyl-	pH 2	254(3.79),262(3.82), 269(3.90),275(3.84)	64-0030-80C
	pH 8	245(3.93),266(3.62), 273(3.67),280(3.64)	64-0030-80C
1H-Benzimidazole, 1-β-D-ribofuranosyl-	pH 2	254(3.70),262(3.74), 270(3.76),276(3.73)	64-0030-80C
	pH 8	245(3.83),273(3.57), 281(3.55)	64-0030-80C
Cyclo-L-tyrosyl-L-serine	MeOH	212(3.86),226(3.94), 280(3.16)	39-0113-80C
1H,7H-Pyrazolo[1,2-a]pyrazole-1,7-dione, 2-(acetoxymethyl)-3,5,6-trimethyl-	dioxan	229(4.09),246s(3.78), 367(3.92)	35-4983-80
$C_{12}H_{14}N_2O_4S_2$			
S,5'-Cyclo-2-thiouridine, 2',3'-O-(1-methylethylidene)-	H_2O	212(4.16),235s(3.98), 280(4.27)	94-0939-80
	pH 13	252(4.27),262(4.27), 305s(3.79)	94-0939-80
$C_{12}H_{14}N_2O_5$			
Thymidine, 2',3'-didehydro-3'-deoxy-	EtOH	267(3.76)	33-2179-80
$C_{12}H_{14}N_2O_5S$			
S^6,5'-Cyclouridine, 2',3'-O-(1-methylethylidene)-	H_2O	212(3.90),292(4.08)	94-0939-80
	pH 13	287(4.02)	94-0939-80
Uridine, 2'-deoxy-5-(2-propynylthio)-	H_2O	281(3.71)	87-0569-80
$C_{12}H_{14}N_2O_5S_2$			
Thieno[2,3-d]pyrimidin-2(1H)-one, 3,4-dihydro-5-methyl-1-β-D-ribofuranosyl-4-thioxo-	pH 1	252(4.36),305(4.13), 353(4.25)	39-1853-80C
	pH 11	231(4.27),256(4.37), 301(4.15),337(4.27)	39-1853-80C
	MeOH	253(4.31),280(4.06), 347(4.30)	39-1853-80C
$C_{12}H_{14}N_2O_6$			
Aspartic acid, 1-methyl 4-[(2-nitrophenyl)methyl] ester, monohydrochloride	H_2O	264(3.72)	22-0133-80
Aspartic acid, 1-methyl 4-[(3-nitrophenyl)methyl] ester, monohydrochloride	H_2O	265(3.86)	22-0133-80
Aspartic acid, 1-methyl 4-[(4-nitrophenyl)methyl] ester, monohydrochloride	H_2O	268(3.96)	22-0133-80
$C_{12}H_{14}N_2O_6S$			
Thieno[2,3-d]pyrimidine-2,4(1H,3H)-dione, 5-methyl-1-β-D-ribofuranosyl-	pH 1	236(4.45),297(3.76)	39-1853-80C
	pH 11	232(4.47),293(3.64)	39-1853-80C
	MeOH	234(4.43),295(3.72)	
$C_{12}H_{14}N_4$			
Methanimidamide, N,N-dimethyl-N'-(1-	EtOH	250(4.15)	114-0127-80C

Compound	Solvent	$\lambda_{max}(\log \epsilon)$	Ref.
phenyl-1H-pyrazol-5-yl)- (cont.)			114-0127-80C
2,2a,4,5-Tetraazabenz[cd]azulene, 3,4- dihydro-1,3,3-trimethyl-	MeOH	222(4.48),293(3.68), 350(4.01)	118-0331-80
$C_{12}H_{14}N_4O$			
1H-Imidazole-4-carboxamide, 5-(methyl- amino)-1-(phenylmethyl)-	pH 1 pH 7 pH 13 EtOH	257(3.89) 269(4.00) 269(4.00) 270(4.02)	94-2819-80 94-2819-80 94-2819-80 94-2819-80
1H-Imidazole-4-carboxamide, 1-methyl- 5-[(phenylmethyl)amino]-	pH 1 pH 7 pH 13 EtOH	253(3.86) 269(3.95) 268(3.94) 270(4.00)	94-2819-80 94-2819-80 94-2819-80 94-2819-80
6H-Pyrrolo[1,2-c]pyrimidine-1-carbo- nitrile, 2,5,7,8-tetrahydro-8-[(di- methylamino)methylene]-4-methyl-2-oxo-	pH 13	292(3.86)	103-0873-80
$C_{12}H_{14}N_4O_2$			
Ethanimidic acid, N-(1,5-dihydro-5-oxo- 3-phenyl-4H-1,2,4-triazol-4-yl)-, ethyl ester	EtOH	260(4.00)	4-1691-80
3H-Pyrazol-3-one, 1,2-dihydro-1,5-di- methyl-4-(methylnitrosoamino)-2- phenyl-	CH_2Cl_2	283(4.05)	94-1820-80
3,5-Pyridinedicarbonitrile, 1,4-dihy- dro-1,2,4-tetramethyl-6-(nitro- methyl)- (first six spectra in EtOH)	pH 0.4	220(4.24),225(4.24), 352(3.75)	73-2938-80
	pH 4.8	221(4.24),350(3.37)	73-2938-80
	pH 7.75	220(4.18),340(3.61)	73-2938-80
	pH 9.0	216(4.12),220(4.10), 296(3.75),325(3.87), 360(3.41)	73-2938-80
	pH 12.7	214(4.13),296s(3.8), 319(3.92),352(3.49)	73-2938-80
	pH 13.2	208(4.39),296s(3.9), 319(3.94),352(3.52)	73-2938-80
(last eight spectra in 50% DMF)	pH 0.86	292(3.31),360(3.49)	73-2938-80
	pH 2.7	283(3.39),354(3.52)	73-2938-80
	pH 3.15	283(2.95),354(3.75)	73-2938-80
	pH 4.81	354(3.41)	73-2938-80
	pH 6.4	292(3.31),342(3.54)	73-2938-80
	pH 7.2	300(3.72),328(3.77), 365(3.59)	73-2938-80
	pH 10.2	299(3.89),320(3.82), 361(3.54)	73-2938-80
	pH 12.6	297(3.87),318(3.80), 367(3.52)	73-2938-80
$C_{12}H_{14}N_4O_2S$			
Hydrazine, 1,1'-(sulfonyldi-4,1-phen- ylene)bis-	mineral oil	206(4.5),216s(4.3), 266(4.2),303(4.4)	103-1146-80
$C_{12}H_{14}N_4O_4$			
2,4(1H,3H)-Pyrimidinedione, 1-[3-(3,4- dihydro-2,4-dioxo-1(2H)-pyrimidinyl)- propyl]-5-methyl-	pH 2 pH 7 pH 12	236(3.61),267(4.17) 235(3.60),267(4.16) 246(3.66),278(4.16)	56-2357-80 56-2357-80 56-2357-80
2,4(1H,3H)-Pyrimidinedione, 1-[3-(3,6- dihydro-2,6-dioxo-1(2H)-pyrimidinyl)- propyl]-6-methyl-	pH 2 pH 7 pH 12	233(3.60),265(4.25) 232(3.59),265(4.25) 243(3.65),274(4.17)	56-2357-80 56-2357-80 56-2357-80
2,4(1H,3H)-Pyrimidinedione, 3-[3-(3,4- dihydro-2,4-dioxo-1(2H)-pyrimidinyl)- propyl]-5-methyl-	pH 2 pH 7 pH 12	235(3.64),267(4.23) 234(3.54),267(4.21) 245(3.75),270(4.04)	56-2357-80 56-2357-80 56-2357-80

Compound	Solvent	$\lambda_{max}(\log \epsilon)$	Ref.
$C_{12}H_{14}N_4O_7$			
2,4,7(1H,3H,8H)-Pteridinetrione, 6-methyl-1-β-D-ribofuranosyl-	pH 1.0	260(3.91),286s(3.71), 319(4.09)	24-1524-80
	pH 6.0	277(4.02),325(4.24), 338s(4.10)	24-1524-80
	pH 13.0	247(4.08),273(3.83), 331(4.24),344s(4.12)	24-1524-80
2,4,7(1H,3H,8H)-Pteridinetrione, 6-methyl-3-β-D-ribofuranosyl-	pH 1.0	282(3.99),324(4.11)	24-1524-80
	pH 7.0	209(4.46),233s(3.97), 281(3.98),328(4.22), 340s(4.11)	24-1524-80
	pH 13.0	225(4.56),261(4.08), 284(3.99),340(4.13)	24-1524-80
2,4,7(1H,3H,8H)-Pteridinetrione, 6-methyl-8-β-D-ribofuranosyl-, ammonium salt	pH 1	280(3.99),328(3.98)	24-1535-80
	pH 6.0	209(4.38),291(3.93), 328s(3.95),342(3.98)	24-1535-80
	2M KOH	259(3.96),281s(3.72), 354(3.94)	24-1535-80
$C_{12}H_{14}N_4O_8$			
D-Ribitol, 1-deoxy-1-(3,4-dihydro-6-nitro-2,4-pyrido[2,3-d]pyrimidin-8(2H)-yl)-	pH 1	350(4.16)	39-2645-80C
	pH 13	246s(3.91),265s(3.77), 463(4.40)	39-2645-80C
$C_{12}H_{14}N_5O_8PS$			
Acetic acid, [[6-amino-9-(3,5-O-phosphinico-β-D-ribofuranosyl)-9H-purin-8-yl]thio]-, monosodium salt	pH 1	278(4.28)	87-0242-80
	pH 11	279(4.26)	87-0242-80
$C_{12}H_{14}N_6O$			
4(1H)-Pteridinone, 2-amino-6(and 7)-(4-pyridinylmethyl)-5,6,7,8-tetrahydro-	pH 1	163(4.29)[sic]	150-0549-80
$C_{12}H_{14}N_6O_4$			
Imidazolidine, 1,3-dimethyl-2-[nitro-[(4-nitrophenyl)azo]methylene]-	MeCN	249(4.08),345(3.65), 464(4.48)	48-0087-80
$C_{12}H_{14}O$			
Benzofuran, 2,3-dihydro-5-methyl-2-(1-methylethenyl)-	MeOH	206(4.02),228(3.71), 287(3.41)	150-0127-80
3,5,7-Decatrien-9-yn-2-one, 3,8-dimethyl-	EtOH	237(3.81),332(4.53), 343s(4.53)	39-0473-80C
2-Hexen-1-one, 1-phenyl-	EtOH	211(4.06),255(4.18)	12-1537-80
1-Naphthalenol, 5,6-dihydro-4,5-dimethyl-	EtOH	259(3.85),266(3.89), 276(3.73),309(3.59), 316(3.56)	83-0048-80
2-Oxabicyclo[4.1.0]heptane, 7-phenyl-, endo	C_6H_{12}	208(3.81),217(3.75)	4-1097-80
exo	C_6H_{12}	204(3.88),222(3.81)	4-1097-80
1-Penten-3-one, 2-methyl-1-phenyl-	EtOH	280(4.20)	101-0367-80K
Spiro[cyclopentane-1,1'(3'H)-isobenzofuran]	EtOH	265(3.06),272(3.09)	44-1828-80
$C_{12}H_{14}O_2$			
Benzene, 4-(1,3-butadienyl)-1,2-dimethoxy-, (E)-	EtOH	203(4.26),222s(3.90), 260s(3.64),298s(3.30), 310s(3.20)	94-2948-80
5-Benzofurancarboxaldehyde, 2,3-dihydro-2-(1-methylethyl)-, (R)-	MeOH	207(4.00),229(4.02), 280s(4.01),296(4.08)	150-0127-80

Compound	Solvent	λ_{max}(log ϵ)	Ref.
5-Benzofuranmethanol, 2,3-dihydro-2-(1-methylethenyl)-	MeOH	208(4.01),233(3.95), 284(3.56),290s(3.52)	150-0127-80
(S)-	MeOH	208(4.01),233(3.95), 284(3.57),290s(3.52)	150-0127-80
2-Butenoic acid, 2-methyl-3-(4-methylphenyl)-, (E)-	EtOH	244(3.98)	32-0327-80
(Z)-	EtOH	247(3.92)	32-0327-80
2(1H)-Naphthalenone, 3,4-dihydro-8-methoxy-1-methyl-	EtOH	270(3.69)	78-2513-80
$C_{12}H_{14}O_3$			
Benzeneacetic acid, 4-acetyl-, ethyl ester (enol)	anion in DMSO	453(4.24)	18-1656-80
2-Butenoic acid, 3-(4-methoxyphenyl)-2-methyl-, (E)-	EtOH	254(3.96)	32-0327-80
(Z)-	EtOH	253(3.92)	32-0327-80
Mellein, 5-methyl-, methyl ether, (±)-	n.s.g.	226(4.99),268(4.4), 335(4.28)	2-0009-80
Spiro[1,3-benzodioxole-2,1'-cyclohexan]-5-ol	EtOH	236(3.49),299(3.69)	12-0527-80
$C_{12}H_{14}O_3S$			
14-Oxa-6-thiabicyclo[9.2.1]tetradeca-11,13-diene-4,8-dione	C_6H_{12}	<u>220(3.9),298(2.3)</u>	138-0397-80
$C_{12}H_{14}O_3W$			
Tungsten, tricarbonylethyl[(1,2,3,4,5-η)-1-ethyl-2,4-cyclopentadien-1-yl]-	hexane	254s(4.00),315(3.37), 356s(3.02)	24-1033-80
$C_{12}H_{14}O_4$			
1,3-Benzodioxole-5,6-dione, 2-butyl-2-methyl-	EtOH	293(4.27),395(3.20)	12-0527-80
1,3-Benzodioxol-5-ol, 2-ethyl-2-methyl-, acetate	EtOH	234(3.48),286(3.59)	12-0527-80
5-Benzofuranacetic acid, 2,3-dihydro-2-(1-hydroxyethyl)-	MeOH	232(3.801),286(3.468)	36-0164-80
5-Benzofuranacetic acid, 2,3-dihydro-2-(2-hydroxyethyl)-	MeOH	232(3.823),286(3.475)	36-0164-80
5-Benzofuranacetic acid, 2-ethyl-2,3-dihydro-3-hydroxy-	MeOH	232(3.850),286(3.426)	36-0164-80
4H-1-Benzopyran-4-one, 2,3-dihydro-5,7-dimethoxy-2-methyl-	MeOH	227(4.31),283(4.31)	94-3070-80
	MeOH	225(4.17),282(4.21)	107-0851-80
2-Buten-1-one, 1-(2-hydroxy-4,6-dimethoxyphenyl)-	MeOH	240(3.83),310(4.29)	107-0851-80
Ethanone, 1-[4-(2-acetoxyethoxy)phenyl]-	CHCl₃	268(4.38),323(2.48)	73-1826-80
Spiro[1,3-benzodioxole-2,1'-cyclohexane]-5,6-diol	EtOH	295(3.94)	12-0527-80
$C_{12}H_{14}O_4S_2$			
2-Butenoic acid, 4-[(ethoxythioxomethyl)thio]-3-(2-furanyl)-, methyl ester, (E)-	EtOH	210(3.96),309(4.22)	73-0142-80
$C_{12}H_{14}O_5$			
4H-1-Benzopyran-4-one, 2,3-dihydro-5-hydroxy-ar,ar-dimethoxy-2-methyl-	MeOH	212(4.29),245(4.09), 288(4.16),349(3.68)	94-3070-80
Butanoic acid, 1-acetoxy-6-oxo-2,4-cyclohexadien-1-yl ester	EtOH	226(3.54),306(3.52)	12-1553-80
Butanoic acid, 2-acetoxy-, 2-hydroxyphenyl ester	EtOH	220(3.80),278(3.49)	12-1553-80

Compound	Solvent	$\lambda_{max}(\log \epsilon)$	Ref.
7-Oxabicyclo[2.2.1]hepta-2,5-diene-2,3-dicarboxylic acid, 3-(1,1-dimethylethyl) ester	EtOH	222s(3.64),285(3.10)	24-0531-80
$C_{12}H_{14}O_6$ 1,2-Benzenediol, 4,5-dimethoxy-, diacetate	EtOH	229(3.88),282(3.57)	12-0527-80
$C_{12}H_{14}O_6S$ 2,3,5-Thiophenetricarboxylic acid, 4-methyl-, 5-ethyl 2,3-dimethyl ester	EtOH	275(4.27)	18-3308-80
$C_{12}H_{15}$ Cyclopropenylium, tricyclopropyl-, chloride	pH 3.7	210(4.36)	88-1221-80
tetrafluoroborate	MeCN	213(4.36)	88-0947-80
$C_{12}H_{15}BrN_2$ 1H-Indole-3-ethanamine, 5-bromo-N,N-dimethyl-	MeOH	225(4.59),285(3.64), 305(3.43)	44-1435-80
$C_{12}H_{15}ClNO_3P$ Phosphonic acid, (8-quinolinylmethyl)-, monoethyl ester, hydrochloride	H_2O	243(4.51),317(3.74)	4-0685-80
$C_{12}H_{15}ClN_2O_5$ Uridine, 5'-chloro-5'-deoxy-2',3'-O-(1-methylethylidene)-	pH 7	262(4.01)	78-2337-80
$C_{12}H_{15}ClN_2O_6$ Aspartic acid, 1-methyl 4-[(2-nitrophenyl)methyl] ester, monohydrochloride	H_2O	264(3.72)	22-0133-80
Aspartic acid, 1-methyl 4-[(3-nitrophenyl)methyl] ester, monohydrochloride	H_2O	265(3.86)	22-0133-80
Aspartic acid, 1-methyl 4-[(4-nitrophenyl)methyl] ester, monohydrochloride	H_2O	268(3.96)	22-0133-80
$C_{12}H_{15}ClN_4O_2$ Acetic acid, [4-chloro-3,5-bis(dimethylamino)-2H-pyrrol-2-ylidene]-cyano-, methyl ester	CH_2Cl_2	268(3.57),398(4.37)	88-2883-80
$C_{12}H_{15}F_3O_3$ 1-Cyclohexene-1-propanoic acid, 5-methyl-6-oxo-2-(2,2,2-trifluoroethyl)-	$CHCl_3$	243(3.82)	39-1114-80C
$C_{12}H_{15}F_5O_3Si$ Silane, triethoxy(pentafluorophenyl)-	gas	203(3.97),268(3.02)	109-0158-80
$C_{12}H_{15}IO$ 2,4,6-Cyclooctatrien-1-one, 8-(4-iodobutyl)-	ether	219(4.30)	12-1569-80
$C_{12}H_{15}N$ Benzenamine, 4-(1,3-butadienyl)-N,N-dimethyl-, trans	C_6H_{12}	235(4.13),321(4.48)	39-0805-80B
1H-Indole, 1-butyl-	EtOH	229(4.18),283(3.85), 293s(3.73)	104-0766-80

Compound	Solvent	λ$_{max}$(log ε)	Ref.
2H-Isoindole, 2-(1,1-dimethylethyl)-	MeOH	223(4.68),266(3.25), 270(3.22),277(3.27), 289(3.09),329(3.59)	89-0320-80
perchlorate	MeOH-HClO$_4$	217(3.98),224(3.86), 275(4.16)	89-0320-80
C$_{12}$H$_{15}$NO			
3-Buten-2-one, 3-methyl-4-(methylphenylamino)-	EtOH	228(3.72),324(4.39)	4-0033-80
1H-Indole, 3-(2-methoxyethyl)-2-methyl-	EtOH	226(4.48),284(3.81), 291(3.75)	80-0245-80
1-Penten-3-one, 1-(methylphenylamino)-	EtOH	228(3.90),321(4.50)	4-0033-80
2-Propen-1-one, 3-(dimethylamino)-2-methyl-1-phenyl-	EtOH	234(3.92),314(4.38)	4-1201-80
C$_{12}$H$_{15}$NOS			
2-Azetidinethione, 4-(4-methoxyphenyl)-1,3-dimethyl-, cis	isooctane	265(4.2),320s(2.3), 332s(2.2),352s(1.9)	24-3010-80
trans	isooctane	266(4.3),338(1.9)	24-3010-80
2,4-Pentadien-1-one, 5-(dimethylamino)-1-(5-methyl-2-thienyl)-	EtOH	312s(4.02),438(4.73)	70-0980-80
C$_{12}$H$_{15}$NO$_2$			
Formamide, N-methyl-N-(2-oxo-4-phenylbutyl)-	MeOH	218(3.68)	4-1081-80
1H-Indole-2-ethanol, 3-(hydroxymethyl)-1-methyl-	EtOH	225(4.58),283(3.95), 292s(3.89)	39-1688-80C
5-Isoxazolol, 4,5-dihydro-3,4,4-trimethyl-5-phenyl-	EtOH	207(4.5),215s(--), 250(2.3),256(2.4), 260(2.3),262(2.3), 266(2.1)	24-1507-80
2,4-Pentadien-1-one, 5-(dimethylamino)-1-(5-methyl-2-furanyl)-, (E,E)-	EtOH	305s(4.04),440(4.74)	70-0980-80
2-Propen-1-one, 3-(dimethylamino)-1-(4-methoxyphenyl)-	EtOH	267(4.13),337(4.46)	44-4522-80
C$_{12}$H$_{15}$NO$_3$			
2H-[1,3]Oxazin-2-one, 3,4,5,6-tetrahydro-4-(2-hydroxyphenyl)-3,6-dimethyl-	EtOH	215(3.87),274(3.46), 280s(3.41)	4-0277-80
C$_{12}$H$_{15}$NO$_6$			
2-Oxa-7-azaspiro[4.5]decane-10-carboxylic acid, 7-methyl-1,6,8-trioxo-, ethyl ester	MeOH	214(3.87)	118-0698-80
4aH-Pyrano[4,3-c]pyridine-4a-carboxylic acid, octahydro-3,6-dimethyl-1,5,7-trioxo-, methyl ester	MeOH	208(4.8)	118-0698-80
4aH-Pyrano[4,3-c]pyridine-4a-carboxylic acid, octahydro-3-methyl-1,5,7-trioxo-, ethyl ester	MeOH	202(4.18)	118-0698-80
C$_{12}$H$_{15}$NO$_7$			
D-Glucopyranose, 6-(3-pyridinecarboxylate)	EtOH	257(4.55),262(4.59), 269(4.48)	44-4999-80
C$_{12}$H$_{15}$N$_3$			
1,3-Propanediamine, N-4-quinolinyl-	EtOH	240(4.21),320(4.09)	22-0316-80
C$_{12}$H$_{15}$N$_3$O			
1H-Benzimidazole, 2-methyl-4-morpholino-	M HCl	269(3.86),276(3.88)	104-1458-80

Compound	Solvent	λ_{max} (log ϵ)	Ref.
$C_{12}H_{15}N_3O_2S_2$			
2-Butenoic acid, 3-[[4-amino-5-cyano-2-(methylthio)-3-thienyl]amino]-, ethyl ester	EtOH	220(4.06),281(4.47)	95-0699-80
$C_{12}H_{15}N_3O_4$			
Acetamide, N-(3-morpholino-2-nitrophenyl)-	EtOH	230(4.17),321s(2.93)	104-1458-80
$C_{12}H_{15}N_3O_4S$			
S^6,5-Cycloisocytidine, 2',3'-O-(1-methylethylidene)-	H_2O	210(4.28),225s(4.09), 286(3.92)	94-0939-80
$C_{12}H_{15}N_3O_5S$			
Thieno[2,3-d]pyrimidin-2(1H)-one, 4-amino-1-β-D-arabinofuranosyl-5-methyl-	pH 1	244(4.37),264s(3.96), 321(3.64)	39-1853-80C
	pH 11	239(4.45),301(3.61)	39-1853-80C
	MeOH	240(4.45),302(3.58)	39-1853-80C
Thieno[2,3-d]pyrimidin-2(1H)-one, 4-amino-5-methyl-1-β-D-ribofuranosyl-	pH 1	243(4.40),263s(4.03), 317(3.70)	39-1853-80C
	pH 11	239(4.49),301(3.60)	39-1853-80C
	MeOH	237(4.48),301(3.58)	39-1853-80C
$C_{12}H_{15}N_5O_4$			
8,5'(R)-Cycloadenosine, 5'-deoxy-5'-(2-hydroxyethyl)-	pH 1	261.5(4.21)	94-0876-80
	H_2O	264.5(4.21)	94-0876-80
(S)-	pH 1	261(4.20)	94-0876-80
	H_2O	264(4.21)	94-0876-80
$C_{12}H_{15}N_5O_4S_3$			
1H-Pyrazolo[3,4-d]pyrimidine-3-carbothioamide, 4,5-dihydro-6-(methylthio)-1-β-D-ribofuranosyl-4-thioxo-	EtOH	205(4.34),252(4.41), 334(4.03)	103-0182-80
$C_{12}H_{15}N_5O_5$			
Adenosine, 5'-acetate	EtOH	259(4.07)	39-0563-80C
$C_{12}H_{15}N_7O_2$			
Adenosine, 5'-[(aminoacetyl)amino]-2',3'-didehydro-2',3',5'-trideoxy-	H_2O	261(4.07)	136-0067-80A
$C_{12}H_{16}BrN_3O_5$			
4(1H)-Pyrimidinone, 2-amino-5-bromo-1-[2,3-O-(1-methylethylidene)-β-D-ribofuranosyl]-	H_2O	272(3.77)	94-0939-80
$C_{12}H_{16}BrN_5O_4$			
4,11-Epoxy-1,3-dioxolo[4,5-f]imidazo[1,5-a][1,3]diazocine-7-carboxylic acid, 9-bromo-3a,4,5,6,11,11a-hexahydro-2,2-dimethyl-, hydrazide, [3aR-(3aα,4β,11β,11aα)]-	MeOH	277(3.94)	78-3509-80
$C_{12}H_{16}ClN_5O_2$			
Hydrazinecarboxamide, N-[3-(4-chlorophenyl)-2-(methylhydrazono)-1-oxopropyl]-2-methyl-	EtOH	225(4.10),265(3.95)	12-0619-80
$C_{12}H_{16}Cl_4$			
Bicyclo[2.2.2]oct-2-ene, tetrakis-(chloromethyl)-, (±)-	EtOH	210(2.00)(end abs.)	78-0149-80

Compound	Solvent	$\lambda_{max}(\log \epsilon)$	Ref.
$C_{12}H_{16}Cl_4O$ 3-Oxatricyclo[3.2.2.0^{2,4}]nonane, 6,7,8,9-tetrakis(chloromethyl)-	EtOH	210(2.00)(end abs.)	78-0149-80
$C_{12}H_{16}N$ 1H-Isoindolium, 2-(1,1-dimethylethyl)-, perchlorate	MeOH-HClO$_4$	217(3.98),224(3.86), 275(4.16)	89-0320-80
$C_{12}H_{16}NO_2$ Isoquinolinium, 3,4-dihydro-6,7-di-methoxy-N-methyl-	EtOH-HCl	244(4.35),308(4.03), 358(4.00)	73-1950-80
	EtOH-NaOH	222(4.26),285(3.54)	73-1950-80
Isoquinolinium, 3,4-dihydro-7,8-di-methoxy-N-methyl-	EtOH-HCl	219(4.43),244(4.03), 300(4.03),380(3.38)	73-1950-80
	EtOH-NaOH	223(4.32),254(3.43), 287(3.43)	73-1950-80
$C_{12}H_{16}N_2$ Propanedinitrile, [4-methyl-3-(1-meth-ylethyl)-2-pentenylidene]-	EtOH	313(4.43)	35-0711-80
$C_{12}H_{16}N_2O$ 5H-Pyrido[1,2-a][1,8]naphthyridin-5-one, 1,2,3,4,7,8,9,10-octahydro-	EtOH	233(4.56),285(4.04)	94-0220-80
$C_{12}H_{16}N_2O_2$ [2,2'-Bi-3H-pyrrole]-3,3'-dione, 4,4',5,5'-tetrahydro-4,4,4',4'-tetramethyl-	C_6H_{12}	215(3.79),252(2.91), 387(2.37)	5-2039-80
	EtOH	208(c. 4.0),405(c. 2.5)	5-2039-80
1,3-Butanedione, 2,2-dimethyl-1-phen-yl-, (E,E)-	EtOH	192(4.3),223(4.2)	24-1507-80
Hydroperoxide, 1,3-diethyl-2,3-dihydro-2-imino-1H-indol-3-yl	n.s.g.	265(4.03),297(3.2)	103-0917-80
Quinoline, 1,2,3,4-tetrahydro-6-nitro-1-propyl-	EtOH	385(4.22)	103-0386-80
Quinoline, 1,2,3,4-tetrahydro-8-nitro-1-propyl-	EtOH	255(4.06),435(3.43)	103-0386-80
$C_{12}H_{16}N_2O_2S_2$ Pyrrolidine, 1,1'-(2,3-dioxo-1,4-di-thioxo-1,4-butanediyl)bis-	CHCl$_3$	276(4.08),332(3.84), 393s(3.26),457(3.28)	97-0436-80
$C_{12}H_{16}N_2O_3$ 1H-Azepine, hexahydro-1-[2-(5-nitro-2-furanyl)ethenyl]-, (E)-	MeOH	280(3.94),514(4.17)	73-0155-80
$C_{12}H_{16}N_2O_4S_2$ Morpholine, 4,4'-(2,3-dioxo-1,4-di-thioxo-1,4-butanediyl)bis-	CH$_2$Cl$_2$	240(4.28),270(4.25), 333(4.02),391s(3.57), 447(3.41)	97-0436-80
$C_{12}H_{16}N_2O_5$ Propanamide, N-[2-hydroxy-1-(hydroxy-methyl)-2-(4-nitrophenyl)ethyl]-, [R-(R*,R*)]-	pH 7	279(4.01)	87-1299-80
5-Pyrimidinecarboxylic acid, 1,2,3,4-tetrahydro-2,4-dioxo-3-(tetrahydro-2H-pyran-2-yl)-, ethyl ester	EtOH	222(3.90),276(4.00)	142-0769-80
sodium salt	EtOH	224(3.28),242(3.46), 301(3.63)	142-0769-80

Compound	Solvent	$\lambda_{max}(\log \epsilon)$	Ref.
$C_{12}H_{16}N_2O_5S$ Uridine, 2'-deoxy-5-(2-propenylthio)-	H_2O	206(3.98),280(3.71)	87-0569-80
$C_{12}H_{16}N_2O_6$ 2(1H)-Pyrimidinone, 3,4-dihydro-4-(2-oxopropylidene)-1-β-D-ribofuranosyl-	H_2O pH 13	265(3.59),338s(4.37), 351(5.42),370s(4.32) 270s(3.75),361(4.59)	94-0157-80 94-0157-80
$C_{12}H_{16}N_2O_6S$ 2(1H)-Pyrimidinone, 4-[(2-oxopropyl)-thio]-1-β-D-ribofuranosyl-	H_2O	265s(3.92),301(4.12)	94-0157-80
$C_{12}H_{16}N_3O_5P$ Phosphonic acid, [(5(or 6)-nitro-1H-benzimidazol-1-yl)methyl]-, diethyl ester	EtOH	235(<u>4.3</u>),300(<u>4.0</u>)	65-1217-80
$C_{12}H_{16}N_4$ 1H-1,2,3-Triazol-5-amine, 1-(1,1-dimethylethyl)-N-phenyl-	EtOH	207(4.06),238(3.95), 263(3.81)	49-0635-80
1H-1,2,3-Triazol-5-amine, 1-(2-methyl-phenyl)-N-phenyl-	EtOH	208(4.07),240(3.81), 265(4.08)	49-0635-80
$C_{12}H_{16}N_4O$ Imidazo[5,1-f][1,2,4]triazin-4(1H)-one, 7-cyclopentyl-2,5-dimethyl-	EtOH EtOH-NaOH	224(4.38),255(3.96), 265(3.80) 235(--),259(--), 269s(--),300(--)	39-1139-80C 39-1139-80C
3H-1,2,4-Triazol-3-one, 4-amino-2-butyl-2,4-dihydro-5-phenyl-	EtOH	262(4.03)	4-1691-80
$C_{12}H_{16}N_4O_4$ 9H-Purine, 6-ethyl-9-β-D-ribofuranosyl-	H_2O	247s(3.80),263(3.92)	94-0150-80
$C_{12}H_{16}N_4O_5$ 5H-Imidazo[4,5-b]pyridin-5-one, 3,4-dihydro-7-(methylamino)-3-β-D-ribofuranosyl-	H_2O	227(4.28),265(4.30), 282(4.17)	142-1049-80B
$C_{12}H_{16}N_6O_4$ 1,1-Ethenediamine, N,N'-diethyl-2-nitro-2-[(4-nitrophenyl)azo]-	MeCN	254s(3.87),349(3.67), 473(4.52)	48-0087-80
$C_{12}H_{16}N_6O_4S_2$ 1H-Pyrazolo[3,4-d]pyrimidine-3-carbo-thioamide, 4-amino-6-(methylthio)-1-β-D-ribofuranosyl-	EtOH	202(4.18),253(4.32), 347(3.60)	103-0182-80
$C_{12}H_{16}N_6O_5$ 8,11-Epoxy[1,3]diazocino[1,2-e]purin-4(3H)-one, 2-amino-6,7,8,9,10,11-hexahydro-9,10-dihydroxy-3-(methoxymethyl)-, monohydrochloride, [8R-(8α,9α,10α,11α)]-	MeOH	260(4.24),292(3.89)	78-3509-80
β-D-Ribofuranoside, (2,4-diamino-6-pteridinyl) methyl	pH 1.0 pH 7.0	244(4.19),287(3.69), 336(4.00),348s(3.93) 225(4.06),259(4.36), 370(3.86)	24-1514-80 24-1514-80
$C_{12}H_{16}O$ 3H-Cyclopenta[1,3]cyclopropa[1,2]benzen-	MeOH	234(3.89),267(3.63)	44-3790-80

Compound	Solvent	λ$_{max}$(log ε)	Ref.
3-one, 3a,3b,4,5,6,7-hexahydro-1,3b-dimethyl- (cont.)			44-3790-80
2H-Inden-2-one, 1,4,5,7a-tetrahydro-4,4,7a-trimethyl-	EtOH	234(4.16)	23-1810-80
2-Naphthalenemethanol, 5,6,7,8-tetrahydro-α-methyl-	n.s.g.	207(3.96),269(2.91), 277(2.94)	56-0453-80
1(4H)-Naphthalenone, 4a,5,6,7-tetrahydro-4a,5-dimethyl-	EtOH	239(3.78),266(3.61), 318(1.54)	83-0048-80
2(4aH)-Naphthalenone, 5,6,7,8-tetrahydro-4,4a-dimethyl-	MeOH	245(4.27)	44-3790-80
2-Propanone, 1-(2,4,6-trimethylphenyl)-	dioxan	268(2.50),274(2.46), 294(2.11)	24-2462-80
Spiro[4.5]deca-6,9-dien-8-one, 6,10-dimethyl-	MeOH	245(4.09)	44-3790-80
C$_{12}$H$_{16}$OS			
Benzene, 1,3,5-trimethyl-2-(2-propenylsulfinyl)-	MeOH	264(3.58),287s(3.28)	12-2635-80
C$_{12}$H$_{16}$OS$_2$			
1,3-Dithiane-2-ethanol, α-phenyl-	EtOH	205(4.07),208s(4.06), 248(2.96),251(2.96)	35-3095-80
C$_{12}$H$_{16}$O$_2$			
Benzene, 4-(1-butenyl)-1,2-dimethoxy-, (E)-	EtOH	213(4.34),260(4.17), 266s(4.15),298s(3.67)	94-2948-80
Benzene, [[2-(1-methylethoxy)cyclopropyl]oxy]-, cis	hexane	221(4.20),264s(--), 270(3.45),276(3.40)	70-1928-80
trans	hexane	220(4.04),263s(--), 269(3.43),276(3.40)	70-1928-80
Benzenemethanol, 2-(1-hydroxycyclopentyl)-	EtOH	261(2.32)	44-1828-80
5-Benzofuranmethanol, 2,3-dihydro-2-(1-methylethyl)-, (+)-	MeOH	207(3.95),233(3.75), 285(3.34),290(3.32)	150-0127-80
(-)-	MeOH	207(3.79),233(3.75), 285(3.34),290(3.32)	150-0127-80
5H-Cyclohepta[b]furan-5-one, 4,6,7,8-tetrahydro-2,8,8-trimethyl-	pentane	275s(2.34)	33-2221-80
2-Cyclopenten-1-one, 2,4,4-trimethyl-5-[(2-propenyloxy)methylene]-, (E)-	n.s.g.	251(3.59),285(3.69)	39-1516-80C
(Z)-	n.s.g.	235(3.87),287(4.01)	39-1516-80C
2-Cyclopenten-1-one, 3,4,4-trimethyl-5-[(2-propenyloxy)methylene]-	n.s.g.	249(4.02),285(4.0)	39-1516-80C
2,6-Naphthalenedione, 1,3,4,7,8,8a-hexahydro-5,8a-dimethyl-, (±)-	EtOH	247.5(4.15)	2-0904-80
	EtOH	244(4.07)	44-3278-80
Spiro[4.5]dec-6-ene-2,8-dione, 6,10-dimethyl-	EtOH	241(4.16)	23-2460-80
C$_{12}$H$_{16}$O$_2$S			
2-Pentanone, 4-methyl-4-(phenylsulfinyl)-	CHCl$_3$	267(3.15)	39-0237-80C
C$_{12}$H$_{16}$O$_2$S$_2$			
2,5-Cyclohexadiene-1,4-dione, 2,3-dimethyl-5,6-bis[(methylthio)methyl]-	EtOH	264s(4.20),270(4.21), 367(3.05)	39-0289-80C
3(2H)-Thiophenone, 2-(4,5-dihydro-4,4-dimethyl-3-oxo-2(3H)-thienylidene)-4,5-dihydro-4,4-dimethyl-	CHCl$_3$	458(4.07)	24-1708-80
C$_{12}$H$_{16}$O$_2$S$_4$			
2,5-Cyclohexadiene-1,4-dione, 2,5-bis-	EtOH	250(4.20),388(3.68)	39-0289-80C

Compound	Solvent	$\lambda_{max}(\log \epsilon)$	Ref.
(methylthio)-3,6-bis[(methylthio)-methyl]- (cont.)			39-0289-80C
2,5-Cyclohexadiene-1,4-dione, 3,5-bis-(methylthio)-2,6-bis[(methylthio)-methyl]-	EtOH	247(4.05),387(3.52)	39-0289-80C
$C_{12}H_{16}O_3$			
Benzenemethanol, 3-hydroxy-2,4,6-tri-methyl-, α-acetate	MeOH	285(3.38)	24-2227-80
1,3-Benzodioxol-5-ol, 2-butyl-2-methyl-	EtOH	235(3.51),299(3.72)	12-0527-80
3-Buten-1-ol, 4-(3,4-dimethoxyphenyl)-, (E)-	EtOH	214(4.32),260(4.18), 266s(4.16),298s(3.70)	94-2948-80
	CHCl₃	260(4.15),264(4.14), 290(3.66),300(3.62)	64-0156-80C
2,4-Cyclohexadien-1-one, 6-acetoxy-2,3,4,6-tetramethyl-	hexane	308(3.66),365(2.61), 385s(2.40)	24-2227-80
	MeOH	313(3.62)	24-2227-80
	CF₃CH₂OH	317(3.59)	24-2227-80
mixt. with 2,4,5,6-tetramethyl isomer	MeOH	329(2.44)	24-2227-80
2,4-Cyclohexadien-1-one, 6-acetoxy-2,4,5,6-tetramethyl-	hexane	315(3.71),365s(2.97), 382(2.83)	24-2227-80
	MeOH	320(3.63),364s(3.33)	24-2227-80
	CF₃CH₂OH	323(3.58),360(3.49)	24-2227-80
2,5-Cyclohexadien-1-one, 4-acetoxy-2,3,4,6-tetramethyl-	MeOH	246(4.08)	24-2227-80
2,4,7-Nonatrienoic acid, 7-methyl-6-oxo-, ethyl ester	n.s.g.	210(3.92),287(4.38), 355(2.48)	70-0425-80
2,4,7-Nonatrienoic acid, 8-methyl-6-oxo-, ethyl ester	n.s.g.	210(4.00),294(4.45), 385(2.27)	70-0425-80
Spiro[1,3-benzodioxole-2,1'-cyclohex-an]-5(4H)-one, 3a,7a-dihydro-, (3aR-cis)-	EtOH	217(3.94)	35-0857-80
$C_{12}H_{16}O_3S$			
2-Butenoic acid, 4-(ethylthio)-3-(2-furanyl)-, ethyl ester, (E)-	EtOH	221(4.07),329(4.24)	73-0142-80
$C_{12}H_{16}O_4$			
4H-1-Benzopyran-4-one, 6-ethyl-5,6,7,8-tetrahydro-5-hydroxy-3-(hydroxymethyl)-, trans (diplodiol)	EtOH	217(3.90),251(3.90)	98-0135-80
Oxiranebutanoic acid, 3-(5-oxo-1,3-pentadienyl)-, methyl ester	EtOH	273(4.43)	35-1436-80
$C_{12}H_{16}O_4S$			
2(4aH)-Naphthalenone, 5,6,7,8-tetra-hydro-4a-[[(methylsulfonyl)oxy]-methyl]-	EtOH	236(4.15)	44-5088-80
$C_{12}H_{16}O_5$			
1-Butanone, 3-hydroxy-1-(2-hydroxy-4,6-dimethoxyphenyl)-	MeOH	226(4.26),286(4.407)	107-0851-80
2-Furanpropanoic acid, 3-(methoxy-carbonyl)-4,5-dimethyl-, methyl ester	MeOH	262(3.59)	24-0699-80
$C_{12}H_{16}O_5S$			
α-D-Galactopyranoside, phenyl 1-thio-	EtOH	248(3.88)	88-3771-80
β-D-Galactopyranoside, phenyl 1-thio-	EtOH	249(3.85)	88-3771-80
α-D-Glucopyranoside, phenyl 1-thio-	EtOH	249(3.84)	88-3771-80
β-D-Glucopyranoside, phenyl 1-thio-	EtOH	248.5(3.86)	88-3771-80
α-D-Mannopyranoside, phenyl 1-thio-	EtOH	247(3.82)	88-3771-80

Compound	Solvent	$\lambda_{max}(\log \epsilon)$	Ref.
β-D-Mannopyranoside, phenyl 1-thio-	EtOH	247.5(3.89)	88-3771-80
β-D-Xylopyranoside, phenyl 1-thio-	EtOH	249(3.82)	88-3771-80
$C_{12}H_{16}O_6$			
α-D-Galactopyranoside, phenyl	EtOH	211(3.85),217s(--), 267(2.99)	88-3771-80
β-D-Galactopyranoside, phenyl	EtOH	211(3.80),217s(--), 267(2.94)	88-3771-80
α-D-Glucopyranoside, phenyl	EtOH	211(3.85),217s(--), 267(2.97)	88-3771-80
β-D-Glucopyranoside, phenyl	EtOH	211(3.84),217s(--), 267(2.99)	88-3771-80
2-Propenoic acid, 3-(4-formyl-2,5-di- hydro-2,5-dimethoxy-3-furanyl)-, ethyl ester, trans	EtOH	257(4.30)	118-0950-80
$C_{12}H_{16}S$			
Benzene, 1,3,5-trimethyl-2-(2-propenyl- thio)-	MeOH	269(3.39)	12-1345-80
$C_{12}H_{17}ClN_4O_3S$			
D-erythro-Pentitol, 1-C-(6-chloro-9H- purin-9-yl)-2-deoxy-1-S-ethyl-1- thio-, (1R,1S)-	MeOH	264(3.6)	136-0356-80C
$C_{12}H_{17}ClN_4O_5S$			
D-Glucitol, 1-C-(6-chloro-9H-purin- 9-yl)-1-S-methyl-1-thio-, (S)-	pH 1 pH 13 MeOH	266(4.11) 265(4.11) 266(4.11)	136-0241-80C 136-0241-80C 136-0241-80C
$C_{12}H_{17}FN_3O_7P$			
Uridine, 2'-deoxy-5-fluoro-5'-O-(tetra- hydro-2H-1,3,2-oxazaphosphorin-2-yl)-, P-oxide	pH 7	270(3.92)	78-2337-80
$C_{12}H_{17}N$			
Methanamine, N-[1-(2,4,6-trimethylphen- yl)ethylidene]-	hexane	196(4.66),215s(4.02), 256(2.89),263s(2.83), 272s(2.76)	32-0597-80
	C_6H_{12}	197(4.66),217s(4.02), 256s(2.73),266s(2.66), 273s(2.54)	32-0597-80
	MeOH	212s(4.11),265s(2.76), 271s(2.74)	32-0597-80
	EtOH	212(4.08),266s(2.64), 271s(2.60)	32-0597-80
$C_{12}H_{17}NO$			
2-Cyclohexen-1-one, 3-[4-(dimethylami- no)-1,3-butadienyl]-, (E,E)-	EtOH	435(4.84)	70-0980-80
1,3,6,8-Decatetraen-5-one, 1-(dimethyl- amino)-, (all-E)-	EtOH	440(4.72)	70-0980-80
Phenol, 2-(1-piperidinylmethyl)-	pH 9.18 pH 10.10 pH 13.3	238(3.75),294(3.38) 238(3.81),294(3.44) 238(3.89),294(3.53)	70-0558-80 70-0558-80 70-0558-80
$C_{12}H_{17}NOS$			
2-Propenesulfenamide, N-(3,5-dimethyl- 4-oxo-2,5-cyclohexadien-1-ylidene)- 2-methyl-	hexane	405(4.38)	18-0775-80

Compound	Solvent	$\lambda_{max}(\log \epsilon)$	Ref.
$C_{12}H_{17}NO_2$			
Carbamic acid, (2,6-dimethylphenyl)-, propyl ester	C_6H_{12}	259(--),264(2.42), 272(--)	44-2195-80
Isoquinoline, 1,2,3,4-tetrahydro-6,7-dimethoxy-2-methyl-	H_2O	210(4.4),217(3.6), 282(3.4),288(3.3)	102-0673-80
$C_{12}H_{17}NO_2S$			
Acetamide, N-[1-(ethylthio)-2,6-dimethyl-4-oxo-2,5-cyclohexadien-1-yl]-	MeCN	220(3.85),255(4.02)	87-1153-80
Ethanone, 1,1'-(1,3-dimethyl-7-thia-2-azabicyclo[3.2.1]oct-3-ene-4,8-diyl)bis-, syn	EtOH	273(3.42),325(4.13)	23-0794-80
$C_{12}H_{17}NO_3$			
Acetamide, N-(1-ethoxy-2,6-dimethyl-4-oxo-2,5-cyclohexadien-1-yl)-	MeCN	219(3.94),242(3.92), 277(3.36)	87-1153-80
1H-Indole-2-carboxylic acid, 4,5,6,7-tetrahydro-3-hydroxy-1-methyl-, ethyl ester	MeOH CHCl₃	279(4.41) 282(4.52)	5-0564-80 5-0564-80
1H-Indole-2-carboxylic acid, 4,5,6,7-tetrahydro-3-methoxy-, ethyl ester	MeOH CHCl₃	278(4.45) 278.5(4.44)	5-0564-80 5-0564-80
Isoquinoline, 1,2,3,4-tetrahydro-5,6,7-trimethoxy- (nortehuanine)	H_2O	203(4.4),223s(3.7), 281(3.2),292s(3.0)	102-0673-80
3-Pyridinecarboxylic acid, 5-butyl-1,4-dihydro-4-oxo-, ethyl ester	EtOH	255s(3.88),260(3.91), 286(3.68)	4-0359-80
3-Pyridinecarboxylic acid, 5-butyl-1-ethyl-1,4-dihydro-4-oxo-	EtOH	260(4.03),287(3.71)	4-0359-80
$C_{12}H_{17}NO_4$			
1H-Pyrrole-3,4-dicarboxylic acid, 1-(1,1-dimethylethyl)-, dimethyl ester	MeOH	250(3.91),388s(3.10)	44-4573-80
$C_{12}H_{17}NO_4S$			
7-Thia-2-azabicyclo[3.2.1]oct-3-ene-4,8-dicarboxylic acid, 1,3-dimethyl-, dimethyl ester, syn	EtOH	268(3.59),303(4.04)	23-0794-80
$C_{12}H_{17}N_2O_3P$			
Phosphonic acid, (1-benzimidazol-1-yl-methyl)-, diethyl ester	EtOH	206(4.2),244(3.8) 273(3.7),279(3.7)	65-1217-80
$C_{12}H_{17}N_3O_2$			
1H-Cyclopentapyrimidine-2,4(3H,5H)-dione, 6,7-dihydro-7-imino-1,3,5,6,6-pentamethyl-	MeCN	306(3.88)	35-3948-80
5-Pyrimidinepropanenitrile, 1,2,3,4-tetrahydro-α,α,β,1,3-pentamethyl-2,4-dioxo-	MeCN	271(3.90)	35-3948-80
$C_{12}H_{17}N_3O_5$			
5-Pyrimidinepentanoic acid, 1,4-dihydro-6-hydroxy-4-oxo-2-[(1-oxopropyl)amino]-	50%MeOH-HCl + NaOH	249(3.97),281(4.00) 231(4.16),265(3.99)	73-3583-80 73-3583-80
$C_{12}H_{17}N_3S$			
4H-Thiazolo[5,4-c]azepin-6-amine, N,N-diethyl-2-methyl-	MeOH	220(4.147),307(3.833)	39-2362-80C
$C_{12}H_{17}N_5O$			
6H-Purin-6-imine, 1-ethoxy-1,9-dihydro-	pH 1	261(4.12)	94-3443-80

Compound	Solvent	$\lambda_{max}(\log \epsilon)$	Ref.
9-(3-methyl-2-butenyl)-, monohydro-bromide (cont.)	pH 7	261(4.12)	94-3443-80
	pH 13	259(4.15),266s(4.11) (changing)	94-3443-80
	EtOH	260(4.12)	94-3443-80
$C_{12}H_{17}N_5O_3$			
Adenosine, 2'-deoxy-N,N-dimethyl-	pH 7	275(4.24)	39-2787-80C
$C_{12}H_{17}N_5O_4$			
Adenosine, N-ethyl-	pH 1	263(4.25)	35-0770-80
	pH 7	267(4.22)	35-0770-80
	pH 13	267(4.23)	35-0770-80
Adenosine, 1-ethyl-, hydriodide	pH 1-7	258(4.13)	4-0583-80
	pH 13	259(4.14),267s(4.08)	4-0583-80
Adenosine, N-methyl-2'-O-methyl-	pH 7	266(4.18)	44-3865-80
Adenosine, N-methyl-3'-O-methyl-	pH 7	266(4.18)	44-3865-80
$C_{12}H_{17}N_5O_5$			
Guanosine, 1-methyl-3'-O-methyl-	pH 1	258(3.95)	39-2787-80C
	pH 7	254(4.04)	39-2787-80C
	pH 7	254(4.04),277s(--)	44-3865-80
	pH 13	255(4.02)	39-2787-80C
6H-Purin-6-one, 9-β-D-arabinofuranosyl-2-(ethylamino)-1,9-dihydro-	pH 1	262(4.16),285s(3.87)	88-0479-80
	pH 13	260(4.08),272s(4.03)	88-0479-80
$C_{12}H_{17}N_7O_4S$			
1H-Pyrazolo[3,4-d]pyrimidine-3-carbox-imidamide, 4-amino-6-(methylthio)-1-β-D-ribofuranosyl-	EtOH	201(4.28),250(4.41), 290(3.94)	103-0182-80
$C_{12}H_{18}$			
Cyclopropane, 1,1,2,2-tetramethyl-3-(3-methyl-1,2-butadienylidene)-	heptane	236s(3.59),264(4.03), 306s(2.18)	35-6813-80
4H-Indene, 3a,5,6,7-tetrahydro-3a,7,7-trimethyl-	EtOH	256(4.02)	23-1810-80
$(C_{12}H_{18})_n$			
1,3-Cyclopentadiene, 5-(1-propylbutyli-dene)-, homopolymer	THF	252(4.10)	126-0031-80
$C_{12}H_{18}ClN_2O_3PS_2$			
Phosphorodithioic acid, O-[5-chloro-1,6-dihydro-6-oxo-1-(2-propenyl)-4-pyridazinyl] O-ethyl S-propyl ester	MeOH	213(4.42),295(4.42)	73-2247-80
$C_{12}H_{18}ClN_3O_6S$			
Methanaminium, N-[(dimethylamino)-[[(4-nitrophenyl)methyl]thio]-methylene]-N-methyl-, perchlorate	MeOH	269(3.96)	78-2675-80
$C_{12}H_{18}Cl_2O_4$			
D-arabino-1-Hexenitol, 1,1-dichloro-1,2-dideoxy-3,4:5,6-bis-O-(1-meth-ylethylidene)-	EtOH	209(3.64)	33-1644-80
$C_{12}H_{18}NO$			
Ethanaminium, N-(3,5-dimethyl-4-oxo-2,5-cyclohexadien-1-ylidene)-N-ethyl-	H_2O	297(4.29)	39-1601-80B

Compound	Solvent	$\lambda_{max}(\log \epsilon)$	Ref.
$C_{12}H_{18}N_2O$			
1,8-Naphthyridine, 5-ethoxy-1,2,3,4-tetrahydro-1,7-dimethyl-	EtOH dioxan	263(<u>4.0</u>),297(<u>3.7</u>) 263(<u>4.0</u>),297(<u>3.6</u>)	103-0260-80
5H-Pyrido[1,2-a][1,8]naphthyridin-5-one, 1,2,3,4,6,6a,7,8,9,10-decahydro-	EtOH	239(3.86),308(4.23)	94-0220-80
$C_{12}H_{18}N_2O_2$			
Benzenamine, N-butyl-3,5-dimethyl-2-nitro-	EtOH	242(3.25),300(2.60), 420(2.60)	103-0962-80
Benzenamine, 3,5-dimethyl-N-(1-methylpropyl)-2-nitro-	EtOH	245(3.29),300(2.62), 420(2.66)	103-0962-80
Benzenamine, 3,5-dimethyl-N-(2-methylpropyl)-4-nitro-	EtOH	243(3.36),300(2.68), 420(2.72)	103-0962-80
3-Pyridinecarboxamide, 1,4-dihydro-1-(2-hydroxycyclohexyl)-	MeOH	354(3.80)	23-0387-80
3-Pyrrolidinone, 2-(4,4-dimethyl-3-oxo-2-pyrrolidinylidene)-4,4-dimethyl-	gas C_6H_{12} benzene EtOH HCOOH $C_2H_2Cl_4$ DMSO	449(--) 204(3.98),473(4.05) 483(4.05) 480(3.99) 366(4.07) 487(4.00) 498(--)	5-2039-80 5-2039-80 5-2039-80 5-2039-80 5-2039-80 5-2039-80 5-2039-80
Spiro[cycloheptimidazole-2(4H),1'-cyclopentane], 5,6,7,8-tetrahydro-, 1,3-dioxide	EtOH	220(3.90),350(3.90)	103-0628-80
$C_{12}H_{18}N_2O_3$			
1-Propanamine, N-[2-(5-nitro-2-furanyl)ethenyl]-N-propyl-	MeOH	280(3.95),514(4.16)	73-0155-80
2-Propanamine, N-(1-methylethyl)-N-[2-(5-nitro-2-furanyl)ethenyl]-, (E)-	MeOH	280(3.97),516(4.09)	73-0155-80
Pyrazinecarboxylic acid, 3,4-dihydro-6-methyl-5-(2-methylpropyl)-3-oxo-, ethyl ester	EtOH	234(3.81),322(3.74), 365(3.66)	70-0774-80
$C_{12}H_{18}N_2O_5$			
1H-Pyrazole-1-acetic acid, 4-(ethoxycarbonyl)-5-(hydroxymethyl)-3-methyl-, ethyl ester	EtOH	236(3.97)	118-0875-80
$C_{12}H_{18}N_2O_6$			
Uridine, 3-methyl-2',3'-di-O-methyl-	pH 7	262(3.93)	44-3865-80
$C_{12}H_{18}N_3O_2S$			
Methanaminium, N-[(dimethylamino)-[[(4-nitrophenyl)methyl]thio]-methylene]-N-methyl-, perchlorate	MeOH	269(3.96)	78-2675-80
$C_{12}H_{18}N_4$			
Pyrazino[2,3-b:5,6-b']bisazepine, 1,2,3,4,5,6,8,9,10,11-decahydro-	MeOH-HCl CHCl$_3$	260(3.94),336(3.57), 413(3.43) 260(3.93),352(3.82)	88-2679-80 88-2679-80
$C_{12}H_{18}N_4O_2$			
Cyclopentanecarboxamide, N-[1-(2,5-dihydro-3-methyl-5-oxo-1,2,4-triazin-6-yl)ethyl]-, (S)-	EtOH EtOH-NaOH	235(3.92),265s(3.70) 232(--),283(--)	39-1139-80C 39-1139-80C
1,4-Diazocine-1,4-dicarboxamide, N,N,N',N'-tetramethyl-	MeCN	233s(4.24),272(4.03), 290s(3.75)	24-3161-80

Compound	Solvent	$\lambda_{max}(\log \epsilon)$	Ref.
Propanedinitrile, [[1-(diethoxymethyl)-2-(dimethylamino)ethenyl]imino]-	EtOH	421(4.62)	88-3759-80
$C_{12}H_{18}N_4O_2S$			
3-Pyridinecarboxylic acid, 5-butyl-1,4-dihydro-4-oxo-2-[(methylamino)-thioxomethyl]hydrazide	EtOH	245(4.20),287(3.85)	4-0175-80
$C_{12}H_{18}N_4O_5S_2$			
D-Glucitol, 1-C-(1,6-dihydro-6-thioxo-9H-purin-9-yl)-1-S-methyl-1-thio-	pH 1	326(4.36)	136-0241-80C
	pH 13	237(4.29),320(4.42)	136-0241-80C
	MeOH	220(4.16),324(4.40)	136-0241-80C
$C_{12}H_{18}O$			
Ethanone, 1-(1,2,3,4,5,6,7,8-octahydro-1-naphthalenyl)-	EtOH	207(3.65)	56-0453-80
Ethanone, 1-(1,2,3,4,5,6,7,8-octahydro-2-naphthalenyl)-	EtOH	207(3.58)	56-0453-80
Ethanone, 1-(1,2,3,4,5-pentamethyl-2,4-cyclopentadien-1-yl)-	MeOH	217(3.68),255(3.81)	44-2091-80
1(2H)-Naphthalenone, 3,4,5,6,7,8-hexa-hydro-2,2-dimethyl-	hexane	236(3.86)	150-1551-80
1(2H)-Naphthalenone, 3,4,5,6,7,8-hexa-hydro-5,5-dimethyl-	MeOH	245(4.10)	77-0399-80
1(4H)-Naphthalenone, 4a,5,6,7,8,8a-hexahydro-4a,5-dimethyl-	EtOH	228(3.91)	39-0963-80C
2-Propyn-1-one, 1-(1,2,2,3-tetramethyl-cyclopentyl)-, (1R-cis)-	MeCN	212(3.6),321(1.6)	24-1855-80
$C_{12}H_{18}OSn$			
Stannane, [2-(4-methoxyphenyl)ethen-yl]trimethyl-, cis	MeOH	267(4.23)	101-0233-80R
trans	MeOH	268(4.39)	101-0233-80R
$C_{12}H_{18}O_2$			
Bicyclo[4.1.0]heptan-2-one, 6-acetyl-4,4,7-trimethyl-	n.s.g.	289(1.80)	33-1499-80
isomer B	n.s.g.	295(1.78)	33-1499-80
2-Cyclohexen-1-one, 2-acetyl-3-ethyl-5,5-dimethyl-	n.s.g.	232(4.13),307(2.27)	33-1499-80
$C_{12}H_{18}O_3$			
Cyclohexaneacetic acid, 3-methyl-α-methylene-4-oxo-, ethyl ester	EtOH	204.5(4.08)	39-1752-80C
Cyclohexanecarboxylic acid, 2-oxo-1-(2-propenyl)-, ethyl ester	C_6H_{12}	290(1.45)	151-0305-80A
1-Cyclopentene-1-pentanoic acid, 5-oxo-, ethyl ester	MeOH	228(4.01)	44-4702-80
2-Cyclopenten-1-one, 2-(5-acetoxy-pentyl)-	MeOH	228(3.89)	44-4702-80
1-Naphthalenecarboxylic acid, deca-hydro-8-oxo-, methyl ester	hexane	207(2.52),285(1.34),290(1.33),300(1.24),311s(0.94)	39-0950-80C
	MeOH	280s(1.45)	39-0950-80C
2H-Pyran-2-one, 5,6-dihydro-6-(3-hy-droxy-1-heptenyl)-	EtOH	207(3.92)	64-1459-80B
$C_{12}H_{18}O_4$			
Benzene, 2-(1,1-dimethoxyethyl)-1,4-dimethoxy-	n.s.g.	227(3.91),291(3.47)	44-0501-80

Compound	Solvent	λ_{max}(log ϵ)	Ref.
Bicyclo[3.3.1]non-2-ene-2-carboxylic acid, 3,5-dihydroxy-4-methyl-, methyl ester	EtOH	258(3.99)	44-3545-80
2,5-Cyclohexadien-1-one, 4-(1,1-dimethylethyl)-2-hydroxy-4,5-dimethoxy-	MeOH	254.4(4.13)	44-4210-80
2,4-Hexadienedioic acid, 3-(1,1-dimethylethyl)-, dimethyl ester	MeOH	207.5(2.18)	44-4210-80
$C_{12}H_{18}O_4S$			
2(3H)-Naphthalenone, 4,4a,5,6,7,8-hexahydro-4a-[[(methylsulfonyl)oxy]-methyl]-	EtOH	234(4.19)	44-5088-80
$C_{12}H_{18}O_6$			
Cyclopenta[c]pyran-4-carboxylic acid, 1,4a,5,6,7,7a-hexahydro-6-hydroxy-7-(hydroxymethyl)-1-methoxy-, methyl ester	MeOH MeOH	237(4.01) 236(4.03)	44-4233-80 44-4233-80
$C_{12}H_{18}O_6S$			
Phenol, 2-(1,1-dimethoxyethyl)-4-methoxy-, methanesulfonate	n.s.g.	205(4.08),227(4.03), 279(3.32),286(3.27)	44-0501-80
Sulfone, methyl 2-hydroxy-2-(3,4,5-trimethoxyphenyl)ethyl	EtOH	215s(4.01),266(2.70)	87-0535-80
$C_{12}H_{18}S$			
Bicyclo[3.3.1]non-2-ene-9-thione, 1,2,5-trimethyl-	isooctane	233(3.97),270(2.90), 505(1.00)	24-2255-80
$C_{12}H_{18}Sn$			
Stannane, trimethyl[2-(4-methylphenyl)-ethenyl]-, cis	MeOH	297(2.89)	101-0233-80R
trans	MeOH	297(3.40)	101-0233-80R
$C_{12}H_{19}BrO_4S_2$			
Sulfonium, [(4-bromophenyl)methyl]-ethylmethyl-, ethyl sulfate	H_2O	231(4.18)	124-0957-80
$C_{12}H_{19}F_3Si_2$			
Disilane, pentamethyl[3-(trifluoromethyl)phenyl]-	isooctane	234(4.00)	101-0261-80Q
Disilane, pentamethyl[4-(trifluoromethyl)phenyl]-	isooctane	241(4.00)	101-0261-80Q
$C_{12}H_{19}NO$			
1-Butanone, 1-(1,2,3,5,6,8a-hexahydro-8-indolizinyl)-, (±)-	EtOH	229(3.99)	142-1433-80
Cyclohexanone, 2-[3-(dimethylamino)-2-methyl-2-propenylidene]-	hexane	225(3.58),283(3.82)	70-1643-80
	MeOH	293(3.82)	70-1643-80
	10% MeOH	235s(3.49),293(3.80), 418(3.19)	70-1643-80
	EtOH	225s(3.62),286(3.72), 410(3.20)	70-1643-80
	CHCl₃	290(3.67),400(3.30)	70-1643-80
	MeCN	294(3.61),395(3.19)	70-1643-80
1-Octen-3-one, 1-(2,5-dihydro-1H-pyrrol-1-yl)-, (E)-	EtOH	307(4.29)	54-0087-80
14-Oxa-12-azabicyclo[9.2.1]tetradeca-11,13-diene	EtOH	217(3.72)	138-0659-80
2-Pentenal, 4-(3,4-dihydro-3,3-dimethyl-2H-pyrrol-5-yl)-4-methyl-	MeOH	219(4.02),300s(2.56)	83-0858-80

Compound	Solvent	$\lambda_{max}(\log \epsilon)$	Ref.
2-Propenal, 3-[2,3-dihydro-3,3-dimethyl-5-(1-methylethyl)-1H-pyrrol-1-yl]-, (E)-	MeOH	211(3.70),231(3.66), 324(4.32)	83-0858-80
2H-Pyrrole-5-ethanol, α-ethynyl-3,4-dihydro-β,β,3,3-tetramethyl-	MeOH	204(2.86),218(2.56)	83-0858-80
$C_{12}H_{19}NOS$			
2-Azaspiro[3.5]nonan-1-one, 5,5,9,9-tetramethyl-3-thioxo-	isooctane	257(4.1),405(1.2)	88-4247-80
$C_{12}H_{19}NO_2$			
Acetic acid, (octahydro-3(2H)-isoquinolinylidene)-, methyl ester, [4aR-(3Z,4aα,8aβ)]-	n.s.g.	289(4.34)	33-1158-80
7(1H)-Indolizinone, hexahydro-8-(1-oxobutyl)-	EtOH EtOH-NaOH	295(3.46) 308(4.12)	142-1433-80 142-1433-80
$C_{12}H_{19}NO_3$			
1-Azabicyclo[5.2.0]nonan-9-one, 8-acetyl-7-ethoxy-	MeOH	206(3.03),311(3.06)	44-0936-80
Butanoic acid, 2-(hexahydro-2H-azepin-2-ylidene)-3-oxo-, ethyl ester	MeOH	249(3.75),310(4.25)	44-0936-80
1-Cyclopentene-1-butanoic acid, 5-(methoxyimino)-, ethyl ester	MeOH	243(4.09)	44-4702-80
$C_{12}H_{19}NO_4$			
1-Cyclopentene-1-carboxylic acid, 2-[(2-ethoxy-2-oxoethyl)amino]-, ethyl ester	MeOH CHCl$_3$	291.5(4.20) 292(4.10)	5-0564-80 5-0564-80
$C_{12}H_{19}NO_6$			
3,5-Isoxazoledicarboxylic acid, 4,5-dihydro-4-pentyl-, dimethyl ester, 2-oxide, trans	MeOH	266(3.39)	94-0479-80
$C_{12}H_{19}N_2O_4PS_2$			
3(2H)-Pyridazinone, 5-[(5,5-dimethyl-1,3,2-dioxaphosphorinan-2-yl)oxy]-4-(ethylthio)-2-methyl-, P-sulfide	MeOH	212(4.16),321(3.86)	73-2343-80
$C_{12}H_{19}N_2O_5PS$			
3(2H)-Pyridazinone, 5-[(5,5-dimethyl-1,3,2-dioxaphosphorinan-2-yl)oxy]-4-ethoxy-2-methyl-, P-sulfide	MeOH	215(4.26),286(3.64)	73-2343-80
$C_{12}H_{19}N_3O_3$			
2(1H)-Pyrimidinone, 4-(dimethylamino)-1-[2-hydroxy-4-(hydroxymethyl)cyclopentyl]-	pH 1 pH 7	220(3.96),292(4.20) 283(4.12)	4-0353-80 4-0353-80
$C_{12}H_{19}N_3O_4$			
2(1H)-Pyrimidinone, 1-[2,3-dihydroxy-4-(hydroxymethyl)cyclopentyl]-4-(dimethylamino)-, (1α,2β,3β,4α)-(±)-	pH 1 pH 13	222(3.96),292(4.22) 283(4.14)	4-0353-80 4-0353-80
$C_{12}H_{19}N_9O_4S$			
1H-Pyrazolo[3,4-d]pyrimidine-3-carboximidic acid, 4-hydrazino-6-(methylthio)-1-β-D-ribofuranosyl-, hydrazide	EtOH	205(4.23),227(4.25), 251(4.30),288(4.15)	103-0182-80

Compound	Solvent	λ_{max}(log ϵ)	Ref.
$C_{12}H_{20}$			
Cyclobutane, 1,2,4-triethyl-3-ethylidene-	hexane	256(3.81)	18-3329-80
$C_{12}H_{20}NO_3$			
1-Piperidinyloxy, 2,2,6,6-tetramethyl-4-[(1-oxo-2-propenyl)oxy]-	MeOH	238(3.28),448(1.04)	126-0595-80
$(C_{12}H_{20}NO_3)_n$			
1-Piperidinyloxy, 2,2,6,6-tetramethyl-4-[(1-oxo-2-propenyl)oxy]-, polymer	MeOH	238(3.13),450(0.88)	126-0595-80
$C_{12}H_{20}N_2O$			
1,6-Naphthyridin-4(1H)-one, 2,3,6,7,8-8a-hexahydro-3,3,8,8-tetramethyl-	MeOH	303(4.46)	5-2039-80
	CHCl$_3$	298(4.38)	5-2039-80
$C_{12}H_{20}N_2O_2S_2$			
Butanedithioamide, N,N,N',N'-tetraethyl-2,3-dioxo-	CHCl$_3$	269(4.21),329(3.86), 389s(3.38),449(3.36)	97-0436-80
$C_{12}H_{20}N_4$			
Imidazo[5,1-f][1,2,4]triazine, 1,4-dihydro-2,4,5-trimethyl-7-(2-methyl-propyl)-	EtOH	254(3.99)	39-1139-80C
$C_{12}H_{20}N_4O_2S_2$			
2H-1,3,5-Thiadiazine-3(4H)-carboxylic acid, 6-(dimethylamino)-4-[(1,1-dimethylethyl)imino]-2-thioxo-, ethyl ester	CH$_2$Cl$_2$	232(4.04),272(4.35), 339(3.86)	24-0079-80
$C_{12}H_{20}N_4O_7$			
D-Glucitol, 1-[(6-amino-1,2,3,4-tetra-hydro-1,3-dimethyl-2,4-dioxo-5-pyrimidinyl)imino]-1-deoxy-	EtOH	276(4.12)	94-2835-80
$C_{12}H_{20}N_5$			
3H-Purinium, 6-(diethylamino)-3-ethyl-9-methyl-, iodide	pH 1	223(4.38),292(4.27)	94-2522-80
	pH 7	223(4.38),292(4.27)	94-2522-80
	EtOH	293(4.28)	94-2522-80
3H-Purinium, 6-(diethylamino)-9-ethyl-3-methyl-, iodide	pH 1	223(4.36),290(4.28)	94-2522-80
	pH 7	223(4.36),290(4.27)	94-2522-80
	EtOH	291(4.28)	94-2522-80
$C_{12}H_{20}N_8O_2$			
1H-Pyrrole-2-carboxamide, 4-[[[(amino-iminomethyl)amino]acetyl]amino]-N-(3-amino-3-iminopropyl)-1-methyl-, dihydrochloride	EtOH	238(4.18),274(4.06)	87-1144-80
1H-Pyrrole-2-carboxamide, 5-[[[(amino-iminomethyl)amino]acetyl]amino]-N-(3-amino-3-iminopropyl)-1-methyl-, dihydrochloride	EtOH	235(4.32)	36-1334-80
$C_{12}H_{20}O$			
Bicyclo[4.1.0]heptane-7-methanol, 1,5,5-trimethyl-2-methylene-, (1α,6α,7α)-	pentane	207(3.85)	33-1856-80
5-Hepten-3-one, 4-(1-methylethylidene)-2,6-dimethyl-	n.s.g.	300(2.27)	33-1499-80

Compound	Solvent	$\lambda_{max}(\log \epsilon)$	Ref.
1-Naphthalenemethanol, 1,2,3,4,5,6,7,8-octahydro-α-methyl-	EtOH	207(3.90)	56-0453-80
diastereomer	EtOH	208(3.69)	56-0453-80
2-Naphthalenemethanol, 1,2,3,4,5,6,7,8-octahydro-α-methyl-	EtOH	207(3.62)	56-0453-80
5,7-Nonadien-3-one, 2,5,8-trimethyl-	n.s.g.	247(4.34)	33-1499-80
isomer	n.s.g.	248(4.40)	33-1499-80
5,7-Octadien-3-one, 2,4,4,7-tetramethyl-, (E)-	n.s.g.	227s(4.26),233(4.35), 238s(4.25),294s(2.71), 300(2.74),308s(2.65), 320s(2.33)	33-1499-80
5,7-Octadien-3-one, 2,4,4,7-tetramethyl-, (Z)-	n.s.g.	225s(3.82),233(3.84), 240s(3.76),293s(2.35), 298(2.36),306s(2.30)	33-1499-80
1-Propanone, 1-[2,2-dimethyl-3-(1-methylethenyl)cyclopropyl]-2-methyl-	n.s.g.	287(1.64)	33-1499-80
$C_{12}H_{20}O_2$			
2-Benzofuranmethanol, 2,4,5,6,7,7a-hexahydro-4,4,7a-trimethyl-, cis	pentane	204(3.81)	33-1833-80
trans	pentane	205(3.84)	33-1833-80
Cycloheptanone, 5-acetyl-3,3,6-trimethyl-	pentane	292(1.76)	33-1499-80
isomer B	pentane	290(1.72)	33-1499-80
Cyclopentene, 1-(3,3-dimethoxy-1-propenyl)-4,4-dimethyl-, (E)-	EtOH	235(4.37)	78-3361-80
$C_{12}H_{20}O_3$			
Cyclohexanecarboxylic acid, 2-oxo-1-propyl-, ethyl ester	C_6H_{12}	290(1.32)	151-0305-80A
Cyclopentanecarboxylic acid, 1-(2-methylpropyl)-2-oxo-, ethyl ester	C_6H_{12}	303(1.79)	151-0305-80A
2(5H)-Furanone, 5-methoxy-3,4-dimethyl-5-pentyl-	MeOH	211(3.98)	138-0955-80
$C_{12}H_{20}O_3Si$			
Silane, triethoxyphenyl-	gas	211(3.94),253(2.42), 260(2.60),264(2.68), 271(2.59)	109-0158-80
$C_{12}H_{20}O_4$			
Bicyclo[2.2.2]oct-7-ene-2,3,5,6-tetramethanol, (1α,2α,3β,4α,5α,6β)-(±)-	EtOH	210(2.07)(end abs.)	78-0149-80
$C_{12}H_{20}O_4S_2$			
Sulfonium, ethylmethyl(phenylmethyl)-, ethyl sulfate	H_2O	208(3.95),250(2.45), 260(2.53)	124-0957-80
$C_{12}H_{20}S_3Si$			
Silane, tris(ethylthio)phenyl-	hexane	218s(--),240s(3.43), 266(2.48),273(2.70)	101-0147-80A +131-0099-80C
$C_{12}H_{21}F_9O_3Si_3$			
Cyclotrisiloxane, 2,4,6-trimethyl-2,4,6-tris(3,3,3-trifluoropropyl)-	heptane MeCN	187.8(1.60) 199.2(1.85)	65-1280-80 65-1280-80
$C_{12}H_{21}NO$			
9-Azabicyclo[3.3.1]nonan-3-one, 9-(1,1-dimethylethyl)-	MeCN	234(3.1),268s(2.8)	35-5482-80

Compound	Solvent	$\lambda_{max}(\log \epsilon)$	Ref.
$C_{12}H_{21}N_2O_2$			
1-Piperidinyloxy, 2,2,6,6-tetramethyl-4-[(1-oxo-2-propenyl)amino]-	MeOH	224(3.91),448(1.06)	126-0595-80
$C_{12}H_{21}N_2O_4PS_2$			
Phosphorodithioic acid, O-(5-ethoxy-1,6-dihydro-1-methyl-6-oxo-4-pyridazinyl) O-ethyl S-propyl ester	MeOH	213(4.37),286(3.71)	73-2247-80
$C_{12}H_{21}N_3O$			
1-Propanamine, N,N-dimethyl-3-[(4,5,6-7-tetrahydro-1H-indazol-3-yl)oxy]-	EtOH	226(3.76)	18-0825-80
$C_{12}H_{22}NO_5$			
1,2,4,5-Tetraoxa-9-azaspiro[5.5]undec-9-yloxy, 3,3,8,8,10,10-hexamethyl-	EtOH	238(3.37),435(0.98)	97-0053-80
$C_{12}H_{22}N_2O_2$			
Acetic acid, [(2,2,6,6-tetramethyl-1-piperidinyl)imino]-, methyl ester	MeOH	282(4.42)	70-0765-80
2-Pentanone, 4,4'-azobis[4-methyl-	hexane	213(3.37),284(1.83),365(1.49)	78-1753-80
$C_{12}H_{22}O$			
Cyclopentanemethanol, α-ethenyl-1,2,2,3-tetramethyl-, [1R-[1α(S*),3α]]-	MeCN	196(3.3),222(3.0)	24-1663-80
3-Nonanone, 4-(1-methylethylidene)-	EtOH	240(3.75),310(1.85)	101-0367-80K
4-Nonen-3-one, 4-(1-methylethyl)-	EtOH	235(3.77),300(1.74)	101-0367-80K
5,7-Octadien-3-ol, 2,4,4,7-tetramethyl-, (E)-	n.s.g.	224s(4.41),230(4.44)	33-1499-80
$C_{12}H_{22}OSi$			
Bicyclo[3.2.0]heptan-2-one, 6,6-dimethyl-1-(trimethylsilyl)-	pentane	305(1.95)	44-4462-80
$C_{12}H_{22}OSi_2$			
Disilane, (4-methoxyphenyl)pentamethyl-	isooctane	239(4.32)	101-0261-80Q
$C_{12}H_{22}O_2$			
Iso-p-menthan-3-one, 4-ethoxy-, (1R,4S)-	MeOH	299(1.60)	28-0255-80B
p-Menthan-3-one, 2-ethoxy-, (1R,2S,4S)-	MeOH	284(1.60)	28-0255-80B
p-Menthan-3-one, 4-ethoxy-, (1R,4R)-	MeOH	306(1.66)	28-0255-80B
$C_{12}H_{22}O_2Si_2$			
Disilane, (4-methoxyphenoxy)pentamethyl-	hexane	227(4.015),288(3.404)	65-0491-80
Silane, [1,2-phenylenebis(oxy)]bis-[trimethyl-	hexane	202(4.02),216(3.891),271(3.297)	65-0491-80
Silane, [1,4-phenylenebis(oxy)]bis-[trimethyl-	hexane	224(3.961),281(3.335)	65-0491-80
$C_{12}H_{22}O_5S$			
α-D-Glucofuranose, 6-S-ethyl-3-O-methyl-1,2-O-(1-methylethylidene)-6-thio-	EtOH	209(3.05),223(3.17)	33-0016-80
$C_{12}H_{22}Si_2$			
Disilane, pentamethyl(2-methylphenyl)-	C_6H_{12}	233(4.04)	65-1621-80
Disilane, pentamethyl(3-methylphenyl)-	isooctane	232(4.17)	101-0261-80Q
Disilane, pentamethyl(4-methylphenyl)-	C_6H_{12}	232(4.12)	65-1615-80
	isooctane	233(4.11)	101-0261-80Q

Compound	Solvent	$\lambda_{max}(\log \epsilon)$	Ref.
Silane, 1,2-phenylenebis[trimethyl-	C_6H_{12}	222s(3.98),270f(3.2)	65-1615-80
$C_{12}H_{23}N$ 9-Azabicyclo[3.3.1]nonane, 9-(1,1-di- methylethyl)-	MeCN	254s(2.8)	35-5482-80
1-Propanamine, N-[(1,1-dimethylethyl)- cyclopropylidene]-2,2-dimethyl-	C_6H_{12}	270(2.14)	5-1814-80
$C_{12}H_{23}NO_2$ 5,6-Decanedione, 4,7-dimethyl-, mono- oxime	EtOH	323(1.68)	90-0441-80
$C_{12}H_{23}N_3$ 1-Propanamine, N-(3,5-dihydro-3,3,5,5- tetramethyl-4H-pyrazol-4-ylidene)- 2,2-dimethyl-	hexane	275(1.911),342(2.308)	89-0049-80
$C_{12}H_{24}BrCoN_7$ Cobalt(1+), azidobromo(5,12-dimethyl- 1,4,8,11-tetraazacyclotetradeca-4,11- diene-N^1,N^4,N^8,N^{11})-, (OC-6-23)-, perchlorate	MeCN HNO$_3$	348(3.95),583(2.52) 363s(3.94),584(2.47)	12-0273-80 12-0273-80
$C_{12}H_{24}ClCoN_7$ Cobalt(1+), azidochloro(5,12-dimethyl- 1,4,8,11-tetraazacyclotetradeca-4,11- diene-N^1,N^4,N^8,N^{11})-, (OC-6-23)-, perchlorate	MeCN HNO$_3$	341(3.91),574(2.50) 358s(3.91),573(2.44)	12-0273-80 12-0273-80
$C_{12}H_{24}O$ 5-Decanone, 4,7-dimethyl-	EtOH	286(1.59)	90-0441-80
$C_{12}H_{30}N_6Rh$ Rhodium(3+), bis(octahydro-1H-1,4,7- triazonine-N^1,N^4,N^7)-, tribromide	H_2O	249(2.33),294(2.42)	24-0036-80
$C_{12}H_{32}Si_4$ Silane, [1,2-bis(dimethylsilyl)-1,2- ethenediyl]bis[trimethyl-, (Z)-	hexane	224(4.22),344(2.57)	88-3077-80
$C_{12}H_{33}N_6O_3Rh_2$ Rhodium(3+), tri-μ-hydroxybis(octahy- dro-1H-1,4,7-triazonine-N^1,N^4,N^7)di-, triperchlorate	H_2O	340(2.64)	24-0036-80
$C_{12}H_{34}N_6O_4Rh_2$ Rhodium(2+), di-μ-dihydroxybis(octahy- dro-1H-1,4,7-triazonine-N^1,N^4,N^7)di-, diperchlorate	pH 10	340(2.70)	24-0036-80
$C_{12}H_{36}N_6O_4Rh_2$ Rhodium(4+), diaquadi-μ-hydroxybis- (octahydro-1H-1,4,7-triazonine- N^1,N^4,N^7)di-, tetraperchlorate, tetrahydrate	M HClO$_4$	340(2.83)	24-0036-80
$C_{12}H_{36}Si_5$ Pentasilane, dodecamethyl-	isooctane	250(4.27)	101-0159-80N
$C_{12}H_{36}Si_6$ Cyclohexasilane, dodecamethyl-	isooctane	197(4.64),236(3.76), 260(3.03)	101-0159-80N

Compound	Solvent	$\lambda_{max}(\log \epsilon)$	Ref.
$C_{13}H_4Cl_{10}$ 1,4-Methanobiphenylene, 1,2,3,4,5,6,7-8,9,9-decachloro-1,4,4a,4b,8a,8b-hexahydro-, (1α,4α,4aβ,4bα,8aα,8bβ)-	EtOH	285(3.53),294(3.68), 306(3.66),320(3.40)	78-3033-80
$C_{13}H_4F_{18}OP_2$ 1,4-Diphosphabicyclo[2.2.2]octa-2,5-diene, 7-methoxy-2,3,5,6,7,8-hexakis-(trifluoromethyl)-	n.s.g.	243(3.29),332(3.00)	35-0252-80
$C_{13}H_5Cl_2N_5O_3S$ 5H-Pyrido[3',2':5,6][1,4]thiazino[2,3-b]quinoxaline, 2,8-dichloro-9-nitro-, 12-oxide	MeOH	310(4.21),382(4.18)	4-0149-80
$C_{13}H_5N_3O_7$ Fluorenone, trinitro-	EtOH	280(4.51),342(3.90)	116-0240-80
$C_{13}H_6Cl_2N_4S$ 5H-Pyrido[3',2':5,6][1,4]thiazino[2,3-b]quinoxaline, 2,8-dichloro-	MeOH	245(4.63),285(3.57), 332(3.43),410(3.92)	4-0159-80
$C_{13}H_6O_5S$ 4H-[1]Benzothieno[3,2-b]pyran-3-acetic acid, α,4-dioxo-	MeOH	249(4.32),290(4.25), 324(3.87)	83-0385-80
$C_{13}H_6S_4$ 1,5,9,9a-Tetrathia(9a-S^{IV})cyclopent-[mno]aceanthrylene	benzene EtOH	518(3.86),560(3.83) 213s(4.18),247(4.04), 261(4.11),282(4.41)	150-3172-80 150-3172-80
$C_{13}H_7BrCl_2N_2$ 2H-Cyclopenta[d]pyridazine, 6-bromo-5,7-dichloro-2-phenyl-	ether	268(4.51),295(4.56), 322(3.88),424(3.49)	44-1695-80
$C_{13}H_7BrO_2$ 6H-Benzo[3,4]cyclobuta[1,2]cyclohepten-6-one, 9-bromo-5-hydroxy-	EtOH	213(4.47),280(4.27), 313(4.63),347(4.01), 392(3.42)	18-2334-80
$C_{13}H_7Br_2ClN_2$ 2H-Cyclopenta[d]pyridazine, 5,7-dibromo-6-chloro-2-phenyl-	ether	268(4.59),295(4.64), 322s(3.98),422(3.53)	44-1695-80
$C_{13}H_7Br_2NO$ 2,1-Benzisoxazole, 5,7-dibromo-3-phenyl-	EtOH	255(4.15),262(4.19), 363(4.19)	12-0091-80
$C_{13}H_7ClN_4S$ 5H-Pyrido[3',2':5,6][1,4]thiazino[2,3-b]quinoxaline, 2-chloro- 5H-Pyrido[3',2':5,6][1,4]thiazino[2,3-b]quinoxaline, 8-chloro-	MeOH MeOH	243(4.40),285s(3.81), 337(3.88),390s(3.76) 242(4.28),355(4.02)	4-0149-80 4-0149-80
$C_{13}H_7ClO_2$ 9H-Fluoren-9-one, 4-chloro-1-hydroxy-	EtOH	254(4.76),299(3.35), 382(3.61)	18-2334-80
$C_{13}H_7Cl_2NO$ 2,1-Benzisoxazole, 5-chloro-3-(2-chloro-phenyl)-	MeOH	247(3.98),255(4.00), 336(4.08)	73-3593-80

Compound	Solvent	λ_{max}(log ϵ)	Ref.
$C_{13}H_7F_3N_2O$ Butanenitrile, 4,4,4-trifluoro-3-oxo-2-(quinolin-2(1H)-ylidene)-	EtOH	220(4.63),237(4.23), 289(4.26),390s(4.28), 394(4.30)	94-2892-80
$C_{13}H_7N$ 1-Azulenecarbonitrile, 4-ethynyl-	CHCl₃	268(4.62),303(4.72), 317(4.74),353(3.72), 367(3.78),370(3.65), 382(3.58),460(2.17), 505(2.47),575(2.70), 620(2.60)	18-1647-80
1-Azulenecarbonitrile, 8-ethynyl-	CHCl₃	272(4.65),303(4.59), 315(4.58),350(3.75), 360(3.82),378(3.73), 580(2.77),630(2.68)	18-1647-80
$C_{13}H_7NO_2$ 1-Azulenecarbonitrile, 2,3-diformyl-	CHCl₃	303(4.64),312(4.64), 350(3.98),377(3.84), 570(3.18)	18-3696-80
$C_{13}H_7N_2S_2$ Propanedinitrile, [2-[4-(methylthio)-phenyl]-3-thioxo-1-cyclopropen-1-yl]-, ion(1-), potassium	EtOH	279(4.3),348s(4.3), 360(4.3),378s(4.1)	5-1409-80
$C_{13}H_7N_3$ Ethenetricarbonitrile, (4-ethenylphen-yl)-	THF	243(4.04),350(3.95)	116-0244-80
$C_{13}H_8BrNO$ Indeno[1,2-d]azepin-4(3H)-one, 10-bromo-	EtOH	286(4.7),350s(--), 368s(--),500(3.0)	18-3232-80
$C_{13}H_8Br_2N_2$ 2H-Cyclopenta[d]pyridazine, 5,7-di-bromo-2-phenyl-	ether	255(4.20),260(4.20), 291(4.43),330(3.61), 430(3.43)	44-1695-80
$C_{13}H_8ClNO$ Indeno[1,2-d]azepin-4(3H)-one, 10-chloro-	EtOH	285(4.7),350s(--), 368s(--),515(2.9)	18-3232-80
$C_{13}H_8ClNO_2$ 9-Acridinol, 2-chloro-, 10-oxide	MeOH	253(4.58),260(4.56), 258s(4.49),275s(4.38), 304(3.69),318(3.67), 404(3.82),422(3.81)	73-3593-80
1-Azulenecarboxylic acid, 2-chloro-3-cyano-, methyl ester	CHCl₃	297(4.89),307(4.98), 353(4.15),370(3.99), 496(3.09),510(3.08)	18-1647-80
Furo[2,3-c]pyridin-2(6H)-one, 3-chloro-6-phenyl-	MeCN	235(3.00),366(4.70)	39-1176-80(
$C_{13}H_8ClNO_3$ 4H-Furo[3,2-b]pyrrole-5-carboxylic acid, 2-(4-chlorophenyl)-	MeOH	343(4.67),357(4.66)	73-2949-80
Methanone, (2-chlorophenyl)(3-nitro-phenyl)-	MeOH	265(4.27)	73-3593-80

Compound	Solvent	λ_{max}(log ϵ)	Ref.
C$_{13}$H$_8$Cl$_3$NO$_8$S			
2-Furancarboxylic acid, 5-[2-(5-nitro-2-furanyl)-1-[(trichloromethyl)sulfonyl]ethenyl]-, methyl ester, (E)-	EtOH	202(4.01),250s(4.33), 312(4.15),384(4.02)	73-0746-80
C$_{13}$H$_8$FNO$_3$			
Methanone, (2-fluorophenyl)(4-nitrophenyl)-	MeOH	264(4.29)	73-3593-80
C$_{13}$H$_8$Fe$_2$O$_6$			
Iron, hexacarbonyl[μ-(η^5-2,4-cyclopentadien-1-ylidene)-1,2-ethanediyl]]di-	hexane	269s(4.0),315s(3.8), 348s(3.7),490(2.9)	24-2211-80
C$_{13}$H$_8$N$_2$OS$_2$			
3-Furancarbonitrile, 2-amino-4,5-di-2-thienyl-	MeOH	208(4.15),233(4.13), 262(4.15),340(4.09)	73-1581-80
C$_{13}$H$_8$N$_2$O$_2$			
2-Propenoic acid, 2-(2,2-dicyanoethenyl)phenyl ester	EtOH	295(3.99)	116-0244-80
2-Propenoic acid, 4-(2,2-dicyanoethenyl)phenyl ester	EtOH	234(4.10),323(4.16)	116-0244-80
Pyridinium, 5,7-dihydro-5,7-dioxo-6H-1-pyrindin-6-ylide	50% EtOH	209(4.391),228(4.338), 239(4.265),284s(3.531), 382(4.210)	103-1239-80
Pyridinium, 5,7-dihydro-5,7-dioxo-6H-2-pyrindin-6-ylide	50% EtOH	214(4.309),230s(4.134), 248s(4.033),286s(3.68), 296(3.682),307(3.74), 370(4.012)	103-1239-80
C$_{13}$H$_8$N$_2$O$_3$			
1H-Phenalen-1-one, 2-amino-6-nitro-	EtOH	213(4.32),225s(4.24), 270(3.67),289(3.80), 358(3.94),528(3.82)	104-1820-80
[2,2':3',2"-Terfuran]-4'-carbonitrile, 5'-amino-	MeOH	201(4.17),230(4.17), 260(4.24),333(4.22)	73-1581-80
C$_{13}$H$_8$N$_4$			
1H-Imidazo[4,5-f][1,8]phenanthroline	MeOH	242(4.15),276(3.79), 367(2.96)	56-2365-80
C$_{13}$H$_8$N$_4$OS			
1,3,5-Triazino[1',2':1,6]pyrido[3,4-b]-indol-4(3H)-one, 2,7-dihydro-2-thioxo-	MeOH	222(4.22),241(4.29), 258(4.31),296(4.35), 341(4.08)	2-0045-80
C$_{13}$H$_8$N$_4$O$_4$			
1H-Cyclopenta[gh]perimidine, 6,7-dihydro-4,9-dinitro-	MeOH	240(4.20),280(4.27), 475(4.23)	103-0071-80
	acid	455(4.13)	103-0071-80
	base	563(4.35)	103-0071-80
Imidazo[1,5-a]pyridine, 3-nitro-1-(4-nitrophenyl)-	MeOH	208(4.245),229(4.09), 280(4.23),342(3.69), 436(4.19)	39-0959-80C
C$_{13}$H$_8$N$_4$S			
5H-Pyrido[3',2':5,6][1,4]thiazino[2,3-b]quinoxaline	MeOH	240(4.23),280(3.44), 322(3.36),405(3.63)	4-0149-80
C$_{13}$H$_8$O			
1H-Phenalen-1-one	dioxan	357(4.02),375(3.93)	104-1813-80

Compound	Solvent	$\lambda_{max}(\log \epsilon)$	Ref.
$C_{13}H_8O_2$			
1H-Phenalen-1-one, 9-hydroxy-	MeOH	235(4.43),350(4.29), 415(3.95),444(4.00)	2-0859-80
$C_{13}H_8O_3$			
1,2,3-Azulenetricarboxaldehyde	CHCl₃	304(4.64),315(4.66), 351(3.98),377(3.84), 560(3.14)	18-3696-80
$C_{13}H_8O_3S_2$			
4H-[1]Benzothieno[3,2-b]pyran-2-carbox-ylic acid, 4-thioxo-, methyl ester	MeOH	286(3.97),310(4.12), 401(4.25)	83-0385-80
$C_{13}H_8O_4$			
Indeno[1,2-b]pyran-2-carboxylic acid, 4,5-dihydro-4-oxo-	MeOH	246(4.02),279(4.04), 309(4.23)	83-0429-80
9H-Xanthen-9-one, 2,6-dihydroxy-	EtOH	236(4.76),264(4.32), 280(3.11),408(3.05)	2-0463-80
	EtOH-NaOAc	205(4.85),236(3.56), 280(4.65),408(3.11)	2-0463-80
$C_{13}H_8O_4S$			
4H-[1]Benzothieno[3,2-b]pyran-2-carbox-ylic acid, 4-oxo-, methyl ester	MeOH	217(4.41),229(4.36), 236(4.37),251(4.26), 300(4.19),335(3.89)	83-0385-80
4H-Pyrano[3,2-b]benzofuran-2-carboxylic acid, 4-thioxo-, methyl ester	MeOH	227(4.15),310(4.14), 390(4.27)	83-0385-80
$C_{13}H_8O_5$			
4H-Pyrano[3,2-b]benzofuran-2-carboxylic acid, 4-oxo-, methyl ester	MeOH	216(4.41),243(4.08), 301(4.28)	83-0385-80
$C_{13}H_9AsO$			
1,3-Benzoxarsole, 2-phenyl-	MeOH	228(4.41),274s(3.54), 406(c. 2)	101-0039-80C
$C_{13}H_9BrN_2O_2$			
Benzenamine, 4-bromo-N-[(4-nitrophen-yl)methylene]-	THF	347(4.19)	56-1177-80
$C_{13}H_9BrN_4$			
Pyridine, 2-[5-(4-bromophenyl)-1H-1,2,4-triazol-3-yl]-	MeOH	260(4.38)	56-1067-80
$C_{13}H_9ClN_2O_2$			
Benzenamine, 4-chloro-N-[(4-nitrophen-yl)methylene]-	THF	346(4.15)	56-1177-80
$C_{13}H_9ClN_4$			
Pyridine, 2-[5-(3-chlorophenyl)-1H-1,2,4-triazol-3-yl]-	MeOH	250(4.23)	56-1067-80
$C_{13}H_9ClOS_2$			
2,4-Pentadien-1-one, 5-chloro-1,5-di-2-thienyl-, (Z,E)-	EtOH	369(4.41)	40-1804-80
$C_{13}H_9Cl_2N$			
Benzenamine, 3-chloro-N-[(4-chlorophen-yl)methylene]-, bis(trichloroacetate)	benzene	360(2.48)	65-1870-80
Benzenamine, 4-chloro-N-[(3-chlorophen-yl)methylene]-, bis(trichloroacetate)	benzene	380(2.95)	65-1870-80

Compound	Solvent	$\lambda_{max}(\log \epsilon)$	Ref.
$C_{13}H_9Cl_2NO$			
Methanone, (2-amino-5-chlorophenyl)-(2-chlorophenyl)-	MeOH	234(4.36),260s(3.90), 389(3.84)	73-3593-80
$C_{13}H_9Cl_3O_6S$			
2-Furancarboxylic acid, 5-[2-(2-furanyl)-1-[(trichloromethyl)sulfonyl]-ethenyl]-, methyl ester, (E)-	EtOH	277(4.32),351(4.22)	73-0746-80
$C_{13}H_9FN_2O_2$			
Benzenamine, 4-fluoro-N-[(4-nitrophenyl)methylene]-	THF	348(4.08)	56-1177-80
$C_{13}H_9IN_2O_2$			
Benzenamine, 4-iodo-N-[(4-nitrophenyl)-methylene]-	THF	350(4.02)	56-1177-80
$C_{13}H_9N$			
Benz[g]isoquinoline	$CHCl_3$	253(4.86),270s(4.09), 315(3.34),330(3.58), 348(3.68),372s(3.54), 392(3.46)	103-0525-80
Benzo[g]quinoline	$CHCl_3$	254(4.96),274s(4.24), 330(3.60),350(3.68), 370(3.78),392(3.71), 430(2.25)	103-0525-80
$C_{13}H_9NO$			
2,1-Benzisoxazole, 3-phenyl-	EtOH	244(4.03),250(4.04), 340(4.04)	12-0091-80
Indeno[1,2-d]azepin-4(3H)-one	EtOH	283(4.7),345s(--), 510(2.9)	18-3232-80
Naphth[1,2-d][1,3]oxazepine	C_6H_{12}	230(4.4),263(4.2), 310(2.6)	39-1159-80B
Naphth[2,1-d][1,3]oxazepine	C_6H_{12}	252(4.5),310(2.5)	39-1159-80B
2,4-Pentadiyn-1-ol, 5-(1H-indol-3-yl)-	EtOH	217(4.48),226(4.50), 267(4.09),282(4.01), 298(4.12),308(4.13)	104-0665-80
1H-Phenalen-1-one, 2-amino-	dioxan	481(3.64)	104-1813-80
cation	dioxan	366(4.02),388(3.98)	104-1813-80
1H-Phenalen-1-one, 3-amino-	$MeNO_2$	417(3.45)	104-1813-80
cation	$MeNO_2$	385(4.04),425(3.79)	104-1813-80
1H-Phenalen-1-one, 4-amino-	$MeNO_2$	456(4.17),477(4.11)	104-1813-80
cation	$MeNO_2$	448(4.28),474(4.27)	104-1813-80
1H-Phenalen-1-one, 5-amino-	dioxan	456(3.60)	104-1813-80
cation	dioxan	355(4.02),370s(3.93)	104-1813-80
1H-Phenalen-1-one, 6-amino-	$MeNO_2$	490(4.04)	104-1813-80
cation	$MeNO_2$	500(4.13),521(4.13)	104-1813-80
1H-Phenalen-1-one, 7-amino-	$MeNO_2$	450(4.09)	104-1813-80
cation	$MeNO_2$	455(4.26),479(4.22)	104-1813-80
1H-Phenalen-1-one, 9-amino-	$MeNO_2$	430(3.99),456(4.12)	104-1813-80
cation	$MeNO_2$	430(4.03),456(4.06)	104-1813-80
$C_{13}H_9NO_2$			
2H-Benz[f]isoindole-4,9-dione, 2-methyl-	MeOH	245(4.40),263(4.21), 272s(4.13),330s(3.68), 354(3.69)	39-0282-80C
3H-Phenoxazin-3-one, 1-methyl-	EtOH	350(4.20),447(4.01)	78-0529-80
3H-Phenoxazin-3-one, 4-methyl-	EtOH	345(4.09),460(3.92)	78-0529-80
3H-Phenoxazin-3-one, 7-methyl-	EtOH	366(4.05),452(4.07)	78-0529-80

Compound	Solvent	$\lambda_{max}(\log \epsilon)$	Ref.
$C_{13}H_9NO_3$			
Indeno[2,1-b]pyran-2-carboxamide, 4,5-dihydro-4-oxo-	MeOH	246(4.00),280(3.98), 310(4.17)	83-0429-80
$C_{13}H_9NO_4$			
Oxazolo[3,2-a]quinolinium, 5-acetoxy-2-hydroxy-, hydroxide, inner salt	EtOH	231(4.41),263(4.08), 322(3.44)	78-1385-80
	MeCN	262(4.03),325(3.54)	78-1385-80
Pyrano[3,2-b]indole-2-carboxylic acid, 4,5-dihydro-5-methyl-4-oxo-	MeOH	221(4.54),255(4.11), 264(4.08),309(4.26)	83-0405-80
$C_{13}H_9NO_5$			
Oxazolo[3,2-a]quinolinium, 5-acetoxy-2,8-dihydroxy-, hydroxide, inner salt	EtOH	213(4.09),251(4.53), 316(3.94)	78-1385-80
$C_{13}H_9N_3$			
Benzonitrile, 4-(phenylazo)-	EtOH	323(4.59)	62-0158-80
$C_{13}H_9N_3O_2$			
1H-Cyclopenta[gh]perimidine, 6,7-dihydro-4-nitro-	MeOH	290(3.89),325s(3.48), 485(3.69)	103-0071-80
	acid	460(3.69)	103-0071-80
	base	530(4.12)	103-0071-80
Imidazo[1,5-a]pyridine, 3-nitro-1-phenyl-	MeOH	208(4.245),229(4.09), 280(4.23),342(3.69), 436(4.19)	39-0959-80(
$C_{13}H_9N_3O_3$			
Diazene, benzoyl(4-nitrophenyl)-	CHCl_3	286(4.38),460(2.18)	39-1212-80(
2,4,6(1H,3H,5H)-Pyrimidinetrione, 5-(2-quinolinyl)-	EtOH	234(3.97),282(3.24), 386(3.81),400(3.80)	142-1083-80!
Quinolinium, tetrahydro-2,4,6-trioxo-5(2H)-pyrimidinylide	EtOH	209(3.87),236(4.08),	142-1083-80!
$C_{13}H_{10}$			
Fluorene	C_6H_{12}	255s(4.22),262(4.28), 265(4.27),273(4.12), 278s(3.94),289(3.79), 294(3.71),301(3.98)	95-0718-80
$C_{13}H_{10}ClN$			
Acridine, 2-chloro-9,10-dihydro-	MeOH	251(4.54),290(4.10)	73-3593-80
Benzenamine, 2-chloro-N-(phenylmethylene)-, trichloroacetate	benzene	270(2.51)	65-1870-80
Benzenamine, 4-chloro-N-(phenylmethylene)-, trichloroacetate	benzene	280(2.60)	65-1870-80
$C_{13}H_{10}ClNO$			
4H-Furo[3.2-b]pyrrole, 2-(4-chlorophenyl)-5-methyl-	MeOH	348.2(4.51)	73-2949-80
$C_{13}H_{10}ClN_3O_2$			
8-Azabicyclo[3.2.1]oct-3-ene-6-carbonitrile, 6-chloro-2-oxo-8-(4-pyridinyl)-, N-oxide	EtOH	210(4.32),292(4.42)	150-3337-80
Furo[2,3-c]pyridin-2(6H)-one, 3-chloro-6-(4,6-dimethyl-2-pyrimidinyl)-	MeCN	237(3.08),374(4.06), 396(4.46)	39-1176-80(
$C_{13}H_{10}Cl_2N_2O$			
3-Pyridinecarboxaldehyde, 2-[[(2,6-dichlorophenyl)methyl]amino]-	CH_2Cl_2	270(3.9),368(3.7)	64-0490-80

Compound	Solvent	$\lambda_{max}(\log \epsilon)$	Ref.
3-Pyridinecarboxaldehyde, 1-[(2,6-di-chlorophenyl)methyl]-1,2-dihydro-2-imino-	EtOH	265(3.6),383(3.7), 405s(3.7)	64-0490-80B
$C_{13}H_{10}Cl_2N_4$ Formazan, 1,5-bis(4-chlorophenyl)-	EtOH	240(4.38),294(4.21), 367(4.48),446(4.00)	104-0751-80
$C_{13}H_{10}Cl_3NO_6S$ Furan, 2-[2-(5-methyl-2-furanyl)-1-[(trichloromethyl)sulfonyl]cyclo-propyl]-5-nitro-, trans-(±)-	MeOH	216(4.22),311(4.07)	73-1704-80
$C_{13}H_{10}F_3N_3$ Propanedinitrile, [1-[4-(dimethylami-no)phenyl]-2,2,2-trifluoroethyli-dene]-	EtOH	202(4.12),257(3.96), 310(3.40),366(4.32), 492(3.83)	104-1441-80
$C_{13}H_{10}FeO_4$ Iron, tricarbonyl[η^4-2,3,5,6-tetrakis-(methylene)-7-oxabicyclo[2.2.1]hep-tane]-	isooctane	220(4.34),298(3.60)	101-0247-80C
$C_{13}H_{10}N_2$ 9-Acridinamine	H_2O	<u>312(3.2),326(3.2), 380(3.9)</u>,401(4.01), <u>422(3.9)</u>	18-1922-80
Benzo[b][1,6]naphthyridine, 3-methyl-	MeOH	252(4.99),322s(3.73), 329s(3.89),338s(3.89), 345(4.04)	39-0522-80C
Imidazo[3,4-a]pyridine, 3-phenyl-	C_6H_{12}	209(4.42),231(4.29), 318(4.13)	142-0369-80B
1H-Indazole, 3-phenyl-	EtOH	250(3.79),c.273(3.69), 300(3.87)	5-0908-80
$C_{13}H_{10}N_2O$ Benzo[b][1,6]naphthyridin-1(2H)-one, 3-methyl-	MeOH	208(4.25),234(4.58), 246(4.54),252(4.50), 265s(4.32),274(4.42), 295(4.19),318s(3.83), 390(3.74)	39-0522-80C
	acid	230(4.45),252s(4.34), 258(4.40),272s(4.10), 284(4.31),311(4.04), 352(3.47),425(3.96)	39-0522-80C
Butanenitrile, 2-(1(2H)-isoquinolin-ylidene)-3-oxo-	EtOH	220(4.63),255(3.99), 298(4.05),316s(3.85), 385(4.28),401(4.29)	95-1261-80
Butanenitrile, 3-oxo-2-(2(1H)-quinolin-ylidene)-	EtOH	200(4.74),238(4.04), 289(4.31),398(4.27), 412s(4.21)	94-0795-80
1H-Phenalen-1-one, 2,6-diamino-	EtOH	210(4.40),244(4.08), 290(4.20),579(3.81)	104-1820-80
2H-Pyrimido[2,1-a]isoquinolin-2-one, 4-methyl-	EtOH	240(4.55),250(4.54), 280s(4.01),291(4.20), 303(4.03),340(3.58), 356(3.48)	95-1261-80
$C_{13}H_{10}N_2OS_3$ Methanone, [4-amino-3-(methylthio)thi-eno[2,3-c]isothiazol-5-yl]phenyl-	MeOH	262(4.11),297(3.93), 323(3.76),390(3.20)	48-1021-80

Compound	Solvent	$\lambda_{max}(\log \epsilon)$	Ref.
$C_{13}H_{10}N_2O_2$			
Benzenamine, 4-nitro-N-(phenylmethylene)-	C_6H_{12}	210(4.21),224(4.17), 298(4.22),321(4.17)	18-1993-80
1H-Pyrrolo[3,4-b]quinoline-1,3(2H)-dione, 2,9-dimethyl-	EtOH	211(4.33),258(4.71)	94-3457-80
$C_{13}H_{10}N_2O_2S$			
5H-Imidazo[2,1-b][1,3]thiazinium, 6,7-dihydro-1-methyl-5,7-dioxo-6-phenyl-, hydroxide, inner salt	MeOH	206(4.16),246(4.14), 290s(3.64)	44-2474-80
5H-Thiazolo[3,2-a]pyrimidinium, 6,7-dihydro-8-methyl-5,7-dioxo-6-phenyl-, hydroxide, inner salt	MeOH	204(4.22),250(4.39), 298(3.73),320s(3.70)	44-2474-80
$C_{13}H_{10}N_2O_3$			
Phenol, 4-[[(4-nitrophenyl)methylene]-amino]-	THF	383(4.17)	56-1177-80
$C_{13}H_{10}N_2O_3S$			
Pyrrolo[1,2-a]quinazolin-1(3aH)-one, 3-acetyl-4,5-dihydro-2-hydroxy-5-thioxo-	EtOH	265(4.20),321(4.09)	4-0945-80
$C_{13}H_{10}N_2S$			
1,2-Benzisothiazol-3-amine, N-phenyl-	MeOH	239(4.41),265(4.20), 332(3.94)	24-2490-80
hydrochloride	MeOH-HCl	239(4.41),265(4.20), 332(3.94)	24-2490-80
$C_{13}H_{10}N_4$			
Pyridine, 2-(5-phenyl-1H-1,2,4-triazol-3-yl)-	MeOH	235(4.27)	56-1067-80
$C_{13}H_{10}N_4O$			
1,2,4-Benzotriazin-3(2H)-one, 6-amino-2-phenyl-	EtOH	227(4.47),269(4.36), 389(4.33)	73-1379-80
hydrochloride	pH 2	212(4.51),258(4.16), 410(4.39)	73-1379-80
Phenol, 2-[5-(2-pyridinyl)-1H-1,2,4-triazol-3-yl]-	MeOH	250(4.22),295(4.12)	56-1067-80
Phenol, 4-[5-(2-pyridinyl)-1H-1,2,4-triazol-5-yl]-	MeOH	265(4.38)	56-1067-80
Pyridazino[4,5-c]pyridazin-8(7H)-one, 3-methyl-5-phenyl-	EtOH	228(4.04),260(3.80), 355(3.30)	4-0529-80
Pyridazino[4,5-c]pyridazin-8(7H)-one, 5-methyl-3-phenyl-	EtOH	270(4.34),330(3.60)	4-0529-80
$C_{13}H_{10}N_4O_3$			
2,4,7(1H,3H,8H)-Pteridinetrione, 1-methyl-6-phenyl-	pH 1.0	203(4.55),220s(4.20), 281(4.13),345(4.23)	24-1524-80
	pH 7.0	217(4.50),235s(4.15), 290(4.09),347(4.29)	24-1524-80
	pH 13.0	235(4.19),257(4.06), 285(3.88),355(4.33)	24-1524-80
2,4,7(1H,3H,8H)-Pteridinetrione, 3-methyl-6-phenyl-	pH 1.0	231(4.11),281(4.03), 348(4.28)	24-1524-80
	pH 7.0	214(4.59),233s(4.15), 287(4.07),348(4.29)	24-1524-80
	pH 13.0	229(4.62),275s(4.02), 290(4.04),356(4.29)	24-1524-80

Compound	Solvent	$\lambda_{max}(\log \epsilon)$	Ref.
$C_{13}H_{10}N_4S$			
Tetrazolium, dihydro-2,3-diphenyl-5-thioxo-, hydroxide, inner salt	H_2O	380(3.21)	39-0139-80B
	MeOH	406(3.08)	39-0139-80B
	EtOH	415(3.00)	39-0139-80B
	PrOH	421(3.07)	39-0139-80B
	MeCN	445(3.08)	39-0139-80B
$C_{13}H_{10}N_6$			
Bis[1,2,4]triazolo[1,5-a:1',5'-c]pyrimidine, 5-methyl-8-phenyl-	EtOH	216(4.49),229s(3.99), 258s(4.07),264(4.07), 276s(3.83)	12-1147-80
$C_{13}H_{10}O$			
Methanone, diphenyl-	hexane	253(4.3),286s(3.3), 300f(4.2)	135-0160-80
Cr(CO)₃ complex	C_6H_{12}	254(4.2),331(3.8), 430(3.5)	110-0749-80
3H-Naphtho[2,1-b]pyran	MeOH	242(4.51),262(3.29), 290s(3.24),302(3.42), 315(3.46),347(3.35)	39-1233-80C
9H-Xanthene	EtOH	239(4.08),282(3.49), 336(3.05)	115-0423-80
$C_{13}H_{10}O_2$			
Bicyclo[4.4.1]undeca-1,3,5,7,9-pentaene-2,7-dicarboxaldehyde	MeCN	202(4.26),222(4.19), 268(4.45),352(4.12), 400s(3.72),408s(3.70), 424s(3.57)	89-0204-80
$C_{13}H_{10}O_3$			
1-Azulenecarboxylic acid, 2-formyl-, methyl ester	MeOH	238(4.32),291(4.61), 301(4.68),335s(3.79), 350(3.84),369(3.75), 573(2.98),606(3.02), 650s(2.70)	18-3696-80
$C_{13}H_{10}O_4$			
1,4-Naphthalenedione, 2-hydroxy-3-(2-oxopropyl)-	EtOH	252(4.29),278(4.26)	103-0578-80
2H-Pyran-2,4(3H)-dione, 3-benzoyl-6-methyl-	MeOH	234(4.20),300(3.90)	136-0219-80B
$C_{13}H_{10}O_4S$			
2H-Pyran-2-one, 4-hydroxy-6-methyl-3-[1-oxo-3-(2-thienyl)-2-propenyl]-	MeOH	381(4.4)	83-0344-80
$C_{13}H_{10}O_5$			
2-Butenoic acid, 4-(1,3-dihydro-1-oxo-2H-inden-2-ylidene)-2,4-dihydroxy-, (Z,Z)-	MeOH	243(3.82),309(3.97), 378(4.08)	83-0429-80
2H-Pyran-2-one, 3-[3-(2-furanyl)-1-oxo-2-propenyl]-4-hydroxy-6-methyl-	MeOH	382(4.5)	83-0344-80
$C_{13}H_{10}O_5S$			
Benzo[b]thiophene-2-butanoic acid, 3-hydroxy-α,γ-dioxo-, methyl ester	MeOH	204(4.33),262(4.12), 303(4.11),343(4.02)	83-0385-80
$C_{13}H_{10}O_6$			
Acetic acid, (8-methoxy-2,7-dioxo-[1]benzopyran-6-ylidene)-, methyl ester	MeOH	205(4.68),228s(4.30), 295(3.81),323(4.25), 380s(3.01)	44-1470-80

Compound	Solvent	$\lambda_{max}(\log \epsilon)$	Ref.
Benzofuran-2-butanoic acid, 3-hydroxy-α,γ-dioxo-, methyl ester	MeOH	203(4.26),319(4.08), 376(4.21)	83-0385-80
$C_{13}H_{10}O_7$			
Naphtho[2,3-d]-1,3-dioxole-5,8-dione, 4,6-dihydroxy-9-methoxy-7-methyl- (or isomer with 6 and 7 substituents interchanged) (nepenthone A)	MeOH	213(4.29),234(4.31), 273(4.41),342(3.88), 410(3.63),505s(3.28)	12-1073-80
$C_{13}H_{11}BrN_2$			
Cyclobuta[1,2-c:4,3-c']dipyridinium, 2-(2-propenyl)-, bromide	H_2O	246(4.26),301(3.15), 315(3.14),331(2.11)	150-2911-80
Propanedinitrile, (2-bromo-2-methyl-1-phenylpropylidene)-	dioxan	280(3.61)	1-0289-80
$C_{13}H_{11}BrN_2O_2$			
2(1H)-Pyrimidinone, 4-[2-(4-bromophenyl)-2-oxoethylidene]-3,4-dihydro-1-methyl-	6M HCl	265(4.10),315(4.01), 395(4.16)	44-3651-80
	EtOH	268(4.00),381(4.57), 395s(4.51)	44-3651-80
2(1H)-Pyrimidinone, 4-[2-(4-bromophenyl)-2-oxoethylidene]-3,4-dihydro-3-methyl-	6M HCl	267(4.21),316(4.04), 390(3.53)	44-3651-80
	pH 6	270(4.04),380(4.49)	44-3651-80
	pH 13	257(4.22),285s(3.70), 400(4.55)	44-3651-80
$C_{13}H_{11}BrN_2O_2S$			
2(1H)-Pyrimidinone, 4-[[2-(4-bromophenyl)-2-oxoethyl]thio]-1-methyl-	pH 4 and 9	263(4.34),298(4.17)	44-3651-80
$C_{13}H_{11}BrN_4O$			
4H-Imidazol-4-one, 2-amino-5-[(5-bromo-1H-indol-3-yl)methylene]-3,5-dihydro-3-methyl-	MeOH	385(4.43)	44-0735-80
4H-Imidazol-4-one, 2-amino-5-[(6-bromo-1H-indol-3-yl)methylene]-3,5-dihydro-3-methyl-	MeOH	390(4.36)	44-0735-80
$C_{13}H_{11}ClNO_4S$			
10H-Phenothiazine, 10-methyl-, perchlorate	CH_2Cl_2	451(3.88),520(4.37), 709(3.42),784(3.65), 880(3.65)	4-1053-80
$C_{13}H_{11}ClN_2O_2$			
1H-1,2-Diazepine, 1-(4-chlorobenzoyl)-3-methoxy-	EtOH	230(4.10),250(3.91), 326(2.88)	44-5095-80
2-Pyridinecarboxylic acid, 5-[[(3-chlorophenyl)methyl]amino]-, monosodium salt	MeOH	278(4.26)	87-1405-80
Pyridinium, 1-[(4-chlorobenzoyl)amino]-2-methoxy-, hydroxide, inner salt	EtOH	230(4.09),285(3.81), 303(3.57)	44-5095-80
$C_{13}H_{11}ClN_2S$			
1,2-Benzisothiazol-3-amine, N-phenyl-, hydrochloride	MeOH-HCl	239(4.41),265(4.20), 332(3.94)	24-2490-80
$C_{13}H_{11}ClN_4O$			
1,2,4-Benzotriazin-3(2H)-one, 6-amino-2-phenyl-, monohydrochloride	pH 2	212(4.51),258(4.16), 410(4.39)	73-1379-80

Compound	Solvent	$\lambda_{max}(\log \epsilon)$	Ref.
$C_{13}H_{11}ClO$			
2-Naphthalenol, 1-(2-chloro-1-methyl-ethenyl)-	MeOH	265(3.68),275(3.78), 284(3.68),321(3.43), 330(3.48)	142-0777-80B
geometric isomer	MeOH	265(3.57),275(3.68), 287(3.57),318(3.30), 330(3.36)	142-0777-80B
$C_{13}H_{11}ClO_3S$			
3-Thiophenecarboxylic acid, 5-[(4-chlorophenyl)methylene]-2,5-di-hydro-4-hydroxy-, methyl ester, (Z)-	EtOH	245(4.01),286(3.88), 351(4.50),369(4.47)	33-1542-80
3-Thiophenecarboxylic acid, 5-[(4-chlorophenyl)methyl]-4-hydroxy-, methyl ester	EtOH	251(3.99),305(3.48)	33-1542-80
$C_{13}H_{11}ClO_5$			
Acetic acid, chloro-, (7-methoxy-2-oxo-2H-1-benzopyran-4-yl)methyl ester	EtOH	323(4.17)	95-0744-80
$C_{13}H_{11}Cl_2N_3O$			
Benzenemethanamine, 2,6-dichloro-N-[(1,2-dihydro-1-hydroxy-2-imino-3-pyridinyl)methylene]-	CH_2Cl_2	250(3.7),366(3.5)	64-0896-80B
$C_{13}H_{11}N$			
Benzenamine, N-(phenylmethylene)-	C_6H_{12}	210(4.25),222(4.14), 236s(4.01),264(4.24), 315(3.85)	18-1993-80
cis	$C_6H_{11}Me$ at $-100°$	225s(--),235s(--), 243(4.42),285s(--), 343(3.11)	39-1282-80B
trans	$C_6H_{11}Me$ at $-100°$	218(4.28),226s(--), 237(4.20),264(4.38), 318(3.98)	39-1282-80B
9H-Carbazole, 9-methyl-	isopentane	282(4.13),288(4.26), 293(4.50),318(3.49), 328(3.76),343(3.89)	110-0294-80
1H-Indeno[2,1-b]pyridine, 1-methyl-	EtOH	304(4.50),326s(4.12), 455s(3.46),580(3.78)	103-1149-80
perchlorate	EtOH	234(4.34),280(4.36), 300(4.40),330s(4.05), 345s(3.80),470(2.94), 580(3.48)	103-1149-80
picrate	EtOH	232(4.60),283s(4.45), 302(4.53),330(4.34), 360(4.37),375(4.36), 510s(3.92),590(4.24)	103-1149-80
2H-Indeno[1,2-c]pyridine, 2-methyl-	EtOH	258(4.40),375(3.70), 620(3.97)	103-1153-80
$C_{13}H_{11}NO$			
2,5-Cyclohexadien-1-one, 4-[(4-methyl-phenyl)imino]-	hexane	461(3.60)	104-2020-80
	+ CF_3COOH	434(3.98)	104-2020-80
	benzene	472(3.61)	104-2020-80
	+ CF_3COOH	437(4.01)	104-2020-80
	CH_2Cl_2	473(3.67)	104-2020-80
	+ CF_3COOH	448(4.09)	104-2020-80
	$CHCl_3$	477(3.68)	104-2020-80
	+ CF_3COOH	451(3.87)	104-2020-80

Compound	Solvent	$\lambda_{max}(\log \epsilon)$	Ref.
Formamide, N,N-diphenyl-	C_6H_{12}	243(4.2)	65-1739-80
GaCl₃ complex (1:1)	C_6H_{12}	243(4.2)	65-1739-80
GaCl₃ complex (1:2)	C_6H_{12}	245(3.8)	65-1739-80
Indeno[1,2-d]azepin-4(1H)-one, 2,3-dihydro-	EtOH	260(4.5),330(3.9), 380s(--)	18-3232-80

$C_{13}H_{11}NOS$

Compound	Solvent	$\lambda_{max}(\log \epsilon)$	Ref.
Benzenesulfenamide, 4-methyl-N-(4-oxo-2,5-cyclohexadien-1-ylidene)-	hexane	438(4.23)	18-0775-80
Benzothiazole, 6-methyl-2-(2-methyl-3-furanyl)-	EtOH	201(4.20),219(4.38), 295s(4.18),303(4.20), 314(4.12)	128-0069-80
Benzothiazole, 6-methyl-2-(5-methyl-2-furanyl)-	EtOH	213(4.22),231s(4.06), 334(4.43)	128-0069-80
Benzo[b]thiophene, 2-methyl-7-(2-methyl-7-(2-methyl-5-oxazolyl)-	MeOH	212s(4.06),216s(4.20), 223s(4.34),224(4.54), 250(4.56),253s(4.56), 293(4.36),304s(4.28), 311s(4.09),319(3.94), 323(3.49)	39-1185-80C
3-Pyridinecarboxaldehyde, 2-[(phenylmethyl)thio]-	EtOH	218(3.60),254(3.74), 278(3.91),338(3.25)	118-0405-80
10H-Thieno[2,3-b][1]benzazepine-10-carboxaldehyde, 4,5-dihydro-	EtOH	248(3.86)	142-1227-80B

$C_{13}H_{11}NO_2$

Compound	Solvent	$\lambda_{max}(\log \epsilon)$	Ref.
Benzamide, N-hydroxy-N-phenyl-	pH 1	206(4.40),260(3.90)	140-1561-80
	pH 6	198(4.52),260(3.90)	140-1561-80
	pH 10	198(4.49),290(3.70)	140-1561-80
Benz[cd]indol-5(1H)-one, 3-hydroxy-1,2-dimethyl-	CH_2Cl_2	246(4.78),322(4.25), 550(4.18)	5-0971-80
Benzoic acid, 2-(phenylamino)-	MeOH-HCl	284(4.15),350(3.85)	44-2127-80
2H-1-Benzopyran-3-carbonitrile, 4-(1-methylethyl)-2-oxo-	EtOH	295(4.14),303(4.13), 338(3.87)	39-2937-80C
2,5-Cyclohexadien-1-one, 4-[(4-methoxyphenyl)imino]-	hexane	486(3.81)	104-2020-80
	+ CF₃COOH	510(4.18)	104-2020-80
	benzene	494(3.86)	104-2020-80
	+ CF₃COOH	523(4.21)	104-2020-80
	CH_2Cl_2	496(3.90)	104-2020-80
	+ CF₃COOH	527(4.23)	104-2020-80
	CHCl₃	500(3.91)	104-2020-80
	+ CF₃COOH	521(4.23)	104-2020-80
1H-Naphth[1,2-e][1,3]oxazine-2(3H)-carboxaldehyde	MeOH	230(4.35),265(3.18), 275(3.31),285(3.58), 314(3.19),328(3.30)	2-0859-80
5H-Oxazolo[3,2-a]quinolin-5-one, 1,2-dimethyl-	EtOH	259(4.18),329(4.05)	78-1385-80
Pyrano[4,3-b]indol-1(5H)-one, 3,5-dimethyl-	EtOH	243(4.62),247(4.78), 313(4.15)	39-1688-80C

$C_{13}H_{11}NO_3$

Compound	Solvent	$\lambda_{max}(\log \epsilon)$	Ref.
Glycine, N-(1-naphthalenylcarbonyl)-	H_2O	250(4.11)	103-0701-80
2H-Naphth[1,2-b]-1,4-oxazine-2,3(4H)-dione, 5,6-dihydro-4-methyl-	EtOH	213(4.06),225(4.06), 279s(3.96),287(3.98), 299s(3.88),347(3.71)	39-2126-80C

$C_{13}H_{11}NO_4$

Compound	Solvent	$\lambda_{max}(\log \epsilon)$	Ref.
Acetamide, N-[3-[(5-formyl-2-furanyl)oxy]phenyl]-	MeOH	205(4.33),244(4.19), 302(4.37)	73-0423-80
5(4H)-Oxazolone, 4-[4-(acetoxyphenyl)-methylene]-2-methyl-, (Z)-	CHCl₃	338(4.44)	70-0576-80

Compound	Solvent	λ_{max} (log ϵ)	Ref.
2H-Pyran-2-one, 4-hydroxy-6-methyl-3-[1-oxo-3-(1H-pyrrol-2-yl)-2-propenyl]-	MeOH	428(4.5)	83-0344-80
1H-Pyrrole-3,4-dicarboxylic acid, 2-methyl-1-phenyl-	EtOH	229(4.30),260s(3.95)	78-2125-80
$C_{13}H_{11}NO_5$			
2-Furancarboxylic acid, 5-[3-(acetyl-amino)phenoxy]-	MeOH	249(4.34),284s(3.97)	73-0910-80
$C_{13}H_{11}NS_2$			
Propanenitrile, 2-(4-methyl-5-phenyl-3H-1,2-dithiol-3-ylidene)-	CHCl$_3$	265(4.19),310(3.84), 368(4.36)	104-0395-80
$C_{13}H_{11}N_2$			
Cyclobuta[1,2-c:4,3-c']dipyridinium, 2-(2-propenyl)-, bromide	H$_2$O	246(4.26),301(3.15), 315(3.14),331(2.11)	150-2911-80
Phenazinium, 5-methyl-, methyl sulfate	pH 7	390(4.4)	46-1909-80
$C_{13}H_{11}N_3O$			
Phenol, 2-(2H-benzotriazol-2-yl)-4-methyl-	EtOH	240s(4.1),295(4.1), 340(4.1)	109-0034-80
4(1H)-Pyrimidinone, 5-(1H-indol-3-yl)-2-methyl-	EtOH	207s(4.27),223(4.37), 278(3.98),337(4.11)	103-0045-80
$C_{13}H_{11}N_3OS$			
4(1H)-Pyrimidinone, 5-(1H-indol-3-yl)-6-methyl-2-thioxo-	EtOH	207s(4.39),219(4.58), 285(4.30),315s(4.08)	103-0045-80
$C_{13}H_{11}N_3O_2$			
1,4-Benzenediamine, N-[(4-nitrophenyl)-methylene]-	THF	426(4.22)	56-1177-80
1H-Pyrazole-5-acetonitrile, 4-acetoxy-1-phenyl-	MeOH	205(4.17),243(3.95)	73-0150-80
Pyridazino[4,5-b]quinoline-1,4-dione, 2,3-dihydro-2,10-dimethyl-	EtOH	215(4.34),249(4.69), 290(3.98)	94-3457-80
compd. with methylhydrazine (1:1)	EtOH	214(4.39),249(4.71), 293(3.98)	142-0267-80
1H-Pyrrolo[3,4-b]quinoline-1,3(2H)-di-one, 9-methyl-2-(methylamino)-	EtOH	213(4.33),262(4.68)	94-3457-80
	EtOH	214(4.39),249(4.71), 293(3.98)	142-0267-80
$C_{13}H_{11}N_3O_2S$			
Pyrimido[4,5-b]quinoline-2,4(1H,3H)-di-one, 5-mercapto-1,3-dimethyl-	EtOH	239(4.51),251(4.54), 265(4.56),325(3.95), 394(3.84)	142-0679-80B
1,3,5-Triazine-2,4(1H,3H)-dione, 3-(4-methylphenyl)-6-(2-prop-ynylthio)-	MeOH	254(4.35)	73-2804-80
$C_{13}H_{11}N_3O_3$			
Diazene, (4-methoxyphenyl)(4-nitro-phenyl)-	EtOH	370(3.12)	62-0158-80
Pyrimido[4,5-b]quinoline-2,4(3H,10H)-dione, 7-hydroxy-3,10-dimethyl-	M HCl	266(4.56),331(4.23), 395(3.85)	83-0937-80
	pH 4	262(4.66),278s(4.32), 329(4.10),420(4.05)	83-0937-80
	pH 13	271(4.53),295(4.55), 336s(4.07),347(4.15), 473(3.93)	83-0937-80

Compound	Solvent	$\lambda_{max}(\log \epsilon)$	Ref.
Pyrimido[4,5-b]quinoline-2,4(3H,10H)-dione, 8-hydroxy-3,10-dimethyl-	M HCl	245s(4.52),257(4.41), 373(4.54)	83-0937-80
	pH 4	251(4.51),265s(4.41), 275s(4.34),325s(3.86), 386s(4.35),394(4.35)	83-0937-80
	pH 13	244(4.48),265s(4.42), 291(4.02),417(4.62)	83-0937-80
	EtOH	235(4.18),251(4.27), 407(4.06)	39-0978-80C
	50% EtOH-HCl	233(4.33),254(4.21), 381(4.11)	39-0978-80C
$C_{13}H_{11}N_3O_4$ 4-Pyridazinecarboxylic acid, 5-[[(2-hydroxyphenyl)amino]carbonyl]-, methyl ester	n.s.g.	275(3.7)	39-1339-80B
$C_{13}H_{11}N_5O_2S$ 1,4-Pentanedione, 5-diazo-1-[5-(phenylamino)-1,2,3-thiadiazol-4-yl]-	MeOH	204(4.40),231(4.19), 240s(4.14),277(4.09), 328(4.24)	103-0151-80
$C_{13}H_{11}N_6O_6P$ 3H-Imidazo[2,1-i]purine-5-carbonitrile, 3-(3,5-O-phosphinico-β-D-ribofuranosyl)-	pH 1	243(4.53),249s(4.49), 273s(3.72),281(3.74), 294(3.72),324(3.76)	94-0115-80
$C_{13}H_{11}O_2$ 5H-Indeno[1,2-b]pyrylium, 4-methoxy-, perchlorate	MeOH	243(4.01),334(4.36)	83-0429-80
$C_{13}H_{12}$ Benzene, 1,1'-methylenebis-, Cr(CO)₃ complex	C_6H_{12}	261(3.9),318(4.0)	110-0749-80
$(C_{13}H_{12})_n$ Benzene, [1-(2,4-cyclopentadien-1-ylidene)ethyl]-, homopolymer	dioxan	282(3.93)	126-0031-80
$C_{13}H_{12}BrCl_3O_3$ Butanoic acid, 4,4,4-trichloro-3-methyl-, 2-(4-bromophenyl)-2-oxoethyl ester, (R)-	MeOH	257(4.26)	78-2133-80
$C_{13}H_{12}ClNO_2$ 2-Propenoic acid, 3-chloro-3-(3-methyl-1H-indol-2-yl)-, methyl ester, (E)-	EtOH	254(3.98),340(4.25)	78-2125-80
$C_{13}H_{12}ClN_3O_2S$ 1,4-Pentanedione, 5-chloro-1-[5-(phenylamino)-1,2,3-thiadiazol-4-yl]-	MeOH	211(4.03),223(3.90), 325(4.11)	103-0151-80
$C_{13}H_{12}Cl_2$ 1H-Cyclobuta[b]cyclopropa[g]naphthalene, 1,1-dichloro-1a,2,4,5,7,7a-hexahydro-	hexane	220(3.71),266(3.30), 271(3.44),275(3.53), 281(3.53),285(3.19)	44-4183-80
$C_{13}H_{12}Cl_5N_2OSb$ Antimony, pentachloro[(2-methylphenyl)phenyldiazene 2-oxide-O]-, (OC-6-21)-	CHCl₃	242(4.02),325(3.89)	78-3177-80

Compound	Solvent	$\lambda_{max}(\log \epsilon)$	Ref.
Antimony, pentachloro[(4-methylphenyl)-phenyldiazene 1-oxide-O]-, (OC-6-21)-	CHCl$_3$	243(2.96),327(4.05)	78-3177-80
Antimony, pentachloro[(4-methylphenyl)-phenyldiazene 2-oxide-O]-, (OC-6-21)-	CHCl$_3$	241(3.86),324(4.08)	78-3177-80
$C_{13}H_{12}DNO_6$			
3,5-Isoxazole-4-d-dicarboxylic acid, 4,5-dihydro-4-phenyl-, dimethyl ester, 2-oxide	MeOH	267(4.02)	94-0479-80
$C_{13}H_{12}FN_3O$			
2-Pyridinecarboxamide, 5-[[(4-fluoro-phenyl)methyl]amino]-	MeOH	287(4.28),308(4.19)	87-1405-80
$C_{13}H_{12}NOS$			
Benzothiazolium, 3-methyl-2-(2-methyl-3-furanyl)-, iodide	EtOH	200(4.45),218(4.45), 247s(3.81),285(3.69), 330(4.16)	128-0069-80
Benzothiazolium, 3-methyl-2-(5-methyl-2-furanyl)-, iodide	EtOH	213(4.53),368(4.60)	128-0069-80
$C_{13}H_{12}N_2$			
Diazene, (4-methylphenyl)phenyl-	EtOH	333(4.37)	62-0158-80
Methanone, diphenyl-, hydrazone	MeOH	281(4.36)	18-3225-80
	dioxan	278(4.06)	18-3225-80
$C_{13}H_{12}N_2O$			
Benzo[f]quinoxalin-6(2H)-one, 3,4-di-hydro-5-methyl-	EtOH	235(4.23),276(4.36), 438(3.54)	83-0603-80
Diazene, (4-methoxyphenyl)phenyl-	EtOH	345(4.16)	62-0158-80
1H-Perimidin-2(3H)-one, 1,3-dimethyl-	CHCl$_3$	321(4.08),336(4.01)	104-1890-80
Phenol, 4-[(2-methylphenyl)azo]-	n.s.g.	352(4.23)	150-2415-80
Phenol, 4-[(4-methylphenyl)azo]-	n.s.g.	349(4.39)	150-2415-80
$C_{13}H_{12}N_2OS$			
Benzenepropanenitrile, α-[1-aziridinyl-(methylthio)methylene]-β-oxo-	MeOH	253(3.63),335(3.80)	78-1791-80
$C_{13}H_{12}N_2O_2$			
1,3-Benzenediol, 4-[(2-methylphenyl)-azo]-	n.s.g.	383(4.23)	150-2415-80
1,3-Benzenediol, 4-[(4-methylphenyl)-azo]-	n.s.g.	385(4.34)	150-2415-80
3H-1,2a-Diazacyclopent[cd]azulene-4-carboxylic acid, ethyl ester	EtOH	223(4.36),253s(4.18), 359(4.13),375(4.08), 424(3.57),448(3.61), 477(3.55),513(3.35), 555s(2.95)	18-1773-80
1H-1,2-Diazepine, 1-benzoyl-3-methoxy-	EtOH	250(3.91),315(3.15)	44-5095-80
Phenol, 4-[(2-methoxyphenyl)azo]-	n.s.g.	335(c. 4.26)	150-2415-80
Phenol, 2-methoxy-4-[(2-pyridinylimi-no)methyl]-	n.s.g.	288(3.93),340(3.15)	90-0349-80
2-Pyridinecarboxylic acid, 5-(phenyl-amino)-, methyl ester	MeOH	329(4.30)	87-1405-80
Pyridinium, 1-(benzoylamino)-2-methoxy-, hydroxide, inner salt	EtOH	230(4.04),286(3.88), 308(3.57)	44-5095-80
$C_{13}H_{12}N_2O_2S$			
5H-Imidazo[2,1-b][1,3]thiazinium, 2,3,6,7-tetrahydro-1-methyl-5,7-di-oxo-6-phenyl-, hydroxide, inner salt	MeOH	208(4.27),222(4.33), 289(3.88)	44-2474-80

Compound	Solvent	$\lambda_{max}(\log \epsilon)$	Ref.
$C_{13}H_{12}N_2O_3$			
Benzenebutanenitrile, 4-(2-cyanoeth-oxy)-β-hydroxy-γ-oxo-	MeOH	271(3.89)	44-5383-80
Isoxazole, 3-methyl-5-[2-(4-methylphen-yl)ethenyl]-4-nitro-	MeOH	250s(3.92),265(3.95), 357(4.20)	4-0621-80
2,4(1H,3H)-Pyrimidinedione, 5-benzoyl-1,3-dimethyl-	MeOH	251(4.10),286(4.22)	24-2566-80
$C_{13}H_{12}N_2O_3S$			
5-Thiazolidineacetamide, N-(4-ethenyl-phenyl)-2,4-dioxo-	MeOH	212(4.29),275(4.36)	80-1097-80
$C_{13}H_{12}N_2O_4$			
Acetic acid, cyano[(2-oxo-2-phenyleth-oxy)imino]-, ethyl ester, (E)-	EtOH	250(4.25),327s(2.40)	5-1623-80
Acetic acid, [2,5-dihydro-3-(4-methyl-phenyl)-5-oxo-6H-1,2,4-oxadiazin-6-ylidene]-, methyl ester, (E)-	MeOH	258(4.20),305(3.92)	4-1101-80
Acetic acid, (2,5-dihydro-5-oxo-3-phen-yl-6H-1,2,4-oxadiazin-6-ylidene)-, ethyl ester, (E)-	MeOH	235(4.16),260(4.12), 305(3.89)	4-1101-80
(Z)-	MeOH	230(4.10),260(4.08), 305(3.83)	4-1101-80
Glycine, N-(carboxymethyl)-N-8-quino-linyl-	anion	257(4.28),350(3.51)	69-2396-80
Isoxazole, 5-[2-(4-methoxyphenyl)ethen-yl]-3-methyl-4-nitro-	MeOH	252(4.02),280(4.05), 387(4.39)	4-0621-80
$C_{13}H_{12}N_2O_5$			
Acetic acid, [2,5-dihydro-3-(4-methoxy-phenyl)-5-oxo-6H-1,2,4-oxadiazin-6-ylidene]-, methyl ester, (E)-	MeOH	271(4.35),320s(3.87)	4-1101-80
$C_{13}H_{12}N_2O_9S$			
α-L-threo-Hex-4-enopyranosiduronic acid, 2,4-dinitrophenyl 4-deoxy-1-thio-, methyl ester	MeOH	242(4.16),317(4.03)	106-0460-80
$C_{13}H_{12}N_2S$			
1H-Perimidine-2(3H)-thione, 1,3-di-methyl-	CHCl₃	318(4.19),328(4.20)	104-1890-80
$C_{13}H_{12}N_4$			
Formazan, 1,5-diphenyl-	EtOH	240(4.46),296(3.18), 365(4.00),436(2.26)	104-0751-80
$C_{13}H_{12}N_4O$			
4H-Imidazol-4-one, 2-amino-1,5-dihydro-5-(1H-indol-3-ylmethylene)-1-methyl-	MeOH	385(4.48)	44-0735-80
4H-Imidazol-4-one, 2-amino-3,5-dihydro-5-(1H-indol-3-ylmethylene)-3-methyl-	MeOH	385(4.40)	44-0735-80
Pyridazino[4,5-c]pyridazin-8(4H)-one, 1,7-dihydro-3-methyl-5-phenyl-	EtOH	228(4.36),257(4.14), 335(4.01)	4-0529-80
Pyridazino[4,5-c]pyridazin-8(4H)-one, 1,7-dihydro-5-methyl-3-phenyl-	EtOH	225(4.11),267(3.90), 365(3.95)	4-0529-80
$C_{13}H_{12}N_4O_2$			
Benzo[g]pteridine-2,4(3H,10H)-dione, 7,8,10-trimethyl-	DMF-Et₄N-ClO₄	340(3.9),448(4.1)	35-7591-80
radical anion	n.s.g.	320(3.9),448(4.1)	35-7591-80

Compound	Solvent	λ_{max}(log ϵ)	Ref.
1H-Pyrazolo[3,4-d]pyrimidine-4,6(5H-7H)-dione, 5,7-dimethyl-3-phenyl-	MeOH	267(3.89)	24-2566-80
Pyridazino[3,4-b]quinoxaline-4-carboxylic acid, 1,2-dihydro-, ethyl ester	EtOH	245(4.62),418(3.97), 444(4.02),469s(3.87)	94-3537-80
$C_{13}H_{12}N_4O_3$			
4-Pyridazinecarboxylic acid, 5-[[(2-aminophenyl)amino]carbonyl]-, methyl ester	DMSO	<u>310(4.1)</u>	39-1339-80B
$C_{13}H_{12}N_4O_3S_2$			
Benzenesulfonic acid, 3-[[(aminothioxomethyl)hydrazono]-2-pyridinylmethyl]-	H₂O	318(4.31)	86-0923-80
	EtOH	335(4.25)	86-0923-80
	acetone	350(4.18)	86-0923-80
	MeisoBu-ketone	355(4.06)	86-0923-80
$C_{13}H_{12}N_5O_8P$			
3H-Imidazo[2,1-i]purine-5-carboxylic acid, 3-(3,5-O-phosphinico-β-D-ribofuranosyl)-	pH 1	238(4.46),277(3.91), 284s(3.91),306s(3.73)	94-0115-80
	pH 13	238(4.51),270s(3.77), 322(3.60)	94-0115-80
$C_{13}H_{12}N_6O_4$			
Propanedinitrile, (9-β-D-ribofuranosyl-6H-purin-6-yl)-	H₂O	236s(3.86),333(4.53)	94-0150-80
$C_{13}H_{12}N_6O_8$			
1H-1,2,3-Triazole-5-acetic acid, 1-[(2,4-dinitrophenyl)amino]-4-(methoxycarbonyl)-, methyl ester	pH 1	213(4.33),261(4.09), 312(4.10)	4-0159-80
	pH 7	215(4.35),256s(4.02), 315(4.13),391(4.18)	4-0159-80
	pH 11	229(4.27),255s(3.92), 392(4.36)	4-0159-80
$C_{13}H_{12}N_6S_2$			
Thieno[2,3-d]pyrimidine-4,5,6-tricarbonitrile, 2-mercapto-, tetramethylammonium salt (also other maxima)	n.s.g.	241(4.36),438(4.26)	44-5113-80
$C_{13}H_{12}O$			
Benzeneethanol, β-2,4-cyclopentadien-1-ylidene-	EtOH	240(3.85),294(4.11), 385s(2.4)	34-0185-80
3-Buten-2-one, 4-(2-ethynylphenyl)-3-methyl-	ether	238(4.16),277(3.92)	39-0466-80C
2,4-Cyclohexadien-1-one, 6-methyl-6-phenyl-	C_6H_{12}	299(3.60),365(2.16), 381(2.16),397s(2.00), 415(1.58)	24-2227-80
	MeOH	308(3.57),356s(2.55)	24-2227-80
	CF₃CH₂OH	313(3.57)	24-2227-80
5,9-Methano-6H-benzocyclohepten-6-one, 5,9-dihydro-9-methyl-	EtOH	231(4.00)	22-0267-80
1H-Naphtho[2,1-b]pyran, 2,3-dihydro-	MeOH	233(4.54),257s(3.30), 268(3.46),278(3.54), 289(3.42),308s(2.90), 321(3.13),335(3.22)	39-1233-80C
$C_{13}H_{12}O_2$			
1H-2-Benzopyran-1-one, 3-(1-butenyl)-(artimidine)	EtOH	229(4.84),242(4.75), 251(4.70),279(4.67), 303(4.74),335(4.28)	25-0084-80

Compound	Solvent	$\lambda_{max}(\log \epsilon)$	Ref.
1H-Indene-1,3(2H)-dione, 2-(2-methyl-1-propenyl)-	CH_2Cl_2	250(4.26),300(3.32), 312(3.1)	49-0309-80
1H-Indene-1,3(2H)-dione, 2-(2-methyl-propylidene)- (corrected)	hexane	249(4.65),267s(--), 299(3.7),309(3.53), 373(1.94)	24-1020-80
1H-Inden-1-one, 3-hydroxy-2-(2-methyl-1-propenyl)- (corrected)	MeOH	251(4.7),300(3.68), 437(2.97)	49-0309-80
$C_{13}H_{12}O_2S$			
1,4-Naphthalenedione, 2-methyl-3-[(methylthio)methyl]-	EtOH	252(4.16),269(4.15), 330(3.51)	39-0282-80C
$C_{13}H_{12}O_2S_2$			
1,3-Dithiole-4-carboxylic acid, 2-(phenylmethylene)-, ethyl ester	EtOH	228(4.23),326(4.26), 340s(4.23),385(3.52)	116-0240-80
1,4-Naphthalenedione, 2-(methylthio)-3-[(methylthio)methyl]-	EtOH	250s(4.16),261(4.21), 323(3.56),434(3.36)	39-0282-80C
$C_{13}H_{12}O_3S$			
3-Thiophenecarboxylic acid, 2,5-dihydro-4-hydroxy-5-(phenylmethylene)-, methyl ester, (Z)-	EtOH	240(3.95),285(3.86), 347(4.45),364(4.41)	33-1542-80
3-Thiophenecarboxylic acid, 4-hydroxy-5-(phenylmethyl)-, methyl ester	EtOH	251(3.93),305(3.40)	33-1542-80
$C_{13}H_{12}O_4$			
2H-1-Benzopyran-2-one, 7-hydroxy-8-methoxy-6-(2-propenyl)-	MeOH	205(4.22),328(4.16), 349s(3.95)	44-1470-80
2H-1-Benzopyran-2-one, 8-methoxy-7-(2-propenyloxy)-	MeOH	245s(3.65),255(3.70), 316(4.18)	44-1470-80
2,8-Decadiene-4,6-diynoic acid, 10-acetoxy-, methyl ester, (Z,Z)-	MeOH	233(4.19),246(4.26), 258(4.22),289(3.97), 308(4.09),329(4.00)	102-0563-80
1H-Indene-1,3(2H)-dione, 2-(2-hydro-peroxy-2-methylpropylidene)-	CH_2Cl_2	254(4.27),301(3.26), 312(3.40),360(2.10)	49-0309-80
Spiro[2H-indene-2,2'-oxirane]-1,3-di-one, 3'-(1-hydroxy-1-methylethyl)-	$CHCl_3$	256s(4.03),311(2.87)	49-0309-80
$C_{13}H_{12}O_4$			
2H-1-Benzopyran-4-carboxylic acid, 7-methoxy-2-oxo-, ethyl ester	EtOH	344(4.04)	95-0289-80
2H-1-Benzopyran-2-one, 4-(acetoxymeth-yl)-7-methoxy-	EtOH	323(4.27)	95-0744-80
2H-1-Benzopyran-2-one, 7-methoxy-6-(oxiranylmethyl)-	EtOH	293(2.74),340(3.06)	2-0495-80
2-Heptene-4,6-diynoic acid, 7-(3-acet-oxymethyl)oxiranyl]-, methyl ester	MeOH	225(4.33),285s(3.60), 272(3.86),287(3.04), 304(3.98)	102-0563-80
$C_{13}H_{12}O_6$			
Acetic acid, hydroxy-, (7-methoxy-2-oxo-2H-1-benzopyran-4-yl)methyl ester	EtOH	323(4.17)	95-0744-80
2H-1-Benzopyran-6-acetic acid, 7-hy-droxy-8-methoxy-2-oxo-, methyl ester	MeOH	204(4.65),225s(4.18), 257(3.62),327(4.13)	44-1470-80
1,4-Naphthalenedione, 3,8-dihydroxy-2,5-dimethoxy-6-methyl-	MeOH	239(4.21),270(4.24), 407(3.59),484(3.51)	12-1073-80
$C_{13}H_{12}O_6S$			
2-Butenoic acid, 3-(2-furanyl)-4-(2-furanylsulfonyl)-, methyl ester, (E)-	EtOH	217(4.12),316(4.19)	73-0142-80

Compound	Solvent	$\lambda_{max}(\log \epsilon)$	Ref.
$C_{13}H_{12}O_8S_2Se_2$ 1,6-Dithia-4,9-diselenaspiro[4.4]nona- 2,7-diene-2,3,7,8-tetracarboxylic acid, tetramethyl ester	C_6H_{12}	283(4.11),360(3.86)	44-2632-80
$C_{13}H_{12}S$ Dispiro[cyclopropane-1,1'-[1H]indene- 3'(2'H),1"-cyclopropane]-2'-thione	isooctane	207(4.54),230(4.04), 267s(3.74),273(3.83), 281(3.83),324(3.58), 454(1.14)	24-2255-80
$C_{13}H_{12}S_3$ 2H-Thiopyran-2-thione, 3-methyl- 6-(methylthio)-4-phenyl-	C_6H_{12}	236(4.27),288(4.13), 325(3.91),467(3.81)	22-0539-80
	EtOH	242(4.26),297(4.18), 325s(3.91),473(3.91)	22-0539-80
$C_{13}H_{13}$ 1,4-Ethano-1H-benzocycloheptenylium, 4,?-dihydro-, (deloc-4a,5,6,7,8,9- 9a)-, tetrafluoroborate	CH_2Cl_2	236(4.58),279(3.78), 334(3.14)	89-0545-80
	MeCN	231(4.65),276(3.77), 325(3.15)	89-0545-80
$C_{13}H_{13}Br$ Azulene, 4-(bromomethyl)-6,8-dimethyl-	hexane	250(4.39),294(4.59), 314s(3.86),348(3.50), 356(3.50),578(2.65), 598s(2.61),624s(2.53), 658s(2.26),688s(2.01)	89-0621-80
$C_{13}H_{13}Cl$ Azulene, 4-(chloromethyl)-6,8-dimethyl-	hexane	215(3.45),247(4.38), 288s(4.64),291(4.65), 311s(3.81),330s(3.40), 340s(3.50),343(3.52), 353(3.55),394s(1.74), 563s(2.61),575(2.62), 595s(2.58),622s(2.48), 653s(2.22),683s(1.92)	89-0621-80
$C_{13}H_{13}ClN_2$ 3H-Indole, 6-chloro-3-(1-pyrrolidinyl- methylene)-	$CHCl_3$	284s(4.24),289(4.31), 364(4.49)	94-1711-80
$C_{13}H_{13}ClN_2O$ 2-Pyridinemethanol, 5-[[(3-chlorophen- yl)methyl]amino]-	MeOH	254(4.26),314(4.59)	87-1405-80
$C_{13}H_{13}ClN_2O_3$ 2-Quinoxalinecarboxylic acid, 3-chloro- 5-methoxy-6,7-dimethyl-, methyl ester	MeOH	259(4.60),343(3.86)	54-0115-80
$C_{13}H_{13}ClN_2O_5$ 2-Butenedioic acid, 2-[[[(4-chlorophen- yl)iminomethyl]amino]oxy]-, dimethyl ester, (E)-	MeOH	229(4.23),275(3.97)	4-1101-80
$C_{13}H_{13}ClN_3O$ Pyridinium, 1-[(4-chlorophenyl)methyl]- 3-[(hydroxyamino)iminomethyl]-, chloride, monohydrochloride	pH 1 pH 7 pH 11.7	256(3.7) 256(3.7),286s(3.4) 256(3.8),321(3.6)	64-0896-80B 64-0896-80B 64-0896-80B

Compound	Solvent	$\lambda_{max}(\log \epsilon)$	Ref.
$C_{13}H_{13}ClN_4O$			
Methanimidamide, N'-[1-(4-chlorophenyl)-4-formyl-1H-pyrazol-5-yl]-N,N-dimethyl-	EtOH	258(4.43),338(3.82)	114-0127-80C
$C_{13}H_{13}ClN_4O_7$			
Benzo[g]pteridinium, 1,2,3,4-tetrahydro-6-hydroxy-1,3,10-trimethyl-2,4-dioxo-, perchlorate	M HCl	210(4.21),255(3.97), 295(4.37),395(4.19)	151-0133-80B
$C_{13}H_{13}ClO$			
2-Cyclohexen-1-one, 3-(3-chlorophenyl)-4-methyl-	EtOH	230(4.16)	22-0295-80
2-Cyclohexen-1-one, 3-(4-chlorophenyl)-4-methyl-	EtOH	230(4.20)	22-0295-80
2-Cyclohexen-1-one, 4-(3-chlorophenyl)-4-methyl-	EtOH	223(4.6)	22-0295-80
2-Cyclohexen-1-one, 4-(4-chlorophenyl)-4-methyl-	EtOH	225(4.24)	22-0295-80
$C_{13}H_{13}ClO_2$			
5H-Benzocycloheptene-8-carboxaldehyde, 9-chloro-6,7-dihydro-3-methoxy-	EtOH	317(4.3)	118-0326-80
1,3-Cyclohexadiene-1,3-diol, 5-(4-chlorophenyl)-5-methyl-	EtOH	221(4.09),260(4.18)	104-1298-80
1H-Inden-1-one, 2,3-dihydro-3-methyl-3-(2-oxopropyl)-5-chloro-	EtOH	252(4.08),289(3.41), 294(3.45)	104-1298-80
$C_{13}H_{13}Cl_2NO_3S$			
2H,6H-[1,3]Thiazino[3,2-b]isoquinolin-6-one, 11,11a-dichloro-3,4,11,11a-tetrahydro-11-methyl-, 1,1-dioxide	MeOH	210(4.3)	94-1131-80
$C_{13}H_{13}Cl_2NO_4S$			
2(1H)-Isoquinolinepropanesulfonyl chloride, 4-chloro-3,4-dihydro-4-methyl-1,3-dioxo-	MeOH	219(4.2)	94-1131-80
$C_{13}H_{13}Cl_2N_3O$			
Pyridinium, 1-[(4-chlorophenyl)methyl]-3-[(hydroxyamino)imino]methyl]-, chloride, monohydrochloride	pH 1	256(3.7)	64-0896-80B
	pH 7	256(3.7),286s(3.4)	64-0896-80B
	pH 11.7	256(3.8),321(3.6)	64-0896-80B
$C_{13}H_{13}N$			
Pyridine, 3-(2-phenylethyl)-	EtOH	222(3.92),258(3.42), 264(3.48),270(3.36)	39-0072-80C
	EtOH-HCl	232(3.96),267(3.79)	39-0072-80C
$C_{13}H_{13}NO$			
Benzocyclohepten-5,8-imin-9-one, 10-ethyl-5,8-dihydro-	EtOH	218(4.25),262(3.59)	39-2077-80C
5H-Benzocyclohepten-5-one, 7-(dimethylamino)-	EtOH	213(4.22),283(4.55), 290(4.56),358(4.00)	39-2077-80C
5H-Benzocyclohepten-5-one, 7-(ethylamino)-	EtOH	275(4.62),284(4.64), 346(3.96)	39-2077-80C
1H-Carbazol-1-one, 2,3,4,9-tetrahydro-9-methyl-	ether	238(4.29),304(4.37)	78-1585-80
2H-Carbazol-2-one, 1,3,4,9-tetrahydro-9-methyl-	EtOH	227(4.60),285(3.98)	39-1512-80C
Indeno[1,2-d]azepin-4(1H)-one, 2,3,5,10-tetrahydro-	EtOH	207(4.28),260(4.01)	18-3232-80

Compound	Solvent	$\lambda_{max}(\log \epsilon)$	Ref.
Phenol, 2-[(2-aminophenyl)methyl]-	MeOH	220(4.58),228(4.70), 283(4.38)	39-0522-80C
	acid	220(4.55),225(4.55), 276(4.29),280s(4.25)	39-0522-80C
	base	220(4.60),230(4.78), 294(4.51)	39-0522-80C
2-Propenal, 3-(2,3-dihydro-5-phenyl-1H-pyrrol-1-yl)-, (E)-	MeOH	205(4.08),228(3.89), 317(4.50)	83-0858-80
2(1H)-Quinolinone, 3-methyl-4-(1-methylethenyl)-	MeOH	221(4.54),271(3.87), 325(3.90),339(3.74)	88-1645-80

$C_{13}H_{13}NOS$
2H-1-Benzopyran-2-thione, 4-[2-(dimethylamino)ethenyl]-	MeCN	360(4.49),372(4.62), 468(4.71),490(4.70)	124-0965-80
4H-1-Benzopyran-4-thione, 2-[2-(dimethylamino)ethenyl]-	MeCN	375(4.53),424(4.21), 450(4.20)	124-0965-80
2-Furancarbothioamide, 5-methyl-N-(4-methylphenyl)-	EtOH	199(4.24),228s(3.93), 322(4.32)	128-0069-80
3-Furancarbothioamide, N,2-dimethyl-N-phenyl-	EtOH	202(4.27),294(4.17)	128-0069-80
3-Furancarbothioamide, 2-methyl-N-(4-methylphenyl)-	EtOH	206(4.31),293(4.05)	128-0069-80
3-Furancarbothioamide, 2-methyl-N-(phenylmethyl)-	EtOH	207(4.31),275(2.97)	128-0069-80

$C_{13}H_{13}NOS_3$
| Ethanethioic acid, O-[5-(ethylthio)-4-phenyl-3-isothiazolyl] ester | CHCl$_3$ | 316(3.79),378(4.20) | 39-2693-80C |

$C_{13}H_{13}NO_2$
5H-Benzocyclohepten-5,8-imin-9-one, 5,8-dihydro-10-(2-hydroxyethyl)-	EtOH	218(4.27),261(3.62)	39-2077-80C
5H-Benzocyclohepten-5-one, 7-[(2-hydroxyethyl)amino]-	EtOH	274(4.63),283(4.63), 342(3.95)	39-2077-80C
5H-Benzocyclohepten-5-one, 2-methoxy-7-(methylamino)-	EtOH	222(4.09),274(4.73), 340(3.94)	39-2077-80C
1H-Carbazol-1-one, 2,3,4,9-tetrahydro-5-hydroxy-6-methyl-	MeOH	205(4.32),247(4.41), 309(4.43),354(3.78)	5-0241-80
1H-Carbazol-1-one, 2,3,4,9-tetrahydro-7-hydroxy-6-methyl-	MeOH	206(4.30),237(4.00), 260(3.76),341(4.44)	5-0241-80
2-Furancarboxamide, 2-methyl-N-(4-methylphenyl)-	EtOH	202(4.12),286(4.33)	128-0069-80
3-Furancarboxamide, N,2-dimethyl-N-phenyl-	EtOH	202(4.12),244(3.83)	128-0069-80
3-Furancarboxamide, 2-methyl-N-(phenylmethyl)-	EtOH	210(4.22),237s(3.85)	128-0069-80
2-Propenoic acid, 3-(3-methyl-1H-indol-2-yl)-, methyl ester	EtOH	255(4.08),350(4.62)	78-2125-80
2H-Pyrrol-2-one, 1,3-dihydro-3-(1-hydroxyethylidene)-5-(phenylmethyl)-, (Z)-	EtOH	207s(4.20),238(4.01), 325(3.76)	33-0121-80

$C_{13}H_{13}NO_2S$
| 2-Propen-1-one, 3-(dimethylamino)-1-(3-hydroxybenzo[b]thien-2-yl)- | MeOH | 225(4.19),272(4.01), 295(3.82),306(3.84), 374(4.42) | 83-0385-80 |
| 4-Quinolinecarboxylic acid, 1,2-dihydro-2-thioxo-, propyl ester | EtOH | 222(4.53),288(4.32), 418(3.99) | 94-0049-80 |

$C_{13}H_{13}NO_3$
| Ethanone, 1-(3-acetoxy-1-methyl-1H- | MeOH | 238(4.26),306(4.30) | 83-0405-80 |

Compound	Solvent	$\lambda_{max}(\log \epsilon)$	Ref.
indol-2-yl)- (cont.)			83-0405-80
Ethanone, 1-(5,7-dimethoxy-8-isoquino-linyl)-	EtOH	221(4.29),241(4.52), 290s(3.84),300(3.88), 350(3.84)	39-0072-80C
	EtOH-HCl	224(4.39),262(4.53), 305(3.73),388(3.82)	39-0072-80C
1H-Indole-3-acetic acid, α-(methoxy-methylene)-, methyl ester	EtOH	205s(4.28),223(4.56), 281(3.92),290(3.92)	103-0045-80
5H-Pyrano[3,2-c]quinolin-5-one, 2,3,4,6-tetrahydro-2-hydroxy-2-methyl-	MeOH	225(4.66),260(3.90), 273(3.90),283(3.93), 314(4.10),324(3.85)	39-0512-80C
	MeOH-base	226(4.56),250s(4.20), 310(4.16)	39-0512-80C
2H-Pyrrol-2-one, 3-acetyl-1,5-dihydro-4-hydroxy-5-(phenylmethyl)-	EtOH	203s(4.11),272(4.14)	33-0121-80
$C_{13}H_{13}NO_3S$			
2-Quinolinecarbothioic acid, 4,8-di-methoxy-, S-methyl ester	MeOH	211(4.53),252(4.50), 355(3.71)	64-1569-80B
2H,6H-[1,3]Thiazino[3,2-b]isoquinolin-6-one, 3,4-dihydro-11-methyl-, 1,1-dioxide	MeOH	211(4.7),230s(4.4), 298(4.1)	94-1131-80
$C_{13}H_{13}NO_4$			
2H-1-Benzopyran-4-carboxamide, N-ethyl-7-methoxy-2-oxo-	EtOH	331(4.19)	95-0289-80
2H-1-Benzopyran-4-carboxamide, 7-meth-oxy-N,N-dimethyl-2-oxo-	EtOH	330(4.19)	95-0289-80
2-Furanacetic acid, 2,5-dihydro-4-meth-yl-5-oxo-3-(phenylamino)-	MeOH	205(3.88),288(4.17)	48-0559-80
2H-1,4-Oxazin-2-one, 3-(methoxycarbo-nylmethylene)-5-phenyl-3,4,5,6-tetrahydro-, (R)-	n.s.g.	325(3.92)	18-0561-80
1(2H)-Quinolineacetic acid, 4-methoxy-2-oxo-, methyl ester	EtOH	259s(3.73),289s(3.46)	78-1385-80
2-Quinolinecarboxylic acid, 4,8-di-methoxy-, methyl ester	MeOH	211(4.30),248(4.46), 310(3.46),345(3.54)	64-1569-80B
$C_{13}H_{13}NO_4S$			
3H-1,6-Methano-2,6-benzothiazonine-7,12(1H)-dione, 4,5-dihydro-1-methyl-, 2,2-dioxide	MeOH	206(4.4),273s(3.4)	94-1131-80
3H,7H-1,2,6-Oxathiazepino[6,7-b]iso-quinolin-7-one, 4,5-dihydro-12-methyl-, 2,2-dioxide	MeOH	209(4.5),228(4.3), 282(4.0)	94-1131-80
$C_{13}H_{13}NO_6$			
3,5-Isoxazoledicarboxylic acid, 4,5-di-hydro-5-hydroxy-4-phenyl-, dimethyl ester, cis	MeOH	224s(3.83),324(3.41)	94-0479-80
3,5-Isoxazoledicarboxylic acid, 4,5-di-hydro-4-phenyl-, dimethyl ester, 2-oxide	MeOH	267(3.99)	94-0479-80
$C_{13}H_{13}NO_{10}P_2$			
Diphosphoric acid, P-(4-methoxyphenyl) P'-(4-nitrophenyl) ester	pH 7	290(4.00)	94-1626-80
$C_{13}H_{13}N_2O_5PS$			
3(2H)-Pyridazinone, 5-(1,3,2-dioxaphos-pholan-2-yloxy)-4-methoxy-2-phenyl-, P-sulfide	MeOH	213(4.30),288(3.78)	73-2343-80

Compound	Solvent	$\lambda_{max}(\log \epsilon)$	Ref.
$C_{13}H_{13}N_3$			
Azulene, 4-(azidomethyl)-6,8-dimethyl-	hexane	246(4.37),286(4.67), 290(4.66),307s(3.85), 336(3.53),352(3.63), 390s(1.46),538s(2.57), 557(2.63),571(2.63), 593(2.58),619s(2.44), 650s(2.17),681s(1.76)	89-0621-80
Benzenamine, 4-[(4-methylphenyl)azo]-	EtOH	386(4.38)	7-0173-80
Imidazo[4,5-c]carbazole, 1,6,7,8,9,10-hexahydro-	EtOH	283(4.03),294(4.07), 303(4.06)	103-0062-80
1H-Perimidin-2(3H)-imine, 1,3-dimethyl-	CHCl₃	324(4.05),346(4.01)	104-1890-80
$C_{13}H_{13}N_3O$			
Benzenamine, 4-[(4-methoxyphenyl)azo]-	EtOH	387(4.41)	7-0173-80
Benzenepropanenitrile, α-[1-aziridinyl-(methylamino)methylene]-β-oxo-	MeOH	229(3.90),308(3.96)	78-1791-80
Benzenepropanenitrile, α-(1-methyl-2-imidazolidinylidene)-β-oxo-	MeOH	228(4.19),293(4.17)	78-1791-80
Methanone, [5-(dimethylamino)-2-pyridinyl]-3-pyridinyl-	n.s.g.	370(3.4)	25-0572-80
$C_{13}H_{13}N_3OS$			
2-Propanone, 1-[[5-(2-phenylethenyl)-1,3,4-thiadiazol-2-yl]amino]-	EtOH	317(4.46),327(4.45)	94-2116-80
$C_{13}H_{13}N_3O_2S$			
Acetamide, N-[5-acetyl-3-(3-methylphenyl)-1,3,4-thiadiazol-2(3H)-ylidene]-	EtOH	228s(3.85),283(3.81), 314(3.88)	4-1713-80
Acetamide, N-[5-acetyl-3-(4-methylphenyl)-1,3,4-thiadiazol-2(3H)-ylidene]-	EtOH	228s(3.96),285(4.26), 317(4.08)	4-1713-80
Acetamide, N-[5-(benzoylmethylene)-4,5-dihydro-4-methyl-1,3,4-thiadiazol-2-yl]-	EtOH	247(4.05),294(3.62), 378(4.39)	94-0447-80
Propenenitrile, 3,3-bis(1-aziridinyl)-2-(phenylsulfonyl)-	MeOH	220(4.26),289(4.30)	78-1791-80
4,6(1H,5H)-Pyrimidinedione, 5-[[4-(dimethylamino)phenyl]methylene]dihydro-2-thioxo-	benzene	484(4.9)	94-2518-80
$C_{13}H_{13}N_3O_2Se$			
Acetamide, N-[5-acetyl-3-(4-methylphenyl)-1,3,4-selenadiazol-2(3H)-ylidene]-	EtOH	258(4.14),321(4.07)	4-1185-80
$C_{13}H_{13}N_3O_3$			
Propanoic acid, 3-cyano-3-[(4-methylphenyl)hydrazono]-2-oxo-, ethyl ester	EtOH	247(3.79),363(4.01)	104-0751-80
3(2H)-Pyridazinone, 5-hydroxy-4-[[(1-methylethylidene)amino]oxy]-2-phenyl-	MeOH	212(4.25),233s(--), 302(4.06)	73-0127-80
2-Pyridinamine, N-[methoxy(4-nitrophenyl)methyl]-	MeOH	270(4.09),290(4.08)	48-0336-80
$C_{13}H_{13}N_3O_3S$			
Acetamide, N-[5-acetyl-3-(4-methoxyphenyl)-1,3,4-thiadiazol-2(3H)-ylidene]-	EtOH	227s(4.01),283(4.24), 317(3.97)	4-1713-80
$C_{13}H_{13}N_3O_3S_2$			
Acetic acid, [6-cyano-4,5-dihydro-8-(methylthio)-4-oxo-1H-thieno[3,4-b]-	EtOH	230(4.14),294(4.44), 350(4.15)	95-0699-80

Compound	Solvent	$\lambda_{max}(\log \epsilon)$	Ref.
[1,4]diazepin-2(3H)-ylidene]-, ethyl ester (cont.)			95-0699-80
$C_{13}H_{13}N_3O_3Se$			
1,3,4-Selenadiazole-2-carboxylic acid, 5-acetylamino-4,5-dihydro-4-phenyl-, ethyl ester	EtOH	318(3.98)	4-1185-80
$C_{13}H_{13}N_3O_4$			
Propanoic acid, 3-cyano-3-[(4-methoxyphenyl)hydrazono]-2-oxo-, ethyl ester	EtOH	247(4.03),375(4.41)	104-0751-80
4(1H)-Pyridazinone, 3-acetyl-5,6-dihydro-1-(4-nitrophenyl)-	EtOH	225(3.93),243(4.01), 384(4.45)	118-0623-80
2(1H)-Quinoxalinone, 3,4-dihydro-6-nitro-3-(2-oxocyclopentyl)-	EtOH	268(4.22),313(3.76), 394(3.66)	104-0938-80
1,2,4-Triazolidine-3,5-dione, 1-(1-acetyl-2-oxopropyl)-4-phenyl-	MeCN	272(3.602)	44-1232-80
$C_{13}H_{13}N_3O_7$			
2-Butenedioic acid, 2-[[[imino(4-nitrophenyl)methyl]amino]oxy]-, dimethyl ester, (E)-	MeOH	215(4.09),257(4.10), 300(3.86)	4-1101-80
$C_{13}H_{13}N_4O_2$			
Benzo[g]pteridinium, 4,10-dihydro-2-methoxy-3,10-dimethyl-4-oxo-, perchlorate	MeOH	420(4.18)	88-0739-80
$C_{13}H_{13}N_4O_3$			
Benzo[g]pteridinium, 1,2,3,4-tetrahydro-6-hydroxy-1,3,10-trimethyl-2,4-dioxo-, perchlorate	M HCl	210(4.21),255(3.97), 295(4.37),395(4.19)	151-0133-80B
Pyridinium, 3-[(hydroxyamino)iminomethyl]-1-(4-nitrophenyl)methyl]-, chloride, hydrochloride	pH 7	263(4.2)	64-0896-80B
	pH 11.5	259(4.2),324s(3.7)	64-0896-80B
	M NaOH	269(4.0),393(4.0)	64-0896-80B
$C_{13}H_{13}N_6O_7P$			
3H-Imidazo[2,1-i]purine-5-carboxamide, 3-(3,5-O-phosphinico-β-D-ribofuranosyl)-	pH 1	240(4.49),278(3.86), 309(3.79)	94-0115-80
$C_{13}H_{13}N_7O_2$			
1H-Pyrazole-4-carbonitrile, 5-(2-butenylideneamino)-1-methyl-3-(1-methyl-5-nitro-1H-imidazol-2-yl)-	MeOH-HCl	229(2.94),275(4.23)	83-0108-80
2,4(1H,3H)-Pyrimidinedione, 5-amino-1,3-dimethyl-6-(5-phenyl-2H-tetrazol-2-yl)-	EtOH	242s(4.24),275(4.09)	142-0285-80B
$C_{13}H_{14}$			
Azulene, 4,6,8-trimethyl-	EtOH	205(4.26),248(4.35), 290(4.5),339(3.52), 355(3.61),565(2.3)	103-0807-80
Benzene, (6-methyl-1,3-cyclohexadien-1-yl)-	EtOH	305(4.10)	78-3187-80
1,2,5-Heptatriene, 5-phenyl-	EtOH	273(4.31)	78-3187-80
1,3,5-Heptatriene, 5-phenyl-, (E,E)-	EtOH	254(4.45),265(4.32)	78-3187-80
(E,Z)-	EtOH	255(4.44),265(4.52), 275(4.43)	78-3187-80
(Z,E)-	EtOH	235(4.16)	78-3187-80

Compound	Solvent	$\lambda_{max}(\log \epsilon)$	Ref.
1,3,5-Heptatriene, 5-phenyl-, (Z,Z)-	EtOH	255(4.37),265(4.42), 275(4.35)	78-3187-80
$C_{13}H_{14}BrN_3O$			
Pyridinium, 2-[(hydroxyamino)iminometh-yl]-1-(phenylmethyl)-, bromide	H_2O pH 10.7	259(3.7),312(3.0) 259(3.8),383(3.1)	64-0896-80B 64-0896-80B
$C_{13}H_{14}ClN_3OS$			
6H-Pyrimido[4,5-b][1,4]benzothiazine, 4-chloro-7,8-dihydro-9-methoxy-7,7-dimethyl-	EtOH	223(4.25),257(4.18), 275s(3.98),352(3.97), 420s(3.51)	103-0580-80
5H-Pyrimido[4,5-b][1,4]benzothiazin-9(6H)-one, 4-chloro-7,8-dihydro-5,7,7-trimethyl-	EtOH	221(4.23),248(3.95), 358(3.85)	103-0580-80
$C_{13}H_{14}N_2$			
2,3'-Bipyridine, 2',5',6'-trimethyl-	MeOH	262(3.9),268(4.0)	103-0951-80
1H-Cyclopent[2,3]azirino[1,2-b]pyra-zole, 4a,5,6,7-tetrahydro-2-phenyl-	EtOH	253.4(4.09)	35-1176-80
3H-Indole, 3-(1-pyrrolidinylmethylene)-	$CHCl_3$	277(4.24),282(4.29), 362(4.45)	94-1711-80
hydrochloride	MeOH	249s(3.98),258s(4.04), 268s(3.87),276(3.82), 348(4.29)	94-1711-80
1H-Perimidine, 2,3-dihydro-1,3-dimeth-yl-	50% H_2SO_4	236(4.48),280(3.58), 300(3.65),315(3.77), 334(3.81),390(2.77), 400(2.77),425(2.69), 460(2.7),490(2.72), 520(2.58),530(2.52)	103-0541-80
	18M H_2SO_4	224(4.22),285(4.09), 325(3.8),372(3.28), 385(3.31),450(2.86), 480(3.1),520(3.56), 540(3.8)	103-0541-80
Perimidine, 2,3-dihydro-1,3-dimethyl-	$CHCl_3$	344(4.27)	104-1890-80
1H-Pyrazole, 1,5-dimethyl-4-(2-phenyl-ethenyl)-	EtOH	298(4.35)	65-1922-80
Pyridazine, 3-phenyl-5-propyl-	EtOH EtOH-HCl	219(3.96),252(4.03) 220(3.99),241(4.01), 262(4.02)	39-0072-80C 39-0072-80C
$C_{13}H_{14}N_2O$			
Azepino[4,5-e]indol-9(3H)-one, 6,7,8,10-tetrahydro-3-methyl-	EtOH	276(3.84),288(3.80), 300(3.68)	94-0900-80
Azepino[4,5-f]indol-6(1H)-one, 5,7,8,9-tetrahydro-1-methyl-	EtOH	280(3.81),286(3.81)	94-0900-80
Azepino[4,5-f]indol-8(1H)-one, 5,6,7,9-tetrahydro-1-methyl-	EtOH	279(3.82),286(3.81)	94-0900-80
1,3-Diazabicyclo[2.2.0]hex-5-en-2-one, 4,6-dimethyl-3-(2-methylphenyl)-	EtOH	229(4.00),267s(2.91)	39-0607-80C
1,3-Diazabicyclo[2.2.0]hex-5-en-2-one, 4,6-dimethyl-3-(4-methylphenyl)-	EtOH	243(4.79),276s(4.17), 285(4.02)	39-0607-80C
Ethanone, 1-[5-methyl-2-(4-methylphen-yl)-1H-imidazol-4-yl]-	EtOH	287(4.31)	4-1723-80
3H-Indole, 3-(morpholinomethylene)-	$CHCl_3$	277s(3.96),283(4.02), 364(4.02)	94-1711-80
4-Isoquinolinecarbonitrile, 3-ethoxy-1,2-dihydro-1-methyl-	n.s.g.	262(4.04),312(3.95)	88-0865-80
3-Pyridinecarboxamide, 1,4-dihydro-1-(phenylmethyl)-	DMF	346(3.80)	35-7591-80

Compound	Solvent	$\lambda_{max}(\log \epsilon)$	Ref.
1H-Pyrido[3,4-b]indol-1-one, 2,3,4,9-tetrahydro-2,6-dimethyl-	isoPrOH	228(4.41),306(4.28)	103-0244-80
1H-Pyrido[3,4-b]indol-1-one, 2,3,4,9-tetrahydro-2,8-dimethyl-	isoPrOH	231(4.41),239s(4.39), 304(4.25),324s(3.87)	103-0244-80
1H-Pyrido[3,4-b]indol-1-one, 2,3,4,9-tetrahydro-2,9-dimethyl-	isoPrOH	225s(4.28),230(4.30), 240s(4.24),302(4.19), 327s(3.77)	103-0244-80
$(C_{13}H_{14}N_2O)_n$ 3H-Indole, 3-(morpholinomethylene)-, polymer	CHCl₃	279s(3.80),286(3.86)	94-1711-80
$C_{13}H_{14}N_2OS$ Pyrimidine, 2-[(3-phenoxypropyl)thio]-	EtOH	221(3.971),251(4.168), 283s(3.238)	112-0001-80
	CH₂Cl₂	252(4.188),283s(3.263)	112-0001-80
$C_{13}H_{14}N_2O_2$ 1H-1,3-Benzodiazepine-1-carboxylic acid, 2-methyl-, ethyl ester	EtOH	240(3.95),285(3.72)	94-2602-80
Ethanone, 1-[2-(4-methoxyphenyl)-5-methyl-1H-imidazol-4-yl]-	EtOH	289(4.29)	4-1723-80
1H-Imidazole-4-carboxylic acid, 5-methyl-2-phenyl-, ethyl ester	EtOH	277(4.36)	4-1723-80
4(1H)-Pyridazinone, 3-acetyl-5,6-dihydro-6-methyl-1-phenyl-	EtOH	224(3.76),251(3.98), 370(4.22)	118-0623-80
3(2H)-Pyridinone, 1-acetyl-1,6-dihydro-5-(phenylamino)-	EtOH	308(4.34)	4-0001-80
1H-Pyrido[3,4-b]indol-1-one, 2,3,4,9-tetrahydro-6-methoxy-2-methyl-	isoPrOH	216(4.53),221s(4.52), 300s(4.35),309(4.39), 336s(3.83)	103-0244-80
4(1H)-Pyrimidinone, 5-(4-ethoxyphenyl)-1-methyl-	EtOH	223(4.28),297(4.06)	22-0559-80
4(3H)-Pyrimidinone, 5-(4-ethoxyphenyl)-3-methyl-	EtOH	223(3.93),312(4.07)	22-0559-80
$C_{13}H_{14}N_2O_3$ Benzenebutanenitrile, 4-(2-cyanoethoxy)-β,γ-dihydroxy-	MeOH	273(2.98)	44-5383-80
1,8-Naphthyridine-3-acetic acid, 1,4-dihydro-7-methyl-4-oxo-, ethyl ester	EtOH	247(4.23),276(3.46), 286(3.40),333(3.90)	39-0227-80C
2-Propenoic acid, 2-cyano-3-[5-(1-pyrrolidinyl)-2-furanyl]-, methyl ester	MeOH	208(3.75),235(4.13), 471(4.74)	73-1831-80
1H-Pyrazole-3-carboxylic acid, 4-hydroxy-1-(4-methylphenyl)-, ethyl ester	EtOH	251(4.01),295(4.14)	142-0697-80B
Pyrido[1,2-a]pyrimidine-3-acetic acid, 6-methyl-4-oxo-, ethyl ester	EtOH	248(3.99),360(3.99)	39-0227-80C
1H-Pyrrole-3-carboxylic acid, 2,5-dihydro-1-(6-methyl-2-pyridinyl)-5-oxo-, ethyl ester	EtOH	229(4.16),305(3.88)	39-0227-80C
1H-Pyrrole-3-carboxylic acid, 4,5-dihydro-1-(6-methyl-2-pyridinyl)-5-oxo-, ethyl ester	EtOH	249(4.07),294(4.15)	39-0227-80C
$C_{13}H_{14}N_2O_4$ 6-Phthalazinecarboxylic acid, 3,4-dihydro-1-(hydroxymethyl)-4-oxo-, 1-methylethyl ester	EtOH	251(3.87),261(3.86), 307(3.90)	94-2770-80
2-Propenoic acid, 2-cyano-3-(5-morpholino-2-furanyl)-, methyl ester	MeOH	211(4.15),237(4.29), 462(4.68)	73-1831-80

Compound	Solvent	$\lambda_{max}(\log \epsilon)$	Ref.
1H-Pyrazole-3-carboxylic acid, 4-hydroxy-1-(4-methoxyphenyl)-, ethyl ester	EtOH	260(3.98),291(4.19)	142-0697-80B
2(1H)-Pyridinone, 3,3'-methylenebis[4-hydroxy-6-methyl-	MeOH	210(4.44),290(4.03)	39-0522-80C
	acid	210(4.42),226(4.13), 285(4.02)	39-0522-80C
	base	216(4.67),284(4.03)	39-0522-80C
2-Quinoxalinecarboxylic acid, 3,4-dihydro-5-methoxy-6,7-dimethyl-3-oxo-, methyl ester	MeOH	237(4.42),262(3.83), 304(3.71)	54-0115-80
$C_{13}H_{14}N_2O_5$			
2-Butenedioic acid, 2-[[(iminophenylmethyl)amino]oxy]-, dimethyl ester, (E)-	MeOH	224(4.07),273(3.19)	4-1101-80
(Z)-	MeOH	222(4.07),276(4.16)	4-1101-80
2-Quinoxalinecarboxylic acid, 3,4-dihydro-5-methoxy-6,7-dimethyl-3-oxo-, methyl ester, 1-oxide	MeOH	232(4.56),264(4.34), 279(3.81),304(4.00)	54-0115-80
$C_{13}H_{14}N_2O_{10}S$			
β-D-Glucopyranosiduronic acid, 2,4-dinitrophenyl 1-thio-, methyl ester	MeOH	317(4.11)	106-0460-80
$C_{13}H_{14}N_2O_{11}$			
β-D-Glucopyranosiduronic acid, 2,4-dinitrophenyl, methyl ester	MeOH	283(4.15)	106-0460-80
$C_{13}H_{14}N_2S_2$			
Propanedinitrile, [[5-[(3-methylbutyl)-thio]-2-thienyl]methylene]-	MeOH	206(4.05),242(3.77), 284(3.63),343(4.30)	73-2360-80
$C_{13}H_{14}N_3O$			
Pyridinium, 2-[(hydroxyamino)iminomethyl]-1-(phenylmethyl)-, bromide	H_2O	259(3.7),312(3.0)	64-0896-80B
	pH 10.7	259(3.8),383(3.1)	64-0896-80B
$C_{13}H_{14}N_4O_2$			
Benzamide, N-[1-(2,5-dihydro-3-methyl-5-oxo-1,2,4-triazin-6-yl)ethyl]-	EtOH	231(4.27),266s(3.81)	39-1139-80C
Benzo[g]pteridine-2,4(1H,3H)-dione, 5,10-dihydro-7,8,10-trimethyl-	DMF-Et_4NClO_4	342(3.7),440(3.6)	35-7591-80
1,3,5-Triazin-2(5H)-one, 4-morpholino-6-phenyl-	n.s.g.	231(4.36)	115-0243-80
$C_{13}H_{14}N_4O_4$			
Imidazo[1,2-a]pyrido[2,3-d]pyrimidine-7-carboxylic acid, 9-ethyl-1,2,3,5-6,9-hexahydro-1-methyl-5,6-dioxo-	EtOH	268(4.27),290s(3.64)	95-1187-80
$C_{13}H_{14}N_4O_8$			
Pentanedioic acid, 3-[(2,4-dinitrophenyl)hydrazono]-, dimethyl ester	pH 1 and 7	223(4.12),258(4.03), 362(4.32)	4-0159-80
	pH 11	230(4.14),242s(4.11), 332(3.99)	4-0159-80
$C_{13}H_{14}N_4S$			
2H-1,2,4-Triazino[5,6-b]indole, 2,6,7-trimethyl-3-(methylthio)-	EtOH	232(4.03),278(4.56), 336(3.70)	142-1139-80
	EtOH-HCl	236(4.01),284(4.55), 354(3.71)	142-1139-80

Compound	Solvent	λ_{max}(log ϵ)	Ref.
4H-1,2,4-Triazino[5,6-b]indole, 4,6,7- trimethyl-3-(methylthio)-	EtOH EtOH-HCl	266(4.37),364(4.06) 228(4.05),270(4.35), 370(4.03)	142-1139-80 142-1139-80
5H-1,2,4-Triazino[5,6-b]indole, 5,6,7- trimethyl-3-(methylthio)-	EtOH	232(4.15),272(4.43), 354(3.89)	142-1139-80
3H-1,2,4-Triazino[5,6-b]indole-3-thi- one, 2,4-dihydro-2,4,6,7-tetramethyl-	EtOH	248(3.83),262(4.09), 290(4.49),382(3.92)	142-1139-80
3H-1,2,4-Triazino[5,6-b]indole-3-thi- one, 2,5-dihydro-2,5,6,7-tetramethyl-	EtOH	242(4.19),268(4.24), 306(4.92),370(3.73)	142-1139-80
C₁₃H₁₄N₆O			
Acetic acid, 2-methyl-2-(2-methyl- [1,2,4]triazolo[1,5-a]quinazolin- 5-yl)hydrazide	n.s.g.	223(4.53),290(3.75), 302(3.83),327(3.89)	33-0001-80
Pyridazino[3,4-b]quinoxaline-4-carbox- ylic acid, 1,2-dihydro-1-methyl-, 1-methylhydrazide	EtOH	255(4.64),412(4.06), 448(4.06)	94-3537-80
C₁₃H₁₄N₆O₄			
Acetamide, N,N'-[6-(acetoxymethyl)- 2,4-pteridinediyl]bis-	MeOH	210s(4.22),232(4.12), 260(4.49),350(3.93)	24-1514-80
C₁₃H₁₄O			
4-Azulenemethanol, 6,8-dimethyl-	dioxan	234s(4.21),248(4.38), 288(4.67),291s(4.66), 297s(4.59),329s(3.51), 335(3.59),345s(3.63), 350(3.70),550(2.68), 581s(2.63),635s(2.22)	89-0621-80
1H-Benz[e]inden-1-one, 2,3,6,7,8,9- hexahydro-	EtOH	252(4.09)	23-1344-80
1H-Benz[f]inden-1-one, 2,3,5,6,7,8- hexahydro-	EtOH	255(4.15)	23-1344-80
3H-Benz[e]inden-3-one, 1,2,6,7,8,9- hexahydro-	EtOH	261(3.93)	23-1344-80
5H-Benz[f]inden-5-one, 1,2,3,6,7,8- hexahydro-	EtOH	261(4.06)	23-1344-80
6H-Benz[e]inden-6-one, 1,2,3,7,8,9- hexahydro-	EtOH	263(4.19)	23-1344-80
9H-Benz[e]inden-9-one, 1,2,3,6,7,8- hexahydro-	EtOH	253(4.17)	23-1344-80
2-Cyclohexen-1-one, 2-methyl-3-phenyl-	EtOH	266(4.146)	104-0037-80
2-Cyclohexen-1-one, 4-methyl-3-phenyl-	EtOH EtOH	280(4.15) 270(4.06)	22-0267-80 78-3187-80
2-Cyclohexen-1-one, 4-methyl-4-phenyl-	EtOH	220(4.04)	22-0267-80
3,5,7,9-Dodecatetraen-11-yn-2-one, 10-methyl-	ether	246s(3.83),254(3.93), 333s(4.73),349(4.88), 365(4.85)	44-3564-80
2,4-Pentadienal, 3-methyl-5-(4-methyl- phenyl)-	EtOH	246(4.06),328(4.34)	118-0815-80
4-Pentenal, 3-methyl-2-(phenylmethyl- ene)-, (E)-	EtOH	226(4.28),282(4.25)	39-1477-80C
4-Pentenal, 4-methyl-2-(phenylmethyl- ene)-, (E)-	EtOH	218(4.00),225(3.95), 283(4.32)	39-1477-80C
C₁₃H₁₄OS₂			
1,2-Dithiol-1-ium, 3-(1,1-dimethyleth- yl)-4-hydroxy-5-phenyl-, hydroxide, inner salt	EtOH dioxan MeCN	465(4.03) 521(3.90) 502(3.96)	139-0079-80A 139-0079-80A 139-0079-80A

Compound	Solvent	$\lambda_{max}(\log \epsilon)$	Ref.
$C_{13}H_{14}O_2$			
2-Cyclohexen-1-one, 3-hydroxy-5-methyl-5-phenyl-	EtOH	257(4.20)	104-1298-80
1H-Inden-1-one, 2,3-dihydro-3-methyl-3-(2-oxopropyl)-	EtOH	212(4.04),246(3.97), 286(3.36)	104-1298-80
2-Naphthalenecarboxylic acid, 3,4-dihydro-5,8-dimethyl-	EtOH	220(4.65),305(5.02)	2-0753-80
2,4-Pentadienal, 5-(4-methoxyphenyl)-3-methyl-	EtOH	250(4.02),352(4.29)	118-0815-80
2,4-Pentadienoic acid, 3-methyl-5-(4-methylphenyl)-	EtOH	240(4.00),320(4.47)	118-0815-80
Spiro[cyclohexane-1,1'(3'H)-isobenzofuran]-3'-one	EtOH	274(3.30),282(3.29)	44-1828-80
Spiro[1,3-dioxolane-2,2'(3'H)-[3a,7a]-etheno[1H]indene]	EtOH	<u>222f(3.4)</u>,266(<u>3.5</u>)	88-3583-80
$C_{13}H_{14}O_2S_2$			
Spiro[1,3-dithiane-2,2'(1'H)-naphthalene]-5',8'-dione, 3',4'-dihydro-	EtOH	250(4.1),335(2.8)	118-0753-80
$C_{13}H_{14}O_3$			
1,3-Cyclopentanedione, 2-(2-methoxyphenyl)-2-methyl-	n.s.g.	272(3.27),279(3.26)	44-0501-80
1,3-Dioxen-4-one, 2-ethyl-2-methyl-6-phenyl- (general spectrum of class)	EtOH	285-315(3.98-4.25)	104-1995-80
Naphthalene, 1,3,8-trimethoxy-	CHCl$_3$	281s(3.65),289(3.75), 300(3.76),323(3.59), 336(3.66)	12-2531-80
2,4-Pentadienoic acid, 5-(4-methoxyphenyl)-3-methyl-	EtOH	242(4.03),331(4.43)	118-0815-80
$C_{13}H_{14}O_3S$			
Ethanone, 1-[3-(phenylsulfonyl)-1-cyclopenten-1-yl]-	EtOH	242(4.11)	35-1602-80
$C_{13}H_{14}O_4$			
2-Benzofurancarboxylic acid, 3-ethoxy-, ethyl ester	EtOH	286(4.53)	23-0786-80
2-Benzofurancarboxylic acid, 2-ethyl-2,3-dihydro-3-oxo-, ethyl ester	EtOH	253(4.08),328(3.70)	23-0786-80
4H-1-Benzopyran-4-one, 2,3-dihydro-2-hydroxy-7-methyl-6-(2-propenyloxy)-	MeOH MeOH-NaOH	228(4.80),324(4.22) 227(4.37),324(4.20)	42-0532-80 42-0532-80
1H-Cyclopenta[b]benzofuran-1-one, 2,3,3a,8b-tetrahydro-3a-hydroxy-7-methoxy-8b-methyl-, cis	n.s.g.	287(3.42)	44-0501-80
2(3H)-Furanone, 3-acetyldihydro-3-(4-methoxyphenyl)-	MeOH	230(3.99),275(3.20), 280(3.15)	12-0113-80
1(3H)-Isobenzofuranone, 5-hydroxy-7-[(3-methyl-2-butenyl)oxy]-	EtOH	218(4.42),258(4.06), 292(3.90)	2-0927-80
1(4H)-Naphthalenone, 3,4,4-trimethoxy-	MeOH	248(4.03),284(3.90)	44-3422-80
2(1H)-Naphthalenone, 1,1,4-trimethoxy-	MeOH	229(4.29),316(3.95)	44-3422-80
Spiro[1,3-benzodioxole-2,1'-cycloheptane]-5,6-dione	EtOH	293(4.13),396(3.15)	12-0527-80
Spiro[1,3-benzodioxole-2,1'-cyclohexane]-5-carboxylic acid	EtOH	220(4.32),265(3.81), 299(3.85)	12-0527-80
Spiro[1,3-benzodioxole-2,1'-cyclopentane], 5-acetoxy-	EtOH	235(3.50),287(3.64)	12-0527-80
$C_{13}H_{14}O_4S$			
2-Propenoic acid, 3-[(2-methoxy-2-oxoethyl)thio]-3-phenyl-, methyl ester, (Z)-	EtOH	210(4.04),276(4.03)	18-1739-80

Compound	Solvent	$\lambda_{max}(\log \epsilon)$	Ref.
$C_{13}H_{14}O_6$ 1,2,3-Benzenetricarboxylic acid, 5-methyl-, trimethyl ester	MeOH	287(2.96),295(2.89)	44-4573-80
$C_{13}H_{14}S$ Bicyclo[2.2.1]hept-2-ene, 5-(phenyl- thio)-, exo	THF	256(3.78)	39-0237-80C
$C_{13}H_{15}$ 1,4-Ethano-1H-benzocycloheptenylium, 2,3,4,?-tetrahydro-, (deloc-4a,5,6- 7,8,9,9a)-, tetrafluoroborate	CH₂Cl₂ MeCN	230(4.57),285(3.70), 300(3.66) 225(4.64),284(3.68), 297s(3.64)	89-0545-80 89-0545-80
$C_{13}H_{15}BrN$ Quinolinium, 1-(3-bromopropyl)- 4-methyl-, bromide	H₂O	315(4.3)	104-2044-80
$C_{13}H_{15}ClN_2$ 3H-Indole, 3-(1-pyrrolidinylmethyl- ene)-, hydrochloride	MeOH	249s(3.98),258s(4.04), 268s(3.87),276(3.82), 348(4.29)	94-1711-80
$C_{13}H_{15}ClN_2O$ Acetamide, 2-chloro-N-[2-(1-methyl-1H- indol-5-yl)ethyl]- Acetamide, 2-chloro-N-[2-(1-methyl-1H- indol-6-yl)ethyl]-	EtOH EtOH	274(3.81),283(3.83), 293(3.74) 275(3.77),287(3.74), 298(3.58)	94-0900-80 94-0900-80
$C_{13}H_{15}ClN_4O_5$ 9H-Purine, 2-chloro-6-(2-propenyloxy)- 9-β-D-ribopyranosyl-	pH 1,7 and 12	258s(4.10)	4-0461-80
$C_{13}H_{15}Cl_2N_3O$ 1H-Benzotriazole, 4,5-dichloro-1-(cy- cloheptyloxy)-	EtOH	209(4.42),265(3.90), 272(3.91),294(3.75)	4-1115-80
$C_{13}H_{15}N$ 1H-Pyrrole, 2,3-dimethyl-1-(phenyl- methyl)-	EtOH	205(4.24),258(2.91), 263(2.85),269(2.67)	44-2741-80
$C_{13}H_{15}NO$ 1-Azaspiro[2.5]octan-4-one, 2-phenyl-, cis trans 1H-Carbazol-1-ol, 2,3,4,9-tetrahydro- 9-methyl- 2-Cyclohexen-1-one, 2-(methylphenyl- amino)- Isoquinoline, 7-methoxy-1-propyl- 3-Penten-2-one, 4-[(1-phenylethyli- dene)amino]-, (Z,?)-	ether ether ether ether MeOH n.s.g.	213(3.68),234(3.55), 286(2.33) 232(3.71),288(2.61) 228(4.41),286(3.72) 292(3.40) 234(4.52),271(4.19), 288(4.04),322(3.39), 332(3.42) 213(4.58),247(4.57), 316(4.62)	88-2947-80 88-2947-80 78-1585-80 78-1585-80 142-1151-80 39-1866-80C
$C_{13}H_{15}NO_2$ Cyclobuta[c]quinolin-3(1H)-one, 2,2a,4,8b-tetrahydro-8b-hydroxy- 1,1-dimethyl- 1H-Isoindol-1-one, 2-ethyl-2,3-dihydro- 3-(2-oxopropyl)-	MeOH EtOH	211(4.42),251(4.00), 282(3.82),292s(3.30) 222(4.00),229(3.99), 279(3.23)	94-3150-80 39-2077-80C

Compound	Solvent	$\lambda_{max}(\log \epsilon)$	Ref.
$C_{13}H_{15}NO_3S$ Sulfonium, dimethyl-, 1-[(benzoylamino)carbonyl]-2-oxopropylide	EtOH	236(4.47),279(4.11)	94-0795-80
$C_{13}H_{15}NO_4S$ Pyrrolo[2,1-b]thiazole-6,7-dicarboxylic acid, 3-methyl-, diethyl ester	EtOH	225(4.18),235(4.18), 243(4.18),291(3.96)	18-3308-80
$C_{13}H_{15}NO_5$ 2H-1-Benzopyran, 2,4-diethoxy-3-nitro-	EtOH	238(3.30),310(3.47), 350(3.41)	39-2049-80C
1-Benzoxepin, 2-ethoxy-2,3-dihydro-5-methoxy-4-nitro-	EtOH	235(3.83),302(3.93)	39-2049-80C
$C_{13}H_{15}N_3$ Pyridinium, 1-methyl-4-[[(1-methylpyridinium-4-yl)imino]methyl]-, diiodide	pH 5.95	278(4.27)	12-1397-80
$C_{13}H_{15}N_3O$ Pyrrolo[3,2-e]benzimidazole-3(6H)-ethanol, 7,8-dimethyl-	EtOH	301(4.22)	103-0062-80
$C_{13}H_{15}N_3OS$ 4-Imidazolidinone, 5-imino-1-(phenylmethyl)-3-propyl-2-thioxo-	EtOH	309.5(4.20)	18-0442-80
$C_{13}H_{15}N_3O_2$ 1,3-Dioxolo[4,5-g]quinazolin-8-amine, N-butyl-	EtOH	210(4.34),222s(4.20), 242(4.40),278(3.79), 290(3.82),306s(3.86), 318(4.05),328s(3.92), 333(4.03)	114-0253-80B
Ethanone, 1-(5,7-dimethoxy-8-isoquinolinyl)-, hydrazone	EtOH	214(4.38),239(4.44), 291s(3.77),300(3.79), 349(3.67)	39-0072-80C
	EtOH-HCl	220(4.39),261(4.43), 310(3.71),388(3.57)	39-0072-80C
$C_{13}H_{15}N_3O_2S$ 5H-Pyrimido[4,5-b][1,4]benzothiazin-9(6H)-one, 7,8-dihydro-4-methoxy-7,7-dimethyl-	EtOH	217(4.23),255(4.21), 293(3.90),333(3.98), 464(4.32)	103-0580-80
Thiourea, N-[7-(dimethylamino)-4-methyl-2-oxo-2H-1-benzopyran-3-yl]-	EtOH	256(4.18),309(3.56), 322(3.53),403(4.59)	95-0289-80
$C_{13}H_{15}N_3O_3$ 2-Quinoxalinecarboxylic acid, 5-methoxy-6,7-dimethyl-3-(methylamino)-	MeOH	222(4.50),262(4.52), 331(3.72),416(3.68)	54-0115-80
$C_{13}H_{15}N_3O_4$ D-Ribitol, 1,4-anhydro-1-C-(5-phenyl-1H-1,2,4-triazol-3-yl)-, (S)-	H_2O	244(4.17)	44-0203-80
1,2,3-Triazole, 4-α-D-lyxofuranosyl-	MeOH	266(4.3)	88-0183-80 136-0093-80H
1,2,3-Triazole, 4-β-D-lyxofuranosyl-	MeOH	265(4.4)	88-0183-80
$C_{13}H_{15}N_3O_5$ L-Leucine, N-(5-benzofurazanylcarbonyl)-, N-oxide	EtOH	223(4.43),260s(3.57), 315s(3.40),333s(3.51), 366(3.70)	4-0213-80

Compound	Solvent	$\lambda_{max}(\log \epsilon)$	Ref.
L-Leucine, N-(5-benzofurazanylcarbonyl)-, N-oxide (cont.)	MeCN	222(4.39),265s(3.34), 315s(3.38),332s(3.49), 365(3.82)	4-0213-80
L-Valine, N-(5-benzofurazanylcarbonyl)-, N-oxide, methyl ester	EtOH	223(4.44),265s(3.59), 315s(3.49),333s(3.58), 365(3.88)	4-0213-80
	MeCN	222(4.47),265s(3.51), 315s(3.46),332s(3.58), 364(3.88)	4-0213-80
$C_{13}H_{15}N_5O_2$ Methanimidamide, N,N-dimethyl-N'-[3-methyl-1-(4-nitrophenyl)-1H-pyrazol-5-yl]-	EtOH	287(4.22),325(4.19)	114-0127-80C
$C_{13}H_{15}N_5O_2S$ Hydrazinecarbothioamide, 2-methyl-N-phenyl-2-(1,2,3,6-tetrahydro-1-methyl-2,6-dioxo-4-pyrimidinyl)-	MeOH	268(4.25)	4-1305-80
$C_{13}H_{15}N_5O_3$ 4,12-Epoxy-4H-1,3-dioxolo[5,6]azepino-[1,2-e]purin-7-amine, 3a,5,12,12a-tetrahydro-2,2-dimethyl-, [3aR-(3aα,4β,12β,12aα)]-	EtOH	264(4.18)	78-1579-80
$C_{13}H_{15}N_7O_5$ 2H-Pyrrolo[2,3-d:5,4-d']dipyrimidin-2-one, 4,5-diamino-1,9-dihydro-9-β-D-ribofuranosyl-	pH 1 pH 11 MeOH	287(4.14),311(4.06) 307(4.22) 294.5(4.24)	88-1599-80 88-1599-80 88-1599-80
4H-Pyrrolo[2,3-d:5,4-d']dipyrimidin-4-one, 2,5-diamino-1,9-dihydro-9-β-D-ribofuranosyl-	pH 1 pH 11 MeOH	303(4.23) 303.5(4.18) 303(4.27),313(4.21)	88-1599-80 88-1599-80 88-1599-80
$C_{13}H_{15}P$ 1H-Phosphole, 3,4-dimethyl-1-(phenylmethyl)-, PdCl$_2$ complex (2:1)	CHCl$_3$	244(4.52),262(4.57), 349(3.60)	125-0709-80
$C_{13}H_{16}$ Benzene, 2-(1,3-butadienyl)-1,3,5-trimethyl-	C_6H_{12}	219(4.35),270(4.22)	39-0805-80B
Bicyclo[4.1.0]heptane, 2-phenyl-, trans	pentane	259(2.67)	33-0588-80
$C_{13}H_{16}AsCl_2N$ 1H-Arsindole-2-methanamine, 1,3-dichloro-N,N-diethyl-, hydrochloride	EtOH	<u>227(4.4),312(3.7)</u>	4-1341-80
$C_{13}H_{16}ClNO$ Ethanone, 1-(2-chlorophenyl)-2-(1-methyl-1-pyrrolidinyl)-, hydrochloride	EtOH	240(3.74)	48-0475-80 +115-0265-80
Ethanone, 1-(4-chlorophenyl)-2-(1-methyl-1-pyrrolidinyl)-, hydrochloride	EtOH	255(4.24)	48-0475-80 +115-0265-80
$C_{13}H_{16}IN_5O_3$ Adenosine, 5'-deoxy-5'-iodo-2',3'-O-(1-methylethylidene)-	MeOH	259(4.15)	44-0788-80
$C_{13}H_{16}IN_5O_4$ Adenosine, 5'-deoxy-5'-iodo-2',3'-O-(1-methylethylidene)-, 1-oxide	MeOH	233(4.58),261(3.91), 296(3.38)	44-0788-80
	MeOH-HCl	257(4.05)	44-0788-80

Compound	Solvent	$\lambda_{max}(\log \epsilon)$	Ref.
Adenosine, 5'-deoxy-5'-iodo-2',3'-O-(1-methylethylidene)-, 1-oxide (cont.)	MeOH-NaOH	233(4.33),267(3.86), 314(3.56)	44-0788-80
$C_{13}H_{16}N_2$			
Ethanamine, N-ethyl-N-(3H-indol-3-ylidenemethyl)-	CHCl$_3$	277s(4.21),282(4.30), 364(4.30)	94-1711-80
1,8-Naphthalenediamine, N,N,N'-trimethyl-	CHCl$_3$	351(3.98)	104-1890-80
$C_{13}H_{16}N_2O$			
5-Oxazolamine, 4-methyl-N-(1-methylethyl)-N-phenyl-	EtOH	242(4.16)	4-0705-80
4(3H)-Quinazolinone, 2-methyl-3-(1-methylpropyl)-	EtOH	207(4.33),226(4.42), 268(3.95),297(3.48), 306(3.56),318(3.45)	1-0637-80
$C_{13}H_{16}N_2O_2$			
2-Butenamide, 2-acetyl-3-amino-N-(phenylmethyl)-	MeOH	240(3.42),302(4.14)	44-0936-80
Imidazo[2,1-a]isoquinoline, 2,3,5,6-tetrahydro-8,9-dimethoxy-	EtOH	223(4.37),264(4.06)	94-1810-80
$C_{13}H_{16}N_2O_3$			
1(2H)-Isoquinolinone, 3-(dimethylamino)-6,7-dimethoxy-	EtOH	248(4.56),302(4.20), 344(3.72)	95-0826-80
2-Propenoic acid, 2-cyano-3-[5-(diethylamino)-2-furanyl]-, methyl ester	MeOH	237(4.21),464(4.91)	73-1831-80
$C_{13}H_{16}N_2O_5$			
2,5'-Anhydrouridine, 2',3'-O-(1-methylethylidene)-5-methyl-	EtOH	244(4.06)	33-2179-80
1H-Benzimidazole-1,3(2H)-dicarboxylic acid, 2-hydroxy-, ethyl ester	CHCl$_3$	246(4.17),285(3.63), 291(3.54)	35-6784-80
Carbamic acid, [2-[(ethoxycarbonyl)-amino]phenyl]formyl-, ethyl ester	H$_2$O	228(4.01),271(2.90)	35-6784-80
Cyclopropanecarboxamide, N-[2-hydroxy-1-(hydroxymethyl)-2-(4-nitrophenyl)-ethyl]-, [R-(R*,R*)]-	pH 7	280(3.98)	87-1299-80
4,11-Epoxy-8H-1,3-dioxolo[5,6]oxocino-[2,3-d]pyrimidin-8-one, 3a,4,5,7,11-11a-hexahydro-2,2,11a-trimethyl-, [3aR-(3aα,4β,11β,11aα)]-	MeOH	293(3.49)	88-1971-80
Uridine, 4',5'-didehydro-5'-deoxy-5-methyl-2',3'-O-(1-methylethylidene)-	EtOH	264(3.84)	33-2179-80
$C_{13}H_{16}N_2O_5S$			
4,12-Epoxy-5H,8H-1,3-dioxolo[4,5-e]-pyrimido[6,1-b][1,3]thiazocin-8-one, 3a,4,12,12a-tetrahydro-10-methoxy-2,2-dimethyl-	H$_2$O	248(3.91),284(4.10)	94-0939-80
$C_{13}H_{16}N_2O_6$			
Glutamic acid, 1-methyl 5-[(2-nitrophenyl)methyl] ester, monohydrochloride	H$_2$O	266(3.76)	22-0133-80
Glutamic acid, 1-methyl 5-[(3-nitrophenyl)methyl] ester, monohydrochloride	H$_2$O	267(3.89)	22-0133-80
Glutamic acid, 1-methyl 5-[(4-nitrophenyl)methyl] ester, monohydrochloride	H$_2$O	271(3.96)	22-0133-80

Compound	Solvent	$\lambda_{max}(\log \epsilon)$	Ref.
$C_{13}H_{16}N_4$			
3H-Imidazo[1,5-a]benzimidazole, N-butyl-	EtOH	285(3.835)	106-0798-80
	EtOH-HCl	275(4.947),283(4.890)	106-0798-80
Methanimidamide, N,N-dimethyl-N'-(3-methyl-1-phenyl-1H-pyrazol-5-yl)-	EtOH	255(4.18),280(4.17)	114-0127-80C
2,2a,4,5-Tetraazabenz[cd]azulene, 3-ethyl-3,4-dihydro-1,3-dimethyl-	MeOH	222(4.41),293(3.63), 354(3.92)	118-0331-80
$C_{13}H_{16}N_4O$			
1,3,5-Triazin-2(5H)-one, 4-(butyl-amino)-6-phenyl-	n.s.g.	221(4.30),267(3.91)	115-0243-80
$C_{13}H_{16}N_4O_2$			
Hydrazinecarboxamide, 2-[2-(2,3-dihydro-2-methyl-3-oxo-1H-isoindol-1-yl)-1-methylethylidene]-	EtOH	229(4.31),279(3.20)	39-2077-80C
Propanimidic acid, N-(1,5-dihydro-5-oxo-3-phenyl-4H-1,2,4-triazol-4-yl)-, ethyl ester	EtOH	262(4.02)	4-1691-80
$C_{13}H_{16}N_4O_4$			
Imidazo[1,2-a]pyrido[2,3-d]pyrimidine-7-carboxylic acid, 9-ethyl-1,2,3,5-6,9-hexahydro-5-hydroxy-1-methyl-6-oxo-	EtOH	247(4.32),270(4.49), 295(4.18)	95-1187-80
2,4(1H,3H)-Pyrimidinedione, 1-[3-(3,6-dihydro-2,6-dioxo-1(2H)-pyrimidinyl)-propyl]-6-ethyl-	pH 2	235(3.64),266(4.23)	56-2357-80
	pH 7	233(3.56),266(4.22)	56-2357-80
	pH 12	244(3.67),274(4.15)	56-2357-80
2,4(1H,3H)-Pyrimidinedione, 3-[3-(3,6-dihydro-2,6-dioxo-1(2H)-pyrimidinyl)-propyl]-5-ethyl-	pH 2	236(3.69),267(4.22)	56-2357-80
	pH 7	235(3.56),267(4.22)	56-2357-80
	pH 12	246(3.77),271(4.06)	56-2357-80
2,4(1H,3H)-Pyrimidinedione, 1-[3-(3,6-dihydro-5-methyl-2,6-dioxo-1(2H)-pyrimidinyl)propyl]-5-methyl-	pH 2	237(3.64),269(4.19)	56-2357-80
	pH 7	237(3.59),270(4.18)	56-2357-80
	pH 12	248(3.70),279(4.11)	56-2357-80
2,4(1H,3H)-Pyrimidinedione, 1-[3-(3,6-dihydro-5-methyl-2,6-dioxo-1(2H)-pyrimidinyl)propyl]-6-methyl-	pH 2	235(3.66),267(4.26)	56-2357-80
	pH 7	235(3.50),268(4.24)	56-2357-80
	pH 12	245(3.75),271(4.12)	56-2357-80
$C_{13}H_{16}N_4O_5$			
2-Propanone, 1-(9-β-D-ribofuranosyl-9H-purin-6-yl)-	H_2O	268(3.86),345s(3.95), 360(4.10)	94-0157-80
	pH 13	241(3.94),359(4.41)	94-0157-80
$C_{13}H_{16}N_4O_5S$			
2-Propanone, 1-[(9-β-D-ribofuranosyl-9H-purin-6-yl)thio]-	H_2O	218(3.92),281(4.10)	94-0157-80
$C_{13}H_{16}N_4O_6S_2$			
1H-Pyrazolo[3,4-d]pyrimidine-3-carbox-ylic acid, 4,6-bis(methylthio)-1-β-D-ribofuranosyl-	EtOH	202(4.00),252(4.12), 291(3.89)	103-0182-80
$C_{13}H_{16}N_4O_7$			
7(8H)-Pteridinone, 2,4-dimethoxy-8-β-D-ribofuranosyl-	MeOH	244(3.89),249(3.96), 270s(3.57),317(4.05), 342s(3.81)	24-1535-80
$C_{13}H_{16}N_5O_4$			
Imidazo[2,1-i]purin-6-ium, 3,9-dihydro-9-methyl-3-β-D-ribofuranosyl-, chloride	pH 1 or 7	276(4.00)	35-0770-80

Compound	Solvent	$\lambda_{max}(\log \epsilon)$	Ref.
$C_{13}H_{16}N_5O_6PS$			
Adenosine, 8-(2-propenylthio)-, cyclic 3',5'-(hydrogen phosphate)	pH 1	282(4.27)	87-0242-80
	pH 11	280(4.22)	87-0242-80
$C_{13}H_{16}N_8O_3$			
Adenosine, 5'-azido-5'-deoxy-2',3'-O-(1-methylethylidene)-	MeOH	259(4.16)	44-0788-80
$C_{13}H_{16}N_8O_4$			
Adenosine, 5'-azido-5'-deoxy-2',3'-O-(1-methylethylidene)-, 1-oxide	MeOH	234(4.58),261(3.88), 297(3.36)	44-0788-80
	MeOH-HCl	257(4.09)	44-0788-80
	MeOH-NaOH	233(4.33),267(3.86), 312(3.60)	44-0788-80
$C_{13}H_{16}O$			
2H-Inden-2-one, 1,4,5,7a-tetrahydro-4,4,7a-trimethyl-1-methylene-	EtOH	252(3.50)	23-1810-80
3-Penten-1-one, 2,2-dimethyl-1-phenyl-, (E)-	C_6H_{12}	241(4.03)	39-0592-80B
Spiro[cyclohexane-1,1'(3'H)-isobenzofuran]	EtOH	265(3.00),272(3.02)	44-1828-80
$C_{13}H_{16}O_2$			
1,3-Benzenediol, 4-(1-cyclohexen-1-yl)-5-methyl-	EtOH	283(3.72)	94-2460-80
4H-Pyran-4-one, 2-(1-cyclohexen-1-yl-methyl)-6-methyl-	EtOH	247(4.21)	94-2460-80
Spiro[2H-1,5-benzodioxepin-3(4H),1'-cyclopentane]	$CHCl_3$	276(3.18)	49-0413-80
$C_{13}H_{16}O_3$			
Ethanone, 1-[4-hydroxy-3-(4-hydroxy-3-methyl-2-butenyl)phenyl]-	EtOH	229(4.15),285(3.99)	102-2781-80
2-Naphthalenecarboxylic acid, 3,4,4a-5,6,8a-hexahydro-8a-hydroxy-5-methylene-, methyl ester, trans	EtOH	230(3.74)	44-0357-80
Phenol, 2-[(3,3-dimethyloxiranyl)-methyl]-, acetate	MeOH	216(3.36),261(2.34), 267(2.23)	150-0127-80
Spiro[1,3-benzodioxole-2,1'-cyclohept-an]-5-ol	EtOH	235(3.51),298(3.73)	12-0527-80
Spiro[1,3-benzodioxole-2,1'-cyclohex-ane], 5-methoxy-	EtOH	236(3.55),297(3.74)	12-0527-80
Spiro[4.5]deca-2,6-diene-2-carboxylic acid, 6,10-dimethyl-8-oxo-, cis-(±)-	EtOH	238(4.13)	23-2460-80
Spiro[4.5]deca-3,6-diene-2-carboxylic acid, 6,10-dimethyl-8-oxo-, [5a(S*),10]-(±)-	EtOH	240(4.20)	23-2460-80
$C_{13}H_{16}O_4$			
Benzeneacetic acid, α-acetyl-4-meth-oxy-, ethyl ester	MeOH	231(4.03),266s(3.40), 274(3.42),280s(3.36)	12-0113-80
Benzeneacetic acid, 4-(ethoxycarbonyl)-, ethyl ester (enolate anion)	DMSO	428(3.92)	18-1656-80
4H-1-Benzopyran-4-one, 2-ethyl-2,3-di-hydro-5,7-dimethoxy-	MeOH	228(4.41),284(4.41)	94-3070-80
2-Buten-1-one, 1-(2,4,6-trimethoxy-phenyl)-, (E)-	MeOH	224(4.29),302(3.49)	94-3070-80
3aH-Cyclopenta[b]benzofuran-1,3a-diol, 1,2,3,8b-tetrahydro-7-methoxy-8b-methyl-, (1α,3aβ,8bβ)-	n.s.g.	297(3.33)	44-0501-80

Compound	Solvent	$\lambda_{max}(\log \epsilon)$	Ref.
1-Propanone, 1-[4-[2-(acetoxyethoxy)-phenyl]-	$CHCl_3$	268(4.70),313(2.38)	73-1826-80
$C_{13}H_{16}O_4S_2$ 2-Butenoic acid, 3-(2-furanyl)-4-[[(1-methylethoxy)thioxomethyl]thio]-, methyl ester, (E)-	EtOH	221(3.92),300(4.24)	73-0142-80
$C_{13}H_{16}O_5$ 2(3H)-Isobenzofuranone, 3-ethoxy-5,6-dimethoxy-3-methyl-	EtOH	223(4.14),261(3.62), 293(3.50),300s(3.48)	39-0911-80C
$C_{13}H_{16}S$ 1H-Indene-1-thione, 2,3-dihydro-2,2,3,3-tetramethyl-	isooctane	205s(3.91),210s(3.86), 229(3.83),234(3.80), 249s(3.22),297s(3.93), 306(3.97),321(3.95), 328s(2.93),546(1.12), 574(1.11),622(0.40)	24-2255-80
2H-Indene-2-thione, 1,3-dihydro-1,1,3,3-tetramethyl-	isooctane	207(4.10),231(3.99), 255(3.60),261(3.50), 320s(1.05),503(0.94), 527(0.91)	24-2255-80
$C_{13}H_{16}Se$ 2H-Indene-2-selone, 1,3-dihydro-1,1,3,3-tetramethyl-	C_6H_{12}	208s(4.08),269(4.03), 297s(3.40),636(1.48), 667(1.53)	24-2255-80
$C_{13}H_{17}BrN_2O$ 4H-1,3-Oxazin-2-amine, N-(4-bromophen-yl)-5,6-dihydro-4,4,6-trimethyl-	heptane	256(4.38),280s(3.44), 292s(3.37),303s(3.17), 310s(2.93)	110-0172-80
$C_{13}H_{17}ClN_2O$ 4H-1,3-Oxazin-2-amine, N-(3-chlorophen-yl)-5,6-dihydro-4,4,6-trimethyl-	heptane	212(4.41),252(4.29), 276(3.35),285(3.31), 294(3.24)	110-0172-80
$C_{13}H_{17}IN_2O_5$ Uridine, 5'-deoxy-5'-iodo-5-methyl-2',3'-O-(1-methylethylidene)-	EtOH	262(4.07)	33-2179-80
$C_{13}H_{17}MnNO_3$ Manganese(1+), tricarbonyl[(1,2,3,4,5-n)-1-[1-(trimethylammonio)ethyl]-2,4-cyclopentadien-1-yl]-, iodide	$MeOCH_2CH_2OH$ MeCN	333(3.09) 332(3.05)	101-0301-80R 101-0301-80R
$C_{13}H_{17}N$ 1H-Indole, 1-butyl-3-methyl-	EtOH	233(3.41),284s(3.19), 292(3.22)	104-0766-80
$C_{13}H_{17}NO$ Ethanone, 2-(1-methyl-2-pyrrolidinyl)-1-phenyl-, hydrochloride	EtOH	243(4.05)	48-0475-80 +115-0265-80
1-Penten-3-one, 4-methyl-1-(methyl-phenylamino)-	EtOH	228(3.61),324(4.21)	4-0507-80
$C_{13}H_{17}NO_2$ 2-Propenoic acid, 3-[4-(dimethylamino)-phenyl]-, ethyl ester	EtOH	244(4.01),364(4.42)	104-1200-80

Compound	Solvent	$\lambda_{max}(\log \epsilon)$	Ref.
$C_{13}H_{17}NO_4$			
4-Morpholinepropanoic acid, α-(2-furanylmethylene)-, methyl ester, (Z)-	EtOH	308(4.34)	73-0906-80
$C_{13}H_{17}NO_5$			
4H-Indol-4-one, 1,5,6,7-tetrahydro-2-β-D-lyxopyranosyl-	EtOH	246(3.71),284(3.62)	136-0037-80C
3,5-Pyridinedicarboxylic acid, 1-ethyl-1,4-dihydro-4-oxo-, diethyl ester	EtOH	256(3.99),263(4.00), 312(3.77)	4-0359-80
$C_{13}H_{17}NO_6$			
4aH-Pyrano[4,3-c]pyridine-4a-carboxylic acid, octahydro-3,6-dimethyl-1,5,7-trioxo-, ethyl ester	MeOH	211(4.05)	118-0698-80
$C_{13}H_{17}N_2$			
Quinolinium, 1-methyl-4-(propylamino)-, iodide	EtOH	246(4.17),336(4.29), 350(4.31)	22-0316-80
Quinolizinium, 2-(diethylamino)-, bromide	MeOH	241(4.39),321(4.34)	142-0213-80B
$C_{13}H_{17}N_3$			
Benzenecarboximidic acid cyclohexylidenehydrazide	MeOH	220(4.12),272(3.96)	104-0822-80
1H-Benzimidazole, 2-methyl-4-piperidino-	M HCl	238(3.79),269(3.86), 277(3.90)	104-1458-80
4-Quinazolinamine, 2-methyl-N-(1-methylpropyl)-	EtOH	211(4.23),238s(4.02), 289(3.84),318(3.85)	1-0637-80
$C_{13}H_{17}N_3O_2$			
Hexanenitrile, 2-[(1,2,3,4-tetrahydro-1,3-dimethyl-2,4-dioxo-5-pyrimidinyl)methylene]-, (E)-	MeCN	259(3.92),313(4.05)	35-3948-80
(Z)-	MeCN	258(3.79),303(4.02)	35-3948-80
$C_{13}H_{17}N_3O_3$			
Acetamide, N-[2-nitro-3-(1-piperidinyl)phenyl]-	EtOH	230(4.45),333s(2.83)	104-1458-80
$C_{13}H_{17}N_3O_5$			
4,12-Epoxy-5H-1,3-dioxolo[4,5-f]pyrimido[1,6-a][1,3]diazocine-8,10(6H,9H)-dione, 3a,4,12,12a-tetrahydro-2,2,6-trimethyl-, [3aR-(3aα,4β,12β,12aα)]-	H₂O pH 13	284(4.32) 282(4.19)	94-0939-80 94-0939-80
$C_{13}H_{17}N_5O$			
1H-Pyrazole, 1-acetyl-3-[[4-(dimethylamino)phenyl]azo]-4,5-dihydro-	CHCl₃	471(4.67)	104-1143-80
$C_{13}H_{17}N_5O_5$			
Adenosine, 2',3'-O-(1-methylethylidene)-, 1-oxide	MeOH	233(4.58),261(3.86), 299(3.28)	44-0788-80
	MeOH-HCl	257(4.08)	44-0788-80
	MeOH-NaOH	231(4.39),267(3.90), 311(3.60)	44-0788-80
β-D-ribo-Hexofuranuronic acid, 1-(6-amino-9H-purin-9-yl)-1,5-dideoxy-, ethyl ester	H₂O	258(4.25)	24-2530-80
4H-1,2,3-Triazolo[4,5-c]pyridin-4-one, 6-amino-1,5-dihydro-1-[2,3-O-(1-methylethylidene)-β-D-ribofuranosyl]-	pH 1 pH 7 pH 11	220(3.11),286(3.20) 218(3.34),286(3.20) 227(3.59),286(3.11),	4-0159-80 4-0159-80 4-0159-80

Compound	Solvent	$\lambda_{max}(\log \epsilon)$	Ref.
(cont.) 4H-1,2,3-Triazolo[4,5-c]pyridin-4-one, 6-amino-2,5-dihydro-2-[2,3-O-(1-meth- ylethylidene)-β-D-ribofuranosyl]-	pH 1 pH 7 pH 11	312s(3.11) 228s(3.90),248(3.94) 223(4.33),267(3.85), 339s(3.36) 232(4.35),263s(3.51), 348s(3.36)	4-0159-80 4-0159-80 4-0159-80 4-0159-80
$C_{13}H_{17}N_7O_2$ Adenosine, 2',3'-didehydro-2',3',5'- trideoxy-5'-[(methylamino)acetyl]- amino]-	H_2O	260.5(4.16)	136-0067-80A
$C_{13}H_{18}$ Benzene, (2-methylcyclohexyl)-, trans 4,7-Methano-1H-indene, 3a,4,5,6,7,7a- hexahydro-1-(1-methylethylidene)-	pentane dioxan	260(2.74) 252(4.17)	33-0588-80 126-0037-80
$C_{13}H_{18}BrN_3O_3S$ Methanaminium, N-[(dimethylamino)- [[2-(4-nitrophenyl)-2-oxoethyl]- thio]methylene]-N-methyl-, bromide	MeOH	260(4.04),376(3.61)	78-2675-80
$C_{13}H_{18}Br_2O_5$ α-D-galacto-Hept-6-enopyranose, 7,7-di- bromo-6,7-dideoxy-1,2:3,4-bis-O-(1- methylethylidene)- β-D-arabino-Hept-1-en-3-ulopyranose, 1,1-dibromo-1,2-dideoxy-3,4:5,6- bis-O-(1-methylethylidene)-	EtOH EtOH	211(3.82) 213(3.77)	33-1181-80 33-1181-80
$C_{13}H_{18}ClFO_5$ β-D-arabino-Hept-1-en-3-ulopyranose, 1-chloro-1,2-dideoxy-1-fluoro-3,4- 5,6-bis-O-(1-methylethylidene)-	EtOH	207(2.82)	33-1644-80
$C_{13}H_{18}ClNO_3$ 2H-Pyran-2-one, 3-chloro-6-(1,1-di- methylethyl)-4-morpholino-	EtOH	237(4.20),276(3.96), 322(4.06)	4-0507-80
$C_{13}H_{18}Cl_2IN_4O_5P$ Uridine, 5'-[[[bis(2-chloroethyl)ami- no]hydroxyphosphinyl]amino]-2',5'- dideoxy-5'-iodo-, intramol. 5',3'- ester	EtOH	283(3.87)	87-1235-80
$C_{13}H_{18}Cl_2O_5$ α-D-galacto-Hept-6-enopyranose, 7,7-di- chloro-6,7-dideoxy-1,2:3,4-bis-O-(1- methylethylidene)- β-D-arabino-Hept-1-en-3-ulopyranose, 1,1-dichloro-1,2-dideoxy-3,4:5,6- bis-O-(1-methylethylidene)-	EtOH EtOH	209(3.50) 209(3.56)	33-1644-80 33-1644-80
$C_{13}H_{18}N_2O$ 4H-1,3-Oxazin-2-amine, 5,6-dihydro- 4,4,6-trimethyl-N-phenyl-	heptane	204(4.45),248(4.42), 273s(3.31),284s(3.30), 290s(3.18)	110-0172-80
$C_{13}H_{18}N_2O_2$ Quinoline, 1-butyl-1,2,3,4-tetrahydro- 8-nitro-	EtOH	255(4.07),440(3.36)	103-0386-80

Compound	Solvent	$\lambda_{max}(\log \epsilon)$	Ref.
$C_{13}H_{18}N_2O_2S$			
Imidazo[2,1-b]thiazole-2-carboxylic acid, 6-(1,1-dimethylethyl)-3-methyl-, ethyl ester	EtOH	274(4.18)	18-3308-80
$C_{13}H_{18}N_2O_3$			
Benzoic acid, 4-hydroxy-, 3-amino-hexahydro-1H-azepin-4-yl ester	MeOH	198(4.03),255(3.99)	24-2221-80
Cyclohexanamine, N-methyl-N-[2-(5-nitro-2-furanyl)ethenyl]-, (E)-	MeOH	276(4.13),504(4.20)	73-0155-80
$C_{13}H_{18}N_2O_4$			
L-Glutamine, N-[2-(4-hydroxyphenyl)-ethyl]-	M HCl	230(3.8),280(3.23)	102-1225-80
Octanamide, N-(1,2,5,6-tetrahydro-2,5,6-trioxo-3-pyridinyl)-	EtOH	220(4.02),263(4.14), 349(3.80)	39-1782-80C
$C_{13}H_{18}N_2O_5$			
Butanamide, N-[2-hydroxy-1-(hydroxymethyl)-2-(4-nitrophenyl)ethyl]-, [R-(R*,R*)]-	pH 7	280(3.99)	87-1299-80
2,4(1H,3H)-Pyrimidinedione, 1-[5-deoxy-2,3-0-(1-methylethylidene)-α-L-lyxofuranosyl]-5-methyl-	EtOH	266(3.92)	33-2179-80
Uridine, 5'-deoxy-5-methyl-2',3'-0-(1-methylethylidene)-	EtOH	264(3.90)	33-2179-80
$C_{13}H_{18}N_2O_5S$			
Uridine, 5-methyl-2',3'-0-(1-methylethylidene)-5'-thio-	EtOH	264(3.98)	33-2179-80
$C_{13}H_{18}N_2O_5S_2$			
4(1H)-Pyrimidinone, 1-β-D-arabinofuranosyl-2-(1,3-dithian-2-yl)-	MeOH	245(4.20)	136-0033-80A
$C_{13}H_{18}N_2O_6$			
2H-Benzimidazole-4,7-diol, 4,5,6,7-tetrahydro-2,2-dimethyl-, diacetate, 1,3-dioxide	EtOH	228(3.90),255(3.30), 360(3.70)	103-0628-80
Uridine, 5-methyl-2',3'-0-(1-methylethylidene)-	EtOH	265(3.96)	33-2179-80
$C_{13}H_{18}N_2O_7$			
2,4(1H,3H)-Pyrimidinedione, 5-[4-C-(hydroxymethyl)-2,3-0-(1-methylethylidene)-β-D-erythro-pentofuranosyl]-	pH 13	284(3.67)	88-2535-80
$C_{13}H_{18}N_3O_3S$			
Methanaminium, N-[(dimethylamino)[[2-(4-nitrophenyl)-2-oxoethyl]thio]methylene]-N-methyl-, bromide	MeOH	260(4.04),376(3.61)	78-2675-80
$(C_{13}H_{18}N_4O_4)_n$			
Poly[imino[2-(3,4-dihydro-2,4-dioxo-1(2H)-pyrimidinyl)-1,3-dioxo-1,3-propanediyl]imino-1,6-hexanediyl]	aq HCl / DMSO	269(3.95) / 269(3.94)	47-0949-80 / 47-0949-80
low molecular weight	aq HCl / DMSO	269(3.94) / 269(3.92)	47-0949-80 / 47-0949-80
$C_{13}H_{18}N_4O_7$			
D-Ribitol, 1-deoxy-1-(2,4-dimethoxy-	MeOH	207(4.51),269(4.08),	24-1535-80

Compound	Solvent	$\lambda_{max}(\log \epsilon)$	Ref.
7-oxo-8(7H)-pteridinyl)- (cont.)		316(4.12),327(4.12)	24-1535-80
$C_{13}H_{18}N_4S$ Thiourea, N-(1H-benzimidazol-2-ylmethyl)-N'-butyl-	EtOH	244(5.268),274(4.902), 282(4.386)	106-0798-80
	EtOH-HCl	240(5.32),270(5.106), 277(5.103)	106-0798-80
$C_{13}H_{18}N_5O_5$ 3H-Imidazo[2,1-i]purinium, 7,8-dihydro-8-hydroxy-9-methyl-3-β-D-ribofuranosyl-, chloride	pH 1 and 7 pH 13	215(4.35),262(4.14) 263(4.03)	35-0770-80 35-0770-80
$C_{13}H_{18}N_5O_6PS$ Adenosine, 8-[(1-methylethyl)thio]-, cyclic 3',5'-(hydrogen phosphate) Adenosine, 8-(propylthio)-, cyclic 3',5'-(hydrogen phosphate)	pH 1 pH 11 pH 1 pH 11	282(4.22) 281(4.21) 283(4.30) 280(4.28)	87-0242-80 87-0242-80 87-0242-80 87-0242-80
$C_{13}H_{18}N_6O_5S_2$ 1H-Pyrazolo[3,4-d]pyrimidine-3-carboximidamide, N-hydroxy-4,6-bis(methylthio)-1-β-D-ribofuranosyl-	EtOH	202(4.21),249(4.30), 262(4.24),289(4.08), 308(4.11)	103-0182-80
$C_{13}H_{18}N_6O_6$ β-D-Glucopyranoside, (2,4-diamino-6-pteridinyl)methyl	pH 2.0	243(4.23),290(3.70), 335(4.01)	24-1514-80
	pH 7.0	258(4.37),370(3.87)	24-1514-80
$C_{13}H_{18}O$ 2-Propanone, 1-(2,3,5,6-tetramethylphenyl)-	dioxan	272(2.76),277(2.74), 281(2.76)	24-2462-80
$C_{13}H_{18}OS$ 14-Thiabicyclo[9.2.1]tetradeca-11,13-dien-2-one	MeCN	290(4.01)	44-1906-80
$C_{13}H_{18}O_2$ Benzene, [(2-butoxycyclopropyl)oxy]-, cis	hexane	221(4.05),265s(--), 270(3.30),276(3.27)	70-1928-80
trans	hexane	220(4.05),264s(--), 270(3.32),276s(3.30)	70-1928-80
Benzene, [[2-(1,1-dimethylethoxy)cyclopropyl]oxy]-, cis	hexane	221(4.35),264s(--), 270(3.34),276(3.30)	70-1928-80
trans	hexane	220(4.22),264s(--), 270(3.32),276(3.34)	70-1928-80
Benzenemethanol, 2-(1-hydroxycyclohexyl)-	EtOH	260(2.29)	44-1828-80
3-Buten-2-one, 4-(5-acetyl-2,2-dimethylbicyclo[2.1.0]pent-1-yl)-, [1α(E),4α,5α]-	pentane	242(4.09)	33-2212-80
Ethanone, 1,1'-(7,7-dimethyl-1,3-cycloheptadiene-1,3-diyl)bis-	pentane	213(3.93),240(3.62), 277(3.80)	33-2230-80
Ethanone, 1-(7,7-dimethyl-3-methylene-2-oxabicyclo[4.3.0]non-4-en-6-yl)-	pentane	234s(4.00),241s(4.03), 256(4.05),305s(2.01), 315s(1.85)	33-2230-80
8-Oxabicyclo[3.2.1]octa-3,6-dien-2-one, 1,3,4,5,6,7-hexamethyl-	EtOH	230(3.81),270(2.91), 340(2.70)	44-2096-80
4-Oxatricyclo[4.2.0.0^{3,5}]oct-7-en-2-one, 1,3,5,6,7,8-hexamethyl-	MeOH	215(3.29),237(3.13), 315(2.51)	44-2091-80

Compound	Solvent	λ_{max}(log ϵ)	Ref.
7-Oxatricyclo[3.3.0.0^{6,8}]oct-3-en-2-one, 1,3,4,5,6,8-hexamethyl-	EtOH	215(3.81),245(3.78)	44-2091-80
Phenol, pentamethyl-, acetate	MeOH	227(3.48)	44-2091-80
2H-Pyran, tetrahydro-2-[2-(1,3-cyclo-pentadien-1-ylidene)propoxy]-	EtOH	241(4.11),282(4.23), 385s(2.3)	34-0184-80
$C_{13}H_{18}O_2S_3$			
2,5-Cyclohexadiene-1,4-dione, 2-methyl-3,5,6-tris[(methylthio)methyl]-	EtOH	271(4.05),376(3.04)	39-0289-80C
$C_{13}H_{18}O_3$			
Benzene, 1-(1-butenyl)-2,4,5-trimeth-oxy-, (E)-	EtOH	207(4.37),259(4.02), 267s(3.96),314(3.76)	94-2948-80
2,4-Cyclohexadien-1-one, 6-acetoxy-2,3,4,5,6-pentamethyl-	hexane	315(3.71)	24-2227-80
	MeOH	321(3.63)	24-2227-80
	CF$_3$CH$_2$OH	324(3.57),357(3.55)	24-2227-80
Cyclopenta[c]pyran-1(3H)-one, hexa-hydro-4a,7a-dimethyl-3-(2-oxo-propylidene)-, (3Z,4aα,7aα)-	n.s.g.	247(4.26)	88-3123-80
2-Cyclopenten-1-one, 3-acetoxy-2-(3-methyl-4-pentenyl)-	C_6H_{12}	255(4.11),300(1.62)	33-1198-80
3,8-Dioxatetracyclo[4.3.0.0^{2,4}.0^{7,9}]-nonan-5-one, 1,2,4,6,7,9-hexamethyl-	MeOH	218(2.92),308(1.70)	44-2091-80
isomer	MeOH	215(3.05),310(1.78)	44-2091-80
3aH-Indene-3a-propanoic acid, hexahydro-6-oxo-, methyl ester	MeOH	238(4.18),293(2.00)	44-0570-80
3aH-Indene-3a-propanoic acid, 2,3,4,5-6,7-hexahydro-2-oxo-, methyl ester	MeOH	228(4.08),298(1.65)	44-0570-80
1-Naphthaleneacetic acid, 1,2,3,4,4a-5,6,7-octahydro-4a-methyl-7-oxo-, cis	1% MeOH	247.5(4.16)	44-1645-80
trans	1% MeOH	245.5(4.16)	44-1645-80
Spiro[1,3-dioxolane-2,2'(6'H)-naphtha-len]-6'-one, 1',3',4',7',8',8'a-hexahydro-8'a-methyl-	EtOH	236(4.18)	39-2511-80C
$C_{13}H_{18}O_3S$			
2-Butenoic acid, 3-(2-furanyl)-4-[(1-methylethyl)thio]-, ethyl ester, (E)-	EtOH	213(4.16),306(4.24)	73-0142-80
2-Butenoic acid, 3-(2-furanyl)-4-(pro-pylthio)-, ethyl ester, (E)-	EtOH	212(4.19),311(4.23)	73-0142-80
$C_{13}H_{18}O_4$			
1,3-Benzodioxole-2-methanol, α-butyl-2-methoxy-	EtOH	212(3.57),274s(3.54), 278(3.57),283s(3.45)	12-1553-80
Bicyclo[2.2.2]oct-5-ene-2-carboxylic acid, 5-formyl-1-methoxy-8-methyl-, methyl ester	EtOH	233(3.94)	18-1049-80
2H-Pyran-2-one, 6-ethyl-4-hydroxy-5-methyl-3-(3-oxopentyl)-	CHCl$_3$	295(3.88)	102-0639-80
$C_{13}H_{18}O_5$			
1-Butanone, 3-hydroxy-1-(2,4,6-trimeth-oxyphenyl)-	MeOH	276(3.76)	94-3070-80
α-D-galacto-Heptopyranose, 6,6,7,7-tetradehydro-6,7-dideoxy-1,2:3,4-bis-O-(1-methylethylidene)-	EtOH	209(2.22)	33-1181-80
β-D-arabino-Heptulopyranose, 1,1,2,2-tetradehydro-1,2-dideoxy-3,4:5,6-bis-O-(1-methylethylidene)-	EtOH	217(2.18)	33-1181-80

Compound	Solvent	$\lambda_{max}(\log \epsilon)$	Ref.
$C_{13}H_{18}O_6$ 1-Cyclohexene-1,2,3-tricarboxylic acid, 3-methyl-, trimethyl ester	EtOH	213(3.88)	2-0601-80
$C_{13}H_{19}ClN_4O_4S$ D-arabino-Hexitol, 1-C-(6-chloro-9H-purin-9-yl)-2-deoxy-1-S-ethyl-1-thio-	MeOH	265(3.7)	136-0356-80C
$C_{13}H_{19}ClN_4O_5S$ D-Glucitol, 1-C-(6-chloro-9H-purin-9-yl)-1-S-ethyl-1-thio-	MeOH	264(4.11)	136-0241-80C
$C_{13}H_{19}ClN_6$ 2-Pyrimidinamine, 4-chloro-N-(5-hexyl-1H-1,2,4-triazol-3-yl)-6-methyl-	EtOH	257(4.38),295(3.54)	103-1275-80
$C_{13}H_{19}NO$ Cyclohexanone, 2-[3-(dimethylamino)-2-propenylidene]-6-ethylidene-, (E,E,E)-	EtOH	440(4.48)	70-0980-80
$C_{13}H_{19}NOS_2$ 2(1H)-Pyridinone, 3-(2-butyl-1,3-dithiolan-2-yl)-6-methyl-	CH_2Cl_2	237(3.79),310(4.00)	44-1354-80
$C_{13}H_{19}NO_2$ Carbamic acid, (2,4,6-trimethylphenyl)-, propyl ester	C_6H_{12}	267(2.42)	44-2195-80
1,3-Cyclohexanedione, 2-[3-(dimethylamino)-2-propenylidene]-5,5-dimethyl-	hexane EtOH CHCl$_3$	255(3.96),410(4.64) 280(3.96),415(4.56) 278(3.51),420(4.69)	70-1643-80 70-1643-80 70-1643-80
$C_{13}H_{19}NO_3$ 1H-Indole-2-carboxylic acid, 4,5,6,7-tetrahydro-3-methoxy-1-methyl-, ethyl ester	MeOH	280(4.27)	5-0564-80
Isoquinoline, 1,2,3,4-tetrahydro-5,6,7-trimethoxy-2-methyl- (tehuanine)	H_2O	203(4.35),211s(3.68), 280(2.92),289s(2.61)	102-0673-80
2-Propenoic acid, 2-[(diethylamino)methyl]-3-(2-furanyl)-, methyl ester, (E)-	EtOH	303(4.40)	73-0906-80
2-Propenoic acid, 2-[[(1,1-dimethylethyl)amino]methyl]-3-(2-furanyl)-, methyl ester, (E)-	EtOH	305(4.20)	73-0906-80
3-Pyridinecarboxylic acid, 5-heptyl-1,4-dihydro-4-oxo-	EtOH	254(3.85),282(3.62)	4-0359-80
1H-Pyrrole-3-carboxylic acid, 1-butyl-4-formyl-2-methyl-, ethyl ester	EtOH	267(3.96),288(3.92)	39-1199-80C
$C_{13}H_{19}NO_4$ Isoquinoline, 1,2,3,4-tetrahydro-5,6,7,8-tetramethoxy-	H_2O	205(4),223s(3.5), 282(2.9),292s(2.8)	102-0673-80
$C_{13}H_{19}NO_4S$ 7-Thia-2-azabicyclo[3.2.1]oct-3-ene-4,8-dicarboxylic acid, 1,2,3-trimethyl-, dimethyl ester, syn		261(3.45),316(4.09)	23-0794-80
$C_{13}H_{19}NO_6$ 1,3-Cyclohexanedicarboxylic acid, 4-(aminocarbonyl)-5-oxo-, diethyl ester	EtOH	256(3.79)	23-1860-80

Compound	Solvent	$\lambda_{max}(\log \epsilon)$	Ref.
4-Indolone, 2-(D-galacto-pentitol-1-yl)-4,5,6,7-tetrahydro-	H_2O	212(4.12),247(3.83), 288(3.81)	136-0017-80A
4-Indolone, 2-(D-manno-pentitol-1-yl)-4,5,6,7-tetrahydro-	H_2O	212(4.12),246(3.83), 286(3.76)	136-0017-80A
$C_{13}H_{19}NO_7$			
Butanedioic acid, [3-(ethoxycarbonyl)-tetrahydro-2-imino-4,5-dimethyl-3-furanyl]-	MeOH	220(4.34),311(1.50)	118-0698-80
$C_{13}H_{19}N_3$			
1H-Indole-3-butanamine, 2-amino-1-methyl-, dihydrochloride	EtOH	214(4.32),265(4.06)	103-0368-80
$C_{13}H_{19}N_3O_5$			
Isocytidine, 5-methyl-2',3'-O-(1-methylethylidene)-	EtOH	235s(3.81),259s(4.04)	33-2179-80
$C_{13}H_{19}N_3S$			
1-Pyrazolidinecarbothioamide, 3,3,5-trimethyl-2-phenyl-	EtOH	253(4.30)	103-0169-80
$C_{13}H_{19}N_5O_2S$			
L-Arginine, N^2-[(phenylamino)thioxomethyl]-, sodium salt	H_2O	245(4.143)	130-0248-80
$C_{13}H_{20}BrN_7$			
1H-Pyrazol-5-amine, 4-[[4-bromo-3-methyl-1-(1-methylethyl)-1H-pyrazol-5-yl]azo]-1-ethyl-3-methyl-	MeOH	385(4.71),410(4.71)	103-1160-80
$C_{13}H_{20}ClNO_2$			
2H-Pyran-2-one, 3-chloro-4-(diethylamino)-6-(1,1-dimethylethyl)-	EtOH	236(4.29),270(3.91), 317(4.04)	4-0507-80
$C_{13}H_{20}NO_6$			
1-Piperidinyloxy, 3,5-bis(methoxycarbonyl)-2,2,6,6-tetramethyl-4-oxo-	hexane	253(3.97),451(1.00)	94-3178-80
	H_2O	249(3.98)	94-3178-80
	EtOH	251(4.00),440(1.00)	94-3178-80
	MeCN	250(3.99),445(1.00)	94-3178-80
$C_{13}H_{20}N_2O$			
Azepino[3,2-c]quinolizin-6(1H)-one, 2,3,4,5,7,7a,8,9,10,11-decahydro-	EtOH	228(3.93),318(4.34)	94-0220-80
$C_{13}H_{20}N_2O_5$			
1H-Pyrazole-1-acetic acid, 4-(ethoxycarbonyl)-5-(1-hydroxyethyl)-3-methyl-, ethyl ester	EtOH	235(3.88)	118-0875-80
$C_{13}H_{20}N_2O_6$			
Uridine, 3'-C-butyl-	H_2O	260(4.02)	136-0219-80B
	pH 13	260(3.88)	136-0219-80B
$C_{13}H_{20}N_2O_6S_2$			
Furo[2,3-d]oxazole-3(2H)-propanamide, β-1,3-dithian-2-yltetrahydro-6-hydroxy-5-(hydroxymethyl)-2-oxo-, [3aR-[3S*],3aα,5β,6α,6aα]]-	MeOH	225(3.54),232(3.48), 245(3.18)	136-0033-80A
2,4(1H,3H)-Pyrimidinedione, 1-β-D-arabinofuranosyl-6-(1,3-dithian-2-yl)-	MeOH	245(3.23)	136-0033-80A

Compound	Solvent	$\lambda_{max}(\log \epsilon)$	Ref.
5,6-dihydro-, (S)- (cont.)			136-0033-80A
$C_{13}H_{20}N_3O_7P$ Thymidine, 5'-O-(tetrahydro-2H-1,3,2- oxazaphosphorin-2-yl)-, P-oxide	EtOH	267(3.99)	78-2337-80
$C_{13}H_{20}N_4$ Imidazo[5,1-f][1,2,4]triazine, 5-meth- yl-2-(1-methylethyl)-7-(2-methyl- propyl)-, hydrochloride	EtOH	230(3.99),252(3.95), 357(2.42)	39-1139-80C
$C_{13}H_{20}N_4O$ Imidazo[5,1-f][1,2,4]triazin-4(1H)-one, 5-methyl-2-(1-methylethyl)-7-(2-meth- ylpropyl)-	EtOH EtOH-NaOH	222(4.37),251(3.95), 266s(--),285s(--) 261(--),270s(--), 297(--)	39-1139-80C 39-1139-80C
$C_{13}H_{20}N_4O_5S_2$ D-Glucitol, 1-S-methyl-1-C-[6-(methyl- thio)-9H-purin-9-yl]-1-thio-	pH 1 pH 13 MeOH	229(4.11),293(4.32) 226(4.14),284(4.34), 290(4.33) 226(4.15),284(4.36), 290(4.36)	136-0241-80C 136-0241-80C 136-0241-80C
$C_{13}H_{20}N_6O$ 4(1H)-Pyrimidinone, 2-[(5-hexyl-1H- 1,2,4-triazol-3-yl)amino]-6-methyl-	EtOH	242(4.13),276(4.03)	103-1275-80
$C_{13}H_{20}O$ Bicyclo[2.2.1]heptan-2-one, 1,7,7-tri- methyl-3-(1-methylethylidene)- 2-Butanone, 4-(2,5,6-trimethyl-2-cyclo- hexen-1-ylidene)-, (1E,5α,6α)-(±)- (1E,5α,6β)-(±)- 3-Buten-2-one, 4-(2,5,6-trimethyl-1- cyclohexen-1-yl)-, [1(E),5α,6α]-(±)- [1(E),5α,6β]-(±)- 4H-Inden-4-one, 1,2,3,5,6,7-hexahydro- 1-methyl-1-(1-methylethyl)-	$C_6H_{11}Me$ EtOH EtOH EtOH EtOH EtOH	241(4.11),328(2.24) 241(4.29),294(3.21) 242(4.24),292(3.04) 300(4.26) 300(4.31) 249(4.10)	44-3518-80 33-0293-80 33-0293-80 33-0293-80 33-0293-80 77-0399-80
$C_{13}H_{20}OSi$ Silane, trimethyl[(4a.5.8.8a-tetrahy- dro-1-naphthalenyl)oxy]-	C_6H_{12}	220s(3.72),276(3.48)	88-2799-80
$C_{13}H_{20}O_2$ Bicyclo[4.1.0]heptane-7-carboxylic acid, 1,5,5-trimethyl-2-methylene-, methyl ester, (1α,6α,7α)- α-Ionone, 4,5-epoxy-4,5-dihydro-, (4R,5S,6S)-(-)- β-Ionone, 4-hydroxy-, (R)-(-)- Tricyclo[3.3.1.0^{1,3}]nonan-9-one, 4-(hy- droxymethyl)-3,6,6-trimethyl-, (1α,3α,4β,5α)- 5,9-Undecadiene-2,8-dione, 6,10-di- methyl-, (E)-	pentane MeOH MeOH EtOH EtOH	210(3.89) 225(4.15) 219(3.96),285(3.95) 293(1.62) 239(4.02)	33-1856-80 33-0010-80 33-0010-80 33-1856-80 102-2759-80
$C_{13}H_{20}O_2S$ Benzene, (2,2-diethoxypropyl)thio-	dioxan	254(3.97)	24-2462-80

Compound	Solvent	$\lambda_{max}(\log \epsilon)$	Ref.

$C_{13}H_{20}O_3$

Compound	Solvent	$\lambda_{max}(\log \epsilon)$	Ref.
Bicyclo[5.1.0]octane-8-carboxylic acid, 1,5,5-trimethyl-6-oxo-, methyl ester	pentane	286(1.83)	33-1833-80
2-Butenoic acid, 4-oxo-4-(1,2,2-tri-methylcyclopentyl)-, methyl ester, (E)-	pentane	225(4.19),350(1.52)	33-1833-80
3-Buten-2-one, 4-(1-acetyl-5-hydroxy-2,2-dimethylcyclopentyl)-, [1α,1(E),5α]-	pentane	222(3.89)	33-2230-80
3-Buten-2-one, 4-(1,2-dihydroxy-2,6,6-trimethyl-3-cyclohexen-1-yl)-, (3E)-	pentane	310(1.91)	33-2212-80
3-Buten-2-one, 4-(1,4-dihydroxy-2,6,6-trimethyl-2-cyclohexen-1-yl)-, (3E)-	EtOH	233(4.10),312(1.92)	33-2212-80
Cyclopentanecarboxaldehyde, 2-hydroxy-2,4,4-trimethyl-3-(3-oxo-1-butenyl)-, (E)-	pentane	221(4.11)	33-2230-80
1-Cyclopentene-1-hexanoic acid, 5-oxo-, ethyl ester	MeOH	228(3.99)	44-4702-80
1-Cyclopentene-1-octanoic acid, 5-oxo-	MeOH	228(4.00)	44-4702-80
2,3-Decadienoic acid, 5,5-dimethyl-9-oxo-, methyl ester	pentane	211(4.07)	33-1833-80
Ethanone, 1-(5-hydroxy-2,2,9-trimethyl-8-oxabicyclo[4.3.0]non-9-en-7-yl)-, (5R*,6R*,7S*)-	pentane	303(1.62)	33-2230-80
2-Furanpropanal, α,2,4-triethyl-2,5-di-hydro-5-oxo-	MeOH	223(4.00)	44-3396-80
2-Heptanone, 6-(5-methoxy-2-furanyl)-6-methyl-	pentane	225(3.96),280(1.42)	33-1833-80
9-Oxabicyclo[4.2.1]non-8-ene-7-carbox-ylic acid, 2,2,6-trimethyl-, methyl ester	pentane	220(3.67)	33-1833-80
7-Oxabicyclo[4.3.0]non-9-ene-8-carbox-ylic acid, 2,2,6-trimethyl-, methyl ester, (6R*,8R*)-	pentane	203(3.76),220s(3.34)	33-1833-80
(6R*,8S*)-	pentane	203(3.81),220s(3.46)	33-1833-80
Propanoic acid, 3-(5-acetyl-2,2-dimeth-ylcyclopentylidene)-, methyl ester, (E)-	pentane	204(3.79),246(2.76), 290(2.07),297(2.04), 306s(1.94),317s(1.60)	33-1833-80
(Z)-	pentane	285(1.81)	33-1833-80
2-Propenoic acid, 3-(1-acetyl-2,2-di-methylcyclopentyl)-, methyl ester, (E)-	pentane	227(3.96),292(2.28)	33-1833-80
(Z)-	pentane	207(3.92),240s(3.40)	33-1833-80
2-Propenoic acid, 3-(5-acetyl-2,2-di-methylcyclopentyl)-, methyl ester, [1α(E),5α]-	pentane	213(4.17)	33-1833-80
[1α(Z),5α]-	pentane	212(4.05)	33-1833-80
2-Propenoic acid, 3-(1,6-epoxy-2,2,6-trimethylcyclohexyl)-, methyl ester, (E)-	pentane	221(4.06)	33-1833-80
(Z)-	pentane	203(3.91)	33-1833-80
2-Propenoic acid, 3-(1,2,2-trimethyl-6-oxocyclohexyl)-, methyl ester, (E)-	pentane	205(4.08),227s(3.85), 284s(2.53),293(2.58), 300(2.57),310s(2.48), 320(2.18)	33-1833-80
(Z)-	pentane	204(3.97),240s(3.23)	33-1833-80
8-Undecene-2,5,7-trione, 6,6-dimethyl-, (E)-	pentane	218(4.16),284(2.03)	33-2212-80

Compound	Solvent	$\lambda_{max}(\log \epsilon)$	Ref.
$C_{13}H_{20}O_3S$ Acetic acid, [[4-(5-oxo-1-cyclopenten-1-yl)butyl]thio]-, ethyl ester	MeOH	228(4.06)	44-4702-80
$C_{13}H_{20}O_4$ Acetic acid, [4-(5-oxo-1-cyclopenten-1-yl)butoxy]-, ethyl ester	MeOH	228(4.03)	44-4702-80
$C_{13}H_{20}O_5$ 2,4-Hexadienedioic acid, 4-(1,1-dimeth-ylethyl)-2-methoxy-, dimethyl ester	MeOH	212(3.98),270s(3.58)	44-1153-80
$C_{13}H_{21}ClN_4$ Imidazo[5,1-f][1,2,4]triazine, 5-meth-yl-2-(1-methylethyl)-7-(2-methyl-propyl)-, hydrochloride	EtOH	230(3.99),252(3.95), 357(2.42)	39-1139-80C
$C_{13}H_{21}Cl_2N_3$ 1H-Indole-3-butanamine, 2-amino-1-meth-yl-, dihydrochloride	EtOH	214(4.32),265(4.06)	103-0368-80
$C_{13}H_{21}NO$ Cyclooctanone, 2-[3-(dimethylamino)-2-propenylidene]-	EtOH	390(4.40)	70-0987-80
Ethanone, 1-bicyclo[2.2.1]hept-5-en-2-yl-2-(diethylamino)-	benzene	290(1.81)	44-1286-80
14-Oxa-12-azabicyclo[9.2.1]tetradeca-11,13-diene, 13-methyl-	EtOH	224(3.71)	138-0659-80
$C_{13}H_{21}NOS$ 2-Azaspiro[3.5]nonan-1-one, 2,5,5,9,9-pentamethyl-3-thioxo-	isooctane	265(4.2),396(1.4)	88-4247-80
2-Azaspiro[3.5]non-2-en-1-one, 5,5,9,9-tetramethyl-3-(methylthio)-	isooctane	252(4.1),320(1.9)	88-4247-80
$C_{13}H_{21}NO_3$ 1-Cyclopentene-1-pentanoic acid, 5-(methoxyimino)-, ethyl ester	MeOH	243(4.13)	44-4702-80
2-Cyclopenten-1-one, 2-(5-acetoxy-pentyl)-, 1-(O-methyloxime)	MeOH	243(3.93)	44-4702-80
$C_{13}H_{21}NO_3S$ Methanesulfonamide, N-cyclohexyl-N-(6-oxo-1-cyclohexen-1-yl)-	ether	221(3.94),254(3.02), 310(2.23)	78-1585-80
$C_{13}H_{21}NO_3S_2$ 2-Azaspiro[3.5]nonan-1-one, 5,5,9,9-tetramethyl-2-(methylsulfonyl)-3-thioxo-	isooctane	235(4.2),258(4.2), 431(1.3)	88-4247-80
$C_{13}H_{21}N_2O_4PS_2$ 3(2H)-Pyridazinone, 5-[(5,5-dimethyl-1,3,2-dioxaphosphorinan-2-yl)oxy]-2-methyl-4-(propylthio)-, P-sulfide	MeOH	212(4.14),321(3.87)	73-2343-80
$C_{13}H_{21}N_3O$ 1,3-Cyclopentadiene-1-carboxamide, 5-[bis(dimethylamino)methylene]-N,N-dimethyl-	dioxan	253(4.14),356(4.27)	89-0199-80

Compound	Solvent	$\lambda_{max}(\log \epsilon)$	Ref.

$C_{13}H_{22}$
  1,3-Cyclopentadiene, 1,3-bis(1,1-di-
  methylethyl)-
	C_6H_{12}	256(3.58)	126-0037-80

$C_{13}H_{22}ClN_2O_3PS_2$
  Phosphorodithioic acid, O-(1-butyl-
  5-chloro-1,6-dihydro-6-oxo-4-pyri-
  dazinyl) O-ethyl S-propyl ester
	MeOH	213(4.42),297(3.67)	73-2247-80

$C_{13}H_{22}N_2$
  12,14-Diazabicyclo[9.2.1]tetradeca-
  1(14),13-diene, 12-methyl-
	EtOH	217(3.78)	138-0659-80

$C_{13}H_{22}N_4$
  Imidazo[5,1-f][1,2,4]triazine, 1,4-di-
  hydro-5-methyl-2-(1-methylethyl)-
  7-(2-methylpropyl)-, monohydro-
  chloride
	EtOH	254(3.98)	39-1139-80C

$C_{13}H_{22}N_4O_2$
  Butanamide, N-[1-[2,5-dihydro-3-(1-
  methylethyl)-5-oxo-1,2,4-triazin-
  6-yl]ethyl]-3-methyl-
	EtOH	235(3.97),260s(3.73)	39-1139-80C

$C_{13}H_{22}N_4O_5$ Cytidine, N-(4-aminobutyl)-	H_2O	272(3.98)	44-2704-80

$C_{13}H_{22}N_8$
  4(1H)-Pyrimidinone, 2-[(5-hexyl-1H-
  1,2,4-triazol-3-yl)amino]-6-methyl-,
  hydrazone
	EtOH	234(4.28),244(4.24),
		  249(4.23)
			103-1275-80

$C_{13}H_{22}O$
  Cyclopropanal, 2,2-dimethyl-1-(1-meth-
  ylethenyl)-
	pentane	293(1.51)	33-0154-80

Spiro[4.4]nonan-2-one, 1,1,6,6-tetra- methyl-	pentane	296(1.53)	33-0154-80

$C_{13}H_{22}OSi_2$
  Bicyclo[3.2.0]hepta-1,4-dien-3-one,
  2,4-bis(trimethylsilyl)-
	C_6H_{12}	393(3.12)	89-1023-80

Disilane, 1-(4-acetylphenyl)pentameth- yl-	isooctane	264(4.24)	101-0261-80Q

$C_{13}H_{22}O_2$
  α-Ionone, 4,5-dihydro-5-hydroxy-,
  (5R,6S)-(-)-
	EtOH	228(4.16)	33-0010-80

$C_{13}H_{22}O_3$
  Cyclohexanecarboxylic acid, 1-(2-meth-
  ylpropyl)-2-oxo-, ethyl ester
	C_6H_{12}	290(1.45)	151-0305-80A

Cyclohexanepropanoic acid, 1,2,2-tri- methyl-6-oxo-, methyl ester	pentane	293(1.43)	33-1833-80
Cyclopentanepropanoic acid, 1-acetyl- 2,2-dimethyl-, methyl ester	pentane	210s(1.95),295(1.42)	33-1833-80
Cyclopentanepropanoic acid, 5-acetyl- 2,2-dimethyl-, methyl ester	pentane	285(1.30)	33-1833-80
1,3-Dioxolane-2-propanol, α-(5-methyl- 1,3-hexadienyl)-, (E,E)-(±)-	EtOH	229(4.45)	35-1390-80

Compound	Solvent	$\lambda_{max}(\log \epsilon)$	Ref.
$C_{13}H_{22}O_4$ Decanoic acid, 5,5-dimethyl-4,9-dioxo-, methyl ester	pentane	285(1.75)	33-1833-80
$C_{13}H_{22}O_4S_2$ Sulfonium, diethyl(phenylmethyl)-, ethyl sulfate	H_2O	208(3.93),258(2.65)	124-0957-80
$C_{13}H_{22}O_4Si$ Silane, triethoxy(phenoxymethyl)-	hexane	221(3.826),265(3.06), 271(3.211),278(3.203)	65-0491-80
$C_{13}H_{23}ClN_4$ Imidazo[5,1-f][1,2,4]triazine, 1,4-di-hydro-5-methyl-2-(1-methylethyl)-7-(2-methylpropyl)-, monohydro-chloride	EtOH	254(3.98)	39-1139-80C
$C_{13}H_{23}N$ 2,6,8-Nonatrien-1-amine, N,N-diethyl-	EtOH	227(4.53)	70-0263-80
$C_{13}H_{23}NO$ 3H-Pyrrol-3-one, 1,2-bis(1,1-dimethyl-ethyl)-1,2-dihydro-5-methyl-	isooctane EtOH	288(3.84),350(3.29) 288(3.72),344(3.73)	77-0889-80 77-0889-80
$C_{13}H_{23}NO_2$ 2-Cyclopenten-1-one, 2-(7-hydroxyhept-yl)-, O-methyloxime	MeOH	243(4.15)	44-4702-80
$C_{13}H_{23}N_3$ 4H-Pyrazol-4-imine, N-cyclohexyl-3,5-dihydro-3,3,5,5-tetramethyl-	hexane	273(1.871),342(2.282)	89-0049-80
$C_{13}H_{23}N_3O$ Ethanamine, N,N-diethyl-2-[(4,5,6,7-tetrahydro-1H-indazol-3-yl)oxy]-	EtOH	225(3.79)	18-0825-80
$C_{13}H_{23}N_3O_5S$ D-Xylitol, 1-C-(4-amino-2-oxo-1(2H)-pyrimidinyl)-1-S-(2-methylpropyl)-1-thio-, (R)-(+)- (S)-(-)-	H_2O H_2O	274(3.91) 273(3.94)	136-0364-80C 136-0364-80C
$C_{13}H_{24}N_4O_4S$ 2-Morpholinol, 4-[4-[3-[(1,1-dimethyl-ethyl)amino]-2-hydroxypropoxy]-1,2,5-thiadiazol-3-yl]-, hemifumarate	EtOH	215(4.07),300(3.88)	87-1178-80
$C_{13}H_{24}N_4O_5S$ Glycine, N-[4-[3-[(1,1-dimethylethyl)-amino]-2-hydroxypropoxy]-1,2,5-thia-diazol-3-yl]-N-(2-hydroxyethyl)-, (S)-	MeOH	205(3.70),310(3.98)	87-1178-80
$C_{13}H_{24}O_2$ 2-Dodecenoic acid, 3-methyl-, (E)- (Z)-	MeOH MeOH	216(3.12) 218(3.04)	12-1799-80 12-1799-80
$C_{13}H_{24}Si_2$ Silane, trimethyl[2-[(trimethylsilyl)-methyl]phenyl]-	C_6H_{12}	222(3.94)	65-1621-80

Compound	Solvent	$\lambda_{max}(\log \epsilon)$	Ref.
$C_{13}H_{25}NSi_2$ Benzenamine, N,N-dimethyl-4-(pentamethyldisilanyl)-	isooctane	270(4.49)	101-0261-80Q
$C_{13}H_{26}Si_3$ Trisilane, 1,1,1,2,3,3,3-heptamethyl-2-phenyl-	isooctane	243.0(4.11)	101-0261-80Q
$C_{13}H_{27}NS_2$ Carbamodithioic acid, dodecyl-, monoammonium salt	EtOH	254(3.99),290(4.11)	90-0775-80
$C_{13}H_{32}BrNiP_4$ Nickel(1+), bromo(6,10-dimethyl-2,6,10,14-tetraphosphapentadecane-P,P',P'',P''')-, bromide, (SP-5-13)-	MeOH CH_2Cl_2	250(3.96),275s(--), 405(2.83),430s(--) 250(4.16),280s(--), 410s(--),440(3.00)	24-1356-80 24-1356-80
$C_{13}H_{32}N_6O_5Rh_2$ Rhodium(2+), [μ-(carbonato(2-)-O:O')]]-di-μ-hydroxybis(octahydro-1H-1,4,7-triazonine-N^1,N^4,N^7)di-, diperchlorate	H_2O	339(2.63)	24-0036-80
$C_{13}H_{34}Si_4$ Silane, [1-(dimethylsilyl)-1-ethenyl-2-ylidene]tris[trimethyl-	hexane	224(4.26),357(2.69)	88-3077-80
$C_{13}H_{39}NSi_6$ Azahexasilacycloheptane, tridecamethyl-	isooctane	228(3.93),249(3.40)	101-0159-80N
$C_{13}H_{39}PSi_6$ Phosphahexasilacycloheptane, tridecamethyl-	isooctane	210(4.00),242(3.85), 261(3.72)	101-0159-80N

Compound	Solvent	$\lambda_{max}(\log \epsilon)$	Ref.
$C_{14}Cl_{10}$ Benzene, 1,1'-(1,2-ethynediyl)bis- [2,3,4,5,6-pentachloro-	$CHCl_3$	245(4.60),254(4.55), 295s(4.33),303s(4.41), 314(4.60),320s(4.49), 335(4.60)	88-2845-80
$C_{14}HF_7O_3$ 9H-Fluorene-1-carboxylic acid, 2,3,4,5,6,7,8-heptafluoro-9-oxo-	EtOH	206(4.27),247(4.60), 302(3.49),315(3.49), 330(3.47),380(3.15)	39-1726-80C
$C_{14}H_2N_6O_2$ Propanedinitrile, 2,2',2"-(4,5-dihy- droxy-4-cyclopentene-1,2,3-tri- ylidene)tris-	H_2O	232(3.98),278(4.06), 318(4.08),378s(4.04), 400s(4.08),520s(4.20), 600(4.74)	44-1338-80
dipotassium salt	H_2O	234(4.15),285(4.20), 314(4.26),378(4.11), 398(4.08),538s(4.51), 599(4.74)	44-1338-80
$C_{14}H_4F_{17}NO_2$ 1,3-Cyclohexanedione, 4,4,5,5,6,6-hexa- fluoro-2-[[[(undecafluorocyclohexyl)- methyl]amino]methylene]-	n.s.g.	264(4.16),282(4.04), 307(3.90)	39-1507-80C
$C_{14}H_5Br_4N$ 4H-Benzo[def]carbazole, 1,3,5,7-tetra- bromo-	EtOH	242(4.66),248(4.70), 272(4.26),288(4.28), 298(4.13),353(4.28), 372(4.33)	18-0494-80
$C_{14}H_5Cl_3O_2$ 1,10-Anthracenedione, 2,4,9-trichloro-	hexane	298(--),309(--), 325(--),451s(--), 470(3.6),495s(--)	110-0200-80
$C_{14}H_6Br_2S_2$ [1]Benzothieno[3,2-b][1]benzothiophene, 2,7-dibromo-	dioxan	220(4.63),243(4.40), 270(4.61),318(4.52), 324(4.49),336(4.31)	104-0383-80
$C_{14}H_6ClNO_2S_2$ [1]Benzothieno[3,2-b][1]benzothiophene, 2-chloro-7-nitro-	dioxan	216(4.54),248(4.37), 274(4.12),340(4.39)	104-0383-80
$C_{14}H_6Cl_2S_2$ [1]Benzothieno[3,2-b][1]benzothiophene, 2,7-dichloro-	dioxan	218(4.59),242(4.37), 271(4.52),316(4.47), 322(4.41),334(4.24)	104-0383-80
$C_{14}H_6N_2$ 1,3-Azulenedicarbonitrile, 4-ethynyl-	$CHCl_3$	245(4.46),275(4.33), 310(4.50),325s(4.44), 355(3.95),365(3.91), 373(3.87),382(3.99), 440(3.38),530s(2.88), 550(2.90),560(2.88), 600(2.71),640(2.39), 650s(2.32)	18-1647-80

Compound	Solvent	$\lambda_{max}(\log \epsilon)$	Ref.
1,3-Azulenedicarbonitrile, 6-ethynyl-	CHCl$_3$	260(2.79),310(4.23), 324(4.36),353(3.70), 370(3.71),380(3.66), 450(2.36),525(2.48), 570(2.39),600(2.67), 620(2.07),640(1.98)	18-1647-80
$C_{14}H_6N_2O_4S_2$ [1]Benzothieno[3,2-b][1]benzothiophene, 2,7-dinitro-	dioxan	212(4.54),238(4.19), 272(4.01),346(4.27), 404(3.97)	104-0383-80
$C_{14}H_6OS_3$ 5H-Benzo[cd][1,2]benzodithiolo[4,3,2- ghi][1,2]benzodithiol-10-S^{IV}-5-one	benzene	310s(3.81),353(3.68), 447(3.58),471(3.76), 624(3.87)	150-3172-80
	EtOH	212(4.18),252(4.41), 267s(3.99)	150-3172-80
$C_{14}H_6O_4$ 1,4,9,10-Anthracenetetrone	CHCl$_3$	254(4.17),365(3.23)	39-1007-80C
$C_{14}H_6O_5$ 4a,9a-Epoxyanthracene-1,4,9,10-tetrone	EtOH	212s(4.18),233(4.27)	39-1007-80C
$C_{14}H_7Br_2N$ Cyclopent[4,5]azepino[2,1,7-cd]pyrroli- zine, 6,8-dibromo-	EtOH	275(4.46),295(4.47), 313(4.32),344s(4.77), 357(4.95),396(3.85), 405s(3.84),423s(3.84), 430(3.87),448(3.90), 457(3.93),576(2.60), 616(2.56),685s(1.98)	39-1324-80C
$C_{14}H_7Br_2N_3$ 6H-Indolo[2,3-b]quinoxaline, 7,9-di- bromo-	dioxan	228(4.62),244(4.51), 299(4.25),357(4.19), 372(4.20)	4-0813-80
$C_{14}H_7ClN_2$ 9-Acridinecarbonitrile, 2-chloro-	MeOH	217(4.40),253s(4.80), 259(5.17),280(3.70), 333s(3.91),375(4.07), 403(3.70)	73-3593-80
$C_{14}H_7ClN_2O$ 9-Acridinecarbonitrile, 2-chloro-, 10-oxide	MeOH	277(4.82),373(3.49), 394(3.81),421(3.96), 448(4.11)	73-3593-80
$C_{14}H_7ClN_2S_2$ Propanedinitrile, [[5-[(4-chlorophen- yl)thio]-2-thienyl]methylene]-	MeOH	205(4.38),228(4.15), 252(3.97),306(3.87), 417(4.29)	73-2360-80
$C_{14}H_7Cl_2N_3$ 6H-Indolo[2,3-b]quinoxaline, 7,9-di- chloro-	dioxan	225(4.57),244(4.47), 299(4.17),354(4.13), 371(4.14)	4-0813-80

Compound	Solvent	$\lambda_{max}(\log \epsilon)$	Ref.
$C_{14}H_7NO_2S_2$			
[1]Benzothieno[3,2-b][1]benzothiophene, 2-nitro-	dioxan	216(4.55),224(4.50), 244(3.31),254(3.27), 340(4.32)	104-0391-80
[1]Benzothieno[3,2-b][1]benzothiophene, 4-nitro-	dioxan	208(4.54),228(4.34), 254(4.24),298(4.06), 308(4.13),372(3.64)	104-0391-80
$C_{14}H_7NO_3S_2$			
[1]Benzothieno[3,2-b][1]benzothiophene-2-ol, 7-nitro-	EtOH	216(4.37),228(4.31), 246(4.19),280(3.87), 360(4.10),398(4.14)	104-0383-80
$C_{14}H_7N_3O_2$			
2-Propenoic acid, 4-(tricyanoethenyl)-phenyl ester	THF	247(3.76),350(4.01)	116-0244-80
$C_{14}H_8BrClO_2$			
9H-Xanthen-9-one, 2-(bromomethyl)-5-chloro-	EtOH	242(4.50),344(3.70)	56-1281-80
9H-Xanthen-9-one, 2-(bromomethyl)-6-chloro-	EtOH	245(4.46),298(3.72), 338(3.68)	56-1281-80
9H-Xanthen-9-one, 2-(bromomethyl)-7-chloro-	EtOH	248(4.38),298(3.50), 350(3.68)	56-1281-80
$C_{14}H_8BrN_3$			
5H-Indolo[2,3-b]quinoxaline, 9-bromo-	dioxan	223(4.44),249(4.49), 299(4.22),352(4.11), 360(4.05)	4-0813-80
$C_{14}H_8Br_2Cl_2O_4S_2$			
Benzenesulfonyl chloride, 2,2'-(1,2-ethenediyl)bis[5-bromo-	dioxan	227(4.30),286(4.15), 336(4.35)	104-0383-80
$C_{14}H_8Br_2S_2$			
[1]Benzothieno[3,2-b][1]benzothiophene, 2,7-dibromo-4b,9b-dihydro-	dioxan	226(4.73),245(4.33), 304(3.86)	104-0383-80
$C_{14}H_8Br_6O_5$			
1,2-Benzenediol, 4,4'-[oxybis(methylene)]bis[3,5,6-tribromo-	EtOH	297(3.65)	102-0141-80
$C_{14}H_8ClNS_2$			
[1]Benzothieno[3,2-b][1]benzothiophen-2-amine, 1-chloro-	dioxan	222(4.47),240(4.42), 268(4.27),276(4.27), 324(4.45),338(4.44)	104-0391-80
[1]Benzothieno[3,2-b][1]benzothiophen-2-amine, 7-chloro-	dioxan	220(4.41),242(4.42), 284(4.27),340(4.27)	104-0383-80
$C_{14}H_8ClN_3$			
6H-Indolo[2,3-b]quinoxaline, 9-chloro-	dioxan	225(4.35),244(4.22), 302(3.97),352(3.98), 370(3.97)	4-0813-80
$C_{14}H_8ClN_5O_4S$			
5H-Pyrido[3',2':5,6][1,4]thiazino[2,3-b]quinoxaline, 8-chloro-2-methoxy-9-nitro-, 12-oxide	MeOH	260s(4.20),364(3.97)	4-0149-80
$C_{14}H_8Cl_2$			
Anthracene, 9,10-dichloro-	n.s.g.	362(3.84),382(4.08),	5-0954-80

Compound	Solvent	$\lambda_{max}(\log \epsilon)$	Ref.
Anthracene, 9,10-dichloro- (cont.)		404(4.07)	5-0954-80
$C_{14}H_8Cl_2N_2O_8S_2$ Benzenesulfonyl chloride, 2,2'-(1,2-ethenediyl)bis[5-nitro-	dioxan	339(4.42)	104-0383-80
$C_{14}H_8Cl_2O$ 9(10H)-Anthracenone, 1,8-dichloro-	C_6H_{12}	220(4.20),227(4.19), 235(4.11),264(4.20), 301(3.51),310(3.45), 315(3.58)	44-1807-80
9(10H)-Anthracenone, 4,5-dichloro-	EtOH	275(4.06),310s(3.53)	44-1807-80
$C_{14}H_8Cl_2S_2$ [1]Benzothieno[3,2-b][1]benzothiophene, 2,7-dichloro-4b,9b-dihydro-	dioxan	214(4.82),252(4.32), 301(3.74)	104-0383-80
$C_{14}H_8Cl_3NO_6S_2$ Benzenesulfonyl chloride, 2-[2-[4-chloro-2-(chlorosulfonyl)phenyl]-ethenyl]-5-nitro-	dioxan	340(4.41)	104-0383-80
$C_{14}H_8Cl_4O_4S_2$ Benzenesulfonyl chloride, 2,2'-(1,2-ethenediyl)bis-	dioxan	235(4.04),314(4.33)	104-0383-80
$C_{14}H_8F_2OS$ Dibenzo[b,f]thiepin-10(11H)-one, 6,9-difluoro-	MeOH	245s(4.41),330(3.71)	73-2688-80
$C_{14}H_8F_2S$ Dibenzo[b,f]thiepin, 1,4-difluoro-	MeOH	257(4.26),305(3.94)	73-2688-80
$C_{14}H_8F_3NO$ Ethanone, 1-(1H-benz[g]indol-2-yl)-2,2,2-trifluoro-	EtOH	225(4.4),285(4.4), 335(4.4)	104-1836-80
Ethanone, 1-(1H-benz[g]indol-3-yl)-2,2,2-trifluoro-	EtOH	251(4.7),285(4.4), 328(4.1)	104-1836-80
$C_{14}H_8F_3NO_4$ Pyrano[4,3-b]indole-1,3-dione, 4,5-di-hydro-5-methyl-4-(trifluoroacetyl)-	EtOH	225(4.20),249(4.39), 318(4.04)	39-1688-80C
$C_{14}H_8N_2O_2$ Cyclopent[4,5]azepino[2,1,7-cd]pyrro-lizine, 6-nitro-	EtOH	242(4.07),271(4.59), 305s(4.03),376(4.62), 474(4.18),520s(3.74), 558s(3.15)	39-1324-80C
6H-Indolo[3,2,1-de][1,5]naphthyridin-6-one, 11-hydroxy- (amarorine)	EtOH	325(3.96),385(4.25)	39-1614-80C
$C_{14}H_8N_2O_2S_2$ [1]Benzothieno[3,2-b][1]benzothiophen-2-amine, 7-nitro-	dioxan	214(4.54),238(4.46), 280(4.42),418(4.42)	104-0383-80
Propanedinitrile, [[5-(phenylsulfonyl)-2-thienyl]methylene]-	MeOH	205(4.17),241(3.88), 344(4.40)	73-2360-80
$C_{14}H_8N_2O_8S_2$ Benzoic acid, 3,3'-dithiobis[6-nitro-, ion(2-)-	DMF-base	502(4.43)	3-1851-80

Compound	Solvent	λ_{max} (log ϵ)	Ref.
$C_{14}H_8N_2S$			
Propanedinitrile, [5-(2,4,6-cyclohepta- trien-1-ylidene)-2(5H)-thienylidene]-	acetone	554(4.56)	138-1485-80
	MeCN	312(3.63),388(3.22), 556(4.55)	138-1485-80
	DMSO	586(4.55)	138-1485-80
$C_{14}H_8N_2S_2$			
Propanedinitrile, [[5-(phenylthio)- 2-thienyl]methylene]-	MeOH	205(4.33),249(3.86), 299(3.78),412(4.30)	73-2360-80
$C_{14}H_8N_4O_2$			
5H-Indolo[2,3-b]quinoxaline, 9-nitro-	dioxan	240(3.98),301(3.89), 357(3.96)	4-0813-80
$C_{14}H_8N_4O_5$			
1,3,4-Oxadiazole, 2,5-bis(2-nitrophen- yl)-	n.s.g.	252(4.22)	39-0773-80B
1,3,4-Oxadiazole, 2,5-bis(3-nitrophen- yl)-	n.s.g.	267(4.49)	39-0773-80B
1,3,4-Oxadiazole, 2,5-bis(4-nitrophen- yl)-	n.s.g.	317(4.45)	39-0773-80B
1,3,4-Oxadiazole, 2-(2-nitrophenyl)- 5-(3-nitrophenyl)-	n.s.g.	256(4.34)	39-0773-80B
1,3,4-Oxadiazole, 2-(2-nitrophenyl)- 5-(4-nitrophenyl)-	n.s.g.	294(4.30)	39-0773-80B
1,3,4-Oxadiazole, 2-(3-nitrophenyl)- 5-(4-nitrophenyl)-	n.s.g.	251(4.26),306(4.41)	39-0773-80B
$C_{14}H_8O_2$			
Naphtho[1,2-c:3,4-c']difuran	C_6H_{12}	219(4.16),226(4.21), 233(4.31),242(4.33), 263(3.95),274(4.00), 285(3.95),295s(3.20), 306(3.08),309s(2.94), 320(2.97),332(2.28)	88-3831-80
9,10-Phenanthrenedione	tert-BuOH	414(3.21)	35-4472-80
$C_{14}H_8O_2S_2$			
[1]Benzothieno[3,2-b][1]benzothiophene, 5,5-dioxide	dioxan	230(4.29),253(4.52), 267(4.27),302(3.84), 329(3.87)	104-0379-80
$C_{14}H_8O_4S_2$			
[1]Benzothieno[3,2-b][1]benzothiophene, 5,5,10,10-tetraoxide	dioxan	268(2.94),275(2.83)	104-0379-80
$C_{14}H_8O_5S$			
4H-[1]Benzothieno[3,2-b]pyran-3-acetic acid, α,4-dioxo-, methyl ester	MeOH	249(4.29),290(4.25), 328(3.95),366(3.71)	83-0395-80
$C_{14}H_8S_2$			
[1]Benzothieno[3,2-b][1]benzothiophene	dioxan	238(4.44),256(4.23), 264(4.51),295(4.42), 303(4.52),330(4.18)	104-0379-80
$C_{14}H_9Br$			
Anthracene, 9-bromo-	EtOH	246(4.94),252(5.15), 337(3.43),354(3.74), 372(3.93),390(3.87)	44-1807-80
	n.s.g.	354(3.81),372(3.99), 393(3.94)	5-0954-80

Compound	Solvent	$\lambda_{max}(\log \epsilon)$	Ref.
$C_{14}H_9BrO_2$			
6H-Benzo[3,4]cyclobuta[1,2]cyclohepten-6-one, 7-bromo-5-methoxy-	EtOH	284(4.39),306(4.59), 337(4.22)	18-2334-80
6H-Benzo[3,4]cyclobuta[1,2]cyclohepten-6-one, 9-bromo-5-methoxy-	EtOH	273(4.28),314(4.60)	18-2334-80
9H-Fluoren-9-one, 2-bromo-1-methoxy-	EtOH	264(4.79),295(3.44), 332(3.29),407(3.04)	18-2334-80
9H-Fluoren-9-one, 4-bromo-1-methoxy-	EtOH	255(4.65),302(3.22), 314(3.22),376(3.53)	18-2334-80
9H-Xanthen-9-one, 2-(bromomethyl)-	EtOH	240(4.43),289(3.32), 338(3.60)	56-1281-80
$(C_{14}H_9Br_2N)_n$			
9H-Carbazole, 3,6-dibromo-9-ethenyl-, homopolymer	$C_2H_4Cl_2$	232(4.74),272(4.19), 306(3.93),348(3.32), 361(3.29)	126-1209-80
$C_{14}H_9Cl$			
Anthracene, 9-chloro-	n.s.g.	353(3.79),371(3.99), 392(3.97)	5-0954-80
$C_{14}H_9ClN_2O$			
9-Acridinecarboxamide, 2-chloro-	MeOH	254(5.01),347(3.88), 362(3.85)	73-3593-80
$C_{14}H_9ClN_4OS$			
5H-Pyrido[3',2':5,6][1,4]thiazino[2,3-b]quinoxaline, 8-chloro-2-methoxy-	MeOH	244(4.57),326(3.77), 430(3.88)	4-0149-80
$C_{14}H_9ClO_2$			
6H-Benzo[3,4]cyclobuta[1,2]cyclohepten-6-one, 5-chloro-7-methoxy-	EtOH	298(4.73),364(3.95), 379(3.87)	18-2334-80
6H-Benzo[3,4]cyclobuta[1,2]cyclohepten-6-one, 7-chloro-5-methoxy-	EtOH	306(4.52),336(4.06), 365(3.37)	18-2334-80
6H-Benzo[3,4]cyclobuta[1,2]cyclohepten-6-one, 9-chloro-5-methoxy-	EtOH	288(4.12),312(4.54), 345(3.68),387(3.92)	18-2334-80
9H-Fluoren-9-one, 2-chloro-1-methoxy-	EtOH	264(4.85),300(3.56), 328(3.50),405(3.18)	18-2334-80
9H-Fluoren-9-one, 4-chloro-1-methoxy-	EtOH	254(4.72),302(3.34), 370(3.65)	18-2334-80
$C_{14}H_9ClO_2S$			
9H-Thioxanthen-9-one, 2-chloro-3-methoxy-	MeOH	257(4.66),269(4.67), 309s(3.66),361(3.79)	73-3166-80
9H-Thioxanthen-9-one, 2-chloro-4-methoxy-	MeOH	260(4.65),300(3.83), 311(4.00),378s(3.73), 391(3.80)	73-3166-80
9H-Thioxanthen-9-one, 2-chloro-6-methoxy-	MeOH	257(4.55),270(4.55), 278(4.58),316(3.82), 362(3.74)	73-3166-80
9H-Thioxanthen-9-one, 2-chloro-7-methoxy-	MeOH	251(4.58),272(4.44), 282(4.43),301s(3.54), 378(3.81)	73-3166-80
9H-Xanthen-9-one, 2-chloro-7-(mercaptomethyl)-	EtOH	240(4.60),298(3.50), 350(3.75)	56-1281-80
9H-Xanthen-9-one, 6-chloro-2-(mercaptomethyl)-	EtOH	243(4.56),294(3.96), 364(3.81)	56-1281-80
$C_{14}H_9ClO_2S_2$			
Disulfide, benzoyl 4-chlorobenzoyl	CH_2Cl_2	263(4.37)	118-0721-80

Compound	Solvent	$\lambda_{max}(\log \epsilon)$	Ref.
$C_{14}H_9Cl_2N$ 9H-Carbazole, 3,6-dichloro-9-ethenyl-, homopolymer	$C_2H_4Cl_2$	231(4.54),270(4.12), 304(3.92),347(3.33), 361(3.34)	126-1209-80
$C_{14}H_9Cl_2NO$ 1H-Pyrrolizin-1-one, 2-[(2,4-dichlorophenyl)methylene]-2,3-dihydro-	EtOH	350(4.10)	145-1135-80
1H-Pyrrolizin-1-one, 2-[(2,6-dichlorophenyl)methylene]-2,3-dihydro-	EtOH	333(4.28)	145-1135-80
1H-Pyrrolizin-1-one, 2-[(3,4-dichlorophenyl)methylene]-2,3-dihydro-	EtOH	333(4.28)	145-1135-80
$C_{14}H_9Cl_2NO_6S_2$ Benzenesulfonyl chloride, 2-[2-[2-(chlorosulfonyl)phenyl]ethenyl]-5-nitro-	dioxan	338(4.37)	104-0391-80
$C_{14}H_9Cl_3FNO_5S$ Furan, 2-[2-(2-fluorophenyl)-1-[(trichloromethyl)sulfonyl]cyclopropyl]-5-nitro-, trans-(±)-	MeOH	206(4.02),312(3.72)	73-1704-80
$C_{14}H_9Cl_3N_2O_7S$ Furan, 2-nitro-5-[2-(3-nitrophenyl)-1-[(trichloromethyl)sulfonyl]cyclopropyl]-, trans-(±)-	MeOH	210(4.50),308(4.07)	73-1704-80
Furan, 2-nitro-5-[2-(4-nitrophenyl)-1-[(trichloromethyl)sulfonyl]cyclopropyl]-, trans-(±)-	MeOH	203(4.41),316(4.10)	73-1704-80
$C_{14}H_9Cl_4NO_5S$ Furan, 2-[2-(2-chlorophenyl)-1-[(trichloromethyl)sulfonyl]cyclopropyl]-5-nitro-, trans-(±)-	MeOH	204(4.46),312(3.97)	73-1704-80
Furan, 2-[2-(3-chlorophenyl)-1-[(trichloromethyl)sulfonyl]cyclopropyl]-5-nitro-, trans-(±)-	MeOH	205(4.63),312(4.10)	73-1704-80
$C_{14}H_9FN_2S$ 1,2,3-Thiadiazole, 4-(4-fluorophenyl)-5-phenyl-	EtOH	304(3.25)	24-0183-80
1,2,3-Thiadiazole, 5-(4-fluorophenyl)-4-phenyl-	EtOH	303(3.31)	24-0183-80
$C_{14}H_9FOS$ Dibenzo[b,f]thiepin-10(11H)-one, 7-fluoro-	MeOH	245(4.26),263(4.00), 271s(3.90),319(3.56)	73-1086-80
$C_{14}H_9N$ 4H-Benzo[def]carbazole	EtOH	234(4.80),273(4.25), 283(4.13),332(4.09), 346(4.04)	18-0494-80
Cyclopenta[4,5]azepino[2,1,7-cd]pyrrolizine	EtOH	273(4.27),294(4.45), 306(4.38),328(4.60), 341(4.75),387(3.68), 406(3.77),415s(3.67), 438(3.47),516(2.43), 544(2.42),560s(2.39), 589(2.35),655(1.82)	39-1324-80C

Compound	Solvent	λ$_{max}$(log ε)	Ref.
Cyclopenta[4,5]azepino[2,1,7-cd]pyrrolizine (cont.)	EtOH-HClO$_4$	248(4.19),292(4.73), 335s(4.22),348(4.47), 398(3.76)	39-1324-80C
C$_{14}$H$_9$NO$_2$			
Anthracene, 9-nitro-	n.s.g.	348(3.60),365(3.69), 385(3.62)	5-0954-80
1H-Indene-1,3(2H)-dione, 2-(2-pyridinyl)-	5M NaOH	254s(4.27),280(4.42), 333(4.26),342(4.24), 425(3.65)	4-0961-80
1H-Indene-1,3(2H)-dione, 2-(4(1H)-pyridinylidene)-	EtOH	385(4.68)	4-0997-80
	THF	403(4.76)	4-0997-80
1(2H)-Isobenzofuranone, 3-(2-pyridinylmethylene)-	EtOH	214(4.24),228(4.15), 251(4.11),293(4.22), 304(4.31),330(4.35)	4-0961-80
Pyridinium, 1,3-dihydro-1,3-dioxo-2H-inden-2-ylide	50% EtOH	239(4.52),303(3.64), 314(3.72),385(4.18)	103-1239-80
C$_{14}$H$_9$NO$_3$			
9,10-Anthracenedione, 1-amino-4-hydroxy-	gas	496(3.80)	135-0344-80
	film	536(--)	135-0344-80
	crystal	538(--)	135-0344-80
	hexane	520(--)	135-0344-80
	DMF	533(3.92)	135-0344-80
1-Azulenecarboxylic acid, 3-cyano-2-formyl-, methyl ester	MeOH	235(4.55),267(4.34), 293(4.63),303(4.73), 340(3.90),367(3.89)	18-3696-80
C$_{14}$H$_9$NO$_4$			
3H-Phenoxazine-1-carboxylic acid, 3-oxo-, methyl ester	EtOH	355(4.01),459(4.01)	78-0529-80
C$_{14}$H$_9$NS			
Indolo[4,5-d]benzo[b]thiophene	EtOH	213(4.23),248(4.66), 255(4.63),286(4.14), 303(4.23),321(3.75)	103-0146-80
Indolo[5,4-d]benzo[b]thiophene	EtOH	217(4.39),252(4.77), 285(4.24),303(3.36)	103-0146-80
Indolo[5,6-d]benzo[b]thiophene	EtOH	217(4.42),247(4.59), 264(4.60),303(3.52), 316(3.91),345(3.28)	103-0146-80
Indolo[6,5-d]benzo[b]thiophene	EtOH	224(4.66),236(4.63), 266(4.01),311(4.30)	103-0146-80
C$_{14}$H$_9$NS$_2$			
[1]Benzothieno[3,2-b][1]benzothiophen-2-amine	dioxan	218(4.55),246(4.45), 276(4.23),332(4.43)	104-0391-80
[1]Benzothieno[3,2-b][1]benzothiophen-4-amine	dioxan	226(4.54),266(4.40), 294(4.10),316(3.93), 338(3.99),356(4.07)	104-0391-80
C$_{14}$H$_9$N$_3$			
5H-Indolo[2,3-b]quinoxaline	dioxan	222(4.513),265(4.454), 334(4.102),350(4.134)	4-0813-80
2,3,7b-Triazacyclopent[cd]indene, 1-phenyl-	EtOH	221(4.26),262(4.35), 301(3.82),488(4.09)	88-4193-80
C$_{14}$H$_9$N$_3$OS			
3,5-Pyridinedicarbonitrile, 1,2-dihydro-4-(methylthio)-2-oxo-6-phenyl-	MeOH	260(4.26),346(3.91)	118-1022-80

Compound	Solvent	$\lambda_{max}(\log \epsilon)$	Ref.
$C_{14}H_9N_3OS_2$ Furo[2,3-b]pyrimidin-4-amine, 5,6-di-2-thienyl-	MeOH	208(4.34),243(4.00), 269(3.91),320(4.27), 335(4.36)	73-1581-80
$C_{14}H_9N_3O_3$ Furo[2,3-b]pyrimidin-4-amine, 5,6-di-2-furanyl-	MeOH	208(4.18),236(4.01), 278(3.90),333(4.22)	73-1581-80
1,3,4-Oxadiazole, 2-(2-nitrophenyl)-5-phenyl-	n.s.g.	258(4.15)	39-0773-80B
1,3,4-Oxadiazole, 2-(3-nitrophenyl)-5-phenyl-	n.s.g.	276(4.40)	39-0773-80B
1,3,4-Oxadiazole, 2-(4-nitrophenyl)-5-phenyl-	n.s.g.	312(4.41)	39-0773-80B
$C_{14}H_9N_5O$ Tetrazolo[1,5-a]quinazolin-5(4H)-one, 4-phenyl-	MeOH	292(3.43)	2-0638-80
$C_{14}H_9N_5O_2$ Isoxazolo[4,5-b]pyridine-3-carboxamide, 5-amino-6-cyano-7-phenyl-	DMF	294(3.84),397(3.85)	5-1623-80
$C_{14}H_9OS_2$ Thieno[3,2,1-de]thianthren-11-ium, 1,2-dihydro-2-oxo-, perchlorate	MeOH	211(4.69),255s(4.17), 282s(3.92),326s(3.73)	39-1185-80C
$C_{14}H_{10}$ Anthracene	n.s.g.	341.5(3.75),359(3.93), 378(3.91)	5-0954-80
$C_{14}H_{10}BNS_2$ Dithieno[2,3-c:3',2'-e][1,2]azaborine, 4,5-dihydro-5-phenyl-	C_6H_{12}	192(4.72),229(4.50), 257(4.15),288(3.77), 321(4.14)	11-0023-80A
$(C_{14}H_{10}BrN)_n$ 9H-Carbazole, 3-bromo-9-ethenyl-, homopolymer	$C_2H_4Cl_2$	232(4.49),263(4.16), 300(3.92),339(3.33), 354(3.36)	126-1209-80
$C_{14}H_{10}BrNO$ Indeno[1,2-d]azepin-4(3H)-one, 10-bromo-3-methyl-	EtOH	280(4.64),354(3.76), 372(3.66),500(2.98)	18-3232-80
$C_{14}H_{10}BrN_3$ 2H-1,2,3-Triazole, 2-(4-bromophenyl)-4-phenyl-	MeOH	299(4.37)	39-0744-80C
$C_{14}H_{10}Br_2N_2O_4$ Ethane, bis[(4-bromophenyl)-aci-nitro]-	MeOH	220(--),295(4.23)	104-2059-80
$C_{14}H_{10}Br_2S_2$ Benzenethiol, 2,2'-(1,2-ethenediyl)-bis[5-bromo-	EtOH-1%NaOH dioxan	278(4.28),308(3.26) 257(4.25),299(4.19), 338(4.08)	104-0383-80 104-0383-80
$C_{14}H_{10}ClN$ 9H-Carbazole, 3-chloro-9-ethenyl-, homopolymer	$C_2H_4Cl_2$	238(4.50),266(4.15), 298(3.96),340(3.51), 356(3.48)	126-1209-80

Compound	Solvent	$\lambda_{max}(\log \epsilon)$	Ref.
$C_{14}H_{10}ClNO$			
Indeno[1,2-d]azepin-4(3H)-one, 10-chloro-3-methyl-	EtOH	277(4.66),330(3.82), 345(3.75),490(3.08)	18-3232-80
1H-Pyrrolizin-1-one, 2-[(2-chlorophenyl)methylene]-2,3-dihydro-	EtOH	345(4.29)	145-1135-80
1H-Pyrrolizin-1-one, 2-[(4-chlorophenyl)methylene]-2,3-dihydro-	EtOH	351(4.43)	145-1135-80
$C_{14}H_{10}ClNO_2$			
Furo[2,3-c]pyridin-2(6H)-one, 3-chloro-6-(phenylmethyl)-	MeCN	265(3.80),396(4.37), 408(4.47)	39-1176-80C
$C_{14}H_{10}ClN_2O_4$			
Pyridinium, 1-[3-(2-chloro-5-nitrophenyl)-3-oxo-1-propenyl]-3-hydroxy-, chloride	EtOH	262(4.53)	39-0362-80C
$C_{14}H_{10}ClN_3O$			
Benzamide, N-1H-benzimidazol-2-yl-2-chloro-	CHCl$_3$	258(2.99),297(3.28)	48-0055-80
2H-1,3,4-Benzotriazepin-2-one, 7-chloro-1,3-dihydro-5-phenyl-	EtOH	226(4.42),250s(4.17), 303(3.75)	106-0332-80
$C_{14}H_{10}ClN_3S$			
3H-1,2,4-Triazole-3-thione, 2-(4-chlorophenyl)-1,2-dihydro-4-phenyl-	MeOH	232(4.45),290s(--)	73-2804-80
$C_{14}H_{10}ClN_5O$			
1H-Pyrazole-4,5-dione, 3-(3-pyridinyl)-, 4-[(2-chlorophenyl)hydrazone]	H$_2$O ion	415(4.01) 380(3.91)	2-0789-80A 2-0789-80A
1H-Pyrazole-4,5-dione, 3-(3-pyridinyl)-, 4-[(4-chlorophenyl)hydrazone]	H$_2$O ion	420(3.99) 370(3.92)	2-0789-80A 2-0789-80A
$C_{14}H_{10}Cl_2N_2O_4$			
Benzene, 1,1'-(1,2-ethanediyl)bis[4-chloro-2-nitro-?	acetone	248(--),315(4.39)	104-2059-80
$C_{14}H_{10}Cl_2O_2$			
Phenol, 4-[2,2-dichloro-1-(4-hydroxyphenyl)ethenyl]-	CF$_3$SO$_3$H	343(3.58),520(4.33)	88-3131-80
$C_{14}H_{10}Cl_2O_4S_2$			
Benzenesulfonyl chloride, 2,2'-(1,2-ethenediyl)bis-	dioxan	234(4.41),277(4.14), 323(4.24)	104-0342-80
$C_{14}H_{10}Cl_3NO_5S$			
Furan, 2-nitro-5-[2-phenyl-1-[(trichloromethyl)sulfonyl]cyclopropyl]-, trans-(±)-	MeOH	207(4.27),312(4.05)	73-1704-80
$C_{14}H_{10}Cl_3NO_8S$			
2-Furancarboxylic acid, 5-[2-(5-nitro-2-furanyl)-2-[(trichloromethyl)sulfonyl]cyclopropyl]-, methyl ester, trans-(±)-	MeOH	207(4.14),311(3.98)	73-1704-80
$C_{14}H_{10}Cl_4N_2O_2$			
Acetamide, N-[2,3,5,6-tetrachloro-4-oxo-1-(phenylamino)-2,5-cyclohexadien-1-yl]-	MeCN	238(3.93),272(3.80)	12-2299-80

Compound	Solvent	$\lambda_{max}(\log \epsilon)$	Ref.
$C_{14}H_{10}INO_2S$ 4H-Cyclopenta[b]thiophene-5-carbox-amide, 2-iodo-6-(4-methylphenyl)-4-oxo-	MeOH	250(4.60)	2-0156-80
$C_{14}H_{10}N_2O$ 1,3,4-Oxadiazole, 2,5-diphenyl-	n.s.g.	282(4.40)	39-0773-80B
1-(Pyrrolo[1',2':3,4]pyrimido[2,1,6-cd]pyrrolizin-8-yl)ethanone	C_6H_{12}	221(4.42),240(4.19), 277(4.24),282(4.26), 293(4.05),302(3.95), 332(4.22),348(4.53), 387(3.92),410(4.07)	24-0614-80
$C_{14}H_{10}N_2OS$ Benzamide, N-2-benzothiazolyl-	CHCl$_3$	240(3.99),302(4.20)	48-0055-80
$C_{14}H_{10}N_2O_2$ 9,10-Anthracenedione, 1,4-diamino-	gas	512(3.90)	135-0344-80
	film	554(--)	135-0344-80
	crystal	560(--)	135-0344-80
	hexane	522(--)	135-0344-80
	DMF	552(4.09)	135-0344-80
Benzamide, N-2-benzoxazolyl-	CHCl$_3$	246(4.12),305(4.46)	48-0055-80
2H-1,3-Benzoxazin-2-one, 4-(phenyl-amino)-	EtOH	206(4.53),251(4.11), 305(4.08)	70-0468-80
2-Propenoic acid, 2-methyl-, 4-(2,2-di-cyanoethenyl)phenyl ester	EtOH	318(4.17)	116-0244-80
4(1H)-Quinazolinone, 2-(2-hydroxyphen-yl)-	EtOH	219(5.53),284(4.78), 298(4.79),327(4.81)	70-0468-80
$C_{14}H_{10}N_2O_2S$ 2H-1,4-Benzothiazine, 3-(4-nitrophen-yl)-	EtOH	240(4.37),274(4.27), 304(4.13),347(4.02)	39-2923-80C
$C_{14}H_{10}N_2O_3$ Acridine, 9-methoxy-1-nitro-	pH 1	248(4.08),352(3.48)	56-1291-80
	pH 7	245(4.14),356(3.65)	56-1291-80
$C_{14}H_{10}N_2O_4$ Acridine, 9-methoxy-1-nitro-, 10-oxide	pH 1	265(4.41),430(3.76)	56-1291-80
	pH 7	267(4.52),432(3.93)	56-1291-80
2H-1,4-Benzoxazin-2-ol, 7-nitro-3-phenyl-	MeOH	228(4.18),317(4.20), 357(4.23)	4-1625-80
3H-Phenoxazine-1-carboxylic acid, 2-amino-3-oxo-, methyl ester	EtOH EtOH-acid	432(4.08) 424s(--),457(--), 494s(--)	78-0529-80 78-0529-80
$C_{14}H_{10}N_2O_4S_2$ Benzenethiol, 2,2'-(1,2-ethenediyl)bis-[5-nitro-	EtOH-1% NaOH	294(4.47),367(4.29), 565(4.00)	104-0383-80
	dioxan	340(4.25)	104-0383-80
$C_{14}H_{10}N_2S$ Naphtho[2',1':5,6]thiopyrano[4,3-c]-pyrazole, 2,11-dihydro-	EtOH	211(4.44),234(4.42), 255(4.43),278(4.57), 326(3.89)	4-0121-80
$C_{14}H_{10}N_2S_2$ [1]Benzothieno[3,2-b][1]benzothiophene-2,7-diamine	dioxan	238(4.51),272(4.24), 282(4.40),343(4.47)	104-0383-80

Compound	Solvent	$\lambda_{max}(\log \epsilon)$	Ref.
Propanedinitrile, [2-(methylthio)-3-[4-(methylthio)phenyl]-2-cyclopropen-1-ylidene]-	CH_2Cl_2	240(4.2),280(4.3), 304s(4.1),359(4.4), 369(4.4),388(4.2)	5-1409-80
$C_{14}H_{10}N_4$			
Tetracyanoethene adduct of 2,3-bis-(methylene)bicyclo[2.1.1]hexane	MeCN	227.5(3.54)	33-1176-80
1,2,4,5-Tetrazine, 3,6-diphenyl-	MeOH	294(4.55),544(2.62)	24-2566-80
	EtOH	294(4.32)	39-2184-80C
$C_{14}H_{10}N_4O$			
6H-Benzo[h]pyrazolo[3,4-b][1,6]naphthyridin-6-one, 5,10-dihydro-5-methyl-	MeOH	229(4.49),251(4.25), 277(4.11),323(3.81)	39-0512-80C
	MeOH-acid	222s(4.57),228(4.67), 252(4.56),276(4.49), 326(4.11),350s(3.93)	39-0512-80C
$C_{14}H_{10}N_4OS$			
5H-Pyrido[3',2':5,6][1,4]thiazino[2,3-b]quinoxaline, 2-methoxy-	MeOH	231(3.88),241(4.65), 426(3.93)	4-0149-80
$C_{14}H_{10}N_4O_2$			
2,3-Pyrazinedicarbonitrile, 5-(3,4-dimethoxyphenyl)-	MeCN	369(4.29)	138-0921-80
$C_{14}H_{10}N_4O_2S$			
3H-1,2,4-Triazole-3-thione, 1,2-dihydro-2-(4-nitrophenyl)-5-phenyl-	MeOH	242(4.18),288(3.90)	73-2804-80
$C_{14}H_{10}N_4O_2Se$			
1,3,4-Selenadiazol-2(3H)-imine, 3-(4-nitrophenyl)-5-phenyl-	EtOH	253(4.56),350(4.22)	4-1185-80
$C_{14}H_{10}N_4O_3$			
1H-Imidazole-4-carboxylic acid, 5-[(2-hydroxy-1-naphthalenyl)azo]-	EtOH	207s(4.43),225(4.53), 301(3.91),480(4.19)	103-1171-80
3H,8H-Imidazo[1,2,3-ij]pteridine-3,8,10(9H)-trione, 5,6-dihydro-2-phenyl-	pH 5.0	214(4.22),235(3.93), 284(3.91),350(4.12)	142-0437-80B
	pH 12.0	212(4.35),235s(4.11), 262(4.10),360(4.30)	142-0437-80B
$C_{14}H_{10}N_4O_4$			
1H-Cyclopenta[gh]perimidine, 6,7-dihydro-2-methyl-4,9-dinitro-	MeOH	280(4.40),330s(3.65), 390s(3.80),480(4.40)	103-0071-80
$C_{14}H_{10}N_4O_6$			
2,2'-Bibenzoxazole, 2,2',3,3'-tetrahydro-6,6'-dinitro-	MeOH	245s(--),259(4.16), 315s(--),368(4.40)	4-1629-80
	0.5M NaOH	230(4.23),278(4.30), 365(4.05),462(4.26)	4-1629-80
$C_{14}H_{10}N_6O_4$			
1H-Benzimidazole, 2,3-dihydro-2-[nitro-[(4-nitrophenyl)azo]methylene]-	MeCN	243(4.04),305(4.23), 430(4.52)	48-0087-80
$C_{14}H_{10}O$			
9(10H)-Anthracenone	EtOH	259(4.28),268(4.25), 308(3.64)	44-1807-80
2,3-Homophenalenone	C_6H_{12}	212(4.56),248(4.35), 319(3.75),334(3.74),	108-0244-80

Compound	Solvent	$\lambda_{max}(\log \epsilon)$	Ref.
2,3-Homophenalenone (cont.)		350s(3.45),365s(3.18), 383s(2.65)	108-0244-80
	EtOH	212(4.53),249(4.29), 323(3.69),335(3.74), 355s(3.62)	108-0244-80
	CF$_3$COOH	240(4.03),295(3.40), 364(3.71),440s(3.14)	108-0244-80
$C_{14}H_{10}OS$			
Dibenzo[b,f]thiepin-3-ol	MeOH	230(4.37),267(4.36), 300s(3.76),335(3.51)	73-1086-80
2H-Naphtho[1,2-b]thiopyran-2-one, 4-methyl-	EtOH	275(4.42),286(4.40), 319(3.78),333(3.78), 373(3.38),390s(3.28)	18-2046-80
2H-Naphtho[2,3-b]thiopyran-2-one, 4-methyl-	EtOH	246(4.73),281(4.34), 295(4.36),333(4.08), 380(3.30)	18-2046-80
$C_{14}H_{10}O_2$			
2(3H)-Benzofuranone, 3-phenyl-	n.s.g.	226(3.85),280(3.30)	150-3901-80
1H-Phenalen-1-one, 9-hydroxy-3-methyl-	MeOH	235(4.18),350(4.09), 415(3.80),435(3.86)	2-0859-80
9H-Xanthen-9-one, 2-methyl-	EtOH	231(4.44),240(4.47), 264(4.03),291(3.58), 348(3.72)	56-1281-80
$C_{14}H_{10}O_2S$			
9H-Xanthen-9-one, 2-(mercaptomethyl)-	EtOH	240(4.64),292(3.60), 370(3.81)	56-1281-80
$C_{14}H_{10}O_2S_2$			
Butanedial, bis(2-thienylmethylene)-	CHCl$_3$	285s(4.3),324(4.6)	118-0898-80
$C_{14}H_{10}O_3S$			
Indeno[1,2-b]pyran-2-carboxylic acid, 4,5-dihydro-4-thioxo-, methyl ester	MeOH	238(4.12),310(4.21), 395(4.33)	83-0429-80
$C_{14}H_{10}O_3S_2$			
4H-[1]Benzothieno[3,2-b]pyran-2-carboxylic acid, 4-thioxo-, ethyl ester	MeOH	286(4.02),310(4.14), 401(4.26)	83-0385-80
$C_{14}H_{10}O_4$			
Butanedial, bis(2-furanylmethylene)-	CHCl$_3$	314(4.6)	118-0898-80
4H-1,3-Dioxin-4-one, 2-(2-furanyl)- (general spectrum of class)	EtOH	285-315(3.98-4.25)	104-1995-80
Indeno[1,2-b]pyran-2-carboxylic acid, 4,5-dihydro-4-oxo-, methyl ester	MeOH	238(4.02),248(4.04), 255(4.03),312(4.20)	83-0429-80
9H-Xanthen-9-one, 3-hydroxy-2-methoxy-	EtOH	242(4.23),275(2.08), 310(4.00),348(4.02)	2-0463-80
	EtOH-NaOAc	240(4.22),275(3.08), 310(4.02),358(4.13)	2-0463-80
9H-Xanthen-9-one, 5-hydroxy-1-methoxy-	EtOH	236(4.03),247(4.89), 305(3.02),352(3.00)	2-0463-80
$C_{14}H_{10}O_4S$			
4H-Pyrano[3,2-b]benzofuran-2-carboxylic acid, 4-thioxo-, ethyl ester	MeOH	226(4.21),308(4.19), 390(4.33)	83-0385-80
$C_{14}H_{10}O_6$			
Bellidifolin	EtOH	234(4.0),255(4.2), 279(4.0),302s(3.7), 334(3.9)	2-0929-80

Compound	Solvent	$\lambda_{max}(\log \epsilon)$	Ref.
$C_{14}H_{10}S_2$			
[1]Benzothieno[3,2-b][1]benzothiophene, 4b,9b-dihydro-	EtOH	248(4.28),298(3.55)	104-0379-80
Dibenzo[c,g][1,2]dithiocin	EtOH	247(4.23),285s(3.66), 320s(3.07)	104-0342-80
$C_{14}H_{11}BrClN_3$			
Acetaldehyde, [(4-chlorophenyl)imino]-, (4-bromophenyl)hydrazone	hexane	296(3.76),410(4.34)	65-2072-80
	EtOH	313(3.90),380(4.59)	65-2072-80
$C_{14}H_{11}BrNO_2$			
Pyridinium, 3-(4-bromophenyl)-3-oxo-1-propenyl]-3-hydroxy-, chloride, (E)-	EtOH	290(4.38)	39-0362-80C
$C_{14}H_{11}BrN_2O_2$			
5H-1-Pyrindinium, 6,7-dihydro-1-methyl-5,7-dioxo-6-pyridinio-, bromide hydroxide, inner salt	50% EtOH	205(4.504),236(3.924), 270(3.482),375(4.129)	103-1239-80
5H-1-Pyrindinium, 6,7-dihydro-2-methyl-5,7-dioxo-6-pyridinio-, bromide hydroxide, inner salt	50% EtOH	209(4.484),228(4.371), 268s(4.0),277(4.194), 292s(4.0),303s(3.84), 359(4.226),420(3.37)	103-1239-80
$C_{14}H_{11}BrN_2O_3$			
Ethanone, 2-[(4-bromophenyl)amino]-1-(4-nitrophenyl)-	CH_2Cl_2	365(2.95)	83-0315-80
$C_{14}H_{11}BrO_3$			
2H,8H-Benzo[1,2-b:3,4-b']dipyran-2-one, 8-(bromomethyl)-8-methyl-	EtOH	217(4.45),261(3.81), 294(4.18),330(4.15)	2-0341-80
$C_{14}H_{11}BrO_6$			
2H-1-Benzopyran-6-acetaldehyde, 7-acetoxy-α-bromo-8-methoxy-2-oxo-	MeOH	228s(4.16),238s(4.11), 290(4.03),322s(3.74)	44-1470-80
$C_{14}H_{11}BrO_7$			
2H-1-Benzopyran-6-acetic acid, 7-acetoxy-α-bromo-8-methoxy-2-oxo-	MeOH	242(4.08),288(3.95), 325s(3.51),365s(2.76)	44-1470-80
$C_{14}H_{11}Br_2N$			
9H-Carbazole, 3,6-dibromo-9-ethyl-	$C_2H_4Cl_2$	243(4.65),275(4.51), 306(4.23),348(3.49), 365(3.51)	126-1209-80
$C_{14}H_{11}Br_2N_3$			
Acetaldehyde, [(4-bromophenyl)imino]-, (4-bromophenyl)hydrazone	hexane	292(3.72),412(4.35)	65-2072-80
	EtOH	312(3.86),382(4.57)	65-2072-80
$C_{14}H_{11}ClNO_2$			
Pyridinium, 1-[3-(4-chlorophenyl)-3-oxo-1-propenyl]-3-hydroxy-, chloride, (E)-	EtOH	270(4.32)	39-0362-80C
$C_{14}H_{11}ClN_2O$			
Benzoic acid, [(3-chlorophenyl)methylene]hydrazide	C_6H_{12}	291(4.47)	115-0013-80
	benzene	295(4.55)	115-0013-80
	EtOH	298(4.50)	115-0013-80
	ether	294(4.47)	115-0013-80
	dioxan	294(4.47)	115-0013-80
	$CHCl_3$	294(4.40)	115-0013-80
	CCl_4	292(4.50)	115-0013-80

Compound	Solvent	$\lambda_{max}(\log \epsilon)$	Ref.
Benzoic acid, [(4-chlorophenyl)methyl-ene]hydrazide	C_6H_{12}	295(4.40)	115-0013-80
	benzene	300(4.42)	115-0013-80
	EtOH	299(4.57)	115-0013-80
	ether	299(4.45)	115-0013-80
	dioxan	298(4.42)	115-0013-80
	$CHCl_3$	291(4.45)	115-0013-80
	CCl_4	297(4.48)	115-0013-80
$C_{14}H_{11}ClN_2OPt$			
Platinum, [2-[[(2-aminophenyl)methyl-ene]amino]benzaldehydato-N,N',O]-chloro-	n.s.g.	560(4.00)(changing)	35-7939-80
final spectrum	n.s.g.	470(3.60)	35-7939-80
$C_{14}H_{11}ClN_2O_2$			
1H-Pyrazolo[1,2-a]pyrazol-4-ium, 2-(4-chlorophenyl)-3-hydroxy-5,7-dimethyl-1-oxo-, hydroxide, inner salt	MeCN	214(4.362),276(4.408), 420(2.849)	64-1002-80B
$C_{14}H_{11}ClN_2O_3$			
Ethanone, 2-[(4-chlorophenyl)amino]-1-(4-nitrophenyl)-	CH_2Cl_2	370(3.04)	83-0315-80
$C_{14}H_{11}ClN_4O_2$			
Acetaldehyde, [)4-chlorophenyl)imino]-, (4-nitrophenyl)hydrazone	hexane	292(--),407(--)	65-2072-80
	EtOH	306(3.78),402(4.72)	65-2072-80
$C_{14}H_{11}Cl_2N$			
9H-Carbazole, 3,6-dichloro-N-ethyl-	$C_2H_4Cl_2$	240(4.64),274(4.43), 304(4.25),350(3.66), 365(4.62)	126-1209-80
$C_{14}H_{11}Cl_2N_3$			
Acetaldehyde, [(4-chlorophenyl)imino]-, (4-chlorophenyl)hydrazone	hexane	295(3.73),413(4.35)	65-2072-80
	EtOH	312(3.96),382(4.61)	65-2072-80
$C_{14}H_{11}N$			
Benz[g]isoquinoline, 8-methyl-	$CHCl_3$	256(5.00),274s(4.44), 314(3.32),329(3.52), 345(3.53),355(3.53), 375(3.71),394(3.64)	103-0525-80
4H-Benzo[def]carbazole, 8,9-dihydro-	EtOH	216(4.61),246(4.54), 255(4.38),294(4.08), 316(3.56),329(3.48)	18-0494-80
Benzo[g]quinoline, 7-methyl-	$CHCl_3$	262(5.24),346s(3.56), 354s(3.60),362(3.62), 370(3.62),393(3.44)	103-0525-80
$(C_{14}H_{11}N)_n$			
9H-Carbazole, 9-ethenyl-, homopolymer	$C_2H_4Cl_2$	238(4.48),262(4.12), 295(4.02),330(3.52), 334(3.53)	126-1209-80
$C_{14}H_{11}NO$			
Acridine, 9-methoxy-	pH 1	256(4.452),348(3.307), 385(3.105),404(3.044)	56-1291-80
	pH 7	251(4.496),336(3.338), 353(3.478),371(3.349)	56-1291-80
Ethanone, 1-(1H-benz[g]indol-3-yl)-	EtOH	255(4.8)	104-1836-80
Indeno[1,2-d]azepin-4(3H)-one, 3-meth-yl-	EtOH	275(4.2),330s(--), 505(2.9)	18-3232-80

Compound	Solvent	$\lambda_{max}(\log \epsilon)$	Ref.
1H-Pyrrolizin-1-one, 2,3-dihydro-2-(phenylmethylene)-	EtOH	348(4.35)	145-1135-80
$C_{14}H_{11}NOS$ Phenol, 2-(2H-1,4-benzothiazin-3-yl)-	EtOH	277(4.11),323s(3.82), 374(3.94)	39-2923-80C
$C_{14}H_{11}NO_2$ 1H-Benz[de]isoquinoline-1,3(2H)-dione, 2-ethyl-	dioxan	240(4.33),333(4.11), 348(4.07)	56-0107-80
$C_{14}H_{11}NO_3$ 9H-Pyrrolo[1,2-a]indole-2-carboxylic acid, 1-methyl-9-oxo-, methyl ester	EtOH	256(4.53),272(4.40), 282(4.33),332(3.95)	78-2125-80
$C_{14}H_{11}NO_3S$ Pyrano[3,2-b]indole-2-carboxylic acid, 4,5-dihydro-5-methyl-4-thioxo-, methyl ester	MeOH	236(4.32),282(4.03), 320(4.11),382(4.12), 424(4.33)	83-0405-80
$C_{14}H_{11}NO_4$ Oxazolo[3,2-a]quinolinium, 5-acetoxy-2-hydroxy-4-methyl-, hydroxide, inner salt	EtOH	234(4.33),269(4.09), 329(3.45)	78-1385-80
Pyrano[3,2-b]indole-2-carboxylic acid, 4,5-dihydro-5,8-dimethyl-4-oxo-	MeOH	217(4.56),254(4.18), 262(4.13),307(4.30)	83-0405-80
Pyrano[3,2-b]indole-2-carboxylic acid, 4,5-dihydro-5-methyl-4-oxo-, methyl ester	MeOH	221(4.55),256(4.13), 264(4.10),309(4.26)	83-0405-80
Pyrrolo[2,1,5-cd]indolizine-1,2-dicarboxylic acid, dimethyl ester	EtOH	270(4.57),317(3.63), 422(3.28)	39-1319-80C
$C_{14}H_{11}NO_4S$ Pyrrolo[2,1-b]benzothiazole-2,3-dicarboxylic acid, dimethyl ester	EtOH	241(4.62),268s(4.13), 288(4.13)	18-3308-80
$C_{14}H_{11}N_2O_2$ 5H-1-Pyrindinium, 6,7-dihydro-1-methyl-5,7-dioxo-6-pyridinio-, bromide hydroxide, inner salt	50% EtOH	205(4.504),236(3.924), 270(3.482),375(4.129)	103-1239-80
5H-2-Pyrindinium, 6,7-dihydro-2-methyl-5,7-dioxo-6-pyridinio-, bromide hydroxide, inner salt	50% EtOH	209(4.484),228(4.371), 268s(4.0),277(4.194), 292s(4.0),303s(3.84), 359(4.226),420(3.37)	103-1239-80
$C_{14}H_{11}N_3O$ Benzamide, N-1H-benzimidazol-2-yl-	CHCl$_3$	244(3.72),304(3.85)	48-0055-80
2H-Indazole, 2-[(2-nitrosophenyl)methyl-	EtOH	220(4.15),285(4.10)	44-4597-80
$C_{14}H_{11}N_3O_2$ 1H-Cyclopenta[gh]perimidine, 6,7-dihydro-1-methyl-4-nitro-	MeOH	290(4.14),315(4.00), 330(3.98),390s(3.56), 470(4.05)	103-0071-80
	acid	465(3.81)	103-0071-80
1H-Cyclopenta[gh]perimidine, 6,7-dihydro-2-methyl-4-nitro-	MeOH	290(3.98),328s(3.64), 385(3.27),485(3.76)	103-0071-80
Imidazo[1,5-a]pyridine, 3-methyl-1-(4-nitrophenyl)-	MeOH	207(4.32),224(4.26), 288s(3.95),420(4.28)	39-0959-80C
Pyridinium, 1-[(4-cyanobenzoyl)amino]-2-methoxy-, hydroxide, inner salt	EtOH	230(4.13),280(3.90), 305(3.63)	44-5095-80

Compound	Solvent	$\lambda_{max}(\log \epsilon)$	Ref.
$C_{14}H_{11}N_3O_2S_2$			
3H-1,5-Benzodiazepine, 4-(methylthio)-7-nitro-2-(2-thienyl)-	EtOH	281(4.35),364(4.23)	142-0007-80
$C_{14}H_{11}N_3O_3$			
Benzoic acid, [(2-nitrophenyl)methylene]hydrazide	C_6H_{12}	285(4.15)	115-0013-80
	benzene	292(4.20)	115-0013-80
	EtOH	293(4.33)	115-0013-80
	ether	293(4.33)	115-0013-80
	dioxan	290(4.23)	115-0013-80
	$CHCl_3$	295(4.32)	115-0013-80
	CCl_4	293(4.28)	115-0013-80
Benzoic acid, [(3-nitrophenyl)methylene]hydrazide	C_6H_{12}	292(4.12)	115-0013-80
	benzene	290(4.57)	115-0013-80
	EtOH	293(4.44)	115-0013-80
	ether	292(4.38)	115-0013-80
	dioxan	295(4.45)	115-0013-80
	$CHCl_3$	290(4.36)	115-0013-80
	CCl_4	290(4.48)	115-0013-80
Benzoic acid, [(4-nitrophenyl)methylene]hydrazide	C_6H_{12}	280(4.54)	115-0013-80
	EtOH	282(4.61)	115-0013-80
	ether	280(4.47)	115-0013-80
	dioxan	280(4.41)	115-0013-80
	$CHCl_3$	280(4.51)	115-0013-80
Pyridazino[4,5-b]quinolin-1(2H)-one, 4-acetoxy-10-methyl-	EtOH	229(4.32),254(4.69), 296(3.87),340(3.74), 358(3.66)	94-3457-80 +142-0267-80
$C_{14}H_{11}N_3O_6S$			
4H-[1]Benzothieno[3,2-d][1,3]oxazin-4-one, 7-nitro-2-pyrrolidino-, 5,5-dioxide	MeOH	219(4.51)	24-2818-80
$C_{14}H_{11}N_3S$			
3H-1,2,4-Triazole-3-thione, 1,2-dihydro-1,5-diphenyl-	MeOH	233(4.44),291(4.20)	73-2804-80
$C_{14}H_{11}N_5$			
2H-1,2,3-Triazole, 2-phenyl-4-(phenylazo)-	EtOH	229(4.15),275(3.99), 338(4.39),425s(2.94)	24-1226-80
	dioxan	230(4.15),274(4.00), 339(4.38),430s(2.92)	24-1226-80
$C_{14}H_{11}N_5O$			
1H-Benzimidazole, 2-[[(hydroxyimino)phenylmethyl]azo]-	50% EtOH	380(4.23)	103-0857-80
Diazene, 1,1'-(2-nitrosoethenylidene)-bis[phenyl-	EtOH	236(4.27),326(4.33), 430s(2.99)	24-1226-80
	dioxan	238(4.23),323(4.26), 440s(2.92)	24-1226-80
1H-Pyrazole-4,5-dione, 3-(3-pyridinyl)-, 4-(phenylhydrazone)	H_2O	425(3.86)	2-0789-80A
	ion	380(3.53)	2-0789-80A
$C_{14}H_{11}N_5O_2$			
1H-Benzimidazole, 2,3-dihydro-2-[nitro-(phenylazo)methylene]-	MeCN	251(4.13),256s(4.08), 312(4.28),422(4.35)	48-0087-80
$C_{14}H_{11}O_2P$			
5H-Dibenzo[b,f]phosphepin, 5-hydroxy-, 5-oxide	EtOH	224(4.52),272(4.00), 294(4.16)	139-0243-80A

Compound	Solvent	$\lambda_{max}(\log \epsilon)$	Ref.
$C_{14}H_{12}$			
9H-Fluorene, 9-methyl-	isopentane	292(3.81),296(3.68), 303(4.05)	110-0294-80
Phenanthrene, 9,10-dihydro-	C_6H_{12}	265(4.24),300(3.65)	95-0718-80
Stilbene, trans-, Cr(CO)$_3$ complex	C_6H_{12}	286(4.4),325(4.1), 422(3.5)	110-0749-80
$C_{14}H_{12}BrCl_2O_4P$			
Phosphoric acid, 2-bromo-2,3-dichloro- ethyl diphenyl ester	MeOH	254(2.74),260(2.80), 266(2.66)	5-0557-80
$C_{14}H_{12}BrN$			
9H-Carbazole, 3-bromo-9-ethyl-	$C_2H_4Cl_2$	242(4.64),270(4.45), 302(4.18),341(3.51), 344(3.51)	126-1209-80
$C_{14}H_{12}BrNO_4$			
1H-Pyrrole-3,4-dicarboxylic acid, 1-(4- bromophenyl)-, dimethyl ester	MeOH	241(4.51)	44-4573-80
$C_{14}H_{12}BrN_3$			
Acetaldehyde, [(4-bromophenyl)imino]-, phenylhydrazone	hexane EtOH	287(3.69),412(4.31) 292(3.76),380(4.58)	65-2072-80 65-2072-80
$C_{14}H_{12}Br_3O_4P$			
Phosphoric acid, diphenyl 2,2,2-tri- bromoethyl ester	MeOH	254(3.00),260(2.96), 265(2.79)	5-0557-80
$C_{14}H_{12}ClN$			
9H-Carbazole, 3-chloro-9-ethyl-	$C_2H_4Cl_2$	240(4.62),268(4.42), 301(4.23),341(4.57), 357(3.60)	126-1209-80
$C_{14}H_{12}ClNO$			
Benzenamine, 2-chloro-N-[(4-methoxy- phenyl)methylene]-, bis(trichloro- acetate)	benzene	380(3.08)	65-1870-80
Benzenamine, 4-chloro-N-[(4-methoxy- phenyl)methylene]-, trichloroacetate	benzene	330(3.04)	65-1870-80
Benzenamine, N-[(2-chlorophenyl)meth- ylene]-4-methoxy-, bis(trichloro- acetate)	benzene	350(3.18)	65-1870-80
Benzenamine, N-[(3-chlorophenyl)meth- ylene]-4-methoxy-, bis(trichloro- acetate)	benzene	350(3.15)	65-1870-80
$C_{14}H_{12}ClNO_3$			
2H,5H-Pyrano[3,2-c][1]benzopyran-2-one, 3-chloro-4-(dimethylamino)-	EtOH	245(3.91),270(4.09), 305(3.83),350(4.07)	4-0061-80
$C_{14}H_{12}ClNO_4$			
1-Pyrrolidinepropanoic acid, 4-[(4- chlorophenyl)methylene]-2,3-dioxo-	EtOH	233(3.89),334(4.39)	4-1231-80
$C_{14}H_{12}ClN_3$			
Acetaldehyde, [(4-chlorophenyl)imino]-, phenylhydrazone	hexane EtOH	287(3.67),410(4.27) 294s(3.92),380(4.51)	65-2072-80 65-2072-80
$C_{14}H_{12}ClN_3O$			
2H-1,3,4-Benzotriazepin-2-one, 7-chlo- ro-1,3,4,5-tetrahydro-5-phenyl-	EtOH	254(4.14),294(3.08)	106-0332-80

Compound	Solvent	$\lambda_{max}(\log \epsilon)$	Ref.
$C_{14}H_{12}Cl_2N_2O$			
3-Pyridinecarbonitrile, 1-[(2,6-dichlorophenyl)methyl]-1,6-dihydro-6-methoxy-	CH_2Cl_2	313(3.8),357(2.3)	5-1350-80
$C_{14}H_{12}Cl_2O_2S$			
4H-Pyran-4-one, 3,5-dichloro-2-phenyl-6-(propylthio)-	heptane	195(4.42),253(4.49), 285(4.23)	5-1960-80
$C_{14}H_{12}Cl_2O_4S_2$			
Benzenesulfonyl chloride, 2,2'-(1,2-ethanediyl)bis-	dioxan	239(4.06),284(3.71)	104-0342-80
$C_{14}H_{12}Cl_3O_4P$			
Phosphoric acid, diphenyl 2,2,2-trichloroethyl ester	MeOH	254(2.70),260(2.77), 266(2.64)	5-0557-80
$C_{14}H_{12}Cl_4OS$			
2,4-Pentadienethioic acid, 2,3,4,5-tetrachloro-5-phenyl-, S-propyl ester, (Z,Z)-	heptane	198(4.26),238(4.11)	5-1960-80
$C_{14}H_{12}FN_5O_4$			
Benzenamine, 4-[(5-fluoro-2,4-dinitrophenyl)azo]-N,N-dimethyl-	$CHCl_3$	530(4.28)	49-0529-80
$C_{14}H_{12}N$			
Benzo[g]quinolinium, 1-methyl-, ion	MeOH	345(3.5),360(3.8), 421(3.3)	97-0378-80
$C_{14}H_{12}NO$			
Acridinium, 3-hydroxy-N-methyl-	M HCl	417(3.93)	138-1235-80
	pH 11.2	347(4.18),362(4.24), 458(4.22)	138-1235-80
$C_{14}H_{12}N_2$			
Benzaldehyde, (phenylmethylene)hydrazone	C_6H_{12}	217(4.16),300(4.56), 312s(4.51),325s(4.17)	59-0207-80
	benzene	304(4.56),315s(4.46)	59-0207-80
	MeOH	207(4.38),300(4.65), 310s(4.60)	59-0207-80
	acetone	328.5(4.13)	59-0207-80
	HOAc	207(4.38),210s(4.60), 300(4.65)	59-0207-80
	EtOAc	300(4.57),311s(4.52)	59-0207-80
	MeCN	298(4.34),310s(4.28), 325s(3.94)	59-0207-80
	pyridine	307(4.47),316s(4.43), 337s(4.14)	59-0207-80
	$CHCl_3$	303(4.51),313s(4.45)	59-0207-80
	DMSO	305(4.53),315s(4.48)	59-0207-80
	H_2SO_4	215(4.02),297(4.59), 375(4.21)	59-0207-80
	50% dioxan	220(4.08),303(4.61)	59-0207-80
2H-Indazole, 5-methyl-2-phenyl-	MeOH	237(4.70),294(4.50)	44-1334-80
1H-Indole, 1-methyl-2-(4-pyridinyl)-	n.s.g.	250(4.17),325(4.22), 440(4.07)	103-0585-80
Phenazine, 1,6-dimethyl-	MeOH	254(5.03),362(4.07)	18-2933-80
Pyridine, 2,2'-(1,3-butadiene-1,4-diyl)bis-	CH_2Cl_2	218(4.58),283(4.20), 325(4.64),336(4.76), 353(4.61)	5-0291-80

Compound	Solvent	$\lambda_{max}(\log \epsilon)$	Ref.
Pyridine, 4,4'-(1,3-butadiene-1,4-diyl)bis-	CH_2Cl_2	229(4.03),300s(4.43), 314(4.62),327(4.72), 343(4.58)	5-0291-80
Pyridine, 2-[4-(4-pyridinyl)-1,3-butadienyl]-	CH_2Cl_2	227(3.90),323s(4.57), 334(4.66),350(4.53)	5-0291-80
Pyrrolo[2,3-b]pyridine, 7-(phenylmethyl)-	MeOH	249(4.08),310(3.81), 392(3.10)	48-0517-80
monohydrobromide	MeOH	226(4.22),299(3.90)	48-0517-80
$C_{14}H_{12}N_2O$			
Benzeneacetaldehyde, α-oxo-, aldehydo-(phenylhydrazone)	EtOH	377(4.28)	65-2072-80
	hexane	295(--),347(--)	65-2072-80
Benzoic acid, (phenylmethylene)hydrazide	C_6H_{12}	293(4.54)	115-0013-80
	benzene	292(4.53)	115-0013-80
	EtOH	299(4.53)	115-0013-80
	ether	294(4.47)	115-0013-80
	dioxan	295(4.04)	115-0013-80
	$CHCl_3$	295(4.46)	115-0013-80
	CCl_4	293(4.51)	115-0013-80
Benzo[b][1,6]naphthyridin-1(2H)-one, 2,3-dimethyl-	MeOH	208(4.60),244(4.83), 277(4.66),300s(4.35), 320s(4.05),390(3.93)	39-0522-80C
	MeOH-acid	208s(4.54),229(4.66), 258(4.62),285(4.61), 315(4.18),352(3.77), 433(4.13)	39-0522-80C
Dibenzo[c,g][1,2]diazocine, 11,12-dihydro-, 5-oxide	PrOH	240(4.04),308(3.18)	44-4597-80
Ethanone, 1-(3,4-dihydropyrrolo[1',2'-3,4]pyrimido[2,1,6-cd]pyrrolizin-8-yl)-	EtOH	205(3.67),220(3.68), 280(3.40),295(3.29), 320(3.14),358(3.53)	24-0614-80
Methanone, (1-ethenyl-1H-pyrrol-2-yl)-3H-pyrrolizin-3-yl-	EtOH	227(4.19),361(4.43), 379(4.44)	24-0614-80
Pentanenitrile, 3-oxo-2-(2(1H)-quinolinylidene)-	EtOH	220(4.74),238(4.16), 290(4.37),398(4.30), 412s(4.24)	94-0795-80
$C_{14}H_{12}N_2OS$			
2H-Pyrimido[2,1-a]isoquinolin-2-one, 4-methyl-3-(methylthio)-	EtOH	240s(4.47),261(4.58), 300(4.24),330s(3.71), 347(3.64)	95-1261-80
$C_{14}H_{12}N_2O_2$			
Benzaldehyde, 2-hydroxy-, [(2-hydroxyphenyl)methylene]hydrazone	C_6H_{12}	225(4.48),294(4.47), 300s(4.43),364(4.42)	59-0207-80
	benzene	296(4.35),360(4.32)	59-0207-80
	MeOH	215(4.42),295(4.42), 360(4.51)	59-0207-80
	EtOH	220(4.45),295(4.47), 362(4.42)	59-0207-80
	75% EtOH	220(4.26),295(4.34), 356(4.29)	59-0207-80
	50% EtOH	225(4.16),297(4.19), 352(4.13)	59-0207-80
	PrOH	240(4.17),297(4.41), 364(4.37)	59-0207-80
	BuOH	225(4.35),297(4.44), 363(4.39)	59-0207-80
	dioxan	220(4.41),289(4.44)	59-0207-80
	50% dioxan	249s(4.19),255s(4.28), 261s(4.27)	59-0207-80

Compound	Solvent	λ_{max}(log ϵ)	Ref.
Benzaldehyde, 2-hydroxy-, [(2-hydroxy-	acetone	360(4.35)	59-0207-80
phenyl)methylene]hydrazone (cont.)	HOAc	295(4.28),294(4.49)	59-0207-80
	EtOAc	295(4.47),360(4.41)	59-0207-80
	MeCN	223(4.41),294(4.49),	59-0207-80
		355(4.41)	
	pyridine	306(4.32),360(4.38)	59-0207-80
	CHCl_3	295(4.47),362(4.41)	59-0207-80
	CCl_4	296(4.55),363(4.51)	59-0207-80
	CS_2	385(4.35)	59-0207-80
	DMSO	297(4.39),358(4.45)	59-0207-80
	H_2SO_4	224(4.59),284(4.35),	59-0207-80
		363(3.76)	
Benzaldehyde, 3-hydroxy-, [(3-hydroxy-	MeOH	215(4.49),297(4.49)	59-0207-80
phenyl)methylene]hydrazone	EtOH	213(4.40),245s(4.04),	59-0207-80
		300(4.62),325s(4.50)	
	PrOH	213(4.45),300(4.50),	59-0207-80
		325s(4.40)	
	BuOH	215(4.52),300(4.56),	59-0207-80
		325s(4.45)	
	dioxan	217(4.56),300(4.56),	59-0207-80
		325s(4.48)	
	50% dioxan	216(4.41),302(4.46)	59-0207-80
	acetone	223(4.53),330(4.39)	59-0207-80
	HOAc	219(4.51),240(4.46),	59-0207-80
		297(4.55)	
	EtOAc	210(4.57),299(4.52),	59-0207-80
		325s(4.42)	
	MeCN	215(4.56),298(4.51),	59-0207-80
		325s(4.41)	
	pyridine	222(4.62),305(4.47)	59-0207-80
	DMSO	220(4.58),305(4.37),	59-0207-80
		325s(4.32)	
	H_2SO_4	206(4.79),255(4.79),	59-0207-80
		297(4.57)	
	75% EtOH	215(4.41),300(4.47)	59-0207-80
	50% EtOH	214(4.46),302(4.50)	59-0207-80
Benzaldehyde, 4-hydroxy-, [(4-hydroxy-	MeOH	227(4.32),332(4.71)	59-0207-80
phenyl)methylene]hydrazone	EtOH	235(3.86),332(4.73)	59-0207-80
	PrOH	240(3.76),335(4.57)	59-0207-80
	BuOH	230(4.16),335(4.63)	59-0207-80
	dioxan	225(4.31),325(4.65)	59-0207-80
	50% dioxan	227(4.14),332(4.54)	59-0207-80
	acetone	330(4.66)	59-0207-80
	HOAc	325(4.41)	59-0207-80
	EtOAc	325(4.70)	59-0207-80
	MeCN	229(4.31),325(4.64)	59-0207-80
	pyridine	335(4.64)	59-0207-80
	DMSO	333(4.62)	59-0207-80
	H_2SO_4	224(4.16),418(4.72)	59-0207-80
	75% EtOH	229(4.18),332(4.67)	59-0207-80
	50% EtOH	227(4.18),332(4.58)	59-0207-80
Benzenamine, 2-methyl-4-nitro-N-(phen-	C_6H_12	209(4.34),225(4.21),	18-1993-80
ylmethylene)-		268s(4.08),295(4.23),	
		327(4.13)	
Benzenamine, 4-methyl-N-[(4-nitrophen-	THF	357(4.11)	56-1177-80
yl)methylene]-			
Benzoic acid, [(2-hydroxyphenyl)meth-	C_6H_12	284(4.61),295(4.56)	115-0013-80
ylene]hydrazide	benzene	286(4.55),296(4.53)	115-0013-80
	EtOH	286(4.70),297(4.70)	115-0013-80
	ether	284(4.58),296(4.56)	115-0013-80
	dioxan	286(4.59),297(4.58)	115-0013-80

Compound	Solvent	$\lambda_{max}(\log \epsilon)$	Ref.
Benzoic acid, [(2-hydroxyphenyl)meth-ylene]hydrazide (cont.)	$CHCl_3$	286(4.69),297(4.64)	115-0013-80
	CCl_4	285(4.50),296(4.47)	115-0013-80
Benzo[b][1,6]naphthyridin-1(2H)-one, 6-hydroxy-2,3-dimethyl-	MeOH	209(4.29),264(4.55), 280s(4.12),306s(4.06), 318(4.14)	39-0522-80C
	acid	210(4.01),273(4.16), 289s(3.83),331(3.87), 400(3.53),450(3.38)	39-0522-80C
	base	216(4.29),268(4.11), 317s(3.92),328(3.99)	39-0522-80C
Dibenzo[c,g][1,2]diazocine, 11,12-di-hydro-, 5,6-dioxide	dioxan	292(3.96),783(1.28)	44-4597-80
1,4-Methano-1H-indene-6,7-dicarboni-trile, 2,3,3a,4,5,7a-hexahydro-3a,4-dimethyl-3,8-dioxo-	MeOH	234(3.90)	35-6604-80
1H-Pyrazolo[1,2-a]pyrazol-4-ium, 3-hy-droxy-5,7-dimethyl-1-oxo-2-phenyl-, hydroxide, inner salt	benzene	434.5(2.963)	64-1002-80B
	EtOH	430(2.834)	64-1002-80B
	MeCN	212(4.483),266(4.458), 280s(4.278),425(3.029)	64-1002-80B
9H-Pyrido[3,4-b]indole-3-carboxylic acid, 1-methyl-, methyl ester	MeOH	254(4.58),268(4.20), 335(3.59),347(3.60)	4-0595-80
$C_{14}H_{12}N_2O_3$			
Benzenamine, 4-methoxy-N-[(4-nitrophen-yl)methylene]-	THF	376(4.21)	56-1177-80
mono(trichloroacetate)	benzene	370(3.20)	65-1870-80
Benzenamine, N-[(4-methoxyphenyl)meth-ylene]-4-nitro-, bis(trichloroacet-ate)	benzene	300(3.08)	65-1870-80
Benzenemethanol, 4-[[(4-nitrophenyl)-methylene]amino]-	THF	355(4.15)	56-1177-80
Ethanone, 1-(4-nitrophenyl)-2-(phenyl-amino)-	CH_2Cl_2	<u>258(4.0)</u>,390(2.86)	83-0315-80
Pyrano[3,2-b]indole-2-carboxamide, 5-ethyl-4,5-dihydro-4-oxo-	MeOH	221(4.35),254(4.06), 263(4.01),309(4.21)	83-0405-80
$C_{14}H_{12}N_2O_4$			
Ethanone, 2-[(2-hydroxyphenyl)amino]-1-(4-nitrophenyl)-	CH_2Cl_2	370(2.91)	83-0315-80
Ethanone, 2-[(3-hydroxyphenyl)amino]-1-(4-nitrophenyl)-	CH_2Cl_2	370(3.06)	83-0315-80
Ethanone, 2-[(4-hydroxyphenyl)amino]-1-(4-nitrophenyl)-	CH_2Cl_2	370(2.79)	83-0315-80
Pyrrolo[1,2-a]quinazoline-1,5-dione, 3-acetyl-3a,4-dihydro-2-hydroxy-4-methyl-	EtOH	246(4.25),304(3.95), 327(3.81)	4-0945-80
$C_{14}H_{12}N_2O_4S$			
4H-[1]Benzothieno[3,2-d][1,3]oxazin-4-one, 2-pyrrolidino-, 5,5-dioxide	MeOH	255(4.60)	24-2818-80
$C_{14}H_{12}N_2O_5$			
2-Furancarboxylic acid, 5-[[(4-nitro-phenyl)methylene]amino]-, ethyl ester	MeOH	371(4.17)	73-0135-80
3-Pyridinecarboxylic acid, 1,4-dihydro-5-(4-nitrophenyl)-4-oxo-, ethyl ester	EtOH	255(3.98),330(3.90)	4-0359-80
3-Pyridinecarboxylic acid, 1-ethyl-1,4-dihydro-5-(4-nitrophenyl)-4-oxo-	EtOH	257(4.14),326(4.07)	4-0359-80
$C_{14}H_{12}N_2O_5S_2$			
4-Thia-1-azabicyclo[3.2.0]hept-2-ene-	dioxan	260(4.21),339(4.04)	88-0619-80

Compound	Solvent	$\lambda_{max}(\log \epsilon)$	Ref.
2-carboxylic acid, 3-(methylthio)-7-oxo-, (4-nitrophenyl)methyl ester	EtOH	260(4.21),340(4.04)	94-3232-80
$C_{14}H_{12}N_2O_6$ 1H-Pyrrole-3,4-dicarboxylic acid, 1-(4-nitrophenyl)-, dimethyl ester	MeOH	251(4.08),302(4.24)	44-4573-80
$C_{14}H_{12}N_2O_{10}S_2$ Benzenesulfonic acid, 2,2'-(1,2-ethanediyl)bis[5-nitro-, disodium salt	H_2O	282(4.35)	104-0342-80
$C_{14}H_{12}N_4$ 2H-1,2,3-Triazol-4-amine, 2,5-diphenyl-	EtOH	227(4.15),322(4.38)	24-1226-80
$C_{14}H_{12}N_4O_2S_2$ 1,3-Thiazetidine-2-thione, 3-(6-methoxy-3-pyridinyl)-4-[(6-methoxy-3-pyridinyl)imino]-	EtOH	230s(4.24),253(4.30), 280(4.19),302s(4.10), 333(4.07)	44-4219-80
$C_{14}H_{12}N_4O_2S_3$ 1,2,4-Dithiazolidine-3-thione, 4-(6-methoxy-3-pyridinyl)-5-[(6-methoxy-3-pyridinyl)imino]-	$CHCl_3$	290(4.03),322s(3.73), 385s(2.66)	44-4219-80
$C_{14}H_{12}N_4O_3$ 2,4,7(1H,3H,8H)-Pteridinetrione, 1,3-dimethyl-6-phenyl-	pH 1.0 pH 6.0	284(4.15),349(4.26) 291(4.12),350(4.31)	24-1524-80 24-1524-80
2,4,7(1H,3H,8H)-Pteridinetrione, 8-ethyl-6-phenyl-	pH 1.0	202(4.59),230(4.08), 287(4.07),352(4.29)	24-1524-80
	pH 7.0	217(4.57),240s(4.01), 263s(3.78),295(4.10), 370(4.34)	24-1524-80
	3M NaOH	254(4.63),272(3.97), 295s(4.08),386(4.27)	24-1524-80
$C_{14}H_{12}N_4O_4$ 2,4,7(1H,3H,8H)-Pteridinetrione, 8-(2-hydroxyethyl)-6-phenyl-	pH 0.0	232(4.13),288(4.07), 353(4.29)	142-0437-80B
	pH 7.0	217(4.54),242s(4.00), 297(4.08),372(4.32)	142-0437-80B
$C_{14}H_{12}N_4O_6$ Acetamide, N-[5-[5-(acetylamino)-1,6-dihydro-2,6-dioxo-3(2H)-pyridinylidene]-1,2,5,6-tetrahydro-2,6-dioxo-3-pyridinyl]-	HOAc	500(4.38)	39-1788-80C
$C_{14}H_{12}O_2$ 1H-Benz[e]inden-1-one, 2,3-dihydro-8-methoxy-	EtOH	229(4.75),258(4.05), 262(4.06),314(3.79), 341(3.80)	87-0512-80
Bicyclo[5.4.1]dodeca-2,5,7,9,11-pentaene-3,5-dicarboxaldehyde	dioxan	288(4.77),369(3.66)	89-0041-80
3-Dibenzofuranol, 6,9-dimethyl-	EtOH	226(4.53),260(4.20), 288(4.19),297(4.21)	12-1817-80
Methanone, (2-hydroxy-5-methylphenyl)-phenyl-	EtOH	260(4.08),350(3.61)	90-0431-80
2-Naphthalenecarboxylic acid, 1-methylethenyl ester	C_6H_{12}	238(4.82),260(3.67), 273(3.82),291(3.91), 292(3.85),318(3.09), 334(3.27)	39-1659-80B

Compound	Solvent	λ_{max}(log ϵ)	Ref.
$C_{14}H_{12}O_3$			
1,3-Benzodioxol-5-ol, 2-methyl-2-phen-yl-	EtOH	233(3.50),299(3.73)	12-0527-80
1,4-Naphthalenedione, 2-allyl-3-meth-oxy-	MeOH	251(4.36),256s(4.32), 274(4.29),278(4.26), 333(3.48),391(3.24)	44-1260-80
$C_{14}H_{12}O_3S$			
15-Oxa-16-thiatricyclo[10.2.1.1^{5,8}]-hexadeca-5,7,12,14-tetraene-4,9-dione	C_6H_{12}	225(4.1),290(3.9), 350s(3.5)	138-0397-80
	CHCl$_3$	295(4.0),360s(3.6)	138-0397-80
$C_{14}H_{12}O_4$			
2H-1-Benzopyran-2-one, 8-acetyl-7-(2-propenyloxy)-	MeOH	254(3.63),300s(4.10), 320(4.20)	44-1470-80
Dibenzo[b,d]pyran-6,7(8H)-dione, 9,10-dihydro-3-methoxy-	EtOH	235(4.07),348(4.27)	118-0715-80
2,8,3,4-Ethanediylidenefuro[2',3':3,4]-cyclobut[1,2-f]isobenzofuran-5,7-di-one, decahydro-	EtOH	225(c. 3.27)	39-2174-80C
Fulvoplumierin	EtOH	270(3.70),366(4.56)	100-0649-80
7H-Furo[3,2-g][1]benzopyran-7-one, 9-hydroxy-2-(1-methylethyl)-	EtOH	254(4.22),262(4.12), 268(4.11),314(3.95)	102-1556-80
$C_{14}H_{12}O_4S_2$			
1,3-Dithiole-4,5-dicarboxylic acid, 2-(phenylmethylene)-, dimethyl ester	CHCl$_3$	245(4.15),328(4.21), 410(3.20)	116-0240-80
$C_{14}H_{12}O_5$			
Benzoic acid, 4-[(5-formyl-2-furanyl)-oxy]-, ethyl ester	MeOH	223(4.00),243(3.93), 298(4.30)	73-0423-80
2-Butenoic acid, 4-(1,3-dihydro-1-oxo-2H-inden-2-ylidene)-2,4-dihydroxy-, methyl ester, (Z,Z)-	MeOH	241(3.80),252(3.82), 308(4.00),390(4.11)	83-0429-80
1,4-Naphthalenedione, 5-acetoxy-8-eth-oxy-	MeOH	206(4.36),226(4.11), 245s(--),395(3.56)	24-1575-80
2-Propenoic acid, (7-methoxy-2-oxo-2H-1-benzopyran-4-yl)methyl ester	EtOH	323(4.17)	95-0744-80
$C_{14}H_{12}O_5S$			
Benzo[b]thiophene-2-butanoic acid, 3-hydroxy-α,γ-dioxo-, ethyl ester	MeOH	203(4.34),262(4.03), 303(4.04),343(3.98)	83-0385-80
$C_{14}H_{12}O_6$			
2-Benzofuranbutanoic acid, 3-hydroxy-α,γ-dioxo-, ethyl ester	MeOH	202(4.15),318(4.03), 377(4.11)	83-0385-80
2H-1-Benzopyran-6-acetaldehyde, 7-acet-oxy-8-methoxy-2-oxo-	MeOH	223s(4.22),249(3.63), 287(4.06),325s(3.62)	44-1470-80
2-Furancarboxylic acid, 5-[4-(ethoxy-carbonyl)phenoxy]-	MeOH	262(4.33)	73-0910-80
1,4-Methanonaphthalene-1,2,3(2H)-tri-carboxylic acid, 3,4-dihydro-	EtOH	246s(2.12),251s(2.31), 256(2.54),263(2.71), 270(2.71)	44-3456-80
$C_{14}H_{12}O_6S_2$			
Benzenesulfonic acid, 2,2'-(1,2-ethene-diyl)bis-, dipotassium salt	H_2O	228(4.21),301(4.31)	104-0342-80
$C_{14}H_{12}O_7$			
2H-1-Benzopyran-6-acetic acid, 7-acet-oxy-8-methoxy-2-oxo-	MeOH	223s(4.18),247(3.60), 287(4.07),330s(3.48)	44-1470-80

Compound	Solvent	$\lambda_{max}(\log \epsilon)$	Ref.
C₁₄H₁₂O₈S₂Se₂			
1,3-Thiaselenole-4,5-dicarboxylic acid, 2-[4,5-bis(methoxycarbonyl)-1,3-thiaselenol-2-ylidene]-, dimethyl ester	C₆H₁₂	250(4.39),290(4.43), 325(4.03),434(3.44)	44-2632-80
C₁₄H₁₂S₂			
Dibenzo[c,g][1,2]dithiocin, 11,12-dihydro-	EtOH	224(4.41),259(3.69)	104-0342-80
C₁₄H₁₃BrN₂			
7H-Pyrrolo[2,3-b]pyridine, 7-(phenylmethyl)-, monohydrobromide	MeOH	226(4.22),299(3.90)	48-0517-80
C₁₄H₁₃BrN₂O			
Benzaldehyde, (2-bromo-3-hydroxyphenyl)methylhydrazone	n.s.g.	220s(4.21),312(4.34)	24-2579-80
C₁₄H₁₃BrN₂O₃			
Acetamide, N-[2-[(3-bromo-1,4-dihydro-1,4-dioxo-2-naphthalenyl)amino]-ethyl]-	EtOH	272(4.34),460(3.48)	83-0603-80
C₁₄H₁₃ClNO₄S			
10H-Phenothiazine, 10-ethyl-, perchlorate	CH₂Cl₂	452(4.06),519(4.44), 711(3.74),782(3.85), 878(3.86)	4-1053-80
C₁₄H₁₃ClN₂O₂			
2-Pyridinecarboxylic acid, 5-[[(3-chlorophenyl)methyl]amino]-, methyl ester	MeOH	212(4.20),291(4.28), 307(4.26)	87-1405-80
2-Pyridinecarboxylic acid, 5-[[(3-chlorophenyl)methyl]methylamino]-	MeOH	282(4.24),311(3.99)	87-1405-80
C₁₄H₁₃ClN₂O₂S			
4(5H)-Thiazolone, 5-[(2-chlorophenyl)-methylene]-2-morpholino-	MeOH	325(4.39)	48-0835-80
C₁₄H₁₃ClN₂O₃			
Acetamide, N-[2-[(3-chloro-1,4-dihydro-1,4-dioxo-2-naphthalenyl)amino]-ethyl]-	EtOH	271(4.38),460(3.53)	83-0603-80
C₁₄H₁₃ClN₄			
Formazan, 1-(4-chlorophenyl)-5-(4-methylphenyl)-	EtOH	241(4.35),295(4.10), 368(4.54),448(3.91)	104-0751-80
C₁₄H₁₃ClO₅			
4H-1,3-Dioxin-2-carboxylic acid, 6-(4-chlorophenyl)-2-methyl-4-oxo-, ethyl ester (general spectrum of class)	EtOH	285-315(3.98-4.25)	104-1995-80
Propanoic acid, 3-chloro-, (7-methoxy-2-oxo-2H-1-benzopyran-4-yl)methyl ester	EtOH	323(4.17)	95-0744-80
C₁₄H₁₃Cl₂NO₂			
2,3-Pyrrolidinedione, 4-[(2,4-dichlorophenyl)methylene]-1-(1-methylethyl)-	EtOH	326(3.85)	145-1135-80
2,3-Pyrrolidinedione, 4-[(2,6-dichlorophenyl)methylene]-1-(1-methylethyl)-	EtOH	290(4.15)	145-1135-80

Compound	Solvent	$\lambda_{max}(\log \epsilon)$	Ref.
$C_{14}H_{13}Cl_2O_4P$			
Phosphoric acid, 2,2-dichloroethyl diphenyl ester	MeOH	255(2.75),260(2.78), 266(2.69)	5-0557-80
$C_{14}H_{13}Cl_3N_4O_5$			
α-D-Ribofuranuronic acid, 1-deoxy-2,3-O-(1-methylethylidene)-1-(2,6,8-tri-chloro-9H-purin-9-yl)-, methyl ester	MeOH	205(4.27),216(4.29), 248s(--),254(3.79), 278(4.04),284s(--)	24-2891-80
β-D-Ribofuranuronic acid, 1-deoxy-2,3-O-(1-methylethylidene)-1-(2,6,8-tri-chloro-9H-purin-9-yl)-, methyl ester	MeOH	204(4.23),216(4.33), 248s(--),254(3.82), 278(4.08),285s(--)	24-2891-80
$C_{14}H_{13}N$			
Benzenamine, 2-methyl-N-(phenylmeth-ylene)-	C_6H_{12}	212(4.26),228(4.07), 237s(4.09),248s(4.15), 263(4.23),330(3.67)	18-1993-80
Benzenamine, N-(1-phenylethylidene)-, cis	C_6H_{11}Me at -100°	237(4.30),314(3.38)	39-1282-80B
trans	C_6H_{11}Me at -100°	248(4.42),323(3.43)	39-1282-80B
Benzenemethanimine, 2-methyl-α-phenyl-	C_6H_{12}	241(4.13),270s(3.24)	44-2541-80
3H-Benzo[def]carbazole, 3a,4,8,9-tetra-hydro-	EtOH	230(4.50),283(3.76)	18-0494-80
9H-Carbazole, 9-ethyl-	$C_2H_4Cl_2$	238(4.65),264(4.37), 296(4.21),324(3.56), 347(3.61)	126-1209-80
2-Propenenitrile, 3-(1,3-dimethyl-1H-inden-2-yl)-, (E)-	EtOH	239s(3.84),246(3.96), 254(3.90),336(4.48)	39-0714-80C
Pyridine, 2-(1-methyl-2-phenylethenyl)-, cis	hexane	283(3.96)	46-0847-80
trans	hexane	290(4.25)	46-0847-80
Pyridine, 3-(1-methyl-2-phenylethenyl)-, cis	hexane	260(4.05)	46-0847-80
trans	hexane	270(4.21)	46-0847-80
Pyridine, 4-(1-methyl-2-phenylethenyl)-, cis	hexane	263(3.98)	46-0847-80
trans	hexane	275(4.26)	46-0847-80
$C_{14}H_{13}NO$			
Benzenamine, N-[(2-methoxyphenyl)meth-ylene]-	benzene	270-330(2.78)	65-1870-80
Benzenamine, N-[(3-methoxyphenyl)meth-ylene]-	benzene	270-330(2.78)	65-1870-80
Benzenamine, N-[(4-methoxyphenyl)meth-ylene]-	benzene	300(2.60)	65-1870-80
Benzenamine, 2-methoxy-N-(phenylmeth-ylene)-, bis(trichloroacetate)	benzene	300(2.65)	65-1870-80
Benzenamine, 4-methoxy-N-(phenylmeth-ylene)-, bis(trichloroacetate)	benzene	360(3.26)	65-1870-80
2,5-Cyclohexadien-1-one, 2,6-dimethyl-4-(phenylimino)-	hexane	214(3.75),227(3.78), 273(4.28),284(4.33), 448(3.45)	87-1153-80
	hexane	445(3.44)	104-2020-80
	+ CF_3COOH	383(4.01)	104-2020-80
	benzene	451(3.45)	104-2020-80
	+ CF_3COOH	398(4.01)	104-2020-80
	CH_2Cl_2	448(3.51)	104-2020-80
	+ CF_3COOH	397(4.06)	104-2020-80
	$CHCl_3$	451(3.51)	104-2020-80
	+ CF_3COOH	396(4.04)	104-2020-80
perchlorate	CH_2Cl_2	403(4.05)	104-2020-80

Compound	Solvent	$\lambda_{max}(\log \epsilon)$	Ref.
Ethanone, 2-(5-methyl-3-pyridinyl)-1-phenyl-	EtOH	245(4.16),268s(3.57), 278s(3.17)	39-0072-80C
	EtOH-HCl	250(4.32),278s(3.34)	39-0072-80C
2(1H)-Naphthalenone, 1-[3-(methylamino)-2-propenylidene]-	MeOH	310(3.98),350(3.99), 420(3.89),510(3.92)	103-0799-80
	MeCN	312(3.66),350(3.51), 520(2.48)	103-0799-80
	PhCN	315(4.10),355(3.96), 520(3.00)	103-0799-80
	DMSO	318(3.76),358(3.72), 520(3.76)	103-0799-80
	CCl_4	315(3.81),355(3.66)	103-0799-80
1-Propanone, 1-phenyl-2-(3-pyridinyl)-	EtOH	247(4.12),269s(3.56)	39-0072-80C
	EtOH-HCl	252(4.22),271s(3.69)	39-0072-80C
Pyrrolo[3,2,1-jk]carbazol-5(1H)-one, 2,3,3a,4-tetrahydro-	EtOH	238(4.29),262(4.04), 290(3.42)	39-0097-80C

$C_{14}H_{13}NOS$

Compound	Solvent	$\lambda_{max}(\log \epsilon)$	Ref.
1,4-Oxathiino[3,2-b]pyridine, 2,3-dihydro-6-methyl-2-phenyl-	EtOH	250s(3.50),311(3.85)	1-0619-80
	EtOH-HCl	255(3.56),340(3.99)	1-0619-80

$C_{14}H_{13}NO_2$

Compound	Solvent	$\lambda_{max}(\log \epsilon)$	Ref.
Methanone, (2-hydroxy-5-methylphenyl)-phenyl-, oxime, (E)-	EtOH	260(3.93),316(3.60)	90-0431-80

$C_{14}H_{13}NO_2S$

Compound	Solvent	$\lambda_{max}(\log \epsilon)$	Ref.
Spiro[1,3-dioxolane-2,10'-[10H]thieno-[3,2-b][1]benzazepine], 4',9'-dihydro-	EtOH	232(4.10),257(3.87), 301(4.00)	142-1227-80B

$C_{14}H_{13}NO_3$

Compound	Solvent	$\lambda_{max}(\log \epsilon)$	Ref.
1-Azabicyclo[3.2.0]hept-2-ene-2-carboxylic acid, 7-oxo-3-phenyl-, methyl ester	EtOH	222(3.90),303(3.96)	94-3494-80
1,4-Naphthalenedione, 2-morpholino-	heptane	428(3.48)	70-0897-80
	isoPrOH	457(3.61)	70-0897-80
3-Pyridinecarboxylic acid, 1,4-dihydro-4-oxo-5-phenyl-, ethyl ester	EtOH	260(3.64),305(3.76)	4-0359-80
3-Pyridinecarboxylic acid, 1-ethyl-1,4-dihydro-4-oxo-5-phenyl-	EtOH	268(3.77),308(3.85)	4-0359-80
1H-Pyrrole-2-carboxylic acid, 4-acetyl-3-methyl-1-phenyl-	EtOH	239(4.31),271s(4.02)	78-2125-80
	EtOH-base	248(4.31),271s(4.14)	78-2125-80

$C_{14}H_{13}NO_4$

Compound	Solvent	$\lambda_{max}(\log \epsilon)$	Ref.
Furo[2,3-b]quinoline, 4,6,7-trimethoxy-(kokusaginine)	EtOH	244(4.37),251(4.39), 307(3.97),319(4.01), 333(3.95)	100-0498-80
1H-Pyrrole-3,4-dicarboxylic acid, 1-phenyl-, dimethyl ester	MeOH	233(4.47),249s(4.33)	44-4573-80
1-Pyrrolidinepropanoic acid, 2,3-dioxo-4-(phenylmethylene)-	EtOH	229(3.83),239(3.77), 329(4.41)	4-1231-80
2,3-Quinolinedicarboxylic acid, 4-methyl-, 3-ethyl ester	EtOH	213(4.46),238(4.62), 288(3.68)	94-3457-80

$C_{14}H_{13}NO_5$

Compound	Solvent	$\lambda_{max}(\log \epsilon)$	Ref.
1H-Indole-2-butanoic acid, 3-hydroxy-1-methyl-α,γ-dioxo-, methyl ester	MeOH	238(4.28),312(4.31), 363(3.88)	83-0405-80
5(4H)-Oxazolone, 4-[(4-acetoxy-3-methoxyphenyl)methylene]-2-methyl-	$CHCl_3$	320s(4.25),333(4.32), 417s(2.73)	70-0576-80

Compound	Solvent	$\lambda_{max}(\log \epsilon)$	Ref.
$C_{14}H_{13}NO_6$ 1H-Indole-4,5,6-tricarboxylic acid, trimethyl ester	MeOH	250(4.47),322(3.91)	44-4573-80
$C_{14}H_{13}NS$ 10H-Phenothiazine, 10-ethyl-, perchlorate	CH_2Cl_2	452(4.06),519(4.44), 711(3.74),782(3.85), 878(3.86)	4-1053-80
$C_{14}H_{13}N_2$ Pyridinium, 1-(1H-indol-3-ylmethyl)-, bromide	MeOH	265(3.79),300s(2.90), 390(1.70)	103-0921-80
$C_{14}H_{13}N_3$ Acetaldehyde, (phenylimino)-, phenyl-hydrazone	hexane EtOH	285(3.57),405(4.27) 298(3.89),375(4.52)	65-2072-80 65-2072-80
Benzenecarboximidic acid, (phenylmethylene)hydrazide	MeOH	230(4.17),315(4.31)	104-0822-80
$C_{14}H_{13}N_3O$ Acetaldehyde, [(2-hydroxyphenyl)imino]-, phenylhydrazone	hexane EtOH	299(3.69),388(4.44) 296(3.72),375(4.39)	65-2072-80 65-2072-80
Benzenecarboximidamide, N-(iminophenylmethoxy)-	EtOH	226(4.22),260s(3.99)	39-1792-80B
2H-Benzotriazole, 2-(2-methoxy-5-methylphenyl)-	EtOH	<u>290(4.1)</u>,350s(3.9)	109-0034-80
Tetracyclo[6.5.0.0^{9,13}.0^{10,12}]trideca-2,4,6-triene-11-carbonyl azide, (1α,8α,9α,10β,11β,12β,13α)-	dioxan	258(3.28)	89-0207-80
$C_{14}H_{13}N_3O_2$ 1,4-Benzenediamine, N-methyl-N'-[(4-nitrophenyl)methylene]-	THF	442(4.29)	56-1177-80
11H-Dibenzo[c,h][1,2,6]triazonine, 12,13-dihydro-, 5,6-dioxide	EtOH	208(4.26),278(3.98)	44-4597-80
$C_{14}H_{13}N_3O_2S$ Pyrimido[4,5-b]quinoline-2,4(1H,3H)-dione, 1,3-dimethyl-5-(methylthio)-	EtOH	220(4.33),246(4.54), 268(4.54),322(3.85), 386(3.77)	142-0679-80B
$C_{14}H_{13}N_3O_3$ Ethanone, 2-[(4-aminophenyl)amino]-1-(4-nitrophenyl)-	CH_2Cl_2	<u>270(4.2)</u>,425(3.42)	83-0315-80
Pyrimido[4,5-b]quinoline-2,4(3H,10H)-dione, 8-hydroxy-3,7,10-trimethyl-	M HCl pH 4	258(4.50),369(4.56) 247(4.69),270s(4.29), 345s(3.87),392s(4.37), 402s(4.35)	83-0937-80 83-0937-80
	pH 13	253(4.51),265(4.42), 291(4.00),424(4.66)	83-0937-80
Pyrimido[4,5-b]quinoline-2,4(3H,10H)-dione, 8-methoxy-3,10-dimethyl-	EtOH	233(4.56),254(4.49), 402(4.29)	39-0978-80C
	50% EtOH-HCl	233(4.63),254(4.52), 377(4.39)	39-0978-80C
$C_{14}H_{13}N_3O_4$ Diazene, (2,4-dimethoxyphenyl)(4-nitrophenyl)-	EtOH	407(4.48)	62-0158-80
Diazene, (3,4-dimethoxyphenyl)(4-nitrophenyl)-	EtOH	393(4.31)	62-0158-80

Compound	Solvent	$\lambda_{max}(\log \epsilon)$	Ref.
4-Pyridazinecarboxylic acid, 5-[[(2-methoxyphenyl)amino]carbonyl]-, methyl ester	DMSO	<u>282(3.8)</u>	39-1339-80C
1,2,4-Triazolidine-3,5-dione, 1-(2,6-dioxocyclohexyl)-4-phenyl-	MeCN	226(4.0,8),244(4.0), 269(3.667)	44-1232-80
$C_{14}H_{13}N_3O_5S$			
Benzenesulfonamide, 4-[[2-(4-nitrophenyl)-2-oxoethyl]amino]-	CH_2Cl_2	350(3.06)	83-0315-80
$C_{14}H_{13}N_5$			
1H-Benzimidazole-2-carboximidic acid, 2-phenylhydrazide	EtOH	252(3.97),280(4.03), 349(4.39)	48-0087-80
$C_{14}H_{13}N_5O_2$			
Acetaldehyde, [(4-aminophenyl)imino]-, (4-nitrophenyl)hydrazone	EtOH	305(3.83),427(4.63)	65-2072-80
$C_{14}H_{13}N_5O_4$			
Benzenamine, 4-[(2,4-dinitrophenyl)-azo]-N,N-dimethyl-	EtOH	514(4.46)	62-0158-80
$C_{14}H_{13}N_5O_6$			
Acetamide, N-[5-[[5-(acetylamino)-1,6-dihydro-2,6-dioxo-3(2H)-pyridinylidene]amino]-1,2,5,6-tetrahydro-2,6-dioxo-3-pyridinyl]-	HOAc	630(4.75)	39-1788-80C
$C_{14}H_{13}O_2P$			
5H-Dibenzo[b,f]phsophepin, 10,11-dihydro-5-hydroxy-, 5-oxide	EtOH	230(4.00),270(3.20), 277(3.15)	139-0243-80A
$C_{14}H_{14}$			
Benzene, 1,1'-(1,2-ethanediyl)bis-, Cr(CO)₃ complex	C_6H_{12}	262(3.8),318(4.0)	110-0749-80
Bicyclo[2.2.2]octane, 2,3,5,6,7,8-hexakis(methylene)-	isooctane	247(4.27)	89-1003-80
Phenanthrene-1,4-$^{13}C_2$, 1,2,3,4-tetrahydro-	EtOH	215s(4.41),225s(4.70), 230(4.80),253(3.58), 266s(3.62),271s(3.67), 276(3.70),282(3.72), 284s(3.72),291s(3.92), 309(3.17),316(3.11), 323(3.16)	33-2295-80
$C_{14}H_{14}BrN_7$			
1H-Pyrazol-5-amine, 4-[(4-bromo-5-methyl-1H-pyrazol-3-yl)azo]-3-methyl-1-phenyl-	MeOH	241(4.10),375(4.56), 410(4.55)	103-1166-80
$C_{14}H_{14}Br_2N_2O$			
Benzaldehyde, (2,6-dibromo-3-oxo-1-cyclohexen-1-yl)methylhydrazone	n.s.g.	281(3.91),363(4.34)	24-2579-80
$C_{14}H_{14}ClNO_2$			
1,4-Naphthalenedione, 2-chloro-3-(diethylamino)-	heptane	494(3.49)	70-0897-80
	isoPrOH	505(3.61)	70-0897-80
2H-Pyran-2-one, 3-chloro-4-(dimethylamino)-5-methyl-6-phenyl-	EtOH	261(3.55),312(3.45)	4-1201-80
2,3-Pyrrolidinedione, 4-[(2-chlorophenyl)methylene]-1-(1-methylethyl)-	EtOH	318(4.37)	145-1135-80

Compound	Solvent	$\lambda_{max}(\log \epsilon)$	Ref.
2,3-Pyrrolidinedione, 4-[(4-chlorophenyl)methylene]-1-(1-methylethyl)-	EtOH	230(4.05),330(4.53)	145-1135-80
$C_{14}H_{14}ClN_2O_4PS$ 3(2H)-Pyridazinone, 4-chloro-5-[(4,5-dimethyl-1,3,2-dioxaphospholan-2-yl)oxy]-2-phenyl-, P-sulfide	MeOH	212(4.26),302(3.71)	73-2343-80
3(2H)-Pyridazinone, 4-chloro-5-[(4-methyl-1,3,2-dioxaphosphorinan-2-yl)oxy]-2-phenyl-, P-sulfide	MeOH	212(4.17),309(3.70)	73-2343-80
$C_{14}H_{14}ClN_3$ Benzenamine, 4-[(4-chlorophenyl)azo]-N,N-dimethyl-	EtOH	414(4.55)	62-0158-80
$C_{14}H_{14}Cl_2N_2$ 2,5-Cyclohexadien-1-one, 4-(dichloromethyl)-4-methyl-, phenylhydrazone	MeOH	253(4.1),294(4.0), 369(4.4)	44-1334-80
$C_{14}H_{14}Cl_2N_2O$ 3-Pyridinecarboxamide, 1-[(2,6-dichlorophenyl)methyl]-1,4-dihydro-N-methyl-	CH$_2$Cl$_2$	355(4.1)	64-1431-80B
$C_{14}H_{14}Cl_2N_4O_5$ α-D-Lyxofuranuronic acid, 1-deoxy-1-(2,6-dichloro-9H-purin-9-yl)-2,3-O-(1-methylethylidene)-, methyl ester	MeOH	205s(--),214(4.32), 253(3.70),274(3.94), 281s(--)	24-2891-80
β-D-Lyxofuranuronic acid, 1-deoxy-1-(2,6-dichloro-7H-purin-7-yl)-2,3-O-(1-methylethylidene)-, methyl ester	MeOH	205s(--),217(4.38), 258s(--),280(3.86), 291s(--)	24-2891-80
β-D-Lyxofuranuronic acid, 1-deoxy-1-(2,6-dichloro-9H-purin-9-yl)-2,3-O-(1-methylethylidene)-, methyl ester	MeOH	206s(--),213(4.21), 255s(--),275(3.83), 281s(--)	24-2891-80
α-D-Ribofuranuronic acid, 1-deoxy-1-(2,6-dichloro-7H-purin-7-yl)-2,3-O-(1-methylethylidene)-, methyl ester	MeOH	216(4.34),257(3.64), 281(3.81),290s(--)	24-2891-80
α-D-Ribofuranuronic acid, 1-deoxy-1-(2,6-dichloro-9H-purin-9-yl)-2,3-O-(1-methylethylidene)-, methyl ester	MeOH	213(4.31),253(3.71), 273(3.96)	24-2891-80
β-D-Ribofuranuronic acid, 1-deoxy-1-(2,6-dichloro-7H-purin-7-yl)-2,3-O-(1-methylethylidene)-, methyl ester	MeOH	215(4.36),255(3.63), 281(3.83),290s(--)	24-2891-80
β-D-Ribofuranuronic acid, 1-deoxy-1-(2,6-dichloro-9H-purin-9-yl)-2,3-O-(1-methylethylidene)-, methyl ester	MeOH	215(4.28),253(3.68), 274(3.92)	24-2891-80
$C_{14}H_{14}Cl_2N_4O_6$ β-D-Ribofuranuronic acid, 1-deoxy-1-(2,6-dichloro-8-hydroxy-9H-purin-9-yl)-2,3-O-(1-methylethylidene)-, methyl ester	MeOH	206(4.29),251(3.75), 287(4.03),318s(--)	24-2891-80

Compound	Solvent	$\lambda_{max}(\log \epsilon)$	Ref.
$C_{14}H_{14}Cl_5N_2OSb$			
Antimony, [bis(2-methylphenyl)diazene 1-oxide-O]pentachloro-, (OC-6-21)-	CHCl$_3$	244(3.96),311(3.78)	78-3177-80
Antimony, [bis(3-methylphenyl)diazene 1-oxide-O]pentachloro-, (OC-6-21)-	CHCl$_3$	243(3.96),325(3.89)	78-3177-80
$C_{14}H_{14}IO_4P$			
Phosphoric acid, 2-iodoethyl diphenyl ester	MeOH	254(2.97),260(3.01), 266(2.88)	5-0557-80
$C_{14}H_{14}NO$			
Pyridinium, 1-methyl-3-(2-oxo-2-phenyl-ethyl)-, iodide	EtOH	247(4.24),270s(3.89), 286s(3.19)	39-0072-80C
	EtOH-NaOH	248(4.21),374(4.47)	39-0072-80C
$C_{14}H_{14}NOS$			
Benzothiazolium, 3,6-dimethyl-2-(2-methyl-3-furanyl)-, iodide	EtOH	199(4.44),217(4.47), 243s(3.82),284s(3.72), 325(3.93)	128-0069-80
Benzothiazolium, 3,6-dimethyl-2-(5-methyl-2-furanyl)-, iodide	EtOH	200(4.30),214(4.50), 369(4.54)	128-0069-80
methyl sulfate	EtOH	212(4.24),368(4.53)	128-0069-80
$C_{14}H_{14}N_2$			
Isoquinoline, 5,6,7,8-tetrahydro-8-(4-pyridinyl)-	MeOH	256(3.7),290(2.3)	103-0945-80
Methanone, (4-methylphenyl)phenyl-, hydrazone	MeOH	272(4.08)	18-3225-80
	dioxan	277(4.08)	18-3225-80
Phenazine, 5,10-dihydro-5,10-dimethyl-	benzene	330(4.3)	46-1841-80
$C_{14}H_{14}N_2O$			
Benzaldehyde, (3-hydroxyphenyl)hydra-zone	n.s.g.	238(4.22),299s(3.91), 327(4.40)	24-2579-80
Benzo[f]quinoxalin-6(2H)-one, 5-ethyl-3,4-dihydro-	EtOH	240(4.19),276(4.37), 438(3.62)	83-0603-80
2,5-Cyclohexadien-1-one, 4-[[4-(dimeth-ylamino)phenyl]imino]-	hexane	553(4.22)	104-2020-80
	+ CF$_3$COOH	644(4.35)	104-2020-80
	benzene	584(4.24)	104-2020-80
	+ CF$_3$COOH	604(4.06)	104-2020-80
	CH$_2$Cl$_2$	604(4.33)	104-2020-80
	+ CF$_3$COOH	625(4.30)	104-2020-80
	CHCl$_3$	610(4.36)	104-2020-80
	+ CF$_3$COOH	710(4.37)	104-2020-80
6H-Indolo[3,2,1-de][1,5]naphthyridin-6-one,1,2,3,3a,4,5-hexahydro-	EtOH	242(4.02),266(3.75), 274s(3.72),294(3.46), 304(3.46)	22-0490-80
Methanone, (4-methoxyphenyl)phenyl-, hydrazone	MeOH	278(4.24)	18-3225-80
	dioxan	278(4.18)	18-3225-80
Phenol, 4-[(2,4-dimethylphenyl)azo]-	n.s.g.	352(4.23)	150-2415-80
2-Pyridinol, 1,2-dihydro-4-(1H-indol-2-yl)-1-methyl-	n.s.g.	205(3.98),225(3.76), 255(3.57),380(3.84)	103-0585-80
1H-Pyrido[4,3-b]indol-1-one, 2,5-di-hydro-2,3,5-trimethyl-	EtOH	243(4.72),249(4.79), 311(4.23),25(4.30)	39-1688-80C
$C_{14}H_{14}N_2O_2$			
1,4-Naphthalenedione, 2-amino-3-(2,2-dimethyl-1-aziridinyl)-	EtOH	238(4.10),245(4.11), 289(4.25),520(3.28)	4-0181-80
$C_{14}H_{14}N_2O_3$			
Acetamide, N-[2-[(1,4-dihydro-1,4-di-oxo-2-naphthalenyl)amino]ethyl]-	EtOH	266(4.39),450(3.58)	83-0603-80

Compound	Solvent	λ_{max}(log ϵ)	Ref.
1H-1,2-Diazepine, 3-methoxy-1-(4-meth-oxybenzoyl)-	EtOH	220(4.01),265(4.06), 324(3.00)	44-5095-80
3-Pyridinecarboxylic acid, 5-(4-amino-phenyl)-1-ethyl-1,4-dihydro-4-oxo-	EtOH	249(4.27),331(3.94)	4-0359-80
Pyridinium, 2-methoxy-1-[(4-methoxy-benzoyl)amino]-, hydroxide, inner salt	EtOH	250(4.24),282(3.97), 303(3.74)	44-5095-80
2-Pyrimidinecarboxylic acid, 1,4-di-hydro-4-oxo-1-(phenylmethyl)-, ethyl ester	EtOH	247(4.14)	142-0843-80B
$C_{14}H_{14}N_2O_4$			
Acetamide, N-(2-acetoxy-1-acetyl-1H-indol-3-yl)-	EtOH	234(4.06),272s(3.42), 300s(3.20)	103-0828-80
Acetamide, N-(1,3-diacetyl-2,3-dihydro-2-oxo-1H-indol-3-yl)-	EtOH	240s(3.90)	103-0828-80
2H-1-Benzopyran-4-carboxylic acid, 7-methoxy-2-oxo-, (1-methyleth-ylidene)hydrazide	EtOH	331(4.21)	95-0289-80
1,3-Dioxolo[4,5-g]quinazoline, 8-(1,4-dioxan-2-yl)-6-methyl-	EtOH	224s(4.33),236(4.38), 290s(3.58),307s(3.67), 316(3.88),333(3.91)	114-0253-80B
7-Oxa-1,5-diazabicyclo[4.1.0]hept-3-ene-6-carboxylic acid, 2-oxo-5-(phenylmethyl)-, ethyl ester	EtOH	250(3.86),307(3.38)	142-0843-80B
2,3-Pyrrolidinedione, 1-(1-methyleth-yl)-4-[(4-nitrophenyl)methylene]-	EtOH	322(4.08)	145-1135-80
$C_{14}H_{14}N_2O_6$			
2-Furancarboxamide, N-[2-hydroxy-1-(hy-droxymethyl)-2-(4-nitrophenyl)ethyl]-, [R-(R*,R*)]-	pH 7	261(4.32)	87-1299-80
$C_{14}H_{14}N_2O_7S$			
1H-Pyrrolo[1,2-a]indole-9-carboxylic acid, 7-amino-2,3,5,8-tetrahydro-6-methyl-2-[(methylsulfonyl)oxy]-5,8-dioxo-	n.s.g.	243(4.234),307(4.063), 350s(3.677),520(2.983)	142-0161-80B
$C_{14}H_{14}N_4$			
Acetaldehyde, [(4-aminophenyl)imino]-, phenylhydrazone	EtOH hexane	305(3.88),394(4.55) 305(--),416(--)	65-2072-80 65-2072-80
Pyrrolo[3,2-e]benzimidazole-3(6H)-propanenitrile, 7,8-dimethyl-	EtOH	301(4.32)	103-1039-80
$C_{14}H_{14}N_4O$			
Pyrazolo[3,4-d]pyridazine, 7-ethoxy-4-methyl-1-phenyl-	EtOH	285(3.74)	4-0231-80
$C_{14}H_{14}N_4O_2$			
Benzenamine, N,N-dimethyl-4-[(2-nitro-phenyl)azo]-	EtOH	440(4.35)	62-0158-80
Benzenamine, N,N-dimethyl-4-[(3-nitro-phenyl)azo]-	EtOH	431(4.46)	62-0158-80
Benzenamine, N,N-dimethyl-4-[(4-nitro-phenyl)azo]-	EtOH	470(4.48)	62-0158-80
Benzo[g]pteridine-2,4(3H,10H)-dione, 3,7,8,10-tetramethyl-	H O	368(4.00),443(4.08)	138-0749-80
Pyrimido[4,5-b]quinoline-2,4(3H,10H)-dione, 8-amino-3,7,10-trimethyl-	12M HCl	255(4.51),329(4.10), 357(3.92)	83-0937-80

Compound	Solvent	λ_{max}(log ϵ)	Ref.
Pyrimido[4,5-b]quinoline-2,4(3H,10H)-dione, 8-amino-3,7,10-trimethyl-(cont.)	M HCl	240(4.52),293(4.10), 357(3.92)	83-0937-80
	pH 6	245(4.62),265s(--), 293s(--),421(4.57)	83-0937-80
$C_{14}H_{14}N_4O_2S$			
Benzenesulfonamide, 4-[[(phenylhydrazono)ethylidene]amino]-	EtOH	293(3.73),385(4.51)	65-2072-80
$C_{14}H_{14}N_4O_3$			
4H,12aH-Benz[g]imidazo[1,2,3-ij]pteridine-4,6(5H)-dione, 1,2-dihydro-12a-methoxy-5-methyl-	MeCN	404(3.63)	88-0739-80
4-Pyridazinecarboxylic acid, 5-[[(2-aminophenyl)amino]carbonyl]-3,6-dimethyl-	DMSO	313(4.0)	39-1339-80B
	MeOH	300(3.6)	39-1339-80B
Pyrido[2,3-d]pyrimidine-6-carboxylic acid, 2-(2,3-dihydro-1H-pyrrol-1-yl)-8-ethyl-5,8-dihydro-5-oxo-	EtOH	227(4.10),304(4.62)	94-2531-80
Spiro[benzo[g]pteridine-2(3H),2'-[1,3]-dioxolan]-4(10H)-one, 3,10-dimethyl-	MeOH	446(3.92)	88-0739-80
$C_{14}H_{14}N_4O_4$			
2H-Benzotriazol-4-ol, 4,5,6,7-tetrahydro-2-(4-nitrophenyl)-, acetate	CHCl$_3$	323(4.29)	39-0744-80C
$C_{14}H_{14}N_4O_5$			
1,5,7-Triazabicyclo[4.1.0]hept-3-ene-6-carboxylic acid, 5-methyl-7-(4-nitrophenyl)-2-oxo-, ethyl ester	EtOH	232(4.09),255(4.03), 333(4.02)	142-0843-80B
$C_{14}H_{14}N_4S$			
Formazan, 3-(methylthio)-1,5-diphenyl-	CHCl$_3$	270(--),550(4.09)	77-0763-80
after standing in dark	CHCl$_3$	280(--),420(4.25), 540(--)	77-0763-80
$C_{14}H_{14}O$			
2,5-Cyclohexadien-1-one, 2,4-dimethyl-4-phenyl-	EtOH	236(4.08)	22-0267-80
1,3-Cyclopentadiene, 5-(2-methoxy-1-phenylethylidene)-	hexane	237s(3.85),294(4.08), 365(2.48)	34-0184-80
2-Propenal, 3-(1,3-dimethyl-1H-inden-1-yl)-, (E)-	EtOH	258s(3.96),287s(3.57), 296(3.53)	39-0714-80C
2-Propenal, 3-(1,3-dimethyl-1H-inden-2-yl)-, (E)-	EtOH	230(3.74),249(3.86), 257(3.85),353(4.48)	39-0714-80C
$C_{14}H_{14}OS_3$			
2H-Thiopyran-2-thione, 4-(4-methoxyphenyl)-3-methyl-6-(methylthio)-	C$_6$H$_{12}$	240(4.34),315(4.25), 334(4.09),468(3.81)	22-0539-80
	EtOH	244(4.58),312(4.45), 348(4.13),474(4.16)	22-0539-80
$C_{14}H_{14}O_2$			
1H-Indene-1,3(2H)-dione, 2-(1,2-dimethylpropylidene)-	CHCl$_3$	256(4.81),301(3.91), 312(3.72),375(2.16)	49-0309-80
1H-Indene-1,3(2H)-dione, 2-(2,2-dimethylpropylidene)-	hexane	249(4.60),270s(--), 299(3.64),308(3.62), 374(1.90)	24-1020-80
1H-Inden-1-one, 3-methoxy-2-(2-methyl-1-propenyl)-	MeOH	247(4.53),299s(--), 413(2.94)	49-0309-80
	CH$_2$Cl$_2$	407(2.89)	49-0309-80

Compound	Solvent	$\lambda_{max}(\log \epsilon)$	Ref.
1,4-Naphthalenedione, 2,3-diethyl-	n.s.g.	330(3.37),440(1.85)	18-0757-80
1H-Naphtho[2,1-d][1,3]dioxin, 1,3-di-methyl-	EtOH	224(3.4),266(3.6), 276(3.7),287(3.6), 317(3.2),331(3.3)	118-0724-80
Spiro[cyclopropane-1,2'-[2H]indene]-1',3'-dione, 2-(1-methylethyl)-	CHCl$_3$	256s(3.62),303(2.69)	49-0309-80
Tetracyclo[6.5.0.0^{9,13}.0^{10,12}]trideca-2,4,6-triene-11-carboxylic acid, (1α,8α,9α,10β,11β,12β,13α)-	MeOH	253(3.20)	89-0207-80
$C_{14}H_{14}O_2S_2$			
1,4-Naphthalenedione, 2,3-bis[(methyl-thio)methyl]-	EtOH	253(4.19),267(4.15), 273s(4.14),335(3.50)	39-0282-80C
$C_{14}H_{14}O_3$			
2H-1-Benzopyran-2-one, 7-hydroxy-8-(3-methyl-2-butenyl)-	EtOH	252s(3.67),260(3.70), 329(4.21)	94-1847-80
2-Cyclobutene-1-carboxylic acid, 4-benzoyl-2,3-dimethyl-, cis	MeOH	244(4.1)	24-2779-80
6,10-Dioxaspiro[4.5]dec-8-en-7-one, 9-phenyl- (general spectrum of class)	EtOH	285-315(3.98-4.25)	104-1995-80
1,2-Naphthalenedione, 7-hydroxy-3-meth-yl-5-(1-methylethyl)- (hibiscoquin-one C)	EtOH	284(4.23),362(3.20), 500(3.34)	39-0249-80C
	EtOH-base	319(--),392(--), 680(--)	39-0249-80C
$C_{14}H_{14}O_3S$			
3-Thiophenecarboxylic acid, 2,5-dihy-dro-4-hydroxy-5-(phenylmethylene)-, ethyl ester, (Z)-	EtOH	240(3.97),286(3.87), 349(4.47),366(4.43)	33-1542-80
$C_{14}H_{14}O_4$			
1,3-Cyclopentanedione, 2-(2-acetoxy-phenyl)-2-methyl-	n.s.g.	264(2.58),284(2.34)	44-0501-80
Marmesin	EtOH	226(3.88),250(3.45), 260(3.38),300s(3.63), 337(4.08)	94-1847-80
1,2-Naphthalenedione, 7,8-dihydroxy-3-methyl-5-(1-methylethyl)-	MeOH	228(4.12),276(4.35), 317s(3.51),415(3.33), 534(3.40)	39-0249-80C
	MeOH-base	256(--),338(--), 498(--),670(--)	39-0249-80C
$C_{14}H_{14}O_4S_2$			
Benzenesulfonothioic acid, 4-methoxy-, S-(4-methoxyphenyl) ester	MeOH	247(4.28),269(4.20)	12-2635-80
$C_{14}H_{14}O_5$			
1-Azulenecarboxylic acid, 2,3-dihydro-3-hydroxy-3-methoxy-2-oxo-, ethyl ester	MeOH	233(4.22),257(4.13), 400(4.18)	138-0197-80
2H-1-Benzopyran-4-carboxylic acid, 7-methoxy-2-oxo-, 1-methylethyl ester	EtOH	344(4.14)	95-0289-80
2H-1-Benzopyran-4-carboxylic acid, 7-methoxy-2-oxo-, propyl ester	EtOH	344(4.07)	95-0289-80
2H-1-Benzopyran-2-one, 7-methoxy-4-[(1-oxopropoxy)methyl]-	EtOH	323(4.17)	95-0744-80
4H-1,3-Dioxin-2-carboxylic acid, 2-methyl-4-oxo-6-phenyl-, ethyl ester	EtOH	285-315(3.98-4.25)	104-1995-80
2-Naphthalenecarboxylic acid, 4,5,7-trimethoxy-	CHCl$_3$	284(3.81),293(3.80), 302s(3.59),343s(3.39),	12-2531-80

Compound	Solvent	$\lambda_{max}(\log \epsilon)$	Ref.
(cont.)		359(3.63),372(3.65)	12-2531-80
1,2-Naphthalenedicarboxylic acid, 5,6,7,8-tetrahydro-5-oxo-, dimethyl ester	MeCN	205(4.14),255(4.10), 260s(4.06),302(3.49), 312s(3.42)	24-3249-80
1,2-Naphthalenedicarboxylic acid, 5,6,7,8-tetrahydro-8-oxo-, dimethyl ester	MeCN	225(4.32),248s(3.93), 290(2.93),302(2.93)	24-3249-80
$C_{14}H_{14}O_6$			
1,3-Benzenedipropanoic acid, β,β'-di-oxo-, dimethyl ester	MeOH	226(4.42),245(4.19), 288(3.82)	47-3029-80
1,4-Benzenedipropanoic acid, β,β'-di-oxo-, dimethyl ester	MeOH	257(4.16),304(4.06)	47-3029-80
1,2-Naphthalenedicarboxylic acid, 5,6,7,8-tetrahydro-3-hydroxy-5-oxo-, dimethyl ester	EtOH	220(4.36),257(4.05), 341(3.66)	24-3249-80
1,2-Naphthalenedicarboxylic acid, 5,6,7,8-tetrahydro-4-hydroxy-8-oxo-, dimethyl ester	EtOH	234(4.27),322(3.20)	24-3249-80
Spiro[bicyclo[2.2.2]octa-5,7-diene-2,2'-oxirane]-5,6-dicarboxylic acid, 4-methyl-3-oxo-, dimethyl ester, $(1\alpha,2\beta,4\alpha)$-	EtOH	240s(3.62),305s(2.59), 314(2.61),326s(2.44)	44-2189-80
Spiro[bicyclo[2.2.2]octa-5,7-diene-2,2'-oxirane]-5,6-dicarboxylic acid, 7-methyl-3-oxo-, dimethyl ester	EtOH	227s(3.65),245s(3.57), 306(2.60),313(2.59), 330s(2.36)	44-2189-80
Spiro[cyclopropa[cd]pentalene-1(2H),2'-oxirane]-2b,4b(2aH,4aH)-dicarboxylic acid, 2a-methyl-2-oxo-, dimethyl ester, $(1\alpha,2a\alpha,2b\alpha,4a\alpha,4b\alpha)$-	EtOH	250s(2.76),312s(1.85), 326s(1.78),339s(1.48)	44-2189-80
Spiro[cyclopropa[cd]pentalene-1(2H),2'-oxirane]-2b,4b(2aH,4aH)-dicarboxylic acid, 4-methyl-2-oxo-, dimethyl ester, $(1\alpha,2a\alpha,2b\alpha,4a\alpha,4b\alpha)$-	EtOH	252s(2.72),312s(1.78), 327s(1.70),340s(1.40)	44-2189-80
$C_{14}H_{14}O_6S_2$			
Benzenesulfonic acid, 2,2'-(1,2-ethane-diyl)bis-, dipotassium salt	H_2O	267(3.46),274(3.44)	104-0342-80
$C_{14}H_{14}S_2Si$			
1,3-Dithia-2-silacyclopentane, 2,2-di-phenyl-	hexane	197(4.83),221(4.20), 245s(3.55),274(2.88)	101-0147-80A +131-0099-80C
$C_{14}H_{14}S_3$			
1-Propanethione, 2-(4,5-dimethyl-1,3-dithiol-2-ylidene)-1-phenyl-	MeOH	253(3.70),270s(3.68), 314s(3.20),478(4.08), 583(2.34)	104-1775-80
2H-Thiopyran-2-thione, 3,5-dimethyl-6-(methylthio)-4-phenyl-	C_6H_{12}	238(4.33),279s(3.79), 310s(3.84),331(3.91), 474(3.63)	22-0539-80
	EtOH	249(4.05),287s(3.83), 310(3.96),320s(3.93), 394s(3.45),482(3.91)	22-0539-80
2H-Thiopyran-2-thione, 3-methyl-4-(4-methylphenyl)-6-(methylthio)-	C_6H_{12}	237(4.31),302(4.23), 328s(3.91),468(3.80)	22-0539-80
	EtOH	244(4.18),306(4.14), 328s(3.90),474(3.78)	22-0539-80
2H-Thiopyran-2-thione, 3-methyl-5-(4-methylphenyl)-6-(methylthio)-	C_6H_{12}	238(4.13),290(3.90), 320s(4.00),335(4.03), 475(3.90)	22-0539-80
	EtOH	239(4.37),320(4.03), 483(3.96)	22-0539-80

Compound	Solvent	$\lambda_{max}(\log \epsilon)$	Ref.
$C_{14}H_{15}BrN_2O$			
Acetamide, 2-bromo-N-[4-(dimethylamino)-1-naphthalenyl]-	EtOH	217(4.63),231(4.13), 323(3.87)	94-1722-80
Benzaldehyde, (6-bromo-3-oxo-1-cyclohexen-1-yl)methylhydrazone	n.s.g.	233s(3.98),357(4.66)	24-2579-80
$C_{14}H_{15}ClN_4O$			
Acetamide, N-[4-amino-5-(4-chlorophenyl)-6-ethyl-2-pyrimidinyl]-	EtOH	220(4.48),250(4.12), 285(4.00)	142-0471-80
Methanimidamide, N'-[1-(4-chlorophenyl)-4-formyl-3-methyl-1H-pyrazol-5-yl]-N,N-dimethyl-	EtOH	260(4.42),338(3.69)	114-0127-80C
$C_{14}H_{15}ClN_4O_5$			
α-D-Lyxofuranuronic acid, 1-(6-chloro-9H-purin-9-yl)-1-deoxy-2,3-0-(1-methylethylidene)-, methyl ester	MeOH	205(4.27),251s(--), 264(3.91)	24-2891-80
β-D-Lyxofuranuronic acid, 1-(6-chloro-7H-purin-7-yl)-1-deoxy-2,3-0-(1-methylethylidene)-, methyl ester	MeOH	207(4.23),254s(--), 270(3.78)	24-2891-80
β-D-Lyxofuranuronic acid, 1-(6-chloro-9H-purin-9-yl)-1-deoxy-2,3-0-(1-methylethylidene)-, methyl ester	MeOH	206(4.27),250s(--), 264(3.91)	24-2891-80
α-D-Ribofuranuronic acid, 1-(2-chloro-7H-purin-7-yl)-1-deoxy-2,3-0-(1-methylethylidene)-, methyl ester	MeOH	211(4.32),255(3.63), 275(3.77),288s(--)	24-2891-80
α-D-Ribofuranuronic acid, 1-(2-chloro-9H-purin-9-yl)-1-deoxy-2,3-0-(1-methylethylidene)-, methyl ester	MeOH	210(4.31),248(3.65), 270(3.89)	24-2891-80
α-D-Ribofuranuronic acid, 1-(6-chloro-7H-purin-7-yl)-1-deoxy-2,3-0-(1-methylethylidene)-, methyl ester	MeOH	209(4.28),252s(--), 271(3.85),280s(--)	24-2891-80
β-D-Ribofuranuronic acid, 1-(6-chloro-7H-purin-7-yl)-1-deoxy-2,3-0-(1-methylethylidene)-, methyl ester	MeOH	210(4.34),256(3.65), 275(3.79),287s(--)	24-2891-80
β-D-Ribofuranuronic acid, 1-(2-chloro-9H-purin-9-yl)-1-deoxy-2,3-0-(1-methylethylidene)-, methyl ester	MeOH	210(4.31),249(3.53), 272(3.85)	24-2891-80
β-D-Ribofuranuronic acid, 1-(6-chloro-9H-purin-9-yl)-1-deoxy-2,3-0-(1-methylethylidene)-, methyl ester	MeOH	207(4.30),251s(--), 265(4.00)	24-2891-80
$C_{14}H_{15}Cl_2N_5O_4$			
α-D-Ribofuranuronamide, 1-deoxy-1-(2,6-dichloro-9H-purin-9-yl)-N-methyl-2,3-0-(1-methylethylidene)-	MeOH	211(4.34),254s(--), 274(3.95)	24-2891-80
β-	MeOH	205s(--),212(4.28), 254(3.70),274(3.89)	24-2891-80
$C_{14}H_{15}FO_3$			
Cyclopentanecarboxylic acid, 1-(4-fluorophenyl)-2-oxo-, ethyl ester	EtOH	210(3.79),258(2.72), 264(2.81),270(2.81)	12-0113-80
$C_{14}H_{15}F_3N_2O_7$			
Thymidine, 2'-deoxy-α,α,α-trifluoro-, 3',5'-diacetate	MeOH MeOH-acid MeOH-base	260(3.98) 260(4.01) 260(3.81)	39-2755-80C 39-2755-80C 39-2755-80C
$C_{14}H_{15}F_3O_2S$			
Sulfonium, diethyl-, 1-benzoyl-3,3,3-trifluoro-2-oxopropylide	50% EtOH	243(4.13),287(3.86)	104-0729-80

Compound	Solvent	$\lambda_{max}(\log \epsilon)$	Ref.
$C_{14}H_{15}N$			
Pyrrolo[3,2,1-jk]carbazole, 1,2,3,3a,4,5-hexahydro-	EtOH	232(4.44),279s(3.78), 282(3.79),292s(3.72)	39-0097-80C
Pyrrolo[3,2,1-jk]carbazole, 4,5,7,8,9,10-hexahydro-	MeOH	235(4.53),292(3.91)	39-0535-80C
$C_{14}H_{15}NO$			
9H-Benzocyclohepten-5,8-imin-9-one, 5,8-dihydro-10-(1-methylethyl)-	EtOH	219(4.31),264(3.66)	39-2077-80C
5H-Benzocyclohepten-5-one, 7-[(1-methylethyl)amino]-	EtOH	210(4.09),276(4.45), 285(4.49),346(3.82)	39-2077-80C
1H-Carbazol-1-one, 9-ethyl-2,3,4,9-tetrahydro-	ether	237(4.27),306(4.29)	78-1585-80
3-Oxa-10-azacyclopenta[jk]fluorene, 1,2,4,5-tetrahydro-2a-methyl-	EtOH	202s(4.29),230(4.54), 276(3.82),295s(3.60)	39-2870-80C
Pyridinium, 1-(2-hydroxyphenyl)-2,4,6-trimethyl-, hydroxide, inner salt	EtOH	220(4.27),288(4.18), 305s(3.85)	39-1870-80C
$C_{14}H_{15}NOS$			
2-Propanesulfenamide, 2-methyl-N-(4-oxo-1(4H)-naphthalenylidene)-	hexane	418(4.28)	18-0775-80
$C_{14}H_{15}NO_2$			
1H-Indole-2-acetic acid, 1-methyl-α-methylene-, ethyl ester	MeOH	223(5.00),275(4.42), 283(4.40),295(4.37)	44-1657-80
1H-Pyrrole-2,5-dione, 1-(2,6-diethylphenyl)-	n.s.g.	290(2.66)	116-0826-80
$C_{14}H_{15}NO_2S$			
4-Quinolinecarboxylic acid, 1,2-dihydro-2-thioxo-, butyl ester	EtOH	222(4.53),289(4.27), 420(3.97)	94-0049-80
4-Quinolinecarboxylic acid, 1,2-dihydro-2-thioxo-, 2-methylpropyl ester	EtOH	221(4.54),288(4.31), 418(3.96)	94-0049-80
$C_{14}H_{15}NO_3$			
2H-1,3-Benzoxazin-2-one, 3,4-dihydro-3-methyl-4-(2-oxocyclopentyl)-	EtOH	266(3.00),272(2.98)	4-0277-80
Ethanone, 1-[3-acetoxy-1-ethyl-1H-indol-2-yl]-	MeOH	237(4.26),306(4.31)	83-0405-80
Ethanone, 1-[5-(acetoxymethyl)-3-methyl-2-indolizinyl]-	n.s.g.	244s(4.37),248(4.38), 268s(3.74),300s(3.04), 352s(3.15),372(3.27), 385(3.28),407s(3.08)	1-0079-80
1H-Indole-2-propanoic acid, 3-methyl-β-oxo-, ethyl ester	EtOH EtOH-base	239(4.17),317(4.32) 337(4.41)	78-2125-80 78-2125-80
5H-Pyrano[3,2-c]quinolin-5-one, 2,3,4,6-tetrahydro-2-hydroxy-2,6-dimethyl-	MeOH	226(4.70),262s(3.92), 276(3.89),287(3.93), 317(4.05),330s(3.91)	39-0512-80C
	MeOH-base	218(4.84),256s(4.29), 312(4.29)	39-0512-80C
$C_{14}H_{15}NO_4$			
2H-1-Benzopyran-4-carboxamide, 7-methoxy-2-oxo-N-propyl-	EtOH	331(4.15)	95-0289-80
2-Furanacetic acid, 2,5-dihydro-4-methyl-5-oxo-3-(phenylamino)-, methyl ester	MeOH	206(4.12),288(4.45)	48-0559-80
1H-Indole-2-acetic acid, 3-carboxy-1-methyl-, 2-ethyl ester	EtOH	216(4.30),230s(4.20), 250s(3.72),288(3.95)	39-1688-80C
1H-Indole-3-carboxylic acid, 1-methyl-, 2-acetoxyethyl ester	EtOH	206(4.47),231s(4.28), 290(4.07)	39-1688-80C

Compound	Solvent	λ_{max}(log ϵ)	Ref.
C$_{14}$H$_{15}$NO$_6$ 3,5-Isoxazoledicarboxylic acid, 4,5-di-hydro-4-phenyl-, 5-ethyl 3-methyl ester, 2-oxide, trans	MeOH	267(4.01)	94-0479-80
C$_{14}$H$_{15}$NO$_6$S Pyrrolo[2,1-b]thiazole-2,6,7-tricarbox-ylic acid, 3-methyl-, 2-ethyl 6,7-di-methyl ester	EtOH	226(4.34),257s(4.43), 265(4.48),292(3.82), 316s(3.58)	18-3308-80
C$_{14}$H$_{15}$N$_3$ Benzenamine, N,N-dimethyl-4-(phenyl-azo)-	EtOH	407(4.45)	62-0158-80
C$_{14}$H$_{15}$N$_3$OS Morpholine, 4-[5-(2-phenylethenyl)-1,3,4-thiadiazol-2-yl]-	EtOH	338(4.45)	94-2116-80
C$_{14}$H$_{15}$N$_3$O$_2$ 3H-1,2-Diazepin-3-one, 1-[4-(dimethyl-amino)benzoyl]-1,2-dihydro-	EtOH	315(4.04)	44-5095-80
C$_{14}$H$_{15}$N$_3$O$_2$S 2-Propenenitrile, 3,3-bis(1-aziridin-yl)-2-[(4-methylphenyl)sulfonyl]-	MeOH	223(4.03),290(4.02)	78-1791-80
C$_{14}$H$_{15}$N$_3$O$_3$ 1,3-Dioxolo[4,5-g]quinazoline, 6-methyl-8-morpholino-	EtOH	218(4.38),230s(4.27), 250(4.32),285(3.78), 294(3.72),339(4.01)	114-0253-80B
C$_{14}$H$_{15}$N$_3$O$_4$ 2H-1,3-Benzoxazin-2-one, 4-(2,3-dihy-dro-5-methyl-3-oxo-1H-pyrazol-4-yl)-3,4-dihydro-8-methoxy-3-methyl-	EtOH	226s(4.10),260s(3.36), 281(3.30),290(3.29)	4-0519-80
4(1H)-Pyridazinone, 3-acetyl-5,6-di-hydro-6,6-dimethyl-1-(4-nitrophenyl)-	EtOH	225(4.00),244(4.04), 348(4.25)	118-0623-80
2(1H)-Quinoxalinone, 3,4-dihydro-6-nitro-3-(2-oxocyclohexyl)-	EtOH	269(4.14),316(3.72), 395(3.56)	104-0938-80
1,2,4-Triazolidine-3,5-dione, 1-(1-acetyl-2-oxopropyl)-4-(4-methyl-phenyl)-	MeCN	272(3.591)	44-1232-80
C$_{14}$H$_{15}$N$_3$O$_5$ 3-Pyridazinecarboxylic acid, 1,4,5,6-tetrahydro-6-methyl-1-(4-nitrophen-yl)-4-oxo-, ethyl ester	EtOH	226s(4.03),234(4.06), 385(4.44)	118-0623-80
1,2,4-Triazolidine-1-acetic acid, α-acetyl-3,5-dioxo-4-phenyl-, ethyl ester	MeCN	233-250s(3.66)	44-1232-80
C$_{14}$H$_{15}$N$_3$O$_6$ 2-Quinoxalineacetic acid, α-acetyl-1,2,3,4-tetrahydro-7-nitro-3-oxo-, ethyl ester	EtOH	268(4.26),313(3.85), 396(3.66)	104-0938-80
C$_{14}$H$_{15}$N$_5$ 3H-Purin-6-amine, N,N-dimethyl-3-(phen-ylmethyl)-	pH 1 pH 7 pH 13 EtOH	292(4.35) 296(4.23) 296(4.22) 301(4.19)	94-1920-80 94-1920-80 94-1920-80 94-1920-80

Compound	Solvent	$\lambda_{max}(\log \epsilon)$	Ref.
9H-Purin-6-amine, N,N-dimethyl-9-(phenylmethyl)-	pH 1	269(4.30)	94-1920-80
	pH 7	278(4.30)	94-1920-80
	pH 13	278(4.30)	94-1920-80
	EtOH	277(4.29)	94-1920-80
$C_{14}H_{15}N_5O_3$			
Acetamide, N-[4,7-dihydro-7-(1-hydroxyethyl)-5-phenyl[1,2,5]oxadiazolo[3,4-d]pyrimidin-7-yl]-	n.s.g.	239(4.07),288(3.94)	44-3827-80
$C_{14}H_{15}N_5O_8$			
D-Ribitol, 1-deoxy-1-(1,3,4,6,7,8-hexahydro-2,4,6,8-tetraoxopyrido[2,3-d:6,5-d']dipyrimidin-10(2H)-yl)-	pH 1	262(3.78),298(3.88), 372(4.20)	39-2645-80C
	pH 13	278(4.00),393(4.44)	39-2645-80C
$C_{14}H_{15}OP$			
Phosphinous acid, diphenyl-, ethyl ester	EtOH	221(3.17),238(3.18), 285(3.18)	65-0945-80
	MeCN	218(3.12),247(3.18), 273(3.18)	65-0945-80
$C_{14}H_{15}OS$			
Thiophenium, tetrahydro-1-(4-hydroxy-1-naphthalenyl)-, tetrafluoroborate	n.s.g.	317(3.91),327(3.91), 366(3.70)	47-1021-80
$C_{14}H_{15}O_2P$			
Phosphonous acid, ethyl-, diphenyl ester	EtOH	212(2.90),270(2.34)	65-0945-80
	MeCN	225(3.13),270(3.13)	65-0945-80
$C_{14}H_{16}$			
Benzo[3,4]cyclobuta[1,2]cyclooctene, 4b,5,6,9,10,10a-hexahydro-, cis	n.s.g.	213(3.80),260(3.15), 266(3.31),273(3.30)	88-3025-80
trans	n.s.g.	215(3.75),260(3.14), 266(3.33),273(3.31)	88-3025-80
Bicyclo[3.2.1]oct-2-ene, 3-phenyl-	EtOH	220(3.96),253(4.08), 292s(2.70)	23-1847-80
Spiro[cyclobuta[b]naphthalene-4(1H),1'-cyclopropane], 2,5,6,7-tetrahydro-	hexane	277(3.42),282(3.53), 287(3.53),292(3.54)	18-0709-80
Tricyclo[3.2.1.0^{2,4}]octane, 3-phenyl-	C_6H_{12}	260(2.47)	44-2813-80
$C_{14}H_{16}BrN_3O_3$			
Phenol, 4-[[(2-amino-3-bromo-4-pyridinyl)amino]methyl]-2,6-dimethoxy-	pH 2	204(4.65),224(4.56), 279(4.13)	87-0384-80
	pH 13	257(4.25),280s(3.96)	87-0384-80
Phenol, 4-[(4,6-diamino-5-bromo-3-pyridinyl)methyl]-2,6-dimethoxy-	pH 1	205(4.68),222(4.68), 277(3.98)	87-0384-80
	pH 13	250s(4.20),283s(3.88)	87-0384-80
$C_{14}H_{16}BrN_5$			
Pyrazolo[3,4-d]-1,2,3-triazole, 2-(2-bromo-4-methylphenyl)-2,4-dihydro-6-methyl-4-(1-methylethyl)-	CHCl₃	410(4.00)	103-1166-80
$C_{14}H_{16}ClN$			
1H-Carbazole, 1-(2-chloroethyl)-2,3,4,9-tetrahydro-	EtOH	228(4.73),276s(4.06), 283(4.09),291(4.03)	39-0097-80C
$C_{14}H_{16}ClN_5O_5$			
α-D-Ribofuranuronic acid, 1-(2-amino-6-chloro-7H-purin-7-yl)-1-deoxy-2,3-O-(1-methylethylidene)-, methyl ester	MeOH	222(4.28),252s(--), 322(3.61),383(3.10)	24-2891-80

Compound	Solvent	$\lambda_{max}(\log \epsilon)$	Ref.
α-D-Ribofuranuronic acid, 1-(2-amino-6-chloro-9H-purin-9-yl)-1-deoxy-2,3-O-(1-methylethylidene)-, methyl ester	MeOH	221(4.25),248(3.75), 309(3.75),253s(--)	24-2891-80
α-D-Ribofuranuronic acid, 1-(6-amino-2-chloro-7H-purin-7-yl)-1-deoxy-2,3-O-(1-methylethylidene)-, methyl ester	MeOH	217(4.28),248(3.70), 277(3.86),289s(--)	24-2891-80
α-D-Ribofuranuronic acid, 1-(6-amino-2-chloro-9H-purin-9-yl)-1-deoxy-2,3-O-(1-methylethylidene)-, methyl ester	MeOH	212(4.31),263(4.08)	24-2891-80
β-D-Ribofuranuronic acid, 1-(2-amino-6-chloro-9H-purin-9-yl)-1-deoxy-2,3-O-(1-methylethylidene)-, methyl ester	MeOH	221(4.20),247(3.70), 310(3.64),253s(--)	24-2891-80
β-D-Ribofuranuronic acid, 1-(6-amino-2-chloro-9H-purin-9-yl)-1-deoxy-2,3-O-(1-methylethylidene)-, methyl ester	MeOH	212(4.34),264(4.13)	24-2891-80

$C_{14}H_{16}ClN_7O$
Hydrazinecarboxamide, 2-[[1-(4-chloro-phenyl)-5-[[(dimethylamino)methyl-ene]amino]-1H-pyrazol-4-yl]methyl-ene]-	EtOH	273(4.50),305(4.22)	114-0127-80C

$C_{14}H_{16}ClN_7S$
Hydrazinecarbothioamide, 2-[[1-(4-chlorophenyl)-5-[[(dimethylamino)-methylene]amino]-1H-pyrazol-4-yl]-methylene]-	EtOH	286(4.49),327(4.43)	114-0127-80C

$C_{14}H_{16}Cl_2N_2O_5$
L-Glutamic acid, N-(4-amino-3,5-di-chlorobenzoyl)-, dimethyl ester	EtOH	278(4.30)	44-0527-80

$C_{14}H_{16}Cl_3N_3O_6$
D-Leucine, 5,5,5-trichloro-N-(2,4-di-nitrophenyl)-N-methyl-, methyl ester	MeOH	365(4.09)	78-2133-80
L-isomer	MeOH	365(4.10)	78-2133-80

$C_{14}H_{16}FN_3O_3$
Phenol, 4-[[(2-amino-3-fluoro-4-pyri-dinyl)amino]methyl]-2,6-dimethoxy-	pH 2	205(4.71),228s(4.46), 281(4.23)	87-0384-80
	pH 8.7	205(4.72),246(4.18), 280s(3.61)	87-0384-80
	pH 13	254.5(4.30)	87-0384-80
Phenol, 4-[(4,6-diamino-6-fluoro-3-pyridinyl)methyl]-2,6-dimethoxy-	pH 2	205(4.68),215s(4.65), 259s(3.95),276(4.02)	87-0384-80
	pH 8.7	208(4.71),240s(4.14), 272(3.61)	87-0384-80
	pH 13	250(4.10),283s(3.81)	87-0384-80

$C_{14}H_{16}F_3NO_4S$
2-Propenoic acid, 3-[4-(dimethylamino)-phenyl]-2-[(trifluoromethyl)sulfon-yl]-, ethyl ester	EtOH	261(4.14),415(4.42)	104-1200-80

$C_{14}H_{16}F_3N_3O_6$
Cytidine, 2'-deoxy-5-(trifluorometh-yl)-, 3',5'-diacetate	MeOH	267(3.85)	39-2755-80C
	MeOH-acid	280(4.09)	39-2755-80C
	MeOH-base	275(3.87)	39-2755-80C

Compound	Solvent	$\lambda_{max}(\log \epsilon)$	Ref.
$C_{14}H_{16}GaNO$			
Gallium, dimethyl[1-[(methylimino)methyl]-2-naphthalenolato-N,O]-, (T-4)-	hexane	313(3.88),325(3.94), 400(3.81),412(3.79)	101-0001-80I
	MeCN	317(3.76),323(3.83), 393(3.74),405(3.75)	101-0001-80I
$C_{14}H_{16}NO_3$			
Isoquinolinium, 8-acetyl-5,7-dimethoxy-2-methyl-, iodide	EtOH	225(4.56),264(4.52), 305(3.74),390(3.76)	39-0072-80C
$C_{14}H_{16}N_2$			
1H,6H-Benz[2,3]azirino[1,2-b]pyrazole, 4a,5,7,8-tetrahydro-2-phenyl-	EtOH	254.5(4.10)	35-1176-80
Cyclobuta[1,2-c:4,3-c']dipyridinium, 2,7-diethyl-, dibromide	H_2O	244(3.33),253(3.53), 298(3.17),312(3.17), 327(3.12)	150-2911-80
3H-Indole, 6-methyl-3-(1-pyrrolidinylmethylene)-	$CHCl_3$	282s(4.26),287(4.31), 366(4.43)	94-1711-80
3H-Indole, 3-(piperidinomethylene)-	$CHCl_3$	276s(4.07),282(4.11), 364(4.13)	94-1711-80
1H-Perimidine, 2,3-dihydro-1,2,3-trimethyl-	$CHCl_3$	348(4.13)	104-1890-80
Pyridazine, 5-(2-methylpropyl)-3-phenyl-	EtOH	222(3.96),254(4.08)	39-0072-80C
	EtOH-HCl	223(4.00),242(4.03), 264(4.07)	39-0072-80C
$(C_{14}H_{16}N_2)_n$			
3H-Indole, 3-(piperidinomethylene)-, polymer	$CHCl_3$	278(3.89),287(3.61)	94-1711-80
$C_{14}H_{16}N_2O$			
Acetamide, N-[4-(dimethylamino)-1-naphthalenyl]-	EtOH	212(4.63),242(4.16), 350(3.92)	94-1722-80
Azepino[3,4-b]indol-1(2H)-one, 3,4,5,10-tetrahydro-2,10-dimethyl-	EtOH	226(4.44),295(4.20)	39-1512-80C
[2,3'-Bipyridin]-5'-ol, 6'-methyl-2'-propyl-	MeOH	297(4.3)	103-0951-80
3H-Indole, 5-methoxy-3-(1-pyrrolidinylmethylene)-	$CHCl_3$	287(4.28),294s(4.06), 357(4.38)	94-1711-80
Urea, tetracyclo[6.5.0.0^{9,13}.0^{10,12}]-trideca-2,4,6-trien-11-yl-, (1α,8α,9α,10β,11β,12β,13α)-	dioxan	250(3.23)	89-0207-80
$C_{14}H_{16}N_2O_2$			
1H-1,3-Benzodiazepine-1-carboxylic acid, 2,4-dimethyl-, ethyl ester	EtOH	244(3.96),285(3.76)	94-2602-80
1H-1,3-Benzodiazepine-1-carboxylic acid, 2,5-dimethyl-, ethyl ester	EtOH	240(3.96),283(3.75)	94-2602-80
6H,12H-Indazolo[2,1-a]indazole-6,12-dione, 1,2,3,4,7,8,9,10-octahydro-	dioxan	254(3.51),317(4.16)	35-4983-80
10H,12H-Indazolo[1,2-a]indazole-10,12-dione, 1,2,3,4,6,7,8,9-octahydro-	dioxan	232(4.27),255s(3.81), 354(3.81)	35-4983-80
Pyrazineethanol, α-(4-methoxyphenyl)-3-methyl-	EtOH	211(3.97),224(4.03), 275(3.95),300s(3.15)	44-0999-80
Pyrazineethanol, α-(4-methoxyphenyl)-5-methyl-	EtOH	210(4.03),224(4.05), 276(3.95),300s(3.23)	44-0999-80
Pyrazineethanol, α-(4-methoxyphenyl)-6-methyl-	EtOH	210(4.27),224(4.24), 275(4.19),306s(3.34)	44-0999-80
4(1H)-Pyridazinone, 3-acetyl-5,6-dihydro-6,6-dimethyl-1-phenyl-	EtOH	226s(3.73),248(3.95), 336(4.14)	118-0623-80

Compound	Solvent	λ_{max}(log ϵ)	Ref.
4(1H)-Pyridazinone, 3-acetyl-5,6-di-hydro-6-methyl-1-(4-methylphenyl)-	EtOH	227(3.79),255(3.99),376(4.23)	118-0623-80
C₁₄H₁₆N₂O₃			
1,8-Naphthyridine-3-propanoic acid, 1,4-dihydro-7-methyl-4-oxo-, ethyl ester	EtOH	247(4.27),274(3.32),335(3.91)	39-0227-80C
Phenol, 2,6-dimethoxy-4-[(4-pyridinyl-amino)methyl]-	pH 7.2 pH 13	273(4.35) 255(4.39),290s(3.77)	87-0384-80 87-0384-80
2-Propenoic acid, 2-cyano-3-[5-(1-pip-eridinyl)-2-furanyl]-, methyl ester	MeOH	213(4.14),238(4.43),465(5.04)	73-1831-80
3-Pyridazinecarboxylic acid, 1,4,5,6-tetrahydro-6-methyl-4-oxo-1-phenyl-, ethyl ester	EtOH	225s(3.80),245(4.04),372(4.15)	118-0623-80
4H-Pyrido[1,2-a]pyrimidine-3-propanoic acid, 6-methyl-4-oxo-, ethyl ester	EtOH	248(4.02),360(4.00)	39-0227-80C
C₁₄H₁₆N₂O₄			
6-Phthalazinecarboxylic acid, 3,4-di-hydro-1-(hydroxymethyl)-5,7-dimeth-yl-4-oxo-, ethyl ester	EtOH	218(--),259(3.90),292(3.79),309(3.71),321(3.58)	94-2770-80
6-Phthalazinecarboxylic acid, 3,4-di-hydro-1-(hydroxymethyl)-4-oxo-, 1,1-dimethylethyl ester	EtOH	252(3.83),261(3.82),306(3.86)	94-2770-80
2(1H)-Pyridinone, 6-amino-3-[(4-hy-droxy-3,5-dimethoxyphenyl)methyl]-	2M HCl	235(4.27),285s(3.40),322(4.09)	87-0384-80
	pH 7	232(4.16),270s(3.28),330(4.17)	87-0384-80
	pH 13	245(4.21),274s(3.69),306(4.01)	87-0384-80
2(1H)-Pyridinone, 6-amino-5-[(4-hy-droxy-3,5-dimethoxyphenyl)methyl]-	2M HCl	230(4.21),285s(3.42),318(4.09)	87-0384-80
	pH 7	234(4.21),270s(3.27),330(4.16)	87-0384-80
	pH 13	240(4.20),307(4.03)	87-0384-80
C₁₄H₁₆N₂O₅S			
Sulfonium, dimethyl-, 1-[[[(4-nitro-phenyl)acetyl]amino]carbonyl]-2-oxopropylide	EtOH	217(4.33),274(4.38)	94-0795-80
C₁₄H₁₆N₂O₆			
2-Butenedioic acid, 2-[[[imino(4-meth-oxyphenyl)methyl]amino]oxy]-, dimethyl ester, (E)-	MeOH	213(4.08),247(4.15),278s(4.03)	4-1101-80
C₁₄H₁₆N₂O₆S₂			
Benzenesulfonic acid, 2,2'-(1,2-ethane-diyl)bis[5-amino-	0.5% NaOH	246(4.37),296(3.71)	104-0342-80
C₁₄H₁₆N₂O₇			
L-Aspartic acid, N-acetyl-, 1-methyl 4-[(2-nitrophenyl)methyl] ester	TMP	260(3.71)	22-0133-80
L-Aspartic acid, N-acetyl-, 1-methyl 4-[(3-nitrophenyl)methyl] ester	TMP	262(3.85)	22-0133-80
L-Aspartic acid, N-acetyl-, 1-methyl 4-[(4-nitrophenyl)methyl] ester	TMP	268(3.97)	22-0133-80
C₁₄H₁₆N₂S			
Isoquinolinium, 2-[(2,2-dimethyl-1-thioxopropyl)amino]-, hydroxide,	EtOH	221(4.46),259(4.05),285(3.89),325s(3.62),	114-0259-80A

Compound	Solvent	λ_{max}(log ϵ)	Ref.
inner salt (cont.)		354s(4.42)	114-0259-80A
$C_{14}H_{16}N_4O$ Methanimidamide, N'-(4-formyl-3-methyl- 1-phenyl-1H-pyrazol-5-yl)-N,N-dimeth- yl-	EtOH	252(4.39),338(3.64)	114-0127-80C
$C_{14}H_{16}N_4O_2$ 8-Azaspiro[4.5]deca-6,9-diene-6,10-di- carbonitrile, 7,8-dimethyl-9-(nitro- methyl)- (all spectra in EtOH)	pH 0.5 pH 2.39 pH 7.75 pH 12.6 pH 13.0	227(4.14),351(3.54) 224(4.15),351(3.51) 220(4.15),343(3.52) 214(4.32),300s(3.95) 320(3.86),363(3.57) 213(4.38),300s(4.0), 311(3.91),355(3.66)	73-2938-80 73-2938-80 73-2938-80 73-2938-80 73-2938-80
$C_{14}H_{16}N_4O_3$ 4H-Pyrimido[1,6-a]pyrimidine-3-carbox- ylic acid, 4-oxo-8-pyrrolidino-, ethyl ester	$CHCl_3$	254(3.88),339s(4.29), 368(4.44),384(4.36)	94-2148-80
$C_{14}H_{16}N_4O_4$ Pyrido[2,3-d]pyrimidine-6-carboxylic acid, 8-ethyl-5,8-dihydro-2-(2-hy- droxy-1-pyrrolidinyl)-5-oxo-	EtOH	218(4.09),275(4.67), 325(3.95)	94-2531-80
Pyrido[2,3-d]pyrimidine-6-carboxylic acid, 8-ethyl-5,8-dihydro-2-(3-hy- droxy-1-pyrrolidinyl)-5-oxo-	EtOH	219(4.11),280(4.70), 326(3.91)	94-2531-80
$C_{14}H_{16}N_4O_5$ Pyrido[2,3-d]pyrimidine-6-carboxylic acid, 2-[(3-carboxypropyl)amino]- 8-ethyl-5,8-dihydro-5-oxo-	EtOH	215(3.98),273(4.63), 324(3.84)	94-2531-80
α-D-Ribofuranuronic acid, 1-deoxy-2,3- O-(1-methylethylidene)-1-(7H-purin- 7-yl)-, methyl ester	MeOH	205(4.24),249s(--), 265(3.83),270s(--)	24-2891-80
α-D-Ribofuranuronic acid, 1-deoxy-2,3- O-(1-methylethylidene)-1-(9H-purin- 9-yl)-, methyl ester	MeOH	204(4.25),246s(--), 261(3.84)	24-2891-80
β-D-Ribofuranuronic acid, 1-deoxy-2,3- O-(1-methylethylidene)-1-(7H-purin- 7-yl)-, methyl ester	MeOH	206(4.20),250s(--), 265(3.83),271s(--)	24-2891-80
β-D-Ribofuranuronic acid, 1-deoxy-2,3- O-(1-methylethylidene)-1-(9H-purin- 9-yl)-, methyl ester	MeOH	205(4.24),247s(--), 263(3.84)	24-2891-80
$C_{14}H_{16}N_6O$ Pyrimido[5,4-e]-1,2,4-triazin-5(1H)- one, 7-amino-2,6-dihydro-1,2-di- methyl-3-(phenylmethyl)-	pH 1	278(4.21)	150-3630-80
$C_{14}H_{16}N_6O_3$ β-D-ribo-Hexofuranurononitrile, 1-(6- amino-9H-purin-9-yl)-1,5-dideoxy- 2,3-O-(1-methylethylidene)-	H_2O	258(4.18)	24-2530-80
$C_{14}H_{16}N_6O_4$ Benzeneacetic acid, 2-(2-amino-1,6-di- hydro-5-nitro-6-oxo-4-pyrimidinyl)- 1,2-dimethylhydrazide	pH 1 pH 13	217(4.33),250s(3.97), 272(3.84),362(3.53) 221(4.32),252(3.94), 372(3.52)	150-3630-80 150-3630-80

Compound	Solvent	$\lambda_{max}(\log \epsilon)$	Ref.
$C_{14}H_{16}O$			
1(2H)-Anthracenone, 3,4,5,6,7,8-hexa-hydro-	EtOH	262(4.14)	23-1344-80
Cyclohept[e]inden-1(2H)-one, 3,6,7,8,9,10-hexahydro-	EtOH	250(4.03)	23-1344-80
Cyclohept[e]inden-3(2H)-one, 1,6,7,8,9,10-hexahydro-	EtOH	260(4.05)	23-1344-80
Cyclohept[e]inden-6(7H)-one, 1,2,3,8,9,10-hexahydro-	EtOH	258(3.98)	23-1344-80
Cyclohept[e]inden-10(9H)-one, 1,2,3,6,7,8-hexahydro-	EtOH	252(3.86)	23-1344-80
Cyclohept[f]inden-1(2H)-one, 3,5,6,7,8,9-hexahydro-	EtOH	252(4.16)	23-1344-80
Cyclohept[f]inden-5(6H)-one, 1,2,3,7,8,9-hexahydro-	EtOH	259(4.10)	23-1344-80
2-Cyclohexen-1-one, 2,4-dimethyl-3-phenyl-	EtOH	258(4.05)	22-0267-80
2-Cyclohexen-1-one, 2,4-dimethyl-4-phenyl-	EtOH	234(4.12)	22-0267-80
2-Cyclohexen-1-one, 3,4-dimethyl-4-phenyl-	EtOH	233(4.20)	22-0267-80
2-Cyclohexen-1-one, 4-methyl-4-(3-meth-ylphenyl)-	EtOH	220(4.12)	22-0295-80
2-Naphthalenol, 4-isobutyl-	EtOH	324(3.30),335(3.37)	44-0240-80
4-Pentenal, 3,3-dimethyl-2-(phenyl-methylene)-, (Z)-	EtOH	274(4.00),345(2.53)	39-1477-80C
1(2H)-Phenanthrenone, 3,4,5,6,7,8-hexa-hydro-	EtOH	264(4.14)	23-1344-80
4(1H)-Phenanthrenone, 2,3,5,6,7,8-hexa-hydro-	EtOH	257(4.00)	23-1344-80
9(1H)-Phenanthrenone, 2,3,4,4a,10,10a-hexahydro-	EtOH	244(4.08),280(3.00)	33-0588-80
$C_{14}H_{16}OS$			
15-Oxa-16-thiatricyclo[10.2.1.1^{5,8}]-hexadeca-5,7,12,14-tetraene	C_6H_{12}	<u>225(4.1)</u>	138-0397-80
$C_{14}H_{16}OS_2$			
Dithieno[2,3-c:3',2'-e]oxepin, 4,6-di-hydro-4,4,6,6-tetramethyl-	heptane	218(4.39),231s(4.25), 238s(4.11),278(3.79), 294s(3.50)	4-0321-80
	MeCN	217(4.38),231s(4.28), 239s(4.12),272s(3.78), 279(--),295s(3.49)	4-0321-80
Dithieno[3,2-c:2',3'-e]oxepin, 4,6-di-hydro-4,4,6,6-tetramethyl-	heptane	211(3.91),245(3.72), 257(3.73),298s(4.02), 312(4.11),328s(3.90)	4-0321-80
	MeCN	213(3.88),247(3.74), 257(3.74),300s(4.05), 312(4.12),328s(3.94)	4-0321-80
4H,6H-Dithieno[3,4-c:3',4'-e]oxepin, 4,4,6,6-tetramethyl-	heptane	209(4.40),226s(4.05), 233s(3.94),265(4.06)	4-0321-80
	MeCN	208(4.41),226s(4.08), 233s(3.95),265(4.03)	4-0321-80
$C_{14}H_{16}OS_3$			
1-Propanethione, 2-(4-ethoxy-1,3-di-thiolan-2-ylidene)-1-phenyl-	MeOH	249(4.12),316(3.89), 425(4.27),590(2.40)	104-0395-80
$C_{14}H_{16}O_2$			
3H-Benz[e]inden-3-one, 1,2,6,7,8,9-hexahydro-5-methoxy-	EtOH	263(4.16),316(3.82)	78-2513-80

Compound	Solvent	$\lambda_{max}(\log \epsilon)$	Ref.
5,9(6H,10H)-Benzocyclooctenedione, 7,8-dihydro-7,7-dimethyl-	EtOH	253(3.92),295(3.33)	44-0240-80
5(6H)-Benzocyclooctenone, 9-ethoxy-7,8-dihydro-	EtOH	243(4.37),272(3.90), 336(3.63)	44-0240-80
Cyclobuta[a]naphthalen-8b(1H)-ol, 3-ethoxy-2,2a-dihydro-	EtOH	272(4.10),280s(4.05), 300s(3.54)	44-0240-80
2-Cyclohexen-1-one, 3-methoxy-5-methyl-5-phenyl-	EtOH	251(4.15)	104-1298-80
2,5-Methano-1-benzoxepin, 2,3,4,5-tetrahydro-7-methoxy-5-methyl-10-methylene-, (2R)-	n.s.g.	208(4.02),232(3.86), 298(3.57)	87-0096-80
2H-Pyran-2-one, 3,6-dihydro-4-methyl-6-(2-phenylethyl)-	EtOH	end absorption	94-1509-80

$C_{14}H_{16}O_3$

4a,8a-Ethanonaphthalen-9-one, 10-acetoxy-1,4,5,8-tetrahydro-	MeOH	310(1.70)	44-0177-80

$C_{14}H_{16}O_3S$

Ethanone, 1-[1-methyl-3-(phenylsulfonyl)-2-cyclopenten-1-yl]-	EtOH	242(4.00)	35-1602-80

$C_{14}H_{16}O_4$

1H-Cyclopenta[b]benzo[b]furan-1-one, 2,3,3a,8b-tetrahydro-3a,7-dimethoxy-8b-methyl-, cis	n.s.g.	225(3.72),315(3.47)	44-0501-80
1,3-Cyclopentanedione, 2-(2,5-dimethoxyphenyl)-2-methyl-	n.s.g.	227(3.58),295(3.43)	44-0501-80
Ethanone, 1,1'-(2,3-dihydro-5,5'-dimethyl[2,2'-bifuran]-4,4'-diyl)bis-	EtOH	208(4.08),275(3.97)	103-0678-80
1H-Indene-5-acetic acid, 2,3-dihydro-1-hydroxy-2,4,6-trimethyl-3-oxo-	EtOH	217(4.51),261(4.12), 307(3.36)	102-1743-80
1H-Indene-5-acetic acid, 2,3-dihydro-3-hydroxy-2,4,6-trimethyl-1-oxo-	MeOH	212(4.34),261(3.97), 305(3.20)	102-1743-80
1-Naphthalenepropanoic acid, 5,6,7,8-tetrahydro-4-methoxy-6-oxo-	EtOH	275(3.30),283(3.29)	78-2513-80
1(4H)-Naphthalenone, 2,4,4-trimethoxy-3-methyl-	MeOH	224(4.01),249(3.98), 287(3.74)	44-3422-80
1(4H)-Naphthalenone, 3,4,4-trimethoxy-2-methyl-	MeOH	230(4.11),248(3.99), 294(3.77),310s(3.67)	44-3422-80
2(1H)-Naphthalenone, 1,1,4-trimethoxy-3-methyl-	MeOH	232(4.27),325(3.86)	44-3422-80
2H-Pyran-2-one, 3-(1-cyclohexen-1-yl-acetyl)-4-hydroxy-6-methyl-	EtOH	313(4.46)	94-2460-80
Spiro[1,3-benzodioxole-2,1'-cyclohexan]-5-ol, acetate	EtOH	235(3.42),290(3.42)	12-0527-80
Spiro[cyclohexane-1,2'-[2H,5H]pyrano-[4,3-b]pyran-4',5'(3'H)-dione, 7'-methyl-	EtOH	310(4.24)	94-2460-80

$C_{14}H_{16}O_5$

5H-Indeno[1,2-c]-1,2-dioxin-5-one, 3,4,4a,9b-tetrahydro-9b-hydroxy-4-methoxy-3,3-dimethyl-	CHCl$_3$	245(4.10),282(3.20), 290(3.14),313(2.15)	49-0309-80

$C_{14}H_{16}O_6$

Bicyclo[2.2.2]octa-2,5-diene-2,3-di-carboxylic acid, 8-hydroxy-1,8-di-methyl-7-oxo-, dimethyl ester, (1α,4α,8R*)-	EtOH	225s(3.60),243(3.51), 305(2.58),312(2.58), 327s(2.40)	44-2189-80

Compound	Solvent	$\lambda_{max}(\log \epsilon)$	Ref.
Butanedioic acid, [(3,5-dimethoxyphen-yl)methylene]-, 1-methyl ester	CHCl$_3$	282(4.08)	12-2531-80
Cyclopropa[cd]pentalene-2a,4b-dicarb-oxylic acid, 2b,3,4,4a-tetrahydro-4-hydroxy-2b,4-dimethyl-3-oxo-, dimethyl ester, (2aα,2bα,4α,4aα,4bα)-	EtOH	245s(2.85),310s(1.60)	44-2189-80
1,2-Naphthalenedicarboxylic acid, 5,6,7,8-tetrahydro-3,5-dihydroxy-, dimethyl ester	EtOH	215(4.41),250(3.92), 320(3.70)	24-3249-80
Propanedioic acid, [(3,4-dimethoxyphen-yl)methylene]-, dimethyl ester	MeOH	241(4.04),302(4.11), 327(4.26)	35-3056-80
C$_{14}$H$_{16}$O$_6$S			
1,3-Cyclopentanedione, 2-[5-methoxy-2-[(methylsulfonyl)oxy]phenyl]-2-methyl-	n.s.g.	204(4.44),223(4.00), 283(3.36)	44-0501-80
C$_{14}$H$_{16}$O$_9$			
7-Oxabicyclo[2.2.1]hept-2-ene-2,3,5,6-tetracarboxylic acid, tetramethyl ester, (endo,endo)	EtOH	220(3.71)(end abs.)	33-1149-80
C$_{14}$H$_{16}$O$_9$P$_2$			
Diphosphoric acid, P.P'-bis(4-methoxy-phenyl) ester	pH 7	274(3.43)	94-1626-80
C$_{14}$H$_{16}$S			
Azulene, 4,6-dimethyl-8-[(methylthio)-methyl]-	hexane	245(4.42),290(4.73), 332s(3.48),337(3.54), 349s(3.61),352(3.64), 363s(3.02),550(2.69), 563(2.69),587(2.66), 610s(2.66),640(2.28)	89-0621-80
C$_{14}$H$_{16}$S$_2$			
15,16-Dithiatricyclo[10.2.1.1^{5,8}]hexa-deca-5,7,12,14-tetraene	n.s.g.	<u>220(4.1),250s(4.1)</u>	138-0397-80
C$_{14}$H$_{16}$S$_4$			
1,3-Benzodithiole, 4,5,6,7-tetrahydro-2-(4,5,6,7-tetrahydro-1,3-benzodi-thiol-2-ylidene)-	MeCN	297(4.03),323s(3.98), 472(2.29)	11-0196-80A
C$_{14}$H$_{16}$Si			
Silane, dimethyldiphenyl-	C$_6$H$_{12}$	212s(4.29),<u>260f(2.8)</u>	65-1615-80
C$_{14}$H$_{17}$BrN$_2$OS			
2-Propenamide, 3-(4-bromophenyl)-N-[(butylamino)thioxomethyl]-	dioxan	305(4.43)	73-2334-80
C$_{14}$H$_{17}$ClN$_2$OS			
2-Propenamide, N-[(butylamino)thioxo-methyl]-3-(4-chlorophenyl)-	dioxan	302(4.41)	73-2334-80
C$_{14}$H$_{17}$I$_2$N$_3$			
1,3-Propanediamine, N'-(7,8-diiodo-4-quinolinyl)-N,N-dimethyl-	hexane	243(4.45),261(4.26), 336(4.05)	103-0754-80
C$_{14}$H$_{17}$N			
Bicyclo[3.2.1]oct-3-en-2-amine, 3-phenyl-, hydrochloride, exo	EtOH	244(4.05)	23-1847-80

Compound	Solvent	$\lambda_{max}(\log \epsilon)$	Ref.
2-Naphthalenemethanamine, N,N,3-tri-methyl-	EtOH	227(5.06),270s(3.63), 277(3.66),288s(3.49), 303s(2.79),311(2.92), 318(2.80),325(3.03)	39-1477-80C
$C_{14}H_{17}NO$			
1H-Carbazole-1-ethanol, 2,3,4,9-tetra-hydro-	EtOH	228(4.40),275s(3.72), 280(3.76),292s(3.70)	39-0097-80C
1H-Carbazol-1-ol, 9-ethyl-2,3,4,9-tetrahydro-	ether	230(4.44),287(3.77)	78-1585-80
2-Cyclohexen-1-one, 2-(ethylphenyl-amino)-	ether	216(2.97),241(3.03), 280(2.35)	78-1585-80
Pyrano[4,3-b]indole, 1,3,4,5-tetra-hydro-1,1,5-trimethyl-	EtOH	217(4.40),286(3.86), 292(3.85)	39-1688-80C
$C_{14}H_{17}NO_2$			
2(1H)-Naphthalenone, 1-[(dimethylami-no)methylene]-3,4-dihydro-8-methoxy-	MeOH	215(4.21),278(3.99), 351(4.17)	118-0236-80
Pyrano[3,4-b]indole-1-ethanol, 1,3,4,9-tetrahydro-1-methyl-	EtOH	225(4.30),282(3.66), 290s(3.61)	39-2870-80C
$C_{14}H_{17}NO_3$			
1H-Carbazole-1-ethanol, 2,3,4,4a-tetrahydro-4a-hydroperoxy-	n.s.g.	219(4.42),250s(3.74)	39-0097-80C
Cyclopent[e]-1,3-oxazin-2(3H)-one, hexahydro-4-(2-hydroxyphenyl)-3-methyl-	EtOH	217(3.86),277(3.42)	4-0277-80
$C_{14}H_{17}NO_3S$			
Sulfonium, dimethyl-, 2-oxo-1-[[(phen-ylacetyl)amino]carbonyl]propylide	EtOH	273(4.18)	94-0795-80
$C_{14}H_{17}NO_5$			
4H-1-Benzopyran-4-one, 2-(1-ethoxy-1-methylethyl)-2,3-dihydro-3-nitro-	EtOH	213(3.78),256(3.50), 328(3.11),388(2.84)	39-2049-80C
1-Benzoxepin-5(2H)-one, 2-(1,1-dimeth-ylethoxy)-3,4-dihydro-4-nitro-	EtOH	251(3.89),305(3.42), 360(3.63)	39-2049-80C
3,5-Pyridinedicarboxylic acid, 1,4-di-hydro-4-oxo-1-(2-propenyl)-, diethyl ester	EtOH	256(4.04),262(4.03), 308(3.77)	4-0359-80
$C_{14}H_{17}N_2$			
3H-Indolium, 1-methyl-3-(1-pyrrolidin-ylmethylene)-, iodide	MeOH	249s(4.12),258(4.18), 268s(3.97),276(3.92), 348(4.36)	94-1711-80
Quinolizinium, 2-piperidino-, bromide	MeOH	242(4.36),324(4.32)	142-0213-80B
$C_{14}H_{17}N_2O_2S$			
Pyridinium, 4-(dimethylamino)-1-[(4-methylphenyl)sulfonyl]-, chloride	H_2O	303(4.41)	77-0993-80
$C_{14}H_{17}N_2O_3$			
2-Furanmethanaminium, N,N,N-trimethyl-5-(2-nitrophenyl)-, bromide	MeOH	255(4.36)	73-1715-80
2-Furanmethanaminium, N,N,N-trimethyl-5-(3-nitrophenyl)-, bromide	MeOH	272(4.50),283(4.50)	73-1715-80
2-Furanmethanaminium, N,N,N-trimethyl-5-(4-nitrophenyl)-, bromide	MeOH	336(4.34)	73-1715-80
$C_{14}H_{17}N_3$			
3,5-Pyridinedicarbonitrile, 1,4-di-	MeOH	223(4.43),347(3.85)	73-3370-80

Compound	Solvent	$\lambda_{max}(\log \epsilon)$	Ref.
hydro-2,4,4,6-tetramethyl-1-(2-propenyl)- (cont.)			73-3370-80
$C_{14}H_{17}N_3OS$			
4-Imidazolidinone, 1-butyl-5-imino-3-(phenylmethyl)-2-thioxo-	EtOH	314(4.17)	18-0442-80
4-Imidazolidinone, 3-butyl-5-imino-1-(phenylmethyl)-2-thioxo-	EtOH	310(4.18)	18-0442-80
$C_{14}H_{17}N_3O_2$			
1,3-Dioxolo[4,5-g]quinazolin-8-amine, N-butyl-6-methyl-	EtOH	212(4.40),224s(4.22), 246(4.42),281(3.78), 292(3.77),326(4.02), 340(3.98)	114-0253-80B
$C_{14}H_{17}N_3O_2S$			
5H-Pyrimido[4,5-b][1,4]benzothiazin-9(6H)-one, 7,8-dihydro-4-methoxy-5,7,7-trimethyl-	EtOH	224(4.33),255(4.11), 323(4.01),425(3.30)	103-0580-80
Thiourea, N-[7-(dimethylamino)-4-methyl-2-oxo-2H-1-benzopyran-3-yl]-N'-methyl-	EtOH	244(4.43),379(4.41)	95-0289-80
$C_{14}H_{17}N_3O_3$			
2-Propenoic acid, 2-cyano-3-[5-(4-methyl-1-piperazinyl)-2-furanyl]-, methyl ester	MeOH	211(3.92),229(4.57), 465(4.93)	73-1831-80
2-Pyridinamine, 6-[(4-hydroxy-3,5-dimethoxyphenyl)methylamino]-	pH 2	238(4.11),280s(3.08), 338(4.24)	87-0384-80
	pH 8.6	235s(4.08),281s(3.42), 311(3.96)	87-0384-80
	pH 13	248(4.21),310(4.00)	87-0384-80
2,4-Pyridinediamine, 3-[(4-hydroxy-3,5-dimethoxyphenyl)methyl]-	pH 1	219s(4.61),272(3.98)	87-0384-80
	pH 13	240s(4.16),278(3.83)	87-0384-80
2,4-Pyridinediamine, 5-[(4-hydroxy-3,5-dimethoxyphenyl)methyl]-	pH 2	220(4.72),263(4.00)	87-0384-80
2-Quinoxalinecarboxylic acid, 5-methoxy-6,7-dimethyl-3-(methylamino)-, methyl ester	MeOH	225(4.45),263(4.54), 336(3.81),431(3.67)	54-0115-80
$C_{14}H_{17}N_3O_3S$			
2-Propenamide, N-[(butylamino)thioxomethyl]-3-(4-nitrophenyl)-	dioxan	314(4.38)	73-2334-80
$C_{14}H_{17}N_3O_5$			
L-Leucine, N-(5-benzofurazanylcarbonyl)-, methyl ester, N-oxide	EtOH	223(4.40),265s(3.54), 315s(3.36),334s(3.48), 366(3.79)	4-0213-80
	MeCN	222(4.39),265s(3.34), 315s(3.38),332s(3.49), 365(3.82)	4-0213-80
$C_{14}H_{17}N_4OS$			
Thiazolium, 5-(2-hydroxyethyl)-4-methyl-3-[(5-methylimidazo[1,2-c]pyrimidin-8-yl)methyl]-, chloride	n.s.g.	260(3.81),295s(3.43)	69-3773-80
$C_{14}H_{17}N_5O_2$			
Pyridazino[4,5-b]quinolin-1(2H)-one, 4-hydroxy-2,10-dimethyl-, monomethylhydrazinium salt	EtOH	214(4.39),249(4.71), 293(3.98)	94-3457-80

Compound	Solvent	$\lambda_{max}(\log \epsilon)$	Ref.
$C_{14}H_{17}N_5O_3$			
8,5'-Cycloadenosine, 5'-deoxy-5'-methyl-2',3'-O-(1-methylethylidene-, (S)-	H_2O	264(4.20)	94-0876-80
$C_{14}H_{17}N_5O_5$			
9H-Imidazo[1,2-a]purin-9-one, 3,4-dihydro-4,6-dimethyl-3-β-D-ribofuranosyl-	pH 2	230(4.55),277(4.07)	77-1158-80
	pH 7	236(4.54),296(3.90)	77-1158-80
	pH 13	236(4.55),295(3.91)	77-1158-80
	EtOH	235(4.52),293(3.91)	77-1158-80
Imidazo[1,2-a]pyrido[2,3-d]pyrimidine-7-carboxylic acid, 9-ethyl-1,2,3,5-6,9-hexahydro-1-methyl-5-(nitromethyl)-6-oxo-	EtOH	244(4.25),274(4.34), 316(4.04)	95-1187-80
$C_{14}H_{17}N_5O_6$			
9H-Purin-6-amine, 9-(3,5-di-O-acetyl-β-D-xylofuranosyl)-	EtOH	260(4.16)	39-0563-80C
$C_{14}H_{17}N_5O_7$			
Guanosine, N-acetyl-, 5'-acetate	EtOH	257(4.08),279(3.93)	39-0563-80C
$C_{14}H_{18}$			
Cyclopropane, 1,1,2,2-tetramethyl-3-(5-methyl-5-hexene-1,3-diynyl)-	hexane	216(4.63),219(4.62), 243(3.73),256(3.93), 271(4.05),287(3.92)	35-5406-80
Spiro[cyclopropane-1,1'(2'H)-naphthalene], 7'-ethyl-3',4'-dihydro-	hexane	268s(2.83),274(3.01), 283(2.52)	18-0709-80
$C_{14}H_{18}D_5NS_2$			
2-Propanesulfenamide, N-[(1,1-dimethylethyl)thio]-2-methyl-N-(phenyl-d_5)-	hexane	252(4.05)	18-0720-80
$C_{14}H_{18}IN_3$			
1,3-Propanediamine, N-(7-iodo-4-quinolinyl)-N',N'-dimethyl-	hexane	228(4.47),263(4.28), 329(3.85)	103-0754-80
$C_{14}H_{18}NO_2S$			
Thiazolium, 5-(2-hydroxyethyl)-2-(hydroxyphenylmethyl)-3,4-dimethyl-, iodide	buffer	267(4.00)	18-2340-80
$C_{14}H_{18}N_2$			
Azepino[3,4-b]indole, 1,2,3,4,5,10-hexahydro-2,10-dimethyl-	EtOH	226(4.34),295(4.12)	39-1512-80C
4,4'-Bipyridinium, 1-methyl-1'-propyl-, diiodide	H_2O	255(4.36)	98-1026-80
4,4'-Bipyridinium, 1,1'-diethyl-, diiodide	H_2O	254(4.12)	98-1026-80
1,8-Naphthalenediamine, N,N,N',N'-tetramethyl-	$CHCl_3$	341(4.09)	104-1890-80
$C_{14}H_{18}N_2OS$			
2-Propenamide, N-[(butylamino)thioxomethyl]-3-phenyl-	dioxan	298(4.43)	73-2334-80
$C_{14}H_{18}N_2O_4S$			
Glycine, N-[[(4-ethoxybenzoyl)amino]thioxomethyl]-, ethyl ester	$CHCl_3$	255(4.31)	73-2334-80
$C_{14}H_{18}N_2O_5$			
Cyclobutanecarboxamide, N-[2-hydroxy-	pH 7	279(4.00)	87-1299-80

Compound	Solvent	$\lambda_{max}(\log \epsilon)$	Ref.
1-(hydroxymethyl)-2-(4-nitrophenyl)-ethyl]-, [R-(R*,R*)] (cont.)			87-1299-80
$C_{14}H_{18}N_2O_7$ 3,6,9,16-Tetraoxa-12,13-diazabicyclo-[9.3.3]heptadeca-12,14-diene-2,10-dione, 11-acetyl-14-methyl-	MeCN	236(3.62),294(4.05)	44-2854-80
$C_{14}H_{18}N_4$ 2,2a,4,5-Tetraazabenz[cd]azulene, 3,3-diethyl-3,4-dihydro-1-methyl-	MeOH	223(4.46),295(3.70), 356(3.98)	118-0331-80
1H-1,2,3-Triazol-5-amine, 1-cyclohexyl-N-phenyl-	EtOH	207(4.13),238(3.89), 264(4.09)	49-0635-80
$C_{14}H_{18}N_4O$ 2,4-Pyrimidinediamine, 5-[(4-methoxy-3,5-dimethylphenyl)methyl]-	pH 2 pH 12	220s(4.49),271(3.73) 240s(4.02),286(3.87)	87-0535-80 87-0535-80
$C_{14}H_{18}N_4OS$ 5H-Pyrimido[4,5-b][1,4]benzothiazin-9(6H)-one, 4-(dimethylamino)-7,8-dihydro-7,7-dimethyl-	EtOH	224(4.26),261(4.01), 298(4.04),348(4.06)	103-0580-80
$C_{14}H_{18}N_4O_2$ Hydrazinecarboxamide, 2-[2-(2-ethyl-2,3-dihydro-3-oxo-1H-isoindol-1-yl)-1-methylethylidene]-	EtOH	229(4.27),279(3.20)	39-2077-80C
2-Quinoxalinecarboxamide, 5-methoxy-N,6,7-trimethyl-3-(methylamino)-	MeOH	224(4.50),261(4.52), 329(3.75),419(3.76)	54-0115-80
$C_{14}H_{18}N_4O_4$ Imidazo[1,2-a]pyrido[2,3-d]pyrimidine-7-carboxylic acid, 9-ethyl-1,2,3,5,8-9-hexahydro-5-methoxy-1-methyl-6-oxo-	EtOH	247(4.34),271(4.50), 296(4.20)	95-1187-80
2,4(1H,3H)-Pyrimidinedione, 1-[3-(3,6-dihydro-5-methyl-2,6-dioxo-1(2H)-pyrimidinyl)propyl]-6-ethyl-	pH 2 pH 7 pH 12	236(3.58),269(4.24) 236(3.59),268(4.24) 246(3.66),273(4.10)	56-2357-80 56-2357-80 56-2357-80
2,4(1H,3H)-Pyrimidinedione, 1-[3-(5-ethyl-3,6-dihydro-2,6-dioxo-1(2H)-pyrimidinyl)propyl]-5-methyl-	pH 2 pH 7 pH 12	238(3.65),269(4.19) 237(3.60),269(4.18) 248(3.74),278(4.12)	56-2357-80 56-2357-80 56-2357-80
2,4(1H,3H)-Pyrimidinedione, 1-[3-(5-ethyl-3,6-dihydro-2,6-dioxo-1(2H)-pyrimidinyl)propyl]-6-methyl-	pH 2 pH 7 pH 12	236(3.66),268(4.26) 235(3.50),267(4.24) 246(3.78),271(4.13)	56-2357-80 56-2357-80 56-2357-80
$C_{14}H_{18}N_4O_6S$ Acetic acid, [(9-β-D-ribofuranosyl-9H-purin-6-yl)thio]-, ethyl ester	H_2O	227(3.93),280(4.11), 287s(4.07)	94-0157-80
$C_{14}H_{18}N_4O_7$ 3H-Imidazo[4,5-b]pyridine-6-carboxylic acid, 4,5-dihydro-7-(methylamino)-5-oxo-3-β-D-ribofuranosyl-, methyl ester	H_2O	243(4.46),288s(4.03), 297(4.05)	142-1049-80B
$C_{14}H_{18}N_6O_4$ 9H-Purine, 6-(4,5-dihydro-2-methyl-1H-imidazol-1-yl)-9-β-D-ribofuranosyl-	H_2O	211(4.35),268(4.33)	87-0781-80
$C_{14}H_{18}O$ 3-Cyclopenten-1-ol, 1,2,2-trimethyl-3-phenyl-	pentane	243(3.91)	33-0154-80

Compound	Solvent	$\lambda_{max}(\log \epsilon)$	Ref.
4-Hexen-1-one, 4,5-dimethyl-1-phenyl-	pentane	238(4.14),279(2.91), 287(2.73)	33-0154-80
2(4aH)-Naphthalenone, 5,6,7,8-tetra-hydro-4a-methyl-7-(1-methylethenyl)-	EtOH	241(4.26)	44-3790-80
1-Pentanone, 1-(2-ethenylphenyl)-4-methyl-	EtOH	249s(4.00),298(3.19)	44-0240-80
3-Penten-1-one, 2,2,4-trimethyl-1-phenyl-	C_6H_{12}	239(4.02),325(2.08)	39-0592-80B
$C_{14}H_{18}O_2$			
4H-1,4-Epoxy-4a,8-methanobenzocyclo-octen-10(5H)-one, 1,6,7,8,9,10a-hexahydro-10a-methyl-	EtOH	289(1.48)	44-3545-80
1H-Inden-1-one, 2,3-dihydro-5-(2-hy-droxyethyl)-2,4,6-trimethyl-	MeOH	215(4.50),263(4.21), 307(3.55)	102-1743-80
2-Naphthalenecarboxylic acid, 3,4,4a-5,6,8a-hexahydro-8a-methyl-5-methyl-ene-, methyl ester, trans-(±)-	EtOH	222(3.79)	44-0367-80
2(1H)-Naphthalenone, 7-ethynyl-4a,5,6,7,8,8a-hexahydro-1-hydroxy-1,4a-dimethyl-	MeOH	228(3.87)	18-1039-80
$C_{14}H_{18}O_2S_2$			
3(2H)-Thiophenone, 2,2'-ethanediyli-denebis[dihydro-4,4-dimethyl-	CHCl₃	456(4.33)	24-1708-80
$C_{14}H_{18}O_3$			
2,4,6,8-Decatetraenoic acid, 3,7-di-methyl-10-oxo-, ethyl ester, (all-E)-	hexane	224(3.30),239(3.51), 357(3.48)	33-0716-80
1H-Indene-1,5(6H)-dione, 2,3,7,7a-tetrahydro-7a-methyl-4-(3-oxobutyl)-	EtOH	251(4.16)	150-1801-80
Isopterosin C	MeOH	215(4.53),263(4.20), 302(3.39)	102-1743-80
1-Naphthalenepropanoic acid, 5,6,7,8-tetrahydro-4-methoxy-	EtOH	274(3.23)	78-2513-80
4a(2H)-Naphthalenepropanoic acid, 3,4,5,6-tetrahydro-2-oxo-, methyl ester	MeOH	279(4.29)	44-0570-80
Naphtho[2,3-b]furan-2,6(3H,4H)-dione, 3a,7,8,8a,9,9a-hexahydro-5,8a-di-methyl-, (3aα,8aβ,9aα)-(±)-	EtOH	243(4.01)	44-3278-80
Spiro[4.5]deca-2,6-diene-2-carboxylic acid, 6,10-dimethyl-8-oxo-, methyl ester, cis-(±)-	EtOH	235(4.24)	23-2460-80
Spiro[4.5]deca-3,6-diene-2-carboxylic acid, 6,10-dimethyl-8-oxo-, methyl ester	EtOH	237(4.20)	23-2460-80
$C_{14}H_{18}O_4$			
Benzeneacetic acid, α-acetyl-4-methoxy-α-methyl-, ethyl ester	EtOH	230(3.96),274(3.23), 280(3.18)	12-0113-80
1,3-Benzodioxol-5-ol, 2-butyl-2-meth-yl-, acetate	EtOH	236(3.46),287(3.61)	12-0527-80
Bicyclo[2.2.2]octa-2,5-diene-2,3-di-carboxylic acid, mono(1,1-dimethyl-ethyl) ester	EtOH	213(3.84),228s(3.73), 240s(3.46)	24-0531-80
1H-Cyclopenta[b]benzo[b]furan-1-ol, 2,3,3a,8b-tetrahydro-3a,7-dimethoxy-8b-methyl-, (1α,3aβ,8bβ)-	n.s.g.	298(3.58)	44-0501-80
Ethanone, 1-[2,6-dihydroxy-4-methoxy-3-(3-methyl-2-butenyl)phenyl]-	MeOH	290(3.91),325(3.12)	42-1238-80

Compound	Solvent	$\lambda_{max}(\log \epsilon)$	Ref.
Spiro[1,3-benzodioxole-2,1'-cyclohexane], 5,6-dimethoxy-	EtOH	236(3.68),306(3.85)	12-0527-80
$C_{14}H_{18}O_5$			
Hexanoic acid, 2-acetoxy-, 2-hydroxyphenyl ester	EtOH	214(4.03),277(3.71)	12-1553-80
Setulosopterosin	MeOH	214(4.49),259(4.06), 305(3.27)	102-1743-80
$C_{14}H_{18}O_6$			
Bicyclo[2.2.2]oct-2-ene-2,3-dicarboxylic acid, 5-hydroxy-1,5-dimethyl-6-oxo-, dimethyl ester	EtOH	245(3.53),307(2.71), 313(2.70),327s(2.50)	44-2189-80
Bicyclo[2.2.2]oct-5-ene-2,3-dicarboxylic acid, 8-hydroxy-1,8-dimethyl-7-oxo-, dimethyl ester	EtOH	309(2.00)	44-2189-80
1,7-Dioxacyclotetradec-3-ene-2,8,11,12-tetrone, 6,14-dimethyl-	EtOH	426(1.20)	88-0681-80
Propanedioic acid, [(3,4-dimethoxyphenyl)methyl]-, dimethyl ester	MeOH	230(3.85),280(3.31), 285s(--)	35-3056-80
Propanoic acid, 2-methoxy-, 1,4-phenylene ester, [S-(R*,R*)]-	MeCN	200(3.94),215(3.82), 262(2.76),268(2.70)	108-0142-80
$C_{14}H_{18}O_7$			
β-D-Glucopyranoside, 2-(4-hydroxyphenyl)ethenyl	MeOH	257(4.17),288s(3.47), 299s(3.33)	102-0471-80
2-Propenoic acid, 3,3'-(2,5-dihydro-2,5-dihydroxy-3,4-furandiyl)bis-, diethyl ester	ether	275s(4.13),288(4.40), 301(4.53),314(4.41)	118-0950-80
$C_{14}H_{18}O_9$			
7-Oxabicyclo[2.2.1]heptane-2,3,5,6-tetracarboxylic acid, all-endo	EtOH	220(2.38)(end abs.)	33-1149-80
exo,endo,endo,endo	EtOH	210(2.45)(end abs.)	33-1149-80
exo,endo,exo,endo	EtOH	230(2.40)(end abs.)	33-1149-80
$C_{14}H_{18}SSi$			
1,4-Pentadiene-1-thione, 3-phenyl-2-(trimethylsilyl)-	isooctane	208(4.5),260s(c.3.3), 497(1.4)	24-3024-80
$C_{14}H_{19}BrN_2O$			
Benzenamine, 4-bromo-N-(tetrahydro-3,4,4,6-tetramethyl-2H-1,3-oxazin-2-ylidene)-	heptane	200(4.23),208s(4.18), 267(4.25)	110-0172-80
4H-1,3-Oxazin-2-amine, N-(4-bromophenyl)-5,6-dihydro-N,4,4,6-tetramethyl-	heptane	208s(4.38),220s(3.52), 265(4.39)	110-0172-80
$C_{14}H_{19}BrN_5O_6P$			
Adenosine, 8-bromo-N-butyl-, cyclic 3',5'-(hydrogen phosphate)	pH 1	293(4.31)	87-0242-80
	pH 11	296(4.22)	87-0242-80
$C_{14}H_{19}ClN_2O$			
Benzenamine, 3-chloro-N-(tetrahydro-3,4,4,6-tetramethyl-2H-1,3-oxazin-2-ylidene)-	heptane	206(4.36),217(4.31), 263(4.23)	110-0172-80
4H-1,3-Oxazin-2-amine, N-(3-chlorophenyl)-5,6-dihydro-N,4,4,6-tetramethyl-	heptane	212s(4.28),261(4.15), 294s(3.17)	110-0172-80
$C_{14}H_{19}IN_4O_3$			
Pyrimidinium, 2,4-diamino-5-[(4-hy-	pH 1	222(4.55),273(3.79)	87-0379-80

Compound	Solvent	$\lambda_{max}(\log \epsilon)$	Ref.
droxy-3,5-dimethoxyphenyl)methyl]- 1-methyl-, iodide (cont.)	pH 12	274s(3.94)	87-0379-80
$C_{14}H_{19}N$ 1H-Indole, 1-butyl-2,3-dimethyl-	EtOH	234(3.61),287(3.05), 295s(3.02)	104-0766-80
$C_{14}H_{19}NO$ 1,3,6,8,10-Dodecapentaen-5-one, 1-(di- methylamino)-, (all-E)-	EtOH	462(4.80)	70-0980-80
Ethanone, 1-(2-methylphenyl)-2-(1-meth- yl-2-pyrrolidinyl)-, hydrochloride	EtOH	245(4.00)	48-0475-80 +115-0265-80
Ethanone, 1-(4-methylphenyl)-2-(1-meth- yl-2-pyrrolidinyl)-, nitrate	EtOH	253(4.22)	48-0475-80
1-Penten-3-one, 4,4-dimethyl-1-(methyl- phenylamino)-	EtOH	230(4.15),325(4.63)	4-0507-80
2-Propen-1-one, 3-(diethylamino)-2- methyl-1-phenyl-	EtOH	233(3.78),313(4.16)	4-1201-80
$C_{14}H_{19}NO_2$ Ethanone, 1-(2-methoxyphenyl)-2-(1- methyl-2-pyrrolidinyl)-, nitrate	EtOH	246(4.07)	48-0475-80 +115-0265-80
Ethanone, 1-(4-methoxyphenyl)-2-(1- methyl-2-pyrrolidinyl)-, nitrate	EtOH	275(4.20)	48-0475-80 +115-0265-80
$C_{14}H_{19}NO_3$ Carbamic acid, methyl(2-oxo-2-phenyl- ethyl)-, 1,1-dimethylethyl ester	EtOH	241(4.10),278(3.08)	33-1915-80
2H-Furo[4,3,2-ij]isoquinoline, 6,7,8,8a-tetrahydro-3,5-di- methoxy-2,8-dimethyl-	EtOH	232(3.94),283(3.38), 305(3.06),385(2.19)	39-0072-80C
	EtOH-HCl	230(4.10),304(3.92), 390(3.24)	39-0072-80C
	EtOH-NaOH	232(4.00),283(3.40)	39-0072-80C
1-Piperidinepropanoic acid, α-(2-fur- anylmethylene)-, methyl ester, (E)-	EtOH	299(4.35)	73-0906-80
3-Pyridinecarboxylic acid, 5-cyclohex- yl-1,4-dihydro-4-oxo-, ethyl ester	EtOH	260(3.64)	4-0359-80
3-Pyridinecarboxylic acid, 5-cyclohex- yl-1-ethyl-1,4-dihydro-4-oxo-	EtOH	262(4.03),289(3.71)	4-0359-80
$C_{14}H_{19}NO_4$ 1,3-Benzodioxole-5-carboxylic acid, 6-[2-(dimethylamino)ethyl]-, ethyl ester	EtOH	218(4.45),262(3.87), 298(3.78)	88-1693-80
2H-[1,3]Oxazin-2-one, tetrahydro-5-(1- hydroxyethyl)-4-(2-hydroxyphenyl)- 3,6-dimethyl-	EtOH	277(3.45)	4-0277-80
$C_{14}H_{19}NO_6$ 1H-Pyrrole-2,3,4-tricarboxylic acid, 1-butyl-, trimethyl ester	MeOH	263(4.02),268s(4.01)	44-457 3-80
3,6,9,13-Tetraoxa-16-azabicyclo[9.3.3]- heptadeca-1(15),11(17)-diene-2,10- dione, 15,17-dimethyl-	MeCN	282(4.19)	44-2854-80
$C_{14}H_{19}NO_8$ Thalictoside	H_2O	218(3.88),270(3.03)	88-0759-80
$C_{14}H_{19}N_2S$ Cyclopropenylium, bis(dimethylamino)- [4-(methylthio)phenyl]-, chloride	EtOH	314(4.3)	5-1409-80

Compound	Solvent	$\lambda_{max}(\log \epsilon)$	Ref.
$C_{14}H_{19}N_3O_6$ 4-Pyridinecarboxylic acid, 1,2,3,6-tetrahydro-5-nitroso-2,6-dioxo-3-[(1-oxooctyl)amino]-	EtOH	265(3.98)	39-1788-80C
$C_{14}H_{19}N_3O_7$ Uridine, 5-(aminomethyl)-2'-deoxy-, 3',5'-diacetate	pH 2 pH 12	264(4.02) 245(3.75)	87-0127-80 87-0127-80
$C_{14}H_{19}N_5O_5$ β-D-ribo-Hexofuranuronic acid, 1-(6-amino-9H-purin-9-yl)-1,5-dideoxy-, 1-methylethyl ester	H_2O	258(4.25)	24-2530-80
$C_{14}H_{19}N_5O_5S_2$ Pyrazolo[3,4-d]pyrimidine-3-carboximidic acid, 4,6-bis(methylthio)-1-β-D-ribofuranosyl-, methyl ester	EtOH	206(4.05),251(4.20), 292(4.03)	103-0182-80
$C_{14}H_{19}N_5O_6S$ 1H-Pyrazolo[3,4-d]pyrimidine-3-carboximidic acid, 4-methoxy-6-(methylthio)-1-β-D-ribofuranosyl-, methyl ester	EtOH	200(4.09),246(4.39), 281(3.94)	103-0182-80
$(C_{14}H_{19}N_7O_2)_n$ Poly[imino[1-[4-[[3-(6-amino-9H-purin-9-yl)-1-oxopropyl]amino]butyl]-2-oxo-1,2-ethanediyl]], (S)-	aq HCl DMSO	261.0(4.11) 266.0(4.09)	47-0949-80 47-0949-80
$C_{14}H_{20}$ Benzene, 1-ethyl-4-(4-methyl-4-pentenyl)-	hexane	255s(2.26),260(2.49), 266(2.62),268(2.60), 274(2.68)	18-0709-80
Cyclobuta[b]naphthalene, 1,2,2a,3a,4-5,6,7-octahydro-7,7-dimethyl-	hexane	212s(4.08)	18-0709-80
$C_{14}H_{20}F_2O_5$ β-D-arabino-Oct-1-en-4-ulopyranose, 1,2,3-trideoxy-1,1-difluoro-4,5:6,7-bis-O-(1-methylethylidene)-	EtOH	205(2.30),248(1.90), 271(2.00)	33-1644-80
$C_{14}H_{20}N$ 1H-Isoindolium, 2-(1,1-dimethylethyl)-3-ethyl-, tetrafluoroborate	MeOH-HClO$_4$	216(3.96),223(3.82), 272(4.15)	89-0320-80
$C_{14}H_{20}NOS$ Sulfonium, dimethyl[2-(4-morpholinyl)-1-phenylethenyl]-, (E)-, fluorosulfate	MeCN	254(3.7)	118-0466-80
$C_{14}H_{20}N_2$ Benzenamine, N,N-dimethyl-4-[3-[(1-methylethyl)imino]-1-propenyl]-	pH 7.24 12M HCl MeCN MeCN-HCl	454(4.65) 312(4.47) 348(4.42) 458(4.67)	35-3062-80 35-3062-80 35-3062-80 35-3062-80
$C_{14}H_{20}N_2O$ Benzenamine, 3-methyl-N-(tetrahydro-4,4,6-trimethyl-2H-1,3-oxazin-2-ylidene)-	heptane	208(4.40),250(4.30), 284s(3.26),290s(3.18)	110-0172-80

Compound	Solvent	$\lambda_{max}(\log \epsilon)$	Ref.
Benzenamine, 4-methyl-N-(tetrahydro-4,4,6-trimethyl-2H-1,3-oxazin-2-ylidene)-	heptane	204(4.41),250(4.37), 281s(3.18),287(3.22), 296s(3.08)	110-0172-80
Benzenamine, N-(tetrahydro-3,4,4,6-tetramethyl-2H-1,3-oxazin-2-ylidene)-	heptane	208s(4.30),257(4.19)	110-0172-80
4H-1,3-Oxazin-2-amine, 5,6-dihydro-N,4,4,6-tetramethyl-N-phenyl-	heptane	200(4.21),256(4.06)	110-0172-80
$C_{14}H_{20}N_2O_2S_2$			
Piperidine, 1,1'-(2,3-dioxo-1,4-dithioxo-1,4-butanediyl)bis-	EtOH	238(4.22),267(4.18), 327(3.88),385s(3.34), 447(3.30)	97-0436-80
$C_{14}H_{20}N_2O_3$			
3-Pyridinecarboxamide, 1-(2-acetoxycyclohexyl)-1,4-dihydro-, (1S-trans)-	EtOH	348(3.84)	23-0387-80
$C_{14}H_{20}N_2O_6$			
4,8-Cycloheptimidazolediol, 2,4,5,6,7-8-hexahydro-2,2-dimethyl-, diacetate, 1,3-dioxide	EtOH	228(4.02),355(3.90)	103-0628-80
1H-Imidazole-4-carboxylic acid, 1-[2,3-O-(1-methylethylidene)-α-D-ribofuranosyl]-, ethyl ester	pH 2	221(4.05)	65-1723-80
	pH 6-7	235(4.04)	65-1723-80
	pH 12	235(4.04)	65-1723-80
β-	pH 2	221(4.05)	65-1723-80
	pH 6-7	234(4.03)	65-1723-80
	pH 12	234(4.03)	65-1723-80
1H-Pyrazole-5-carboxylic acid, 1-methyl-4-(tetrahydro-6-methoxy-2,2-dimethylfuro[2,3-d]-1,3-dioxol-5-yl)-, methyl ester, [3aR-(3aα,5α,6α,6aα)]-	EtOH	232(3.58),250(3.51)	33-1181-80
$C_{14}H_{20}N_2O_8S$			
Uridine, 5-methyl-2',3'-O-(1-methylethylidene)-, 5'-methanesulfonate	EtOH	263(3.92)	33-2179-80
$C_{14}H_{20}N_2S_4$			
Methanamine, N,N'-[dithiobis(carbonothioyl-2-cyclopentyl-1-ylidene)]bis-	$CHCl_3$	312(3.92),407(4.47)	118-0566-80
$C_{14}H_{20}N_3$			
Methanaminium, N-[5-(dimethylamino)-3-(4-pyridinyl)-2,4-pentadienylidene]-N-methyl-, perchlorate	EtOH	418(4.63),445(4.52)	118-0030-80
$C_{14}H_{20}N_4O_3$			
Pyrrolo[2,3-c]azepine-2-carboxylic acid, 1,4,5,6,7,8-hexahydro-8-oxo-3-[[(dimethylamino)methylene]amino]-, ethyl ester	EtOH	223(4.18),266(4.41)	103-0853-80
$(C_{14}H_{20}N_4O_4)_n$			
Poly[imino[1-[4-[[3-(3,4-dihydro-5-methyl-2,4-dioxo-1(2H)-pyrimidinyl)-1-oxopropyl]amino]butyl]-2-oxo-1,2-ethanediyl]]-, (S)	aq HCl	273.5(3.93)	47-0949-80
	DMSO	273.5(3.94)	47-0949-80
high molecular weight	aq HCl	273.0(3.93)	47-0949-80
	DMSO	273.0(3.95)	47-0949-80
$C_{14}H_{20}N_4S_4$			
Carbamodithioic acid, diethyl-, 1,2-di-	EtOH	241(4.32),280(4.23),	44-5113-80

Compound	Solvent	λ_{max}(log ϵ)	Ref.
cyano-1,2-ethenediyl ester (cont.)		325s(3.80),390s(3.47)	44-5113-80
$C_{14}H_{20}N_5O_6PS$			
Adenosine, 8-(butylthio)-, cyclic 3',5'-(hydrogen phosphate)	pH 1 pH 11	282(4.30) 280(4.27)	87-0242-80 87-0242-80
$C_{14}H_{20}N_6$			
Propanedinitrile, [2,5-bis(diethyl-amino)-4H-imidazol-4-ylidene]-	CHCl$_3$	360(4.23),465(4.05)	88-2879-80
$C_{14}H_{20}O$			
Benzenemethanol, 4-cyclohexyl-α-methyl-	EtOH	218(3.89),246(3.46), 257(2.44),271(2.44)	56-0453-80
2(3H)-Naphthalenone, 4,4a,5,6,7,8-hexa-hydro-4-methyl-6-(1-methylethenyl)-(4α,4aα,6β)-(±)-	EtOH	237(4.18)	18-1049-80
2(3H)-Naphthalenone, 4,4a,5,6,7,8-hexa-hydro-4a-methyl-7-(1-methylethenyl)-	EtOH	238(4.18)	44-3790-80
2(3H)-Naphthalenone, 4,4a,5,6,7,8-hexa-hydro-4-methyl-6-(1-methylethylidene)-	EtOH	232(4.12)	18-1049-80
$C_{14}H_{20}OS$			
15-Thiabicyclo[10.2.1]pentadeca-1(14),12-dien-2-one	MeCN	295(4.05)	44-1906-80
$C_{14}H_{20}O_2$			
4H-1,3-Benzodioxin, 2,4-bis(1-methyl-ethyl)-	EtOH	218(3.8),269(3.0), 275(4.0)	118-0724-80
2,5-Cyclohexadiene-1,4-dione, 2,6-bis-(1,1-dimethylethyl)-	PrOH	285(2.7),435(2.2)	70-1087-80
3,5-Cyclohexadiene-1,2-dione, 3,5-bis-(1,1-dimethylethyl)-	tert-BuOH	398(3.28)	35-4472-80
1,4-Cyclopentadiene-1-carboxaldehyde, 2,4-bis(1,1-dimethylethyl)-3-oxo-	C$_6$H$_{12}$	416(2.76)	88-4097-80
1,3-Cyclopentanediol, 1,2,2-trimethyl-3-phenyl-	pentane	243(1.97),248(2.08), 253(2.18),259(1.26), 265(2.14)	33-0154-80
Glutinose, 3-epimer	EtOH	237(4.08)	18-1049-80
1-Heptanone, 1-(2-hydroxy-5-methyl-phenyl)-	EtOH	255(3.99),338(3.59)	90-0431-80
2-Heptanone, 6-methyl-3-methylene-6-(5-methyl-2-furanyl)-	pentane	217(4.18),327(1.61)	33-2221-80
2(3H)-Naphthalenone, 7-ethenyl-4,4a,5-6,7,8-hexahydro-7-hydroxy-8,8-di-methyl-	EtOH	243(4.14)	88-1577-80
2(3H)-Naphthalenone, 4,4a,5,6,7,8-hexa-hydro-3-hydroxy-4-methyl-6-(1-methyl-ethenyl)- (glutinosone)	EtOH	237(4.16)	18-1045-80
1-Octanone, 1-(2-hydroxyphenyl)-	EtOH	251(4.01),325(3.59)	90-0436-80
1-Octanone, 1-(4-hydroxyphenyl)-	EtOH	278(4.18)	90-0436-80
8-Oxabicyclo[5.3.0]dec-9-en-2-one, 3,3,7,9-tetramethyl-6-methylene-	pentane	292(1.95),301(1.90), 311s(1.78)	33-2221-80
Spiro[4.5]deca-2,6-diene-2-carboxylic acid, 6,10-dimethyl-, methyl ester, cis-(±)-	EtOH	225(3.84)	23-2460-80
$C_{14}H_{20}O_2S$			
1-Pentanone, 1,1'-(2,5-thiophenediyl)-bis-	C$_6$H$_{12}$	221s(3.7),290(4.2), 350s(2.3)	138-0397-80

Compound	Solvent	$\lambda_{max}(\log \epsilon)$	Ref.
$C_{14}H_{20}O_3$			
Bicyclo[2.2.2]oct-5-ene-2-carboxylic acid, 5-ethenyl-1-methoxy-8-methyl-, methyl ester	EtOH	235(4.27)	18-1049-80
1H-Cyclopentacyclooctene-5-carboxylic acid, 2,3,3a,6,7,8,9,9a-octahydro-4-methyl-1-oxo-, methyl ester, trans	hexane	230(3.87)	77-1011-80
1,4-Dioxadispiro[4.1.5.2]tetradec-8-en-10-one, 8,12-dimethyl-	EtOH	242(4.14)	23-2460-80
4a,8a-Ethanonaphthalen-9-one, 10-acet-oxyoctahydro-	MeOH	295(1.89)	44-0177-80
2-Hexenoic acid, 5-(3,3-dimethylcyclo-pentylidene)-4-oxo-, methyl ester	pentane	230(4.08),289(3.74)	33-1856-80
3aH-Indene-3a-propanoic acid, 1,2,3,4-5,6-hexahydro-7-methyl-2-oxo-, methyl ester	MeOH	242(4.03)	44-0570-80
4a(2H)-Naphthalenepropanoic acid, 1,3,4,5,6,7-hexahydro-1-oxo-, methyl ester	MeOH	243(3.91)	44-0570-80
4a(2H)-Naphthalenepropanoic acid, 3,4,5,6,7,8-hexahydro-2-oxo-, methyl ester	MeOH	240(4.04)	44-0570-80
2(3H)-Naphthalenone, 4,4a,5,6,7,8-hexa-hydro-3,4a-dihydroxy-4-methyl-6-(1-methylethenyl)- (oxyglutinosone)	EtOH	230(4.08)	18-1045-80
2,7-Oxepindione, 3,5-bis(1,1-dimethyl-ethyl)-	C_6H_{12}	247.5(3.24)	44-1153-80
Spiro[4.5]deca-2,6-diene-2-carboxylic acid, 8-hydroxy-6,10-dimethyl-, methyl ester, (5α,8α,10α)-(±)-	EtOH	224(3.93)	23-2460-80
Spiro[1,3-dioxolane-2,2'(4'H)-naphtha-len]-6'-one, 1',3',4',7',8',8'a-hexahydro-5',8'a-dimethyl-	EtOH	247.5(4.11)	2-0904-80
Tricyclo[3.3.1.0^{1,3}]nonane-4-carboxylic acid, 3,6,6-trimethyl-9-oxo-, methyl ester, (1α,3α,4β,5α)-	pentane	295(1.57)	33-1856-80
$C_{14}H_{20}O_3S$			
2-Butenoic acid, 4-(butylthio)-3-(2-furanyl)-, ethyl ester, (E)-	EtOH	213(3.95),307(4.22)	73-0142-80
$C_{14}H_{20}O_4$			
1,4-Cycloheptanedione, 2-(2-acetoxy-1-propenyl)-7,7-dimethyl-	pentane	292(2.03)	33-2221-80
2H-Pyran-2-one, 6-(3-acetoxy-1-hepten-yl)-5,6-dihydro-	EtOH	204(4.06)	64-1459-80B
$C_{14}H_{20}O_4S$			
2-Butenoic acid, 4-(butylsulfinyl)-3-(2-furanyl)-, ethyl ester, (E)-	EtOH	212(4.01),309(4.26)	73-0142-80
$C_{14}H_{20}O_5$			
1-Butanone, 3-methoxy-1-(2,4,6-tri-methoxyphenyl)-	MeOH	279(3.79)	94-3070-80
Ethanone, 1,1'-(5-ethoxy-4,5-dihydro-2,6a-dimethylfuro[2,3-b]furan-3,3a(6aH)-diyl)bis-	MeOH	265(4.08)	23-1645-80
Ethanone, 1,1',1"-(2-ethoxy-2,3-dihydro-6-methyl-4H-pyran-5-yl-4-ylidene)-tris-	MeOH	259(4.01)	23-1645-80

Compound	Solvent	$\lambda_{max}(\log \epsilon)$	Ref.
Propanedioic acid, (3-oxobicyclo[3.3.1]-non-1-yl)-, dimethyl ester	EtOH	275(1.28)	44-1800-80
$C_{14}H_{20}O_5S$ 2-Butenoic acid, 4-(butylsulfonyl)-3-(2-furanyl)-, ethyl ester, (E)-	EtOH	212(4.04),315(4.25)	73-0142-80
$C_{14}H_{20}O_6$ Bicyclo[2.2.2]octane-2,3-dicarboxylic acid, 5-hydroxy-1,5-dimethyl-6-oxo-, dimethyl ester, ($1\alpha,2\beta,3\beta,4\alpha,5\beta$)-	EtOH	308(1.48)	44-2189-80
$C_{14}H_{20}O_8$ β-D-Glucopyranose, monoglucoside with 4-(2-hydroxyethyl)-1,2-benzene-diol (lemairin)	H_2O	278(3.2)	100-0411-80
$C_{14}H_{20}O_{10}$ Stilbericoside	H_2O	197(3.97)	100-0649-80
$C_{14}H_{20}S$ 8H-Indeno[b]thiophene, 4,4a,5,6,7,7a-hexahydro-4,8,8-trimethyl-, cis	EtOH	228(3.62),247(3.49)	70-1833-80
Thiophene, 2-(3,7-dimethyl-2,6-octa-dienyl)-	EtOH	234(3.94),284(2.87)	70-1833-80
$C_{14}H_{21}BrO_2$ Phenol, 3-[(8-bromooctyl)oxy]-	DMSO	278(3.39)	44-3923-80
Phenol, 4-[(8-bromooctyl)oxy]-	DMSO	297(3.48)	44-3923-80
$C_{14}H_{21}Cl_2N_4O_5P$ Thymidine, 5'-[[[bis(2-chloroethyl)-amino]hydrox y phosphinyl]amino]-5'-deoxy-, intramol. 5',3'-ester	EtOH	267(3.89)	87-1235-80
$C_{14}H_{21}FO_3$ 1-Cyclopentene-1-heptanoic acid, α-fluoro-5-oxo-, ethyl ester	MeOH	228(4.01)	44-4702-80
$C_{14}H_{21}NO_2$ 5H-1-Benzopyran-5-one, 2-(dimethyl-amino)-2,6,7,8-tetrahydro-3,7,7-trimethyl-	H_2O	220(3.88),295(4.16), 360(3.99)	70-1643-80
	MeOH	218(3.82),294(4.07)	70-1643-80
	MeCN	208(4.05),245s(3.83), 290(3.97),373(4.00)	70-1643-80
	CHCl₃	250(3.99),290(3.83)	70-1643-80
1,3-Cyclohexanedione, 2-[3-(dimethyl-amino)-2-methyl-2-propenylidene]-5,5-dimethyl-	hexane	245(3.81),254s(3.80), 263s(3.64),300(3.62)	70-1643-80
	H_2O	240(3.91),295(4.19), 400(4.33)	70-1643-80
	MeOH	250(4.15),300(3.83), 408(3.13)	70-1643-80
	67% MeOH	210(3.95),245(3.93), 293(4.02),408(4.16)	70-1643-80
	EtOH	240(3.76),295(4.05), 400(4.08)	70-1643-80
	MeCN	247(4.07),305(3.82)	70-1643-80
	CHCl₃	250(3.99),305(3.83)	70-1643-80
1-Heptanone, 1-(2-hydroxy-5-methyl-phenyl)-, oxime	EtOH	257(3.93),338(3.59)	90-0431-80

Compound	Solvent	$\lambda_{max}(\log \epsilon)$	Ref.
1-Octanone, 1-(2-hydroxyphenyl)-, oxime	EtOH	251(4.01),304(3.60)	90-0431-80
Pyrrolo[1,2-a]quinolin-6(1H)-one, 2,3,3a,4,5,7,8,9-octahydro-1-(2-hydroxyethyl)-, trans-(±)-	MeOH	319(4.49)	35-7154-80
$C_{14}H_{21}NO_3$			
8-Isoquinolinemethanol, 1,2,3,4-tetra-hydro-5,7-dimethoxy- ,2-dimethyl-	EtOH	228(3.87),285(3.36)	39-0072-80C
3-Pyridinecarboxylic acid, 1-ethyl-5-hexyl-1,4-dihydro-4-oxo-	EtOH	260(4.03),287(3.70)	4-0359-80
3-Pyridinecarboxylic acid, 5-hexyl-1,4-dihydro-4-oxo-, ethyl ester	EtOH	255s(3.89),260(3.93), 286(3.71)	4-0359-80
$C_{14}H_{21}NO_4S$			
7-Thia-2-azabicyclo[3.2.1]oct-3-ene-4,8-dicarboxylic acid, 1,3-dimethyl-, diethyl ester, syn	EtOH	262(3.58),302(3.96)	23-0794-80
$C_{14}H_{21}N_3O_4$			
Benzenamine, N,N-dibutyl-2,4-dinitro-	DMF	390(4.18)(changing)	104-0891-80
$C_{14}H_{21}N_5O_3S$			
Cytidine, 5'-[[2-amino-4-(methylthio)-1-oxobutyl]amino]-2',3'-didehydro-2',3',5'-trideoxy-, (S)-	H_2O	271(3.88)	136-0067-80A
$C_{14}H_{21}N_5O_4$			
Adenosine, N-methyl-2',3',5'-tri-0-methyl-	pH 1.8	261(4.20)	44-4073-80
	pH 7	265(4.16)	44-4073-80
	pH 13	265(4.16)	44-4073-80
$C_{14}H_{22}BrNS_2$			
2-Propanesulfenamide, N-(4-bromophen-yl)-N-[(1,1-dimethylethyl)thio]-2-methyl-	hexane	260(4.21)	18-0720-80
$C_{14}H_{22}BrN_7$			
1H-Pyrazol-5-amine, 4-[(4-bromo-3-meth-yl-1-(1-methylethyl)-1H-pyrazol-5-yl]azo]-3-methyl-1-(1-methylethyl)-	MeOH	390(4.57),410(4.57)	103-1160-80
$C_{14}H_{22}ClNS_2$			
2-Propanesulfenamide, N-(3-chlorophen-yl)-N-[(1,1-dimethylethyl)thio]-2-methyl-	hexane	255(4.06)	18-0720-80
2-Propanesulfenamide, N-(4-chlorophen-yl)-N-[(1,1-dimethylethyl)thio]-2-methyl-	hexane	258(4.18)	18-0720-80
$C_{14}H_{22}Cl_2N_5O_4P$			
Thymidine, 3',5'-[[bis(2-chloroethyl)-amino]phosphoryl]-3',5'-diamino-3',5'-dideoxy-	EtOH	267(3.95)	87-1235-80
$C_{14}H_{22}NO_4$			
Oxazolium, 5-(2-acetoxy-1,1-dimethyl-ethyl)-4,5-dihydro-3-methyl-2-(2-methyl-1-propenyl)-4-oxo-, per-chlorate	HOAc	285(4.15)	103-0023-80

Compound	Solvent	$\lambda_{max}(\log \epsilon)$	Ref.
$C_{14}H_{22}N_2O$			
Pyridine, 4-butyl-3-(4,5-dihydro-4,4-dimethyl-2-oxazolyl)-1,4-dihydro-	EtOH	329(3.840)	39-2070-80C
Pyridine, 3-(4,5-dihydro-4,4-dimethyl-2-oxazolyl)-1,4-dihydro-4-(1-methylpropyl)-	EtOH	329(3.964)	39-2070-80C
Pyridine, 3-(4,5-dihydro-4,4-dimethyl-2-oxazolyl)-4-(1,1-dimethylethyl)-1,4-dihydro-	EtOH	318(3.796)	39-2070-80C
Pyridine, 5-(4,5-dihydro-4,4-dimethyl-2-oxazolyl)-2-(1,1-dimethylethyl)-1,2-dihydro-	EtOH	267(4.509),277s(4.435), 339(3.977)	39-2070-80C
$C_{14}H_{22}N_2O_3$			
1-Butanamine, N-butyl-N-[2-(5-nitro-2-furanyl)ethenyl]-, (E)-	MeOH	280(4.11),520(4.32)	73-0155-80
$C_{14}H_{22}N_4O_5S_2$			
D-Glucitol, 1-S-ethyl-1-C-[6-(methylthio)-9H-purin-9-yl]-1-thio-	MeOH	284(4.21)	136-0241-80C
$C_{14}H_{22}O$			
2-Butanone, 4-(2,2-dimethyl-6-methylenecycloheptylidene)-	pentane	288(1.85),295s(1.81), 306s(1.66)	33-1520-80
2-Butanone, 4-(3,7,7-trimethyl-2-cyclohepten-1-ylidene)-	pentane	230(4.04),280s(2.29), 288s(2.27),297s(2.21), 306s(2.05)	33-1520-80
3-Buten-2-one, 4-(2,2-dimethyl-6-methylenecycloheptyl)-, (E)-	pentane	223(4.22),326(1.65), 337s(1.63),352s(1.43)	33-1520-80
3-Buten-2-one, 4-(5,5-dimethylspiro[2.5]oct-4-yl)-, (E)-	pentane	222(4.17),325(1.70), 338s(1.66),355s(1.49)	33-1520-80
3-Buten-2-one, 4-(1,3,3-trimethylbicyclo[4.1.0]hept-2-yl)-, (E)-	pentane	222(4.24),325(1.67), 338s(1.62),350s(1.48)	33-1520-80
3-Buten-2-one, 4-(2,2,6-trimethylbicyclo[4.1.0]hept-1-yl)-	pentane	326s(1.85),339s(1.79), 352s(1.62)	33-1520-80
2-Cyclohexene-1-acetaldehyde, 5-(1,1-dimethylethyl)-2-ethenyl-, trans	C_6H_{12}	231(c. 4.11)	35-0314-80
5H-Cycloprop[e]azulen-5-one, decahydro-3,3,7b-trimethyl-, [1aS-(1aα,4aα-7aβ,7bα)]-	MeCN	305(1.40)	31-0891-80
Ethanone, 1-(4-cyclohexyl-3-cyclohexen-1-yl)-	EtOH	205(3.41)	56-0453-80
Ethanone, 1-(1-ethenyl-3,7,7-trimethyl-2-cyclohepten-1-yl)-	pentane	300(2.26)	33-1520-80
Furan, 2-methyl-5-(1,1,5-trimethyl-5-hexenyl)-	pentane	219(4.00)	33-1520-80
2H-Inden-2-one, 1,4,5,6,7,7a-hexahydro-1,1,4,4,7a-pentamethyl-	EtOH	237(4.09)	23-1810-80
1(4H)-Naphthalenone, 4a,5,6,7,8,8a-hexahydro-2,5,5,8a-tetramethyl-, (4aS trans)-	EtOH	236.7(3.87)	65-0176-80
2-Oxabicyclo[4.4.1]undeca-3,5-diene, 1,3,7,7-tetramethyl-	pentane	260(3.92)	33-1520-80
Oxirane, 2-methyl-2-[2-(2,6,6-trimethyl-1-cyclohexen-1-yl)ethenyl]-, (E)-(±)-	EtOH	240(3.79)	33-1665-80
Oxirane, 2-(4,8-dimethyl-1,3,7-nonatrienyl)-2-methyl-	EtOH	240(4.32)	33-1665-80
$C_{14}H_{22}O_2$			
3-Oxabicyclo[4.4.1]undeca-1,4-dien-	pentane	303(1.70)	33-2221-80

Compound	Solvent	$\lambda_{max}(\log \epsilon)$	Ref.
7-one, 2,4,8,8-tetramethyl- (cont.)			33-2221-80
$C_{14}H_{22}O_2S_2$			
1,4-Dithiaspiro[4.5]decane-8-acetic acid, 6-methyl-α-methylene-, ethyl ester	EtOH	205(4.20)	39-1752-80C
$C_{14}H_{22}O_2Si$			
Benzenemethanol, 4-methoxy-2-methyl-α-[1-(trimethylsilyl)ethenyl]-, (±)-	C_6H_{12}	233(3.93),278(3.13), 284(3.11)	89-1027-80
$C_{14}H_{22}O_3$			
1-Cyclopentene-1-heptanoic acid, α-ethyl-5-oxo-	MeOH	228(4.00)	44-4702-80
1-Cyclopentene-1-heptanoic acid, 5-oxo-, ethyl ester	MeOH	228(4.02)	44-4702-80
1-Cyclopentene-1-heptanoic acid, α-methyl-5-oxo-, methyl ester	MeOH	228(4.00)	44-4702-80
1-Cyclopentene-1-nonanoic acid, 5-oxo-	MeOH	227(4.01)	44-4702-80
2,7,9-Dodecatrienoic acid, 6-hydroxy-11-methyl-, methyl ester, (E,E,E)- (>95%)	EtOH	231(4.35)	35-1390-80
(E,E,Z)-	EtOH	228(4.52)	35-1390-80
2H-Pyran-2-one, 4-hydroxy-6-nonyl-	EtOH	203(4.32),238(3.86), 282(3.85)	23-2158-80
$C_{14}H_{22}O_4$			
2-Propenoic acid, 3-[3-[2-(3,3-dimethyloxiranyl)ethyl]-3-methyloxiranyl]-, ethyl ester	EtOH	224(3.97)	70-0754-80
$C_{14}H_{22}O_5$			
1-Cyclopentene-1-heptanoic acid, 3-(2-hydroxyethoxy)-5-oxo-, (±)-	MeOH	219(3.81)	87-0903-80
4H,5H-Pyrano[2,3-d]-1,3-dioxin-4-one, 7-ethoxy-6,7-dihydro-2,2-dimethyl-6-(1-methylethyl)-, cis	MeCN	253(3.95)	24-1020-80
$C_{14}H_{22}O_6$			
4H,5H-Pyrano[2,3-d]-1,3-dioxin-4-one, 6,7-dihydro-7,7-dimethoxy-2,2-dimethyl-6-(1-methylethyl)-	MeCN	251(3.89)	24-1020-80
$C_{14}H_{22}Si$			
Silane, triethyl(6-methyl-1,2,3,4,5-heptapentaenyl)-	hexane	226(3.86),239(3.77), 251(3.84),268s(3.93), 300(4.34),318(4.32), 368(2.24),398(1.72)	35-5406-80
$C_{14}H_{23}N$			
Piperidine, 1-(2,6,8-nonatrienyl)-, (E,E)-	EtOH	227(4.55)	70-0263-80
$C_{14}H_{23}NS_2$			
2-Propanesulfenamide, N-[(1,1-dimethylethyl)thio]-2-methyl-N-phenyl-	hexane	252(4.04)	18-0720-80
$C_{14}H_{23}N_3O_3$			
3,5-Isoxazoledicarboxamide, N',N'-dibutyl-4-methyl-	MeOH	245(4.03)	94-0479-80

Compound	Solvent	$\lambda_{max}(\log \epsilon)$	Ref.
$C_{14}H_{24}N_2$			
12,14-Diazabicyclo[9.2.1]tetradeca-11(14),13-diene, 12,13-dimethyl-	EtOH	227(3.76)	138-0659-80
$C_{14}H_{24}N_2O_2Si$			
Spiro[cyclohexane-1,8'-[2,4]diazabicyclo[4.2.0]octane]-3',5'-dione, 6'-(trimethylsilyl)-	MeOH	225(3.03)	44-4462-80
$C_{14}H_{24}O$			
2-Butanone, 4-(5,5-dimethylspiro[2.5]-oct-4-yl)-, (E)-	pentane	285(1.40)	33-1520-80
2-Butanone, 4-(1,3,3-trimethylbicyclo[4.1.0]hept-2-yl)-	pentane	281(1.42)	33-1520-80
2-Butanone, 4-(2,2,6-trimethylbicyclo[4.1.0]hept-1-yl)-	pentane	281(1.30)	33-1520-80
3-Cyclohexene-1-methanol, 4-cyclohexyl--methyl-	EtOH	205(3.35)	56-0453-80
$C_{14}H_{24}OSi_2$			
2(4H)-Pentalenone, 5,6-dihydro-1,3-bis(trimethylsilyl)-	C_6H_{12}	396(2.91)	89-1023-80
$C_{14}H_{24}O_2$			
2-Butanone, 4-(6-hydroxy-2,2,6-trimethylcycloheptylidene)-	pentane	281(2.25)	33-1520-80
5,7-Octadien-3-ol, 2,4,4,7-tetramethyl-, acetate, (E)-	n.s.g.	215s(4.44),230(4.47), 237s(4.30)	33-1499-80
1,13-Tetradecadien-3-one, 1-hydroxy-, (Z)-	hexane	272(3.79)	88-5001-80
$C_{14}H_{24}O_6S$			
α-D-Glucofuranose, 6-S-ethyl-3-O-methyl-1,2-O-(1-methylethylidene)-6-thio-, acetate	EtOH	207(3.11),222(3.19)	33-0016-80
$C_{14}H_{25}NO_4S$			
2-Cyclopenten-1-one, 2-[7-[(methylsulfonyl)oxy]heptyl]-, O-methyloxime	MeOH	242(4.09)	44-4702-80
$C_{14}H_{25}N_3O_4$			
3,5-Isoxazoledicarboxamide, N,N'-dibutyl-4,5-dihydro-4-methyl-, 2-oxide, trans	MeOH	256(3.95)	94-0479-80
$C_{14}H_{26}OSi$			
Cyclohexanol, 1-[1-ethenyl-3-(trimethylsilyl)-2-propenyl]-, (E)-	hexane	213(3.08)	33-0555-80
Cyclohexanol, 1-[5-(trimethylsilyl)-2,4-pentadienyl]-, (E,E)-	hexane	235(4.11)	33-0555-80
$C_{14}H_{26}O_2Si_2$			
Silane, [[3,4-bis(methylene)-1-cyclobutene-1,2-diyl]bis(methyleneoxy)]-bis[trimethyl-	EtOH	218(4.26),247(3.81)	5-1786-80
$C_{14}H_{27}N$			
3-Pentanamine, N-[(1,1-dimethylethyl)-cyclopropylidene]-2,4-dimethyl-	C_6H_{12}	271(2.19)	5-1814-80

Compound	Solvent	$\lambda_{max}(\log \epsilon)$	Ref.
$C_{14}H_{28}N_4O_4S_2$			
1,9,12,20-Tetraoxa-4,6,15,17-tetraaza-cyclodocosane-5,16-dithione	H_2O H_2O	209(4.37),238(4.31) 209(4.33),238(4.29)	88-0313-80 104-1124-80
$C_{14}H_{35}N_6O_4Rh_2$			
Rhodium(3+), [μ-(acetato-O:O')]di-μ-hydroxybis(octahydro-1H-1,4,7-triazonine-N^1,N^4,N^7)di-, triperchlorate	H_2O	339(2.62)	24-0036-80
$C_{14}H_{36}Si_4$			
Silane, 1,2-ethenediylidenetetrakis-[trimethyl-	hexane	224(4.25),370(2.85)	88-3077-80
$C_{14}H_{42}Si_6$			
Hexasilane, tetradecamethyl-	isooctane	220(4.15),260(4.32)	101-0159-80N
$C_{14}H_{42}Si_7$			
Cycloheptasilane, tetradecamethyl-	isooctane	221(3.96),239(3.66), 249(3.56)	101-0159-80N

Compound	Solvent	λ_{max}(log ϵ)	Ref.
$C_{15}H_7BrN_2$ Cyclopent[4,5]azepino[2,1,7-cd]pyrro- lizine-6-carbonitrile, 8-bromo-	EtOH	234(4.25),276(4.26), 292(4.26),318(4.10), 347s(4.58),363(4.77), 413(3.74),434s(3.75), 454(3.82),528(2.79)	39-1324-80C
$C_{15}H_7ClN_2O_2$ Indolo[2,1-b]quinazoline-6,12-dione, 2-^{35}Cl-	CHCl$_3$	252(4.53),258(4.61), 282s(3.84),305(3.85), 317(3.89),325s(3.88), 343(3.93),360(3.92), 398(3.91)	150-2601-80
Indolo[2,1-b]quinazoline-6,12-dione, 8-chloro-	CHCl$_3$	251(4.65),258(4.76), 285(3.94),296(3.85), 310(3.83),343(3.91), 358(3.87),410(3.81)	150-2601-80
$C_{15}H_8ClNO_2$ Benzofuro[2,3-b]quinoline, 11-chloro-, 6-oxide	EtOH	225(4.42),259(4.63), 267(4.65),291s(4.12), 325(4.11),340(4.16)	18-1057-80
$C_{15}H_8F_3NO_5$ Oxazolo[3,2-a]quinolinium, 5-acetoxy- 2-hydroxy-1-(trifluoroacetyl)-, hydroxide, inner salt	EtOH	278(3.76),362(4.30)	78-1385-80
$C_{15}H_8Fe_2O_8$ Iron, octacarbonyl[μ-[(4,5-η:6,7-η)- spiro[2.4]hepta-4,6-diene]]di-	hexane	249s(4.3),305(4.2)	24-2211-80
$C_{15}H_8N_2O$ Benzonitrile, 3,3'-carbonylbis-	EtOH	221(4.68),248(4.18), 286s(3.08),335(1.04)	23-2537-80
$C_{15}H_8N_2O_2$ Indolo[2,1-b]quinazoline-6,12-dione	CHCl$_3$	248(4.58),254(4.68), 272(3.88),283(3.87), 305(3.91),337(3.89), 353(3.84),400(3.85)	150-2601-80
$C_{15}H_8O_2S$ 2H-[1]Benzothiepino[4,3,2-cd]isobenzo- furan-2-one	MeOH	257(4.33),278(4.31), 288(4.31),322(4.07), 400(3.49)	73-1086-80
$C_{15}H_8O_5$ 6H-Benzofuro[3,2-c][1]benzopyran-6-one, 3,9-dihydroxy- (coumestrol)	pH −8.2 pH −6.9 pH −4.3 pH −2.8 pH −2.1 pH −0.9 pH 0.8 pH 5 pH 8 pH 11 pH 13 EtOH	365(4.11) 365(4.11) 352(4.12) 343(4.17) 342(4.19) 342(4.20) 342(4.20) 342(4.20) 362(4.39) 384(4.44) 384(4.44) 243(4.19),304(3.63), 345(4.32),357s(--)	149-0143-80B 149-0143-80B 149-0143-80B 149-0143-80B 149-0143-80B 149-0143-80B 149-0143-80B 149-0143-80B 149-0143-80B 149-0143-80B 149-0143-80B 149-0143-80B

Compound	Solvent	$\lambda_{max}(\log \epsilon)$	Ref.
6H-Benzofuro[3,2-c][1]benzopyran-6-one, 3,9-dihydroxy- (cont.)	ether	242(4.18),304(3.74), 341(4.35),351s(--), 359s(--)	149-0143-80B
	MeCN	241(4.21),303(3.71), 340(4.35),354s(--)	149-0143-80B
	DMSO	306(3.71),345(4.34), 361s(--)	149-0143-80B
	CCl$_4$	324(--),350(--), 356(--)	149-0143-80B
$C_{15}H_9Br$ 4H-Cyclopenta[def]phenanthrene, 4-bromo-	EtOH	227(4.75),243(4.34), 257(4.32),285(4.13), 298(4.07)	18-0494-80
4H-Cyclopenta[def]phenanthrene, 8-bromo-	EtOH	206(4.43),223(4.53), 251(4.69),257(4.65), 267(4.34),283(3.98), 295(4.15),308(4.19)	18-0494-80
$C_{15}H_9BrO_4$ 9,10-Anthracenedione, 3-(bromomethyl)- 1,8-dihydroxy-	MeOH	227(4.51),254(4.23), 259(4.23),277(3.95), 287(3.93),430(3.96), 455s(3.80)	44-0024-80
$C_{15}H_9BrO_5$ 9,10-Anthracenedione, 1-bromo-4,5-di- hydroxy-2-(hydroxymethyl)-	EtOH	228(4.42),258(4.28), 292(3.87),412s(3.89), 433(3.96),452s(3.86)	44-0020-80
$C_{15}H_9Br_2N_3O_4$ 1H-Pyrrole-2,5-dione, 3,3'-(3,5-pyri- dinediyl)bis[4-bromo-1-methyl-	MeOH	215(2.94),230(3.19), 337(3.64),367(3.66)	24-2884-80
$C_{15}H_9ClNO_2$ Pyridinium, 1-(3-chloro-1,4-dihydro- 1,4-dioxo-2-naphthalenyl)-, chloride	MeCN	221s(4.15),257s(4.27), 263(4.27),368(3.49)	44-5139-80
perchlorate	EtOH	213(4.47),245(4.30), 283s(4.01),325(3.73)	44-5139-80
$(C_{15}H_9F_3O)_n$ Methanone, phenyl[4-(trifluoroethenyl)- phenyl]-, polymer	CHCl$_3$	340(2.19)	44-2903-80
$C_{15}H_9F_3S$ Dibenzo[b,f]thiepin, 3-(trifluoro- methyl)-	MeOH	223(4.32),261(4.33), 298(3.92),340s(2.96)	73-1086-80
$C_{15}H_9N$ 9-Anthracenecarbonitrile	n.s.g.	365(3.90),382(3.94), 403(3.84)	5-0954-80
$C_{15}H_9NO$ Cyclopent[4,5]azepino[2,1,7-cd]pyrro- lizine-6-carboxaldehyde	EtOH	240(4.38),258(4.55), 305s(4.25),313(4.26), 350s(4.70),366(4.94), 462(4.15),510(3.43), 592s(2.16)	39-1324-80C
$C_{15}H_9NO_2$ 1-Azulenecarboxylic acid, 3-cyano-4-	C_6H_{12}	250(4.39),263(4.06),	18-1647-80

Compound	Solvent	$\lambda_{max}(\log \epsilon)$	Ref.
ethynyl-, methyl ester (cont.)		278(4.13),315(4.31), 360(3.62),390(3.65), 540s(2.62),558(2.67), 605(2.61),655(2.26)	18-1647-80
1-Azulenecarboxylic acid, 3-cyano-6-ethynyl-, methyl ester	$CHCl_3$	260(4.09),309s(4.67), 317s(4.78),321s(4.87), 345(4.05),353(4.10), 358(4.08),376(3.61), 545(2.77),580s(2.70)	18-1647-80
1-Azulenecarboxylic acid, 3-cyano-8-ethynyl-, methyl ester	C_6H_{12}	265(4.40),310s(4.60), 318(4.64),363(3.95), 383(3.78),578(2.81)	18-1647-80
$C_{15}H_9NO_2S$			
Indolo[4,5-d]benzo[b]thiophene-2-carboxylic acid	EtOH	208(4.32),257(4.66), 312(4.49)	103-0146-80
Indolo[5,4-d]benzo[b]thiophene-2-carboxylic acid	EtOH	212(4.28),259(4.59), 277(4.60),317(3.94)	103-0146-80
Indolo[6,5-d]benzo[b]thiophene-2-carboxylic acid	EtOH	205(3.29),232(4.62), 281(3.96),292(4.07), 322(4.36),339(4.33)	103-0146-80
$C_{15}H_9NO_3S_2$			
[1]Benzothieno[3,2-b][1]benzothiophene, 2-methoxy-7-nitro-	EtOH	213(4.49),248(4.26), 360(4.15),391(4.15)	104-0383-80
$C_{15}H_9NO_6$			
2H-1-Benzopyran-2-one, 4,7-dihydroxy-3-(4-nitrophenyl)-	EtOH	247(4.23),307(4.17)	114-0271-80A
$C_{15}H_9NS_2$			
3H-Indole, 3-(1,3-benzodithiol-2-ylidene)-	benzene	417(4.55)	18-1661-80
$C_{15}H_9N_3O$			
Benzo[h]pyrido[2,3-b][1,6]naphthyridin-6(5H)-one	MeOH	226(4.04),254(3.89), 370(3.82)	39-0512-80C
	MeOH-acid	227(3.97),315(3.53), 367(3.44)	39-0512-80C
	MeOH-base	284(3.67),324(3.60), 356(3.62)	39-0512-80C
$C_{15}H_9N_3O_2$			
1H-Pyrrolo[3,4-f][3,8]phenanthroline-1,3(2H)-dione, 2-methyl-	MeOH	223(3.74),245(3.76), 408(3.80)	24-2884-80
$C_{15}H_9N_7O_3$			
Tetrazolo[1,5-a]quinolin-8-ol, 4-[(4-nitrophenyl)azo]-	DMSO	456(5.32)	103-1286-80
$C_{15}H_{10}$			
4H-Cyclopenta[def]phenanthrene	EtOH	210(4.39),220s(4.43), 222(4.45),225(4.39), 249s(4.68),252(4.71), 261(4.26),275(3.94), 287(4.03),299(4.11)	18-0494-80
$C_{15}H_{10}BrNO_3$			
9,10-Anthracenedione, 1-amino-4-bromo-2-(hydroxymethyl)-	EtOH	472(3.86)	18-3007-80 +146-0513-80

Compound	Solvent	$\lambda_{max}(\log \epsilon)$	Ref.
$C_{15}H_{10}BrNO_3S$			
4H-1-Benzothiopyran-4-one, 3-bromo- 2-(phenylamino)-, 1,1-dioxide	EtOH	250(4.17),298s(3.55), 392(3.73)	150-0139-80
$C_{15}H_{10}BrNS$			
2(1H)-Quinolinethione, 6-bromo- 4-phenyl-	EtOH	228(4.56),294(4.40), 403(3.98)	94-0049-80
2(1H)-Quinolinethione, 7-bromo- 4-phenyl-	EtOH	227(4.58),287(4.37), 398(4.03)	94-0049-80
$C_{15}H_{10}Br_2N_2O_2$			
4H-Pyrazole, 4,4-dibromo-3,5-diphenyl-, 1,2-dioxide	CHCl₃	255(4.43),380(3.73)	44-0076-80
$C_{15}H_{10}Br_2O_3$			
2H-Naphtho[2,3-b]pyran-5,10-dione, 2,2-bis(bromomethyl)-	n.s.g.	235(3.88),250(4.0), 285(3.89),320(3.19)	2-1078-80
2H-Naphtho[2,3-b]pyran-5,10-dione, 3,4-dibromo-2,2-dimethyl-	n.s.g.	210(4.6),225(4.55), 260(4.7)	2-1078-80
$C_{15}H_{10}ClNO$			
2(1H)-Quinolinone, 3-chloro-1-phenyl-	CHCl₃	243(4.14),274s(3.?2), 282(3.94),291(3.88), 328s(3.72),337(3.80), 352(3.63)	150-0414-80S
$C_{15}H_{10}ClNO_2S$			
4H-1-Benzothiopyran-4-one, 3-chloro- 2-(phenylamino)-, 1-oxide	EtOH	229(4.23),252(4.18), 400(3.85)	150-0139-80
$C_{15}H_{10}ClNO_6$			
2H-Pyran-2-one, 3-[3-(4-chloro-3-nitro- phenyl)-1-oxo-2-propenyl]-4-hydroxy- 6-methyl-	MeOH	353(4.4)	83-0344-80
$C_{15}H_{10}ClNS$			
1,2-Benzisothiazole, 3-[1-(4-chloro- phenyl)ethenyl]-	EtOH	221(4.36),242s(4.24), 255s(4.10),310(3.72)	39-2830-80C
2(1H)-Quinolinethione, 6-chloro- 4-phenyl-	EtOH	225(4.59),293(4.40), 402(3.98)	94-0049-80
2(1H)-Quinolinethione, 7-chloro- 4-phenyl-	EtOH	225(4.63),286(4.36), 398(4.04)	94-0049-80
$C_{15}H_{10}Cl_2N_2O$			
2H-1,4-Benzodiazepin-2-one, 7-chloro- 5-(2-chlorophenyl)-1,3-dihydro-	MeOH	230(4.47),251s(4.12), 319(3.32)	73-3593-80
4H-Pyrazole, 4,4-dichloro-3,5-diphen- yl-, 1-oxide	CHCl₃	270(4.12),289(4.05), 400(3.76)	44-0076-80
$C_{15}H_{10}Cl_2N_2O_2$			
4H-Pyrazole, 4,4-dichloro-3,5-diphen- yl-, 1,2-dioxide	CHCl₃	249(4.41),260s(4.32), 365(3.94)	44-0076-80
$C_{15}H_{10}Cl_2O_4$			
2H-Pyran-2-one, 3-[3-(3,4-dichloro- phenyl)-1-oxo-2-propenyl]-4-hydroxy- 6-methyl-	MeOH	355(4.4)	83-0344-80
$C_{15}H_{10}Cl_3IO_5S$			
2-Furancarboxylic acid, 5-[2-(4-iodo- phenyl)-1-[(trichloromethyl)sulfon-	EtOH	203(4.37),240(4.29), 264(4.32),327(4.26)	73-0746-80

Compound	Solvent	$\lambda_{max}(\log \epsilon)$	Ref.
yl]ethenyl]-, methyl ester, (E)-			73-0746-80
$C_{15}H_{10}Cl_3NO_7S$			
2-Furancarboxylic acid, 5-[2-(4-nitro-phenyl)-1-[(trichloromethyl)sulfon-yl]ethenyl]-, methyl ester, (E)-	EtOH	203(4.38),269s(4.14), 345(3.92)	73-0746-80
$C_{15}H_{10}Cl_4O_4$			
3,10-Methanobenzo[b]cyclopenta[e][1,4]-dioxepin-11-ol, 5,6,7,8-tetrachloro-3,3a,10,10a-tetrahydro-, acetate, (3α,3aβ,10α,10aβ,11R*)-	CHCl₃	294s(3.13),299(3.19)	78-0267-80
1,4-Methanodibenzo[b,e][1,4]dioxin-11-ol, 6,7,8,9-tetrachloro-1,4,4a-10a-tetrahydro-, acetate	CHCl₃	293s(3.05),299(3.11)	78-0267-80
Spiro[3,5-cyclohexadiene-1,4'-[3]oxa-tricyclo[4.2.1.0²,⁵]non[7]en]-2-one, 9'-acetoxy-3,4,5,6-tetrachloro-, (1'α,2'β,4'β,5'β,6'α,9'S*)-	MeCN	219(4.06),251(3.71), 335(3.43),374(3.22)	78-0267-80
$C_{15}H_{10}Cl_4O_5S$			
2-Furancarboxylic acid, 5-[2-(4-chloro-phenyl)-1-[(trichloromethyl)sulfon-yl]ethenyl]-, methyl ester, (E)-	EtOH	203(4.36),232(4.20), 267(4.43),299(4.23), 333s(4.13)	73-0746-80
$C_{15}H_{10}NS_2$			
1,3-Benzodithiol-1-ium, 2-(1H-indol-3-yl)-, tetrafluoroborate	MeCN	453(4.69)	18-1661-80
$C_{15}H_{10}N_2$			
1H-Phenanthro[1,2-d]imidazole	EtOH	258(4.85),306(4.17)	4-0679-80
1H-Phenanthro[9,10-d]imidazole	MeOH	253(4.56),299(4.03), 350(3.59)	56-2365-80
Pyrazino[2,1,6-cd]pyrrolizine, 1-phen-yl-	EtOH	220(4.32),250s(4.19), 276(4.55),319(4.13), 394(3.13)	39-1319-80C
$C_{15}H_{10}N_2O$			
Benzoxazole, 2-(1H-indol-3-yl)-	EtOH	218(4.55),264(4.14), 316(4.51)	103-0501-80
Indolo[7,6-g]indole-2-carboxaldehyde, 3,8-dihydro-	EtOH	206(3.19),245s(3.58), 254(3.66),275s(3.37), 287(3.52),366(3.42)	103-1139-80
$C_{15}H_{10}N_2OS$			
Naphtho[2',1':5,6]thiopyrano[4,3-c]-pyrazol-1-(2H)-one, 2-methyl-	EtOH	240(4.53),261(4.48), 305(3.88)	4-0121-80
$C_{15}H_{10}N_2O_2$			
Amororidine	n.s.g.	246(3.89),325(3.68), 389(3.74)	39-1614-80C
6-Canthinone, 8-methoxy-	MeOH	225s(5.25),264s(5.34), 272(5.53),307(4.94), 355(5.15)	102-0313-80
	MeOH-HCl	278(5.40),313s(5.02), 320(5.08),380(5.27)	102-0313-80
1H-Dipyrrolo[1,2-a:3',4'-c]quinoline-1,3(2H)-dione, 2-methyl-	CHCl₃	277s(4.26),375(3.60), 467(3.72)	24-2884-80
$C_{15}H_{10}N_2O_3$			
10H-[1]Benzopyrano[2,3-b]oxazolo[4,5-e]-	EtOH	205(4.32),238(4.70),	44-1964-80

Compound	Solvent	$\lambda_{max}(\log \epsilon)$	Ref.
pyridin-10-one, 2,8-dimethyl- (cont.)		298(4.34),348(4.15)	44-1964-80
2,6-Canthindione, 3-methoxy-	MeOH	226(4.16),247(4.13), 253s(3.04),290(3.63), 302(3.65),325(3.43), 400s(3.59),422(3.85), 446(3.90)	102-0313-80
$C_{15}H_{10}N_2O_4$			
Acetamide, N-(6-nitro-1-oxo-1H-phena- len-2-yl)-	EtOH	209(4.31),233(4.14), 265(3.91),372(3.93), 436(4.01)	104-1820-80
$C_{15}H_{10}N_2O_5$			
1,3-Benzenediol, 4-[4-(4-nitrophenyl)- 5-isoxazolyl]-	EtOH	275(4.04)	114-0271-80A +114-0389-80B
Benzenepropanenitrile, 2,4-dihydroxy- α-(4-nitrophenyl)-β-oxo-	EtOH	288(4.06)	114-0271-80A
2H-1-Benzopyran-4,7-diol, 2-imino-3-(4- nitrophenyl)-	EtOH	248(4.17),306(4.14)	114-0271-80A
$C_{15}H_{10}N_4$			
Bicyclo[5.3.1]undeca-1,3,5-triene- 8,8,9,9-tetracarbonitrile	EtOH	218(3.49),257s(--)	88-2447-80
Cycloprop[d]azulene-6,6,7,7(1H,8H)- tetracarbonitrile, 1a,5a-dihydro-	EtOH	203(3.59),258(3.46)	88-2447-80
$C_{15}H_{10}N_4O$			
1,2,4-Triazolo[3,4-b]oxadiazole, 3,6-diphenyl-	EtOH	260(4.79)	4-1691-80
[1,2,4]Triazolo[4,3-a]quinazolin- 5(4H)-one, 4-phenyl-	MeOH	292(3.56)	2-0638-80
$C_{15}H_{10}N_4OS$			
[1,2,4]Triazolo[4,3-a]quinazolin-5(1H)- one, 2,4-dihydro-4-phenyl-1-thioxo-	MeOH	284(4.17)	2-0638-80
$C_{15}H_{10}OS$			
Benzo[b]thiophen-3(2H)-one, 2-(phenyl- methylene)-	EtOH	433(3.90)	44-4611-80
$C_{15}H_{10}OS_2$			
1,2-Dithiol-1-ium, 4-hydroxy-3,5-di- phenyl-, hydroxide, inner salt	EtOH dioxan MeCN	498(4.45) 579(3.76) 528(4.36)	139-0079-80A 139-0079-80A 139-0079-80A
$C_{15}H_{10}OSe_2$			
3H-1,2-Diselenol-3-one, 4,5-diphenyl-	MeOH	224s(4.30),272(4.27), 356(3.69)	142-1921-80
$C_{15}H_{10}O_2$			
4H-1-Benzopyran-4-one, 2-phenyl-	MeOH	250(4.24),295(4.58)	118-0874-80
8H-Cyclohepta[b]furan-8-one, 3-phenyl-	MeOH	232(4.35),282(4.20), 338s(3.67),356s(3.45)	18-0745-80
$C_{15}H_{10}O_3$			
2H-1-Benzopyran-2-one, 7-hydroxy- 4-phenyl-	pH 1.0 pH 5.0 pH 10.0 MeOH CH_2Cl_2	330(4.19) 330(4.19) 379(4.25) 332(4.20) 327(4.17)	61-1115-80 61-1115-80 61-1115-80 61-1115-80 61-1115-80

Compound	Solvent	$\lambda_{max}(\log \epsilon)$	Ref.
2H-1-Benzopyran-2-one, 7-hydroxy- 4-phenyl- (cont.)	60% H_2SO_4	353(4.06),370s(--)	61-1115-80
	20% H_2SO_4	330(4.19),345s(--)	61-1115-80
	DMSO	333(4.19)	61-1115-80
4H-1-Benzopyran-4-one, 7-hydroxy- 2-phenyl-	pH 4.5	250(4.38),311(4.47)	86-0977-80
	pH 10.5	266(4.51),305s(3.90), 361(4.16)	86-0977-80
4H-1-Benzopyran-4-one, 7-hydroxy- 3-phenyl-	pH 4.5	243(4.46),301(4.12)	86-0977-80
	pH 10.5	263(4.50),309s(3.95), 337(4.46)	86-0977-80
$C_{15}H_{10}O_3S$			
Dibenzo[b,f]thiepin-1-carboxylic acid, 10,11-dihydro-11-oxo-	MeOH	244(4.12),333(3.80)	73-1086-80
Dibenzo[b,f]thiepin-3-carboxylic acid, 10,11-dihydro-11-oxo-	MeOH	247(4.35),345(3.56)	73-1086-80
$C_{15}H_{10}O_4$			
9,10-Anthracenedione, 1-hydroxy-4-meth- oxy-	MeOH	223(4.44),243s(--), 250(4.45),272(4.10), 321(3.44),457(3.90)	24-2994-80
9,10-Anthracenedione, 1-hydroxy-2-(hy- droxymethyl)-	EtOH	408(3.83)	18-3007-80 +146-0513-80
4H-1-Benzopyran-4-one, 7-hydroxy-2-(4- hydroxyphenyl)-	MeOH	255s(3.79),314s(4.10), 330(4.15)	102-2179-80
	MeOH-NaOMe	253(4.05),264(4.06), 330(3.91),387(5.50)	102-2179-80
6a-Pterocarpen, 3,9-dihydroxy-	MeOH	228(4.26),239(4.24), 247s(4.22),290s(3.95), 318s(4.33),333(4.56), 350(4.51)	94-1172-80
$C_{15}H_{10}O_5$			
9,10-Anthracenedione, 1,4-dihydroxy- 2-(hydroxymethyl)-	EtOH	480(3.98)	18-3007-80 +146-0513-80
9,10-Anthracenedione, 1,4,5-trihydroxy- 2-methyl- (islandicin)	MeOH	230(4.50),251(4.29), 288(3.89),461s(--), 475s(--),489(4.09), 508s(--),523(3.91)	24-1575-80
9,10-Anthracenedione, 1,4,8-trihydroxy- 2-methyl-	MeOH	231(4.67),252s(--), 289(3.97),465s(--), 476s(--),488(4.08), 511s(--),521(3.91)	24-1575-80
4H-1-Benzopyran-4-one, 5,7-dihydroxy- 2-(4-hydroxyphenyl)- (apigenin)	EtOH	265(4.44),336(4.48)	36-0053-80
4H-1-Benzopyran-4-one, 2-(2,4-di- hydroxyphenyl)-7-hydroxy-	MeOH	241(4.33),249(4.36), 259s(4.27),289(4.15)	102-0921-80
$C_{15}H_{10}O_5S$			
4H-[1]Benzothieno[3,2-b]pyran-3-acetic acid, α,4-dioxo-, ethyl ester	MeOH	251(4.27),292(4.22), 330(3.94),366(3.67)	83-0385-80
$C_{15}H_{10}O_6$			
4H-Pyrano[3,2-b]benzofuran-3-acetic acid, α,4-dioxo-, ethyl ester	MeOH	207(4.29),288(4.33), 362(3.73)	83-0385-80
$C_{15}H_{10}O_8$			
Benzoic acid, 4-(2-carboxy-6-hydroxy- benzoyl)-3,5-dihydroxy-	MeOH	203(4.02),285(3.48), 365(2.72)	24-2221-80
$C_{15}H_{11}BrN_2O_2$			
[2,3'-Bi-1H-pyrrole]-2',5'-dione,	$CHCl_3$	295(3.62),417(3.98)	24-2884-80

Compound	Solvent	$\lambda_{max}(\log \epsilon)$	Ref.
4'-bromo-1'-methyl-1-phenyl- (cont.)			24-2884-80
$C_{15}H_{11}BrOS$			
1-Propanone, 1-(4-bromophenyl)-3-phenyl-3-thioxo-	C_6H_{12}	271(4.03),328(4.09), 409(4.26),520s(2.12) (anom.)	39-1768-80B
anion	EtOH	266(4.20),405(4.30)	39-1768-80B
$C_{15}H_{11}BrO_3$			
2H-Naphtho[2,3-b]pyran-5,10-dione, 3-bromo-2,2-dimethyl-	EtOH	261(4.41),276(4.34), 350(3.76),415(3.43), 440(3.47)	2-0013-80
$C_{15}H_{11}Cl$			
Anthracene, 2-(chloromethyl)-	hexane	256(5.00),325(2.95), 339(3.15),353(3.28), 363(3.20)	44-4183-80
Anthracene, 9-chloro-10-methyl-	EtOH	252(4.90),259(5.20), 326(3.01),341(3.40), 358(3.66),378(3.93), 399(3.92)	44-1807-80
$C_{15}H_{11}ClN_2O$			
1(2H)-Isoquinolinone, 6-chloro-3-(phenylamino)-	EtOH	240(4.44),321(4.33), 319(4.37)	95-0826-80
1(2H)-Isoquinolinone, 7-chloro-3-(phenylamino)-	EtOH .	222(4.34),319(4.37), 383(3.68)	95-0826-80
3H-Pyrazol-3-ol, 4-chloro-3,5-diphenyl-	$CHCl_3$	245(4.30),320(3.56), 385s(2.54)	44-0076-80
$C_{15}H_{11}ClN_2O_3$			
9,10-Anthracenedione, 1,8-diamino-4-chloro-2-(hydroxymethyl)-	EtOH	475(3.86)	18-3007-80 +146-0513-80
$C_{15}H_{11}ClOS$			
5H-Dibenzo[b,g]thiocin-5-one, 3-chloro-6,7-dihydro-	MeOH	235(4.25),261s(--), 324(3.38)	73-0491-80
1H-Inden-1-one, 4-[(4-chlorophenyl)-thio]-2,3-dihydro-	MeOH	244(4.44),259s(4.16), 281s(3.73),312(3.48)	73-0491-80
$C_{15}H_{11}ClO_2S_2$			
Disulfide, 4-chlorobenzoyl 4-methylbenzoyl	CH_2Cl_2	276(4.48)	118-0721-80
$C_{15}H_{11}ClO_3S_2$			
Disulfide, 4-chlorobenzoyl 4-methoxybenzoyl	CH_2Cl_2	261(4.11)	118-0721-80
$C_{15}H_{11}ClO_4$			
2H-Pyran-2-one, 3-[3-(2-chlorophenyl)-1-oxo-2-propenyl]-4-hydroxy-6-methyl-	MeOH	353(4.3)	83-0344-80
2H-Pyran-2-one, 3-[3-(3-chlorophenyl)-1-oxo-2-propenyl]-4-hydroxy-6-methyl-	MeOH	354(4.4)	83-0344-80
2H-Pyran-2-one, 3-[3-(4-chlorophenyl)-1-oxo-2-propenyl]-4-hydroxy-6-methyl-	MeOH	357(4.5)	83-0344-80
$C_{15}H_{11}Cl_3O_5S$			
2-Furancarboxylic acid, 5-[2-phenyl-1-[(trichloromethyl)sulfonyl]ethenyl]-, methyl ester, (E)-	EtOH	203(4.45),226(4.16), 265(4.47),291s(4.17), 326s(4.17)	73-0746-80

Compound	Solvent	λ_{max}(log ϵ)	Ref.
$C_{15}H_{11}Cl_3O_6S$			
2-Furancarboxylic acid, 5-[2-(4-hy-droxyphenyl)-1-[(trichloromethyl)-sulfonyl]ethenyl]-, methyl ester, (E)-	EtOH	201(4.18),249(4.21), 278(4.22),353(4.30)	73-0746-80
$C_{15}H_{11}FO_4$			
2H-Pyran-2-one, 3-[3-(3-fluorophenyl)-1-oxo-2-propenyl]-4-hydroxy-6-methyl-	MeOH	354(4.4)	83-0344-80
2H-Pyran-2-one, 3-[3-(4-fluorophenyl)-1-oxo-2-propenyl]-4-hydroxy-6-methyl-	MeOH	355(4.4)	83-0344-80
$C_{15}H_{11}F_3$			
Stilbene, α-(trifluoromethyl)-, (E)-	MeOH	256(4.13),265s(4.0)	24-3384-80
	CHCl₃	257(4.12),265s(4.08)	24-3384-80
$C_{15}H_{11}F_3O$			
Methanone, (4-methylphenyl)[4-(tri-fluoromethyl)phenyl]-	EtOH	243(4.33),268(4.42), 332(2.31)	23-2537-80
$C_{15}H_{11}N$			
Cyclopent[4,5]azepino[2,1,7-cd]pyrro-lizine, 6-methyl-	EtOH	272(4.14),299(4.42), 333s(4.54),344(4.63), 394(3.57),422(3.58), 443(3.52),452s(3.47), 548s(2.13),572(2.21), 621(2.16),693(1.58)	39-1324-80C
Pyridine, 4-(6-azulenyl)-	EtOH	295(4.43),335(3.68), 348(3.77),365(3.60), 600(2.53),645s(2.44), 720s(1.95)	118-0030-80
$C_{15}H_{11}NOS_2$			
[1]Benzothieno[3,2-b][1]benzothiophen-2-amine, 7-methoxy-	EtOH	209(4.39),216(4.36), 226(4.30),241(4.35), 278(4.30),337(4.35)	104-0383-80
$C_{15}H_{11}NO_2$			
9,10-Anthracenedione, 1-(methylamino)-	gas	463(3.71)	135-0344-80
	film	512(--)	135-0344-80
	crystal	527(--)	135-0344-80
	hexane	490(--)	135-0344-80
	DMF	512(3.85)	135-0344-80
1,3-Benzenediol, 4-(2-quinolinyl)-	EtOH	223(3.81),275(3.58), 350(3.41)	104-1092-80
1,3-Benzenediol, 4-(4-quinolinyl)-	EtOH	227(4.98),280(4.04)	104-1092-80
Benzenepropanenitrile, 2-hydroxy-β-oxo-α-phenyl-	EtOH	285(4.00)	114-0271-80A
2H-1-Benzopyran-2-imine, 4-hydroxy-3-phenyl-	EtOH	262(3.88),302(4.06)	114-0271-80A
1H-Indene-1,3(2H)-dione, 2-(1-methyl-4(1H)-pyridinylidene)-	EtOH	203(4.27),217(4.13), 235(4.56),255s(3.98), 285s(3.48),296(3.74), 306(3.88),392(4.76)	4-0997-80
	THF	408(4.69)	4-0997-80
1H-Indene-1,3(2H)-dione, 2-(2-methyl-4(1H)-pyridinylidene)-	EtOH	385(4.75)	4-0997-80
	THF	396(4.77)	4-0997-80
1H-Indene-1,3(2H)-dione, 2-(3-methyl-4(1H)-pyridinylidene)-	EtOH	204(4.61),236(4.46), 247(4.34),298(3.57), 308(3.59),399(4.42)	4-0961-80
	EtOH	399(4.42)	4-0997-80
	THF	417(4.50)	4-0997-80

Compound	Solvent	λ$_{max}$(log ε)	Ref.
1H-Indene-1,3(2H)-dione, 2-(6-methyl-2(1H)-pyridinylidene)-	5M NaOH	228(4.88),282(4.04), 344(4.18)	4-0961-80
1(3H)-Isobenzofuranone, 3-[(3-methyl-4-pyridinyl)methylene]-	EtOH	212(3.71),252(3.51), 290(3.61),304(3.61), 330(3.63)	4-0961-80
1(3H)-Isobenzofuranone, 3-[1-(2-pyridinyl)ethylidene]-	EtOH	233(4.02),248(4.09), 293(4.16),325(4.16)	4-0961-80
Phenol, 2-(4-phenyl-5-isoxazolyl)-	EtOH	228(4.28),263(4.03)	114-0271-80A
	EtOH	263(4.03)	114-0389-80B
C$_{15}$H$_{11}$NO$_2$S			
2H-1,4-Benzothiazin-2-one, 3-(4-methoxyphenyl)-	EtOH	234(4.16),366(3.66)	39-2923-80C
C$_{15}$H$_{11}$NO$_2$S$_2$			
2-Propenoic acid, 2-cyano-3-[5-(phenylthio)-2-thienyl]-, methyl ester	MeOH	205(4.32),247(4.09), 303(4.00),400(4.25)	73-2360-80
C$_{15}$H$_{11}$NO$_3$			
10(9H)-Acridineacetic acid, 9-oxo-	MeOH	256(4.70),293s(3.40), 386s(3.89),398(3.93)	73-3593-80
9,10-Anthracenedione, 1-amino-2-(hydroxymethyl)-	EtOH	472(3.86)	18-3007-80 +146-0513-80
1,3-Benzenediol, 4-(4-phenyl-5-isoxazolyl)-	EtOH	280(3.84)	114-0389-80B
C$_{15}$H$_{11}$NO$_3$S			
2-Propenoic acid, 2-cyano-3-[5-(phenylthio)-2-furanyl]-, methyl ester	MeOH	210(4.22),241s(4.00), 371(4.33)	73-1831-80
C$_{15}$H$_{11}$NO$_4$			
9,10-Anthracenedione, 1-amino-4-hydroxy-2-methoxy-	gas	488(3.94)	135-0344-80
	film	517(--)	135-0344-80
	crystal	523(--)	135-0344-80
	hexane	509(--)	135-0344-80
	DMF	515(4.10)	135-0344-80
C$_{15}$H$_{11}$NO$_4$S$_2$			
1,3-Dithiole-4,5-dicarboxylic acid, 2-(cyanophenylmethylene)-, dimethyl ester	CHCl$_3$	349(4.32)	39-2693-80C
2-Propenoic acid, 2-cyano-3-[5-(phenylsulfonyl)-2-thienyl]-, methyl ester	MeOH	205(4.22),242(3.90), 341(3.38)	73-2360-80
C$_{15}$H$_{11}$NO$_5$			
Pyrano[3,2-b]indole-3-acetic acid, 4,5-dihydro-5-methyl-α,4-dioxo-, methyl ester	MeOH	214(4.38),302(4.31)	83-0405-80
C$_{15}$H$_{11}$NO$_6$			
2H-Pyran-2-one, 4-hydroxy-6-methyl-3-[3-(2-nitrophenyl)-1-oxo-2-propenyl]-	MeOH	350(4.3)	83-0344-80
2H-Pyran-2-one, 4-hydroxy-6-methyl-3-[3-(3-nitrophenyl)-1-oxo-2-propenyl]-	MeOH	349(4.4)	83-0344-80
2H-Pyran-2-one, 4-hydroxy-6-methyl-3-[3-(4-nitrophenyl)-1-oxo-2-propenyl]-	MeOH	356(4.4)	83-0344-80
C$_{15}$H$_{11}$NS			
1,2-Benzisothiazole, 3-(1-phenylethenyl)-	EtOH	219(3.87),255s(3.43), 306(3.18)	39-2830-80C

Compound	Solvent	$\lambda_{max}(\log \epsilon)$	Ref.
$C_{15}H_{11}N_3$			
1H-Benzimidazole, 2-(1H-indol-3-yl)-	EtOH	221(4.55),314(4.40)	103-0501-80
Isoquinoline, 4-(2-pyrazinylethenyl)-, (E)-	MeCN	230(4.35),340(4.29)	44-1557-80
$C_{15}H_{11}N_3OS$			
Phenol, 2-[[(5-phenyl-1,3,4-thiadiazol-2-yl)imino]methyl]-	EtOH	209(4.40),256(4.18), 305(4.24),374(3.97), 465(2.48)	2-0144-80A
	DMF	312(4.30),376(3.95), 462(3.08)	2-0144-80A
	CHCl$_3$	307(4.24),374(3.90)	2-0144-80A
	CCl$_4$	305(4.24),374(3.97)	2-0144-80A
Phenol, 4-[[(5-phenyl-1,3,4-thiadiazol-2-yl)imino]methyl]-	EtOH	204(4.58),231(4.09), 265s(3.88),436(4.44)	2-0144-80A
	DMF	362(4.33),470(4.03)	2-0144-80A
	CHCl$_3$	350(4.43)	2-0144-80A
	CCl$_4$	360(4.40)	2-0144-80A
$C_{15}H_{11}N_3OS_2$			
1H-Thieno[3,4-b][1,4]diazepine-6-carbonitrile, 2,3-dihydro-8-(methylthio)-2-oxo-4-phenyl-	EtOH	220(4.30),275(4.35), 338(4.25)	95-0699-80
1H-Thieno[3,4-b][1,4]diazepine-8-carbonitrile, 2,3-dihydro-6-(methylthio)-2-oxo-4-phenyl-	EtOH	281(4.36),307(4.35)	95-0699-80
$C_{15}H_{11}N_3O_2$			
Benzeneacetonitrile, 4-[[(4-nitrophenyl)methylene]amino]-	THF	342(4.12)	56-1177-80
$C_{15}H_{11}N_3O_3S$			
1,2,3-Thiadiazole, 4-(4-methoxyphenyl)-5-(4-nitrophenyl)-	EtOH	259(3.82),336s(3.29)	24-0183-80
$C_{15}H_{11}N_3S$			
1,3,4-Thiadiazol-2-amine, 5-phenyl-N-(phenylmethylene)-	EtOH	209(4.51),220s(4.37), 300(4.53),350(3.48)	2-0144-80A
	DMF	308(4.61),350(3.60)	2-0144-80A
	CHCl$_3$	293(4.56),350(3.48)	2-0144-80A
	CCl$_4$	300(4.56),350(3.48)	2-0144-80A
$C_{15}H_{11}OS_2$			
Thieno[3,2,1-de]thianthren-11-ium, 2-methoxy-, perchlorate	MeOH	211(4.39),266s(4.27), 250(4.10),314(3.40)	39-1185-80C
$C_{15}H_{12}$			
Anthracene, 2-methyl-	C$_6$H$_{12}$	323(5.04),325(3.03), 342(3.25),360(3.40), 380(3.32)	44-1807-80
Anthracene, 9-methyl-	EtOH	251s(5.01),256(5.29), 316s(2.81),330(3.36), 347(3.72),365(3.95), 385(3.93)	44-1807-80
	n.s.g.	351(3.78),369(3.99), 389(3.97)	5-0954-80
1H-Trindene, 4,7-dihydro-	C$_6$H$_{12}$	220(4.125),227(4.088), 257(4.378),265(4.379), 282(3.992),297(4.046), 308(3.961),329(2.887)	35-1058-80

Compound	Solvent	$\lambda_{max}(\log \epsilon)$	Ref.
$C_{15}H_{12}BrNO$ Indeno[1,2-d]azepine, 10-bromo-4-eth-oxy-	EtOH	290(4.60),352(3.65), 370(3.74),390(3.64), 544(2.59)	18-3232-80
$C_{15}H_{12}BrNO_2$ 2-Propen-1-one, 1-(4-bromophenyl)-3-(2-hydroxyphenyl)amino]-, (Z)-	dioxan	264(4.19),387(4.46)	48-0099-80
$C_{15}H_{12}Br_6$ 1H-Trindene, 1,3,4,6,7,9-hexabromo-2,3,4,5,6,7,8,9-octahydro-	MeCN	243(5.033)	35-1058-80
$C_{15}H_{12}ClNO_2$ 2-Propen-1-one, 1-(4-chlorophenyl)-3-[(2-hydroxyphenyl)amino]-, (Z)-	dioxan	258(4.18),385(4.47)	48-0099-80
$C_{15}H_{12}ClNO_3$ 4H-Furo[3,2-b]pyrrole-5-carboxylic acid, 2-(4-chlorophenyl)-4-ethyl-	MeOH	343.3(4.78)	73-2949-80
$C_{15}H_{12}ClNO_4S_3$ 1,3-Dithiole-4,5-dicarboxylic acid, 2-[2-amino-1-(4-chlorophenyl)-2-thioxoethylidene]-, dimethyl ester	CHCl$_3$	314(4.09),390(4.24)	39-2693-80C
$C_{15}H_{12}ClN_3$ 1H-Pyrazol-5-amine, 1-(4-chlorophenyl)-4-(2,4-cyclopentadien-1-ylidene-methyl)-	EtOH	249(4.10),286(3.88), 368(4.35)	114-0127-80C
2(1H)-Quinolinone, 6-chloro-4-phenyl-, hydrazone	EtOH	219(4.54),249(4.58), 275s(4.12),354(3.71)	4-0575-80
$C_{15}H_{12}Cl_2$ 1H-Cycloprop[a]anthracene, 1,1-dichloro-1a,2,3,9b-tetrahydro-	hexane	227(4.85),265(3.59), 275(3.68),284(3.68), 294(3.47)	44-4183-80
1H-Cycloprop[b]anthracene, 1,1-dichloro-1a,2,9,9a-tetrahydro-	hexane	227(4.80),259(3.41), 268(3.54),278(3.58), 288(3.45)	44-4183-80
$C_{15}H_{12}Cl_2O_2$ Cyclopropane, 1,1-dichloro-2,2-diphen-oxy-	hexane	216(4.56),258(3.20), 265(3.28),271(3.23)	70-1928-80
$C_{15}H_{12}Cl_4O_4$ Spiro[3,5-cyclohexadiene-1,4'-[3]oxa-tricyclo[4.2.1.0^{2,5}]non[7]ene]-2,9'-diol, 3,4,5,6-tetrachloro-, 9'-acet-ate	CHCl$_3$	294s(3.74),302(3.78)	78-0155-80
$C_{15}H_{12}FNO_2$ 2-Propen-1-one, 1-(4-fluorophenyl)-3-[(2-hydroxyphenyl)amino]-, (Z)-	dioxan	245(4.12),255s(4.06), 379(4.45)	48-0099-80
$C_{15}H_{12}INO_2$ 2-Propen-1-one, 3-[(2-hydroxyphenyl)-amino]-1-(4-iodophenyl)-, (Z)-	dioxan	270(4.20),387(4.48)	48-0099-80
$C_{15}H_{12}N_2$ 1H-Imidazole, 4-[2-(1-naphthalenyl)-	EtOH	220(4.74),292(3.83)	4-0679-80

Compound	Solvent	$\lambda_{max}(\log \epsilon)$	Ref.
ethenyl]-, cis (cont.)			4-0679-80
trans	EtOH	229(4.52),322(4.30)	4-0679-80
Isoindolo[1,2-b]quinazoline, 10,12-di-hydro-	MeOH	206(4.51),242(4.37), 336(3.98)	83-0729-80
Isoindolo[2,1-a]quinazoline, 5,11-di-hydro-	MeOH	206(4.58),238(4.35), 275(3.69),282(3.78), 312(3.73)	83-0729-80
$C_{15}H_{12}N_2O$			
8(1H)-Cycloheptapyrazolone, 3-methyl-1-phenyl-	MeOH	233(4.38),305(4.01), 316(4.04),365(3.82)	4-1293-80
8(2H)-Cycloheptapyrazolone, 3-methyl-2-phenyl-	MeOH	229(4.41),246(4.38), 288(3.92),303(3.79), 379(3.94)	4-1293-80
Ethanone, 1-phenyl-2-(7H-pyrrolo[2,3-b]pyridin-7-yl)-	MeOH	242(4.08),307(3.94), 392(3.15)	48-0517-80
monohydrobromide	MeOH	244(4.35),297(4.05)	48-0517-80
3H-Pyrazol-3-one, 1,2-dihydro-4,5-di-phenyl-	MeOH	238(4.16),264s(4.06)	142-1921-80
Pyrimidine, 4-methoxy-5-(1-naphthal-enyl)-	EtOH	282(4.26),292(4.26)	22-0559-80
4(1H)-Pyrimidinone, 1-methyl-5-(1-naph-thalenyl)-	EtOH	282(3.99),292(3.97)	22-0559-80
4(3H)-Pyrimidinone, 3-methyl-5-(1-naph-thalenyl)-	EtOH	282(3.98),292(4.00)	22-0559-80
$C_{15}H_{12}N_2OS_2$			
4-Thiazolidinone, 5-(1-methyl-2(1H)-pyridinylidene)-3-phenyl-2-thioxo-	EtOH	457(4.37)	103-0227-80
$C_{15}H_{12}N_2O_2$			
Acetamide, N-(6-amino-1-oxo-1H-phena-len-2-yl)-	EtOH	203(4.54),214s(4.42), 238s(4.14),278s(4.17), 300(4.43),370(3.44), 560(4.07)	104-1820-80
2,6(1H,3H)-Pyridinedione, 3-(1(2H)-iso-quinolinylidene)-4-methyl-	EtOH	220(4.66),323(4.18), 468(3.35)	95-1261-80
2,6(1H,3H)-Pyridinedione, 4-methyl-3-(2(1H)-quinolinylidene)-	EtOH	244s(4.08),284(3.93), 333(4.20),445(4.40)	94-2892-80
$C_{15}H_{12}N_2O_2S$			
Benzamide, N-2-benzothiazolyl-4-meth-oxy-	CHCl$_3$	244(4.04),306(4.13)	48-0055-80
$C_{15}H_{12}N_2O_3$			
9,10-Anthracenedione, 1,4-diamino-2-(hydroxymethyl)-	EtOH	548(4.16)	18-3007-80 +146-0513-80
9,10-Anthracenedione, 1,4-diamino-2-methoxy-	gas	500(4.06)	135-0344-80
	film	539(--)	135-0344-80
	crystal	550(--)	135-0344-80
	hexane	536(--)	135-0344-80
	DMF	536(4.19)	135-0344-80
Propanetrione, diphenyl-, 1,3-dioxime, (E,Z)-	EtOH	232(4.3)	24-1507-80
1H-Pyrido[3,4-b]indole-2-carboxylic acid, 4-acetyl-, methyl ester	EtOH	270(4.47),286(4.66), 374(3.86)	4-0595-80
$C_{15}H_{12}N_2O_4$			
2-Propen-1-one, 3-[(2-hydroxyphenyl)-amino]-1-(4-nitrophenyl)-, (Z)-	dioxan	?(4.14),413(4.31)	48-0099-80

Compound	Solvent	$\lambda_{max}(\log \epsilon)$	Ref.
$C_{15}H_{12}N_2O_5S$			
4-Thia-1-azabicyclo[3.2.0]hept-2-ene-2-carboxylic acid, 3-ethenyl-7-oxo-, (4-nitrophenyl)methyl ester, (±)-	EtOH	264(4.21),348(3.92)	88-0561-80
$C_{15}H_{12}N_2S$			
Naphtho[2',1':5,6]thiopyrano[4,3-c]-pyrazole, 2,11-dihydro-2-methyl-	EtOH	213(4.42),236(4.33), 256(4.34),273(4.47), 282(4.52),327(3.86)	4-0121-80
Naphtho[2',1':5,6]thiopyrano[4,3-c]-pyrazole, 3,11-dimethyl-3-methyl-	EtOH	213(4.40),234(4.41), 275(4.31)	4-0121-80
$C_{15}H_{12}N_4O$			
10H-Indazolo[5,4-b][1,6]naphthyridin-10-one, 3,9-dihydro-8,9-dimethyl-	MeOH	223(3.90),236(3.92), 289(3.88),300s(3.81), 320s(3.42),396(2.99)	39-0522-80C
	acid	223(3.85),245(3.86), 256s(3.75),315(3.70), 440(2.86)	39-0522-80C
1,3,5-Triazin-2(5H)-one, 6-phenyl-4-(phenylamino)-	n.s.g.	247(4.54)	115-0243-80
$C_{15}H_{12}N_4O_2$			
Benzamide, N-(1,5-dihydro-5-oxo-3-phen-yl-4H-1,2,4-triazol-4-yl)-	EtOH	224(4.24),265(4.04)	4-1691-80
3H-1,2,4-Triazol-3-one, 4-amino-2-benz-oyl-2,4-dihydro-5-phenyl-	EtOH	235(4.25),272(3.98)	4-1691-80
$C_{15}H_{12}N_4O_3S$			
3H-1,2,4-Triazole-3-thione, 1,2-dihy-dro-1-(4-methoxyphenyl)-5-(4-nitro-phenyl)-	MeOH	256(4.48)	73-2804-80
$C_{15}H_{12}N_6$			
1H-Pyrazole, 1,1',1''-(1,3,5-benzene-triyl)tris-	EtOH	259(4.78)	24-2755-80
$C_{15}H_{12}N_9O_2$			
2,5'-Bi-2H-tetrazolium, 2'-methyl-3-(4-nitrophenyl)-5-phenyl-, perchlorate	EtOH	250(4.56)	103-0094-80
2H-Tetrazolium, 2-(1-methyl-1H-tetra-zol-5-yl)-3-(3-nitrophenyl)-, per-chlorate	EtOH	244(4.36)	103-0094-80
2H-Tetrazolium, 2-(1-methyl-1H-tetra-zol-5-yl)-3-(4-nitrophenyl)-, per-chlorate	EtOH	250(4.49),300(4.09)	103-0094-80
$C_{15}H_{12}O$			
Anthracene, 9-methoxy-	n.s.g.	352(3.74),370(3.93), 390(3.87)	5-0954-80
2,4,10,12-Cyclotridecatetraene-6,8-diyn-1-one, 5,10-dimethyl-	ether	250s(4.41),262(4.58), 273(4.60),387(4.00)	39-0466-80C
$C_{15}H_{12}OS$			
1-Propanone, 1,3-diphenyl-3-thioxo-	C_6H_{12}	262(3.96),325(4.09), 408(4.21),515s(1.36) (anom.)	39-1768-80B
anion	EtOH	257(4.09),400(4.28)	39-1768-80B
$C_{15}H_{12}O_2$			
1-Azulenecarboxylic acid, 4-ethynyl-,	C_6H_{12}	265(4.38),304(4.70),	18-1647-80

Compound	Solvent	$\lambda_{max}(\log \epsilon)$	Ref.
ethyl ester (cont.)		318(4.75),365(3.77), 375(3.61),387(3.65), 576(2.67),628(2.56)	18-1647-80
1-Azulenecarboxylic acid, 8-ethynyl-, ethyl ester	C_6H_{12}	270(4.49),305(4.50), 350(3.57),363(3.65), 380(3.10),440(2.30), 550(2.51),605(2.62), 660(2.50)	18-1647-80
4H-1-Benzopyran-4-one, 2,3-dihydro- 2-phenyl-	benzene EtOH	311(3.5) 252(3.95),320(3.55)	18-0518-80 18-2938-80
4H-Cyclopenta[def]phenanthrene-8,9-diol, 8,9-dihydro-, dl-	EtOH	270(4.10),296(3.45), 308(3.30)	18-1179-80
meso-	EtOH	268(4.14),295(3.40), 307(3.41)	18-1179-80
1H-Phenalen-1-one, 3-ethoxy-	EtOH	206s(4.56),225s(4.36), 245(4.37),328(4.09), 353(4.06)	78-2291-80
9(10H)-Phenanthrenone, 10-hydroxy- 10-methyl-	tert-BuOH	326(3.48)	35-4472-80
2-Propen-1-one, 1-(2-hydroxyphenyl)- 3-phenyl-	benzene	313(4.2),335(4.0)	18-0518-80
$C_{15}H_{12}O_2S_2$ Disulfide, benzoyl 4-methylbenzoyl	CH_2Cl_2	272(4.42)	118-0721-80
$C_{15}H_{12}O_3$ Benzoic acid, 2-(4-methylbenzoyl)-	EtOH	255(4.1)	40-1749-80
4H-1-Benzopyran-4-one, 2,3-dihydro- 7-hydroxy-3-phenyl-	MeOH	275(5.17),315(3.99)	42-0208-80
[1,1'-Biphenyl]-2-carboxylic acid, 2'-acetyl-	tert-BuOH	288(3.47)	35-4472-80
2H-Naphtho[2,3-b]pyran-5,10-dione, 2,2-dimethyl-	EtOH	249(4.36),294(4.46), 350(3.78),415(3.37), 485(3.25)	2-0013-80
1,3-Propanedione, 1-(2-hydroxyphenyl)- 3-phenyl-	MeOH	205(4.01),210(3.96), 250(3.59),360(4.16)	118-0874-80
$C_{15}H_{12}O_3Ru$ Ruthenium, tricarbonyl[η^4-5,6,7,8- tetrakis(methylene)bicyclo[2.2.2]- oct-2-ene]-, endo	isooctane	243s(3.71),247(3.72), 259s(3.59),282(3.33)	101-0103-80K
exo	isooctane	214(4.07),239(4.02), 246(4.03),257s(3.93), 286(3.68)	101-0103-80K
$C_{15}H_{12}O_3S$ Indeno[1,2-b]pyran-2-carboxylic acid, 4,5-dihydro-4-thioxo-, ethyl ester	MeOH	239(4.13),310(4.23), 396(4.34)	83-0429-80
$C_{15}H_{12}O_3S_2$ Dibenzo[b,f]thiepin-10(11H)-one, 2-(methylsulfonyl)-, 5-oxide	MeOH	251s(4.30),284(3.82)	73-0529-80
$C_{15}H_{12}O_3S_6$ 1,3,5-Cyclohexanetrione, 2,4,6-tris- (1,3-dithiolan-2-ylidene)-	MeCN	262(4.21),322(4.67), 404(4.65)	44-3719-80
$C_{15}H_{12}O_4$ 4H-1-Benzopyran-4-one, 2,3-dihydro- 5,7-dihydroxy-3-phenyl-	MeOH	290(4.31)	42-0208-80

Compound	Solvent	$\lambda_{max}(\log \epsilon)$	Ref.
Indeno[1,2-b]pyran-2-carboxylic acid, 4,5-dihydro-4-oxo-, ethyl ester	MeOH	237(4.05),248(4.07), 312(4.23)	83-0429-80
1,3-Propanedione, 1,3-bis(4-hydroxyphenyl)-	EtOH	227(4.18),292(4.12), 364(4.71)	102-2179-80
	EtOH-NaOEt	239(4.14),345(4.65), 425(4.53)	102-2179-80
2H-Pyran-2-one, 4-hydroxy-6-methyl-3-(1-oxo-3-phenyl-2-propenyl)-	MeOH	353(4.4)	83-0344-80

$C_{15}H_{12}O_4S$

Compound	Solvent	$\lambda_{max}(\log \epsilon)$	Ref.
Benzoic acid, 3-[[2-(carboxymethyl)-phenyl]thio]-	MeOH	225(4.27),250(4.05), 275s(3.77),310s(3.18)	73-1086-80

$C_{15}H_{12}O_5$

Compound	Solvent	$\lambda_{max}(\log \epsilon)$	Ref.
1,3-Azulenedicarboxylic acid, 2-formyl-, dimethyl ester	MeOH	234(4.53),275s(4.43), 292(4.62),302(4.70), 340(3.89),368(4.00)	18-3696-80
	CHCl$_3$	525(2.97)	18-3696-80
1,3-Azulenedicarboxylic acid, 5-formyl-, dimethyl ester	CHCl$_3$	275(4.39),308(4.53), 333(4.11),406(4.23), 520(3.13)	18-3696-80
2,4-Cyclohexadien-1-one, 6-acetoxy-6-benzoyloxy-	EtOH	235(4.15),313(3.46)	12-1553-80
2H-Naphtho[1,8-bc]furan-5-carboxaldehyde, 6,7-dihydro-4-hydroxy-2,2,8-trimethyl-6,7-dioxo-	MeOH	233(4.28),282(4.02), 295s(4.00),337(3.93), 520(3.12)	39-0249-80C
	MeOH-base	296(--),357(--), 596(--)	39-0249-80C
4H-Naphtho[2,3-b]pyran-4-one, 5,6-dihydroxy-8-methoxy-2-methyl-(rubrofusarin)	MeOH	225(4.45),278(4.68), 406(3.74)	39-2474-80C
1,3-Propanedione, 1-(2,4-dihydroxyphenyl)-3-(4-hydroxyphenyl)-(licodione)	MeOH	285(4.28),376(4.55)	102-2179-80
	MeOH-NaOMe	242(4.10),342(4.69), 415(4.19)	102-2179-80

$C_{15}H_{12}O_6$

Compound	Solvent	$\lambda_{max}(\log \epsilon)$	Ref.
Anhydrofusarubin	EtOH	237(4.25),290(4.22), 348(3.56),540(3.84)	23-1380-80
4H-1-Benzopyran-4-one, 2-(3,4-dihydroxyphenyl)-2,3-dihydro-5,7-dihydroxy- (eriodictyol)	MeOH	227s(4.71),289(4.66), 324s(4.19)	100-0739-80
	MeOH-NaOMe	245(--),323(--)	100-0739-80
1,3-Propanedione, 1,3-bis(2,4-dihydroxyphenyl)-	EtOH	231(4.23),283(4.45), 325(4.28),383(3.89), 400(3.89)	102-2179-80
	EtOH-NaOEt	281(3.99),324(4.26), 356(4.19)	102-2179-80
9H-Xanthen-9-one, 1,7-dihydroxy-3,6-dimethoxy-	MeOH	236(4.40),255(4.54), 307(4.17),362(3.99)	39-2353-80C

$C_{15}H_{12}O_7$

Compound	Solvent	$\lambda_{max}(\log \epsilon)$	Ref.
4H-1-Benzopyran-4-one, 2,3-dihydro-3,7-dihydroxy-2-(3,4,5-trihydroxyphenyl)- (taxifolin)	MeOH	229(4.48),291(4.49), 332s(--)	102-0893-80
	MeOH-NaOH	223(4.53),326(4.76)	102-0893-80
	MeOH-AlCl$_3$	227(4.6),315(4.61)	102-0893-80

$C_{15}H_{12}O_8$

Compound	Solvent	$\lambda_{max}(\log \epsilon)$	Ref.
4H-1-Benzopyran-4-one, 2,3-dihydro-3,5,7-trihydroxy-2-(3,4,5-trihydroxyphenyl)-	MeOH	229(4.00),293(4.70)	102-0893-80
	MeOH-AlCl$_3$	229(4.97),315(4.90)	102-0893-80

Compound	Solvent	$\lambda_{max}(\log \epsilon)$	Ref.
$C_{15}H_{13}BrNO_2$ Pyridinium, 1-[3-(4-bromophenyl)-3-oxo-1-propenyl]-5-hydroxy-2-methyl-, chloride, (E)-	EtOH	230(4.38),280(4.34)	39-0362-80C
$C_{15}H_{13}BrN_2O$ Ethanone, 1-phenyl-2-(7H-pyrrolo[2,3-b]pyridin-7-yl)-, monohydrobromide	MeOH	244(4.35),297(4.05)	48-0517-80
$C_{15}H_{13}BrN_2O_2$ 1H,7H-Pyrazolo[1,2-a]pyrazole-1,7-dione, 3-(bromomethyl)-2,5-dimethyl-6-phenyl-	dioxan	226s(4.10),254(4.18), 391(3.85)	35-4983-80
$C_{15}H_{13}BrO_3$ Naphtho[1,2-b]furan-4,5-dione, 2-(1-bromo-1-methylethyl)-2,3-dihydro-	EtOH	248(4.26),261(4.38), 290(3.87),331(3.38), 442(3.24)	2-0017-80
2H-Naphtho[1,2-b]pyran-5,6-dione, 3-bromo-3,4-dihydro-2,2-dimethyl-	EtOH	256(4.42),282(3.96), 334(3.21),410(3.18), 442(3.12)	2-0017-80
$C_{15}H_{13}BrO_4$ 2H-Naphtho[1,2-b]pyran-5,6-dione, 3-bromo-3,4-dihydro-4-hydroxy-2,2-dimethyl-	EtOH	253(4.42),277(3.89), 333(3.38),380(3.19), 415(3.24),440(3.12)	2-0013-80
$C_{15}H_{13}ClN_2$ Indole, 2-chloro-3-[1-(3-pyridinyl)-ethyl]-	EtOH	221(4.55),272(3.99), 291(3.82)	118-0365-80
2(1H)-Quinazolinone, 6-chloro-3,4-di-hydro-3-methyl-4-phenyl-	EtOH	260(4.04),300(3.30)	106-0751-80
$C_{15}H_{13}ClN_2O_2$ 4H-Furo[3,2-b]pyrrole-5-carboxamide, 2-(4-chlorophenyl)-4-ethyl-	MeOH	343(4.75),359(4.70)	73-2949-80
$C_{15}H_{13}ClN_2O_2S$ Acetamide, N-[6-chloro-2-[(2-oxo-2-phenylethyl)thio]-3-pyridinyl]-	n.s.g.	253(4.33),302(3.81)	103-0607-80
$C_{15}H_{13}ClN_2S$ Benzenamine, N-(6-chloro-2-ethyl-1,2-benzisothiazol-3(2H)-ylidene)-	MeOH	235(4.29),294(3.66), 357(3.76)	24-2490-80
	MeOH-HCl	244(4.35),339(3.94)	24-2490-80
$C_{15}H_{13}ClN_4O_3$ 6H-Pyrrolo[3,4-d]pyrimidine-6-propanoic acid, 2-amino-4-(4-chlorophenyl)-5,7-dihydro-7-oxo-	EtOH	254(4.23),268(4.23), 350(3.92)	4-1231-80
$C_{15}H_{13}ClO_4$ 2H-Pyran-2-one, 3-[3-(4-chlorophenyl)-1-oxopropyl]-4-hydroxy-6-methyl-	MeOH	309(4.1)	83-0344-80
$C_{15}H_{13}N$ Benz[g]isoquinoline, 6,8-dimethyl-	CHCl$_3$	256(5.32),316(3.52), 330(3.68),346(3.70), 358(3.70),380(3.88), 398(3.76)	103-0525-80

Compound	Solvent	$\lambda_{max}(\log \epsilon)$	Ref.
Benz[g]isoquinoline, 7,8-dimethyl-	CHCl$_3$	230(4.65),258(5.34), 320(3.34),335(3.54), 366(3.64),380(3.72), 400(3.62)	103-0525-80
Benzo[g]quinoline, 7,8-dimethyl-	CHCl$_3$	263(5.25),348(3.68), 356s(3.74),366(3.80), 380s(3.71),398(3.56)	103-0525-80
Benzo[g]quinoline, 7,9-dimethyl-	CHCl$_3$	260(5.28),306s(3.28), 320(3.52),338(3.72), 347s(3.74),356(3.76), 366s(3.74),384(3.60)	103-0525-80
1,6-Imino-8,13-methano[14]annulene, anti	EtOH	269(3.53),336(2.55)	89-1015-80
syn	EtOH	284(4.48),314(4.76), 375(3.98),518(2.93)	89-1015-80
1H-Indole, 3-methyl-2-phenyl-	EtOH	229(4.36),310(4.30)	39-0339-80B
C$_{15}$H$_{13}$NO			
2-Azetidinone, 1,4-diphenyl-	dioxan	251(3.96),285(2.75)	23-2061-80
Indeno[1,2-d]azepine, 4-ethoxy-	EtOH	288(4.5),345(3.6), 361(3.6),382(3.5), 544(2.6)	18-3232-80
1H-Indole, 1-hydroxy-3-methyl-2-phenyl-	EtOH	232(4.37),304(4.22)	39-0339-80B
2-Propen-1-one, 1,3-diphenyl-, oxime,	EtOH	290(4.31)	150-4726-80
(E,E)-	EtOH-base	263(--),324(--)	150-4726-80
(E,Z)-	EtOH	288(4.53)	150-4726-80
	EtOH-base	315(--)	150-4726-80
1H-Pyrrolizin-1-one, 2,3-dihydro-2-[(4-methylphenyl)methylene]-	EtOH	352(4.45)	145-1135-80
C$_{15}$H$_{13}$NOS			
2H-1,4-Benzothiazine, 3-(4-methoxy-phenyl)-	EtOH	234s(4.19),275(4.20), 309(4.10),323(4.10), 351s(3.96)	39-2923-80C
C$_{15}$H$_{13}$NO$_2$			
3H-Benz[e]indene-2-acetamide, 8-hydroxy-	EtOH	234(4.98),274(3.80), 294(3.73),318(3.38), 330(3.41)	87-0512-80
2-Propen-1-one, 3-[(2-hydroxyphenyl)-amino]-1-phenyl-, (Z)-	dioxan	247(4.16),382(4.45)	48-0099-80
1H-Pyrrolizin-1-one, 2,3-dihydro-2-[(2-methoxyphenyl)methylene]-	EtOH	361(4.35)	145-1135-80
1H-Pyrrolizin-1-one, 2,3-dihydro-2-[(4-methoxyphenyl)methylene]-	EtOH	360(4.49)	145-1135-80
Pyrrolo[2,1-a]isoquinoline-1-carboxylic acid, 2-methyl-, methyl ester	EtOH	223(4.44),243(4.15), 272s(4.45),281(4.62), 331(4.06)	18-0297-80
C$_{15}$H$_{13}$NO$_3$			
9(10H)-Acridinone, 1,3-dimethoxy-	EtOH	223(4.10),245s(4.40), 256(4.59),265(4.66), 285(4.05),314(3.75), 374(3.84)	100-0498-80
Benz[e]indene-2-acetamide, 2,3-dihydro-8-hydroxy-1-oxo-	EtOH	223(4.58),263(3.98), 317(3.78),349(3.87)	87-0512-80
1H-Benz[de]isoquinoline-1,3(2H)-dione, 2-ethyl-5-methoxy-	dioxan	246(4.33),333(3.99), 377(3.88)	56-0107-80
1H-Benz[de]isoquinoline-1,3(2H)-dione, 2-ethyl-6-methoxy-	dioxan	252(4.35),361(4.11)	56-0107-80

Compound	Solvent	$\lambda_{max}(\log \epsilon)$	Ref.
Benzo[5,6]cyclohepta[1,2-b]pyrrole-2-acetic acid, 1,4,5,10-tetrahydro-10-oxo-	MeOH	213(4.07),224(4.01), 228(4.01),240(3.96), 260(3.64),328(4.00)	4-1081-80
Glycine, N-([1,1'-biphenyl]-4-ylcarbonyl)-	H_2O	240(4.30)	103-0701-80
Phenol, 2-[4,5-dihydro-5-(4-hydroxyphenyl)-3-isoxazolyl]-	EtOH	220(4.27),265(4.11), 275(3.98),308(3.77)	142-1319-80
1-Propanone, 1-(2-nitroso-4-phenoxyphenyl)-	CHCl$_3$	760(1.53)	104-1780-80
$C_{15}H_{13}NO_3S$ Pyrano[3,2-b]indole-2-carboxylic acid, 4,5-dihydro-5-methyl-4-thioxo-, ethyl ester	MeOH	238(4.30),283(4.02), 322(4.12),382(4.10), 426(4.16)	83-0405-80
$C_{15}H_{13}NO_4$ Pyrano[3,2-b]indole-2-carboxylic acid, 4,5-dihydro-5-methyl-4-oxo-, ethyl ester	MeOH	222(4.54),257(4.12), 265(4.10),310(4.25)	83-0405-80
Pyrano[3,2-b]indole-2-carboxylic acid, 5-ethyl-4,5-dihydro-4-oxo-, methyl ester	MeOH	222(4.53),256(4.08), 264(4.05),308(4.23)	83-0405-80
$C_{15}H_{13}NO_4S_3$ 1,3-Dithiole-4,5-dicarboxylic acid, 2-(2-amino-1-phenyl-2-thioxoethylidene)-, dimethyl ester	CHCl$_3$	317(4.16),391(4.34)	39-2693-80C
$C_{15}H_{13}NO_5$ 9(10H)-Acridinone, 1,5-dihydroxy-2,3-dimethoxy-	EtOH	269(4.28),333(4.02), 347s(3.42),362s(3.05)	102-1566-80
	EtOH-HCl	276(4.62),318(4.30), 332(3.98),349(3.42), 367(3.28)	102-1566-80
	EtOH-NaOMe	272(4.42),318s(4.36), 334(3.28)	102-1566-80
$C_{15}H_{13}NS$ Benzene, 1,1'-(1-isothiocyanato-1,2-ethanediyl)bis-, (+)-	heptane	260(3.40),296(3.34)	104-0683-80
1H-Indole, 3-(methylthio)-2-phenyl-	H_2O dioxan	235(4.34),299(4.20) 237(4.15),301(4.11)	44-0780-80 44-0780-80
$C_{15}H_{13}N_3OS$ 3H-1,2,4-Triazole-3-thione, 1,2-dihydro-1-(4-methoxyphenyl)-5-phenyl-	MeOH	256(4.40)	73-2804-80
$C_{15}H_{13}N_3OS_2$ Naphtho[2',1':5,6]thiopyrano[4,3-c]-pyrazole-3(3aH)-carbothioamide, 11,11a-dihydro-3a-hydroxy-	EtOH	220(4.44),274(4.46)	4-0121-80
$C_{15}H_{13}N_3O_2$ 1H-Cyclopenta[gh]perimidine, 6,7-dihydro-1,2-dimethyl-4-nitro-	MeOH	285(4.10),315s(3.97), 355s(3.50),375s(3.54), 470(3.98)	103-0071-80
Pyrido[3,2-d]pyrimidine-2,4(1H,3H)-dione, 1,3-dimethyl-6-phenyl-	EtOH	277(4.33),335(3.66)	118-0479-80
$C_{15}H_{13}N_3O_2S$ Naphtho[2',1':5,6]thiopyrano[4,3-c]-	EtOH	225(4.42),273(4.26)	4-0121-80

Compound	Solvent	$\lambda_{max}(\log \epsilon)$	Ref.
pyrazole-3(3aH)-carboxamide, 11,11a-dihydro-3a-hydroxy- (cont.)			4-0121-80
$C_{15}H_{13}N_3O_2S_2$			
Benzenepropanamide, N-[4-amino-5-cyano-2-(methylthio)-3-thienyl]-β-oxo-	EtOH	223(4.22),280(4.21), 330(4.12)	95-0699-80
$C_{15}H_{13}N_3O_3$			
Acetamide, N-[4-[[(4-nitrophenyl)methylene]amino]phenyl]-	THF	382(4.29)	56-1177-80
Pyridazino[4,5-b]quinolin-1(2H)-one, 4-acetoxy-2,10-dimethyl-	EtOH	230(4.30),254(4.68), 300(3.82),340(3.77), 360(3.79)	94-3457-80 +142-0267-80
$C_{15}H_{13}N_3O_4$			
1H-Cyclohepta[c]furan-4,8-imine-1,3,5-trione, 9-(4,6-dimethyl-2-pyrimidinyl)-3a,4,8,8a-tetrahydro-, (3aα,4β,8β,8aα)-	$CHCl_3$	246(3.66),280(3.11)	39-0331-80C
$C_{15}H_{13}N_3S$			
Propanedinitrile, [2-(dimethylamino)-3-[4-(methylthio)phenyl]-2-cyclopropen-1-ylidene]-	CH_2Cl_2	357(4.6),376(4.4)	5-1409-80
$C_{15}H_{13}N_5O$			
1H-Pyrazole-4,5-dione, 3-(3-pyridinyl)-, 4-[(2-methylphenyl)hydrazone]	H_2O ion	436(3.88) 384(3.75)	2-0789-80A 2-0789-80A
1H-Pyrazole-4,5-dione, 3-(3-pyridinyl)-, 4-[(4-methylphenyl)hydrazone]	H_2O ion	440(3.91) 385(3.88)	2-0789-80A 2-0789-80A
$C_{15}H_{13}N_5O_2$			
1H-Pyrazole-4,5-dione, 3-(3-pyridinyl)-, 4-[(2-methoxyphenyl)hydrazone]	H_2O ion	452(3.32) 384(3.87)	2-0789-80A 2-0789-80A
1H-Pyrazole-4,5-dione, 3-(3-pyridinyl)-, 4-[(4-methoxyphenyl)hydrazone]	H_2O ion	456(3.81) 390(3.51)	2-0789-80A 2-0789-80A
$C_{15}H_{13}N_8$			
2,5'-Bi-2H-tetrazolium, 2'-methyl-3,5-diphenyl-, perchlorate	EtOH	250(4.60),295(3.88)	103-0094-80
2H-Tetrazolium, 2-(1-methyl-1H-tetrazol-5-yl)-3,5-diphenyl-, chloride	EtOH	249(4.49),320(3.68)	103-0094-80
$C_{15}H_{13}N_8O$			
3,5'-Bi-2H-tetrazolium, 2-(4-hydroxyphenyl)-2'-methyl-5-phenyl-, perchlorate	EtOH	245(4.37),372(3.61), 520(3.52)	103-0094-80
2H-Tetrazolium, 2-(4-hydroxyphenyl)-3-(1-methyl-1H-tetrazol-5-yl)-5-phenyl-, perchlorate	EtOH	245(4.44),395(3.75), 542(3.78)	103-0094-80
$C_{15}H_{13}OP$			
5H-Dibenzo[b,f]phosphepin, 5-methyl-, 5-oxide	EtOH	225(4.51),269(3.89), 300(4.12)	139-0243-80A
$C_{15}H_{14}$			
5H-Dibenzo[a,c]cycloheptene, 6,7-dihydro-	C_6H_{12}	248(4.20),280s(3.08)	95-0718-80
Stilbene, α-methyl-, cis	hexane	263(4.07)	46-0847-80
Stilbene, α-methyl-, trans	hexane	273(4.32)	46-0847-80
	3-Mepentane at 77° K	280(4.44)	46-0847-80

Compound	Solvent	$\lambda_{max}(\log \epsilon)$	Ref.
$C_{15}H_{14}BrN_3$			
Acetaldehyde, [(4-methylphenyl)imino]-, (4-bromophenyl)hydrazone	hexane	293(3.65),410(4.37)	65-2072-80
	EtOH	312(3.60),377(4.57)	65-2072-80
$C_{15}H_{14}ClNO_2$			
4H-Furo[3,2-b]pyrrole-5-methanol, 2-(4-chlorophenyl)-4-ethyl-	MeOH	341.3(4.69)	73-2949-80
$C_{15}H_{14}ClNO_3$			
3-Pyridinecarboxylic acid, 1,4-dihydro-4-oxo-5-[(4-chlorophenyl)methyl]-, ethyl ester	EtOH	256s(3.88),260(3.90), 287(3.72)	4-0359-80
3-Pyridinecarboxylic acid, 5-[(4-chlorophenyl)methyl]-1-ethyl-1,4-dihydro-4-oxo-	EtOH	261(3.99),292(3.70)	4-0359-80
$C_{15}H_{14}ClNO_4$			
1H-Pyrrole-2-acetic acid, 5-(4-chlorobenzoyl)-4-(hydroxymethyl)-1-methyl-	MeCN	254(4.11),315(4.05)	87-0098-80
1-Pyrrolidinebutanoic acid, 4-[(4-chlorophenyl)methylene]-2,3-dioxo-	EtOH	233(3.88),333(4.45)	4-1231-80
$C_{15}H_{14}Cl_2N_2O$			
3-Pyridinecarbonitrile, 1-[(2,6-dichlorophenyl)methyl]-6-ethoxy-1,6-dihydro-	CH_2Cl_2	313(3.8),358s(3.2)	5-1350-80
$C_{15}H_{14}Cl_2O_2S$			
4H-Pyran-4-one, 3,5-dichloro-2-[(1,1-dimethylethyl)thio]-6-phenyl-	heptane	201(4.26),250(4.25), 280(4.12)	5-1960-80
$C_{15}H_{14}Cl_4OS$			
2,4-Pentadienethioic acid, 2,3,4,5-tetrachloro-5-phenyl-, S-(1,1-dimethylethyl) ester, (Z,Z)-	heptane	202(4.27),240(4.11)	5-1960-80
$C_{15}H_{14}FN_3O_5$			
1(2H)-Pyrimidinebutanoic acid, γ-(benzoylamino)-5-fluoro-3,4-dihydro-2,4-dioxo-	MeOH	270(4.00)	94-1137-80
$C_{15}H_{14}N_2$			
Diazene, (2-cyclopropylphenyl)phenyl-	EtOH	221(3.00),328(3.06), 448(2.75)	104-0534-80
1H-Indol-1-amine, 2-methyl-N-phenyl-	EtOH	203(4.82),222(4.76), 276(3.98),283(3.99), 291(3.87)	104-0534-80
$C_{15}H_{14}N_2O$			
Acetic acid, (diphenylmethylene)hydrazide	MeOH	281(4.36)	18-3225-80
	dioxan	286(4.27)	18-3225-80
Azetidine, 1-nitroso-2,4-diphenyl-, cis	C_6H_{12}	241(3.79),398(1.95)	4-0219-80
trans	C_6H_{12}	245(3.72),398(1.92)	4-0219-80
Benzoic acid, [(3-methylphenyl)methylene]hydrazide	C_6H_{12}	294(4.50)	115-0013-80
	benzene	297(4.42)	115-0013-80
	EtOH	298(4.57)	115-0013-80
	ether	293(4.50)	115-0013-80
	dioxan	295(4.42)	115-0013-80
	$CHCl_3$	297(4.48)	115-0013-80
	CCl_4	296(4.43)	115-0013-80

Compound	Solvent	$\lambda_{max}(\log \epsilon)$	Ref.
Benzoic acid, [(4-methylphenyl)meth-ylene]hydrazide	C_6H_{12}	297(4.37)	115-0013-80
	benzene	297(4.54)	115-0013-80
	EtOH	301(4.40)	115-0013-80
	ether	295(4.36)	115-0013-80
	dioxan	297(4.45)	115-0013-80
	$CHCl_3$	300(4.45)	115-0013-80
	CCl_4	299(4.41)	115-0013-80
9H-Carbazole-9-propanenitrile, 1,2,3,4-tetrahydro-1-oxo-	EtOH	237(3.98),306(4.09)	39-0097-80C
Diazene, (2-cyclopropylphenyl)phenyl-, 2-oxide	EtOH	253(4.12),335(4.03)	104-0534-80
1-Propanone, 1-[2-(phenylazo)phenyl]-	EtOH	228(3.05),322(4.30), 445(2.73)	104-0534-80
$C_{15}H_{14}N_2OS$			
Phenol, 4-[(2-ethyl-1,2-benzisothiazol-3(2H)-ylidene)amino]-	MeOH	230(4.17),287(3.36), 340(3.77)	24-2490-80
	MeOH-HCl	235(4.23),339(3.90)	24-2490-80
$C_{15}H_{14}N_2O_2$			
Benzenamine, 2,6-dimethyl-4-nitro-N-(phenylmethylene)-, (E)-	C_6H_{12}	208(4.45),233(4.10), 254(4.11),296s(4.12)	18-1993-80
Benzenamine, 4-ethyl-N-[(4-nitrophen-yl)methylene]-	THF	356(4.17)	56-1177-80
Benzoic acid, 2-(phenylazo)-, ethyl ester	EtOH	231(4.11),323(4.38), 446(1.71)	104-0534-80
Benzo[b][1,6]naphthyridin-1(2H)-one, 6-methoxy-2,3-dimethyl-	MeOH	212(4.50),260(4.77), 278(4.38),300s(4.45), 310(4.52),400(4.01)	39-0522-80C
	MeOH-acid	208(4.21),268(4.35), 287s(3.95),325(4.09), 390(3.77),440(3.68)	39-0522-80C
2,4,6-Cycloheptatrien-1-one, 2-hydroxy-3-[1-(phenylhydrazono)ethyl]-, (E)-	MeOH	242(4.33),335(4.01), 396(4.05)	4-1293-80
1H,5H-Pyrazolo[1,2-a]pyrazole-1,5-di-one, 2,3,7-trimethyl-6-phenyl-	dioxan	234(4.00),332(4.16)	35-4983-80
1H,7H-Pyrazolo[1,2-a]pyrazole-1,7-di-one, 2,3,6-trimethyl-5-phenyl-	dioxan	223(4.44),255(4.18), 380(4.04)	35-4983-80
1H-Pyrazolo[1,2-a]pyrazol-4-ium, 3-hy-droxy-5,7-dimethyl-1-oxo-2-(phenyl-methyl)-, hydroxide, inner salt	benzene	402(3.049)	35-4983-80
	EtOH	398(3.056)	35-4983-80
	MeCN	210(4.362),250s(4.056), 260s(3.828),394(3.027)	35-4983-80
3H-Pyrrolizine-2-carboxylic acid, 1-amino-3-phenyl-, methyl ester	CH_2Cl_2	252(4.04),262s(3.95), 331(4.21)	150-3078-80
$C_{15}H_{14}N_2O_2S$			
Imidazo[2,1-b]thiazole-2-carboxylic acid, 3-methyl-6-phenyl-, ethyl ester	EtOH	257s(4.37),265(4.38), 280(4.38),287(4.38), 294s(4.36)	18-3308-80
$C_{15}H_{14}N_2O_3$			
Benzenamine, 4-ethoxy-N-[(4-nitrophen-yl)methylene]-	THF	377(4.27)	56-1177-80
Benzoic acid, 2-[(2-amino-2-oxoethyl)-phenylamino]-	MeOH	218(4.12),237(4.13), 291(3.95)	73-3593-80
Ethanone, 2-[(4-methylphenyl)amino]-1-(4-nitrophenyl)-	CH_2Cl_2	380(2.80)	83-0315-80
10H-Phenoxazine, 2-nitro-10-propyl-	MeCN	328(3.65)	44-2331-80
Pyrano[4,3-b]indole-1,3-dione, 4-(dimethylaminomethylene)-4,5-dihydro-5-methyl-	EtOH	218(4.46),237(4.46), 291(4.14),365(3.93)	39-1688-80C

Compound	Solvent	$\lambda_{max}(\log \epsilon)$	Ref.
$C_{15}H_{14}N_2O_4$			
4H-Pyrazolo[5,1-c][1,4]oxazine-3-carb-	EtOH	212(3.84),238(4.00)	118-0875-80
oxylic acid, 6,7-dihydro-6-oxo-2-			
phenyl-, ethyl ester			
$C_{15}H_{14}N_2O_4S_2$			
4-Thiazolecarboxylic acid, 4,5-dihydro-	THF	272(3.92),332(4.25)	35-3199-80
2-(6-hydroxy-2-benzothiazolyl)-,			
1-ethoxyethenyl ester, (S)-			
$C_{15}H_{14}N_2O_4Se$			
Selenonium, bis(phenylmethyl)-,	MeCN	340(3.97)	70-0123-80
dinitromethylide			
$C_{15}H_{14}N_2O_5$			
2-Furancarboxylic acid, 5-[2-(4-nitro-	MeOH	205(4.12),214(4.05),	73-0135-80
phenyl)-1-aziridinyl]-, ethyl ester		288(4.35)	
$C_{15}H_{14}N_2O_5S_2$			
4-Thia-1-azabicyclo[3.2.0]hept-2-ene-	EtOH	261(4.17),337(4.01)	33-1093-80
2-carboxylic acid, 3-(ethylthio)-			
7-oxo-, (4-nitrophenyl)methyl ester			
$C_{15}H_{14}N_2O_6S$			
4-Aza-1,3-indanedione, N-methyl-2-(N-	50% EtOH	211(4.447),238(3.915),	103-1239-80
pyridiumyl)-, betaine, methyl sulfate		263(3.370),381(4.114)	
5-Aza-1,3-indanedione, N-methyl-2-(N-	50% EtOH	209(4.446),227(4.342),	103-1239-80
pyridiniumyl)-, betaine, methyl sul-		270s(4.0),277(4.057),	
fate		292s(3.89),304s(3.78),	
		359(4.10),405-24(3.38)	
$C_{15}H_{14}N_2S$			
Benzenamine, N-(2-ethyl-1,2-benzisothi-	MeOH	348(3.87)	24-2490-80
azol-3(2H)-ylidene)-	MeOH-HCl	339(4.02)	24-2490-80
$C_{15}H_{14}N_4$			
Benzonitrile, 4-[[4-(dimethylamino)-	EtOH	451(4.52)	62-0158-80
phenyl]azo]-			
$C_{15}H_{14}N_4O$			
2-Naphthalenol, 1-[(1,3-dimethyl-1H-	EtOH	256(3.82),407(4.12)	65-1705-80
pyrazol-4-yl)azo]-			
3H-Pyrazolo[3,4-c]pyridinium, 6-(benz-	EtOH	228(4.23),335(3.74)	88-4507-80
oylamino)-3,3-dimethyl-, hydroxide,			
inner salt			
$C_{15}H_{14}N_4O_2$			
Acetaldehyde, [(4-methylphenyl)imino]-,	EtOH	403(4.71)	65-2072-80
(4-nitrophenyl)hydrazone	hexane	303(--),408(--)	65-2072-80
2-Propenoic acid, 2-methyl-, 4-[(1,1-	CHCl$_3$	290(4.10)	126-1565-80
dicyanoethyl)azo]phenyl]methyl ester			
1H-Pyrazole, 1-acetyl-4,5-dihydro-	CHCl$_3$	486(4.28)	104-1143-80
3-[(2-hydroxy-1-naphthalenyl)azo]-			
$C_{15}H_{14}N_4O_2S$			
Acetic acid, [(1,5-diphenylformazan-	benzene	421(4.30)	39-0139-80B
yl)thio]-	benzene	420(4.31),538(3.74)	88-0899-80
	H$_2$O	424(4.36)	39-0139-80B
	MeOH	418(4.39)	39-0139-80B
	EtOH	420(4.30)	39-0139-80B
	PrOH	424(4.40)	39-0139-80B

Compound	Solvent	$\lambda_{max}(\log \epsilon)$	Ref.
Acetic acid, [(1,5-diphenylformazan-yl)thio]- (cont.)	BuOH	423(4.32)	39-0139-80B
	acetone	420(4.11)	39-0139-80B
	acetone	414(4.12),535(3.98)	88-0899-80
	ether	411(4.25)	39-0139-80B
	EtOAc	416(4.17)	39-0139-80B
	HCONH$_2$	428(4.24)	39-0139-80B
	MeCN	422(4.25)	39-0139-80B
	pyridine	431(4.25)	39-0139-80B
	DMSO	443(4.16)	39-0139-80B
	DMSO	430(4.04),547(3.96)	88-0899-80
	CHCl$_3$	420(4.29)	39-0139-80B
	CHCl$_3$	418(4.35),530s(3.68)	88-0899-80
	neutral	420(4.45)	39-0139-80B
	anion	500(4.64)	39-0139-80B
	cation	512(4.68)	39-0139-80B
Carbamic acid, [(9H-pyrido[3,4-b]indol-3-ylamino)thioxomethyl]-, ethyl ester	MeOH	226(4.40),232(4.41), 241(4.44),261(5.47), 293(4.37),355(3.80)	2-0045-80
$C_{15}H_{14}N_4O_3$			
Acetaldehyde, [(4-methoxyphenyl)imino]-, (4-nitrophenyl)hydrazone	EtOH	300(3.75),397(4.55)	65-2072-80
6H-Pyrrolo[3,4-d]pyrimidine-6-propanoic acid, 2-amino-5,7-dihydro-7-oxo-4-phenyl-	EtOH	248(4.32),265(4.22), 347(4.05)	4-1231-80
$C_{15}H_{14}N_4O_4$			
2,4,7(1H,3H,8H)-Pteridinetrione, 8-(2-hydroxyethyl)-6-(phenylmethyl)-	pH 1	283(4.03),332(4.16)	39-2645-80C
	pH 13	290(3.99),353(4.20)	39-2645-80C
$C_{15}H_{14}N_4O_6$			
Piperidine, 1-(2,4,5-trinitro-1-naphthalenyl)-	DMSO	430(3.92)	18-2921-80
$C_{15}H_{14}O$			
Benzene, (1-phenoxy-1-propenyl)-	hexane	250(4.12),276s(--), 290s(--)	118-0847-80
Ethanone, 2-bicyclo[2.2.1]hepta-2,5-dien-7-yl-1-phenyl-	EtOH	243(4.20),277(2.92), 315(1.85)	78-0397-80
3,5-Hexadien-2-one, 6-(2-ethynylphenyl)-3-methyl-	EtOH	220(4.04),233(3.95), 248s(3.97),255(4.10), 263(4.08),327(4.40), 331(4.41)	39-0473-80C
4(1H)-Phenanthrenone, 2,3-dihydro-3-methyl-, (±)-	EtOH	215(4.52),310(3.72)	56-2247-80
2-Propanone, 1-[1,1'-biphenyl]-4-yl-	dioxan	254.5(4.32)	24-2462-80
$C_{15}H_{14}O_2$			
2H-1-Benzopyran-7-ol, 3,4-dihydro-2-phenyl-	EtOH	211(4.41),285(3.49), 290(3.43)	102-0889-80
[1,1'-Biphenyl]-4-carboxylic acid, ethyl ester	MeOH	274(3.34),330(--)	33-0456-80
1H-Cyclopropa[f]naphtho[2,3-b][1,4]-dioxocin, 1a,2,11,11a-tetrahydro-	CHCl$_3$	245(4.15),283(3.74), 317(3.30)	48-0909-80
$C_{15}H_{14}O_2S_2$			
1,3-Dithiole-4-carboxylic acid, 2-[(4-ethenylphenyl)methylene]-, ethyl ester	EtOH	246(4.26),355s(4.45), 363(4.46),405s(3.54)	116-0240-80

Compound	Solvent	$\lambda_{max}(\log \epsilon)$	Ref.
$C_{15}H_{14}O_3$			
Benzeneacetic acid, 2-methoxy-, phenyl ester	EtOH	221(3.91),272(3.36), 278(3.33)	49-0081-80
Benzeneacetic acid, 4-methoxy-, phenyl ester	EtOH	229(3.89),276(3.19), 283(3.12)	49-0081-80
2H-1-Benzopyran-7-ol, 3,4-dihydro-2-(4-hydroxyphenyl)-	EtOH	226(4.27),284(3.67), 290s(3.53)	102-0889-80
2H-1-Benzopyran-2-one, 7-methoxy-6-(3-methyl-1,3-butadienyl)-, (E)-	EtOH	220(4.20),276(4.34), 283s(4.32),341(4.03)	12-0395-80
Ethanone, 1-(4-hydroxyphenyl)-2-(2-methoxyphenyl)-	EtOH	221(4.15),280(4.24)	49-0081-80
Ethanone, 1-(4-hydroxyphenyl)-2-(4-methoxyphenyl)-	EtOH	222(4.23),280(4.24)	49-0081-80
Methanone, [4-(2-hydroxyethoxy)phenyl]-phenyl-	CHCl$_3$	286(4.36),339(2.64)	73-1826-80
Naphtho[1,2-b]furan-4,5-dione, 2,3-dihydro-2-(1-methylethyl)-	EtOH	251(4.22),262(4.38), 288(3.81),350(3.46), 422(3.21)	2-0017-80
$C_{15}H_{14}O_3S$			
2-Butenoic acid, 3-(2-furanyl)-4-(phenylthio)-, methyl ester, (E)-	EtOH	217(4.13),309(4.13)	73-0142-80
$C_{15}H_{14}O_4$			
1,3-Azulenedicarboxylic acid, 2-methyl-, dimethyl ester	MeOH	237(4.50),270(4.38), 295(4.57),305(4.66), 343(3.90),371(3.93), 490(2.95)	18-3276-80
2H-1-Benzopyran-2-one, 6-(3-formyl-2-butenyl)-7-methoxy-, (E)-	EtOH	226(4.40),284(3.79), 295(3.88),318s(4.13), 325(4.15)	12-0395-80
2H-1-Benzopyran-2-one, 7-methoxy-8-(3-methyl-1-oxo-2-butenyl)-	EtOH	235(4.20),322(4.20)	2-0341-80
7H-Furo[3,2-g][1]benzopyran-7-one, 9-methoxy-2-(1-methylethyl)-	EtOH	219(4.52),252(4.60), 302(4.05)	102-1556-80
1-Naphthalenecarboxaldehyde, 7,8-dihydro-2-hydroxy-6-methyl-4-(1-methylethyl)-7,8-dioxo-	EtOH	229(4.12),262(3.93), 309(3.86),342s(3.54), 484(3.01)	39-0249-80C
1,4-Naphthalenedione, 2-hydroxy-3-(2-hydroxy-3-methyl-3-butenyl)-	EtOH	251(4.49),280(4.26), 332(3.42)	2-0017-80
2H-Naphtho[1,8-bc]furan-2-one, 3,8-dihydroxy-7-methyl-5-(1-methylethyl)-	MeOH	234(4.28),263(4.32), 356(4.03)	39-0249-80C
	MeOH-base	271(--),398(--)	39-0249-80C
Spiro[1,3-dioxolane-2,3'(4'H)-[2H]-naphthaleno[2,3-b][1,4]dioxepin]	CHCl$_3$	243(4.54),276(3.81), 286(3.80),314(3.35), 328(3.46)	49-0413-80
$C_{15}H_{14}O_5$			
2H-1-Benzopyran-2-one, 7-acetoxy-8-methoxy-6-(2-propenyl)-	MeOH	204(4.63),224s(4.30), 287(4.11),325s(3.63)	44-1470-80
2-Butenoic acid, 4-(1,3-dihydro-1-oxo-2H-inden-2-ylidene)-2,4-dihydroxy-, ethyl ester, (Z,Z)-	MeOH	241(3.81),252(3.83), 307(4.02),389(4.09)	83-0429-80
1-Naphthalenecarboxaldehyde, 7,8-dihydro-2,3-dihydroxy-6-methyl-4-(1-methylethyl)-7,8-dioxo- (o-hemigossypolone)	CHCl$_3$	276(4.12),334(4.09), 400(3.46),488(3.18)	102-1735-80
1-Propanone, 3-(4-hydroxyphenyl)-1-(2,4,6-trihydroxyphenyl)- (phloretin)	MeOH	225(4.38),286(4.35)	100-0739-80
	MeOH-NaOMe	321(4.46)	100-0739-80

Compound	Solvent	$\lambda_{max}(\log \epsilon)$	Ref.
$C_{15}H_{14}O_5S$			
2-Butenoic acid, 3-(2-furanyl)-4-(phenylsulfonyl)-, methyl ester, (E)-	EtOH	221(4.07),315(4.26)	73-0142-80
$C_{15}H_{14}O_6$			
Isoplumericin	EtOH	215(4.24)	100-0649-80
Plumericin	EtOH	215(4.24)	100-0649-80
1-Propanone, 3-(3,4-dihydroxyphenyl)-1-(2,4,6-trihydroxyphenyl)-	MeOH	225(4.19),287(4.20),325s(3.49)	100-0739-80
(3-hydroxyphloretin)	EtOH	206(4.31),225(4.17),288(4.16)	102-0476-80
2H,5H-Pyrano[3,2-c][1]benzopyran-3-carboxylic acid, 7,8,9,10-tetrahydro-2,5-dioxo-, ethyl ester	EtOH	373(4.20)	49-0093-80
$C_{15}H_{14}O_7$			
Fusarubin	EtOH	225(4.49),302(3.94),470(3.82),495(3.88),532(3.70)	23-1380-80
Naphtho[1,2-d]-1,3-dioxole-6,9-dione, 4,5,7-trimethoxy-8-methyl-	MeOH	225(4.32),273(4.06),302(3.84),405(3.84)	12-1073-80
Naphtho[2,3-d]-1,3-dioxole-5,8-dione, 4,6,9-trimethoxy-7-methyl-	MeOH	220(4.36),272(4.29),304(3.78),380(3,43)	12-1073-80
$C_{15}H_{14}Se_3$			
Carbonotriselenoic acid, bis(phenylmethyl) ester	80% DMSO	360(4.15),546(2.29)	78-1451-80
$C_{15}H_{15}BrO_3$			
2H-1-Benzopyran-2-one, 6-(2-bromo-3-methyl-2-butenyl)-7-methoxy-	EtOH	224(4.34),239(3.85),253(3.75),298(3.91),328s(4.18),347s(3.96)	12-0395-80
$C_{15}H_{15}BrO_3S$			
Benzenesulfonic acid, 4-bromo-, 5,6-bis(methylene)bicyclo[2.2.1]hept-2-yl ester, endo	EtOH	235.5(4.40)	33-1016-80
exo	EtOH	234(4.38)	33-1016-80
$C_{15}H_{15}ClN_2OS$			
4(5H)-Thiazolone, 5-[(2-chlorophenyl)-methylene]-2-piperidino-	MeOH	325(4.35)	48-0835-80
$C_{15}H_{15}ClN_4O_7$			
α-D-Ribofuranuronic acid, 1-(6-chloro-9H-purin-9-yl)-1-deoxy-, methyl ester, 2,3-diacetate	MeOH	205(4.24),250s(--),264(3.88)	24-2891-80
β-	MeOH	204(4.21),251s(--),264(3.83)	24-2891-80
$C_{15}H_{15}ClO_3$			
2H-1-Benzopyran-2-one, 6-(2-chloro-3-methyl-3-butenyl)-7-methoxy-	EtOH	224(4.30),243(3.79),253(3.64),298(3.90),327(4.16),345s(3.94)	12-0395-80
$C_{15}H_{15}Cl_2NO_3$			
3-Pyridinecarboxylic acid, 1-[(2,6-dichlorophenyl)methyl]-1,6-dihydro-6-methoxy-, methyl ester	CH_2Cl_2	255(4.1),314(4.0)	5-1350-80

Compound	Solvent	$\lambda_{max}(\log \epsilon)$	Ref.
$C_{15}H_{15}IO_5$			
2-Naphthalenecarboxylic acid, 8-iodo-4,5,7-trimethoxy-, methyl ester	$CHCl_3$	294(3.80),306(3.82), 319(3.81),375(3.81)	12-2531-80
$C_{15}H_{15}N$			
Acridine, 9,10-dihydro-9,9-dimethyl-	C_6H_{12}	215(4.31),281(4.25)	24-0358-80
	EtOH	218(4.18),288(4.28)	24-0358-80
15-Azatricyclo[8.4.1.1^{3,8}]hexadeca-3,5,7,10,12,14-hexaene	hexane	255s(3.74),360s(2.23)	89-1015-80
Benzenamine, 2,6-dimethyl-N-(phenyl-methylene)-	C_6H_{12}	213(4.33),253(4.35), 340(3.26)	18-1993-80
$C_{15}H_{15}NO$			
Benzenamine, N-(1-methyl-2-phenoxy-ethylidene)-	dioxan	265s(3.51),271(3.60), 278(3.58)	24-2462-80
3H-Indol-3-one, ,2,4,5,6,7-hexahydro-2-(phenylmethylene)-	MeOH	314(4.49),428(3.98)	5-0564-80
	$CHCl_3$	310(4.36),412(3.87)	5-0564-80
Pyridine, 2-[2-(4-methoxyphenyl)-1-methylethenyl]-	EtOH	228(4.166),271(4.317), 295(4.412)	83-0826-80
$C_{15}H_{15}NOS$			
Benzenamine, N-[1-methyl-2-(phenylsul-finyl)ethylidene]-	dioxan	272(3.86),289(3.87)	24-2462-80
$C_{15}H_{15}NO_2$			
5H-Benzocyclohepten-5-one, 7-morpho-lino-	EtOH	286(4.48),347(3.92)	39-2077-80C
Benzoic acid, 2-[(2,3-dimethylphenyl)-amino]-	MeOH-HCl	279(3.93),350(3.85)	44-2127-80
2H-1-Benzopyran-3-carbonitrile, 4-(2,2-dimethylpropyl)-2-oxo-	EtOH	297(4.12),304(4.11), 340(3.86)	39-2937-80C
2,5-Cyclohexadien-1-one, 4-[(4-methoxy-phenyl)imino]-2,6-dimethyl-, per-chlorate	CH_2Cl_2	502(4.10)	104-2020-80
$C_{15}H_{15}NO_2S$			
Benzenamine, N-[1-methyl-2-(phenylsul-fonyl)ethenyl]-	dioxan	293(4.21)	24-2462-80
Benzenamine, N-[1-methyl-2-(phenylsul-fonyl)ethylidene]-	dioxan	294(3.94)	24-2462-80
Pyridine, 3-(1,3-dioxolan-2-yl)-2-[(phenylmethyl)thio]-	EtOH	252(4.09),290(3.65)	118-0405-80
$C_{15}H_{15}NO_3$			
1H-Pyrrole-3-carboxylic acid, 4-formyl-2-methyl-1-(phenylmethyl)-, methyl ester	EtOH	266(3.92),287(3.85)	39-1199-80C
$C_{15}H_{15}NO_3S$			
8H-Thieno[3,2-c]azepin-8-one, 4,5,6,7-tetrahydro-5-[(4-methylphenyl)sul-fonyl]-	EtOH	203(4.08),232(3.96), 271(4.04)	138-1389-80
$C_{15}H_{15}NO_4$			
1H-1-Benzazepine-3,4-dicarboxylic acid, 1-methyl-, dimethyl ester	EtOH	239(4.20),259(4.39), 293(4.10),317(3.54)	44-0456-80
1H-Pyrrole-2-carboxylic acid, 4-acetyl-3-hydroxy-1-phenyl-, ethyl ester	EtOH	246(4.23)	78-2125-80
	EtOH-base	245(4.12),268(4.10), 358(3.59)	78-2125-80
1H-Pyrrole-2,4-dicarboxylic acid, 3-methyl-1-phenyl-, 2-ethyl ester	EtOH	226(4.45),255(4.12)	78-2125-80
	EtOH-base	226(4.38),266(4.17)	78-2125-80

Compound	Solvent	$\lambda_{max}(\log \epsilon)$	Ref.
1H-Pyrrole-3,4-dicarboxylic acid, 2-methyl-1-phenyl-, 3-ethyl ester	EtOH	226(4.22),262(3.90)	78-2125-80
1-Pyrrolidinebutanoic acid, 2,3-dioxo-4-(phenylmethylene)-	EtOH	229(3.83),235(3.79), 328(4.43)	4-1231-80
$C_{15}H_{15}NO_4S$			
Acetic acid, (7-oxo-4-oxa-1-azabicyclo-[3.2.0]hept-3-ylidene)(phenylthio)-, ethyl ester	EtOH	245(4.21),300s(--)	142-1999-80
$C_{15}H_{15}NO_5$			
1H-Indole-2-butanoic acid, 3-hydroxy-1-methyl-α,γ-dioxo-, ethyl ester	MeOH	238(4.26),312(4.28), 362(3.82)	83-0405-80
1H-Pyrrole-3,4-dicarboxylic acid, 1-(4-methoxyphenyl)-, dimethyl ester	MeOH	242(4.43)	44-4573-80
1-Pyrrolidinepropanoic acid, 4-[(4-methoxyphenyl)methylene]-2,3-dioxo-	EtOH	247(4.09),370(4.59)	4-1231-80
$C_{15}H_{15}NO_6$			
Propanedioic acid, [1-(methoxycarbo-nyl)-1H-indol-3-yl]-, dimethyl ester	EtOH	225(4.33),255(3.96), 262(3.96),288(3.77)	103-0045-80
$C_{15}H_{15}NO_7$			
2-Naphthalenecarboxylic acid, 4,5,7-trimethoxy-8-nitro-, methyl ester	CHCl$_3$	301(3.75),312(3.66), 346s(3.54),368(3.67), 397s(3.45)	12-2531-80
$C_{15}H_{15}NS$			
Benzenamine, N-[1-methyl-2-(phenyl-thio)ethylidene]-	dioxan	247s(3.86),286s(3.53)	24-2462-80
$C_{15}H_{15}N_2$			
Pyridinium, 1-[2-(1H-indol-3-yl)ethyl]-, bromide	MeOH	274(4.28),293(3.90), 505(2.64)	103-0921-80
Pyridinium, 1-methyl-4-(1-methyl-1H-indol-2-yl)-, iodide	n.s.g.	220(4.09),245(3.65), 388(4.12)	103-0585-80
$C_{15}H_{15}N_3$			
Acetaldehyde, [(2-methylphenyl)imino]-, phenylhydrazone	hexane EtOH	289(3.79),408(4.27) 300(3.74),368(4.46)	65-2072-80 65-2072-80
Acetaldehyde, [(4-methylphenyl)imino]-, phenylhydrazone	hexane EtOH	287(3.83),407(4.33) 295(3.76),376(4.54)	65-2072-80 65-2072-80
Benzenecarboximidic acid, (1-phenyl-ethylidene)hydrazide	MeOH	228(4.07),308(4.06)	104-0822-80
$C_{15}H_{15}N_3O$			
Acetaldehyde, [(2-methoxyphenyl)-imino]-, phenylhydrazone	hexane EtOH	294(3.53),417(4.32) 296(3.77),375(4.46)	65-2072-80 65-2072-80
Acetaldehyde, [(4-methoxyphenyl)-imino]-, phenylhydrazone	hexane EtOH	294(3.71),412(4.32) 300(3.81),383(4.57)	65-2072-80 65-2072-80
$C_{15}H_{15}N_3O_2$			
1,4-Benzenediamine, N,N-dimethyl-N'-[(4-nitrophenyl)methylene]-	THF	446(4.30)	56-1177-80
Pyrido[2,3-d]pyrimidin-2(1H)-one, 3,4-dihydro-4-(2-hydroxyphenyl)-1,3-dimethyl-	MeOH	263(3.78),285(3.90)	44-1918-80
2,4(1H,3H)-Pyrimidinedione, 1,3-di-methyl-5-(3-methyl-1H-indol-2-yl)-	MeCN	260(3.95),291(3.98), 340(3.72)	35-7535-80
Pyrimido[4,5-b]quinoline-2,4(3H,10H)-dione, 3,7,8,10-tetramethyl-	M HCl pH 6	259(4.57),351(4.27) 259(4.57),329(4.00),	83-0937-80 83-0937-80

Compound	Solvent	$\lambda_{max}(\log \epsilon)$	Ref.
(cont.) Urea, N-(5H-[1]benzopyrano[2,3-b]pyridin-5-yl)-N,N'-dimethyl-	MeOH	401(4.08) 235(3.77),269(3.36), 290(3.44)	83-0937-80 44-1918-80
$C_{15}H_{15}N_3O_2S$ Pyrimido[4,5-b]quinoline-2,4(1H,3H)-dione, 1,3,7-trimethyl-5-(methylthio)-	EtOH	226(4.30),254(4.55), 270(4.58),324(3.80), 396(3.77)	142-0679-80B
$C_{15}H_{15}N_3O_3$ Pyrimido[4,5-b]quinoline-2,4(3H,10H)-dione, 8-methoxy-3,7,10-trimethyl-	M HCl pH 4	257(4.50),378(4.55) 251(4.48),274(4.27), 343(3.83),393s(4.30), 403(4.30)	83-0937-80 83-0937-80
$C_{15}H_{15}N_3O_3S$ Pyrimido[4,5-b]quinoline-2,4(1H,3H)-dione, 7-methoxy-1,3-dimethyl-5-(methylthio)-	EtOH	224(4.32),268(4.67), 317(3.71),406(3.74)	142-0679-80B
Pyrimido[4,5-b]quinoline-2,4(1H,3H)-dione, 8-methoxy-1,3-dimethyl-5-(methylthio)-	EtOH	230(4.44),272(4.65), 348(4.22)	142-0679-80B
Pyrimido[4,5-b]quinoline-2,4(1H,3H)-dione, 9-methoxy-1,3-dimethyl-5-(methylthio)-	EtOH	230(4.34),248(4.39), 283(4.64),324(3.74), 400(3.65)	142-0679-80B
$C_{15}H_{15}N_3O_4$ Piperidine, 1-(2,4-dinitro-1-naphthalenyl)-	DMSO	422(3.90)	18-2921-80
$C_{15}H_{15}N_5O_2$ 1H-Indole-2,3-dione, 3-[(5-ethyl-1,4-dihydro-6-methyl-4-oxo-2-pyrimidinyl)hydrazone]	EtOH	205(4.38),250(4.17), 286s(3.70),385(4.31)	103-1279-80
$C_{15}H_{15}N_5O_3$ 4(1H)-Pteridinone, 6-(1,2-dihydroxypropyl)-2-(phenylamino)-, [S-(R*,S*)]-	pH -1.0 pH 4.5 pH 9.5	255(4.20),324(3.90) 236(4.03),289(4.32), 352(3.78) 243s(4.05),284(4.38), 374(3.91)	18-2344-80 18-2344-80 18-2344-80
$C_{15}H_{15}N_5O_4$ Acetamide, N-[4-(1-acetyl-5,6,7,8-tetrahydro-8-oxopyrrolo[2,3-c]-azepin-4(1H)-ylidene)-4,5-dihydro-5-oxo-1H-imidazol-2-yl]-	MeOH	235(4.21),281(3.92), 376(4.29)	77-0435-80
4(1H)-Pteridinone, 2-(phenylamino)-6-(1,2,3-trihydroxypropyl)-, [R-(R*,S*)]-	pH -1.0 pH 4.5 pH 9.5	255(4.21),324(3.91) 237(4.05),289(4.33), 353(3.80) 240s(4.06),284(4.39), 374(3.92)	18-2344-80 18-2344-80 18-2344-80
[S-(R*,S*)]-	pH -1.0 pH 4.5 pH 9.5	255(4.21),324(3.91) 237(4.05),289(4.34), 353(3.80) 240s(4.06),285(4.38), 375(3.92)	18-2344-80 18-2344-80 18-2344-80
$C_{15}H_{15}OP$ 5H-Dibenzo[b,f]phosphepin, 10,11-dihydro-5-methyl-, 5-oxide	EtOH	225(3.88),264s(3.10), 271(3.21),278(3.15),	139-0243-80A

Compound	Solvent	$\lambda_{max}(\log \epsilon)$	Ref.
(cont.)		302s(2.30)	139-0243-80A
$C_{15}H_{15}OS$ 5H-Cyclopenta[b]thiopyrylium, 6,7-di- hydro-2-(4-methoxyphenyl)-, per- chlorate	CH_2Cl_2	258(4.00),442(4.21)	104-0170-80
$C_{15}H_{16}BrNO_3S$ 4H-1-Benzothiopyran-4-one, 3-bromo- 2-[2-(diethylamino)ethenyl]-, 1,1- dioxide	EtOH	236(3.74),290(4.08), 469(4.55)	150-0139-80
$C_{15}H_{16}ClNO_2$ 2H-Pyran-2-one, 3-chloro-6-(1-methyl- ethyl)-4-(methylphenylamino)-	EtOH	213(4.09),238(4.04), 250s(4.01),280(3.88), 329(4.02)	4-0507-80
$C_{15}H_{16}ClNO_2S$ 4H-1-Benzothiopyran-4-one, 3-chloro- 2-[2-(diethylamino)ethenyl]-, 1-oxide	EtOH	257(3.98),304(4.01), 466(4.49)	150-0139-80
$C_{15}H_{16}ClN_5S$ 2H-Pyrrole-3,5-diamine, 2-(2,1-benz- isothiazol-3-ylimino)-4-chloro- N,N,N',N'-tetramethyl-	$CHCl_3$	311(4.03),371(3.88), 388(3.86),472(4.25), 501(4.25),545(3.97)	88-2883-80
2H-Pyrrole-3,5-diamine, 2-(2-benzothia- zolylimino)-4-chloro-N,N,N',N'-tetra- methyl-	$CHCl_3$	254(3.95),281(3.85), 295(3.86),395(4.26), 418(4.33),445(4.25), 482(3.88)	88-2883-80
$C_{15}H_{16}FN_6O_6P$ Uridine, 2'-deoxy-5-fluoro-, 5'-(di- 1H-imidazol-1-ylphosphinate)	MeOH	269(3.96)	87-1229-80
$C_{15}H_{16}F_3N_5O_5$ Adenosine, 2'-deoxy-8-(trifluoromethyl)-, 3',5'-diacetate	MeOH MeOH-acid MeOH-base	264(4.06) 262(4.19) 264(4.09)	39-2755-80C 39-2755-80C 39-2755-80C
$C_{15}H_{16}NO$ Pyridinium, 1,3-dimethyl-5-(2-oxo- 2-phenylethyl)-, iodide	EtOH	247(4.2),271s(3.96), 288s(3.31)	39-0072-80C
	EtOH-NaOH	253(4.19),373(4.38)	39-0072-80C
$C_{15}H_{16}NO_2S$ Pyridinium, 3-(1,3-dioxolan-2-yl)- 2-(methylthio)-1-phenyl-, iodide	EtOH	217(4.31),281(3.80), 325s(--)	118-0405-80
$C_{15}H_{16}N_2O$ Benzeneethanol, α-methyl-2-(phenylazo)-	EtOH	230(2.72),325(2.88), 453(1.69)	104-0534-80
Benzenemethanol, α-ethyl-2-(phenylazo)-	EtOH	230(2.78),325(2.96), 453(1.69)	104-0534-80
4H-Benzimidazol-4-one, 1,5,6,7-tetra- hydro-6,6-dimethyl-2-phenyl-2-phenyl-	EtOH	218(4.18),298(4.37)	4-1723-80
Indolo[2,3-a]quinolizin-4(1H)-one, 2,3,6,7,12,12b-hexahydro-	EtOH	223(4.62),274s(3.89), 281(3.90),290(3.78)	94-2527-80
Urea, (1,2-diphenylethyl)-	EtOH	242(2.30),248(2.46), 253(2.58),258(2.66), 264(2.56),268(2.42)	104-0683-80

Compound	Solvent	$\lambda_{max}(\log \epsilon)$	Ref.
$C_{15}H_{16}N_2O_2$			
9H-Carbazole-9-propanamide, 1,2,3,4-tetrahydro-1-oxo-	EtOH	239(4.20),308(4.30)	39-0097-80C
$C_{15}H_{16}N_2O_2S$			
Sulfonium, dimethyl-, 1-[(1-isoquinolinylamino)carbonyl]-2-oxopropylide	EtOH	214(4.64),230(4.53), 290(4.04),300(4.03), 329(4.01),342s(3.89)	95-1261-80
Sulfonium, dimethyl-, 2-oxo-1-[(2-quinolinylamino)carbonyl]propylide	EtOH	243(4.62),276(4.44), 326(4.12),338(4.09)	94-0795-80
$C_{15}H_{16}N_2O_3$			
Acetamide, N-[2-[(1,4-dihydro-3-methyl-1,4-dioxo-2-naphthalenyl)amino]-ethyl]-	EtOH	272(4.32),460(3.44)	83-0603-80
1H-1,2-Diazepine, 1-(4-ethoxybenzoyl)-3-methoxy-	EtOH	220(3.95),265(4.02), 324(2.90)	44-5095-80
6-Oxa-2,7-diazabicyclo[3.2.2]nona-3,8-diene-2-carboxylic acid, 7-phenyl-, ethyl ester	EtOH	220(3.61),255(3.74)	88-0319-80
Pyridinium, 1-[(4-ethoxybenzoyl)amino]-2-methoxy-, hydroxide, inner salt	EtOH	250(4.21),283(3.94), 303(3.74)	44-5095-80
$C_{15}H_{16}N_2O_3S$			
2(1H)-Pyrimidinone, 1-[4-(benzoyloxy)-butyl]-3,4-dihydro-4-thioxo-	MeOH	228(4.17),251s(3.76), 332(4.29)	78-0865-80
4(5H)-Thiazolone, 5-[(3-methoxyphenyl)-methylene]-2-morpholino-	MeOH	320(4.36),333(4.40)	48-0835-80
4(5H)-Thiazolone, 5-[(4-methoxyphenyl)-methylene]-2-morpholino-	MeOH	308s(4.31),325s(4.43)	48-0835-80
$C_{15}H_{16}N_2O_4$			
1H-1,3-Benzodiazepine-1,2-dicarboxylic acid, diethyl ester	EtOH	248(4.20),266s(--)	94-2602-80
Phenol, 2-[4-nitro-2-(propylamino)-phenoxy]-	MeCN	398(3.61)	44-2331-80
Phenol, 2-[5-nitro-2-(propylamino)-phenoxy]-	MeCN	395(4.30)	44-2331-80
2H-Pyrano[4,3-d]pyrimidine-2,4(3H)-di-one, 1,5,7,8-tetrahydro-5-hydroxy-1,3-dimethyl-7-phenyl-	EtOH	270(3.95)	142-0289-80B
1H-Pyrazole-3-carboxylic acid, 5-benz-oyl-4-hydroxy-, butyl ester	MeOH	235(4.73),270s(3.88), 280s(2.78)	39-2670-80C
2,4(1H,3H)-Pyrimidinedione, 1-[4-(benz-oyloxy)butyl]-	MeOH	226(4.15)	78-0865-80
$C_{15}H_{16}N_2O_5S$			
4(1H)-Pyrimidinone, 2,3-dihydro-5-(4-C-phenyl-β-D-ribofuranosyl)-2-thioxo-	pH 1	276(4.13),289(4.14)	142-0761-80
	pH 13	216(4.29),264(4.14), 289(4.14)	142-0761-80
	MeOH	276(4.22),290(4.17)	142-0761-80
$C_{15}H_{16}N_2O_6$			
5(2H)-Isoxazolone, 2-(1,1-dimethyl-3-oxobutyl)-3-hydroxy-4-(4-nitro-phenyl)-	neutral	388(4.13)	4-0299-80
	anion	236(4.33),438(4.17)	4-0299-80
	MeOH	242(4.18),385(4.13)	4-0299-80
2,4(1H,3H)-Pyrimidinedione, 5-(4-C-phenyl-β-D-ribofuranosyl)-	pH 1	263(3.94)	142-0761-80
	pH 13	288(3.71)	142-0761-80
	MeOH	264(3.73)	142-0761-80
Uridine, 5-phenyl-	MeCN	235(4.57),280(4.57)	88-2813-80

Compound	Solvent	$\lambda_{max}(\log \epsilon)$	Ref.
$C_{15}H_{16}N_4$			
Formazan, 1,5-bis(4-methylphenyl)-	EtOH	242(4.37),297(4.01), 369(4.60),450(3.85)	104-0751-80
1,2-Phenazinediamine, N^2-propyl-	MeOH	387(3.73),555(3.46)	32-0135-80
$C_{15}H_{16}N_4O$			
Imidazo[5,1-f][1,2,4]triazin-4(1H)-one, 2-methyl-5-phenyl-7-propyl-	EtOH	275(4.01),295(4.00), 311(4.00)	39-1139-80C
$C_{15}H_{16}N_6O$			
3H-Pyrazol-3-one, 4-[(1,3-dimethyl-1H-pyrazol-4-yl)azo]-2,4-dihydro-5-methyl-2-phenyl-	EtOH	247(4.36),402(4.24)	65-1705-80
$C_{15}H_{16}N_6O_4$			
1H-Pyrrole-2-carboxamide, N-[5-[[(2-cyanoethyl)amino]carbonyl]-1-methyl-1H-pyrrol-2-yl]-1-methyl-5-nitro-	EtOH	271(4.23),345(4.15)	36-1334-80
$C_{15}H_{16}O$			
Ethanone, 2-bicyclo[2.2.1]hept-2-en-7-yl-1-phenyl-, anti	EtOH	243(4.15),282(3.07), 314(1.96)	78-0397-80
syn	EtOH	243(4.03),277(2.98), 315(1.86)	78-0397-80
Ethanone, 1-(2,3,4,9-tetrahydro-1H-fluoren-2-yl)-	EtOH	208(4.28),259(4.07)	56-0453-80
4H-Fluoren-4-one, 1,2,3,4a-tetrahydro-4a,9-dimethyl-	EtOH	254(3.86),268(3.87), 294(3.30)	39-1909-80C
3-Oxatricyclo[4.2.1.0^{2,5}]non-7-ene, 4-methyl-4-phenyl-	EtOH	250(2.64)	78-0397-80
4(1H)-Phenanthrenone, 2,3,4a,9-tetrahydro-4a-methyl-	EtOH	206(4.04),226(2.92)	56-2247-80
$C_{15}H_{16}O_2$			
3-Benzofurancarboxaldehyde, 6-cyclohexyl-	MeOH	230(4.35),266(3.84)	118-0236-80
Cycloprop[2,3]indeno[5,6-b]furan-2(4H)-one, 4a,5,5a,6,6a,6b-hexahydro-3,6b-dimethyl-5-methylene- (chloranthalactone A)	MeOH	279(4.10)	94-0092-80
1,9-Phenanthrenedione, 2,3,4,4a,10-10a-hexahydro-10a-methyl-, trans	EtOH	253(4.15),294(3.30)	104-0037-80
Propanoic acid, 2,2-dimethyl-, 1-naphthalenyl ester	THF	272(3.75),281(3.80), 291(3.65),313(2.59), 317(2.35)	116-1138-80
$C_{15}H_{16}O_3$			
Chloranthalactone A SeO$_2$ oxidn. product	MeOH	273(4.26)	94-0092-80
3H-Cycloprop[2,5]oxireno[4,5]indeno-[5,6-b]furan-3-one, 5,5a,6,6a,7,7a-7b,7c-octahydro-4,7b-dimethyl-6-methylene- (chloranthalactone B)	MeOH	226(4.11)	94-0092-80
3H-Naphtho[1,8-bc]furan-3-one, 4,5-dihydro-8-hydroxy-7-methyl-5-(1-methylethyl)-, (R)- (hibiscone D)	EtOH	229s(3.98),243s(3.93), 330(3.12)	39-0249-80C
	EtOH-base	230s(--),268(--), 405(--)	39-0249-80C
$C_{15}H_{16}O_3S$			
3-Thiophenecarboxylic acid, 2,5-dihydro-4-hydroxy-2-methyl-5-(phenylmethylene)-, ethyl ester, (Z)-	EtOH	240(3.96),289(3.89), 347(4.47),365(4.44)	33-1542-80

Compound	Solvent	$\lambda_{max}(\log \epsilon)$	Ref.
$C_{15}H_{16}O_4$			
2H-1-Benzopyran-2-one, 6-(2-hydroxy-3-methyl-3-butenyl)-7-methoxy-	EtOH	224(4.28),244s(3.77), 254(3.66),298s(3.84), 330(4.14)	12-0395-80
2H-1-Benzopyran-2-one, 6-(4-hydroxy-3-methyl-2-butenyl)-7-methoxy-	EtOH	224(4.30),244s(3.76), 254(3.66),298(3.86), 331(4.18)	12-0395-80
2H-1-Benzopyran-2-one, 6-methoxy-7-[(3-methyl-2-butenyl)oxy]-	EtOH	231(4.26),253(3.81), 263s(3.69),288s(3.72), 297(3.78),346(4.10)	94-1847-80
3-Butenoic acid, 4-[2-(3-methoxy-3-oxo-1-propenyl)phenyl]-, methyl ester, (E,E)-	EtOH	246(4.28),284(4.25)	44-0357-80
Cyclopenta[g]-2-benzopyran-1,6-dione, 3,4,7,8-tetrahydro-8-hydroxy-5,7,7-trimethyl- (pterolactone A)	MeOH	260(4.22),323(3.45)	94-1869-80
Matricarin, 11,13-dehydrodeacetyl-	EtOH	211(4.03),252(4.09)	102-0103-80
Pergillin	EtOH	225(3.98),287(4.03)	98-0989-80
$C_{15}H_{16}O_5$			
5H-Benzocycloheptene-1,2-dicarboxylic acid, 6,7,8,9-tetrahydro-5-oxo-, dimethyl ester	MeCN	205(4.52),250(4.19), 295(3.41)	24-1584-80
2H-1-Benzopyran-4-carboxylic acid, 7-methoxy-2-oxo-, butyl ester	EtOH	345(4.08)	95-0289-80
2H-1-Benzopyran-2-one, 8-(3,4-dihydroxy-3-methyl-1-butenyl)-7-methoxy-, (E)-(±)- (casegravol)	EtOH	245(3.68),255(3.73), 321(4.15)	25-0154-80
2H-1-Benzopyran-2-one, 6-(2,3-epoxy-1-hydroxy-3-methylbutyl)-7-methoxy-	EtOH	223(4.28),243(3.74), 252(3.60),297(3.92), 326(4.16),344s(3.89)	12-0395-80
2H-1-Benzopyran-2-one, 6-(2-hydroperoxy-3-methyl-3-butenyl)-7-methoxy-	EtOH	224(4.29),244(3.77), 254(3.69),299s(3.93), 330(4.15),347s(3.96)	12-0395-80
2H-1-Benzopyran-2-one, 8-hydroxy-6-methoxy-7-[(3-methyl-2-butenyl)oxy]-	EtOH	230(4.10),259(3.66), 315(3.94)	105-0558-80
Butanoic acid, (7-methoxy-2-oxo-2H-1-benzopyran-4-yl)methyl ester	EtOH	323(4.18)	95-0744-80
Cyclohept[cd]isobenzofuran-3-carboxylic acid, 2,6,7,8,9,9a-hexahydro-9a-methoxy-2-oxo-, methyl ester	MeCN	207(4.65),237(3.93), 287(3.32)	24-1584-80
Cyclopenta[g]-2-benzopyran-1,6-dione, 3,4,7,8-tetrahydro-8-hydroxy-7-(hydroxymethyl)-5,7-dimethyl- (pterolactone B)	CHCl$_3$	260(4.06),325(3.27)	94-1869-80
1,3-Cyclopentanedione, 2-(2-acetoxy-5-methoxyphenyl)-2-methyl-	n.s.g.	281(3.23)	44-0501-80
1-Naphthalenecarboxaldehyde, 2,3,7,8-tetrahydroxy-6-methyl-4-(1-methylethyl)- (2-hydroxyhemigossypol)	EtOH	238(4.27),274(3.79), 295s(--),304s(--), 399(3.63)	102-1735-80
	EtOH-HCl	232(4.32),279(3.71), 348s(--),389(3.49)	102-1735-80
	EtOH-NaOH	290(3.75),384(3.51), 450(3.42)	102-1735-80
2-Naphthalenecarboxylic acid, 4,5,7-trimethoxy-, methyl ester	CHCl$_3$	285(3.85),290(3.84), 303s(3.64),341s(3.48), 357(3.68),372(3.68)	12-2531-80
1,4-Naphthalenedione, 2-(2,3-dihydroxy-3-methylbutyl)-3-hydroxy-	EtOH	240(4.13),253(4.24), 278(4.31),287(4.21), 335(3.44),390(3.15)	2-0017-80
Toxol, 13-acetoxy-	CHCl$_3$	275(4.09)	102-0639-80

Compound	Solvent	$\lambda_{max}(\log \epsilon)$	Ref.
$C_{15}H_{16}O_6$			
Allamdin	EtOH	238(4.15)	100-0649-80
2H-1-Benzopyran-2-one, 8-hydroxy-7-(4-hydroxy-3-methyl-2-butenyl)oxy]-6-methoxy-	EtOH	229(4.15),258(3.71), 315(3.95)	105-0558-80
Plumericin, dihydro-	EtOH	240(3.97)	100-0649-80
Spiro[1,3-benzodioxole-2,1'-cyclopentane], 5,6-diacetoxy-	EtOH	240(3.75),290(3.96)	12-0527-80
Spiro[bicyclo[2.2.2]octa-5,7-diene-2,2'-oxirane]-5,6-dicarboxylic acid, 4,7-dimethyl-3-oxo-, dimethyl ester	EtOH	232(3.72),244s(3.68), 305s(2.60),315(2.64), 328s(2.49)	44-2189-80
Spiro[bicyclo[2.2.2]octa-5,7-diene-2,2'-oxirane]-5,6-dicarboxylic acid, 7,8-dimethyl-3-oxo-, dimethyl ester	EtOH	239(3.69),306(2.76), 313(2.76),330s(2.56)	44-2189-80
Spiro[cyclopropa[cd]pentalen-1(2H),2'-oxirane]-2b,4b(2aH,4aH)-dicarboxylic acid, 2a,4-dimethyl-2-oxo-, dimethyl ester	EtOH	255s(2.69),313s(1.95), 325s(1.85),340s(1.48)	44-2189-80
Spiro[cyclopropa[cd]pentalen-1(2H),2'-oxirane]-2b,4b(2aH,4aH)-dicarboxylic acid, 3,4-dimethyl-2-oxo-, dimethyl ester	EtOH	258(2.60),313s(1.81), 326s(1.74),341s(1.40)	44-2189-80
$C_{15}H_{16}O_7$			
Allamandicin	EtOH	238(4.06)	100-0649-80
$C_{15}H_{16}O_{10}$			
2H-1-Benzopyran-2-one, 7-(β-D-glucopyranosyloxy)-6,8-dihydroxy- (erioside)	MeOH	267(3.66),329(3.95)	102-1554-80
$C_{15}H_{16}S_2Si$			
1,3-Dithia-2-silacyclohexane, 2,2-diphenyl-	hexane	194(4.73),220(4.15), 260s(2.94),273(2.79), 276(2.91)	101-0147-80A +131-0099-80C
1,3-Dithia-2-silacyclopentane, 4-methyl-2,2-diphenyl-	hexane	223(4.27),245(3.63), 273(2.86)	101-0147-80A +131-0099-80C
$C_{15}H_{16}S_4$			
1,3-Dithiolane, 2,2'-(2-phenyl-1,3-propanediylidene)bis-	EtOH	211(3.33),246(3.35), 254(3.34),257s(3.33), 265s(3.27),269s(3.16), 359(2.50)	35-3095-80
$C_{15}H_{17}BrNO$			
1H-Indolizinium, 3-(bromomethyl)-5-(2-furanyl)-2,3-dihydro-3,8-dimethyl-, bromide, (±)-	EtOH	204(4.24),248(3.75), 330(4.00)	19-0009-80
1H-Indolizinium, 3-(bromomethyl)-5-(3-furanyl)-2,3-dihydro-3,8-dimethyl-, bromide, (±)-	EtOH	207(4.02),282(3.72)	19-0009-80
$C_{15}H_{17}BrO_3$			
2H-Pyran-2-one, 5-bromotetrahydro-4-hydroxy-4,5-dimethyl-6-(2-phenylethenyl)-	EtOH	250(4.34)	94-1509-80
$C_{15}H_{17}BrO_4$			
2H-1-Benzopyran-2-one, 6-(2-bromo-3-hydroxy-3-methylbutyl)-7-methoxy-	EtOH	222(4.23),242(3.75), 252(3.63),295(3.83), 327(4.10)	12-0395-80

Compound	Solvent	$\lambda_{max}(\log \epsilon)$	Ref.
$C_{15}H_{17}ClN_2O$			
1(2H)-Isoquinolinone, 6-chloro-3-(cy-clohexylamino)-	EtOH	241(4.48),312(4.34), 381(3.57)	95-0826-80
1(2H)-Isoquinolinone, 7-chloro-3-(cy-clohexylamino)-	EtOH	228(4.38),312(4.38), 391(3.55)	95-0826-80
Pyrazineethanol, α-(4-chlorophenyl)-3,5,6-trimethyl-	EtOH	214(4.32),281(4.08), 300s(3.81)	44-0999-80
$C_{15}H_{17}ClN_2O_3$			
2H-1,3-Benzoxazin-2-one, 6-chloro-3,4-dihydro-3-methyl-4-(1-methyl-4-oxo-3-piperidinyl)-	EtOH	224(3.92),276(3.11)	4-0277-80
$C_{15}H_{17}ClN_4$			
Piperidine, 1-[[[1-(4-chlorophenyl)-1H-pyrazol-5-yl]imino]methyl]-	EtOH	254(4.19),290(4.10)	114-0127-80C
$C_{15}H_{17}ClO_2$			
1,7-Naphthalenedione, 2-chloro-4,4a,5,6-tetrahydro-4a,5-dimethyl-4-(1-methylethenyl)-	EtOH	266(3.91),283(3.97)	83-0048-80
$C_{15}H_{17}Cl_2N_5O_4$			
α-D-Ribofuranuronamide, 1-deoxy-1-(2,6-dichloro-7H-purin-7-yl)-N-ethyl-2,3-O-(1-methylethylidene)-	MeOH	216(4.38),258s(--), 282(3.84),292s(--)	24-2891-80
α-D-Ribofuranuronamide, 1-deoxy-1-(2,6-dichloro-9H-purin-9-yl)-N-ethyl-2,3-O-(1-methylethylidene)-	MeOH	211(4.36),254s(--), 274(3.98)	24-2891-80
β-	MeOH	205(4.32),212(4.29), 255s(--),275(3.88)	24-2891-80
$C_{15}H_{17}N$			
1H-Indole, 4,5,6,7-tetrahydro-1-(phen-ylmethyl)-	EtOH	207(4.19),258(3.05), 264(2.96),270(2.85), 310(2.79)	44-2741-80
1H-Pyrido[3,2,1-jk]carbazole, 2,3,3a,4,5,6-hexahydro-	EtOH	232(4.60),285(3.96)	39-0097-80C
$C_{15}H_{17}NOS$			
4H-[1]Benzothieno[4,5-c]quinolizin-4-one, 5,5a,6,7,8,9,11,12-octahydro-	EtOH	216(4.08),248(4:38), 285(4.08)	4-0403-80
$C_{15}H_{17}NO_2$			
Acetamide, N-[4-(1-methyl-4-oxo-2-cy-clohexen-1-yl)phenyl]-	EtOH	244(4.32)	22-0295-80
Acetamide, N-[4-(6-methyl-3-oxo-1-cy-clohexen-1-yl)phenyl]-	EtOH	233(4.14)	22-0295-80
Benzamide, N-ethyl-N-(6-oxo-1-cyclo-hexen-1-yl)-	ether	215(4.08),325s(2.35)	78-1585-80
2-Cyclohexen-1-one, 3-benzoyl-2-(ethyl-amino)-	ether	222(4.12)	78-1585-80
7(1H)-Indolizinone, 2,3,5,6-tetrahydro-6-(4-methoxyphenyl)-	EtOH	224(4.06),278s(3.52), 285s(3.62),318(4.18)	44-1713-80
	EtOH-acid	224(4.06),276s(3.72), 284s(3.83),307(4.00)	44-1713-80
1H-Pyrrole-3-carboxylic acid, 2,5-di-methyl-1-phenyl-, ethyl ester	EtOH	237(4.04),265s(3.68)	78-2125-80
$C_{15}H_{17}NO_2S$			
Pyridine, 3-(dimethoxymethyl)-2-[(phen-	EtOH	251(4.12),290(3.70)	118-0405-80

Compound	Solvent	$\lambda_{max}(\log \epsilon)$	Ref.
ylmethyl)thio]- (cont.)			118-0405-80
4-Quinolinecarboxylic acid, 1,2-di-hydro-2-thioxo-, 3-methylbutyl ester	EtOH	221(4.53),289(4.31), 418(3.98)	94-0049-80
4-Quinolinecarboxylic acid, 1,2-di-hydro-2-thioxo-, pentyl ester	EtOH	221(4.51),289(4.28), 418(3.98)	94-0049-80
$C_{15}H_{17}NO_3$			
2,3-Pyrrolidinedione, 4-[(2-methoxy-phenyl)methylene]-1-(1-methylethyl)-	EtOH	366(4.08)	145-1135-80
$C_{15}H_{17}NO_4$			
2H-1-Benzopyran-4-carboxamide, N-butyl-7-methoxy-2-oxo-	EtOH	331(4.21)	95-0289-80
3-Isoquinolineacetic acid, 1,2,3,4-tetrahydro-1-(2-methoxy-2-oxoeth-ylidene)-, methyl ester, (R)-	EtOH	251(4.15),333(4.11)	44-0357-80
5(2H)-Isoxazolone, 2-(1,1-dimethyl-3-oxobutyl)-3-hydroxy-4-phenyl-	neutral anion	253(4.35) 224(4.22),236(4.16), 275(4.09)	4-0299-80 4-0299-80
	MeOH	250s(4.12)	4-0299-80
Propanedioic acid, ethyl-1H-indol-3-yl-, dimethyl ester	EtOH	220(4.53),283(3.82), 292(3.76)	103-0045-80
$C_{15}H_{17}NO_5$			
2H-1,3-Benzoxazine-4-acetic acid, 3,4-dihydro-α-(1-hydroxyethylidene)-3-methyl-2-oxo-, ethyl ester	EtOH	225s(4.01),246(3.91), 286s(3.00)	4-0519-80
$C_{15}H_{17}NS$			
2H-Azeto[2,1-a]isoquinoline-2-thione, 1,4,5,9b-tetrahydro-1-(1-methyl-2-propenyl)-	CHCl$_3$	273(4.2),329s(2.0)	24-3024-80
$C_{15}H_{17}N_2O_5PS$			
3(2H)-Pyridazinone, 5-[(4,5-dimethyl-1,3,2-dioxaphospholan-2-yl)oxy]-4-methoxy-2-phenyl-, P-sulfide	MeOH	214(4.30),296(3.70)	73-2343-80
3(2H)-Pyridazinone, 4-methoxy-5-[(4-methyl-1,3,2-dioxaphosphorinan-2-yl)oxy]-2-phenyl-, P-sulfide	MeOH	212(4.36),297(3.72)	73-2343-80
$C_{15}H_{17}N_3O_2$			
Benzamide, N-(1,1-dimethylethyl)-2-(1H-imidazol-2-ylcarbonyl)-	EtOH EtOH-5M HCl dioxan + HCl CHCl$_3$	292(3.78) 260s(3.56) 292(4.08) 270s(3.62) 293(4.11)	103-0247-80 103-0247-80 103-0247-80 103-0247-80 103-0247-80
1H-1,2-Diazepine, 1-[4-(dimethylamino)-benzoyl]-3-methoxy-	EtOH	225(4.13),315(4.26)	44-5095-80
Pyridinium, 1-[[4-(dimethylamino)benz-oyl]amino]-2-methoxy-, hydroxide, inner salt	EtOH	285(4.03),322(4.51)	44-5095-80
$C_{15}H_{17}N_3O_3$			
2H-1,3-Benzoxazin-2-one, 4-(3,5-dimeth-yl-1H-pyrazol-4-yl)-3,4-dihydro-8-methoxy-3-methyl-	EtOH	273(3.27),280(3.27)	4-0519-80
Pyrazineethanol, 3,5,6-trimethyl-α-(4-nitrophenyl)-	EtOH	213(4.08),281(4.13), 300(3.96)	44-0999-80

Compound	Solvent	$\lambda_{max}(\log \epsilon)$	Ref.
$C_{15}H_{17}N_3O_4$ 2H-1,3-Benzoxazin-2-one, 4-(2,5-dihy- dro-1,3-dimethyl-5-oxo-1H-pyrazol- 4-yl)-3,4-dihydro-8-methoxy-3-methyl-	EtOH	225s(4.11),254(3.83), 280s(3.30)	4-0519-80
$C_{15}H_{17}N_3O_5$ 3-Pyridazinecarboxylic acid, 1,4,5,6- tetrahydro-6,6-dimethyl-1-(4-nitro- phenyl)-4-oxo-, ethyl ester	EtOH	225(4.12),230s(4.07), 346(4.25)	118-0623-80
4(1H)-Pyrimidinone, 2-amino-5-(4-C- phenyl-β-D-ribofuranosyl)-	pH 1 pH 13 MeOH	263(3.90) 231(4.15),276(3.99) 217(4.25),262(3.98)	142-0761-80 142-0761-80 142-0761-80
$C_{15}H_{17}N_3O_7$ Acetamide, N-[3-acetoxy-2-(acetoxy- methyl)-2,3,3a,9a-tetrahydro-6H- furo[2',3':4,5]oxazolo[3,2-a]pyrimi- din-6-ylidene]-, [2R-(2α,3β,3aα,9aβ)]-, monotetrafluoroborate	MeOH	245(3.91),283(4.13)	44-1577-80
$C_{15}H_{17}N_5O_6$ 9H-Purine-6-acetic acid, α-cyano-9-β-D- ribofuranosyl-	H_2O	327s(4.54),338(4.60)	94-0150-80
$C_{15}H_{18}BrClO_2$ 4,9-Dioxabicyclo[6.1.0]nonane, 3-(1- bromopropylidene)-6-chloro-5-(2- penten-4-ynyl)- (venustin A)	EtOH	213(4.30),222s(4.28), 232(4.11)	138-1177-80
$C_{15}H_{18}BrN_3O_3$ 2,4-Pyridinediamine, 3-bromo-5-[(3,4,5- trimethoxyphenyl)methyl]-	pH 1 pH 12	204(4.66),222(4.67), 278(3.95) 215(4.70),278s(3.51)	87-0384-80 87-0384-80
$C_{15}H_{18}ClN_3$ 2-Pyrimidinamine, N-(4-butylphenyl)- 4-chloro-6-methyl-	EtOH EtOH-HCl	278(4.51) 260(4.30)	103-0309-80 103-0309-80
$C_{15}H_{18}Cl_3NO_6Si$ Silicon, [[2,2',2"-nitrilotris[ethanol- ato]](3-)-N,O,O',O"][[[(2,4,5-tri- chlorophenoxy)acetyl]oxy]methyl]-, (TB-5-23)-	MeCN	207(4.78),230s(3.93), 290(3.38),298(3.36)	65-0481-80
$C_{15}H_{18}IN_3O_7$ Cytidine, N-acetyl-2'-deoxy-5-iodo-, 3',5'-diacetate	MeOH MeOH-acid MeOH-base	319(3.74) 307(3.88) 295(3.78)	39-2755-80C 39-2755-80C 39-2755-80C
$C_{15}H_{18}NO_2S$ Pyridinium, 3-(dimethoxymethyl)- 2-(methylthio)-1-phenyl-, iodide	EtOH	217(4.40),279(3.90), 322(3.42)	118-0405-80
$C_{15}H_{18}N_2$ 1,4-Benzenediamine, N-(1-methylethyl)- N'-phenyl-	H_2O	279(4.16)	152-0615-80
1H-Cyclohept[2,3]azirino[1,2-b]pyra- zole, 4a,5,6,7,8,9-hexahydro-2-phenyl-	EtOH	254(4.13)	35-1176-80
1H-Perimidine, 2,3-dihydro-1,2,2,3- tetramethyl-	$CHCl_3$	346(4.11)	104-1890-80

Compound	Solvent	$\lambda_{max}(\log \epsilon)$	Ref.
$C_{15}H_{18}N_2O$			
5H-Benzocyclohepten-5-one, 7-[[2-(di-methylamino)ethyl]amino]-	EtOH	276(4.61),284(4.63), 342(3.96)	39-2077-80C
hydrochloride	EtOH	273(4.59),281(4.60), 334(3.87)	39-2077-80C
2-Propanone, 1-(2,3,4,9-tetrahydro-2-methyl-1H-pyrido[3,4-b]indol-1-yl)-, (±)-	EtOH	225(4.10),282(3.55), 290(3.52)	102-1282-80
Pyrazineethanol, 3,5,6-trimethyl-α-phenyl-	EtOH	215(4.08),281(3.98), 300s(3.72)	44-0999-80
1H-Pyrido[3,4-b]indol-1-one, 2-butyl-2,3,4,9-tetrahydro-	isoPrOH	224s(4.35),228(4.36), 240s(4.24),304(4.23), 324s(3.83)	103-0244-80
$C_{15}H_{18}N_2O_2$			
4(1H)-Pyridazinone, 3-acetyl-5,6-di-hydro-6,6-dimethyl-1-(4-methylphenyl)-	EtOH	226s(3.79),249(3.98), 338(4.17)	118-0623-80
$C_{15}H_{18}N_2O_3$			
2-Propenoic acid, 2-cyano-3-[5-(hexa-hydro-1H-azepin-1-yl)-2-furanyl]-, methyl ester	MeOH	209(4.12),238(4.35), 470(4.92)	73-1831-80
3-Pyridazinecarboxylic acid, 1,4,5,6-tetrahydro-6,6-dimethyl-4-oxo-1-phenyl-, ethyl ester	EtOH	225s(3.92),235(3.93), 336(4.11)	118-0623-80
3-Pyridazinecarboxylic acid, 1,4,5,6-tetrahydro-6-methyl-1-(4-methylphen-yl)-4-oxo-, ethyl ester	EtOH	225(3.88),247(4.04), 375(4.17)	118-0623-80
2(1H)-Pyridinone, 3-[(2-amino-3-meth-oxyphenyl)methyl]-4-hydroxy-1,6-di-methyl-	MeOH acid	216(4.43),294(4.03) 213(4.44),274(3.94)	39-0522-80C 39-0522-80C
$C_{15}H_{18}N_2O_4$			
2(1H)-Pyridinone, 3,3'-methylenebis-[4-hydroxy-1,6-dimethyl-	MeOH acid base	217(4.64),293(4.55) 216(4.64),288(4.52) 220(4.70),226(4.71), 292(4.43)	39-0522-80C 39-0522-80C 39-0522-80C
$C_{15}H_{18}N_2O_5S_2$			
1H-Thieno[3,4-b][1,4]diazepine-6-carb-oxylic acid, 2-(2-ethoxy-2-oxoethyl-idene)-2,3,4,5-tetrahydro-8-(methyl-thio)-4-oxo-, ethyl ester	EtOH	230(4.06),300(4.47), 355(4.07)	95-0699-80
$C_{15}H_{18}N_2O_7$			
L-Glutamic acid, N-acetyl-, 1-methyl 5-[(2-nitrophenyl)methyl] ester	TMP	259(3.72)	22-0133-80
L-Glutamic acid, N-acetyl-, 1-methyl 5-[(3-nitrophenyl)methyl] ester	TMP	262.5(3.83)	22-0133-80
L-Glutamic acid, N-acetyl-, 1-methyl 5-[(4-nitrophenyl)methyl ester	TMP	267(3.98)	22-0133-80
$C_{15}H_{18}N_2O_9S$			
Carbonic acid, 1-[2-[(2-hydroxyethyl)-sulfonyl]-4-oxo-3-azetidinyl] ethyl (4-nitrophenyl)methyl ester	EtOH	262(3.91)	35-2039-80
isomer	EtOH	263(3.98)	35-2039-80
$C_{15}H_{18}N_4O$			
Morpholine, 4-[1-(2-quinolinylhydra-zono)ethyl]-, monohydriodide	MeOH	285(4.47),380(4.16)	56-0661-80

Compound	Solvent	λ_{max}(log ϵ)	Ref.
Phenol, 5-(diethylamino)-2-(2-pyridin-ylazo)-	10% EtOH-pH 1.0	440(3.60)	140-0314-80
C$_{15}$H$_{18}$N$_4$O$_2$			
3-Azaspiro[5.5]undeca-1,4-diene-1,5-di-carbonitrile, 2,3-dimethyl-4-(nitro-methyl)- (all spectra in ethanol)	pH 0.5	228(4.38),343(3.57)	73-2938-80
	pH 2.9	228(4.19),340(3.70)	73-2938-80
	pH 6.65	219(4.38),223(4.39),335(3.67)	73-2938-80
	pH 9.95	215(4.15),305s(3.8),324(4.05),354s(3.8)	73-2938-80
	pH 12.5	204(4.41),305s(3.9),322(4.12),354s(3.8)	73-2938-80
Butanamide, N-[(2,5-dihydro-3-methyl-5-oxo-1,2,4-triazin-6-yl)phenyl-methyl]-	EtOH	234(3.98),264(3.72)	39-1139-80C
	EtOH-NaOH	233(--),286(--)	39-1139-80C
C$_{15}$H$_{18}$N$_4$O$_3$			
Urea, N-ethyl-N,N'-bis(6-methoxy-3-pyridinyl)-	EtOH	236s(4.14),246(4.17),290s(3.82)	44-4219-80
C$_{15}$H$_{18}$N$_4$O$_4$			
Pyrido[2,3-d]pyrimidine-6-carboxylic acid, 8-ethyl-5,8-dihydro-5-oxo-2-(2-methoxy-1-pyrrolidinyl)-	EtOH	219(4.08),274(4.69),325(4.02)	94-2531-80
C$_{15}$H$_{18}$N$_5$			
3H-Purinium, 6-(dimethylamino)-3-meth-yl-9-(phenylmethyl)-, bromide	pH 1	288(4.27)	94-2522-80
	pH 7	288(4.27)	94-2522-80
	EtOH	289(4.32)	94-2522-80
C$_{15}$H$_{18}$O			
5(6H)-Benzocyclooctenone, 7,8-dihydro-7,7,9-trimethyl-	EtOH	234(4.28),262(3.80),320(3.58)	44-0240-80
1H-Cyclohepta[b]naphthalen-1-one, 2,3,4,6,7,8,9,10-octahydro-	EtOH	260(3.92)	23-1344-80
4H-Cyclohepta[a]naphthalen-4-one, 1,2,3,7,8,9,10,11-octahydro-	EtOH	262(4.09)	23-1344-80
6H-Cyclohepta[b]naphthalen-6-one, 1,2,3,4,7,8,9,10-octahydro-	EtOH	260(4.10)	23-1344-80
7H-Cyclohepta[a]naphthalen-7-one, 1,2,3,4,8,9,10,11-octahydro-	EtOH	258(4.05)	23-1344-80
11H-Cyclohepta[a]naphthalen-11-one, 1,2,3,4,7,8,9,10-octahydro-	EtOH	254(3.62)	23-1344-80
1H-Fluorene-2-methanol, 2,3,4,9-tetra-hydro-α-methyl-	EtOH	209(4.19),260(4.01)	56-0453-80
1H-Fluoren-4-ol, 2,3,4,4a-tetrahydro-4a,9-dimethyl-	EtOH	262.5(4.06)	39-1909-80C
C$_{15}$H$_{18}$OSe			
2-Cyclohexen-1-one, 2,6,6-trimethyl-4-(phenylseleno)-	hexane	240(4.23)	24-2227-80
C$_{15}$H$_{18}$O$_2$			
2-Cyclohexen-1-one, 2-[(3-methoxyphen-yl)methyl]-3-methyl-	EtOH	225(4.14)	39-0804-80C
5,8-Epoxy-4H-indeno[5,6-b]furan, 4a,5,6,7,7a,8-hexahydro-4a,7,7a-tri-methyl-4-methylene-, [4aS-(4aα,5β-7α,7aα,8β)]- (dehydropinguisanin)	EtOH	212(3.39),218(3.36),238(3.35)	102-2651-80
4,6-Heptadien-3-one, 2-hydroxy-2,6-di-methyl-7-phenyl-, (E,E)-	EtOH	225(4.0),318(4.4)	88-4561-80

Compound	Solvent	$\lambda_{max}(\log \epsilon)$	Ref.
Ligularenolide, (±)-	EtOH	331(4.32)	94-3265-80
2,6-Naphthalenedione, tetrahydro-1,8a-dimethyl-7-(1-methylethenyl)-(6,9,11-eremophilatriene-3,8-dione)	EtOH	241(4.15)	94-3265-80
1,8-Propanonaphthalene, 1,6,7,8-tetrahydro-4-methoxy-8-methyl-9-oxo-	EtOH	279(3.50)	150-1801-80
Xantholide A	MeOH	204.5(4.00)	88-1861-80
$C_{15}H_{18}O_2S_2$			
Naphtho[2,1-b:6,5-b']dithiophene, 2,3,4,5,8b,9,10,10a-octahydro-10a-methyl-, 1,1-dioxide, (8bS-trans)-	MeOH	230(3.92),247(3.59)	13-0133-80A
$C_{15}H_{18}O_3$			
Cyclohexanecarboxylic acid, 1-(4-methylphenyl)-2-oxo-, methyl ester	MeOH	258(2.45),265(2.49),273(2.34)	12-0113-80
3-Cyclohexene-1-carboxaldehyde, 2-(3,4-dimethoxyphenyl)-, cis	MeOH	211(4.04),232(3.88),280(3.44)	12-0913-80
trans	MeOH	213(4.12),231(4.09),281(3.68)	12-0913-80
Cycloprop[2,3]indeno[5,6-b]furan-2(4H)-one, 4a,5,5a,6,6a,6b,7,7a-octahydro-7a-hydroxy-3,6b-dimethyl-5-methylene- (chloranthalactone D)	MeOH MeOH-NaOH	298(4.24) 264(3.97)	94-0092-80 94-0092-80
Furoscrobiculin A	EtOH	207(3.82),234(3.65),276(3.19)	100-0319-80
1-Naphthalenecarboxylic acid, 5,6,7,8-tetrahydro-2-hydroxy-4-methyl-7-(1-methylethenyl)-, (R)- (manicol)	EtOH	260(4.61),332(3.81),380(3.97)	39-2065-80C
Naphtho[2,3-b]furan-2,6(3H,4H)-dione, 3a,7,8,8a,9,9a-hexahydro-5,8a-dimethyl-3-methylene- (3-oxodiplophyllin)	EtOH	246(4.16)	44-3278-80
3H-Naphtho[1,8-bc]furan-3,8(4H)-dione, 5,5a,6,7-tetrahydro-7-methyl-5-(1-methylethyl)- (hibiscone C)	EtOH EtOH-base	232(4.10),267(4.09) 258(3.71),414(4.59)	39-0249-80C 39-0249-80C
Ryomenin	MeOH	211(4.51),252(3.98),310(3.58)	94-3070-80
$C_{15}H_{18}O_4$			
Cyclohexanecarboxylic acid, 1-(4-methoxyphenyl)-2-oxo-, methyl ester	EtOH	231(3.98),276(3.15),282(3.08)	12-0113-80
Cyclopentanecarboxylic acid, 1-(4-methoxyphenyl)-2-oxo-, ethyl ester	MeOH	227(3.96),266s(3.15),274(3.18),279(3.15)	12-0113-80
Isomarasmic acid	EtOH	237(4.00)	78-3361-80
Marasmic acid, (±)-	EtOH	239(3.96)	78-3367-80
1-Naphthalenepropanoic acid, 5,6,7,8-tetrahydro-4-methoxy-6-oxo-, methyl ester	EtOH	275(3.28),283(3.29)	78-2513-80
Spiro[1,3-benzodioxole-2,1'-cycloheptan]-5-ol, acetate	EtOH	235(3.44),290(3.47)	12-0527-80
$C_{15}H_{18}O_5$			
1H-Indene-3-carboxylic acid, 5-acetyl-3a,4,7,7a-tetrahydro-6-hydroxy-1,2,3a-trimethyl-4-oxo-, (1α,3aα,7aα)-	EtOH	225s(3.99),273(4.26)	94-1590-80
$C_{15}H_{18}O_6$			
Bicyclo[2.2.2]octa-2,5-diene-2,3-dicarboxylic acid, 8-hydroxy-1,5,8-trimethyl-7-oxo-, dimethyl ester	EtOH	222s(3.74),245s(3.58),312(2.62),325s(2.51)	44-2189-80

Compound	Solvent	$\lambda_{max}(\log \epsilon)$	Ref.
Cyclopropa[cd]pentalene-2a,4b-dicarbox-ylic acid, 2b,3,4,4a-tetrahydro-4-hy-droxy-1,2b,4-trimethyl-3-oxo-, di-methyl ester, (2aα,2bα,4α,4aα,4bα)-	EtOH	250s(2.86),310s(1.70)	44-2189-80
2H-2,4a-Epoxynaphthalene-3,4-dicarbox-ylic acid, 5,6,7,8-tetrahydro-7-hy-droxy-2-methyl-, dimethyl ester	MeCN	204(3.97),230s(3.59), 300(2.76)	24-3249-80
$C_{15}H_{18}S$			
Azulene, 3a,4-dihydro-6,8-dimethyl-4-methylene-3a-[(methylthio)methyl]-	hexane	219(4.04),261(4.22), 290s(3.22),370(3.66)	89-0621-80
Azulene, 4,6,8-trimethyl-1-[(methyl-thio)methyl]-	hexane	247(4.41),292(4.67), 296(4.67),301s(4.64), 332s(3.50),345s(3.64), 352(3.76),355s(3.52), 369(2.65),563(2.57), 600s(2.57),658(2.11)	89-0621-80
Azulene, 4,6,8-trimethyl-5-[(methyl-thio)methyl]-	hexane	249(4.46),293s(4.69), 296(4.70),308s(3.99), 331s(3.47),346s(3.65), 352(3.75),368(3.52), 493s(2.64),558(2.69), 521s(2.67),600(2.63), 657(2.21)	89-0621-80
$C_{15}H_{19}ClN_5$			
Methanaminium, N-[[1-(4-chlorophenyl)-5-[[(dimethylamino)methylene]amino]-1H-pyrazol-4-yl]methylene]-N-methyl-perchlorate	EtOH	259(3.77),330s(4.31)	114-0127-80C
	EtOH	259(3.80),330s(4.34)	114-0127-80C
$C_{15}H_{19}ClO$			
1(4H)-Naphthalenone, 2-chloro-4a,5,6,7-tetrahydro-4a,5-dimethyl-4-(1-methyl-ethenyl)-	EtOH	263(3.83)	83-0048-80
1(4H)-Naphthalenone, 3-chloro-4a,5,6,7-tetrahydro-4a,5-dimethyl-4-(1-methyl-ethenyl)-	EtOH	294(3.78)	83-0048-80
$C_{15}H_{19}ClO_2$			
1H-Inden-1-one, 6-(2-chloroethyl)-2,3-dihydro-4-hydroxy-2,2,5,7-tetrameth-yl- (pterosin R)	MeOH	234(4.36),270(4.05), 324(3.55)	102-1743-80
$C_{15}H_{19}I_2N_3$			
1,3-Propanediamine, N'-(7,8-diiodo-4-quinolinyl)-N,N,2-trimethyl-	hexane	242(4.47),261(4.28), 336(4.08)	103-0754-80
$C_{15}H_{19}N$			
Azulene, 4-(dimethylaminomethyl)-6,8-dimethyl-	hexane	244(4.42),287s(4.62), 290(4.66),304s(3.93), 323s(3.40),330s(3.48), 335(3.55),346s(3.60), 350(3.66),360s(3.04), 367s(2.54),387s(1.43), 530s(2.61),548(2.67), 566(2.66),589(2.63), 613s(2.44),642(2.24), 678s(1.56)	89-0621-80

Compound	Solvent	$\lambda_{max}(\log \epsilon)$	Ref.
$C_{15}H_{19}NO$			
2-Cyclohexen-1-one, 2-(ethylamino)-3-(4-methylphenyl)-	MeOH	250(3.61),310(3.21)	78-1585-80
2-Cyclohexen-1-one, 2-[(1-methylethyl)-amino]-3-phenyl-	ether	284(3.85)	78-1585-80
4a(4H)-Naphthalenecarboxamide, N-(1,1-dimethylethyl)-	MeCN	310(3.66)	142-0459-80B
$C_{15}H_{19}NO_3$			
2H-1,3-Benzoxazin-2-one, octahydro-4-(2-hydroxyphenyl)-3-methyl-	EtOH	215(3.16),274(2.76)	4-0277-80
$C_{15}H_{19}NO_3S$			
7-Azabicyclo[4.2.0]octan-5-one, 8-methyl-7-[(4-methylphenyl)sulfonyl]-, (1α,6α,8β)-	ether	227(4.07),300(1.60)	78-1585-80
Benzenesulfonamide, N-ethyl-4-methyl-N-(6-oxo-1-cyclohexen-1-yl)-	ether	228(4.10),336(2.11)	78-1585-80
Benzenesulfonamide, N-(1-methylethyl)-N-(6-oxo-1-cyclohexen-1-yl)-	ether	263(3.89)	78-1585-80
1-Pyrrolidinepropanoic acid, α-(4-methoxyphenyl)-2-thioxo-, methyl ester	EtOH	229(4.07),270(4.19)	44-1713-80
$C_{15}H_{19}NO_6$			
3,6,9,12-Tetraoxa-16-azabicyclo[12.3.1]-octadeca-1(18),14,16-triene-2,13-dione, 15,17-dimethyl-	MeCN	236(4.09),273(3.57), 280(3.48)	44-2854-80
$C_{15}H_{19}NO_7$			
α-D-Glucofuranose, 1,2-O-(1-methylethylidene)-, 6-(3-pyridinecarboxylate)	EtOH	257(4.85),262(4.86), 269(4.75)	44-4999-80
$C_{15}H_{19}NS$			
2-Azetidinethione, 3-(1,1-dimethyl-2-propenyl)-1-methyl-4-phenyl-	3:1 isooctane-CHCl$_3$	268(4.2),328s(2.0)	24-3024-80
$C_{15}H_{19}N_3$			
Pyrrolo[3,2-e]benzimidazole, 3-butyl-3,6-dihydro-7,8-dimethyl-	EtOH	301(4.21)	103-0062-80
	EtOH	301(4.19)	103-1039-80
$C_{15}H_{19}N_3O$			
4(1H)-Pyrimidinone, 2-[(4-butylphenyl)-amino]-6-methyl-	EtOH	260(4.46),286s(4.39)	103-0309-80
	EtOH-HCl	260(4.54)	103-0309-80
	EtOH-KOH	295(4.34),303(4.38)	103-0309-80
$C_{15}H_{19}N_3O_3$			
2,4-Pyridinediamine, 5-[(3,4,5-trimethoxyphenyl)methyl]-	pH 1	222(4.71),265(3.98)	87-0384-80
	pH 12	220s(4.68),277(3.46)	87-0384-80
$C_{15}H_{19}N_3O_6$			
6H-Furo[2',3':4,5]oxazolo[3,2-a]pyrimidine-2-methanol, 2,3,3a,9a-tetrahydro-6-imino-3-(1-oxopropoxy)-, propanoate, [2R-(2α,3β,3aβ,9aβ)]-, tetrafluoroborate	MeOH	235(4.07),264(4.12)	44-1577-80
$C_{15}H_{19}N_3O_8$			
Acetamide, N-[1-(3,5-di-O-acetyl-β-D-arabinofuranosyl)-1,2-dihydro-2-oxo-4-pyrimidinyl]-	MeOH	248(4.19),300(3.87)	44-1577-80

Compound	Solvent	$\lambda_{max}(\log \epsilon)$	Ref.
$C_{15}H_{19}N_5O_6$ 4,13-Epoxy-1,3-dioxolo[6,7][1,3]diazo- cino[1,2-e]purine-8,10(9H,11H)-dione, 3a,4,5,6,13,13a-hexahydro-9-(methoxy- methyl)-2,2-dimethyl-, [3aR- (3aα,4β,13β,13aα)]-	MeOH	209(4.39),254(4.22), 304(3.92)	78-3509-80
$C_{15}H_{19}N_7S$ Hydrazinecarbothioamide, 2-[[5-[[(di- methylamino)methylene]amino]-3-meth- yl-1-phenyl-1H-pyrazol-4-yl]methyl- ene]-	EtOH	283(4.43),323(4.45)	114-0127-80C
$C_{15}H_{19}S$ Sulfonium, [(6,8-dimethyl-4-azulenyl)- methyl]dimethyl-, tetrafluoroborate	MeOH	248(4.39),289(4.65), 309s(3.39),342(3.50), 356(3.54),370s(2.74), 572(2.69),597s(2.64), 665s(2.20)	89-0621-80
$C_{15}H_{20}BrN_3$ 3,5-Pyridinedicarbonitrile, 1-(4-bromo- butyl)-1,4-dihydro-2,4,4,6-tetrameth- yl)-	MeOH	224(4.36),344(3.81)	73-3370-80
$C_{15}H_{20}BrN_5O_4$ 4,11-Epoxy-1,3-dioxolo[4,5-f]imidazo- [1,5-a][1,3]diazocine-7-carboxylic acid, 9-bromo-3a,4,5,6,11,11a-hexa- hydro-2,2-dimethyl-, (1-methyleth- ylidene)hydrazide, [3aR-(3aα,4β,11β- 11aα)]-	MeOH	224(4.24),287(4.36)	78-3509-80
$C_{15}H_{20}Br_2O_2$ Furan, 3-bromo-5-[1-bromo-2-[3-(2-pent- en-4-ynyl)oxiranyl]ethyl]-2-ethyl- tetrahydro- (laureepoxide)	n.s.g.	224(4.23),230s(4.10)	88-1471-80
$C_{15}H_{20}ClNO_6Si$ Silicon, [[[(4-chlorophenoxy)acetyl]- oxy]methyl][[2,2',2"-nitrilotris- [ethanolato]](3-)-N,O,O',O"]-, (TB-5-23)-	MeCN	226(3.83),282(3.04), 287(2.99)	65-0481-80
$C_{15}H_{20}IN_3$ 1,3-Propanediamine, N'-(7-iodo-4-quino- linyl)-N,N,2-trimethyl-	hexane	220(4.53),257(4.33), 322(3.94)	103-0754-80
$C_{15}H_{20}N$ Benz[f]isoindolium, 2,3,3a,4-tetrahy- dro-2,2,4-trimethyl-, bromide	EtOH	212(4.31),217(4.36), 223(4.29),266(4.04), 327(1.77)	39-1477-80C
2-Naphthalenemethanaminium, N,N,N,3- tetramethyl-, iodide	EtOH	228(5.04),270s(3.63), 278(3.66),288s(3.51), 313(3.00),319(2.90), 328(3.14)	39-1477-80C
$C_{15}H_{20}N_2$ Pyridinium, 1,1'-(1,3-propanediyl)bis- [2-methyl-	H_2O	263(4.0)	104-2044-80

Compound	Solvent	$\lambda_{max}(\log \epsilon)$	Ref.
Pyridinium, 1,1'-(1,3-propanediyl)bis-[3-methyl-, dibromide	H_2O	262(3.9)	104-2044-80
Pyridinium, 1,1'-(1,3-propanediyl)bis-[4-methyl-, dibromide	H_2O	254(4.2)	104-2044-80
$C_{15}H_{20}N_2OS$			
2-Propenamide, N-[(butylamino)thioxomethyl]-3-(4-methylphenyl)-	dioxan	311(4.53)	73-2334-80
$C_{15}H_{20}N_2O_2$			
3a,7-Methano-3aH-pyrrolo[2,3-b]azocine-2,6(1H,3H)-dione, 7,8-dihydro-8,8-dimethyl-1-(1-methylethyl)-	MeOH	230(4.2),258(3.04)	24-0669-80
$C_{15}H_{20}N_2O_2S$			
2-Propenamide, N-[(butylamino)thioxomethyl]-3-(4-methoxyphenyl)-	dioxan	327(4.52)	73-2334-80
$C_{15}H_{20}N_2O_5$			
1H-Benzimidazole-1,3(2H)-dicarboxylic acid, 2-ethoxy-, diethyl ester	H_2O	243(4.12),282(3.53),290s(3.49)	35-6784-80
$C_{15}H_{20}N_4OS$			
5H-Pyrimido[4,5-b][1,4]benzothiazin-9(6H)-one, 4-(dimethylamino)-7,8-dihydro-5,7,7-trimethyl-	EtOH	252(4.18),290s(3.93),334(3.15),421(3.40)	103-0580-80
$C_{15}H_{20}N_4O_4$			
Imidazo[1,2-a]pyrido[2,3-d]pyrimidine-7-carboxylic acid, 5-ethoxy-9-ethyl-1,2,3,5,6,9-hexahydro-1-methyl-6-oxo-	EtOH	247(4.35),271(4.52),295(4.22)	95-1187-80
2,4(1H,3H)-Pyrimidinedione, 6-ethyl-1-[3-(5-ethyl-3,6-dihydro-2,6-dioxo-1(2H)-pyrimidinyl)propyl]-	pH 2	236(3.66),267(4.25)	56-2357-80
	pH 7	235(3.61),268(4.24)	56-2357-80
	pH 12	247(3.74),272(4.11)	56-2357-80
$C_{15}H_{20}N_6O_5$			
4,13-Epoxy-1,3-dioxolo[6,7][1,3]diazocino[1,2-e]purin-8(9H)-one, 10-amino-3a,4,5,6,13,13a-hexahydro-9-(methoxymethyl)-2,2-dimethyl-, [3aR-(3aα,4β,13β,13aα)]-	MeOH	260(4.27),293(3.95)	78-3509-80
$C_{15}H_{20}O$			
Benzofuran, 4,5,6,7-tetrahydro-7-methyl-7-(4-methyl-1,3-pentadienyl)-, (E)-	EtOH	225(4.36),231(4.37),246(4.29)	12-2729-80
Cyclodeca[b]furan, 4,7,8,9,10,11-hexahydro-3,6-dimethyl-10-methylene-, (E)-	EtOH	220(3.85)	12-0927-80
Cyclodeca[b]furan, 4,7,8,11-tetrahydro-3,6,10-trimethyl-, (E,E)-	EtOH	220(4.04)	12-0927-80
3H-Cyclopenta[1,3]cyclopropa[1,2]benzen-3-one, 3a,3b,4,5,6,7-hexahydro-1,3b-dimethyl-5-(1-methylethenyl)-	MeOH	234(3.49),268(3.25)	44-3790-80
3H-Cyclopenta[1,3]cyclopropa[1,2]benzen-3-one, 3a,3b,4,5,6,7-hexahydro-1,3b-dimethyl-5-(1-methylethylidene)-, (±)-	MeOH	232(3.79),267(3.52)	44-3790-80
6,9-Ethanocycloocta[b]furan, 4,5,6,9-tetrahydro-6,7,11-trimethyl-, (6 ,9 ,11S*)-(+) (nakafuran-8)	hexane	228(3.79)	33-2159-80

Compound	Solvent	$\lambda_{max}(\log \epsilon)$	Ref.
6,10-Methano-4H-cyclonona[b]furan, 5,6,9,10-tetrahydro-6,7,8-tri-methyl- (nakafuran-9)	hexane	219(3.63)	33-2159-80
2(3H)-Naphthalenone, 4,4a,5,6-tetra-hydro-4a,5-dimethyl-3-(1-methyleth-ylidene)-	EtOH	203(3.98),270(4.12), 300s(3.98)	39-0963-80C
2(4aH)-Naphthalenone, 5,6,7,8-tetra-hydro-4,4a-dimethyl-7-(1-methyl-ethenyl)-	MeOH	245(4.28)	44-3790-80
2(4aH)-Naphthalenone, 5,6,7,8-tetra-hydro-4,4a-dimethyl-6-(1-methyl-ethylidene)-	MeOH	236(4.21),263(4.10)	44-3790-80
Naphtho[2,3-b]furan, 4,4a,5,6,7,8,8a,9-octahydro-3,8a-dimethyl-5-methylene-, trans (atractylone)	EtOH	220(3.85)	12-0927-80
Spiro[cycloprop[e]indene-2(1H),2'-oxir-ane], 1a,3,3a,6b-tetrahydro-3',3',3a-6,6-tetramethyl-, [1aR-(1aα,2β,3aα-6bα)]-	EtOH	262(3.93)	102-0603-80
Spiro[4,5]deca-6,9-dien-8-one, 6,10-di-methyl-2-(1-methylethenyl)-, (R)-	MeOH	246(4.11)	44-3790-80
β-Vetivone, dehydro-	EtOH	244(4.23)	23-2460-80
	MeOH	244(3.81)	44-3790-80
$C_{15}H_{20}O_2$			
Azuleno[5,6-c]furan-4-ol, 4,4a,5,6,8,9-hexahydro-6,6,8-trimethyl- (furosard-onin A)	EtOH	223(3.42)	102-0093-80
Caespitenone	EtOH	205(3.80),277(3.50)	102-0603-80
Costunolide	n.s.g.	210(4.05)(end abs.)	100-0527-80
4H-Cyclopropa[3,4]cyclohepta[1,2-c]-pyran-4-one, 4a,5,6,7,7a,8,8a,8b-octahydro-1,8,8-trimethyl-5-meth-ylene-	EtOH	205(3.12)	102-2147-80
4H-Cyclopropa[b]naphthalen-4-one, 1,1a,2,5,6,6a,7,7a-octahydro-5-(hy-droxymethylene)-1,1,6a-trimethyl-, [1aR-(1aα,6aβ,7aα)]-	EtOH	256(4.06)	39-0176-80C
Eremophila-6,9,11-trien-8-one, 3β-hy-droxy-	EtOH	250(4.11)	94-3265-80
Furo[2,3-b]naphthalen-9(4H)-one, 4a,5,6,7,8,8a-hexahydro-3,4,a,5-trimethyl- (10α-furanoeremophilone)	EtOH	279(4.05)	39-0963-80C
4H-Indeno[5,6-b]furan-8-ol, 4a,5,6,7-7a,8-hexahydro-4a,7,7a-trimethyl-4-methylene-, [4aS-(4aα,7α,7aα,8β)]-	EtOH	213(3.46),218(3.46), 236(3.46)	102-2651-80
Isodrimenin, 6β-acetoxy-	MeOH	212(3.77)	100-0365-80
1(4H)-Naphthalenone, 4a,5,6,7-tetrahy-dro-2-hydroxy-4a,5-dimethyl-4-(1-methylethenyl)-, [4S-(4α,4aβ,5β)]-	EtOH	278(3.76),300(3.77)	83-0048-80
	EtOH-KOH	233(--),266(--), 346(--)	83-0048-80
1(4H)-Naphthalenone, 4a,5,6,7-tetrahy-dro-8-hydroxy-4a,5-dimethyl-4-(1-methylethenyl)-	EtOH	230(3.93),334(3.70)	83-0048-80
	EtOH-KOH	233(--),348(--)	83-0048-80
Naphtho[1,2-b]furan-2(4H)-one, 5,5a,6-9,9a,9b-hexahydro-3,5a,9-trimethyl-	MeOH	265(3.67)	35-5337-80
8H-Naphtho[1,8-bc]furan-8-one, 3,4,5-5a,6,7-hexahydro-7-methyl-5-(1-methylethyl)-, [5R-(5α,5aα,7α)]- (hibiscone A)	EtOH	280(4.09)	39-0249-80C

Compound	Solvent	$\lambda_{max}(\log \epsilon)$	Ref.
$C_{15}H_{20}O_2S$			
4H-Indeno[2,1-b]thiophene-2-carboxylic acid, 3b,7,7-trimethyl-3b,5,6,7,7a,8-hexahydro-	EtOH	250(3.91),294(4.03)	70-1833-80
2-Thiophenecarboxylic acid, 5-(3,7-dimethyl-2,6-octadienyl)-, (E)-	EtOH	257(3.89),280(4.01)	70-1833-80
2-Thiophenecarboxylic acid, 5-[(2,6,6-trimethyl-1-cyclohexen-1-yl)methyl]-	EtOH	255(3.83),280(4.04)	70-1833-80
$C_{15}H_{20}O_3$			
Atractylenolide III	MeOH	218(4.04)	94-0092-80
Cyclodeca[b]furan-2,9(3H,4H)-dione, 3a,5,8,10,11,11a-hexahydro-6,10-dimethyl-3-methylene-, [3aS-(3aR*,10R*,11aS*)]- (tansanin)	EtOH	210(4.11),295(2.39)	105-0452-80
Eremofortine B	CHCl$_3$	249(4.20)	78-2989-80
Ethanone, 1-[2,2-bis(1-methylethyl)-1,3-benzodioxol-5-yl]-	MeOH	223(4.28),277(3.75), 314(3.95)	35-3056-80
Hibiscone B	EtOH	276(4.18)	39-0249-80C
Lactaroscrobiculide B	EtOH	208(4.06),276(3.68)	100-0319-80
Pinguisenal	EtOH	203(3.55),234(3.81)	102-2651-80
Reynosin	n.s.g.	210(3.96)(end abs.)	100-0527-80
Santamarine	n.s.g.	210(4.30)(end abs.)	100-0527-80
$C_{15}H_{20}O_4$			
1,3-Benzodioxole-5,6-dione, 2-heptyl-2-methyl-	EtOH	290(4.12),395(3.21)	12-0527-80
2-Cyclohexene-1-carboxylic acid, 1,3-dimethyl-4-oxo-2-(3-oxo-1-butenyl)-, ethyl ester, (E)-	EtOH	292(4.06)	104-1951-80
1H-Cyclopropa[a]naphthalene-5-acetic acid, 1a,2,4,5,6,7,7a,7b-octahydro-6-hydroxy- ,7a-dimethyl-2-oxo-	MeOH	236(4.11)	94-0092-80
3-Epiphomenone, (±)-	EtOH	247(4.05)	94-3265-80
Ovatifolin, deacetyl-	MeOH	210(3.91)	102-2765-80
Tulirinol, deacetyl-	n.s.g.	207(4.16)	44-1441-80
Verlotorin	n.s.g.	210(3.95)(end abs.)	100-0527-80
$C_{15}H_{20}O_5$			
1,3-Benzodioxole-2-methanol, α-butyl-2-methoxy-, acetate	EtOH	211(3.60),272s(3.52), 276(3.55),282(3.43)	12-1553-80
1H-Inden-1-one, 2,3-dihydro-3-hydroxy-6-(2-hydroxyethyl)-2,5-bis(hydroxymethyl)-2,7-dimethyl-, (2S-trans)- (pterosin Y)	MeOH	216(4.44),259(4.08), 305(3.27)	102-1743-80
2,4a(2H)-Naphthalenedicarboxylic acid, 1,3,4,5,6,7-hexahydro-8-methyl-7-oxo-, dimethyl ester	EtOH	246(4.09)	18-1049-80
$C_{15}H_{21}ClO_2$			
1-Octanone, 1-(3-chloro-2-hydroxy-5-methylphenyl)-	EtOH	258(3.96),343(3.59)	90-0431-80
$C_{15}H_{21}Cl_3O_3Si$			
Acetic acid, (2,4,5-trichlorophenoxy)-, (triethylsilyl)methyl ester	MeCN	207(4.88),239s(3.97), 289(3.45),298(3.42)	65-0481-80
$C_{15}H_{21}N$			
Benzenamine, N-[(1,1-dimethylethyl)-cyclopropylidene]-2,6-dimethyl-	C$_6$H$_{12}$	202(4.48),228s(--), 278(2.89),304(2.91)	5-1814-80

Compound	Solvent	$\lambda_{max}(\log \epsilon)$	Ref.
$C_{15}H_{21}NO$ Cyclohexanone, 2-(2-butenylidene)-6- [3-(dimethylamino)-2-propenyli- dene]-, (all-E)-	EtOH	472(4.51)	70-0980-80
$C_{15}H_{21}NOS$ 2-Azetidinethione, 3-(1,1-dimethyleth- yl)-4-(4-methoxyphenyl)-1-methyl-, trans	isooctane	268(4.3),343(1.6)	24-3010-80
$C_{15}H_{21}NO_2$ Ethanone, 1-(4-ethoxyphenyl)-2-(1-meth- yl-2-pyrrolidinyl)-, nitrate	EtOH	275(4.25)	48-0475-80 115-0265-80
$C_{15}H_{21}NO_3$ 1-Cyclohexene-1-carboxylic acid, 3- [3-(dimethylamino)-2-propenylidene]- 2-methyl-4-oxo-, ethyl ester, (E,E)- 3-Pyridinecarboxylic acid, 1,4-dihydro- 5-(8-nonenyl)-4-oxo-	EtOH EtOH	440(4.71) 254(3.80),283(3.60)	70-0980-80 4-0359-80
$C_{15}H_{21}NO_4$ 1-Octanone, 1-(2-hydroxy-5-methyl- 3-nitrophenyl)-	EtOH	239(4.16),353(3.71)	90-0431-80
$C_{15}H_{21}NO_5$ 4H-Indol-4-one, 2-α-D-arabinofuranosyl- 1,5,6,7-tetrahydro-6,6-dimethyl- 4H-Indol-4-one, 1,5,6,7-tetrahydro- 2-β-D-lyxopyranosyl-6,6-dimethyl-	EtOH EtOH	246(3.69),287(3.62) 246(3.66),287(3.61)	136-0037-80C 136-0037-80C
$C_{15}H_{21}N_4O_3$ Pyrimidinium, 2,4-diamino-1-methyl- 5-[(3,4,5-trimethoxyphenyl)methyl]-, iodide	pH 2 and 12	223(4.64),273(3.84)	87-0379-80
$C_{15}H_{21}N_5$ Pyrimidine, 2-(3,5-dimethyl-1H-pyrazol- 1-yl)-4-methyl-6-piperidino- 4(1H)-Pyrimidinone, 2-[(4-butylphenyl)- amino]-6-methyl-, hydrazone	EtOH EtOH EtOH-HCl	250(4.6),290(4.0) 271(4.54) 254(4.48)	103-0868-80 103-0309-80 103-0309-80
$C_{15}H_{21}N_5O$ Ethanol, 2-[[4-[(1,3-dimethyl-1H-pyra- zol-4-yl)azo]phenyl]ethylamino]-	EtOH	266(4.17),400(4.35), 432(4.34)	65-1705-80
$C_{15}H_{21}N_7O_2S$ Adenosine, 5'-[[2-amino-4-(methylthio)- 1-oxobutyl]amino]-2',3'-didehydro- 2',3',5'-trideoxy-, (S)-	H_2O	261(4.13)	136-0067-80A
$C_{15}H_{21}N_7O_5$ 4,13-Epoxy-1,3-dioxolo[6,7][1,3]diazo- cino[1,2-e]purin-8(9H)-one, 6,10-di- amino-3a,4,5,6,13,13a-hexahydro-9- (methoxymethyl)-2,2-dimethyl-, [3aR-(3aα,4β,13β,13aα)]-	MeOH	260(4.23),287(3.93)	78-3509-80
$C_{15}H_{22}$ Caespitene	EtOH	251(3.37)	102-0603-80

Compound	Solvent	$\lambda_{max}(\log \epsilon)$	Ref.
4H-Cyclopenta[def]phenanthrene, 8,9-di-hydro-	EtOH	214(4.57),228(4.18), 273(4.26),282(4.15)	18-0494-80
1,3,5,8,10-Dodecapentaene, 3,7,11-tri-methyl-, (E,E,E)-(+)-	EtOH	236(4.31),264(4.51), 270(4.59),279(4.56)	44-2523-80
(E,Z,E)-(+)-	EtOH	237(4.40),264(4.60), 271(4.71),279(4.67)	44-2523-80
$C_{15}H_{22}ClNO_2$			
1-Octanone, 1-(3-chloro-2-hydroxy-5-methylphenyl)-, oxime	EtOH	259(3.99),318(3.60)	90-0431-80
$C_{15}H_{22}Cl_2O_3$			
2-Propenoic acid, 3-[3-[2-(2,2-dichloro-3,3-dimethylcyclopropyl)ethyl]-3-methyloxiranyl]-, ethyl ester	EtOH	224(4.01)	70-0754-80
$C_{15}H_{22}N_2$			
1H-Indole-3-ethanamine, N,N-diethyl-2-methyl-, monohydrochloride	EtOH	226(4.32),284(3.83), 290(3.76)	80-0245-80
$C_{15}H_{22}N_2O$			
Benzenamine, 3-methyl-N-(tetrahydro-3,4,4,6-tetramethyl-2H-1,3-oxazin-2-ylidene)-	heptane	202(4.38),214s(4.35), 259(4.16)	110-0172-80
Benzenamine, 4-methyl-N-(tetrahydro-3,4,4,6-tetramethyl-2H-1,3-oxazin-2-ylidene)-	heptane	208s(4.28),260(4.18)	110-0172-80
Ethanol, 2-[ethyl-[2-(2-methyl-1H-indol-3-yl)ethyl]amino]-, monohydro-chloride	EtOH	226(4.34),284(3.84), 290(3.76)	80-0245-80
4H-1,3-Oxazin-2-amine, 5,6-dihydro-N,4,4,6-tetramethyl-N-(3-methyl-phenyl)-	heptane	205(4.32),257(4.18)	110-0172-80
4H-1,3-Oxazin-2-amine, 5,6-dihydro-N,4,4,6-tetramethyl-N-(4-methyl-phenyl)-	heptane	204(4.31),256(4.18), 285s(3.16)	110-0172-80
1,3,6,8,10-Undecapentaen-5-one, 1,11-bis(dimethylamino)-, (all-E)-	EtOH	507(4.93)	70-0980-80
$C_{15}H_{22}N_2O_2$			
Benzenamine, 4-ethoxy-N-(tetrahydro-4,4,6-trimethyl-2H-1,3-oxazin-2-ylidene)-	heptane	200(4.30),248(4.24), 298(3.30),308s(3.20)	110-0172-80
$C_{15}H_{22}N_2O_4$			
1-Octanone, 1-(2-hydroxy-5-methyl-3-nitrophenyl)-, oxime	EtOH	248(4.09),353(3.58)	90-0431-80
$C_{15}H_{22}N_2O_6$			
4(1H)-Pyrimidinone, 2-ethoxy-5-methyl-1-[2,3-O-(1-methylethylidene)-β-D-ribofuranosyl]-	EtOH	233s(3.92),254(4.03)	33-2179-80
$C_{15}H_{22}N_3O_8P$			
Thymidine, 5'-O-(tetrahydro-2H-1,3,2-oxazaphosphorin-2-yl)-, 3'-acetate, P-oxide	EtOH	267(3.97)	78-2337-80
Uridine, 2',3'-O-(1-methylethylidene)-5'-O-(tetrahydro-2H-1,3,2-oxazaphos-phorin-2-yl)-, P-oxide	EtOH	262(3.97)	78-2337-80

Compound	Solvent	$\lambda_{max}(\log \epsilon)$	Ref.
$C_{15}H_{22}N_4$			
1H-Tetrazole, 5-[2-methyl-4-(2,6,6-tri-methyl-1-cyclohexen-1-yl)-1,3-buta-dienyl]-, (E,E)-	EtOH	292(4.27)	87-1013-80
$C_{15}H_{22}N_4OS$			
4(1H)-Pyridinone, 3-(4,5-dihydro-4-methyl-5-thioxo-1H-1,2,4-triazol-3-yl)-5-heptyl-	EtOH	254(3.31)	4-0175-80
$C_{15}H_{22}N_4O_6$			
D-Ribitol, 1-deoxy-1-(3,4-dihydro-7-methyl-2,4-dioxo-6-propyl-8(2H)-pteridinyl)-	pH 1	257(4.13),275s(3.98), 405(3.93)	39-2645-80C
	pH 13	282(4.03),315(3.88)	39-2645-80C
$C_{15}H_{22}N_5O_6PS$			
Adenosine, 8-(pentylthio)-, cyclic 3',5'-(hydrogen phosphate)	pH 1	282(4.32)	87-0242-80
	pH 11	280(4.28)	87-0242-80
$C_{15}H_{22}O$			
2(1H)-Azulenone, 6,7,8,8a-tetrahydro-3,8-dimethyl-5-(1-methylethyl)-	EtOH	293(4.32)	18-0785-80
Cyclopenta[c]pentalen-3(3aH)-one, 1,2,5a,6,7,8-hexahydro-1,3a,4,5a-tetramethyl-, (1α,3aα,5β,8aR*)-	EtOH	307(2.53)	102-1477-80
2H-Cyclopropa[a]naphthalen-2-one, 1,1a,4,5,6,7,7a,7b-octahydro-1,1,7,7a-tetramethyl-, (1aα,7α-7aα,7bα)-(+)- (dihydroaristolone)	EtOH	208(3.35)	102-0603-80
Dehydrofukinone, (±)-	EtOH	249(4.09),276(3.88)	39-0963-80C
1-Pentyn-3-ol, 3-methyl-5-(2,5,6-tri-methyl-2-cyclohexen-1-ylidene)-, (3RS,5'RS,6'SR)-	EtOH	241(4.21)	33-0293-80
(3RS,5'SR,6'SR)-	EtOH	241(4.19)	33-0293-80
Spirolaurenone, dehydrobromo-	EtOH	270(3.67)	78-1551-80
Tetracyclo[5.3.3.0³,⁶]tridecan-2-one, 3,6-dimethyl-	EtOH	306(1.53)	44-3999-80
Vitrenal, (+)-	n.s.g.	242(4.12)	77-1220-80
$C_{15}H_{22}OSi$			
Benzenemethanol, α-[1-ethenyl-3-(tri-methylsilyl)-2-propenyl]-, (E)-	hexane	210(3.90),287(3.30)	33-0555-80
more polar diastereoisomer	hexane	212(3.99),234(3.79)	33-0555-80
Benzenemethanol, α-[5-(trimethylsilyl)-2,4-pentadienyl]-, (E,E)-	hexane	235(4.22)	33-0555-80
$C_{15}H_{22}O_2$			
Benzaldehyde, 2-hydroxy-5-(1,1,3,3-tetramethylbutyl)-	EtOH	259(4.04),338(3.54)	90-0431-80
Caespitenone, dihydro-	EtOH	208(3.46),235s(2.79)	102-0603-80
1-Hexanone, 2-ethyl-1-(2-hydroxy-5-methylphenyl)-	EtOH	257(4.00),341(3.60)	90-0431-80
2-Naphthalenecarboxylic acid, 5-ethyli-dene-3,4,4a,5,6,7,8,8a-octahydro-8a-methyl-, methyl ester	EtOH	223(3.74)	44-0367-80
2(1H)-Naphthalenone, 6,7,8,8a-tetra-hydro-6-(1-hydroxy-1-methylethyl)-4,8a-dimethyl-, (6R-cis)-	EtOH	293(4.10)	78-0371-80
Naphtho[2,3-b]furan-2(4H)-one, 4a,5,6-7,8,8a,9,9a-octahydro-3,4a,5-tri-methyl-	EtOH	220.5(4.21)	94-3265-80

Compound	Solvent	$\lambda_{max}(\log \epsilon)$	Ref.
1-Octanone, 1-(2-hydroxy-5-methyl-phenyl)-	EtOH	255(3.99),338(3.59)	90-0431-80
12-Oxabicyclo[9.1.0]dodeca-5,9-dien-2-one, 1,5,8,8-tetramethyl-, [1S-(1R*,5E,9E,11R*)]-	n.s.g.	230(4.09),325(2.11)	2-0093-80
Propanoic acid, 2-(3,4,6,7,8,8a-hexa-hydro-8,8a-dimethyl-2(1H)-naphtha-lenylidene)-, (2E,8α,8aα)-(±)-	EtOH	226(3.91)	39-1752-80C
(Z)-	EtOH	225(3.90)	39-1752-80C
Spiro[4.5]deca-1,6-dien-8-one, 3-(1-hy-droxy-1-methylethyl)-6,10-dimethyl-, [3α,5β(S*)]-(±)-	EtOH	239(4.18)	23-2460-80

$C_{15}H_{22}O_3$

Compound	Solvent	$\lambda_{max}(\log \epsilon)$	Ref.
1,3-Benzodioxol-5-ol, 2-heptyl-2-methyl-	EtOH	235(3.52),299(3.72)	12-0527-80
6,9-Ethanocycloocta[b]furan-7,8-diol, 6,7,11-trimethyl-	MeOH	218(3.75)	33-2159-80
4a,8a-Ethanonaphthalen-9-one, octahy-dro-10-(1-oxopropoxy)-	MeOH	295(1.90)	44-0177-80
β-Ionone, 4-acetoxy-	MeOH	279(3.79)	33-0010-80
2-Naphthalenecarboxylic acid, 3,4,4a-5,6,7,8,8a-octahydro-8a-hydroxy-7,7-dimethyl-5-methylene-, methyl ester, trans	EtOH	223(3.68)	44-0365-80
2-Naphthalenecarboxylic acid, 3,4,4a-5,6,7,8,8a-octahydro-8a-(methoxy-methyl)-5-methylene-, methyl ester	EtOH	222(3.95)	44-0367-80
2(3H)-Naphthalenone, 6-[1-(formyloxy)-1-methylethyl]-4,4a,5,6,7,8-hexahy-dro-4-methyl-	EtOH	236(4.16)	18-1049-80
Naphtho[1,2-c]furan-1(3H)-one, 4,5,5a-6,7,8,9,9a-octahydro-5-hydroxy-6,6,9a-trimethyl-	MeOH	218(3.95)	94-2185-80

$C_{15}H_{22}O_3S$

Compound	Solvent	$\lambda_{max}(\log \epsilon)$	Ref.
3H-2,1-Benzoxathiole, 3,3-dimethyl-5,7-bis(1-methylethyl)-, 1,1-dioxide	EtOH	266(2.83),275(2.83)	39-1076-80C
2-Butenoic acid, 3-(2-furanyl)-4-[(3-methylbutyl)thio]-, ethyl ester, (E)-	EtOH	213(4.03),309(4.28)	73-0142-80

$C_{15}H_{22}O_4$

Compound	Solvent	$\lambda_{max}(\log \epsilon)$	Ref.
Acetic acid, [3,4,4-trimethyl-2-oxo-3-(3-oxo-1-butenyl)-1-cyclohexyl] ester, (E)-	pentane	213(4.16),302(1.82)	33-2230-80
(Z)-	pentane	221(3.86)	33-2230-80
3-Buten-2-one, 4-(5-acetoxy-2,2,6-tri-methyl-7-oxabicyclo[4.1.0]hept-1-yl)-, [1α(E),5β,6α]-	pentane	227(4.10)	33-2230-80
2-Cyclohexene-1-carboxylic acid, 2-(3-hydroxy-1-butenyl)-1,3-dimethyl-4-oxo-, ethyl ester	EtOH	282(3.93)	104-1951-80
2,11-Dioxabicyclo[4.4.1]undeca-3,5-dien-10-ol, 1,3,7,7-tetramethyl-, acetate	pentane	263(4.03)	33-2230-80
isomer	pentane	253(3.88)	33-2230-80
4a(2H)-Naphthalenepropanoic acid, 3,4,5,6,7,8-hexahydro-1-methoxy-2-oxo-, methyl ester	MeOH	254(3.52)	44-0570-80
Spiro[bicyclo[4.1.0]heptane-2,2'-oxir-ane]-4-acetic acid, 3',3',4,6-tetra-methyl-5-oxo-, methyl ester	EtOH	202(2.28)	102-0603-80

Compound	Solvent	λ_{max}(log ϵ)	Ref.
$C_{15}H_{22}O_8$			
Antirrhide	n.s.g.	206(3.6)	100-0649-80
Butanedioic acid, [3-(ethoxycarbonyl)-tetrahydro-4,5-dimethyl-2-oxo-3-furanyl]-, dimethyl ester	MeOH	214(3.64)	118-0698-80
β-D-Glucopyranoside, 1,4a,5,7a-tetrahydro-7-(hydroxymethyl)cyclopenta-[c]pyran-1-yl (bartsioside)	EtOH	209(3.2)	100-0649-80
Linaride	n.s.g.	204(3.7)	100-0649-80
Loasaside	MeOH	207(3.55)	100-0649-80
$C_{15}H_{22}O_9$			
Aucubin	H_2O	210(3.4)	100-0649-80
Decaloside	n.s.g.	204(3.68)	100-0649-80
Galiridoside	H_2O	189.5(4.18)	100-0649-80
Mentzeloside	n.s.g.	205(3.53)	100-0649-80
$C_{15}H_{22}O_9S$			
Cyclopenta[c]pyran-4-carboxylic acid, 6-acetoxy-1,4a,5,6,7,7a-hexahydro-1-methoxy-7-[[(methylsulfonyl)oxy]methyl]-, methyl ester	MeOH	235(4.02)	44-4233-80
$C_{15}H_{22}O_{10}$			
Antirrinoside	EtOH	267(3.4)	100-0649-80
Catalpol	H_2O	193(3.9)	100-0649-80
Scabroside	n.s.g.	208(3.6)	100-0649-80
$C_{15}H_{22}O_{11}$			
Macfadienoside	MeOH	204(3.4)	100-0649-80
$C_{15}H_{22}S$			
1-Propanethione, 1-[4-(1,1-dimethylethyl)phenyl]-2,2-dimethyl-	isooctane	215s(4.05),226s(4.01),308(3.75),565(2.17)	24-2255-80
$C_{15}H_{22}Si$			
Silane, trimethyl[3-(phenylmethyl)-1,4-pentadienyl]-, (E)-	hexane	215(3.35),256(2.34)	33-0555-80
$C_{15}H_{23}BrO_2$			
Phenol, 3-[(9-bromononyl)oxy]-	n.s.g.	278(3.36)	44-3923-80
$C_{15}H_{23}ClN_6$			
2-Pyrimidinamine, 4-chloro-5-ethyl-N-(5-hexyl-1H-1,2,4-triazol-3-yl)-6-methyl-	EtOH	256(4.24),288(3.66)	103-1275-80
$C_{15}H_{23}ClO_3Si$			
Acetic acid, (4-chlorophenoxy)-, (triethylsilyl)methyl ester	MeCN	227(3.76),281(3.15),289(3.04)	65-0481-80
$C_{15}H_{23}ClO_6Si$			
Acetic acid, (4-chlorophenoxy)-, (triethoxysilyl)methyl ester	MeCN	227(3.84),274s(--),281(3.14),289(3.04)	65-0481-80
$C_{15}H_{23}ClO_9$			
Deutziol, 7-chloro-	MeOH	205(3.5)	100-0649-80
$C_{15}H_{23}Cl_2N_4O_5P$			
Thymidine, 5'-[[[bis(2-chloroethyl)amino]hydroxyphosphinyl]methylamino]-5'-	EtOH	266(3.94)	87-1235-80

Compound	Solvent	$\lambda_{max}(\log \epsilon)$	Ref.
deoxy-, intramol. 5',3'-ester (cont.)			87-1235-80
$C_{15}H_{23}NOS$			
2-Octanesulfenamide, 2-methyl-N-(4-oxo-2,5-cyclohexadien-1-ylidene)-	hexane	405(4.43)	18-0775-80
$C_{15}H_{23}NO_2$			
Benzaldehyde, 2-hydroxy-5-(1,1,3,3-tetramethylbutyl)-, oxime	EtOH	261(4.06),313(3.57)	90-0431-80
1-Hexanone, 2-ethyl-1-(2-hydroxy-5-methylphenyl)-, oxime	EtOH	256(3.85),313(3.56)	90-0431-80
1-Octanone, 1-(2-hydroxy-5-methyl-phenyl)-, oxime	EtOH	257(3.93),313(3.60)	90-0431-80
$C_{15}H_{23}NO_3$			
3-Pyridinecarboxylic acid, 1-ethyl-5-heptyl-1,4-dihydro-4-oxo-	EtOH	261(3.97),287(3.66)	4-0359-80
3-Pyridinecarboxylic acid, 5-heptyl-1,4-dihydro-4-oxo-, ethyl ester	EtOH	260(3.89),285(3.70)	4-0359-80
$C_{15}H_{23}NO_6$			
4H-Indol-4-one, 6,6-dimethyl-2-(D-galacto-pentitol-1-yl)-	H_2O	211(4.12),246(3.80),288(3.70)	136-0017-80A
4H-Indol-4-one, 6,6-dimethyl-2-(D-gluco-pentitol-1-yl)-	H_2O	211(4.12),245(3.74),287(3.65)	136-0017-80A
4H-Indol-4-one, 6,6-dimethyl-2-(D-manno-pentitol-1-yl)-	H_2O	211(4.12),246(3.76),288(3.68)	136-0017-80A
$C_{15}H_{23}N_3$			
Benzenamine, 4-[2-(1,3-dimethyl-2-imidazolidinyl)ethenyl]-N,N-dimethyl-	MeCN MeCN-acid	297(4.31) 480(4.60)	35-3062-80 35-3062-80
Cyclopenta[c]pyrrole-1,3-diamine, 5-(1,1-dimethylethyl)-N,N,N',N'-tetramethyl-	CH_2Cl_2	225(4.35),298(4.32),308(4.32),388(3.11),563(2.71)	89-0199-80
$C_{15}H_{23}N_3O_6$			
1H-Imidazole-4-carboxylic acid, 5-amino-2-methyl-1-[2,3-O-(1-methylethylidene)-β-D-ribofuranosyl]-	pH 2 pH 6-7 pH 12	250s(4.05),267(4.16) 240s(3.76),273(4.14) 240s(3.76),273(4.14)	65-1723-80 65-1723-80 65-1723-80
$C_{15}H_{23}N_3O_6S$			
2-Thiazolebutanoic acid, 4-[[(2-ethoxy-2-oxoethyl)amino]carbonyl]-α-(formyl-amino)-4,5-dihydro-, ethyl ester, [R-(R*,S*)]-	35% HCl	268(3.69)	18-2592-80
$C_{15}H_{23}N_3S$			
1-Pyrazolidinecarbothioamide, N-ethyl-3,3,5-trimethyl-2-phenyl-	EtOH	244(4.02)	103-0169-80
$C_{15}H_{23}N_5O_4$			
Adenosine, N,N-dimethyl-2',3',5'-tri-O-methyl-	pH 6.6	211(4.21),272(4.29)	44-4073-80
$C_{15}H_{24}$			
1,3,7-Cyclodecatriene, 1,7-dimethyl-4-(1-methylethyl)-, (E,E,E)-	EtOH	253(4.05)	12-1833-80
$C_{15}H_{24}ClN_2O_3PS_2$			
Phosphorodithioic acid, O-(5-chloro-1-cyclohexyl-1,6-dihydro-6-oxo-4-pyri-	MeOH	214(4.42),298(3.75)	73-2247-80

Compound	Solvent	$\lambda_{max}(\log \epsilon)$	Ref.
dazinyl) O-ethyl S-propyl ester (cont.)			73-2247-80
$C_{15}H_{24}N_2O$			
1,3-Cyclopentadiene-1-carboxamide, 5-[(dimethylamino)methylene]-3-(1,1-dimethylethyl)-N,N-dimethyl-	dioxan	243(4.06),342(4.41)	89-0199-80
$C_{15}H_{24}N_4$			
2H-Cyclopenta[d]pyridazine-1,4-diamine, 6-(1,1-dimethylethyl)-N,N,N',N'-tetramethyl-	CH_2Cl_2	249(4.49),298s(3.90), 592(1.08)	89-0199-80
$C_{15}H_{24}N_4O_2S$			
3-Pyridinecarboxylic acid, 5-heptyl-1,4-dihydro-4-oxo-, 2-[(methylamino)-thioxomethyl]hydrazide	EtOH	245(4.24),288(3.85)	4-0175-80
$C_{15}H_{24}N_4O_3$			
3-Pyridinecarboxylic acid, 5-butyl-1,4-dihydro-4-oxo-, 2-[(butylamino)carbonyl]hydrazide	EtOH	254(3.91),286(3.78)	4-0175-80
$C_{15}H_{24}N_6O$			
2-Pyrimidinamine, 4-ethoxy-N-(5-hexyl-1H-1,2,4-triazol-3-yl)-6-methyl-	EtOH	251(4.33)	103-1275-80
4(1H)-Pyrimidinone, 5-ethyl-2-[(5-hexyl-1H-1,2,4-triazol-3-yl)amino]-6-methyl-	EtOH	249(4.01),271(3.95), 291(3.88)	103-1275-80
$C_{15}H_{24}O$			
Acorenone B	MeOH	242(4.21),310(1.22)	100-0598-80
1-Azulenol, 1,2,6,7,8,8a-hexahydro-5,8a-dimethyl-3-(1-methylethyl)-, cis	EtOH	245(4.05)	88-0201-80
Methanone, bicyclo[2.2.2]oct-1-yl-cyclohexyl-	C_6H_{11}Me-iso-pentane	297.5(1.36)	44-3933-80
2(1H)-Naphthalenone, 4a,5,6,7,8,8a-hexahydro-3,4,4a,8,8-pentamethyl-	EtOH	249.5(4.14)	65-0176-80
2(3H)-Naphthalenone, 4,4a,5,6,7,8-hexahydro-1,4a-dimethyl-7-(1-methylethyl)-	EtOH	251(4.16)	44-3088-80
2,4-Pentadien-1-ol, 3-methyl-5-(2,6,6-trimethyl-1-cyclohexen-1-yl)-, (E,E)-	3-Mepentane	239(4.15),263(4.14)	149-0739-80B
at 77° K	3-Mepentane	203(--),235s(4.08), 264(4.17)	149-0739-80B
(Z,E)-	3-Mepentane	240(4.02),267(4.05)	149-0739-80B
at 77° K	3-Mepentane	205(--),235s(3.90), 265(4.03)	149-0739-80B
$C_{15}H_{24}O_2$			
2(1H)-Azulenone, 4,5,6,7,8,8a-hexahydro-5-(1-hydroxy-1-methylethyl)-3,8-dimethyl-	EtOH	242(4.22)	18-0785-80
Bicyclo[2.2.2]oct-5-ene-2-methanol, 5-ethenyl-1-methoxy-α,α,8-trimethyl-	EtOH	235(4.26)	18-1049-80
1(4H)-Naphthalenone, 4a,5,6,7,8,8a-hexahydro-4-(hydroxymethyl)-3,4a,8,8-tetramethyl-, [4S-(4α,4aα,8aβ)]-(6-oxodrimenol)	MeOH	239.5(3.76)	39-0221-80C
$C_{15}H_{24}O_2S$			
Benzenesulfinic acid, 2,4,6-tris(1-methylethyl)-	EtOH	273(3.15),282(3.08)	39-1076-80C

Compound	Solvent	$\lambda_{max}(\log \epsilon)$	Ref.
$C_{15}H_{24}O_3$			
1-Cyclopentene-1-heptanoic acid, α-ethyl-5-oxo-, methyl ester	MeOH	228(3.98)	44-4702-80
1-Cyclopentene-1-heptanoic acid, α-methyl-5-oxo-, ethyl ester	MeOH	228(3.99)	44-4702-80
1-Cyclopentene-1-octanoic acid, 5-oxo-, ethyl ester	MeOH	228(3.99)	44-4702-80
1(4H)-Naphthalenone, 4a,5,6,7,8,8a-hexahydro-7-hydroxy-4-(hydroxymethyl)-3,4a,8,8-tetramethyl-	MeOH	239.5(3.83)	39-0221-80C
Naphtho[1,2-c]furan-1(3H)-one, 4-hydroxy-6,6,9a-trimethyl- (futronolide)	MeOH	218(4.84)	100-0365-80
2H-Pyran-2-one, 4-methoxy-6-nonyl-	EtOH	279(3.99)	23-2158-80
Uvidin A	MeOH	204(3.18),233s(--)	39-0221-80C
$C_{15}H_{24}O_4$			
Cyclopentaneacetic acid, 3-octyl-α,2-dioxo-	MeOH	299(3.67)	44-4702-80
Uvidin B	MeOH	206(3.01)	39-0221-80C
$C_{15}H_{24}O_7$			
D-manno-Oct-2-enonic acid, 2,3-dideoxy-4,5:7,8-bis-O-(1-methylethylidene)-, methyl ester, (E)-	MeOH	215(3.78)	136-00C4-80C
$C_{15}H_{24}O_8$			
Gluroside	H_2O	190(3.8)	100-0649-80
$C_{15}H_{24}O_9$			
Deutziol	MeOH	218(2.97)	100-0649-80
Harpagide, 6-deoxy-	H_2O	189(3.9)	100-0649-80
Mioporoside	MeOH	204(3.51)	100-0649-80
$C_{15}H_{24}S$			
12-Thiabicyclo[9.1.0]dodeca-3,7-diene, 1,5,5,8-tetramethyl-	EtOH	266(2.34)	39-0311-80C
$C_{15}H_{25}NO$			
Cyclodecanone, 2-[3-(dimethylamino)-2-propenylidene]-	hexane	235(3.84),340(3.75)	70-0987-80
	EtOH	378(4.50)	70-0987-80
	CHCl$_3$	367(4.40)	70-0987-80
$C_{15}H_{25}NOS_2$			
2-Propanesulfenamide, N-[(1,1-dimethylethyl)thio]-N-(3-methoxyphenyl)-2-methyl-	hexane	252(3.95),286(3.64), 293(3.48)	18-0720-80
2-Propanesulfenamide, N-[(1,1-dimethylethyl)thio]-N-(4-methoxyphenyl)-2-methyl-	hexane	254(4.09),305(3.34)	18-0720-80
$C_{15}H_{25}NO_3$			
1-Cyclopentene-1-heptanoic acid, 5-(methoxyimino)-, ethyl ester	MeOH	243(4.12)	44-4702-80
$C_{15}H_{25}NS_2$			
2-Propanesulfenamide, N-[(1,1-dimethylethyl)thio]-2-methyl-N-(4-methylphenyl)-	hexane	254(4.10)	18-0720-80
$C_{15}H_{25}N_3O_3$			
3,5-Isoxazoledicarboxamide, N,N'-di-	MeOH	244(4.02)	94-0479-80

Compound	Solvent	$\lambda_{max}(\log \epsilon)$	Ref.
butyl-4-ethyl- (cont.)			94-0479-80
$C_{15}H_{26}N_8$			
4(1H)-Pyrimidinone, 5-ethyl-2-[(5-hexyl-1H-1,2,4-triazol-3-yl)amino]-6-methyl-, hydrazone	EtOH	233(4.27),255(4.24), 287(3.92)	103-1275-80
$C_{15}H_{26}O$			
Acorenone B, dihydro-	MeOH	283(1.42)	100-0598-80
epimer	MeOH	278(1.34)	100-0598-80
$C_{15}H_{26}OSi_2$			
2H-Inden-2-one, 4,5,6,7-tetrahydro-1,3-bis(trimethylsilyl)-	C_6H_{12}	441(2.86),444s(2.70)	89-1023-80
$C_{15}H_{26}O_2$			
1(2H)-Naphthalenone, octahydro-4-(hydroxymethyl)-3,4a,8,8-tetramethyl-(6-oxodrimanol)	MeOH	203(2.97)	39-0221-80C
8-Oxaspiro[4.6]undecan-7-one, 1,9-dimethyl-4-(1-methylethyl)-	hexane	218(1.99)	100-0598-80
$C_{15}H_{26}O_3$			
Drimanol, 3β-hydroxy-6-oxo-	MeOH	204(2.78)	39-0221-80C
Drimanol, 8β-hydroxy-6-oxo-	MeOH	204(2.99)	39-0221-80C
$C_{15}H_{27}I$			
2,6-Dodecadiene, 12-iodo-2,6,10-trimethyl-, (E)-	heptane	259(2.76)	78-1455-80
(Z)-	heptane	259(2.71)	78-1455-80
$C_{15}H_{27}N_3O_4$			
3,5-Isoxazoledicarboxamide, N,N'-dibutyl-4-ethyl-4,5-dihydro-, 2-oxide, trans	MeOH	258(3.94)	94-0479-80
$C_{15}H_{28}OTe$			
Propanetelluroic acid, 2,2-dimethyl-, O-[5-methyl-2-(1-methylethyl)cyclohexyl] ester, [1R-(1α,2β,5α)]-	C_6H_{12}	241(3.54),265(2.79), 346(3.82),589(2.38)	39-2191-80C
$C_{15}H_{30}Si_3$			
Disilane, pentamethyl[[2-(trimethylsilyl)methyl]phenyl]-	C_6H_{12}	233(4.03)	65-1621-80
Disilane, pentamethyl[[4-(trimethylsilyl)methyl]phenyl]-	isooctane	240.5(4.32)	101-0261-80Q
$C_{15}H_{31}NS_2$			
Carbamodithioic acid, tetradecyl-, monoammonium salt	EtOH	254(3.97),290(4.10)	90-0775-80
$C_{15}H_{31}N_3$			
1H-Imidazole-1-ethanamine, 2-decyl-4,5-dihydro-	hexane	226(--)	135-0860-80
	EtOH	230(3.82)	135-0860-80

Compound	Solvent	$\lambda_{max}(\log \epsilon)$	Ref.
$C_{16}F_{10}$			
Fluoranthene, decafluoro-	MeOH	208(4.53),236(4.51), 272(3.91),283(3.85), 322(3.79),354(3.98)	104-1794-80
	EtOH	210(4.49),235(4.55), 254(4.16),271(3.95), 282(3.87),305(3.53), 318(3.83),353(4.03), 370(3.93)	39-1726-80C
$C_{16}HF_9$			
Fluoranthene, 1,2,3,4,6,7,8,9,10-nona-fluoro-	MeOH	208(4.56),237(4.51), 269(3.99),281(3.94), 319(3.73),358(3.96)	104-1794-80
$C_{16}H_4O_6$			
1,2,3,6,7,8-Pyrenehexone	MeCN	203(4.36),234(4.67), 266(4.04),342(4.15), 355(4.15),533s(2.10)	89-0715-80
$C_{16}H_6Cl_3NO_3$			
11H-Benzo[b]phenoxazine-6,11(12H)-dione, 1,2,4-trichloro-	DMSO	307(4.33),584(4.04), 642(2.04)	44-5144-80
$C_{16}H_7Cl_2NO_3$			
11H-Benzo[b]phenoxazine-6,11(12H)-dione, 2,4-dichloro-	dioxan	235(4.35),306(4.41), 573(3.00)	44-5144-80
$C_{16}H_7F_3N_2O_3S_2$			
Acetamide, 2,2,2-trifluoro-N-(7-nitro-[1]benzothiopheno[3,2-b][1]benzo-thien-2-yl)-	dioxan	218(4.48),258(4.30), 348(4.34)	104-0383-80
$C_{16}H_8ClNO_3$			
11H-Benzo[b]phenoxazine-6,11(12H)-dione, 2-chloro-	DMSO	304(4.21),556s(2.68)	44-5144-80
$C_{16}H_8Cl_2N_2O_4$			
1,4-Naphthalenedione, 2-chloro-3-[(4-chlorophenyl)amino]-5-nitro-	EtOH	276(4.37),502(3.68)	40-1862-80
1,4-Naphthalenedione, 3-chloro-2-[(4-chlorophenyl)amino]-5-nitro-	EtOH	278(4.43),500(3.71)	40-1862-80
$C_{16}H_8Cl_4N_2O_2$			
1,4-Naphthalenedione, 5-amino-2,6,8-trichloro-3-[(4-chlorophenyl)amino]-	EtOH	282(4.49),544(3.97)	40-1862-80
1,4-Naphthalenedione, 5-amino-3,6,8-trichloro-2-[(4-chlorophenyl)amino]-	EtOH	283(4.49),540(3.97)	40-1862-80
$C_{16}H_8D_2N_4$			
1,1,2,2-Ethanetetracarbonitrile, 1-(1,2-dihydro-2-naphthalenyl-1,2-d_2)	CH_2Cl_2	228(4.2),271(4.0)	24-0024-80
$C_{16}H_8F_3NOS_2$			
Acetamide, N-[1]benzothieno[3,2-b][1]-benzothien-2-yl-2,2,2-trifluoro-	dioxan	216(4.56),240(4.32), 277(4.44),324(4.52), 340(4.36)	104-0391-80
$C_{16}H_8F_6O_2$			
Ethanedione, bis[4-(trifluoromethyl)-phenyl]-	MeCN	254(4.31),393(1.77)	44-2883-80

Compound	Solvent	$\lambda_{max}(\log \epsilon)$	Ref.
$C_{16}H_8F_{12}$			
4H-1,4:4a,7-Dimethanonaphthalene, 1,7-dihydro-2,3,5,6-tetrakis-(trifluoromethyl)-	C_6H_{12}	208(3.42),242s(2.70)	77-0670-80
$C_{16}H_8N_2O$			
Benzofuro[2,3-b]quinoline-11-carbonitrile	EtOH	222(4.65),262(4.64), 277s(3.99),349(4.33), 366(4.35)	18-1057-80
Benzofuro[3,2-c]quinoline-6-carbonitrile	EtOH	211(4.36),229(4.32), 257s(4.66),265(4.70), 286(4.26),298(4.14), 348(3.52),360(3.50)	18-1057-80
$C_{16}H_8N_2O_2$			
Benzofuro[2,3-b]quinoline-11-carbonitrile, 6-oxide	EtOH	211(4.45),233s(4.27), 270(4.47),362(4.16)	18-1057-80
$C_{16}H_8N_2O_5$			
11H-Benzo[b]phenoxazine-6,11(12H)-dione, 2-nitro-	DMSO	305(4.42),437(3.62), 559(2.50)	44-5144-80
11H-Benzo[b]phenoxazine-6,11(12H)-dione, 3-nitro-	DMSO	306(4.44),441(3.38), 642(2.07)	44-5144-80
$C_{16}H_8O_2S_2$			
Benzo[b]thiophen-3(2H)-one, 2-(3-oxo-benzo[b]thien-2(3H)-ylidene)-	$CHCl_3$	541(4.19)	24-1708-80
$C_{16}H_9BrN_2O_4S$			
Benzenesulfonic acid, 4-bromo-, 6-diazo-5,6-dihydro-5-oxo-1-naphthalenyl ester	EPA	214(4.12),226(4.25), 263(3.89),348(3.82), 402(3.79)	135-0064-80
$C_{16}H_9BrO_6$			
1,4,9,10-Anthracenetetrone, 4a-acetoxy-9a-bromo-4a,9a-dihydro-	EtOH	213s(4.15),232(4.41), 263s(3.86),309(3.30)	39-1007-80C
$C_{16}H_9ClN_2O_4$			
1,4-Naphthalenedione, 2-chloro-5-nitro-3-(phenylamino)-	EtOH	272(4.33),497(3.66)	40-1862-80
1,4-Naphthalenedione, 3-chloro-5-nitro-2-(phenylamino)-	EtOH	274(4.35),493(3.72)	40-1862-80
$C_{16}H_9ClN_2O_4S$			
Benzenesulfonic acid, 4-chloro-, 6-diazo-5,6-dihydro-5-oxo-1-naphthalenyl ester	EPA	214(4.00),226(4.15), 263(3.94),345(3.78), 400(3.71)	135-0064-80
$C_{16}H_9ClN_4O$			
2H-Pyrido[1,2-a]pyrimidin-2-one, 3-(3-chloro-2-quinoxalinyl)-	EtOH	207(4.65),246(4.53), 365(4.32)	94-2527-80
$C_{16}H_9Cl_2NO_3$			
7H-Benzo[c]phenoxazin-5(12aH)-one, 6,9-dichloro-12a-hydroxy-	dioxan	262(4.28),373(4.01)	44-2155-80
$C_{16}H_9Cl_3N_2O_2$			
1,4-Naphthalenedione, 5-amino-2,6,8-trichloro-3-(phenylamino)-	EtOH	270(4.48),480(3.91)	40-1862-80
1,4-Naphthalenedione, 5-amino-3,6,8-trichloro-2-(phenylamino)-	EtOH	276(4.53),530(3.95)	40-1862-80

Compound	Solvent	$\lambda_{max}(\log \epsilon)$	Ref.
$C_{16}H_9Cl_4NO_4$			
Benzamide, N-methyl-N-(5,6,7,8-tetra-chloro-2,3-dihydro-3-oxo-1,4-benzo-dioxin-2-yl)-	MeCN	214(4.77),290(3.19), 299(3.22)	5-1836-80
$C_{16}H_9F_3N_2O_2$			
Pyridinium, 4-cyano-, 1-benzoyl-3,3,3-trifluoro-2-oxopropylide	50% EtOH	230(4.15),257(4.05), 280s(3.87),487(3.72)	104-0729-80
	85% EtOH	492(--)	104-0729-80
	$CHCl_3$	502(--)	104-0729-80
$C_{16}H_9NO_2$			
5H-Benzo[a]phenoxazin-5-one	50% EtOH	370(4.06),439(4.12)	86-0349-80
9H-Benzo[a]phenoxazin-9-one	EtOH	407(3.76),505(4.27)	86-0349-80
10H-Benzo[c]phenoxazin-10-one	50% EtOH	376(3.87),505(3.95)	86-0349-80
6H-[1]Benzopyrano[4,3-b]quinolin-6-one	MeOH	228(4.20),265s(4.38), 273(4.54),302s(3.69), 340(3.39),355(3.43), 370(3.35)	39-0522-80C
	acid	218(4.48),248(4.49), 266s(4.45),275(4.52), 360(3.87),370(3.87)	39-0522-80C
Cyclopent[4,5]azepino[2,1,7-cd]pyrro-lizine-6,8-dicarboxaldehyde	EtOH	273(4.54),298(4.50), 372(4.77),460(4.04), 505(3.71)	39-1324-80C
$C_{16}H_9NO_2S_2$			
2H-[1,3]Thiazino[2,3-b]benzothiazolium, 3,4-dihydro-2,4-dioxo-3-phenyl-, hydroxide, inner salt	MeOH	228(4.18),235s(4.16), 324(4.42)	44-2474-80
$C_{16}H_9NO_3S$			
2H-[1,3]Thiazino[2,3-b]benzoxazolium, 3,4-dihydro-2,4-dioxo-3-phenyl-, hydroxide, inner salt	MeOH	258(3.99),298(4.44)	44-2474-80
$C_{16}H_9N_3O_5S$			
Benzenesulfonic acid, 4-nitroso-, 6-di-azo-5,6-dihydro-5-oxo-1-naphthalenyl ester	EPA	212(4.15),226(4.00), 260(4.18),351(3.83), 402(3.82)	135-0064-80
$C_{16}H_9N_3O_6S$			
Benzenesulfonic acid, 4-nitro-, 6-di-azo-5,6-dihydro-5-oxo-1-naphthalenyl ester	EPA	210(4.07),226(4.00), 268(4.00),328(3.67), 405(3.78)	135-0064-80
$C_{16}H_{10}$			
Anthracene, 9-ethynyl-	EtOH	249s(4.91),257(5.17), 343(3.49),361(3.84), 380(4.05),400(4.03)	44-1807-80
$C_{16}H_{10}BrClN_2OS$			
Phenol, 4-bromo-2-[[[4-(4-chlorophen-yl)-2-thiazolyl]imino]methyl]-	pH 5	390(3.56)	2-0492-80
$C_{16}H_{10}BrNOS$			
[1]Benzothieno[3,2-b]quinolin-11(5H)-one, 2-bromo-5-methyl-	MeOH	242(4.37),254(4.42), 275(4.60),284(4.80), 302(4.01),313(4.03), 381(3.99),400(4.11)	83-0027-80

Compound	Solvent	$\lambda_{max}(\log \epsilon)$	Ref.
$C_{16}H_{10}BrNO_3$ 2H-Anthra[1,2-d][1,3]oxazine-7,12-dione, 6-bromo-1,4-dihydro-	EtOH	489(3.69)	18-3007-80 +146-0513-80
$C_{16}H_{10}BrN_3OS$ 4(3H)-Quinazolinone, 3-(2-benzothiazolyl)-6-bromo-2-methyl-	n.s.g.	282(3.90),340(4.04)	18-2389-80
$C_{16}H_{10}BrN_3O_2$ 4(3H)-Quinazolinone, 3-(2-benzoxazolyl)-6-bromo-2-methyl-	n.s.g.	287(3.95),335(3.60)	18-2389-80
$C_{16}H_{10}Br_2N_2$ Pyrimidine, 4,6-bis(3-bromophenyl)-	CHCl$_3$	250(4.36),290(4.31)	24-2739-80
$C_{16}H_{10}ClNOS$ Thiocyanic acid, 3-(4-chlorophenyl)-3-oxo-1-phenyl-1-propenyl ester	EtOH	310(4.30)	2-0266-80
$C_{16}H_{10}ClNOS_2$ Acetamide, N-(7-chloro[1]benzothieno[3,2-b][1]benzothien-2-yl)-	dioxan	222(4.54),244(4.42), 268(4.33),278(4.45), 328(4.57),342(4.56)	104-0383-80
$C_{16}H_{10}ClNOS_3$ Benzenecarbothioic acid, S-[4-(4-chlorophenyl)-2,5-dihydro-5-thioxo-3-isothiazolyl] ester	CHCl$_3$	316(4.22),420(4.14)	39-2693-80C
$C_{16}H_{10}ClNO_2$ 1,2-Naphthalenedione, 4-[(3-chlorophenyl)amino]-	EtOH	242(4.34),285(4.19), 335(3.82),448(3.66)	94-1207-80
1,2-Naphthalenedione, 4-[(4-chlorophenyl)amino]-	EtOH	243(4.40),285(4.18), 330s(3.81),458(3.70)	94-1207-80
1,4-Naphthalenedione, 2-chloro-3-(phenylamino)-	EtOH	277(4.40),331(3.51), 480(3.49)	150-0139-80
$C_{16}H_{10}ClNO_3$ 7H-Benzo[c]phenoxazin-5(12aH)-one, 6-chloro-12a-hydroxy-	EtOH	255(4.39),390(4.28)	44-2155-80
$C_{16}H_{10}ClN_3$ Quino[3,2-c][1,8]naphthyridine, 3-chloro-7-methyl-	EtOH	212(4.49),255s(4.53), 264(4.54),294s(4.34), 304(4.44)	4-1225-80
$C_{16}H_{10}ClN_5O$ 1H-Indole-2,3-dione, 3-[(3-chloro-2(1H)-quinoxalinylidene)hydrazone], (E,Z)-	EtOH	330(3.96),430s(4.17), 452s(4.2),472(4.22), 492s(4.15)	103-1073-80
$C_{16}H_{10}Cl_2N_2$ 11H-Indeno[1,2-c]isoquinolin-5-amine, 2,9-dichloro-	EtOH-H$_2$SO$_4$	212(4.45),258(4.47), 324(4.29),337(4.32), 375(4.14),392(4.02)	18-2885-80
11H-Indeno[1,2-c]isoquinolin-5-amine, 3,8-dichloro-	EtOH-H$_2$SO$_4$	223(4.72),234s(4.55), 324(4.36),338(4.37), 380(4.11),400(4.03)	18-2885-80
$C_{16}H_{10}Cl_2N_2O_2$ 1,4-Naphthalenedione, 5-amino-2-chloro-	EtOH	268(4.47),474(4.05)	40-1862-80

Compound	Solvent	$\lambda_{max}(\log \epsilon)$	Ref.
3-[(4-chlorophenyl)amino]- (cont.) 1,4-Naphthalenedione, 5-amino-3-chloro-2-[(4-chlorophenyl)amino]-	EtOH	283(4.48),546(3.93)	40-1862-80 40-1862-80
$C_{16}H_{10}Cl_3NO_5S$ 2-Furancarboxylic acid, 5-[2-(4-cyanophenyl)-1-[(trichloromethyl)sulfonyl]ethenyl]-, methyl ester, (E)-	EtOH	202(4.22),261(4.43), 283s(4.14),345(3.92)	73-0746-80
$C_{16}H_{10}Cl_4N_2O_4$ 1H-Pyrazolo[1,2-a]pyrazol-4-ium, 3-hydroxy-5,7-dimethyl-1-oxo-2-(5,6,7,8-tetrachloro-2,3-dihydro-1,4-benzodioxin-2-yl)-, hydroxide, inner salt	MeCN	218(4.483),230s(4.429), 250s(4.273),295s(3.416), 302(3.529),365(3.015)	64-1002-80B
$C_{16}H_{10}Cl_4O_3$ 4,9-Ethenobiphenyleno[2,3-c]furan-1,3-dione, 5,6,7,8-tetrachloro-3a,4,4a,4b-8a,8b,9,9a-octahydro-, (3aα,4β,4aα-4bβ,8aβ,8bα,9β,9aα)-	MeCN	295(3.66)	78-3033-80
$C_{16}H_{10}F_3IO_2$ Iodonium, phenyl-, 1-benzoyl-3,3,3-trifluoro-2-oxopropylide	50% EtOH	228(4.09),253(4.09), 330s(3.11)	104-0729-80
$C_{16}H_{10}F_3NO_2$ Phenol, 2-[4-phenyl-3-(trifluoromethyl)-5-isoxazolyl]-	EtOH	255(3.94)	114-0389-80B
$C_{16}H_{10}F_3NO_5$ Oxazolo[3,2-a]quinolinium, 5-acetoxy-2-hydroxy-4-methyl-1-(trifluoroacetyl)-, hydroxide, inner salt	EtOH	280(4.00),362(4.58)	78-1385-80
$C_{16}H_{10}F_5NO$ 5H-Dibenz[b,f]azepine, 10-(pentafluoroethoxy)-	EtOH	255(4.79),290s(3.78)	44-4122-80
$C_{16}H_{10}Fe_2O_7$ Iron, hexacarbonyl[μ-[η⁴:η⁴-[3-methyl-5,6-bis(methylene)-4-oxo-2-cyclohexene-1,2-diyl]methylene]]di-	isooctane	233(4.13),244s(4.10), 307s(3.80)	101-0247-80C
Iron, tricarbonyl[μ-[η⁴:η⁴-2,3,5,6-tetrakis(methylene)-7-oxabicyclo-2.2.1]heptane]]di-	isooctane	223(4.52),302(3.74)	101-0247-80C
$C_{16}H_{10}N_2$ Naphtho[2,3-g]phthalazine	CHCl₃	293(5.18),377(3.25), 382(3.15),400(3.25), 422(3.51),445(3.68), 473(3.58)	118-0689-80
Propanedinitrile, [4-(2,4,6-cycloheptatrien-1-ylidene)-2,5-cyclohexadien-1-ylidene]-	acetone MeCN	660(4.40) 668(4.47)	138-1485-80 138-1485-80
$C_{16}H_{10}N_2O$ 2,7-Ethanonaphth[2,3-b]oxirene-4,5-dicarbonitrile, 1a,2,7,7a-tetrahydro-8,9-bis(methylene)-, (1aα,2α,7α,7aα)-(1aα,2β,7β,7aα)-	EtOH dioxan EtOH dioxan.	227(4.62),253(4.18) 227(4.68),252(4.23) 223(4.64),247(4.20) 223(4.68),243s(4.34)	78-0149-80 78-0149-80 78-0149-80 78-0149-80

Compound	Solvent	$\lambda_{max}(\log \epsilon)$	Ref.
$C_{16}H_{10}N_2O_2$			
Benzofuro[2,3-b]quinoline-11-carbox-amide	EtOH	221(4.67),250s(4.57), 258(4.73),325(4.34), 339s(4.26)	18-1057-80
3-Quinolinecarbonitrile, 1,4-dihydro-2-hydroxy-4-oxo-1-phenyl-	MeOH	226(4.21),287(3.49), 297(3.55)	78-1791-80
$C_{16}H_{10}N_2O_2S$			
4H-[1,3]Thiazino[3,2-a]benzimidazol-4-one, 2-hydroxy-3-phenyl-	MeOH	210(4.43),245(4.29), 278(4.18),295s(4.26), 305(4.33)	44-2474-80
$C_{16}H_{10}N_2O_4$			
1,2-Naphthalenedione, 4-[(3-nitrophen-yl)amino]-	EtOH	222(4.14),245(4.15), 288(4.04),338(3.68), 435(3.37)	94-1207-80
1,2-Naphthalenedione, 4-[(4-nitrophen-yl)amino]-	EtOH	240s(--),285s(--), 304(4.22),343(4.10), 400(--),441(3.80)	94-1207-80
$C_{16}H_{10}N_2O_4S$			
1-Naphthalenesulfonic acid, 6-diazo-5,6-dihydro-5-oxo-, phenyl ester	EPA	213(4.18),228(4.32), 260(4.11),345(3.79), 402(3.71)	135-0064-80
$C_{16}H_{10}N_4$			
Cyclobuta[a]naphthalene-1,1,2,2-tetra-carbonitrile, 2a,3,4,8b-tetrahydro-	MeCN	203(4.2),268(2.9), 275(2.9)	24-0024-80
Cyclobutane-1,1,2,2-tetracarbonitrile, 3-(2-phenylethenyl)-, (Z)-	CH_2Cl_2	263(4.23),286s(3.79), 295s(3.38)	24-1663-80
$C_{16}H_{10}N_4O_2$			
2(1H)-Quinoxalinone, 3-(2-oxo-2H-pyri-do[1,2-a]pyrimidin-3-yl)-	EtOH	214(4.64),297(4.04), 380(4.40)	94-3537-80
[1,2,4]Triazolo[4,3-a]quinoline, 1-(4-nitrophenyl)-	MeOH	290(4.15)	56-0661-80
$C_{16}H_{10}N_4O_3$			
1H-Isoindole-1,3(2H)-dione, 2-(1,5-di-hydro-5-oxo-3-phenyl-4H-1,2,4-tria-zol-4-yl)-	EtOH	218(4.84),262(4.18)	4-1691-80
$C_{16}H_{10}N_4O_5$			
1-Naphthalenol, 4-[(2,4-dinitrophenyl)-azo]-	benzene	460(4.24)	32-0527-80
	toluene	458(4.47)	32-0527-80
	MeOH	455(--),628(--)	32-0527-80
	EtOH	457(--),638(--)	32-0527-80
	ether	450(4.21)	32-0527-80
	dioxan	455(4.55)	32-0527-80
	EtOAc	452(4.53)	32-0527-80
	HCOOEt	453(4.64)	32-0527-80
	HOAc	457(4.56)	32-0527-80
	THF	458(4.30)	32-0527-80
	Ac_2O	458(4.55)	32-0527-80
	$HCONH_2$	640(4.85)	32-0527-80
	aniline	470(4.39)	32-0527-80
	2-picoline	645(4.89)	32-0527-80
	3-picoline	644(4.88)	32-0527-80
	4-picoline	644(4.89)	32-0527-80
	CH_2Cl_2	457(4.54)	32-0527-80
	$CHCl_3$	457(4.53)	32-0527-80

Compound	Solvent	$\lambda_{max}(\log \epsilon)$	Ref.
(cont.)	CCl_4	450(4.22)	32-0527-80
	PhCl	459(4.49)	32-0527-80
	BuBr	466(4.51)	32-0527-80
(also other solvents)	CS_2	460(4.30)	32-0527-80
$C_{16}H_{10}O$			
Phenanthro[9,10-c]furan	C_6H_{12}	238s(4.24),246(4.38), 252(4.38),262(4.14), 292(3.56),302(3.56), 317(3.34),332(3.46)	88-3831-80
$C_{16}H_{10}O_2$			
2,3-Anthracenedicarboxaldehyde	$CHCl_3$	275(4.57),295(4.68), 315s(4.33),345(3.57), 375s(3.60),392(3.80), 415(3.87)	118-0689-80
2,5-Cyclohexadiene-1,4-dione, 2-(1-naphthalenyl)-	CH_2Cl_2	434(3.0)	18-1703-80
	CF_3COOH	500(2.9)	18-1703-80
1H-Indene-1,3(2H)-dione, 2-(phenyl-methylene)-	C_6H_{12}	240(4.59),342(4.56), 407(2.74)	24-1020-80
	$CHCl_3$	344(4.52)	18-1703-80
Indeno[2,1-a]indene-5,10-dione, 4b,9b-dihydro-, (4bS-cis)-	EtOH	202(4.63),210s(4.57), 237s(4.37),246(4.33), 253s(4.23),291(3.52), 297s(3.51),333(2.59), 346(2.54),364(2.21)	18-0291-80
$C_{16}H_{10}O_4$			
1,4,5,8-Anthracenetetrone, 2,3-dimethyl-	CH_2Cl_2	252(4.65),304s(3.56), 355(3.67),360s(3.65)	23-1161-80
$C_{16}H_{10}O_6$			
9,10-Anthracenedione, 4-acetoxy-1,5-dihydroxy-	MeOH	248(4.30),283(3.96), 420(3.82),436(3.86)	24-2994-80
$C_{16}H_{10}O_7$			
9,10-Anthracenedione, 1-acetyl-2,4,5,7-tetrahydroxy-	MeOH-1% HOAc	233(4.13),257(4.04), 266(4.04),296(4.28), 322(3.78),457(3.83)	12-2781-80
$C_{16}H_{10}S$			
Phenanthro[1,2-b]thiophene	C_6H_{12}	211(4.53),271(4.89), 288s(4.37),300(4.30), 311(3.99)	4-1259-80
Phenanthro[2,1-b]thiophene	C_6H_{12}	207(4.48),233(4.53), 254s(4.72),261(4.82), 290(4.34),302(4.22), 316(4.27)	4-1259-80
Phenanthro[2,3-b]thiophene	C_6H_{12}	222(4.50),254s(4.43), 275(4.86),284(4.74), 309s(3.93),320(4.06), 334(4.10),347(3.15), 366(2.65)	4-1259-80
Phenanthro[3,2-b]thiophene	C_6H_{12}	210(4.47),243(4.45), 272(4.78),282(4.88), 302(4.03),314(4.04), 328s(3.98),352(3.17), 370(3.17)	4-1259-80
Phenanthro[3,4-b]thiophene	C_6H_{12}	229(4.35),269(4.65), 278(4.78),298s(4.15), 310s(3.88)	4-1259-80

Compound	Solvent	$\lambda_{max}(\log \epsilon)$	Ref.
Phenanthro[4,3-b]thiophene	C_6H_{12}	211(4.56),234s(4.26), 272(4.76),291s(4.13), 304(4.02),317(4.06)	4-1259-80
Phenanthro[9,10-b]thiophene	C_6H_{12}	254(4.76),259s(4.71), 279s(4.12),289(4.21), 309(3.92)	4-1259-80
$C_{16}H_{11}BrN_2OS$			
Phenol, 4-bromo-2-[[(4-phenyl-2-thiazo-lyl)imino]methyl]-	pH 5	390(3.97)	2-0492-80
$C_{16}H_{11}BrN_2O_2$			
5,8-Quinolinedione, 7-bromo-6-[(2-meth-ylphenyl)amino]-	n.s.g.	235(4.27),270(4.18), 480(3.54)	2-0512-80
5,8-Quinolinedione, 7-bromo-6-[(4-meth-ylphenyl)amino]-	n.s.g.	236(4.26),272(4.28), 496(3.64)	2-0512-80
$C_{16}H_{11}BrO_4$			
9,10-Anthracenedione, 5-bromo-1,3-di-methoxy-	MeOH	233(4.33),243(4.30), 277(4.33),350(3.64), 387(3.71)	12-1805-80
9,10-Anthracenedione, 6-bromo-1,3-di-methoxy-	MeOH	231(4.24),250(4.35), 254(4.37),283(4.39), 327(3.48),400(3.71)	12-1805-80
9,10-Anthracenedione, 7-bromo-1,3-di-methoxy-	MeOH	233(4.32),254(4.28), 285(4.41),334(3.57), 398(3.66)	12-1805-80
9,10-Anthracenedione, 8-bromo-1,3-di-methoxy-	MeOH	234(4.31),246(4.31), 281(4.28),354(3.57), 394(3.67)	12-1805-80
$C_{16}H_{11}ClN_2OS$			
4-Imidazolidinone, 5-[(2-chlorophenyl)-methylene]-3-phenyl-2-thioxo-	EtOH	364(4.55)	56-0683-80
4-Imidazolidinone, 5-[(3-chlorophenyl)-methylene]-3-phenyl-2-thioxo-	EtOH	376(4.64)	56-0683-80
4-Imidazolidinone, 5-[(4-chlorophenyl)-methylene]-3-phenyl-2-thioxo-	EtOH	380(4.69)	56-0683-80
Phenol, 2-[[4-(4-chlorophenyl)-2-thia-zolyl]imino]methyl]-	pH 5	380(4.14)	2-0492-80
$C_{16}H_{11}ClN_2OS_3$			
2(5H)-Isothiazolecarboxamide, N-(4-chlorophenyl)-3-mercapto-4-phenyl-5-thioxo-, acetonitrile adduct	EtOH	320(4.65),407(4.52)	142-0785-80
2(5H)-Isothiazolecarboxamide, 4-(4-chlorophenyl)-3-mercapto-N-phenyl-5-thioxo-, acetone adduct	EtOH	320(4.42),406(4.36)	142-0785-80
$C_{16}H_{11}ClN_2OSe$			
4-Imidazolidinone, 5-[(2-chlorophenyl)-methylene]-3-phenyl-2-selenoxo-	EtOH	395(4.48)	56-0683-80
4-Imidazolidinone, 5-[(3-chlorophenyl)-methylene]-3-phenyl-2-selenoxo-	EtOH	395(4.52)	56-0683-80
4-Imidazolidinone, 5-[(4-chlorophenyl)-methylene]-3-phenyl-2-selenoxo-	EtOH	400(4.53)	56-0683-80
$C_{16}H_{11}ClN_2O_2$			
2,4-Imidazolidinedione, 5-[(2-chloro-phenyl)methylene]-3-phenyl-	EtOH	320(4.34)	56-0683-80

Compound	Solvent	$\lambda_{max}(\log \epsilon)$	Ref.
2,4-Imidazolidinedione, 5-[(3-chloro-phenyl)methylene]-3-phenyl-	EtOH	320(4.43)	56-0683-80
2,4-Imidazolidinedione, 5-[(4-chloro-phenyl)methylene]-3-phenyl-	EtOH	324(4.46)	56-0683-80
1,4-Naphthalenedione, 5-amino-2-chloro-3-(phenylamino)-	EtOH	264(4.60),463(4.23)	40-1862-80
1,4-Naphthalenedione, 5-amino-3-chloro-2-(phenylamino)-	EtOH	279(4.63),535(4.08)	40-1862-80
$C_{16}H_{11}ClN_4$ Benzo[1,2-b:3,4-b']dipyrrole, 3-[(4-chlorophenyl)azo]-1,6-dihydro-	EtOH	207(4.32),222(4.28), 256s(4.14),269(4.21), 454(3.50)	103-0495-80
$C_{16}H_{11}ClN_4O$ 1H-[1,2,4]Triazolo[4,3-a][1,4]benzodi-azepin-1-one, 8-chloro-2,4-dihydro-6-phenyl-	EtOH	214(4.54),250(4.19), 305s(3.19)	87-0402-80
$C_{16}H_{11}ClN_4O_3$ Benzenemethanamine, 4-chloro-α-[[3-(4-nitrophenyl)-1,2,4-oxadiazol-5-yl]-methylene]-	EtOH	258(4.38),338(4.23)	39-1635-80C
$C_{16}H_{11}ClO$ 2-Naphthalenol, 4-chloro-1-phenyl-	EtOH	235(4.79),285(3.84), 297(3.82),343(3.66)	104-1463-80
$C_{16}H_{11}ClO_4$ 9,10-Anthracenedione, 6-chloro-1,3-di-methoxy-	MeOH	232(4.26),249(4.36), 280(4.37),327s(3.45), 398(3.70)	12-1805-80
9,10-Anthracenedione, 7-chloro-1,3-di-methoxy-	MeOH	233(4.36),244(4.34), 282(4.42),320(3.47), 396(3.68)	12-1805-80
9,10-Anthracenedione, 2-(chloromethyl)-1-hydroxy-4-methoxy-	MeOH	225(4.27),248(4.35), 275(3.92),440s(--), 460(3.78)	24-2994-80
$C_{16}H_{11}Cl_2NO_2$ 1H-Indole-2-carboxylic acid, 5-chloro-3-(2-chlorophenyl)-1-methyl-	EtOH	220(4.43),238(4.47), 301(4.13),325s(3.81)	87-0764-80
$C_{16}H_{11}Cl_2N_3O$ Benzenemethanamine, 4-chloro-α-[[3-(4-chlorophenyl)-1,2,4-oxadiazol-5-yl]-methylene]-	EtOH	250(4.30),335(4.18)	39-1635-80C
1,2,4-Triazine, 5,6-bis(4-chlorophen-yl)-3-methoxy-	EtOH	218s(4.37),259(4.20), 326(3.95)	44-4587-80
$C_{16}H_{11}Cl_2N_3S$ 1,2,4-Triazine, 5,6-bis(4-chlorophen-yl)-3-(methylthio)-	EtOH	220s(3.93),282(4.12), 350(3.32)	44-4587-80
$C_{16}H_{11}F_5O$ Benzene, 1,1'-[1-(pentafluoroethoxy)-1,2-ethenediyl]bis-	EtOH	220(4.16),282(4.42)	44-4122-80
$C_{16}H_{11}N$ 1H-Indole, 3-(phenylethynyl)-	EtOH	205(4.42),225(4.50), 241(4.27),253(4.06),	103-0741-80

Compound	Solvent	$\lambda_{max}(\log \epsilon)$	Ref.
(cont.)		281(4.14),308(4.31), 322(4.25)	103-0741-80
$C_{16}H_{11}NOS$			
[1]Benzothieno[3,2-b]quinolin-11(5H)-one, 5-methyl-	MeOH	236(4.25),268(4.57), 277(4.66),305(3.99), 375(4.02),393(4.18)	83-0027-80
Oxazole, 5-(4-dibenzothienyl)-2-methyl-, perchlorate	MeOH	215(4.37),242(4.63), 261(4.51),285(4.32), 295s(4.03),326(3.72), 339(3.83)	39-1185-80C
Thiocyanic acid, 3-oxo-1,3-diphenyl-1-propenyl ester	EtOH	307.5(4.39)	2-0266-80
$C_{16}H_{11}NOS_3$			
Benzenecarbothioic acid, S-(2,5-dihydro-4-phenyl-5-thioxo-3-isothiazolyl) ester	$CHCl_3$	317(4.34),423(4.24)	39-2693-80C
$C_{16}H_{11}NO_2$			
Benzofuro[2,3-b]quinoline, 11-methoxy-	EtOH	222(4.59),250(4.69), 258(4.86),275(3.87), 287s(3.80),304s(4.18), 316(4.36),330(4.18), 342s(3.81)	18-1057-80
Benzofuro[2,3-b]quinolin-11(6H)-one, 6-methyl-	EtOH	222(4.49),258s(4.49), 265(4.62),288(4.00), 302(3.94),326(4.03), 339(4.08),356(3.81)	18-1057-80
1,2-Naphthalenedione, 4-(phenylamino)-	EtOH	243(4.36),283(4.13), 340s(3.74),460(3.69)	94-1207-80
5(4H)-Oxazolone, 2-phenyl-4-(phenylmethylene)- (E)-	toluene	365(4.59),385(4.59)	135-0930-80
	dioxan	226(4.18),239(4.18), 246(4.13),340s(4.61), 360(4.68),380s(4.53)	70-0576-80
(Z)-	dioxan	242(4.10),250(4.15), 260(4.16),350(4.42), 365(4.53),386(4.36)	70-0576-80
1H-Pyrrole-2,5-dione, 3,4-diphenyl-	60% dioxan	354(3.72)	40-0837-80
$C_{16}H_{11}NO_3$			
4H-Anthra[1,2-d][1,3]oxazine-7,12-dione, 1,2-dihydro-	EtOH	495(3.95)	18-3007-80 +146-0513-80
1H-Benzo[f]pyrrolo[1,2-a]indole-11-carboxaldehyde, 2,3,5,10-tetrahydro-5,10-dioxo-	MeOH	252(4.59),282s(4.16), 324(3.88),399(3.50)	44-1260-80
1,2-Naphthalenedione, 4-[(3-hydroxyphenyl)amino]-	EtOH	243(4.36),283(4.21), 340s(--),466(3.70)	94-1207-80
1,2-Naphthalenedione, 4-[(4-hydroxyphenyl)amino]-	EtOH	245(4.43),280(4.21), 347(4.14),484(3.77)	94-1207-80
$C_{16}H_{11}NO_4$			
Benzonitrile, 4-[3-(4-hydroxy-6-methyl-2-oxo-2H-pyran-3-yl)-3-oxo-1-propenyl]-	MeOH	355(4.4)	83-0344-80
$C_{16}H_{11}NO_6$			
9,10-Anthracenedione, 1,3-dimethoxy-5-nitro-	MeOH	235(4.37),275(4.24), 402(3.63)	12-1805-80

Compound	Solvent	$\lambda_{max}(\log \epsilon)$	Ref.
9,10-Anthracenedione, 1,3-dimethoxy-6-nitro-	MeOH	259(4.45),269s(4.40), 405(3.68)	12-1805-80
9,10-Anthracenedione, 1,3-dimethoxy-7-nitro-	MeOH	251s(4.24),259s(4.26), 280(4.36),298s(4.09), 404(3.68)	12-1805-80
9,10-Anthracenedione, 1,3-dimethoxy-8-nitro-	MeOH	241(4.37),275(4.22), 401(3.69)	12-1805-80
3H-Phenoxazine-1,6-dicarboxylic acid, 3-oxo-, ethyl ester	EtOH	340(4.14),456(4.01)	78-0529-80
3H-Phenoxazine-1,8-dicarboxylic acid, 3-oxo-, dimethyl ester	EtOH	330(3.99),430(4.14)	78-0529-80
$C_{16}H_{11}NS_2$ [1]Benzothieno[3,2-b]quinoline-11(5H)-thione, 5-methyl-	MeOH	229(4.57),252(4.49), 304(4.34),327(3.99), 340(4.06),458(4.39)	83-0027-80
3H-Indole, 3-(1,3-benzodithiol-2-ylidene)-2-methyl-	benzene	400(4.40)	18-1661-80
$C_{16}H_{11}N_3$ [1,2,4]Triazolo[4,3-a]quinoline, 1-phenyl-	MeOH	290(3.93)	56-0661-80
$C_{16}H_{11}N_3O$ Dibenzo[b,h][1,6]naphthyridin-6(5H)-one, 11-amino-	MeOH	222(4.68),294(4.58), 336s(3.81),386(3.54)	39-0512-80C
Phenol, 2-[1,2,4]triazolo[4,3-a]quinolin-1-yl-	MeOH	285(4.07)	56-0661-80
Phenol, 4-[1,2,4]triazolo[4,3-a]quinolin-1-yl-	MeOH	255(4.17)	56-0661-80
$C_{16}H_{11}N_3OS$ Imidazo[1,5-a]quinazolin-5(1H)-one, 2,4-dihydro-4-phenyl-1-thioxo-	MeOH	289(4.11),324(4.00)	2-0638-80
$C_{16}H_{11}N_3O_2$ 4-Cyclohexene-1,2-dicarboximide, 1,2-dicyano-4-phenyl-	EtOH	246(4.15)	24-1663-80
Indolo[7,6-g]indole, 3,8-dihydro-1-(2-nitroethenyl)-	EtOH	206(4.04),267(4.58), 283s(3.99),294(4.02), 350(3.93),414(4.11)	103-1139-80
$C_{16}H_{11}N_3O_2S$ 1,3,4-Thiadiazol-2-amine, N-(1,3-benzodioxol-5-ylmethylene)-5-phenyl-	EtOH	207(4.40),228(4.16), 303(4.25),368(4.10)	2-0144-80A
	CHCl$_3$	303(4.23),364(4.09)	2-0144-80A
	CCl$_4$	305(4.23),360(4.07)	2-0144-80A
	DMF	311(4.23),368(4.08)	2-0144-80A
$C_{16}H_{11}N_3O_4S$ Benzenesulfonic acid, 4-amino-, 6-diazo-5,6-dihydro-5-oxo-1-naphthalenyl ester	EPA	212(4.27),228(4.25), 265(4.02),328(3.72), 405(3.41)	135-0064-80
$C_{16}H_{12}$ Anthracene, 9-ethenyl-	EtOH	253(5.12),337s(3.38), 352(3.66),368(3.82), 386(3.77)	44-1807-80
$C_{16}H_{12}BNS_2$ Thieno[2,3-e]-1,2-azaborine, 1,2-di-	EtOH	220(4.28),238s(4.32),	11-0145-80A

Compound	Solvent	$\lambda_{max}(\log \epsilon)$	Ref.
hydro-2-phenyl-3-(2-thienyl)- (cont.)		249(4.34),335(4.24)	11-0145-80A
Thieno[3,2-e]-1,2-azaborine, 1,2-di-hydro-2-phenyl-3-(2-thienyl)-	EtOH	232(4.31),271(4.03), 341(4.34)	11-0135-80A
$C_{16}H_{12}BrClN_2O$ 1H-Pyrazole, 4-bromo-3-(4-chlorophenyl)-5-(4-methoxyphenyl)-	EtOH	259(3.81)	2-0364-80
$C_{16}H_{12}BrNO_2S$ Methanone, [5-bromo-2-(methylamino)-phenyl](3-hydroxybenzo[b]thien-2-yl)-	MeOH	259(4.39),318(4.09), 381(3.87),436(4.04)	83-0027-80
$C_{16}H_{12}BrN_3O_2$ 2H-1,2,3-Triazol-4-ol, 2-(4-bromophenyl)-5-phenyl-, acetate	MeOH	302(4.57)	39-0744-80C
$C_{16}H_{12}BrN_3O_3$ 1H-Pyrazole, 4-bromo-3-(4-methoxyphenyl)-5-(4-nitrophenyl)-	MeOH	305(3.72)	2-0364-80
$C_{16}H_{12}BrN_3S_3$ 3H-Thieno[3,4-b][1,4]diazepine-6-carbonitrile, 4-(4-bromophenyl)-2,8-bis-(methylthio)-	EtOH	233(4.22),288(4.56)	95-0699-80
$C_{16}H_{12}Br_2$ Anthracene, 9-(1,2-dibromoethyl)-	EtOH	257(4.92),365(3.83), 382(4.00),401(3.93)	44-1807-80
$C_{16}H_{12}ClN$ Isoquinoline, 5-chloro-3-methyl-1-phenyl-	MeOH-acid	238(4.50),286(3.86), 366(3.94)	56-2209-80
	MeOH-base	227(4.57),294(3.89), 341(3.93)	56-2209-80
Isoquinoline, 6-chloro-3-methyl-1-phenyl-	MeOH-acid	252(4.80),275(4.05), 353(3.97)	56-2209-80
	MeOH-base	233(4.79),285(3.78), 336(3.79)	56-2209-80
Isoquinoline, 7-chloro-3-methyl-1-phenyl-	MeOH-acid	238(4.74),281(3.99), 363(3.91)	56-2209-80
	MeOH-base	227(4.78),277(3.99), 342(3.83)	56-2209-80
$C_{16}H_{12}ClNO$ 2(1H)-Quinolinone, 3-(chloromethyl)-1-phenyl-	CHCl₃	245(4.21),278s(3.88), 282(3.81),332(3.75), 338s(3.74)	150-0414-80S
$C_{16}H_{12}ClNO_3$ 9H-Pyrrolo[1,2-a]indole-2-carboxylic acid, 1-chloro-9-(oxoethylidene)-, ethyl ester	EtOH	255s(4.21),263s(4.26), 270(4.27),333(3.87), 359(3.98)	78-2125-80
$C_{16}H_{12}ClNO_5$ 4H-Furo[3,2-b]pyrrole-4-propanoic acid, 5-carboxy-2-(4-chlorophenyl)-	MeOH	342(4.69),357(4.65)	73-2949-80
$C_{16}H_{12}ClN_3$ 5-Pyrimidinamine, 2-chloro-4,6-diphenyl-	EtOH	238(3.30),358(3.00)	103-0970-80

Compound	Solvent	$\lambda_{max}(\log \epsilon)$	Ref.
$C_{16}H_{12}ClN_3O_2S$ 3H-1,5-Benzodiazepine, 2-(4-chlorophen-yl)-4-(methylthio)-7-nitro-	EtOH	236(4.28),282(4.49), 336(4.15)	142-0007-80
$C_{16}H_{12}ClN_3S_3$ 3H-Thieno[3,4-b][1,4]diazepine-6-carbo-nitrile, 4-(4-chlorophenyl)-2,8-bis-(methylthio)-	EtOH	230(4.24),286(4.55)	95-0699-80
$C_{16}H_{12}ClN_5O$ Acetic acid, [(4-chlorophenyl)hydra-zono]cyano-, (phenylmethylene)hy-drazide	EtOH	282(4.48),372(3.86)	104-1536-80
$C_{16}H_{12}Cl_2N_2O$ 1H-Indole-2-carboxamide, 5-chloro-3-(2-chlorophenyl)-1-methyl-	EtOH	222(4.49),242s(4.37), 300(4.07)	87-0764-80
$C_{16}H_{12}Cl_2N_2O_4$ 2-Butene, 1,4-bis[(4-chlorophenyl)-aci-nitro]-	MeOH	220(--),246(4.16), 337(4.00)	104-2059-80
$C_{16}H_{12}Cl_2N_2S$ 3H-1,5-Benzodiazepine, 7-chloro-2-(4-chlorophenyl)-4-(methylthio)-	EtOH	270(4.57),340(3.84)	142-0007-80
$C_{16}H_{12}Cl_2O$ 2-Buten-1-one, 1,3-bis(2-chlorophenyl)-, (E)-	CH_2Cl_2	266(4.07)	118-0041-80
(Z)-	CH_2Cl_2	240(4.14)	118-0041-80
3,8-Ethenocyclobuta[3,4]cyclobuta[1,2-b]naphthalen-1(2H)-one, 2,2-dichloro-2a,2b,3,8,8a,8b-hexahydro-, (2aα,2bβ-3α,8α,8aβ,8bα)-	hexane	258s(2.73),263(2.83), 272(2.79),313(2.02), 328s(1.98)	89-0307-80
$C_{16}H_{12}Cl_2O_4$ 1,3-Benzodioxole, 5,5'-(1,2-dichloro-1,2-ethanediyl)bis-, (R*,S*)-	MeOH	232(3.97),282(3.76)	2-0556-80
$C_{16}H_{12}NS_2$ 1,3-Benzodithiol-1-ium, 2-(2-methyl-1H-indol-3-yl)-, tetrafluoroborate	MeCN	441(4.57)	18-1661-80
1,3-Benzodithiol-1-ium, 2-(3-methyl-1H-indol-2-yl)-, tetrafluoroborate	MeCN	467(4.70)	18-1661-80
$C_{16}H_{12}N_2$ Cycloheptimidazole, 4-(2-phenyletheny1)-	EtOH	256(4.41),292s(4.23), 371(4.31),433(4.04)	18-1406-80
Diazene, 1-naphthalenylphenyl-	EtOH	372(4.10)	62-0158-80
Diazene, 2-naphthalenylphenyl-	EtOH	328(4.28)	62-0158-80
11H-Indeno[1,2-c]isoquinolin-5-amine	EtOH-H_2SO_4	213(4.52),244(4.37), 316(4.17),330(4.17), 374(4.00),388s(3.91)	18-2885-80
Isoquinoline, 4-[2-(3-pyridinyl)ethen-yl]-	C_6H_{12}	224(4.48),257(4.14), 332(4.25)	44-1557-80
$C_{16}H_{12}N_2O$ Benzoxazole, 2-(1H-indol-3-ylmethyl)-	EtOH	209(4.69),221(4.68), 244(3.94),275(4.15), 282(4.17),290(3.81)	103-0501-80
[2,3'-Bipyridin]-5'-ol, 6'-phenyl-	MeOH	240(4.4),320(4.3)	103-0951-80

Compound	Solvent	$\lambda_{max}(\log \epsilon)$	Ref.
[3,4'-Bipyridin]-5-ol, 6-phenyl-	MeOH	245(4.1),321(3.9)	103-0951-80
Phenol, 4-(1-naphthalenylazo)-	n.s.g.	379(4.27)	150-2415-80
$C_{16}H_{12}N_2OS$			
Naphtho[2',1':5,6]thiopyrano[4,3-c]-pyrazole, 2-acetyl-2,11-dihydro-	EtOH	210(4.19),235(4.22), 255(4.28),278(4.36), 326(3.86)	4-0121-80
Phenol, 2-[[(4-phenyl-2-thiazolyl)-imino]methyl]-	pH 5	375(4.20)	2-0492-80
2-Propenamide, N-2-benzothiazolyl-3-phenyl-	MeOH	290(4.81),315(4.97)	48-0434-80
$C_{16}H_{12}N_2OS_3$			
2(5H)-Isothiazolecarboxamide, 3-mercap-to-N,4-diphenyl-5-thioxo-	EtOH	319(4.20),405(4.09)	142-0785-80
$C_{16}H_{12}N_2O_2$			
Isoquinoline, 3-methyl-5-nitro-1-phen-yl-	MeOH-acid	232(4.56),274(3.89), 364(4.01)	56-2209-80
	MeOH-base	269(3.92),356(3.90)	56-2209-80
Isoquinoline, 3-methyl-7-nitro-1-phen-yl-	MeOH-acid	252(4.36),342(3.98)	56-2209-80
	MeOH-base	263(4.32),338(3.97)	56-2209-80
Methanone, (4-amino-3-phenyl-5-isoxazo-lyl)phenyl-	EtOH	226(4.31),257(4.16), 361(4.21)	5-1623-80
2-Propenamide, N-2-benzoxazolyl-3-phenyl-	MeOH	221(4.71),225(4.46), 302(4.98)	48-0434-80
$C_{16}H_{12}N_2O_2Se$			
1,3,4-Selenadiazol-2(3H)-one, 5-benz-oyl-3-(4-methylphenyl)-	EtOH	324(4.07)	4-1185-80
$C_{16}H_{12}N_2O_3$			
Naphtho[2,3-f]quinoxaline-7,12-dione, 1,2,3,4-tetrahydro-6-hydroxy-	benzene	510s(4.04),544(4.29), 585(4.30)	138-0743-80
3(2H)-Pyridazinone, 5-hydroxy-6-phen-oxy-2-phenyl-	MeOH	211(4.48),226s(--), 284(3.87)	73-0127-80
$C_{16}H_{12}N_2O_4$			
Benzo[f]quinoxaline-2,3-dicarboxylic acid, dimethyl ester	MeOH	236(4.56),286(4.51)	44-3182-80
$C_{16}H_{12}N_2O_5$			
2-Buten-1-one, 1,3-bis(2-nitrophenyl)-, (E)-	CHCl$_3$	257(4.23)	118-0041-80
2-Buten-1-one, 1,3-bis(4-nitrophenyl)-, (E)-	CHCl$_3$	280(4.31),308(4.40)	118-0041-80
(Z)-	CHCl$_3$	264(4.35)	118-0041-80
$C_{16}H_{12}N_2O_9S_2$			
2,7-Naphthalenedisulfonic acid, 4-[(2,4-dihydroxyphenyl)azo]-5-hydroxy-	pH 1 pH 6 pH 11	370(3.88),490(3.99) 355(3.94),490(4.03) 380(4.08),490(4.05)	140-1105-80 140-1105-80 140-1105-80
$C_{16}H_{12}N_4$			
Benzo[1,2-b:3,4-b']dipyrrole, 1,6-di-hydro-3-(phenylazo)-	EtOH	205(4.21),227(4.18), 269(4.14),444(4.52)	103-0495-80
2,2a,4,5-Tetraazabenz[cd]azulene, 1-methyl-3-phenyl-	MeOH	271(3.93),359(3.71), 440s(2.89),466(2.95), 495(2.93),530s(2.77), 578s(2.42)	4-1057-80

Compound	Solvent	$\lambda_{max}(\log \epsilon)$	Ref.
$C_{16}H_{12}N_4O_2$			
Acetonitrile, [(2-oxo-2-phenylethoxy)-imino](phenylazo)-, (E)-	EtOH	244(4.24),329(4.76)	5-1623-80
Indolo[7,6-g]indole-1,6-dicarboxalde-hyde, 3,8-dihydro-, dioxime, syn-syn	EtOH	210(4.35),278(4.78), 319(4.07),339(3.47), 353(4.42)	103-1139-80
Methanone, [4-amino-3-(phenylazo)-5-isoxazolyl]phenyl-	EtOH	228(4.15),261s(3.91), 318(3.80),377(2.93)	5-1623-80
$C_{16}H_{12}N_4O_2Se$			
Methanone, [4,5-dihydro-4-(4-methyl-phenyl)-5-(nitrosoimino)-1,3,4-sel-enadiazol-2-yl]phenyl-	EtOH	256(3.99),284(3.86), 480(1.78)	4-1185-80
Methanone, [4,5-dihydro-5-(nitrosoimi-no)-4-phenyl-1,3,4-selenadiazol-2-yl](4-methylphenyl)-	EtOH	255(3.95),283(3.89), 480(1.76)	4-1185-80
$C_{16}H_{12}N_4O_3Se$			
Acetamide, N-[3-(4-nitrophenyl)-5-phen-yl-1,3,4-selenadiazol-2(3H)-ylidene]-	EtOH	250(4.40),348(4.22)	4-1185-80
$C_{16}H_{12}N_4O_8$			
2-Butene, 1,4-bis[(4-nitrophenyl)-aci-nitro]-	MeOH	263(4.02),360(4.15)	104-2059-80
$C_{16}H_{12}N_4S$			
2H-1,2,4-Triazino[5,6-b]indole, 3-[(phenylmethyl)thio]-	MeOH-HCl	283(4.67),344(3.65)	83-0108-80
$C_{16}H_{12}N_8S$			
Tetramethylammonium 2-(dicyanomethyl)-4,5,6-tricyanothieno[2,3-c]pyrimi-dinide	n.s.g.	487(4.59)	44-5113-80
$C_{16}H_{12}O$			
Anthracene, 1,2,3,4-tetrahydro-2,3-bis(methylene)-	EtOH	242(4.50),272(3.65), 281(3.61),295s(3.35), 309(3.13),315s(2.90), 323(3.23)	33-0232-80
Indeno[2,1-a]inden-5(4bH)-one, 9b,10-dihydro-, (4bS-cis)-	EtOH	209(4.47),247(4.09), 269(3.42),276(3.49), 286(3.33),294(3.34), 332(2.47)	18-0291-80
2-Naphthalenol, 3-phenyl-	MeOH	214(4.59),248(4.72), 268(3.90),339(3.36)	103-0965-80
$C_{16}H_{12}OS$			
4H-1-Benzothiopyran-4-one, 2,3-dihydro-3-(phenylmethylene)-	EtOH	248(4.42),305(4.25)	2-0955-80
$C_{16}H_{12}O_2Se$			
Selenonium, methylphenyl-, 1,3-dihydro-1,3-dioxo-2H-inden-2-ylide	EtOH	218(4.41),250(4.25), 268(4.21),300(3.57), 312(3.42),370(3.17)	104-0119-80
$C_{16}H_{12}O_3$			
3-Benzofurancarboxaldehyde, 2-(4-meth-oxyphenyl)-	MeOH	251(4.28),331(4.26)	18-0179-80
2H-1-Benzopyran-2-one, 7-hydroxy-3-methyl-2-phenyl-	pH 4.5 pH 10.5	246(4.14),306(4.21) 262(4.49),309(3.97), 347(4.18)	86-0977-80 86-0977-80

Compound	Solvent	λ_{max} (log ϵ)	Ref.
2H-1-Benzopyran-2-one, 7-methoxy-4-phenyl-	pH 5.0	328(4.18)	61-1115-80
	pH 10.0	328(4.19)	61-1115-80
	20% H_2SO_4	329(4.18)	61-1115-80
	60% H_2SO_4	353(4.07),370s(--)	61-1115-80
	MeOH	327(4.16)	61-1115-80
4H-1-Benzopyran-4-one, 7-hydroxy-2-methyl-3-phenyl-	pH 4.5	230(4.44),242s(4.39), 297(4.20)	86-0977-80
	pH 10.5	259(4.50),303s(3.94), 335(4.20)	86-0977-80
1H-Indene-1-carboxylic acid, 2,3-di-hydro-3-oxo-2-phenyl-, (-)-	EtOH	208(4.38),244(3.98), 287s(3.26),293(3.26), 335s(2.04)	18-0291-80
Methanone, (6-methoxy-2-benzofuranyl)-phenyl-	MeOH	236s(3.99),259(4.00), 345(4.34)	18-1769-80
$C_{16}H_{12}O_3Se$ 2H-1-Benzopyran-2-one, 6-methoxy-3-(phenylseleno)-	EtOH	352(3.93)	44-4611-80
$C_{16}H_{12}O_4$ 1,4-Anthracenedione, 10-hydroxy-8-methoxy-2-methyl-	$CHCl_3$	498(3.88)	44-0012-80
9,10-Anthracenedione, 6-ethyl-1,4-di-hydroxy-	MeOH	208(4.30),225(4.35), 258(4.42),281(3.96), 465(3.89),477(3.91), 510(3.69)	24-2976-80
1,3-Benzodioxole, 5,5'-(1,2-ethenedi-yl)bis-, (E)-	MeOH	295(4.02),320(3.96)	2-0556-80
3(2H)-Benzofuranone, 2-acetoxy-2-phenyl-	MeOH	257(4.11),329(3.55)	18-0179-80
4H-1-Benzopyran-4-one, 5,7-dihydroxy-3-methyl-2-phenyl-	MeOH	235(3.85),267(4.16), 349(3.38)	2-0101-80
1-Oxaspiro[4.5]deca-3,7,9-triene-2,6-dione, 8-methoxy-3-phenyl-	MeOH	225(4.38),276(4.26)	18-0179-80
$C_{16}H_{12}O_5$ 9,10-Anthracenedione, 1,4-dihydroxy-5-methoxy-2-methyl-	MeOH	230(4.50),248(4.30), 285(3.92),378(3.44), 478(3.99),490(4.00), 526(3.75)	24-1575-80
9,10-Anthracenedione, 1,4-dihydroxy-8-methoxy-2-methyl-	MeOH	230(4.65),250(4.20), 284(3.90),384(3.48), 475(4.01),494(4.01), 521(3.76)	24-1575-80
9,10-Anthracenedione, 4-hydroxy-1,5-di-methoxy-	MeOH	226(4.41),252(3.95), 280s(--),370s(--), 460(3.70)	24-2994-80
9,10-Anthracenedione, 1-hydroxy-2-(hy-droxymethyl)-4-methoxy-	MeOH	226(4.38),245(4.45), 250(4.47),277(4.00), 320(3.36),458(3.85)	24-2994-80
4H-1-Benzopyran-4-one, 5-hydroxy-2-(4-hydroxyphenyl)-7-methoxy- (genkwanin)	EtOH	268(4.40),337(4.47)	36-0053-80
$C_{16}H_{12}O_6$ 9,10-Anthracenedione, 1,4-dihydroxy-2-(hydroxymethyl)-5-methoxy-	MeOH	230(4.55),249(4.31), 284(3.93),465(4.00), 491(4.00),526(3.74)	24-1575-80
9,10-Anthracenedione, 1,4-dihydroxy-3-(hydroxymethyl)-5-methoxy-	MeOH	229(4.51),247(4.23), 284(3.87),376(3.37), 445s(--),472(3.97), 485(3.96),522(3.67)	24-2994-80

Compound	Solvent	$\lambda_{max}(\log \epsilon)$	Ref.
Azuleno[1,2-c]furan-9-carboxylic acid, 1-acetoxy-1,3-dihydro-3-oxo-, methyl ester	MeOH	234(4.73),271(4.66), 300(4.87),327(3.93), 355(4.09),367(4.17), 492(2.96)	18-3696-80
4H-1-Benzopyran-4-one, 5,8-dihydroxy-2-(2-hydroxyphenyl)-7-methoxy-	MeOH	271(4.39),338(4.27)	95-1220-80
	MeOH-NaOMe	238s(4.49),272(4.35), 290s(3.97),464(4.33)	95-1220-80
	MeOH-NaOAc	270(4.41),340(4.23)	95-1220-80
	MeOH-AlCl₃	256(4.14),280s(4.38), 286(4.41),360(4.31)	95-1220-80
	MeOH-AlCl₃-HCl	254(4.11),280s(4.37), 285(4.39)	95-1220-80
4H-1-Benzopyran-4-one, 5,6,7-trihydroxy-8-methoxy-2-phenyl-	EtOH	285(4.16),352(4.16)	40-1397-80
	EtOH-NaOAc	263(4.48),382(4.03)	40-1397-80
	EtOH-AlCl₃	275s(4.35),288(4.40), 265(4.13)	40-1397-80
2,5-Cyclohexadiene-1,4-dione, 2-acetyl-3-(3-acetyl-4-hydroxyphenoxy)-	MeCN	223(4.33),250(4.33), 346(3.62),440s(2.93)	44-1421-80
Pinselin	MeOH	238(4.43),257s(4.45), 265(4.55),295(3.98), 387(3.80)	94-3649-80
$C_{16}H_{12}O_7$			
4H-1-Benzopyran-4-one, 5,6,7-trihydroxy-2-(4-hydroxyphenyl)-8-methoxy-	EtOH	278(4.31),345(4.16)	40-1397-80
	EtOH-NaOAc	278(4.31),310(4.20), 383(4.20)	40-1397-80
	EtOH-AlCl₃	308(4.37),375(4.37)	40-1397-80
$C_{16}H_{12}O_8$			
Benzoic acid, 2-hydroxy-5-[[2-(methoxycarbonyl)-3,6-dioxo-1,4-cyclohexadien-1-yl]oxy]-, methyl ester	MeCN	214(4.46),240(4.26), 250s(4.22),320(3.65), 370s(3.08),480s(2.40)	44-1421-80
$C_{16}H_{12}S_3$			
1-Propanethione, 2-(1,3-benzodithiol-2-ylidene)-1-phenyl-	MeOH	253(4.02),319(3.76), 428(4.23),592(2.24)	104-1775-80
$C_{16}H_{13}BrCl_3NO_7S$			
1H-Pyrrolo[1,2-a]indole-9-carboxylic acid, 7-bromo-2,3,5,8-tetrahydro-6-methyl-2-[(methylsulfonyl)oxy]-5,8-dioxo-, 2,2,2-trichloroethyl ester	n.s.g.	287(3.87),325(3.35), 418(2.95)	142-0161-80B
$C_{16}H_{13}BrN_2$			
1H-1,5-Benzodiazepine, 2-(4-bromophenyl)-4-methyl-	H₂O	470(3.21)	96-0165-80
$C_{16}H_{13}BrN_2O$			
4(3H)-Quinazolinone, 6-bromo-2-methyl-3-(4-methylphenyl)-	n.s.g.	285(3.85),325(3.48)	18-2389-80
$C_{16}H_{13}BrN_2S$			
4(3H)-Quinazolinethione, 6-bromo-2-methyl-3-(4-methylphenyl)-	n.s.g.	287(3.70),353(3.60), 370(3.70),383(3.48)	18-2389-80
$C_{16}H_{13}BrOS$			
1-Propanone, 1-(4-bromophenyl)-3-(4-methylphenyl)-3-thioxo-	C₆H₁₂	272(--),346(--), 411(--),520s(--)(anom.)	39-1768-80B
anion	EtOH	265(4.15),400(4.31)	39-1768-80B

Compound	Solvent	$\lambda_{max}(\log \epsilon)$	Ref.
$C_{16}H_{13}BrO_2S$			
1-Propanone, 1-(4-bromophenyl)-3-(4-methoxyphenyl)-3-thioxo-	C_6H_{12}	264(--),378(--), 410s(--),520s(--) (anom.)	39-1768-80B
anion	EtOH	266(4.20),411(4.39)	39-1768-80B
$C_{16}H_{13}BrO_3$			
1H-Inden-1-one, 2-(2-bromophenyl)-2,3-dihydro-3-hydroxy-3-methoxy-, anion	n.s.g.	430(3.31)	73-1072-80
1H-Inden-1-one, 2-(3-bromophenyl)-2,3-dihydro-3-hydroxy-3-methoxy-, anion	n.s.g.	454(3.26)	73-1072-80
1H-Inden-1-one, 2-(4-bromophenyl)-2,3-dihydro-3-hydroxy-3-methoxy-, anion	n.s.g.	459(3.27)	73-1072-80
$C_{16}H_{13}ClN_2$			
1H-1,5-Benzodiazepine, 2-(4-chlorophenyl)-4-methyl-	H_2O	485(3.20)	96-0165-80
$C_{16}H_{13}ClN_2O$			
1(2H)-Isoquinolinone, 6-chloro-3-[(phenylmethyl)amino]-	EtOH	241(4.44),310(4.25), 375(3.59)	95-0826-80
1(2H)-Isoquinolinone, 7-chloro-3-[(phenylmethyl)amino]-	EtOH	225(4.35),310(4.32), 386(3.59)	95-0826-80
3(2H)-Pyridazinone, 6-(4-chlorophenyl)-1,6-dihydro-6-phenyl-	EtOH	270(4.16)	118-0457-80
$C_{16}H_{13}ClN_2O_3$			
Quinoline, 1-(2-chlorobenzoyl)-1,2,3,4-tetrahydro-6-nitro-	EtOH	317(3.95)	103-0386-80
$C_{16}H_{13}ClN_4O_2$			
[4,5'-Bipyrimidine]-2',4'(1'H,3'H)-di-one, 2-chloro-1',3'-dimethyl-6-phenyl-	EtOH	206(4.39),259(4.36), 330(4.41)	103-0303-80
$C_{16}H_{13}ClO$			
3,8-Ethenocyclobuta[3,4]cyclobuta[1,2-b]naphthalen-1(2H)-one, 2-chloro-2a,2b,3,8,8a,8b-hexahydro-, (2α,2aα,2bβ,3α,8α,8aβ,8bα)-	hexane	257s(2.57),263(2.68), 270(2.65),309(2.22)	89-0307-80
2-Propen-1-one, 3-(2-chlorophenyl)-2-methyl-1-phenyl-	MeOH	273(4.39)	56-2209-80
2-Propen-1-one, 3-(3-chlorophenyl)-2-methyl-1-phenyl-	MeOH	253(4.09),282(4.03)	56-2209-80
2-Propen-1-one, 3-(4-chlorophenyl)-2-methyl-1-phenyl-	MeOH	248(4.05),291(4.16)	56-2209-80
$C_{16}H_{13}ClO_3$			
1H-Inden-1-one, 2-(2-chlorophenyl)-2,3-dihydro-3-hydroxy-3-methoxy-, anion	n.s.g.	430(3.33)	73-1072-80
1H-Inden-1-one, 2-(4-chlorophenyl)-2,3-dihydro-3-hydroxy-3-methoxy-, anion	n.s.g.	460(3.26)	73-1072-80
$C_{16}H_{13}ClO_4S$			
Benzenepropanoic acid, 2-[(2-carboxy-4-chlorophenyl)thio]-	MeOH	257(4.09),327(3.58)	73-0491-80
$C_{16}H_{13}Cl_2N_3O$			
1,2,4-Triazine, 5,6-bis(4-chlorophenyl)-2,5-dihydro-3-methoxy-	EtOH	221(4.29),298(3.98)	44-4587-80

Compound	Solvent	$\lambda_{max}(\log \epsilon)$	Ref.
$C_{16}H_{13}Cl_2N_3S$			
1,2,4-Triazine, 5,6-bis(4-chlorophenyl)-2,5-dihydro-3-(methylthio)-	EtOH	218s(4.35),238s(4.19), 304(4.00)	44-4587-80
$C_{16}H_{13}Cl_3O_6S$			
2-Furancarboxylic acid, 5-[2-(4-methoxyphenyl)-1-[(trichloromethyl)sulfonyl]ethenyl]-, methyl ester, (E)-	EtOH	204(4.17),242(4.23), 275(4.27),345(4.35)	73-0746-80
$C_{16}H_{13}FO_3$			
1H-Inden-1-one, 2-(2-fluorophenyl)-2,3-dihydro-3-hydroxy-3-methoxy-, anion	n.s.g.	436(3.33)	73-1072-80
1H-Inden-1-one, 2-(3-fluorophenyl)-2,3-dihydro-3-hydroxy-3-methoxy-, anion	n.s.g.	457(3.27)	73-1072-80
1H-Inden-1-one, 2-(4-fluorophenyl)-2,3-dihydro-3-hydroxy-3-methoxy-, anion	n.s.g.	463(3.26)	73-1072-80
$C_{16}H_{13}FeP$			
Ferrocene, 1,1'-(phenylphosphinidene)-	C_6H_{12}	501(2.63)	101-0345-80J
$C_{16}H_{13}IO_3$			
1H-Inden-1-one, 2,3-dihydro-3-hydroxy-2-(2-iodophenyl)-3-methoxy-, anion	n.s.g.	428(3.33)	73-1072-80
1H-Inden-1-one, 2,3-dihydro-3-hydroxy-2-(4-iodophenyl)-3-methoxy-, anion	n.s.g.	458(3.26)	73-1072-80
$C_{16}H_{13}N$			
Cyclopent[4,5]azepino[2,1,7-cd]pyrrolizine, 6,8-dimethyl-	EtOH	275(4.12),305(4.44), 335s(4.50),346(4.61), 395(3.58),429(3.62), 450s(3.62),458(3.66), 554s(2.20),602(2.26), 648(2.17), >700	39-1324-80C
Isoquinoline, 3-methyl-1-phenyl-	MeOH-acid	234(4.70),272(4.00), 353(3.94)	56-2209-80
	MeOH-base	223(4.75),277(3.83), 334(3.83)	56-2209-80
1H-Pyrrole, 2,3-diphenyl-	hexane	202(4.31),242(4.08), 248(4.04),297(3.95)	103-0488-80
1H-Pyrrole, 2,5-diphenyl-	EtOH	208(4.13),232(4.05), 327(4.48)	103-0448-80
$C_{16}H_{13}NO$			
4bH-Azirino[2,1,3-cd]dibenzo[a,f]pyrrolizine, 8b,8c-dihydro-4b-methoxy-	EtOH	202(4.49),220s(4.48), 240(3.87),255(3.27)	44-1310-80
Formamide, N-(9,10-dihydro-10-methylene-9-anthracenyl)-	MeOH	256(5.20),354(3.78), 372(3.96),393(3.94)	73-0517-80
2H-1,3-Oxazine, 4,6-diphenyl-	n.s.g.	253(4.03),328(3.54)	39-1866-80C
$C_{16}H_{13}NOS$			
Isothiazolium, 4-hydroxy-2-methyl-3,5-diphenyl-, hydroxide, inner salt	EtOH	414(4.29)	139-0079-80A
	dioxan	491(4.27)	139-0079-80A
	MeCN	466(4.26)	139-0079-80A
$C_{16}H_{13}NO_2$			
1,3-Dioxolo[4,5-g]isoquinoline, 7,8-dihydro-7-phenyl-	MeOH	286(3.84),314(3.99)	2-0556-80
10,5-(Iminomethano)-11H-dibenzo[a,d]cyclohepten-11-one, 5,10-dihydro-10-hydroxy-	EtOH	207(4.41),239(3.93), 256s(3.86),277s(3.54), 344(2.67)	95-1127-80

Compound	Solvent	$\lambda_{max}(\log \epsilon)$	Ref.
1H-Indene-1,3(2H)-dione, 2-(1,2-dimeth-yl-4(1H)-pyridinylidene)-	EtOH	388(4.73)	4-0997-80
	THF	405(4.76)	4-0997-80
1H-Indene-1,3(2H)-dione, 2-(1,3-dimeth-yl-4(1H)-pyridinylidene)-	EtOH	239(4.43),250s(4.32), 283(3.20),298(3.15), 308(3.26),416(4.45)	4-0997-80
	THF	429(4.50)	4-0997-80
1H-Indene-1,3(2H)-dione, 2-(2,6-dimeth-yl-4(1H)-pyridinylidene)-	EtOH	384(4.76)	4-0997-80
	THF	398(4.80)	4-0997-80
1H-Indene-1,3(2H)-dione, 2-(3,6-dimeth-yl-2(1H)-pyridinylidene)-	EtOH	230(4.19),250s(4.02), 276s(3.98),286(4.15), 304(3.74),317(3.57), 387(4.18)	4-0961-80
1H-Indene-1,3(2H)-dione, 2-(5,6-dimeth-yl-2(1H)-pyridinylidene)-	EtOH	229(4.34),255s(3.95), 278(4.18),287(4.27), 307(3.98),320(3.88), 389(4.40)	4-0961-80
1H-Indene-1,3(2H)-dione, 2-(3-ethyl-4(1H)-pyridinylidene)-	EtOH	400(4.38)	4-0997-80
	THF	416(4.48)	4-0997-80
1H-Indole-3-carboxylic acid, 2-phenyl-, methyl ester	MeOH	243(4.48),300(4.20)	94-1157-80
9,10-(Methanomethano)anthracen-11-one, 9,10-dihydro-10-hydroxy-	EtOH	263(2.89),271(2.88)	95-1127-80
Phenol, 2-methyl-6-(4-phenyl-5-isoxazo-lyl)-	EtOH	265(4.09)	114-0389-80B
Phenol, 2-(3-methyl-4-phenyl-5-isoxazo-lyl)-	EtOH	275(3.88)	114-0389-80B
$C_{16}H_{13}NO_2S$			
Methanone, (3-hydroxybenzo[b]thien-2-yl)[2-(methylamino)phenyl]-	MeOH	247(4.29),319(4.07), 380(3.87),430(4.04)	83-0027-80
$C_{16}H_{13}NO_3$			
10(9H)-Acridineacetic acid, 9-oxo-, methyl ester	MeOH	253(4.71),379(3.91), 393(3.98)	73-3593-80
Benzenepropanenitrile, 2-hydroxy-4-methoxy-β-oxo-α-phenyl-	EtOH	286(3.98)	114-0271-80A
Benzenepropanenitrile, 2-hydroxy-α-(4-methoxyphenyl)-β-oxo-	EtOH	282(3.97)	114-0271-80A
2H-1-Benzopyran-4-ol, 2-imino-3-(4-methoxyphenyl)-	EtOH	257(3.97),307(3.95)	114-0271-80A
2H-1-Benzopyran-4-ol, 2-imino-7-meth-oxy-3-phenyl-	EtOH	253(4.20),305(4.14)	114-0271-80A
1H-Benzo[f]pyrrolo[1,2-a]indole-5,10-dione, 2,3-dihydro-11-(hydroxy-methyl)-	MeOH	262(4.48),266s(4.47), 335(3.74),419(3.56)	44-1260-80
Phenol, 2-[4-(2-methoxyphenyl)-5-isoxa-zolyl]-	EtOH	291(3.83)	114-0389-80B
Phenol, 2-[4-(4-methoxyphenyl)-5-isoxa-zolyl]-	EtOH	236(4.16),279(3.96)	114-0271-80A
Phenol, 5-methoxy-2-(4-phenyl-5-isoxa-zolyl)-	EtOH	233(4.17),276(3.90)	114-0271-80A +114-0389-80B
2-Propen-1-one, 2-methyl-3-(2-nitro-phenyl)-1-phenyl-	MeOH	253(4.34)	56-2209-80
2-Propen-1-one, 2-methyl-3-(4-nitro-phenyl)-1-phenyl-	MeOH	257(4.06),307(4.33)	56-2209-80
$C_{16}H_{13}NO_4$			
9,10-Anthracenedione, 5-amino-1,3-di-methoxy-	MeOH	229(4.46),275(4.17), 282s(4.07),393(3.56), 476(3.76)	12-1805-80

Compound	Solvent	$\lambda_{max}(\log \epsilon)$	Ref.
9,10-Anthracenedione, 8-amino-1,3-di-methoxy-	MeOH	228(4.56),271(4.30), 284s(4.09),380s(3.32), 480(3.87)	12-1805-80
Phenol, 2-[5-(1,3-benzodioxol-5-yl)-4,5-dihydro-3-isoxazolyl]-	EtOH	218(4.20),265(4.15), 274(4.05),288(4.09), 308(3.87)	142-1319-80
9H-Pyrrolo[1,2-a]indole-2-carboxylic acid, 9-(2-methoxy-2-oxoethylidene)-, methyl ester	EtOH	243(4.32),265(4.62), 303(4.11),316(4.15), 344(4.15)	78-2125-80
$C_{16}H_{13}NO_4S$			
2H-Pyran-3-carboxylic acid, 5-cyano-4-(methylthio)-2-oxo-6-phenyl-, ethyl ester	MeOH	268(4.10),308(3.96)	118-1022-80
$C_{16}H_{13}NO_5$			
Benzo[5,6]cyclohepta[1,2-b]pyrrole-2-acetic acid, 3-carboxy-1,4,5,10-tetrahydro-10-oxo-	MeOH	212(4.25),227(4.14), 242(4.12),260(4.33), 330(4.16)	4-1081-80
1,3-Dioxolo[4,5-b]acridin-10(5H)-one, 4,11-dimethoxy-	EtOH	260s(4.32),271(4.60), 287(4.10),386(3.80)	100-0498-80
1H-Inden-1-one, 2,3-dihydro-3-hydroxy-3-methoxy-2-(2-nitrophenyl)-, anion	n.s.g.	418(3.33)	73-1072-80
1H-Inden-1-one, 2,3-dihydro-3-hydroxy-3-methoxy-2-(4-nitrophenyl)-, anion	n.s.g.	439(4.37)	73-1072-80
Pyrano[3,2-b]indole-3-acetic acid, 4,5-dihydro-5-methyl-α,4-dioxo-, ethyl ester	MeOH	212(4.42),299(4.35)	83-0405-80
$C_{16}H_{13}NO_6S$			
Benzenepropanoic acid, 2-[(2-carboxy-4-nitrophenyl)thio]-	MeOH	250(3.85),343(4.18)	73-0491-80
$C_{16}H_{13}NS$			
1,2-Benzisothiazole, 3-[1-(phenylmeth-yl)ethenyl]-	EtOH	224(4.34),262s(3.63), 307(3.83),316(3.81)	39-2830-80C
$C_{16}H_{13}N_2O_3$			
Pyridinium, 1-[[5-(2-nitrophenyl)-2-furanyl]methyl]-, bromide	MeOH	259(4.53)	73-1715-80
Pyridinium, 1-[[5-(3-nitrophenyl)-2-furanyl]methyl]-, bromide	MeOH	266(4.47),283(4.42)	73-1715-80
Pyridinium, 1-[[5-(4-nitrophenyl)-2-furanyl]methyl]-, bromide	MeOH	339(4.31)	73-1715-80
$C_{16}H_{13}N_3$			
1H-Benzimidazole, 2-(1H-indol-3-yl-methyl)-	EtOH	210(4.68),221(4.67), 252(4.17),266(4.21), 290(3.84)	103-0501-80
Pyrrolo[3,2-e]benzimidazole, 1,6-di-hydro-8-methyl-7-phenyl-	EtOH	255(4.25),313(4.42)	103-0062-80
$C_{16}H_{13}N_3O$			
9H-Indolo[5,6-b][1,6]naphthyridin-9-one, 1,8-dihydro-7,8-dimethyl-	MeOH	234(3.86),253(3.82), 262s(3.72),293(3.97), 311(3.89),388(3.35)	39-0522-80C
	MeOH-acid	230(3.96),244s(3.81), 261s(3.64),273(3.74), 312(3.86),328(3.79), 438(3.61)	39-0522-80C

Compound	Solvent	$\lambda_{max}(\log \epsilon)$	Ref.
2-Propenamide, N-1H-benzimidazol-2-yl-3-phenyl-	MeOH	226(4.39),235(3.99), 280(4.43),313(4.64)	48-0434-80
$C_{16}H_{13}N_3OS$			
4-Imidazolidinone, 5-imino-3-phenyl-1-(phenylmethyl)-2-thioxo-	EtOH	310(4.20)	18-0442-80
1,3,4-Thiadiazol-2-amine, N-[(4-methoxyphenyl)methylene]-5-phenyl-	EtOH	212(4.26),225s(4.20), 300(4.48),358(3.66)	2-0144-80A
	DMF	309(4.37),660(3.73)	2-0144-80A
	$CHCl_3$	298(4.39),350(3.73)	2-0144-80A
	CCl_4	303(4.37),350(3.73)	2-0144-80A
$C_{16}H_{13}N_3OSe$			
Methanone, [4,5-dihydro-5-imino-4-(4-methylphenyl)-1,3,4-selenadiazol-2-yl]phenyl-	EtOH	263(4.31),361(4.13)	4-1185-80
Methanone, (4,5-dihydro-5-imino-4-phenyl-1,3,4-selenadiazol-2-yl)(4-methylphenyl)-	EtOH	265(4.22),362(4.00)	4-1185-80
$C_{16}H_{13}N_3O_2$			
1H-1,5-Benzodiazepine, 4-methyl-2-(3-nitrophenyl)-	H_2O	465(3.18)	96-0165-80
1H-Cyclobuta[d][1,2,4]triazolo[1,2-a]-pyridazine-1,3(2H)-dione, 5,6,7,8-tetrahydro-6,7-bis(methylene)-2-phenyl-	EtOH	210(4.61),245(3.81)	5-1786-80
1H-Pyrrole-2,5-dione, 3-amino-1-phenyl-4-(phenylamino)-	MeOH	252(4.33),415(3.41)	78-1801-80
$C_{16}H_{13}N_3O_2S$			
3H-1-5-Benzodiazepine, 4-(methylthio)-7-nitro-2-phenyl-	EtOH	234(4.26),279(4.46), 340(4.12)	142-0007-80
$C_{16}H_{13}N_3O_3$			
Methanone, [4,5-dihydro-4-(4-nitrophenyl)-1H-pyrazol-5-yl]phenyl-	MeOH	328(3.50)	2-0980-80
$C_{16}H_{13}N_3O_4$			
Pyridazino[4,5-b]quinolin-1(2H)-one, 4-acetoxy-2-acetyl-10-methyl-	EtOH	229(4.24),256(4.63)	94-3457-80
$C_{16}H_{13}N_3O_5$			
L-Phenylalanine, N-(5-benzofurazanylcarbonyl)-, N-oxide	EtOH	333?(4.46),265s(3.59), 315s(3.40),333s(3.52), 365(3.85)	4-0213-80
	MeCN	222(4.48),265s(3.51), 315s(3.51),333s(3.59), 365(3.89)	4-0213-80
$C_{16}H_{13}N_3S_3$			
3H-Thieno[3,4-b][1,4]diazepine-6-carbonitrile, 2,8-bis(methylthio)-4-phenyl-	EtOH	230(4.12),290(4.50)	95-0699-80
$C_{16}H_{13}N_5O$			
Acetic acid, cyano(phenylhydrazono)-, (phenylmethylene)hydrazide	EtOH	280(4.36),352(4.00)	104-1536-80
$C_{16}H_{13}N_5O_2$			
Benzaldehyde, 4-nitro-, (3-methyl-8(1H)-cycloheptapyrazolylidene)hydrazone	MeOH	278(3.63),313(3.10), 434(4.02)	118-0331-80

Compound	Solvent	$\lambda_{max}(\log \epsilon)$	Ref.
$C_{16}H_{13}S$			
2-Benzothiopyrylium, 1-methyl-3-phenyl-, perchlorate	CF_3COOH	278(4.63),316(3.80), 424(3.39)	103-0599-80
$C_{16}H_{14}$			
Anthracene, 2,7-dimethyl-	EtOH	255(5.28),326(3.40), 340(3.62),356(3.73), 376(3.54)	2-0341-80
Anthracene, 9,10-dimethyl-	n.s.g.	360(3.79),379(4.02), 401(4.01)	5-0954-80
Anthracene, 9-ethyl-	n.s.g.	351(3.80),369(4.01), 389(4.00)	5-0954-80
9,10-Benzotricyclo[6.2.2.0^{2,7}]dodeca-3,5,9,11-tetraene	hexane	264(3.53),271(3.60), 282(3.51),293(3.19)	89-0307-80
1,3-Butadiene, 1,4-diphenyl-, trans-trans	CH_2Cl_2	319(4.68),333(4.76), 349(4.56)	24-1663-80
1,6,2,5-Ethanediylidenebenzo[a]cyclobuta[c]cyclooctene, 1,2,2a,5,6,10b-hexahydro-	hexane	251s(2.31),256(2.47), 263(2.60),270(2.57)	89-0307-80
1H-Indene, 2-(phenylmethyl)-	EtOH	258(4.22)	2-0955-80
Indeno[2,1-a]indene, 4b,5,9b,10-tetrahydro-, (4bS-cis)-	EtOH	196(4.81),209(4.31), 213(4.28),218(4.24), 254(2.95),261(3.25), 267(3.47),274(3.59)	18-0291-80
$C_{16}H_{14}BrNO_2$			
1H-Indole, 2-(4-bromophenyl)-4,6-dimethoxy-	EtOH	254(4.23),335(4.31)	12-0343-80
1H-Indole, 3-(4-bromophenyl)-4,6-dimethoxy-	EtOH	248(4.30),275(4.19), 300s(4.10)	12-0343-80
$C_{16}H_{14}BrNO_4$			
L-Proline, 1-(3-bromo-1,4-dihydro-1,4-dioxo-2-naphthalenyl)-, methyl ester	MeOH	236(4.17),283(4.35), 478(3.68)	44-1260-80
$C_{16}H_{14}BrN_3O$			
Acetaldehyde, [(4-acetylphenyl)imino]-, 1-[(4-bromophenyl)hydrazono]-	EtOH	303(3.90),394(4.57)	65-2072-80
$C_{16}H_{14}BrN_5O_2$			
2,4-Quinazolinediamine, 6-bromo-N^2,N^2-dimethyl-N^4-(2-nitrophenyl)-	dioxan	244(4.52),287(4.54), 294(4.51),354(3.75), 419(3.85)	73-1079-80
2,4-Quinazolinediamine, 6-bromo-N^2,N^2-dimethyl-N^4-(4-nitrophenyl)-	dioxan	250(4.45),285(4.32), 292(4.32),402(3.60)	73-1079-80
$C_{16}H_{14}BrO_2S_2$			
Thianthrenium, 1-(2-bromo-1-methoxyethenyl)-5-methoxy-, perchlorate	MeOH	212s(4.26),218s(4.29), 223(4.31),242s(4.16), 258(3.99),305(3.52)	39-1185-80C
$C_{16}H_{14}Br_2N_2O_4$			
Benzene, 1,1'-(1,2-dibromo-3-methyl-1,3-propanediyl)bis[4-methyl-	MeOH	272(4.33)	73-2120-80
$C_{16}H_{14}Br_4O_2$			
Tricyclo[5.1.0.0^{3,5}]octan-1-ol, 4,4,8,8-tetrabromo-3-methyl-, benzoate	EtOH	231(4.21)	80-0559-80
Tricyclo[5.1.0.0^{3,5}]octan-1-ol, 4,4,8,8-tetrabromo-5-methyl-, benzoate	EtOH	231(4.17)	80-0559-80

Compound	Solvent	$\lambda_{max}(\log \epsilon)$	Ref.
$C_{16}H_{14}ClNO$			
Benzenamine, 2-chloro-N-[3-(4-methoxy-phenyl)-2-propenylidene]-, bis(tri-chloroacetate)	benzene	300(3.23),400(2.99)	65-1870-80
Benzenamine, 4-chloro-N-[3-(4-methoxy-phenyl)-2-propenylidene]-, bis(tri-chloroacetate)	benzene	290(3.08),400(3.26)	65-1870-80
2-Propen-1-one, 3-(2-chlorophenyl)-2-methyl-1-phenyl-, oxime, (Z,?)-	MeOH	273(4.36)	56-2209-80
2-Propen-1-one, 3-(3-chlorophenyl)-2-methyl-1-phenyl-, oxime, (Z,?)-	MeOH	268(4.40)	56-2209-80
2-Propen-1-one, 3-(4-chlorophenyl)-2-methyl-1-phenyl-, oxime, (Z,?)-	MeOH	280(4.33)	56-2209-80
$C_{16}H_{14}ClNO_3$			
Benzene, 1-[2-chloro-2-(4-methoxyphen-yl)-1-methylethenyl]-4-nitro-, (E)-	EtOH	260(4.23),336(3.82)	44-4309-80
(Z)-	EtOH	254(4.22),308s(3.95)	44-4309-80
4H-Furo[3,2-b]pyrrole-5-carboxylic acid, 2-(4-chlorophenyl)-4-methyl-, ethyl ester	MeOH	341.6(4.49),358.1(4.69)	73-2949-80
$C_{16}H_{14}ClN_3O_2$			
1H-Pyrazole, 5-(4-chlorophenyl)-4,5-di-hydro-3-(4-methoxyphenyl)-1-nitroso-	EtOH	262(3.93)	2-0364-80
$C_{16}H_{14}Cl_2N_2$			
1H-Indole-2-methanamine, 5-chloro-3-(2-chlorophenyl)-1-methyl-, hydrochlor-ide	EtOH	230(4.57),282(3.95), 298(3.88),310s(3.78)	87-0764-80
$C_{16}H_{14}Cl_2O_2$			
Benzene, 1,1'-(dichloroethenylidene)-bis[4-methoxy-	CF_3SO_3H	351(3.50),545(4.14)	88-3131-80
$C_{16}H_{14}N_2$			
1H-1,5-Benzodiazepine, 4-methyl-2-phen-yl-	H_2O	485(3.14)	96-0165-80
1,2-Diazabicyclo[3.1.0]hex-2-ene, 3,6-diphenyl-	n.s.g.	257(4.06)	88-1009-80
1H-Indene-2-carbonitrile, 2,3-dihydro-2-(phenylamino)-	dioxan	244(4.17),267(3.50), 273(3.53),287(3.24)	24-2462-80
3H-Indole, 3-[(1-methyl-2(1H)-pyridin-ylidene)ethylidene]-	MeOH-KOH	227(5.60),310(3.67), 530(4.50)	103-1031-80
Pyridine, 2,2'-(1,3,5-hexatriene-1,6-diyl)bis-	CH_2Cl_2	346s(4.59),360(4.73), 380(4.70),403s(4.28)	5-0291-80
Pyridine, 4,4'-(1,3,5-hexatriene-1,6-diyl)bis-	CH_2Cl_2	341s(4.54),354(4.66), 373(4.62),400(4.31)	5-0291-80
$C_{16}H_{14}N_2O$			
3(2H)-Pyridazinone, 1,6-dihydro-6,6-di-phenyl-	EtOH	270(4.14)	118-0457-80
$C_{16}H_{14}N_2O_2$			
1,4,2,5-Dioxadiazine, 3,6-bis(4-methyl-phenyl)-	MeCN	282(3.13)	12-2447-80
1H-Indole-2-carboxamide, 3-hydroxy-1-methyl-N-phenyl-	MeOH	236(4.30),262(4.25), 312(4.42)	83-0405-80
2H-Indol-2-one, 3-(1,3,4,5,6,7-hexa-hydro-3-oxo-2H-indol-2-ylidene)-1,3-dihydro-	$CHCl_3$	355(4.05),500(3.89)	5-0564-80

Compound	Solvent	$\lambda_{max}(\log \epsilon)$	Ref.
3H-Indol-3-one, 2-(1,3-dihydro-3-oxo-2H-indol-2-ylidene)-1,2,4,5,6,7-hexahydro-	CHCl₃ tert-BuOH + base	315(4.47),565(4.32) 567(--) 730(--)	5-0564-80 5-0564-80 5-0564-80
1(2H)-Isoquinolinone, 6-methoxy-3-(phenylamino)-	EtOH	249(4.45),316(4.15), 350(3.68)	95-0826-80
1(2H)-Isoquinolinone, 7-methoxy-3-(phenylamino)-	EtOH	223(4.41),307(4.22), 381(3.87)	95-0826-80
C₁₆H₁₄N₂O₂S			
Hexanenitrile, 4-(methylthio)-3,5-di-oxo-2-(2(1H)-quinolinylidene)-	EtOH	222(4.56),241(3.97), 293(4.20),400(4.30), 415(4.28)	94-2892-80
4H-1,3-Oxazin-4-one, 2-(1(2H)-isoquino-linylidenemethyl)-6-methyl-5-(methyl-thio)-	EtOH	225(4.55),255(3.84), 264(3.89),298(4.31), 400s(4.22),421(4.58), 446(4.68)	95-1261-80
4H-1,3-Oxazin-4-one, 6-methyl-5-(meth-ylthio)-2-(2(1H)-quinolinylidenemeth-yl)-	EtOH	219(4.77),299s(4.21), 312(4.26),322(4.25), 415(4.32),432(4.60), 461(4.57)	94-0795-80
2,6(1H,3H)-Pyridinedione, 3-(1(2H)-iso-quinolinylidene)-4-methyl-5-(methyl-thio)-	EtOH	220(4.53),261(3.85), 335(4.06),474(3.00)	95-1261-80
2,6(1H,3H)-Pyridinedione, 3-(2(1H)-quinolinylidene)-4-methyl-5-(methyl-thio)-	EtOH	223(4.52),245s(4.18), 290s(3.96),340(4.12), 460(4.38)	94-2892-80
C₁₆H₁₄N₂O₃			
Acetamide, N-(2-ethyl-2,3-dihydro-1,3-dioxo-1H-benz[de]isoquinolin-5-yl)-	dioxan	256(4.60),339(4.02), 375(3.73)	56-0107-80
Acetamide, N-(2-ethyl-2,3-dihydro-1,3-dioxo-1H-benz[de]isoquinolin-6-yl)-	dioxan	247(4.40),368(4.15)	56-0107-80
2-Propen-1-one, 2-methyl-3-(2-nitro-phenyl)-1-phenyl-, oxime, (Z,?)-	MeOH	251(4.27)	56-2209-80
2-Propen-1-one, 2-methyl-3-(4-nitro-phenyl)-1-phenyl-, oxime	MeOH	329(4.18)	56-2209-80
Quinoline, 1-benzoyl-1,2,3,4-tetra-hydro-6-nitro-	EtOH	325(4.02)	103-0386-80
Quinoline, 1-benzoyl-1,2,3,4-tetra-hydro-8-nitro-	EtOH	242(4.26),335(3.48)	103-0386-80
C₁₆H₁₄N₂O₄			
Benzene, 1,1'-(3-methyl-1-propene-1,3-diyl)bis[4-nitro-, cis	MeOH	293(4.30)	73-2120-80
trans	MeOH	313(4.36)	73-2120-80
Ethanone, 2-[(4-acetylphenyl)amino]-1-(4-nitrophenyl)-	CH₂Cl₂	370(2.89)	83-0315-80
C₁₆H₁₄N₂O₅S₂			
5-Thia-1-azabicyclo[4.2.0]oct-2-ene-2-carboxylic acid, 3-(acetoxymethyl)-8-oxo-7-[(phenylthio)imino]-, sodium salt, (R)-	MeOH	326(4.03)	35-1690-80
C₁₆H₁₄N₂O₇S			
4-Thia-1-azabicyclo[3.2.0]hept-2-ene-2-carboxylic acid, 3-(acetoxymethyl)-7-oxo-, (4-nitrophenyl)methyl ester	n.s.g.	265(4.04),322(3.85)	77-0070-80
C₁₆H₁₄N₂S			
2H-Pyrimido[2,1-b]benzothiazole, 3,4-	EtOH	222(4.80),265(4.13),	103-0169-80

Compound	Solvent	$\lambda_{max}(\log \epsilon)$	Ref.
dihydro-4-phenyl- (cont.)		295(3.87)	103-0169-80
$C_{16}H_{14}N_3O$			
4H-1,2,4-Triazolium, 1-(2-oxo-2-phenyl-ethyl)-4-phenyl-, bromide	MeOH	249(4.20)	80-0407-80
$C_{16}H_{14}N_4$			
Benzaldehyde, (3-methyl-8(1H)-cyclo-heptapyrazolylidene)hydrazone	MeOH	221(4.48),367(4.02)	118-0331-80
$C_{16}H_{14}N_4O$			
1,3,5-Triazin-2(5H)-one, 6-phenyl-4-[(phenylmethyl)amino]-	n.s.g.	233(4.60)	115-0243-80
1,3,5-Triazin-2(5H)-one, 4-[(2-methyl-phenyl)amino]-6-phenyl-	n.s.g.	238(4.50)	115-0243-80
1,3,5-Triazin-2(5H)-one, 4-[(4-methyl-phenyl)amino]-6-phenyl-	n.s.g.	248(4.53)	115-0243-80
$C_{16}H_{14}N_4O_2$			
1H-1,2,4-Triazolium, 1-(phenylmethyl)-, 4-[(4-nitrophenyl)methylide]	pH 13	532(4.03)	80-0407-80
$C_{16}H_{14}N_4O_3$			
1H-1,2,4-Triazole-1-carboxylic acid, 4-amino-4,5-dihydro-5-oxo-3-phenyl-, phenylmethyl ester	EtOH	262(4.15)	4-1691-80
$C_{16}H_{14}N_4O_4$			
1H-Pyrazole, 4,5-dihydro-3-(4-methoxy-phenyl)-5-(4-nitrophenyl)-1-nitroso-	MeOH	296(4.01)	2-0364-80
$C_{16}H_{14}N_4O_4S_3$			
5-Thia-1-azabicyclo[4.2.0]oct-2-ene-2-carboxylic acid, 3-(5-methyl-1,3,4-thiadiazol-2-yl)-8-oxo-7-[(2-thien-ylacetyl)amino]-, (6R-trans)-, mono-sodium salt	H_2O	305(4.11)	94-2116-80
$C_{16}H_{14}N_6O_2$			
1H-Isoindole-1,3(2H)-dione, 2-[3-(6-am-ino-3H-purin-3-yl)propyl]-, mono-hydrobromide	MeOH	240(4.12),276(4.09)	24-2043-80
$C_{16}H_{14}O$			
2-Buten-1-one, 1,3-diphenyl-, (E)-	EtOH	265(4.03),296(4.21)	118-0041-80
(Z)-	EtOH	251(4.14),280(4.06)	118-0041-80
2,4,10,12-Cyclotridecatetraene-6,8-di-yn-1-one, 2,5,10-trimethyl-	ether	250s(4.39),265(4.68), 276(4.70),390s(3.15)	39-0466-80C
1,4-Epoxyanthracene, 1,2,3,4,9,10-hexa-hydro-2,3-bis(methylene)-	EtOH	212(4.15),225s(4.04), 233s(3.99),243s(3.86), 273(2.90)	33-0232-80
2-Propen-1-one, 2-methyl-1,3-diphenyl-	MeOH	254(4.05),289(4.14)	56-2209-80
$C_{16}H_{14}OS$			
4H-1-Benzothiopyran-4-one, 2,3-dihydro-3-(phenylmethyl)-	EtOH	240(4.50),261(3.90)	2-0955-80
1-Propanone, 1-(4-methylphenyl)-3-phenyl-3-thioxo-	C_6H_{12}	268(3.97),323(4.10), 413(4.29),515s(2.30) (anom.)	39-1768-80B
anion	EtOH	269(4.24),401(4.37)	39-1768-80B

Compound	Solvent	$\lambda_{max}(\log \epsilon)$	Ref.
1-Propanone, 3-(4-methylphenyl)-1-phenyl-3-thioxo-	C_6H_{12}	261(--),340(--), 408(--),520s(--)	39-1768-80B
anion	EtOH	256(4.05),280s(3.97), 404(4.22)	39-1768-80B
$C_{16}H_{14}O_2$			
Anthracene, 9,10-dimethoxy-	n.s.g.	363(3.77),383(3.96), 405(3.89)	5-0954-80
Tricyclo[3.2.2.0^{2,4}]non-8-ene-6,7-dione, 3-methyl-3-phenyl-	CCl$_4$	445(2.05)	30-0456-80
$C_{16}H_{14}O_2S$			
1-Propanone, 1-(4-methoxyphenyl)-3-phenyl-3-thioxo-	C_6H_{12}	245(--),252s(--), 326(--),423(--), 513s(--)	39-1768-80B
anion	EtOH	282(4.13),399(4.34)	39-1768-80B
1-Propanone, 3-(4-methoxyphenyl)-1-phenyl-3-thioxo-	C_6H_{12}	233s(--),259(--), 372(--),407(--), 515s(--)	39-1768-80B
anion	EtOH	300(3.92),404(4.33)	39-1768-80B
$C_{16}H_{14}O_2S_2$			
Ethanone, 1,1'-(dithiodi-2,1-phenylene)bis-	MeOH	230(4.57),329(3.91)	142-0955-80
$C_{16}H_{14}O_2S_3$			
Ethanone, 1,1'-(trithiodi-2,1-phenylene)bis-	MeOH	229(4.45),329(3.94)	142-0955-80
$C_{16}H_{14}O_3$			
4H-1-Benzopyran-4-one, 2,3-dihydro-2-(4-methoxyphenyl)-	EtOH	320(4.52)	18-2938-80
4H-1-Benzopyran-4-one, 2,3-dihydro-6-methoxy-2-phenyl-	EtOH	254(3.79),352(3.55)	18-2938-80
4H-1-Benzopyran-4-one, 2,3-dihydro-7-methoxy-2-phenyl-	isoPrOH	272(4.07),310(3.75)	18-2938-80
5H-Furo[3,2-b]xanthen-5-one, 6,7,8,9-tetrahydro-11-methyl-	CHCl$_3$	246(4.74),278(4.6)	42-1011-80
1H-Inden-1-one, 2,3-dihydro-3-hydroxy-3-methoxy-2-phenyl-, anion	n.s.g.	461(4.20)	73-1072-80
1(3H)-Isobenzofuranone, 3-methoxy-3-(4-methoxyphenyl)-	n.s.g.	220(4.1),280(3.0)	40-1749-80
Naphtho[2,3-b]pyran-5,10-dione, 2,2,7-trimethyl- (6-methyldehydro-α-lapachone)	MeOH	206(4.47),265(4.31), 276s(4.27),333s(3.76), 444(3.14)	102-0277-80
Naphtho[2,3-b]pyran-5,10-dione, 2,2,8-trimethyl-	MeOH	205(4.38),260(4.31), 285s(4.12),338s(3.56), 443(3.08)	102-0277-80
$C_{16}H_{14}O_3S$			
2-Propenoic acid, 3-(2-methoxyphenyl)-2-(phenylthio)-	MeOH	205(4.35),265(4.09), 320(4.08)	25-0791-80
2-Propenoic acid, 3-(2-methoxyphenyl)-3-(phenylthio)-	MeOH	205(4.22),285(3.95)	25-0791-80
$C_{16}H_{14}O_4$			
Alloisoimperatorin	EtOH	224(4.46),245(4.14), 253(4.21),268(4.27), 274(4.27),317(4.08)	94-1847-80
Alpinetin	MeOH	227(3.99),285(4.00)	102-1262-80

Compound	Solvent	$\lambda_{max}(\log \epsilon)$	Ref.
1,3-Benzodioxol-5-ol, 2-methyl-2-phenyl-, acetate	EtOH	232(3.56),285(3.70)	12-0527-80
4H-1-Benzopyran-4-one, 2,3-dihydro-5-hydroxy-7-methoxy-2-phenyl-	isoPrOH	285(4.23),320(3.48)	18-2938-80
[1,1'-Biphenyl]-2,2'-dicarboxylic acid, monoethyl ester	tert-BuOH	283(3.49)	35-4472-80
7bH-Cyclopent[cd]indene-1,2-dicarboxylic acid, 7b-methyl-, dimethyl ester	EtOH	217(3.99),262(3.82), 305(4.60),336(3.84), 471(3.25)	77-0691-80
7H-Furo[3,2-g]-1-benzopyran-2-one, 9-[(3-methyl-2-butenyl)oxy]- (imperatorin)	EtOH	220(4.41),245s(4.35), 250(4.37),264s(4.13), 301(4.08)	94-1847-80
Isoimperatorin	EtOH	223(4.25),244s(4.07), 251(4.13),260(4.08), 269(4.07),310(4.02)	94-1847-80
	n.s.g.	222(4.32),250(4.27), 310(4.17)	106-0503-80
2-Propen-1-one, 3-(4-hydroxy-2-methoxyphenyl)-1-(4-hydroxyphenyl)-, (E)- (echinatin)	EtOH	237(3.79),312(3.94), 370(4.20)	102-2179-80
	EtOH-NaOEt	252(3.79),271(3.80), 435(4.41)	102-2179-80
$C_{16}H_{14}O_4S_2$ 1,3-Dithiole-4,5-dicarboxylic acid, 2-[(4-ethenylphenyl)methylene]-, dimethyl ester	EtOH	245(4.24),345(4.38), 359s(4.36),410(2.70)	116-0240-80
$(C_{16}H_{14}O_4S_2)_n$ 1,3-Dithiole-4,5-dicarboxylic acid, 2-[(4-ethenylphenyl)methylene]-, dimethyl ester, homopolymer	CHCl$_3$	255s(4.06),326(4.12), 405(3.02)	116-0240-80
polymer formed in sulfuric acid	CHCl$_3$	238(4.11),328(4.10), 405(3.00)	116-0240-80
$C_{16}H_{14}O_4S_3$ 1,3-Dithiole-4,5-dicarboxylic acid, 2-(1-methyl-2-phenyl-2-thioxoethylidene)-, dimethyl ester	MeOH	262(4.26),327(3.84), 460(4.35),580(2.53)	104-1775-80
$C_{16}H_{14}O_5$ 4H-1-Benzopyran-4-one, 2,3-dihydro-5,7-dihydroxy-6-methoxy-2-phenyl-	EtOH	294(4.14),334(3.88)	95-1220-80
	EtOH-NaOAc	295(4.04),334(4.12)	95-1220-80
	EtOH-AlCl$_3$	313(4.28),390(3.39)	95-1220-80
7H-Furo[3,2-g][1]benzopyran-7-one, 9-acetoxy-2-(1-methylethyl)-	EtOH	215(4.32),250(4.73), 296(4.04)	102-1556-80
4H-Naphtho[1,2-b]pyran-4-one, 5-hydroxy-8,10-dimethoxy-2-methyl- (flavosperone)	MeOH	241(4.65),262(4.41), 370(3.66)	39-2474-80C
4H-Naphtho[2,3-b]pyran-4-one, 5-hydroxy-6,8-dimethoxy-2-methyl- (heminigerone)	MeOH	225(4.40),242(4.51), 247(4.50),277(4.53), 376(3.65)	39-2474-80C
1,3-Propanedione, 1-(2,4-dihydroxyphenyl)-3-(4-methoxyphenyl)-	EtOH	269s(4.05),283(4.12), 376(4.56),388s(4.52)	102-2331-80
	EtOH-NaOEt	256(4.12),290s(3.99), 388(4.71)	102-2331-80
1,3-Propanedione, 1-(2-hydroxy-4-methoxyphenyl)-3-(4-hydroxyphenyl)-	EtOH	283(4.07),378(4.52), 390s(4.49)	102-2331-80
	EtOH-NaOEt	383(4.51)	102-2331-80
1,3-Propanedione, 1-(4-hydroxy-2-methoxyphenyl)-3-(4-hydroxyphenyl)-	EtOH	275(4.20),308(4.20), 368(4.66)	102-2331-80

Compound	Solvent	$\lambda_{max}(\log \epsilon)$	Ref.
(cont.)	EtOH–NaOEt	242(4.13),339(4.65), 428(4.08)	102-2331-80
$C_{16}H_{14}O_6$			
Benzoic acid, 4-methoxy-, 1-acetoxy-6-oxo-2,4-cyclohexadien-1-yl ester	EtOH	264(4.58),310(3.81)	12-1553-80
4H-1-Benzopyran-4-one, 2,3-dihydro-5,7-dihydroxy-2-(4-hydroxyphenyl)-6-methoxy-	MeOH	293(4.23),331(3.68)	95-1220-80
	MeOH–NaOMe	247(4.30),329(4.44)	95-1220-80
	MeOH–NaOAc	294(4.07),330(4.19)	95-1220-80
	MeOH–AlCl₃	225(4.42),300s(4.12), 316(4.21),394(3.41)	95-1220-80
	MeOH–AlCl₃-HCl	225(4.47),314(4.32), 394(3.41)	95-1220-80
4H-1-Benzopyran-4-one, 2-(1,4-dihydroxy-2,5-cyclohexadien-1-yl)-5-hydroxy-7-methoxy-	EtOH	231(4.34),250(4.38), 257s(4.35),293(3.99), 324s(3.73)	88-1227-80
$C_{16}H_{14}O_7$			
Benzoic acid, 2-(2,6-dihydroxy-4-methylbenzoyl)-3,5-dihydroxy-, methyl ester	EtOH	282(4.10),324s(3.79)	32-0629-80
4H-1-Benzopyran-4-one, 2-(3,4-dihydroxyphenyl)-2,3-dihydro-3,5,7-trihydroxy-6-methyl-	MeOH	228(4.21),295(4.24), 334s(--)	102-0893-80
	MeOH–AlCl₃	227(4.29),318(4.30)	102-0893-80
	MeOH–AlCl₃-HCl	228(4.37),319(4.33)	102-0893-80
	MeOH–NaOAc-H_3BO_3	228(4.26),295(4.26)	102-0893-80
$C_{16}H_{14}O_8$			
4H-1-Benzopyran-4-one, 2,3-dihydro-3,5,7-trihydroxy-2-(3,4,5-trihydroxyphenyl)-6-methyl-	MeOH	231(4.86),296(4.75), 342s(--)	102-0893-80
	MeOH–NaOAc	231(5.27),296(4.68)	102-0893-80
	MeOH–AlCl₃	231(5.64),318(4.86)	102-0893-80
$C_{16}H_{14}S$			
2H-1-Benzothiopyran, 3-(phenylmethyl)-	EtOH	248(4.43)	2-0955-80
Thiophene, 2-(4,8-dimethyl-6-azulenyl)-	EtOH	205(4.48),245(4.36), 264(4.20),292(4.08), 327(4.60),580(2.8)	103-0807-80
$C_{16}H_{15}BrN_2$			
2H-Indol-2-imine, 3-[(4-bromophenyl)methyl]-1,3-dihydro-1-methyl-, monohydrochloride	n.s.g.	215(4.2),260(3.9)	103-0917-80
$C_{16}H_{15}BrN_2O_2$			
Hydroperoxide, 3-[(4-bromophenyl)methyl]-2,3-dihydro-2-imino-1-methyl-1H-indol-3-yl	n.s.g.	265(4.1),298(3.3)	103-0917-80
$C_{16}H_{15}BrN_5O_6PS$			
Adenosine, 8-[(4-bromophenyl)thio]-, cyclic 3',5'-(hydrogen phosphate)	pH 1	280(4.25)	87-0242-80
	pH 11	283(4.22)	87-0242-80
$C_{16}H_{15}BrO_4$			
2H-Naphtho[1,2-b]pyran-5,6-dione, 3-bromo-3,4-dihydro-4-methoxy-2,2-dimethyl-	EtOH	252(4.48),280(3.93), 332(3.42),380(3.19), 420(3.25)	2-0013-80

Compound	Solvent	$\lambda_{max}(\log \epsilon)$	Ref.
$C_{16}H_{15}Br_2NO_2S$			
Isoquinoline, 1-[(2,5-dibromo-3-thien-yl)methyl]-3,4-dihydro-6,7-dimeth-oxy-, hydrochloride	MeOH	230(2.75),308(2.43), 360(2.30)	2-1028-80
$C_{16}H_{15}ClN_2O$			
3(2H)-Pyridazinone, 6-(4-chlorophenyl)-tetrahydro-6-phenyl-	EtOH	285(4.46)	48-0617-80
$C_{16}H_{15}ClN_2O_3$			
Acetamide, 2-chloro-N-[3-(2,2-dimethyl-aziridino)-1,4-dihydro-1,4-dioxo-2-naphthalenyl]-	EtOH	248(4.20),254(4.21), 287(3.96),340(3.39)	4-0181-80
$C_{16}H_{15}ClN_4O_3$			
6H-Pyrrolo[3,4-d]pyrimidine-6-butanoic acid, 2-amino-4-(4-chlorophenyl)-5,7-dihydro-7-oxo-	EtOH	255(4.29),269(4.29), 349(3.99)	4-1231-80
$C_{16}H_{15}Cl_3N_2$			
1H-Indole-2-methanamine, 5-chloro-3-(2-chlorophenyl)-1-methyl-, hydrochlor-ide	EtOH	230(4.57),282(3.95), 298(3.88),310s(3.78)	87-0764-80
$C_{16}H_{15}N$			
1H-Indole, 3-ethyl-2-phenyl-	EtOH	207(4.46),228(4.40), 308(4.26)	39-0339-80B
$C_{16}H_{15}NO$			
Benzamide, N-[2-(1-propenyl)phenyl]-, (E)-	MeOH	235(4.35)	44-1549-80
Benzenamine, 4-methoxy-N-(3-phenyl-2-propenylidene)-, trichloroacetate	benzene	290(2.45)	65-1870-80
1H-Indole, 5-methoxy-3-methyl-2-phenyl-	tert-BuOH	226s(4.46),314(4.34)	35-7559-80
2-Propen-1-one, 2-methyl-1,3-diphenyl-, oxime	MeOH	275(4.37)	56-2209-80
$C_{16}H_{15}NO_2$			
Benzo[g]pyrrolo[1,2-a]quinolin-5(1H)-one, 2,3,3a,4-tetrahydro-6-hydroxy-	MeOH	244(4.60),292(4.65), 315(4.06),332(3.68), 467(3.41)	44-1260-80
1H-Inden-1-one, 2,3-dihydro-3-hydroxy-3-methoxy-2-(4-nitrophenyl)-, anion	n.s.g.	475(3.18)	73-1072-80
1H-Indole, 4,6-dimethoxy-2-phenyl-	EtOH	250(4.23),325(4.24)	12-0343-80
3H-Indol-3-ol, 5-methoxy-3-methyl-2-phenyl-	tert-BuOH	244(4.16),303(3.91), 339(4.08)	35-7559-80
2-Propen-1-one, 3-[(2-hydroxyphenyl)-amino]-1-(4-methylphenyl)-, (Z)-	dioxan	248(4.08),263(4.12), 382(4.49)	48-0099-80
$C_{16}H_{15}NO_2S$			
Ethanedione, diphenyl-, mono[O-(methyl-thio)methyl]oxime, (Z)-	EtOH	253(4.48)	150-4501-80
Ethanone, [[(methylthio)methyl]imino]-diphenyl-, N-oxide, (E)-	EtOH	262(4.30),288(4.20)	150-4501-80
(Z)-	EtOH	256(4.27),288s(3.98)	150-4501-80
Ethene, 1-(ethylthio)-2-nitro-1,2-di-phenyl-, (Z)-	MeOH-pH 10.6	360(3.82)	28-0021-80A
$C_{16}H_{15}NO_3$			
9(10H)-Acridinone, 1,3-dimethoxy-10-methyl-	EtOH	225(4.14),260(4.68), 268(4.69),290(4.12),	100-0498-80

Compound	Solvent	$\lambda_{max}(\log \epsilon)$	Ref.
(cont.)		314(3.72),379(3.92)	100-0498-80
Benzamide, N-(2-acetyl-4-methoxyphenyl)-	tert-BuOH	227(4.37),283(4.05),	35-7559-80
		362(3.78)	
1H-Benz[e]indene-2-acetamide, 2,3-di-	EtOH	229(4.76),264(4.07),	87-0512-80
hydro-8-methoxy-1-oxo-		317(3.84),343(3.88)	
Benzo[5,6]cyclohepta[1,2-b]pyrrole-	MeOH	230(3.69),256(3.55),	4-1081-80
2-acetic acid, 1,4,5,10-tetrahydro-		334(4.05)	
1-methyl-10-oxo-			
Butanoic acid, 4-(diphenylamino)-4-oxo-	MeOH	234(4.03)	73-3593-80
Hydroperoxide, 5-methoxy-3-methyl-	tert-BuOH	242(4.21),302(3.97),	35-7559-80
2-phenyl-3H-indol-3-yl		339(4.10)	
Indeno[1,2-d]azepine-3(2H)-carboxylic	EtOH	224(4.22),277(4.34),	18-3232-80
acid, 1,10-dihydro-10-oxo-, ethyl		455(2.93)	
ester			
3H-Naphth[1,2-e][1,3]oxazin-3-one,	EtOH	228(4.81),255s(3.48),	4-0277-80
1,2-dihydro-2-methyl-1-(2-oxopropyl)-		266s(3.62),276(3.70),	
		308(3.08),322(3.20)	
Phenol, 2-[4,5-dihydro-5-(4-methoxy-	EtOH	222(4.30),264(4.11),	142-1319-80
phenyl)-3-isoxazolyl]-		274(4.00),308(3.76)	
2-Propen-1-one, 3-[(2-hydroxyphenyl)-	dioxan	241(3.95),281(4.00),	48-0099-80
amino]-1-(4-methoxyphenyl)-, (Z)-		381(4.54)	
$C_{16}H_{15}NO_3S$			
1H-2,1-Benzothiazin-4(3H)-one, 1-(2,3-	MeOH	224(4.39),258(3.89),	44-2127-80
dimethylphenyl)-, 2,2-dioxide		335(3.59)	
	MeOH-KOH	240(4.01),299(3.90)	44-2127-80
$C_{16}H_{15}NO_4$			
L-Proline, 1-(1,4-dihydro-1,4-dioxo-	MeOH	236(4.24),243(4.18),	44-1260-80
2-naphthalenyl)-, methyl ester		268(4.35),274(4.41),	
		299(3.91),327(3.48)	
Pyrano[3,2-b]indole-2-carboxylic acid,	MeOH	221(4.53),256(4.10),	83-0405-80
5-ethyl-4,5-dihydro-4-oxo-, ethyl		264(4.07),309(4.24)	
ester			
$C_{16}H_{15}NO_4S$			
Benzenemethanol, α-[3-[(4-nitrophenyl)-	MeOH	260(4.02)	12-2635-80
sulfinyl]-2-propenyl]-, (E)-			
$C_{16}H_{15}NO_7$			
2H,5H-Pyrano[2,3-b]quinolizine-3,11-di-	EtOH	397(4.31)	49-0093-80
carboxylic acid, 7,8,9,10-tetrahydro-			
2,5-dioxo-, 3-ethyl ester			
$C_{16}H_{15}NS$			
Benzenecarbothioamide, N-[2-(1-propen-	MeOH	245(4.40),300s(3.83)	44-1549-80
yl)phenyl]-, (E)-			
Ethanethioamide, N-[2-(2-phenylethen-	MeCN	225(4.41),286(4.56),	44-1549-80
yl)phenyl]-, (E)-		310s(4.52)	
Sulfonium, dimethyl(2-phenyl-1H-indol-	H_2O	237(4.40),291(4.15)	44-0780-80
3-yl)-, hydroxide, inner salt	dioxan	237(4.23),301(4.04)	44-0780-80
$C_{16}H_{15}N_3$			
1H-Pyrazol-5-amine, 4-(2,4-cyclopenta-	EtOH	244(4.10),303(3.76),	114-0127-80C
dien-1-ylidenemethyl)-3-methyl-		368(4.23)	
1-phenyl-			
1,2,4-Triazine, 2,5-dihydro-3-methyl-	EtOH	230s(4.08),303(3.81)	44-4587-80
5,6-diphenyl-			
$C_{16}H_{15}N_3O$			
Acetaldehyde, [(4-acetylphenyl)imino]-,	EtOH	296(3.79),394(4.40)	65-2072-80

Compound	Solvent	$\lambda_{max}(\log \epsilon)$	Ref.
1-(phenylhydrazone) (cont.)			65-2072-80
Imidazo[2,1-b]quinazolin-5-ol, 1,2,3,5-tetrahydro-5-phenyl-	pH 1	244(4.43)	94-2024-80
	pH 13	268(4.19)	94-2024-80
	EtOH	273(4.19)	94-2024-80
4H-Pyrimido[6,1-a]isoquinolin-4-one, 2-(1-pyrrolidinyl)-	EtOH	223s(4.62),244(4.36), 280s(4.42),290(4.58), 320s(3.92),344(4.30), 363(4.71),381(4.34), 404(4.25)	95-1261-80
1,2,4-Triazine, 2,5-dihydro-3-methoxy-5,6-diphenyl-	EtOH	224s(4.22),292(3.96)	44-4587-80
$C_{16}H_{15}N_3O_2$			
Benzamidoxime, O-(N-acetylbenzimidoyl)-	EtOH	238(4.28),265s(4.00)	39-1792-80B
$C_{16}H_{15}N_3O_3$			
1H-Pyrazole, 4,5-dihydro-3-(4-methoxyphenyl)-5-(4-nitrophenyl)-	MeOH	288(4.40)	2-0364-80
$C_{16}H_{15}N_3O_4$			
12H-Dibenzo[c,h][1,2,6]triazonine-12-carboxylic acid, 11,13-dihydro-, methyl ester, 5,6-dioxide	EtOH	217(4.19),268(4.06)	44-4597-80
$C_{16}H_{15}N_3O_5$			
Butanoic acid, 4-[(3-pyridinylcarbonyl)amino]-, 4-nitrophenyl ester	EtOH	264(4.11),350(2.45)	65-1339-80
Pyrimido[4,5-b]quinoline-2-carboxylic acid, 1,4-dihydro-7,8-dimethoxy-4-oxo-, ethyl ester	CHCl₃	382(4.32)	117-0219-80
$C_{16}H_{15}N_3O_5S$			
5-Thia-1-azabicyclo[4.2.0]oct-2-ene-2-carboxylic acid, 7-[(aminophenylacetyl)amino]-3-methyl-4,8-dioxo-	pH 3.0	288(3.65),317(3.63) (changing)	33-0201-80
	EtOH-1% HCOOH	290s(3.67),313(3.70) (changing)	33-0201-80
$C_{16}H_{15}N_3S$			
1,2,4-Triazine, 2,5-dihydro-3-(methylthio)-5,6-diphenyl-	EtOH	234s(4.14),300(3.94)	44-4587-80
$C_{16}H_{15}N_4O_2$			
1H-1,2,4-Triazolium, 4-[(4-nitrophenyl)methyl]-1-(phenylmethyl)-, bromide	MeOH	258(4.02)	80-0407-80
$C_{16}H_{15}N_5O$			
1H-Benzimidazole, 2-[[1-(hydroxyimino)-ethyl]azo]-1-(phenylmethyl)-	50% EtOH	375(4.30)	103-0857-80
$C_{16}H_{15}N_8$			
3,5'-Bi-2H-tetrazolium, 2'-methyl-2-(2-methylphenyl)-5-phenyl-, perchlorate	EtOH	249(4.48),310(3.65)	103-0094-80
3,5'-Bi-2H-tetrazolium, 2'-methyl-2-(4-methylphenyl)-5-phenyl-, perchlorate	EtOH	245(4.44),312(3.78)	103-0094-80
2H-Tetrazolium, 2-(2-methylphenyl)-3-(1-methyl-1H-tetrazol-5-yl)-5-phenyl-, chloride	EtOH	250(4.46),325(3.86)	103-0094-80
2H-Tetrazolium, 2-(4-methylphenyl)-3-(1-methyl-1H-tetrazol-5-yl)-5-	EtOH	245(4.45),330(3.77)	103-0094-80

Compound	Solvent	$\lambda_{max}(\log \epsilon)$	Ref.
5-phenyl-, chloride (cont.)			103-0094-80
$C_{16}H_{15}N_8O$			
3,5'-Bi-2H-tetrazolium, 2-(4-methoxy-phenyl)-2'-methyl-5-phenyl-, per-chlorate	EtOH	245(4.45),357(4.03)	103-0094-80
2H-Tetrazolium, 2-(4-methoxyphenyl)-3-(1-methyl-1H-tetrazol-5-yl)-5-phenyl-, perchlorate	EtOH	246(4.35),290(4.16), 380(3.81)	103-0094-80
$C_{16}H_{16}$			
1-Butene, 1,3-diphenyl-	MeOH	253(4.30)	33-0154-80
1,3-Cyclopentadiene, 1,5,5-trimethyl-4-phenyl-	pentane	224(4.08),232s(4.02), 240s(3.82),306(4.15), 330s(3.87)	33-0154-80
Dibenzo[a,c]cyclooctene, 5,6,7,8-tetra-hydro-	C_6H_{12}	235(4.15),265s(3.08)	95-0718-80
$C_{16}H_{16}Br_2$			
Butane, 1,2-dibromo-1,3-diphenyl-	MeOH	219(4.410)	73-2120-80
$C_{16}H_{16}ClNO_2$			
1,4-Naphthalenedione, 2-chloro-3-[2-(di-ethylamino)ethenyl]-	EtOH	234(3.96),324(4.42), 582(4.13)	150-0139-80
$C_{16}H_{16}ClN_5$			
Pyrido[3,2-e][1,2,4]triazolo[1,5-a]-pyrimidine, 9-[(2-chlorophenyl)meth-yl]-6,7,8,9-tetrahydro-5-methyl-	EtOH	216(4.41),268(3.65), 315(4.24)	87-0927-80
$C_{16}H_{16}FN_3O_5$			
1(2H)-Pyrimidinepropanoic acid, β-(ace-tylamino)-5-fluoro-3,4-dihydro-2,4-dioxo-, phenylmethyl ester	MeOH	268(3.93)	94-1137-80
$C_{16}H_{16}NS$			
Sulfonium, dimethyl(2-phenyl-1H-indol-3-yl)-, iodide	H₂O	235(4.15),288(4.00)	44-0780-80
	dioxan	276(3.93),301(4.04)	44-0780-80
$C_{16}H_{16}N_2$			
Cyclobuta[1,2-c:4,3-c']dipyridinium, 2,7-di-2-propenyl-, dibromide	H₂O	246(3.93),252(4.13), 299(2.11),313(2.11), 329(2.10)	150-2911-80
Diazirino[3,1-a]isoquinoline, 1,3,4,8b-tetrahydro-1-(4-methylphenyl)-	C_6H_{12}	210(4.42),232(4.23)	88-4877-80
1H-Indol-2-amine, 1-methyl-3-(phenyl-methyl)-, monohydrochloride	n.s.g.	210(4.1),260(3.5)	103-0917-80
$C_{16}H_{16}N_2O$			
Acetic acid, [(4-methylphenyl)phenyl-methylene]hydrazide	MeOH	285(4.30)	18-3225-80
	dioxan	288(4.28)	18-3225-80
Benz[f]imidazo[2,1-a]isoquinoline, 1,2,10,11-tetrahydro-7-methoxy-	EtOH	254(4.71),300(4.10)	94-1810-80
13H-Isoquino[2,1-a][1,8]naphthyridin-13-one, 1,2,3,4,6,7-hexahydro-	EtOH	249(4.46),308(3.96)	94-0220-80
Propanenitrile, 2-methyl-3-phenoxy-2-(phenylamino)-	dioxan	265s(3.25),270(3.38), 277(3.40),315s(3.16)	24-2462-80
3(2H)-Pyridazinone, tetrahydro-6,6-di-phenyl-	EtOH	289(4.39)	48-0617-80

Compound	Solvent	λ_{max}(log ϵ)	Ref.
C₁₆H₁₆N₂OS			
Propanenitrile, 2-methyl-2-(phenyl-amino)-3-(phenylsulfinyl)-	dioxan	242(4.21),286s(3.23)	24-2462-80
C₁₆H₁₆N₂O₂			
Acetic acid, [(4-methoxyphenyl)phenyl-methylene]hydrazide	MeOH	287(4.35)	18-3225-80
	dioxan	285(4.27)	18-3225-80
Benzamide, N-[2-(methylphenylamino)-2-oxoethyl]-	MeOH	228(4.21)	73-3593-80
Benzenamine, 4-(1-methylethyl)-N-[(4-nitrophenyl)methylene]-	THF	362(4.20)	56-1177-80
2,4,6-Cycloheptatrien-1-one, 2-methoxy-7-[1-(phenylhydrazono)ethyl]-	MeOH	242(4.37),270s(4.20), 330(3.99),402(4.02)	4-1293-80
Hydroperoxide, 2,3-dihydro-2-imino-1-methyl-3-(phenylmethyl)-1H-indol-3-yl	n.s.g.	263(4.0),295(3.3)	103-0917-80
Hydroperoxide, 2,3-dihydro-2-imino-3-methyl-1-(phenylmethyl)-1H-indol-3-yl	n.s.g.	264(4.07),298(3.3)	103-0917-80
3H-Pyrrolizine-2-carboxylic acid, 1-amino-3-phenyl-, ethyl ester	CH₂Cl₂	252(4.04),262s(3.92), 332(4.22)	150-3078-80
C₁₆H₁₆N₂O₂S			
Propanenitrile, 2-methyl-2-(phenyl-amino)-3-(phenylsulfonyl)-	dioxan	266(3.33),273(3.34), 282(3.21)	24-2462-80
C₁₆H₁₆N₂O₃			
Benzoic acid, 2-[methyl(2-oxo-2-phenyl-aminoethyl)amino]-	MeOH	235(4.29)	83-0402-80
Indolo[2,3-a]quinolizine-3-carboxylic acid, 1,2,3,4,6,7,12,12b-octahydro-4-oxo-	EtOH	224(4.59),274s(3.88), 281(3.89),290(3.79)	94-2527-80
C₁₆H₁₆N₂O₃S			
4-Oxa-2,6-diazabicyclo[3.2.0]hept-2-en-7-one, 6-(2,2-dimethyl-4-oxo-3-thiet-anyl)-2-(phenylmethyl)-, [1S-[1α,5α,6(R*)]]-	EtOH	214(3.94)	39-0388-80C
[1S-[1α,5α,6(S*)]]-	EtOH	213(4.05)	39-0388-80C
2,6-Piperidinedione, 4-hydroxy-3-(1-isoquinolinyl)-4-methyl-5-(methyl-thio)-	EtOH	220(4.67),263s(3.73), 275(3.78),287s(3.64), 313(3.59),325(3.69)	95-1261-80
2-Propenoic acid, 2-cyano-3-(methyl-thio)-3-[(1-oxo-3-phenyl-2-prop-enyl)amino]-, ethyl ester	MeOH	293(4.21)	48-0434-80
C₁₆H₁₆N₂O₄			
8-Azabicyclo[3.2.1]oct-3-en-2-one, 6(or 7)-(2-acetoxyethyl)-8-(4-pyridinyl)-, N-oxide	EtOH	255(3.80),310(4.20)	150-3337-80
Ethanone, 2-[(4-ethoxyphenyl)amino]-1-(4-nitrophenyl)-	CH₂Cl₂	405(2.69)	83-0315-80
2-Furancarboxylic acid, 5-(acetylami-no)-4-[(phenylmethylene)amino]-, ethyl ester	MeOH	200(4.44),222(4.33), 258(4.30),315(4.30)	73-0135-80
4H-Pyrazolo[5,1-c][1,4]oxazine-3-carb-oxylic acid, 6,7-dihydro-4-methyl-6-oxo-2-phenyl-, ethyl ester	EtOH	212(3.83),234(3.96)	118-0875-80
C₁₆H₁₆N₂O₅			
Ethanone, 2-[(2,5-dimethoxyphenyl)-	CH₂Cl₂	425(2.83)	83-0315-80

Compound	Solvent	$\lambda_{max}(\log \epsilon)$	Ref.
amino]-1-(4-nitrophenyl)- (cont.)			83-0315-80
$C_{16}H_{16}N_2O_5S_2$			
4-Thia-1-azabicyclo[3.2.0]hept-2-ene-2-carboxylic acid, 7-oxo-3-(propyl-thio)-, (4-nitrophenyl)methyl ester	EtOH	262(4.22),339(4.06)	94-3232-80
$C_{16}H_{16}N_2O_6$			
Isoxazole, 3-(4-nitrophenyl)-5-(tetra-hydro-2,2-dimethylfuro[3,4-d]-1,3-dioxol-4-yl)-, [3aS-(3aα,4α,6aα)]-	CHCl$_3$	280(4.26)	33-1181-80
$C_{16}H_{16}N_2O_8$			
Imidazo[1,2-a]pyridine-5,6,7,8-tetra-carboxylic acid, 3-methyl-, tetra-methyl ester (picrate)	EtOH	255(4.56),315s(4.03),354(4.31)	18-3308-80
$C_{16}H_{16}N_2O_8S_2$			
4-Thia-1-azabicyclo[3.2.0]hept-2-ene-2-carboxylic acid, 3-[2-[(methyl-sulfonyl)oxy]ethyl]-7-oxo-, (4-ni-trophenyl)methyl ester, (±)-	CHCl$_3$	266(4.10),318(3.96)	88-0561-80
$C_{16}H_{16}N_4O_2S$			
Acetic acid, [(1,5-diphenylformazanyl)-thio]-, methyl ester	benzene	541(4.14)(changing)	88-0899-80
after five days	benzene	413(4.18),540(3.89)	88-0899-80
	acetone	412(4.09),535(4.02)	88-0899-80
	DMSO	429(3.94),541(4.07)	88-0899-80
	CHCl$_3$	535(4.15)(changing)	88-0899-80
after five days	CHCl$_3$	414(4.29),530(3.77)	88-0899-80
Propanoic acid, 2-[(1,5-diphenylforma-zanyl)thio]-	neutral	423(4.45)	39-0139-80B
	anion	502(4.66)	39-0139-80B
	cation	516(4.68)	39-0139-80B
Propanoic acid, 3-[(1,5-diphenylforma-zanyl)thio]-	neutral	422(4.46)	39-0139-80B
	anion	500(4.68)	39-0139-80B
	cation	517(4.69)	39-0139-80B
$C_{16}H_{16}N_4O_3$			
6H-Pyrrolo[3,4-d]pyrimidine-6-butanoic acid, 2-amino-5,7-dihydro-7-oxo-4-phenyl-	EtOH	249(4.19),268(4.09),348(3.77)	4-1231-80
$C_{16}H_{16}N_4O_4$			
6H-Pyrrolo[3,4-d]pyrimidine-6-propanoic acid, 2-amino-5,7-dihydro-4-(4-meth-oxyphenyl)-7-oxo-	EtOH	234(4.49),295(4.12),349(4.17)	4-1231-80
$C_{16}H_{16}N_5O_6PS$			
Adenosine, 8-(phenylthio)-, cyclic 3',5'-(hydrogen phosphate)	pH 1	282(4.24)	87-0242-80
	pH 11	282(4.19)	87-0242-80
$C_{16}H_{16}O$			
4H-6a,10-Methanocyclohepta[de]naphtha-len-7(10H)-one, 5,6-dihydro-10-meth-yl-	EtOH	232(4.0)	22-0304-80
Methanone, phenyl(2,4,6-trimethylphen-yl)-	hexane	217(4.22),238s(4.23),243(4.24),250s(4.16),272(3.52),280s(3.47),290s(3.26),330s(1.76),340(1.81),353(1.81),368s(1.65)	104-1316-80

Compound	Solvent	$\lambda_{max}(\log \epsilon)$	Ref.
C₁₆H₁₆OS			
Benzenemethanol, α-[1-(phenylthio)-2-propenyl]-	MeOH	258(3.90)	12-1345-80
Benzenemethanol, α-[3-(phenylthio)-2-propenyl]-, (E)-	MeOH	251(4.03),267(4.03)	12-1345-80
(Z)-	MeOH	250(3.81),266(3.81)	12-1345-80
C₁₆H₁₆O₂			
2,5-Cyclohexadiene-1,4-dione, 2-(1,1-dimethylethyl)-6-phenyl-	PrOH	<u>367(3.5)</u>	70-1087-80
1,4a-Ethano-4aH-fluorene-9,11(2H)-dione, 1,3,4,9a-tetrahydro-1-methyl-, (1α,4aα,9aβ)-(±)-	EtOH	248(3.9),295(3.3)	39-2881-80C
C₁₆H₁₆O₂S			
Benzenemethanol, α-[3-(phenylsulfinyl)-2-propenyl]-, (E)-	MeOH	230s(4.82),260s(4.94), 273s(3.64)	12-2635-80
C₁₆H₁₆O₃			
Benzeneacetic acid, (2-methoxyphenyl)-methyl ester	MeCN	220s(3.85),274(3.33)	39-0838-80B
Benzeneacetic acid, (4-methoxyphenyl)-methyl ester	MeCN	226(4.08),274(3.14), 281(3.08)	39-0838-80B
Benzeneacetic acid, 2-methoxy-, 2-methylphenyl ester	EtOH	214(4.00),272(3.38), 278(3.33)	49-0081-80
Benzeneacetic acid, 2-methoxy-, 4-methylphenyl ester	EtOH	219(4.12),272(3.44), 278(3.36)	49-0081-80
Benzeneacetic acid, 4-methoxy-, 2-methylphenyl ester	EtOH	228(3.99),270(3.19), 277(3.22),284(3.15)	49-0081-80
Benzeneacetic acid, 4-methoxy-, 4-methylphenyl ester	EtOH	226(3.62),267(3.17), 272(3.24),282(3.11)	49-0081-80
Benzeneacetic acid, 4-methoxy-, phenylmethyl ester	MeCN	277(3.18),283.5(3.11)	39-0838-80B
1H-Benz[e]inden-1-one, 2,3-dihydro-7,8-dimethoxy-3-methyl-	MeOH	220(4.65),245(4.56), 320(3.98)	25-0466-80
1H-Benz[f]inden-1-one, 2,3-dihydro-6,7-dimethoxy-3-methyl-	MeOH	205(4.34),265(4.86), 310(4.32)	25-0466-80
2H-1-Benzopyran-7-ol, 3,4-dihydro-2-(4-methoxyphenyl)- (broussin)	EtOH	224(4.37),282(3.73), 289s(3.57)	138-1459-80
2H-1-Benzopyran-7-ol, 3,4-dihydro-2-(4-hydroxyphenyl)-8-methyl-	EtOH	225(4.27),279(3.60), 283s(3.59)	102-0889-80
Ethanone, 1-[4-(2-hydroxyethoxy)phenyl]-2-phenyl-	CHCl₃	276(4.33),323(2.52)	73-1826-80
Ethanone, 1-(2-hydroxy-3-methylphenyl)-2-(4-methoxyphenyl)-	EtOH	221(4.29),261(4.05), 338(3.59)	49-0081-80
Ethanone, 1-(2-hydroxy-5-methylphenyl)-2-(2-methoxyphenyl)-	EtOH	224(4.22),257(4.05), 339(3.64)	49-0081-80
Ethanone, 1-(2-hydroxy-5-methylphenyl)-2-(4-methoxyphenyl)-	EtOH	223(4.35),258(4.04), 343(3.64)	49-0081-80
Ethanone, 1-(4-hydroxy-3-methylphenyl)-2-(2-methoxyphenyl)-	EtOH	224(4.18),281(4.21)	49-0081-80
Ethanone, 1-(4-hydroxy-3-methylphenyl)-2-(4-methoxyphenyl)-	EtOH	228(4.19),284(4.20)	49-0081-80
Ethanone, 1-[5-methoxy-2-(phenylmethoxy)phenyl]-	n.s.g.	248(3.79),335(3.59)	44-0501-80
Isolapachol, 6-methyl-	MeOH	214s(4.29),271(4.42), 291s(4.39),296(4.40), 303(4.37),437(3.43)	102-0277-80
Isolapachol, 7-methyl-	MeOH	205(4.23),238(4.22), 267(4.35),282s(4.28), 307s(4.16),442(3.34)	102-0277-80

Compound	Solvent	$\lambda_{max}(\log \epsilon)$	Ref.
$C_{16}H_{16}O_4$			
2H-1-Benzopyran-7-ol, 3,4-dihydro-2-(4-hydroxy-3-methoxyphenyl)-	EtOH	228(3.64),278(3.68)	102-0455-80
	EtOH-NaOH	248(3.82),288(3.66)	102-0455-80
Dibenz[b,d]oxepin-1(2H)-one, 3,4-dihydro-9,10-dimethoxy-	C_6H_{12}	225(4.44),235(4.44), 245(4.46),285(3.88), 330(3.42)	24-3249-80
	MeCN	237(4.29),246s(4.27), 272s(3.85),330(3.35)	24-3249-80
4,11b-Epoxy-11bH-naphtho[1,2-c]-1,2-dioxepin-7(3H)-one, 4,5-dihydro-3,3,6-trimethyl-	$CFCl_3$ at $-30°$	357(1.9)	88-3459-80
Naphtho[1,2-b]furan-4,5-dione, 2,3-dihydro-7-hydroxy-2,3,3,9-tetramethyl- (trypethelone)	MeOH	274(4.54),283(4.55), 316(3.89),516(3.51)	5-0779-80
3H-Naphtho[1,8-bc]furan-3-one, 4-hydroxy-8-methoxy-7-methyl-5-(1-methylethyl)- (anhydroraimondal)	$CHCl_3$	252s(--),270(4.24), 312(3.57),340(3.56), 465(3.70)	102-1735-80
Phenol, 4-(2,3-dihydro-3-methyl-1,4-benzodioxin-2-yl)-2-methoxy-, trans	EtOH	279(3.69),283s(3.65)	39-0775-80C
1-Propanone, 1-(2,4-dihydroxy-6-methoxyphenyl)-3-phenyl- (uvangoletin)	MeOH	220(3.88),289(4.01)	102-2036-80
$C_{16}H_{16}O_4S$			
2-Butenoic acid, 3-(2-furanyl)-4-[(methoxyphenyl)thio]-, methyl ester, (E)-	EtOH	219(3.98),305(4.24)	73-0142-80
$C_{16}H_{16}O_5$			
Auriculin	MeOH	222(5.68),278(5.08), 286s(4.91)	102-1560-80
1-Propanone, 3-(4-methoxyphenyl)-1-(2,4,6-trihydroxyphenyl)-	MeOH	225(4.1),284(4.00)	100-0739-80
$C_{16}H_{16}O_5S$			
2-Butenoic acid, 3-(2-furanyl)-4-[(methylphenyl)sulfonyl]-, methyl ester, (E)-	EtOH	222(4.19),316(4.28)	73-0142-80
$C_{16}H_{16}O_6$			
9,10-Anthracenedione, 3c-ethyl-1,2,3,4-tetrahydro-1r,3t,5,8-tetrahydroxy-	MeOH	215(4.60),278(3.98), 480(3.83),507(3.87), 544(3.64)	24-2976-80
9,10-Anthracenedione, 3t-ethyl-1,2,3,4-tetrahydro-1r,3c,5,8-tetrahydroxy-	MeOH	215(4.60),280(3.97), 480(3.83),508(3.87), 545(3.63)	24-2976-80
2H-Cyclohepta[b]pyrano[2,3-d]pyran-3-carboxylic acid, 5,7,8,9,10,11-hexahydro-2,5-dioxo-, ethyl ester	EtOH	275(3.84),397(4.29)	49-0093-80
2-Naphthalenecarboxylic acid, 4-acetoxy-5,7-dimethoxy-, methyl ester	$CHCl_3$	281(3.80),288(3.78), 300s(3.54),351(3.47), 366(3.47)	12-2531-80
$C_{16}H_{16}S_2$			
Benzene, 1,1'-(1,2-ethenediyl)bis[2-(methylthio)-	EtOH	250(4.34),290(3.90), 335(3.41)	104-0342-80
$C_{16}H_{17}BrN_2O$			
Benzenepropanoic acid, 4-bromo-, 2-methyl-2-phenylhydrazide	n.s.g.	238(4.0),285(3.3)	103-0917-80

Compound	Solvent	$\lambda_{max}(\log \epsilon)$	Ref.
$C_{16}H_{17}BrN_2O_3$ Benzaldehyde, 3,4-dimethoxy-, (2-bromo-3-hydroxyphenyl)methylhydrazone	n.s.g.	320(4.40)	24-2579-80
$C_{16}H_{17}BrN_4O_7$ 9H-Purine, 6-bromo-9-(2,3,5-tri-O-acetyl-β-D-ribofuranosyl)-	MeOH	266.2(3.97)	44-3969-80
$C_{16}H_{17}BrO_2$ 2(3H)-Phenanthrenone, 8-bromo-4,4a,9,10-tetrahydro-5-methoxy-4a-methyl-, (±)-	EtOH	230(4.41),280(3.46)	78-2513-80
$C_{16}H_{17}Br_2NO_2S$ Isoquinoline, 1-[(2,5-dibromo-3-thienyl)methyl]-1,2,3,4-tetrahydro-6,7-dimethoxy-, hydrochloride	MeOH	220(2.71),285(2.31)	2-1028-80
$C_{16}H_{17}Br_2NO_3S$ 3-Thiopheneacetamide, 2,5-dibromo-N-[2-(3,4-dimethoxyphenyl)ethyl]-	MeOH	228(2.81),271(2.43)	2-1028-80
$C_{16}H_{17}ClN_4O$ Piperidine, 1-[[[1-(4-chlorophenyl)-4-formyl-1H-pyrazol-5-yl]imino]-methyl]-	EtOH	258(4.44),333(3.88)	114-0127-80C
$C_{16}H_{17}ClN_4O_2$ Acetamide, N,N'-[5-(4-chlorophenyl)-6-ethyl-2,4-pyrimidinediyl]bis-	EtOH	205s(4.24),225(4.54), 247s(4.30),280s(4.01)	142-0471-80
$C_{16}H_{17}ClN_4O_7$ 9H-Purine, 6-chloro-9-(2,3,5-tri-O-acetyl-β-D-ribofuranosyl)-	MeOH MeOH	205(4.27),250s(--), 264(3.92) 263.5(3.99)	24-2891-80 44-3969-80
$C_{16}H_{17}Cl_2NO_3$ 3-Pyridinecarboxylic acid, 1-[(2,6-dichlorophenyl)methyl]-6-ethoxy-1,6-dihydro-, methyl ester	CH_2Cl_2	255(3.9),315(3.8)	5-1350-80
$C_{16}H_{17}F_3N_2O_9$ Uridine, 5-(trifluoromethyl)-, 2',3',5'-triacetate	MeOH-acid MeOH-base	258(3.96) 260(3.81)	39-2755-80C 39-2755-80C
$C_{16}H_{17}IN_4O_7$ 9H-Purine, 6-iodo-9-(2,3,5-tri-O-acetyl-β-D-ribofuranosyl)-	MeOH	273.5(4.02)	44-3969-80
$C_{16}H_{17}N$ Benzenamine, 2,6-dimethyl-N-(1-phenyl-ethylidene)-, cis trans	CH_2Cl_2 at -70° CH_2Cl_2 at -70°	238(4.44),315(2.90) 244(4.57),322(2.94)	39-1282-80B 39-1282-80B
Benzenamine, N-[1-methyl-2-(4-methyl-phenyl)ethylidene]-	CCl₄	327(2.39)	24-2462-80
Benzenamine, N-[1-(phenylmethyl)prop-ylidene]-	dioxan	284(3.57)	24-2462-80
Benzenamine, 2,4,6-trimethyl-N-(phenyl-methylene)-, cis	$C_6H_{11}Me$ at -100°	222s(--),230(4.20), 250(4.40),278(3.49), 285(3.32),380(2.65)	39-1282-80B

Compound	Solvent	$\lambda_{max}(\log \epsilon)$	Ref.
Benzenamine, 2,4,6-trimethyl-N-(phenyl-methylene)-, trans	$C_6H_{11}Me$ at $-100°$	220s(--),230s(--), 254(4.46),288(3.30), 344(3.42)	39-1282-80B
$C_{16}H_{17}NO$			
Benzenamine, N-[2-(4-methoxyphenyl)-1-methylethylidene]-	dioxan	278(3.66),285(3.62), 297s(3.28)	24-2462-80
Benzo[a]cyclopenta[f]quinolizin-1(2H)-one, 3,5,6,10b,11,12-hexahydro-	MeOH	210(4.06),294(4.57)	135-0956-80
2,3-Benzoxazepine, 1,3,4,5-tetrahydro-3-methyl-1-phenyl-	MeOH	252s(2.83),259(2.85), 263s(2.81),267s(2.86), 272s(2.62)	12-0833-80
3H-Indol-3-one, 1,2,4,5,6,7-hexahydro-1-methyl-2-(phenylmethylene)-, (E)-	CHCl$_3$	273(4.19),319(4.35), 460(3.75)	5-0564-80
(Z)-	CHCl$_3$	298(4.29),438(3.70)	5-0564-80
2(1H)-Naphthalenone, 1-[3-[(1-methyl-ethyl)amino]-2-propenylidene]-	MeOH	315(3.94),360(3.92), 510(4.08)	103-0799-80
	MeOH-NaOMe	310(3.95),363(3.77), 450(4.16)	103-0799-80
	PhCN	317(4.20),357(3.97), 520(2.85)	103-0799-80
	DMSO	320(4.00),358(3.97), 502(3.81),520(3.92)	103-0799-80
	CCl$_4$	315(3.80),355(3.66)	103-0799-80
$C_{16}H_{17}NO_2$			
Benzenepropanoic acid, β-(phenylamino)-, methyl ester	MeOH	213(3.82),248(3.92), 295(3.11)	23-2061-80
Carbamic acid, (1,2-diphenylethyl)-, methyl ester	EtOH	208(4.38),242(2.32), 248(2.46),253(2.58), 258(2.67),264(2.57), 268(2.40)	104-0683-80
2,3-Pyrrolidinedione, 1-(1-methylethyl)-4-(3-phenyl-2-propenylidene)-	EtOH	368(4.48)	145-1135-80
$C_{16}H_{17}NO_3$			
1-Azabicyclo[3.2.0]hept-2-ene-2-carbox-ylic acid, 4,4-dimethyl-7-oxo-, phenylmethyl ester	EtOH	270(3.67)	88-4009-80
Indeno[1,2-d]azepine-3(2H)-carboxylic acid, 1,4,5,10-tetrahydro-10-oxo-, ethyl ester	EtOH	237(4.54),244(4.55), 305(2.95)	18-3232-80
Lycoramine, O-demethyl-	MeOH	228s(3.90),283(3.38)	94-3433-80
2H-1,3-Oxazin-2-one, tetrahydro-4-(2-hydroxy-1-naphthalenyl)-3,6-dimethyl-	EtOH	231(4.81),270(3.26), 280(3.32),292(3.28), 338(3.00)	4-0277-80
2-Propenoic acid, 3-(2-furanyl)-2-[(methylphenylamino)methyl]-, methyl ester, (E)-	EtOH	252(4.42)	73-0906-80
3-Pyridinecarboxylic acid, 1-ethyl-1,4-dihydro-4-oxo-5-phenyl-, ethyl ester	EtOH	230(4.12),270(3.83), 312(3.85)	4-0359-80
1H-Pyrrole-2-carboxylic acid, 4-acetyl-3-methyl-1-phenyl-, ethyl ester	EtOH	238(4.40),272s(3.88)	78-2125-80
1H-Pyrrole-3-carboxylic acid, 4-acetyl-5-methyl-1-phenyl-, ethyl ester	EtOH	234(4.21),270s(3.84)	78-2125-80
1H-Pyrrole-3-carboxylic acid, 4-formyl-2-methyl-1-(phenylmethyl)-, ethyl ester	EtOH	267(3.88),288(3.84)	39-1199-80C

Compound	Solvent	$\lambda_{max}(\log \epsilon)$	Ref.
$C_{16}H_{17}NO_4$			
1H-1-Benzazepine-3,4-dicarboxylic acid, 1,2-dimethyl-, dimethyl ester	EtOH	220(4.06),258(4.32), 292(3.90),370(2.91)	44-0456-80
1H-1-Benzazepine-3,4-dicarboxylic acid, 1,5-dimethyl-, dimethyl ester	EtOH	245(4.23),283(3.86), 312(3.65)	44-0462-80
2-Butenedioic acid, 2-(1,3-dimethyl-1H-indol-2-yl)-, dimethyl ester, (E)-	EtOH	227(4.52),259(3.82), 277(3.76),340(3.86)	44-0462-80
(Z)-	EtOH	228(4.56),296(3.79)	44-0462-80
3H-Cyclobut[b]indole-1,2-dicarboxylic acid, 2a,7b-dihydro-3,7b-dimethyl-, dimethyl ester	EtOH	251(3.61),302(3.14), 435(2.97)	44-0462-80
8-Indolizinecarboxylic acid, 1,2,3,5-6,7-hexahydro-6-(4-methoxyphenyl)-7-oxo-	EtOH and EtOH-acid	232(4.19),241(4.23), 285s(3.84),307(4.09)	44-1713-80
	EtOH-base	226(4.20),241s(3.92), 284s(3.56),322(4.12)	44-1713-80
Piperidine, 1-[(7-methoxy-2-oxo-2H-1-benzopyran-4-yl)carbonyl]-	EtOH	330(4.18)	95-0289-80
1H-Pyrrole-2-acetic acid, 3-carboxy-1-methyl-4-(2-phenylethyl)-	MeOH	243(3.82),262(3.77)	4-1081-80
$C_{16}H_{17}NO_5$			
1H-Pyrrole-2,4-dicarboxylic acid, 3-hy-droxy-1-phenyl-, diethyl ester	EtOH	230(4.44),262(4.07)	78-2125-80
	EtOH-base	233(4.41),250s(4.26), 283s(3.87),330(3.97)	78-2125-80
1-Pyrrolidinebutanoic acid, 4-[(4-meth-oxyphenyl)methylene]-2,3-dioxo-	EtOH	246(3.92),370(4.41)	4-1231-80
$C_{16}H_{17}N_2$			
Pyridinium, 1-[3-(1H-indol-3-yl)prop-yl]-, chloride	MeOH	275(4.34),290(3.79), 550(2.91)	103-0921-80
Pyridinium, 1-[2-(2-methyl-1H-indol-3-yl)ethyl]-, bromide	MeOH	226(4.34),276(4.04), 470(3.06)	103-0921-80
Pyridinium, 1-[2-(7-methyl-1H-indol-3-yl)ethyl]-, bromide	MeOH	232(4.47),280(4.08), 332(3.31),558(3.01)	103-0921-80
$C_{16}H_{17}N_2O$			
Pyridinium, 1-[2-(5-methoxy-1H-indol-3-yl)ethyl]-, bromide	MeOH	234(4.01),281(3.85), 314(3.64),585(3.17)	103-0921-80
$C_{16}H_{17}N_3$			
Acetaldehyde, [(4-methylphenyl)imino]-, methylphenylhydrazone	hexane	302(3.99),351(4.51)	65-2072-80
	EtOH	299(3.76),364(4.54)	65-2072-80
$C_{16}H_{17}N_3O$			
4H-Pyrimido[6,1-a]isoquinolin-4-one, 2-(diethylamino)-	EtOH	224s(4.49),245(4.24), 281s(4.34),290(4.51), 325s(3.83),342(3.91), 360(4.04),380(4.21), 402(4.11)	95-1261-80
$C_{16}H_{17}N_3O_2$			
Piperidine, 1-[2-(1H-imidazol-2-yl-carbonyl)benzoyl]-	EtOH	298(4.16)	103-0247-80
	dioxan	299(4.14)	103-0247-80
	CHCl$_3$	303(4.16)	103-0247-80
Pyrido[2,3-d]pyrimidin-2(1H)-one, 3,4-dihydro-4-(2-hydroxyphenyl)-1,3,4-trimethyl-	MeOH	240(4.21),271(3.96), 283(3.90),324(3.85)	44-1918-80
2,4(1H,3H)-Pyrimidinedione, 5-(1,3-di-methyl-1H-indol-2-yl)-1,3-dimethyl-	MeCN	230(4.05),284(3.60), 326(3.16)	35-7535-80

Compound	Solvent	$\lambda_{max}(\log \epsilon)$	Ref.
$C_{16}H_{17}N_3O_5S$			
Cytidine, 2',3'-didehydro-2',3'-dide-oxy-, 5'-(4-methylbenzenesulfonate)	MeOH	226(4.34),270(3.92)	136-0067-80A
$C_{16}H_{17}N_3O_7$			
D-Ribitol, 1-deoxy-1-(3,4-dihydro-8-hy-droxy-2,4-dioxopyrimido[4,5-b]quino-lin-10(2H)-yl)-	pH 13	232(4.71),287(4.01), 419(4.71)	4-1709-80
$C_{16}H_{17}N_3S$			
3(2H)-Benzothiazolepropanamine, 2-(phenylimino)-	EtOH	221(4.65),298(4.19)	103-0169-80
1-Pyrazolidinecarbothioamide, N,2-di-phenyl-	EtOH	237(4.25),257(4.30)	103-0169-80
1-Pyrazolidinecarbothioamide, 2,3-di-phenyl-	EtOH	251(4.30)	103-0169-80
$C_{16}H_{17}N_5$			
4-Pyrimidinamine, 2-(3,5-dimethyl-1H-pyrazol-1-yl)-6-methyl-N-phenyl-	EtOH	<u>256(4.5)</u>,285s(4.4)	103-0868-80
$C_{16}H_{17}N_5O_4$			
1-Propanone, 2-amino-2-methyl-1-phenyl-, 2,4-dinitrophenylhydrazone, (E)-	EtOH	198(4.3),222(4.2), 254(4.1),357(4.4)	5-1016-80
4(1H)-Pteridinone, 6-(1,2-dihydroxy-propyl)-2-[(4-methoxyphenyl)amino]-, [S-(R*,S*)]-	pH -1.0	228(4.26),256(4.20), 325(3.94)	18-2344-80
	pH 4.5	236(4.16),287(4.37), 354(3.81)	18-2344-80
	pH 9.5	265s(4.28),287(4.38), 377(3.93)	18-2344-80
$C_{16}H_{17}N_5O_5$			
4(1H)-Pteridinone, 2-[(4-methoxyphen-yl)amino]-6-(1,2,3-trihydroxypropyl)-, D-erythro-	pH -1.0	228(4.27),256(4.20), 325(3.94)	18-2344-80
	pH 4.5	233(4.17),287(4.35), 353(3.79)	18-2344-80
	pH 9.5	265s(4.25),287(4.35), 377(3.90)	18-2344-80
L-isomer	pH -1.0	228(4.26),256(4.19), 325(3.92)	18-2344-80
	pH 4.5	235(4.16),287(4.34), 354(3.78)	18-2344-80
	pH 9.5	264s(4.26),287(4.35), 377(3.90)	18-2344-80
$C_{16}H_{17}N_6O_6PS$			
Adenosine, 8-[(3-pyridinylmethyl)thio]-, cyclic 3',5'-(hydrogen phosphate)	pH 1 pH 11	276(4.24) 283(4.15)	87-0242-80 87-0242-80
$C_{16}H_{17}OS$			
1-Benzothiopyrylium, 5,6,7,8-tetra-hydro-2-(4-methoxyphenyl)-, per-chlorate	CH_2Cl_2	264(4.11),440(4.33)	104-0170-80
$C_{16}H_{18}$			
1H-Fluorene, 2,4a-dihydro-4,4a,9-tri-methyl-, (+)-	EtOH	265(4.00),287s(3.19)	39-1909-80C
1H-Fluorene, 2,3,4,4a-tetrahydro-4a,9-dimethyl-4-methylene-, (+)-	EtOH	268(4.01),287s(3.41), 295(2.93)	39-1909-80C

Compound	Solvent	$\lambda_{max}(\log \epsilon)$	Ref.
$C_{16}H_{18}BrN_7$			
1H-Pyrazol-5-amine, 4-[(4-bromo-3-methyl-1-phenyl-1H-pyrazol-5-yl)azo]-1-ethyl-3-methyl-	MeOH	390(4.52),420(4.53)	103-1160-80
$C_{16}H_{18}Br_2N_2O_3$			
Benzaldehyde, 3,4-dimethoxy-, (2,6-dibromo-3-oxo-1-cyclohexen-1-yl)methylhydrazone	n.s.g.	284(4.09),378(4.51)	24-2579-80
$C_{16}H_{18}Br_2O_4$			
α-D-xylo-Hex-5-enofuranose, 6,6-dibromo-5,6-dideoxy-1,2-O-(1-methylethylidene)-3-O-(phenylmethyl)-	EtOH	215(3.80)	33-1181-80
$C_{16}H_{18}ClNO_2$			
2H-Pyran-2-one, 3-chloro-4-(diethylamino)-5-methyl-6-phenyl-	EtOH	261(4.05),318(4.09)	4-1201-80
2H-Pyran-2-one, 3-chloro-6-(1,1-dimethylethyl)-4-(methylphenylamino)-	EtOH	240(4.07),251(4.07), 278(3.99),328(4.03)	4-0507-80
$C_{16}H_{18}ClNO_5S$			
Benzenepropanoic acid, 2-[(4-amino-2-carboxyphenyl)thio]-, hydrochloride, hydrate	MeOH	267(4.15),325(3.24)	73-0491-80
$C_{16}H_{18}ClN_5$			
4H-[1,2,4]Triazolo[4,3-a][1,4]benzodiazepine, 8-chloro-1-methyl-6-piperidino-	EtOH	213(4.62),237s(4.16), 287s(3.53),294(3.54)	87-0873-80
6H-[1,2,4]Triazolo[4,3-a][1,4]benzodiazepine, 8-chloro-1-methyl-4-piperidino-	EtOH	221s(4.26),230s(4.24), 258s(3.87),264(3.83), 267s(3.83),273(3.81), 276(3.81),283(3.80)	87-0873-80
$C_{16}H_{18}Cl_2N_6O_3$			
1,2-Cyclopentanediol, 3-[[2-amino-6-chloro-5-[(4-chlorophenyl)azo]-4-pyrimidinyl]amino]-5-(hydroxymethyl)-, (1α,2β,3β,5β)-(±)-	pH 1	228(4.38),266(--), 372(4.44)	36-1019-80
	H₂O	226(4.24),278(4.06), 386(4.47)	36-1019-80
	pH 13	267(4.14),386(4.48)	36-1019-80
$C_{16}H_{18}Cl_2O_4$			
α-D-xylo-Hex-5-enofuranose, 6,6-dichloro-5,6-dideoxy-1,2-O-(1-methylethylidene)-3-O-(phenylmethyl)-	EtOH	208(4.08)	33-1644-80
$C_{16}H_{18}F_3N_3O_8$			
Cytidine, 5-(trifluoromethyl)-, 2',3',5'-triacetate	MeOH	260(3.83)	39-2755-80C
	MeOH-acid	277(4.06)	39-2755-80C
	MeOH-base	275(3.85)	39-2755-80C
2(1H)-Pyrimidinone, 4-amino-1-(2,3,5-tri-O-acetyl-β-D-arabinofuranosyl)-5-(trifluoromethyl)-	MeOH	263(3.90)	39-2755-80C
	MeOH-acid	278(4.10)	39-2755-80C
	MeOH-base	277(3.93)	39-2755-80C
$C_{16}H_{18}I_2N$			
Benzenemethanaminium, 2-iodo-N-[(2-iodophenyl)methyl]-N,N-dimethyl-, bromide	MeOH	269(3.25),275(3.33), 282(3.30)	73-0504-80

Compound	Solvent	$\lambda_{max}(\log \epsilon)$	Ref.
$C_{16}H_{18}N_2$			
Pyridine, 5-ethenyl-2-methyl-, dimer	MeOH	252(4.0),260(4.0), 266(4.0)	103-0945-80
Quinoline, 5,6,7,8-tetrahydro-6,7-di-methyl-5-(2-pyridinyl)-	MeOH	262(3.9),268(3.8)	103-0945-80
$C_{16}H_{18}N_2O$			
Benzenamine, 4-[[(4-methoxyphenyl)imi-no]methyl]-N,N-dimethyl-, mono(tri-chloroacetate)	benzene	400(2.40)	65-1870-80
bis(trichloroacetate)	benzene	380(3.23)	65-1870-80
1,4-Benzenediamine, N'-[(4-methoxyphen-yl)methylene]-N,N-dimethyl-, bis(tri-chloroacetate)	benzene	340(2.70),450(2.54)	65-1870-80
Benzenepropanoic acid, 2-methyl-2-phen-ylhydrazide	n.s.g.	240(4.1),285(3.3)	103-0917-80
13H-Isoquino[2,1-a][1,8]naphthyridin-13-one, 1,2,3,4,6,7,11b,12-octahydro-	EtOH	238(4.00),309(4.28)	94-0220-80
Isoquino[1,2-f]pyrido[2,1-b]pyrimidin-13-one, 1,2,3,4,4a,6,7,13-octahydro-	EtOH	252(4.36),366(3.91)	94-0220-80
Pyridine, 3-(4,5-dihydro-4,4-dimethyl-2-oxazolyl)-1,4-dihydro-4-phenyl-	EtOH	332(3.383)	39-2070-80C
$C_{16}H_{18}N_2OS$			
2(1H)-Quinazolinethione, 3-acetyl-3,4,5,6,7,8-hexahydro-4-phenyl-	EtOH	276(3.74),332(4.06)	114-0147-80B
$C_{16}H_{18}N_2O_2$			
Acetamide, N-[2,6-dimethyl-4-oxo-1-(phenylamino)-2,5-cyclohexadien-1-yl]-	MeCN	214s(4.09),244(4.43), 283(3.71)	87-1153-80
1H-Azepino[5,4,3-cd]indole-4-carboxylic acid, 3,4,5,6-tetrahydro-6-(2-methyl-1-propenyl)- (clavicipitic acid)	EtOH	225(4.58),288(3.81)	44-1117-80
3H-Indol-3-one, 2-(1,3,4,5,6,7-hexa-hydro-3-oxo-2H-indol-2-ylidene)-1,2,4,5,6,7-hexahydro-	gas	483(--)	5-2039-80
	C_6H_{12}	226(4.37),305(4.22), 505(3.92)	5-2039-80
	benzene	514(3.89)	5-2039-80
	H_2O	321(--),530(--)	5-0564-80
	MeOH	317(4.60),524(4.05)	5-0564-80
	EtOH	527(3.88)	5-2039-80
	HCOOH	416(4.76),520(2.67)	5-2039-80
	$CHCl_3$	316(4.38),520(4.11)	5-0564-80
	$CHCl_3$	520(3.89)	5-2039-80
	CCl_4	310(--),506(--)	5-0564-80
	DMSO	528(3.87)	5-2039-80
hydrochloride	$CHCl_3$	277(4.25),343(4.42), 536(3.78)	5-0564-80
2(1H)-Quinazolinone, 3-acetyl-3,4,5,6-7,8-hexahydro-4-phenyl-	EtOH	263(3.69)	114-0147-80B
$C_{16}H_{18}N_2O_2S$			
4(5H)-Thiazolone, 5-[(2-methoxyphenyl)-methylene]-2-piperidino-	MeOH	242(3.89),327(4.37)	48-0835-80
4(5H)-Thiazolone, 5-[(3-methoxyphenyl)-methylene]-2-piperidino-	MeOH	248s(3.85),254(3.88), 298(4.32)	48-0835-80
$C_{16}H_{18}N_2O_3$			
Benzaldehyde, 3,4-dimethoxy-, (3-hy-droxyphenyl)methylhydrazone	n.s.g.	242(4.18),341(4.44)	24-2579-80

Compound	Solvent	$\lambda_{max}(\log \epsilon)$	Ref.
$C_{16}H_{18}N_2O_4$			
4,7-Etheno-3H-benzo[3,4]cyclobuta[1,2-c]pyrazole-5,6-dicarboxylic acid, 3a,3b,4,7,7a,7b-hexahydro-3-methyl-, $(3\alpha,3a\alpha,3b\beta,4\alpha,7\alpha,7a\beta,7b\alpha)-$	EtOH	328(2.33)	142-1115-80
2,4(1H,3H)-Pyrimidinedione, 1-[5-(benzoyloxy)pentyl]-	MeOH	225(4.43),264(4.32)	78-0865-80
$C_{16}H_{18}N_4$			
Imidazo[5,1-f][1,2,4]triazine, 5-methyl-7-(2-methylpropyl)-2-phenyl-	EtOH	228(4.15),267(4.53), 275s(4.47),280(3.13)	39-1139-80C
1,2-Phenazinediamine, N-(1,1-dimethylethyl)-	MeOH	384(3.75),535(3.34)	32-0135-80
$C_{16}H_{18}N_4O$			
Imidazo[5,1-f][1,2,4]triazin-4(1H)-one, 5-methyl-7-(2-methylpropyl)-2-phenyl-	EtOH	243(4.38),264s(4.30)	39-1139-80C
Imidazo[5,1-f][1,2,4]triazin-4(1H)-one, 5-methyl-2-(phenylmethyl)-7-propyl-	EtOH	221(4.40),254(4.00), 265s(3.86)	39-1139-80C
Piperidine, 1-[[(4-formyl-1-phenyl-1H-pyrazol-5-yl)imino]methyl]-	EtOH	252(4.39),330(3.85)	114-0127-80C
$C_{16}H_{18}N_4O_2$			
Benzenamine, N,N-diethyl-4-[(4-nitrophenyl)azo]-	toluene	476(4.54)	5-2055-80
-dication	20% MeOH	495(4.56)	39-0937-80B
	H_2SO_4	411(4.54)	39-0937-80B
1-Propanone, 2-amino-2-methyl-1-(3-nitrophenyl)-, phenylhydrazone, monohydrochloride, (E)-	EtOH	201(4.5),267(4.3), 298(4.00)	5-1016-80
1-Propanone, 2-amino-2-methyl-1-phenyl-, (4-nitrophenyl)hydrazone, monohydrochloride, (E)-	EtOH	199(4.5),240(3.7), 379(4.4)	5-1016-80
Pyrimido[4,5-b]quinoline-2,4(3H,10H)-dione, 8-(dimethylamino)-3,7,10-trimethyl-	6M HCl	256(4.62),325(4.22), 358(4.00),371s(3.91)	83-0937-80
	pH 1	246(4.57),309(4.00), 448(4.24)	83-0937-80
	pH 5	251(4.62),270s(4.40), 305s(3.70),432(4.51)	83-0937-80
$C_{16}H_{18}N_4O_3S$			
4(5H)-Thiazolone, 5-[(4-nitrophenyl)methylene]-2-[(1-piperidinylmethyl)amino]-	EtOH	224(4.03),294(4.11), 355(4.28)	103-0718-80
$C_{16}H_{18}N_4O_7$			
9H-Purine, 9-(2,3,5-tri-O-acetyl-β-D-ribofuranosyl)-	MeOH	262.0(3.88)	44-3969-80
$C_{16}H_{18}N_4S$			
Formazan, 1,5-bis(2-methylphenyl)-3-(methylthio)-	$CHCl_3$	420(4.47)(changing)	77-0763-80
Formazan, 1,5-bis(4-methylphenyl)-3-(methylthio)-	$CHCl_3$	550(4.15)(changing)	77-0763-80
$C_{16}H_{18}O$			
Ethanone, 1-(2,3,4,9-tetrahydro-1-methyl-1H-fluoren-1-yl)-	EtOH	260(4.10)	44-1081-80
$C_{16}H_{18}OS$			
Ethanone, 1-bicyclo[2.2.1]hept-5-en-2-yl-2-[(phenylmethyl)thio]-	C_6H_{12} benzene	307(2.40) 306(2.39)	44-1286-80 44-1286-80

Compound	Solvent	$\lambda_{max}(\log \epsilon)$	Ref.
$C_{16}H_{18}O_2$			
1H-Naphtho[2,1-b]pyran, 3-ethoxy-2,3-dihydro-3-methyl-	MeOH	231(4.92),285s(3.46), 267(3.65),278(3.74), 289(3.61),305s(2.99), 319(3.27),332(3.38)	39-1233-80C
2-Phenanthrenecarboxylic acid, 1,2,3,4-9,10-hexahydro-2-methyl-	EtOH	260(4.26)	44-1081-80
2(3H)-Phenanthrenone, 4,4a,9,10-tetrahydro-5-methoxy-4a-methyl-	EtOH	228(4.30),272(3.43)	78-2513-80
2-Propenoic acid, 3-(1,3-dimethyl-1H-inden-1-yl)-, ethyl ester, (E)-	EtOH	253(3.99),285s(3.56), 294s(3.39)	39-0714-80C
2-Propenoic acid, 3-(1,3-dimethyl-1H-inden-2-yl)-, ethyl ester, (E)-	EtOH	237s(3.73),246(3.88), 254(3.83),338(4.42)	39-0714-80C
Tetracyclo[6.5.0.0^{9,13}.0^{10,12}]trideca-2,4,6-triene-11-carboxylic acid, ethyl ester	C_6H_{12}	250(3.23)	89-0207-80
$C_{16}H_{18}O_3$			
2H-1-Benzopyran-2-one, 3-acetyl-4-(2,2-dimethylpropyl)-	EtOH	290(3.93),320s(3.76)	39-2937-80C
Cyclopropa[c][1]benzopyran-2(1H)-one, 1a-acetyl-1-(1,1-dimethylethyl)-1a,7b-dihydro-, (1R*,1aR*,7bR*)-	EtOH	226(3.45),269(2.96), 276(2.92)	39-2937-80C
1H-Fluorene-1-carboxylic acid, 2,3,4,9-tetrahydro-7-methoxy-1-methyl-	EtOH	266(4.3)	39-0804-80C
Phenol, 2-[3-(4-hydroxyphenyl)propyl]-5-methoxy-	EtOH	225(4.24),280(3.70), 287s(3.63)	138-0339-80
Phenol, 4-[3-(4-hydroxyphenyl)propyl]-3-methoxy- (broussonin B)	EtOH	225(4.21),280(3.63), 287s(3.61)	138-0339-80
$C_{16}H_{18}O_4$			
α-D-xylo-Hexofuranose, 5,5,6,6-tetradehydro-5,6-dideoxy-1,2-O-(1-methylethylidene)-3-O-(phenylmethyl)-	EtOH	215(3.33),253(2.40)	33-1181-80
$C_{16}H_{18}O_5$			
2H-1-Benzopyran-2-one, 6-[(3,3-dimethyloxiranyl)methoxymethyl]-7-methoxy-	EtOH	242s(3.79),252s(3.64), 292(3.89),325(4.11)	12-0395-80
4H-1-Benzopyran-4-one, 5-hydroxy-2-(4-hydroxycyclohexyl)-7-methoxy-	EtOH	230(4.09),248(4.16), 255s(4.13),290(3.76), 320s(3.51)	88-1227-80
1-Naphthalenecarboxaldehyde, 2,3,8-trihydroxy-7-methoxy-6-methyl-4-(1-methylethyl)- (raimondal)	EtOH	236(4.62),276(4.11), 288s(--),298s(--), 387(3.96)	102-1735-80
	CHCl₃	270s(--),278(4.10), 287s(--),376(4.00)	102-1735-80
1,2-Naphthalenedicarboxylic acid, 5,6,7,8-tetrahydro-6,6-dimethyl-8-oxo-, dimethyl ester	MeCN	225(4.20),243s(3.99), 291(2.91),302(2.90)	24-3249-80
1,2-Naphthalenedicarboxylic acid, 5,6,7,8-tetrahydro-7,7-dimethyl-5-oxo-, dimethyl ester	MeCN	205(4.57),254(4.29), 260s(4.23),302(3.54), 310s(3.48)	24-3249-80
$C_{16}H_{18}O_5W$			
Tungsten, [2,3-bis(1,1-dimethylethyl)-2-cyclopropen-1-ylidene]pentacarbonyl-, (OC-6-21)-	heptane	240(4.86),288(3.91), 331(4.00)	101-0087-80I
$C_{16}H_{18}O_6$			
2H-1-Benzopyran-2-one, 8-(3-hydroxy-	EtOH	207(4.30),218(4.30),	94-1782-80

Compound	Solvent	$\lambda_{max}(\log \epsilon)$	Ref.
3-methyl-1-oxobutyl)-5,7-dimethoxy-1,2-Naphthalenedicarboxylic acid, 5,6,7,8-tetrahydro-3-hydroxy-7,7-dimethyl-5-oxo-, dimethyl ester	MeCN	259(3.85),321(4.26) 220(4.26),258(4.02), 347(3.58)	94-1782-80 24-3249-80
1,2-Naphthalenedicarboxylic acid, 5,6,7,8-tetrahydro-4-hydroxy-6,6-dimethyl-8-oxo-, dimethyl ester	MeCN	232(4.52),318(3.46)	24-3249-80
Spiro[1,3-benzodioxole-2,1'-cyclohexane]-5,6-diol, diacetate	EtOH	238(3.65),293(3.90)	12-0527-80
Spiro[1,3-dioxolane-2,1'(2'H)-naphthalene]-7',8'-dicarboxylic acid, 3',4'-dihydro-	MeCN	202(4.33),240(3.88), 275s(2.79),286s(2.59)	24-3249-80
$C_{16}H_{18}O_7$			
Cyclohept[cd]isobenzofuran-3-carboxylic acid, 2,6,7,8,9,9a-hexahydro-5-hydroxy-5a-(2-hydroxyethoxy)-2-oxo-, methyl ester	MeCN	221s(4.30),229(4.35), 272(3.93),304s(3.59), 334s(3.21)	24-1584-80
Spiro[1-benzoxepin-6(7H),2'-[1,3]dioxolane]-4,5-dicarboxylic acid, 8,9-dihydro-, dimethyl ester	C_6H_{12}	205(4.17),270(3.38), 312(3.27)	24-3249-80
Spiro[1,3-dioxolane-2,8'(5'H)-[2H-2,4a]epoxynaphthalene]-3',4'-dicarboxylic acid, 6',7'-dihydro-, dimethyl ester	MeCN	205(3.86),230s(3.47), 285(2.84)	24-3249-80
$C_{16}H_{18}O_9$			
Scopoletin 7-O-β-D-glucopyranoside	EtOH	229(3.87),280(3.28), 339(2.78)	105-0125-80
$C_{16}H_{18}S_2$			
Benzene, 1,1'-(1,2-ethanediyl)bis[2-(methylthio)-	EtOH	252(4.25),280s(3.44)	104-0342-80
$C_{16}H_{18}S_3$			
1-Propanethione, 2-(hexahydro-1,3-benzodithiol-2-ylidene)-1-phenyl-, cis	MeOH	255(4.17),320(3.96), 431(4.41),580(2.57)	104-0395-80
1-Propanethione, 1-phenyl-2-(1,6,6-trimethyl-2,4-dithiabicyclo[3.1.0]hex-3-ylidene)-	MeOH	255(4.05),319(3.75), 432(4.25),588(2.37)	104-0395-80
$C_{16}H_{19}BrNO_5$			
Oxazolium, 5-(2-acetoxy-1,1-dimethylethyl)-2-[2-(5-bromo-2-furanyl)ethenyl]-4,5-dihydro-3-methyl-4-oxo-, perchlorate	HOAc	418(4.05)	103-0023-80
$C_{16}H_{19}BrN_2O_3$			
Benzaldehyde, 3,4-dimethoxy-, (6-bromo-3-oxo-1-cyclohexen-1-yl)methylhydrazone	n.s.g.	230s(4.07),275(3.86), 377(4.63)	24-2579-80
$C_{16}H_{19}BrO_4$			
2H-1-Benzopyran-2-one, 6-(2-bromo-3-methoxy-3-methylbutyl)-7-methoxy-	EtOH	222(4.22),242(3.73), 252(3.60),294(3.84), 327(4.11)	12-0395-80
$C_{16}H_{19}INO_5$			
Oxazolium, 5-(2-acetoxy-1,1-dimethylethyl)-4,5-dihydro-2-[2-(5-iodo-2-	HOAc	430(4.18)	103-0023-80

Compound	Solvent	λ_{max}(log ϵ)	Ref.
furanyl)ethenyl]-3-methyl-4-oxo-, perchlorate (cont.)			103-0023-80
C₁₆H₁₉NO			
2-Cyclohexen-1-one, 3-(4-methylphenyl)-2-(2-propenylamino)-	ether	240(3.91),338(3.86)	78-1585-80
1(2H)-Naphthalenone, 2-[3-(dimethyl-amino)-2-methyl-2-propenylidene]-3,4-dihydro-	hexane	230(3.89),245(3.79), 253(3.76),345(4.09)	70-1643-80
	MeOH	235(4.03),242(3.98), 250(3.88),330(4.15), 460(2.94)	70-1643-80
	10% MeOH	235(3.73),242(3.71), 250(3.67),330(3.99), 460(3.60)	70-1643-80
	EtOH	240s(3.75),335(4.00), 455(3.68)	70-1643-80
	MeCN	250(3.85),344(4.02), 438(3.68)	70-1643-80
	CHCl₃	350(3.99),440(3.62)	70-1643-80
C₁₆H₁₉NO₂			
Methanone, (1,6-dihydro-6-methoxy-1-propyl-3-pyridinyl)phenyl-	CH₂Cl₂	298(3.8),326(3.8)	5-1350-80
C₁₆H₁₉NO₃			
2H-Benzo[a]quinolizin-2-one, 1,6,7,11b-tetrahydro-9,10-dimethoxy-4-methyl-	MeOH	228(4.02),293(3.90), 321(4.20)	135-0956-80
2H-1,3-Benzoxazin-2-one, 3,4-dihydro-3-methyl-4-(3-methyl-2-oxocyclohexyl)-	EtOH	266(2.99),272(2.95)	4-0277-80
2,4-Pentadienoic acid, 2-acetyl-6-(di-methylamino)-4-phenyl-, methyl ester	hexane	205(4.54),235(4.37), 260s(4.19),325(4.15)	70-1643-80
	H₂O	400(4.73)	70-1643-80
	MeOH	205(4.40),235(4.19), 262s(4.08),333(3.98), 385(4.00)	70-1643-80
	67% MeOH	392(4.55)	70-1643-80
	50% MeOH	392(4.64)	70-1643-80
	10% MeOH	290(3.32),396(4.66)	70-1643-80
	CHCl₃	330(3.94),400(2.89)	70-1643-80
C₁₆H₁₉NO₃S			
7-Azabicyclo[4.2.0]octan-5-one, 8-eth-enyl-7-[(4-methylphenyl)sulfonyl]-	EtOH	296s(1.82)	78-1585-80
7-Azabicyclo[4.2.0]oct-5-en-1-ol, 8-ethenyl-7-[(4-methylphenyl)sulfonyl]-	EtOH	222(4.09),246s(3.63)	78-1585-80
Benzenesulfonamide, 4-methyl-N-(6-oxo-1-cyclohexen-1-yl)-N-2-propenyl-	EtOH	228(4.19),314(2.30)	78-1585-80
C₁₆H₁₉NO₄S			
1H-Cyclopenta[5,6]thiopyrano[4,3-b]ind-ol-3-ol, 2,3,3a,5,10,10b-hexahydro-8-methoxy-3a-methyl-, 4,4-dioxide, (3α,3aβ,10bβ)-(±)-	MeOH	223(4.30),295(3.78), 327(3.14)	13-0599-80A
C₁₆H₁₉NO₅			
5(2H)-Isoxazolone, 2-(1,1-dimethyl-3-oxobutyl)-3-hydroxy-4-(4-meth-oxyphenyl)-	MeOH neutral anion	250(4.06),278(4.23) 254(4.36) 245(4.30),271s(--)	4-0299-80 4-0299-80 4-0299-80
C₁₆H₁₉NO₆			
2H-1,3-Benzoxaz ine -4-acetic acid,	EtOH	225(4.06),251(3.88),	4-0519-80

Compound	Solvent	$\lambda_{max}(\log \epsilon)$	Ref.
α-acetyl-3,4-dihydro-8-methoxy-3-methyl-2-oxo-, ethyl ester (cont.)		281(3.51)	4-0519-80
2H-1,3-Benzoxazine-4-acetic acid, 3,4-dihydro-α-(1-hydroxyethylidene)-8-methoxy-3-methyl-2-oxo-, ethyl ester	EtOH	225s(4.06),252(3.87), 280s(3.54)	4-0519-80
$C_{16}H_{19}NO_6S$			
Pyrrolo[2,1-b]thiazole-2,6,7-tricarboxylic acid, 3-methyl-, triethyl ester	EtOH	226(4.19),257s(4.42), 265(4.49),292s(3.92), 316(3.67)	18-3308-80
$C_{16}H_{19}NS$			
2H-Azeto[2,1-a]isoquinoline-2-thione, 1-(1,1-dimethyl-2-propenyl)-1,4,5,9b-tetrahydro-	CHCl$_3$	273(4.2),337(1.9)	24-3024-80
$C_{16}H_{19}NS_2$			
2H-Thiopyran-2-thione, 6-(diethylamino)-5-methyl-3-phenyl-	C$_6$H$_{12}$	232(4.34),252s(4.16), 327(3.92),478(3.85)	22-0530-80
	EtOH	230(4.32),252s(4.21), 326(3.93),503(4.06)	22-0530-80
2H-Thiopyran-2-thione, 6-(diethylamino)-5-methyl-4-phenyl-	C$_6$H$_{12}$	262(4.14),280(4.17), 322(4.01),473(3.85)	22-0539-80
	EtOH	241(3.86),293(3.95), 317s(3.84),500(3.80)	22-0539-80
4H-Thiopyran-4-thione, 2-(diethylamino)-3-methyl-6-phenyl-	C$_6$H$_{12}$	231(4.42),271(4.22), 329(4.39),466(3.89)	22-0539-80
	EtOH	232(4.63),287(4.52), 319(4.65),354(4.37), 443(4.36)	22-0539-80
$C_{16}H_{19}NSe$			
2H-Azeto[2,1-a]isoquinoline-2-selone, 1-(1,1-dimethyl-2-propenyl)-1,4,5,9b-tetrahydro-	MeCN	299(4.2),383(2.3)	88-4251-80
$C_{16}H_{19}N_2O_5PS$			
3(2H)-Pyridazinone, 5-[(5,5-dimethyl-1,3,2-dioxaphosphorinan-2-yl)oxy]-4-methoxy-2-phenyl-, P-sulfide	MeOH	216(4.02),296(3.56)	73-2343-80
$C_{16}H_{19}N_2O_7$			
Oxazolium, 5-(2-acetoxy-1,1-dimethylethyl)-4,5-dihydro-3-methyl-2-[2-(5-nitro-2-furanyl)ethenyl]-4-oxo-, perchlorate	HOAc	350(3.52)	103-0023-80
$C_{16}H_{19}N_3$			
Benzenamine, N,N-diethyl-4-(phenylazo)-	20% MeOH	423(4.49)	39-0937-80B
dication	H$_2$SO$_4$	416(4.70)	39-0937-80B
1-Propanone, 2-amino-2-methyl-1-phenyl-, phenylhydrazone, monohydrochloride, (E)-	EtOH	199(4.5),271(4.2), 298(4.0)	5-1016-80
$C_{16}H_{19}N_3O$			
1H-1,2,4-Triazole, 1-[(2-phenylcyclohexyl)acetyl]-, trans	THF	217(4.03),280s(3.78)	33-0588-80
$C_{16}H_{19}N_3OS$			
4(5H)-Thiazolone, 5-(phenylmethylene)-2-[(1-piperidinylmethylene)amino]-	EtOH	231(4.06),286(4.10), 331(4.31)	103-0718-80

Compound	Solvent	$\lambda_{max}(\log \epsilon)$	Ref.
$C_{16}H_{19}N_3O_4$			
Benzenamine, 4-[(3,5-dimethoxyphenyl)-azo]-3,5-dimethoxy-, monohydrochloride	EtOH	455(4.40)	12-0343-80
1H-1,2,4-Triazolium, 4-[2-ethoxy-1-(ethoxycarbonyl)-2-oxoethyl]-1-(phenylmethyl)-, hydroxide, inner salt	MeOH	248(4.13)	80-0407-80
$C_{16}H_{19}N_3O_8$			
Carbamic acid, [3-acetoxy-2-(acetoxymethyl)-2,3,3a,7a-tetrahydro-6H-furo[2',3':4,5]oxazolo[3,2-a]pyrimidin-6-ylidene]-, ethyl ester, [2R-(2α,3β,3aβ,9aβ)]-, monotetrafluoroborate	MeOH	243(4.06),280(4.28)	44-1577-80
$C_{16}H_{19}N_5$			
3H-Purin-6-amine, N,N-diethyl-3-(phenylmethyl)-	pH 1	294(4.39)	94-1920-80
	pH 7	298(4.25)	94-1920-80
	pH 13	298(4.24)	94-1920-80
	EtOH	303(4.21)	94-1920-80
9H-Purin-6-amine, N,N-diethyl-9-(phenylmethyl)-	pH 1	271(4.31)	94-1920-80
	pH 7	280(4.31)	94-1920-80
	pH 13	280(4.31)	94-1920-80
	EtOH	279(4.31)	94-1920-80
$C_{16}H_{19}OP$			
Phosphine oxide, dimethyl[2-(2-phenylethyl)phenyl]-	EtOH	225(3.86),264s(3.27), 270(3.32),277(3.25), 296s(2.52)	139-0243-80A
$C_{16}H_{20}$			
Butane, 2,2-dimethyl-3-(1-naphthalenyl)-, (R)-	heptane	225f(5.0),282f(3.8), 313(2.9)	35-6859-80
2,5-Cyclohexadiene, 1,1-dimethyl-4-(4,4-dimethyl-2,5-cyclohexadien-1-ylidene)-	C_6H_{12}	340.5(4.80)	5-2039-80
Dibenzo[a,e]cyclooctene, 2,3,5,6,8,9-11,12-octahydro-	hexane	263(3.74)	24-0586-80
Tricyclo[9.3.1.0³,⁸]pentadeca-3,7,11-triene, 15-methylene-	hexane	230s(3.88),265(3.45)	24-0586-80
$C_{16}H_{20}Br_2N_2O_7$			
1H-Pyrazole, 4-bromo-5-(bromomethyl)-3-methyl-1-(2,3,5-tri-O-acetyl-β-D-ribofuranosyl)-	EtOH	247(3.88)	4-0113-80
$C_{16}H_{20}ClN_3O_8$			
1H-Pyrazole-3-carboxamide, 5-(chloromethyl)-1-(2,3,5-tri-O-acetyl-β-D-ribofuranosyl)-	EtOH	218(3.90)	87-0657-80
1H-Pyrazole-5-carboxamide, 3-(chloromethyl)-1-(2,3,5-tri-O-acetyl-β-D-ribofuranosyl)-	EtOH	226(4.01)	87-0657-80
$C_{16}H_{20}IN_3O_8$			
1H-Pyrazole-3-carboxamide, 5-(iodomethyl)-1-(2,3,5-tri-O-acetyl-β-D-ribofuranosyl)-	EtOH	221(4.19),240s(4.04)	87-0657-80
1H-Pyrazole-5-carboxamide, 3-(iodomethyl)-1-(2,3,5-tri-O-acetyl-β-D-ribo-	EtOH	227(4.24)	87-0657-80

Compound	Solvent	$\lambda_{max}(\log \epsilon)$	Ref.
furanosyl)- (cont.)			87-0657-80
$C_{16}H_{20}NO$			
Furo[3,2-c]pyridinium, 4,5,6,7-tetra-hydro-5,5-dimethyl-4-(phenylmethyl)-, iodide	MeOH	217.5(4.34)	83-0805-80
$C_{16}H_{20}NOT1$			
Thallium, diethyl[1-[(methylimino)meth-yl]-2-naphthalenolato-N,O]-, (T-4)-	benzene	309(4.03),365(3.70), 408(--),425(3.70)	104-2004-80
	BuOH	308(4.00),330(3.72), 405(--),420(4.00)	104-2004-80
	MeCN	305(4.02),367(3.56), 405(--),420(3.93)	104-2004-80
	$C_2H_4Cl_2$	310(4.11),367(3.65), 400(--),420(3.93)	104-2004-80
$C_{16}H_{20}NO_5$			
Oxazolium, 5-(2-acetoxy-1,1-dimethyl-ethyl)-2-[2-(2-furanyl)ethenyl]-4,5-dihydro-3-methyl-4-oxo-, perchlorate	HOAc	400(3.94)	103-0023-80
$C_{16}H_{20}N_2$			
1H-Pyrido[3,4-b]indole, 2,3,4,9-tetra-hydro-2-methyl-1-(2-methyl-2-propen-yl)- (isoborverine)	EtOH	225(4.06),282(3.51), 290(3.48)	102-1282-80
Spiro[2,3-diazabicyclo[2.2.2]oct-2-ene-5,2'(1'H)-naphthalene], 3',4',6',7'-tetrahydro-6-methylene-	EtOH	265(3.59),383(1.90)	24-0586-80
$C_{16}H_{20}N_2O$			
5H-Benzocyclohepten-5-one, 7-[[3-(di-methylamino)propyl]amino]-	EtOH	276(4.60),284(4.63), 342(3.95)	39-2077-80C
Pyrazineethanol, 3,5,6-trimethyl-α-(4-methylphenyl)-	EtOH	216(4.26),281(3.99), 300s(3.74)	44-0999-80
$C_{16}H_{20}N_2O_2$			
1(2H)-Isoquinolinone, 3-(cyclohexyl-amino)-6-methoxy-	EtOH	249(4.63),307(4.30), 357(3.67)	95-0826-80
1(2H)-Isoquinolinone, 3-(cyclohexyl-amino)-7-methoxy-	EtOH	231(4.31),298(4.23), 394(3.58)	95-0826-80
Pyrazineethanol, α-(4-methoxyphenyl)-3,5,6-trimethyl-	EtOH	214(4.09),282(3.99), 300s(3.68)	44-0999-80
$C_{16}H_{20}N_2O_3$			
2H-1,3-Benzoxazin-2-one, 3,4-dihydro-4-(1,3-dimethyl-4-oxo-3-piperidin-yl)-3-methyl-	EtOH	267(3.09),274(3.06)	4-0277-80
3-Pyridazinecarboxylic acid, 1,4,5,6-tetrahydro-6,6-dimethyl-1-(4-methyl-phenyl)-4-oxo-, ethyl ester	EtOH	225s(3.94),235(4.01), 337(4.12)	118-0623-80
1H-Pyrrole-3-propanoic acid, 5-[(3-eth-enyl-2,5-dihydro-4-methyl-5-oxo-1H-pyrrol-2-ylidene)methyl]-, methyl ester	CHCl$_3$ +CF$_3$COOH	409(4.70) 434(4.69)	77-0178-80 77-0178-80
$C_{16}H_{20}N_2O_4S_2$			
2-Azaspiro[4.4]non-3-ene-4-carboxylic acid, 2,3-dimethyl-1,8-dioxo-6-(2-thioxo-3-thiazolidinyl)-, ethyl ester, trans-(±)-	dioxan	281(3.50)	24-3405-80

Compound	Solvent	$\lambda_{max}(\log \epsilon)$	Ref.
1H-Indole-3-carboxylic acid, 5,6,7,7a-tetrahydro-7a-hydroxy-1,2-dimethyl-5-oxo-7-(2-thioxo-3-thiazolidinyl)-, ethyl ester, trans-(±)-	MeOH	288(3.73),406(3.50)	24-3405-80
Pyridine, 2,2'-dithiobis[3-(dimethoxymethyl)-	EtOH	241(4.15),283(3.78)	118-0405-80
$C_{16}H_{20}N_2O_5$			
7-Oxa-1,5-diazabicyclo[4.1.0]heptane-6-carboxylic acid, 4-ethoxy-2-oxo-5-(phenylmethyl)-, ethyl ester	EtOH	295(3.46)	142-0843-80B
$C_{16}H_{20}N_2O_8$			
L-Aspartic acid, N-[(1,1-dimethylethoxy)carbonyl]-, 4-[(2-nitrophenyl)methyl] ester, compd. with dicyclohexylamine	CHCl₃	263(3.75)	22-0133-80
L-Aspartic acid, N-[(1,1-dimethylethoxy)carbonyl]-, 4-[(3-nitrophenyl)methyl] ester	CHCl₃	263(3.91)	22-0133-80
compd. with dicyclohexylamine	CHCl₃	264(3.93)	22-0133-80
L-Aspartic acid, N-[(1,1-dimethylethoxy)carbonyl]-, 4-[(4-nitrophenyl)methyl] ester	CHCl₃	267.5(4.02)	22-0133-80
compd. with dicyclohexylamine	CHCl₃	270(4.01)	22-0133-80
$C_{16}H_{20}N_4$			
Imidazo[5,1-f][1,2,4]triazine, 1,4-dihydro-5-methyl-7-(2-methylpropyl)-2-phenyl-	EtOH	224(4.19),298(3.96)	39-1139-80C
$C_{16}H_{20}N_4O_2$			
Butanamide, N-[1-[1,6-dihydro-6-oxo-3-(phenylmethyl)-1,2,4-triazin-5-yl]ethyl]-, (S)-	EtOH	225(4.09),259(3.28), 266(3.29),271(3.59), 306(3.59)	39-1139-80C
Butanamide, N-[1-[2,5-dihydro-5-oxo-3-(phenylmethyl)-1,2,4-triazin-6-yl]ethyl]-, (S)-	EtOH	235(3.98),260s(3.78)	39-1139-80C
$C_{16}H_{20}N_4O_4$			
Benzo[g]pteridine-2,4(3H,4aH)-dione, 5-ethyl-5,10-dihydro-4a-hydroperoxy-3,7,8,10-tetramethyl-	n.s.g.	370(3.85)	35-7559-80
Imidazo[1,2-a]pyrido[2,3-d]pyrimidine-7-carboxylic acid, 1-methyl-6-oxo-5-(2-oxopropyl)-	EtOH	244(4.30),273(4.32), 321(4.13)	95-1187-80
Pyrido[2,3-d]Pyrimidine-6-carboxylic acid, 2-(2-ethoxy-1-pyrrolidinyl)-8-ethyl-5,8-dihydro-5-oxo-	EtOH	219(4.08),274(4.69), 325(4.02)	94-2531-80
$C_{16}H_{20}N_4O_5$			
Bicyclo[3.3.1]nonan-3-one, 1-methoxy-, 2,4-dinitrophenylhydrazone	EtOH	228(4.23),260s(4.07), 360(4.40)	44-1800-80
Pyrido[2,3-d]pyrimidine-6-carboxylic acid, 2-[(4-ethoxy-4-oxobutyl)amino]-8-ethyl-5,8-dihydro-5-oxo-	EtOH	219(4.03),271(4.69), 323(4.05)	94-2531-80
$C_{16}H_{20}O$			
Benzo[1,2:3,4]dicyclohepten-1(2H)-one, 3,4,5,6,7,8,9,10-octahydro-	EtOH	260(3.65)	23-1344-80

Compound	Solvent	$\lambda_{max}(\log \epsilon)$	Ref.
Benzo[1,2:4,5]dicyclohepten-1(2H)-one, 3,4,5,7,8,9,10,11-octahydro-	EtOH	258(3.81)	23-1344-80
Ethanone, 1-(1,2,3,4,5,6,7,8-octahydro-2-phenanthrenyl)-	EtOH	205(4.46)	56-0453-80
Ethanone, 1-(1,2,3,4,5,6,7,8-octahydro-3-phenanthrenyl)-	EtOH	205(4.49),255(2.78), 270(2.71),278(2.63)	56-0453-80
2,6-Octadien-1-one, 3,7-dimethyl-1-phenyl-, (E)-	n.s.g.	258(4.35)	33-0571-80
(Z)-	n.s.g.	258(4.27)	33-0571-80
$C_{16}H_{20}OS$			
5(6H)-Benzocyclooctenone, 9-(ethylthio)-7,8-dihydro-7,7-dimethyl-	EtOH	258(4.22),288(3.96), 347(3.84)	44-0240-80
Cyclobuta[a]naphthalen-8b(1H)-ol, 3-(ethylthio)-2,2a-dihydro-2,2-dimethyl-	EtOH	297(4.24),288s(4.19), 307s(4.05),321s(3.95)	44-0240-80
$C_{16}H_{20}O_2$			
5(6H)-Benzocyclooctenone, 9-ethoxy-7,8-dihydro-7,7-dimethyl-	EtOH	245(4.46),273(3.96), 339(3.72)	44-0240-80
Cyclobuta[a]naphthalen-8b(1H)-ol, 3-ethoxy-2,2a-dihydro-2,2-dimethyl-	EtOH	272(4.11),280(4.07), 303(3.52)	44-0240-80
2-Naphthalenemethanol, 3-methoxy-α,α,5,8-tetramethyl-	EtOH	235(4.58)	2-0578-80
2(1H)-Phenanthrenone, 3,4,4a,9,10,10a-hexahydro-5-methoxy-4a-methyl-, cis	EtOH	271(3.16),279(3.19)	78-2513-80
trans	EtOH	271(3.14),279(3.16)	78-2513-80
$C_{16}H_{20}O_3$			
Cyclohexaneacetic acid, 1-methyl-2-oxo-6-phenyl-, methyl ester, trans	EtOH	248(2.32),253(2.36), 259(2.40),265(2.34), 268(2.26)	104-0037-80
1H-Fluorene-1-carboxylic acid, 2,3,4,4a,9,9a-hexahydro-7-methoxy-1-methyl-, (1α,4aβ,9aα)-($\pm$)-	EtOH	280(3.4)	39-0804-80C
(1α,4aβ,9aβ)-($\pm$)-	EtOH	255(2.7),260(2.8), 280(3.4)	39-0804-80C
$C_{16}H_{20}O_3S$			
Ethanone, 1-[3,5,5-trimethyl-3-(phenyl-sulfonyl)-1-cyclopenten-1-yl]-	EtOH	240(4.09)	35-1602-80
$C_{16}H_{20}O_4$			
Cyclohexanecarboxylic acid, 2-[(3-meth-oxyphenyl)methyl]-1-methyl-3-oxo-	EtOH	273(3.3),280(3.28)	39-0804-80C
3-Cyclohexene-1-carboxylic acid, 2-(3,4-dimethoxyphenyl)-, methyl ester, cis	MeOH	210(4.14),230(4.03), 279(3.54)	12-0913-80
trans	MeOH	215(3.80),230(3.86), 297(3.46)	12-0913-80
1-Naphthalenepropanoic acid, 5,6,7,8-tetrahydro-4-methoxy-5-methyl-6-oxo-, methyl ester	EtOH	276(3.28),283(3.29)	78-2513-80
Scorpioidine	MeOH	218(4.18)	77-0802-80
$C_{16}H_{20}O_6$			
1,3-Benzodioxole-2-methanol, 2-acetoxy-α-butyl-, acetate	EtOH	273s(3.43),277(3.45), 284s(3.31)	12-1553-80
$C_{16}H_{20}O_8$			
1H-Indene-1,1-dicarboxylic acid, 6-acetyl-2,3,3a,4,7,7a-hexahydro-2,5-	EtOH	242(3.86),274(3.95)	94-1590-80

Compound	Solvent	$\lambda_{max}(\log \epsilon)$	Ref.
dihydroxy-2,3,7a-trimethyl-7-oxo-, (2α,3α,3aα,7aα)-(±)- (cont.)			94-1590-80
$C_{16}H_{20}O_9$ Gentiopicroside	EtOH	247s(3.84),255s(3.93), 270(3.97)	100-0649-80
$C_{16}H_{20}O_{10}$ Asperuloside, deacetyl-	n.s.g.	239(3.66)	100-0649-80
$C_{16}H_{20}S_2Si$ Silane, bis(ethylthio)diphenyl-	hexane	195(4.85),222s(4.28), 245s(3.50),261(3.01), 266(2.99),273(2.85)	101-0147-80A +131-0099-80C
$C_{16}H_{20}Si_2$ Silanthrene, 5,10-dihydro-5,5,10,10-tetramethyl-	C_6H_{12}	217s(4.42),270f(3.0)	65-1615-80
$C_{16}H_{21}BrN_2O_7$ 1H-Pyrazole, 4-bromo-3,5-dimethyl-1-(2,3,5-tri-O-acetyl-β-D-ribofuranosyl)-	EtOH	233(3.80)	4-0113-80
1H-Pyrazole, 5-(bromomethyl)-3-methyl-1-(2,3,5-tri-O-acetyl-β-D-ribofuranosyl)-	EtOH	238(3.93)	4-0113-80
$C_{16}H_{21}BrN_6O_5$ Guanosine, 8-bromo-N-[(dimethylamino)-methylene]-2',3'-O-(1-methylethylidene)-	MeOH	235(4.16),305(4.38)	78-3509-80
$C_{16}H_{21}BrO_3$ 2-Naphthaleneacetic acid, 8-(bromomethyl)-1,2,3,4,4a,7-hexahydro-α,4a-dimethyl-7-oxo-, methyl ester, [2R-[2α(S*),4aα]]-	EtOH	240(4.09)	94-3244-80
$C_{16}H_{21}Cl_3N_3O_9P$ 5-Ethynyluridinephosphoromorpholidic acid 2,2,2-trichloroethyl ester	n.s.g.	228(3.89),288(3.96)	78-0155-80
$C_{16}H_{21}NO$ 2-Cyclohexen-1-one, 2-[(1-methylethyl)-amino]-3-(4-methylphenyl)-	ether	218(4.11),241(4.08), 342(4.00)	78-1585-80
1,3,6,8,10,12-Tetradecahexaen-5-one, 1-(dimethylamino)-, (all-E)-	EtOH	475(4.66)	70-0980-80
$C_{16}H_{21}NO_2$ 2-Cyclohexen-1-one, 3-(4-methoxyphenyl)-2-[(1-methylethyl)amino]-	ether	246(3.52),250(3.40), 212(3.65)	78-1585-80
$C_{16}H_{21}NO_3$ 2H-1,3-Benzoxazin-2-one, 3,4-dihydro-4-(2-hydroxy-3-methylcyclohexyl)-3-methyl-	EtOH	265(3.00),272(2.95)	4-0277-80
2H-1,3-Benzoxazin-2-one, 3,4,4a,5,6,7-8,8a-octahydro-4-(2-hydroxyphenyl)-3,8-dimethyl-	EtOH	216(3.16),274(2.78)	4-0277-80

Compound	Solvent	$\lambda_{max}(\log \epsilon)$	Ref.
$C_{16}H_{21}NO_3S$ Benzenesulfonamide, 4-methyl-N-(1-meth-ylethyl)-N-(6-oxo-1-cyclohexen-1-yl)-	ether	226(4.24),326(1.81)	78-1585-80
$C_{16}H_{21}NO_4$ Edulinine	EtOH	230(4.44),245s(4.02), 267s(3.74),275(3.68), 285(3.82),316s(3.72), 326(3.82),337s(3.69)	105-0574-80
Propanedioic acid, [[4-(dimethylamino)-phenyl]methylene]-, diethyl ester	EtOH	249(4.03),376(4.58)	104-1200-80
$C_{16}H_{21}NO_4S$ Benzenesulfonamide, 4-methoxy-N-(1-methylethyl)-N-(6-oxo-1-cyclohexen-1-yl)-	MeOH	240(3.23),320s(2.18)	78-1585-80
$C_{16}H_{21}NS$ 2H-Azeto[2,1-a]isoquinoline-2-thione, 1-(1,1-dimethylethyl)-1,4,5,9b-tetra-hydro-1-methyl-	isooctane	270(3.9),352(1.5)	24-3010-80
$C_{16}H_{21}N_2O_4PS_2$ Phosphorodithioic acid, O-(1,6-dihydro-5-methoxy-6-oxo-1-phenyl-4-pyridazin-yl) O-ethyl S-propyl ester	MeOH	211(4.29),297(3.87)	73-2247-80
$C_{16}H_{21}N_3O$ Phenol, 4-[(2,6-diamino-3-pyridinyl)-methyl]-2,6-diethyl-	pH 2	242(4.12),279(3.28), 336(4.18)	87-0384-80
	pH 13	241(4.21),304(4.09)	87-0384-80
$C_{16}H_{21}N_3O_3$ Ethanedione, (2,5-dihydro-1,2,2,5,5-pentamethyl-1H-imidazol-4-yl)-phenyl-, 1-oxime, N-oxide	EtOH	251(4.12),289(3.85)	70-0956-80
$C_{16}H_{21}N_3O_9$ Carbamic acid, [1-(3,5-di-O-acetyl-β-D-arabinofuranosyl)-1,2-dihydro-2-oxo-4-pyrimidinyl]-, ethyl ester	MeOH	242(4.20),294(3.94)	44-1577-80
$C_{16}H_{22}BrN_3$ 3,5-Pyridinedicarbonitrile, 1-(5-bromo-pentyl)-1,4-dihydro-2,4,4,6-tetra-methyl-	MeOH	224(4.39),346(3.79)	73-3370-80
$C_{16}H_{22}BrN_5O_8S$ Guanosine, 8-bromo-1-(methoxymethyl)-2',3'-O-(1-methylethylidene)-, 5'-methanesulfonate	MeOH	261(4.11),280s(3.96)	78-3509-80
$C_{16}H_{22}HgSi_2$ Mercury, bis(dimethylphenylsilyl)-	C_6H_{12}	265(3.95),330(2.99), 387(2.26)	101-0169-80N
$C_{16}H_{22}N$ 1H-Benz[f]isoindolium, 2,3,3a,4-tetra-hydro-2,2,4,4-tetramethyl-	EtOH	212(4.25),217(4.34), 224(4.24),265(4.05), 272(4.04)	39-1477-80C

Compound	Solvent	$\lambda_{max}(\log \epsilon)$	Ref.
2-Naphthalenemethanaminium. N,N,N,1,3-pentamethyl-, iodide	EtOH	232(4.97),253s(3.59), 273s(3.65),282(3.70), 291s(3.59),317(3.05), 332(3.16)	39-1477-80C
2-Naphthalenemethanaminium, N,N,N,3,4-pentamethyl-, iodide	EtOH	233(5.00),275s(3.61), 280s(3.66),284(3.68), 295s(3.56),316(3.08), 331(3.21)	39-1477-80C
$C_{16}H_{22}N_2$			
4,4'-Bipyridinium, 1,1'-bis(1-methylethyl)-, diiodide	H_2O	257(4.03)	98-1026-80
4,4'-Bipyridinium, 1,1'-dipropyl-, diiodide	H_2O	258(4.24)	98-1026-80
$C_{16}H_{22}N_2O$			
1H-Pyrido[3,4-b]indole-1-ethanol, 2,3,4,9-tetrahydro-α,α,2-trimethyl-	EtOH	225(4.08),282(3.52), 290(3.47)	102-1282-80
$C_{16}H_{22}N_2O_2$			
Ethanone, 2-(3-hydroxy-1,2,2,5,5-pentamethyl-4-imidazolidinylidene)-1-phenyl-	EtOH	238(3.68),350(3.98)	70-0956-80
$C_{16}H_{22}N_2O_7$			
1H-Pyrazole, 3,5-dimethyl-1-(2,3,5-tri-O-acetyl-β-D-ribofuranosyl)-	EtOH	225(3.72)	4-0113-80
$C_{16}H_{22}N_4$			
Benzo[1,2-b:3,4-b']dipyrrole-3,8-dimethanamine, 1,6-dihydro-N,N,N',N'-tetramethyl-	EtOH	206s(4.33),238(4.56), 270s(4.01),282(4.12), 296s(3.92),308s(3.71)	103-0495-80
$C_{16}H_{22}N_5O_6PS$			
Adenosine, 8-(cyclohexylthio)-, cyclic (hydrogen phosphate)	pH 1 pH 11	283(4.28) 281(4.24)	87-0242-80 87-0242-80
$C_{16}H_{22}O$			
Methanone, phenyl(1,2,2,3-tetramethylcyclopentyl)-, (1R-cis)-	MeCN	237(3.86),266s(2.68), 325(2.18)	108-0142-80
2-Phenanthrenemethanol, 1,2,3,4,5,6,7,8-octahydro-α-methyl-	EtOH	206(4.50),270(2.69), 280(2.61)	56-0453-80
3-Phenanthrenemethanol, 1,2,3,4,5,6,7,8-octahydro-α-methyl-	EtOH	205(4.48),269(3.17)	56-0453-80
$C_{16}H_{22}O_2$			
Spiro[1,3-benzodioxole-2,1'-cyclohexane], 5-(1,1-dimethylethyl)-	EtOH	232(3.52),289(3.49)	12-0527-80
$C_{16}H_{22}O_3$			
1H-Inden-1-one, 2,3-dihydro-3-hydroxy-6-(2-methoxyethyl)-2,2,5,7-tetramethyl-, (S)- (dennstopterosin)	MeOH	217(4.47),260(4.13), 304(3.38)	94-1869-80
2(3H)-Naphthalenone, 3-acetoxy-4,4a,5,6,7,8-hexahydro-4-methyl-6-(1-methylethenyl)- (glutinosone acetate)	EtOH	236(4.18)	18-1045-80
$C_{16}H_{22}O_3S$			
2-Butenoic acid, 4-(cyclohexylthio)-3-(2-furanyl)-, ethyl ester, (E)-	EtOH	206(4.08),310(4.23)	73-0142-80

Compound	Solvent	λ_{max}(log ϵ)	Ref.
$C_{16}H_{22}O_4$			
1,2-Benzenedicarboxylic acid, bis(1,1-dimethylethyl) ester	EtOH	222(3.93),272(3.11), 280s(3.05)	24-0531-80
2-Naphthaleneacetic acid, 1,2,3,4,4a-5,6,7-octahydro-4a,8-dimethyl-3,7-dioxo-, ethyl ester	EtOH	241(4.08)	44-3278-80
4a(2H)-Naphthaleneacetic acid, 1,3,4-7,8,8a-hexahydro-6-(methoxycarbonyl)-1-methylene-, methyl ester, trans-(±)-	EtOH	222(3.86)	44-0367-80
2(3H)-Naphthalenone, 3-acetoxy-4,4a,5-6,7,8-hexahydro-4a-hydroxy-4-methyl-6-(1-methylethenyl)-	EtOH	230(4.08)	18-1045-80
Spiro[5H-cyclopenta[1,3]cyclopropa[1,2]-benzene-5,2'-[1,3]dioxolane]-2-carboxylic acid, 1,3a,3b,4,6,7-hexahydro-3b,7-dimethyl-, methyl ester, (3aα,3bβ,7β,7aS*)-(±)-	EtOH	265(3.92)	23-2460-80
Spiro[4.5]deca-2,6-diene-2-carboxylic acid, 8-acetoxy-6,10-dimethyl-, methyl ester, (5α,8α,10α)-(±)-	EtOH	222(3.93)	23-2460-80
$C_{16}H_{22}O_4S$			
2-Butenoic acid, 4-(cyclohexylsulfinyl)-3-(2-furanyl)-, ethyl ester, (E)-	EtOH	218(4.16),307(4.27)	73-0142-80
$C_{16}H_{22}O_5$			
2-Naphthaleneacetic acid, 1,2,3,5,6,7-8,8a-octahydro-α-hydroxy-α,8,8a-tri-methyl-3,7-dioxo-, dimethyl ester isomer b	EtOH	235.5(4.20)	94-3265-80
isomer b	EtOH	235(4.20)	94-3265-80
7-Oxabicyclo[2.2.1]hepta-2,5-diene-2,3-dicarboxylic acid, bis(1,1-di-methylethyl) ester	EtOH	218s(3.90),227s(3.84), 286(3.19)	24-0531-80
2H-Pyran-3-carboxaldehyde, 4-methoxy-2-oxo-6-(1-oxononyl)-	EtOH	223(4.13),272(3.28), 342(3.97)	23-2158-80
$C_{16}H_{22}O_5S$			
2-Butenoic acid, 4-(cyclohexylsulfonyl)-3-(2-furanyl)-, ethyl ester, (E)-	EtOH	215(3.99),314(4.23)	73-0142-80
$C_{16}H_{22}O_7$			
2-Propenoic acid, 3,3'-(2,5-dihydro-2,5-dimethoxy-3,4-furandiyl)bis-, diethyl ester, [2α,3(E),4(E),5β]-	EtOH	276s(4.17),289s(4.41), 301(4.52),315(4.40)	118-0950-80
$C_{16}H_{22}O_9$			
Cyclopenta[c]pyran-4-carboxaldehyde, 1-(β-D-glucopyranosyloxy)-1,4a,5,7a-tetrahydro-7-(hydroxymethyl)-, [1S-(1α,4aα,7aα)]- (tarennoside)	MeOH	250(4.10)	100-0649-80
Sweroside	n.s.g.	246(3.92)	100-0649-80
$C_{16}H_{22}O_{10}$			
Cyclopenta[c]pyran-4-carboxylic acid, 1-(β-D-glucopyranosyloxy)-1,4a,5,6,7-7a-hexahydro-6-hydroxy-7-methylene-(gardoside)	MeOH	235.5(3.98)	100-0649-80
Cyclopenta[c]pyran-4-carboxylic acid, 1-(β-D-glucopyranosyloxy)-1,4a,5,7a-tetrahydro-7-(hydroxymethyl)-(geniposidic acid)	MeOH	237(3.64)	100-0649-80

Compound	Solvent	$\lambda_{max}(\log \epsilon)$	Ref.
$C_{16}H_{22}O_{11}$			
Cyclopenta[c]pyran-4-carboxylic acid, 1-(β-D-glucopyranosyloxy)-1,4a,5,7a-tetrahydro-5-hydroxy-7-(hydroxymethyl)-	n.s.g.	235(4.16)	100-0649-80
Eustomoside	MeOH	235.5(3.94)	100-0649-80
Forsythide	MeOH	234(4.06)	100-0649-80
Ixoside, 11-methyl-	MeOH	220(4.2),230s(--)	100-0649-80
Monotropein	EtOH	235(3.98)	100-0649-80
Swertiamarin	n.s.g.	206(3.2),234(4.0)	100-0649-80
Theveside	EtOH	231(3.85)	100-0649-80
$C_{16}H_{22}S_2$			
1,3-Dithiepin, 2-[2,3-bis(1,1-dimethylethyl)-2-cyclopropen-1-ylidene]-	CH_2Cl_2	234(4.41),308s(3.85), 354s(3.77)	138-1427-80
$C_{16}H_{22}Si_2$			
Disilane, 1,1,2,2-tetramethyl-1,2-diphenyl-	C_6H_{12}	236(4.46)	65-1615-80
	isooctane	238(4.27)	101-0261-80Q
$C_{16}H_{23}ClO_{11}$			
1H,3H-Pyrano[3,4-c]pyran-1-one, 5-(2-chloro-1-hydroxyethyl)-6-(β-D-glucopyranosyloxy)-4,4a,5,6-tetrahydro-4a-hydroxy-, [4aβ-[(4aβ,5α(S*),6β]]-(eustoside)	MeOH	237(3.86)	100-0649-80
$C_{16}H_{23}N$			
Benzenamine, N-[(1,1-dimethylethyl)-cyclopropylidene]-2,4,6-trimethyl-	C_6H_{12}	205(4.83),228s(--), 278(3.39),304(3.35)	5-1814-80
$C_{16}H_{23}NO_7S_2$			
β-D-Glucopyranose, 1-deoxy-1-[[4-(1-methylpropyl)-2-nitrophenyl]dithio]-	EtOH	235(4.16),366(3.53)	44-4216-80
	20% EtOH-pH 7.0	232(4.02),368(3.53)	44-4216-80
plus dithioerythritol	EtOH	235(4.16),366(3.53)	44-4216-80
	20% EtOH-pH 7.0	262(4.24),424(3.18)	44-4216-80
$C_{16}H_{23}N_5O_3$			
2,4,6-Pyrimidinetriamine, N^4,N^4-dimethyl-5-[(3,4,5-trimethoxyphenyl)methyl]-	pH 12	225s(4.47),286(4.13)	87-0535-80
$C_{16}H_{24}$			
Benzene, [2-(1,1-dimethylethyl)-3,3-dimethyl-1-butenyl]-	C_6H_{12}	212(4.08)(end abs.)	5-1207-80
Benzene, [(1,2,3,4-tetramethylcyclopentyl)methyl]-	MeCN	195(4.45),209(4.03), 248(2.11),253(2.23), 259(2.28),262s(2.26), 265(2.18),269(2.15)	108-0142-80
$C_{16}H_{24}N_2O_2$			
Acetic acid, cyano(octahydro-3(2H)-isoquinolinylidene)-, 1,1-dimethylethyl ester, (3Z,4aα,8aβ)-(±)-	n.s.g.	285(4.33)	33-1158-80
9-Azoniabicyclo[3.3.1]nonane, 3-oxo-9-(3-oxo-9-azoniabicyclo[3.3.1]non-1-ylidene)-	MeCN	257(3.3)	35-5482-80
Benzenamine, 4-ethoxy-N-(tetrahydro-3,4,4,6-tetramethyl-2H-1,3-oxazin-2-ylidene)-	heptane	208s(4.23),261(4.19), 303s(3.47)	110-0172-80

Compound	Solvent	λ_{max}(log ϵ)	Ref.
1H-Imidazole-4-ethanol, 2,5-dihydro-1,2,2,5,5-pentamethyl-α-phenyl-, 3-oxide	EtOH	234(3.91)	70-0956-80
4H-1,3-Oxazin-2-amine, N-(4-ethoxyphenyl)-5,6-dihydro-N,4,4,6-tetramethyl-	heptane	208s(4.17),222s(3.81), 252(4.07),285(3.35)	110-0172-80
$C_{16}H_{24}N_2O_5$			
1,4,7,10-Tetraoxa-13-azacyclopentadecane, 13-(4-nitrosophenyl)-	MeCN	416(4.97)	24-0457-80
$C_{16}H_{24}N_2O_{11}$			
α-D-Glucopyranosiduronic acid, [(1-methylethyl)nitrosoamino]methyl, 2,3,4-triacetate	MeOH	230(3.63),300(2.54)	89-0400-80
α-D-Glucopyranosiduronic acid, (nitrosopropylamino)methyl, 2,3,4-triacetate	MeOH	230(3.63),300(2.30)	89-0400-80
$C_{16}H_{24}N_2S_4$			
Ethanamine, N,N'-[dithiobis(carbonothioyl-2-cyclopentyl-1-ylidene)]bis-	CHCl₃	312(3.48),412(4.18)	118-0566-80
$C_{16}H_{24}N_4OS$			
4(1H)-Pyridinone, 3-heptyl-5-[4-methyl-5-(methylthio)-4H-1,2,4-triazol-3-yl]-	EtOH	264(3.99)	4-0175-80
$C_{16}H_{24}N_4O_2$			
9-Azabicyclo[3,3,1]nonan-3-one, 9,9'-azobis-	MeCN	260s(3.8),288(4.0)	35-5482-80
$C_{16}H_{24}O$			
Benzenemethanol, α-(1,2,2,3-tetramethylcyclopentyl)-	MeCN	198(4.31),209(3.86), 247(2.11),252(2.23), 257(2.30),264(2.18), 267s(1.90)	108-0142-80
isomer	MeCN	197(3.99),203s(3.91), 216s(3.70),247(2.34), 252(2.36),259(2.34), 265(2.20)	108-0142-80
$C_{16}H_{24}OS$			
17-Thiabicyclo[12.2.1]heptadeca-14,16-dien-2-one	MeCN	295(4.04)	44-1906-80
16-Thiabicyclo[11.2.1]heptadeca-1(15),13-dien-2-one, 15-methyl-	MeCN	293(4.06)	44-1906-80
$C_{16}H_{24}O_2$			
Ethanone, 1-(3-heptyl-2-hydroxy-5-methylphenyl)-	EtOH	261(4.01),347(3.60)	90-0431-80
Ethanone, 1-(2-hydroxy-5-octylphenyl)-	EtOH	255(3.99),338(3.55)	90-0431-80
Naphtho[2,1-b]furan-2(3aH)-one, 4,5,5a,6,7,8,9,9a-octahydro-3a,6,6,9a-tetramethyl-, [3aR-(3aα,5aβ,9aα)]-	EtOH	214.5(4.78)	65-0180-80
Propanoic acid, 2-(3,4,6,7,8,8a-hexahydro-8,8a-dimethyl-2(1H)-naphthalenylidene)-, methyl ester, (E)-	EtOH	224(3.98)	39-1752-80C
(Z)-	EtOH	224.5(3.95)	39-1752-80C
$C_{16}H_{24}O_3$			
2-Naphthalenecarboxylic acid,	EtOH	223(3.64)	44-0357-80

Compound	Solvent	$\lambda_{max}(\log \epsilon)$	Ref.
3,4,4a,5,6,7,8,8a-octahydro-8a-hydroxy-5-methylene-8-(1-methylethyl)-, methyl ester (cont.)			44-0357-80
13-Norisomarasman-5-oic acid, 7-oxo-, ethyl ester	EtOH	206(3.61)	94-0500-80
13-Normarasman-5-oic acid, 7-oxo-, ethyl ester	EtOH	205(3.43)	94-0500-80
$C_{16}H_{24}O_4$			
Butanoic acid, 2-[[3-methyl-3-(4-methyl-3-pentenyl)oxiranyl]methylene]-3-oxo-, ethyl ester	EtOH	252(3.70)	70-0754-80
1,4-Cyclohexadiene-1,2-dicarboxylic acid, bis(1,1-dimethylethyl) ester	EtOH	234(3.34)	24-0531-80
2H-Pyran-3-carboxaldehyde, 4-methoxy-6-nonyl-2-oxo-	EtOH	227(3.17),247(2.76), 322(3.08)	23-2158-80
$C_{16}H_{24}O_5$			
2-Furanpropanoic acid, 3-(methoxycarbonyl)-4-methyl-5-pentyl-, methyl ester	MeOH	262(3.57)	24-0699-80
$C_{16}H_{24}O_6S$			
Cyclopenta[c]pyran-4-carboxylic acid, 6-acetoxy-7-[(ethylthio)methyl]-1,4a,5,6,7,7a-hexahydro-1-methoxy-, methyl ester, (1α,4aβ,6β,7β,7aβ)-(±)-	MeOH	236(4.01)	44-4233-80
$C_{16}H_{24}O_7$			
β-D-Glucopyranoside, 3-hydroxy-2-methyl-5-(1-methylethyl)phenyl	MeOH	260(3.41),275(3.59), 320(3.14)	102-2215-80
$C_{16}H_{24}O_8$			
Cyclopenta[c]pyran-4-carboxaldehyde, 1-(β-D-glucopyranosyloxy)-1,4a,5,6-7,7a-hexahydro-7-methyl-, [1S-(1α,4aα,7β,7aα)]- (boschnaloside)	EtOH n.s.g.	249(4.16) 249(4.08)	94-1730-80 100-0649-80
$C_{16}H_{24}O_9$			
Cyclopenta[c]pyran-4-carboxaldehyde, 1-(β-D-glucopyranosyloxy)-4a-hydroxy-7-methyl- (yuheinoside)	MeOH	243(4.09)	100-0649-80
Cyclopenta[c]pyran-4-carboxaldehyde, 1-(β-D-glucopyranosyloxy)-1,4a,5,6-7,7a-hexahydro-7-hydroxy-7-methyl- (ixoroside)	MeOH	249(4.09)	100-0649-80
Cyclopenta[c]pyran-4-carboxylic acid, 1-(β-D-glucopyranosyloxy)-1,4a,5,6-7,7a-hexahydro-7-methyl- (desoxyloganic acid)	n.s.g.	231(3.29)	100-0649-80
$C_{16}H_{24}O_{10}$			
Asperulosidol	MeOH	206(3.60)	78-1613-80
Loganic acid	EtOH	230(4.2),234(3.97)	100-0649-80
Tecomoside	EtOH	241(4.01)	100-0649-80
$C_{16}H_{24}O_{11}$			
Shanzhiside	n.s.g.	229(4.04)	100-0649-80
$C_{16}H_{24}O_{12}$			
Eustomorusside	MeOH	236.5(3.76)	100-0649-80

Compound	Solvent	$\lambda_{max}(\log \epsilon)$	Ref.
$C_{16}H_{25}BrO_2$			
Phenol, 3-[(10-bromodecyl)oxy]-	n.s.g.	278(3.40)	44-3923-80
Phenol, 4-[(10-bromodecyl)oxy]-	n.s.g.	297(3.49)	44-3923-80
$C_{16}H_{25}IO$			
[1,1'-Bibicyclo[2.2.2]octan]-4-ol, 4'-iodo-	EtOH	260.0(3.00)	44-3933-80
$C_{16}H_{25}NOS_2$			
2-Propanesulfenamide, N-(3-acetylphenyl)-N-(1,1-dimethylethyl)thio-2-methyl-	hexane	239(4.38),328(3.64)	18-0720-80
2-Propanesulfenamide, N-(4-acetylphenyl)-N-(1,1-dimethylethyl)thio-2-methyl-	hexane	303(4.35)	18-0720-80
$C_{16}H_{25}NO_2$			
Ethanone, 1-(3-heptyl-2-hydroxy-5-methylphenyl)-, oxime	EtOH	258(4.01),317(3.16)	90-0431-80
Ethanone, 1-(2-hydroxy-5-octylphenyl)-, oxime	EtOH	255(3.99),338(3.55)	90-0431-80
$C_{16}H_{25}NO_3$			
3-Pyridinecarboxylic acid, 1,4-dihydro-5-octyl-4-oxo-, ethyl ester	EtOH	255s(3.91),260(3.94), 286(3.74)	4-0359-80
3-Pyridinecarboxylic acid, 1-ethyl-1,4-dihydro-5-octyl-4-oxo-	EtOH	260(4.02),287(3.68)	4-0359-80
$C_{16}H_{25}NO_5$			
Propanedioic acid, [7-[5-(methoxyimino)-1-cyclopenten-1-yl]heptyl]-	MeOH	243(4.12)	44-4702-80
$C_{16}H_{25}NO_6$			
3,5-Isoxazoledicarboxylic acid, 4-(2,6-dimethyl-5-heptenyl)-4,5-dihydro-, dimethyl ester, 2-oxide	MeOH	268(3.73)	94-0479-80
$C_{16}H_{25}N_2O_5PS$			
3(2H)-Pyridazinone, 2-cyclohexyl-5-[(5,5-dimethyl-1,3,2-dioxaphosphorinan-2-yl)oxy]-4-methoxy-, P-sulfide	MeOH	215(4.30),287(3.67)	73-2343-80
$C_{16}H_{25}N_3O_2$			
1,5,9-Triazacyclotridecan-4-one, 9-hydroxy-2-phenyl-, (S)- (mayfoline)	EtOH	251(2.33),257(2.39), 262(2.33),264s(2.32), 268(2.21)	102-0162-80
$C_{16}H_{25}N_3O_{10}$			
α-D-Glucopyranosiduronamide, (nitrosopropylamino)methyl, 2,3,4-triacetate	MeOH	230(3.78),300(2.28)	89-0400-80
$C_{16}H_{26}$			
2,4,8-Decatriene, 2,5,9-trimethyl-7-(1-methylethenyl)-	n.s.g.	248(4.38)	33-1499-80
$C_{16}H_{26}BrN_3O$			
Spirolaurenone semicarbazone (spectrum of parent compound)	EtOH	288(2.04)	78-1551-80
$C_{16}H_{26}CuN_4O_4S_2$			
Copper, bis[ethyl (1-pyrrolidinylthioxo-	CHCl$_3$	257(4.56),346(3.76),	97-0268-80

Compound	Solvent	$\lambda_{max}(\log \epsilon)$	Ref.
methyl)carbamato-O',S^N]- (cont.)		421s(3.23),566(2.39)	97-0268-80
$C_{16}H_{26}CuN_4O_6S_2$ Copper, bis[ethyl (4-morpholinylthioxo-methyl)carbamato]-	CHCl$_3$	260(4.26),347(3.81), 421s(3.27),562(2.33)	97-0268-80
$C_{16}H_{26}N_2O$ [9,9'-Bi-9-azabicyclo[3.3.1]nonan]-3-one	MeCN	260s(2.9),280(3.0)	35-5482-80
$C_{16}H_{26}N_2O_3$ 1-Butanamine, 3-methyl-N-(3-methylbut-yl)-N-[2-(5-nitro-2-furanyl)ethenyl]-, (E)-	MeOH	280(3.98),520(4.07)	73-0155-80
1-Pentanamine, N-[2-(5-nitro-2-furan-yl)ethenyl]-N-pentyl-, (E)-	MeOH	280(3.98),516(4.14)	73-0155-80
$C_{16}H_{26}N_2O_6$ 3-Pyridinecarboxamide, N,N-diethyl-1-β-D-glucopyranosyl-1,4-dihydro-	CHCl$_3$	310(3.40)	23-0387-80
$C_{16}H_{26}N_4NiO_6S_2$ Nickel, bis[ethyl (4-morpholinylthioxo-methyl)carbamato]-	CHCl$_3$	255(4.48),287(4.39), 327s(3.92),420s(2.17), 518(2.26)	97-0268-80
$C_{16}H_{26}N_4O_2$ 2,4-Pentanedione, 3-[2,5-bis(diethyl-amino)-4H-imidazol-4-ylidene]-	CHCl$_3$	345(4.15),450(4.17)	88-2879-80
$C_{16}H_{26}N_4O_4$ Propanedioic acid, [2,5-bis(diethyl-amino)-4H-imidazol-4-ylidene]-, dimethyl ester	benzene MeOH acetone CH$_2$Cl$_2$	350(4.18),455(3.94) 355(3.63),460(3.44) 350(4.18),455(3.92) 355(4.14),460(3.88)	88-2879-80 88-2879-80 88-2879-80 88-2879-80
$C_{16}H_{26}O$ 9,11-Hexadecadiyn-1-ol	EtOH	214(2.69),226(2.61), 241(2.63),254(2.44)	107-0391-80
2(3H)-Naphthalenone, 7-(1,1-dimethyl-ethyl)-4,4a,5,6,7,8-hexahydro-1,4a-dimethyl-	EtOH	253(4.19)	44-3088-80
$C_{16}H_{26}OSi$ 1H-Benz[e]inden-5-ol, 2,3,3a,4,5,7,8,9-octahydro-5-(trimethylsilyl)-	MeOH	256(4.32)	35-4839-80
$C_{16}H_{26}OTe$ Propanetelluroic acid, 2,2-dimethyl-, O-(tricyclo[3.3.1.1^{3,7}]dec-1-yl-methyl) ester	C$_6$H$_{12}$	244(3.58),266s(2.90), 337(3.92),596(2.46)	39-2191-80C
$C_{16}H_{26}O_2$ Bicyclo[4.1.0]heptane-2-propanol, 1,3,3-trimethyl-α-methylene, acetate	pentane	260(end abs.)	33-1520-80
$C_{16}H_{26}O_3$ 1-Cyclopentene-1-heptanoic acid, β,β-di-methyl-5-oxo-, ethyl ester	MeOH	228(4.02)	44-4702-80
1-Cyclopentene-1-heptanoic acid, α-eth-yl-5-oxo-, ethyl ester	MeOH	228(4.05)	44-4702-80

Compound	Solvent	$\lambda_{max}(\log \epsilon)$	Ref.
1-Cyclopentene-1-nonanoic acid, 5-oxo-, ethyl ester	MeOH	228(4.00)	44-4702-80
$C_{16}H_{26}O_3Si$ Acetic acid, (2-methylphenoxy)-, (triethylsilyl)methyl ester	MeCN	216(3.95),272(3.20), 278(3.18)	65-0481-80
$C_{16}H_{26}O_7$ Picrocrocine	H_2O	250.5(4.09)	33-1463-80
$C_{16}H_{26}O_{11}$ Ixoside	H_2O	219(4.16)	100-0649-80
$C_{16}H_{27}N_2O_4PS_2$ Phosphorodithioic acid, O-(1-cyclohexyl-1,6-dihydro-5-methoxy-6-oxo-4-pyridazinyl) O-ethyl S-propyl ester	MeOH	217(4.32),290(3.71)	73-2247-80
$C_{16}H_{27}N_3O_3$ 3,5-Isoxazoledicarboxamide, N,N'-dibutyl-4-propyl-	MeOH	246(4.03)	94-0479-80
$C_{16}H_{28}NO_4$ 1-Piperidinyloxy, 4-[(4,4-dimethyl-1,3-dioxopentyl)oxy]-2,2,6,6-tetramethyl-	C_6H_{12}	246(3.81),305(2.49), 475(1.11)	22-0147-80
	MeOH	245(3.56),450(1.11)	22-0147-80
$C_{16}H_{28}N_2$ 9-Azoniabicyclo[3.3.1]nonane, 9-(9-azoniabicyclo[3.3.1]non-9-ylidene)-	MeCN	240s(2.2)	35-5482-80
14,16-Diazabicyclo[11.2.1]hexadeca-13(16),15-diene, 14,15-dimethyl-	EtOH	226(3.65)	138-0659-80
$C_{16}H_{28}N_4$ 9-Azabicyclo[3.3.1]nonane, 9,9'-azobis-	MeCN	264s(3.7),293(4.0)	35-5482-80
$C_{16}H_{28}N_4O_2S_2$ 2H-1,3,5-Thiadiazine-3(4H)-carboxylic acid, 6-[bis(1-methylethyl)-1-piperazinyl]-	CH_2Cl_2	238(4.16),275(4.32), 349(4.06)	24-0079-80
$C_{16}H_{28}O$ 9,11-Hexadecadienal, (Z,Z)-	EtOH	230(4.41),237(4.44)	107-0391-80
$C_{16}H_{28}O_3$ Cyclopentaneacetic acid, 2-methyl-5-(1-methylethyl)-1-(3-oxobutyl)-, methyl ester, [1S-(1α,2α,5α)]-	hexane	223(2.19),279(1.73)	100-0598-80
$C_{16}H_{28}O_4Si$ Silane, (phenoxymethyl)tris(1-methylethoxy)-	hexane	221(3.953),265(3.098), 272(3.241),277(3.235)	65-0491-80
$C_{16}H_{28}S_4$ Thiophene, 2,3,5-tris[(1,1-dimethylethyl)thio]-	heptane	195(4.31),256(4.04)	24-3342-80
$C_{16}H_{29}NO_3$ Pentanoic acid, 4,4-dimethyl-3-oxo-, 2,2,6,6-tetramethyl-4-piperidinyl ester	pentane	247(3.90),284(2.37), 306(1.88)	22-0147-80
	MeOH	247(3.15)	22-0147-80

Compound	Solvent	$\lambda_{max}(\log \epsilon)$	Ref.
$C_{16}H_{29}N_3O_4$			
3,5-Isoxazoledicarboxamide, N,N'-dibut-yl-4,5-dihydro-4-(1-methylethyl)-, 2-oxide, trans	MeOH	258(3.91)	94-0479-80
3,5-Isoxazoledicarboxamide, N,N'-dibut-yl-4,5-dihydro-4-propyl-, 2-oxide, trans	MeOH	257(3.90)	94-0479-80
$C_{16}H_{30}O$			
9,11-Hexadecadien-1-ol, (Z,Z)-	EtOH	230s(4.42),237(4.46)	107-0391-80
$C_{16}H_{31}NO_2$			
6,7-Dodecanedione, 5,8-diethyl-, mono-oxime	EtOH	326(1.76)	90-0441-80
$C_{16}H_{32}O$			
6-Dodecanone, 5,8-diethyl-	EtOH	287(1.67)	90-0441-80
$C_{16}H_{32}O_2$			
6-Dodecanone, 5,8-diethyl-7-hydroxy-	EtOH	284(1.75)	90-0441-80
$C_{16}H_{34}Si_4$			
Disilane, 1,1'-(1,3-phenylene)bis-[1,1,2,2,2-pentamethyl-	isooctane	231(4.39)	101-0261-80Q
Disilane, 1,1'-(1,4-phenylene)bis-[1,1,2,2,2-pentamethyl-	isooctane	248(4.39)	101-0261-80Q

Compound	Solvent	$\lambda_{max}(\log \epsilon)$	Ref.
$C_{17}H_3F_9$ Fluoranthene, 1,2,3,4,6,7,8,9,10-nona- fluoro-5-methyl-	MeOH	211(4.57),238(4.58), 272(3.96),284(3.92), 320(3.85),358(4.02)	104-1794-80
$C_{17}H_5Cl_7O_2S$ 4H-Pyran-4-one, 3,5-dichloro-2-[(penta- chlorophenyl)thio]-6-phenyl-	heptane	200(4.41),217(4.72), 245(4.53),281(4.21)	5-1960-80
$C_{17}H_5Cl_9OS$ 2,4-Pentadienethioic acid, 2,3,4,5- tetrachloro-5-phenyl-, S-(penta- chlorophenyl) ester, (Z,Z)-	heptane	217(4.78)	5-1960-80
$C_{17}H_9Cl_2N_3$ 11H-Indeno[1,2-c]isoquinoline-11-carbo- nitrile, 5-amino-2,9-dichloro-, hydrochloride	EtOH-H_2SO_4	213(4.44),260(4.51), 327s(4.26),335(4.29), 366(4.13),384(4.03)	18-2885-80
11H-Indeno[1,2-c]isoquinoline-11-carbo- nitrile, 5-amino-3,8-dichloro-, hydrochloride	EtOH-H_2SO_4	223(4.61),233(4.56), 325s(4.21),337(4.24), 372(4.04),390(3.92)	18-2885-80
$C_{17}H_9Cl_5OS$ 2,4-Pentadienethioic acid, 2,3,4,5- tetrachloro-5-phenyl-, S-(4-chloro- phenyl) ester	heptane	199(4.65),262(4.39)	5-1960-80
$C_{17}H_9NO_2$ Naphtho[2,3-h]quinoline-7,12-dione	50% EtOH	240(4.2),256s(--), 267(4.3),295s(--), 350(3.6)	104-1248-80
$C_{17}H_9NO_3$ Liriodenine	EtOH	247(4.49),268(4.41), 310(3.91),413(3.80)	88-3307-80
$C_{17}H_9NO_4$ 8H-Benzo[g]-1,3-benzodioxolo[6,5,4-de]- quinolin-8-one, 10-hydroxy- (oxoanolobine)	MeOH	217(4.24),249(4.43), 274(4.35),324s(3.84), 370(3.65),442(3.76)	142-1977-80
	MeOH-HCl	220(4.29),260(4.41), 287(4.31),345(3.72), 395(3.73),510(3.51)	142-1977-80
	MeOH-NaOH	222(4.29),253(4.38), 291(4.42),334s(4.01), 372(3.48),506(3.42)	142-1977-80
$(C_{17}H_9N_3O_{10})_n$ 9H-Fluorene-2-carboxylic acid, 4,5,7- trinitro-9-oxo-, oxiranylmethyl ester, homopolymer	THF	370(3.99)	116-0782-80
$C_{17}H_{10}Cl_3NO_7S$ 4H-1-Benzopyran-4-one, 3-[2-(5-nitro- 2-furanyl)-2-[(trichloromethyl)sul- fonyl]cyclopropyl]-, trans-(±)-	MeOH	206(4.25),325(3.80)	73-1704-80
$C_{17}H_{10}Cl_4OS$ 2,4-Pentadienethioic acid, 2,3,4,5- tetrachloro-5-phenyl-, S-phenyl ester, (Z,Z)-	heptane	201(4.52),250s(4.00)	5-1960-80

Compound	Solvent	$\lambda_{max}(\log \epsilon)$	Ref.
$C_{17}H_{10}F_4OS_2$ 2-Cyclopenten-1-one, 4,4,5,5-tetra-fluoro-2,3-bis(phenylthio)-	isooctane	244(4.05),327(4.03)	44-4429-80
$C_{17}H_{10}N_2O_2$ Benzonitrile, 4-[(3,4-dihydro-3,4-di-oxo-1-naphthalenyl)amino]-	EtOH	250(4.24),290(4.15), 337(3.76),440(3.53)	94-1207-80
$C_{17}H_{10}N_6O_8$ Acetonitrile, (dimethylamino)(2,4,5,7-tetranitro-9H-fluoren-9-ylidene)-	MeCN	354(4.20),442(4.00), 532(4.04)	104-0740-80
$C_{17}H_{10}N_6S$ Thieno[2,3-d]pyrimidine-4,5,6-tricarbo-nitrile, 2-[4-(dimethylamino)phenyl]-	n.s.g.	256(4.18),307(3.86), 330(3.81),568(4.59)	44-5113-80
$C_{17}H_{10}O_2$ 12H-Benzo[a]xanthen-12-one	MeOH	236(4.51),262(4.11), 298(3.89),322(4.13)	2-0615B-80
$C_{17}H_{10}O_4$ 4H-Furo[2,3-h]-1-benzopyran-4-one, 5-hydroxy-2-phenyl- (pongaglabol)	EtOH and EtOH-base	221(4.48),257(4.29), 281(4.47)	102-1199-80
	EtOH-AlCl$_3$	224(4.43),265(4.29), 306(4.48)	102-1199-80
5H-Furo[3,2-g][1]benzopyran-5-one, 4-hydroxy-7-phenyl-	EtOH	214(4.48),260(4.39), 278(4.56)	102-1199-80
	EtOH-AlCl$_3$	213(4.44),268(4.33), 295(4.52)	102-1199-80
$C_{17}H_{10}O_7$ Tephrosol	MeOH	245(4.59),285(4.10), 315(3.97),355(4.45)	102-1272-80
	MeOH-NaOAc	385(4.59)	102-1272-80
$C_{17}H_{11}BrO_6$ 2-Anthracenecarboxylic acid, 1-bromo-9,10-dihydro-4,5-dimethoxy-9,10-di-oxo-	EtOH	223(4.43),266(4.28), 370(3.70)	44-0020-80
$C_{17}H_{11}ClF_3N_3O$ Benzenemethanamine, α-[[3-(4-chloro-phenyl)-1,2,4-oxadiazol-5-yl]-methylene]-4-(trifluoromethyl)-	EtOH	246(4.45),332(4.20)	39-1635-80C
$C_{17}H_{11}ClN_2O_4$ 1,4-Naphthalenedione, 2-chloro-3-[(4-methylphenyl)amino]-5-nitro-	EtOH	286(4.43),503(3.64)	40-1862-80
1,4-Naphthalenedione, 3-chloro-2-[(4-methylphenyl)amino]-5-nitro-	EtOH	275(4.33),510(3.70)	40-1862-80
$C_{17}H_{11}ClN_2O_5$ 2,4-Pentadien-1-one, 5-chloro-1,5-bis-(3-nitrophenyl)-, (Z,E)-	EtOH	247(4.39),335(4.43)	40-1804-80
2,4-Pentadien-1-one, 5-chloro-1,5-bis-(4-nitrophenyl)-, (Z,E)-	EtOH	269(4.21),344(4.51)	40-1804-80
$C_{17}H_{11}Cl_3N_2O_2$ 1,4-Naphthalenedione, 5-amino-2,6,8-trichloro-3-[(4-methylphenyl)amino]-	EtOH	271(4.36),490(4.10)	40-1862-80

Compound	Solvent	λ_{max} (log ϵ)	Ref.
1,4-Naphthalenedione, 5-amino-3,6,8-trichloro-2-[(4-methylphenyl)amino]-	EtOH	277(4.49),542(3.92)	40-1862-80
$C_{17}H_{11}Cl_3N_2O_3$ 1,4-Naphthalenedione, 5-amino-2,6,8-trichloro-3-[(4-methoxyphenyl)amino]-	EtOH	272(4.44),492(4.07)	40-1862-80
1,4-Naphthalenedione, 5-amino-3,6,8-trichloro-2-[(4-methoxyphenyl)amino]-	EtOH	280(4.46),550(3.92)	40-1862-80
$C_{17}H_{11}Cl_3O$ 2,4-Pentadien-1-one, 5-chloro-1,5-bis-(4-chlorophenyl)-, (Z,E)-	EtOH	262(4.09),344(4.50)	40-1804-80
$C_{17}H_{11}F_2NO_4S$ 5(4H)-Oxazolone, 4-[[4-[(difluoromethyl)sulfonyl]phenyl]methylene]-2-phenyl-	$CHCl_3$	370(4.70)	103-0701-80
5(4H)-Oxazolone, 2-[4-[(difluoromethyl)sulfonyl]phenyl]-4-(phenylmethylene)-	$CHCl_3$	380(4.53)	103-0701-80
$C_{17}H_{11}F_3N_4O_3$ 1,2,4-Oxadiazole, 3-(4-nitrophenyl)-5-[β-amino-4-(trifluoromethyl)styryl]-	EtOH	268(4.48),330(4.00)	39-1635-80C
$C_{17}H_{11}N$ Benz[a]acridine	MeOH	225(4.43),237(4.38), 278(4.66),284s(4.56), 323s(3.43),333s(3.57), 348(3.69),366(3.82), 385(3.85)	39-1233-80C
$C_{17}H_{11}NO$ Benz[cd]indol-5(1H)-one, 2-phenyl-	CH_2Cl_2	246(4.11),280(4.19), 411(4.32),536(2.95)	5-0971-80
$C_{17}H_{11}NO_3$ 8H,11H-Benzo[a]pyrano[3,2-g]quinolizine-8,11-dione, 9-methyl-	EtOH	212(4.56),219(4.58), 241(4.46),275(4.40), 305(4.30),317(4.29), 413(4.40),431(4.44)	95-0571-80
$C_{17}H_{11}NO_4$ Spiro[2H-indene-2,2'-[2H,9aH]pyrido[2,1-b][1,3]oxazine]-3'-carboxaldehyde, 1,3-dihydro-1,3-dioxo-	MeCN	228(4.70),243s(4.35), 350(4.16)	4-1577-80
$C_{17}H_{11}N_3$ 11H-Indeno[1,2-c]isoquinoline-11-carbonitrile, 5-amino-, monohydrochloride	EtOH-H_2SO_4	213(4.50),239(4.44), 316(4.21),330(4.22), 364(4.05),382(3.98)	18-2885-80
$C_{17}H_{11}N_3O_2S_2$ 1,2,4-Triazolidinium, 3,5-dioxo-4-phenyl-1-(4-phenyl-3H-1,2-dithiol-3-ylidene)-, hydroxide, inner salt	dioxan	227(4.39),300s(3.61), 500(4.02)	104-0188-80
1,2,4-Triazolidinium, 3,5-dioxo-4-phenyl-1-(5-phenyl-3H-1,2-dithiol-3-ylidene)-, hydroxide, inner salt	dioxan	230(4.34),322(4.26), 512(4.14)	104-0188-80

Compound	Solvent	$\lambda_{max}(\log \epsilon)$	Ref.
$C_{17}H_{11}N_3O_3$ Diazene, (2-naphthalenylcarbonyl)(4-nitrophenyl)-	CHCl$_3$	286(4.41),498(2.20)	39-1212-80C
$C_{17}H_{12}$ 3,4-Benzofluorene	C$_6$H$_{12}$	216(4.41),233(4.62), 253(4.26),264(4.27), 300(3.99),312(4.10), 321(4.00),329(3.91), 336(4.13)	44-5163-80
4H-Cycloocta[def]fluorene	C$_6$H$_{12}$	253(4.47),273s(4.33), 300(3.66),246s(3.13)	44-1628-80
1,2:3,4-Fluorenobicyclo[4.2.0]octatriene	C$_6$H$_{12}$	244(4.26),231(4.21), 238(4.09),254(4.03), 263s(4.02),276(4.06), 284(3.97),300s(3.48)	44-1628-80
$C_{17}H_{12}BrNO_2$ 2,3-Pyrrolidinedione, 1-(4-bromophenyl)-4-(phenylmethylene)-	EtOH	232(4.07),336(4.26)	4-1231-80
$C_{17}H_{12}ClN$ Cyclohepta[b]pyrrole, 2-chloro-8-(2-phenylethenyl)-, (E)-	EtOH	247(4.38),282(4.34), 325(4.31),385(4.37), 467(3.36)	18-1406-80
$C_{17}H_{12}ClNO$ Benzeneacetaldehyde, α-(chloro-1H-indol-3-ylmethylene)-	EtOH	208(4.51),217(4.54), 277(4.10),377(4.03)	103-0741-80
$C_{17}H_{12}ClNOS_3$ Benzenecarbothioic acid, 4-chloro-, S-[2,5-dihydro-4-(4-methylphenyl)-5-thioxo-3-isothiazolyl] ester	CHCl$_3$	318(4.28),422(4.20)	39-2693-80C
$C_{17}H_{12}ClNO_2$ 1(4H)-Naphthalenone, 4-[(4-chlorophenyl)imino]-2-methoxy-	EtOH	233(4.31),255s(4.09), 293(4.31),340(3.85), 436(3.58)	94-1207-80
$C_{17}H_{12}ClNO_3$ 7H-Benzo[c]phenoxazin-5(12aH)-one, 6-chloro-12a-hydroxy-9-methyl-	dioxan	262(4.26),382(4.29)	44-2155-80
7H-Benzo[c]phenoxazin-5(12aH)-one, 6-chloro-12a-methoxy-	dioxan	257(4.35),380(4.24)	44-2155-80
$C_{17}H_{12}ClN_3$ [1,2,4]Triazolo[4,3-a]quinoline, 7-chloro-1-methyl-5-phenyl-	EtOH	225s(4.58),232(4.58), 238s(4.54),250s(4.31), 303(3.97),313(3.94), 327(3.78)	4-0575-80
$C_{17}H_{12}ClN_3O$ Oxireno[c][1,2,4]triazolo[4,3-a]quinoline, 8-chloro-1a,9b-dihydro-4-methyl-9b-phenyl-	EtOH	210(4.58),243s(4.19), 251(4.21),281s(3.03), 293(2.76)	4-0575-80
$C_{17}H_{12}ClN_3O_2$ 4H-1,2,4-Triazole-3-carboxaldehyde, 4-(2-benzoyl-4-chlorophenyl)-5-methyl- (methanolate)	EtOH	211s(4.47),253(4.16), 286(3.53)	4-0575-80

Compound	Solvent	λ_{max} (log ϵ)	Ref.
$C_{17}H_{12}ClN_3O_2S$			
Benzamide, N-[5-acetyl-3-(3-chlorophen-yl)-1,3,4-thiadiazol-2(3H)-ylidene]-	EtOH	238(3.98),283s(4.11),330(4.05)	4-1713-80
Benzamide, N-[5-acetyl-3-(4-chlorophen-yl)-1,3,4-thiadiazol-2(3H)-ylidene]-	EtOH	234(4.03),282(4.23),330(4.22)	4-1713-80
$C_{17}H_{12}ClN_3O_4$			
8-Azabicyclo[3.2.1]oct-3-ene-6-carbo-nitrile, 8-[3-(2-chloro-5-nitrophen-yl)-3-oxo-1-propenyl]-2-oxo-, trans	$CHCl_3$	245(4.20),290(4.38)	39-0362-80C
$C_{17}H_{12}ClN_5O$			
1H-Indole-2,3-dione, 1-methyl-, 3-[(3-chloro-2(1H)-quinoxalinylidene)hy-drazone], (E,Z)-	EtOH	332(3.95),425s(4.17),455s(4.27),471(4.29),490s(4.22),522s(3.84)	103-1073-80
(Z,Z)-	EtOH	328s(3.97),408(4.46)	103-1073-80
$C_{17}H_{12}F_3NO_2$			
Phenol, 2-methyl-6-[4-phenyl-3-(tri-fluoromethyl)-5-isoxazolyl]-	EtOH	260(3.85)	114-0389-80B
$C_{17}H_{12}F_3NO_3$			
Phenol, 5-methoxy-2-[4-phenyl-3-(tri-fluoromethyl)-5-isoxazolyl]-	EtOH	260(4.00)	114-0389-80B
$C_{17}H_{12}INOS_3$			
Benzenecarbothioic acid, 2-iodo-, S-[2,5-dihydro-4-(4-methylphenyl)-5-thioxo-3-isothiazolyl] ester	$CHCl_3$	272(4.09),316(4.22),423(4.21)	39-2693-80C
$C_{17}H_{12}N_2$			
Benz[a]acridin-8-amine	MeOH	231(4.48),278s(4.31),290(4.39),303(4.31)	39-1233-80C
	MeOH-acid	226(4.45),233(4.46),277(4.40),287(4.44),297s(4.07),332(3.93),368(3.51),387(3.63),408(3.89)	39-1233-80C
$C_{17}H_{12}N_2O$			
Diazene, (2-naphthalenylcarbonyl)phen-yl-	$CHCl_3$	288(4.25),492(1.98)	39-1212-80C
3-Furancarbonitrile, 2-amino-4,5-di-phenyl-	MeOH	204(4.60),231(4.20),271(4.01),320(4.14)	73-1581-80
6H-Pyrido[4,3-b]carbazole-5-carboxalde-hyde, 11-methyl-	EtOH	210(4.20),225(4.23),231s(4.22),239s(4.15),261(4.14),291(4.39),335(3.54),358(3.56),404(3.44)	88-4027-80
	EtOH-HCl	209(4.17),222s(4.10),241(4.11),251s(4.07),276s(4.04),306(4.35),354(3.84),410(3.96)	88-4027-80
$C_{17}H_{12}N_2O_2$			
Dibenzo[b,h][1,6]naphthyridin-6(5H)-one, 11-methoxy-	MeOH	220(4.70),286(4.82),355(3.79),374(3.77),394s(3.58)	39-0512-80C
	MeOH-acid	218(4.58),286(4.64),310(4.27),352(3.68),373(3.65),398s(3.54),	39-0512-80C

Compound	Solvent	λ_{max}(log ϵ)	Ref.
(cont.) Pyrrolo[3,4-b]indole-1,3(2H,4H)-dione, 6-methyl-2-phenyl-	MeOH	430(3.15) 246(4.41),316(4.08)	39-0512-80C 78-1801-80
C₁₇H₁₂N₂O₂S 2H-Pyrimido[2,1-b]benzothiazolium, 3,4- dihydro-1-methyl-2,4-dioxo-3-phenyl-, hydroxide, inner salt	MeOH	213(4.50),255(4.39), 330(3.65)	44-2474-80
2H-1,3-Thiazino[3,2-a]benzimidazolium, 3,4-dihydro-10-methyl-2,4-dioxo-3- phenyl-, hydroxide, inner salt	CHCl₃	242s(4.13),255(4.23), 323(4.15)	44-2474-80
2H-1,3-Thiazino[3,2-a]benzimidazol- 2-one, 4-methoxy-3-phenyl-	MeOH	218s(4.22),264(4.57), 305(3.67)	44-2474-80
5H-Thiazolo[3,2-a]quinazolinium, 1-hy- droxy-4-methyl-5-oxo-2-phenyl-, hydroxide, inner salt	MeCN	273(4.15),309(4.20), 444(4.06)	2-0638-80
C₁₇H₁₂N₂O₂S₂ Thiazolo[3,2-a]pyridinium, 3-hydroxy- 2-[(3-methyl-2(3H)-benzothiazolyli- dene)acetyl]-, hydroxide, inner salt	EtOH	474(4.46)	103-0227-80
C₁₇H₁₂N₂O₄ 1(4H)-Naphthalenone, 2-methoxy-4-[(4- nitrophenyl)imino]-	EtOH	248(4.12),256(4.10), 304(4.31),406s(3.72)	94-1207-80
C₁₇H₁₂N₂O₄S 1(2H)-Naphthalenone, 2-diazo-5-[[(4- methylphenyl)sulfonyl]oxy]-	EPA	214(4.19),226(4.25), 265(3.88),345(3.71), 400(3.70)	135-0064-80
2,4,6(1H,3H,5H)-Pyrimidinetrione, 5- (4H-[1]benzothieno[3,2-b]pyran-4- ylidene)-1,3-dimethyl-	dioxan	318(4.06),441(4.53)	83-0557-80
C₁₇H₁₂N₂O₅ 2,4,6(1H,3H,5H)-Pyrimidinetrione, 1,3-dimethyl-5-(4H-pyrano[3,2-b]- benzofuran-4-ylidene)-	dioxan	226(4.2),317(4.02), 432(4.44)	83-0557-80
C₁₇H₁₂N₂O₅S Benzenesulfonic acid, 4-methoxy-, 6-diazo-5,6-dihydro-5-oxo-1- naphthalenyl ester	EPA	213(4.20),227(4.28), 266(3.83),345(3.80), 403(3.76)	135-0064-80
C₁₇H₁₂N₃O₈ 4H-Cyclopenta[b]quinoxaline-1,2,3-tri- carboxylic acid, 6-nitro-, trimethyl ester, ion(1-)	MeCN	291(4.53),305(4.53), 345(4.54),505(3.55)	124-0750-80
C₁₇H₁₂N₄ 1H-Pyrazolo[3,4-d]pyrimidine, 1,3-di- phenyl-	EtOH	247(4.36),330(3.72)	114-0127-80C
C₁₇H₁₂N₄O 1H-Pyrazolo[3,4-d]pyrimidine, 1,3-di- methyl-, 5-oxide	EtOH	260(4.17),291(4.30), 384(3.66)	114-0127-80C
C₁₇H₁₂N₄O₄S Benzamide, N-[5-acetyl-3-(3-nitrophen- yl)-1,3,4-thiadiazol-2(3H)-ylidene]-	EtOH	242(3.87),279s(4.20), 328(3.98)	4-1713-80

Compound	Solvent	λ_{max}(log ϵ)	Ref.
Benzamide, N-[5-acetyl-3-(4-nitrophenyl)-1,3,4-thiadiazol-2(3H)-ylidene]-	EtOH	246(4.27),272s(4.31), 325(4.39)	4-1713-80
$C_{17}H_{12}N_6O_4$ 2,5-Pyrrolidinedione, 1-[[4-[(4-azidophenyl)azo]benzoyl]oxy]-	$CHCl_3$	365(4.52)	69-4423-80
$C_{17}H_{12}O$ Ethanone, 1-(4H-cyclopenta[def]phenanthren-1-yl)-	C_6H_{12}	250(4.47),279(3.94), 315(3.93),342(3.44), 359(3.32)	44-1783-80
Ethanone, 1-(4H-cyclopenta[def]phenanthren-2-yl)-	C_6H_{12}	262(4.64),270(4.93), 297(4.19),345(3.21)	44-1783-80
Ethanone, 1-(4H-cyclopenta[def]phenanthren-3-yl)-	C_6H_{12}	252(4.51),284(3.82), 314(4.13),326(4.10), 347(3.29),364(3.28)	44-1783-80
Ethanone, 1-(4H-cyclopenta[def]phenanthren-8-yl)-	C_6H_{12}	255(4.37),279(4.07), 316(3.93),328(3.87)	44-1783-80
$C_{17}H_{12}O_2$ 4H-1-Benzopyran-4-one, 2-(2-phenylethenyl)-, (E)-	MeOH	240(4.10),328(4.52)	2-0615B-80
4H-Pyran-4-one, 2,6-diphenyl-	EtOH	<u>256s(4.3)</u>,290(4.3)	97-0261-80
$C_{17}H_{12}O_4$ Benzeneacetic acid, 2-oxo-2H-1-benzopyran-7-yl ester	EtOH	214(4.28),283(4.02), 313(3.98)	102-2219-80
	EtOH-NaOH	216(4.17),229(3.99), 378(4.33)	102-2219-80
$C_{17}H_{12}O_5$ 6H-Benzofuro[3,2-c][1]benzopyran-6-one, 3,9-dimethoxy-	pH -2.1	342.5(4.12)	149-0143-80B
	pH -4.3	354(4.12)	149-0143-80B
	pH -8.2	370(4.09)	149-0143-80B
	EtOH	301(3.66),342(4.33), 355s(--)	149-0143-80B
	ether	240(4.16),302(3.71), 338(4.30),348(4.16), 356(4.15)	149-0143-80B
	MeCN	241(4.16),303(3.71), 340(4.30),353s(--)	149-0143-80B
	DMSO	304(3.70),339(4.19), 357s(--)	149-0143-80B
2H-1-Benzopyran-4-carboxylic acid, 7-methoxy-2-oxo-, phenyl ester	EtOH	348(4.04)	95-0289-80
4H-1-Benzopyran-4-one, 2-(1,3-benzodioxol-5-yl)-7-methoxy-	MeOH	235(4.37),335(4.26)	118-0874-80
$C_{17}H_{12}O_6$ 2-Anthracenecarboxylic acid, 9,10-dihydro-4,5-dimethoxy-9,10-dioxo-	EtOH	227(4.17),259(3.95), 389(3.54)	44-0020-80
$C_{17}H_{12}O_7$ 2-Anthracenecarboxylic acid, 9,10-dihydro-1-hydroxy-4,5-dimethoxy-9,10-dioxo-	EtOH	228(3.55),258(3.27), 267(3.76),286(2.53), 410s(3.05),434(3.10), 461s(2.88)	44-0020-80
$C_{17}H_{13}BrN_2OS$ Phenol, 4-bromo-2-[[[4-(4-methylphenyl)-2-thiazolyl]imino]methyl]-	pH 5	390(3.98)	2-0492-80

Compound	Solvent	$\lambda_{max}(\log \epsilon)$	Ref.
$C_{17}H_{13}BrN_2O_2$			
5,8-Quinolinedione, 7-bromo-6-[(2,6-di-methylphenyl)amino]-	n.s.g.	234(4.34),272(4.20), 480(3.51)	2-0512-80
$C_{17}H_{13}BrO_5$			
9,10-Anthracenedione, 1-bromo-2-(hy-droxymethyl)-4,5-dimethoxy-	EtOH	261(4.50),280s(4.08), 375(3.80)	44-0020-80
$C_{17}H_{13}Br_2S_2$			
1,4-Dithiinium, 2,5-dibromo-1-methyl-3,6-diphenyl-, tetrafluoroborate	MeCN	282(4.11)	44-0933-80
$C_{17}H_{13}ClN_2O$			
Diazene, (2-chlorophenyl)(2-methoxy-1-naphthalenyl)-	EtOH	370(3.74)	32-0549-80
Diazene, (3-chlorophenyl)(2-methoxy-1-naphthalenyl)-	EtOH	389(3.65)	32-0549-80
Diazene, (4-chlorophenyl)(2-methoxy-1-naphthalenyl)-	EtOH	386(3.66)	32-0549-80
3H-Pyrazol-3-one, 4-[(4-chlorophenyl)-methylene]-2,4-dihydro-5-methyl-2-phenyl-	n.s.g.	250(4.35),330(4.57), 460(2.95)	124-0642-80
$C_{17}H_{13}ClN_2OS$			
4-Imidazolidinone, 5-[(2-chlorophenyl)-methylene]-3-(4-methylphenyl)-2-thi-oxo-	EtOH	364(4.56)	56-0683-80
4-Imidazolidinone, 5-[(3-chlorophenyl)-methylene]-3-(4-methylphenyl)-2-thi-oxo-	EtOH	374(4.59)	56-0683-80
4-Imidazolidinone, 5-[(4-chlorophenyl)-methylene]-3-(4-methylphenyl)-2-thi-oxo-	EtOH	380(4.64)	56-0683-80
4(5H)-Thiazolone, 5-[(2-chlorophenyl)-methylene]-2-[(phenylmethyl)amino]-	MeOH	299(3.84),333(4.31)	48-0835-80
$C_{17}H_{13}ClN_2OSe$			
4-Imidazolidinone, 5-[(2-chlorophenyl)-methylene]-3-(4-methylphenyl)-2-sel-enoxo-	EtOH	395(4.49)	56-0683-80
4-Imidazolidinone, 5-[(3-chlorophenyl)-methylene]-3-(4-methylphenyl)-2-sel-enoxo-	EtOH	400(4.51)	56-0683-80
4-Imidazolidinone, 5-[(3-chlorophenyl)-methylene]-3-(4-methylphenyl)-2-sel-enoxo-	EtOH	400(4.52)	56-0683-80
$C_{17}H_{13}ClN_2O_2$			
8-Azabicyclo[3.2.1]oct-3-ene-6-carbo-nitrile, 8-[3-(4-chlorophenyl-3-oxo-1-propenyl]-2-oxo-, trans-endo	CHCl₃	270(4.13),330(4.32)	39-0362-80C
exo	CHCl₃	265(3.91),325(4.42)	39-0362-80C
2,4-Imidazolidinedione, 5-[(2-chloro-phenyl)methylene]-3-(4-methylphenyl)-	EtOH	320(4.31)	56-0683-80
2,4-Imidazolidinedione, 5-[(3-chloro-phenyl)methylene]-3-(4-methylphenyl)-	EtOH	320(4.41)	56-0683-80
2,4-Imidazolidinedione, 5-[(4-chloro-phenyl)methylene]-3-(4-methylphenyl)-	EtOH	324(4.44)	56-0683-80
1,4-Naphthalenedione, 5-amino-2-chloro-3-[(4-methylphenyl)amino]-	EtOH	265(4.43),480(4.07)	40-1862-80

Compound	Solvent	$\lambda_{max}(\log \epsilon)$	Ref.
1,4-Naphthalenedione, 5-amino-3-chloro-2-[(4-methylphenyl)amino]-	EtOH	281(4.46),550(3.92)	40-1862-80
1,2,4-Oxadiazole, 3-(4-chlorophenyl)-5-(4-methylphenacyl)-	EtOH	255(4.46),315(3.78)	39-1635-80C
3H-Pyrazol-3-ol, 4-chloro-3,5-diphenyl-, acetate	CHCl$_3$	245(4.34),325(3.61), 375s(2.92)	44-0076-80
$C_{17}H_{13}ClN_2O_3$			
Ethanone, 2-[3-(4-chlorophenyl)-1,2,4-oxadiazol-5-yl]-1-(4-methoxyphenyl)-	EtOH	245(4.46),325(3.60)	39-1635-80C
$C_{17}H_{13}ClN_4O$			
4bH,7H-Oxazirino[2,3-d][1,2,4]triazolo-[4,3-a][1,4]benzodiazepine, 3-chloro-10-methyl-4b-phenyl-	EtOH	235s(4.22),263s(2.98), 269s(2.89),275s(2.77), 281s(2.72)	87-0643-80
4H-[1,2,4]Triazolo[4,3-a][1,4]benzodi-azepine, 8-chloro-1-methyl-6-phenyl-, 5-oxide	EtOH	227(4.46),256(4.22), 262s(4.21),308(4.04)	87-0643-80
4H-[1,2,4]Triazolo[4,3-a][1,4]benzodi-azepin-4-ol, 8-chloro-1-methyl-6-phen-yl-, ethanol solvate	EtOH	223(4.53),246s(4.12), 266s(3.79),275s(3.69), 285s(3.56),298s(3.31)	87-0643-80
4H-[1,2,4]Triazolo[4,3-a][1,4]benzodi-azepin-4-one, 8-chloro-5,6-dihydro-1-methyl-6-phenyl-	EtOH	238(4.12),270s(3.27), 280s(2.86)	87-0643-80
$C_{17}H_{13}ClN_4O_3$			
1H-Imidazole-4-carboxamide, N-(4-chloro-phenyl)-5-methyl-2-(4-nitrophenyl)-	EtOH	275(4.44),351(4.36)	4-1723-80
$C_{17}H_{13}ClO$			
2,4-Pentadien-1-one, 5-chloro-1,5-di-phenyl-, (Z,E)-	EtOH	339(4.51)	40-1804-80
$C_{17}H_{13}ClO_3$			
[1,1'-Biphenyl]-4-butanoic acid, 2'-chloro-α-methylene-γ-oxo- (itanoxone)	EtOH	267(4.24)	36-0049-80
[1,1'-Biphenyl]-4-butanoic acid, 2'-chloro-β-methylene-γ-oxo-	EtOH	269(4.15)	36-0049-80
[1,1'-Biphenyl]-4-butanoic acid, 4'-chloro-α-methylene-γ-oxo-	EtOH	285(4.47)	36-0049-80
2-Butenoic acid, 4-(2'-chloro[1,1'-bi-phenyl]-4-yl)-2-methyl-4-oxo-, (E)-	EtOH	287(4.25)	36-0049-80
2(5H)-Furanone, 5-(2'-chloro[1,1'-bi-phenyl]-4-yl)-5-hydroxy-3-methyl-	EtOH	249(4.12)	36-0049-80
2(5H)-Furanone, 5-(2'-chloro[1,1'-bi-phenyl]-4-yl)-5-hydroxy-4-methyl-	EtOH	248(4.16)	36-0049-80
$C_{17}H_{13}ClO_5$			
9,10-Anthracenedione, 2-(chloromethyl)-1-hydroxy-4,8-dimethoxy-	MeOH	229(4.37),251(4.16), 274(3.95),381s(--), 447(3.93),467(3.95), 495s(--)	24-2994-80
$C_{17}H_{13}F_3N_2OS_2$			
4-Thiazolidinone, 3-methyl-5-[[1-meth-yl-2-(trifluoromethyl)-4(1H)-quino-linylidene]ethylidene]-2-thioxo-	MeCN	526(4.64),551(4.69), 588s(4.53)	124-0827-80
4-Thiazolidinone, 3-methyl-5-[[1-meth-yl-4-(trifluoromethyl)-2(1H)-quino-linylidene]ethylidene]-2-thioxo-	MeCN	513s(4.66),540(4.70), 575s(4.49)	124-0827-80

Compound	Solvent	$\lambda_{max}(\log \epsilon)$	Ref.
$C_{17}H_{13}N$			
Benzenamine, N-(2-naphthalenylmethyl-ene)-, cis	CH_2Cl_2 at $-70°$	226(4.54),244(4.73), 253(4.84),280(4.16), 285(4.24),292(4.12), 297(4.19),326(3.63), 332(3.64),339(3.65), 360(3.34)	39-1282-80B
trans	CH_2Cl_2 at $-70°$	233s(--),240(4.49), 249s(--),258(4.58), 285(4.35),297(4.36), 318(4.20),332(4.22), 346(4.16)	39-1282-80B
2-Naphthalenamine, N-(phenylmethylene)-, cis	$C_6H_{11}Me$ at $-100°$	228(3.77),240(3.72), 245s(--),267s(--), 333(3.67),370s(--)	39-1282-80B
trans	$C_6H_{11}Me$ at $-100°$	225(4.66),232s(--), 238(4.59),245(4.50), 252(4.43),269(4.51), 330(4.06),348(3.98)	39-1282-80B
$C_{17}H_{13}NO$			
Ethanone, 1-phenyl-2-(3-quinolinyl)-	EtOH	233(4.41),245s(4.15), 280(3.59),303(3.40), 317(3.40)	39-0072-80C
	EtOH-HCl	238(4.56),310s(3.76), 317(3.79)	39-0072-80C
	EtOH-NaOH	232(4.30),242(4.15), 283(3.78),320(3.58), 360(3.83),420(3.72)	39-0072-80C
$C_{17}H_{13}NOS$			
[1]Benzothieno[3,2-b]quinolin-11(5H)-one, 5-ethyl-	MeOH	237(4.28),268(4.63), 277(4.72),306(4.00), 375(4.06),393(4.18)	83-0027-80
$C_{17}H_{13}NOS_3$			
Benzenecarbothioic acid, S-[2,5-dihy-dro-4-(4-methylphenyl)-5-thioxo-3-isothiazolyl] ester	$CHCl_3$	270(4.25),318(4.31)	39-2693-80C
Benzenecarbothioic acid, O-[5-(methyl-thio)-4-phenyl-3-isothiazolyl] ester	$CHCl_3$	265(4.33),322(3.75), 397(4.49)	39-2693-80C
$C_{17}H_{13}NO_2$			
Benzofuro[2,3-b]quinoline, 11-ethoxy-	EtOH	222(4.57),250(4.70), 258(4.86),275(3.93), 287s(3.89),305s(4.17), 317(4.33),330(4.15), 342s(3.80)	18-1057-80
1,2-Naphthalenedione, 4-(methylphenyl-amino)-	EtOH	246(4.36),274s(4.08), 321(3.77),370(3.61), 466(3.82)	94-1207-80
1,2-Naphthalenedione, 4-[(3-methylphen-yl)amino]-	EtOH	238(4.35),278(4.22), 330s(3.72),450(3.66)	94-1207-80
1,2-Naphthalenedione, 4-[(4-methylphen-yl)amino]-	EtOH	244(4.40),282(4.14), 340s(3.75),467(3.71)	94-1207-80
1(4H)-Naphthalenone, 2-methoxy-4-(phen-ylimino)-	EtOH	246s(4.08),252s(4.06), 288(4.28),336(3.84), 433(3.51)	94-1207-80
5(4H)-Oxazolone, 4-[(4-methylphenyl)-methylene]-2-phenyl-	$CHCl_3$	390(4.65)	103-0701-80
2(1H)-Pyridinone, 3-hydroxy-4,6-diphenyl-	$CHCl_3$	335(4.05)	39-2743-80C

Compound	Solvent	$\lambda_{max}(\log \epsilon)$	Ref.
2(1H)-Pyridinone, 5-hydroxy-4,6-diphenyl-	CHCl₃	333(4.05)	39-2743-80C
1H-Pyrrole-2,5-dione, 1-methyl-3,4-diphenyl-	60% dioxan	365(3.60)	40-0837-80
$C_{17}H_{13}NO_2S$			
Indolo[4,5-d]benzo[b]thiophene-2-carboxylic acid, ethyl ester	EtOH	209(4.27),257(4.52), 275(4.49),318(4.43)	103-0146-80
Indolo[5,4-d]benzo[b]thiophene-2-carboxylic acid, ethyl ester	EtOH	211(4.36),216(4.28), 252(4.66),250(4.68), 282(4.69),318(4.21)	103-0146-80
Indolo[5,6-d]benzo[b]thiophene-2-carboxylic acid, ethyl ester	EtOH	213(2.42),225(4.47), 266(4.38),276(4.53), 298(4.60),339(3.91), 354(3.95)	103-0146-80
Indolo[6,5-d]benzo[b]thiophene-2-carboxylic acid, ethyl ester	EtOH	204(4.34),232(4.68), 282(4.07),292(4.24), 327(4.42),342(4.39)	103-0146-80
Thiocyanic acid, 3-(4-methoxyphenyl)-3-oxo-1-phenyl-1-propenyl ester	EtOH	326.5(4.51)	2-0266-80
$C_{17}H_{13}NO_2S_2$			
Acetamide, N-(7-methoxy-[1]benzothieno-[3,2-b][1]benzothien-2-yl)-	EtOH	241(4.38),267(4.28), 277(4.43),324(4.54), 338(4.56)	104-0383-80
Thiophene, 3-(methylthio)-5-nitro-2,4-diphenyl-	MeCN	248(4.05),338(3.90)	44-0933-80
$C_{17}H_{13}NO_2S_3$			
Benzenecarbothioic acid, O-[5-(methyl-thio)-4-phenyl-3-isothiazolyl] ester, S-oxide	CHCl₃	273(4.18),402(4.33)	39-2693-80C
$C_{17}H_{13}NO_3$			
2H-Anthra[1,2-d][1,3]oxazine-7,12-dione, 1,4-dihydro-2-methyl-	EtOH	494(3.84)	18-3007-80 +146-0513-80
8H,11H-Benzo[a]pyrano[3,2-g]quinolizine-8,11-dione, 13,13a-dihydro-9-methyl-	EtOH	238(3.87),306(3.76)	95-0571-80
3,1-Benzoxazepine-5-carboxylic acid, 2-phenyl-, methyl ester	MeOH	255(4.43),314(3.86)	94-1157-80
5(4H)-Oxazolone, 4-[(4-methoxyphenyl)-methylene]-2-phenyl-	CHCl₃	380(4.69)	103-0701-80
(E)-	dioxan	228s(4.16),239s(4.19), 243s(4.22),250(4.23), 253(4.21),261(4.14), 278(3.86),390(4.59)	70-0576-80
(Z)-	dioxan	251(4.31),261(4.33), 278s(4.19),365s(4.68), 402s(4.58)	70-0576-80
5(4H)-Oxazolone, 2-(4-methoxyphenyl)-4-(phenylmethylene)-	CHCl₃	375(4.91)	103-0701-80
5(4H)-Oxazolone, 2-(phenylmethoxy)-4-(phenylmethylene)-, (Z)-	CHCl₃	235(3.91),240(3.80), 332(4.53),345(4.40)	39-0858-80C
$C_{17}H_{13}NO_4$			
2H-1-Benzopyran-4-carboxamide, 7-methoxy-2-oxo-N-phenyl-	EtOH	331(4.22)	95-0289-80
1H-Benzo[f]pyrrolo[1,2-a]indole-1-carboxylic acid, 2,3,5,10-tetrahydro-5,10-dioxo-, methyl ester	EtOH	203(4.15),257(4.36), 283(3.93),322(3.64), 334(3.61),338(3.55),	94-1071-80

Compound	Solvent	$\lambda_{max}(\log \epsilon)$	Ref.
(cont.)		348(3.40)	94-1071-80
1,3-Dioxolo[4,5-g]isoquinoline, 7-(1,3-benzodioxol-5-yl)-7,8-dihydro-	MeOH	284(4.11),316(4.04)	2-0556-80
5(4H)-Oxazolone, 4-[(4-hydroxy-3-methoxyphenyl)methylene]-2-phenyl-, (E)-	dioxan	240(4.13),263(4.00),280(3.76),420(4.53)	70-0576-80
(Z)-	dioxan	257s(4.14),266(4.19),280(3.96),400(4.46),417s(4.43)	70-0576-80
$C_{17}H_{13}NO_6S$			
Cyclopenta[b][1,4]benzothiazine-1,2,3-tricarboxylic acid, trimethyl ester	MeCN	287(4.64),372(4.12),390s(4.06),556(3.44)	124-0750-80
$C_{17}H_{13}NO_7$			
Cyclopenta[b][1,4]benzoxazine-1,2,3-tricarboxylic acid, trimethyl ester	MeCN	260(4.55),358(4.27),498(3.28)	124-0750-80
	cation	268(4.54),423(4.25),624(2.90)	124-0750-80
$C_{17}H_{13}N_2O_6$			
4H-Cyclopenta[b]quinoxaline-1,2,3-tricarboxylic acid, trimethyl ester, ion(1-)	EtOH-Et$_3$N	278(4.98),309(4.53),345(4.03),353(4.09),452(3.59)	124-0750-80
$C_{17}H_{13}N_3$			
Benzo[b]pyrido[2,3-h][1,6]naphthyridine, 3,7-dimethyl-	EtOH	212(4.42),253(4.46),266(4.45),291s(4.37),300(4.45)	4-1225-80
Propanedinitrile, (1,2,5-trimethylbenz[cd]indol-3(1H)-ylidene)-	CH$_2$Cl$_2$	271(4.37),342(3.83),490(4.44)	5-0971-80
Quinoline, 4-(1H-benzimidazol-2-yl)-2-methyl-, monoperchlorate	EtOH	205(4.61),236(4.43),320(4.23)	103-1261-80
free base	EtOH	207(4.31),240(4.28),323(4.13)	103-1261-80
Quinoline, 2-(1-methyl-1H-benzimidazol-2-yl)-, monohydriodide	EtOH	206(4.44),245(4.44),285(4.07)	103-1261-80
$C_{17}H_{13}N_3O$			
Pyrido[4,3-b][1,8]phenanthrolin-8(9H)-one, 9,10-dimethyl-	MeOH	213(3.80),243(3.80),255(3.81),269(3.91),276(3.92),323(3.50),338(3.52),404(3.04)	39-0522-80C
	MeOH-acid	261(3.78),279s(3.78),287(3.82),348(3.46),430(2.92)	39-0522-80C
5H-Pyrimido[5,4-b]indole, 2-methoxy-4-phenyl-	EtOH	247(4.28),270(4.15),314(4.30),390(4.00)	103-0970-80
$C_{17}H_{13}N_3O_2$			
[1]Benzopyrano[2,3-b][1,5]benzodiazepin-13(6H)-one, 12-amino-2-methyl-	EtOH	247(4.23),289(4.30),309(4.22)	44-1964-80
Indolo[7,6-g]indole, 3,8-dihydro-1-(2-nitro-1-propenyl)-	EtOH	207(4.31),264(4.84),269(4.86),296(4.28),352(4.44),410(4.60)	103-1139-80
1H-Isoindole-1,3(2H)-dione, 2-(2-amino-1-methyl-1H-indol-3-yl)-, monohydrochloride	EtOH	224(4.54),284(3.92)	103-0368-80
2-Propenamide, 3-phenyl-N-(5-phenyl-1,3,4-oxadiazol-2-yl)-	MeOH	225(4.22),297(4.71)	48-0434-80

Compound	Solvent	$\lambda_{max}(\log \epsilon)$	Ref.
$C_{17}H_{13}N_3O_2S$			
Benzamide, N-(5-acetyl-3-phenyl-1,3,4-thiadiazol-2(3H)-ylidene)-	EtOH	238(3.99),287s(4.29), 332(4.40)	4-1713-80
$C_{17}H_{13}N_3O_2S_3$			
2-Thiophenecarbonitrile, 3-amino-4-[[(1,3-dihydro-1,3-dioxo-2H-inden-2-ylidene)(methylthio)methyl]amino]-5-(methylthio)-	EtOH	230(4.47),240(4.45), 305(4.39),352(4.47)	95-0699-80
$C_{17}H_{13}N_3O_2Se$			
Benzamide, N-(5-acetyl-3-phenyl-1,3,4-selenadiazol-2(3H)-ylidene)-	EtOH	277(4.16),338(4.25)	4-1185-80
$C_{17}H_{13}N_3O_3$			
3H-Pyrazol-3-one, 2,4-dihydro-5-methyl-4-[(4-nitrophenyl)methylene]-2-phenyl-	n.s.g.	247(4.44),320(4.56), 480(3.15)	124-0642-80
Pyrimidine, 2-methoxy-5-nitro-4,6-diphenyl-	EtOH	253(4.24),299(4.20)	103-0970-80
$C_{17}H_{13}N_3O_8$			
4H-Cyclopenta[b]quinoxaline-1,2,3-tricarboxylic acid, 6-nitro-, trimethyl ester	MeCN	273(4.63),330(4.50), 520(3.37)	124-0750-80
	anion	291(4.53),305(4.35), 345(4.54),505(3.55)	124-0750-80
	cation	270(4.53),320(4.40), 390s(4.13),405(4.27), 640(2.96)	124-0750-80
$C_{17}H_{13}N_5$			
5H-Pyrazolo[1',2':2,3][1,2,3]triazolo-[4,5-a]phenazin-4-ium, 1,3-dimethyl-, hydroxide, inner salt	C_6H_{12}	<u>348(5.5),550(4.9)</u>, 596(4.92)	39-2904-80C
	$CHCl_3$	573(4.87)	39-2904-80C
	$CHCl_3$-MeOH	575(4.88)	39-2904-80C
[1,2,4]Triazolo[1,5-a]pyrimidin-2-amine, 5,7-diphenyl-	EtOH	205(4.57),225(4.36), 255(4.38),270(4.40), 355(4.11)	124-0835-80
[1,2,4]Triazolo[4,3-a]pyrimidin-3-amine, 5,7-diphenyl-	EtOH	203(4.42),240(4.00), 275(4.46),390(3.53)	124-0835-80
$C_{17}H_{13}N_5O$			
Pyrimidine, 5-azido-2-methoxy-4,6-diphenyl-	EtOH	255(4.32),330(3.81)	103-0970-80
$C_{17}H_{14}BrNO_2$			
1H-Isoindole-1,3(2H)-dione, 2-[1-(bromomethyl)-2-phenylethyl]-, (S)-	EtOH	294(3.30)	44-4006-80
$C_{17}H_{14}BrNO_3$			
Acetamide, N-[2-[[3-(4-bromophenyl)-3-oxo-1-propenyl]oxy]phenyl]-, (E)-	dioxan	249(4.22),276(4.33)	48-0099-80
2-Propen-1-one, 3-[(2-acetoxyphenyl)-amino]-1-(4-bromophenyl)-, (Z)-	dioxan	261(4.17),379(4.50)	48-0099-80
$C_{17}H_{14}BrN_3O$			
1H-1,2,4-Triazolium, 1-(phenylmethyl)-, 4-[2-(4-bromophenyl)-2-oxoethylide]	pH 13	322(4.02)	80-0407-80
$C_{17}H_{14}ClNO$			
2(1H)-Quinolinone, 3-(2-chloroethyl)-	$CHCl_3$	243(4.09),275(3.82),	150-0414-80S

Compound	Solvent	$\lambda_{max}(\log \epsilon)$	Ref.
1-phenyl- (cont.)		284(3.79),323s(3.66), 332(3.73),346s(3.57)	150-0414-80S
$C_{17}H_{14}ClNO_3$			
Acetamide, N-[2-[[3-(4-chlorophenyl)- 3-oxo-1-propenyl]oxy]phenyl]-	dioxan	250(4.27),276(4.31)	48-0099-80
2-Butenoic acid, 2-(benzoylamino)- 3-(4-chlorophenyl)-, (Z)-	EtOH	202(4.45),222(4.25), 260(4.08)	118-0901-80
2-Propen-1-one, 3-[(2-acetoxyphenyl)- amino]-1-(4-chlorophenyl)-, (Z)-	dioxan	260(4.15),378(4.48)	48-0099-80
$C_{17}H_{14}ClNO_4$			
4H-Furo[3,2-b]pyrrole-5-carboxylic acid, 4-acetyl-2-(4-chlorophenyl)-, ethyl ester	MeOH	342(4.77),357(4.74)	73-2949-80
$C_{17}H_{14}ClN_3O$			
Benzenemethanamine, α-[[3-(4-chloro- phenyl)-1,2,4-oxadiazol-5-yl]meth- ylene]-4-methyl-	EtOH	245(4.38),325(4.34)	39-1635-80C
$C_{17}H_{14}ClN_3O_2$			
Benzenemethanamine, α-[[3-(4-chloro- phenyl)-1,2,4-oxadiazol-5-yl]meth- ylene]-4-methoxy-	EtOH	250(4.20),340(4.32)	39-1635-80C
$C_{17}H_{14}ClN_3O_3$			
Methanone, [2-[3,5-bis(hydroxymethyl)- 4H-1,2,4-triazol-4-yl]-5-chloro- phenyl]phenyl-	EtOH	212s(4.43),255(4.11), 285s(3.51)	4-0575-80
$C_{17}H_{14}ClN_5$			
4H-[1,2,4]Triazolo[4,3-a][1,4]benzodi- azepin-4-amine, 8-chloro-1-methyl-6- phenyl-	EtOH	223(4.59),247s(4.17), 265(3.85),290s(3.53)	87-0643-80
6H-[1,2,4]Triazolo[4,3-a][1,4]benzodi- azepin-4-amine, 8-chloro-1-methyl-6- phenyl-	EtOH	274s(3.58),283(3.47)	87-0643-80
$C_{17}H_{14}Cl_2N_2O$			
1H-[1,4]Benzodiazepine-1-carboxalde- hyde, 7-chloro-2-(chloromethyl)- 2,3-dihydro-5-phenyl-	EtOH	222(4.50),249(4.14)	4-0373-80
$C_{17}H_{14}CrO_4$			
Chromium, tricarbonyl[(3b,4,5,6,7,7a- η)-3a,8a-dihydro-3,8a-dimethylcyclo- pent[a]inden-8(1H)-one]-	EtOH	325(3.98),420(3.48)	35-4410-80
Chromium, tricarbonyl[(4b,5,6,7,8,8a- η)-1,2,9,9a-tetrahydro-9a-methyl- 3H-fluoren-3-one]-	EtOH	275(4.15),321(3.85), 450(3.45)	35-4410-80
$C_{17}H_{14}FNO_3$			
Acetamide, N-[2-[[3-(4-fluorophenyl)- 3-oxo-1-propenyl]oxy]phenyl]-, (E)-	dioxan	247(4.31),276(4.26)	48-0099-80
2-Propen-1-one, 3-[(2-acetoxyphenyl)- amino]-1-(4-fluorophenyl)-, (Z)-	dioxan	249(4.09),372(4.47)	48-0099-80
$C_{17}H_{14}F_3N_3$			
Propanedinitrile, [1-[(1,3-dihydro- 1,3,3-trimethyl-2H-indol-2-ylidene)-	EtOH	205(4.25),249(4.00), 481(4.56)	104-1441-80

Compound	Solvent	$\lambda_{max}(\log \epsilon)$	Ref.
methyl]-2,2,2-trifluoroethylidene]-			104-1441-80
$C_{17}H_{14}INO_2$			
1H-Isoindole-1,3(2H)-dione, 2-[1-(iodo-methyl)-2-phenylethyl]-, (S)-	EtOH	293(3.36)	44-4006-80
$C_{17}H_{14}INO_3$			
Acetamide, N-[2-[[3-(4-iodophenyl)-3-oxo-1-propenyl]oxy]phenyl]-, (E)-	dioxan	242(4.20),284(4.38)	48-0099-80
2-Propen-1-one, 3-[(2-acetoxyphenyl)-amino]-1-(4-iodophenyl), (Z)-	dioxan	271(4.09),379(4.51)	48-0099-80
$C_{17}H_{14}NO_2S_2$			
1,4-Dithiinium, 1-methyl-2-nitro-3,6-diphenyl-, tetrafluoroborate	MeCN	230(4.22),288(4.14)	44-0933-80
$C_{17}H_{14}N_2$			
2,3'-Bipyridine, 5'-methyl-6'-phenyl-	MeOH	262(3.9),267(3.9)	103-0951-80
1H-Pyrazole, 3-(2-ethenylphenyl)-5-phenyl-	MeOH	238(4.51),353(4.52)	44-3756-80
6H-Pyrido[4,3-b]carbazole, 5,11-dimethyl- (ellipticine)	EtOH	224(4.48),237s(4.43), 245s(4.34),275(4.76), 285(4.88),293(4.85), 331(3.85),346(3.70), 380(3.58),400(3.58)	100-0294-80
$C_{17}H_{14}N_2O$			
[2,3'-Bipyridine]-5'-ol, 2'-methyl-6'-phenyl-	MeOH	242(4.4),324(4.4)	103-0951-80
[3,4'-Bipyridine]-5-ol, 2-methyl-6-phenyl-	MeOH	239(4.0),318(4.3)	103-0951-80
Diazene, (2-methoxy-1-naphthalenyl)-phenyl-	EtOH	386(3.71)	32-0549-80
Dibenzo[b,h][1,6]naphthyridin-6(5H)-one, 7,12-dihydro-12-methyl-	MeOH	233(4.78),258(4.50), 334(4.17),356s(4.06)	39-0512-80C
11H-Indeno[1,2-c]isoquinolin-5-amine, 4-methoxy-	EtOH-H_2SO_4	216(4.54),245(4.41), 329(4.22),341(4.27), 381(4.03),396s(3.94)	18-2885-80
11H-Indeno[1,2-c]isoquinolin-5-amine, 7-methoxy-	EtOH-H_2SO_4	216(4.49),225s(4.47), 250(4.29),257(4.28), 318(4.13),332(4.16), 380(4.27),400(4.25)	18-2885-80
2(1H)-Pyrazinone, 1-methyl-5,6-diphenyl-	EtOH	266(4.08),347(3.86)	88-2529-80
3H-Pyrazol-3-one, 2,4-dihydro-5-methyl-2-phenyl-4-(phenylmethylene)-	n.s.g.	250(4.32),320(4.51), 445(2.91)	124-0642-80
$C_{17}H_{14}N_2OS$			
1-Naphthaleneacetic acid, [2-(2-thien-yl)methylene]hydrazide	C_6H_{12} EtOH 50% EtOH	307(4.38) 305(4.39) 306(4.57)	115-0151-80 115-0151-80 115-0151-80
Phenol, 2-[[[4-(4-methylphenyl)-2-thia-zolyl]imino]methyl]-	pH 5	380(3.79)	2-0492-80
$C_{17}H_{12}N_2OS_3$			
2(3H)-Isothiazolecarboxamide, 5-(meth-ylthio)-N,4-diphenyl-3-thioxo-	EtOH	272(3.93),380(4.17)	142-0785-80
2(5H)-Isothiazolecarboxamide, 3-mercap-to-4-(4-methylphenyl)-N-phenyl-5-thi-oxo- (chloroform solvate)	EtOH	320(4.25),406(4.17)	142-0785-80

Compound	Solvent	$\lambda_{max}(\log \epsilon)$	Ref.
$C_{17}H_{14}N_2O_2$			
Methanone, (5-hydroxy-3-methyl-1-phenyl-1H-pyrazol-4-yl)phenyl-, m. 115-7°	MeOH	275(4.27)	64-1019-80B
yellow isomer m. 89-90°	MeOH	270(4.82)	64-1019-80B
1-Naphthaleneacetic acid, N-[(2-furanyl)methylene]hydrazide	C_6H_{12}	284(4.42),301(4.49)	115-0151-80
	EtOH	283(4.47),296(4.55)	115-0151-80
	50% EtOH	298(4.58)	115-0151-80
1H-Pyrazol-5-ol, 3-methyl-1-phenyl-, benzoate	MeOH	235(4.49)	64-1019-80B
3H-Pyrazol-3-one, 4-benzoyldihydro-5-methyl-1-phenyl-	EtOH	213(4.50),237(4.57), 276(4.57)	90-1155-80
	n.s.g.	276(4.57)	64-0715-80B
sodium salt	n.s.g.	276(4.31)	64-0715-80B
$C_{17}H_{14}N_2O_3$			
Methanone, [4-(1,3-benzodioxol-5-yl)-4,5-dihydro-1H-pyrazol-5-yl]phenyl-	MeOH	332(3.68)	2-0980-80
Oxazolium, 5-hydroxy-3-methyl-2-phenyl-4-[(phenylamino)carbonyl]-, hydroxide, inner salt	MeCN	229(4.12),270(4.05), 348(4.26)	5-1836-80
$C_{17}H_{14}N_2O_4$			
1H-Benzo[f]pyrrolo[1,2-a]indole-5,10-dione, 11-[[(aminocarbonyl)oxy]methyl]-2,3-dihydro-	MeCN	241s(4.25),261(4.50), 279s(4.28),330(3.76), 412(3.57)	44-1260-80
$C_{17}H_{14}N_2O_5$			
Acetamide, N-[2-[[3-(4-nitrophenyl)-3-oxo-1-propenyl]oxy]phenyl]-	dioxan	247(4.29),270(4.29)	48-0099-80
2-Butenoic acid, 2-(benzoylamino)-3-(3-nitrophenyl)-, (E)-	EtOH	202(4.47),220(4.27), 262(4.27)	118-0901-80
(Z)-	EtOH	202(4.45),224(4.31), 257(4.23)	118-0901-80
2-Butenoic acid, 2-(benzoylamino)-3-(4-nitrophenyl)-, (Z)-	EtOH	202(4.48),224(4.25)	118-0901-80
2-Propen-1-one, 3-[(2-acetoxyphenyl)-amino]-1-(4-nitrophenyl)-, (Z)-	dioxan	265(4.13),399(4.36)	48-0099-80
$C_{17}H_{14}N_2O_6$			
4H-Cyclopenta[b]quinoxaline-1,2,3-tricarboxylic acid, trimethyl ester	MeCN	277(4.82),282(4.82), 348(4.20),369(4.32), 502(3.39)	124-0750-80
	anion	278(4.98),309(4.53), 345(4.03),353(4.09), 452(3.59)	124-0750-80
	cation	280(4.82),405(4.42), 610(3.06)	124-0750-80
$C_{17}H_{14}N_2S$			
Imidazo[2,1-b]thiazole, 2,3-dihydro-5,6-diphenyl-	EtOH	226(4.29),262s(4.06), 297(4.01)	4-0393-80
$C_{17}H_{14}N_4O_2$			
2-Pyrimidinamine, N-methyl-5-nitro-4,6-diphenyl-	EtOH	254(4.34),333(3.60)	103-0970-80
$C_{17}H_{14}N_4O_2S$			
4(1H)-Pyrimidinone, 6-amino-5-nitroso-1-phenyl-2-[(phenylmethyl)thio]-	CHCl$_3$	280s(3.71),310s(2.93), 344(4.13),634(1.78)	95-0515-80
Co(III) chelate	CHCl$_3$	396(4.58)	95-0515-80

Compound	Solvent	$\lambda_{max}(\log \epsilon)$	Ref.
1H-1,2,4-Triazole, 3-(methylthio)-1-(4-nitrophenyl)-5-(2-phenylethenyl)-	MeOH	287(4.85)	48-0434-80
$C_{17}H_{14}N_4O_3$			
Benzenemethanamine, 4-methyl-α-[[3-(4-nitrophenyl)-1,2,4-oxadiazol-5-yl]-methylene]-	EtOH	270(4.34),325(4.32)	39-1635-80C
$C_{17}H_{14}N_4O_3S$			
5H-Pyrazolo[3,4-c]isoquinolin-5-one, 1-amino-3,4-dihydro-4-[(4-methyl-phenyl)sulfonyl]-	EtOH	226(4.58),280(4.22)	95-0456-80
$C_{17}H_{14}N_4O_4$			
Benzenemethanamine, 4-methoxy-α-[[3-(4-nitrophenyl)-1,2,4-oxadiazol-5-yl]-methylene]-	EtOH	270(4.46),333(4.28)	39-1635-80C
$C_{17}H_{14}N_6O$			
2(1H)-Quinoxalinone, 3-(2-oxo-2H-pyrido[1,2-a]pyrimidin-3-yl)-, 2-(2-methylhydrazone)	EtOH	240(4.70),300(4.24), 315(4.25),486(4.20)	94-3537-80
$C_{17}H_{14}O$			
Benzeneacetaldehyde, α-[(2-ethenylphenyl)methylene]-	MeOH	254(4.23),320(4.20)	44-3756-80
2,4,6,12,14-Cyclopentadecapentaene-8,10-diyn-1-one, 7,12-dimethyl-, (E,E,Z,Z,E)-	THF	246(4.12),258(4.16), 305(4.55),385(3.86)	44-3564-80
	CF_3COOH	292(--),352s(--), 367(--),496s(--), 513(--),555(--)	44-3564-80
Ethanone, 1-(8,9-dihydro-4H-cyclopenta-[def]phenanthren-2-yl)-	C_6H_{12}	240(4.01),305(4.29), 322(4.24)	44-1783-80
Naphthalene, 2-methoxy-1-phenyl-	EtOH	233(4.89),273(3.66), 284(3.77),296(3.72), 323(3.38),337(3.45)	104-1463-80
2-Propen-1-one, 3-(2-ethenylphenyl)-1-phenyl-	MeOH	252(4.20),310(4.18)	44-3756-80
$C_{17}H_{14}OS_2$			
1,2-Dithiol-1-ium, 4-hydroxy-3,5-bis(4-methylphenyl)-, hydroxide, inner salt	EtOH	503(4.42)	139-0079-80A
	dioxan	568(4.67)	139-0079-80A
	MeCN	528(4.36)	139-0079-80A
$C_{17}H_{14}O_2$			
Ethanone, 1,1'-(9H-fluorene-4,5-diyl)-bis-	EtOH	246(4.36),275(3.52), 322(3.86)	18-1179-80
$C_{17}H_{14}O_3$			
1,4-Anthracenedione, 5-methoxy-2,3-di-methyl-	CH_2Cl_2	261(4.41),281(4.34), 297(4.13),324(3.56), 433(3.75)	23-1161-80
5H-Indeno[5,6-d]-1,3-dioxol-5-one, 6,7-dihydro-6-(phenylmethyl)-	MeOH	231(4.35),267(3.97), 319(4.04)	35-3056-80
1H-Inden-1-one, 2-(1,3-benzodioxol-5-ylmethyl)-2,3-dihydro-	MeOH	252(4.11),277s(--)	35-3056-80
$C_{17}H_{14}O_3S$			
1H-Inden-1-one, 4,7-dimethoxy-3-(phen-ylthio)-	EtOH	286(3.92),393(3.91)	44-4611-80

Compound	Solvent	$\lambda_{max}(\log \epsilon)$	Ref.
$C_{17}H_{14}O_3S_2$			
1,2-Dithiol-1-ium, 4-hydroxy-3,5-bis(4-methoxyphenyl)-, hydroxide, inner salt	EtOH	520(4.38)	139-0079-80A
	dioxan	571(4.23)	139-0079-80A
	MeCN	556(3.86)	139-0079-80A
$C_{17}H_{14}O_3Se$			
1H-Inden-1-one, 4,7-dimethoxy-3-(phenylseleno)-	EtOH	299(3.89),398(3.95)	44-4611-80
$C_{17}H_{14}O_4$			
4H-1-Benzopyran-4-one, 6-acetoxy-2,3-dihydro-2-phenyl-	EtOH	233(4.92),319(3.84)	18-2938-80
4H-1-Benzopyran-4-one, 2-(4-acetoxyphenyl)-2,3-dihydro-	EtOH	310(3.04)	18-2938-80
4H-1-Benzopyran-4-one, 7-methoxy-2-(4-methoxyphenyl)-	MeOH	230(4.15),255(3.86), 320(4.35)	118-0874-80
4H-1-Benzopyran-4-one, 5,7-dimethoxy-2-phenyl-	MeOH	262(4.32),302(3.91)	118-0874-80
Cyclohepta[de]naphthalene-8-carboxylic acid, 10-hydroxy-6-methoxy-7-methyl-	CHCl$_3$	220(3.76),265(4.14)	120-0250-80
2,5-Furandione, dihydro-4-[1-(2-methoxy-1-naphthalenyl)ethylidene]-	CHCl$_3$	259(4.54)	120-0250-80
Methanone, (6-methoxy-2-benzofuranyl)-(4-methoxyphenyl)-	MeOH	228s(4.23),259s(3.81), 307s(4.07),347(4.33)	18-1769-80
1H-Phenalene-2-acetic acid, 4-methoxy-3-methyl-1-oxo-	CHCl$_3$	257(4.53),315(3.61), 390(2.60)	120-0250-80
Pterocarp-6a-ene, 3,9-dimethoxy-	MeOH	228(4.23),241(4.21), 248s(4.18),290s(3.93), 320s(4.02),333(4.51), 350(4.46)	94-1172-80
9H-Xanthene-2-butanoic acid, γ-oxo-	EtOH	276(4.13)	115-0423-80
$C_{17}H_{14}O_5$			
9,10-Anthracenedione, 1-ethoxy-4-hydroxy-5-methoxy-	MeOH	225(4.44),253(4.00), 449(3.87)	24-1575-80
9,10-Anthracenedione, 4-ethoxy-1-hydroxy-5-methoxy-	MeOH	225(4.47),251(4.10), 444(3.74)	24-1575-80
Benzaldehyde, 2-hydroxy-5-[3-(4-hydroxyphenyl)-1-oxo-2-propenyl]-4-methoxy- (isoneobavachalcone)	EtOH	230(4.18),266(4.36), 306s(4.03),378(4.47)	102-2034-80
	EtOH-NaOMe	266(4.39),328(4.35), 428(4.51)	102-2034-80
	EtOH-NaOAc	255s(4.33),268(4.36), 328(4.39),380(4.32)	102-2034-80
	EtOH-AlCl$_3$	238(--),310s(--), 360(--),425s(--)	102-2034-80
3(2H)-Benzofuranone, 2-acetoxy-2-(4-methoxyphenyl)-	MeOH	225s(4.32),259(4.11), 283s(3.58),330(3.69)	18-0179-80
4H-1-Benzopyran-4-one, 5,7-dihydroxy-3-[(4-hydroxyphenyl)methyl]-8-methyl-	EtOH	222(4.24),264(4.29), 297(3.94),325s(3.94)	94-2039-80
	EtOH	222(4.34),264(4.44), 297(3.78),325s(3.94)	94-2487-80
	EtOH-NaOAc	332(--)	94-2039-80
	EtOH-AlCl$_3$	316(--),364(--)	94-2487-80
2-Cyclopenten-1-one, 3,4-dihydroxy-2,5-bis(4-hydroxyphenyl)-, cis-(+)-(chamonixin)	MeOH	225(4.27),252(4.29), 276s(4.14)	64-0824-80C
1-Oxaspiro[4.5]deca-3,7,9-triene-2,6-dione, 8-methoxy-3-(2-methoxyphenyl)-	MeOH	224(4.40),240s(4.30), 277(4.19),311s(3.88)	18-0179-80

Compound	Solvent	$\lambda_{max}(\log \epsilon)$	Ref.
$C_{17}H_{14}O_6$			
9,10-Anthracenedione, 1,4-dihydroxy-5,7-dimethoxy-3-methyl- (ventinone B)	EtOH	230(4.49),260(4.21), 320(4.01)	2-0097-80
9,10-Anthracenedione, 1-hydroxy-2-(hydroxymethyl)-4,8-dimethoxy-	MeOH	250(4.15),279(3.87), 378s(--),444(3.88), 463(3.89),495s(--)	24-2994-80
9,10-Anthracenedione, 1,4,5-trihydroxy-7-methoxy-2,3-dimethyl- (5λ,4ε) (ventinone A)	EtOH	227(4.14),259(4.02), 280(4.30),480(4.20), 525(?)	2-0097-80
Azuleno[1,2-c]furan-9-carboxylic acid, 1-acetoxy-1,3-dihydro-3-oxo-, ethyl ester	MeOH	235(4.72),271(4.66), 292(4.76),301(4.84), 326(3.90),355(4.09), 368(4.18)	18-3696-80
4H-1-Benzopyran-4-one, 5,6-dihydroxy-7,8-dimethoxy-2-phenyl-	EtOH	285(4.51),325s(4.03)	40-1397-80
	EtOH-AlCl₃	300(4.44),340(4.12)	40-1397-80
2-Cyclopenten-1-one, 5-(3,4-dihydroxyphenyl)-3,4-dihydroxy-2-(4-hydroxyphenyl)-, cis-(-)- (involutin)	MeOH	200(4.73),254(4.18), 279(4.16)	64-0824-80C
1,3-Propanedione, 1-(1,3-benzodioxol-5-yl)-3-(2-hydroxy-4-methoxyphenyl)-	MeOH	205(4.26),225(3.92), 275(3.66),378(4.29)	118-0874-80
9H-Xanthene-1-carboxylic acid, 8-hydroxy-3-methoxy-6-methyl-9-oxo-, methyl ester	EtOH	235(4.45),253(4.31), 267s(4.16),290s(4.10), 303(4.22),353(3.81)	32-0629-80
$C_{17}H_{14}O_7$			
4H-1-Benzopyran-4-one, 5,6-dihydroxy-2-(4-hydroxyphenyl)-7,8-dimethoxy-	EtOH	300(4.36),335(4.39)	40-1397-80
	EtOH-NaOAc	306(4.23),335(4.24), 390(4.24)	40-1397-80
	EtOH-AlCl₃	312(4.39),360(4.45)	40-1397-80
4H-1-Benzopyran-4-one, 5,8-dihydroxy-2-(2-hydroxyphenyl)-6,7-dimethoxy-	MeOH	277(4.42),338(4.19)	95-1220-80
	MeOH-NaOMe	238(4.45),279(4.37), 410(4.30)	95-1220-80
	MeOH-NaOAc	276(4.39),349(4.06)	95-1220-80
	MeOH-AlCl₃	257(4.08),290(4.39), 360(4.24)	95-1220-80
	MeOH-AlCl₃-HCl	255(4.06),289(4.37), 355(4.21)	95-1220-80
$C_{17}H_{14}O_8$			
4H-1-Benzopyran-4-one, 5,6,7-trihydroxy-2-(4-hydroxy-3-methoxyphenyl)-8-methoxy-	EtOH	287(4.28),356(4.20)	40-1397-80
	EtOH-NaOAc	277(4.20),325(4.10), 390(4.21)	40-1397-80
	EtOH-AlCl₃	300(4.20),385(4.38)	40-1397-80
$C_{17}H_{15}BrN_3O$			
1H-1,2,4-Triazolium, 4-[2-(4-bromophenyl)-2-oxoethyl]-1-(phenylmethyl)-, bromide	MeOH	262(4.25)	80-0407-80
$C_{17}H_{15}Br_2NO_2$			
4H-Dibenzo[de,g]quinoline-10,11-diol, 8,9-dibromo-5,6,6a,7-tetrahydro-6-methyl-, hydrobromide, (R)-	EtOH	220(4.48),272(4.22), 320(3.55)	44-3918-80
$C_{17}H_{15}ClFNO_3$			
Butanoic acid, 4-[[(4-chlorophenyl)(5-fluoro-2-hydroxyphenyl)methylene]-amino]-	MeOH	210(4.34),252(4.04), 332(3.62)	87-0702-80
$C_{17}H_{15}ClN_2O$			
3H-Pyrazole, 4-chloro-3-ethoxy-3,5-di-	CHCl₃	242(4.34),320(3.60),	44-0076-80

Compound	Solvent	$\lambda_{max}(\log \epsilon)$	Ref.
phenyl- (cont.)		405(2.46)	44-0076-80
$C_{17}H_{15}ClN_2O_2$			
3H-Pyrazole, 4-chloro-3-ethoxy-3,5-di-phenyl-, 1-oxide	CHCl₃	239(4.25),265s(3.87)	44-0076-80
1H-Pyrazole-1-carboxaldehyde, 5-(4-chlorophenyl)-4,5-dihydro-3-(4-methoxyphenyl)-	MeOH	292(4.17)	2-0364-80
$C_{17}H_{15}ClO_3$			
Benzenepentanoic acid, β-(4-chloro-phenyl)-δ-oxo-	EtOH	243(4.28)	34-0085-80
[1,1'-Biphenyl]-4-butanoic acid, 2'-chloro-α-methyl-γ-oxo-, (±)-	EtOH	262.5(4.21)	36-0049-80
[1,1'-Biphenyl]-4-butanoic acid, 2'-chloro-β-methyl-γ-oxo-, (±)-	EtOH	266(4.23)	36-0049-80
$C_{17}H_{15}Cl_2N_3O$			
1,2,4-Triazine, 5,6-bis(4-chlorophen-yl)-2,5-dihydro-3-methoxy-2-methyl-	EtOH	222(4.27),240s(4.19), 310(3.99)	44-4587-80 +88-1529-80
$C_{17}H_{15}Cl_2N_3S$			
1,2,4-Triazine, 5,6-bis(4-chlorophen-yl)-2,5-dihydro-2-methyl-3-(methyl-thio)-	EtOH	221(4.29),298(3.98)	44-4587-80
$C_{17}H_{15}N$			
Isoquinoline, 3,6-dimethyl-1-phenyl-	MeOH-acid	239(4.63),268(3.91), 351(3.83)	56-2209-80
	MeOH-base	230(4.65),282(3.68), 331(3.70)	56-2209-80
Isoquinoline, 3,7-dimethyl-1-phenyl-	MeOH-acid	237(4.70),273(3.99), 365(3.92)	56-2209-80
	MeOH-base	230(4.71),277(3.80), 344(3.79)	56-2209-80
2-Naphthalenamine, N-methyl-3-phenyl-	MeOH	212(4.58),253(4.72), 286(3.71),365(3.28)	103-0965-80
$C_{17}H_{15}NO$			
Isoquinoline, 5-methoxy-3-methyl-1-phenyl-	MeOH-acid	241(4.32),282(4.06), 382(3.73)	56-2209-80
	MeOH-base	224(4.46),305(3.73), 343(3.71)	56-2209-80
1(2H)-Isoquinolinone, 2-methyl-3-(phen-ylmethyl)-	MeOH	208(4.82),227s(4.78), 250(4.03),285(4.11), 290(4.10),333(3.80)	103-0965-80
$C_{17}H_{15}NOS$			
Isothiazolium, 2-ethyl-4-hydroxy-3,5-diphenyl-, hydroxide, inner salt	EtOH dioxan MeCN	412(4.19) 490(4.25) 463(4.27)	139-0079-80A 139-0079-80A 139-0079-80A
$C_{17}H_{15}NO_2$			
4H-1-Benzopyran-4-one, 2,3-dihydro-3-[(methylphenylamino)methylene]-	EtOH	216s(4.15),233s(4.03), 262(3.97),323(3.90), 377(4.23)	4-0061-80
1,3-Dioxolo[4,5-g]isoquinoline, 7,8-di-hydro-5-methyl-7-phenyl-	MeOH	275(3.75),314(3.93)	2-0556-80
10,5-(Iminomethano)-11H-dibenzo[a,d]-cyclohepten-11-one, 5,10-dihydro-10-hydroxy-12-methyl-	EtOH	216(4.30),243(3.99), 254s(3.93),283(3.52), 368(2.79)	95-1127-80

Compound	Solvent	λ_{max}(log ϵ)	Ref.
1H-Indene-1,3(2H)-dione, 2-(1-ethyl-2-methyl-4(1H)-pyridinylidene)-	EtOH	217(4.11),235(4.51), 250s(4.24),260s(3.88), 283s(3.45),293(3.65), 305(3.86),391(4.74)	4-0997-80
1H-Indene-1,3(2H)-dione, 2-(3-ethyl-1-methyl-4(1H)-pyridinylidene)-	EtOH	405(4.52)	4-0997-80
	THF	419(4.60)	4-0997-80
9,10-(Methaniminomethano)anthracen-11-one, 9,10-dihydro-10-hydroxy-12-methyl-	EtOH	263(2.78),271(2.79)	95-1127-80
4H-1,3-Oxazin-5(6H)-one, 2-phenyl-4-(phenylmethyl)-	MeOH	208(4.38),240(4.12)	103-1000-80
Phenol, 2-methyl-6-(3-methyl-4-phenyl-5-isoxazolyl)-	EtOH	257(3.96)	114-0389-80B
$C_{17}H_{15}NO_2S$			
Methanone, [2-(ethylamino)phenyl](3-hy-droxybenzo[b]thien-2-yl)-	MeOH	250(4.32),319(4.10), 380(3.90),430(4.08)	83-0027-80
$C_{17}H_{15}NO_3$			
Acetamide, N-[2-[(3-oxo-3-phenyl-1-pro-penyl)oxy]phenyl]-, (E)-	dioxan	246(4.33),277(4.22)	48-0099-80
Benzo[4,5]cyclohepta[1,2-b]pyrrolizine-1-carboxylic acid, 1,2,3,5,10,11-hex-ahydro-5-oxo-	MeOH	219(3.91),258(3.83), 337(4.25)	4-1081-80
2-Butenoic acid, 2-(benzoylamino)-3-phenyl-, (E)-	EtOH	202(4.45),223(4.18), 266(4.11)	118-0901-80
(Z)-	EtOH	204(4.35),222(4.21), 250(4.06)	118-0901-80
3-Buten-2-one, 4-[[2-(benzoyloxy)phen-yl]amino]-, (Z)-	dioxan	233(4.33),338(4.33)	48-0099-80
1H-Isoindole-1,3(2H)-dione, 2-(1-hy-droxymethyl)-2-phenylethyl]-, (S)-	EtOH	295(3.26)	44-4006-80
Phenol, 5-methoxy-2-(3-methyl-4-phenyl-5-isoxazolyl)-	EtOH	274(3.94)	114-0389-80B
Pyrrolo[2,1-a]isoquinoline-1-carboxylic acid, 3-acetyl-2-methyl-, methyl ester	EtOH	224s(4.19),249(4.30), 274(4.57),284(4.48) 323(4.11),340(3.91), 357(4.15),375(4.12)	18-0297-80
$C_{17}H_{15}NO_4$			
Phenol, 5-methoxy-2-[4-(4-methoxyphen-yl)-5-isoxazolyl]-	EtOH	279(3.96)	114-0389-80B
2-Propenoic acid, 3-phenyl-2-[[(phenyl-methoxy)carbonyl]amino]-, (Z)-	EtOH	280(4.28)	39-0858-80C
$C_{17}H_{15}NO_4S_2$			
1,3-Dithiole-4,5-dicarboxylic acid, 2-(cyanophenylmethylene)-, diethyl ester	CHCl$_3$	242(4.20),351(4.24)	39-2693-80C
$C_{17}H_{15}NO_5$			
1,3-Dioxolo[4,5-b]acridin-10(5H)-one, 4,11-dimethoxy-5-methyl-(melicopidine)	EtOH	221(4.21),252s(4.37), 276(4.68),302(4.10), 325(3.68),399(3.92)	100-0498-80
1,3-Dioxolo[4,5-c]acridin-6(1H)-one, 4,5-dimethoxy-11-methyl-(melicopine)	EtOH	215(4.25),251(4.41), 271(4.72),302(4.12), 404(3.80)	100-0498-80
$C_{17}H_{15}N_2O_3$			
Pyridinium, 2-methyl-1-[[5-(2-nitro-phenyl)-2-furanyl]methyl]-, bromide	MeOH	265(4.35)	73-1715-80

Compound	Solvent	$\lambda_{max}(\log \epsilon)$	Ref.
Pyridinium, 2-methyl-1-[[5-(3-nitro-phenyl)-2-furanyl]methyl]-, bromide	MeOH	269(4.54)	73-1715-80
Pyridinium, 2-methyl-1-[[5-(4-nitro-phenyl)-2-furanyl]methyl]-, bromide	MeOH	339(4.37)	73-1715-80
Pyridinium, 3-methyl-1-[[5-(2-nitro-phenyl)-2-furanyl]methyl]-, bromide	MeOH	262(4.33)	73-1715-80
Pyridinium, 3-methyl-1-[[5-(3-nitro-phenyl)-2-furanyl]methyl]-, bromide	MeOH	270(4.45)	73-1715-80
Pyridinium, 3-methyl-1-[[5-(4-nitro-phenyl)-2-furanyl]methyl]-, bromide	MeOH	339(4.37)	73-1715-80
$C_{17}H_{15}N_3$			
Pyrrolo[3,2-e]benzimidazole, 1,6-dihy-dro-2,8-dimethyl-7-phenyl-	EtOH	256(4.27),313(4.41)	103-0062-80
Pyrrolo[3,2-e]benzimidazole, 3,6-dihy-dro-3,8-dimethyl-7-phenyl-	EtOH	255s(4.09),320(4.46)	103-0062-80
$C_{17}H_{15}N_3O$			
1-Naphthaleneacetic acid, N-[(2-pyrro-lyl)methylene]hydrazide	C_6H_{12}	314(4.44)	115-0151-80
	EtOH	312(4.33)	115-0151-80
	50% EtOH	284(4.21),313(4.46)	115-0151-80
5-Pyrimidinamine, 2-methoxy-4,6-di-phenyl-	EtOH	235(4.20),364(3.96)	103-0970-80
1H-1,2,4-Triazolium, 1-(phenylmethyl)-, 4-(2-oxo-2-phenylethylide)	pH 13	321(3.93)	80-0407-80
$C_{17}H_{15}N_3O_2$			
3-Diaziridinecarboxylic acid, 3-cyano-1,2-diphenyl-, ethyl ester	hexane	249(4.36)	30-0224-80
1,3-Dioxolo[4,5-g]quinazolin-8-amine, 6-methyl-N-(phenylmethyl)-	EtOH	213(4.45),222s(4.26), 245(4.47),280(3.77), 288(3.77),324(4.01), 336(3.94)	114-0253-80B
$C_{17}H_{15}N_3O_2S$			
Acetonitrile, (1-phenyl-2-imidazolidin-ylidene)(phenylsulfonyl)-	MeOH	273(4.05)	78-1791-80
2-Propenenitrile, 3-(1-aziridinyl)-3-(phenylamino)-2-(phenylsulfonyl)-	MeOH	247(4.04),296(4.34)	78-1791-80
$C_{17}H_{15}N_3O_3$			
1,2,4-Triazine-3,5(2H,4H)-dione, 6-[(4-methoxyphenyl)methyl]-2-phenyl-	EtOH	232(4.24),284(3.77), 335s(4.16)	12-0619-80
$C_{17}H_{15}N_3O_4$			
Methanone, [4,5-dihydro-4-(4-nitrophen-yl)-1H-pyrazol-5-yl](4-methoxyphenyl)-	MeOH	331(3.73)	2-0980-80
1H-Pyrazole-1-caroxaldehyde, 4,5-di-hydro-3-(4-methoxyphenyl)-5-(4-ni-trophenyl)-	MeOH	289(4.14)	2-0364-80
$C_{17}H_{15}N_3O_5$			
L-Phenylalanine, N-(5-benzofurazanyl-carbonyl)-, methyl ester, N-oxide	EtOH	222(4.47),264s(3.60), 315s(3.51),332s(3.59), 365(3.89)	4-0213-80
	MeCN	221(4.49),265s(3.46), 315s(3.51),332s(3.61), 365(3.90)	4-0213-80
$C_{17}H_{15}N_5O$			
Acetic acid, cyano[(4-methylphenyl)hy-	EtOH	250(4.13),290(4.18),	104-1536-80

Compound	Solvent	$\lambda_{max}(\log \epsilon)$	Ref.
drazono]-, (phenylmethyl)hydrazide		380(4.29)	104-1536-80
$C_{17}H_{15}N_5O_2$ 8(1H)-Cycloheptapyrazolone, 3-methyl-, [1-(4-nitrophenyl)ethylidene]hydra- zone	MeOH	275(3.62),432(3.46)	118-0331-80
$C_{17}H_{15}N_5O_2S$ Acetamide, N-[3,7,8,9-tetrahydro-3-(4- methylphenyl)-9-oxo-2H-pyrimido[1,2- c]thiazolo[5,4-e]pyrimidin-2-ylidene]-	EtOH	240(4.24),255(4.24), 280(4.16),340(4.15)	2-0037-80
$C_{17}H_{15}N_5O_3S_3$ 5-Thia-1-azabicyclo[4.2.0]oct-2-ene- 2-carboxylic acid, 3-[5-(acetylami- no)-1,3,4-thiadiazol-2-yl]-8-oxo-7- [(2-thienylacetyl)amino]-, sodium salt, (6R-trans)-	EtOH	254(4.15),317(4.14)	94-2116-80
$C_{17}H_{15}N_7O_4$ Benzenamine, 4-[[1-(2,4-dinitrophenyl)- 1H-pyrazol-3-yl]azo]-N,N-dimethyl-	CHCl$_3$	461(4.31)	104-1143-80
$C_{17}H_{16}$ 6,11-Ethano-4a,12a-methanobenzocyclo- decene, (4aα,6α,11α,12aα)-	C$_6$H$_{12}$	287(4.45),381(3.54)	89-0919-80
1H-Indene, 1,3-dimethyl-2-phenyl-	EtOH	228(4.18),292(4.41)	44-2181-80 +44-4555-80
$C_{17}H_{16}BrNO_3$ 2-Propen-1-one, 1-(3-bromo-2-hydroxy- 5-methylphenyl)-3-(4-methoxyphenyl)-, oxime	CHCl$_3$	270(4.07),325(3.51)	90-0977-80
palladium chelate	CHCl$_3$	248(4.60),265(4.56), 320(3.91),395(3.77)	90-0977-80
$C_{17}H_{16}BrN_7$ 4-Quinolinamine, N-[3-(6-amino-9H- purin-9-yl)propyl]-7-bromo-	EtOH	260(4.38),327(4.09)	22-0316-80
$C_{17}H_{16}ClFN_2O_2$ Butanamide, 4-[[(4-chlorophenyl)(5- fluoro-2-hydroxyphenyl)methylene]- amino]-	MeOH	210(4.38),250(4.03), 332(3.62)	87-0702-80
$C_{17}H_{16}ClNO_2$ 2-Propen-1-one, 1-(4-chlorophenyl)- 3-[(2-hydroxyethyl)amino]-3-phenyl-, (Z)-	EtOH	250(4.1),350(4.3)	114-0235-80C
$C_{17}H_{16}ClNO_3$ 4H-Furo[3,2-b]pyrrole-5-carboxylic acid, 2-(4-chlorophenyl)-4-ethyl-, ethyl ester	MeOH	336.1(4.25),357.1(4.56)	73-2949-80
2H,5H-Pyrano[3,2-c][1]benzopyran-2-one, 3-chloro-4-piperidino-	EtOH	240(3.83),271(3.95), 307(3.75),352(4.01)	4-0061-80
$C_{17}H_{16}ClN_3O_2$ Benzhydrol, 5-chloro-2-[3-(hydroxymeth- yl)-5-methyl-4H-1,2,4-triazol-4-yl)-, isomer A	EtOH	225s(4.22),253(2.57), 258(2.66),264(2.63), 273s(2.32),280s(2.66)	87-0643-80

Compound	Solvent	$\lambda_{max}(\log \epsilon)$	Ref.
isomer B (cont.)	EtOH	225s(4.23),253(2.58), 258(2.68),264(2.66), 275(2.30)	87-0643-80
$C_{17}H_{16}ClN_3O_3$ Acetamide, 2-[(aminoacetyl)amino]-N-(2-benzoyl-4-chloromethyl)-	EtOH	241(4.44),275s(4.03), 340(3.55)	87-0764-80
$C_{17}H_{16}Cl_2O_2S$ 4H-Pyran-4-one, 3,5-dichloro-2-(cyclohexylthio)-6-phenyl-	heptane	195(4.26),254(4.36), 287(4.09)	5-1960-80
$C_{17}H_{16}Cl_2O_4$ 1,3-Benzodioxole, 5-[1,2-dichloro-2-(3,4-dimethoxyphenyl)ethyl]-, (R*,S*)-	MeOH	233(4.32),283(4.07)	2-0556-80
$C_{17}H_{16}Cl_3NO_5S$ 2-Furancarboxylic acid, 5-[2-[4-(dimethylamino)phenyl]-1-[(trichloromethyl)sulfonyl]ethenyl]-, methyl ester, (E)-	EtOH	202(4.11),254(4.11), 299(3.86),419(4.40)	73-0746-80
$C_{17}H_{16}Cl_4OS$ 2,4-Pentadienethioic acid, 2,3,4,5-tetrachloro-5-phenyl-, S-cyclohexyl ester, (Z,Z)-	heptane	200(4.33),257(4.18)	5-1960-80
$C_{17}H_{16}F_9NO_4S$ 2-Propenoic acid, 3-[4-(dimethylamino)phenyl]-2-[(nonafluorobutyl)sulfonyl]-, ethyl ester	EtOH	260(4.10),420(4.54)	104-1200-80
$C_{17}H_{16}GaNOS$ Gallium, dimethyl[2-[(phenylimino)methyl]-3(2H)-benzofuranthionato-N,S]-, (T-4)-	hexane	310(3.93),348(4.20), 470(4.04)	101-0001-80I
	MeCN	305(3.94),346(4.10), 445(3.99),510(3.69)	101-0001-80I
	DMSO	310(4.12),350(3.91), 510(3.30)	101-0001-80I
$C_{17}H_{16}N_2$ 1H-1,5-Benzodiazepine, 4-methyl-2-(4-methylphenyl)-	H_2O	480(3.04)	96-0165-80
4H-Pyrazole, 4,4-dimethyl-3,5-diphenyl-	EtOH	222(3.9),313(4.3)	24-1507-80
$C_{17}H_{16}N_2O$ 1H-1,5-Benzodiazepine, 2-(4-methoxyphenyl)-4-methyl-	H_2O	485(3.24)	96-0165-80
4H-Pyrazole, 4,4-dimethyl-3,5-diphenyl-, N^1-oxide	EtOH	263(4.1),344(4.0)	24-1507-80
3(2H)-Pyridazinone, 1,6-dihydro-6-(4-methylphenyl)-6-phenyl-	EtOH	273(4.18)	118-0457-80
4(3H)-Quinazolinone, 2-phenyl-3-propyl-	EtOH	208(4.54),227(4.46), 303(3.99),327(3.73), 340s(3.60)	1-0637-80
$C_{17}H_{16}N_2OS$ 4H-1,3-Thiazin-5(6H)-one, 2-(phenylamino)-4-(phenylmethyl)-	MeOH	208(4.37),231s(3.92), 276(4.04)	103-1003-80

$C_{17}H_{16}N_2O_2-C_{17}H_{16}N_4O_2$

Compound	Solvent	$\lambda_{max}(\log \epsilon)$	Ref.
$C_{17}H_{16}N_2O_2$			
Acetic acid, acetyl(diphenylmethylene)-hydrazide	MeOH	208(4.40),245(4.20)	18-3225-80
	dioxan	253(4.15)	18-3225-80
1(2H)-Isoquinolinone, 6-methoxy-3-[(phenylmethyl)amino]-	EtOH	250(4.60),306(4.25), 352(3.69)	95-0826-80
1(2H)-Isoquinolinone, 7-methoxy-3-[(phenylmethyl)amino]-	EtOH	228(4.38),298(4.26), 387(3.57)	95-0826-80
Methanone, [4,5-dihydro-4-(4-methoxyphenyl)-1H-pyrazol-5-yl]phenyl-	MeOH	332(3.56)	2-0980-80
3(2H)-Pyridazinone, 1,6-dihydro-6-(4-methoxyphenyl)-6-phenyl-	EtOH	280(4.33)	118-0457-80
2,4(1H,3H)-Quinazolinedione, 1-methyl-3-(2-phenylethyl)-	EtOH	221(4.79),240(--), 310(3.61)	102-0935-80
$C_{17}H_{16}N_2O_2S$			
1H-1,3-Benzodiazepine, 2-methyl-1-[(4-methylphenyl)sulfonyl]-	EtOH	232s(--),259(4.30), 275s(--)	94-2602-80
4H-1,3-Oxazin-4-one, 6-methyl-5-(methylthio)-2-[1-(2(1H)-quinolinylidene)-ethyl]-	EtOH	222(4.70),290s(4.02), 302s(4.09),339(4.17), 440s(4.20),464(4.40), 490(4.31)	94-0795-80
Propanoic acid, 2-(2-dibenzothienyl-hydrazono)-, ethyl ester, anti	EtOH	241(4.59),266(4.38), 302(4.36),328(4.51), 366(4.14)	103-0146-80
syn	EtOH	243(4.60),266(4.44), 300(4.12),344(4.39), 371(4.35)	103-0146-80
Propanoic acid, 2-(3-dibenzothienyl-hydrazono)-, ethyl ester, anti	EtOH	205(3.57),239(3.74), 267(3.35),347(3.81)	103-0146-80
syn	EtOH	206(3.68),236(3.91), 281(3.45)	103-0146-80
$C_{17}H_{16}N_2O_3$			
1(2H)-Isoquinolinone, 6,7-dimethoxy-3-(phenylamino)-	EtOH	245(4.45),310(4.31), 361(3.84)	95-0826-80
$C_{17}H_{16}N_2O_3S$			
1H-Thieno[3,4-b][1,4]diazepine-6-carboxylic acid, 2,5-dihydro-8-(methylthio)-2-oxo-4-phenyl-, ethyl ester	EtOH	245(4.27),280(4.28), 322(4.23)	95-0699-80
$C_{17}H_{16}N_2O_6$			
3,5-Pyridinedicarboxylic acid, 2,6-dimethyl-4-(4-nitrophenyl)-, dimethyl ester	EtOH	273s(4.18)	94-3163-80
$C_{17}H_{16}N_3O$			
1H-1,2,4-Triazolium, 4-(2-oxo-2-phenyl-ethyl)-1-(phenylmethyl)-, bromide	MeOH	247(4.19)	80-0407-80
$C_{17}H_{16}N_4$			
8(1H)-Cycloheptapyrazolone, 3-methyl-, (1-phenylethylidene)hydrazone	MeOH	219(4.46),267(4.05), 359(4.04)	118-0331-80
$C_{17}H_{16}N_4O_2$			
2,3,4(5H)-Furantrione, 5-methyl-, 3,4-bis(phenylhydrazone), (E,E)-	EtOH	262(4.21),354(3.96), 468(4.16)(changing)	78-2955-80
4(1H)-Pyrimidinone, 5-ethyl-2-[(1-hydroxy-2-naphthalenyl)azo]-6-methyl-	EtOH	213(4.28),252(4.31), 263(4.28),272(4.25), 416s(3.97),442(4.07)	103-1279-80

Compound	Solvent	$\lambda_{max}(\log \epsilon)$	Ref.
$C_{17}H_{16}N_4O_3$			
4,5'-Bipyrimidine, 2,2',4'-trimethoxy-6-phenyl-	EtOH	213(4.11),265(4.32), 320(4.36)	103-0303-80
[4,5'-Bipyrimidine]-2',4'(1'H,3'H)-dione, 2-methoxy-1',3'-dimethyl-6-phenyl-	EtOH	207(4.65),256(4.53), 330(4.65)	103-0303-80
[4,5'-Bipyrimidine]-2,2',4'(1H,1'H-3'H)-trione, 1,1',3'-trimethyl-6-phenyl-	EtOH	207(4.53),256(4.39), 335(4.39)	103-0303-80
[4,5'-Bipyrimidine]-2,2',4'(1'H,3H-3'H)-trione, 1',3,3'-trimethyl-6-phenyl-	EtOH	205(4.33),277(4.25), 341(4.08)	103-0303-80
[4,5'-Bipyrimidin]-2'(1'H)-one, 2,4'-dimethoxy-1'-methyl-6-phenyl-	EtOH	206(4.53),256(4.41), 324(4.44)	103-0303-80
$C_{17}H_{16}N_4O_7$			
2,4,7(1H,3H,8H)-Pteridinetrione, 6-phenyl-1-β-D-ribofuranosyl-	pH 1.0	225(4.22),277(4.16), 339(4.21)	24-1524-80
	pH 7.0	208(4.50),233s(4.17), 290(4.12),344(4.29)	24-1524-80
	pH 13.0	237s(4.21),258s(4.01), 287(3.94),351(4.33)	24-1524-80
2,4,7(1H,3H,8H)-Pteridinetrione, 6-phenyl-3-β-D-ribofuranosyl-	pH 1.0	277s(4.08),285(4.03), 348(4.25)	24-1524-80
	pH 7.0	213(4.54),233s(4.14), 293(4.07),348(4.26)	24-1524-80
	pH 13.0	233(4.63),275s(3.97), 297(4.08),359(4.27)	24-1524-80
$C_{17}H_{16}N_4S$			
1,3,4-Thiadiazol-2-amine, N-[[4-(dimethylamino)phenyl]methylene]-5-phenyl-	EtOH	210(4.23),220s(4.08), 300(4.45),425(2.78)	2-0144-80A
	DMF	310(4.45),425(2.76)	2-0144-80A
	CHCl$_3$	300(4.45),419(2.76)	2-0144-80A
	CCl$_4$	300(4.45),408(2.75)	2-0144-80A
$C_{17}H_{16}N_6OS$			
Acetamide, N-[6-(2-cyanoethyl)-6,7-dihydro-7-imino-3-(4-methylphenyl)thiazolo[4,5-d]pyrimidin-2(3H)-ylidene]-	EtOH	233(4.18),325(4.00)	2-0037-80
$C_{17}H_{16}O$			
3H-Cyclopenta[j]fluoren-3-one, 3a,4,5,11-tetrahydro-3a-methyl-	EtOH	220(4.40),253(4.20), 290(3.60)	44-1081-80
3,5,8,10,12-Pentadecapentaene-1,14-diyn-7-one, 3,13-dimethyl-, (E,E,Z,Z,E)-	ether	229s(3.80),247s(3.97), 255s(4.05),273(4.08), 285s(4.06),301s(4.11), 359s(4.50)	44-3564-80
2-Propen-1-one, 2-methyl-3-(3-methylphenyl)-1-phenyl-	MeOH	245(4.05),291(4.04)	56-2209-80
2-Propen-1-one, 2-methyl-3-(4-methylphenyl)-1-phenyl-	MeOH	247(4.21),296(3.96)	56-2209-80
$C_{17}H_{16}OS$			
1-Propanone, 1,3-bis(4-methylphenyl)-3-thioxo-	C$_6$H$_{12}$	268(--),339(--), 413(--),515s(--)	39-1768-80B
anion	EtOH	270(4.11),402(4.29)	39-1768-80B
$C_{17}H_{16}O_2$			
4H-Cyclopenta[def]phenanthrene-8,9-diol, 8,9-dihydro-8,9-dimethyl-	EtOH	273(4.06),294(3.80), 305(3.16)	18-1179-80

Compound	Solvent	$\lambda_{max}(\log \epsilon)$	Ref.
9H-Fluorene-2-carboxylic acid, 9-ethyl-9-methyl-, 1-	EtOH	208(4.61),218(4.48), 229(4.09),237(4.94), 279(4.31),289(4.38), 301(4.30),312(4.40)	56-0901-80
	CHCl$_3$	209(3.64),231(3.84), 242(3.71),284(4.23), 292(4.31),306(4.25), 316(4.37)	56-0901-80
1,3-Propanedione, 2,2-dimethyl-1,3-di-phenyl-	EtOH	248(4.3),319(2.4)	24-1507-80
2-Propen-1-one, 3-(2-methoxyphenyl)-2-methyl-1-phenyl-	MeOH	249(4.14),286(4.12)	56-2209-80
2-Propen-1-one, 3-(4-methoxyphenyl)-2-methyl-1-phenyl-	MeOH	240(4.05),318(4.27)	56-2209-80
Spiro[2H-1,5-benzodioxepin-3(4H),2'-[2H]indene], 1',3'-dihydro-	CHCl$_3$	268(3.52),274(3.58)	49-0413-80
$C_{17}H_{16}O_2S$			
1-Propanone, 1-(3-methoxyphenyl)-3-(4-methylphenyl)-3-thioxo-	C_6H_{12}	252(--),266s(--), 335(--),402(--), 520s(--)(anom.)	39-1768-80C
anion	EtOH	267(4.03),290s(3.92), 405(4.33)	39-1768-80C
1-Propanone, 1-(4-methoxyphenyl)-3-(4-methylphenyl)-3-thioxo-	C_6H_{12}	248s(--),337(--), 422(--),510s(--)(anom.)	39-1768-80C
anion	EtOH	258(4.14),402(4.37)	39-1768-80C
$C_{17}H_{16}O_3$			
Benzene, 1,2-dimethoxy-4-[(4-methoxy-phenyl)ethynyl]-	MeOH	247s(4.04),298(4.49), 310(4.46),319(4.46)	18-0179-80
Benzenepentanoic acid, δ-oxo-β-phenyl-	EtOH	242(4.11)	34-0085-80
4H-1-Benzopyran-4-one, 2,3-dihydro-7-methoxy-2-methyl-2-phenyl-	EtOH	277(4.12),314(3.84)	18-2938-80
1H-Inden-1-one, 2,3-dihydro-3-hydroxy-3-methoxy-2-(2-methylphenyl)-, anion	n.s.g.	437(3.32)	73-1072-80
1H-Inden-1-one, 2,3-dihydro-3-hydroxy-3-methoxy-2-(4-methylphenyl)-, anion	n.s.g.	465(3.26)	73-1072-80
$C_{17}H_{16}O_3S$			
1-Propanone, 1,3-bis(4-methoxyphenyl)-3-thioxo-	C_6H_{12}	253(--),365(--), 421(--),510s(--)(anom.)	39-1768-80B
anion	EtOH	290(4.20),402(4.36)	39-1768-80B
$C_{17}H_{16}O_4$			
Benzeneacetic acid, 4-methoxy-2-[(2-methoxyphenyl)methylene]-, (E)-	MeOH	236(4.12),290s(4.22), 321(4.25)	18-0179-80
1H-Benz[e]indene-2-acetic acid, 2,3-di-hydro-8-hydroxy-1-oxo-, ethyl ester	EtOH	230(4.61),263(3.99), 318(3.77),350(3.86)	87-0512-80
1,3-Benzodioxole, 5-[2-(3,4-dimethoxy-phenyl)ethenyl]-	MeOH	291(4.03),334(3.9)	2-0556-80
1H-Inden-1-one, 2,3-dihydro-3-hydroxy-3-methoxy-2-(2-methoxyphenyl)-, anion	n.s.g.	440(3.33)	73-1072-80
1H-Inden-1-one, 2,3-dihydro-3-hydroxy-3-methoxy-2-(3-methoxyphenyl)-, anion	n.s.g.	461(3.26)	73-1072-80
1H-Inden-1-one, 2,3-dihydro-3-hydroxy-3-methoxy-2-(4-methoxyphenyl)-, anion	n.s.g.	472(3.23)	73-1072-80
Methanone, 4-[2-(acetoxyethoxy)phenyl]-phenyl-	CHCl$_3$	287(4.28),342(2.68)	73-1826-80
1,1'-Spirobi[1H-indene]-4,4',7,7'-tetrol, 2,2',3,3'-tetrahydro-	EtOH	202(5.32),227s(4.60), 290(4.32)	138-0743-80

Compound	Solvent	$\lambda_{max}(\log \epsilon)$	Ref.
$C_{17}H_{16}O_5$			
1,3-Azulenedicarboxylic acid, 5-form-yl-, diethyl ester	CHCl$_3$	275(4.39),308(4.53), 333(4.11),406(4.23), 520(3.13)	18-3696-80
2H-1-Benzopyran-7-ol, 3-(4-hydroxy-2,3-dimethoxyphenyl)-	MeOH	237s(4.23),300s(4.21), 322(4.32)	94-1172-80
Butanedioic acid, [1-(2-methoxy-1-naph-thalenyl)ethylidene]-	CHCl$_3$	240(4.49)	120-0250-80
Cnidilin	EtOH	224(4.41),243(4.16), 251(4.18),270(4.27), 313(4.09)	94-1847-80
2,5-Cyclohexadien-1-one, 3,5-dihydroxy-2-[3-(4-hydroxyphenyl)-1-oxo-2-prop-enyl]-4,4-dimethyl-	EtOH	395(4.5)	138-1095-80
Ethanedione, (3,4-dimethoxyphenyl)(4-methoxyphenyl)-	MeOH	228(4.29),295(4.36), 322s(4.23)	18-0179-80
7H-Furo[3,2-g][1]benzopyran-7-one, 9-(3-hydroxy-3-methyl-1-butenyl)-4-methoxy-	EtOH	235(4.35),244(4.33), 276(4.41),285(4.43), 312(4.11)	2-1046-80
2H-Naphtho[2,3-b]pyran-4-one, 5,8-di-hydroxy-6-methoxy-2-propyl-	EtOH	224(4.27),250(4.24), 275(4.40),324(3.42), 405(3.60)	12-2781-80
1,3-Propanedione, 1-(2-hydroxy-4,6-di-methoxyphenyl)-3-phenyl-	MeOH	205(4.25),220(3.85), 238(3.68),287(3.85), 365(3.7)	118-0874-80
1,3-Propanedione, 1-(2-hydroxy-4-meth-oxyphenyl)-3-(4-methoxyphenyl)-	EtOH	270s(4.16),282(4.20), 376(4.70),387s(4.66)	102-2331-80
	EtOH-NaOEt	263(4.24),372(4.67)	102-2331-80
	MeOH	205(4.15),280(3.76), 375(4.32),385(4.27)	118-0874-80
$C_{17}H_{16}O_6$			
6H-Benzofuro[3,2-c][1]benzopyran-2,8-diol, 6a,11a-dihydro-3,9-dimethoxy-, (6aR-cis)-	EtOH	209(4.57),304(4.04)	102-2003-80
	EtOH-NaOH	238(4.61),323(4.47)	102-2003-80
4H-1-Benzopyran-4-one, 2,3-dihydro-3,5-dihydroxy-7-methoxy-2-(4-meth-oxyphenyl)-, (2R-trans)-	MeOH	228(4.24),292(4.08)	142-1979-80
4H-1-Benzopyran-4-one, 2,3-dihydro-5-hydroxy-2-(4-hydroxyphenyl)-6,7-dimethoxy-, (S)-	EtOH	228(4.34),289(4.22), 343(3.41)	33-0225-80
2H-Pyran-2-one, 3-[3-(3,4-dimethoxy-phenyl)-1-oxo-2-propenyl]-4-hydroxy-6-methyl-	MeOH	386(4.3)	83-0344-80
Spiro[benzofuran-2(3H),1'-[2,5]cyclo-hexadiene]-3,4'-dione, 2',6,6'-tri-methoxy-4-methyl-	EtOH	236(4.42),278(4.44), 313(4.08)	77-0285-80
$C_{17}H_{16}O_7$			
Benzoic acid, 2-(2,6-dihydroxy-4-meth-ylbenzoyl)-3-hydroxy-5-methoxy-, methyl ester	EtOH	284(4.11),327s(3.78)	32-0629-80
Benzoic acid, 2-(2,6-dihydroxy-4-meth-ylbenzoyl)-5-hydroxy-3-methoxy-, methyl ester	EtOH	282(4.09),322s(3.78)	32-0629-80
$C_{17}H_{16}S_3$			
1-Propanethione, 1-phenyl-2-(3a,4,7,7a-tetrahydro-4,7-methano-1,3-benzodi-thiol-2-ylidene)-	MeOH	252(4.02),319(3.76), 428(4.23),592(2.24)	104-0395-80

Compound	Solvent	$\lambda_{max}(\log \epsilon)$	Ref.
$C_{17}H_{16}Si$ Silacyclopenta-2,4-diene, 1-methyl- 2,5-diphenyl-	dioxan	378(4.24)	61-1122-80
$C_{17}H_{17}BrO_4$ 2H-Naphtho[1,2-b]pyran-5,6-dione, 3-bromo-4-ethoxy-3,4-dihydro- 2,2-dimethyl-	EtOH	252(4.45),281(3.88), 332(3.40),380(3.18), 420(3.25)	2-0013-80
$C_{17}H_{17}ClN_2O_3S$ Benzenesulfonamide, 4-chloro-N-[2-(2- hydroxyethyl)-1-methyl-1H-indol-3-yl]-	EtOH	230(4.62),288(3.97), 300(3.83)	39-1688-80C
$C_{17}H_{17}ClN_4O$ 4H-1,2,4-Triazole-3-methanol, 4-[2-(am- inophenylmethyl)-4-chlorophenyl]-5- methyl-	EtOH	220s(4.33),252s(3.00), 258(2.95),264s(2.87), 275s(2.57)	87-0643-80
$C_{17}H_{17}ClN_4O_2S$ Ethanol, 2,2'-[[4-[(4-chloro-2-benzo- thiazolyl)azo]phenyl]imino]bis-	acetone	514(4.67)	7-0167-80
Ethanol, 2,2'-[[4-[(6-chloro-2-benzo- thiazolyl)azo]phenyl]imino]bis-	acetone	513(4.73)	7-0167-80
$C_{17}H_{17}ClN_5O_6PS$ Adenosine, 8-[[(4-chlorophenyl)methyl]- thio]-, cyclic 3',5'-(hydrogen phos- phate)	pH 1 pH 11	283(4.26) 282(4.19)	87-0242-80 87-0242-80
$C_{17}H_{17}Cl_2NO_3$ 2H,5H-Pyrano[3,2-c][1]benzopyran-2-one, 3,3-dichloro-3,4-dihydro-4-piperi- dino-	EtOH	215(4.17),260(4.02), 345(3.60)	4-0061-80
$C_{17}H_{17}Cl_3N_2O_3S_2$ 4-Thia-1-azabicyclo[3.2.0]heptane-2- carboxylic acid, 3,3-dimethyl-6- [[[(4-methylphenyl)thio]imino]-7- oxo-, 2,2,2-trichloroethyl ester, (2S-cis)-	MeOH	226(4.19),267(3.90), 338(3.94)	35-1690-80
$C_{17}H_{17}FN_5O_6PS$ Adenosine, 8-[[(4-fluorophenyl)methyl]- thio]-, cyclic 3',5'-(hydrogen phos- phate)	pH 1 pH 11	282(4.24) 283(4.18)	87-0242-80 87-0242-80
$C_{17}H_{17}F_3N_4O_8$ Inosine, 8-(trifluoromethyl)-, 2',3',5'- triacetate	MeOH MeOH-acid MeOH-base	253(3.99) 252(4.00) 276(3.99)	39-2755-80C 39-2755-80C 39-2755-80C
$C_{17}H_{17}IN_2$ Pyridinium, 1-methyl-2-[2-(1-methyl- 1H-indol-3-yl)ethenyl]-, iodide	MeOH	225(3.94),290(3.15), 438(4.10)	103-1031-80
$C_{17}F_{17}NO$ 9-Anthracenamine, 10-methoxy-N,N-di- methyl-	ether	252(5.14),257s(4.83), 338(3.68),356(3.86), 375(3.92),397(3.68)	78-2453-80
2-Azetidinone, 1-(2,6-dimethylphenyl)- 4-phenyl-	dioxan	245(3.43),287(2.46)	23-2061-80

Compound	Solvent	$\lambda_{max}(\log \epsilon)$	Ref.
2-Propen-1-one, 2-methyl-3-(methyl-phenylamino)-1-phenyl-	EtOH	232(3.74),334(3.99)	4-1201-80
2-Propen-1-one, 2-methyl-3-(3-methyl-phenyl)-1-phenyl-, oxime, (Z,?)-	MeOH	276(4.37)	56-2209-80
2-Propen-1-one, 2-methyl-3-(4-methyl-phenyl)-1-phenyl-, oxime, (Z,?)-	MeOH	278(4.40)	56-2209-80
Quinoline, 5,6,7,8-tetrahydro-8-[(3-methoxyphenyl)methylene]-	EtOH	224(4.685),271(4.169), 316(4.007)	83-0826-80

$C_{17}H_{17}NOS$

Compound	Solvent	$\lambda_{max}(\log \epsilon)$	Ref.
Methanamine, N-(1,3-diphenyl-2-propen-ylidene)-1-(methylthio)-, N-oxide, (E,E)-	EtOH	325(4.28)	150-4726-80
(Z,E)-	EtOH	340(4.47)	150-4726-80
2-Propen-1-one, 1,3-diphenyl-, O-[(methylthio)methyl]oxime, (Z,E)-	EtOH	292(4.56)	150-4726-80

$C_{17}H_{17}NO_2$

Compound	Solvent	$\lambda_{max}(\log \epsilon)$	Ref.
Benzenamine, 4-methoxy-N-[3-(4-methoxy-phenyl)-2-propenylidene]-, bis(tri-chloroacetate)	benzene	300(3.08),350(2.90)	65-1870-80
Benzo[f]pyrrolo[1,2-a]quinolin-11(1H)-one, 2,3,12,12a-tetrahydro-6-methoxy-	MeOH	223(4.39),257s(4.52), 264s(4.63),271(4.70), 305(3.89),318(3.93), 396(3.93),413(3.94)	44-1260-80
Isoquinoline, 3,4-dihydro-6,7-dimeth-oxy-3-phenyl-	MeOH	279(4.18),310(4.14)	2-0556-80
5-Isoxazolol, 4,5-dihydro-4,4-dimethyl-3,5-diphenyl-	EtOH	191(4.7),204s(--), 252(4.0)	24-1507-80
2-Propen-1-one, 3-(2-methoxyphenyl)-2-methyl-1-phenyl-, oxime, (Z,?)-	MeOH	268(4.32)	56-2209-80

$C_{17}H_{17}NO_2S$

Compound	Solvent	$\lambda_{max}(\log \epsilon)$	Ref.
Benzene, 1,1'-[1-nitro-2-(propylthio)-1,2-ethenediyl]bis-, (Z)-	MeOH-pH 10.6	360(3.72)	28-0021-80A

$C_{17}H_{17}NO_3$

Compound	Solvent	$\lambda_{max}(\log \epsilon)$	Ref.
Benzo[g]pyrrolo[1,2-a]quinolin-5(1H)-one, 2,3,3a,4-tetrahydro-6-hydroxy-11-methoxy-	MeOH	249(4.55),297(4.54), 325s(4.02),450(3.47)	44-1260-80
1-Phenanthreneethanamine, 3,5-dihy-droxy-6-methoxy-, hydrochloride	EtOH	240(4.55),257(4.70), 298(4.17),321(4.19)	87-1008-80
Phenol, 2-[5-(4-ethoxyphenyl)-4,5-di-hydro-3-isoxazolyl]-	EtOH	225(4.32),265(4.05), 275(3.96),306(3.77)	142-1319-80

$C_{17}H_{17}NO_4$

Compound	Solvent	$\lambda_{max}(\log \epsilon)$	Ref.
Phenol, 2-[5-(3,4-dimethoxyphenyl)-4,5-dihydro-3-isoxazolyl]-	EtOH	217(4.32),265(4.10), 274(4.03),308(3.80)	142-1319-80
3,5-Pyridinedicarboxylic acid, 2,6-di-methyl-4-phenyl-, dimethyl ester	EtOH	272s(3.68)	94-3163-80
1H-Pyrrole-3-propanoic acid, 4-(1-but-enyl)-2,5-dihydro-2,5-dioxo-1-phen-yl-, (E)-	MeOH	228(4.34),280(3.83), 350(3.40)	39-2134-80C

$C_{17}H_{17}NO_4S$

Compound	Solvent	$\lambda_{max}(\log \epsilon)$	Ref.
2-Butenoic acid, 4-[[(acetylamino)-phenyl]thio]-3-(2-furanyl)-, methyl ester, (E)-	EtOH	220(3.99),305(4.21)	73-0142-80

$C_{17}H_{17}NO_4S_3$

Compound	Solvent	$\lambda_{max}(\log \epsilon)$	Ref.
1,3-Dithiole-4,5-dicarboxylic acid,	CHCl$_3$	317(3.99),391(4.22)	39-2693-80C

Compound	Solvent	$\lambda_{max}(\log \epsilon)$	Ref.
2-(2-amino-1-phenyl-2-thioxoethyli-dene)-, diethyl ester (cont.)			39-2693-80C
$C_{17}H_{17}NO_5$			
9(10H)-Acridinone, 1,2,3,4-tetrameth-oxy-	EtOH	218(4.05),264(4.65), 390(3.72)	100-0498-80
Ethanone, 1-[2,4-diacetoxy-5-(phenyl-methyl)-1H-pyrrol-3-yl]-	EtOH	205(4.31),235s(4.08), 282(3.62)	33-0121-80
$C_{17}H_{17}NO_6S$			
4-Oxa-1-azabicyclo[3.2.0]heptane-2-carboxylic acid, 3-[2-ethoxy-2-oxo-1-ethylidene]-7-oxo-, methyl ester, $(2\alpha,3Z,5\alpha)$-	EtOH	246(4.21),302(3.49)	142-1999-80
$C_{17}H_{17}N_2$			
Pyridinium, 1-methyl-2-[2-(1-methyl-1H-indol-3-yl)ethenyl]-, iodide	MeOH	225(3.94),290(3.15), 438(4.10)	103-1031-80
$C_{17}H_{17}N_3$			
4-Quinazolinamine, 2-phenyl-N-propyl-	EtOH	207(4.57),256(4.49), 322(4.08)	1-0637-80
1,2,4-Triazine, 2,5-dihydro-2,3-dimeth-yl-5,6-diphenyl-	EtOH	230s(4.14),314(3.85)	44-4587-80
$C_{17}H_{17}N_3O$			
3,6-Ethenocycloheptapyrazole-2(1H)-car-boxamide, 3,3a,6,8a-tetrahydro-N-phenyl-	MeCN	246(4.41),277s(3.15), 288s(2.95)	5-1428-80
3,6-Ethenocycloprop[g]indazole-1(2H)-carboxamide, 3,3a,5a,6,6a,6b-hexa-hydro-N-phenyl-	MeCN	246(4.41),277s(3.04), 288s(2.85)	5-1428-80
3,6-Ethenocycloprop[g]indazole-2(1H)-carboxamide, 3,3a,5a,6,6a,6b-hexa-hydro-N-phenyl-	MeCN	246(4.41),277s(3.04), 288s(2.85)	5-1428-80
Imidazo[2,1-b]quinazolin-5-ol, 1,2,3,5-tetrahydro-1-methyl-5-phenyl-	pH 1 pH 13 EtOH	250(4.54) 272(4.20) 273(4.20)	94-2024-80 94-2024-80 94-2024-80
1H,13H-Isoquino[1,2-f]pyrido[2,1-b]-pyrimidine-4-carbonitrile, 2,3,6-7,11b,12-hexahydro-13-oxo-	EtOH	236(4.00),295(4.23)	94-0220-80
1,2,4-Triazine, 2,5-dihydro-3-methoxy-2-methyl-5,6-diphenyl-	EtOH	228s(4.22),303(3.90)	44-4587-80
$C_{17}H_{17}N_3O_3S$			
1H-Benzimidazol-2-amine, 6-benzoyl-1-[(1-methylethyl)sulfonyl]-	MeOH	210(4.53),245(4.25), 316(4.28)	87-0368-80
$C_{17}H_{17}N_3O_6S_2$			
4-Thia-1-azabicyclo[3.2.0]hept-2-ene-2-carboxylic acid, 3-[[2-(acetylam-ino)ethyl]thio]-7-oxo-, (4-nitro-phenyl)methyl ester	EtOH	259(4.23),335(4.06)	33-1093-80
$C_{17}H_{17}N_3O_7$			
Uridine, 2'-deoxy-5-[2-(3-nitrophenyl)-ethenyl]-, (E)-	pH 1 H$_2$O pH 13	298(4.34) 298(4.33) 306(4.34)	35-2033-80 35-2033-80 35-2033-80
Uridine, 2'-deoxy-5-[2-(4-nitrophenyl)-ethenyl]-, (E)-	pH 1 H$_2$O pH 13	360(4.24) 358(4.20) 376(4.24)	35-2033-80 35-2033-80 35-2033-80

Compound	Solvent	$\lambda_{max}(\log \epsilon)$	Ref.
$C_{17}H_{17}N_3S$ 1,2,4-Triazine, 2,5-dihydro-2-methyl-3-(methylthio)-5,6-diphenyl-	EtOH	235s(4.02),309(3.73)	44-4587-80
$C_{17}H_{17}N_4$ 2,2'-Bi-1H-benzimidazolium, 1,1',3-trimethyl-, iodide	EtOH	223(4.79),305(4.39)	103-1261-80
$C_{17}H_{17}N_5$ Benzenamine, N,N-dimethyl-4-[(1-phenyl-1H-pyrazol-3-yl)azo]-	CHCl$_3$	422(4.50)	104-1143-80
$C_{17}H_{17}N_5O_4S$ Ethanol, 2,2'-[[4-(6-nitro-2-benzothiazolylazo)phenyl]imino]bis-	acetone	541(4.60)	7-0167-80
$C_{17}H_{17}N_5O_4S_3$ 5-Thia-1-azabicyclo[4.2.0]oct-2-ene-2-carboxylic acid, 3-[5-(dimethylamino)-1,3,4-thiadiazol-2-yl]-8-oxo-7-[(2-thienylacetyl)amino]-, monosodium salt, (6R-trans)-	H$_2$O	335(4.18)	94-2116-80
$C_{17}H_{17}N_5O_5$ Uridine, 5-[2-(3-azidophenyl)ethenyl]-2'-deoxy-, (E)-	MeOH MeOH-HCl MeOH-NaOH	249(4.30),312(4.26) 249(4.30),312(4.26) 316(4.26)	35-2033-80 35-2033-80 35-2033-80
$C_{17}H_{17}N_6O_8PS$ Adenosine, 8-[[(3-nitrophenyl)methyl]thio]-, cyclic 3',5'-(hydrogen phosphate) Adenosine, 8-[[(4-nitrophenyl)methyl]thio]-, cyclic 3',5'-(hydrogen phosphate)	pH 1 pH 11 pH 1 pH 11	278(4.33) 279(4.27) 272(4.39) 276(4.37)	87-0242-80 87-0242-80 87-0242-80 87-0242-80
$C_{17}H_{17}N_7$ 4-Quinolinamine, N-[3-(6-amino-9H-purin-9-yl)propyl]-	EtOH	248(4.38),320(4.11)	22-0316-80
$C_{17}H_{17}N_7O$ 6H-Purin-6-one, 2-amino-1,9-dihydro-9-[3-(4-quinolinylamino)propyl]-	EtOH	245(4.35),330(4.24), 343(4.26)	22-0316-80
$C_{17}H_{17}N_7O_4$ Benzenamine, 4-[[1-(2,4-dinitrophenyl)-4,5-dihydro-1H-pyrazol-3-yl]azo]-N,N-dimethyl-	CHCl$_3$	534(4.74)	104-1143-80
$C_{17}H_{18}$ 5H-Dibenzo[a,c]cyclononene, 6,7,8,9-tetrahydro-	C$_6$H$_{12}$	253s(2.93),261(3.06), 267(3.13),274(3.11)	95-0718-80
$C_{17}H_{18}BrNO_3S$ 6H-Thieno[2',3':5,6][1,3]oxazepino[2,3-a]isoquinoline, 10-bromo-5,8,12,13a-tetrahydro-2,3-dimethoxy-	MeOH	240(2.85),310(2.37), 369(2.34)	118-1021-80
$C_{17}H_{18}BrNO_4$ α-D-xylo-Hept-5-enofuranurononitrile, 6-bromo-5,6-dideoxy-1,2-O-(1-methyl-	n.s.g.	227(3.80)	136-0187-80H

Compound	Solvent	$\lambda_{max}(\log \epsilon)$	Ref.
ethylidene)-3-O-(phenylmethyl)-, (E)-			136-0187-80H
4(5H)-Oxazolone, 5-(2-acetoxy-1,1-di-	HOAc	326(4.52)	103-0023-80
methylethyl)-2-[2-(4-bromophenyl)-	HOAc-HClO$_4$	362(4.57)	103-0023-80
ethenyl]-, perchlorate			
$C_{17}H_{18}ClNO_5$			
Cyclopentanecarboxylic acid, 1-(6-chlo-	EtOH	223(3.83),276(3.04),	4-0519-80
ro-3,4-dihydro-3-methyl-2-oxo-2H-1,3-		283(3.02)	
benzoxazin-4-yl)-2-oxo-, ethyl ester			
$C_{17}H_{18}ClNO_6$			
2H-1,3-Benzoxazine-4-acetic acid, α-(1-	EtOH	224(4.30),277(3.10),	4-0519-80
acetoxyethylidene)-6-chloro-3,4-dihy-		286(3.08)	
dro-3-methyl-2-oxo-, ethyl ester			
$C_{17}H_{18}Cl_2N_2$			
7-Isoquinolinamine, 6-chloro-4-(3-chlo-	EtOH	212(4.67),247(4.06),	4-1563-80
rophenyl)-1,2,3,4-tetrahydro-3,3-di-		305(3.58)	
methyl-, monohydrochloride			
$C_{17}H_{18}FN_3O_5$			
1(2H)-Pyrimidinebutanoic acid, γ-(acet-	MeOH	269(3.50)	94-1137-80
ylamino)-5-fluoro-3,4-dihydro-2,4-di-			
oxo-, phenylmethyl ester			
$C_{17}H_{18}FN_6O_7P$			
Uridine, 2'-deoxy-5-fluoro-, 3'-acetate	MeOH	269(3.96)	87-1229-80
5'-(di-1H-imidazol-1-ylphosphinate)			
$C_{17}H_{18}F_3N_5O_7$			
Adenosine, 8-(trifluoromethyl)-,	MeOH	265(4.08)	39-2755-80C
2',3',5'-triacetate	MeOH-acid	261.5(4.19)	39-2755-80C
	MeOH-base	263(4.08)	39-2755-80C
$C_{17}H_{18}FeN$			
Methylium, (1-ethyl-1H-pyrrol-2-yl)-	CHCl$_3$	312(4.51),380(4.55),	65-2039-80
ferrocenyl-, perchlorate		602(4.50)	
$C_{17}H_{18}N_2$			
1,4-Benzenediamine, N,N-dimethyl-N'-(3-	12M HCl	364(4.47)	35-3062-80
phenyl-2-propenylidene)-	MeCN	382(4.61)	35-3062-80
	MeCN-HCl	520(4.77)	35-3062-80
Benzenepropanenitrile, α,2-dimethyl-	dioxan	243(4.14),273(3.15),	24-2462-80
α-(phenylamino)-		287(3.19)	
$C_{17}H_{18}N_2O$			
2H-Indol-2-imine, 1,3-dihydro-3-[(2-	n.s.g.	215(4.2),250(3.8)	103-0917-80
methoxyphenyl)methyl]-1-methyl-,			
hydrochloride			
2H-Indol-2-imine, 1,3-dihydro-3-[(4-	n.s.g.	215(4.2),260(3.9)	103-0917-80
methoxyphenyl)methyl]-1-methyl-,			
hydrochloride			
1,2,6-Oxadiazepine, 4,5,6,7-tetrahydro-	THF	214(4.3),251(4.1)	24-3373-80
3-phenyl-6-(phenylmethyl)-			
3(2H)-Pyridazinone, tetrahydro-6-(4-	EtOH	293(4.43)	48-0617-80
methylphenyl)-6-phenyl-			
$C_{17}H_{18}N_2O_2$			
Benzenamine, 4-(1,1-dimethylethyl)-	THF	356(4.09)	56-1177-80
N-[(4-nitrophenyl)methylene]-			

Compound	Solvent	$\lambda_{max}(\log \epsilon)$	Ref.
3(2H)-Pyridazinone, tetrahydro-6-(4-methoxyphenyl)-6-phenyl-	EtOH	299(4.46)	48-0617-80
$C_{17}H_{18}N_2O_2S$			
Benzenesulfonic acid, 4-methyl-, [[2-(2-propenyl)phenyl]methylene]hydrazide	MeOH	278(4.21)	44-3756-80
$C_{17}H_{18}N_2O_3$			
Hydroperoxide, 2,3-dihydro-2-imino-3-[(2-methoxyphenyl)methyl]-1-methyl-1H-indol-3-yl	n.s.g.	270(4.0),295(3.4)	103-0917-80
Hydroperoxide, 2,3-dihydro-2-imino-3-[(4-methoxyphenyl)methyl]-1-methyl-1H-indol-3-yl	n.s.g.	265(4.0),295(3.3)	103-0917-80
$C_{17}H_{18}N_2O_3S$			
4-Oxa-2,6-diazabicyclo[3.2.0]hept-2-en-7-one, 3-(phenylmethyl)-6-(2,2,3-trimethyl-4-oxo-3-thietanyl)-, (R)-	EtOH	218(3.89)	39-0388-80C
(S)-	EtOH	217(3.86)	39-0388-80C
$C_{17}H_{18}N_2O_5$			
Uridine, 2'-deoxy-5-(2-phenylethenyl)-, (E)-	H_2O	305(4.25)	35-2033-80
$C_{17}H_{18}N_2O_5S_2$			
4-Thia-1-azabicyclo[3.2.0]hept-2-ene-2-carboxylic acid, 3-(butylthio)-7-oxo-, (4-methylphenyl)methyl ester	EtOH	262(4.21),339(4.05)	94-3232-80
$C_{17}H_{18}N_2O_6$			
4(5H)-Oxazolone, 5-(2-acetoxy-1,1-dimethylethyl)-2-[2-(3-nitrophenyl)-ethenyl]-, monoperchlorate	HOAc HOAc-HClO₄	300(4.41) 327(4.42)	103-0023-80 103-0023-80
3,5-Pyridinedicarboxylic acid, 1,4-di-hydro-2,6-dimethyl-4-(4-nitrophenyl)-, dimethyl ester	EtOH	234(4.32),282(4.18)	94-3163-80
2(1H)-Pyrimidinone, 3,4-dihydro-4-(2-oxo-2-phenylethylidene)-1-β-D-ribo-furanosyl-	H_2O pH 13	263(3.45),376(4.18) 250(3.66),388(4.23)	94-0157-80 94-0157-80
$C_{17}H_{18}N_2O_6S$			
2(1H)-Pyrimidinone, 4-[(2-oxo-2-phenyl-ethyl)thio]-1-β-D-ribofuranosyl-	H_2O	250(4.20),300(4.17)	94-0157-80
$C_{17}H_{18}N_2O_6S_2$			
4-Thia-1-azabicyclo[3.2.0]hept-2-ene-2-carboxylic acid, 3-[(2-ethoxyeth-yl)thio]-7-oxo-, (4-nitrophenyl)-methyl ester	EtOH	262(4.21),339(4.05)	94-3232-80
$C_{17}H_{18}N_2O_7$			
Isoxazole, 3-(4-nitrophenyl)-5-(tetra-hydro-6-methoxy-2,2-dimethylfuro-[2,3-d]-1,3-dioxol-5-yl)-, [3aR-(3aα,5α,6α,6aα)]-	EtOH	209(3.96),275(4.13)	33-1181-80
$C_{17}H_{18}N_2O_8S$			
2-Propenoic acid, 3-[[3-[1-[[[(4-nitro-phenyl)methoxy]carbonyl]oxy]ethyl]-4-oxo-2-azetidinyl]thio]methyl ester	EtOH	270(4.33)	35-2039-80

$C_{17}H_{18}N_3-C_{17}H_{18}N_5O_6PS$

Compound	Solvent	$\lambda_{max}(\log \epsilon)$	Ref.
$C_{17}H_{18}N_3$			
1,2,4-Benzotriazinium, 3-(1,1-dimethyl-ethyl)-1-phenyl-, perchlorate	HCOOH	248(4.40),327(3.82), 350s(3.65),405(3.56)	24-1205-80
1,2,4-Benzotriazinyl, 3-(1,1-dimethyl-ethyl)-1,?-dihydro-1-phenyl-	MeOH	241(4.40),315(3.91), 348(3.85),419(3.43), 508(3.05),521s(3.04), 542(3.02)	24-1205-80
$C_{17}H_{18}N_3O_2$			
Pyridinium, 1-[3-(2-methyl-5-nitro-1H-indol-3-yl)propyl]-, chloride	MeOH	227(4.00),260(4.08), 405(4.46)	103-0921-80
$C_{17}H_{18}N_3O_{10}P$			
5'-Uridylic acid, 2'-deoxy-5-[2-(3-ni-trophenyl)ethenyl]-, (E)-	pH 1	298(4.23)	35-2033-80
	H_2O	298(4.26)	35-2033-80
	pH 13	306(4.26)	35-2033-80
5'-Uridylic acid, 2'-deoxy-5-[2-(4-ni-trophenyl)ethenyl]-, (E)-	pH 1	363(--)	35-2033-80
	H_2O	363(4.33)	35-2033-80
	pH 13	378(4.29)	35-2033-80
$C_{17}H_{18}N_3O_{11}P$			
5'-Uridylic acid, 5-[2-(3-nitrophenyl)-ethenyl]-, (E)-	pH 1	298(4.23)	35-2033-80
	H_2O	298(4.24)	35-2033-80
	pH 13	306(4.30)	35-2033-80
$C_{17}H_{18}N_4$			
1H-Benzimidazole, 1-ethyl-5,6-dimethyl-2-(phenylazo)-	MeOH	400(3.35)	104-2008-80
1H-Phenazinamine, 2-piperidino-	MeOH	386(3.79),515(3.23)	32-0135-80
$C_{17}H_{18}N_4OS$			
4(1H)-Pyridinone, 3-butyl-5-(4,5-dihy-dro-4-phenyl-5-thioxo-1H-1,2,4-tria-zol-3-yl)-	EtOH	261(4.23)	4-0175-80
$C_{17}H_{18}N_4O_2S$			
Ethanol, 2,2'-[[4-(2-benzothiazolyl-azo)phenyl]imino]bis-	acetone	504(4.69)	7-0167-80
quaternized methyl deriv.	acetone	598(4.94)	7-0167-80
$C_{17}H_{18}N_4O_3S$			
1H-Benzimidazol-2-amine, 6-[(hydroxy-imino)phenylmethyl]-1-[(1-methyl-ethyl)sulfonyl]-, anti	MeOH	218(4.66),290(4.43)	87-0368-80
syn	MeOH	254(4.32),285(4.12)	87-0368-80
$C_{17}H_{18}N_4O_4$			
2-Imidazolidinone, 5-hydroxy-4,4-di-methyl-1-[(4-nitrophenyl)amino]-5-phenyl-	EtOH	199(4.4),224(3.9), 358(4.1)	5-1016-80
2-Imidazolidinone, 5-hydroxy-4,4-di-methyl-5-(3-nitrophenyl)-1-(phenyl-amino)-	EtOH	199(4.6),234(4.1), 281(3.4)	5-1016-80
6H-Pyrrolo[3,4-d]pyrimidine-6-butanoic acid, 2-amino-5,7-dihydro-4-(4-meth-oxyphenyl)-7-oxo-	EtOH	235(4.48),298(4.23), 350(4.26)	4-1231-80
$C_{17}H_{18}N_5O_6PS$			
Adenosine, 8-[(phenylmethyl)thio]-, cyclic 3',5'-(hydrogen phosphate)	pH 1	281(4.23)	87-0242-80
	pH 11	281(4.19)	87-0242-80

Compound	Solvent	$\lambda_{max}(\log \epsilon)$	Ref.
$C_{17}H_{18}N_5O_7PS$			
Adenosine, 8-[(4-methoxyphenyl)thio]-, cyclic 3',5'-(hydrogen phosphate)	pH 1 pH 11	281(4.26) 282(4.23)	87-0242-80 87-0242-80
$C_{17}H_{18}N_5O_8P$			
5'-Uridylic acid, 5-[2-(3-azidophenyl)-ethenyl]-2'-deoxy-, (E)-	pH 1 H_2O pH 13	255(4.30),312(4.27) 255(4.28),312(4.27) 250(4.28),308(4.30)	35-2033-80 35-2033-80 35-2033-80
$C_{17}H_{18}N_6O_5$			
Adenosine, 5'-(phenylcarbamate)	H_2O	237(--),259(4.08)	18-3670-80
$C_{17}H_{18}N_6O_{10}$			
2(1H)-Pyrimidinone, 4-(3-nitro-1H-1,2,4-triazol-1-yl)-1-(2,3,5-tri-O-acetyl-β-D-ribofuranosyl)-	EtOH	249(4.20),323(3.81)	88-2265-80
$C_{17}H_{18}N_9$			
3,5'-Bi-2H-tetrazolium, 2-[4-(dimethyl-amino)phenyl]-2'-methyl-5-phenyl-, perchlorate	EtOH	245(4.44),495(4.09)	103-0094-80
2H-Tetrazolium, 2-[4-(dimethylamino)-phenyl]-3-(1-methyl-1H-tetrazol-5-yl)-5-phenyl-, perchlorate	EtOH	245(4.40),530(4.12)	103-0094-80
picrate	EtOH	245(4.75),345(4.35), 397(3.91),530(4.03)	103-0094-80
$C_{17}H_{18}OS$			
Benzenemethanol, α-[1-methyl-1-(phenyl-thio)-2-propenyl]-	MeOH	237(4.14),263(3.28)	12-1345-80
isomer	MeOH	223(4.28),263(3.26)	12-1345-80
Benzenemethanol, α-[1-methyl-3-(phenyl-thio)-2-propenyl]-	MeOH	247(4.03),266(4.09)	12-1345-80
Benzenemethanol, α-[1-(4-methylphenyl)-thio]-2-propenyl]-	MeOH	213(4.23),258(3.75)	12-1345-80
Benzenemethanol, α-[2-methyl-1-(phenyl-thio)-2-propenyl]-	MeOH	257(3.75)	12-1345-80
Benzenemethanol, α-[2-methyl-3-(phenyl-thio)-2-propenyl]-	MeOH	249(4.03),265(4.07)	12-1345-80
Benzenemethanol, α-[3-(4-methylphenyl)-thio]-2-propenyl]-, (E)-	MeOH	213(4.20),250(4.07), 266(4.03)	12-1345-80
(Z)-	MeOH	217(4.10),248(4.05), 266(4.10)	12-1345-80
Benzenemethanol, α-[3-(phenylthio)-2-butenyl]-	MeOH	247(3.97),262(3.86)	12-1345-80
$C_{17}H_{18}OSi$			
Silane, (9-anthracenyloxy)trimethyl-	C_6H_{12}	247(4.71),252(4.76), 258(4.79),340s(3.43), 359(3.72),378(3.88), 400(3.77)	44-1807-80
$C_{17}H_{18}O_2$			
Spiro[cyclopentane-1,3'(4'H)-[2H]naph-tho[2,3-b][1,4]dioxepin	$CHCl_3$	248(4.19),285(3.72), 315(3.22),330(3.29)	49-0413-80
$C_{17}H_{18}O_2S$			
Benzenemethanol, α-[1-[(4-methoxyphen-yl)thio]-2-propenyl]-	MeOH	235(4.13),261(3.77)	12-1345-80
Benzenemethanol, α-[3-[(4-methoxyphen-yl)thio]-2-propenyl]-, (E)-	MeOH	254(4.06),267(3.97)	12-1345-80

Compound	Solvent	$\lambda_{max}(\log \epsilon)$	Ref.
Benzenemethanol, α-[3-[(4-methoxyphenyl)thio]-2-propenyl]-, (Z)-	MeOH	250(4.04),266(4.03)	12-1345-80
Benzenemethanol, α-[1-[(4-methylphenyl)sulfinyl]-2-propenyl]- isomer	MeOH	221(4.21),251(3.85)	12-2635-80
	MeOH	220s(4.25),251(3.89), 275s(3.28)	12-2635-80
Benzenemethanol, α-[3-[(4-methylphenyl)sulfinyl]-2-propenyl]-, (E)- isomer mixture	MeOH	232(4.17)	12-2635-80
	MeOH	230(4.20)	12-2635-80
Benzenemethanol, α-[1-methyl-3-(phenylsulfinyl)-2-propenyl]-, (E)-	MeOH	end absorption	12-2635-80
Benzenemethanol, α-[2-methyl-1-(phenylsulfinyl)-2-propenyl]-	MeOH	250(3.76)	12-2635-80
Benzenemethanol, α-[2-methyl-3-(phenylsulfinyl)-2-propenyl]-, (E)-	MeOH	226s(4.27)	12-2635-80
(Z)-	MeOH	226s(4.23)	12-2635-80
Benzenemethanol, α-[1-(phenylsulfinyl)-2-butenyl]-	MeOH	252(3.72)	12-2635-80
Benzenemethanol, α-[3-(phenylsulfinyl)-2-butenyl]-	MeOH	225s(4.15),260s(3.36), 272s(3.04)	12-2635-80

$C_{17}H_{18}O_3$

Compound	Solvent	$\lambda_{max}(\log \epsilon)$	Ref.
Benzeneacetic acid, 2-methoxy-, 2,4-dimethylphenyl ester	EtOH	221(3.91),274(3.42), 278(3.35)	49-0081-80
Benzeneacetic acid, 2-methoxy-, 2,6-dimethylphenyl ester	EtOH	211(4.19),272(3.35), 278(3.32)	49-0081-80
Benzeneacetic acid, 4-methoxy-, 2,4-dimethylphenyl ester	EtOH	227(4.01),270(3.24), 274(3.31),283(3.15)	49-0081-80
Benzeneacetic acid, 4-methoxy-, 2,6-dimethylphenyl ester	EtOH	224(3.99),268(3.07), 276(3.20),282(3.12)	49-0081-80
1,4a-Ethanofluorene-9,11(2H)-dione, 1,3,4,9a-tetrahydro-7-methoxy-1-methyl-, (1α,4aα,9aβ)-(±)-	EtOH	222(4.2),252(3.7), 325(3.2)	39-2881-80C
Ethanone, 1-(2-hydroxy-3,5-dimethylphenyl)-2-(2-methoxyphenyl)-	EtOH	223(4.23),263(4.07), 349(3.60)	49-0081-80
Ethanone, 1-(2-hydroxy-3,5-dimethylphenyl)-2-(4-methoxyphenyl)-	EtOH	225(4.40),265(4.11), 350(3.65)	49-0081-80
Ethanone, 1-(4-hydroxy-3,5-dimethylphenyl)-2-(2-methoxyphenyl)-	EtOH	226(4.22),281(4.14)	49-0081-80
Ethanone, 1-(4-hydroxy-3,5-dimethylphenyl)-2-(4-methoxyphenyl)-	EtOH	225(4.22),286(4.19)	49-0081-80

$C_{17}H_{18}O_3S$

Compound	Solvent	$\lambda_{max}(\log \epsilon)$	Ref.
Benzenemethanol, α-[1-[(4-methoxyphenyl)sulfinyl]-2-propenyl]-	MeOH	236(4.07),255(4.05)	12-2635-80
Benzenemethanol, α-[3-[(4-methoxyphenyl)sulfinyl]-2-propenyl]-, (E)-	MeOH	244(4.26)	12-2635-80
2-Butenoic acid, 3-(2-furanyl)-4-[(phenylmethyl)thio]-, ethyl ester, (E)-	EtOH	214(4.13),309(4.16)	73-0142-80

$C_{17}H_{18}O_4$

Compound	Solvent	$\lambda_{max}(\log \epsilon)$	Ref.
Dibenz[b,d]oxepin-1(2H)-one, 3,4-dihydro-9,10-dimethoxy-6-methyl-	MeCN	237(4.30),250s(4.18), 274s(3.85),322s(3.13)	24-3249-80
Naphtho[1,2-b]furan-4,5-dione, 2,3-dihydro-7-methoxy-2,3,3,9-tetramethyl-	MeOH	273(3.63),281(3.64), 314(3.05),499(2.45)	5-0779-80
Phenol, 4-(2,3-dihydro-3,7-dimethyl-1,4-benzodioxin-2-yl)-2-methoxy-	EtOH	282(3.88)	39-0775-80C

$C_{17}H_{18}O_5$

Compound	Solvent	$\lambda_{max}(\log \epsilon)$	Ref.
2H-1-Benzopyran-4-carboxylic acid,	EtOH	343(4.05)	95-0289-80

Compound	Solvent	λ_{max}(log ϵ)	Ref.
7-methoxy-2-oxo-, cyclohexyl ester			95-0289-80
2H-1-Benzopyran-7-ol, 3,4-dihydro-2-(4-hydroxy-2,3-dimethoxyphenyl)-	MeOH	280(3.95),288s(3.81)	94-1172-80
2H-1-Benzopyran-2-one, 6-(4-acetoxy-3-methyl-2-butenyl)-7-methoxy-, (E)-	EtOH	223(4.30),243s(3.78), 253(3.65),298s(3.85), 330(4.16)	12-0395-80
1-Propanone, 1-(2,4-dihydroxy-6-methoxyphenyl)-3-(4-methoxyphenyl)-	EtOH	224(4.44),290(4.38)	102-1195-80
	EtOH-NaOH	210(4.56),245(4.00), 332(4.64)	102-1195-80
	EtOH-AlCl$_3$	220(4.50),308(4.36)	102-1195-80
Spiro[2,5-cyclohexadiene-1,1'(2'H)-naphthalen]-4-one, 3',4'-dihydro-6',7'-dihydroxy-3,5'-dimethoxy-	EtOH	242(3.76),275(3.43)	102-0455-80
$C_{17}H_{18}O_6$ Eremofortine E	CHCl$_3$	250(4.20)	78-2989-80
$C_{17}H_{18}S_3$ 1-Propanethione, 2-(hexahydro-4,7-methano-1,3-benzodithiol-2-ylidene)-1-phenyl-	MeOH	250(4.13),320(3.85), 428(4.36),590(2.39)	104-0395-80
$C_{17}H_{19}BrN_2O_{11}$ β-D-Glucopyranuronic acid, 1-(5-bromo-3,4-dihydro-2,4-dioxo-1(2H)-pyrimidinyl)-1-deoxy-, methyl ester, 2,3,4-triacetate	pH 7 pH 14	273(3.91) 271(3.86)	106-0587-80 106-0587-80
$C_{17}H_{19}BrN_4O_6$ Riboflavin, 6-bromo-	n.s.g.	397(4.1),445(3.99) (approx.)	69-2537-80
$C_{17}H_{19}BrO_6$ Cyclopentanone, 3α-acetoxy-2-(2-acetoxy-5-methoxyphenyl)-5-bromo-2-methyl-	n.s.g.	281(3.13),284(3.11)	44-0501-80
$C_{17}H_{19}ClN_2$ 7-Isoquinolinamine, 4-(4-chlorophenyl)-1,2,3,4-tetrahydro-3,3-dimethyl-	EtOH	295(3.20)	4-1563-80
$C_{17}H_{19}ClN_2O_2$ 3H-Pyrrolo[1,2-a]indole-2-carboxylic acid, 1-chloro-3-(dimethylamino)-9-methyl-, ethyl ester	EtOH	267(3.79),364(4.24)	78-2125-80
$C_{17}H_{19}ClN_2O_{11}$ β-D-Glucopyranuronic acid, 1-(5-chloro-3,4-dihydro-2,4-dioxo-1(2H)-pyrimidinyl)-1-deoxy-, methyl ester, 2,3,4-triacetate	pH 7 pH 14	270(3.96) 264(3.85)	106-0587-80 106-0587-80
$C_{17}H_{19}FN_2O_{11}$ β-D-Glucopyranuronic acid, 1-deoxy-1-(5-fluoro-3,4-dihydro-2,4-dioxo-1(2H)-pyrimidinyl)-, methyl ester, 2,3,4-triacetate	pH 7 pH 14	261(3.99) 262(3.90)	106-0587-80 106-0587-80
$C_{17}H_{19}IN_2O_{11}$ β-D-Glucopyranuronic acid, 1-deoxy-1-(3,4-dihydro-5-iodo-2,4-dioxo-1(2H)-pyrimidinyl)-, methyl ester,	pH 7	279(3.88)	106-0587-80

Compound	Solvent	$\lambda_{max}(\log \epsilon)$	Ref.
2,3,4-triacetate (cont.)			106-0587-80
$C_{17}H_{19}N$			
Benzenamine, 3,5-dimethyl-N-(1-methyl-ethylidene)-	dioxan	270(3.28),285(3.31)	24-2462-80
Benzenamine, N-[2-(3,5-dimethylphenyl)-1-methylethylidene]-	dioxan	268(3.45)	24-2462-80
Benzenamine, 2,4,6-trimethyl-N-(1-phenylethylidene)-, cis	CH_2Cl_2 at -70°	236(4.37),242s(--), 276s(--),285s(--), 324(2.94)	39-1282-80B
trans	CH_2Cl_2 at -70°	245(4.53),276s(--), 285s(--),330(2.96)	39-1282-80B
$C_{17}H_{19}NO$			
1H-Dibenzo[a,f]quinolizin-1-one, 2,3,4,6,7,11b,12,13-octahydro-	MeOH	211(4.09),318(4.50)	135-0956-80
13H-Dibenzo[a,f]quinolizin-13-one, 1,2,3,4,6,7,11b,12-octahydro-	MeOH	211(4.19),335(4.14)	135-0956-80
Ethanone, 2-(1-methyl-2-pyrrolidinyl)-1-(1-naphthalenyl)-, nitrate	EtOH	240(4.25),300(3.85)	48-0475-80 +115-0265-80
7-Isoquinolinol, 1,2,3,4-tetrahydro-3,3-dimethyl-4-phenyl-	EtOH	220s(3.88),228s(3.26), 282(3.30)	4-1563-80
2(1H)-Naphthalenone, 1-(3-butylamino)-2-propenylidene]-	MeOH	315(3.97),330(3.97), 510(4.18)	103-0799-80
	CCl_4	318(3.85),360(3.68)	103-0799-80
	MeCN	314(4.07),353(3.90), 520(2.48)	103-0799-80
	PhCN	315(3.93),352(3.82)	103-0799-80
	DMSO	320(4.00),362(4.03), 520(4.09)	103-0799-80
2(1H)-Naphthalenone, 1-[3-[(1,1-dimethylethyl)amino]-2-propenylidene]-	MeCN	310(3.69),350(3.52), 420(3.15),520(3.85)	103-0799-80
	PhCN	317(4.22),357(4.00), 430(3.51),540(3.04)	103-0799-80
	DMSO	313(3.90),344(3.96), 520(4.10)	103-0799-80
$C_{17}H_{19}NO_2$			
Benzo[a]cyclopenta[f]quinolizin-1(2H)-one, 3,5,6,10b,11,12-hexahydro-8-methoxy-	MeOH	227(3.97),294(4.59)	135-0956-80
Carbamic acid, (1,2-diphenylethyl)-, ethyl ester	EtOH	208(4.38),242(2.34), 248(2.45),253(2.58), 258(2.68),264(2.57), 268(2.40)	104-0683-80
2-Propen-1-one, 1-(3-hydroxy-8-methyl-8-azabicyclo[3.2.1]oct-2-en-2-yl)-3-phenyl-, [1α,2(E),5α]-(+)- (chalcostrobamine)	EtOH	360(3.88)	102-0953-80
Strobamine	EtOH	274(3.86)	102-0953-80
$C_{17}H_{19}NO_3$			
Strobolamine	EtOH	273(3.87)	102-0953-80
$C_{17}H_{19}NO_4$			
2H-1-Benzopyran-4-carboxamide, N-cyclohexyl-7-methoxy-2-oxo-	EtOH	330(4.20)	95-0289-80
8-Indolizinecarboxylic acid, 1,2,3,5,6-7-hexahydro-6-(4-methoxyphenyl)-7-oxo-, methyl ester	EtOH	226(4.01),246(4.14), 285s(3.83),304(4.07)	44-1713-80
	EtOH-acid	226(4.17),244s(3.76), 303(3.91)	44-1713-80

Compound	Solvent	$\lambda_{max}(\log \epsilon)$	Ref.
6,7-Isoquinolinediol, 1-[(3,4-dihydr-oxyphenyl)methyl]-1,2,3,4-tetrahydro-2-methyl-	EtOH	287(3.89)	39-1696-80B
4(5H)-Oxazolone, 5-(2-acetoxy-1,1-di-methylethyl)-2-(2-phenylethenyl)-, perchlorate	HOAc HOAc-HClO₄	318(4.40) 352(4.42)	103-0023-80 103-0023-80
5H-Pyrano[3,2-c]quinolin-5-one, 2,6-di-hydro-7,8-dimethoxy-2,2,6-trimethyl-(veprisine)	EtOH	236(4.51),263(4.21), 273(4.16),334(4.03), 349(4.11),364(3.93)	88-3293-80
3,5-Pyridinedicarboxylic acid, 1,4-di-hydro-2,6-dimethyl-4-phenyl-, di-methyl ester	EtOH	238(4.27),354(3.86)	94-3163-80
Pyrrole-2-acetic acid, 3-(methoxycarbo-nyl)-4-(2-phenylethyl)-, methyl ester	MeOH	213(4.10),233(3.90), 260(3.74)	4-1081-80
1H-Pyrrole-3,4-dicarboxylic acid, 1-(1-methylethyl)-2-phenyl-, dimethyl ester	CCl₄	278.5(3.79)	22-0552-80
1H-Pyrrole-3,4-dicarboxylic acid, 2-methyl-1-phenyl-, diethyl ester	EtOH	229(4.22),256s(3.97)	78-2125-80
$C_{17}H_{19}NO_5$			
2H-1,3-Benzoxazin-2-one, 3,4-dihydro-3-methyl-4-(6-oxo-1,4-dioxaspiro-[4.5]dec-7-yl)-	EtOH	267(3.02),273(3.00)	4-0277-80
Clivonine	MeOH	204(4.21),225(4.31), 266(3.75),305(3.75)	94-1827-80
$C_{17}H_{19}NO_7$			
Ethanedioic acid, 2-(benzoylamino)-1-(ethoxycarbonyl)-1-propenyl ethyl ester	EtOH	233(4.03),308(4.05)	39-1139-80C
$C_{17}H_{19}N_2S$			
Methanaminium, N-[6-(dimethylamino)-3H-thioxanthen-3-ylidene]-N-methyl-, chloride	pH 7 MeOH EtOH	563(4.90) 290f(4.8),540(5.0) 565(5.01)	61-1203-80 61-1203-80 61-1203-80
$C_{17}H_{19}N_3O_2$			
1,4-Benzenediamine, N,N-diethyl-N'-(4-nitrophenyl)-	THF	461(4.30)	56-1177-80
Benzoic acid, 4-[[4-(diethylamino)phen-yl]azo]- dication	20% MeOH anion H₂SO₄	463(4.56) 447(4.59) 413(4.65)	39-0937-80B 39-0937-80B 39-0937-80B
2-Imidazolidinone, 5-hydroxy-4,4-di-methyl-5-phenyl-1-(phenylamino)-	EtOH	199(4.6),235(4.0), 282(3.2)	5-1016-80
$C_{17}H_{19}N_3O_5$			
Uridine, 5-[2-(3-nitrophenyl)ethenyl]-2'-deoxy-, (E)-	pH 1 MeOH	312(4.19) 288(4.11),300(4.10)	35-2033-80 35-2033-80
$C_{17}H_{19}N_3O_7$			
D-Ribitol, 1-deoxy-1-(3,4-dihydro-8-hy-droxy-7-methyl-2,4-dioxopyrimido[4,5-b]quinolin-10(2H)-yl)-	pH 13	244(4.71),288s(3.94), 425(4.72)	4-1709-80
$C_{17}H_{19}N_3S$			
3(2H)-Benzothiazolepropanamine, β-meth-yl-2-(phenylimino)-	EtOH	221(4.54),?98(4.12)	103-0169-80
1-Pyrazolidinecarbothioamide, 4-methyl-N,2-diphenyl-	EtOH	237(4.24),259(4.28)	103-0169-80

Compound	Solvent	$\lambda_{max}(\log \epsilon)$	Ref.
1-Pyrazolidinecarbothioamide, 5-methyl-N,2-diphenyl-	EtOH	237(4.30),260(4.27)	103-0169-80
$C_{17}H_{19}N_5O_2S$ 1H-Pyrazole, 3-[[4-(dimethylamino)phenyl]azo]-4,5-dihydro-1-(phenylsulfonyl)-	CHCl$_3$	466(4.56)	104-1143-80
$C_{17}H_{19}N_5O_3$ Cytidine, 5'-[(aminophenylacetyl)amino]-2',3'-didehydro-2',3',5'-trideoxy-	H$_2$O	271(3.84)	136-0067-80A
$C_{17}H_{19}N_5O_4$ 1-Propanone, 2-amino-2-methyl-1-(4-methylphenyl)-, 2,4-dinitrophenylhydrazone, (E)-	EtOH	198(4.4),218(4.3), 249(4.1),358(4.4)	5-1016-80
4(1H)-Pteridinone, 6-(1,2-dihydroxypropyl)-2-[[2-(4-hydroxyphenyl)ethyl]amino]-	pH -0.5	240(4.18),252s(4.15), 325(3.86)	18-2344-80
	pH 5.0	224(4.20),281(4.28), 354(3.75)	18-2344-80
	pH 9.0	222(4.21),267(4.32), 370(3.80)	18-2344-80
	pH 12.0	241(4.24),265(4.43), 372(3.86)	18-2344-80
4(1H)-Pteridinone, 6-(1,2-dihydroxypropyl)-2-[[(4-methoxyphenyl)methyl]amino]-	pH -0.5	226(4.33),252s(4.24), 324(3.70)	18-2344-80
	pH 5.0	226(4.29),281(4.35), 352(3.80)	18-2344-80
	pH 10.0	225s(4.26),265(4.44), 370(3.88)	18-2344-80
$C_{17}H_{19}N_5O_5$ Acetic acid, (9-amino-3a,4,12,12a-tetrahydro-2,2-dimethyl-4,12-epoxy-11H-1,3-dioxolo[5,6]azepino[1,2-e]purin-11-ylidene)-, ethyl ester, [3aR-(3aα,4β,11E,12β,12aα)]-	H$_2$O	240(4.34),285s(3.81), 328(4.08)	94-0876-80
4(1H)-Pteridinone, 2-[[2-(4-hydroxyphenyl)ethyl]amino]-6-(1,2,3-trihydroxypropyl)-, (R)-	pH -0.5	241(4.22),252s(4.19), 325(3.88)	18-2344-80
	pH 5.0	224(4.27),282(4.32), 353(3.78)	18-2344-80
	pH 9.0	222(4.25),267(4.37), 370(3.85)	18-2344-80
	pH 12.0	240(4.27),265(4.46), 373(3.90)	18-2344-80
(S)-	pH -0.5	241(4.21),252s(4.18), 325(3.88)	18-2344-80
	pH 5.0	224(4.25),282(4.31), 354(3.78)	18-2344-80
	pH 9.0	221(4.25),267(4.36), 370(3.84)	18-2344-80
	pH 12.0	240(4.27),265(4.46), 373(3.89)	18-2344-80
4(1H)-Pteridinone, 2-[[(4-methoxyphenyl)methyl]amino]-6-(1,2,3-trihydroxypropyl)-, (R)-	pH -0.5	226(4.35),250s(4.26), 324(3.90)	18-2344-80
	pH 5.0	226(4.30),281(4.35), 352(3.80)	18-2344-80
	pH 10.0	222(4.25),265(4.44), 370(3.88)	18-2344-80

Compound	Solvent	$\lambda_{max}(\log \epsilon)$	Ref.
4(1H)-Pteridinone, 2-[[(4-methoxyphen-yl)methyl]amino]-6-(1,2,3-trihydroxy-propyl)-, (S)-	pH -0.5	227(4.34),250s(4.26), 324(3.90)	18-2344-80
	pH 5.0	227(4.25),281(4.35), 352(3.80)	18-2344-80
	pH 10.0	222(4.24),265(4.43), 370(3.88)	18-2344-80
$C_{17}H_{19}OSSe$ Sulfonium, [2-methoxy-2-phenyl-1-(phen-ylseleno)ethenyl]dimethyl-, tetra-fluoroborate	n.s.g.	250s(4.30),255s(4.77)	104-0573-80
$C_{17}H_{20}BrN_7$ 1H-Pyrazol-5-amine, 4-[[4-bromo-3-meth-yl-1-(1-methylethyl)-1H-pyrazol-5-yl]azo]-3-methyl-1-phenyl-, (E)-	MeOH	390(4.57),410(4.57)	103-1166-80
$C_{17}H_{20}ClNO$ Benzenemethanol, α-[1-[(4-chlorophen-yl)methylamino]-1-methylethyl]-	EtOH	207(3.85),217(3.87)	4-1563-80
$C_{17}H_{20}Cl_2O_5S_2$ α-D-xylo-Hexofuranos-5-ulose, 6,6-di-C-chloro-3-O-methyl-1,2-O-(1-methyleth-ylidene)-6-S-(phenylmethyl)-6-thio-	EtOH	213(3.99),220(4.01)	33-0016-80
$C_{17}H_{20}Cl_2O_7S$ α-D-xylo-Hexofuranos-5-ulose, 6,6-di-chloro-6-deoxy-3-O-methyl-1,2-O-(1-methylethylidene)-6-[(phenylmethyl)-sulfonyl]-	EtOH	209s(--),216(3.97)	33-0016-80
$C_{17}H_{20}F_2O_4$ α-D-xylo-Hept-6-enofuranose, 5,6,7-tri-deoxy-7,7-difluoro-1,2-O-(1-methyl-ethylidene)-3-O-(phenylmethyl)-	EtOH	211(2.57)	33-1644-80
$C_{17}H_{20}IN_3O_9$ Acetamide, N-[1,2-dihydro-5-iodo-2-oxo-1-(2,3,5-tri-O-acetyl-β-D-arabino-furanosyl)-4-pyrimidinyl]-	MeOH	318(3.68)	39-2755-80C
	MeOH-acid	302(3.82)	39-2755-80C
	MeOH-base	295(3.81)	39-2755-80C
Cytidine, N-acetyl-5-iodo-, 2',3',5'-triacetate	MeOH	319(3.75)	39-2755-80C
	MeOH-acid	308(3.88)	39-2755-80C
	MeOH-base	297(3.80)	39-2755-80C
$C_{17}H_{20}NO$ Acridinium, 10-ethyl-1,2,3,4-tetrahy-dro-3,3-dimethyl-1-oxo-, perchlorate	n.s.g.	255(4.31),330(4.08)	104-1592-80
$C_{17}H_{20}N_2$ Indolo[2,3-a]quinolizine, 3-ethylidene-1,2,3,4,6,7,12,12b-octahydro-(deplancheine)	EtOH	223(4.60),278(3.53), 283(3.54),291(3.48)	88-0063-80
6-Isoquinolinamine, 1,2,3,4-tetrahydro-3,3-dimethyl-4-phenyl-	EtOH	208(4.28),240(3.89), 294(3.29)	4-1563-80
7-Isoquinolinamine, 1,2,3,4-tetrahydro-3,3-dimethyl-4-phenyl-	EtOH	240(4.04),294(3.20)	4-1563-80
8-Isoquinolinamine, 1,2,3,4-tetrahydro-3,3-dimethyl-4-phenyl-	EtOH	286(3.34)	4-1563-80

Compound	Solvent	$\lambda_{max}(\log \epsilon)$	Ref.
$C_{17}H_{20}N_2O$			
Azepino[2,3-f]benzo[a]quinolizin-14(1H)-one, 2,3,4,5,7,8,12b,13-octahydro-	EtOH	240(4.00),316(4.28)	94-0220-80
14H-Azepino[2',1':2,3]pyrimido[6,1-a]-isoquinolin-14-one, 1,2,3,4,5,5a,7,8-octahydro-	EtOH	252(4.34),356(4.00)	94-0220-80
Indolo[2,3-a]quinolizin-4(1H)-one, 3-ethyl-2,3,6,7,12,12b-hexahydro-	EtOH	224(4.56),274s(3.86), 281(3.87),290(3.78)	94-2527-80
more polar form	EtOH	224(4.56),274s(3.87), 280(3.87),290(3.78)	94-2527-80
Pyrazolidine, 3-methoxy-5-methyl-1,2-diphenyl-	n.s.g.	204(4.38),251(4.27), 282s(3.46)	73-2417-80
$C_{17}H_{20}N_2OS$			
2(1H)-Quinazolinethione, 3,4,5,6,7,8-hexahydro-3-(1-oxopropyl)-4-phenyl-	EtOH	277(3.93),330(4.15)	114-0147-80B
$C_{17}H_{20}N_2O_2$			
Benzenepropanoic acid, 2-methoxy-, 2-methyl-2-phenylhydrazide	n.s.g.	240(4.1),280(3.5)	103-0917-80
Benzenepropanoic acid, 4-methoxy-, 2-methyl-2-phenylhydrazide	n.s.g.	240(4.0),285(3.4)	103-0917-80
3H-Indol-3-one, 2-(1,3,4,5,6,7-hexahydro-3-oxo-2H-indol-2-ylidene)-1,2,4,5,6,7-hexahydro-1-methyl-	CHCl$_3$	316(4.28),552(4.00)	5-0564-80
2(1H)-Quinazolinone, 3,4,5,6,7,8-hexahydro-3-(1-oxopropyl)-4-phenyl-	EtOH	264(3.48)	114-0147-80B
$C_{17}H_{20}N_2O_3$			
4H-[1]Benzoxepino[4,3-c]pyrazol-4-one, 3a-acetyl-3,3a,10,10a-tetrahydro-3,3,10,10-tetramethyl-, cis	EtOH	232(3.55),265(2.97), 273(2.85),333(2.55)	39-2937-80C
$C_{17}H_{20}N_2O_4S$			
Imidazo[2,1-b]thiazole-3-carboxylic acid, hexahydro-2,2-dimethyl-5-oxo-7-(phenylacetyl)-, methyl ester, (3S-cis)-	EtOH	215(4.03)	39-2001-80C
$C_{17}H_{20}N_2O_5$			
1H-Pyrazole-1-acetic acid, 4-(ethoxycarbonyl)-5-(hydroxymethyl)-3-phenyl-, ethyl ester	EtOH	234(4.06)	118-0875-80
$C_{17}H_{20}N_2O_8S$			
Thymidine, α-hydroxy-, 5'-(4-methylbenzenesulfonate)	pH 2	265(4.08)	87-0127-80
	pH 12	265(3.94)	87-0127-80
$C_{17}H_{20}N_2O_{11}$			
β-D-Glucopyranuronic acid, 1-deoxy-1-(3,4-dihydro-2,4-dioxo-1(2H)-pyrimidinyl)-, methyl ester, 2,3,4-triacetate	pH 7	255(4.05)	106-0587-80
	pH 14	258(4.02)	106-0587-80
$C_{17}H_{20}N_2S$			
4H-Thieno[3,2-b][1]benzazepine-4-propanamine, N,N-dimethyl-	EtOH	211(4.48),263(4.27), 363(3.18)	142-1227-80B

Compound	Solvent	$\lambda_{max}(\log \epsilon)$	Ref.
$C_{17}H_{20}N_3O_8P$			
5'-Uridylic acid, 5-[2-(3-aminophenyl)-ethenyl]-2'-deoxy-, monohydrochloride, (E)-	pH 1 pH 13	308(4.18) 302(4.16)	35-2033-80 35-2033-80
$C_{17}H_{20}N_3O_9P$			
5'-Uridylic acid, 5-[2-(3-aminophenyl)-ethenyl]-, monohydrochloride, (E)-	pH 1 pH 13	308(4.19) 302(4.18)	35-2033-80 35-2033-80
$C_{17}H_{20}N_4O$			
Imidazo[5,1-f][1,2,4]triazin-4(1H)-one, 5-methyl-7-(2-methylpropyl)-2-(phenylmethyl)-	EtOH EtOH-NaOH	222(4.41),253(4.02), 265s(3.89) 234(--),262(--), 270s(--),300(--)	39-1139-80C 39-1139-80C
Imidazo[5,1-f][1,2,4]triazin-4(1H)-one, 5-methyl-2-(2-phenylethyl)-7-propyl-	EtOH	218(4.41),254(3.99), 265s(--)	39-1139-80C
$C_{17}H_{20}N_4O_2$			
Benzenamine, N,N-diethyl-4-[(2-methyl-4-nitrophenyl)azo]-	toluene	472(4.52)	5-2055-80
2,4(1H,3H)-Pyrimidinedione, 6-[2-(dimethylamino)ethenyl]-1,3-dimethyl-5-[(phenylmethylene)amino]-	EtOH	279(4.40),350(4.14), 395(4.14)	118-0479-80
$C_{17}H_{20}N_4O_2S$			
3-Pyridinecarboxylic acid, 5-butyl-1,4-dihydro-4-oxo-, 2-[(phenylamino)thioxomethyl]hydrazide	EtOH	258(4.26)	4-0175-80
4,6(1H,5H)-Pyrimidinedione, 5-[[4-(dimethylamino)phenyl]-1-pyrrolidinyl-methylene]dihydro-2-thioxo-	MeOH	397(4.54)	97-0020-80
$C_{17}H_{20}N_4O_3$			
3-Pyridinecarboxylic acid, 5-butyl-1,4-dihydro-4-oxo-, 2-[(phenylamino)carbonyl]hydrazide	EtOH	241(4.29),284(3.88)	4-0175-80
2,4,6(1H,3H,5H)-Pyrimidinetrione, 5-[[4-(dimethylamino)phenyl]-1-pyrrolidinylmethylene]-	MeOH	391(4.43)	97-0020-80
$C_{17}H_{20}N_4O_3S$			
4,6(1H,5H)-Pyrimidinedione, 5-[[4-(dimethylamino)phenyl]-4-morpholinyl-methylene]dihydro-2-thioxo-	MeOH	410(4.53)	97-0020-80
$C_{17}H_{20}N_4O_4$			
Bicyclo[5.3.1]undec-7-en-9-one, 2,4-dinitrophenylhydrazone	EtOH	229(4.22),256(4.31), 288s(4.08),386(4.40)	44-1800-80
2,4,6(1H,3H,5H)-Pyrimidinetrione, 5-[[4-(dimethylamino)phenyl]-4-morpholinylmethylene]-	MeOH	403(4.40)	97-0020-80
$C_{17}H_{20}N_4O_6$			
Benzamide, N-[[(1-β-D-arabinofuranosyl-1,2-dihydro-2-oxo-4-pyrimidinyl)-amino]methyl]-	MeOH	227(4.31),275(4.16)	44-1577-80
$C_{17}H_{20}N_4O_7S$			
Thiazole, 5-nitro-2-[(2,3,5,6,8,9,11-12-octahydro-1,4,7,10,13-benzopenta-oxacyclopentadecin-15-yl)azo]-	MeCN	453(4.73)	24-0457-80

Compound	Solvent	$\lambda_{max}(\log \epsilon)$	Ref.
$C_{17}H_{20}O$			
3H-Cyclopenta[j]fluoren-3-one, 1,2,3a-4,5,6,6a,11-octahydro-3a-methyl-, (3aα,6aα,11aR*)-	EtOH	260(2.80),266(3.09), 272(3.10)	44-1081-80
Ethanone, 1-(1,2,3,4,9,10-hexahydro-1-methyl-1-phenanthrenyl)-	EtOH	265(4.10)	44-1081-80
Ethanone, 1-(1,2,3,4,9,10-hexahydro-2-methyl-2-phenanthrenyl)-	EtOH	262(4.07)	44-1081-80
$C_{17}H_{20}OS$			
Benzenemethanol, α-[3-[(4-methylphenyl)thio]propyl]-	MeOH	255(3.89)	12-2635-80
$C_{17}H_{20}O_2S_2$			
Spiro[1,3-dithiolane-2,6'(4'H)-naphtho-[2,3-b]furan]-4'-one, 4'a,5',7',8'-tetrahydro-3',4'a,5'-trimethyl-, cis-(±)-	EtOH	330(4.34)	94-3265-80
$C_{17}H_{20}O_3$			
1H-Fluorene-1-carboxylic acid, 2,3,4,9-tetrahydro-7-methoxy-1-methyl-, methyl ester	EtOH	269(4.2)	39-0804-80C
$C_{17}H_{20}O_4$			
4H-1-Benzopyran-4-one, 5,6,7,8-tetra-hydro-2-[2-(2-hydroxy-1-cyclohexen-1-yl)-2-oxoethyl]-	EtOH	253(4.16),286(3.85)	94-2460-80
Cycloprop[2,3]indeno[5,6-b]furan-2(4H)-one, 5-(acetoxymethyl)-4a,5,5a,6,6a-6b-hexahydro-3,6b-dimethyl-, [4aS-(4aα,5α,5aα,6aα,6bβ)]- (chlorantha-lactone C)	MeOH	281.5(4.30)	94-0092-80
1H-Indene-2-propanoic acid, β-(1,1-di-methylethyl)-2,3-dihydro-1,3-dioxo-, methyl ester	CH_2Cl_2	248(3.97),288(2.89), 301(2.82)	24-1020-80
Indeno[1,2-b]pyran-5(2H)-one, 3,4-di-hydro-2,2-dimethoxy-3-(1-methyleth-yl)-	hexane	230s(--),238(4.65), 246(4.65),295(2.72), 385(2.87)	24-1020-80
2-Penten-4-ynal, 5-(4-acetoxy-2,6,6-trimethyl-3-oxo-1-cyclohexen-1-yl)-3-methyl-, [S-(E)]-	EtOH	245(4.01),315(4.37)	33-1473-80
Spiro[1,3-dioxolane-2,6'(4'H)-naphtho-[2,3-b]furan]-2'(5'H)-one, 4'a,7'-dihydro-3',4'a,5'-trimethyl-, cis-(±)-	EtOH	328.5(4.32)	94-3265-80
$C_{17}H_{20}O_5$			
4H,5H-Pyrano[2,3-d]-1,3-dioxin-4-one, 7-ethoxy-6,7-dihydro-2,2-dimethyl-6-phenyl- (or isomer)	MeCN	251(3.97)	24-1020-80
$C_{17}H_{20}O_6$			
Cyclodeca[b]furan-10-carboxaldehyde, 6-(acetoxymethyl)-2,3,3a,4,7,8,11,11a-octahydro-4-hydroxy-3-methylene-2-oxo-, (3aR*,4S*,11aR*)-	MeOH	203(3.94)	102-0849-80
Cyclopentanone, 3-acetoxy-2-(2-acetoxy-5-methoxyphenyl)-2-methyl-, cis	n.s.g.	202(4.01),261(2.34)	44-0501-80
1,3-Propanediol, 1,2-bis(4-hydroxy-3-methoxyphenyl)-	EtOH	282(3.53)	102-0449-80

Compound	Solvent	$\lambda_{max}(\log \epsilon)$	Ref.
4H,5H-Pyrano[2,3-d]-1,3-dioxin-4-one, 6,7-dihydro-7,7-dimethoxy-2,2-dimethyl-6-phenyl-	MeCN	250(3.83)	24-1020-80
Spiro[5H-benzocycloheptene-5,2'-[1,3]-dioxolane]-3,4-dicarboxylic acid, 6,7,8,9-tetrahydro-, dimethyl ester	MeCN	202(4.58),242(4.03)	24-1584-80
Spiro[bicyclo[2.2.2]octa-5,7-diene-2,2'-oxirane]-5,6-dicarboxylic acid, 7-(1,1-dimethylethyl)-3-oxo-, dimethyl ester	EtOH	225s(3.65),250s(3.52), 310(2.59),325s(2.40)	44-2189-80
Spiro[cyclopropa[cd]pentalene-1(2H),2'-oxirane]-2b,4b(2aH,4aH)-dicarboxylic acid, 4-(1,1-dimethylethyl)-2-oxo-, dimethyl ester	EtOH	250s(2.87),327s(1.60), 340s(1.30)	44-2189-80
isomer	EtOH	250s(2.89),315s(1.70)	44-2189-80
$C_{17}H_{20}O_7$			
Spiro[5H-benzocycloheptene-5,2'-[1,3]-dioxolane]-3,4-dicarboxylic acid, 6,7,8,9-tetrahydro-1-hydroxy-, dimethyl ester	MeCN	213(4.44),248(3.79), 298(3.37)	24-1584-80
Spiro[1,3-dioxolan-2,5'-[1,9a]epoxy-[5H]benzocycloheptene]-3',4'-di-carboxylic acid, 1',6',7',8',9',9'a-hexahydro-, dimethyl ester	MeCN	208(4.15),260(3.54), 285s(3.43)	24-1584-80
	C_6H_{12}	288s(3.34)	24-1584-80
Spiro[1,3-dioxolan-2,5'-[3,9a]epoxy-[5H]benzocycloheptene]-1',2'-di-carboxylic acid, 3',6',7',8',9',9'a-hexahydro-, dimethyl ester	MeCN	204(3.97),227s(3.59), 285(3.01)	24-1584-80
Yomogiartemin	MeOH	218(4.04)	95-0615-80
$C_{17}H_{21}BrN_2O_2$			
3H-Indolium, 1-(2-ethoxy-2-oxoethyl)-3-(1-pyrrolidinylmethylene)-, bromide	MeOH	249(4.17),256(4.15), 269(3.90),276(3.86), 346(4.37)	94-1711-80
$C_{17}H_{21}BrN_2O_2S$			
Benzenesulfonic acid, 4-bromo-, bicyclo-[5.3.1]undec-7-en-9-ylidenehydrazide	EtOH	232(4.46),260(4.44)	44-1800-80
$C_{17}H_{21}BrO_3$			
2-Cyclohexen-1-one, 6-acetoxy-3-(5-bro-mo-3-methyl-3-penten-1-ynyl)-2,4,4-trimethyl-, [S-(E)]-	EtOH	235(3.93),313(4.37)	33-1473-80
$C_{17}H_{21}NO$			
13H-Dibenzo[a,f]quinolizin-13-one, 1,2,3,4,4a,6,7,11b,12,13a-decahydro-	MeOH	210(4.04),257(2.89), 265(2.86),272(2.80)	135-0956-80
$C_{17}H_{21}NOS_2$			
2H-Thiopyran-2-thione, 6-(diethylami-no)-4-(4-methoxyphenyl)-5-methyl-	C_6H_{12}	244(4.22),315(4.31), 340s(3.92),472(3.85)	22-0539-80
	EtOH	245(4.09),316(4.14), 349s(3.76),498(3.88)	22-0539-80
4H-Thiopyran-4-thione, 2-(diethylami-no)-6-(4-methoxyphenyl)-3-methyl-	C_6H_{12}	230(3.87),250(3.84), 309s(3.87),470(3.51)	22-0539-80
	EtOH	224(3.34),255(3.34), 315(3.48),357(3.20), 450(3.12)	22-0539-80
Unknown compd., m. 90°	C_6H_{12}	237(4.19),263s(4.01), 309s(3.89),348s(4.12),	22-0539-80

Compound	Solvent	λ_{max}(log ϵ)	Ref.
(cont.)		396(4.35)	22-0539-80
	EtOH	237(4.00),275(3.76),	22-0539-80
		316(3.81),404(4.23)	
$C_{17}H_{21}NO_2$			
2,3-Cyclodecadien-1-ol, phenylcarbamate	EtOH	236(4.30),264(3.64),	35-5370-80
		272(3.65),280(3.46)	
1-Naphthalenol, 4-methoxy-2-(1-piperi-dinylmethyl)-	n.s.g.	325(3.8),336(3.9)	49-0563-80
$C_{17}H_{21}NO_3$			
Benzenepropanoic acid, α-[3-(dimethyl-amino)-2-methyl-2-propenylidene]-β-oxo-, ethyl ester	hexane	212(4.35),232s(4.14), 315(3.91)	70-1643-80
	MeOH	250(4.04),355(4.12), 410(4.25)	70-1643-80
	67% MeOH	255(4.00),355(4.06), 420(4.40)	70-1643-80
	50% MeOH	255(3.94),355s(3.92), 420(4.42)	70-1643-80
	EtOH	248(3.95),350(4.07), 410(4.15)	70-1643-80
	$CHCl_3$	355(3.94),400(3.91)	70-1643-80
$C_{17}H_{21}NO_4$			
2H-1,3-Benzoxazin-2-one, 4-(2-acetoxy-phenyl)-3,4,4a,5,6,7,8,8a-octahydro-3-methyl-	EtOH	261(2.48),268(2.38)	4-0277-80
$C_{17}H_{21}NO_5$			
Oxireno[c]oxireno[3,4]benz[1,2-f]ind-ole-2,6-diol, 1a,2,4b,5a,6,7,7a,8-octahydro-1a,7,7a-trimethyl-, 6-acetate	$CHCl_3$	248(4.10)	78-2989-80
$C_{17}H_{21}NS$			
2H-Azeto[2,1-a]isoquinoline-2-thione, 1-(1,1-dimethyl-2-propenyl)-1,4,5,9b-tetrahydro-1-methyl-, trans	isooctane-$CHCl_3$	273(4.2)	24-3010-80
$C_{17}H_{21}NS_2$			
2H-Thiopyran-2-thione, 6-(diethylami-no)-3,5-dimethyl-4-phenyl-	C_6H_{12}	247(4.23),274s(3.86), 316(3.94),466(3.85)	22-0539-80
	EtOH	251(4.28),284s(3.87), 314(3.97),492(3.97)	22-0539-80
2H-Thiopyran-2-thione, 6-(diethylami-no)-5-methyl-3-(4-methylphenyl)-	C_6H_{12}	237(4.32),254s(4.17), 327(3.93),476(3.86)	22-0530-80
	EtOH	236(4.34),246s(4.33), 326(4.01),503(4.05)	22-0530-80
2H-Thiopyran-2-thione, 6-(diethylami-no)-5-methyl-4-(4-methylphenyl)-	C_6H_{12}	243(4.12),297(4.20), 321(4.02),472(3.85)	22-0539-80
	EtOH	241(4.03),305(4.12), 499(3.89)	22-0539-80
$C_{17}H_{21}N_2O_2$			
3H-Indolium, 1-(2-ethoxy-2-oxoethyl)-3-(1-pyrrolidinylmethylene)-, bromide	MeOH	249(4.17),256(4.15), 269(3.90),276(3.86), 346(4.37)	94-1711-80
$C_{17}H_{21}N_2O_8P$			
5'-Uridylic acid, 2'-deoxy-5-(2-phenyl-ethyl)-	pH 1 and H_2O	268(3.95)	35-2033-80
	pH 13	267(3.86)	35-2033-80

Compound	Solvent	λ_{max}(log ϵ)	Ref.
C$_{17}$H$_{21}$N$_3$			
Imidazo[4,5-c]carbazole, 3-butyl-3,6,7,8,9,10-hexahydro-	EtOH	302(4.24)	103-0062-80
2-Piperidinecarbonitrile, 3-ethyl-4-(1H-indol-3-yl)-1-methyl-	EtOH	223(4.54),275(3.71), 284(3.76),292(3.65)	35-1064-80
1-Propanone, 2-amino-2-methyl-1-(4-methylphenyl)-, phenylhydrazone, monohydrochloride, (E)-	EtOH	199(4.5),274(4.2), 298(4.0)	5-1016-80
1-Propanone, 2-amino-2-methyl-1-phenyl-, (2-methylphenyl)hydrazone, monohydrochloride, (E)-	EtOH	197(4.5),267(4.2), 293(4.0)	5-1016-80
C$_{17}$H$_{21}$N$_3$O			
Benzenamine, N,N-diethyl-4-[(4-methoxyphenyl)azo]-	20% MeOH	443(4.49)	39-0937-80B
dication	H$_2$SO$_4$	470(4.84)	39-0937-80B
7,8-Diazatetracyclo[4.3.3.0^{2,10}.0^{5,9}]-dodecane-7(or 8)-carboxamide, N-phenyl-	MeCN	246(4.36),276s(3.11), 285(3.00)	5-1428-80
Unidentified compd. m. 129º	MeCN	240(4.15),260(4.35)	5-1428-80
C$_{17}$H$_{21}$N$_3$O$_2$S			
4(5H)-Thiazolone, 5-[(4-methoxyphenyl)-methylene]-2-[(1-piperidinylmethyl)-amino]-	EtOH	246(4.08),293(3.94), 349(4.37)	103-0718-80
C$_{17}$H$_{21}$N$_3$O$_5$			
Uridine, 5-[2-(3-aminophenyl)ethyl]-2'-deoxy-, hydrochloride	MeOH	266(3.94)	35-2033-80
C$_{17}$H$_{21}$N$_5$O$_6$			
Riboflavin, 6-amino-	2M HCl	330(4.1),405(4.2)	69-2537-80
	pH 7	428(4.3),560(3.7)	69-2537-80
	pH 12	425(4.2)	69-2537-80
	70% HClO$_4$	393(4.3)	69-2537-80
C$_{17}$H$_{22}$FNO$_3$			
4-Piperidinone, 1-[3-[2-(4-fluorophenyl)-1,3-dioxolan-2-yl]propyl]-	MeOH	256(2.97),268(2.97)	87-0075-80
C$_{17}$H$_{22}$NO$_2$S			
Pyridinium, 3-(diethoxymethyl)-2-(methylthio)-1-phenyl-, iodide	EtOH	215(4.26),281(3.75), 320s(2.78)	118-0405-80
C$_{17}$H$_{22}$NO$_5$			
Oxazolium, 5-(2-acetoxy-1,1-dimethylethyl)-4,5-dihydro-3-methyl-2-[2-(5-methyl-2-furanyl)ethenyl]-4-oxo-, perchlorate	HOAc	431(4.57)	103-0023-80
	HOAc-HClO$_4$	431(4.82)	103-0023-80
C$_{17}$H$_{22}$N$_2$			
2,3'-Bipyridine, 5'-hexyl-6'-methyl-	MeOH	262(3.9),266(3.8)	103-0951-80
C$_{17}$H$_{22}$N$_2$O			
Benzenemethanol, α-[[[(2-aminophenyl)-methyl]amino]-1-methylethyl]-	EtOH	285(3.85)	4-1563-80
C$_{17}$H$_{22}$N$_2$OS			
2,4-Pentadien-1-one, 5-(dimethylamino)-1-[5-[4-(dimethylamino)-1,3-butadienyl]-2-thienyl]-, (all-E)-	EtOH	400(4.10),500(4.79)	70-0980-80

Compound	Solvent	$\lambda_{max}(\log \epsilon)$	Ref.
$C_{17}H_{22}N_2O_2$			
2,4-Pentadien-1-one, 5-(dimethylamino)-1-[5-[4-(dimethylamino)-1,3-butadienyl]-2-furanyl]-, (all-E)-	EtOH	410(4.26),500(4.70)	70-0980-80
$C_{17}H_{22}N_2O_3$			
1(2H)-Isoquinolinone, 3-(cyclohexylamino)-6,7-dimethoxy-	EtOH	247(4.55),303(4.26), 370(3.68)	95-0826-80
$C_{17}H_{22}N_2O_4$			
Phomamide	MeOH	209(4.09),229(4.13), 277(3.16)	39-0113-80C
$C_{17}H_{22}N_2O_8$			
L-Aspartic acid, N-[(1,1-dimethylethoxy)carbonyl]-, 1-methyl 4-[(3-nitrophenyl)methyl] ester	CHCl$_3$	262.5(3.92)	22-0133-80
L-Aspartic acid, N-[(1,1-dimethylethoxy)carbonyl]-, 1-methyl 4-[(4-nitrophenyl)methyl] ester	CHCl$_3$	268.5(4.03)	22-0133-80
1,2,3-Cyclohexanetriol, 1-methyl-4-(1-methylethyl)-, 3-(3,5-dinitrobenzoate), (1α,2α,3α,4α)-	EtOH$_3$	234(4.13),253s(3.84)	78-0645-80
(1α,2α,3β,4α)-	EtOH	234(4.12),254s(3.88)	78-0645-80
(1α,2α,3β,4β)-	EtOH	234(4.19),254s(3.94)	78-0645-80
L-Glutamic acid, N-[(1,1-dimethylethoxy)carbonyl]-, 5-[(2-nitrophenyl)methyl] ester	CHCl$_3$	263(3.75)	22-0133-80
dicyclohexylamine salt	CHCl$_3$	263(3.76)	22-0133-80
L-Glutamic acid, N-[(1,1-dimethylethoxy)carbonyl]-, 5-[(3-nitrophenyl)methyl] ester	CHCl$_3$	268(3.89)	22-0133-80
dicyclohexylamine salt	CHCl$_3$	262.5(3.94)	22-0133-80
L-Glutamic acid, N-[(1,1-dimethylethoxy)carbonyl]-, 5-[(4-nitrophenyl)methyl] ester	CHCl$_3$	268(4.04)	22-0133-80
dicyclohexylamine salt	CHCl$_3$	270(4.00)	22-0133-80
3-Pyridinecarboxamide, 1,4-dihydro-1-(2,3,4-tri-O-acetyl-β-D-xylopyranosyl)-	MeOH	329(3.74)	23-0387-80
$C_{17}H_{22}N_2S$			
4H-Thieno[3,2-b][1]benzazepine-4-propanamine, 9,10-dihydro-N,N-dimethyl-	EtOH	268(3.76),295(3.67)	142-1227-80B
10H-Thieno[2,3-b][1]benzazepine-10-propanamine, 4,5-dihydro-N,N-dimethyl-	EtOH	280(3.87)	142-1227-80B
$C_{17}H_{22}N_4$			
Imidazo[5,1-f][1,2,4]triazine, 1,4-dihydro-5-methyl-2-(2-phenylethyl)-7-propyl-	EtOH	257(4.00)	39-1139-80C
$C_{17}H_{22}N_4O_2$			
Butanamide, N-[1-[2,5-dihydro-5-oxo-3-(2-phenylethyl)-1,2,4-triazin-6-yl]ethyl]-, (S)-	EtOH	235(3.98),266(3.77)	39-1139-80C
Butanamide, N-[1-[2,5-dihydro-5-oxo-3-(phenylmethyl)-1,2,4-triazin-6-yl]ethyl]-3-methyl-, (S)-	EtOH	237(3.98),265s(3.78)	39-1139-80C

Compound	Solvent	$\lambda_{max}(\log \epsilon)$	Ref.
$C_{17}H_{22}N_4O_2S$ 4,6(1H,5H)-Pyrimidinedione, 5-[(dieth- ylamino)[4-(dimethylamino)phenyl]- methylene]dihydro-2-thioxo-	MeOH	409(4.43)	97-0020-80
$C_{17}H_{20}N_4O_3$ 2,4,6(1H,3H,5H)-Pyrimidinetrione, 5- [(diethylamino)[4-(dimethylamino)- phenyl]methylene]-	MeOH	396(4.37)	97-0020-80
$C_{17}H_{22}N_4O_8S$ Phenol, 2-[2-[2-[2-(2-hydroxyethoxy)- ethoxy]ethoxy]ethoxy]-4-[(5-nitro- 2-thiazolyl)azo]-	MeOH	601(4.72)	24-0457-80
$C_{17}H_{22}N_5$ 3H-Purinium, 6-(diethylamino)-9-methyl- 3-(phenylmethyl)-, bromide	pH 1 pH 7 EtOH	292(4.30) 292(4.30) 294(4.32)	94-2522-80 94-2522-80 94-2522-80
$C_{17}H_{22}N_6$ Pyrimidine, 2,4-bis(3,5-dimethyl-1H- pyrazol-1-yl)-5-ethyl-6-methyl-	EtOH	265(4.43),288(3.96)	103-1279-80
$C_{17}H_{22}N_6O_5$ 9H-Purine, 6-(4,5-dihydro-2-methyl-1H- imidazol-1-yl)-9-[2,3-O-(1-methoxy- ethylidene)-β-D-ribofuranosyl]-	EtOH	267(4.26)	87-0781-80
$C_{17}H_{22}O$ Cyclobuta[a]naphthalen-8b(1H)-ol, 2,2a-dihydro-2,2-dimethyl-3-(1- methylethyl)-	EtOH	260s(3.96),268(4.06), 278s(4.00),293s(3.49), 305s(3.25)	44-0240-80
$C_{17}H_{22}OSi$ 9(3H)-Phenanthrenone, 4,4a,10,10a- tetrahydro-3-(trimethylsilyl)- more polar form	hexane hexane	207(4.18),239(3.94), 284(3.13),292(3.11) 207(4.22),241(4.04), 284(3.20),292(3.18)	33-0555-80 33-0555-80
$C_{17}H_{22}O_2$ A-Norestr-3(5)-ene-2,17-dione	MeOH	233(4.24)	24-2249-80
$C_{17}H_{22}O_3$ Benzenepropanoic acid, α-(2,3-dimethyl- 2-butenyl)-β-oxo- 1H-Benz[e]indene-3,7(2H,3aH)-dione, 4,5,8,9,9a,9b-hexahydro-3a-methyl- 6-(2-oxopropyl)-, [3aS-(3aα,9aα,9bβ)]- Spiro[1,3-benzodioxole-2,1'-cyclohex- ane]-5-carboxaldehyde, 6-(1,1-dimeth- ylethyl)- Spiro[1,3-dioxolane-2,2'(6'H)-naphtha- len]-6'-one, 1',3',4',8'a-tetrahydro- 1',8'a-dimethyl-7'-(1-methylethenyl)-, cis-(±)-	pentane MeOH EtOH EtOH	242(4.11),280(3.28), 290(3.21) 246(4.13) 238(4.38),285(3.92) 243(4.11)	33-0154-80 24-2249-80 12-0527-80 94-3265-80
$C_{17}H_{22}O_3S$ Ethanone, 1-[3-ethyl-5,5-dimethyl- 3-(phenylsulfonyl)-1-cyclopenten- 1-yl]-	EtOH	241(4.33)	35-1602-80

Compound	Solvent	$\lambda_{max}(\log \epsilon)$	Ref.
$C_{17}H_{22}O_4$			
Cyclohexanecarboxylic acid, 2-[(3-methoxyphenyl)methyl]-1-methyl-3-oxo-, methyl ester	EtOH	269(4.01)	39-0804-80C
Cyclooctanecarboxylic acid, 1-(4-methoxyphenyl)-2-oxo-, methyl ester	MeOH	233(3.92),274(3.20), 280(3.15)	12-0113-80
$C_{17}H_{22}O_4S$			
α-D-xylo-Hex-5-enofuranose, 5-deoxy-3-O-methyl-1,2-O-(1-methylethylidene)-6-S-(phenylmethyl)-6-thio-, (E)-	EtOH	216(3.79),232(3.75)	33-0016-80
(Z)-	EtOH	213(3.91),235(3.85)	33-0016-80
α-D-xylo-Hex-5-enofuranose, 6-deoxy-3-O-methyl-1,2-O-(1-methylethylidene)-5-S-(phenylmethyl)-5-thio-	EtOH	211(3.93)	33-0016-80
β-L-threo-Hex-4-enofuranose, 5-deoxy-3-O-methyl-1,2-O-(1-methylethylidene)-6-S-(phenylmethyl)-6-thio-	EtOH	218(4.04)	33-0016-80
$C_{17}H_{22}O_5$			
4H-1-Benzopyran-2-octanoic acid, 5,6,7,8-tetrahydro-ζ,4-dioxo-	EtOH	252(4.13)	94-2460-80
Eremofortine A	CHCl₃	246(4.17)	78-2989-80
Ovatifolin	MeOH	211(4.37)	102-2765-80
Spiro[1,3-dioxolane-2,6'(2'H)-naphth-[1,2-b]oxiren]-2'-one, 1'a,4',5'-7',7'a,7'b-hexahydro-1'a-[1-(hydroxymethyl)ethenyl]-7',7'a-dimethyl-(1'α,7'α,7'aα,7'bα)-(±)-	EtOH	242(4.15)	94-3265-80
Tulirinol	n.s.g.	208(4.33)	44-1441-80
$C_{17}H_{22}O_6$			
Cyclodeca[b]furan-6-carboxaldehyde, 2,3,3a,4,5,8,9,11a-octahydro-5-methoxy-3-(methoxymethyl)-10-methyl-2,4-dioxo-	n.s.g.	230(4.08)(end abs.)	102-0323-80
$C_{17}H_{22}O_6S$			
α-D-xylo-Hexofuranos-5-ulose, 6-deoxy-3-O-methyl-1,2-O-(1-methylethylidene)-6-[(phenylmethyl)sulfinyl]-	EtOH	216(3.90)	33-0016-80
$C_{17}H_{22}O_8$			
1H-Indene-1,1-dicarboxylic acid, 6-acetyl-2,3,3a,4,7,7a-hexahydro-2,5-dihydroxy-2,3,7a-trimethyl-7-oxo-, monomethyl ester	EtOH	274(4.25)	94-1590-80
$C_{17}H_{22}O_{11}$			
Apodanthoside	n.s.g.	232(3.96)	100-0649-80
$C_{17}H_{23}BrCl_2O_3$			
4-Oxocanol, 2-(1-bromopropyl)-5,7-dichloro-8-(2-penten-4-ynyl)-, acetate, [2R-[2α(S*),4β,5α,7β,8β(E)]]-(laurencienyne)	MeOH	225(4.18),232s(4.12)	88-2299-80
$C_{17}H_{23}NO_3S_2$			
2-Azetidinone, 3,3-bis(1,1-dimethylethyl)-1-(phenylsulfonyl)-4-thioxo-	isooctane	234(4.3),261(4.2), 430(1.3)	88-4247-80

Compound	Solvent	$\lambda_{max}(\log \epsilon)$	Ref.
$C_{17}H_{23}NO_4$			
Phellibilidine	EtOH	213(4.02),298(3.11)	102-1279-80
$C_{17}H_{23}NO_7$			
3,6,9,12,15-Pentaoxa-19-azabicyclo-[15.3.1]heneicosa-1(21),17,19-triene-2,16-dione, 18,20-dimethyl-	MeCN	236(4.02),274(3.52), 282(3.42)	44-2854-80
$C_{17}H_{23}N_2O_3$			
2-Furanmethanaminium, N,N,N-triethyl-5-(2-nitrophenyl)-, bromide	MeOH	255(4.31)	73-1715-80
2-Furanmethanaminium, N,N,N-triethyl-5-(3-nitrophenyl)-, bromide	MeOH	275(4.41)	73-1715-80
2-Furanmethanaminium, N,N,N-triethyl-5-(4-nitrophenyl)-, bromide	MeOH	336(4.33)	73-1715-80
$C_{17}H_{23}N_2O_4PS_2$			
Phosphorodithioic acid, O-(5-ethoxy-1,6-dihydro-6-oxo-1-phenyl-4-pyridazinyl) O-ethyl S-propyl ester	MeOH	212(4.40),287(3.80)	73-2247-80
$C_{17}H_{23}N_3O$			
Pyrazineethanol, α-[4-(dimethylamino)-phenyl]-3,5,6-trimethyl-	EtOH	211(3.70),257(3.61), 280(3.43),300s(3.23)	44-0999-80
$C_{17}H_{24}BrN_3$			
3,5-Pyridinedicarbonitrile, 1-(6-bromo-hexyl)-1,4-dihydro-2,4,4,6-tetramethyl-	MeOH	224(4.43),345(3.84)	73-3370-80
$C_{17}H_{24}FNO_3$			
4-Piperidinol, 1-[3-[2-(4-fluorophenyl)-1,3-dioxolan-2-yl]propyl]-	MeOH	256(2.61),262(2.79), 268(2.78)	87-0075-80
$C_{17}H_{24}N$			
2-Naphthalenemethanaminium, 3,4-dihydro-N,N,N,4,4-pentamethyl-3-methylene-, iodide	EtOH	221(4.53),228s(4.42), 236s(4.28),306(4.17)	39-1477-80C
$C_{17}H_{24}N_2$			
1-Butanamine, N-butyl-N-(3H-indol-3-yl-idenemethyl)-	CHCl₃	277s(4.27),282(4.33), 364(4.29)	94-1711-80
$C_{17}H_{24}N_2O$			
2-Cyclohexen-1-one, 3-[4-(dimethylami-no)-1,3-butadienyl]-6-[3-(dimethyl-amino)-2-propenylidene]-, (all-E)-	EtOH CHCl₃	430(4.58),505(4.90) 420(--),478(--)	70-0980-80 70-0980-80
1,3,5,8,10,12-Tridecahexaen-7-one, 1,13-bis(dimethylamino)-, (all-E)-	EtOH CHCl₃	512(4.82) 510(--)	70-0980-80 70-0980-80
$C_{17}H_{24}N_2O_2$			
1-Propanone, 2-(2,5-dihydro-1,2,2,5,5-pentamethyl-1H-imidazol-4-yl)-1-phen-yl-, N-oxide	EtOH	239(4.01)	70-0956-80
$C_{17}H_{24}O$			
1H,8H-3a,8a-Propanobenzo[3,4]cyclobuta-[1,2-a]pentalen-8-one, decahydro-, (3aα,3bα,3cβ,7aβ,7bα,8aα)-	EtOH	295(2.18)	44-3999-80

Compound	Solvent	$\lambda_{max}(\log \epsilon)$	Ref.
$C_{17}H_{24}OSi$			
Benzenemethanol, 2-ethenyl-α-[1-ethenyl-3-(trimethylsilyl)-2-propenyl]-, (E)-	hexane	205(4.32),239(3.20), 282(3.48)	33-0555-80
Benzenemethanol, 2-ethenyl-α-[5-(trimethylsilyl)-2,4-pentadienyl]-, (E,E)-	hexane	208(4.19),236(4.19)	33-0555-80
$C_{17}H_{24}O_2$			
Phenanthro[2,1-b]furan-7(4aH)-one, 2,3,3aβ,4,5,8,9,9a,9b,10,11,11a-dodecahydro-9b-methyl-, (3bβ,9aβ,9bα-11aα)-($\pm$)-	EtOH	242(4.3)	39-2511-80C
$C_{17}H_{24}O_3$			
2(1H)-Naphthalenone, 1-(2-acetoxy-1-methylethenyl)-3,4,6,7,8,8a-hexahydro-8,8a-dimethyl-, [1S-[1α(E),8β,8aβ]]-	EtOH	225(3.81)	12-0885-80
Spiro[bicyclo[4.1.0]heptane-2,1'-[4]cyclopenten]-3'-one, 4'-(acetoxymethyl)-3,7,7-trimethyl-	n.s.g.	227(3.95)	77-1220-80
$C_{17}H_{24}O_4$			
1,3-Benzodioxole-5,6-dione, 2-methyl-2-nonyl-	EtOH	290(4.12),395(3.17)	12-0527-80
1,3-Benzodioxol-5-ol, 2-heptyl-2-methyl-, acetate	EtOH	235(3.48),286(3.64)	12-0527-80
Futronolide acetate	MeOH	216(4.2)	100-0365-80
Naphtho[1,2-b]furan-2(4H)-one, 8-acetoxy-5,5a,6,7,8,9,9a,9b-octahydro-3,5a,9-trimethyl-, [5aR-(5aα,8α,9β,9aβ,9bα)]-	EtOH	218.5(3.64)	94-0282-80
$C_{17}H_{24}O_5$			
Azuleno[5,6-c]furan-1(3H)-one, 3a,4,4a-5,6,7,7a,8-octahydro-3a-hydroxy-6,6,8-trimethyl-, (3aα,4aα,4aα,7aα,8α)-	MeOH	217(3.94)	102-0093-80
1,2-Naphthalenedicarboxaldehyde, 4-acetoxy-1,4,4a,5,6,7,8,8a-octahydro-1-hydroxy-5,5,8a-trimethyl- (cinnamodial)	MeOH	215(4.14)	100-0365-80
Naphtho[1,2-a]furan-1(3H)-one, 5-acetoxy-4,5,5a,6,7,8,9,9a-octahydro-4-hydroxy-6,6,9a-trimethyl- (ugandensolide)	MeOH	212(3.9)	100-0365-80
Naphtho[1,2-c]furan-3(1H)-one, 5-acetoxy-5,5a,6,7,8,9,9a,9b-octahydro-9b-hydroxy-6,6,9a-trimethyl- (cinnamosmolide)	MeOH	212(3.96)	100-0365-80
Spiro[1,3-dioxolane-2,2'(1'H)-naphthalene]-5'-acetic acid, 3',4',6',7'-8',8'a-hexahydro-8'a-methyl-6'-oxo-, ethyl ester	EtOH	243(4.01)	39-2511-80C
$C_{17}H_{24}O_6$			
Cyclodeca[b]furan-6-carboxaldehyde, 2,3,3a,4,5,8,9,11a-octahydro-4-hydroxy-5-methoxy-3-(methoxymethyl)-10-methyl-2-oxo-	MeOH	230(3.98)	102-0323-80

Compound	Solvent	$\lambda_{max}(\log \epsilon)$	Ref.
$C_{17}H_{24}O_6S$			
α-D-Glucofuranose, 6-deoxy-3-O-methyl-1,2-O-(1-methylethylidene)-6-[(phenylmethyl)sulfinyl]-, (R,S)-	EtOH	210(3.75)	33-0016-80
(S,S)-	EtOH	210(3.88)	33-0016-80
$C_{17}H_{24}O_{10}$			
Cyclopenta[c]pyran-4-carboxylic acid, 1-(β-D-glucopyranosyloxy)-1,4a,5,6-7,7a-hexahydro-7-methyl-5-oxo-, methyl ester (cornin)	EtOH	290(2.02)	100-0649-80
Cyclopenta[c]pyran-4-carboxylic acid, 1-(β-D-glucopyranosyloxy)-1,4a,5,6-7,7a-hexahydro-7-methyl-6-oxo-, methyl ester (7-oxologanin)	EtOH	234(4.02)	100-0649-80
Cyclopenta[c]pyran-4-carboxylic acid, 1-(β-D-glucopyranosyloxy)-1,4a,5,7a-tetrahydro-7-(hydroxymethyl)-, methyl ester (geniposide)	MeOH	236.5(4.08)	100-0649-80
2H-Pyran-5-carboxylic acid, 3-ethenyl-2-(β-D-glucopyranosyloxy)-3,4-dihydro-4-(2-oxoethyl)-, methyl ester (loniceroside)	EtOH	236(3.99)	100-0649-80
$C_{17}H_{24}O_{11}$			
Cyclopenta[c]pyran-4-carboxylic acid, 1-(β-D-glucopyranosyloxy)-1,4a,5,6-7,7a-hexahydro-4a-hydroxy-7-methyl-5-oxo-, methyl ester (hastatoside)	H_2O	234(3.98)	100-0649-80
Feretoside	MeOH	235(3.8)	100-0649-80
Forsythide methyl ester	MeOH	233.5(4.05)	100-0649-80
Gardenoside	MeOH	233(3.5)	100-0649-80
Scandoside methyl ester	MeOH	238(3.89)	100-0649-80
Theviridoside	n.s.g.	234(3.9)	100-0649-80
$C_{17}H_{24}O_{12}$			
Secogalioside	EtOH	238(4.05)	100-0649-80
$C_{17}H_{24}Si_2$			
Disilane, 1,1,2,2-tetramethyl-1-(4-methylphenyl)-2-phenyl-	C_6H_{12}	237(4.30)	65-1615-80
$C_{17}H_{25}NO_3$			
3-Pyridinecarboxylic acid, 1,4-dihydro-5-(8-nonenyl)-4-oxo-, ethyl ester	EtOH	255s(3.81),260(3.84), 287(3.68)	4-0359-80
3-Pyridinecarboxylic acid, 1-ethyl-1,4-dihydro-5-(8-nonenyl)-4-oxo-	EtOH	260(3.96),287(3.62)	4-0359-80
$C_{17}H_{25}NSSi$			
2-Azetidinethione, 1-methyl-3-(1-methyl-2-propenyl)-4-phenyl-3-(trimethylsilyl)-	isooctane	265(4.2),336s(2.0)	24-3024-80
$C_{17}H_{26}FN_4O_8P$			
Uridine, 2'-deoxy-5-fluoro-, 5'-(di-4-morpholinylphosphinate)	MeOH	269(3.96)	87-1229-80
$C_{17}H_{26}N_2$			
1H-Indole-3-ethanamine, 2-methyl-N,N-dipropyl-, monohydrochloride	EtOH	226(4.37),283(3.85), 291(3.78)	80-0245-80

Compound	Solvent	$\lambda_{max}(\log \epsilon)$	Ref.
$C_{17}H_{26}N_2O_{11}$			
α-D-Glucopyranosiduronic acid, [(1,1-dimethylethyl)nitrosoamino]methyl 2,3,4-triacetate	MeOH	234(2.71),300(2.00)	89-0400-80
$C_{17}H_{26}N_6O_5$			
Adenosine, N-(4-aminobutyl)-2',3'-O-(1-methoxyethylidene)-	EtOH	267(4.20)	87-0781-80
$C_{17}H_{26}O$			
2,4,6-Heptatrien-1-ol, 5-methyl-7-(2,6,6-trimethyl-1-cyclohexen-1-yl)-, (E,E,E)-	3-Mepentane	225(3.65),290(4.49)	149-0739-80B
at 77°K	3-Mepentane	223(3.82),295(4.47)	149-0739-80B
(E,E,Z)-	3-Mepentane	250(--),287(4.38)	149-0739-80B
at 77°K	3-Mepentane	228(--),250(--), 292s(4.34)	149-0739-80B
$C_{17}H_{26}O_2$			
Propanoic acid, 2-(3,4,6,7,8,8a-hexa-hydro-8,8a-dimethyl-2(1H)-naphthal-enylidene)-, ethyl ester, (E)-	EtOH	225(3.96)	39-1752-80C
(Z)-	EtOH	225.5(3.93)	39-1752-80C
$C_{17}H_{26}O_3$			
1,3-Benzodioxol-5-ol, 2-methyl-2-nonyl-	EtOH	235(3.57),299(3.78)	12-0527-80
A-Nor-1-oxaandrostan-2-one, 17-hydroxy-, (5β,17β)-	n.s.g.	203(3.46)	33-2380-80
$C_{17}H_{26}O_4$			
1,4-Cyclohexadiene-1,2-dicarboxylic acid, 4-methyl-, bis(1,1-dimethyl-ethyl) ester	EtOH	237s(3.32)	24-0531-80
2(1H)-Naphthalenone, 5-acetoxy-4a,5,6-7,8,8a-hexahydro-6-(1-hydroxy-1-methylethyl)-4,8a-dimethyl-, [4aR-(4aα,5α,6β,8aβ)]-	EtOH	241(4.17)	78-0371-80
$C_{17}H_{26}O_9$			
Deoxyloganin	n.s.g.	236(4.03)	100-0649-80
$C_{17}H_{26}O_{10}$			
Cyclopenta[c]pyran-4-carboxylic acid, 1-(β-D-glucopyranosyloxy)-1,4a,5,6-7,7a-hexahydro-5-hydroxy-7-methyl-, methyl ester (dihydrocornin)	EtOH	238(4.05)	100-0649-80
Cyclopenta[c]pyran-4-carboxylic acid, 1-(β-D-glucopyranosyloxy)-1,4a,5,6-7,7a-hexahydro-6-hydroxy-7-methyl-, methyl ester (loganin)	n.s.g.	238(4.03)	100-0649-80
Cyclopenta[c]pyran-4-carboxylic acid, 1-(β-D-glucopyranosyloxy)-1,4a,5,6-7,7a-hexahydro-7-hydroxy-7-methyl-, methyl ester (mussaenoside)	MeOH	238(4.04)	100-0649-80
β-D-Glucopyranoside, 7-acetoxy-1,4a,5-6,7,7a-hexahydro-4a-hydroxy-7-methyl-cyclopenta[c]pyran-1-yl (glucoside VII)	H₂O	205(3.7)	100-0649-80
β-D-Glucopyranoside, 7-acetoxy-1,4a,5-6,7,7a-hexahydro-5-hydroxy-7-methyl-cyclopenta[c]pyran-1-yl (ajugoside)	MeOH	206(3.6)	100-0649-80

Compound	Solvent	$\lambda_{max}(\log \epsilon)$	Ref.
Reptoside	MeOH	205(3.7)	100-0649-80
$C_{17}H_{26}O_{11}$			
β-D-Glucopyranoside, 7-acetoxy-1,4a,5-6,7,7a-hexahydro-4a,5-dihydroxy-7-methylcyclopenta[c]pyran-1-yl (8-acetylharpagide)	n.s.g.	210(3.6)	100-0649-80
Ipolamiide	MeOH	229(4.03)	100-0649-80
$C_{17}H_{26}O_{12}$			
Lamalbid	MeOH	235(3.96)	100-0649-80
Lamiide	EtOH	229(4.02)	100-0649-80
Nyctanthoside	H_2O	237(3.84)	100-0649-80
$C_{17}H_{26}O_{13}$			
Cyclopenta[c]pyran-4-carboxylic acid, 1-(β-D-glucopyranosyloxy)-1,4a,5,6-7,7a-hexahydro-4a,5,6,7-tetrahydroxy-7-methyl-, methyl ester (phlomiol)	MeOH	231(3.83)	100-0649-80
$C_{17}H_{27}N$			
Benzenamine, N-(1-pentylhexylidene)-	CCl_4	288s(3.27)	24-2462-80
$C_{17}H_{27}NO_2$			
2(3H)-Naphthalenone, 4,4a,5,6,7,8-hexahydro-4a-methyl-8-[2-(4-morpholinyl)-ethyl]-, cis	1% MeOH	247(4.04)	44-1645-80
trans	1% MeOH	247(4.04)	44-1645-80
$C_{17}H_{27}NO_3$			
3-Pyridinecarboxylic acid, 1,4-dihydro-5-nonyl-4-oxo-, ethyl ester	EtOH	255s(3.78),260(3.81),290(3.67)	4-0359-80
3-Pyridinecarboxylic acid, 1-ethyl-1,4-dihydro-5-nonyl-4-oxo-	EtOH	260(3.98),284(3.65)	4-0359-80
$C_{17}H_{28}N_6O$			
2-Pyrimidinamine, 4-ethoxy-5-ethyl-N-(5-hexyl-1H-1,2,4-triazol-3-yl)-6-methyl-	EtOH	253(4.23),278(3.80)	103-1275-80
$C_{17}H_{28}O_2$			
Spiro[4.4]nonane-1,6-dione, 3,8-bis-(1,1-dimethylethyl)-, (3R,5R,8R)-(-)-	isooctane	200(3.6),222(3.0), 305(2.1),312(2.1)	88-1243-80
$C_{17}H_{28}O_4$			
Acarenoic acid, (-)-	MeOH	219(3.42)	102-2713-80
Isoacarenoic acid	MeOH	232(3.56)	102-2713-80
$C_{17}H_{29}NO_7$			
D-Arabinitol, 1-C-[1-butyl-4-(ethoxy-carbonyl)-5-methyl-1H-pyrrol-3-yl]-, (S)-	EtOH	244(3.85),258s(--)	39-1199-80C
D-Arabinitol, 5-C-[1-butyl-4-(ethoxy-carbonyl)-5-methyl-1H-pyrrol-3-yl]-, (S)-	EtOH	240(4.11),260(--)	39-1199-80C
$C_{17}H_{29}N_3O$			
1,3-Cyclopentadiene-1-carboxamide, 5-[bis(dimethylamino)methylene]-3-(1,1-dimethylethyl)-N,N-dimethyl-	dioxan	255(4.18),363(4.25)	89-0199-80

Compound	Solvent	$\lambda_{max}(\log \epsilon)$	Ref.
$C_{17}H_{29}N_3O_2S$			
Pentanamide, 4-methyl-2-[methyl(3-meth-yl-1-oxobutyl)amino]-N-[1-(2-thiazol-yl)ethyl]-	MeOH	355(4.10)	78-2133-80
$C_{17}H_{29}N_3O_3$			
3,5-Isoxazoledicarboxamide, N,N'-di-butyl-4-(2-methylpropyl)-	MeOH	245(4.01)	94-0479-80
3,5-Isoxazoledicarboxamide, N,N',4-tri-butyl-	MeOH	246(3.99)	94-0479-80
$C_{17}H_{30}O_4$			
Acaranoic acid, (-)-	MeOH	210(2.85)	102-2713-80
$C_{17}H_{31}N_3O_4$			
3,5-Isoxazoledicarboxamide, N,N'-di-butyl-4,5-dihydro-4-(2-methylprop-yl)-, 2-oxide, trans	MeOH	258(3.95)	94-0479-80
3,5-Isoxazoledicarboxamide, N,N',4-tri-butyl-4,5-dihydro-, 2-oxide, trans	MeOH	258(3.93)	94-0479-80
$C_{17}H_{32}N_2O_9$			
D-galacto-Octonic acid, 2-[1-(butyl-amino)ethylidene]-2,3-dideoxy-3-(ni-tromethyl)-, ethyl ester, [2(Z),3ξ]-	EtOH	297(4.10)	39-1199-80C
$C_{17}H_{32}N_4O$			
1H-Indazole, 4,5,6,7-tetrahydro-3-[3-(dimethylamino)propoxy]-1-[3-(di-methylamino)propyl]-	EtOH	232(3.83)	18-0825-80
$C_{17}H_{32}O_7Si$			
DL-allo-Heptonic acid, 3,6-anhydro-7-O-[(1,1-dimethylethyl)dimethylsilyl]-4,5-O-(1-methylethylidene)-, methyl ester, (2ξ)-	EtOH	294(4.14)	23-2024-80
$C_{17}H_{33}N_3O_7$			
Pentanedioic acid, 2-hydroxy-3-nitro-, bis(cyclohexylamine) salt	pH 13	233(4.00)	69-2358-80
$C_{17}H_{34}NO_5$			
1-Piperidinyloxy, 4,4-bis[(1,1-dimeth-ylethyl)dioxy]-2,2,6,6-tetramethyl-	EtOH	237(3.38),443(0.93)	97-0053-80
$C_{17}H_{35}NS_2$			
Carbamodithioic acid, hexadecyl-, monoammonium salt	dioxan	245(3.93),275(4.01)	90-0775-80

Compound	Solvent	$\lambda_{max}(\log \epsilon)$	Ref.
$C_{18}H_4BrF_8NOS$ 10H-Phenothiazine, 10-(4-bromophenyl)- 1,2,3,4,6,7,8,9-octafluoro-, 5-oxide	EtOH	229(4.61),288(3.89), 320(3.79)	104-0905-80
$C_{18}H_5F_8NOS$ 10H-Phenothiazine, 1,2,3,4,6,7,8,9- octafluoro-10-phenyl-, 5-oxide	EtOH	207(4.43),217(4.43), 288(3.81),320(3.69)	104-0905-80
$C_{18}H_6Br_9N$ Benzenamine, 2,4,6-tribromo-N,N-bis- (2,4,6-tribromophenyl)-	$CHCl_3$	283(4.29)	24-0577-80
$C_{18}H_8Cl_2N_4O_4$ 1,3,4,6-Hexanetetrone, 1,6-bis(4-chlo- rophenyl)-2,5-bis(diazo)-	CH_2Cl_2	261(4.74)	39-2670-80C
$C_{18}H_8Cl_2O_4$ 1H,4H-Furo[3,4-c]furan-1,4-dione, 3,6-bis(4-chlorophenyl)-	CH_2Cl_2	248(4.52),265s(4.18), 295(4.06),387s(4.05), 410(4.48),436(4.78), 466(4.83)	39-2670-80C
$C_{18}H_8F_6N_2O_2S_2$ Acetamide, N,N'-[1]benzothieno[3,2-b]- [1]benzothiophene-2,7-diylbis[2,2,2- trifluoro-	dioxan	222(4.59),244(4.44), 278(4.47),332(4.68), 352(4.61)	104-0383-80
$C_{18}H_8NO_4$ 1H-Indene-1,3(2H)-dione, 2-[(1,3-dihy- dro-1,3-dioxo-2H-inden-2-ylidene)- amino]-, ion(1-)	EtOH	253(4.64),469(4.33), 575(4.28)	23-0201-80
$C_{18}H_8O_4$ 1,4,6,11-Naphthacenetetrone	CH_2Cl_2	259(4.75),300(3.74), 348(3.84),357s(3.79)	23-1161-80
$C_{18}H_9Br_6N$ Benzenamine, 2,4-dibromo-N,N-bis(2,4- dibromophenyl)-	$CHCl_3$	301.5(4.49)	24-0577-80
$C_{18}H_9F_3O$ Ethanone, 1-dicyclopenta[ef,kl]hepta- len-1-yl-2,2,2-trifluoro-	C_6H_{12}	240(4.17),264(4.32), 300(3.96),315(3.87), 334(3.61),354s(2.94), 384(3.38),410(3.08), 438(2.92),475(2.98), 499s(3.22),511(3.71)	44-1312-80
$C_{18}H_9NO_4$ 1H-Indene-1,3(2H)-dione, 2-[(1,3-di- hydro-1,3-dioxo-2H-inden-2-ylidene)- amino]-	$CHCl_3$	485(4.20)	23-0201-80
$C_{18}H_9N_3O_5S$ [2,2':3',2"-Terfuran]-4'-carbonitrile, 5'-[[(5-nitro-2-thienyl)methylene]- amino]-	MeOH	495(3.44)	73-1581-80
$C_{18}H_{10}Br_3N$ 9H-Carbazole, 3,6-dibromo-9-(4-bromo- phenyl)-	$CHCl_3$	260(3.90),274(3.78), 304(3.66)	24-0577-80

Compound	Solvent	$\lambda_{max}(\log \epsilon)$	Ref.
$C_{18}H_{10}Br_5N$ Benzenamine, 2,4-dibromo-N-(4-bromo-phenyl)-N-(2,4-dibromophenyl)-	CHCl$_3$	305(4.43)	24-0577-80
$C_{18}H_{10}ClNO_2$ 5,12-Naphthacenedione, 6-amino-11-chloro-	toluene	389(3.56),468(3.97)	104-1651-80
$C_{18}H_{10}Cl_2N_2O_2$ 1H,5H-Pyrazolo[1,2-a]pyrazole-1,5-dione, 2,6-dichloro-3,7-diphenyl-	dioxan	325(4.19)	35-4983-80
1H,7H-Pyrazolo[1,2-a]pyrazole-1,7-dione, 2,6-dichloro-3,5-diphenyl-	dioxan	235s(4.03),270(4.19), 369(3.81)	35-4983-80
$C_{18}H_{10}Cl_4N_2O_3$ Acetamide, N-[2,4,6-trichloro-7-[(4-chlorophenyl)amino]-5,8-dihydro-5,8-dioxo-1-naphthalenyl]-	EtOH	269(4.36),490(3.69)	40-1862-80
Acetamide, N-[2,4,7-trichloro-6-[(4-chlorophenyl)amino]-5,8-dihydro-5,8-dioxo-1-naphthalenyl]-	EtOH	276(4.44),492(3.76)	40-1862-80
$C_{18}H_{10}Cl_4O_2$ Butanedial, bis[(2,6-dichlorophenyl)-methylene]-	CHCl$_3$	261(4.2)	118-0898-80
$C_{18}H_{10}N_2$ Cyclobuta[1,2-c:4,3-c']diquinoline	C_6H_{12}	253(4.21),265(3.73), 284(3.65),396(3.63), 433(3.91),448(3.92)	150-2911-80
$C_{18}H_{10}N_2OS_3$ 3-Furancarbonitrile, 4,5-di-2-thienyl-2-[(2-thienylmethylene)amino]-	MeOH	423(4.12)	73-1581-80
$C_{18}H_{10}N_2O_3S$ [2,2':3',2"-Terfuran]-4'-carbonitrile, 5'-[(2-thienylmethylene)amino]-	MeOH	435(4.07)	73-1581-80
$C_{18}H_{10}N_2O_4$ [2,2':3',2"-Terfuran]-4'-carbonitrile, 5'-[(2-furanylmethylene)amino]-	MeOH	428(4.23)	73-1581-80
$C_{18}H_{10}N_2O_5S_2$ Methanone, [2-(hydroxy-2-thienylmeth-ylene)-7-nitro-2H-1,4-benzoxazin-3-yl]-2-thienyl-	MeOH	234(4.20),250(4.12), 305(3.90),414(4.63)	4-1625-80
$C_{18}H_{10}N_2O_7$ Methanone, 2-furanyl[2-(2-furanylhydr-oxymethylene)-7-nitro-2H-1,4-benzox-azin-3-yl]-	MeOH	234(4.04),252(3.94), 297(3.88),414(4.67)	4-1625-80
$C_{18}H_{10}N_2S_2$ [1,4]Dithiino[2,3-c:5,6-c']diquinoline	n.s.g.	314.0(4.22)	56-0033-80
[1,4]Dithiino[2,3-c:6,5-c']diquinoline	n.s.g.	322.0(3.99)	56-0033-80
$C_{18}H_{10}N_4O_4$ 1,3,4,6-Hexanetetrone, 2,5-bis(diazo)-1,6-diphenyl-	CH$_2$Cl$_2$	257(4.51)	39-2670-80C

Compound	Solvent	$\lambda_{max}(\log \epsilon)$	Ref.
$C_{18}H_{10}O_2S_2$			
Benzo[b]thiophen-3(2H)-one, 2,2'-(1,2-ethanediylidene)bis-	CHCl$_3$	528(4.23)	24-1708-80
[3,3'-Bi-4H-1-benzothiopyran]-4,4'-dione	CHCl$_3$	528(4.41)	24-1708-80
$C_{18}H_{10}O_3$			
Naphtho[1,2-b]furan-4,5-dione, 2-phenyl-	EtOH	224(4.38),226(4.37), 340(4.47)	103-0578-80
$C_{18}H_{10}O_4$			
1H,4H-Furo[3,4-c]furan-1,4-dione, 3,6-diphenyl-	CH$_2$Cl$_2$	285(3.87),402(4.35), 427(4.63),456(4.67)	39-2670-80C
$C_{18}H_{10}O_6$			
[2,2'-Bi-1H-indene]-1,1',3,3'(2H,2'H)-tetrone, 2,2'-dihydroxy-	EtOH	229(4.90),246(4.30)	23-0201-80
$C_{18}H_{10}S_8$			
1,3-Dithiole, 4,4'-(1,4-phenylene)bis-[2-(1,3-dithiol-2-ylidene)-	dioxan	296(4.30),310(4.34), 320(4.33),440(3.61)	11-0196-80A
$C_{18}H_{11}Br_4N$			
Benzenamine, 2,4-dibromo-N,N-bis(4-bromophenyl)-	CHCl$_3$	307(4.44)	24-0577-80
$C_{18}H_{11}ClN_2O$			
3-Pyridinecarbonitrile, 4-(4-chlorophenyl)-1,2-dihydro-2-oxo-6-phenyl-	pH 13	248(4.31),355(4.27)	4-1521-80
	EtOH	257(4.33),357(4.28)	4-1521-80
	CHCl$_3$	260(4.28),360(4.26)	4-1521-80
$C_{18}H_{11}Cl_3N_2O_3$			
Acetamide, N-[2,4,6-trichloro-5,8-dihydro-5,8-dioxo-7-(phenylamino)-1-naphthalenyl]-	EtOH	264(4.41),485(3.65)	40-1862-80
Acetamide, N-[2,4,7-trichloro-5,8-dihydro-5,8-dioxo-6-(phenylamino)-1-naphthalenyl]-	EtOH	270(4.44),485(3.69)	40-1862-80
$C_{18}H_{11}Cl_3N_2O_8S$			
Furan, 2-[2-(5-nitro-2-furanyl)-2-[(trichloromethyl)sulfonyl]cyclopropyl]-5-(2-nitrophenyl)-, trans-(±)-	MeOH	207(4.43),325(4.02)	73-1704-80
Furan, 2-[2-(5-nitro-2-furanyl)-2-[(trichloromethyl)sulfonyl]cyclopropyl]-5-(4-nitrophenyl)-, trans-(±)-	MeOH	207(4.30),356(4.30)	73-1704-80
$C_{18}H_{11}Cl_4NO_5$			
Benzamide, N-(2-acetyl-5,6,7,8-tetrachloro-2,3-dihydro-1,4-benzodioxin-2-yl)-N-methyl-	MeCN	212(4.61),288(3.06), 297(3.06)	5-1836-80
$C_{18}H_{11}N$			
1H-Indole, 3-(4-phenyl-1,3-butadiynyl)-	EtOH	205(4.55),219(4.60), 228(4.68),252(4.38), 265(4.41),281(4.35), 299(4.29),318(4.29), 332(4.30),351(4.20)	104-0665-80
$C_{18}H_{11}NO_2$			
1H-Benz[f]indole-4,9-dione, 2-phenyl-	CHCl$_3$	293(4.58),345s(3.41),	39-2923-80C

Compound	Solvent	$\lambda_{max}(\log \epsilon)$	Ref.
(cont.)		440(3.66)	39-2923-80C
$C_{18}H_{11}NO_4$			
11H-Benzo[b]phenoxazine-6,11(12H)-dione, 1-acetyl-	DMSO	307(4.23),441(3.70)	44-5144-80
Oxazolo[3,2-a]quinolinium, 5-(benzoyl-oxy)-2-hydroxy-, hydroxide, inner salt	EtOH	232(4.46),265(4.17), 304s(--)	78-1385-80
$C_{18}H_{11}N_3$			
Benz[f]indazolo[4,5-b]quinoline	MeOH	220(3.62),257s(3.35), 285(3.74),290s(3.72), 355(3.75),372(2.87), 392(2.98)	39-1233-80C
	MeOH-acid	228(3.70),273s(3.19), 295(3.68),398s(3.08), 420(3.17)	39-1233-80C
$C_{18}H_{11}N_3O$			
Indolo[2',3':3,4]pyrido[2,1-b]quinazo-lin-5(13H)-one	MeOH	250(4.7),270s(4.4), 330(4.3),370(4.4), 390(4.4)	83-0990-80
$C_{18}H_{11}N_5$			
1H-Imidazo[4,5-f][1,8]phenanthroline, 2-(4-pyridinyl)-	MeOH	220(4.93),250(4.80), 364(3.93)	56-2365-80
$C_{18}H_{12}$			
Naphth[2,1-a]azulene	MeOH	272(4.24),322(4.87), 375(3.92),395(3.54), 411(3.17),580(2.46), 630(2.57)	138-0167-80
Naphth[2,3-a]azulene	MeOH	269(4.41),279(4.38), 316(4.77),326(4.76), 366(3.85),392(3.72), 414(3.66),586(2.52), 647(2.60)	138-0167-80
$C_{18}H_{12}Br_3N$			
Benzenamine, 4-bromo-N,N-bis(4-bromo-phenyl)-	$CHCl_3$	311.5(4.53)	24-0577-80
$C_{18}H_{12}ClNO_3$			
12H-Benzo[a]phenoxazin-5-ol, 6-chloro-, acetate	dioxan	269(4.39),320(3.68), 396(3.68)	44-2155-80
$C_{18}H_{12}ClN_3O_2$			
Pyrimido[4,5-b]quinoline-2,4(3H,10H)-dione, 7-chloro-3-methyl-10-phenyl-	EtOH	226(4.44),268(4.64), 307(3.99),319s(3.95), 393s(3.89),409(3.96), 423s(3.87)	94-3049-80
Pyrimido[4,5-b]quinoline-2,4(3H,10H)-dione, 8-chloro-3-methyl-10-phenyl-	EtOH	256(4.30),322(3.82), 397(3.78),419s(3.51)	94-3049-80
Pyrimido[4,5-b]quinoline-2,4(3H,10H)-dione, 10-(4-chlorophenyl)-3-methyl-	EtOH	264(4.56),316(3.97), 320(3.98),400(4.03), 420s(3.94)	94-3049-80
$C_{18}H_{12}Cl_2N_2O_3$			
Acetamide, N-[6-chloro-7-(4-chlorophen-yl)amino]-5,8-dihydro-5,8-dioxo-1-naphthalenyl]-	EtOH	262(4.38),289(4.41), 435(3.83)	40-1862-80

Compound	Solvent	$\lambda_{max}(\log \epsilon)$	Ref.
Acetamide, N-[7-chloro-6-(4-chlorophenyl)amino]-5,8-dihydro-5,8-dioxo-1-naphthalenyl]-	EtOH	274(4.45),502(3.86)	40-1862-80
$C_{18}H_{12}Cl_2O_2$			
Anthra[1,9-bc]pyran-7(2H)-one, 4,6-dichloro-2,2-dimethyl-	benzene	388(3.69)	104-0159-80
Butanedial, bis[(4-chlorophenyl)methylene]-	CHCl₃	285(4.8)	118-0898-80
$C_{18}H_{12}Cl_2O_4$			
2-Propenoic acid, 3,3'-[1,1'-biphenyl]-4,4'-diylbis[2-chloro-	film	270(3.88)	104-2207-80
$C_{18}H_{12}Cl_2O_5$			
2-Propenoic acid, 3,3'-(oxydi-4,1-phenylene)bis[2-chloro-	film	408(3.88)	104-2207-80
$C_{18}H_{12}Cl_2O_6S$			
2-Propenoic acid, 3,3'-(sulfonyldi-4,1-phenylene)bis[2-chloro-	film	312(3.86)	104-2207-80
$C_{18}H_{12}FN_3O_2$			
Pyrimido[4,5-b]quinoline-2,4(3H,10H)-dione, 10-(4-fluorophenyl)-3-methyl-	EtOH	263(4.51),320(4.00),380s(3.91),401(4.50),419s(4.00)	94-3049-80
$C_{18}H_{12}FeO_6Ru$			
Ruthenium, tricarbonyl[μ-[η⁴:η⁴-5,6,7-8-tetrakis(methylene)bicyclo[2.2.2]oct-2-ene]](tricarbonyliron)-, endo-Fe,exo-Ru	isooctane	255(4.05),328s(3.86)	101-0103-80K
exo-Fe,endo-Ru	isooctane	255(4.06),330s(3.89)	101-0103-80K
exo-Fe,exo-Ru	isooctane	237(3.85),282s(3.51)	101-0103-80K
$C_{18}H_{12}N_2$			
2,2'-Biquinoline	CH₂Cl₂	314(4.30),326(4.36),339(4.27)	5-0291-80
	CH₂Cl₂	259(4.82),313(4.30),325(4.36),339(4.27)	35-7892-80
4,4'-Biquinoline	CH₂Cl₂	288s(3.98),291(3.99),304(3.98),317(3.91)	5-0291-80
1H-Indole, 3,3'-(1,2-ethynediyl)bis-	EtOH	208(4.55),227(4.58),256(4.23),279(4.24),303(4.06),327(3.96)	103-0741-80
$C_{18}H_{12}N_2O$			
3-Pyridinecarbonitrile, 1,2-dihydro-2-oxo-4,6-diphenyl-	pH 13	254(4.35),355(4.16)	4-1521-80
	EtOH	257(4.24),285s(3.86),366(4.10)	4-1521-80
	CHCl₃	260(4.34),284s(4.04),367(4.15)	4-1521-80
$C_{18}H_{12}N_2O_2$			
Benzonitrile, 4-[(3-methoxy-4-oxo-1(4H)-naphthalenylidene)amino]-	EtOH	250(4.39),255s(4.37),289(4.41),296(4.42),341(3.92),410(3.59)	94-1207-80
1H-Pyrrole-1-acetonitrile, 2,5-dihydro-2,5-dioxo-3,4-diphenyl-	60% dioxan	365(3.72)	40-0837-80

Compound	Solvent	$\lambda_{max}(\log \epsilon)$	Ref.
$C_{18}H_{12}N_2O_3$			
Furo[2,3-c]pyridin-2(6H)-one, 3-phenyl-6-(4-pyridinyl)-, N-oxide	EtOH	216(3.97),255(3.76), 405(4.26)	39-1176-80C
Furo[3,2-b]pyridin-2(4H)-one, 3-phenyl-4-(4-pyridinyl)-, N-oxide	EtOH	216(4.11),250(4.01), 291(3.93),391(3.99)	39-1176-80C
$C_{18}H_{12}N_2O_5S$			
2H-Naphtho[2,3-b]-1,4-thiazine-5,10-dione, 3,4-dihydro-3-hydroxy-3-(4-nitrophenyl)-	CHCl$_3$	283(4.52),303s(3.31), 492(3.34)	39-2923-80C
$C_{18}H_{12}N_2O_6S$			
4H-[1]Benzothieno[3,2-b]pyran-2-carboxylic acid, 4-(tetrahydro-1,3-dimethyl-2,4,6-trioxo-5(2H)-pyrimidinylidene)-	dioxan	220(4.53),290(4.04), 329(4.02),455(4.33)	83-0557-80
1H-Indole-2-carboxylic acid, 5,5'-sulfonylbis-	mineral oil	241s(5.1),258(5.2), 305(4.8)	103-1146-80
$C_{18}H_{12}N_2O_7$			
4H-Pyrano[3,2-b]benzofuran-2-carboxylic acid, 4-(tetrahydro-1,3-dimethyl-2,4,6-trioxo-5(2H)-pyrimidinylidene)-	dioxan	222(4.36),317(4.17), 449(4.32)	83-0557-80
$C_{18}H_{12}N_4O$			
12H-Benz[h]indazolo[5,4-b][1,6]naphthyridin-12-one, 3,11-dihydro-11-methyl-	MeOH	226(4.46),246s(4.26), 283(4.59),312s(4.12), 368(3.73),384s(3.62)	39-0512-80C
	MeOH-acid	230(4.62),254s(4.35), 297(4.51),322s(4.35), 388(4.06),412(4.05)	39-0512-80C
2,7-Ethanonaphth[2,3-b]oxirene-4,4,5,5-tetracarbonitrile, 1a,2,3,6,7,7a-hexahydro-8,9-bis(methylene)-,	EtOH	224(3.98),235(4.00), 252s(3.78)	78-0149-80
(1aα, 2α,7α,7aα)-	dioxan	224(3.97),237(4.02), 253s(3.79)	78-0149-80
(1aα,2β,7β,7aα)-	EtOH	225(4.00),231(3.99), 241s(3.91)	78-0149-80
	dioxan	225(4.00),231(3.99), 242s(3.91)	78-0149-80
Pyridazino[4,5-c]pyridazin-8(7H)-one, 3,5-diphenyl-	EtOH	228s(3.90),275(4.48), 340(3.70)	4-0529-80
$C_{18}H_{12}N_4O_2$			
2,4(1H,3H)-Pteridinedione, 6,7-diphenyl-	pH –5.5	235(4.28),292(4.01), 405(4.10)	142-0437-80B
	pH 5.0	220s(4.43),272(4.16), 362(4.17)	142-0437-80B
$C_{18}H_{12}N_4O_4$			
Indolo[7,6-g]indole, 3,8-dihydro-1,6-bis(2-nitroethenyl)-	EtOH	204(4.24),261s(4.39), 269(4.67),293(4.13), 348(4.09),415(4.38)	103-1139-80
$C_{18}H_{12}N_4O_6S$			
2,2'-Bibenzoxazole, 2,2',3,3'-tetrahydro-6,6'-dinitro-2-(2-thienyl)-	0.5M NaOH	252(4.22),272(4.28), 384(4.41),460s(--)	4-1629-80
	MeOH	215s(--),235s(--), 252(4.16),310s(--), 367(4.47)	4-1629-80
2,2'-Bibenzoxazole, 2,2',3,3'-tetrahydro-6,6'-dinitro-2-(3-thienyl)-	0.5M NaOH	251(4.17),276(4.19), 384(4.40),460s(--)	4-1629-80

Compound	Solvent	$\lambda_{max}(\log \epsilon)$	Ref.
(cont.)	MeOH	230s(--),258(4.12), 310s(--),367(4.40)	4-1629-80
$C_{18}H_{12}O$			
Azuleno[2,1-b]furan, 2-phenyl-	MeOH	256(4.22),321(4.77), 331(4.78),365(4.08), 387(4.30),407(4.42), 580(2.63),612(2.65), 640s(--),720s(--)	142-0835-80B
7H-Benzocyclotridecen-7-one, 12,13,14- 15-tetradehydro-11-methyl-	ether	236(4.29),253s(4.49), 273(4.54),290s(4.34), 386(3.26)	39-0466-80C
	CF_3COOH	276s(--),290(--), 350s(--),420s(--)	39-0466-80C
Fluorantheno[3,2-b]furan, 5,6-dihydro-	EtOH	223(4.61),247(4.65), 275(4.37),286(4.60), 319(3.76),329(4.01), 358(3.94),392(3.97)	23-0051-80
$C_{18}H_{12}O_2$			
1H-Indene-1,3(2H)-dione, 2-(3-phenyl- 2-propenylidene)-	$CHCl_3$	385(4.65)	18-1703-80
$C_{18}H_{12}O_2S_2$			
1H-2-Benzothiopyran-4(3H)-one, 3-(4- oxo-1H-2-benzothiopyran-3(4H)-yli- dene)-	EtOH $CHCl_3$	474(4.03) 477(4.03)	24-1708-80 24-1708-80
4H-1-Benzothiopyran-4-one, 2,3-dihydro- 3-(4-oxo-2H-1-benzothiopyran-3(4H)- ylidene)-	$CHCl_3$	379(3.34)	24-1708-80
Spiro[2H-[1]benzothieno[3,2-b]pyran- 2,2'(3'H)-benzo[b]thiophen]-3'-one, 3,4-dihydro-	EtOH	239(4.50),262(3.71), 271s(3.68),294(3.45), 370(3.05)	94-3430-80
$C_{18}H_{12}O_3$			
12H-Benzo[a]xanthen-12-one, 2-methoxy-	MeOH	238(4.52),262(4.44), 355(4.08)	2-0615B-80
12H-Benzo[a]xanthen-12-one, 9-methoxy-	MeOH	228(4.60),258(4.50), 326(4.27)	2-0615B-80
Methanone, 3,4-furandiylbis[phenyl-	EtOH	252(4.78)	44-3187-80
1,4:5,8:9,12-Triepoxytriphenylene, 1,4,5,8,9,12-hexahydro-	EtOH	276(3.97)	77-1075-80
$C_{18}H_{12}O_4$			
2H-1-Benzopyran-2-one, 4-hydroxy-3-(1- oxo-3-phenyl-2-propenyl)-	MeOH	367(4.5)	83-0344-80
5H-Furo[3,2-g][1]benzopyran-5-one, 4-methoxy-7-phenyl- (pinnatin)	EtOH	221(4.57),270(4.49), 305(4.16)	102-1199-80
Pongaglabol methyl ether	EtOH	222(4.51),228(4.50), 256(4.37),274(4.49), 321s(3.76)	102-1199-80
$C_{18}H_{12}O_6$			
4H-1-Benzopyran-4-one, 3-[3-(4-hydroxy- 6-methyl-2-oxo-2H-pyran-3-yl)-3-oxo- 1-propenyl]-	MeOH	355(4.4)	83-0344-80
1,8-Phenanthrenedicarboxylic acid, 9,10-dihydro-9,10-dioxo-, dimethyl ester	benzene	325(3.51),412(3.30)	44-1847-80

Compound	Solvent	$\lambda_{max}(\log \epsilon)$	Ref.

$C_{18}H_{12}O_6RuW$
   Tungsten, tricarbonyl[μ-[η^4:η^4-5,6,7,8-
   tetrakis(methylene)bicyclo[2.2.2]oct-
   2-ene]](tricarbonylruthenium)-
	isooctane	217(4.54),268s(4.04),
		 318(4.19),392s(2.95)
			101-0103-80K

$C_{18}H_{12}O_6Ru_2$
   Ruthenium, hexacarbonyl[μ-[η^4:η^4-
   5,6,7,8-tetrakis(methylene)bicyclo-
   [2.2.2]oct-2-ene]]di-
	isooctane	239(3.92),266s(3.75)	101-0103-80K

$C_{18}H_{12}O_7$
   1,3-Benzodioxole, 5,5'-[2,4-furandiyl-
   bis(oxy)]bis-
	EtOH	219(3.29),235(3.28),
		 288(3.21),316(3.20)
			2-0240-80

Tephrosol monomethyl ether	MeOH	250(4.55),285(4.0), 315(3.77),355(4.15)	102-1272-80

$C_{18}H_{12}S_2$
   1,3-Dithiepin, 2-(9H-fluoren-9-yli-
   dene)-
	CH_2Cl_2	244(4.24),259(4.05),
		 335(3.70),377(3.75)
			138-1427-80

$C_{18}H_{13}Bi$ 5H-Dibenzobismole, 5-phenyl-	isopentane	288(4.05),302(3.83)	110-0294-80

$C_{18}H_{13}BrN_4O$
   7H-Pyrrolo[3,4-d]pyrimidin-7-one,
   2-amino-6-(4-bromophenyl)-5,6-
   dihydro-4-phenyl-
	EtOH	240(4.37),268(4.19),
		 352(4.06)
			4-1231-80

$C_{18}H_{13}BrO$
   3,4,5-Hexatrien-2-one, 6-(4-bromophen-
   yl)-6-phenyl-
	EtOH
	 DMF
		260(4.20),378(4.52)
		 378(4.47)
			78-1331-80
			 78-1331-80

$C_{18}H_{13}BrO_6$
   2-Anthracenecarboxylic acid, 1-bromo-
   9,10-dihydro-4,5-dimethoxy-9,10-di-
   oxo-, methyl ester
	EtOH	228(4.45),260(4.35),
		 275s(4.09),353(3.77),
		 380(3.80)
			44-0020-80

$C_{18}H_{13}ClN_2O_3$
   Acetamide, N-[6-chloro-5,8-dihydro-
   5,8-dioxo-7-(phenylamino)-1-naph-
   thalenyl]-
	EtOH	258(4.41),288(4.40),
		 427(3.86)
			40-1862-80

Acetamide, N-[7-chloro-5,8-dihydro-
   5,8-dioxo-6-(phenylamino)-1-naph-
   thalenyl]-
	EtOH	285(4.47),495(3.85)	40-1862-80

1H-Pyrido[3,4-b]indole-3-carboxylic
   acid, 4-(2-chlorophenyl)-2,3,4,9-
   tetrahydro-1-oxo-
	EtOH	302(4.18)	103-0048-80

$C_{18}H_{13}ClO_5$
   9,10-Anthracenedione, 1-acetoxy-
   2-(chloromethyl)-4-methoxy-
	MeOH	218(4.07),253(4.06),
		 273s(--),386(3.41)
			24-2994-80

Benzoic acid, 4-chloro-, (7-methoxy-
   2-oxo-2H-1-benzopyran-4-yl)methyl
   ester
	EtOH	323(4.10)	95-0744-80

$C_{18}H_{13}Cl_2NO_2S$
   3-Thiophenecarboxamide, N-(4-chloro-
   phenyl)-5-[(4-chlorophenyl)methyl-
   ene]-2,5-dihydro-4-hydroxy-, (Z)-
	EtOH	239(4.30),357(4.57),
		 375(4.51)
			33-1542-80

3-Thiophenecarboxamide, N-(4-chloro- phenyl)-5-[(4-chlorophenyl)methyl]-	EtOH	221s(--),280(4.32)	33-1542-80

Compound	Solvent	$\lambda_{max}(\log \epsilon)$	Ref.
4-hydroxy- (cont.)			33-1542-80
$C_{18}H_{13}Cl_2NO_3$			
7H-Benzo[c]phenoxazin-5(12aH)-one, 6,9-dichloro-12a-ethoxy-	dioxan	259(4.35),377(4.16)	44-2155-80
$C_{18}H_{13}N$			
1H-Azuleno[2,1-b]pyrrole, 2-phenyl-	MeOH	229(4.05),332(4.86), 344(4.87),385(3.87), 404(4.03),425(3.95), 581(2.55),635(2.52), 720s(--)	142-0835-80B
Benz[a]acridine, 10-methyl-	MeOH	225(4.44),238(4.23), 269s(4.40),278(4.59), 287(4.58),348(3.55), 367(3.72),387(3.77)	39-1233-80C
	MeOH-acid	228(4.38),236s(4.29), 254(4.16),262(4.22), 286(4.40),295(4.55), 401(3.89)	39-1233-80C
2H-Dibenzo[3,4:7,8]cycloocta[1,2-c]-pyrrole	C_6H_{12}	218(4.56),232(4.51), 267s(3.76)	44-1505-80
$C_{18}H_{13}NO$			
Benz[a]acridine, 8-methoxy-	MeOH	230(4.55),244s(4.19), 285(4.74),348s(3.51), 366(3.64),384(3.60)	39-1233-80C
	MeOH-acid	230(4.48),236(4.45), 247s(4.14),294(4.68), 308(4.20),384s(3.76), 401(3.91)	39-1233-80C
Benz[cd]indol-5(1H)-one, 1-methyl-2-phenyl-	CH_2Cl_2	248(4.21),277(4.30), 358(3.95),417(4.25), 538(3.40)	5-0971-80
$C_{18}H_{13}NO_2$			
Azulene, 2-[2-(4-nitrophenyl)ethenyl]-	MeOH	231(4.07),282(4.50), 323(4.51),406(4.60), 425(4.51),584(2.67), 627(2.64)	18-3276-80
5(4H)-Oxazolone, 2-(2-phenylethenyl)-4-(phenylmethylene)-	CHCl₃	380(4.61)	103-0701-80
5(4H)-Oxazolone, 2-phenyl-4-(3-phenyl-2-propenylidene)-	CHCl₃	390(4.68)	103-0701-80
$C_{18}H_{13}NO_3$			
Ethanone, 2-(2-furanyl)-1-phenyl-2-(phenylimino)-, N-oxide	MeOH	261(4.51),314(4.82)	73-3546-80
3,4,5-Hexatrien-2-one, 6-(4-nitro-phenyl)-6-phenyl-	EtOH	288(3.94),378(4.20)	78-1331-80
	DMF	380(4.47)	78-1331-80
Lysicamine	EtOH	237(4.38),270(4.31), 312(3.72),400(3.75)	95-0337-80
1,2-Naphthalenedione, 4-[(3-acetyl-phenyl)amino]-	EtOH	225(4.28),286(4.03), 333s(3.70),452(3.51)	94-1207-80
1,2-Naphthalenedione, 4-[(4-acetyl-phenyl)amino]-	EtOH	246(4.30),257s(4.27), 294s(4.33),299(4.34), 334s(3.99),448(3.68)	94-1207-80
$C_{18}H_{13}NO_3S$			
2H-Naphtho[2,3-b]-1,4-thiazine-5,10-di-one, 3,4-dihydro-3-hydroxy-3-phenyl-	CHCl₃	287(4.33),350s(3.19), 500(3.32)	39-2923-80C

Compound	Solvent	λ_{max}(log ϵ)	Ref.
$C_{18}H_{13}NO_4$			
1,3-Benzenediol, 4-[4-(2-benzofuranyl)-3-methyl-5-isoxazolyl]-	EtOH	260(4.37),293(4.26)	103-0685-80
5(4H)-Oxazolone, 4-[(4-acetoxyphenyl)-methylene]-2-phenyl-	dioxan	246(4.28),253(4.30), 260(4.28),263(4.26), 353(4.62),370(4.74), 390(4.57)	70-0576-80
Phenol, 2-[4-(2-benzofuranyl)-5-isoxa-zolyl]-5-methoxy-	EtOH	259(4.29),289(4.25), 310(4.23)	103-0685-80
1H-Pyrrole-1-acetic acid, 2,5-dihydro-2,5-dioxo-3,4-diphenyl-	60% dioxan	364(3.65)	40-0837-80
Spiro[2H-indene-2,2'-[2H,9aH]pyrido-[2,1-b][1,3]oxazine]-3'-carboxalde-hyde, 1,3-dihydro-6'-methyl-1,3-dioxo-	MeCN	228(4.67),246s(4.31), 351(4.12)	4-1577-80
Spiro[2H-indene-2,2'-[2H,9aH]pyrido-[2,1-b][1,3]oxazine]-3'-carboxalde-hyde, 1,3-dihydro-8'-methyl-1,3-dioxo-	MeCN	228(4.70),249s(4.32), 348(4.14)	4-1577-80
Spiro[2H-indene-2,2'-[2H,9aH]pyrido-[2,1-b][1,3]oxazine]-3'-carboxalde-hyde, 1,3-dihydro-9'-methyl-1,3-dioxo-	MeCN	228(4.82),247s(4.47), 351(4.24)	4-1577-80
$C_{18}H_{13}NO_4S$			
12H-[1]Benzothiopyrano[2,3-b]indoliz-ine-6-carboxylic acid, 12-oxo-, ethyl ester, 5-oxide	EtOH	240(4.08),254s(4.33), 304(3.89),321(3.95), 336(4.16),387(4.05)	150-0139-80
$C_{18}H_{13}NO_5S$			
12H-[1]Benzothiopyrano[2,3-b]indoliz-ine-6-carboxylic acid, 12-oxo-, ethyl ester, 5,5-dioxide	EtOH	239(4.48),259(4.18), 304(3.76),317(3.87), 332(4.14),378(4.09)	150-0139-80
12H-[1]Benzothiopyrano[3,2-b]indoliz-ine-11-carboxylic acid, 12-oxo-, ethyl ester, 5,5-dioxide	EtOH	239(4.53),245(4.55), 255s(4.21),261s(4.16), 284(3.86),306(3.84), 320(3.86),333(3.81), 402(4.09)	150-0139-80
$C_{18}H_{13}NS$			
Benz[cd]indole-5(1H)-thione, 1-methyl-2-phenyl-	CH_2Cl_2	242(4.25),323(3.92), 410(3.78),534(4.40)	83-0977-80
$C_{18}H_{13}N_3O$			
Furo[2,3-d]pyrimidin-4-amine, 5,6-di-phenyl-	MeOH	207(4.62),226(4.30), 302(4.39),313(4.46), 327(4.31)	73-1581-80
11H-Indeno[1,2-c]isoquinoline-11-carbo-nitrile, 5-amino-4-methoxy-, mono-hydrochloride	EtOH-H$_2$SO$_4$	227(4.47),248(4.22), 262(4.23),320(4.02), 334(4.07),372(4.22), 392(4.20)	18-2885-80
11H-Indeno[1,2-c]isoquinoline-11-carbo-nitrile, 5-amino-7-methoxy-, mono-hydrochloride	EtOH-H$_2$SO$_4$	218(4.61),245(4.46), 342(4.30),372(4.10), 388s(4.00)	18-2885-80
Pyrimido[4,5-b]quinolin-4(10H)-one, 10-methyl-2-phenyl-	EtOH	233(4.50),259(4.16), 271(4.20),299(4.41), 341(4.08),405s(3.72), 432(4.01),452(4.05)	94-3514-80
$C_{18}H_{13}N_3O_2$			
Pyrimido[4,5-b]quinoline-2,4(1H,3H)-di-one, 3-methyl-5-phenyl-	EtOH	244(4.42),259(4.57), 312(3.98),377s(3.62), 383(3.86),413s(3.82)	94-3049-80

Compound	Solvent	$\lambda_{max}(\log \epsilon)$	Ref.
Pyrimido[4,5-b]quinoline-2,4(3H,10H)-dione, 3-methyl-10-phenyl-	EtOH	264(4.56),321(4.03), 382s(3.98),400(4.08), 417s(4.03)	94-3049-80
Pyrimido[4,5-b]quinoline-2,4(3H,10H)-dione, 10-methyl-3-phenyl-	EtOH	224(4.68),268(4.70), 313s(4.01),323(4.07), 380s(4.00),401(4.15), 420s(4.05)	94-3514-80
$C_{18}H_{13}N_3O_2S$ 5H-[1,2,4]Triazolo[5,1-b][1,3]thiazinium, 6,7-dihydro-3-methyl-5,7-dioxo-2,6-diphenyl-, hydroxide, inner salt	CHCl$_3$	241(4.04),269(3.78), 314(3.97)	44-2474-80
$C_{18}H_{13}N_3O_2S_2$ 1,2-Dithiol-1-ium, 3-(3,5-dioxo-4-phenyl-1,2,4-triazolidin-1-yl)-4-methyl-5-phenyl-, hydroxide, inner salt	dioxan	227(4.41),308(4.02), 503(4.06)	104-0188-80
$C_{18}H_{13}N_3O_9$ 9H-Fluorene-2-carboxylic acid, 4,5,7-trinitro-9-oxo-, butyl ester	THF	350(3.84)	116-0782-80
$C_{18}H_{13}P$ 5H-Dibenzophosphole, 5-phenyl-	isopentane	279(4.32),285(4.29), 300(3.90),310(3.64)	110-0294-80
$C_{18}H_{13}Sb$ 5H-Dibenzostibole, 5-phenyl-	isopentane	288(3.97),293(3.94), 305(3.59),312(4.13)	110-0294-80
$(C_{18}H_{14})_n$ Benzene, (2,4-cyclopentadien-1-ylidenephenylmethyl)-, homopolymer	THF	297(4.04)	126-0031-80
$C_{18}H_{14}BNO_2S_2$ Thieno[2,3-e]-1,2-azaborine-6-carboxylic acid, 1,2-dihydro-2-phenyl-3-(2-thienyl)-, methyl ester	EtOH	267(4.13),374(4.44)	11-0135-80A
$C_{18}H_{14}BrClN_4O_3$ 1H-Pyrazole-3-carboxylic acid, 5-[(4-bromophenyl)azo]-1-(3-chlorophenyl)-4-hydroxy-, ethyl ester	EtOH	253(4.32),355(4.20), 440(4.04)	142-0697-80B
$C_{18}H_{14}BrNO_2$ 1,4-Naphthalenedione, 2-bromo-3-[(methylphenylamino)methyl]-	benzene	587(2.66)	104-0520-80
$C_{18}H_{14}BrNO_2S$ 3-Thiophenecarboxamide, N-(4-bromophenyl)-2,5-dihydro-4-hydroxy-5-(phenylmethylene)-, (Z)-	EtOH	236(4.30),357(4.57), 373(4.51)	33-1542-80
3-Thiophenecarboxamide, N-(4-bromophenyl)-4-hydroxy-5-(phenylmethyl)-	EtOH	227s(--),282(4.33)	33-1542-80
$C_{18}H_{14}BrNO_3$ 2H-Anthra[1,2-d][1,3]oxazine-7,12-dione, 6-bromo-1,4-dihydro-2,2-dimethyl-	EtOH	490(3.88)	18-3007-80 +146-0513-80
2H-Anthra[1,2-d][1,3]oxazine-7,12-dione, 6-bromo-2-ethyl-1,4-dihydro-	EtOH	488(4.64)	18-3007-80 +146-0513-80

Compound	Solvent	$\lambda_{max}(\log \epsilon)$	Ref.
Methanone, (4-bromophenyl)(2,3,3a,6a-tetrahydro-2-phenylfuro[2,3-d]isoxa-aol-3-yl)-, (3α,3aα,6aα)-	MeOH	250(4.25)	49-0909-80
$C_{18}H_{14}Br_2N_2O_2S_2$			
[2,2'-Bi-3H-indole]-3,3'-dione, 6,6'-dibromo-1,1',2,2'-tetrahydro-2,2'-bis(methylthio)-	MeOH	237s(4.37),252(4.51),275s(4.08),350(3.41),402(3.46),598(2.85)	138-0631-80
$C_{18}H_{14}Br_4N_4$			
1H-Pyrazole, 3,3'-(1,4-phenylenedi-2,1-ethenediyl)bis[4,5-dibromo-1-methyl-	dioxan	352(4.58)	65-1922-80
$C_{18}H_{14}ClNOS_3$			
Benzenecarbothioic acid, O-[4-(4-chlorophenyl)-5-(ethylthio)-3-isothiazo-lyl] ester	CHCl₃	267(4.27),323(3.66),397(4.44)	39-2693-80C
$C_{18}H_{14}ClNO_3$			
7H-Benzo[c]phenoxazin-5(12aH)-one, 6-chloro-12a-ethoxy-	dioxan	256(4.35),379(4.24)	44-2155-80
$C_{18}H_{14}ClN_3O$			
Benzenepropanenitrile, α-[1-aziridinyl-(phenylamino)methylene]-2-chloro-β-oxo-	MeOH	317(4.39)	78-1791-80
Benzenepropanenitrile, 2-chloro-β-oxo-α-(1-phenyl-2-imidazolidinylidene)-	MeOH	291(4.27)	78-1791-80
$C_{18}H_{14}ClN_3O_3Se$			
1,3,4-Selenadiazole-2-carboxylic acid, 5-(benzoylimino)-4-(4-chlorophenyl)-4,5-dihydro-, ethyl ester	EtOH	252(4.34),333(4.32)	4-1185-80
$C_{18}H_{14}ClN_5O_3$			
1H-Pyrido[2,3-b]indole-1-acetamide, 6-chloro-2,9-dihydro-α-(1H-imidazol-4-ylmethylene)-3-methoxy-2-oxo-, (E)-	MeOH	234(4.38),320(4.43),336(4.19),340(4.45),374(4.36),450(4.12)	94-2987-80
$C_{18}H_{14}ClN_5O_5$			
1H-Pyrazole-3-carboxylic acid, 1-(3-chlorophenyl)-4-hydroxy-5-[(3-nitro-phenyl)azo]-, ethyl ester	EtOH	255(4.30),345(4.11),440(3.94)	142-0697-80B
1H-Pyrazole-3-carboxylic acid, 1-(3-chlorophenyl)-4-hydroxy-5-[(4-nitro-phenyl)azo]-, ethyl ester	EtOH	246(4.28),360(4.09),520(4.03)	142-0697-80B
$C_{18}H_{14}Cl_2N_4O$			
2,7-Ethanonaphth[2,3-b]oxirene-4,4,5,5-tetracarbonitrile, 8,9-bis(chloro-methyl)-1a,2,3,6,7,7a-hexahydro-, (1aα,2β,7β,7aα,8R*,9R*)-(±)-	EtOH	210(3.34)(end abs.)	78-0149-80
$C_{18}H_{14}Cl_2N_4O_3$			
1H-Pyrazole-3-carboxylic acid, 1-(3-chlorophenyl)-5-[(3-chlorophenyl)-azo]-4-hydroxy-, ethyl ester	EtOH	250(4.32),352(4.18),440(3.90)	142-0697-80B
1H-Pyrazole-3-carboxylic acid, 1-(3-chlorophenyl)-5-[(4-chlorophenyl)-azo]-4-hydroxy-, ethyl ester	EtOH	251(4.31),356(4.20),436(3.95)	142-0697-80B

Compound	Solvent	λ_{max}(log ϵ)	Ref.
C$_{18}$H$_{14}$Ge			
9H-Germafluorene, 9-phenyl-	isopentane	278(4.14),287(4.07), 315(2.76),320(3.28)	110-0294-80
C$_{18}$H$_{14}$N$_2$			
Isoquinoline, 1,2-dihydro-1-(3H-indol-3-ylidene)-2-methyl-	n.s.g.	515(4.71)	103-0743-80
Quinoline, 1,2-dihydro-2-(3H-indol-3-ylidene)-1-methyl-	n.s.g.	510(4.59)	103-0743-80
C$_{18}$H$_{14}$N$_2$O			
Benzo[f]quinoxalin-6(2H)-one, 3,4-dihydro-5-phenyl-	EtOH	203(4.52),277(4.35), 436(3.60)	83-0603-80
Ethanone, 1,2-di-1H-indol-3-yl-	EtOH	208(4.69),220(4.77), 244(4.27),263(4.23), 285(4.28),292(4.29)	103-0741-80
2-Pyridinamine, N-(3H-naphtho[2,1-b]-pyran-3-yl)-	MeOH	315(3.11),350(3.72)	103-0799-80
	PhCN	315(3.97),354(3.69)	103-0799-80
	DMSO	315(4.09),353(3.78), 530(3.11)	103-0799-80
	DMSO-NaOMe	510(4.07)	103-0799-80
	CCl$_4$	315f(4.01),350f(3.72)	103-0799-80
3-Pyridinecarbonitrile, 1,2,3,4-tetrahydro-2-oxo-4,6-diphenyl-	pH 13	251(4.13),352(3.47)	4-1521-80
	EtOH	267s(3.91),362(3.32)	4-1521-80
	CCl$_4$	262(3.74),362(3.13)	4-1521-80
C$_{18}$H$_{14}$N$_2$O$_2$			
Dibenzo[b,h][1,6]naphthyridin-6(5H)-one, 11-methoxy-5-methyl-	MeOH	220(4.57),287(4.67), 358(3.67),370(3.59), 398s(3.33)	39-0512-80C
	MeOH-acid	222(4.53),288(4.63), 356(3.61),376(3.57), 398(3.37),436(2.76)	39-0512-80C
2,5-Piperazinedione, 3,6-bis(phenylmethylene)-, (E,Z)-	EtOH	232(3.89),337(4.30)	39-0419-80C
(Z,Z)-	EtOH	233(3.95),338(4.47)	39-0419-80C
C$_{18}$H$_{14}$N$_2$O$_2$S			
2,2'-Bibenzoxazole, 2,2',3,3'-tetrahydro-2-(2-thienyl)-	0.5M NaOH	249(4.16),304(4.12), 347(4.19)	4-1629-80
	MeOH	240(4.21),285(4.04), 295(4.04),343(4.20)	4-1629-80
2,2'-Bibenzoxazole, 2,2',3,3'-tetrahydro-2-(3-thienyl)-	0.5M NaOH	240(4.33),298(4.28), 320s(--)	4-1629-80
	MeOH	238(4.29),292(4.12), 320s(--)	4-1629-80
C$_{18}$H$_{14}$N$_2$O$_2$S$_2$			
Thiazolo[3,2-a]pyridinium, 2-[(3-ethyl-2(3H)-benzothiazolylidene)acetyl]-3-hydroxy-, hydroxide, inner salt	EtOH	476(4.52)	103-0227-80
C$_{18}$H$_{14}$N$_2$O$_3$			
6H-Anthra[1,9-cd]isoxazol-6-one, 3-morpholino-	dioxan	263(4.51),518(4.45)	103-0704-80
Ethanone, 2-(2-naphthalenylamino)-1-(4-nitrophenyl)-	CH$_2$Cl$_2$	410(2.89)	83-0315-80
Phenol, 2-[[(2,3-dihydro-2-benzoxazolyl)-2-furanylmethylene]amino]-	0.5M NaOH	242(4.23),303(4.27), 335(4.27)	4-1629-80
	MeOH	239(4.22),297(4.15), 330(4.20)	4-1629-80

Compound	Solvent	$\lambda_{max}(\log \epsilon)$	Ref.
$C_{18}H_{14}N_2O_4$			
2H-1-Benzopyran-4-carboxylic acid, 7-methoxy-2-oxo-, (phenylmethylene)hydrazide	EtOH	292(4.41),300(4.41)	95-0289-80
Naphtho[2,3-f]quinoxaline-7,12-dione, 4-acetyl-1,2,3,4-tetrahydro-6-hydroxy-	benzene	520s(3.88),553(4.17), 594(4.10)	138-0743-80
Oxazolium, 4-[(benzoylamino)carbonyl]-5-hydroxy-3-methyl-2-phenyl-, hydroxide, inner salt	MeCN	240(4.15),259s(4.05), 323(3.75)	5-1836-80
2H-Pyrano[2,3-d]pyrimidine-2,4(3H)-dione, 7-(1,3-dihydro-1-oxo-2H-inden-2-ylidene)-1,7-dihydro-1,3-dimethyl-	dioxan	22?(4.07),272(3.99), 336(4.02),353(4.07), 410(4.35),431(4.34)	83-0557-80
2,4,6(1H,3H,5H)-Pyrimidinetrione, 5-(indeno[1,2-b]pyran-4(4H)-ylidene)-1,3-dimethyl-	dioxan	236(4.20),?(4.02), 443(4.42)	83-0557-80
$C_{18}H_{14}N_4O$			
Pyridazino[4,5-c]pyridazin-8(4H)-one, 1,7-dihydro-3,5-diphenyl-	EtOH	240(4.40),270(4.30), 360(3.95)	4-0529-80
Urea, N-phenyl-N'-9H-pyrido[3,4-b]-indol-3-yl-	MeOH	230(4.39),252(4.40), 273(4.48),285(4.52), 364(3.70)	2-0042-80
$C_{18}H_{14}N_4O_5$			
Indolo[7,6-g]indole-1-carboxaldehyde, 3,8-dihydro-6-[2-nitro-1-(nitromethyl)ethyl]-	EtOH	206(4.19),233s(4.22), 259(4.80),280(4.51), 334(3.82),350(3.52)	103-1139-80
$C_{18}H_{14}N_4S$			
2H-Pyrido[3,4-b]indole-2-carbothioamide, 3,9-dihydro-3-imino-N-phenyl-	MeOH	222(4.26),270(4.53), 356(3.51)	2-0042-80
$C_{18}H_{14}N_6NiO_6S_2$			
Nickelate(2-), [7,16-dihydro-8,17-dimethyldibenzo[c,j][1,2,5,8,9,12]hexazacyclotetradecinedisulfonato(4-)-N^5,N^9,N^{14},N^{18}]-, disodium	n.s.g.	438(4.43),616(3.95)	40-1154-80
$C_{18}H_{14}O$			
3,4,5-Hexatrien-2-one, 6,6-diphenyl-	EtOH DMF	252(4.08),375(4.44) 373(4.54)	78-1331-80 78-1331-80
1,4,6-Nonatrien-8-yn-3-one, 1-(2-ethynylphenyl)-7-methyl-	ether	226(4.37),247(4.34), 332(4.47)	39-0466-80C
$C_{18}H_{14}O_2$			
2-Anthracenecarboxylic acid, 1-methylethenyl ester	C_6H_{12}	239(4.38),259(4.94), 270(4.90),324(3.37), 339(3.61),356(3.68), 376(3.68),387(3.72)	39-1659-80B
Butanedial, bis(phenylmethylene)-, (E,E)-	CHCl$_3$	292(4.6)	118-0898-80
4-Cyclopentene-1,3-dione, 4-methyl-2,5-diphenyl-	MeCN	222(4.25),288(3.97)	24-0424-80
$C_{18}H_{14}O_3$			
4H-1-Benzopyran-4-one, 2-[2-(4-methoxyphenyl)ethenyl]-	MeOH	248(4.30),310s(4.08), 357(4.31)	2-0615B-80
4H-1-Benzopyran-4-one, 7-methoxy-2-(2-phenylethenyl)-	MeOH	238(4.27),327(4.41)	2-0615B-80

Compound	Solvent	$\lambda_{max}(\log \epsilon)$	Ref.
$C_{18}H_{14}O_4$			
6H-Benzo[d]naphtho[1,2-b]pyran-6,7(8H)-dione, 9,10-dihydro-2-methoxy-	EtOH	229(4.53),277(4.32), 285(4.33),344(4.12)	118-0715-80
1,8-Phenanthrenedicarboxylic acid, dimethyl ester	EtOH	251(4.53),257(4.58), 284(4.28),305s(4.18)	44-1847-80
$C_{18}H_{14}O_5$			
9,10-Anthracenedione, 5-acetyl-1,3-dimethoxy-	MeOH	237s(4.34),240(4.34), 281(4.36),339(3.45), 400(3.66)	12-1805-80
9,10-Anthracenedione, 6-acetyl-1,3-dimethoxy-	MeOH	250(4.51),283(4.34), 334s(3.45),400(3.74)	12-1805-80
9,10-Anthracenedione, 8-acetyl-1,3-dimethoxy-	MeOH	237(4.35),241(4.36), 282(4.33),345(3.42), 398(3.73)	12-1805-80
2H-1-Benzopyran-4-carboxylic acid, 7-methoxy-2-oxo-, phenylmethyl ester	EtOH	346(4.07)	95-0289-80
2H-1-Benzopyran-2-one, 4-[(benzoyloxy)methyl]-7-methoxy-	EtOH	323(4.14)	95-0744-80
$C_{18}H_{14}O_6$			
2-Anthracenecarboxylic acid, 9,10-dihydro-5,7-dimethoxy-9,10-dioxo-, methyl ester	MeOH	245(4.52),281(4.33), 400(3.73)	12-1805-80
9,10-Anthracenedione, 5-acetoxy-1,3-dimethoxy-	MeOH	233(4.34),238(4.34), 279(4.33),339(3.58), 393(3.68)	12-1805-80
9,10-Anthracenedione, 8-acetoxy-1,3-dimethoxy-	MeOH	233s(4.32),238(4.34), 278(4.30),336(3.47), 394(3.64)	12-1805-80
Benzoic acid, 4-hydroxy-, (7-methoxy-2-oxo-2H-1-benzopyran-4-yl)methyl ester	EtOH	323(3.88)	95-0744-80
4H-1-Benzopyran-4-one, 3-(1,3-benzodioxol-5-ylmethyl)-5,7-dihydroxy-6-methyl- (ophiopogonone A)	EtOH	225(4.21),264(4.24), 295(4.05),330s(3.57)	94-2039-80
	EtOH-NaOAc	332(--)	94-2039-80
	EtOH-AlCl₃	272(--),316(--), 365(--)	94-2039-80
4H-1-Benzopyran-4-one, 3-(1,3-benzodioxol-5-ylmethyl)-5,7-dihydroxy-8-methyl-	EtOH	225(4.32),263(4.52), 291(4.02),330(3.69)	94-2039-80
	EtOH-NaOAc	265(--),277(--), 333(--)	94-2039-80
	EtOH-AlCl₃	273(--),315(--), 368(--)	94-2039-80
8H-1,3-Dioxolo[4,5-g][1]benzopyran-8-one, 9-methoxy-7-(4-methoxyphenyl)-	MeOH	270(4.26),330(3.50)	102-1878-80
$C_{18}H_{14}S_2$			
1,3-Dithiole, 2-[(4-ethenylphenyl)methylene]-4-phenyl-	CH_2Cl_2	230s(4.18),378(4.43)	116-0240-80
$C_{18}H_{14}S_3$			
[1,2]Dithiolo[1,5-b][1,2]dithiole-7-S^{IV}, 3-methyl-2,5-diphenyl-	dioxan	240(4.38),330s(3.81), 286s(4.17),506(3.41)	104-1775-80
1-Propanethione, 1-phenyl-2-(4-phenyl-1,3-dithiol-2-ylidene)-	MeOH	244(4.38),257s(4.36), 328(3.81),476(4.51), 586(2.60)	104-1775-80
$C_{18}H_{14}Si$			
9H-9-Silafluorene, 9-phenyl-	isopentane	280(4.15),291(4.10), 310(3.18),322(3.00)	110-0294-80

Compound	Solvent	$\lambda_{max}(\log \epsilon)$	Ref.
$C_{18}H_{15}BrGe$ Germane, bromotriphenyl-	CH_2Cl_2	253(3.03),258(3.12), 264(3.13),269(3.00)	35-7892-80
$C_{18}H_{15}BrN_2O$ Acetamide, 2-bromo-N-[4-(phenylamino)- 1-naphthalenyl]-	EtOH	218(4.69),255(4.23), 352(3.97)	94-1722-80
$C_{18}H_{15}BrN_4O$ 7H-Pyrrolo[3,4-d]pyrimidin-7-one, 2-am- ino-6-(4-bromophenyl)-1,4,5,6-tetra- hydro-4-phenyl-	EtOH	270(4.34),320(3.45)	4-1231-80
$C_{18}H_{15}ClN_2$ 1H-Indole-3-acetonitrile, α-(2-chloro- phenyl)-1,2-dimethyl-	EtOH	285(3.93)	103-0048-80
$C_{18}H_{15}ClN_2O_2$ 1H-Imidazole-4-carboxylic acid, 1-[(4- chlorophenyl)phenylmethyl]-, methyl ester	n.s.g.	224(4.28)	145-1051-80
1H-Imidazole-5-carboxylic acid, 1-[(4- chlorophenyl)phenylmethyl]-, methyl ester	n.s.g.	240(4.10)	145-1051-80
$C_{18}H_{15}ClN_2O_2S$ Benzenesulfonamide, 4-chloro-N-(2,3-di- hydro-9-methyl-1H-pyrrolo[1,2-a]ind- ol-1-ylidene)-	EtOH	243(4.23),255(4.25), 350(4.32)	39-2870-80C
$C_{18}H_{15}ClN_2O_3$ 4H-Furo[3,2-b]pyrrole-5-carboxylic acid, 2-(4-chlorophenyl)-4-(2-cyanoethyl)-, ethyl ester	MeOH	341(4.56),357(4.70)	73-2949-80
$C_{18}H_{15}ClN_2O_3S$ Benzenesulfonamide, 4-chloro-N-(3-oxo- spiro[cyclopentan-1,3'-[3H]indol]- 2'(1'H)-ylidene)-	EtOH	225(4.44),280(4.21), 292s(4.07)	39-1512-80C
$C_{18}H_{15}ClN_4$ 4H-[1,2,4]Triazolo[4,3-a][1,4]benzodia- zepine, 8-chloro-1,4-dimethyl-6-phen- yl-	EtOH	223(4.61),245s(4.19), 270s(3.75),290s(3.43)	87-0643-80
$C_{18}H_{15}ClN_4O$ 5H-Benzocyclohepten-5,8-imine-6-carbo- nitrile, 6-chloro-10-(4,6-dimethyl- 2-pyrimidinyl)-6,7,8,9-tetrahydro- 9-oxo-, (5α,6α,8α)-	EtOH	216(4.00),247(4.38), 287(3.71)	39-0331-80C
$C_{18}H_{15}ClN_4O_3$ 1H-Pyrazole-3-carboxylic acid, 1-(3- chlorophenyl)-4-hydroxy-5-(phenyl- azo)-, ethyl ester	EtOH	246(4.28),349(4.19), 440(3.94)	142-0697-80B
$C_{18}H_{15}ClO_3S$ Acetic acid, [[3-(4-chlorophenyl)-3- oxo-1-phenyl-1-propenyl]thio]-, methyl ester, (Z)-	EtOH	272(3.99),330(4.26)	18-1739-80

Compound	Solvent	$\lambda_{max}(\log \epsilon)$	Ref.
5H-Dibenzo[b,g]thiocin-6-carboxylic acid, 9-chloro-7-hydroxy-, ethyl ester	MeOH	231s(4.39),260s(4.17), 290s(3.82)	73-0491-80
$C_{18}H_{15}ClSn$ Stannane, chlorotriphenyl-	CH_2Cl_2	253(2.94),259(3.04), 264(3.03),269(2.84)	35-7892-80
$C_{18}H_{15}Cl_2NO_2$ 1H-Indole-2-carboxylic acid, 5-chloro-3-(2-chlorophenyl)-1-methyl-, ethyl ester	EtOH	219(4.48),231(4.49), 240(4.51),303(4.21), 335s(3.80)	87-0764-80
$C_{18}H_{15}N$ Benz[a]acridine, 7,12-dihydro-7-methyl-	MeOH	267s(4.04),275(4.07), 296(3.65),312(3.69), 366(3.12)	39-1233-80C
	MeOH-acid	267s(4.02),275(4.05), 295(3.75),310(3.64), 366(3.11)	39-1233-80C
Benz[a]acridine, 7,12-dihydro-10-methyl-	MeOH	222(4.34),267(3.97), 278(4.00),313(3.71), 374(3.16)	39-1233-80C
	MeOH-acid	222(4.28),253s(3.87), 263(3.97),280(3.99), 294(3.98),315(3.57), 384(3.26)	39-1233-80C
Benzenamine, N-[1-(2-naphthalenyl)eth-ylidene]-, cis	CH_2Cl_2 at -70°	245(4.71),250(4.69), 276(4.11),285(4.11), 329(3.69)	39-1282-80B
trans	CH_2Cl_2 at -70°	248s(--),254(4.84), 274(4.22),284(4.29), 295(4.22),324(3.74), 338(3.67)	39-1282-80B
2-Naphthalenamine, N-(1-phenylethyli-dene)-	CH_2Cl_2 at -70°	242(4.64),320(3.59), 332s(--)	39-1282-80B
trans	CH_2Cl_2 at -70°	247(4.73),278s(--), 288s(--),321(3.65), 332(3.65)	39-1282-80B
$C_{18}H_{15}NO$ Benz[a]acridine, 7,12-dihydro-8-meth-oxy-	MeOH	221(4.39),267(4.03), 278(4.04),325(3.71), 366(3.21)	39-1233-80C
	MeOH-acid	222(4.29),235s(4.05), 249s(3.85),268s(3.97), 282(4.03),294(4.14), 308(3.78),330s(3.51), 380(3.25)	39-1233-80C
Ethanone, 2-(6-methyl-3-quinolinyl)-1-phenyl-	EtOH	236(4.44),247s(4.08), 282(3.46),307(3.30), 321(3.33)	39-0072-80C
	EtOH-HCl	243(4.59),314s(3.95), 322(4.0)	39-0072-80C
	EtOH-NaOH	236(4.29),248(4.06), 285(3.63),321(3.46), 360(3.63),419(3.59)	39-0072-80C
3-Penten-2-one, 4-(9H-fluoren-9-yli-denamino)-, (Z)-	n.s.g.	206(4.45),247(4.70), 255(4.80),270(4.35), 291(4.17),300(4.20)	39-1866-80C

Compound	Solvent	$\lambda_{max}(\log \epsilon)$	Ref.
$C_{18}H_{15}NOS_3$			
Benzenecarbothioic acid, O-[5-(ethyl-thio)-4-phenyl-3-isothiazolyl] ester	$CHCl_3$	323(3.73),397(4.48)	39-2693-80C
Benzenecarbothioic acid, O-[4-(4-meth-ylphenyl)-5-(methylthio)-3-isothia-zolyl] ester	$CHCl_3$	263(4.38),320(3.77), 397(4.52)	39-2693-80C +138-0401-80
$C_{18}H_{15}NO_2$			
1H-Indene-1,3(2H)-dione, 2-[[4-(dimeth-ylamino)phenyl]methylene]-	$CHCl_3$	480(4.94)	18-1703-80
1,2-Naphthalenedione, 4-[methyl(3-meth-ylphenyl)amino]-	EtOH	247(4.37),277(4.08), 322(3.78),468(3.86)	94-1207-80
Oxiranecarbonitrile, 2-phenyl-3-[2-(2-propenyloxy)phenyl]-	EtOH	217s(4.28),234s(4.09), 274s(3.59),282(3.62)	89-0047-80
$C_{18}H_{15}NO_3$			
2H-Anthra[1,2-d][1,3]oxazine-7,12-dione, 1,4-dihydro-2,2-dimethyl-	EtOH	494(3.92)	18-3007-80 +146-0513-80
2H-Anthra[1,2-d][1,3]oxazine-7,12-dione, 2-ethyl-1,4-dihydro-	EtOH	477(4.02)	18-3007-80 +146-0513-80
7H-Benzo[c]phenoxazin-5(12aH)-one, 12a-ethoxy-	EtOH	209(4.46),255(4.37), 388(4.23)	44-2155-80
Dibenz[cd,f]indol-4(5H)-one, 2,9-di-methoxy-5-methyl-	EtOH	235s(4.63),240(4.65), 256(4.31),282(4.18), 293(4.21),312(4.11), 321(4.18),406(3.67)	95-0337-80
Dibenz[cd,f]indol-4(5H)-one, 1,2-di-methoxy-5-methyl-	EtOH	235(4.48),251s(4.31), 264(4.38),280(4.40), 287(4.37),324(3.84), 370s(3.77),386(3.82)	95-0337-80
1H-Indole-3-acetic acid, α-benzoyl-, methyl ester	EtOH	210s(4.52),218(4.57), 245(4.22),279(3.94), 289(3.86)	103-0045-80
1H-Indole-3-carboxylic acid, 4-acetyl-2-phenyl-, methyl ester	MeOH	239(4.46),318(4.09)	94-1157-80
1H-Indole-3-carboxylic acid, 6-acetyl-2-phenyl-, methyl ester	MeOH	221(4.16),267(4.49), 320(4.28)	94-1157-80
3H-Indole-3-carboxylic acid, 3-acetyl-2-phenyl-, methyl ester	MeOH	251(4.16),318(4.20)	94-1157-80
10,13a-Methano-13aH-cyclobuta[c]pyr-rolo[3,2,1-ij]quinoline-7,9,14-tri-one, 4,5,10,11,12,13-hexahydro-	MeOH and MeOH-HClO₄	240(4.24),274s(3.66), 375(3.52)	39-0535-80C
Methanone, phenyl(2,3,3a,6a-tetrahydro-2-phenylfuro[2,3-d]isoxazol-3-yl)-	MeOH	247(4.33)	49-0909-80
1,2-Naphthalenedione, 4-[(3-ethoxy-phenyl)amino]-	EtOH	242(4.41),280(4.23), 335s(3.78),460(3.72)	94-1207-80
1,2-Naphthalenedione, 4-[(4-ethoxy-phenyl)amino]-	EtOH	245(4.38),280(4.17), 348(3.60),480(3.67)	94-1207-80
1(4H)-Naphthalenone, 2-methoxy-4-[(4-methoxyphenyl)imino]-	EtOH	239(4.31),255s(3.98), 289(4.24),334s(3.84), 474(3.75)	94-1207-80
$C_{18}H_{15}NO_4$			
2H-1-Benzopyran-4-carboxamide, 7-meth-oxy-2-oxo-N-(phenylmethyl)-	EtOH	331(4.03)	95-0289-80
1H-Indole-3-carboxylic acid, 2-(benz-oyloxy)ethyl ester	CH_2Cl_2	277(4.05),280(4.06), 293(3.95)	142-1119-80B
$C_{18}H_{15}NO_5$			
Acetamide, N-(9,10-dihydro-6,8-dimeth-oxy-9,10-dioxo-1-anthracenyl)-	MeOH	266(4.37),275(4.34), 416(3.64)	12-1805-80

Compound	Solvent	$\lambda_{max}(\log \epsilon)$	Ref.
Benzo[4,5]cyclohepta[1,2-b]pyrrolizine-1,12-dicarboxylic acid, 1,2,3,5,10,11-hexahydro-5-oxo-	MeOH	218(4.14),233(4.19), 243(4.18),265(3.78), 323(3.17)	4-1081-80
$C_{18}H_{15}NO_7S$			
Cyclopenta[b][1,4]benzothiazine-1,2,3-tricarboxylic acid, 6-methoxy-, trimethyl ester	MeCN	245(4.29),268(4.43), 293(4.53),435(4.31), 530(3.54)	124-0750-80
cation	MeCN	270(4.37),298(4.54), 437(3.72),540(4,31), 675d(3.12)	124-0750-80
$C_{18}H_{15}NO_8$			
Cyclopenta[b][1,4]benzoxazine-1,2,3-tricarboxylic acid, 6-methoxy-, trimethyl ester	MeCN	257(4.48),415(4.37), 475s(3.60)	124-0750-80
cation	MeCN	255(4.43),305s(3.52), 525(4.30),630s(3.20)	124-0750-80
$C_{18}H_{15}N_2O_7$			
4H-Cyclopenta[b]quinoxaline-1,2,3-tricarboxylic acid, 6-methoxy-, trimethyl ester, ion(1-)	MeCN	280(4.87),311(4.54), 360s(4.15),364(4.21), 445(3.62)	124-0750-80
$C_{18}H_{15}N_3$			
Quinoline, 2-methyl-4-(1-methyl-1H-benzimidazol-2-yl)-, monohydriodide	EtOH	205(4.92),323(4.25)	103-1261-80
mono(methyl sulfate)	EtOH	206(4.42),236(4.36), 320(4.19)	103-1261-80
$C_{18}H_{15}N_3O$			
Benzenepropanenitrile, α-[1-aziridinyl-(phenylamino)methylene]-β-oxo-	MeOH	243(4.25),324(4.40)	78-1791-80
Benzenepropanenitrile, β-oxo-α-(1-phenyl-2-imidazolidinylidene)-	MeOH	225s(4.28),299(4.31)	78-1791-80
Benzo[b]pyrido[2,3-h][1,6]naphthyridine, 3-ethoxy-7-methyl-	EtOH	210(4.38),262(4.75), 271(4.64),294s(4.47), 304(4.62)	4-1225-80
1-Naphthaleneacetic acid, (2-pyridinyl-methylene)hydrazide	C_6H_{12}	284(4.48),290(4.47), 294(4.46)	115-0151-80
	EtOH	284(4.48),290(4.49), 294(4.50)	115-0151-80
	50% EtOH	285(4.50),290(4.49), 294(4.47)	115-0151-80
$C_{18}H_{15}N_3OS$			
1,3,4-Thiadiazolium, 5-(benzoylamino)-3-methyl-2-(2-phenylethenyl)-, hydroxide, inner salt	EtOH	238(4.35),298(4.22), 388(4.44)	94-0447-80
$C_{18}H_{15}N_3O_2$			
1H-Isoindole-1,3(2H)-dione, 2-[(2-amino-7-methyl-1H-indol-3-yl)methyl]-, monohydrochloride	EtOH	220(4.75),265(3.89)	103-0368-80
2,4,6-Triazapentacyclo[6.4.3.0^{2,6}-0^{7,12}.0^{9,15}]pentadeca-10,13-diene-3,5-dione, 4-phenyl-	MeCN	221(4.23)	5-1428-80
2,4,6-Triazatetracyclo[8.3.2.0^{2,6}-0^{7,13}]pentadeca-8,11,14-triene-3,5-dione	MeCN	218(4.23)	5-1428-80

Compound	Solvent	λ_{max} (log ϵ)	Ref.
$C_{18}H_{15}N_3O_2S$			
Benzamide, N-[5-acetyl-3-(3-methylphenyl)-1,3,4-thiadiazol-2(3H)-ylidene]-	EtOH	237(4.11),285s(4.19), 330(4.30)	4-1713-80
Benzamide, N-[5-acetyl-3-(4-methylphenyl)-1,3,4-thiadiazol-2(3H)-ylidene]-	EtOH	240(4.06),282s(4.26), 335(4.31)	4-1713-80
Benzamide, N-[4,5-dihydro-4-methyl-5-(2-oxo-2-phenylethylidene)-1,3,4-thiadiazol-2-yl]-	EtOH	243(4.33),382(4.39)	94-0447-80
$C_{18}H_{15}N_3O_2Se$			
Acetamide, N-[5-benzoyl-3-(4-methylphenyl)-1,3,4-selenadiazol-2(3H)-ylidene]-	EtOH	257(4.21),322(4.05)	4-1185-80
Acetamide, N-[5-(4-methylbenzoyl)-3-phenyl-1,3,4-selenadiazol-2(3H)-ylidene]-	EtOH	260(4.23),325(4.01)	4-1185-80
$C_{18}H_{15}N_3O_3S$			
Benzamide, N-[5-acetyl-3-(4-methoxyphenyl)-1,3,4-thiadiazol-2(3H)-ylidene]-	EtOH	235(4.21),272s(4.25), 330(4.17)	4-1713-80
$C_{18}H_{15}N_3O_4$			
2,4,6(1H,3H,5H)-Pyrimidinetrione, 1,3-dimethyl-5-(5-methylpyrano[3,2-b]indol-4(5H)-ylidene)-	dioxan	242(4.4),339(4.04), 483(4.43)	83-0557-80
1,2,4-Triazolidine-3,5-dione, 1-(1-benzoyl-2-oxo-2-phenylethyl)-4-methyl-	MeCN	251(4.309),313(3.503)	44-1232-80
$C_{18}H_{15}N_3S$			
1,3,5-Triazine, 2-(methylthio)-4-phenyl-6-(2-phenylethenyl)-	MeOH	268(4.76),310(4.57)	48-0434-80
$C_{18}H_{15}S$			
Sulfonium, triphenyl-, hexafluoroarsenate	n.s.g.	227(4.32)	47-2697-80
$C_{18}H_{16}$			
Bicyclo[3.1.0]hex-2-ene, 1,2-diphenyl-	EtOH	255(3.90)	44-2181-80
Cyclobutane, 1,2-bis(phenylmethylene)-	C_6H_{12}	328(4.48),344(4.61), 363(3.48)	44-4183-80
1H-Indene, 1-(2,3-dihydro-1H-inden-1-ylidene)-2,3-dihydro-, trans	EtOH	207(4.52),231(4.09), 238(4.11),246(3.95), 290(4.14),309(4.26), 322(4.49),338(4.47)	24-3112-80
Naphthacene, 1,2,3,4-tetrahydro-	C_6H_{12}	255(4.94),265(5.30), 335(3.48),351(3.73), 370(3.86),390(3.74)	78-2311-80
Naphtho[2,3:6,7]dicyclobutene[1,8:4,5]-dicyclopentene	5:2 CH_2Cl_2-MeCN	240(4.68),270s(--), 286(3.67),298(3.78), 309(3.68),335(2.79), 360(2.49)	44-3731-80
Tricyclo[2.2.0.$0^{2,6}$]hexane, 1,2-diphenyl-	EtOH	257(4.04)	44-2181-80
$C_{18}H_{16}BrClN_4O$			
4-Quinazolinamine, N-(4-bromophenyl)-6-chloro-2-(4-morpholinyl)-	dioxan	243(4.61),288(4.52), 377(3.94)	73-1079-80
$C_{18}H_{16}BrN_5O_3$			
4-Quinazolinamine, 6-bromo-2-(4-morpho-	dioxan	246(4.59),287(4.55),	73-1079-80

Compound	Solvent	$\lambda_{max}(\log \epsilon)$	Ref.
linyl)-N-(2-nitrophenyl)- (cont.)		294(4.53),352(3.75), 408(3.85)	73-1079-80
4-Quinazolinamine, 6-bromo-2-(4-morpholinyl)-N-(4-nitrophenyl)-	dioxan	249(4.48),295(4.39), 342(4.14),396(4.12)	73-1079-80
$C_{18}H_{16}Br_2N_4O$			
4-Quinazolinamine, 6-bromo-N-(4-bromophenyl)-2-(4-morpholinyl)-	dioxan	246(4.61),290(4.51), 380(3.90)	73-1079-80
$C_{18}H_{16}Br_2O_4$			
4H-1-Benzopyran, 4,4-dibromo-5,7-dimethoxy-2-(4-methoxyphenyl)-	MeOH	251(4.15)	25-0198-80
$C_{18}H_{16}ClNO_4$			
8-Azabicyclo[3.2.1]oct-3-ene-6-carboxylic acid, 8-[3-(4-chlorophenyl)-3-oxo-1-propenyl]-2-oxo-, methyl ester, [1α,5α,6α,8(E)]-	CHCl$_3$	263(4.11),330(4.36)	39-0362-80C
[1α,5α,6β,8(E)]-	CHCl$_3$	262(4.20),332(4.43)	39-0362-80C
4H-Furo[3,2-b]pyrrole-5-carboxylic acid, 2-(4-chlorophenyl)-4-(oxiranylmethyl)-, ethyl ester	MeOH	342(4.75),358(4.71)	73-2949-80
$C_{18}H_{16}ClN_5O_3$			
4-Quinazolinamine, 6-chloro-2-(4-morpholinyl)-N-(4-nitrophenyl)-	dioxan	247(4.45),293(4.39), 340(4.15),393(4.14)	73-1079-80
$C_{18}H_{16}Cl_2O_2$			
2-Propen-1-ol, 3,3'-[1,1'-biphenyl]-4,4'-diylbis[2-chloro-	film	282(3.91)	104-2207-80
$C_{18}H_{16}Cl_2O_3$			
2-Propen-1-ol, 3,3'-(oxydi-4,1-phenylene)bis[2-chloro-	film	296(3.95)	104-2207-80
$C_{18}H_{16}Cl_2O_4S$			
2-Propen-1-ol, 3,3'-(sulfonyldi-4,1-phenylene)bis[2-chloro-	film	271(3.82)	104-2207-80
$C_{18}H_{16}CrO_4$			
Chromium, tricarbonyl[(1,2,3,4,4a,10a-η)-8,9-dihydro-6,9-dimethyl-5,9-methanobenzocycloocten-10(5H)-one]-	EtOH	325(3.87),425(3.40)	35-4410-80
Chromium, tricarbonyl[(4,5,6,7,8,8a-η)-1,9,10,10a-tetrahydro-10a-methyl-3(2H)-phenanthrenone]-	EtOH	270(4.20),332(3.83), 455(3.46)	35-4410-80
$C_{18}H_{16}Fe_2O_6$			
Iron, [μ-[η^4:η^4-1,4-bis(1-methylethenyl)-1,3-cyclohexadiene]]hexacarbonyldi-, cis	isooctane	272(4.09),330s(3.78)	44-0870-80
trans	isooctane	265s(4.15),330(3.94)	44-0870-80
Iron, [μ-[η^4:η^4-1,4-bis(1-methylethenyl)-1,4-cyclohexadiene]]hexacarbonyldi-, cis	isooctane	303(3.83)	44-0870-80
trans	isooctane	300(3.80)	44-0870-80
Iron, hexacarbonyl[μ-[η^4:η^4-(1,4-cyclohexanediylidene-1,3-propanediyl-2-ylidene]]di-, cis	isooctane	275s(3.34)	44-0870-80
trans	isooctane	275s(3.39)	44-0879-80

Compound	Solvent	$\lambda_{max}(\log \epsilon)$	Ref.
$C_{18}H_{16}GaNO_2$			
Gallium, dimethyl[2-[(phenylimino)meth-yl]-1H-indene-1,3(2H)-dionato-N^2,O^1]-, (T-4)-	hexane	304(3.89),368(4.39), 450(3.98)	101-0001-80I
	MeCN	301(3.71),368(4.42), 445(3.97)	101-0001-80I
	DMSO	305(3.75),372(4.44), 442(4.00)	101-0001-80I
$C_{18}H_{16}NO$			
Quinolinium, 1-methyl-3-(2-oxo-2-phen-ylethyl)-, iodide	EtOH	239(5.71),310s(4.87), 320(4.93)	39-0072-80C
	EtOH-NaOH	277s(5.09),294(5.15), 386(5.48),530(4.99)	39-0072-80C
$C_{18}H_{16}NO_2S_2$			
Sulfonium, dimethyl(5-nitro-2,4-diphen-yl-3-thienyl)-, tetrafluoroborate	MeCN	320(3.97)	44-0933-80
$C_{18}H_{16}N_2O$			
Acetamide, N-[4-(phenylamino)-1-naph-thalenyl]-	EtOH	219(4.62),254(4.20), 350(3.92)	94-1722-80
2,3'-Bipyridine, 5'-methoxy-2'-methyl-6'-phenyl-	MeOH	230(4.9),290(4.5)	103-0951-80
[3,3'-Bipyridin]-5-ol, 2,6'-dimethyl-6-phenyl-	MeOH	240(4.3),311(4.3)	103-0951-80
Diazene, (2-methoxy-1-naphthalenyl)(2-methylphenyl)-	EtOH	383(3.72)	32-0549-80
Diazene, (2-methoxy-1-naphthalenyl)(3-methylphenyl)-	EtOH	377(3.66)	32-0549-80
Diazene, (2-methoxy-1-naphthalenyl)(4-methylphenyl)-	EtOH	375(3.72)	32-0549-80
2(1H)-Pyrazinone, 1-ethyl-5,6-diphenyl-	EtOH	264(4.04),345(3.81)	88-2529-80
3H-Pyrazol-3-one, 2,4-dihydro-5-methyl-4-[(4-methylphenyl)methylene]-2-phen-yl-	n.s.g.	250(4.37),335(4.50), 450(3.06)	124-0642-80
1H-Pyrido[3,4-b]indol-1-one, 2,3,4,9-tetrahydro-2-methyl-9-phenyl-	isoPrOH	224(4.43),236s(4.30), 302(4.20),326s(3.85)	103-0244-80
$C_{18}H_{16}N_2OS$			
6H-Imidazo[2,1-b]thiazin-7-one, 2,3,4,5-tetrahydro-6,6-diphenyl-	EtOH	240(4.21),266(3.96)	78-1079-80
$C_{18}H_{16}N_2O_2$			
8-Azabicyclo[3.2.1]oct-3-en-2-one, 6-phenyl-8-(4-pyridinyl)-, N-oxide, endo	EtOH	212(4.30),298(4.30)	150-3337-80
1H-1,3-Benzodiazepine-1-carboxylic acid, 2-methyl-, phenylmethyl ester	EtOH	240(4.00),285(3.76)	94-2602-80
Diazene, (2-methoxy-1-naphthalenyl)-(2-methoxyphenyl)-	EtOH	387(3.72)	32-0549-80
Diazene, (2-methoxy-1-naphthalenyl)-(3-methoxyphenyl)-	EtOH	398(3.81)	32-0549-80
Diazene, (2-methoxy-1-naphthalenyl)-(4-methoxyphenyl)-	EtOH	374(3.77)	32-0549-80
1H-Imidazole-4-carboxylic acid, 1-(di-phenylmethyl)-, methyl ester	n.s.g.	234(4.15)	145-1051-80
1H-Imidazole-5-carboxylic acid, 1-(di-phenylmethyl)-, methyl ester	n.s.g.	240(4.07)	145-1051-80
11H-Indeno[1,2-c]isoquinolin-5-amine, 2,9-dimethoxy-	EtOH-H_2SO_4	212(4.41),253(4.35), 280(4.59),340(4.31), 370(4.20)	18-2885-80

Compound	Solvent	$\lambda_{max}(\log \epsilon)$	Ref.
11H-Indeno[1,2-c]isoquinolin-5-amine, 3,8-dimethoxy-	EtOH-H$_2$SO$_4$	228(4.62),327(4.28), 340(4.29),392(4.06), 410(4.03)	18-2885-80
11H-Indeno[1,2-c]isoquinolin-5-amine, 4,7-dimethoxy-	EtOH-H$_2$SO$_4$	220(4.57),259(4.33), 328(4.13),342(4.21), 386(4.25),405(4.22)	18-2885-80
1,2-Naphthalenediamine, 4-[[4-(dimethylamino)phenyl]amino]-	EtOH	263(4.56),290s(4.20), 524(3.77)	94-1207-80
5(4H)-Oxazolone, 2-[4-(dimethylamino)-phenyl]-4-(phenylmethylene)-	CHCl$_3$	380(4.70)	103-0701-80
5(4H)-Oxazolone, 4-[[4-(dimethylamino)-phenyl]methylene]-2-phenyl-	CHCl$_3$	470(4.74)	103-0701-80
3H-Pyrazol-3-one, 2,4-dihydro-4-[(4-methoxyphenyl)methylene]-5-methyl-2-phenyl-	n.s.g.	250(4.43),355(4.60), 435(3.27)	124-0642-80
1H-Pyrrole-2,5-dione, 1-(dimethylamino)-3,4-diphenyl-	MeCN	356.5(3.61)	40-0837-80

$C_{18}H_{16}N_2O_2S$

Compound	Solvent	$\lambda_{max}(\log \epsilon)$	Ref.
Isoquinolinium, 2-[[(3,4-dimethoxyphenyl)thioxomethyl]amino]-, hydroxide, inner salt	EtOH	224(4.57),260(4.28), 289(4.29)	114-0259-80A
	EtOH-HCl	225(4.54),259(4.28), 284(4.29)	114-0259-80A
4-Thiazolidinone, 5-[(4-methoxyphenyl)-methylene]-2-(phenylmethylimino)-	MeOH	246(3.98),260(--), 265s(3.88),327(4.24)	48-0835-80
3-Thiophenecarboxamide, 4-hydroxy-N-(6-methyl-2-pyridinyl)-5-(phenyl-methyl)-	EtOH	269(4.16),292(4.35)	33-1542-80
Thiourea, N-(4-methyl-2-oxo-2H-1-benzo-pyran-7-yl)-N'-(phenylmethyl)-	EtOH	339(4.34)	95-0289-80

$C_{18}H_{16}N_2O_3S$

Compound	Solvent	$\lambda_{max}(\log \epsilon)$	Ref.
4-Thiazolidinone, 5-[(4-methoxyphenyl)-methylene]-2-[(4-methoxyphenyl)imino]-	MeOH	237(3.98),310(4.22), 343(4.47)	48-0835-80

$C_{18}H_{16}N_2O_4$

Compound	Solvent	$\lambda_{max}(\log \epsilon)$	Ref.
[1,1'-Biisoquinoline]-6,6',7,7'-tetrol, 3,3',4,4'-tetrahydro-, dihydrobromide	EtOH	243(4.40),300s(4.01), 321(4.11),384(4.00)	33-0938-80
3(2H)-Pyridazinone, 5-hydroxy-4-(2-phenoxyethoxy)-2-phenyl-	MeOH	210(4.38),220s(--), 272(3.82)	73-0127-80

$C_{18}H_{16}N_2O_4S$

Compound	Solvent	$\lambda_{max}(\log \epsilon)$	Ref.
Benzenesulfonamide, N,4-dimethyl-N-(8-nitro-1-naphthalenyl)-	CHCl$_3$	319(3.88)	104-1890-80

$C_{18}H_{16}N_2O_7$

Compound	Solvent	$\lambda_{max}(\log \epsilon)$	Ref.
4H-Cyclopenta[b]quinoxaline-1,2,3-tri-carboxylic acid, 6-methoxy-, trimethyl ester	MeCN	283(4.71),388(4.35), 490(3.41)	124-0750-80
cation	MeCN	260s(4.40),285(4.76), 400s(3.91),450(4.29), 590(3.13)	124-0750-80

$C_{18}H_{16}N_2S$

Compound	Solvent	$\lambda_{max}(\log \epsilon)$	Ref.
5H-Imidazo[2,1-b][1,3]thiazine, 6,7-di-hydro-2,3-diphenyl-	EtOH	222(4.26),269(4.00), 295s(3.99)	4-0393-80

$C_{18}H_{16}N_3$

Compound	Solvent	$\lambda_{max}(\log \epsilon)$	Ref.
1H-Benzimidazolium, 1,3-dimethyl-2-(2-quinolinyl)-, iodide	EtOH	206(4.39),246(4.39), 282(4.02)	103-1261-80

Compound	Solvent	$\lambda_{max}(\log \epsilon)$	Ref.
$C_{18}H_{16}N_4$ 8H,17H-Tetrapyrrolo[1,2-c:2',1'-e:1",2"- h:2"',1"'-j][1,3,6,8]tetrazecine	benzene	277(3.92)	33-1190-80
$C_{18}H_{16}N_4O$ 5H-Benzocyclohepten-5,8-imine-6(and 7)- carbonitrile, 10-(4,6-dimethyl-2- pyrimidinyl)-6,7,8,9-tetrahydro- 9-oxo-, (5α,6(and 7)α,8α)-	EtOH	215(3.48),235(3.60)	39-0331-80C
$C_{18}H_{16}N_4O_2$ 2-Pyrimidinamine, N,N-dimethyl-5-nitro- 4,6-diphenyl-	EtOH	256(4.51),352(3.72)	103-0970-80
$C_{18}H_{16}N_4O_3$ 1H-Imidazole-4-carboxamide, 5-methyl- 2-(4-nitrophenyl)-N-(phenylmethyl)-	EtOH	232(4.26),260s(--), 352(4.23)	4-1723-80
$C_{18}H_{16}N_4O_4S$ Benzoic acid, [(methylthio)[[3-(4-ni- trophenyl)-1-oxo-2-propenyl]amino]- methylene]hydrazide	MeOH	302(4.76)	48-0434-80
$C_{18}H_{16}N_6$ Benzaldehyde, methyl(2-methyl[1,2,4]- triazolo[1,5-a]quinazolin-5-yl)hy- drazone	n.s.g.	224(4.62),270(4.10), 292s(--),306(3.95), 318(4.06),364(4.43)	33-0001-80
$C_{18}H_{16}N_6Ni$ Nickel, [7,16-dihydro-8,17-dimethyldi- benzo[c,j][1,2,5,8,9,12]hexaazacyclo- tetradecinato(2-)-N^5,N^9,N^{14},N^{18}]-	n.s.g.	433(4.98),608(4.58)	40-1154-80
$C_{18}H_{16}N_6O_5$ 4-Quinazolinamine, 2-(4-morpholinyl)- 6-nitro-N-(4-nitrophenyl)-	dioxan	260(4.35),360(4.26), 404(4.30)	73-1079-80
$C_{18}H_{16}N_6O_8$ Methanediamine, N,N,N',N'-tetramethyl- 1-(2,4,5,7-tetranitro-9H-fluoren-9- ylidene)-	MeCN	365(4.51),610(3.59)	104-0740-80
$C_{18}H_{16}O$ Benzenebutanal, γ-methylene-α-(phenyl- methylene)-, (E)-	EtOH	226(4.15),245(4.11), 283(4.28)	39-1477-80C
$C_{18}H_{16}O_2S_2$ 2-Butene-1,4-dione, 2,3-bis(methyl- thio)-1,4-diphenyl- 3-Hexene-2,5-dione, 3,4-bis(phenyl- thio)-	EtOH CHCl₃ CHCl₃	340(3.61) 340(3.60) 313(3.96)	24-1708-80 24-1708-80 24-1708-80
$C_{18}H_{16}O_3$ Naphtho[2,3-b]furan-4,9-dione, 2,2-di- cyclopropyl-2,3-dihydro-	EtOH	249s(4.21),254(4.23), 287(3.95),334(3.30), 397(2.94)	18-0567-80
$C_{18}H_{16}O_3S$ Acetic acid, [(3-oxo-1,3-diphenyl-1- propenyl)thio]-, methyl ester, (Z)-	EtOH	256(3.96),327(4.27)	18-1739-80

Compound	Solvent	$\lambda_{max}(\log \epsilon)$	Ref.
$C_{18}H_{16}O_4$			
1,4-Anthracenedione, 5,8-dimethoxy-2,3-dimethyl-	CH_2Cl_2	256(4.81),355(3.34), 473(3.73)	23-1161-80
1,3-Azulenedicarboxylic acid, 4-ethynyl-, diethyl ester	C_6H_{12}	254(4.48),272s(4.32), 309(4.50),320(4.52), 370(3.88),388(3.90), 565(2.86)	18-1647-80
1,3-Azulenedicarboxylic acid, 6-ethynyl-, diethyl ester	C_6H_{12}	230(4.57),270(4.36), 305s(4.78),320(5.00), 353(4.17),378(3.92), 514(2.68),540(2.76), 582(2.68),644(2.27)	18-1647-80
3-Benzofuranmethanol, 2-(4-methoxyphenyl)-, acetate	MeOH	305(4.47)	18-0179-80
4H-1-Benzopyran-4-one, 5,7-dimethoxy-3-methyl-2-phenyl-	MeOH	234(3.69),269(4.23), 354(3.31)	2-0101-80
Butanoic acid, α-methyl-γ-oxo-γ-2-xanthenyl-	EtOH	249(4.76),278(4.33)	115-0423-80
Butanoic acid, β-methyl-γ-oxo-γ-2-xanthenyl-	EtOH	333(3.99)	115-0423-80
6-Oxaestra-1,3,5(10),8,15-pentaene-7,17-dione, (14β)-	EtOH	216(4.26),247(3.95), 350(4.26)	23-1427-80
$C_{18}H_{16}O_5$			
9,10-Anthracenedione, 1,4,5-trimethoxy-2-methyl-	$CHCl_3$	392(3.85)	44-0012-80
1H-Benz[e]indene-2-acetic acid, 2,3-dihydro-8-methoxy-α,1-dioxo-, ethyl ester	EtOH	222(4.73),255(4.17), 371(4.40)	87-0512-80
2H-1-Benzopyran-2-one, 6,7-dimethoxy-3-(4-methoxyphenyl)-	MeOH	230(4.42),249s(4.15), 370(4.36)	18-0179-80
2H-1-Benzopyran-2-one, 5,6,7-trimethoxy-3-phenyl-	MeOH	232s(4.32),251s(4.04), 351(4.33)	18-0179-80
4H-1-Benzopyran-4-one, 5,7-dihydroxy-3-(4-methoxyphenyl)-6-methyl-	EtOH	226(4.30),262(4.25), 298(3.93),330s(3.62)	94-2039-80
4H-1-Benzopyran-4-one, 5,7-dimethoxy-2-(4-methoxyphenyl)-	MeOH	262(4.25),320(4.29)	118-0874-80
2,4-Cyclohexadien-1-one, 6-acetoxy-3-methoxy-6-(3-oxo-3-phenyl-1-propenyl)-	MeOH	260(3.93),308s(3.72)	18-1769-80
$C_{18}H_{16}O_6$			
9,10-Anthracenedione, 4-ethoxy-1-hydroxy-2-(hydroxymethyl)-5-methoxy-	MeOH	228(4.38),250(4.09), 282s(--),447(3.70)	24-1575-80
9,10-Anthracenedione, 1-hydroxy-2-(hydroxymethyl)-8-methoxy-	MeOH	228(4.54),250(4.21), 286s(--),448(3.89), 463(3.89)	24-1575-80
4H-1-Benzopyran-4-one, 3-(1,3-benzodioxol-5-ylmethyl)-2,3-dihydro-5,7-dihydroxy-6-methyl-	EtOH EtOH-NaOAc EtOH-AlCl$_3$	213(4.14),295(4.28) 335(--) 318(--)	94-2039-80 94-2039-80 94-2039-80
4H-1-Benzopyran-4-one, 5-hydroxy-6,7-dimethoxy-2-(4-methoxyphenyl)- (salvigenin)	EtOH EtOH-NaOAc EtOH-AlCl$_3$	275(4.31),328(4.42) 275(4.31),328(4.41) 298(4.33),348(4.42)	102-2229-80 102-2229-80 102-2229-80
2,5-Cyclohexadiene-1,4-dione, 2-acetyl-3-(5-acetyl-4-hydroxy-2-methylphenoxy)-5-methyl-	MeCN	226(4.34),260(4.43), 340(3.63),480s(2.49)	44-1421-80
1,4-Ethanoanthracene-9,10-dione, 1,4-dihydro-5,8-dihydroxy-6-(hydroxymethyl)-1-methoxy-	MeOH	222(4.49),283(3.80), 485(3.80),519(3.88), 558(3.70)	24-1575-80

Compound	Solvent	$\lambda_{max}(\log \epsilon)$	Ref.
$C_{18}H_{16}O_7$			
4H-1-Benzopyran-4-one, 5,7-dihydroxy-	EtOH	280(4.45),336(4.04)	102-2229-80
6,8-dimethoxy-2-(4-methoxyphenyl)-	EtOH-NaOAc	280(4.48),378(4.06)	102-2229-80
(nevadensin)	EtOH-AlCl$_3$	307(4.39),348(4.34)	102-2229-80
4H-1-Benzopyran-4-one, 5,7-dihydroxy-	MeOH	278(4.50),324(4.07)	102-2795-80
3,6,8-trimethoxy-2-phenyl-	MeOH-NaOMe	284(--),379(--)	102-2795-80
	MeOH-NaOAc	283(--),381(--)	102-2795-80
	MeOH-AlCl$_3$	293(--),349(--)	102-2795-80
4H-1-Benzopyran-4-one, 5,7-dihydroxy-	EtOH	261(4.42),296(4.16)	18-0831-80
3-(2,4,5-trimethoxyphenyl)-			
4H-1-Benzopyran-4-one, 5-hydroxy-3-(4-	EtOH	259(4.41),294(4.15)	142-1283-80
hydroxy-2,5-dimethoxyphenyl)-7-meth-	EtOH-AlCl$_3$	270(4.40),296(4.20),	142-1283-80
oxy-		376(3.58)	
4H-1-Benzopyran-4-one, 5-hydroxy-3-(5-	EtOH	259(4.40),295(4.15)	142-1283-80
hydroxy-2,4-dimethoxyphenyl)-7-meth-	EtOH-AlCl$_3$	271(4.42),299(4.21),	142-1283-80
oxy-		376(3.60)	
$C_{18}H_{16}O_8$			
Benzoic acid, 5-[[2-(ethoxycarbonyl)-	MeCN	214(4.45),242(4.26),	44-1421-80
3,6-dioxo-1,4-cyclohexadien-1-yl]-		250s(4.21),298(3.66),	
oxy]-2-hydroxy-, ethyl ester		370s(3.05),480s(2.40)	
4H-1-Benzopyran-4-one, 5,6-dihydroxy-	EtOH	255(4.08),290(4.27),	40-1397-80
2-(4-hydroxy-3-methoxyphenyl)-7,8-		350(4.38)	
dimethoxy-	EtOH-NaOAc	285(4.16),352(4.16)	40-1397-80
	EtOH-AlCl$_3$	260s(4.07),304(4.26),	40-1397-80
		370(4.44)	
$C_{18}H_{17}Br$			
[2.2.2](1,2,4)Cyclophane, 7-bromo-	EtOH	200(4.77),245(3.73),	24-2358-80
		290(2.76)	
$C_{18}H_{17}BrN_4O$			
4-Quinazolinamine, 6-bromo-2-(4-morpho-	dioxan	245(4.59),290(4.49),	73-1079-80
linyl)-N-phenyl-		377(3.85)	
4-Quinazolinamine, N-(4-bromophenyl)-	dioxan	248(4.51),285(4.42),	73-1079-80
2-(4-morpholinyl)-		292(4.44),339(3.97),	
		396(4.00)	
$C_{18}H_{17}ClN_2$			
1H-Pyrido[3,4-b]indole, 4-(2-chloro-	EtOH	282(3.83)	103-0048-80
phenyl)-2,3,4,9-tetrahydro-9-methyl-			
$C_{18}H_{17}ClN_2O$			
2(3H)-Quinazolinone, 3-butyl-6-chloro-	isoPrOH-HCl	242(4.51),420(3.51)	106-0751-80
4-phenyl-	isoPrOH-	255(4.10),292(3.20),	106-0751-80
	NaOH	234?(4.51),296(4.00),	
		406(3.60)	
$C_{18}H_{17}ClN_2O_2$			
1H-Pyrazole, 1-acetyl-5-(4-chlorophen-	MeOH	295(3.63)	2-0364-80
yl)-4,5-dihydro-3-(4-methoxyphenyl)-			
$C_{18}H_{17}ClN_4$			
Methanimidamide, N'-[1-(4-chlorophen-	EtOH	228(4.20),258(4.21),	114-0127-80C
yl)-4-(2,4-cyclopentadien-1-ylidene-		292(4.26),365(4.42)	
methyl)-1H-pyrazol-5-yl]-N,N-dimethyl-			
Methanimidamide, N'-[1-(4-chlorophen-	EtOH	273(4.49)	114-0127-80C
yl)-3-phenyl-1H-pyrazol-5-yl]-N,N-			
dimethyl-			

Compound	Solvent	$\lambda_{max}(\log \epsilon)$	Ref.
$C_{18}H_{17}ClN_4O$			
Benzenemethanamine, α-[[3-(4-chloro-phenyl)-1,2,4-oxadiazol-5-yl]meth-ylene]-4-(dimethylamino)-	EtOH	235(4.36),315(4.20)	39-1635-80C
4-Quinazolinamine, 6-chloro-2-(4-mor-pholinyl)-N-phenyl-	dioxan	242(4.59),288(4.47), 375(3.87)	73-1079-80
$C_{18}H_{17}ClN_4O_2$			
Hydrazinecarboxylic acid, 2-(7-chloro-5-phenyl-3H-1,4-benzodiazepin-2-yl)-, ethyl ester	EtOH	213(4.49),229(4.44), 258(4.45),339(3.31)	87-0402-80
$C_{18}H_{17}N$			
1-Naphthalenamine, N-methyl-3-(phenyl-methyl)-	MeOH	216(4.76),253(4.47), 337(3.83)	103-0965-80
2-Naphthalenamine, N-ethyl-3-phenyl-	MeOH	212(4.62),253(4.77), 286(3.92),362(3.46)	103-0965-80
2-Naphthalenamine, N-methyl-4-(phenyl-methyl)-	MeOH	213(4.64),251(4.75), 276s(3.86),289(3.91), 300(3.79),355(3.49)	103-0965-80
$C_{18}H_{17}NO$			
2-Buten-1-one, 1-phenyl-3-[(1-phenyl-ethylidene)amino]-, (Z,?)-	n.s.g.	206(4.16),223(3.98), 326(4.01)	39-1866-80C
3-Penten-2-one, 4-[(diphenylmethylene)-amino]-, (Z)-	n.s.g.	207(4.30),279(4.03)	39-1866-80C
Pyrano[4,3-b]indole, 1,3,4,5-tetrahy-dro-5-methyl-1-phenyl-	EtOH	228(4.49),292(3.88)	39-1688-80C
$C_{18}H_{17}NO_2$			
10,5-(Iminomethano)-11H-dibenzo[a,d]-cyclohepten-11-one, 5,10-dihydro-10-methoxy-12-methyl-	EtOH	208(4.38),216(4.37), 240(4.04),255s(3.89), 290(3.50),302s(3.35), 273[sic](2.81)	95-1127-80
10,5-(Iminomethano)-11H-dibenzo[a,d]-cyclohepten-11-one, 12-ethyl-5,10-dihydro-10-hydroxy-	EtOH	243(4.01),287(3.53), 370(2.90)	95-1127-80
1H-Indene-1,3(2H)-dione, 2-(1-ethyl-2,6-dimethyl-4(1H)-pyridinylidene)-	EtOH	236(4.53),293(3.76), 305(3.93),392(4.81)	4-0997-80
	THF	405(4.84)	4-0997-80
Isoquinoline, 6,7-dimethoxy-3-methyl-1-phenyl-	MeOH-acid	255(4.69),315(3.94), 354(3.87)	56-2209-80
	MeOH-base	243(4.71),281(3.76), 338(3.79)	56-2209-80
9,10-(Methaniminomethano)anthracen-11-one, 9,10-dihydro-10-methoxy-12-methyl-	EtOH	207(4.44),257(2.75), 264(2.84),272(2.77)	95-1127-80
9,10-(Methaniminomethano)anthracen-11-one, 12-ethyl-9,10-dihydro-10-hydroxy-	EtOH	263(2.81),271(2.82)	95-1127-80
$C_{18}H_{17}NO_3$			
Acetamide, N-[2-[[3-(4-methylphenyl)-3-oxo-1-propenyl]oxy]phenyl]-, (E)-	dioxan	247(4.26),278(4.35)	48-0099-80
1H-Benzo[f]pyrrolo[1,2-a]indole-11-carboxaldehyde, 2,3-dihydro-5,10-dimethoxy-	MeOH	254(4.85),311(3.91), 327(3.74),342(3.83), 374(4.07),386(4.02)	44-1260-80
2-Butenoic acid, 2-(benzoylamino)-3-(4-methylphenyl)-, (E)-	EtOH	202(4.44),220(4.23), 272(4.14)	118-0901-80
(Z)-	EtOH	204(4.35),220(4.22), 265(4.06)	118-0901-80

Compound	Solvent	$\lambda_{max}(\log \epsilon)$	Ref.
12H-Naphtho[1,2-b]pyrrolo[1,2-d][1,4]-oxazin-12-one, 1,2,3,12a-tetrahydro-6-(2-propenyloxy)-, (S)-	MeOH	254(4.67),315(3.92), 354(3.52)	44-1260-80
Oliveroline, (±)-	EtOH	273(3.92),315(3.42)	88-3307-80
Propanamide, N-[2-[(3-oxo-3-phenyl-1-propenyl)oxy]phenyl]-, (E)-	dioxan	246(4.30),277(4.22)	48-0099-80
2-Propen-1-one, 3-[(2-acetoxyphenyl)-amino]-1-(4-methylphenyl)-, (Z)-	dioxan	259(4.08),373(4.49)	48-0099-80
Ushiinsunine, (±)-	EtOH	272(3.98),323(3.48)	88-3307-80
$C_{18}H_{17}NO_3S$			
Carbamothioic acid, dimethyl-, S-(1-benzoyl-2-oxo-2-phenylethyl) ester	MeOH	251(4.15),335(3.55)	78-2675-80
$C_{18}H_{17}NO_4$			
Acetamide, N-[2-[[3-(4-methoxyphenyl)-3-oxo-1-propenyl]oxy]phenyl]-, (E)-	dioxan	288s(4.38),298(4.44)	48-0099-80
1,3-Dioxolo[4,5-g]isoquinoline, 7-(3,4-dimethoxyphenyl)-7,8-dihydro-	MeOH	278(4.14),314(4.03)	2-0556-80
Glaucine	EtOH	280(4.2),304(4.06)	102-0998-80
Isoquinoline, 3-(1,3-benzodioxol-5-yl)-3,4-dihydro-6,7-dimethoxy-	MeOH	283(4.05),310(3.82)	2-0556-80
Laetine	EtOH	270(4.06),307(3.67)	102-0998-80
2-Propenoic acid, 3-(2-benzoylamino-phenyl)-2-methoxy-, methyl ester	MeOH	226(4.38),252s(4.22)	142-0047-80
2-Propen-1-one, 3-[(2-acetoxyphenyl)-amino]-1-(4-methoxyphenyl)-, (Z)-	dioxan	283(3.98),371(4.57)	48-0099-80
9H-Pyrrolo[1,2-a]indole-2-carboxylic acid, 9-(2-ethoxy-2-oxoethylidene)-1-methyl-, methyl ester	EtOH	247(4.40),267(4.61), 308(4.09),357(4.17)	78-2125-80
$C_{18}H_{17}NO_4S_2$			
1,3-Dithiole-4,5-dicarboxylic acid, 2-[cyano(4-methylphenyl)methylene]-, diethyl ester	$CHCl_3$	243(4.32),350(4.35)	39-2693-80C
$C_{18}H_{17}NO_5$			
Benzo[5,6]cyclohepta[1,2-b]pyrrole-2-acetic acid, 1,4,5,10-tetrahydro-3-(methoxycarbonyl)-10-oxo-, methyl ester	MeOH	211(4.34),228(4.25), 241(4.19),260(3.89), 323(4.19)	4-1081-80
Norledecorine, (±)-	EtOH	240s(3.91),292(3.55)	142-0585-80
$C_{18}H_{17}NO_6$			
Nagosinone, 3,4-dihydro-	EtOH	230s(4.36),298(4.23)	142-0585-80
$C_{18}H_{17}N_2$			
1H-Pyrido[3,4-a]carbazolium, 5-ethyl-2-methyl-, hydroxide	MeOH	221(4.8),245(4.5), 307(4.4),435(3.9)	24-3245-80
$C_{18}H_{17}N_3$			
Benzenamine, N,N-dimethyl-4-(1-naphtha-lenylazo)-	EtOH	431(4.44)	62-0158-80
Benzenamine, N,N-dimethyl-4-(2-naphtha-lenylazo)-	EtOH	421(4.57)	62-0158-80
Benzenamine, N-methyl-2-[(6-phenyl-4-pyridazinyl)methyl]-	EtOH EtOH-HCl	246(4.5),288s(3.76) 254(4.27)	39-0072-80C 39-0072-80C
Pyrrolo[3,2-e]benzimidazole, 3,6-di-hydro-7,8-dimethyl-3-(phenylmethyl)-	EtOH	303(4.41)	103-0062-80

Compound	Solvent	$\lambda_{max}(\log \epsilon)$	Ref.
$C_{18}H_{17}N_3O$			
5-Pyrimidinol, 2-(dimethylamino)-4,6-diphenyl-	EtOH	224(4.46),256(4.42), 375(3.96)	103-0970-80
	EtOH	256(4.42),275(3.96)	103-0970-80
	EtOH-KOH	245(4.34),434(3.03)	103-0970-80
1,2,4-Triazine, 3-methoxy-5,6-bis(4-methylphenyl)-	EtOH	220s(4.36),262(4.12), 334(3.94)	44-4587-80
$C_{18}H_{17}N_3O_2S$			
Acetonitrile, [(4-methylphenyl)sulfonyl](1-phenyl-2-imidazolidinylidene)-	MeOH	221(4.51),272(4.28)	78-1791-80
2-Propenenitrile, 3-(1-aziridinyl)-2-[(4-methylphenyl)sulfonyl]-3-(phenylamino)-	MeOH	223(3.57),247(3.36), 298(3.76)	78-1791-80
1,2,4-Triazine, 5,6-bis(4-methoxyphenyl)-3-(methylthio)-	EtOH	220s(4.22),268s(4.24), 291(4.34),363(3.90)	44-4587-80
$C_{18}H_{17}N_3O_3$			
1,2,4-Triazine, 3-methoxy-5,6-bis(4-methoxyphenyl)-	EtOH	240(4.21),281(4.14), 351(4.03)	44-4587-80
$C_{18}H_{17}N_3O_4$			
1H-Pyrazole, 1-acetyl-4,5-dihydro-3-(4-methoxyphenyl)-5-(4-nitrophenyl)-	MeOH	293(4.20)	2-0364-80
$C_{18}H_{17}N_3O_4S$			
Benzimidazolium, 1-methyl-2-(2-quinolinyl)-, methyl sulfate	EtOH	206(4.31),242(4.28), 333(4.06)	103-1261-80
1-Naphthalenesulfonic acid, 3-[[4-(dimethylamino)phenyl]azo]-4-hydroxy-	pH< 4.2	495(4.0)	18-2666-80
	pH 5.0	510(4.1)	18-2666-80
	pH 8	520(4.3)	18-2666-80
	pH >9	502(4.4)	18-2666-80
$C_{18}H_{17}N_3S$			
1,2,4-Triazine, 5,6-bis(4-methylphenyl)-3-(methylthio)-	EtOH	230s(4.23),282(4.38), 353(3.73)	44-4587-80
$C_{18}H_{17}N_5O_2$			
Acetic acid, cyano[(4-ethoxyphenyl)hydrazono]-, (phenylmethylene)hydrazide	EtOH	256(4.49),295(4.79), 395(4.56)	104-1536-80
Methanimidamide, N,N-dimethyl-N'-[1-(4-nitrophenyl)-3-phenyl-1H-pyrazol-5-yl]-	EtOH	270(4.30),339(4.23)	114-0127-80C
$C_{18}H_{17}N_5O_3$			
4-Quinazolinamine, 2-(4-morpholinyl)-N-(4-nitrophenyl)-	dioxan	247(4.28),294(4.19), 340(3.93),396(3.92)	73-1079-80
$C_{18}H_{18}$			
Anthracene, 9,10-diethyl-	n.s.g.	360(3.81),380(4.05), 401(4.04)	5-0954-80
Anthracene, 2,3,6,7-tetramethyl-	EtOH	215(4.75),260(5.71), 324(4.32),340(4.21), 360(4.11),380(3.97)	2-0341-80
[2.2.2](1,2,3)Cyclophane	CH_2Cl_2	272(2.59),275s(2.58)	108-0288-80
[2.2.2](1,2,4)Cyclophane	EtOH	223(4.08),291(1.64), 305s(2.34)	44-3974-80
$C_{18}H_{18}ClNOS$			
9H-Thioxanthen-2-ol, 7-chloro-9-[3-(dimethylamino)propylidene]-	MeOH	268(4.12),286(3.93), 340s(3.58)	73-3166-80

Compound	Solvent	$\lambda_{max}(\log \epsilon)$	Ref.
9H-Thioxanthen-3-ol, 2-chloro-9-[3-(di-methylamino)propylidene]-	ether	237(4.49),274(4.11), 290s(3.90),323(3.51)	73-3166-80
9H-Thioxanthen-3-ol, 7-chloro-9-[3-(di-methylamino)propylidene]-, (Z)-monohydrate	MeOH	239(4.57),275(4.20), 330s(3.58)	73-3166-80
	MeOH	238(4.54),274(4.19), 332s(3.62)	73-3166-80
9H-Thioxanthen-4-ol, 2-chloro-9-[3-(di-methylamino)propylidene]-, (E)-	ether	272(4.16),328(3.69)	73-3166-80
(Z)-	ether	272(4.16),330(3.69)	73-3166-80
$C_{18}H_{18}ClNO_2$			
4H-Dibenzo[de,g]quinoline-10,11-diol, 6-(2-chloroethyl)-5,6,6a,7-tetrahydro-	EtOH	275(4.169)	87-0594-80
$C_{18}H_{18}ClNO_3$			
8-Azabicyclo[3.2.1]oct-3-en-2-one, 8-[3-(4-chlorophenyl)-3-oxo-2-propenyl]-6-ethoxy-, [1α,5α,6β,8(E)]-	CHCl$_3$	260(4.14),335(4.31)	39-0362-80C
$C_{18}H_{18}ClN_3$			
2H-Isoindole, 1-[(4-chlorophenyl)azo]-2-(1,1-dimethylethyl)-	CH$_2$Cl$_2$	264(3.92),310(3.74), 482(4.54)	89-0320-80
$C_{18}H_{18}Cl_2O_2$			
Phenol, 4,4'-(dichloroethenylidene)-bis[2,6-dimethyl-	CF$_3$SO$_3$H	362(3.56),555(4.36)	88-3131-80
$C_{18}H_{18}CoN_4O_2$			
Cobalt(1+), diamminebis(8-quinolinol-ato-N^1(O^8)-, chloride, (OC-6-13)-	MeOH	321(3.47),337(3.50) 407(3.80)	138-1555-80
$C_{18}H_{18}Fe_2N_2O_3$			
Iron, di-μ-carbonylcarbonylbis(η^5-2,4-cyclopentadien-1-yl)(2,3-diazabicyclo[2.2.1]hept-2-ene-N)di-, (Fe-Fe)-	toluene	286(4.00),351(3.69), 455(3.60)	64-0401-80B
$C_{18}H_{18}Fe_2O_4$			
Iron, di-μ-carbonyldicarbonyl[(1,2,3,4-5-η)-1-ethyl-2,4-cyclopentadien-1-yl]di-, (Fe-Fe)-	hexane	350(4.0),410s(3.3), 524(2.9)	24-3211-80
$C_{18}H_{18}GaNS_2$			
Gallium, dimethyl[2-[[(phenylmethyl)-imino]methyl]benzo[b]thiophene-3(2H)-thionato-N^2,S^3]-, (T-4)-	hexane	282(4.08),340(4.01), 450(3.60),500(3.49)	101-0001-80I
	MeCN	275(3.97),337(3.93), 428(3.52),485(3.48)	101-0001-80I
	DMSO	290(4.03),342(4.09), 470(3.69),495(3.72)	101-0001-80I
$C_{18}H_{18}N_2O$			
Diazene, bis(2-cyclopropylphenyl)-, 1-oxide	EtOH	239(3.53),310(3.34)	104-0534-80
1-Propanone, 1-[2-[(2-methyl-1H-indol-1-yl)amino]phenyl]-	EtOH	224(4.81),262(4.06), 282(3.90),290(3.86), 365(3.72)	104-0534-80
3(2H)-Pyridinone, 1,6-dihydro-5-(phen-ylamino)-1-(phenylmethyl)-	EtOH	310(4.29)	4-0001-80
$C_{18}H_{18}N_2O_2$			
9,10-Anthracenedione, 1-amino-4-[(1-	MeOH	573(4.19),616(4.26)	18-3725-80

Compound	Solvent	$\lambda_{max}(\log \epsilon)$	Ref.
methylphenyl)amino]- (cont.) 3H-Indol-3-one, 2-(1,3,4,5,6,7-hexahy- dro-1-methyl-3-oxo-2H-indol-2-yli- dene)-1,2-dihydro-1-methyl-	$CHCl_3$	328(4.27),621(4.17)	18-3725-80 5-0564-80
$C_{18}H_{18}N_2O_2S$ Benzenesulfonamide, N-(2,3-dihydro-1H- pyrrolo[1,2-a]indol-9-yl)-4-methyl-	EtOH	222(4.68),276s(3.86), 283(3.89),290s(3.83)	39-2870-80C
$C_{18}H_{18}N_2O_3$ 1(2H)-Isoquinolinone, 6,7-dimethoxy- 3-[(phenylmethyl)amino]-	EtOH	247(4.55),302(4.25), 350(3.72)	95-0826-80
Methanone, [4,5-dihydro-4-(4-methoxy- phenyl)-1H-pyrazol-5-yl)(4-methoxy- phenyl)-	MeOH	330(3.68)	2-0980-80
2,4(1H,3H)-Quinazolinedione, 3-[2-(4- methoxyphenyl)ethyl]-1-methyl-	EtOH	222(4.79),242(--), 276(3.51),283(3.51), 310(3.61)	102-0935-80
$C_{18}H_{18}N_2O_6S$ 4-Thiazolidinecarboxylic acid, 2-[2- [2-(methoxycarbonyl)phenyl]-5-oxo- 4(5H)-oxazolylidene]-5,5-dimethyl-, methyl ester	CH_2Cl_2	361(4.43)	44-1481-80
$C_{18}H_{18}N_2O_7S_2$ 4-Thia-1-azabicyclo[3.2.0]hept-2-ene- 2-carboxylic acid, 3-[(3-ethoxy-3- oxopropyl)thio]-7-oxo-, (4-nitro- phenyl)methyl ester	EtOH	261(4.21),338(4.05)	94-3232-80
$C_{18}H_{18}N_4$ Methanimidamide, N'-(1,3-diphenyl-1H- pyrazol-5-yl)-N,N-dimethyl-	EtOH	272(4.54)	114-0127-80C
2,5-Pyrimidinediamine, N^2,N^2-dimethyl- 4,6-diphenyl-	EtOH	230(4.33),241(4.34), 395(3.79)	103-0970-80
$C_{18}H_{18}N_4O$ 1H-Imidazole-4-carboxamide, 1-(phenyl- methyl)-5-[(phenylmethyl)amino]-	pH 1 pH 7 pH 13 EtOH	257(3.89) 268(3.94) 268(3.94) 268(4.00)	94-2819-80 94-2819-80 94-2819-80 94-2819-80
$C_{18}H_{18}N_4O_2$ 2H-Isoindole, 2-(1,1-dimethylethyl)- 1-[(4-nitrophenyl)azo]-	CH_2Cl_2	256(3.92),319(3.77), 530(4.63)	89-0320-80
$C_{18}H_{18}N_4O_2S$ Acetamide, 2-[(1,2-dihydro-2-oxo-4- pyrimidinyl)thio]-N-[4-(dimethyl- amino)-1-naphthalenyl]-	EtOH	216(4.74),245(4.24), 305(4.14)	94-1722-80
Acetamide, 2-[(1,4-dihydro-4-oxo-2- pyrimidinyl)thio]-N-[4-(dimethyl- amino)-1-naphthalenyl]-	EtOH	217(4.73),295(3.98)	94-1722-80
$C_{18}H_{18}N_4O_5$ Ethanone, 1-phenyl-2-(9-β-D-ribofurano- syl-9H-purin-6-yl)-	H_2O pH 13	252(3.54),386(3.88) 245(3.59),384(4.02)	94-0157-80 94-0157-80
$C_{18}H_{18}N_4O_5S$ Ethanone, 1-phenyl-2-[(9-β-D-ribo-	H_2O	226(4.14),252(4.16),	94-0157-80

Compound	Solvent	$\lambda_{max}(\log \epsilon)$	Ref.
furanosyl-9H-purin-6-yl)thio]- (cont.)		284(4.33),292s(4.31)	94-0157-80
$C_{18}H_{18}O$			
2-Buten-1-one, 1,3-bis(2-methylphenyl)-, (E)-	CH_2Cl_2	263(4.22)	118-0041-80
(Z)-	CH_2Cl_2	243(4.05)	118-0041-80
Cyclopenta[j]phenanthren-8(6H)-one, 7,7a,11,12-tetrahydro-7a-methyl-, (7aR*,10aS*)-	EtOH	212(4.50)	44-1081-80
2-Cyclopropene-1-ethanol, 1-methyl-2,3-diphenyl-	EtOH	228(4.20),238(4.09), 319(4.43),337(4.31)	44-2181-80
2-Cyclopropene-1-ethanol, 2-methyl-1,3-diphenyl-	EtOH	263(4.19)	44-2181-80
9H-6a,10-Methanocycloocta[a]naphthalen-9-one, 5,6,10,11-tetrahydro-10-methyl-	EtOH	235(4.51)	44-1081-80
2H-Pyran, 5,6-dihydro-4-methyl-2,3-diphenyl-	EtOH	235(3.82)	44-2181-80
Tricyclo[8.2.2.2^{4,7}]hexadeca-4,6,10,12-13,15-hexaene-5-carboxaldehyde, 12-methyl-	EtOH	212(4.59),292(3.65)	24-2358-80
$C_{18}H_{18}O_2$			
Ethanone, 2-(2,3-dihydro-3,3-dimethyl-2-benzofuranyl)-1-phenyl-	EtOH	247(4.00),277(3.70)	39-2937-80C
$C_{18}H_{18}O_3$			
Benzenepentanoic acid, β-(4-methylphenyl)-δ-oxo-	EtOH	243(4.22)	34-0085-80
2-Buten-1-one, 1,3-bis(4-methoxyphenyl)-, (E)-	CH_2Cl_2	227(4.23),324(4.37)	118-0041-80
Ethanone, 1-(3-hydroxy-3-methyl-4,4-diphenyl-2-oxetanyl)-, trans	EtOH	224(4.30),259(3.54), 290s(3.11)	18-1183-80
1H-Inden-1-one, 2,3-dihydro-5,6-dimethoxy-2-(phenylmethyl)-	MeOH	230(4.30),268(4.05), 314(4.01)	35-3056-80
1H-Inden-1-one, 2-[(3,4-dimethoxyphenyl)methyl]-2,3-dihydro-	MeOH	238(4.16),245s(--), 285(3.65),294s(--)	35-3056-80
2-Propen-1-one, 3-(3,4-dimethoxyphenyl)-2-methyl-1-phenyl-	MeOH	231(4.41),309(3.86)	56-2209-80
$C_{18}H_{18}O_4$			
9-Anthracenol, 1,4,5-trimethoxy-2-methyl-	$CHCl_3$	262(4.78),360(3.74), 379(3.96),388(3.91), 411(3.69)	44-0012-80
Benzenepropanoic acid, α-(4-methoxyphenyl)-α-methyl-β-oxo-, methyl ester	EtOH	230(4.15),240s(4.08), 271(3.53)	12-0113-80
1H-Benz[e]indene-2-acetic acid, 2,3-dihydro-8-methoxy-1-oxo-, ethyl ester	EtOH	230(4.64),263(4.07), 315(3.86),342(3.88)	87-0512-80
Cyclopent[cd]azulene-2,3-dicarboxylic acid, 2a,8b-dihydro-2a,8b-dimethyl-, dimethyl ester	EtOH	268(4.54),355(3.81)	88-1841-80
isomer	EtOH	242(4.29),284(4.70), 382(3.62)	88-1841-80
Ethanone, 1-[4-(2-acetoxyethoxy)phenyl]-2-phenyl-	$CHCl_3$	274(4.28),317(2.56)	73-1826-80
[3.3]Metacyclophanequinhydrone, anti	dioxan	<u>290(4.0)</u>,310s(3.7), 462(3.51)	24-0241-80
syn	dioxan	<u>285(3.9)</u>,447(3.44)	24-0241-80
6-Oxaestra-1,3,5(10),8-tetraene-7,17-dione, 3-methoxy-	EtOH	225(4.06),328(4.15)	23-1427-80

Compound	Solvent	$\lambda_{max}(\log \epsilon)$	Ref.
14β-6-Oxaestra-1,3,5(10),8-tetraene-7,17-dione, 3-methoxy-	EtOH	222(4.06),323(4.30)	23-1427-80
$C_{18}H_{18}O_5$			
Benzeneacetic acid, α-[(2,4-dimethoxyphenyl)methylene]-2-methoxy-, (E)-	MeOH	239s(4.09),294(4.08), 331(4.23)	18-0179-80
Benzeneacetic acid, α-[(2,4-dimethoxyphenyl)methylene]-4-methoxy-, (E)-	MeOH	240(4.17),295(4.07), 336(4.23)	18-0179-80
2H-1-Benzopyran-7-ol, 3,4-dihydro-2-(6-hydroxy-1,3-benzodioxol-5-yl)-5,8-dimethyl-	EtOH	237(4.39),280(4.14), 350(4.09)	102-1195-80
	EtOH-NaOH	245(4.35),280(4.16), 385(4.10)	102-1195-80
2H-1-Benzopyran-7-ol, 3,4-dihydro-2-(6-hydroxy-1,3-benzodioxol-5-yl)-6,8-dimethyl-	EtOH	230(4.30),293(3.95)	102-1195-80
	EtOH-NaOH	232(4.30),308(3.97)	102-1195-80
1,3-Dioxane-4,6-dione, 2,2-dimethyl-5-[(2,4,7-trimethyl-3-benzofuranyl)-methylene]-	EtOH	216(4.37),257(4.24), 394(3.88)	12-1817-80
1,3-Dioxane-4,6-dione, 2,2-dimethyl-5-[(2,4,7-trimethyl-6-benzofuranyl)-methylene]-	EtOH	216(4.29),257(4.19), 397(4.13)	12-1817-80
Ethanone, 2-acetoxy-2-(2,4-dimethoxyphenyl)-1-phenyl-	MeOH	239(4.23),283(3.75), 289s(3.71)	18-0179-80
Ethanone, 2-acetoxy-2-(2-methoxyphenyl)-1-(4-methoxyphenyl)-	MeOH	222(4.25),286(4.27)	18-0179-80
$C_{18}H_{18}O_6$			
4H-1-Benzopyran-4-one, 2,3-dihydro-3-hydroxy-5,7-dimethoxy-2-(4-methoxyphenyl)-	MeOH	257(4.0),308(3.72), 352(4.04)	142-1979-80
1,3-Propanedione, 1-(2-hydroxy-4,6-dimethoxyphenyl)-3-(4-methoxyphenyl)-	MeOH	205(4.04),210(4.10), 285(4.09),375(3.61)	118-0874-80
$C_{18}H_{18}O_7$			
6H-Benzofuro[3,2-c][1]benzopyran-2,8-diol, 6a,11a-dihydro-3,9,10-trimethoxy-, (6aR-cis)-	EtOH	207(4.46),300(3.84)	102-2003-80
	EtOH-NaOH	266(4.42),310(4.28)	102-2003-80
Posoquenin benzylidene deriv.	MeOH	241(3.78)	100-0571-80
$C_{18}H_{19}Br_2NO_3S$			
Isoquinoline, 2-acetyl-1-[(2,5-dibromo-3-thienyl)methyl]-1,2,3,4-tetrahydro-6,7-dimethoxy-	MeOH	230(2.73),278(2.38)	2-1028-80
$C_{18}H_{19}ClN_2O$			
2(1H)-Quinazolinone, 3-butyl-6-chloro-3,4-dihydro-4-phenyl-	EtOH	259(4.04),297(3.30)	106-0751-80
$C_{18}H_{19}ClN_2O_2$			
2(1H)-Quinazolinone, 3-butyl-6-chloro-3,4-dihydro-4-hydroxy-4-phenyl-	EtOH	255(4.11),297(3.23)	106-0751-80
$C_{18}H_{19}ClN_2O_3$			
Cyclohexanepropanenitrile, 3-(6-chloro-3,4-dihydro-3-methyl-2-oxo-2H-1,3-benzoxazin-4-yl)-2-oxo-	EtOH	229(3.89),276(3.10), 285(3.08)	4-0277-80
$C_{18}H_{19}ClN_2O_4$			
4H-Furo[3,2-b]pyrrole-5-carboxylic acid, 4-(3-amino-2-hydroxypropyl)-2-(4-chlorophenyl)-, ethyl ester	MeOH-HCl	343(4.76),359(4.68)	73-2949-80

Compound	Solvent	$\lambda_{max}(\log \epsilon)$	Ref.
$C_{18}H_{19}ClN_3$ 1H-Isoindolium, 1-[(4-chlorophenyl)hy-drazono]-2-(1,1-dimethylethyl)-, tetrafluoroborate	MeOH–HClO$_4$	243(4.37),470(4.05)	89-0320-80
$C_{18}H_{19}ClN_4O_3$ Acetamide, N-acetyl-N-[2-(acetylamino)-5-(4-chlorophenyl)-6-ethyl-4-pyrimi-dinyl]-	EtOH	208(4.16),243(4.39), 280s(3.80)	142-0471-80
$C_{18}H_{19}GaN_2O$ Gallium, [1,3-dihydro-1-methyl-3-[(phenylimino)methyl]-2H-indol-2-onato-N^3,O^2]dimethyl-, (T-4)-	hexane	285(4.19),373(4.32), 386(4.37)	101-0001-80I
	MeCN	285(4.15),372(4.32), 384(4.35)	101-0001-80I
	DMSO	285(4.02),375(4.26), 382(4.26)	101-0001-80I
$C_{18}H_{19}N$ 1H-Indole, 1-butyl-2-phenyl-	EtOH	232(4.30),295(4.20), 300s(4.19)	104-0766-80
$C_{18}H_{19}NO$ 5H-Cyclohepta[b]pyridine, 6,7,8,9-tetrahydro-9-[(3-methoxyphenyl)-methylene]-	EtOH	229(3.960),270.5(4.170)	83-0826-80
1-Penten-3-one, 1-(diphenylamino)-4-methyl-	EtOH	229(3.87),278s(3.75), 333(4.33)	4-0507-80
$C_{18}H_{19}NO_2$ Bisnoratherosperminine, hydrochloride	MeOH	212(4.24),233(4.32), 249(4.65),256(4.78), 274(4.06),304(4.06), 311(4.06)	36-1180-80
1H-Dibenzo[a,f]quinolizine-3,13-dione, 2,3,4,4a,6,7,13,13a-octahydro-13a-methyl-, cis	EtOH	207(4.27),262(4.19), 367(4.09)	48-0554-80
Isoquinoline, 3,4-dihydro-6,7-dimeth-oxy-1-methyl-3-phenyl-	MeOH	270(3.9),306(3.92)	2-0556-80
$C_{18}H_{19}NO_2S$ Benzenamine, N-[1,2-dimethyl-4-(phenyl-sulfonyl)-2-butenylidene]-	EtOH	238(4.41)	104-0849-80
$C_{18}H_{19}NO_3$ Benzo[5,6]cyclohepta[1,2-b]pyrrole-2-acetic acid, 1,4,5,10-tetrahydro-10-oxo-, 1-methylethyl ester	MeOH	211(4.02),225(3.88), 257(3.86),333(4.22)	4-1081-80
Benzo[g]pyrrolo[1,2-a]quinolin-5(1H)-one, 2,3,3a,4-tetrahydro-6,11-di-methoxy-	MeOH	243(4.44),282(4.49), 314s(3.94),459(3.30)	44-1260-80
4H-Dibenzo[de,g]quinoline-10,11-diol, 5,6,6a,7-tetrahydro-6-(2-hydroxy-ethyl)-, hydrochloride	EtOH	275(4.17)	87-0594-80
4H-Dibenzo[de,g]quinolin-11-ol, 5,6,6a,7-tetrahydro-2,10-dimethoxy-, (R)-	EtOH	269(4.14),279(4.15), 300(3.90)	44-2275-80
1-Propanone, 2-[(3,4-dimethoxyphenyl)-methylene]-1-phenyl-, oxime	MeOH	308(3.79)	56-2209-80

Compound	Solvent	$\lambda_{max}(\log \epsilon)$	Ref.
$C_{18}H_{19}NO_3S$			
4H-Benzo[de]thieno[2,3-g]quinoline, 6-acetyl-5,6,6a,7-tetrahydro-1,2-dimethoxy-	MeOH	222(2.72),298(2.52), 314(2.36)	2-1028-80
$C_{18}H_{19}NO_4$			
1H,4H-3a,8b-Ethenocyclopent[b]indole-9,10-dicarboxylic acid, 2,3-dihydro-4-methyl-, dimethyl ester	EtOH	249(3.68),304(3.18), 438(2.88)	44-0456-80
Laurelliptine	MeOH	220(3.18),284(3.76), 304(3.80)	100-0353-80
$C_{18}H_{19}NO_4S_3$			
1,3-Dithiole-4,5-dicarboxylic acid, 2-[2-amino-1-(4-methylphenyl)-2-thioxoethylidene]-, diethyl ester	$CHCl_3$	316(4.02),390(4.23)	39-2693-80C
$C_{18}H_{19}NO_5$			
Phenol, 2-[4,5-dihydro-5-(3,4,5-trimethoxyphenyl)-3-isoxazolyl]-	EtOH	220(4.26),264(4.12), 273(3.99),307(3.75)	142-1319-80
Ungerine	n.s.g.	227(4.36),268(3.72), 306(3.76)	105-0525-80
$C_{18}H_{19}NS$			
9H-Fluorene-2-carbothioamide, 9-ethyl-N,9-dimethyl-, (-)-	EtOH	200(4.31),214(4.34), 253(3.79),290(4.31), 300(4.30),314(4.34), 335(4.32),350(3.63)	56-0901-80
$C_{18}H_{19}N_2$			
Pyridinium, 4-[1-(1H-indol-3-ylmethylene)propyl]-1-methyl-, iodide	MeOH	221(4.7),258(4.1), 280(3.9),287(3.9), 437(4.1)	24-3245-80
$C_{18}H_{19}N_3$			
5H,9cH-2a,4a,9b-Triazapentaleno[1,6-ab]naphthalene, 1,2,3,4-tetrahydro-5-phenyl-, trans	pH 1	246(3.84),291(3.18)	94-2587-80
	pH 13	251(3.95),295(3.30)	94-2587-80
	EtOH	254(3.97),300(3.32)	94-2587-80
$C_{18}H_{19}N_3O$			
7H-Azepino[2',1':2,3]pyrimido[6,1-a]-isoquinoline-5-carbonitrile, 1,2,3-4,8,12b,13,14-octahydro-14-oxo-	EtOH	234(3.92),304(4.11)	94-0220-80
Imidazo[2,1-b]quinazoline, 5-ethoxy-1,2,3,5-tetrahydro-5-phenyl-	pH 1	244(4.41)	94-2024-80
	pH 13	268(4.20)	94-2024-80
	EtOH	272(4.21)	94-2024-80
4,7-Methano-1,4,7-benzotriazecin-13-one, 1,2,3,5,6,8-hexahydro-8-phenyl-	pH 1	258(3.92)	94-2587-80
	pH 13	258(3.92)	94-2587-80
	EtOH	258(3.91)	94-2587-80
	$CHCl_3$	261(3.89),296(3.37)	94-2587-80
2H-Pyrimido[2,1-b]quinazolin-6-ol, 1,3,4,6-tetrahydro-1-methyl-6-phenyl-	pH 1	251(4.46)	94-2024-80
	pH 13	280(4.28)	94-2024-80
	EtOH	284(4.20)	94-2024-80
4(3H)-Quinazolinone, 2-(butylamino)-3-phenyl-	MeOH	269(4.23),335(3.58)	2-0638-80
1,2,4-Triazine, 2,5-dihydro-3-methoxy-5,6-bis(4-methylphenyl)-	EtOH	218s(4.26),292(3.96)	44-4587-80
$C_{18}H_{19}N_3O_2$			
2,4,6-Triazapentacyclo[6.4.3.0^{2,6}-0^{7,12}.0^{9,15}]pentadeca-3,5-dione	MeCN	220(4.21)	5-1428-80

Compound	Solvent	$\lambda_{max}(\log \epsilon)$	Ref.
$C_{18}H_{19}N_3O_2S$ 1,2,4-Triazine, 2,5-dihydro-5,6-bis(4-methoxyphenyl)-3-(methylthio)-	EtOH	223s(4.28),250s(4.03), 283(4.03),303(4.09)	44-4587-80
$C_{18}H_{19}N_3O_3$ 1H-Pyrazole, 1-ethyl-4,5-dihydro-3-(4-methoxyphenyl)-5-(4-nitrophenyl)-	MeOH	288(3.88)	2-0364-80
1,2,4-Triazine, 2,5-dihydro-3-methoxy-5,6-bis(4-methoxyphenyl)-	EtOH	220s(4.23),283s(4.08), 294(4.08)	44-4587-80
$C_{18}H_{19}N_3O_3S$ Hydrazinecarboxamide, N-[2-mercapto-3-(4-methoxyphenyl)-1-oxo-2-propenyl]-2-methyl-2-phenyl-	EtOH	252(4.17),368(4.36)	12-0619-80
$C_{18}H_{19}N_3O_4$ 1H-Indole-3-propanoic acid, 2-(1,2,3,4-tetrahydro-1,3-dimethyl-2,4-dioxo-5-pyrimidinyl)-, methyl ester	MeCN	264(4.00),282(4.01), 333(3.74)	35-7535-80
$C_{18}H_{19}N_3S$ 1,2,4-Triazine, 2,5-dihydro-5,6-bis(4-methylphenyl)-3-(methylthio)-	EtOH	218s(4.33),240s(4.13), 301(3.98)	44-4587-80
$C_{18}H_{19}N_4O_2$ 1H-Isoindolium, 2-(1,1-dimethylethyl)-1-[(4-nitrophenyl)hydrazono]-, tetrafluoroborate	MeOH-HClO$_4$	233(4.23),264(3.95), 325(4.16),458(3.62)	89-0320-80
$C_{18}H_{19}N_5$ Benzenamine, N,N-dimethyl-4-[[1-(4-methylphenyl)-1H-pyrazol-3-yl]azo]-	CHCl$_3$	423(4.50)	104-1143-80
$C_{18}H_{19}N_5O$ 1H-Benzimidazole, 2-[[1-(hydroxyimino)-2-methylpropyl]azo]-1-(phenylmethyl)-	50% EtOH	381(4.34)	103-0857-80
$C_{18}H_{19}N_5O_3$ Acetamide, N-[3,7-dihydro-7-(2-oxocyclohexyl)-5-phenyl[1,2,5]oxadiazolo[3,4-d]pyrimidin-7-yl]-	n.s.g.	239(4.10),284(4.01)	44-3827-80
$C_{18}H_{19}N_5O_6$ 2-Imidazolidinone, 1-[(2,4-dinitrophenyl)amino]-5-hydroxy-4,4-dimethyl-5-(4-methylphenyl)-	EtOH	196(4.3),210(4.3), 256(3.9),336(4.1)	5-1016-80
$C_{18}H_{19}N_7O_2$ Adenosine, 5'-[(aminophenylacetyl)-amino]-2',3'-didehydro-2',3',5'-trideoxy-, (R)-	H$_2$O	261(4.13)	136-0067-80A
$C_{18}H_{20}$ Bicyclo[2.2.2]octane, 1-(1-naphthalenyl)-	4:1 C$_6$H$_{11}$Me-isopentane	260s(3.63),269(3.84), 279(3.93),287(3.76), 292(3.76),312(2.64)	44-3933-80
Bicyclo[2.2.2]octane, 1-(2-naphthalenyl)-	4:1 C$_6$H$_{11}$Me-isopentane	255s(3.45),263(3.60), 266(3.60),273(3.64), 283s(3.47),302(2.54), 316(2.40)	44-3933-80

Compound	Solvent	$\lambda_{max}(\log \epsilon)$	Ref.
Dibenzo[a,c]cyclodecene, 5,6,7,8,9,10-hexahydro-	C_6H_{12}	260(3.00),267(3.04), 273(3.04)	95-0718-80
Dibenzo[a,e]cyclooctene, 5,6,11,12-tetrahydro-2,9-dimethyl-	EtOH	197(4.62),265(3.28)	24-2358-80 +108-0291-80
	EtOH	201(4.49),203(4.50), 204(4.50),262s(2.75), 268(1.96),272(2.87), 277(3.03)	44-3974-80
$C_{18}H_{20}ClN$			
Isoquinoline, 4-(4-chlorophenyl)-1,2,3,4-tetrahydro-2,3,3-trimethyl-	EtOH	203(4.50)	4-1563-80
Isoquinoline, 6-chloro-1,2,3,4-tetrahydro-2,3,3-trimethyl-4-phenyl-	EtOH	205(4.53)	4-1563-80
$C_{18}H_{20}ClNO$			
Isoquinoline, 6-chloro-1,2,3,4-tetrahydro-4-(3-methoxyphenyl)-3,3-dimethyl-, hydrochloride	EtOH	274(3.34)	4-1563-80
$C_{18}H_{20}ClNO_5$			
Cyclohexanecarboxylic acid, 1-(6-chloro-3,4-dihydro-3-methyl-2-oxo-2H-1,3-benzoxazin-4-yl)-2-oxo-, ethyl ester	EtOH	264(3.00),272(2.98)	4-0519-80
$C_{18}H_{20}Cl_2N_2O_4$			
4H-Furo[3,2-b]pyrrole-5-carboxylic acid, 4-(3-amino-2-hydroxypropyl)-2-(4-chlorophenyl)-, ethyl ester, monohydrochloride	MeOH	343(4.76),359(4.68)	73-2949-80
$C_{18}H_{20}Cl_2O_4$			
Benzene, 1,1'-(1,2-dichloro-1,2-ethanediyl)bis[3,4-dimethoxy-, (R*,S*)-	MeOH	232(4.28),284(3.85)	2-0556-80
$C_{18}H_{20}N_2$			
Apparicine	MeOH	304(3.70)	73-1419-80
Benzenepropanenitrile, 4-ethyl-α-methyl-α-(phenylamino)-	dioxan	243(4.19),288(3.20)	24-2462-80
Benzenepropanenitrile, α,3,5-trimethyl-α-(phenylamino)-	dioxan	243(4.16),276(3.18), 288(3.20)	24-2462-80
Pericalline	MeOH	218(4.71),230(4.69), 307(4.62)	102-1213-80
$C_{18}H_{20}N_2O$			
1,2,6-Oxadiazepine, 4,5,6,7-tetrahydro-3-(4-methylphenyl)-6-(phenylmethyl)-	THF	214(4.3),258(4.2)	24-3373-80
$C_{18}H_{20}N_2O_2$			
Deethylibophyllidine	EtOH	226(4.32),298(4.44), 328(4.58)	88-0055-80
13H-Isoquino[2,1-a][1,8]naphthyridin-13-one, 4-acetyl-1,2,3,4,6,7,11b,12-octahydro-	EtOH	235(3.88),337(4.11)	94-0220-80
1,2,6-Oxadiazepine, 4,5,6,7-tetrahydro-3-(4-methoxyphenyl)-6-(phenylmethyl)-	$CHCl_3$	230(3.7),265(4.2)	24-3373-80
3H-Pyrrolizine-2-carboxylic acid, 1-amino-3-phenyl-, 1,1-dimethylethyl ester	CH_2Cl_2	250(4.02),260s(3.93), 331(4.21)	150-3078-80

Compound	Solvent	λ_{max} (log ϵ)	Ref.
$C_{18}H_{20}N_2O_2S$			
Benzenesulfonic acid, [[2-(2-butenyl)-phenyl]methylene]hydrazide, (?,E)-	MeOH	278(4.21)	44-3756-80
Benzenesulfonic acid, [[2-(3-butenyl)-phenyl]methylene]hydrazide	MeOH	278(4.24)	44-3756-80
2H-Benz[g]indazole, 2,3,3a,4,5,9b-hexa-hydro-2-[(4-methylphenyl)sulfonyl]-	MeOH	218(4.12)	44-3756-80
$C_{18}H_{20}N_2O_2S_2$			
Thioperoxydicarbonimidic acid, N,N'-di-phenyl-, diethyl ester	EtOH	225s(4.41)	39-0665-80C
$C_{18}H_{20}N_2O_3$			
Indolo[2,3-a]quinolizine-3-carboxylic acid, 1,2,3,4,6,7,12,12b-octahydro-4-oxo-, ethyl ester	EtOH	223(4.62),274s(3.91), 280(3.92),290(3.81)	94-2527-80
$C_{18}H_{20}N_2O_4$			
1H-Pyrrole-3-propanoic acid, 5-[(4-eth-enyl-1,5-dihydro-3-methyl-5-oxo-2H-	MeOH	275(4.35),408(4.54), 428(4.51)	24-1603-80
pyrrol-2-ylidene)methyl]-2-formyl-4-methyl-, methyl ester	+ Zn(OAc)$_2$	284(4.38),442(4.48), 466(4.54)	24-1603-80
$C_{18}H_{20}N_2O_5S$			
Benzeneacetamide, N-(dihydro-10,10-di-methyl-1,7-dioxo-9H-5,9a-(epithio-methano)-1H,3H,5H-oxazolo[4,3-c]-[1,4]oxazepin-6-yl)-	EtOH	211(4.00),285(3.51)	39-0388-80C
Benzeneacetamide, N-[9,9a-dihydro-9a-(1-mercapto-1-methylethyl)-1,7-dioxo-1H,3H,7H-oxazolo[4,3-c][1,4]oxazepin-6-yl]-, (+)-	EtOH	214(3.91),286(4.04)	39-0388-80C
$C_{18}H_{20}N_2O_6$			
2,4(1H,3H)-Pyrimidinedione, 5-[2,3-O-(1-methylethylidene)-4-C-phenyl-β-D-ribofuranosyl]-	pH 13 MeOH	285(3.88) 263(3.90)	142-0761-80 142-0761-80
$C_{18}H_{20}N_3$			
1,2,4-Benzotriazinyl, 3-(1,1-dimethyl-ethyl)-1,4-dihydro-1-(4-methylphenyl)-	MeOH	242(4.36),320(3.93), 347(3.83),423(3.42), 508(3.08),523s(3.07), 543(3.05)	24-1205-80
1,2,4-Benzotriazinyl, 3-(1,1-dimethyl-ethyl)-1,4-dihydro-5-methyl-1-phenyl-	MeOH	247(4.37),317(3.82), 347(3.77),424(3.44), 478s(3.00),532(3.01), 558(3.00)	24-1205-80
1,2,4-Benzotriazinyl, 3-(1,1-dimethyl-ethyl)-1,4-dihydro-6-methyl-1-phenyl-	MeOH	245(4.41),318(3.95), 357(3.92),430(3.35), 510(3.06),545s(3.02)	24-1205-80
1,2,4-Benzotriazinyl, 3-(1,1-dimethyl-ethyl)-1,4-dihydro-7-methyl-1-phenyl-	MeOH	244(4.22),278s(3.73), 318(3.77),353(3.65), 426(3.13),513(2.70), 550(2.66)	24-1205-80
$C_{18}H_{20}N_4$			
1H-Benzimidazole, 1-ethyl-5,6-dimethyl-2-[(2-methylphenyl)azo]-	MeOH	397(3.37)	104-2008-80
1H-Benzimidazole, 1-ethyl-5,6-dimethyl-2-[(4-methylphenyl)azo]-	MeOH	416(3.45)	104-2008-80

Compound	Solvent	$\lambda_{max}(\log \epsilon)$	Ref.
2,2'-Bi-1H-benzimidazolium, 1,1',3,3'-tetramethyl-, diiodide	EtOH	270(4.22),277(4.25)	103-1261-80
$C_{18}H_{20}N_4OS$ 4(1H)-Pyridinone, 3-butyl-5-[5-(methyl-thio)-4H-1,2,3-triazol-3-yl]-	EtOH	260(4.00)	4-0175-80
$C_{18}H_{20}N_4O_2S$ Ethanol, 2,2'-[[4-[(4-methyl-2-benzo-thiazolyl)azo]phenyl]imino]bis-	acetone	503(4.70)	7-0167-80
Ethanol, 2,2'-[[4-[(6-methyl-2-benzo-thiazolyl)azo]phenyl]imino]bis-	acetone	503(4.69)	7-0167-80
$C_{18}H_{20}N_4O_3S$ Ethanol, 2,2'-[[4-(4-methoxy-2-benzo-thiazolyl)azo]phenyl]imino]bis-	acetone	491(4.57)	7-0167-80
Ethanol, 2,2'-[[4-[(6-methoxy-2-benzo-thiazolyl)azo]phenyl]imino]bis-	acetone	505(4.72)	7-0167-80
$C_{18}H_{20}N_4O_4$ Carbamic acid, [4-(phenylazo)-1,3-phen-ylene]bis-, diethyl ester	EtOH	225(4.41),266(4.11), 379(4.17)	73-1379-80
Carbamic acid, [2-[2-(1,2,3,4-tetra-hydro-1,3-dimethyl-2,4-dioxo-5-pyri-midinyl)-1H-indol-3-yl]ethyl]-, methyl ester	MeCN	224(4.33),261(3.98), 291(3.95),399(3.71)	35-7535-80
$C_{18}H_{20}N_5O_6PS$ Adenosine, N-methyl-8-[(phenylmethyl)-thio]-, cyclic 3',5'-(hydrogen phosphate)	pH 1 pH 11	287(4.31) 291(4.25)	87-0242-80 87-0242-80
Adenosine, 8-[[(2-methylphenyl)methyl]-thio]-, cyclic 3',5'-(hydrogen phosphate)	pH 1 pH 11	283(4.24) 283(4.18)	87-0242-80 87-0242-80
Adenosine, 8-[[(4-methylphenyl)methyl]-thio]-, cyclic 3',5'-(hydrogen phosphate)	pH 1 pH 11	283(4.25) 283(4.18)	87-0242-80 87-0242-80
$C_{18}H_{20}N_5O_7PS$ Adenosine, 8-[[(4-methoxyphenyl)meth-yl]thio]-, cyclic 3',5'-(hydrogen phosphate)	pH 1 pH 11	283(4.25) 283(4.19)	87-0242-80 87-0242-80
$C_{18}H_{20}N_6O_8$ 1H-1,2,3-Triazole-4,5-dicarboxylic acid, 1,1'-[2,3-bis(methylene)-1,4-butanediyl]bis-, tetramethyl ester	EtOH	217(4.39)	44-0870-80
$C_{18}H_{20}N_7$ Quinolinium, 4-[[3-(6-amino-9H-purin-9-yl)propyl]amino]-1-methyl-, iodide	EtOH	237(4.33),255(4.34), 338(4.29),350(4.31)	22-0316-80
$C_{18}H_{20}O$ 9H-6a,10-Methanocycloocta[a]naphthalen-9-one, 5,6,7,8,10,11-hexahydro-10-methyl-	EtOH	258(4.27),288(3.61)	44-1081-80
[2.2]Paracyclophane, 4-(hydroxymethyl)-13-methyl-	EtOH	225(4.45),275(4.21)	24-2358-80
$C_{18}H_{20}O_3$ 6-Oxaestra-1,3,5(10),7-tetraen-17-one,	EtOH	225(4.06),250(3.71),	23-1427-80

Compound	Solvent	$\lambda_{max}(\log \epsilon)$	Ref.
3-methoxy- (cont.)		290(3.67)	23-1427-80
$C_{18}H_{20}O_4$			
Benzene, 1,1'-(1,2-ethenediyl)bis[3,4-dimethoxy-	MeOH	285(3.93),316(3.96)	2-0556-80
Benzeneacetic acid, 4-methoxy-, 1-(4-methoxyphenyl)ethyl ester	MeCN	275(3.54),282(3.47)	39-0838-80B
Bicyclo[5.4.1]dodeca-2,5,7,9,11-penta-ene-3,5-dicarboxylic acid, diethyl ester	dioxan	278(4.63),358(3.70)	89-0041-80
6-Oxaestra-1,3,5(10)-triene-7,17-dione, 3-methoxy-, (8α)-	EtOH	220(4.06),280(3.44), 285(3.42)	23-1427-80
1-Propanone, 1-(2,4-dihydroxy-6-meth-oxy-3,5-dimethylphenyl)-3-phenyl-(angoletin)	MeOH	215(4.13),288(4.10), 325(3.57)	102-2036-80
$C_{18}H_{20}O_5$			
1,4-Benzodioxan-2-methanol, 3-(3,4-di-methoxyphenyl)-6-methyl-	EtOH	281(3.75),284(3.75)	39-0775-80C
1,3-Benzodioxol-5-ol, 6-[3-(4-hydroxy-2-methoxy-5-methylphenyl)propyl]-	EtOH EtOH-NaOH	295(4.26) 303(4.30)	102-1195-80 102-1195-80
Naphtho[1,2-b]furan-4,5-dione, 2,3-di-hydro-6,7-dimethoxy-2,3,3,9-tetra-methyl-	MeOH	278(4.56),363(3.47), 478(3.61)	5-0779-80
1-Propanone, 1-(2-hydroxy-4,6-dimeth-oxyphenyl)-3-(4-methoxyphenyl)-	EtOH EtOH-AlCl₃	224(4.16),287(4.10) 220(4.22),307(4.08)	102-1195-80 102-1195-80
Spiro[dibenz[b,d]oxepin-1(2H),2'-[1,3]dioxolane], 3,4-dihydro-9,10-dimethoxy-	C_6H_{12} MeCN	225(4.32),235(4.31), 248(4.33),280(3.70), 330(3.30) 227(3.80),275s(3.13), 315(3.09)	24-3249-80 24-3249-80
$C_{18}H_{20}O_6$			
4H-1-Benzopyran-3-carboxylic acid, 5,6,7,8-tetrahydro-2-[2-(2-hydroxy-1-cyclohexen-1-yl)-2-oxoethyl]-4-oxo-	EtOH	260(3.85),285(3.90)	94-2460-80
Naphtho[1,2-b]furan-4,5-dione, 2,3-di-hydro-3-(hydroxymethyl)-6,7-dimeth-oxy-2,3,9-trimethyl-	MeOH	277(4.34),368(3.31), 472(3.46)	5-0779-80
1-Propanone, 1-(2-hydroxy-4,6-dimeth-oxyphenyl)-3-(3-hydroxy-4-methoxy-phenyl)-	EtOH	208(4.36),226(4.21), 288(4.17)	102-0476-80
$C_{18}H_{20}O_7$			
Benzaldehyde, 4-[2-hydroxy-2-(4-hydr-oxy-3-methoxyphenyl)-1-(hydroxymeth-yl)ethoxy]-3-methoxy-	EtOH	230(4.24),280(4.03), 310(3.92)	102-0449-80
$C_{18}H_{21}BrNO_4$			
Oxazolium, 5-(2-acetoxy-1,1-dimethyl-ethyl)-2-[2-(4-bromophenyl)ethenyl]-4,5-dihydro-3-methyl-4-oxo-, per-chlorate	HOAc HOAc-HClO₄	370(3.68) 370(4.15)	103-0023-80 103-0023-80
$C_{18}H_{21}ClN_2O_3$			
2H-1,3-Benzoxazine-8-propanenitrile, 3,4,4a,5,6,7,8,8a-octahydro-4-(5-chloro-2-hydroxyphenyl)-3-methyl-2-oxo-	EtOH	285(3.45),288(3.90)	4-0277-80
Cyclohexanepropanenitrile, 3-(6-chloro-3,4-dihydro-3-methyl-2-oxo-2H-1,3-	EtOH	224(3.86),274(3.08), 281(3.04)	4-0277-80

Compound	Solvent	$\lambda_{max}(\log \epsilon)$	Ref.
benzoxazin-4-yl)-2-hydroxy- (cont.)			4-0277-80
$C_{18}H_{21}ClN_6O_2$			
Propanedioic acid, [1-(4-chlorophenyl)-3-hydrazono-3-phenylpropyl]-, dihydrazide	EtOH	257(4.08)	34-0085-80
$C_{18}H_{21}N$			
Benzenamine, N-[1-methyl-2-(2,4,6-trimethylphenyl)ethylidene]-	dioxan	281(3.55)	24-2462-80
$C_{18}H_{21}NO$			
Isoquinoline, 1,2,3,4-tetrahydro-4-(3-methoxyphenyl)-3,3-dimethyl-, hydrochloride	EtOH	204(4.27),274(3.38), 282(3.34)	4-1563-80
$C_{18}H_{21}NO_2$			
Benzenepropanoic acid, β-[(2,6-dimethylphenyl)amino]-, methyl ester	MeOH	218(4.02),244(3.88)	23-2061-80
1H-Pyrrole-3-carboxylic acid, 1-cyclohexyl-2-phenyl-, methyl ester	CCl_4	280(4.02)	22-0552-80
$C_{18}H_{21}NO_3$			
Benzo[a]cyclopenta[f]quinolizin-1(2H)-one, 3,5,6,10b,11,12-hexahydro-8,9-dimethoxy-	MeOH	227(4.01),294(4.63)	135-0956-80
Benzo[a]cyclopenta[f]quinolizin-12(1H)-one, 2,3,5,6,10b,11-hexahydro-8,9-dimethoxy-	MeOH	227(4.08),290(3.73), 331(4.18)	135-0956-80
2,3-Benzoxazepine, 1,3,4,5-tetrahydro-7,8-dimethoxy-3-methyl-1-phenyl-	MeOH	239(3.88),285(3.50)	12-0833-80
7-Isoquinolinol, 1,2,3,4-tetrahydro-6-methoxy-2-[(4-methoxyphenyl)-methyl]- (sendaverine)	EtOH	255(4.33),283(3.70)	2-0160-80
Morphinan-7-one, 5,6-didehydro-4-hydroxy-3-methoxy-17-methyl-, (+)-	MeOH	230(4.18),282(3.34)	44-1901-80
$C_{18}H_{21}NO_4$			
Deoxypretazettine	MeOH	241(3.74),290(3.63)	94-2924-80
3,5-Pyridinedicarboxylic acid, 1,4-dihydro-1,2,6-trimethyl-4-phenyl-, dimethyl ester	EtOH	242(4.18),347(3.82)	94-3163-80
1H-Pyrrole-2-acetic acid, 3-(methoxycarbonyl)-1-methyl-4-(2-phenylethyl)-, methyl ester	n.s.g.	242(3.93),257(3.78)	4-1081-80
$C_{18}H_{21}NO_5$			
Cyclohexanecarboxylic acid, 1-(3,4-dihydro-3-methyl-2-oxo-2H-1,3-benzoxazin-4-yl)-2-oxo-, ethyl ester	EtOH	265(3.00),272(3.00)	4-0519-80
4(5H)-Oxazolone, 5-(2-acetoxy-1,1-dimethylethyl)-2-[2-[(4-methoxyphenyl)-ethenyl]-, perchlorate	HOAc HOAc-$HClO_4$	356(4.56) 413(4.56)	103-0023-80 103-0023-80
Pretazettine	MeOH	241(3.67),291(3.64)	94-2924-80
1H-Pyrrole-3-carboxylic acid, 1-[(3,4-dimethoxyphenyl)methyl]-4-formyl-2-methyl-, ethyl ester	EtOH	270s(3.91),285(3.97)	39-1199-80C
Unsevine	n.s.g.	238(3.76),288(3.64)	105-0525-80
$C_{18}H_{21}NO_8$			
3aH-Indole-2,3,3a,4-tetracarboxylic	MeOH	251(4.11),290(3.05),	44-4573-80

Compound	Solvent	λ_{max}(log ϵ)	Ref.
acid, 1,7a-dihydro-1,6-dimethyl-, tetramethyl ester (cont.)		311s(2.56)	44-4573-80
$C_{18}H_{21}NO_9S$			
Sulfamic acid, [2-[3,5-dihydroxy-4-[3-(3-hydroxy-4-methoxyphenyl)-1-oxopropyl]phenoxy]ethyl]-, mono-potassium salt	H_2O	282(4.30)	44-5371-80
$C_{18}H_{21}N_2O_6$			
Oxazolium, 5-(2-acetoxy-1,1-dimethyl-ethyl)-4,5-dihydro-3-methyl-2-[2-(3-nitrophenyl)ethenyl]-4-oxo-, per-chlorate	HOAc HOAc-HClO4	335(3.72) 335(4.17)	103-0023-80 103-0023-80
Oxazolium, 5-(2-acetoxy-1,1-dimethyl-ethyl)-4,5-dihydro-3-methyl-2-[2-(4-nitrophenyl)ethenyl]-4-oxo-, per-chlorate	HOAc	295(3.79)	103-0023-80
$C_{18}H_{21}N_3O_2$			
Benzoic acid, 4-[[4-(diethylamino)-2-methylphenyl]azo]- dication	20% MeOH anion H_2SO_4	474(4.57) 444(4.54) 431(4.68)	39-0937-80B 39-0937-80B 39-0937-80B
2-Imidazolidinone, 5-hydroxy-4,4-di-methyl-1-[(2-methylphenyl)amino]-5-phenyl-	EtOH	200(4.7),234(4.0), 280(3.2)	5-1016-80
2-Imidazolidinone, 5-hydroxy-4,4-di-methyl-5-(4-methylphenyl)-1-(phenyl-amino)-	EtOH	199(4.7),218(4.2), 236(4.1),281(3.3)	5-1016-80
$C_{18}H_{21}N_3O_4S$			
2H-Isoindole-2-acetic acid, α-[[[(di-methylamino)methylene]amino]thioxo-methyl]-1,3-dihydro-1,3-dioxo-, 1,1-dimethylethyl ester	90% MeOH	214(4.56),240s(4.42), 264(4.48),345(4.40)	4-0767-80
$C_{18}H_{21}N_3O_5S$			
2-Azaspiro[3.5]nonan-1-one, 2-(2,4-di-nitrophenyl)-5,5,9,9-tetramethyl-3-thioxo-	isooctane	258(4.4),297(4.1), 315s(--),430s(--)	88-4247-80
$C_{18}H_{21}N_3S$			
1(2H)-Pyridazinecarbothioamide, tetra-hydro-6-methyl-N,2-diphenyl-	EtOH	246(4.50)	103-0169-80
$C_{18}H_{21}N_4O_2S$			
Benzothiazolium, 2-[[4-[bis(2-hydroxy-ethyl)amino]phenyl]azo]-3-methyl-, methyl sulfate	acetone	572(4.89)	7-0167-80
$C_{18}H_{21}N_5$			
4-Pyrimidinamine, 2-(3,5-dimethyl-1H-pyrazol-1-yl)-5-ethyl-6-methyl-N-phenyl-	EtOH	<u>253(4.5),285s(4.4)</u>	103-0868-80
$C_{18}H_{21}N_5O_7S_3$			
1H-Pyrazolo[3,4-d]pyrimidine-3-carbo-thioamide, 4,5-dihydro-6-(methyl-thio)-4-thioxo-1-(2,3,5-tri-0-acetyl-β-D-ribofuranosyl)-	EtOH	199(4.39),256(4.47), 334(4.16)	103-0182-80

Compound	Solvent	$\lambda_{max}(\log \epsilon)$	Ref.
$C_{18}H_{22}$ 4H-Indene, 5,6,7,7a-tetrahydro-4,4,7a- trimethyl-1-phenyl-	pentane	223(3.91),239s(3.69), 305(4.07)	33-0154-80
$C_{18}H_{22}IN_3$ 1,3-Propanediamine, N'-(7-iodo-4-quino- linyl)-N,N-di-2-propenyl-	hexane	220(4.53),257(4.33), 322(3.94)	103-0754-80
$C_{18}H_{22}NO_4$ Oxazolium, 5-(2-acetoxy-1,1-dimethyl- ethyl)-4,5-dihydro-3-methyl-4-oxo- 2-(2-phenylethenyl)-, perchlorate	HOAc HOAc-HClO$_4$	358(4.09) 358(4.37)	103-0023-80 103-0023-80
$C_{18}H_{22}NO_5$ Oxazolium, 5-(2-acetoxy-1,1-dimethyl- ethyl)-2-[4-(2-furanyl)-1,3-buta- dienyl]-4,5-dihydro-3-methyl-4-oxo-, perchlorate	HOAc	460(4.27)	103-0023-80
$C_{18}H_{22}N_2$ Acetophenone N-butylphenylhydrazone Diazene, bis(1-methyl-1-phenylethyl)-	EtOH hexane C_6H_{12}	235-254(3.41) 367.5(1.65) 252(2.82),258(2.79), 265(2.62),367(1.67)	104-0766-80 35-0259-80 44-4629-80
$C_{18}H_{22}N_2O$ Pyrazolidine, 3-ethoxy-5-methyl-1,2-di- phenyl-	MeOH	202(4.37),251(4.26), 283s(3.44)	73-2417-80
$C_{18}H_{22}N_2O_2$ 3H-Indol-3-one, 2-(1,3,4,5,6,7-hexahy- dro-1-methyl-3-oxo-2H-indol-2-yli- dene)-1,2,4,5,6,7-hexahydro-1-methyl-	CHCl$_3$	330(4.34),582(3.97)	5-0564-80
$C_{18}H_{22}N_2O_4S_3$ Methanaminium, N-[[[bis(phenylsulfon- yl)methyl]thio](dimethylamino)meth- ylene]-N-methyl-, hydroxide, inner salt	MeOH	244(4.15)	78-2675-80
$C_{18}H_{22}N_2O_5$ 1H-Pyrazole-1-acetic acid, 4-(ethoxy- carbonyl)-5-(1-hydroxyethyl)-3-phen- yl-, ethyl ester	EtOH	228(4.01)	118-0875-80
$C_{18}H_{22}N_2O_6$ 1,1-Cyclohexanedicarboxylic acid, 3-(aminocarbonyl)-4-(benzoylamino)-, dimethyl ester, cis trans	EtOH EtOH	227.5(4.06) 228(3.92)	23-1860-80 23-1860-80
$C_{18}H_{22}N_2O_7$ 2H-1,3-Benzoxazine-4-acetic acid, 3,4- dihydro-8-methoxy-3-methyl-α-[1- [[(methylamino)carbonyl]oxy]eth- ylidene]-2-oxo-, ethyl ester	EtOH	246s(3.76),285(3.29)	4-0519-80
$C_{18}H_{22}N_2O_7S$ Carbonic acid, 1-(2,2-dimethyl-9-oxo- 3-oxa-6-thia-1-azabicyclo[5.2.0]- non-8-yl)ethyl (4-nitrophenyl)methyl ester	EtOH	263(4.00)	35-2039-80

Compound	Solvent	$\lambda_{max}(\log \epsilon)$	Ref.
$C_{18}H_{22}N_2O_9S$			
Carbonic acid, 1-(2,2-dimethyl-9-oxo-3-oxa-6-thia-1-azabicyclo[5.2.0]non-8-yl)ethyl (4-nitrophenyl)methyl ester, S,S-dioxide	EtOH	263(3.99)	35-2039-80
$C_{18}H_{22}N_4O_2$			
Benzenamine, N,N-diethyl-4-[(2,6-dimethyl-4-nitrophenyl)azo]-	toluene	414(4.38)	5-2055-80
$C_{18}H_{22}N_4O_2S$			
4,6(1H,5H)-Pyrimidinedione, 5-[[4-(dimethylamino)phenyl]-1-piperidinylmethylene]dihydro-2-thioxo-	MeOH	403(4.54)	97-0020-80
$C_{18}H_{22}N_4O_3$			
2,4,6(1H,3H,5H)-Pyrimidinetrione, 5-[[4-(dimethylamino)phenyl]-1-piperidinylmethylene]-	MeOH	396(4.40)	97-0020-80
$C_{18}H_{22}N_4S$			
Thiodicarbonimidic diamide, N,N,N',N'-tetramethyl-N'',N'''-diphenyl-	EtOH	252(4.25)	39-0665-80C
Thiourea, N-[(dimethylamino)(phenylimino)methyl]-N',N'-dimethyl-N-phenyl-	EtOH	255(4.27)	39-0665-80C
$C_{18}H_{22}N_4S_2$			
Thioperoxydicarbonimidic diamide, N,N,N',N'-tetramethyl-N'',N'''-diphenyl-	EtOH	245(4.37)	39-0665-80C
$C_{18}H_{22}N_6O_2$			
Propanedioic acid, (3-hydrazono-1,3-diphenylpropyl)-, dihydrazide	EtOH	252-270s(4.10)	34-0085-80
$C_{18}H_{22}O$			
Cyclopenta[j]phenanthren-8(4bH)-one, 5,6,7,7a,9,10,11,12-octahydro-7a-methyl-, (4bα,7aα,10aS*)-	EtOH	260(2.50),266(2.70), 273(2.70)	44-1081-80
$C_{18}H_{22}OS$			
2(3H)-Naphthalenone, 4,4a,5,6,7,8-hexahydro-4a,5-dimethyl-1-(phenylthio)-	EtOH	202(4.41),248(4.21)	39-0963-80C
$C_{18}H_{22}O_3$			
Benzeneacetic acid, α-[5-(5-oxo-1-cyclopenten-1-yl)pentyl]-	MeOH	227(4.03)	44-4702-80
1,4-Benzocyclodecenediol, 5,8,9,12-tetrahydro-6,10-dimethyl-, 1-acetate, (E,E)- (wigandol)	EtOH	283(--)	102-2202-80
Pentacyclo[8.2.0.0^{4,9}.0^{5,11}.0^{8,12}]dodecane-3,7,10-trione, 1,2,5,6,6,8-hexamethyl-	MeOH	302(1.90)	44-0034-80
Tricyclo[6.2.2.0^{2,7}]dodeca-4,9-diene-3,6,11-trione, 1,8,9,10,12,12-hexamethyl-	C_6H_{12}	220(3.92),302(1.76)	44-0034-80
Tricyclo[6.2.2.0^{2,7}]dodeca-2,4,6,9-tetraen-11-one, 1,8,9,10,12,12-hexamethyl-3,6-dihydroxy-	MeOH	250(3.43),305(3.27)	44-0034-80
Tricyclo[7.2.1.0^{3,8}]dodeca-3,5,7,10-	C_6H_{12}	256(2.57),357(2.68)	44-0034-80

Compound	Solvent	$\lambda_{max}(\log \epsilon)$	Ref.
tetraen-2-one, 1,9,10,11,12,12-hexa-methyl-4,7-dihydroxy- (cont.)			44-0034-80
$C_{18}H_{22}O_3S$			
17-Thiaestra-1,3,5(10),8(14)-tetraene, 3-methoxy-, 17,17-dioxide	MeOH	277(3.27),282(3.25)	13-0133-80A
$C_{18}H_{22}O_4$			
Benzene, 2-(1,1-dimethoxyethyl)-4-meth-oxy-1-(phenylmethoxy)-	n.s.g.	228(4.05),291(3.52)	44-0501-80
Dispiro[cyclohexane-1,2'-benzo[1,2-c:4,5-d']bis[1,3]dioxole-6',1"-cyclohexane]	EtOH	242(3.16),323(3.84)	12-0527-80
3,6-Ethanonaphth[2,3-b]oxirene-2,7,8-trione, 1a,2a,3,6,6a,7a-hexahydro-3,4,5,6,9,9-hexamethyl-, (1aα,2aβ-3β,6β,6aβ,7aα)-	MeOH	299(2.48)	44-0034-80
Indeno[1,2-b]pyran-5(2H)-one, 4-(1,1-dimethylethyl)-3,4-dihydro-2,2-di-methoxy-	CH_2Cl_2	240(4.58),249(4.58), 300(2.81),392(2.83)	24-1020-80
$C_{18}H_{22}O_6$			
Spiro[cyclopropa[cd]pentalene-1(2H),2'-oxirane]-2b,4b(2aH,4aH)-dicarboxylic acid, 4-(1,1-dimethylethyl)-2a-meth-yl-2-oxo-, dimethyl ester	EtOH	256s(2.72),312s(1.93), 323s(1.81),337s(1.48)	44-2189-80
$C_{18}H_{22}O_7$			
4H-1-Benzopyran-2-octanoic acid, 3-carboxy-5,6,7,8-tetrahydro-ζ,4-dioxo-	EtOH	252(4.05)	94-2460-80
Spiro[1-benzoxepin-6(7H),2'-[1,3]dioxo-lane]-4,5-dicarboxylic acid, 8,9-di-hydro-8,8-dimethyl-, dimethyl ester	MeCN	205(3.97),295(3.49)	24-3249-80
Spiro[1,3-dioxolane-2,8'(5'H)-[2H-2,4a]epoxynaphthalene]-3',4'-di-carboxylic acid, 6',7'-dihydro-6',6'-dimethyl-, dimethyl ester	MeCN	208(3.94),283(2.98)	24-3249-80
$C_{18}H_{22}O_{10}S$			
Paederoside	n.s.g.	235(4.02)	100-0649-80
$C_{18}H_{22}O_{11}$			
Asperuloside	EtOH	234.5(3.83)	100-0649-80
$C_{18}H_{23}BrS_3$			
Thiophene, 3-bromo-2,4-bis[(1,1-dimeth-ylethyl)thio]-5-phenyl-	heptane	197(4.43),280(4.08)	24-3342-80
$C_{18}H_{23}ClN_2O_9$			
1H-Pyrazole-5-carboxylic acid, 3-(chlo-romethyl)-1-(2,3,5-tri-O-acetyl-β-D-ribofuranosyl)-, ethyl ester	EtOH	230(4.24),240s(4.11)	87-0657-80
$C_{18}H_{23}ClN_4O_6S$			
D-erythro-Pentitol, 1-C-(6-chloro-purin-9-yl)-2-deoxy-1-S-ethyl-1-thio-, 3,4,5-triacetate	MeOH	264(3.9)	136-0356-80C
$C_{18}H_{23}IN_2O_9$			
1H-Pyrazole-5-carboxylic acid, 3-(iodo-	EtOH	228(4.31),240s(4.13)	87-0657-80

Compound	Solvent	$\lambda_{max}(\log \epsilon)$	Ref.
methyl)-1-(2,3,5-tri-O-acetyl-β-D-ribofuranosyl)-, ethyl ester (cont.)			87-0657-80
$C_{18}H_{23}NO$ 2H-Pyrrole-5-ethanol, 3,4-dihydro-β,β,3,3-tetramethyl-α-(phenylethynyl)-	MeOH	207(4.14),240(4.20), 249(4.13)	83-0858-80
$C_{18}H_{23}NOS_3$ 3-Thiophenecarbodithioic acid, 4-(diethylamino)-2-(4-methoxyphenyl)-5-methyl-, methyl ester	EtOH	223s(2.99),258s(2.55), 333(2.45),360s(2.39), 467(2.83)	22-0539-80
$C_{18}H_{23}NO_2$ 2,3-Cycloundecadien-1-ol, phenylcarbamate	EtOH	234(4.21),264(3.49), 272(3.52),280(3.38)	35-5370-80
1H-Pyrrole-2-acetic acid, 1-methyl-4-(2-phenylethyl)-, 1-methylethyl ester	MeOH	217(4.06)	4-1081-80
$C_{18}H_{23}NO_3$ Benzo[a]cyclopenta[f]quinolizin-12(1H)-one, 2,3,3a,5,6,10a,11,12a-octahydro-8,9-dimethoxy-	MeOH	227(3.95),284(3.61), 291(3.56)	135-0956-80
$C_{18}H_{23}NO_4$ 2(1H)-Quinolinone, 4,7,8-trimethoxy-1-methyl-3-(3-methyl-2-butenyl)-	EtOH	227(4.42),236(4.37), 253(4.03),262(4.04), 300(3.82),323(3.86), 335(3.76)	88-3293-80
$C_{18}H_{23}NO_5$ 1H-Indol-3-ol, 2,3,3a,6,7,7a-hexahydro-3a-[6-(hydroxymethyl)-1,3-benzodioxol-5-yl]-6-methoxy-1-methyl-	MeOH	242(3.77),288(3.55)	94-2924-80
1-Pyrrolidinepropanoic acid, 2-(2-methoxy-2-oxoethylidene)-α-(4-methoxyphenyl)-, methyl ester, (E)-	EtOH EtOH-acid	229(4.09),280(4.47) 228(4.05),277(3.81), 282(3.82)	44-1713-80 44-1713-80
$C_{18}H_{23}NO_5S$ Spiro[benzothiazole-2(3H),6'(5'H)-furo[2,3-d][1,3]dioxole], 5'-(2,2-dimethyl-1,3-dioxolan-4-yl)-3'a,6'a-dihydro-2',2'-dimethyl-, [3'aR-[3'aα,5'α(R*),6'β,6'aα]]-	EtOH	218(4.23)	33-1779-80
$C_{18}H_{23}NO_6$ 2H-1,3-Oxazin-2-one, 5-(1-acetoxyethyl)-4-(2-acetoxyphenyl)-3,4,5,6-tetrahydro-3,6-dimethyl-	EtOH	263(3.15),270(3.08)	4-0277-80
Spiro[benzoxazole-2(3H),6'(5'H)-furo[2,3-d][1,3]dioxole], 5'-(2,2-dimethyl-1,3-dioxolan-4-yl)-3'a,6'a-dihydro-2',2'-dimethyl-, [3'aR-[3'aα,5'α(R*),6'β,6'aα]]-	EtOH	214(4.32)	33-1779-80
$C_{18}H_{23}NS$ 2H-Azeto[2,1-a]isoquinoline-2-thione, 1-(1,1-dimethylethyl)-1,4,5,9b-tetrahydro-1-(2-propenyl)-, cis	CHCl₃	275(4.2),330s(2.3)	24-3010-80

Compound	Solvent	$\lambda_{max}(\log \epsilon)$	Ref.
$C_{18}H_{23}N_3$			
1-Propanone, 2-amino-2-methyl-1-(4-methylphenyl)-, (2-methylphenyl)hydrazone, monohydrochloride, (E)-	EtOH	199(4.5),270(4.2), 299(4.0)	5-1016-80
$C_{18}H_{23}N_5O_8$			
Guanosine, N-ethyl-, 2',3',5'-triacetate	EtOH	254(4.19),276s(3.98)	118-1025-80
1,2-Hydrazinedicarboxylic acid, 1,1'-(5,6-dimethyl-2H-isoindole-1,3-diyl)bis-, tetramethyl ester	CH_2Cl_2 at -20°	258(3.72),297(3.37), 306s(3.29)	88-3471-80
1,2-Hydrazinedicarboxylic acid, 1,1'-(2-ethyl-2H-isoindole-1,3-diyl)bis-, tetramethyl ester	MeOH	269(3.20),273(3.20), 279(3.52),327(3.92)	88-3471-80
$C_{18}H_{24}$			
Hexamethylradialene	CH_2Cl_2	265s(3.76)	24-1663-80
$C_{18}H_{24}BrN_3O$			
Phenol, 4-[(4,6-diamino-5-bromo-3-pyridinyl)methyl]-2,6-bis(1-methylethyl)-	pH 2	222(4.66),277(3.97)	87-0384-80
	pH 8.7	218(4.64),280(3.60)	87-0384-80
	pH 13	240s(4.29),290(3.78)	87-0384-80
$C_{18}H_{24}NO_5$			
Oxazolium, 5-(2-acetoxy-1,1-dimethylethyl)-4,5-dihydro-3-methyl-2-[2-(5-methyl-2-furanyl)-1-propenyl]-4-oxo-, perchlorate	HOAc	332(3.42),436(3.81)	103-0023-80
$C_{18}H_{24}N_2$			
2,2'-Bipyridine, 4,4'-bis(1,1-dimethylethyl)-	MeCN	246(4.04),253s(4.02), 286(4.20)	33-1675-80
$C_{18}H_{24}N_2O_3$			
3-Pyridinecarboxamide, 1,4-dihydro-N-[2-hydroxy-1-(hydroxymethyl)-2-phenylethyl]-1-propyl-	MeOH	355(3.81)	39-0007-80C
$C_{18}H_{24}N_2O_4$			
2H-1,3-Benzoxazin-2-one, 3,4,4a,5,6,7-8,8a-octahydro-3,8-dimethyl-4-[2-[(methylamino)carbonyl]oxy]phenyl]-	EtOH	264(2.65),270(2.59)	4-0277-80
Butanedioic acid, [bis(dimethylamino)-methylene](phenylmethylene)-, dimethyl ester	n.s.g.	220(4.15)(end abs.)	44-4573-80
$C_{18}H_{24}N_2O_5$			
α-D-ribo-Hexofuranose, 3-[(2-aminophenyl)imino]-3-deoxy-1,2:5,6-bis-O-(1-methylethylidene)-	EtOH	230(3.90),208(3.87), 347(3.38)	33-1779-80
Spiro[2H-benzimidazole-2,6'(5'H)-furo-[2,3-d][1,3]dioxole], 5'-(2,2-dimethyl-1,3-dioxolan-4-yl)-1,3,3'a,6'a-tetrahydro-2',2'-dimethyl-, [3'aR-[3'aα,5'α,6'aα)]-	hexane	211(4.45)	33-1779-80
$C_{18}H_{24}N_2O_8$			
D-Glutamic acid, N-[(1,1-dimethylethoxy)carbonyl]-, 1-methyl 5-[(4-nitrophenyl)methyl] ester	CHCl_3	266(4.02)	22-0133-80

Compound	Solvent	$\lambda_{max}(\log \epsilon)$	Ref.
L-Glutamic acid, N-[(1,1-dimethylethoxy)carbonyl]-, 1-methyl 5-[(2-nitrophenyl)methyl] ester	CHCl$_3$	261.5(3.75)	22-0133-80
L-Glutamic acid, N-[(1,1-dimethylethoxy)carbonyl]-, 1-methyl 5-[(3-nitrophenyl)methyl] ester	CHCl$_3$	263.5(3.91)	22-0133-80
L-Glutamic acid, N-[(1,1-dimethylethoxy)carbonyl]-, 1-methyl-5-[(4-nitrophenyl)methyl] ester	CHCl$_3$	266(4.01)	22-0133-80
$C_{18}H_{24}N_4O_2S_4$			
4-Morpholinecarbodithioic acid, 2,6-dimethyl-, 1,2-dicyano-1,2-ethenediyl ester	EtOH	264(4.17),388(3.85)	44-5113-80
$C_{18}H_{24}N_4O_3$			
2,4,6(1H,3H,5H)-Pyrimidinetrione, 5-[[2-[(1,1-dimethylethyl)amino]-4,5-dimethylphenyl]imino]-1,3-dimethyl-	MeCN	620(4.03)	88-0739-80
$C_{18}H_{24}O$			
2(3H)-Anthracenone, 4,4a,5,6,7,8,10-10a-octahydro-10a-methyl-6-(1-methylethylidene)-, (4aS-cis)-	EtOH	300(4.22)	39-0176-80C
5H-Cycloprop[b]anthracen-5-one, 1,1a,2-6,7,7a,8,8a,9,9a-decahydro-1,1,8a-trimethyl-, [1aR-(1aα,7aβ,8aβ,9aα)]-	EtOH	299(4.48)	39-0176-80C
3aH-Inden-3a-ol, 3,4,5,6,7,7a-hexahydro-4,4,7a-trimethyl-1-phenyl-, trans	pentane	246(3.99)	33-0154-80
$C_{18}H_{24}O_2$			
19-Norandrost-4-ene-3,17-dione	n.s.g.	240(4.30)	19-0001-80
A-Norgon-3(5)-ene-2,17-dione, 13-ethyl-	MeOH	232(4.21)	24-2249-80
$C_{18}H_{24}O_3$			
1H-Benz[e]indene-3,7(2H,3aH)-dione, 3a-ethyl-4,5,8,9,9a,9b-hexahydro-6-(2-oxopropyl)-, [3aS-(3aα,9aα,9bβ)]-	MeOH	247(4.12)	24-2249-80
Ethanone, 1-[4-hydroxy-3-(4-hydroxy-3-methyl-2-butenyl)-5-(3-methyl-2-butenyl)phenyl]-	EtOH	226(4.24),282(4.17)	102-2781-80
$C_{18}H_{24}O_4$			
Ethanone, 1-[3-[(3,3-dimethyloxiranyl)methyl]-4-hydroxy-5-(4-hydroxy-3-methyl-2-butenyl)phenyl]-	EtOH	232(4.22),285(4.14)	102-2781-80
Ethanone, 1-[4-hydroxy-3,5-bis(4-hydroxy-3-methyl-2-butenyl)phenyl]-	EtOH	227(4.35),283(4.21)	102-2781-80
$C_{18}H_{24}O_5$			
Spiro[1,3-benzodioxole-2,1'-cyclohexan]-5(6H)-one, 6-acetoxy-6-(1,1-dimethylethyl)-	EtOH	252(3.66),316(3.46)	12-0527-80
$C_{18}H_{24}O_6$			
1H-Indene-4,5-dicarboxylic acid, 6-(dimethoxymethyl)-2,3-dihydro-2,2-dimethyl-, dimethyl ester	EtOH	289(3.38)	78-3361-80
$C_{18}H_{24}O_6S$			
Estra-1,3,5(10)-triene-2,3,17-triol,	MeOH	286(3.61)	95-0867-80

Compound	Solvent	$\lambda_{max}(\log \epsilon)$	Ref.
17-(hydrogen sulfate), monopotassium salt, (17β)- (cont.)			95-0867-80
$C_{18}H_{24}O_9$			
Propanoic acid, 2-methoxy-, 1,3,5-benzenetriyl ester	MeCN	202(4.04),265s(2.36), 273s(2.11)	108-0142-80
$C_{18}H_{24}O_{11}S$			
Paederosidic acid	n.s.g.	233(4.04)	100-0649-80
6-epi-	EtOH	233(3.91)	100-0649-80
$C_{18}H_{24}O_{12}$			
Asperulosidic acid	EtOH	234(3.95)	100-0649-80
Cyclopenta[c]pyran-4-carboxylic acid, 7-(acetoxymethyl)-1-(β-D-glucopyranosyloxy)-1,4a,5,7a-tetrahydro-5-hydroxy-, [1S-(1α,4aα,5β,7aα)]- (10acetylscandoside)	EtOH	235(3.97)	100-0649-80
Griselinoside	MeOH	235(4.0)	100-0649-80 +102-2685-80
$C_{18}H_{24}O_{13}$			
Aralidioside	MeOH	232(3.99)	100-0649-80 +102-2685-80
$C_{18}H_{25}BrN_6O_6$			
Guanosine, 8-bromo-N-[(dimethylamino)-methylene]-1-(methoxymethyl)-2',3'-O-(1-methylethylidene)-	MeOH	238(4.11),280s(4.11), 313(4.35)	78-3509-80
$C_{18}H_{25}NO$			
9-Azabicyclo[3.3.1]nonan-3-one, 9-[4-(1,1-dimethylethyl)phenyl]-	MeCN	254(4.3),290s(3.5)	35-5482-80
$C_{18}H_{25}NOS$			
2-Azetidinethione, 3-(1,1-dimethylethyl)-4-(4-methoxyphenyl)-1-methyl-3-(2-propenyl)-, trans	isooctane	267(4.2),316(1.9), 340s(1.8)	24-3010-80
$C_{18}H_{25}NO_3$			
3-Pyridinecarboxylic acid, 1,4-dihydro-5-(8-nonenyl)-4-oxo-1-(2-propenyl)-	EtOH	262(3.96),285s(3.64)	4-0359-80
$C_{18}H_{25}NO_8S$			
5H,8H-Pyrano[4,3-d]thiazolo[3,2-a]pyridin-5-one, 9-ethenyl-8-(β-D-glucopyranosyloxy)-2,3,9,9a,10,10a-hexahydro-, [8S-(8α,9β,9aα,10aα)]- (xylostosidine)	MeOH	238(4.23)	33-1045-80
$C_{18}H_{25}N_3O$			
Phenol, 4-[(4,6-diamino-3-pyridinyl)-methyl]-2,6-bis(1-methylethyl)-, monohydrobromide	pH 2 pH 13	222(4.70),266(4.00) 240s(4.26),288(3.75)	87-0384-80 87-0384-80
$C_{18}H_{26}BrN_3$			
3,5-Pyridinedicarbonitrile, 1-(7-bromoheptyl)-1,4-dihydro-2,4,4,6-tetramethyl-	MeOH	223(4.39),346(3.79)	73-3370-80
$C_{18}H_{26}IN_3$			
1,3-Propanediamine, N'-(7-iodo-4-quino-	hexane	231(4.37),266(4.31),	103-0754-80

Compound	Solvent	λ_{max}(log ϵ)	Ref.
linyl)-N,N-dipropyl- (cont.)		333(4.05)	103-0754-80
$C_{18}H_{26}NO_7$			
3,6,9,12,15-Pentaoxa-19-azoniabicyclo-[15.3.1]heneicosa-1(21),17,19-triene, 18,19,20-trimethyl-2,16-dioxo-, per-chlorate	MeCN	228(3.94),280(3.81), 288(3.80),310(2.95)	44-2854-80
$C_{18}H_{26}N_2$			
4,4'-Bipyridinium, 1,1'-dibutyl-, diiodide	H_2O	258(4.35)	98-1026-80
1H-Indole-3-ethanamine, N-cyclohexyl-N,2-dimethyl-, monohydrochloride	EtOH	226(4.38),284(3.84), 291(3.78)	80-0245-80
$C_{18}H_{26}N_2O$			
Cyclohexanone, 2-[5-(dimethylamino)-2,4-pentadienylidene]-6-[3-(dimethylamino)-2-propenylidene]-, (all-E)-	EtOH CHCl$_3$	512(4.82) 492(--)	70-0980-80 70-0980-80
$C_{18}H_{26}N_2O_2$			
3H-Pyrrol-3-one, 4-butyl-2-(4-butyl-1,3-dihydro-5-methyl-3-oxo-2H-pyrrol-2-ylidene)-1,2-dihydro-5-methyl-	MeOH CHCl$_3$ CCl$_4$ C$_6$H$_{12}$ tert-BuOH + base	314(4.40),532(4.12) 317(4.20),529(3.98) 310(4.41),520(4.21) 307(--),503(--) 315(--),536(--) 634(--)	5-0564-80 5-0564-80 5-0564-80 5-0564-80 5-0564-80 5-0564-80
$C_{18}H_{26}N_2O_3$			
Cyclohexanamine, N-cyclohexyl-N-[2-(5-nitro-2-furanyl)ethenyl]-, (E)-	MeOH	280(3.96),522(4.07)	73-0155-80
$C_{18}H_{26}N_4O$			
2,4-Pyrimidinediamine, 5-[[4-methoxy-3,5-bis(1-methylethyl)phenyl]methyl]-	pH 2 pH 12	220s(4.50),272(3.67) 241s(3.97)	87-0535-80 87-0535-80
$C_{18}H_{26}N_4O_5$			
Pyrido[2,3-d]pyrimidine-6-carboxylic acid, 2-[(4,4-diethoxybutyl)amino]-8-ethyl-5,8-dihydro-5-oxo-	EtOH	214(4.01),274(4.62), 325(3.85)	94-2531-80
$C_{18}H_{26}N_8$			
2-Pyrimidinamine, 4-(3,5-dimethyl-1H-pyrazol-1-yl)-N-(5-hexyl-1H-1,2,4-triazol-3-yl)-6-methyl-	EtOH	260(4.58),298(4.01)	103-1275-80
4-Pyrimidinamine, 2-(3,5-dimethyl-1H-pyrazol-1-yl)-N-(5-hexyl-1H-1,2,4-triazol-3-yl)-6-methyl-	EtOH	230(4.01),274(4.27), 300(3.93)	103-1271-80
$C_{18}H_{26}O$			
5H-Cycloprop[b]anthracen-5-one, 1,1a,2-2a,3,6,7,7a,8,8a,9,9a-dodecahydro-1,1,8a-trimethyl-, [1aR-(1aα,2aβ-7aβ,8aβ,9aα)]-	EtOH	240(4.24)	39-0176-80C
$C_{18}H_{26}O_2$			
19-Nortestosterone	n.s.g.	241(4.25)	19-0001-80
$C_{18}H_{26}O_4$			
Bicyclo[3.3.1]nonan-3-one, 1,1'-dioxy-bis-	EtOH	280(1.65)	44-1800-80

Compound	Solvent	$\lambda_{max}(\log \epsilon)$	Ref.
Bicyclo[2.2.2]octa-2,5-diene-2,3-di-carboxylic acid, bis(1,1-dimethyl-ethyl) ester	EtOH	213(3.84),228s(3.73), 240s(3.46)	24-0531-80
$C_{18}H_{26}O_4S_2$ Spiro[1,3-dithiolane-2,2'(1'H)-naphtha-lene]-7'-acetic acid, 3',4',6',7',8'-8'a-hexahydro-α-hydroxy-α,1',8'a-tri-methyl-6'-oxo-, methyl ester	EtOH	238.5(4.18)	94-3265-80
isomer b	EtOH	238(4.26)	94-3265-80
$C_{18}H_{26}O_5S$ α-D-Glucofuranose, 5-C-methyl-3-O-meth-yl-1,2-O-(1-methylethylidene)-6-S-(phenylmethyl)-6-thio-	EtOH	210(3.84)	33-0016-80
$C_{18}H_{26}O_6$ Spiro[1,3-dioxolane-2,2'(1'H)-naphtha-lene]-7'-acetic acid, 3',4',6',7',8'-8'a-hexahydro-α-hydroxy-α,1',8'a-tri-methyl-6'-oxo-, methyl ester	EtOH	237.5(4.20)	94-3265-80
isomer b	EtOH	237(4.18)	94-3265-80
$C_{18}H_{26}O_7$ 1,4,7,10,13-Benzopentaoxacyclopentadec-in-15-methanol, 2,3,5,6,8,9,11,12-octahydro-α-methyl-, acetate	MeOH	278(3.46)	138-0515-80
$C_{18}H_{26}O_9$ 7-Oxabicyclo[2.2.1]heptane-2,3,5,6-tetramethanol, tetraacetate, (2-endo-3-exo,5-endo,6-exo)-	EtOH	220(2.66)	33-1149-80
$C_{18}H_{26}O_{10}$ 1-Butanone, 3-(β-D-allosyloxy)-1-(2-hy-droxy-4,6-dimethoxyphenyl)-	MeOH MeOH-AlCl₃	291(4.28) 310(4.43)	94-3070-80 94-3070-80
$C_{18}H_{27}N$ 9-Azabicyclo[3.3.1]nonane, 9-[4-(1,1-dimethylethyl)phenyl]-	MeCN	261(4.2),303s(3.2)	35-5482-80
Benzenamine, N-cyclododecylidene-	dioxan	297(3.24)	24-2462-80
3H-Indole, 5,7-bis(1,1-dimethylethyl)-3,3-dimethyl-	EtOH	224(4.2),231(4.1), 266(3.9)	18-0205-80
$C_{18}H_{27}NO$ 1H-Pyrrole-2-carboxaldehyde, 5-(12-cya-no-6-dodecenyl)-, (Z)-	MeCN	297(4.20)	44-4980-80
$C_{18}H_{27}NO_2$ 4-Azaandrost-1-en-3-one, 17-hydroxy-, (5β,17β)-	n.s.g.	210(4.02),255(3.42)	33-2380-80
1H-Benz[e]inden-3-ol, 6-ethenyldodeca-hydro-7-isocyanato-3a,6-dimethyl-, [3S-(3α,3aα,5aβ,6β,7β,9aα,9bβ)]-	n.s.g.	203(2.99)	33-2380-80
$C_{18}H_{27}NO_3$ 2-Azaandrostan-3-one, 4,5-epoxy-17-hy-droxy-, (4α,5α,17β)-	n.s.g.	207(3.65),270(2.30)	33-0486-80
2-Aza-B-homo-A-norandrostane-3,6-dione, 17-hydroxy-, (17β)-	n.s.g. + NaOH	212(3.19),260(3.18) 293(3.73)	33-0486-80 33-0486-80
ferric complex	EtOH	600(2.86)	33-0486-80

Compound	Solvent	$\lambda_{max}(\log \epsilon)$	Ref.
3-Pyridinecarboxylic acid, 1,4-dihydro-5-nonyl-4-oxo-1-(2-propenyl)-	EtOH	262(4.02),283(3.68)	4-0359-80
$C_{18}H_{27}NO_7$ 3,6,9,12,15-Pentaoxa-19-azabicyclo-[15.3.1]heneicosa-1(21),17-diene-2,16-dione, 18,19,20-trimethyl-	MeOH	222(4.10),289(4.23), 380(3.85)	44-2854-80
3,6,9,12,15-Pentaoxa-19-azabicyclo-[15.3.1]heneicosa-17,20-diene-2,16-dione, 18,19,20-trimethyl-	MeOH	232(4.16),264(3.96), 360(3.79)	44-2854-80
$C_{18}H_{28}$ Benzene, 1-(4-methyl-4-pentenyl)-4-(4-methylpentyl)-	hexane	255s(2.39),260(2.57), 266(2.69),268(2.60), 275(2.73)	18-0709-80
$C_{18}H_{28}N_2O$ 1H-Indole-3-ethanamine, 5-methoxy-2-methyl-N,N-dipropyl-, mono-hydrochloride	EtOH	226(4.35),284(3.88), 294(3.85)	8-0245-80
$C_{18}H_{28}N_2O_{11}$ α-D-Glucopyranosiduronic acid, [(1,1-dimethylethyl)nitrosoamino]methyl methyl ester, 2,3,4-triacetate	MeOH	234(3.71),300(2.26)	89-0400-80
$C_{18}H_{28}N_2S_4$ 1-Propanamine, N,N'-[dithiobis(carbono-thioyl-2-cyclopentyl-1-ylidene)]bis-	$CHCl_3$	315(3.76),416(4.39)	118-0566-80
$C_{18}H_{28}N_3O_5$ 1,3,8-Triazaspiro[4.5]decyloxy, 7,7,9,9-tetramethyl-3-[3-[(2-methyl-1-oxo-2-propenyl)oxy]propyl]-2,4-dioxo-polymer	MeOH	236s(3.54),432(0.85)	126-0595-80
	$CHCl_3$	442(0.83)	126-0595-80
$C_{18}H_{28}O$ 3-Buten-2-one, 4-(decahydro-5,5,8a-tri-methyl-2-methylene-1-naphthalenyl)-, [1S-[1α(E),4aβ,8aα]]-	EtOH	224(4.33),280s(2.57)	94-3452-80
$C_{18}H_{28}OS$ 19-Thiabicyclo[14.2.1]nonadeca-16,18-dien-2-one	MeCN	295(4.04)	44-1906-80
$C_{18}H_{28}O_2$ 4H-1,3-Benzodioxin, 2,4-dipentyl-	EtOH	216(3.9),273(3.3), 280(3.3)	118-0724-80
2(1H)-Naphthalenone, 4a,5,6,7,8,8a-hexahydro-3,4a,8,8-tetramethyl-4-(3-oxobutyl)-, (4aS-trans)-	EtOH	249(4.17)	65-0162-80
$C_{18}H_{28}O_2S$ 4-Thiepincarboxylic acid, 2,7-bis(1,1-dimethylethyl)-5-methyl-, ethyl ester	C_6H_{12}	234(4.11),356(2.95)	128-0615-80
$C_{18}H_{28}O_3$ 5,9-Methanobenzocycloocten-4(1H)-one, 2,3,5,6,7,8,9,10-octahydro-3,5-di-hydroxy-2,2,7,7,9-pentamethyl-	n.s.g.	250(3.90)	39-0733-80C

Compound	Solvent	$\lambda_{max}(\log \epsilon)$	Ref.
$C_{18}H_{28}O_4$			
1,4-Cyclohexadiene-1,2-dicarboxylic acid, 4,5-dimethyl-, bis(1,1-dimethylethyl) ester	EtOH	254(3.04)	24-0531-80
3-Decanone, 1-(3,4-dimethoxyphenyl)-5-hydroxy-	EtOH	229(3.86),279(3.42)	39-2637-80C
$C_{18}H_{28}O_{11}$			
Lamioside	n.s.g.	208(3.6)	100-0649-80
$C_{18}H_{29}NO_3$			
3-Pyridinecarboxaldehyde, 5-(1,1-dimethylethyl)-6-(2,2-dimethyl-1-oxopropyl)-1,6-dihydro-6-hydroxy-1-(1-methylethyl)-	C_6H_{12}	390(3.36)	88-4097-80
3-Pyridinecarboxylic acid, 5-decyl-1,4-dihydro-4-oxo-, ethyl ester	EtOH	256s(3.84),261(3.86), 287(3.64)	4-0359-80
3-Pyridinecarboxylic acid, 5-decyl-1-ethyl-1,4-dihydro-4-oxo-	EtOH	261(4.10),288(3.66)	4-0359-80
$C_{18}H_{29}NO_6Si$			
1H-Pyrrole-2,5-dione, 3-[5-O-[(1,1-dimethylethyl)dimethylsilyl]-2,3-O-(1-methylethylidene)-β-D-ribofuranosyl]-	EtOH	222(4.13),275s(3.15)	23-2024-80
$C_{18}H_{30}$			
Benzene, 1,3,5-tris(1-methylpropyl)-	MeCN	204(4.01),213s(3.93), 258s(2.20),263(2.28), 268(2.18)	108-0142-80
$C_{18}H_{30}CuN_4O_4S_2$			
Copper, bis[ethyl (1-piperidinylthioxomethyl)carbamato-O',S^N]-	CHCl$_3$	258(4.52),282s(4.17), 348(3.73),426s(3.28), 570(2.45)	97-0268-80
$C_{18}H_{30}N_4NiO_4S_2$			
Nickel, bis[ethyl (1-piperidinylthioxomethyl)carbamato-O',S^N]-	CHCl$_3$	257(4.34),282(4.39), 323(3.68),428s(2.06), 520(2.10)	97-0268-80
$C_{18}H_{30}O$			
1(2H)-Decalenone, 3,4,5,6,7,8,9,10,11-12,13,14,15,16-tetradecahydro-, (E)-(±)-	hexane	307(1.78)	44-3229-80
isomer	hexane	240(2.99),315(1.90)	44-3229-80
$C_{18}H_{30}O_3$			
1,3,5-Benzenetrimethanol, α,α',α''-triethyl-α,α',α''-trimethyl-	MeCN	197(4.69),214(3.92), 243(2.08),248(2.26), 254(2.34),260(2.32), 264s(2.18),268s(2.00)	108-0142-80
5,9-Methanobenzocyclooctene-3,4,5-triol, 1,2,3,4,5,6,7,8,9,10-decahydro-2,2,7,7,9-pentamethyl-	n.s.g.	208(3.66)	39-0733-80C
$C_{18}H_{31}N_3O_3$			
3,5-Isoxazoledicarboxamide, N,N'-dibutyl-4-pentyl-	MeOH	245(4.00)	94-0479-80

Compound	Solvent	$\lambda_{max}(\log \epsilon)$	Ref.
$C_{18}H_{32}O_3$ Cyclopentadecanecarboxylic acid, 2-oxo-, ethyl ester	$CHCl_3$	245(3.02)	103-0711-80
$C_{18}H_{33}N_3O_4$ 3,5-Isoxazoledicarboxamide, N,N'-dibutyl-4,5-dihydro-4-pentyl-, 2-oxide, trans	MeOH	257(3.90)	94-0479-80
$C_{18}H_{36}N_4O_6S_2$ 1,9,12,15,23,26-Hexaoxa-4,6,18,20-tetra-azacyclooctacosane-5,19-dithione	H_2O MeOH	209(4.38),237(4.38) 209(4.30),243(4.33)	104-1124-80 104-1124-80
$C_{18}H_{36}N_4S_2$ 1,3,12,14-Tetraazacyclodocosane-2,13-dithione	MeOH	211(4.38),242(4.29)	104-1124-80
$C_{18}H_{36}O_2P_2$ Phosphine, (1,2-dioxo-1,2-ethanediyl)-bis[bis(1,1-dimethylethyl)-	n.s.g.	610(2.19)	49-0749-80
$C_{18}H_{38}NO_4P$ Phosphonic acid, [2-(diethylamino)-2-oxoethyl]-, dihexyl ester	n.s.g.	215(3.63)	90-1029-80
$C_{18}H_{38}Se_2$ Diselenide, bis[(1,1-dimethylethyl)-2,2-dimethylpropyl]	n.s.g.	319(2.46)	23-0016-80
$C_{18}H_{44}Si_4$ Silane, [2,3-bis[(trimethylsilyl)methyl]-2-butene-1,4-diyl]bis[trimethyl-	hexane	238(3.78)	35-4429-80
$C_{18}H_{54}HgSi_8$ Mercury, bis[2,2,2-trimethyl-1,1-bis-(trimethylsilyl)disilanyl]-	C_6H_{12} THF	205(5.00),249s(4.48), 258s(4.40),275s(4.15), 342(2.88),390(2.36) 251s(4.42),278s(3.88), 341(2.86),390(2.26)	101-0169-80N 101-0169-80N

Compound	Solvent	$\lambda_{max}(\log \epsilon)$	Ref.
$C_{19}HF_{15}N_4$ Formazan, 1,3,5-tris(pentafluorophenyl)-	hexane	268(4.24),446(4.13)	103-0882-80
$C_{19}H_4F_{11}N$ Benzenamine, N-[bis(pentafluorophenyl)-methylene]-2-fluoro-	EtOH	236s(4.24),335(3.51)	70-1149-80
$C_{19}H_6F_{10}N_4$ Formazan, 1,5-bis(pentafluorophenyl)-3-phenyl-	hexane	285(4.3),495(4.0)	103-0882-80
$C_{19}H_7F_8NOS$ 10H-Phenothiazine, 1,2,3,4,6,7,8,9-octafluoro-10-(4-methoxyphenyl)-, 5-oxide	EtOH	207(4.45),228(4.50), 290(3.86),322(3.76)	104-0905-80
$C_{19}H_7F_8NO_2S$ 10H-Phenothiazine, 1,2,3,4,6,7,8,9-octafluoro-10-(4-methoxyphenyl)-, 5-oxide	EtOH	232(4.52),280s(3.78), 290(3.83),322(3.76)	104-0905-80
$C_{19}H_{10}ClNO_4$ 1,3(2H,4H)-Isoquinolinedione, 4-(3-chloro-1,4-dihydro-1,4-dioxo-2-naphthalenyl)-	EtOH	207(4.34),307(4.19), 385(3.46)	2-0836-80
$C_{19}H_{11}BrN_2O_2$ 1H-Indolo[1,2-a]pyrrolo[3,4-c]quinoline-1,3(2H)-dione, 13-bromo-2-methyl-	CHCl$_3$	297(4.48),405(3.71), 525(3.55)	24-2884-80
$C_{19}H_{11}Cl_2N_3O$ Acetamide, N-(2,9-dichloro-11-cyano-11H-indeno[1,2-c]isoquinolin-5-yl)-	EtOH	230s(4.44),243s(4.45), 272(4.62),330(4.18), 356s(3.92),422s(3.58), 458s(3.45),540s(3.00)	18-2885-80
Acetamide, N-(3,8-dichloro-11-cyano-11H-indeno[1,2-c]isoquinolin-5-yl)-	EtOH	220(4.49),234(4.48), 265(4.51),282(4.45), 303(4.31),320(4.22), 330(4.20),366(3.92), 428(3.56),460s(3.40)	18-2885-80
$C_{19}H_{12}BrNO_2$ Furo[2,3-c]pyridin-2(6H)-one, 3-(4-bromophenyl)-6-phenyl-	EtOH	210(4.37),239(3.95), 280(3.95),395(4.42)	39-1176-80C
Furo[3,2-b]pyridin-2(4H)-one, 3-(4-bromophenyl)-4-phenyl-	EtOH	210(4.40),255(4.25), 292(4.04),384(4.22)	39-1176-80C
$C_{19}H_{12}BrNO_4$ 3H-Dibenzo[f,ij]isoquinoline-2,7-dione, 1-acetoxy-6-bromo-3-methyl-	n.s.g.	352(3.92),400(3.81)	124-0755-80
$C_{19}H_{12}Br_2N_2O_2$ 1H-Pyrrole-2,5-dione, 3-bromo-4-(3-bromo-1-phenyl-1H-indol-2-yl)-1-methyl-	CHCl$_3$	277(4.16),377(3.67), 425(3.60)	24-2884-80
$C_{19}H_{12}ClN_3O$ 8H-1,2,4-Oxadiazino[4,5-a]perimidine, 11-(3-chlorophenyl)-	MeOH	232(4.43),328(3.96)	118-0155-80
8H-1,2,4-Oxadiazino[4,5-a]perimidine, 11-(4-chlorophenyl)-	MeOH	232(4.50),328(3.99)	118-0155-80

Compound	Solvent	$\lambda_{max}(\log \epsilon)$	Ref.
$C_{19}H_{12}Cl_3NO_2$			
Benzoic acid, 2-(phenylamino)-, 2,4,5-trichlorophenyl ester	MeOH	212(4.52),222(4.59), 240(4.24),286(4.14), 410(3.98)	73-3593-80
$C_{19}H_{12}F_3NO_2$			
Isoquinolinium, 1-benzoyl-3,3,3-trifluoro-2-oxopropylide	50% EtOH	234(4.69),310(4.13), 390s(3.18)	104-0729-80
	85% EtOH	395(--)	104-0729-80
	$CHCl_3$	405(--)	104-0729-80
Quinolinium, 1-benzoyl-3,3,3-trifluoro-2-oxopropylide	50% EtOH	238(--),312(4.26), 395(2.85)	104-0729-80
	85% EtOH	405(--)	104-0729-80
	$CHCl_3$	442(--)	104-0729-80
$C_{19}H_{12}N_2$			
Benzo[f]indolo[6,5-b]quinoline	MeOH	226(4.39),240(4.11), 253(4.11),262(4.11), 294(4.36),312s(4.23), 358s(3.42),376(3.69), 397(3.77)	39-1233-80C
	MeOH-acid	248s(4.02),306(4.28), 415(3.67)	39-1233-80C
$C_{19}H_{12}N_2O_2$			
1-Azulenecarbonitrile, 2-[2-(4-nitrophenyl)ethenyl]-	MeOH	233(4.27),286(4.20), 333(4.72),404(4.59), 424(4.48)	18-3276-80
$C_{19}H_{12}N_2O_3$			
3-Pyridinecarbonitrile, 4-(1,3-benzodioxol-5-yl)-1,2-dihydro-2-oxo-6-phenyl-	pH 13	258(4.48),358(4.29)	4-1521-80
	EtOH	259(4.31),289(3.95), 368(4.14)	4-1521-80
	$CHCl_3$	260(4.32),298(4.04), 368(4.21)	4-1521-80
$C_{19}H_{12}N_2O_4$			
Furo[2,3-c]pyridin-2(6H)-one, 3-(4-nitrophenyl)-6-phenyl-	EtOH	208(4.30),242(4.04), 432(4.36)	39-1176-80C
$C_{19}H_{12}N_4$			
2-Butenedinitrile, 2-amino-3-[(2,3-diphenyl-2-cyclopropen-1-ylidene)amino]-, (Z)-	MeCN	238(4.20),262(4.13), 334(4.46)	88-3751-80
1H-Imidazole-4,5-dicarbonitrile, 2-(1,2-diphenylethenyl)-, (E)-	MeCN	224(4.24),305(4.32)	88-3751-80
1H-Imidazo[4,5-f][1,8]phenanthroline, 2-phenyl-	MeOH	250(4.14),283(4.08), 442(3.40)	56-2365-80
$C_{19}H_{12}N_4O$			
1,2,4-Triazolo[3,4-b][1,3,4]oxadiazole, 6-(2-naphthalenyl)-3-phenyl-	EtOH	260(4.67),298(4.35)	4-1691-80
$C_{19}H_{12}N_4OS$			
1,3,5-Triazino[1',2':1,6]pyrido[3,4-b]-indol-2(7H)-one, 3,4-dihydro-3-phenyl-4-thioxo-	MeOH	223(4.42),265(4.62)	2-0042-80
$C_{19}H_{12}N_4O_3$			
8H-1,2,4-Oxadiazino[4,5-a]perimidine, 11-(3-nitrophenyl)-	MeOH	233(4.68),331(4.20)	118-0155-80

Compound	Solvent	$\lambda_{max}(\log \epsilon)$	Ref.
8H-1,2,4-Oxadiazino[4,5-a]perimidine, 11-(4-nitrophenyl)-	MeOH	232(4.31)	118-0155-80
$C_{19}H_{12}N_4S$ 1,3,5-Triazino[1',2':1,6]pyrido[3,4-b]-indole-4(7H)-thione, 2-phenyl-	MeOH	211(4.10),236(4.15), 265(4.10),295(3.96), 350(3.44)	2-0045-80
$C_{19}H_{12}N_6O_5$ 2-Naphthalenol, 1-[[1-(2,4-dinitro-phenyl)-1H-pyrazol-3-yl]azo]-	CHCl₃	471(4.28)	104-1143-80
$C_{19}H_{12}N_6O_8$ 1-Pyrrolidineacetonitrile, α-(2,4,5,7-tetranitro-9H-fluoren-9-ylidene)-	MeCN	356(4.20),440(4.04), 538(4.04)	104-0740-80
$C_{19}H_{12}N_6O_9$ 4-Morpholineacetonitrile, α-(2,4,5,7-tetranitro-9H-fluoren-9-ylidene)-	MeCN	358(4.18),446(4.04), 530(4.04)	104-0740-80
$C_{19}H_{12}O$ 1H-Phenalen-1-one, 2-phenyl-	EtOH	232(4.23),253(4.30), 360(3.93),403(3.97)	44-3364-80
$C_{19}H_{12}O_2$ 1H,3H-Naphtho[1,8-cd]pyran-1-one, 3-(phenylmethylene)-	EtOH	225(4.37),234(4.39), 242(4.40),262(4.26), 271(4.15),310(4.20), 384(4.18)	44-3364-80
$C_{19}H_{12}O_4$ 1,4-Methanonaphthacene-6,11-dione, 1,4-dihydro-5,12-dihydroxy-	EtOH	210(4.34),220s(4.12), 247s(4.54),262(4.63), 474s(3.93),490(3.97), 524(3.75)	39-1007-80C
1,4-Methanonaphthacene-5,6,11,12-tetrone, 1,4,4a,12a-tetrahydro-	EtOH	237(4.15),263(4.04), 272s(4.00),278(3.85), 311(3.59),325(3.59), 356(3.66)	39-1007-80C
Naphtho[2,3-d]-1,3-dioxepin-6,11-dione, 4-phenyl-	EtOH	307(4.36),462(3.74)	138-0859-80
$C_{19}H_{12}O_5$ 5a,11a-Epoxy-1,4-methanonaphthacene-5,6,11,12-tetrone, 1,4,4a,12a-tetrahydro-	EtOH	209(3.95),237(4.35), 265(3.85),311(3.36)	39-1007-80C
$C_{19}H_{12}O_8$ Tephrosol monoacetate	MeOH	245(4.79),285(4.47), 315(4.13),355(4.34)	102-1272-80
$C_{19}H_{13}BrN_2O_2$ 1H-Pyrrole-2,5-dione, 3-bromo-1-methyl-4-(1-phenyl-1H-indol-2-yl)-	CHCl₃	277(4.23),412(3.86)	24-2884-80
$C_{19}H_{13}BrO_7$ 9,10-Anthracenedione, 5-acetoxy-2-(ace-toxymethyl)-1-bromo-4-hydroxy-	EtOH	230(4.35),247(4.42), 257(4.42),265s(4.36), 285(4.00),395s(3.79), 412(3.81),435(3.66)	44-0020-80

Compound	Solvent	$\lambda_{max}(\log \epsilon)$	Ref.
$C_{19}H_{13}Cl$ 1H-Cyclopent[a]aceanthrylene, 7-chloro-3a,11c-dihydro-	MeCN	253s(4.95),260(5.09), 335s(3.23),353s(3.57), 368(3.85),387(3.97), 409(3.86)	24-1458-80
$C_{19}H_{13}Cl_2N_3O_2$ 1(2H)-Quinolineacetamide, 6-chloro-4-(2-chlorophenyl)-3-cyano-N-methyl-2-oxo-	EtOH	216(4.68),245(4.62), 292(4.02),303(3.97), 375(3.78)	142-0635-80
$C_{19}H_{13}Cl_2N_3O_3$ 1H-Imidazo[1,5-a][1,4]benzodiazepine-3-carboxylic acid, 8-chloro-6-(2-chlorophenyl)-2,4-dihydro-1-oxo-, methyl ester	isoPrOH	223(4.64),276(4.32), 348s(3.04)	4-1697-80
$C_{19}H_{13}Cl_3N_2O_3$ Acetamide, N-[2,4,6-trichloro-5,8-di-hydro-7-[(4-methylphenyl)amino]-5,8-dioxo-1-naphthalenyl]-	EtOH	261(4.37),500(3.66)	40-1862-80
Acetamide, N-[2,4,7-trichloro-5,8-di-hydro-6-[(4-methylphenyl)amino]-5,8-dioxo-1-naphthalenyl]-	EtOH	273(4.37),500(3.69)	40-1862-80
$C_{19}H_{13}Cl_3N_2O_4$ Acetamide, N-[2,4,6-trichloro-5,8-di-hydro-7-[(4-methoxyphenyl)amino]-5,8-dioxo-1-naphthalenyl]-	EtOH	257(4.37),510(3.61)	40-1862-80
Acetamide, N-[2,4,7-trichloro-5,8-di-hydro-6-[(4-methoxyphenyl)amino]-5,8-dioxo-1-naphthalenyl]-	EtOH	278(4.37),510(3.66)	40-1862-80
$C_{19}H_{13}N$ 1-Azulenecarbonitrile, 2-(2-phenyl-ethenyl)-	MeOH	231(4.27),323(4.75), 335(4.83),388(4.15), 408(4.43),433(4.42), 558(2.72),589(2.75), 653(2.42)	18-3276-80
$C_{19}H_{13}NO$ Bicyclo[3.1.0]hex-2-ene-1-carbonitrile, 4-oxo-6,6-diphenyl-	C_6H_{12}	218s(4.19),262(3.59), 335(2.38),342(2.32), 370(2.22),388(1.83)	44-4864-80
Bicyclo[3.1.0]hex-2-ene-2-carbonitrile, 4-oxo-6,6-diphenyl-	C_6H_{12}	248(3.76),254s(3.74), 292(3.64),364(2.46), 382(2.50),401(2.34), 420(1.78)	44-4864-80
1,4-Cyclohexadiene-1-carbonitrile, 3-oxo-6,6-diphenyl-	EtOH	233(4.31),286s(3.38)	44-4864-80
$C_{19}H_{13}NO_2$ Furo[2,3-c]pyridin-2(6H)-one, 3,6-di-phenyl-	EtOH	211(4.35),267(3.98), 392(4.50)	39-1176-80C
Furo[3,2-b]pyridin-2(4H)-one, 3,4-di-phenyl-	EtOH	207(4.15),252(3.96), 292(3.81),304(3.96)	39-1176-80C
$C_{19}H_{13}NO_3$ 1H-Benz[f]indole-4,9-dione, 2-(4-nitro-phenyl)-	CHCl$_3$	283s(4.20),307(4.25), 349s(3.38),462(3.68)	39-2923-80C

Compound	Solvent	$\lambda_{max}(\log \epsilon)$	Ref.
$C_{19}H_{13}NO_4$			
Benzo[f]pyrido[1,2-a]indole-12-carboxylic acid, 6,11-dihydro-6,11-dioxo-, ethyl ester	EtOH	254(4.67),278s(4.20), 317(4.10),327s(4.06), 349(3.86),460(3.80)	150-0139-80
3H-Dibenz[f,ij]isoquinoline-2,7-dione, 1-acetoxy-3-methyl-	n.s.g.	350(4.09),393(3.88)	124-0755-80
Spiro[5aH-cyclopenta[d]pyrido[2,1-b]-[1,3]oxazine-4(3H),2'-[2H]indene]-1',3,3'-trione, 1,2-dihydro-	MeCN	229(4.71),251(4.36), 340(4.04)	4-1577-80
$C_{19}H_{13}NO_5$			
6H-Benzo[a]pyrrolo[2,1,5-de]quinolizine-4,5-dicarboxylic acid, 6-oxo-, dimethyl ester	CHCl$_3$	263(4.73),307(3.78), 319(3.78),337(3.71), 353(3.87),397(4.28), 418(4.38)	103-0506-80
Dibenzo[de,g]quinolin-7-one, 1,2-dimethoxy-9,10-(methylenedioxy)-	EtOH	243(4.44),264s(4.38), 272(4.46),288s(4.22), 318(3.90),357(3.96), 378s(3.90),426(3.56)	95-0337-80
Dibenzo[de,g]quinolin-7-one, 8,9-dimethoxy-1,2-(methylenedioxy)-	EtOH	249(4.49),276(4.40), 380(3.82),440(4.21)	102-2735-80
Dicentrinone	EtOH	249(4.36),271(4.27), 309s(3.84),348(3.86), 387(3.75),418(3.72)	102-0998-80
	EtOH-HCl	260(4.41),290(4.31), 378(4.01),494(3.38)	102-0998-80
$C_{19}H_{13}N_3O$			
Acetamide, N-(11-cyano-11H-indeno[1,2-c]isoquinolin-5-yl)-	EtOH	212(4.48),261(4.53), 293(4.11),301(4.11), 314(4.14),357(3.83), 420(3.26),460s(3.11)	18-2885-80
6H-Benz[h]indolo[5,6-b][1,6]naphthyridin-6-one, 5,9-dihydro-5-methyl-	MeOH	230(4.65),302(4.69), 380(4.04)	39-0512-80C
	MeOH-acid	230(4.84),300(4.67), 330(4.75),425(4.34)	39-0512-80C
1,2,4-Benzotriazin-7(1H)-one, 1,3-diphenyl-	MeOH	299(4.52),330s(4.14), 540(3.69)	24-1205-80
8H-[1,2,4]Oxadiazino[4,5-a]perimidine, 11-phenyl-	MeOH	231(4.40),328(4.02)	118-0155-80
$C_{19}H_{13}OS_2$			
Pyrylium, 4-phenyl-2,6-di-2-thienyl-, perchlorate	C$_2$H$_4$Cl$_2$	334(4.31),385(4.56), 480(4.45)	150-4041-80
$C_{19}H_{14}$			
Naphth[2,1-a]azulene, 2-methyl-	MeOH	270(3.89),316(4.54), 326(4.59),379(3.89), 395(3.91),599(2.00), 638(2.08)	138-0167-80
$C_{19}H_{14}BrNO_5$			
1,2-Indolizinedicarboxylic acid, 3-benzoyl-5-bromo-, dimethyl ester	CHCl$_3$	240(4.58),295s(4.20), 353(3.99),412(3.45)	103-0506-80
$C_{19}H_{14}BrN_3O_2S$			
4(3H)-Quinazolinone, 6-bromo-3-[4-(4-methoxyphenyl)-2-thiazolyl]-2-methyl-	n.s.g.	287(3.85),340(3.70)	18-2389-80
$C_{19}H_{14}ClNO_2$			
11-Azatricyclo[5.3.1.0^{2,6}]undeca-3,9-	CHCl$_3$	260(4.18),340(4.28)	39-0362-80C

Compound	Solvent	$\lambda_{max}(\log \epsilon)$	Ref.
dien-8-one, 11-[3-(4-chlorophenyl)-3-oxo-1-propenyl]-, endo (cont.)			39-0362-80C
$C_{19}H_{14}ClNO_3$ 2H,5H-Pyrano[3,2-c][1]benzopyran-2-one, 3-chloro-4-(methylphenylamino)-	EtOH	241(4.17),279(3.91), 318s(3.75),374(4.31)	4-0061-80
$C_{19}H_{14}Cl_2$ 7,8:9,10-Dibenzotricyclo[4.2.2.1^{2,5}]-undeca-3,7,9-triene, 1,6-dichloro-	MeCN	262(2.75),271(2.90), 279(3.04)	24-1458-80
8,9:10,11-Dibenzotricyclo[5.2.2.0^{2,6}]-undeca-3,8,10-triene, 1,7-dichloro-	MeCN	255s(2.57),263(2.73), 270(2.79)	24-1458-80
$C_{19}H_{14}Cl_2O_4$ 2-Propenoic acid, 3,3'-(methylenedi-4,1-phenylene)bis[2-chloro-	film	272(3.83)	104-2207-80
$C_{19}H_{14}Cl_3NO_2$ 2,3-Pyrrolidinedione, 1-[2-(4-chloro-phenyl)ethyl]-4-[(3,4-dichlorophen-yl)methylene]-	EtOH	323(4.27)	145-1135-80
$C_{19}H_{14}F_3NO_3S_2$ Benz[c]indolium, 1-methyl-5-mercapto-2-phenyl-1,5-dihydro-, trifluoro-methanesulfonate	CH_2Cl_2	253(4.45),350(4.31), 454(4.65),358(4.26)	83-0977-80
$C_{19}H_{14}F_3NO_4S$ Benz[cd]indolium, 1,5-dihydro-5-hydr-oxy-1-methyl-2-phenyl-, trifluoro-methanesulfonate	CH_2Cl_2	258(4.29),343(4.06), 434(4.47),538(3.44)	83-0977-80
$C_{19}H_{14}NO_4$ Pyridinium, 1-[2-(2,3-dihydro-2-hydr-oxy-1,3-dioxo-1H-inden-2-yl)-3-oxo-1-cyclopenten-1-yl]-, chloride	MeOH-HCl	233(4.71),250s(4.30)	4-1577-80
$C_{19}H_{14}N_2O$ 3-Pyridinecarbonitrile, 1,2-dihydro-4-(3-methylphenyl)-2-oxo-6-phenyl-	pH 13	252(4.53),356(4.37)	4-1521-80
	EtOH	255(4.30),288s(3.77), 364(4.10)	4-1521-80
	CHCl₃	256(4.32),286s(3.80), 366(4.14)	4-1521-80
3-Pyridinecarbonitrile, 1,2-dihydro-4-(4-methylphenyl)-2-oxo-6-phenyl-	pH 13	256(4.33),354(4.15)	4-1521-80
	EtOH	257(4.21),296(3.90), 365(4.07)	4-1521-80
	CHCl₃	259(4.23),310(3.97), 367(4.11)	4-1521-80
3-Pyridinecarbonitrile, 1,2-dihydro-6-(4-methylphenyl)-2-oxo-4-phenyl-	pH 13	257(4.31),357(4.22)	4-1521-80
	EtOH	260(4.29),370(4.26)	4-1521-80
	CCl₄	261(4.31),291s(3.97), 359(4.09)	4-1521-80
$C_{19}H_{14}N_2O_2$ [1,1'-Biphenyl]-4-amine, N-[(4-nitro-phenyl)methylene]-	THF	365(4.26)	56-1177-80
3-Pyridinecarbonitrile, 1,2-dihydro-4-(4-methoxyphenyl)-2-oxo-6-phenyl-	pH 13	256(4.51),356(4.35)	4-1521-80
	EtOH	256(4.34),338(4.28), 357s(4.27)	4-1521-80
	CHCl₃	257(4.10),344(4.08), 362s(4.03)	4-1521-80

Compound	Solvent	$\lambda_{max}(\log \epsilon)$	Ref.
$C_{19}H_{14}N_2O_2S$			
5H-Imidazo[2,1-b][1,3]thiazinium, 6,7-dihydro-1-methyl-5,7-dioxo-2,6-diphenyl-, hydroxide, inner salt	MeOH	206(4.45),253(4.45)	44-2474-80
$C_{19}H_{14}N_2O_3$			
1-Azulenecarboxamide, 2-[2-(4-nitrophenyl)ethenyl]-	MeOH	230(4.97),284(4.50), 327(4.59),404(4.55)	18-3276-80
Benzenamine, N-[(4-nitrophenyl)methylene]-4-phenoxy-	THF	365(4.15)	56-1177-80
3-Pyridinecarbonitrile, 4-(1,3-benzodioxol-5-yl)-1,2,3,4-tetrahydro-2-oxo-6-phenyl-	pH 13	236(4.20),316(3.71), 352s(3.52)	4-1521-80
	EtOH	286(3.98),358(3.21)	4-1521-80
	CCl$_4$	286(3.86),358(3.12)	4-1521-80
$C_{19}H_{14}N_2O_5$			
2H-Pyrano[3,2-c]pyridine-8-carboxylic acid, 3-cyano-5,6-dihydro-7-methyl-2,5-dioxo-6-phenyl-, ethyl ester	EtOH	378(4.22)	49-0093-80
$C_{19}H_{14}N_2O_6$			
Indeno[1,2-b]pyran-2-carboxylic acid, 4,5-dihydro-4-(tetrahydro-1,3-dimethyl-2,4,6-trioxo-5(2H)-pyrimidinylidene)-	dioxan	254(4.07),329(4.08), 461(4.35)	83-0557-80
$C_{19}H_{14}N_3$			
1,2,4-Benzotriazinium, 1,3-diphenyl-, perchlorate	HCOOH	282(4.57),303s(4.17), 358(3.73),447s(3.50)	24-1205-80
1,2,4-Benzotriazinyl, 1,?-dihydro-1,3-diphenyl-	MeOH	260s(4.51),268(4.53), 320(3.86),375(4.71), 420(4.39),500(4.10), 565s(3.78)	70-1159-80
1,2,4-Benzotriazin-4(1H)-yl, 1,3-diphenyl-	MeOH	264s(4.56),267(4.57), 318(3.86),367(3.73), 420s(3.41),490(3.09), 550s(2.77)	24-12105-80
$C_{19}H_{14}N_4$			
2H-Benzotriazole, 2-[4-[2-(3-pyridinyl)ethenyl]phenyl]-	DMF	349(4.72)	33-1311-80
2-Butenedinitrile, 2-amino-3-[(2,3-diphenyl-2-propenylidene)amino]-, (Z,?,E)-	MeCN	232(4.06),270(3.87), 372(4.56)	88-3751-80
Propanedinitrile, [4-[cyano[4-(dimethylamino)phenyl]methylene]-2,5-cyclohexadien-1-ylidene]-	EtOH	280(4.3),325(4.3), 410s(3.9),480(4.0), 700(4.7)	104-1612-80
$C_{19}H_{14}N_4O_2$			
2-Naphthalenecarboxamide, N-(1,5-dihydro-5-oxo-3-phenyl-4H-1,2,4-triazol-4-yl)-	EtOH	234(4.79)	4-1691-80
2,4(1H,3H)-Pteridinedione, 1-methyl-6,7-diphenyl-	pH -5.5	245(4.23),298(3.95), 415(4.05)	142-0437-80B
	pH 0.0	220(4.35),277(4.13), 365(4.09)	142-0437-80B
2,4(1H,3H)-Pteridinedione, 3-methyl-6,7-diphenyl-	pH -5.5	247(4.28),280(4.00), 410(4.14)	142-0437-80B
	pH 0.0	223(4.45),272(4.12), 363(4.19)	142-0437-80B

Compound	Solvent	$\lambda_{max}(\log \epsilon)$	Ref.
2,4(1H,3H)-Pteridinedione, 8-methyl-6,7-diphenyl-	pH -3.0	240s(4.05),255(4.04), 286(4.09),400(4.05)	142-0437-80B
$C_{19}H_{14}N_6O_5$			
2-Naphthalenol, 1-[[1-(2,4-dinitrophenyl)-4,5-dihydro-1H-pyrazol-3-yl]azo]-	CHCl$_3$	535(4.61)	104-1143-80
$C_{19}H_{14}N_6O_8$			
Acetonitrile, (diethylamino)(2,4,5,7-tetranitro-9H-fluoren-9-ylidene)-	MeCN	356(4.20),444(4.04), 530(4.08)	104-0740-80
$C_{19}H_{14}O$			
1-Azulenecarboxaldehyde, 2-(2-phenylethenyl)-	CH$_2$Cl$_2$	345(4.67),365s(4.58), 405(4.02)	18-3696-80
7H-Benzocyclotridecen-7-one, 12,13,14-15-tetradehydro-6,11-dimethyl-	ether	232s(4.49),265s(4.52), 276(4.60),290s(4.40), 378(3.52)	39-0466-80C
7H-Benzocyclotridecen-7-one, 12,13,14-15-tetradehydro-8,11-dimethyl-	ether	235s(4.39),275(4.62), 290s(4.48),380(3.47)	39-0466-80C
	CF$_3$COOH	282s(--),293(--), 346s(--),420s(--)	39-0466-80C
5H-Fluorantheno[3,2-b]pyran, 6,7-dihydro-	EtOH	224(4.59),248(4.61), 278(4.21),289(4.43), 316(3.72),331(3.97), 360(3.86),392(3.83)	23-0051-80
9H-Xanthene, 9-phenyl-	ether	213(4.56),246(3.87), 279(3.38)	35-4659-80
$C_{19}H_{14}O_2$			
5,6-Benzoflavanone	isoPrOH	312(3.88),340(3.62)	18-2938-80
7,8-Benzoflavanone	isoPrOH	280(3.85),360(3.68)	18-2938-80
Ethanone, 1,1'-(4H-cyclopenta[def]phenanthrene-1,5-diyl)bis-	C$_6$H$_{12}$	244(4.51),258(4.58), 322(4.08)	44-1783-80
Ethanone, 1,1'-(4H-cyclopenta[def]phenanthrene-1,6-diyl)bis-	C$_6$H$_{12}$	267(4.63),275(4.62), 286(4.78),330(3.78)	44-1783-80
Ethanone, 1,1'-(4H-cyclopenta[def]phenanthrene-1,7-diyl)bis-	C$_6$H$_{12}$	257(4.48),301(3.98), 330(4.60)	44-1783-80
Ethanone, 1,1'-(4H-cyclopenta[def]phenanthrene-2,6-diyl)bis-	C$_6$H$_{12}$	277(4.79),298(4.25), 317(4.23)	44-1783-80
1-Naphthalenecarboxylic acid, 8-(2-phenylethenyl)-, (E)-	EtOH	231(4.78),272(4.30), 328(4.40)	44-3364-80
1H,3H-Naphtho[1,8-cd]pyran-1-one, 3-(phenylmethyl)-	EtOH	215(4.91),237(4.42), 307(3.41)	44-3364-80
$C_{19}H_{14}O_3$			
1,3-Benzodioxol-5-ol, 2,2-diphenyl-	EtOH	233(3.56),299(3.73)	12-0527-80
$C_{19}H_{14}O_4$			
4H-1-Benzopyran-4-one, 3-(2-benzofuranyl)-6-ethyl-7-hydroxy-	EtOH	285(4.68),295(4.67)	103-0685-80
1,4-Methanonaphthacene-5,12-dione, 1,4,4a,12a-tetrahydro-6,11-dihydroxy-	EtOH	204(4.10),245(4.41), 255(4.43),281(4.36), 289(4.33),386s(3.97), 405(4.12),425(4.13)	39-1007-80C
5,12-Naphthacenedione, 7,10-dihydro-6,11-dihydroxy-8-methyl-	EtOH	209(3.98),227(3.93), 258(4.29),285s(3.68), 325(3.23),456(3.66), 485(3.77),515(3.64)	39-1007-80C
5,6,11,12-Naphthacenetetrone, 1,4,4a-12a-tetrahydro-2-methyl-	EtOH	218(4.27),233(4.26), 257(4.23),322(3.63), 400(3.20),420(3.00)	39-1007-80C

Compound	Solvent	λ_{max}(log ϵ)	Ref.
2H-Pyran-2-one, 4-hydroxy-6-methyl-3-[3-(1-naphthalenyl)-1-oxo-2-propenyl]-	MeOH	326(4.1)	83-0344-80
2H-Pyran-2-one, 4-hydroxy-6-methyl-3-[3-(2-naphthalenyl)-1-oxo-2-propenyl]-	MeOH	363(4.3)	83-0344-80
$C_{19}H_{14}O_4S$			
Naphtho[2,3-b]-1,4-oxathiin-5,10-dione, 2,3-dihydro-2-methoxy-2-phenyl-	CHCl$_3$	275(4.31),250s(3.30), 446(3.32)	39-2923-80C
$C_{19}H_{14}O_5$			
6H-Benzo[b]naphtho[2,3-d]pyran-6-one, 7,12-dihydroxy-11-methoxy-2-methyl-	EtOH	200(4.44),220(4.44), 260(4.59),350(3.66), 365(3.77),395s(3.54), 415(3.70),435(3.64)	44-4071-80
5a,11a-Epoxynaphthacene-5,6,11,12-tetrone, 6a,7,10,10a-tetrahydro-8-methyl-	EtOH	212(3.95),234(4.11), 255(3.92),300s(3.32)	39-1007-80C
2-Propen-1-one, 3-(1,3-benzodioxol-5-yl)-1-(4-methoxy-5-benzofuranyl)-, (E)- (ovalitenin C)	MeOH	245(3.98),310s(--)	102-1558-80
$C_{19}H_{14}O_5S$			
11bH-Thiopyrano[4,3,2-kl]xanthene-2,3-dicarboxylic acid, dimethyl ester	dioxan	252(4.15),288(3.82), 353(3.87)	5-0867-80
$C_{19}H_{14}O_6$			
9,10-Anthracenedione, 1,3-diacetoxy-6-methyl-	MeOH	261(4.60),276s(4.17), 334(3.68)	12-1805-80
1,3-Propanedione, 1-(1,3-benzodioxol-5-yl)-3-(4-methoxy-5-benzofuranyl)-(ovalitenone)	EtOH	240(4.21),288(4.25), 363(4.36)	102-1199-80
$C_{19}H_{15}BrN_2O$			
Ethanone, 1-[4-[2-(4-bromophenyl)-2-phenylethenyl]-1H-pyrazol-3-yl]-	EtOH	237(3.95),316(4.05)	78-1331-80
$C_{19}H_{15}Br_2NO_2STe$			
Tellurilimine, Te,Te-bis(3-bromophenyl)-N-[(phenylmethyl)sulfonyl]-	MeOH	222(4.56),280(3.57)	104-2210-80
Tellurilimine, Te,Te-bis(4-bromophenyl)-N-[(phenylmethyl)sulfonyl]-	MeOH	252(4.46),276(4.14)	104-2210-80
$C_{19}H_{15}Cl$			
7,8:9,10-Dibenzotricyclo[4.2.2.1^{2,5}]-undeca-3,7,9-triene, 1-chloro-	MeCN	264(2.90),272(3.08), 280(3.22)	24-1458-80
8,9:10,11-Dibenzotricyclo[5.2.2.0^{2,6}]-undeca-3,8,10-triene, 1-chloro-	MeCN	251s(2.69),258(2.78), 264(2.91),271(2.99)	24-1458-80
$C_{19}H_{15}ClN_2O$			
3H-Pyrazol-3-one, 4-[3-(4-chlorophenyl)-2-propenylidene]-2,4-dihydro-5-methyl-2-phenyl-	n.s.g.	250(4.48),363(4.70), 490(3.19)	124-0642-80
$C_{19}H_{15}ClN_2O_3$			
Acetamide, N-[6-chloro-5,8-dihydro-7-[(4-methylphenyl)amino]-5,8-dioxo-1-naphthalenyl]-	EtOH	259(4.37),290(4.35), 431(3.81)	40-1862-80
Acetamide, N-[7-chloro-5,8-dihydro-6-[(4-methylphenyl)amino]-5,8-dioxo-1-naphthalenyl]-	EtOH	286(4.43),515(3.81)	40-1862-80

Compound	Solvent	λ_{max}(log ϵ)	Ref.
C$_{19}$H$_{15}$ClN$_4$O$_2$			
4H-1,2,4-Triazolo[4,3-a][1,4]benzodiaz- epin-4-ol, 8-chloro-1-methyl-6-phen- yl-, acetate	EtOH	223(4.58),248s(4.14), 270s(3.84),290s(3.61)	87-0643-80
C$_{19}$H$_{15}$Cl$_2$NO			
Methanone, [1-[(2,6-dichlorophenyl)- methyl]-1,4-dihydro-3-pyridinyl]- phenyl-	CH$_2$Cl$_2$	376(3.0)	64-1431-80B
C$_{19}$H$_{15}$Cl$_2$NO$_2$			
Methanone, [1-(2,6-dichlorophenyl)meth- yl]-1,6-dihydro-6-hydroxy-3-pyridin- yl]phenyl-	CH$_2$Cl$_2$	290s(4.5),326(4.5)	5-1350-80
2,3-Pyrrolidinedione, 1-[2-(4-chloro- phenyl)ethyl]-4-[(4-chlorophenyl)- methylene]-	EtOH	217(4.34),326(4.41)	145-1135-80
2,3-Pyrrolidinedione, 4-[(3,4-dichloro- phenyl)methylene]-1-(2-phenylethyl)-	EtOH	323(4.32)	145-1135-80
C$_{19}$H$_{15}$Cl$_2$NO$_2$S			
3-Thiophenecarboxamide, N-(4-chloro- phenyl)-5-[(4-chlorophenyl)methyl- ene]-2,5-dihydro-4-methoxy-, (Z)-	EtOH	235(4.23),265(4.21), 346s(--),357(4.41)	33-1542-80
3-Thiophenecarboxamide, N-(4-chloro- phenyl)-5-[(4-chlorophenyl)methyl]- 4-methoxy-	EtOH	272(4.35)	33-1542-80
C$_{19}$H$_{15}$Cl$_2$NO$_2$STe			
Tellurilimine, Te,Te-bis(3-chlorophen- yl)-N-[(phenylmethyl)sulfonyl]-	MeOH	220(4.46),280(3.55)	104-2210-80
Tellurilimine, Te,Te-bis(4-chlorophen- yl)-N-[(phenylmethyl)sulfonyl]-	MeOH	244(4.32),274(3.80)	104-2210-80
C$_{19}$H$_{15}$Cl$_2$NO$_3$			
2H,5H-Pyrano[3,2-c][1]benzopyran-2-one, 3,3-dichloro-3,4-dihydro-4-(methyl- phenylamino)-	EtOH	217(4.20),247(4.17), 279s(3.77),326s(3.41)	4-0061-80
C$_{19}$H$_{15}$FeN			
Ferrocene, (3H-indol-3-ylidenemethyl)-, perchlorate	CHCl$_3$	302(5.04),432(5.07), 640(5.05)	65-2039-80
C$_{19}$H$_{15}$IO$_4$S			
Benzo[b]thiophene-6-carboxylic acid, 4-acetoxy-2-iodo-7-(4-methylphenyl)-, methyl ester	MeOH	245(4.52),270(4.38), 310(3.85)	2-0156-80
C$_{19}$H$_{15}$N			
7,8:9,10-Dibenzobicyclo[4.2.2]deca- 3,7,9-triene-1-carbonitrile	MeCN	250s(2.48),256(2.63), 261(2.79),265s(2.61), 269(2.78)	24-1458-80
9,10-Ethanoanthracene-9(10H)-carbo- nitrile, 12-ethenyl-	MeCN	250s(2.62),257(2.79), 263(2.92),270(2.98)	24-1458-80
C$_{19}$H$_{15}$NO			
1-Azulenecarboxamide, 2-(phenylethen- yl)-	MeOH	318(4.64),327(4.72), 405(4.38),426(4.26)	18-3276-80
Azuleno[1,2-c]pyridin-1(2H)-one, 3,4-dihydro-3-phenyl-	MeOH	299(4.65),358(3.91), 376(3.95)	18-3276-80

Compound	Solvent	$\lambda_{max}(\log \epsilon)$	Ref.
$C_{19}H_{15}NO_2$			
Benz[a]acridine, 8,10-dimethoxy-	MeOH	218(4.26),226(4.41), 248s(4.06),278s(4.46), 287(4.60),295s(4.52), 330(3.34),344(3.39), 362(3.40),382(3.57), 402(3.61)	39-1233-80C
	MeOH-acid	231(4.51),266(3.89), 301(4.56),384(3.52), 400(3.61)	39-1233-80C
$C_{19}H_{15}NO_2S$			
2(1H)-Pyridinone, 3-benzoyl-4-(methyl-thio)-6-phenyl-	MeOH	250(4.40),330(3.87)	118-1022-80
$C_{19}H_{15}NO_3$			
Ethanone, 2-(5-methyl-2-furanyl)-1-phenyl-2-(phenylimino)-, N-oxide	MeOH	256(4.50),326(4.87)	73-3546-80
1(4H)-Naphthalenone, 4-[(4-acetylphen-yl)imino]-2-methoxy-	EtOH	250s(--),257(4.24), 299(4.49),340s(3.99), 426(3.62)	94-1207-80
$C_{19}H_{15}NO_3S$			
2H-Naphtho[2,3-b]-1,4-thiazine-5,10-di-one, 3,4-dihydro-3-methoxy-3-phenyl-	$CHCl_3$	290(4.39),355s(3.08), 520(3.33)	39-2923-80C
$C_{19}H_{15}NO_4$			
Cephardione B	EtOH	213(4.54),238(4.58), 244(4.58),274s(4.09), 303(4.15),316(4.18), 440(4.09)	95-0337-80
4H-Dibenzo[de,g]quinoline-4,5(6H)-dione, 2,10-dimethoxy-6-methyl-	MeOH	322(4.54),246(4.62), 322(4.01),473(3.92)	95-0337-80
Phenol, 2-[4-(2-benzofuranyl)-3-methyl-5-isoxazolyl]-5-methoxy-	EtOH	257(4.44),292(4.33)	103-0685-80
Phenol, 2-[4-(2-benzofuranyl)-5-methyl-3-isoxazolyl]-5-methoxy-	EtOH	278(4.32),290(4.31), 302(4.19)	103-0685-80
$C_{19}H_{15}NO_4S$			
2H-Naphtho[2,3-b]-1,4-thiazine-5,10-di-one, 3,4-dihydro-3-hydroxy-3-(4-meth-oxyphenyl)-	$CHCl_3$	285(4.46),352s(3.31), 500(3.44)	39-2923-80C
$C_{19}H_{15}NO_5$			
9H-Azuleno[1,2,3-ij]isoquinolin-9-one, 10-hydroxy-4,5,6-trimethoxy-(grandirubrine)	EtOH	232(4.96),254(4.79), 274s(4.66),296(4.58), 312s(4.46),343s(4.41), 363(4.72),384(4.41), 400(4.19),480(3.90)	142-0943-80
Dibenzo[cd,f]indol-4-one, 8,9-dimeth-oxy-N-methyl-1,2-(methylenedioxy)-	EtOH	213(4.48),245(4.60), 279s(4.51),290(4.62), 356(4.00),374(3.94), 396(3.88)	102-2735-80
Dibenzo[cd,f]indol-4-one, 1,2-dimeth-oxy-5-methyl-9,10-(methylenedioxy)-	EtOH	218(4.47),230s(4.50), 237(4.51),272s(4.42), 279(4.45),289s(4.50), 294s(4.53),301(4.70), 334s(3.82),366s(3.72), 387(3.79)	95-0337-80
7H-Dibenzo[de,g]quinolin-7-one, 10-hy-droxy-1,2,9-trimethoxy-	EtOH	244(4.35),274(4.32), 294s(4.12),359(3.82), 394s(3.73)	142-1131-80

Compound	Solvent	$\lambda_{max}(\log \epsilon)$	Ref.
5(4H)-Oxazolone, 4-[(4-acetoxy-3-meth-oxyphenyl)methylene]-2-phenyl-	dioxan	223(4.19),263(4.25), 361(4.43),380(4.58), 395(4.49)	70-0576-80
$C_{19}H_{15}NO_6$ 1,3-Dioxolo[4,5-g]isoquinoline-6(5H)-carboxaldehyde, 7,8-dihydro-5-[(4-hydroxy-1,3-benzodioxol-5-yl)meth-ylene]-, (Z)-	EtOH	220(4.33),263s(3.83), 330(3.93)	142-0585-80
Rugosinone	MeOH	237(4.57),298(4.13), 329(3.95)	100-0143-80
	MeOH-NaOMe	236(4.60),296(4.05), 327(3.79),380(3.65)	100-0143-80
$C_{19}H_{15}N_3$ 1,2,4-Benzotriazine, 1,4-dihydro-1,3-diphenyl-	MeOH-Pd-H_2	249(4.37),302(3.93), 340s(3.75),417(3.09)	24-1205-80
$C_{19}H_{15}N_3O$ Pyrimido[4,5-b]quinolin-4(10H)-one, 10-ethyl-2-phenyl-	EtOH	233(4.42),260(4.15), 271(4.21),298(4.39), 341(4.02),404s(3.67), 431(3.96),451(4.00)	94-3514-80
$C_{19}H_{15}N_3O_2$ 1,4-Benzenediamine, N-[(4-nitrophenyl)-methylene]-N'-phenyl-	THF	439(4.31)	56-1177-80
Furo[2,3-c]pyridin-2(6H)-one, 6-(4,6-dimethyl-2-pyrimidinyl)-3-phenyl-	EtOH	217(4.13),253(4.07), 407(4.52)	39-1176-80C
Furo[3,2-b]pyridin-2(4H)-one, 4-(4,6-dimethyl-2-pyrimidinyl)-3-phenyl-	EtOH	217(4.28),250(4.40), 285(4.11),402(4.20)	39-1176-80C
11H-Indeno[1,2-c]isoquinoline-11-carbo-nitrile, 5-amino-2,9-dimethoxy-, monohydrochloride	EtOH-H_2SO_4	216(4.40),252(4.34), 280(4.58),338(4.27), 354s(4.21),370s(4.16)	18-2885-80
11H-Indeno[1,2-c]isoquinoline-11-carbo-nitrile, 5-amino-4,7-dimethoxy-, monohydrochloride	EtOH-H_2SO_4	220(4.51),263(4.29), 332s(4.01),344(4.12), 380(4.21),398(4.18)	18-2885-80
Pyrimido[4,5-b]quinoline-2,4(1H,3H)-di-one, 3-methyl-5-(4-methylphenyl)-	EtOH	242(4.65),254(4.46), 310(3.98),313s(3.94), 361(3.81),374s(3.75)	94-3049-80
Pyrimido[4,5-b]quinoline-2,4(3H,10H)-dione, 3,7-dimethyl-10-phenyl-	EtOH	224(4.48),266(4.65), 318s(4.04),325(4.05), 388s(3.93),404(4.09), 429s(4.01)	94-3049-80
Pyrimido[4,5-b]quinoline-2,4(3H,10H)-dione, 3,8-dimethyl-10-phenyl-	EtOH	263(4.40),322(3.96), 399(3.97),414s(3.90)	94-3049-80
Pyrimido[4,5-b]quinoline-2,4(3H,10H)-dione, 3-methyl-10-(4-methylphenyl)-	EtOH	264(4.62),319(4.00), 384s(3.94),400(4.06), 420s(3.97)	94-3049-80
Pyrimido[4,5-b]quinoline-2,4(3H,10H)-dione, 10-ethyl-3-phenyl-	EtOH	225(4.53),268(4.62), 313s(3.93),323(3.99), 379s(3.92),400(4.08), 419s(3.99)	94-3514-80
$C_{19}H_{15}N_3O_3$ Ethanone, 1-[4-[2-(4-nitrophenyl)-2-phenylethenyl]-1H-pyrazol-3-yl]-	EtOH	248(3.96),343(3.76)	78-1331-80
3H-Pyrazol-3-one, 2,4-dihydro-5-methyl-4-[3-(4-nitrophenyl)-2-propenyli-dene]-2-phenyl-	n.s.g.	250(4.49),355(4.72), 485(3.26)	124-0642-80

Compound	Solvent	$\lambda_{max}(\log \epsilon)$	Ref.
Pyrimido[4,5-b]quinoline-2,4(3H,10H)-dione, 7-methoxy-3-methyl-10-phenyl-	EtOH	225(4.26),263(4.42), 313(3.94),329(3.85), 409s(3.75),427(3.87)	94-3049-80
Pyrimido[4,5-b]quinoline-2,4(3H,10H)-dione, 8-methoxy-3-methyl-10-phenyl-	EtOH	257(4.16),336(3.53), 395(3.99),422(3.96)	94-3049-80
Pyrimido[4,5-b]quinoline-2,4(3H,10H)-dione, 10-(4-methoxyphenyl)-3-methyl-	EtOH	264(4.58),320(4.00), 402(4.03),419s(3.94)	94-3049-80
$C_{19}H_{15}N_3O_6$			
Pyrano[3,2-b]indole-2-carboxylic acid, 4,5-dihydro-5-methyl-4-(tetrahydro-1,3-dimethyl-2,4,6-trioxo-5(2H)-pyrimidinylidene)-	dioxan	247(4.33),280(4.10), 350(4.13),514(4.39)	83-0557-80
$C_{19}H_{16}BNO$			
Borinic acid, diphenyl-, 2-(iminomethyl)phenyl ester	CHCl$_3$	285(3.93),392(3.42)	49-0863-80
$C_{19}H_{16}BNO_2$			
Borinic acid, diphenyl-, 2-[(hydroxyimino)methyl]phenyl ester	benzene	309(3.45),365(3.08)	49-0863-80
	EtOH	241(4.47),261(4.53), 266(4.54)	49-0863-80
	CHCl$_3$	365(3.18)	49-0863-80
	MeCN	229(4.6),257s(3.91), 265(3.87),280(3.72), 354(3.20)	49-0863-80
	DMSO	362(3.42)	49-0863-80
$C_{19}H_{16}BrNO_2S$			
3-Thiophenecarboxamide, N-(4-bromophenyl)-2,5-dihydro-4-methoxy-5-(phenylmethylene)-, (Z)-	EtOH	236(4.24),267(4.20), 344s(--),361(4.36)	33-1542-80
3-Thiophenecarboxamide, N-(4-bromophenyl)-4,5-dihydro-2-methyl-4-oxo-5-(phenylmethyl)-	EtOH	227s(--),274(4.36)	33-1542-80
3-Thiophenecarboxamide, N-(4-bromophenyl)-4-methoxy-5-(phenylmethyl)-	EtOH	275(4.37)	33-1542-80
$C_{19}H_{16}BrNO_3$			
7H-Pyrano[2,3-c]acridin-7-one, 9-bromo-3,12-dihydro-6-methoxy-3,3-dimethyl-	MeOH	265(4.43),275(4.63), 295(4.06),325(3.33), 382(3.63)	5-0503-80
$C_{19}H_{16}BrN_3$			
Methanone, (2-amino-5-bromophenyl)phenyl-, phenylhydrazone	n.s.g.	205(4.3),247(4.2), 318(4.0),356(4.0)	124-0823-80
isomer	n.s.g.	204(4.1),240(4.0), 294(3.6),331(3.7)	124-0823-80
$C_{19}H_{16}ClNO_2$			
7-Azatricyclo[4.3.1.1^{2,5}]undeca-3,8-dien-10-one, 7-[3-(4-chlorophenyl)-3-oxo-1-propenyl]-, [1α,2β,5β,6α,7(E)]-	CHCl$_3$	262(4.30),358(4.56)	39-0362-80C
2H-Pyran-2-one, 3-chloro-4-(methylphenylamino)-5-methyl-6-phenyl-	EtOH	241(3.73),273(3.33), 335(3.57)	4-1201-80
2,3-Pyrrolidinedione, 4-[(4-chlorophenyl)methylene]-1-(2-phenylethyl)-	EtOH	327(4.36)	145-1135-80
$C_{19}H_{16}ClNO_3$			
7H-Benzo[c]phenoxazin-5(12aH)-one, 6-chloro-12a-ethoxy-9-methyl-	EtOH	258(4.33),395(4.24)	44-2155-80

Compound	Solvent	$\lambda_{max}(\log \epsilon)$	Ref.
3H-Pyrano[2,3-c]acridin-9-ol, 7-chloro-6-methoxy-3,3-dimethyl-	MeOH	255(4.47),283(4.89), 355(--),370(--), 460(--)	5-0503-80
$C_{19}H_{16}ClN_3O_3$ 2H-1,3-Benzoxazin-2-one, 6-chloro-4-(2,5-dihydro-3-methyl-5-oxo-1-phenyl-1H-pyrazol-4-yl)-3,4-dihydro-3-methyl-	EtOH	226(4.26),272(4.02)	4-0519-80
$C_{19}H_{16}FeO_4$ Ferrocene, [3-(4-hydroxy-6-methyl-2-oxo-2H-pyran-3-yl)-3-oxo-1-propenyl]-	MeOH	362(4.1)	83-0344-80
$C_{19}H_{16}NO$ Acridinium, 1,2,3,4-tetrahydro-1-oxo-10-phenyl-, perchlorate	n.s.g.	222(4.83),314(4.42)	104-1592-80
$C_{19}H_{16}NO_4$ Thalifaurine (chloride)	MeOH	241(4.31),263(4.28), 291(4.66),310s(4.40), 341(4.23),380s(3.83)	36-1061-80
	MeOH-NaOH	253(4.45),311(4.32), 380(4.44)	36-1061-80
$C_{19}H_{16}N_2O$ Ethanone, 1-[4-(2,2-diphenylethenyl)-1H-pyrazol-3-yl]-	EtOH	237(4.22),317(4.08)	78-1331-80
5H-Imidazole, 4-methyl-2-phenyl-5-(3-phenyl-2-propen-1-ylidene)-, N-oxide	n.s.g.	250(4.49),360(4.73), 480(3.20)	124-0642-80
3-Pyridinecarbonitrile, 1,2,3,4-tetra-hydro-4-(3-methylphenyl)-2-oxo-6-phenyl-	pH 13	250(4.21),352(3.53)	4-1521-80
	EtOH	275(3.92),364(2.98)	4-1521-80
	CCl₄	277(3.92),364(2.92)	4-1521-80
3-Pyridinecarbonitrile, 1,2,3,4-tetra-hydro-4-(4-methylphenyl)-2-oxo-6-phenyl-	pH 13	249(4.10),352(3.39)	4-1521-80
	EtOH	266(4.04),360(3.31)	4-1521-80
	CCl₄	266(3.90),362(3.12)	4-1521-80
$C_{19}H_{16}N_2O_2$ 6H-Anthra[1,9-cd]isoxazol-6-one, 5-(cy-clopentylamino)-	dioxan	262(4.38),495(3.98), 530(4.00)	103-0704-80
6H-Anthra[1,9-cd]isoxazol-6-one, 3-piperidino-	dioxan	265(4.53),543(4.50)	103-0704-80
Cecilin	EtOH	232(4.36),248s(4.25), 293s(4.04),299(4.18), 355(3.56),380s(3.56)	102-1859-80
	EtOH-NaOH	238(4.32),248s(4.20), 299(4.04),355(3.48), 380s(3.48)	102-1859-80
3-Pyridinecarbonitrile, 1,2,3,4-tetra-hydro-4-(4-methoxyphenyl)-2-oxo-6-phenyl-	pH 13	252(4.12),354(3.47)	4-1521-80
	EtOH	270(3.95),360(3.34)	4-1521-80
	CCl₄	274(3.84),360(3.21)	4-1521-80
$C_{19}H_{16}N_2O_2S$ Benzenamine, N-[(2,3-dihydro-2-benz-oxazolyl)-2-thienylmethylene]-2-methoxy-	MeOH	242(4.29),284(4.02), 294(4.02),343(4.20)	4-1629-80
Benzenamine, N-[(2,3-dihydro-2-benz-oxazolyl)-3-thienylmethylene]-2-methoxy-	MeOH	242(4.44),288(4.27), 320s(--)	4-1629-80
1-Thia-5,8-diazaspiro[3.4]oct-2-ene-6,7-dione, 5,8-dimethyl-2,3-diphenyl-	dioxan	243(4.60),348(3.94)	5-0873-80

Compound	Solvent	$\lambda_{max}(\log \epsilon)$	Ref.
$C_{19}H_{16}N_2O_3$			
Alangimarine	pH 1	230(4.22),275(4.04), 290(3.79),429(4.41)	88-2667-80
	pH 13	225(4.27),272(4.17), 364(4.22),402(4.18)	88-2667-80
	EtOH	220(4.37),261(4.11), 290s(3.83),365(4.42)	88-2667-80
Benzenamine, N-[(2,3-dihydro-2-benzoxa-zolyl)-2-furanylmethylene]-2-methoxy-	MeOH	241(4.29),295s(--), 332(4.26)	4-1629-80
Benzenemethanamine, N-[2-(5-nitro-2-furanyl)ethenyl]-N-phenyl-, (E)-	MeOH	250(4.23),492(3.92)	73-0155-80
2,5-Piperazinedione, 3-[(4-methoxyphen-yl)methylene]-6-(phenylmethylene)-, (E,Z)-	EtOH	234(3.93),352(4.40)	39-0419-80C
(Z,E)-	EtOH	235(3.96),352(4.47)	39-0419-80C
(Z,Z)-	EtOH	236(3.95),352(4.45)	39-0419-80C
$C_{19}H_{16}N_2O_4$			
Phenol, 2-[4-nitro-2-[(phenylmethyl)am-ino]phenoxy]-	MeCN	393(3.56)	44-2331-80
Phenol, 2-[5-nitro-2-[(phenylmethyl)am-ino]phenoxy]-	MeCN	390(4.24)	44-2331-80
$C_{19}H_{16}N_2O_8$			
Pyrido[1,2-a]benzimidazole-1,2,3,4-tetracarboxylic acid, tetramethyl ester	EtOH	277(4.60),285s(4.56), 326(3.68),375(3.45)	18-3308-80
$C_{19}H_{16}N_4$			
3-Pyridinecarbonitrile, 4-amino-6-(methylphenylamino)-5-phenyl-	EtOH	243(4.26),266(4.20), 346(4.24)	88-2097-80
$C_{19}H_{16}N_4O$			
7H-Pyrrolo[3,4-d]pyrimidin-7-one, 2-amino-5,6-dihydro-4-phenyl-6-(phenylmethyl)-	EtOH	250(4.28),342(3.81)	4-1231-80
$C_{19}H_{16}N_4O_2$			
2,4(1H,3H)-Pteridinedione, 7,8-dihydro-8-methyl-6,7-diphenyl-	pH -2.0	242s(4.08),275(4.46), 417(4.10)	142-0437-80B
	pH 3.0	237(4.27),292(4.26), 373(4.07)	142-0437-80B
	pH 8.0	250(4.27),287s(4.11), 385(4.11)	142-0437-80B
$C_{19}H_{16}N_4O_3S$			
1H-Pyrazole, 4,5-dihydro-3-[(2-hydroxy-1-naphthalenyl)azo]-1-(phenylsulfon-yl)-	CHCl₃	480(4.18)	104-1143-80
$C_{19}H_{16}N_4O_3S_2$			
Benzenesulfonic acid, 3-[[[(phenylami-no)thioxomethyl]hydrazono]-2-pyri-dinylmethyl]-	H₂O	325(4.38),340(4.38), 352(4.32),365(4.17)	86-0923-80
$C_{19}H_{16}O$			
2,4,6,12,14,16-Cycloheptadecahexaene-8,10-diyn-1-one, 7,12-dimethyl-	THF	264s(4.29),279s(4.62), 296(4.80),306(4.83), 350s(3.62)	39-0473-80C
	THF	265(4.24),282(4.50), 297(4.66),306(4.67),	44-3564-80

Compound	Solvent	$\lambda_{max}(\log \epsilon)$	Ref.
(cont.)		403s(3.56)	44-3564-80
	CF_3COOH	331(--),343s(--),	39-0473-80C
		380(--)	+44-3564-80
3,4,5-Hexatrien-2-one, 6-(4-methylphen-yl)-6-phenyl-	EtOH	255(4.22),382(4.33)	78-1331-80
	DMF	382(4.47)	78-1331-80
Naphthalene, 2-[(1-phenyl-1-propenyl)-oxy]-	hexane	250s(--),282s(--), 314(3.12),312(3.04), 328(3.27)	118-0847-80
1,4,6-Nonatrien-8-yn-3-one, 1-(2-ethyn-ylphenyl)-2,7-dimethyl-	ether	225(4.37),243(4.30), 316(4.39)	39-0466-80C
1,4,6-Nonatrien-8-yn-3-one, 1-(2-ethyn-ylphenyl)-4,7-dimethyl-	ether	227(4.42),249(4.48), 254(4.47),325(4.46)	39-0466-80C
$C_{19}H_{16}O_2$			
Benzenemethanol, 2-hydroxy-α,α-diphen-yl-	EtOH	271(3.70)	35-4659-80
	ether	274(3.47)	35-4659-80
Bicyclo[3.1.0]hex-3-en-2-one, 4-meth-oxy-6,6-diphenyl-	C_6H_{12}	245s(3.90),314(2.60)	44-4864-80
Bicyclo[3.1.0]hex-3-en-2-one, 5-meth-oxy-6,6-diphenyl-	C_6H_{12}	270(3.15),357(2.10)	44-4876-80
Cyclobuta[b]naphthalene-3,8-dione, 1,2,2a,8a-tetrahydro-2a-methyl-1-phenyl-, syn	$CHCl_3$	244(4.05),254(4.08), 299(3.22),308(3.19), 340(2.32)	18-0757-80
Cyclobuta[b]naphthalene-3,8-dione, 1,2,2a,8a-tetrahydro-8a-methyl-1-phenyl-, anti	$CHCl_3$	255(4.11),298(3.36), 308(3.34),335(2.40)	18-0757-80
2,5-Cyclohexadien-1-one, 3-methoxy-4,4-diphenyl-	EtOH	242(4.03),275s(3.79)	44-4876-80
Ethanone, 1,1'-(8,9-dihydro-4H-cyclo-penta[def]phenanthrene-2,6-diyl)bis-	C_6H_{12}	244(3.94),325(4.39)	44-1783-80
1,5-Heptadiene-3,5-dione, 1,7-diphenyl-	EtOH	233(4.06),300(4.08), 392(4.56)	102-2643-80
	EtOH-HOAc	392(4.58)	102-2643-80
	EtOH-NaOH	292(4.35),408(4.40)	102-2643-80
3,4,5-Hexatrien-2-one, 6-(4-methoxy-phenyl)-6-phenyl-	EtOH	255(4.12),402(4.33)	78-1331-80
	DMF	402(4.41)	78-1331-80
4H-Pyran-4-one, 2,6-dimethyl-3,5-di-phenyl-	MeOH	260s(4.1)	18-0469-80
[1,1':2',1"-Terphenyl]-4'-ol, 6'-meth-oxy-	EtOH	226s(4.42),240s(4.30), 294(3.59)	44-4876-80
[1,1':2',1"-Terphenyl]-3'-ol, 5'-meth-oxy-	EtOH	232s(4.38),296(3.62)	44-4876-80
Tricyclo[8.5.1.1³,⁸]heptadeca-1,3,5,7-9,11,14-heptaene-12,14-dicarboxalde-hyde	dioxan	326(4.91),334(4.91), 409(3.72)	89-0041-80
$C_{19}H_{16}O_2S$			
1,4-Naphthalenedione, 2-methyl-3-[[(4-methylphenyl)thio]methyl]-	EtOH	251(4.27),262(4.20), 333(3.45)	39-0282-80C
1,4-Naphthalenedione, 2-methyl-3-[[(phenylmethyl)thio]methyl]-	EtOH	247s(4.18),251(4.20), 264(4.12),269s(4.12), 331(3.47)	39-0282-80C
$C_{19}H_{16}O_3$			
2H-1-Benzopyran-2-one, 3-benzoyl-4-(1-methylethyl)-	EtOH	254(4.03),280(4.00), 310(3.79)	39-2937-80C
1-Benzoxepin-2(5H)-one, 3-benzoyl-5,5-dimethyl-	EtOH	252(4.04)	39-2937-80C
Cyclopropa[c][1]benzopyran-2(1aH)-one, 1a-benzoyl-1,7b-dihydro-1,1-dimeth-yl-, (1aR*,7bS*)-	EtOH	252(4.08)	39-2937-80C

Compound	Solvent	$\lambda_{max}(\log \epsilon)$	Ref.
$C_{19}H_{16}O_4$			
4H-1-Benzopyran-4-one, 7-methoxy-2-[2-(4-methoxyphenyl)ethenyl]-, (E)-	MeOH	242(4.24),311(4.08), 359(4.11)	2-0615B-80
5,12-Naphthacenedione, 1,4,4a,12a-tetrahydro-6,11-dihydroxy-2-methyl-	EtOH	208(4.07),237(4.40), 251(4.40),280(4.27), 288(4.22),386s(3.79), 400(4.00),418(4.00), 423(3.96)	39-1007-80C
$C_{19}H_{16}O_5$			
6H-Benzofuro[3,2-c]furo[3,2-g][1]benzopyran, (6aR-cis)- (ambonane)	MeOH	250(3.72),295(3.57), 350(3.23),365(3.19)	39-1804-80C
Benzoic acid, 4-methyl-, (7-methoxy-2-oxo-2H-1-benzopyran-4-yl)methyl ester	EtOH	323(4.12)	95-0744-80
2(5H)-Furanone, 5-acetoxy-4-(2-methoxyphenyl)-5-phenyl-	MeOH	236s(4.03),283(4.19), 334(3.89)	18-0179-80
1,4-Naphthalenedione, 8-(3,4-dimethoxyphenyl)-2-methoxy-	EtOH	204(4.75),236(4.39), 248s(4.32),275(4.31)	94-2948-80
$C_{19}H_{16}O_6$			
9,10-Anthracenedione, 1,4,8-trihydroxy-2-(3-oxopentyl)-	MeOH	232(4.45),250(4.23), 289(3.78),406(3.33), 463(3.96),477(4.00), 490(4.05),508(3.89), 522(3.84)	24-2994-80
Benzoic acid, 4-methoxy-, (7-methoxy-2-oxo-2H-1-benzopyran-4-yl)methyl ester	EtOH	323(4.12)	95-0744-80
4H-1-Benzopyran-4-one, 3-(1,3-benzodioxol-5-ylmethyl)-5,7-dihydroxy-6,8-dimethyl-	EtOH	231s(4.47),266(4.62), 297s(4.20),340s(3.87)	94-1477-80
	EtOH-NaOAc	278(--),345(--)	94-1477-80
	EtOH-AlCl₃	322(--),392(--)	94-1477-80
4H-1-Benzopyran-4-one, 3-(1,3-benzodioxol-5-ylmethyl)-5-hydroxy-7-methoxy-6-methyl-	EtOH	234(4.10),256(4.07), 263(4.09),292(3.84), 330s(3.39)	94-2039-80
4H-1-Benzopyran-4-one, 3-(1,3-benzodioxol-5-ylmethyl)-5-hydroxy-7-methoxy-8-methyl-	EtOH	229(4.16),248(4.23), 256(4.32),263(4.35), 290(3.87),331(3.59)	94-2039-80
	EtOH	229(4.22),248(4.28), 256(4.37),263(4.42), 290(3.92),331(3.64)	94-2487-80
	EtOH-AlCl₃	273(--),315(--), 370(--)	94-2487-80
6H-Furo[2,3-c]xanthen-6-one, 1,2-dihydro-10-hydroxy-5-methoxy-2-(2-methyloxiranyl)- (psorospermin)	EtOH	240s(--),247(4.61), 300s(--),310(4.24), 340s(--)	100-0296-80
$C_{19}H_{16}O_7$			
2-Anthracenecarboxylic acid, 9,10-dihydro-1,4,5-trimethoxy-9,10-dioxo-, methyl ester	EtOH	227(4.25),260(4.15), 370(3.62)	44-0020-80
$C_{19}H_{16}O_8$			
Anhydrofusarubin diacetate	EtOH	217(4.33),285(4.20), 455(3.59)	23-1380-80
$C_{19}H_{16}O_9$			
Cryptostictic acid	EtOH	214(4.54),267(3.98), 316(3.51)	102-0328-80

Compound	Solvent	$\lambda_{max}(\log \epsilon)$	Ref.
$C_{19}H_{17}BN_2O$ Boron, (2-hydroxybenzaldehyde hydrazonato)diphenyl-, (T-4)-	CHCl$_3$	280(3.99),370(3.34)	49-0863-80
$C_{19}H_{17}BrN_2O_3$ Spiro[2H-1-benzopyran-2,2'-[2H]indole], 8-bromo-1',3'-dihydro-1',3',3'-trimethyl-6-nitro-	EtOH	530(4.45)	103-0041-80
$C_{19}H_{17}Cl$ 11H-9,10[1',3']-endo-Cyclopentanthracene, 9-chloro-9,10,11,12,13,14,15-hexahydro-	MeCN	253s(2.66),262(2.78), 268(2.90),275(2.98)	24-1458-80
$C_{19}H_{17}ClN_2O_2$ Ethanol, 2-[(6-chloro-4-phenyl-2-quinolinyl)amino]-, acetate	EtOH	250(4.7),352(3.7)	106-0751-80
$C_{19}H_{17}ClN_2O_3S$ Benzenesulfonamide, 4-chloro-N-(1'-methyl-3-oxospiro[cyclopentan-1,3'-[3H]indol]-2'(1'H)-ylidene)-	EtOH	226(4.52),285(4.32), 298s(4.22)	39-1512-80C
$C_{19}H_{17}ClN_2O_6$ 8-Azabicyclo[3.2.1]oct-3-ene-6-carboxylic acid, 8-[trans-3-(2-chloro-5-nitrophenyl)-3-oxo-1-propenyl]-, ethyl ester, endo	CHCl$_3$	228(4.13),307(4.16)	39-0362-80C
exo	CHCl$_3$	250(4.39),303(4.66)	39-0362-80C
$C_{19}H_{17}ClN_4O$ Methanimidamide, N'-[1-(4-chlorophenyl)-4-formyl-3-phenyl-1H-pyrazol-5-yl]-N,N-dimethyl-	EtOH	258(4.48),338(3.82)	114-0127-80C
$C_{19}H_{17}ClN_4O_3$ 1H-Pyrazole-3-carboxylic acid, 1-(3-chlorophenyl)-4-hydroxy-5-[(4-methylphenyl)azo]-, ethyl ester	EtOH	251(4.28),362(4.21), 443(3.77)	142-0697-80B
$C_{19}H_{17}ClN_4O_4$ 1H-Pyrazole-3-carboxylic acid, 1-(3-chlorophenyl)-4-hydroxy-5-[(4-methoxyphenyl)azo]-, ethyl ester	EtOH	255(4.33),358(4.21), 525(3.59)	142-0697-80B
$C_{19}H_{17}ClO$ 2,4-Pentadien-1-one, 5-chloro-1,5-bis(4-methylphenyl)-, (Z,E)-	EtOH	347(4.53)	40-1804-80
$C_{19}H_{17}ClO_6$ 6H-Furo[2,3-c]xanthen-6-one, 2-(2-chloro-1-hydroxy-1-methylethyl)-1,2-dihydro-10-hydroxy-5-methoxy-	EtOH	238(4.31),244(4.34), 257(4.23),319(4.06)	100-0296-80
$C_{19}H_{17}N$ Benzenamine, N-[1-methyl-2-(1-naphthalenyl)ethylidene]-	dioxan	283(3.98)	24-2462-80
3H-3a,8-Methanodibenzo[3,4:6,7]cyclohepta[1,2-c]pyrrole, 2,8-dihydro-2-methyl-	C$_6$H$_{12}$	337(3.95)	44-1505-80

Compound	Solvent	$\lambda_{max}(\log \epsilon)$	Ref.
$C_{19}H_{17}NO_2$			
1H-Indene, 1,3-dimethyl-1-[2-(4-nitrophenyl)ethenyl]-, (E)-(+)-	EtOH	260s(3.96),327(4.19)	39-0714-80C
(Z)-	EtOH	263(4.05),295(3.95)	39-0714-80C
1H-Indene, 1,3-dimethyl-2-[2-(4-nitrophenyl)ethenyl]-, (E)-(+)-	EtOH	257(4.02),305(3.97), 405(4.50)	39-0714-80C
Oxiranecarbonitrile, 3-[2-(3-butenyloxy)phenyl]-2-phenyl-	EtOH	217s(4.30),231s(4.08), 274s(3.58),282(3.63)	89-0047-80
$C_{19}H_{17}NO_2S$			
3-Thiophenecarboxamide, 2,5-dihydro-4-hydroxy-N-(4-methylphenyl)-5-(phenylmethylene)-, (Z)-	EtOH	231(4.26),353(4.55), 368s(--)	33-1542-80
2-Thiophenecarboxamide, 4-hydroxy-N-(4-methylphenyl)-5-(phenylmethyl)-	EtOH	225s(--),281(4.23)	33-1542-80
$C_{19}H_{17}NO_2STe$			
Tellurilimine, Te,Te-diphenyl-N-[(phenylmethyl)sulfonyl]-	MeOH	222(4.45),274(3.75)	104-2210-80
$C_{19}H_{17}NO_3$			
Acetamide, N-[(10,11-dihydro-10,11-dioxo-5H-dibenzo[a,d]cyclohepten-5-yl)methyl]-N-methyl-	EtOH	209(4.47),282(3.87), 420s(1.79)	95-1127-80
5H-[1]Benzopyrano[3,4-c]pyridin-5-one, 1,2,3,4-tetrahydro-10-hydroxy-3-(phenylmethyl)-	EtOH	324(4.17)	2-0495-80
2H-1,3-Benzoxazin-2-one, 3,4-dihydro-3-methyl-4-(1,2,3,4-tetrahydro-1-oxo-2-naphthalenyl)-	EtOH	223(4.16),277(4.23), 288s(4.20)	4-0277-80
$C_{19}H_{17}NO_3S$			
Methanone, phenyl[2,3,3a,6a-tetrahydro-5-(mercaptomethyl)-2-phenylfuro[2,3-d]isoxazol-3-yl]-, (3α,3aα,6aα)-	MeOH	246(4.68)	73-3546-80
$C_{19}H_{17}NO_4$			
Methanone, phenyl[2,3,3a,6a-tetrahydro-5-(hydroxymethyl)-2-phenylfuro[2,3-d]isoxazol-3-yl]-, (3α,3aα,6aα)-	MeOH	246(4.54)	73-3546-80
7H-Pyrano[2,3-c]acridin-7-one, 3,4-dihydro-9-hydroxy-6-methoxy-3,3-dimethyl-	MeOH	278(4.72),300s(--), 320s(--),340s(--), 412(3.78)	5-0503-80
Stesakine, dehydro-	MeOH	247s(4.32),271(4.73), 296s(4.12),338(4.10)	102-2735-80
	MeOH-NaOH	289(4.69),298(4.66)	102-2735-80
$C_{19}H_{17}N_2O_2S$			
Thiazolium, 3-ethyl-2-[2-(4-nitrophenyl)ethenyl]-4-phenyl-, iodide	EtOH	520(3.45)	49-0657-80
$C_{19}H_{17}N_3O_2$			
Acetamide, N-(2-methoxy-4,6-diphenyl-5-pyrimidinyl)-	EtOH	246(4.15),293(4.07)	103-0970-80
2H-1,3-Benzoxazin-2-one, 3,4-dihydro-3-methyl-4-(3-methyl-5-phenyl-1H-pyrazol-4-yl)-	EtOH	240s(3.95),276(3.20)	4-0519-80
1H-Isoindole-1,3(2H)-dione, 2-[2-(2-amino-1-methyl-1H-indol-3-yl)ethyl]-, monohydrochloride	EtOH	218(4.72),265(3.85)	103-0368-80

Compound	Solvent	$\lambda_{max}(\log \epsilon)$	Ref.
$C_{19}H_{17}N_3O_3$			
2H-1,3-Benzoxazin-2-one, 4-(2,5-dihydro-3-methyl-5-oxo-1-phenyl-1H-pyrazol-4-yl)-3,4-dihydro-3-methyl-	EtOH	247(4.14)	4-0519-80
$C_{19}H_{17}N_5O$			
4-Pyrimidinecarboxamide, N-[bis(phenylamino)methylene]-2-methyl-	MeOH	252(4.25)	39-1667-80C
$C_{19}H_{17}N_7O_4S$			
1H-Indole-3-propanamide, α-(acetylamino)-2-[(4-azido-2-nitrophenyl)thio]-, (S)-	HOAc	263(4.35),286(4.40), 390(3.63)	69-3280-80
	2M HOAc	263(4.37),286(4.40), 400(3.59)	69-3280-80
1H-Indole-3-propanamide, α-(acetylamino)-2-[(5-azido-2-nitrophenyl)thio]-, (S)-	HOAc	285(4.29),293(4.29)	69-3280-80
	2M HOAc	288(4.27),327(4.06)	69-3280-80
$C_{19}H_{18}$			
Benzene, 1,1'-[3-methyl-1-(2-propenyl)-2-cyclopropene-1,2-diyl]bis-	EtOH	262(4.21)	35-2797-80
Benzene, 1,1'-[3-methyl-3-(2-propenyl)-1-cyclopropene-1,2-diyl]bis-	EtOH	229(4.26),320(4.46), 338(4.33)	35-2797-80
Bicyclo[3.1.0]hex-2-ene, 3-methyl-1,2-diphenyl-	EtOH	256(4.04)	44-2181-80
1H-Indene, 1,3-dimethyl-2-(2-phenylethenyl)-, (E)-	EtOH	241(4.10),259(3.86), 330(4.52),344(4.62), 356(4.45)	39-0714-80C
(Z)-	EtOH	238(4.15),316(4.13)	39-0714-80C
1H-Indene, 2-methyl-1-phenyl-3-(2-propenyl)-	EtOH	220(4.25),263(3.83)	44-4555-80
Tricyclo[2.2.0.0^{2,6}]hexane, 2-methyl-1,6-diphenyl-	EtOH	240(4.03)	35-2797-80 +44-2181-80
$C_{19}H_{18}BrNO$			
Spiro[2H-1-benzopyran-2,2'-[2H]indole], 6-bromo-1',3'-dihydro-1',3',3'-trimethyl-	20% MeOH	298(3.73)	32-0613-80
	pH –2	360s(4.15),435(4.49)	32-0613-80
protonated	20% MeOH	320s(3.79),435(4.21)	32-0613-80
$C_{19}H_{18}BrNO_4$			
4H-Pyrano[2,3-h]quinoline-2-carboxaldehyde, 3-(2-bromo-2-propenyl)-1,8-dihydro-5-methoxy-8,8-dimethyl-4-oxo-	MeOH	251(4.77),275(4.61), 284(4.60),345(4.03)	5-0503-80
$C_{19}H_{18}ClNO_4$			
4H-Pyrano[2,3-h]quinoline-2-carboxaldehyde, 3-(2-chloro-2-propenyl)-1,8-dihydro-5-methoxy-8,8-dimethyl-4-oxo-	MeOH	243(4.43),260(4.32), 270(4.36),320(3.81)	5-0503-80
$C_{19}H_{18}ClN_3O_3S$			
Benzenesulfonamide, 4-chloro-N-(1,1'-dimethyl-2'-oxospiro[3H-indole-3,3'-pyrrolidin]-2(1H)-ylidene)-	EtOH	228(4.50),288(4.25), 302(4.18)	39-1512-80C
$C_{19}H_{18}ClN_5$			
Methanimidamide, N'-[1-(4-chlorophenyl)-4-[(phenylimino)methyl]-1H-pyrazol-5-yl]-N,N-dimethyl-	EtOH	264(4.31),325(3.95)	114-0127-80C

Compound	Solvent	$\lambda_{max}(\log \epsilon)$	Ref.
$C_{19}H_{18}NO$			
Quinolinium, 1,6-dimethyl-3-(2-oxo-2-phenylethyl)-, iodide	EtOH	243(5.74),315s(4.86), 325(4.94)	39-0072-80C
	EtOH-NaOH	279s(5.00),296(5.09), 333(5.46),531(4.82)	39-0072-80C
$C_{19}H_{18}NOS$			
Thiazolium, 3-ethyl-2-[2-(2-hydroxyphenyl)ethenyl]-4-phenyl-, iodide	EtOH	520(4.21)	49-0657-80
	EtOH	218(4.54),265(4.08), 390(3.93),525(3.56)	49-1213-80
	DMF	387(3.78),580(3.82)	49-1213-80
	DMSO	388(3.94),577(3.53)	49-1213-80
	$CHCl_3$	405(3.90),565(3.08)	49-1213-80
Thiazolium, 3-ethyl-2-[2-(4-hydroxyphenyl)ethenyl]-4-phenyl-, iodide	EtOH	550(4.09)	49-0657-80
	EtOH	220(4.51),250s(--), 404(4.55),522(3.60)	49-1213-80
	DMF	401(4.38),564(4.20)	49-1213-80
	DMSO	402(4.54),565(3.42)	49-1213-80
	$CHCl_3$	414(4.46),565(3.20)	49-1213-80
$C_{19}H_{18}NS$			
Thiazolium, 3-ethyl-4-phenyl-2-(2-phenylethenyl)-, iodide	EtOH	520(3.51)	49-0657-80
	EtOH	225(4.33),270(3.78), 350(3.56),480(2.74)	49-1213-80
	DMF	280(3.81),355(3.68), 480(2.74)	49-1213-80
	DMSO	280(3.81),355(3.64), 480(2.74)	49-1213-80
	$CHCl_3$	285(3.79),360(3.62), 480(2.74)	49-1213-80
$C_{19}H_{18}N_2$			
Benzo[g]indolo[2,3-a]quinolizine, 5,7,8,13,13b,14-hexahydro-	n.s.g.	225(4.57),273(3.90), 281(3.80),291(3.70)	107-0523-80
1H-Perimidine, 2,3-dihydro-1,3-dimethyl-2-phenyl-	$CHCl_3$	351(4.15)	104-1890-80
$C_{19}H_{18}N_2O$			
6,7-Diazabicyclo[3.2.0]hept-3-en-2-one, 1,3-dimethyl-4,5-diphenyl-, (E)-	EtOH	280(4.13)	23-1316-80
1H-Pyrido[3,4-b]indol-1-one, 2,3,4,9-tetrahydro-2-methyl-9-(phenylmethyl)-	isoPrOH	227s(4.25),231(4.25), 302(4.11),309s(4.07), 327s(3.69)	103-0244-80
$C_{19}H_{18}N_2O_2$			
Acetic acid, cyano(1,2,5-trimethylbenz[cd]indol-3(1H)-ylidene)-, ethyl ester, (E)-	CH_2Cl_2	230(4.51),253(4.46), 275(4.50),348(4.11), 492(4.60)	5-0971-80
1,17-Cyclocorynan-17,21-dione, 19,20-didehydro-	MeOH	245(4.21),270(4.08), 295(3.68),305(3.66)	142-0935-80B
1(4H)-Naphthalenone, 4-[[4-(dimethylamino)phenyl]imino]-2-methoxy-	EtOH	249(4.33),292(4.28), 327s(4.05),570(3.99)	94-1207-80
$C_{19}H_{18}N_2O_2S$			
Benzenesulfonamide, N-(2,3-dihydro-9-methyl-1H-pyrrolo[1,2-a]indol-1-ylidene)-4-methyl-	$CHCl_3$	255(4.36),350(4.43)	39-2870-80C
3-Thiophenecarboxamide, 4-methoxy-N-(6-methyl-2-pyridinyl)-5-(phenylmethyl)-	EtOH	267(4.16),288(4.33)	33-1542-80

Compound	Solvent	$\lambda_{max}(\log \epsilon)$	Ref.
$C_{19}H_{18}N_2O_3$			
8H-Isoquino[2,1-b][2,7]naphthyridin-8-one, 12-ethenyl-5,6,13,13a-tetrahydro-2-hydroxy-3-methoxy-	pH 1	220(4.42),254(4.00), 284(3.90)	88-2667-80
	pH 13	221(4.54),246(4.25), 301(3.76)	88-2667-80
	EtOH	220(4.53),255(4.00), 284(3.84)	88-2667-80
8H-Isoquino[2,1-b][2,7]naphthyridin-8-one, 12-ethyl-5,6-dihydro-2-hydroxy-3-methoxy-	pH 1	213(4.48),224(4.45), 266(4.14),420(4.54)	88-2667-80
	pH 13	215(4.54),252(4.33), 358(4.32),367s(4.29), 411(3.77)	88-2667-80
	EtOH	220(4.51),255(4.24), 299(3.71),357(4.45), 373s(4.40)	88-2667-80
3-Pyridazinecarboxylic acid, 1,4,5,6-tetrahydro-4-oxo-1,6-diphenyl-, ethyl ester	EtOH	225(3.98),245(4.09), 372(4.19)	118-0623-80
Spiro[2H-1-benzopyran-2,2'-[2H]indole], 1',3'-dihydro-1',3',3'-trimethyl-6-nitro-	EtOH	532(4.53)	103-0041-80
	20% MeOH	246s(4.43),340(4.00)	32-0613-80
	protonated	265(4.17),345(4.06), 520(3.89)	32-0613-80
	pH −2	310(4.27),400(4.36)	32-0613-80
Spiro[2H-1-benzopyran-2,2'-[2H]indole], 1',3'-dihydro-1',3',3'-trimethyl-8-nitro-	EtOH	550(4.43)	103-0041-80
$C_{19}H_{18}N_2O_4$			
8H-Isoquino[2,1-b][2,7]naphthyridin-8-one, 5,6-dihydro-2-hydroxy-12-(1-hydroxyethyl)-3-methoxy- (alamarine)	pH 1	220(4.32),269(4.12), 301(3.78),422(4.53)	88-2667-80
	pH 13	231(4.37),259(4.36), 360(4.23),400(4.19)	88-2667-80
	EtOH	220(4.37),253(4.20), 363(4.44)	88-2667-80
8H-Isoquino[2,1-b][2,7]naphthyridin-8-one, 5,6-dihydro-3-hydroxy-12-(1-hydroxyethyl)-2-methoxy-	pH 1	220(4.21),266(3.97), 301(3.60),424(4.41)	88-2667-80
	pH 13	223(4.25),259(4.03), 306(3.74),418(4.42)	88-2667-80
	EtOH	220(4.25),253(4.04), 364(4.29)	88-2667-80
$C_{19}H_{18}N_2O_4S_2$			
Acetic acid, [6-benzoyl-4,5-dihydro-8-(methylthio)-4-oxo-1H-thieno[3,4-b][1,4]diazepin-2(3H)-ylidene]-, ethyl ester	EtOH	282(4.38),380(4.32)	95-0699-80
Benzoic acid, 2-[1-cyano-2-[[(4-methylphenyl)sulfonyl]amino]-2-(methylthio)ethenyl]-, methyl ester	EtOH	310(3.94),322(4.48)	95-0456-80
$C_{19}H_{18}N_2O_5$			
Acetamide, N-[3-[(1,4-dihydroxy-9,10-dioxo-2-anthracenyl)amino]propyl]-	MeOH	514(4.09),534s(4.04)	138-0743-80
Pyrimido[1,2-a]indole-4,10-dicarboxylic acid, 3-acetyl-, diethyl ester	EtOH	238(4.32),244(4.32), 300(4.38),307(4.44), 350(4.08),360(4.06)	94-2972-80
$C_{19}H_{18}N_2O_5S$			
Acetic acid, (3,6-dihydro-5-formyl-2H-1,3-thiazin-2-ylidene)(phthalimido)-, 1,1-dimethylethyl ester	MeOH	218(4.48),238s(4.32), 346(4.45)	4-0767-80

Compound	Solvent	$\lambda_{max}(\log \epsilon)$	Ref.
$C_{19}H_{18}N_2O_6$ 3-Azabicyclo[3.3.1]nonane-1-carboxylic acid, 6-(1,3-dihydro-1,3-dioxo-2H-isoindol-2-yl)-2,4-dioxo-, ethyl ester, exo	EtOH	222(4.59)	23-1860-80
$C_{19}H_{18}N_2O_9S$ 4-Thia-1-azabicyclo[3.2.0]hept-2-ene-2-carboxylic acid, 6-[1-[[[(4-nitrophenyl)methoxy]carbonyl]oxy]ethyl]-7-oxo-, 2-oxopropyl ester, erythro	EtOH	261(4.10),315(3.90)	35-2039-80
threo	EtOH	261(4.10),315(3.90)	35-2039-80
$C_{19}H_{18}N_4O$ Methanimidamide, N'-(4-formyl-1,3-diphenyl-1H-pyrazol-3-yl)-N,N-dimethyl-	EtOH	251(4.49),335(3.74)	114-0127-80C
$C_{19}H_{18}N_4O_7$ 2-Pyridinecarboxamide, N-[3-acetoxy-2-(acetoxymethyl)-2,3,3a,9a-tetrahydro-6H-furo[2',3':4,5]oxazolo[3,2-a]pyrimidin-6-ylidene]-, [2R-(2α,3β-3aβ,9aβ)]-, monotetrafluoroborate	MeOH	248(4.15),294(4.36)	44-1577-80
$C_{19}H_{18}N_6O_4$ 3H-Purine-3-butanoic acid, 6-amino-α-(1,3-dihydro-1,3-dioxo-2H-isoindol-2-yl)-, ethyl ester, (S)-	MeOH	278(4.07)	24-2043-80
4-Quinazolinamine, 6-nitro-N-(4-nitrophenyl)-2-(1-piperidinyl)-	dioxan	253(4.47),360(4.76), 407(4.29)	73-1079-80
$C_{19}H_{18}O$ 2-Cyclohexen-1-one, 4-methyl-2,4-diphenyl-	EtOH	220(4.28)	22-0267-80
3,5,7,10,12,14-Heptadecahexaene-1,16-diyn-9-one, 3,15-dimethyl-, (E,E,Z,Z,E,E)-	ether	268s(4.31),279(4.37), 289(4.36),320s(4.37), 378(4.74)	44-3564-80
2-Propanone, 1-(1-methyl-3-phenyl-1H-inden-1-yl)-	EtOH	237(4.08),268(3.62)	104-1298-80
$C_{19}H_{18}O_2$ 2-Cyclohexen-1-one, 3-methoxy-4,4-diphenyl-	EtOH	249(4.29)	44-4876-80
$C_{19}H_{18}O_3$ 1,4-Naphthalenedione, 2-(2,2-dicyclopropylethenyl)-3-methoxy-	EtOH	255s(4.06),272(4.11), 327(3.34),424(3.15)	18-0567-80
$C_{19}H_{18}O_4$ 1,3-Azulenedicarboxylic acid, 6-ethynyl-5-methyl-, diethyl ester	C_6H_{12}	237(4.42),276(4.27), 313s(4.70),325(4.84), 355(4.40),382(3.82), 552(2.86),590s(2.80), 645s(2.46)	18-1647-80
$C_{19}H_{18}O_4S$ Acetic acid, [[3-(4-methoxyphenyl)-3-oxo-1-phenyl-1-propenyl]thio]-, methyl ester, (E)-	EtOH	323(4.30)	18-1739-80
(Z)-	EtOH	283s(4.08),332(4.39)	18-1739-80

Compound	Solvent	$\lambda_{max}(\log \epsilon)$	Ref.
$C_{19}H_{18}O_5$			
2H-1-Benzopyran-2-one, 7-[[4-(2,5-dihydro-4-methyl-5-oxo-2-furanyl)-3-methyl-2-butenyl]oxy]-	MeOH	323(4.19)	2-0820-80
4H-1-Benzopyran-4-one, 5,7-dihydroxy-3-[(4-methoxyphenyl)methyl]-6,8-dimethyl-	EtOH	221s(4.29),266(4.31), 305(3.74),329s(3.47)	94-1477-80
	EtOH-NaOAc	342(--)	94-1477-80
	EtOH-AlCl₃	277(--),322(--), 366(--)	94-1477-80
4H-1-Benzopyran-4-one, 5-hydroxy-7-methoxy-3-[(4-methoxyphenyl)methyl]-6-methyl-	EtOH	230(4.00),262(4.01), 290(3.82),323s(2.82)	94-2039-80
4H-1-Benzopyran-4-one, 5-hydroxy-7-methoxy-3-[(4-methoxyphenyl)methyl]-8-methyl-	EtOH	224(4.38),244s(4.29), 256s(4.41),263(4.46), 285(3.80),298(3.73), 333(3.64)	94-2487-80
3,12-Dioxatricyclo[12.2.2.2⁶,⁹]eicosa-1(16),6,8,14,17,19-hexaene-4,11-dione, 15-methoxy-	MeOH	269(3.77)	44-4496-80
1,4-Ethanoanthracene-9,10-dione, 5-ethoxy-1,4-dihydro-8-hydroxy-1-methoxy-	MeOH	214(4.38),276(3.88), 479(3.70)	24-1575-80
1,4-Ethanoanthracene-9,10-dione, 8-ethoxy-1,4-dihydro-5-hydroxy-1-methoxy-	MeOH	215(4.30),274(3.80), 477(3.57)	24-1575-80
$C_{19}H_{18}O_6$			
4H-1-Benzopyran-4-one, 3-(1,3-benzodioxol-5-ylmethyl)-2,3-dihydro-5,7-dihydroxy-6,8-dimethyl-	EtOH	214(4.73),298(4.87)	94-1477-80
	EtOH-NaOAc	345(--)	94-1477-80
	EtOH-AlCl₃	322(--)	94-1477-80
4H-1-Benzopyran-4-one, 2-(3,4-dimethoxyphenyl)-5,7-dimethoxy-	MeOH	240(4.01),265(3.86), 330(4.07)	118-0874-80
4H-1-Benzopyran-4-one, 7-methoxy-2-(3,4,5-trimethoxyphenyl)-	MeOH	230(4.16),310(4.18)	118-0874-80
2,4-Cyclohexadien-1-one, 6-acetoxy-3-methoxy-6-[3-(4-methoxyphenyl)-3-oxo-1-propenyl]-	MeOH	225(4.26),295(4.19)	18-1769-80
1,4-Ethanoanthracene-9,10-dione, 5-acetoxy-1,4,4a,9a-tetrahydro-8-hydroxy-1-methoxy-	MeOH	235(4.19),353(3.60)	24-1575-80
2-Propen-1-one, 3-(1,3-benzodioxol-5-yl)-1-(2-hydroxy-4,6-dimethoxy-3-methylphenyl)-	EtOH	370(4.48)	94-2487-80
	EtOH-AlCl₃	418(--)	94-2487-80
$C_{19}H_{18}O_7$			
4H-1-Benzopyran-4-one, 2-(3,4-dimethoxyphenyl)-3-hydroxy-5,7-dimethoxy-	MeOH	224(4.54),257(4.43), 300(6.65),361(4.30)	36-0360-80
	MeOH-AlCl₃	227(4.52),265(4.49), 422(4.40)	36-0360-80
	MeOH-AlCl₃-HCl	220(4.50),262(4.38), 360(4.05),420(4.03)	36-0360-80
4H-1-Benzopyran-4-one, 5-hydroxy-7-methoxy-3-(2,4,5-trimethoxyphenyl)- (robustigenin)	EtOH	260(4.41)	18-0831-80
$C_{19}H_{18}O_9$			
4H-1-Benzopyran-4-one, 2-(2,4-dihydroxy-5-methoxyphenyl)-5-hydroxy-6,7,8-trimethoxy-	MeOH	273(4.14),380(4.21)	102-2439-80
	MeOH-NaOAc	272(--),430(--)	102-2439-80
	MeOH-AlCl₃	284(--),302(--), 418(--)	102-2439-80
$C_{19}H_{18}S_4$			
7H,15H-6a,14a-Methano-6H,14H-[1,6]-	CHCl₃	257(4.11),266(4.10)	48-0909-80

Compound	Solvent	$\lambda_{max}(\log \epsilon)$	Ref.
benzodithiecino[3,4-c][1,6]benzodithiocin (cont.)			48-0909-80
$C_{19}H_{19}BrClNO_4$ 7H-Pyrano[2,3-c]acridin-7-one, 9-bromo-9-chloro-3,8,9,10,11,12-hexahydro-11-hydroxy-6-methoxy-3,3-dimethyl-	MeOH	251(4.41),275(4.38), 281(4.39),345(3.77)	5-0503-80
$C_{19}H_{19}BrO_4$ Propanedioic acid, (bromomethyl)methyl-, bis(phenylmethyl) ester	EtOH	225(2.34)	24-0650-80
$C_{19}H_{19}BrO_7$ α-D-xylo-Heptofuranuronic acid, 5,5,6,6-tetradehydro-5,6-dideoxy-3-O-methyl-1,2-O-(1-methylethylidene)-, 2-(4-bromophenyl)-2-oxoethyl ester	EtOH	205(4.07),255(4.24)	33-1181-80
$C_{19}H_{19}ClN_2O_2$ 1H-Pyrazole, 5-(4-chlorophenyl)-4,5-dihydro-3-(4-methoxyphenyl)-1-(1-oxopropyl)-	MeOH	297(3.79)	2-0364-80
$C_{19}H_{19}ClN_6$ Methanimidamide, N'-[1-(4-chlorophenyl)-4-[(phenylhydrazono)methyl]-1H-pyrazol-5-yl]-N,N-dimethyl-	EtOH	250(4.31),284(4.39), 341(4.19)	114-0127-80C
$C_{19}H_{19}FN_2S$ Piperazine, 1-(7-fluorodibenzo[b,f]thiepin-10-yl)-4-methyl-	MeOH	269(4.11),305(3.93)	73-1086-80
$C_{19}H_{19}N$ 1-Naphthalenamine, N-ethyl-3-(phenylmethyl)-	MeOH	216(4.76),253(4.47), 337(3.92)	103-0965-80
2-Naphthalenamine, N-ethyl-4-(phenylmethyl)-	MeOH	213(4.65),251(4.78), 276s(3.86),289(3.92), 300(3.79),355(3.49)	103-0965-80
$C_{19}H_{19}NO$ Benzenepentanenitrile, α,α-dimethyl-δ-oxo-β-phenyl-	EtOH	242(4.10),278(3.03)	78-0631-80
Spiro[2H-1-benzopyran-2,2'-[2H]indole], 1',3'-dihydro-1',3',3'-trimethyl-	20% MeOH protonated pH -2	250s(4.28),300(3.89) 300(3.79),435(4.26) 435(4.56)	32-0613-80 32-0613-80 32-0613-80
$C_{19}H_{19}NO_2$ 4H-Dibenzo[de,g]quinoline, 5,6-dihydro-2,10-dimethoxy-6-methyl-	EtOH	245(4.60),260s(4.55), 293(4.26),324(3.96), 384(3.34)	95-0337-80
4H-Dibenzo[de,g]quinoline-10,11-diol, 5,6,6a,7-tetrahydro-6-(2-propenyl)-, (R)- (N-allylapomorphine)	EtOH	273(4.15),281(4.22), 320(3.48)	44-3465-80
1H-Indole-2,3-dione, 4-(5-bromopentyl)-	EtOH	<u>240(4.1)</u>,<u>305(3.6)</u>, <u>420(3.3)</u>	78-2441-80
Pyrano[4,3-b]indole, 1,3,4,5-tetrahydro-1-(4-methoxyphenyl)-5-methyl-	EtOH	228(4.47),287(3.85)	39-1688-80C
Spiro[2H-1-benzopyran-2,2'-[2H]indol]-6-ol, 1',3'-dihydro-1',3',3'-trimethyl-	20% MeOH anion	290(3.72),335s(3.62), 470(3.04) 360(3.45),452(3.21)	32-0613-80 32-0613-80

Compound	Solvent	$\lambda_{max}(\log \epsilon)$	Ref.
(cont.)	protonated	375(4.17),470(4.26)	32-0613-80

$C_{19}H_{19}NO_3$

2-Butenamide, 4-(2,5-dimethylphenyl)-N-(4-methoxyphenyl)-4-oxo-, trans	EtOH	237(4.39),283(3.92), 335(3.98)	115-0401-80
Cyclopropanecarboxylic acid, 2-[(hydroxyimino)phenylmethyl]-3-phenyl-, ethyl ester	MeOH	225(3.12)	4-0541-80
2H-Naphth[2,1-e][1,3]oxazin-2-one, 3,4,4a,5,6,10b-hexahydro-4-(2-hydroxyphenyl)-3-methyl-	EtOH	272(3.50),280s(3.43)	4-0277-80
3H-Naphth[1,2-e][1,3]oxazin-3-one, 1,2-dihydro-2-methyl-1-(2-oxocyclohexyl)-	EtOH	268s(3.64),274s(3.72), 277(3.74),284(3.66), 288(3.65),309(3.11), 315(3.00),323(3.24)	4-0277-80

$C_{19}H_{19}NO_4$

Acetic acid, (1',2'-dihydro-2,4'-dioxospiro[cyclohexane-1,6'-[6H]pyrrolo-3,2,1-ij]quinolin]-5'(4'H)-ylidene)-, methyl ester	MeOH and MeOH-HClO$_4$	233(4.18),326(3.54)	39-0535-80C
12H-Benzo[a]-1,3-benzodioxolo[4,5-g]-quinolizin-9-ol, 6,6a,11,14-tetrahydro-8-methoxy-	MeOH MeOH-NaOH	230s(4.00),290(3.94) 240s(4.01),296(4.04)	36-1061-80 36-1061-80
1,3-Dioxolo[4,5-g]isoquinoline, 7-(3,4-dimethoxyphenyl)-7,8-dihydro-5-methyl-	MeOH	278(3.97),316(4.10)	2-0556-80
Glaucine methyl deriv.	EtOH	260(3.55),303(3.24)	102-0998-80
Isoquinoline, 3-(1,3-benzodioxol-5-yl)-3,4-dihydro-6,7-dimethoxy-1-methyl-	MeOH	282(3.95),306(4.04)	2-0556-80
4H-1,3-Oxazin-5(6H)-one, 2-(3,4-dimethoxyphenyl)-4-(phenylmethyl)-	MeOH	210(4.32),217s(4.29), 265(3.96),295(3.75)	103-1000-80
Stesakine	EtOH	218(4.47),240s(4.10), 281(4.23),320s(3.69)	102-2735-80
	EtOH-NaOH	235s(4.26),313(4.28), 327(4.26)	102-2735-80

$C_{19}H_{19}NO_5$

Benzo[5,6]cyclohepta[1,2-b]pyrrole-2-acetic acid, 3-carboxy-1,4,5,10-tetrahydro-10-oxo-, α-(1-methylethyl) ester	MeOH	212(4.32),225(4.21), 240(4.14),260(3.83), 328(4.19)	4-1081-80
Ledecorine, (±)-	EtOH	240s(3.89),292(3.53)	142-0585-80
2H-Naphth[2,3-e]-1,3-oxazine-1-acetic acid, α-acetyl-3,4-dihydro-3-methyl-2-oxo-, ethyl ester	EtOH	229(4.79),255s(3.93), 264(3.93),274s(3.89), 289(3.70),310(3.20), 324(3.23)	4-0519-80

$C_{19}H_{19}NS$

| Benz[cd]indolium, 1,5-dihydro-1-methyl-5-(methylthio)-2-phenyl-, tetrafluoroborate | CH$_2$Cl$_2$ | 243(4.25),366(3.89), 483(4.36) | 83-0977-80 |

$C_{19}H_{19}N_3$

Benzenamine, N,4-dimethyl-2-[(6-phenyl-4-pyridazinyl)methyl]-	EtOH EtOH-HCl	247(4.45),289s(3.66) 258(4.27)	39-0072-80C 39-0072-80C
Pyrrolo[3,2-e]benzimidazole, 3,6-dihydro-2,7,8-trimethyl-3-(phenylmethyl)-	EtOH	300(4.30)	103-0062-80
Pyrrolo[3,2-e]benzimidazole, 3,6-dihydro-6,7,8-trimethyl-3-(phenylmethyl)-	EtOH	290s(4.18),305(4.20), 315s(4.16)	103-1039-80

Compound	Solvent	$\lambda_{max}(\log \epsilon)$	Ref.
$C_{19}H_{19}N_3O_2$ 4H-Imidazol-4-one, 1,5-dihydro-2-(4-morpholinyl)-5,5-diphenyl-	EtOH	222.2(4.58)	56-2217-80
$C_{19}H_{19}N_3O_3$ 2-Propenoic acid, 2-cyano-3-[5-(4-phenyl-1-piperazinyl)-2-furanyl]-, methyl ester	MeOH	211(4.39),244(4.42), 466(4.79)	73-1831-80
$C_{19}H_{19}N_3O_4$ 1H-Pyrazole, 4,5-dihydro-3-(4-methoxyphenyl)-5-(4-nitrophenyl)-1-(1-oxopropyl)-	MeOH	292(4.42)	2-0364-80
$C_{19}H_{19}N_3O_6S$ 4-Thia-1-azabicyclo[3.2.0]heptane-2-carboxylic acid, 6-[[(1,3-dihydro-1,3-dioxo-2H-isoindol-2-yl)acetyl]-amino]-3,3-dimethyl-7-oxo-, methyl ester, [2S-(2α,5α,6β)]-	EtOH	219(4.65),223s(4.58), 232s(4.11),240(3.94)	128-0449-80
$C_{19}H_{19}N_5O_2$ 4-Quinazolinamine, N-(4-nitrophenyl)-2-(1-piperidinyl)-	dioxan	248(4.29),295(4.38), 342(4.11),402(4.03)	73-1079-80
$C_{19}H_{19}N_6$ [1,2,4]Triazolo[1,5-a:4,3-a']dipyrimidin-5-ium, 10-[2-[4-(dimethylamino)-phenyl]ethenyl]-8-methyl-, perchlorate	EtOH	550(4.42)	124-0835-80
$C_{19}H_{20}$ [3.2.2](1,2,5)Cyclophane	EtOH	227(4.26),291(2.30), 302s(2.20)	44-3974-80
Cyclopropene, 3-(1,1-dimethylethyl)-1,2-diphenyl-	EtOH	230(4.26),238(4.16), 313(4.38),322(4.43), 340(4.28)	35-5648-80
$C_{19}H_{20}ClNOS$ 1-Propanamine, 3-(2-chloro-6-methoxy-9H-thioxanthen-9-ylidene)-N,N-dimethyl-	MeOH	239(4.63),273(4.20), 322(3.46)	73-3166-80
1-Propanamine, 3-(2-chloro-7-methoxy-9H-thioxanthen-9-ylidene)-N,N-dimethyl-	MeOH	226(4.53),268(4.11), 286s(3.92),338(3.53)	73-3166-80
$C_{19}H_{20}ClNO_2$ 4H-Dibenzo[de,g]quinolin-11-ol, 6-(2-chloroethyl)-5,6,6a,7-tetrahydro-10-methoxy-	EtOH	274(3.99)	44-2275-80
$C_{19}H_{20}ClN_3O_2S$ Benzenesulfonamide, 4-chloro-N-(1,1'-dimethylspiro[3H-indole-3,3'-pyrrolidin]-2(1H)-ylidene)-	EtOH	225(4.54),288(4.26), 297s(4.21)	39-1512-80C
$C_{19}H_{20}ClN_6O_7P$ Adenosine, N-[(2-chlorophenoxy)(2-cyanoethoxy)phosphinyl]-	pH 4.0	257(4.26),264s(4.14), 278s(3.58)	142-0761-80B
	pH 10.0	212s(4.39),269(4.35)	142-0761-80B

Compound	Solvent	$\lambda_{max}(\log \epsilon)$	Ref.
(cont.)	MeOH	261(4.20),268s(4.12), 283s(3.44)	142-0761-80B
$C_{19}H_{20}F_2N_2S$ Piperazine, 1-(6,9-difluoro-10,11-di-hydrodibenzo[b,f]thiepin-10-yl)-4-methyl-	MeOH	222(3.98),259(3.75), 291(3.72)	73-2688-80
$C_{19}H_{20}F_2O_5$ Gibb-3-ene-1α,4aα-carbolactone, 10β-carboxy-8,8-difluoro-1β-methyl-2-oxo-	n.s.g.	232(3.60)	77-1097-80
$C_{19}H_{20}NO_2$ 5H-Benzo[g]-1,3-benzodioxolo[6,5,4-de]-quinolinium, 6,7,7a,8-tetrahydro-7,7-dimethyl-, iodide, (S)-	MeOH	210(4.50),271(4.24), 314(3.66)	73-0914-80
$C_{19}H_{20}N_2$ 4H-Pyrazole, 4,4-diethyl-3,5-diphenyl-	EtOH	220(3.9),307(4.3)	24-1507-80
$C_{19}H_{20}N_2O$ Benzenepropanenitrile, 4-methoxy-3,5-dimethyl-α-[(phenylamino)methylene]-	EtOH	210s(4.36),285(4.42), 306(4.44)	87-0535-80
Eburnamonine	MeOH	242(4.13),266(4.07), 293(3.68),302(3.68)	73-1419-80
4H-Pyrazole, 4,4-diethyl-3,5-diphenyl-, 1-oxide	EtOH	198(4.4),263(4.2), 345(4.0)	24-1507-80
$C_{19}H_{20}N_2O_3$ 3H-Naphth[1,2-e][1,3]oxazin-3-one, 1,2-dihydro-2-methyl-1-(1-methyl-4-oxo-3-piperidinyl)-, monohydro-chloride	EtOH	230(4.84),255s(3.11), 289s(3.64),323(3.23)	4-0277-80
$C_{19}H_{20}N_2O_3S$ 2-Thietanone, 4,4-dimethyl-3-[7-oxo-3-(phenylmethyl)-4-oxa-2,6-diaza-bicyclo[3.2.0]hept-2-en-6-yl]-3-(2-propenyl)-	EtOH	224(3.68)	39-0388-80C
$C_{19}H_{20}N_2O_5$ Pyrimido[1,2-a]indole-4,10-dicarboxylic acid, 3-acetyl-1,4-dihydro-, diethyl ester	EtOH	260(3.85),365(4.21)	94-2972-80
$C_{19}H_{20}N_2O_6$ 1H-Indole-3-carboxylic acid, α-[(2-ace-tyl-4-ethoxy-3,4-dioxo-1-butenyl)ami-no]-, ethyl ester	EtOH	258(4.06),367(4.25)	94-2972-80
Pyrimido[1,2-a]indole-4,10-dicarboxylic acid, 3-acetyl-1,4-dihydro-4-hydroxy-, diethyl ester	EtOH	256(4.05),360(4.36)	94-2972-80
$C_{19}H_{20}N_2O_7$ Morphinan-10-one, 6,7-didehydro-4,5-epoxy-8-hydroxy-3,6-dimethoxy-17-methyl-14-nitro-, (5α,8β)-	n.s.g.	241(4.09),288(4.04), 320(3.84)	77-0022-80
$C_{19}H_{20}N_2O_8S_2$ 5-Thia-1-azabicyclo[4.2.0]oct-2-ene-2-carboxylic acid, 3-(1,2-diacetoxy-	n.s.g.	237(4.09),260(3.87)	32-0519-80

Compound	Solvent	$\lambda_{max}(\log \epsilon)$	Ref.
ethyl)-8-oxo-7-[(2-thienylacetyl)am- ino]-, [6R-(6α,7β)]- (cont.)			32-0519-80
$C_{19}H_{20}N_2O_{13}S$ β-D-Glucopyranosiduronic acid, 2,4-di- nitrophenyl 1-thio-, methyl ester, 2,3,4-triacetate	MeOH	309(4.11)	106-0460-80
$C_{19}H_{20}N_2O_{14}$ β-D-Glucopyranosiduronic acid, 2,4-di- nitrophenyl, methyl ester, 2,3,4- triacetate	MeOH	285(4.25)	106-0460-80
$C_{19}H_{20}N_2S_2$ Piperazine, 1-[8-(methylthio)dibenzo- [b,f]thiepin-10-yl]-	MeOH	275(4.38),311(3.96)	73-0504-80
$C_{19}H_{20}N_3$ Pyrrolo[3,2-e]benzimidazolium, 1,6-di- hydro-1,7,8-trimethyl-3-(phenylmeth- yl)-, iodide	EtOH	253(4.18),310(4.00)	103-1039-80
$C_{19}H_{20}N_3O$ Pyridinium, 4-[2-(2,3-dihydro-1,5-di- methyl-3-oxo-2-phenyl-1H-pyrazol-4- yl)ethenyl]-1-methyl-, perchlorate	HOAc	400(4.38)	48-0543-80
$C_{19}H_{20}N_4$ Methanimidamide, N'-[4-(2,4-cyclopenta- dien-1-ylidenemethyl)-3-methyl-1-phen- yl-1H-pyrazol-5-yl]-N,N-dimethyl-	EtOH	225(4.24),255(4.19), 285(4.26),364(4.18)	114-0127-80C
$C_{19}H_{20}N_4O$ 4H-Imidazol-4-one, 1,5-dihydro-5,5-di- phenyl-2-(1-piperazinyl)-	EtOH	222.2(4.55)	56-2217-80
$C_{19}H_{20}N_4O_8$ 2-Pyridinecarboxamide, N-[1-(3,5-di-O- acetyl-β-D-arabinofuranosyl)-1,2-di- hydro-2-oxo-4-pyrimidinyl]-	MeOH	264(4.20),309(3.95)	44-1577-80
$C_{19}H_{20}N_5O_4$ Imidazo[2,1-i]purin-6-ium, 3,9-dihydro- 9-(phenylmethyl)-3-β-D-ribofuranosyl-, chloride	pH 1 and 7	277(4.11)	35-0770-80
$C_{19}H_{20}N_7O_{11}PS$ Araadenosine, 2',6-anhydro-6-hydroxy- arauridylyl-(3'→5')-2'-deoxy-2',8- epithio-	pH 2 pH 7 pH 12	255(4.38),277(4.31) 255(4.38),276(4.28) 256(4.31),276(4.29)	94-0189-80 94-0189-80 94-0189-80
$C_{19}H_{20}Ni_2O_3$ Nickel, di-μ-carbonyl[μ-[(1,2,3,4,5- η:1',2',3',4',5'-η)-(1,5-dimethyl- 3-oxo-1,5-pentanediyl]di-2,4-cyclo- pentadien-1-ylidene]]di-, (Ni-Ni)	hexane	224s(3.8),245s(3.6), 296s(3.7),312(3.7), 367(3.6),502(3.04)	24-1420-80
Nickel, di-μ-carbonyl[μ-[(1,2,3,4,5- η:1',2',3',4',5'-η)-(2,4-dimethyl- 3-oxo-1,5-pentanediyl)di-2,4-cyclo- pentadien-1-ylidene]]di-, (Ni-Ni)	hexane	226s(4.2),244s(4.1), 292(4.2),307(4.1), 363(4.1),503(3.6)	24-1420-80

Compound	Solvent	$\lambda_{max}(\log \epsilon)$	Ref.
$C_{19}H_{20}O$			
Anthracene, 2-[(1,1-dimethylethoxy)-methyl]-	C_6H_{12}	308(4.95),323(3.10), 338(3.30),356(2.39), 376(3.30)	44-4183-80
Benzeneethanol, α-methyl-β-(phenylmethylene)-α-2-propenyl-, (E)-	MeOH	255(4.18)	44-2181-80
$C_{19}H_{20}O_2$			
Benzenepentanal, α,α-dimethyl-δ-oxo-β-phenyl-	EtOH	245(4.06),277(3.01)	78-0631-80
1,3-Propanedione, 2,2-diethyl-1,3-diphenyl-	EtOH	249(4.3),290s(--), 323(2.5)	24-1507-80
1,1'-Spiro[bi[1H-indene]-4,4'-diol, 2,2',3,3'-tetrahydro-7,7'-dimethyl-	EtOH	206(4.94),228s(4.45), 277(3.53),284(3.94)	138-0743-80
Spiro[cyclopentane-1,7'(8'H)-[6H]dibenzo[f,h][1,5]dioxonin]	CHCl₃	247(3.96),284(3.72)	49-0413-80
$C_{19}H_{20}O_4$			
Butanedioic acid, methyl-, bis(phenylmethyl) ester	EtOH	260(2.33)	24-0650-80
Propanedioic acid, dimethyl-, bis(phenylmethyl) ester	CHCl₃	255(2.32)	24-0650-80
Tricyclo[11.3.1.1⁵,⁹]octadeca-1(17),5-8,13,15-pentaene-7,18-dione, 15-hydroxy-17-methoxy-, anti	CHCl₃ dioxan	397(3.50) 393(3.53)	24-0241-80 24-0241-80
Tricyclo[11.3.1.1⁵,⁹]octadeca-1(17),5-8,13,15-pentaene-7,18-dione, 17-hydroxy-15-methoxy-, anti	CHCl₃ dioxan	403(3.33) 394(3.39)	24-0241-80 24-0241-80
syn	dioxan	438(3.42)	24-0241-80
$C_{19}H_{20}O_5$			
Benzenemethanol, α-[(2,4-dimethoxyphenyl)methylene]-4-methoxy-, acetate, (Z)-	MeOH	237s(4.05),300s(4.33), 325(4.41)	18-0179-80
Benzenemethanol, α-[(3,4-dimethoxyphenyl)methylene]-4-methoxy-, acetate, (Z)-	MeOH	320(4.48)	18-0179-80
1,4-Benzodioxin-2-methanol, 2,3-dihydro-3-(4-hydroxy-3-methoxyphenyl)-6-(1-propenyl)-, trans	EtOH	259(4.23),266(4.23), 287s(3.92),302(3.74)	39-0775-80C
1,4-Benzodioxin-2-methanol, 2,3-dihydro-3-(4-hydroxy-3-methoxyphenyl)-6-(2-propenyl)-, trans	EtOH	227(4.24),282(3.87)	39-0775-80C
2H-1-Benzopyran, 7-methoxy-3-(2,3,4-trimethoxyphenyl)-	MeOH	238s(4.29),300s(4.23), 322(4.34)	94-1172-80
4H-1-Benzopyran-4-one, 2,3-dihydro-5,7-dihydroxy-3-[(4-methoxyphenyl)methyl]-6,8-dimethyl-	EtOH EtOH-NaOAc EtOH-AlCl₃	220(4.62),298(4.53) 344(--) 323(--)	94-1477-80 94-1477-80 94-1477-80
5,11a-Epoxy-11aH-dibenz[b,g]oxocin-7,10(9H,11H)-dione, 5,6-dihydro-8-hydroxy-9,9,11,11-tetramethyl-, (±)-vafzelin)	dioxan	218(3.59),250s(3.42), 283(3.65)	35-7365-80
1,4-Ethanoanthracene-9,10-dione, 5-ethoxy-1,4,4a,9a-tetrahydro-8-hydroxy-1-methoxy-	MeOH	237(4.11),379(3.62)	24-1575-80
3-Pentenoic acid, 2-(ethoxycarbonyl)-3-(2-methoxy-1-naphthalenyl)-, (E)-	CHCl₃	255(4.41),312(3.62)	120-0250-80
2-Propen-1-one, 1-(2-hydroxy-4,6-dimethoxy-3-methylphenyl)-3-(4-methoxyphenyl)-	EtOH EtOH-AlCl₃	378(4.67) 412(--)	94-2487-80 94-2487-80
$C_{19}H_{20}O_6$			
2H-1-Benzopyran-5-ol, 3,4-dihydro-	EtOH	287(4.41),301(4.52)	102-1195-80

Compound	Solvent	$\lambda_{max}(\log \epsilon)$	Ref.
2-(6-hydroxy-1,3-benzodioxol-5-yl)-7-methoxy-6,8-dimethyl- (cont.)	EtOH-NaOH	287(4.30),312(4.44)	102-1195-80
Ethanone, 2-acetoxy-2-(2,4-dimethoxyphenyl)-1-(2-methoxyphenyl)-	MeOH	236s(4.05),253(3.94), 288(3.65),313(3.58)	18-0179-80
1-Propanone, 3-(1,3-benzodioxol-5-yl)-1-(2-hydroxy-4,6-dimethoxy-3-methylphenyl)-	EtOH EtOH-AlCl$_3$	282(4.28) 318(--)	94-2487-80 94-2487-80
$C_{19}H_{20}O_7$			
6H-Benzofuro[3,2-c][1]benzopyran-8-ol, 6a,11a-dihydro-3,4,9,10-tetramethoxy-, (6aR-cis)-	EtOH EtOH-NaOH	232(4.54),298(4.06) 274(4.26),315(4.30)	102-2003-80 102-2003-80
1,3-Propanedione, 1-(3,4-dimethoxyphenyl)-3-(2-hydroxy-4,6-dimethoxyphenyl)-	MeOH	205(4.21),225(4.13), 290(4.04),380(3.6)	118-0874-80
1,3-Propanedione, 1-(2-hydroxy-4-methoxyphenyl)-3-(3,4,5-trimethoxyphenyl)-	MeOH	205(4.33),270(3.60), 385(4.18)	118-0874-80
$C_{19}H_{20}O_8$			
6H-Benzofuro[3,2-c][1]benzopyran-2,8-diol, 6a,11a-dihydro-3,4,9,10-tetramethoxy-, (6aR-cis)-	EtOH EtOH-NaOH	225(4.39),297(4.11) 241(4.41),307(3.48)	102-2003-80 102-2003-80
$C_{19}H_{21}NO$			
2-Cyclohexen-1-one, 2-[(1-methylethyl)amino]-3-(1-naphthalenyl)-	ether	218(4.74),290(3.84), 340(3.81)	78-1585-80
2-Cyclohexen-1-one, 2-[(1-methylethyl)amino]-3-(2-naphthalenyl)-	ether	218(4.71),222(4.68), 290(4.13),340(4.08)	78-1585-80
1-Penten-3-one, 1-(diphenylamino)-4,4-dimethyl-	EtOH	230(3.94),280s(3.84), 335(4.35)	4-0507-80
2-Propen-1-one, 3-(diethylamino)-1,2-diphenyl-	EtOH	240(3.99),312(4.22)	4-1201-80
$C_{19}H_{21}NO_2$			
Benzenebutanamide, α,2,5-trimethyl-N-phenyl-	EtOH	245(4.43)	115-0401-80
Isoxazole, 5-ethoxy-4,5-dihydro-4,4-dimethyl-3,5-diphenyl-	EtOH	191(4.7),203s(--), 252(4.0)	24-1507-80
5-Isoxazolol, 4,4-diethyl-4,5-dihydro-3,5-diphenyl-	EtOH	252(4.0)	24-1507-80
3-Penten-2-one, 4-[(2-hydroxy-2,2-diphenylethyl)amino]-	EtOH	313(4.26),318s(4.23)	18-1183-80
$C_{19}H_{21}NO_2S$			
Benzenamine, N-[1,2-dimethyl-4-[(4-methylphenyl)sulfonyl]-2-butenylidene]-	EtOH	234(4.79)	104-0849-80
$C_{19}H_{21}NO_3$			
Benzo[5,6]cyclohepta[1,2-b]pyrrole-2-acetic acid, 1,4,5,10-tetrahydro-1-methyl-10-oxo-, 1-methylethyl ester	MeOH	226(3.80),256(3.69), 328(4.12)	4-1081-80
Carbamic acid, [2-hydroxy-2-methyl-1-(phenylmethylene)propyl]-, phenylmethyl ester, (Z)-	EtOH	260(4.18)	39-0858-80C
4H-Dibenzo[de,g]quinolin-9-ol, 5,6,6a,7-tetrahydro-1,2-dimethoxy-6-methyl-	EtOH	213(4.17),235s(3.91), 280(3.84)	88-0723-80
4H-Dibenzo[de,g]quinolin-11-ol, 5,6,6a,7-tetrahydro-2,10-dimethoxy-6-methyl-	EtOH	268(4.17),278(4.18), 300(3.91)	44-2275-80
Norapocodeine, 6-(2-hydroxyethyl)-	EtOH	274(3.62)	44-2275-80

Compound	Solvent	$\lambda_{max}(\log \epsilon)$	Ref.
$C_{19}H_{21}NO_3S$			
Benzenamine, N-[1,2-dimethyl-4-(phenyl-sulfonyl)-2-butenylidene]-4-methoxy-	EtOH	240(4.20)	104-0849-80
1-Naphthalenesulfonamide, N-(1-methyl-ethyl)-N-(6-oxo-1-cyclohexen-1-yl)-	MeOH	221(4.74),286(3.87)	78-1585-80
2-Naphthalenesulfonamide, N-(1-methyl-ethyl)-N-(6-oxo-1-cyclohexen-1-yl)-	ether	228(4.41),270(4.72)	78-1585-80
$C_{19}H_{21}NO_4$			
4H-Dibenzo[de,g]quinoline-1,10-diol, 5,6,6a,7-tetrahydro-2,11-dimethoxy-6-methyl-, (S)-	EtOH	225(4.39),275(3.87), 313(3.67)	105-0177-80
4H-Dibenzo[de,g]quinolin-10-ol, 5,6,6a,7-tetrahydro-1,2,9-tri-methoxy- (norlirioferine)	EtOH	220(4.45),273s(3.95), 280(4.02),305(3.98), 316s(3.91)	142-1131-80
Isoquinoline, 3-(3,4-dimethoxyphenyl)-3,4-dihydro-6,7-dimethoxy-	n.s.g.	278(4.24),312(4.03)	2-0556-80
Isosinoacutine	MeOH	235(4.08),283(3.81)	25-0662-80
	MeOH-base	240(--),284(--)	25-0662-80
3H-7,12b-Methanodibenzo[c,e]azocin-3-one, 5,6,7,8-tetrahydro-2,10,11-trimethoxy-, hydrochloride	EtOH	238(4.24),275(3.78)	89-1018-80
Norcorydine	EtOH	223(4.36),270(3.81), 310(3.40)	105-0177-80
Norisocorydine	EtOH	220(4.34),270(3.84), 308(3.46)	105-0177-80
4(5H)-Oxazolone, 5-(2-acetoxy-1,1-di-methylethyl)-2-(4-phenyl-1,3-buta-dienyl)-, perchlorate	HOAc	354(4.59)	103-0023-80
	HOAc-HClO_4	406(4.50)	103-0023-80
1H-Pyrrole-2-acetic acid, 1-ethenyl-3-(methoxycarbonyl)-4-(2-phenyl-ethyl)-, methyl ester	MeOH	220(4.27),231(4.30), 263(4.17)	4-1081-80
1H-Pyrrolizine-1,7-dicarboxylic acid, 2,3-dihydro-6-(2-phenylethyl)-, dimethyl ester	MeOH	215(4.16),240(3.94), 260(3.80)	4-1081-80
$C_{19}H_{21}N_3$			
1H,11H-4,5-Ethanopyrimido[1,2-a]quin-azoline, 2,3,4,4a,5,6-hexahydro-6-phenyl-	pH 1	242(3.94),287(3.20)	94-2587-80
	pH 13	243(3.92),288(3.23)	94-2587-80
	EtOH	250(3.99),293(3.28)	94-2587-80
10H-3,4-Propanoimidazo[1,2-a]quinazo-line, 1,2,3,3a,4,5-hexahydro-5-phen-yl-	pH 1	247(3.99),293(3.32)	94-2587-80
	pH 13	252(3.97),299(3.32)	94-2587-80
	EtOH	255(4.04),303(3.45)	94-2587-80
$C_{19}H_{21}N_3O$			
1,3-Ethano-1,3,7-benzotriazecin-2-one, 1,2,3,4,5,6,7,8-octahydro-8-phenyl-	pH 1	256(3.99)	94-2587-80
	pH 13	259(3.99)	94-2587-80
	EtOH	256(3.99)	94-2587-80
	CHCl_3	250(3.86)(end abs.)	94-2587-80
5,7-Ethano-1,5,7-benzotriazecin-6-one, 1,2,3,4,5,6,7,8-octahydro-8-phenyl-	pH 1 and 13	259(3.89)	94-2587-80
	EtOH	261(3.92),265(3.91), 308(3.40)	94-2587-80
	CHCl_3	264s(3.89),268(3.90), 311(3.49)	94-2587-80
Imidazo[2,1-b]quinazoline, 5-ethoxy-1,2,3,5-tetrahydro-1-methyl-5-phenyl-	pH 1	250(4.52)	94-2024-80
	pH 13	272(4.20)	94-2024-80
	EtOH	274(4.21)	94-2024-80
1,2,4-Triazine, 2,5-dihydro-3-methoxy-2-methyl-5,6-bis(4-methylphenyl)-	EtOH	220s(4.23),234s(4.14), 304(3.96)	44-4587-80 +88-1529-80

Compound	Solvent	$\lambda_{max}(\log \epsilon)$	Ref.
$C_{19}H_{21}N_3O_2$ 2,5-Piperazinedione, 3-[[2-(1,1-dimeth-yl-2-propenyl)-1H-indol-3-yl]methyl-ene]-6-methyl- (neoechinulin A)	MeOH	223(4.48),283(3.94), 289(3.93),335(4.02)	88-2817-80
$C_{19}H_{21}N_3O_2S$ 1,2,4-Triazine, 2,5-dihydro-5,6-bis(4-methoxyphenyl)-2-methyl-3-(methyl-thio)-	EtOH	225s(4.33),245s(4.14), 282(3.92),312(4.08)	44-4587-80 +88-1529-80
$C_{19}H_{21}N_3O_3$ 1,2,4-Triazine, 2,5-dihydro-3-methoxy-5,6-bis(4-methoxyphenyl)-2-methyl-	EtOH	223s(4.25),252s(4.00), 284s(3.95),305(4.06)	44-4587-80 +88-1529-80
$C_{19}H_{21}N_3O_4$ 12H-Dibenzo[c,h][1,2,6]triazonine-12-carboxylic acid, 1,1-dimethylethyl ester, 5,6-dioxide	EtOH	207(4.26),280(3.99)	44-4597-80
$C_{19}H_{21}N_3S$ 1,2,4-Triazine, 2,5-dihydro-2-methyl-5,6-bis(4-methylphenyl)-3-(methyl-thio)-	EtOH	220s(4.26),235s(4.15), 310(3.90)	44-4587-80 +88-1529-80
$C_{19}H_{21}N_5O_7S_2$ 1H-Pyrazolo[3,4-d]pyrimidine-3-carbo-nitrile, 4,6-bis(methylthio)-1-(2,3,5-tri-O-acetyl-β-D-ribofuranosyl)-	EtOH	205(4.28),254(4.4), 296(4.19),322(4.04)	103-0182-80
$C_{19}H_{21}N_6O_7P$ Adenosine, N-[(2-cyanoethoxy)phenoxy-phosphinyl]-	pH 4.0	261(4.23),268s(4.15), 285s(3.43)	142-0761-80B
	pH 10.0	208s(4.39),275(4.38)	142-0761-80B
	MeOH	259(4.21),269s(4.09), 280s(3.56)	142-0761-80B
$C_{19}H_{21}N_7O_2$ Adenosine, 5'-[(2-amino-1-oxo-3-phenyl-propyl)amino]-2',3'-didehydro-2',3',5'-trideoxy-	H_2O	261(4.14)	136-0067-80A
$C_{19}H_{22}ClNO_4$ 1H-Pyrrole-2-acetic acid, 1-(2-chloro-ethyl)-3-(methoxycarbonyl)-4-(2-phenylethyl)-, methyl ester	MeOH	215(4.25),239(4.01), 260(3.81)	4-1081-80
$C_{19}H_{22}N_2O$ Acetamide, N-(1,2,3,4-tetrahydro-3,3-dimethyl-4-phenyl-6-isoquinolinyl)-	EtOH	208s(4.59),247(4.18)	4-1563-80
Benzenamine, N,N-dimethyl-4-[2-(3-phen-yl-2-oxazolidinyl)ethenyl]-	MeCN	248(4.20),302(4.39)	44-2099-80
	50% dioxan-pH 4.82	498(4.81)	44-2099-80
	50% dioxan-KOH	303(4.41)(changing)	44-2099-80
$C_{19}H_{22}N_2O_2$ Indolizino[8,1-ef][1]benzazonin-6(5H)-one, 8a-ethyl-7,8,8a,9,10,11-hexahy-dro-7-hydroxy-	MeOH	220(4.11),268(3.90)	78-0511-80

Compound	Solvent	$\lambda_{max}(\log \epsilon)$	Ref.
$C_{19}H_{22}N_2O_3$			
1H-Indolizino[8,7-b]indole-2-propanoic acid, α-ethyl-2,3,5,6,11,11b-hexahydro-3-oxo-	EtOH	223(4.52),281(3.83), 298(4.19)	78-1063-80
$C_{19}H_{22}N_2O_4S$			
2-Azaspiro[4.4]non-3-ene-4-carboxylic acid, 6-[(2-aminophenyl)thio]-2,3-dimethyl-1,8-dioxo-, ethyl ester	MeOH	235(4.28),300(4.22)	24-3405-80
1H-Indole-3-carboxylic acid, 7-[(2-aminophenyl)thio]-5,6,7,7a-tetrahydro-7a-hydroxy-1,2-dimethyl-5-oxo-, ethyl ester	MeOH	237(4.27),290(4.32), 405(4.27)	24-3405-80
$C_{19}H_{22}N_2O_5S$			
Benzeneacetamide, N-[9,9a-dihydro-9a-[1-methyl-1-(methylthio)ethyl]-1,7-dioxo-1H,3H,7H-oxazolo[4,3-c][1,4]-oxazepin-6-yl]-	EtOH	208(3.95),285(3.83)	39-0388-80C
$C_{19}H_{22}N_2O_8$			
Imidazo[1,2-a]pyridine-5,6,7,8-tetracarboxylic acid, 3-(1,1-dimethylethyl)-, tetramethyl ester	EtOH	261(4.34),302(3.52), 358(3.60)	18-3308-80
$C_{19}H_{22}N_2S$			
Aspidospermidine-8-thione, 1,2-didehydro-, (±)-	EtOH	223(4.23),274(4.30)	4-1133-80
$C_{19}H_{22}N_3O_2S$			
Pyridinium, 4-(dimethylamino)-1-[[5-(dimethylamino)-1-naphthalenyl]sulfonyl]-, chloride	H_2O	303(4.48),350(3.78)	77-0993-80
$C_{19}H_{22}N_4$			
1H-Benzimidazole, 2-[(2,3-dimethylphenyl)azo]-1-ethyl-5,6-dimethyl-	MeOH	402(3.38)	104-2008-80
1H-Benzimidazole, 2-[(2,4-dimethylphenyl)azo]-1-ethyl-5,6-dimethyl-	MeOH	405(3.55)	104-2008-80
1H-Benzimidazole, 2-[(2,5-dimethylphenyl)azo]-1-ethyl-5,6-dimethyl-	MeOH	403(3.49)	104-2008-80
1H-Benzimidazole, 2-[(2,6-dimethylphenyl)azo]-1-ethyl-5,6-dimethyl-	MeOH	384(3.34)	104-2008-80
1H-Benzimidazole, 2-[(3,4-dimethylphenyl)azo]-1-ethyl-5,6-dimethyl-	MeOH	415(3.49)	104-2008-80
$C_{19}H_{22}N_4OS$			
4(1H)-Pyridinone, 3-(4,5-dihydro-4-phenyl-5-thioxo-1H-1,2,4-triazol-3-yl)-5-hexyl-	EtOH	260(4.23)	4-0175-80
$C_{19}H_{22}N_4O_6$			
D-Ribitol, 1-deoxy-1-(3,4-dihydro-7-methyl-2,4-dioxo-6-(phenylmethyl)-8(2H)-pteridinyl]-	pH 1	258(4.27),278s(4.12), 405(4.08)	39-2645-80C
	pH 13	281(4.22),316(4.11)	39-2645-80C
$C_{19}H_{22}N_5O_6PS$			
Adenosine, N-ethyl-8-[(phenylmethyl)thio]-, cyclic 3',5'-(hydrogen phosphate)	pH 1	286(4.32)	87-0242-80
	pH 7	291(4.23)	87-0242-80

Compound	Solvent	$\lambda_{max}(\log \epsilon)$	Ref.
$C_{19}H_{22}N_6O_7$			
Octanamide, N-[[(2,4-dinitrophenyl)-hydrazonyl]-1,2,5,6-tetrahydrodioxo-3-pyridinyl]-	$CHCl_3$	460(4.65)	39-1782-80C
$C_{19}H_{22}N_6O_8$			
Acetamide, N-[5-[bis(2-hydroxyethyl)-amino]-2-[(2,4-dinitrophenyl)azo]-4-methoxyphenyl]-	EtOH	575(4.09)	62-0158-80
$C_{19}H_{22}O$			
D-Homo-C,18-dinorandrosta-4,13,15,17-tetraen-3-one, 17a-methyl-	EtOH	219(3.88),237(3.92), 272(2.48)	18-0243-80
$C_{19}H_{22}OS$			
Benzenemethanol, α-[1-[(2,4,6-trimeth-ylphenyl)thio]-2-propenyl]-	MeOH	233(4.16),268(3.52)	12-1345-80
Benzenemethanol, α-[3-[(2,4,6-trimeth-ylphenyl)thio]-2-propenyl]-, (E)-	MeOH	234(4.18),272(3.45)	12-1345-80
(Z)-	MeOH	239(4.15),270(3.67)	12-1345-80
$C_{19}H_{22}O_2$			
Estra-1,3,5(10),9(11)-tetraen-17-one, 3-methoxy-, (±)-	MeOH	262(4.29),296s(3.53)	89-1027-80
Spiro[benzofuran-2(3H),1'-[3,5]cyclo-hexadien]-2'-one, 3',4,5,5',6',7-hexamethyl- (4λ,3ε)	EtOH	220(5.09),283(4.53), 289(4.55),340(?)	39-1986-80C
$C_{19}H_{22}O_2S$			
Benzenemethanol, α-[3-[(2,4,6-trimeth-ylphenyl)sulfinyl]-2-propenyl]-, (E)-	MeOH	239(4.15),278s(3.46), 287s(3.34)	12-2635-80
$C_{19}H_{22}O_3$			
1H-Cyclopenta[a]phenanthrene-3,17(2H-4H)-dione, 5,6,7,10,15,16-hexahydro-11-methoxy-10-methyl-, cis	EtOH	259(4.15),317(3.76)	78-2513-80
trans	EtOH	264(4.19),319(3.82)	78-2513-80
18-Nor-5α-androsta-8(9),11,13(14)-tri-ene-3,17-dione, 11-methoxy-, (±)-	EtOH	264(4.19),319(3.81)	78-2513-80
$C_{19}H_{22}O_4$			
Bicyclo[6.4.1]trideca-2,6,8,10,12-pentaene-3,6-dicarboxylic acid, diethyl ester	dioxan	275(4.62),356(3.88)	89-0919-80
1,3-Cyclopentanedione, 2-[3-(2,4-di-methoxyphenyl)-2,4-pentadienyl]-2-methyl-	EtOH	228(4.36),280(3.79)	2-0433-80
Milanjilactone B	EtOH	257(4.11)	31-0028-80
1-Phenanthreneacetic acid, 2,3,4,4a-9,10-hexahydro-7-methoxy-4a-methyl-2-oxo-, methyl ester, (±)-	EtOH	227(4.2),247(4.2)	39-2511-80C
1-Phenanthrenepropanoic acid, 4b,5,6-7,9,10-hexahydro-4-methoxy-4b-methyl-7-oxo-, (±)-	EtOH	230(4.28)	78-2513-80
1-Phenanthrenepropanoic acid, 4b,5,6-7,9,10-hexahydro-4-methoxy-7-oxo-, methyl ester	EtOH	227(4.20),265(3.62)	78-2513-80
$C_{19}H_{22}O_5$			
Benzoic acid, 2-[(2,5-dimethoxy-4-meth-ylphenyl)methyl]-3-methoxy-, methyl ester	$CHCl_3$	295(3.85)	44-0012-80

Compound	Solvent	$\lambda_{max}(\log \epsilon)$	Ref.
Bicyclo[3.2.1]octan-3-one, 7-(1,3-ben-zodioxol-5-yl)-2,8-dihydroxy-6-meth-yl-5-(2-propenyl)-, [1S-(2-endo,6-exo,6-exo,8-anti)]-	MeOH	234(3.72),286(3.66)	102-0474-80
Milanjilactone A	EtOH	220(4.00)	31-0028-80
1-Propanone, 1-(2-hydroxy-4,6-dimeth-oxy-3-methylphenyl)-3-(4-methoxy-phenyl)-	EtOH	220(4.34),290(4.32)	94-2487-80
	EtOH-AlCl$_3$	317(--)	94-2487-80
Spiro[dibenz[b,d]oxepin-1(2H),2'-[1,3]-dioxolane], 3,4-dihydro-9,10-dimeth-oxy-6-methyl-	MeCN	205(4.45),227(4.40), 311(3.83)	24-3249-80
$C_{19}H_{22}O_6$			
5-Benzofuranpropanol, 2,3-dihydro-7-hy-droxy-2-(4-hydroxy-3-methoxyphenyl)-3-(hydroxymethyl)- (cedrusin)	MeOH	217(4.04),224(4.24), 279(3.94)	102-1260-80
2H-1-Benzopyran-3,4,7-triol, 3,4-dihy-dro-5-methoxy-2-(4-methoxyphenyl)-6,8-dimethyl-, [2R-(2α,3β,4β)]-	MeOH	227(3.66),275(2.51), 282(2.45)	94-1884-80
1-Propanone, 3-(3,4-dimethoxyphenyl)-1-(2-hydroxy-4,6-dimethoxyphenyl)-	MeOH	286(4.26)	100-0739-80
	EtOH	207(4.37),220(4.25), 288(4.23)	102-0476-80
$C_{19}H_{22}O_7$			
Ethanone, 1-(2-hydroxy-4,6-dimethoxy-phenyl)-2-(2,4,5-trimethoxyphenyl)-	EtOH	289(4.35)	18-0831-80
$C_{19}H_{22}O_8$			
2H-Oxireno[h][2]benzoxacyclotetradecin-2,8(1aH)-dione, 5,6,13,14,15,15a-hexahydro-9,13,14-trihydroxy-11-methoxy-6-methyl- (hypothemycin)	MeOH	220(4.58),267(4.15), 307(3.85)	88-2011-80
$C_{19}H_{23}BrO_3$			
Benzenemethanol, 3-[(3-bromo-2-hydroxy-5-methylphenyl)methyl]-5-(1,1-dimeth-ylethyl)-2-hydroxy-	dioxan	280s(3.76),287(3.78)	126-0461-80B
$C_{19}H_{23}N$			
Benzenamine, N-[1-methyl-2-(2,3,5,6-tetramethylphenyl)ethylidene]-	dioxan	272f(3.80)	24-2462-80
Benzenamine, 2,4,6-trimethyl-N-[(2,4,6-trimethylphenyl)methylene]-, cis	$C_6H_{12}Me$ at $-100°$	227(4.20),247(4.15), 257s(--),327(2.48)	39-1282-80B
trans	$C_6H_{11}Me$ at $-100°$	224s(--),267(4.43), 304s(--),337(2.40)	39-1282-80B
$C_{19}H_{23}NO$			
1H-Dibenzo[a,f]quinolizin-1-one, 2,3,4,6,7,11b,12,13-octahydro-3,3-dimethyl-	MeOH	211(4.07),319(4.49)	135-0956-80
$C_{19}H_{23}NO_3$			
1H-2,3-Benzoxazocine, 3,4,5,6-tetra-hydro-8,9-dimethoxy-3-methyl-1-phenyl-	MeOH	235s(3.93),283s(3.54), 286(3.55),290s(2.51)	12-1323-80
1H-Dibenzo[a,f]quinolizin-1-one, 2,3,4,6,7,11b,12,13-octahydro-9,10-dimethoxy-	MeOH	227(3.98),318(4.52)	135-0956-80
$C_{19}H_{23}NO_4$			
3H-Cyclobut[b]indole-1,2-dicarboxylic	EtOH	252(3.62),295(3.21),	44-0456-80

Compound	Solvent	$\lambda_{max}(\log \epsilon)$	Ref.
acid, 7b-(1,1-dimethylethyl)-2a,7b-dihydro-3-methyl-, dimethyl ester		411(2.81)	44-0456-80
6,7-Isoquinolinediol, 1-[(3,4-dimethoxyphenyl)methyl]-1,2,3,4-tetrahydro-2-methyl-	EtOH	284(3.83)	39-1696-80B
1H-Pyrrole-2-acetic acid, 3-carboxy-1-methyl-4-(2-phenylethyl)-, α-(1-methylethyl) ester	MeOH	243(3.88),260(3.73)	4-1081-80
Reticuline	EtOH	286(4.10)	105-0177-80
$C_{19}H_{23}NO_5$			
1H-Pyrrole-2-acetic acid, 1-(1-hydroxyethyl)-3-(methoxycarbonyl)-4-(2-phenylethyl)-, methyl ester	MeOH	213(4.18),239(3.95), 260(3.78)	4-1081-80
1H-Pyrrole-2-acetic acid, 1-(2-hydroxyethyl)-3-(methoxycarbonyl)-4-(2-phenylethyl)-, methyl ester	MeOH	217(4.14),242(3.95), 261(3.79)	4-1081-80
$C_{19}H_{23}N_2$			
Methanaminium, N-[3-(6-azulenyl)-5-(dimethylamino)-2,4-pentadienylidene]-N-methyl-, perchlorate	EtOH	277(4.61),285(4.58), 308(4.16),346(3.98), 446(4.68),463(4.10), 590(3.59),638(3.49), 705(2.07)	118-0030-80
$C_{19}H_{23}N_2O$			
3H-Indolium, 2-[2-[5-(dimethylamino)-2-furanyl]ethenyl]-1,3,3-trimethyl-	H_2O	560(4.73)	140-1570-80
protonated	H_2O	298(4.40)	140-1570-80
hydroxide	H_2O	270(4.43)	140-1570-80
$C_{19}H_{23}N_2O_3P$			
Phosphonic acid, [[2-(phenylmethyl)-1H-benzimidazol-1-yl]methyl-, diethyl ester	EtOH	245(<u>4.0</u>),275(<u>4.1</u>), 282(<u>4.1</u>)	65-1217-80
$C_{19}H_{23}N_2S$			
3H-Indolium, 2-[2-[5-(dimethylamino)-2-thienyl]ethenyl]-1,3,3-trimethyl-	H_2O	568(4.80)	140-1570-80
protonated	H_2O	355(4.73)	140-1570-80
hydroxide	H_2O	380(4.60)	140-1570-80
$C_{19}H_{23}N_3$			
1,2-Ethanediamine, N,N,N'-trimethyl-N'-(3-phenyl-1H-indol-1-yl)-	pH 1	222(4.45),263(4.16)	145-0919-80
$C_{19}H_{23}N_3O_2$			
2-Imidazolidinone, 5-ethoxy-4,4-dimethyl-5-phenyl-1-(phenylamino)-	EtOH	209(4.2),234(4.1), 280(3.3)	5-1016-80
2-Imidazolidinone, 5-hydroxy-4,4-dimethyl-5-(4-methylphenyl)-1-[(2-methylphenyl)amino]-	EtOH	198(4.7),217(4.2), 233(4.1),281(3.3)	5-1016-80
$C_{19}H_{23}N_3O_3$			
Benzoic acid, 4-[[4-(diethylamino)-2-ethoxyphenyl]azo]-	20% MeOH	480(4.57)	39-0937-80B
anion	463(4.58)	39-0937-80B
dication	H_2SO_4	384(4.41),465(4.37)	39-0937-80B
$C_{19}H_{23}N_3S$			
1-Pyrazolidinecarbothioamide, 3,3,5-trimethyl-N,2-diphenyl-	EtOH	263(4.37)	103-0169-80

Compound	Solvent	$\lambda_{max}(\log \epsilon)$	Ref.
$C_{19}H_{23}N_4O_2S$			
Benzothiazolium, 2-[[4-[bis(2-hydroxy-ethyl)amino]phenyl]azo]-3,4-dimeth-yl-, methyl sulfate	acetone	605(4.93)	7-0167-80
Benzothiazolium, 2-[[4-[bis(2-hydroxy-ethyl)amino]phenyl]azo]-3,6-dimeth-yl-, methyl sulfate	acetone	604(4.94)	7-0167-80
$C_{19}H_{23}N_4O_3S$			
Benzothiazolium, 2-[[4-[bis(2-hydroxy-ethyl)amino]phenyl]azo]-4-methoxy-3-methyl-, methyl sulfate	acetone	609(4.81)	7-0167-80
Benzothiazolium, 2-[[4-[bis(2-hydroxy-ethyl)amino]phenyl]azo]-6-methoxy-3-methyl-, methyl sulfate	acetone	617(4.89)	7-0167-80
$C_{19}H_{23}N_5O_4$			
Adenosine, N,N-dimethyl-5'-O-(phenyl-methyl)-	EtOH	275(4.25)	44-4006-80
Cytidine, 5'-[[2-amino-3-(4-methoxy-phenyl)-1-oxopropyl]amino]-2',3'-di-dehydro-2',3',5'-trideoxy-	H_2O	272.5(4.01)	136-0067-80A
$C_{19}H_{23}N_5O_6$			
Acetamide, N-[5-[bis(2-hydroxyethyl)-amino]-4-methoxy-2-[(4-nitrophenyl)-azo]phenyl]-	EtOH	531(4.51)	62-0158-80
$C_{19}H_{23}N_5O_7S_3$			
1H-Pyrazolo[3,4-d]pyrimidine-3-carbo-thioamide, 4,6-bis(methylthio)-1-(2,3,5-tri-O-acetyl-β-D-ribofurano-syl)-	EtOH	198(4.34),254(4.37), 298(4.15)	103-0182-80
$C_{19}H_{24}Br_2N_2O_9$			
1H-Pyrazole, 4-bromo-5-(bromomethyl)-3-methyl-1-(2,3,4,6-tetra-O-acetyl-β-D-glucopyranosyl)-	EtOH	250(4.12)	4-0113-80
$C_{19}H_{24}ClN_3O_{10}$			
1H-Pyrazole-5-carboxamide, 3-(chloro-methyl)-1-(2,3,4,6-tetra-O-acetyl-α-D-glucopyranosyl)-	EtOH	227(3.99)	87-0657-80
β-	EtOH	227(3.98)	87-0657-80
$C_{19}H_{24}IN_3O_{10}$			
1H-Pyrazole-5-carboxamide, 3-(iodometh-yl)-1-(2,3,4,6-tetra-O-acetyl-β-D-glucopyranosyl)-	EtOH	228(4.10)	87-0657-80
$C_{19}H_{24}NOP$			
5H-Dibenzo[b,f]phosphepin-5-propanam-ine, 10,11-dihydro-N,N-dimethyl-, 5-oxide	EtOH	227s(4.10),263s(3.14), 270(3.27),277(3.23), 301(2.54)	139-0243-80A
$C_{19}H_{24}NO_3$			
Isoquinolinium, 1,2,3,4-tetrahydro-8-hydroxy-1-[(4-hydroxyphenyl)methyl]-7-methoxy-2,2-dimethyl-, iodide (oblongine)	EtOH	234(4.08),284(3.81), 362(3.22)	102-1882-80

Compound	Solvent	$\lambda_{max}(\log \epsilon)$	Ref.
$C_{19}H_{24}NO_4$ Oxazolium, 5-(2-acetoxy-1,1-dimethyl-ethyl)-4,5-dihydro-3-methyl-4-oxo-2-(2-phenyl-1-propenyl)-, perchlorate	HOAc	337(3.85),364(3.90)	103-0023-80
$C_{19}H_{24}NO_5$ Oxazolium, 5-(2-acetoxy-1,1-dimethyl-ethyl)-4,5-dihydro-2-[2-(4-methoxy-phenyl)ethenyl]-3-methyl-4-oxo-, perchlorate	HOAc HOAc-HClO₄	420(4.23) 420(4.16)	103-0023-80 103-0023-80
$C_{19}H_{24}N_2$ Ibogamine	MeOH	225(4.58),285(3.96), 293(3.94)	64-0219-80B
6-Isoquinolinamine, 1,2,3,4-tetrahydro-N,N,3,3-tetramethyl-4-phenyl-	EtOH	208(4.52),259(4.05), 307s(3.32)	4-1563-80
$C_{19}H_{24}N_2O$ Ibogamine pseudoindoxyl	MeOH	228(4.28),250(3.60), 255s(3.82),400(3.60)	64-0219-80B
Ibogamin-20-ol, (20R)-	MeOH	227(4.49),276s(3.73), 283(3.89),291(3.81)	64-0219-80B
Urea, N-butyl-N'-(1,2-diphenylethyl)-	EtOH	247(2.43),252(2.57), 258(2.61),264(2.56), 268(2.43)	104-0683-80
$C_{19}H_{24}N_2O_2$ Dihydrocleavamine, 16-hydroxy-21-oxo-	EtOH	225(4.63),278s(3.90), 285(3.93),294(3.87)	78-1057-80
Ibogamine pseudoindoxyl, 20-hydroxy-, (20R)-	MeOH	228(4.30),251(3.59), 256s(3.82),402(3.58)	64-0219-80B
1H-Indolizino[8,7-b]indole-2-propanoic acid, α-ethyl-2,3,5,6,11,11b-hexahy-dro-	EtOH	223(4.51),274(3.85), 279(3.84),281s(3.84), 289(3.75)	78-1057-80
$C_{19}H_{24}N_2O_5S$ 1,4-Oxazepine-3-carboxylic acid, 2,3,4,7-tetrahydro-3-[1-methyl-1-(methylthio)ethyl]-7-oxo-6-[(phenylacetyl)amino]-, methyl ester	EtOH	209(4.13),285(4.18)	39-0388-80C
$C_{19}H_{24}N_4O_2S$ 3-Pyridinecarboxylic acid, 5-hexyl-1,4-dihydro-4-oxo-, 2-[(phenylamino)-thioxomethyl]hydrazide	EtOH	257(4.07)	4-0175-80
$C_{19}H_{24}N_4O_8$ Pentanedioic acid, bis[2-(3,4-dihydro-5-methyl-2,4-dioxo-1(2H)-pyrimidin-yl)ethyl] ester	DMF	271.0(4.24)	47-0427-80
$C_{19}H_{24}N_4O_8S$ Thiazole, 2-[(2,3,5,6,8,9,11,12,14,15-decahydro-1,4,7,10,13,16-benzohexa-oxacyclooctadecin-18-yl)azo]-5-nitro-	MeCN	451(4.64)	24-0457-80
$C_{19}H_{24}N_6O_2$ Propanedioic acid, [3-hydrazono-1-(4-methylphenyl)-3-phenylpropyl]-, di-hydrazide	EtOH	248-270s(4.15)	34-0085-80

Compound	Solvent	$\lambda_{max}(\log \epsilon)$	Ref.
$C_{19}H_{24}N_6O_8S_2$ 1H-Pyrazolo[3,4-d]pyrimidine-3-carbox-imidamide, N-hydroxy-4,6-bis(methyl-thio)-1-(2,3,5-tri-O-acetyl-β-D-ribofuranosyl)-	EtOH	212(4.13),247(4.21), 264(4.20),292(4.05), 306(4.06)	103-0182-80
$C_{19}H_{24}N_6O_9$ Imidodicarbonic diamide, 2-[4-cyano-1-(2,3,5-tri-O-acetyl-β-D-ribofur-anosyl)-1H-imidazol-5-yl]-N,N'-di-methyl-	pH 1 MeOH	226s(3.98) 227s(4.06)	44-4020-80 44-4020-80
$C_{19}H_{24}N_8S_2$ Bis(tetramethylammonium) 2-mercapto-1,2-dicyanovinyl-1,2,3,3-tetracyano-propenidosulfide	EtOH	215(3.96),407(4.24)	44-5113-80
$C_{19}H_{24}O_2$ Androsta-4,6-diene-3,17-dione	EtOH	282(4.43)	39-2535-80C
$C_{19}H_{24}O_3$ Androst-4-ene-3,6,17-trione	EtOH	250(4.22)	64-0102-80B
Cyclopentanone, 3-ethenyl-2-[3-(4-meth-oxy-2-methylphenyl)-3-oxopropyl]-2-methyl-	hexane	224s(4.11),264(4.24), 290s(3.20),310s(2.36)	89-1027-80
C,18-Dinorandrost-4-ene-3,17-dione, 13α-acetyl-	EtOH	237(4.00)	18-0243-80
D-Homo-C,18-dinorandrosta-4,8(14)-di-ene-3,17-dione, 17a-hydroxy-17a-methyl-, (13α,17aβ)-	EtOH	206(3.90),232(4.00)	18-0243-80
D-Homo-C,18-dinorandrost-4-ene-3,17-di-one, 13,17a-epoxy-17a-methyl-, (13α,17aα)-	EtOH	237(3.98)	18-0243-80
$C_{19}H_{24}O_3S_2$ Cycloprop[e]indene-6b(1H)-carboxylic acid, 1a-(1,3-dithian-2-yl)-2-formyl-1a,5,6,6a-tetrahydro-5,5-dimethyl-, methyl ester, (1aα,6aβ,6bα)-(±)-	EtOH	315(4.03)	78-3367-80
$C_{19}H_{24}O_4$ Bicyclo[2.2.1]heptane-2-exo-carboxylic acid, endo-2-(4-methoxyphenyl)-4,7,7-trimethyl-3-oxo-, methyl ester	EtOH	234(4.00),275(3.11), 281(3.08)	12-0113-80
17-Norkaur-9(11)-en-18-oic acid, 12,16-dioxo-, (4α)-	MeOH	257(3.96)	39-1270-80C
1-Phenanthrenepropanoic acid, 4b,5,6-7,8,8a,9,10-octahydro-4-methoxy-4b-methyl-7-oxo-, trans-(±)-	EtOH	276(3.26),283(3.26)	78-2513-80
$C_{19}H_{24}O_6$ Ovatifolin acetate	MeOH	212(4.00)	102-2765-80
$C_{19}H_{25}BrN_2O_9$ 1H-Pyrazole, 4-bromo-3,5-dimethyl-1-(2,3,4,6-tetra-O-acetyl-β-D-glucopyranosyl)-	EtOH	235(3.96)	4-0113-80
1H-Pyrazole, 5-(bromomethyl)-3-methyl-1-(2,3,4,6-tetra-O-acetyl-β-D-gluco-pyranosyl)-	EtOH	238(3.96)	4-0113-80

Compound	Solvent	$\lambda_{max}(\log \epsilon)$	Ref.
$C_{19}H_{25}FN_2O_{10}S$			
D-Arabinitol, 1-S-ethyl-1-C-(5-fluoro-3,4-dihydro-2,4-dioxo-1(2H)-pyrimidinyl)-1-thio-, 2,3,4,5-tetraacetate, (R)-	MeOH	270(3.9)	136-0263-80C
D-Lyxitol, 1-S-ethyl-1-C-(5-fluoro-3,4-dihydro-2,4-dioxo-1(2H)-pyrimidinyl)-1-thio-, 2,3,4,5-tetraacetate	MeOH	270(3.9)	136-0263-80C
D-Ribitol, 1-S-ethyl-1-C-(5-fluoro-3,4-dihydro-2,4-dioxo-1(2H)-pyrimidinyl)-1-thio-, 2,3,4,5-tetraacetate	MeOH	268(4.1)	136-0263-80C
D-Xylitol, 1-S-ethyl-1-C-(5-fluoro-3,4-dihydro-2,4-dioxo-1(2H)-pyrimidinyl)-1-thio-, 2,3,4,5-tetraacetate, (S)-	MeOH	270(3.9)	136-0263-80C
$C_{19}H_{25}FO_2$			
Androst-4-ene-3,17-dione, 14α-fluoro-	EtOH	239(4.11)	152-0239-80
$C_{19}H_{25}NO_3S$			
7-Azabicyclo[4.2.0]oct-5-en-1-ol, 8-ethenyl-3,3,5-trimethyl-7-[(4-methylphenyl)sulfonyl]-	ether	226(4.07),252s(3.72)	78-1585-80
Benzenesulfonamide, 4-methyl-N-2-propenyl-N-(2,4,4-trimethyl-6-oxo-1-cyclohexen-1-yl)-	ether	230(4.36),320s(2.35)	78-1585-80
$C_{19}H_{25}NO_4$			
Harnovine, N,O-dimethyl-	EtOH	270(3.91),300(3.5)	102-0998-80
$C_{19}H_{25}NO_6$			
Benzenamine, 2,4,6-trimethoxy-N-methyl-N-(2,4,6-trimethoxyphenyl)-	MeCN	224(4.32),290(4.10)	152-0389-80
$C_{19}H_{25}NO_7$			
D-Arabinitol, 1-C-[4-(methoxycarbonyl)-5-methyl-1-(phenylmethyl)-1H-pyrrol-3-yl]-, (S)-	EtOH	239(3.82),262s(--)	39-1199-80C
$C_{19}H_{25}NS$			
2H-Azeto[2,1-a]isoquinoline-2-thione, 1-(1,1-dimethylethyl)-1,4,5,9b-tetrahydro-1-(1-methyl-2-propenyl)-	3:2 isooctane-CHCl₃	272(4.2),331(1.9)	24-3010-80
$C_{19}H_{25}N_3O_2$			
Benzamide, 2-(1H-imidazol-2-ylcarbonyl)-N-(1,1,3,3-tetramethylbutyl)-	dioxan	293(4.08)	103-0247-80
$C_{19}H_{25}N_5O_6S$			
1,4,7,10-Tetraoxa-13-azacyclopentadecane, 13-[4-[(5-nitro-2-thiazolyl)azo]phenyl]-	MeCN	570(4.06)	24-0457-80
$C_{19}H_{26}N_2$			
Quebrachamine, (±)-	EtOH	229(4.11),290(3.29)	4-1133-80
$C_{19}H_{26}N_2O$			
Aspidosine	MeOH	246(3.91),289(3.42)	73-1419-80
1H-Indolizino[8,7-b]indole-2-propanol, β-ethyl-2,3,5,6,11,11b-hexahydro-, trans-(±)-	EtOH	225(4.38),265(3.71), 292(3.73),300(3.69)	78-1063-80

Compound	Solvent	$\lambda_{max}(\log \epsilon)$	Ref.
$C_{19}H_{26}N_2O_3$			
5,8-Etheno-10H-pyrrolo[1,2-e][1,5,8]-oxadiazacyclotetradecine-1,12(2H-11H)-dione, 3,4,14,15,16,16a-hexa-hydro-10-(1-methylethyl)-, (10R-trans)-	MeCN	271(2.79),276(2.75)	44-4813-80
$C_{19}H_{26}N_2O_9$			
Propanedioic acid, [2,3-dihydro-1-[2,3-O-(1-methylethylidene)-2-oxo-4(1H)-pyrimidinylidene]-, diethyl ester	H$_2$O	237(3.80),325s(4.34),336(4.36),355s(4.15)	94-0157-80
	pH 13	257(3.86),344(4.43)	94-0157-80
$C_{19}H_{26}N_2O_{10}S$			
D-Lyxitol, 1-C-(3,4-dihydro-2,4-dioxo-1(2H)-pyrimidinyl)-1-S-ethyl-1-thio-, 2,3,4,5-tetraacetate, (S)-	MeOH	266(3.98)	136-0364-80C
D-Ribitol, 1-C-(3,4-dihydro-2,4-dioxo-1(2H)-pyrimidinyl)-1-S-ethyl-1-thio-, 2,3,4,5-tetraacetate	MeOH	265(4.01)	136-0364-80C
$C_{19}H_{26}O$			
2(3H)-Anthracenone, 4,4a,5,6,10,10a-hexahydro-1,10a-dimethyl-7-(1-meth-ylethyl)-, (4aS-cis)-	EtOH	345(4.48)	39-0176-80C
2(3H)-Anthracenone, 4,4a,5,6,7,8,10,10a-octahydro-1,10a-dimethyl-6-(1-methyl-ethylidene)-, (4aS-cis)-	EtOH	302.5(4.26)	39-0176-80C
5H-Cycloprop[b]anthracen-5-one, 1,1a,2,6,7,7a,8,8a,9,9a-decahydro-1,1,4,8a-tetramethyl-, [1aR-(1aα,7aβ,8aβ,9aα)]-	EtOH	305(4.45)	39-0176-80C
2,4,6,8-Nonatetraenal, 7-methyl-9-(2,6,6-trimethyl-1-cyclohexen-1-yl)-, (all-E)-	3-Mepentane	366(4.63)	46-0134-80
7-Z	3-Mepentane	356(4.41)	46-0134-80
9-Z	3-Mepentane	362(4.48)	46-0134-80
11-Z	3-Mepentane	365(4.43)	46-0134-80
$C_{19}H_{26}O_2$			
Androst-5-ene-3,17-dione (as ethylene acetal)	EtOH	239(4.08)	18-0259-80
$C_{19}H_{26}O_3$			
Androst-4-ene-3,17-dione, 14α-hydroxy-	EtOH	235(4.11)	39-2535-80C
5α-Androst-4-ene-3,17-dione, 19-hy-droxy-	n.s.g.	242(4.16)	19-0001-80
Androst-5-ene-7,17-dione, 3β-hydroxy-	EtOH	238(4.11)	39-2535-80C
Androst-5-ene-7,17-dione, 14α-hydroxy-	EtOH	239(4.12)	39-2535-80C
Cyclohexanecarboxylic acid, 5-(1,1-di-methylethyl)-1-(4-methylphenyl)-2-oxo-, methyl ester, trans	EtOH	221s(3.89),260(2.46),266(2.51),271(2.40),275(2.36)	12-0113-80
D-Homo-C,18-dinorandrosta-4,8(14)-dien-3-one, 17,17a-dihydroxy-17a-methyl-, (13α,17α,17aβ)-	EtOH	208(3.95),234(4.04)	18-0243-80
(13α,17β,17aβ)-	EtOH	208(4.00),234(4.08)	18-0243-80
D-Homo-C,18-dinorandrosta-4,13-dien-3-one, 17,17a-dihydroxy-17a-methyl-, (17β,17aα)-	EtOH	237(3.98)	18-0243-80
D-Homo-C,18-dinorandrost-4-en-3-one, 14,17-epoxy-17a-hydroxy-17a-methyl-,	EtOH	237(4.04)	18-0243-80

Compound	Solvent	$\lambda_{max}(\log \epsilon)$	Ref.
(13α,14β,17β,17aβ)- (cont.) 1H-Inden-1-one, octahydro-4-[(5-hydroxy-2-oxocyclohexylidene)ethylidene]-3a,7a-dimethyl-	EtOH	312(4.46)	18-0243-80 44-2013-80
17-Norkaur-9(11)-en-18-oic acid, 16-oxo-, (4α)-	MeOH	254(2.70)	39-1270-80C
$C_{19}H_{26}O_4$			
Androstane-3,6,17-trione, 5-hydroxy-, (5β)-	EtOH	240(2.97),280(2.61)	39-2535-80C
Androst-5-ene-7,17-dione, 3β,14α-dihydroxy-	EtOH	238(4.12)	39-2535-80C
2,5-Cyclohexadien-1-one, 2-acetyl-3-hydroxy-5-methoxy-4,4-bis(3-methyl-2-butenyl)-	MeOH	260(4.02),270(4.02), 310(4.32)	42-1238-80
Cyclohexanecarboxylic acid, 5-(1,1-dimethylethyl)-1-(4-methoxyphenyl)-2-oxo-, methyl ester, trans	EtOH	233(3.92),278(3.11), 285(3.04)	12-0113-80
Marasmic acid, 1,1-dimethylethyl ester	EtOH	243(3.89)	78-3367-80
4,7-Methanobenz[d]indene-8,11(1H)-dione, 2,3,3a,4,5,6,6a,7-octahydro-6a-(methoxymethoxy)-4,5,10-trimethyl-	EtOH	242(3.95)	44-1540-80
Plagiochiline C	EtOH	205(3.12)	102-2147-80
$C_{19}H_{26}O_6$			
1,3-Benzodioxole-5,6-diol, 2-heptyl-2-methyl-, diacetate	EtOH	240(3.58),295(3.75)	12-0527-80
Plagiochiline A	EtOH	205(3.12)	102-2147-80
$C_{19}H_{26}O_6S$			
α-D-Glucofuranose, 3-O-methyl-1,2-O-(1-methylethylidene)-6-S-(phenylmethyl)-6-thio-, acetate	EtOH	213(3.76)	33-0016-80
$C_{19}H_{26}O_{11}$			
Apodanthoside, 10-ethyl-	n.s.g.	232(3.92)	100-0649-80
Shanzhiside, methyl ester	MeOH	238(3.93)	100-0649-80
$C_{19}H_{26}O_{12}$			
Barlerin	n.s.g.	235(3.76)	100-0649-80
Daphylloside	MeOH	235(3.95)	100-0649-80
$C_{19}H_{27}NO_{12}$			
Phenol, 4-(2-nitroethyl)-, primaveroside	EtOH	267s(3.01),274(3.05), 279(2.98)	102-1251-80
$C_{19}H_{27}NSSi$			
2-Azetidinethione, 3-(2-cyclohexen-1-yl)-1-methyl-4-phenyl-3-(trimethylsilyl)-	3:1 isooctane-CHCl₃	266(4.1),330s(2.2)	24-3024-80
$C_{19}H_{27}N_3O$			
1-Propanamine, N,N-dimethyl-3-[[4,5,6,7-tetrahydro-1-(phenylmethyl)-1H-indazol-3-yl]oxy]-	EtOH	233(3.96)	18-0825-80
hydrochloride	EtOH	232(3.93)	18-0825-80
$C_{19}H_{27}N_3O_4$			
3,5-Isoxazoledicarboxamide, N,N'-dibutyl-4,5-dihydro-4-phenyl-, 2-oxide, trans	MeOH	252(4.00)	94-0479-80

Compound	Solvent	λ_{max}(log ϵ)	Ref.
$C_{19}H_{27}N_3O_9S$			
D-Arabinitol, 1-C-(4-amino-2-oxo-1(2H)-pyrimidinyl)-1-S-ethyl-1-thio-, 2,3,4,5-tetraacetate, (+)-	MeOH	278(3.95)	136-0364-80C
(-)-	MeOH	278(4.0)	136-0364-80C
D-Lyxitol, 1-C-(4-amino-2-oxo-1(2H)-pyrimidinyl)-1-S-ethyl-1-thio-, 2,3,4,5-tetraacetate	MeOH	278(3.98)	136-0364-80C
D-Ribitol, 1-C-(4-amino-2-oxo-1(2H)-pyrimidinyl)-1-S-ethyl-1-thio-, 2,3,4,5-tetraacetate	MeOH	278(3.98)	136-0364-80C
D-Xylitol, 1-C-(4-amino-2-oxo-1(2H)-pyrimidinyl)-1-S-ethyl-1-thio-, 2,3,4,5-tetraacetate, (+)-	MeOH	277(4.05)	136-0364-80C
(-)-	MeOH	277(3.99)	136-0364-80C
$C_{19}H_{28}FN_4O_9P$			
Uridine, 2'-deoxy-5-fluoro-, 3'-acetate 5'-(di-4-morpholinylphosphinate)	MeOH	269(3.96)	87-1229-80
$C_{19}H_{28}N_2O_2$			
Androst-4-ene-3,17-dione, dioxime	MeOH	241(4.43)	36-0995-80
isomer m. 223-6°	MeOH	243(4.36)	36-0995-80
$C_{19}H_{28}N_2O_6$			
Cyclopent[e]indazole-3a,8b(1H,4H)-dicarboxylic acid, 4-(dimethoxymethyl)-6,7,8,8a-tetrahydro-7,7-dimethyl-, dimethyl ester, (3aα,4β,8aα,8bα)-	EtOH	323(2.63)	78-3361-80
Cyclopent[g]indazole-3a,8b(3H,4H)-dicarboxylic acid, 4-(dimethoxymethyl)-6,7,8,8a-tetrahydro-7,7-dimethyl-, dimethyl ester, (3aα,4β,8aα,8bα)-	EtOH	320(2.46)	78-3361-80
$C_{19}H_{28}N_4$			
2,4-Pyrimidinediamine, N^4-butyl-N^2-(4-butylphenyl)-6-methyl-	EtOH	272(4.61),290s(4.43)	103-0309-80
	EtOH-HCl	260(4.47)	103-0309-80
$C_{19}H_{28}O$			
5H-Cycloprop[b]anthracen-5-one, 1,1a-2,2a,6,7,7a,8,8a,9,9a-dodecahydro-1,1,4,8a-tetramethyl-, [1aR-(1aα,2aβ-7aβ,8aβ,9aα)]-	EtOH	248(4.16)	39-0176-80C
$C_{19}H_{28}O_3$			
Androst-4-en-3-one, 17β,19-dihydroxy-	n.s.g.	244(4.11)	19-0001-80
Androst-5-en-7-one, 3β,16β-dihydroxy-	EtOH	238(4.05)	39-2535-80C
$C_{19}H_{28}O_4$			
1,3-Benzodioxole-5,6-dione, 2-methyl-2-undecyl-	EtOH	287(4.06),394(3.18)	12-0527-80
1,3-Benzodioxol-5-ol, 2-methyl-2-nonyl-, acetate	EtOH	235(3.35),286(3.50)	12-0527-80
D-Homo-C,18-dinorandrost-4-en-3-one, 13,17,17a-trihydroxy-17a-methyl-, (13α,17β,17aβ)-	EtOH	239(4.04)	18-0243-80
Spiro[5H-cyclopenta[1,3]cycloprop[1,2]-benzene-5,2'-[1,3]dioxolane]-2-carboxylic acid, 1,3a,3b,4,6,7-hexahydro-3b,7-dimethyl-, 1,1-dimethylethyl ester, (3aα,3bβ,7β,7aS*)-($\pm$)-	EtOH	251(3.88)	23-2460-80

Compound	Solvent	$\lambda_{max}(\log \epsilon)$	Ref.
$C_{19}H_{28}O_{12}$ Cyclopenta[c]pyran-4-carboxylic acid, 7-acetoxy-1-(β-D-glucopyranosyloxy)-1,4a,5,6,7,7a-hexahydro-4a-hydroxy-7-methyl-, methyl ester, [1S-(1α,4aα,7α,7aα)]- (ipolamiidoside)	MeOH	229(3.90)	100-0649-80
$C_{19}H_{29}NO_2$ 2-Azaandrost-4-en-3-one, 17β-hydroxy-N-methyl-	n.s.g.	217(3.84),250(3.16)	33-2380-80
4-Aza-5β-androst-1-en-3-one, 17β-hydroxy-N-methyl-	n.s.g.	210(3.85),255(3.08)	33-2380-80
$C_{19}H_{29}NO_4$ 2H-Benzo[a]quinolizine-2-ethanol, 3-ethyl-1,3,4,6,7,11b-hexahydro-8-hydroxy-9,10-dimethoxy- (ankorine)	pH 13 EtOH	287(3.37) 273(2.98)	44-1889-80 44-1889-80
$C_{19}H_{30}N_2$ 1H-Indole-3-ethanamine, N,N-dibutyl-2-methyl-, monohydrochloride	EtOH	226(4.39),283(3.85), 291(3.79)	80-0245-80
$C_{19}H_{30}O$ Benzene, [1-(decyloxy)-1-propenyl]-	hexane	250(4.01)	118-0847-80
$C_{19}H_{30}O_3$ Acetic acid, [3,5-diethyl-5-(2-ethyl-3-hexenyl)-2(5H)-furanylidene]-, methyl ester	MeOH	282(3.92)	44-3396-80
1,3-Benzodioxol-5-ol, 2-methyl-2-undecyl-	EtOH	235(3.51),299(3.71)	12-0527-80
$C_{19}H_{31}NO_3$ 2-Aza-1,10-secoandrost-5(10)-en-3-one, 17β-hydroxy-1-methoxy-	n.s.g.	205(3.76),270(3.02)	33-2380-80
5H-Indeno[4,5-e]azecin-5-one, 1,2,3,4-6,8a,9,10,10a,11,12,13,13a,13b-tetradecahydro-11-hydroxy-3-methoxy-8,10a-dimethyl-	n.s.g.	207(3.58)	33-2380-80
3-Pyridinecarboxaldehyde, 5-(1,1-dimethylethyl)-6-(2,2-dimethyl-1-oxopropyl)-1,6-dihydro-6-hydroxy-1-(2-methylpropyl)-	C_6H_{12}	397(3.38)	88-4097-80
$C_{19}H_{31}NO_4$ 1-Pyrrolidineheptanoic acid, 2-oxo-5-(3-oxo-1-heptenyl)-, methyl ester, [R-(E)]-	MeOH	215(4.15)	94-1449-80
$C_{19}H_{31}N_3O_3$ Dodecanamide, N-methyl-2-[(4-nitrophenyl)amino]-, (±)-	20% MeCN	387(4.32)	18-1361-80
monohydrobromide	20% MeCN	285(3.99)	18-1361-80
$C_{19}H_{32}N_2O$ Androstan-17-one, 3-hydroxy-, hydrazone	MeOH	198(3.59)	39-1356-80C
2,5-Cyclohexadien-1-one, 4-[bis(dimethylamino)methylene]-2,6-bis(1,1-dimethylethyl)-	isooctane	417(4.41)	73-2675-80

Compound	Solvent	$\lambda_{max}(\log \epsilon)$	Ref.
$C_{19}H_{32}N_2O_6$			
2,4(1H,3H)-Pyrimidinedione, 1-[tetra- hydro-3,4-dihydroxy-5-(hydroxymeth- yl)-1,5-dipentyl-2-furanyl]-	pH 1 pH 13 MeOH	265(3.36) 290(3.86) 265(3.86)	138-0679-80 138-0679-80 138-0679-80
$C_{19}H_{32}N_2O_7Si$			
2,4(1H,3H)-Pyrimidinedione, 5-[2-C- [[[(1,1-dimethylethyl)dimethylsilyl]- oxy]methyl]-2,3-O-(1-methylethyli- dene)-β-DL-ribofuranosyl]-	pH 13 MeOH	289(3.79) 266(3.86)	142-0321-80B 142-0321-80B
$C_{19}H_{32}O_2$			
2,9,12-Octadecatrienoic acid, methyl ester, (E,Z,Z)-	n.s.g.	202(4.33)	54-0132-80
$C_{19}H_{32}O_5$			
2-Furanundecanoic acid, 2,5-dihydro- 2-methoxy-3,4-dimethyl-5-oxo-, methyl ester	MeOH	211(3.97)	138-0955-80
$C_{19}H_{33}NO$			
Cyclotetradecanone, 2-[3-(dimethyl- amino)-2-propenylidene]-	EtOH CHCl$_3$	378(4.60) 367(4.56)	70-0987-80 70-0987-80
$C_{19}H_{33}N_3O_5$			
4(1H)-Pyrimidinone, 2-amino-5-[tetra- hydro-3,4-dihydroxy-5-(hydroxymeth- yl)-1,5-dipentyl-2-furanyl]-	pH 1 pH 13 MeOH	265(3.57) 230(3.83),278(3.59) 263(3.72)	138-0679-80 138-0679-80 138-0679-80
$C_{19}H_{36}N_4O$			
2H-Tetrazole, 2-(1-oxooctadecyl)-	THF	214(3.82)	33-0588-80
$C_{19}H_{36}N_4O_3$			
2-Propanol, 1,3-bis(2,5-dihydro- 1,2,2,5,5-pentamethyl-1H-imidazol- 4-yl)-, N^1,N^3-dioxide	EtOH	234(4.10)	70-0956-80

Compound	Solvent	$\lambda_{max}(\log \epsilon)$	Ref.
$C_{20}H_2F_{15}N_4$ 1,2,4,5-Tetrazin-1(2H)-yl, 3,4-dihydro-2,4,6-tris(pentafluorophenyl)-	hexane	314(4.9),575(3.45)	103-0882-80
$C_{20}H_4Cl_4I_4O_5$ Spiro[isobenzofuran-1(3H),9'-[9H]xanthen]-3-one, 4,5,6,7-tetrachloro-3',6'-dihydroxy-2',4',5',7'-tetraiodo-	protonated	485(4.59)	110-0843-80
$C_{20}H_4Cl_{10}O_5$ Dinaphtho[2,1-b:1',2'-d]furan-5,9-dione, 1,3,6,6,6a,7a,8,8,11,13-decachloro-6,6a,7a,8-tetrahydro-4,10-dihydroxy-	$CHCl_3$	325(4.06),349(4.05), 435(4.30)	12-2531-80
$C_{20}H_5Cl_5O_5$ Dinaphtho[2,1-b:1',2'-d]furan-5,9-dione, pentachloro-4,10-dihydroxy-	$CHCl_3$	401(4.03),565(4.31)	12-2531-80
$C_{20}H_6Br_4Cl_2O_5$ Spiro[isobenzofuran-1(3H),9'-[9H]xanthen]-3-one, 2',4',5',7'-tetrabromo-4,7-dichloro-3',6'-dihydroxy- (phloxin)	protonated	453(4.47)	110-0843-80
$C_{20}H_6Cl_2I_4O_5$ Spiro[isobenzofuran-1(3H),9'-[9H]xanthen]-3-one, 4,7-dichloro-3',6'-dihydroxy-2',4',5',7'-tetraiodo-	protonated	463(4.57)	110-0843-80
$C_{20}H_6Cl_4O_5$ Dinaphtho[2,1-b:1',2'-d]furan-5,9-dione, tetrachloro-4,10-dihydroxy-	$CHCl_3$	400(4.04),560(4.26)	12-2531-80
$C_{20}H_7Cl_3O_5$ Dinaphtho[2,1-b:1',2'-d]furan-5,9-dione, trichloro-4,10-dihydroxy-	$CHCl_3$	399(4.10),557(4.23)	12-2531-80
$C_{20}H_7F_{10}N$ Benzenamine, N-[bis(pentafluorophenyl)-methylene]-2-methyl-	EtOH	236s(4.18),343(3.48)	70-1149-80
Benzenamine, N-[bis(pentafluorophenyl)-methylene]-4-methyl-	EtOH	218s(4.30),233s(4.20), 343(3.98)	70-1149-80
$C_{20}H_7F_{10}NO$ Benzenamine, N-[bis(pentafluorophenyl)-methylene]-3-methoxy-	EtOH	240s(4.16),340(3.45)	70-1149-80
Benzenamine, N-[bis(pentafluorophenyl)-methylene]-4-methoxy-	EtOH	223(4.29),236s(4.21), 357(3.70)	70-1149-80
$C_{20}H_7F_{10}N_4$ 1,2,4,5-Tetrazin-1(2H)-yl, 3,4-dihydro-2,4-bis(pentafluorophenyl)-6-phenyl-	hexane	360(4.8),625(3.4)	103-0882-80
$C_{20}H_8Br_4O_5$ Spiro[isobenzofuran-1(3H),9'-[9H]xanthen]-3-one, 2',4',5',7'-tetrabromo-3',6'-dihydroxy-, dianion (eosin)	H_2O	517(4.97)	40-0675-80
	MeOH	524(4.97)	40-0675-80
	EtOH	526(5.04)	40-0675-80
	isoPrOH	531(5.00)	40-0675-80
	BuOH	530(5.11)	40-0675-80
	pentanol	533(4.99)	40-0675-80
	hexanol	534(5.11)	40-0675-80

Compound	Solvent	$\lambda_{max}(\log \epsilon)$	Ref.
Eosin (cont.)	cyclohexanol	541(5.11)	40-0675-80
	acetone	534(4.94)	40-0675-80
	THF	538(4.64)	40-0675-80
	EtOAc	535(4.76)	40-0675-80
	$HCONH_2$	529(5.04)	40-0675-80
	DMF	536(5.00)	40-0675-80
	MeCN	532(4.87)	40-0675-80
	$MeNO_2$	539(4.26)	40-0675-80
	pyridine	543(4.98)	40-0675-80
	PhCN	545(4.91)	40-0675-80
	quinoline	548(4.54)	40-0675-80
	DMSO	542(5.00)	40-0675-80
	protonated	454(4.65)	110-0843-80
$C_{20}H_8Cl_2O_5$ Dinaphtho[2,1-b:1',2'-d]furan-5,9-di- one, dichloro-4,10-dihydroxy-	$CHCl_3$	397(4.10),558(4.14)	12-2531-80
$C_{20}H_8F_{10}N_4$ 1,2,4,5-Tetrazine, 1,2,5,6-tetrahydro- 1,5-bis(pentafluorophenyl)-3-phenyl-	hexane	292(4.0)	103-0882-80
$C_{20}H_8I_4O_5$ Spiro[isobenzofuran-1(3H),9'-[9H]xanth- en]-3-one, 3',6'-dihydroxy- 2',4',5',7'-tetraiodo-	protonated	462(4.66)	110-0843-80
$C_{20}H_9Cl_3O_2$ 1,10-Anthracenedione, 2,4-dichloro- 9-(4-chlorophenyl)-	benzene	485(3.90)	104-0159-80
$C_{20}H_{10}ClNO_4$ 8H-Naphtho[2,3-a]phenoxazine-8,13(14H)- dione, 2-chloro-7-hydroxy-	THF	267(4.38),585(4.23), 630(4.13)	104-1884-80
8H-Naphtho[2,3-a]phenoxazine-8,13(14H)- dione, 4-chloro-7-hydroxy-	THF	267(4.71),600(4.20), 650(4.11)	104-1884-80
$C_{20}H_{10}ClN_3O_4$ 9,10-Anthracenedione, 1-azido-2-(2- chlorophenoxy)-4-hydroxy-	THF	250(4.59),440(3.85)	104-1884-80
9,10-Anthracenedione, 1-azido-2-(4- chlorophenoxy)-4-hydroxy-	THF	250(4.58),440(3.80)	104-1884-80
$C_{20}H_{10}Cl_2O_2$ 1,10-Anthracenedione, 2,4-dichloro- 9-phenyl-	benzene	485(4.06)	104-0159-80
$C_{20}H_{10}Cl_3NO_2S$ 2,5-Cyclohexadiene-1,4-dione, 2,3,5- trichloro-6-[2-(10H-phenothiazin- 10-yl)ethenyl]-	$CHCl_3$	256(4.44),284s(--), 379(4.37),725(4.08)	104-2026-80
$C_{20}H_{10}Cl_4O_2$ 9(10H)-Anthracenone, 1,3,10-trichloro- 10-(4-chlorophenyl)-4-hydroxy-	benzene	340(3.65)	104-0159-80
$C_{20}H_{10}Cl_6N_6Se_2$ Pyrazinamine, N,N'-[diselenobis(5- chloro-2,1-phenylene)]bis[3,6-di- chloro-	EtOH	273(4.52),362(4.06)	78-2681-80

Compound	Solvent	$\lambda_{max}(\log \epsilon)$	Ref.
$C_{20}H_{10}Cl_6O_2$ 1-Oxaspiro[3.5]nona-5,8-dien-7-one, 5,6,8,9-tetrachloro-2,3-bis(4- chlorophenyl)-, trans	THF	261(4.13),296(3.86)	18-0726-80
$C_{20}H_{10}N_2O_2S_4$ Methanone, [1,4]dithiino[2,3-c:5,6-c']- diisothiazole-3,7-diylbis[phenyl- (not all dissolved)	MeCN	234(4.15),266(4.04), 300(4.00),405(3.83)	44-5122-80
$C_{20}H_{10}N_2O_4$ 5H-[1]Benzopyrano[2,3-d]pyrimidin-5- one, 2-(4-oxo-4H-1-benzopyran-3-yl)-	EtOH	209(4.50),244(4.43), 312(4.21)	44-1964-80
$C_{20}H_{10}N_2O_4S_4$ [1,4]Dithiino[2,3-c:5,6-c']diisothia- zole-3,7-dicarboxylic acid, diphenyl ester	MeCN	220(4.54),283(3.99), 375(4.08)	44-5122-80
$C_{20}H_{10}O_3$ Naphthaceno[5,6-bc]pyran-2,8-dione	toluene	419(3.76),444(3.68)	104-1646-80
$C_{20}H_{10}O_4$ Dinaphtho[1,2-b:2',1'-d]furan-5,6-di- one, 8-hydroxy-	EtOH	260s(4.63),273s(4.74), 279(4.77),314s(3.98), 332(3.90),348(3.90), 530(3.51)	39-0090-80C
$C_{20}H_{10}O_5$ Dinaphtho[2,1-b:1',2'-d]furan-5,9-di- one, 4,10-dihydroxy-	CHCl₃	278(3.76),383(4.35), 395s(4.32),541(4.19)	12-2531-80
$C_{20}H_{10}O_5W$ Tungsten, pentacarbonyl(2,3-diphenyl- 2-cyclopropen-1-ylidene)-	heptane	196(4.96),242(4.55), 270s(--),280s(--), 351(3.91),430s(--)	101-0087-80I
$C_{20}H_{10}O_6$ [2,2'-Binaphthalene]-1,1',4,4'-tetrone, 5,5'-dihydroxy-	CHCl₃	248(4.28),274(4.27), 339(3.34),440(3.94)	5-1321-80
[2,2'-Binaphthalene]-1,1',4,4'-tetrone, 8,8'-dihydroxy-	CHCl₃	249(4.28),269(4.27), 335(3.42),437(3.92)	5-1321-80
$C_{20}H_{11}BrN_2O_2$ 6H-Anthra[1,9-cd]isoxazol-6-one, 5-[(4-bromophenyl)amino]-	dioxan	273(4.31),490(4.13), 519(4.17)	103-0704-80
$C_{20}H_{11}ClN_2O_2$ 6H-Anthra[1,9-cd]isoxazol-6-one, 5-[(4-chlorophenyl)amino]-	dioxan	272(4.27),490(4.11), 515(4.16)	103-0704-80
$C_{20}H_{11}Cl_3O_2$ 9(10H)-Anthracenone, 1,3,10-trichloro- 4-hydroxy-10-phenyl-	benzene	345(3.71)	104-0159-80
$C_{20}H_{11}NO_2$ 5H-Dibenzo[a,h]phenoxazin-5-one 5H-Dibenzo[a,j]phenoxazin-5-one	50% EtOH EtOH	376(4.01),490(4.18) 387(3.72),490(4.32)	86-0349-80 86-0349-80
$C_{20}H_{11}NO_4$ Naphtho[2',3':4,5]furo[2,3-c]isoquino-	CHCl₃	290(4.23),336(3.93),	2-0836-80

Compound	Solvent	$\lambda_{max}(\log \epsilon)$	Ref.
line-5,8,13(6H)-trione, 6-methyl- 8H-Naphtho[2,3-a]phenoxazine-8,13(14H)- dione, 7-hydroxy-	THF	347(3.88),488(3.86) 267(4.58),590(4.15), 660(4.05)	2-0836-80 104-1884-80
$C_{20}H_{11}N_3O_3$			
5H-Indolo[2,3-a]pyrrolo[3,4-c]carbazole- 5,7(6H)-dione, 12,13-dihydro-2-hy- droxy-	MeOH	229(4.07),271(3.70), 280(3.75),323(4.11), 414(3.19)	89-0459-80
1H-Pyrrolo[3',4':4,5]oxepino[2,3-b:7,6- b']diindole-1,3(2H)-dione, 8,10-di- hydro-	MeOH	226(4.44),273(3.82), 283s(3.83),362(3.51), 471(3.68)	89-0459-80
$C_{20}H_{11}N_3O_4$			
9,10-Anthracenedione, 1-azido-4-hydroxy- 2-phenoxy-	THF	250(4.55),450(3.86)	104-1884-80
5H-Indolo[2,3-a]pyrrolo[3,4-c]carbaz- ole-5,7(6H)-dione, 12,13-dihydro- 2,10-dihydroxy-	MeOH	229(4.14),255s(3.77), 270(3.66),280(3.70), 318s(4.09),331(4.29), 422(3.34)	89-0459-80
$C_{20}H_{11}N_3O_5$			
[2,2':3',2"-Terfuran]-4'-carbonitrile, 5'-[[(4-nitrophenyl)methylene]amino]-	MeOH	455(3.62)	73-1581-80
$C_{20}H_{12}$			
Perylene	EtOH	<u>270(4.7)</u>,436f(<u>4.7</u>)	61-1140-80
radical cation	EtOH	<u>546(4.8)</u>	61-1140-80
$C_{20}H_{12}BrNO_4$			
2H-Anthra[1,2-d][1,3]oxazine-7,12-di- one, 6-bromo-2-(2-furanyl)-1,4-di- hydro-	EtOH	486(3.69)	18-3007-80 +146-0513-80
$C_{20}H_{12}ClNO_4$			
1,3(2H,4H)-Isoquinolinedione, 4-(3- chloro-1,4-dihydro-1,4-dioxo-2- naphthalenyl)-2-methyl-	EtOH	204(4.53),236(4.46), 278(4.09),308(4.23), 392(3.38)	2-0836-80
$C_{20}H_{12}Cl_2N_2O_2$			
9,10-Anthracenedione, 1-amino-2-chloro- 4-[(4-chlorophenyl)amino]-	n.s.g.	579(4.11),616(4.11)	93-1963-80
$C_{20}H_{12}Cl_3N$			
1H-Indole, 5-chloro-2,3-bis(2-chloro- phenyl)-	MeOH	302(4.19)	73-3593-80
$C_{20}H_{12}Cl_4N_2O_4$			
1H-Pyrazole, 3,5-dimethyl-1-[(5,6,7,8- tetrachloro-2,3-dihydro-3-oxo-2-phen- yl-1,4-benzodioxin-2-yl)carbonyl]-	MeCN	213(4.446),240s(4.116), 299(3.110)	64-1002-80B
$C_{20}H_{12}Cl_4N_3O_2P_3$			
1,1-(1,1'-Dioxy-2,2'-binaphthalenyl)- cyclotriphosphazene, 3,3,5,5-tetra- chloro-	C_6H_{12}	215(4.59),259(5.03), 272(4.49),283(4.32)	44-1672-80
1,1-(2,2'-Dioxy-1,1'-binaphthalenyl)- cyclotriphosphazene, 3,3,5,5-tetra- chloro-	C_6H_{12}	216(5.08),263(3.87), 305(4.13)	44-1672-80
$C_{20}H_{12}Cl_4O_2$			
1-Oxaspiro[3.5]nona-5,8-dien-7-one,	THF	259(4.06),295(3.84)	18-0726-80

Compound	Solvent	$\lambda_{max}(\log \epsilon)$	Ref.
5,6,8,9-tetrachloro-2,3-diphenyl-, trans (cont.)			18-0726-80
$(C_{20}H_{12}I_2N_2O_2)_n$ Poly[imino-1,3-phenyleneiminocarbonyl-(2,2'-diiodo[1,1'-biphenyl]-4,4'-diyl)carbonyl]	DMSO	285(4.89)	126-0333-80
$C_{20}H_{12}N_2$ 1H-Indole, 3,3'-(1,3-butadiyne-1,4-diyl)bis-	EtOH	206(4.55),226(4.75), 265(4.78),282(4.38), 305(4.38),324(4.29)	104-0665-80
Naphtho[2,1-b][1,8]phenanthroline	MeOH	218(4.57),245(4.34), 251(4.32),258(4.32), 264(4.31),290(4.86), 317(5.13),332(5.14), 359(4.45),378(4.80), 399(4.92)	39-1233-80C
	MeOH-acid	217(4.62),230(4.41), 251(4.54),257(4.57), 263s(4.46),275(4.28), 304(4.76),340(4.17), 398(3.57),420(3.59)	39-1233-80C
$C_{20}H_{12}N_2O_2$ 6H-Anthra[1,9-cd]isoxazol-6-one, 5-(phenylamino)-	dioxan	261(4.37),498(4.22), 526(4.26)	103-0704-80
$C_{20}H_{12}N_2O_4$ [2,2':3',2"-Terfuran]-4'-carbonitrile, 5'-[[(2-hydroxyphenyl)methylene]-amino]-	MeOH	431(4.46)	73-1581-80
$C_{20}H_{12}O$ Benzo[a]pyren-3-ol	50% EtOH	228(4.71),258(4.87), 268(4.85),293(4.68), 306(4.78),345(4.00), 362(4.45),381(4.68), 399(4.37),423(4.39)	94-0657-80
$C_{20}H_{12}O_2$ 1H-Indene-1,3(2H)-dione, 2-(1-naphthalenylmethylene)-	$CHCl_3$	405(4.25)	18-1703-80
1H-Indene-1,3(2H)-dione, 2-(2-naphthalenylmethylene)-	$CHCl_3$	366(4.46)	18-1703-80
2,3-Naphthacenedicarboxaldehyde	$CHCl_3$	274(4.60),292(4.50), 312s(4.66),324(4.84), 390(4.37),425s(3.60), 445(3.85),473(3.70), 508(3.51)	118-0689-80
$C_{20}H_{12}O_4S$ Benzo[a]pyren-3-ol, hydrogen sulfate, potassium salt	50% EtOH	222(4.67),226(4.71), 256(4.85),265(4.88), 267(4.89),277(4.63), 289(4.86),301(4.94), 334(3.91),351(4.32), 362(4.50),368(4.59), 381(4.65),388(4.60), 408(4.00)	94-0657-80

Compound	Solvent	$\lambda_{max}(\log \epsilon)$	Ref.
$C_{20}H_{12}O_6$ Furo[3',4':6,7]naphtho[1,2-d]-1,3-diox-ol-7(9H)-one, 10-(1,3-benzodioxol-5-yl)- (helioxanthin)	CHCl₃	268(4.68),295(3.82), 361(3.92)	100-0482-80
$C_{20}H_{12}O_7$ Furo[3',4':6,7]naphtho[1,2-d]-1,3-di-oxol-7(9H)-one, 10-(7-hydroxy-1,3-benzodioxol-5-yl)- (justicinol)	CHCl₃	270(4.70),297(3.80), 361(3.93)	100-0482-80
$C_{20}H_{12}S$ Dibenzo[d,j]thiacyclotridecin, 14,15,16,17-tetrahydro-, (E,E)-	THF	218(4.61),227s(4.58), 247(4.29),261(4.25), 308(4.54),346(4.03), 360s(3.94),388s(3.49)	18-1127-80
$C_{20}H_{13}BrFeO_2$ Ferrocene, 1,1'-[2-[(3-bromophenyl)-methylene]-1,3-dioxo-1,3-propane-diyl]-	dioxan MeOH	305(4.11) 304(--)	73-1290-80 73-1290-80
Ferrocene, 1,1'-[2-[(4-bromophenyl)-methylene]-1,3-dioxo-1,3-propane-diyl]-	dioxan MeOH	320(4.14) 322(--)	73-1290-80 73-1290-80
$C_{20}H_{13}BrN_2$ Benzenamine, 4-bromo-N-(2-phenyl-3H-indol-3-ylidene)-	EtOH	430(3.66)	7-0009-80
$C_{20}H_{13}BrN_2O$ Methanone, [6-bromo-1-(2-pyridinyl)-3-indolizinyl]phenyl-	CHCl₃	250(4.49),281(4.39), 310(4.36),388(4.22)	103-0506-80
Methanone, [6-bromo-1-(4-pyridinyl)-3-indolizinyl]phenyl-	CHCl₃	250(4.41),278(4.39), 302(4.29),383(4.22)	103-0506-80
$C_{20}H_{13}ClFeO_2$ Ferrocene, 1,1'-[2-[(3-chlorophenyl)-methylene]-1,3-dioxo-1,3-propane-diyl]-	dioxan MeOH	304(4.10) 303(--)	73-1290-80 73-1290-80
Ferrocene, 1,1'-[2-[(4-chlorophenyl)-methylene]-1,3-dioxo-1,3-propane-diyl]-	dioxan MeOH	318(4.21) 321(--)	73-1290-80 73-1290-80
$C_{20}H_{13}ClN_2$ Benzenamine, 4-chloro-N-(2-phenyl-3H-indol-3-ylidene)-	EtOH	435(3.65)	7-0009-80
$C_{20}H_{13}ClN_2OS$ Methanone, (6-chloro-2-phenyl-1H-pyri-do[2,3-b][1,4]thiazin-3-yl)phenyl-	n.s.g.	264(3.81)	103-0607-80
$C_{20}H_{13}ClN_2O_2$ 9,10-Anthracenedione, 1-amino-2-chloro-4-(methylamino)-	n.s.g.	583(4.10),620(4.13)	93-1963-80
$C_{20}H_{13}ClO_4$ 2H-Pyran-2-one, 3-[3-(4-chlorophenyl)-1-oxo-2-propenyl]-4-hydroxy-6-phenyl-	MeOH	376(4.5)	83-0344-80
$C_{20}H_{13}Cl_2N_5O_2$ 7H,13H-[1,2,4]Triazino[1',6':3,4]imid-	isoPrOH	218(4.59),244(4.53),	4-1697-80

Compound	Solvent	$\lambda_{max}(\log \epsilon)$	Ref.
azo[1,5-a][1,4]benzodiazepine-8,13(9H)-dione, 3-chloro-5-(2-chlorophenyl)-10-methyl- (cont.)		250s(4.52),303s(3.69), 239[sic](3.79)	4-1697-80
$C_{20}H_{13}FeNO_4$			
Ferrocene, 1,1'-[2-[(4-nitrophenyl)-methylene]-1,3-dioxo-1,3-propane-diyl]-	dioxan	308(4.17)	73-1290-80
	MeOH	305(--)	73-1290-80
$C_{20}H_{13}NO_2$			
1-Azulenecarboxylic acid, 3-cyano-2-(2-phenylethenyl)-	MeOH	230(4.46),340(4.76), 409(4.23),560(2.72)	18-3276-80
5(4H)-Oxazolone, 4-(1-naphthalenyl-methylene)-2-phenyl-	CHCl$_3$	405(4.48)	103-0701-80
5(4H)-Oxazolone, 2-(1-naphthalenyl)-4-(phenylmethylene)-	CHCl$_3$	380(4.48)	103-0701-80
$C_{20}H_{13}NO_3S$			
2H-Pyran-5-carbonitrile, 3-benzoyl-4-(methylthio)-2-oxo-6-phenyl-	MeOH	260(3.47),312(3.23)	118-1022-80
$C_{20}H_{13}NO_4$			
9,10-Anthracenedione, 1-amino-4-hy-droxy-2-phenoxy-	gas	492(4.09)	135-0344-80
	film	522(--)	135-0344-80
	crystal	532(--)	135-0344-80
	hexane	512(--)	135-0344-80
	DMF	520(4.16)	135-0344-80
$C_{20}H_{13}N_3$			
1H-Phenanthro[9,10-d]imidazole, 2-(4-pyridinyl)-	MeOH	230(5.10),268(4.91), 348(4.22)	56-2365-80
$C_{20}H_{13}N_3O$			
Benzo[h]isoquino[5,6-b][1,6]naphthyri-din-6(5H)-one, 5-methyl-	MeOH	228(4.70),260(4.80), 270(4.80),287(4.79), 295s(4.77),379(3.17), 399(3.66)	39-0512-80C
	MeOH-acid	230(4.67),278(4.85), 335s(4.07),400(3.19), 415(3.19)	39-0512-80C
$C_{20}H_{13}N_3O_3$			
Methanone, (4-nitrophenyl)[1-(2-pyri-dinyl)-3-indolizinyl]-	CHCl$_3$	258(4.45),274(4.46), 243[sic](4.14),412(4.1)	103-0506-80
Methanone, (4-nitrophenyl)[1-(4-pyri-dinyl)-3-indolizinyl]-	CHCl$_3$	255(4.29),275(4.29), 298(4.26),340(3.98), 400(4.07)	103-0506-80
1H-Pyrrole-2,5-dione, 3-(6-hydroxy-1H-indol-3-yl)-4-(1H-indol-3-yl)-	MeOH	281(3.93),392s(3.57), 465(3.77)	89-0459-80
$C_{20}H_{13}N_3O_4$			
1H-Pyrrole-2,5-dione, 3,4-bis(6-hy-droxy-1H-indol-3-yl)-	MeOH	283(3.93),474(3.76)	89-0459-80
$(C_{20}H_{13}N_3O_{11})_n$			
9H-Fluorene-2-carboxylic acid, 4,5,7-trinitro-9-oxo-, 2-[(2-methyl-1-oxo-2-propenyl)oxy]ethyl ester, homo-polymer	THF	345(3.82)	116-0782-80

Compound	Solvent	$\lambda_{max}(\log \epsilon)$	Ref.
$C_{20}H_{14}$			
Anthracene, 9-phenyl-	n.s.g.	348.5(3.83),366.5(4.04), 386(4.01)	5-0954-80
6H-Benzo[cd]pyrene, 6-methyl-	hexane	269(4.39),278(4.64), 289(4.75),312(3.95), 325(3.97),338(3.77)	18-2036-80
6,6'-Biazulene	EtOH	310(5.05),382(4.23), 600(2.87),700(2.38)	118-0030-80
$C_{20}H_{14}BrN$			
3H-Indole, 3-bromo-2,3-diphenyl-	CH_2Cl_2	260(4.03),318(3.70)	142-0867-80
$C_{20}H_{14}BrNO_2$			
Furo[2,3-c]pyridin-2(6H)-one, 3-(4-bromophenyl)-6-(phenylmethyl)-	EtOH	211(4.29),240(3.79), 281(3.88),382(4.34)	39-1176-80C
Furo[3,2-b]pyridin-2(4H)-one, 3-(4-bromophenyl)-4-(phenylmethyl)-	EtOH	208(4.05),281(3.80), 370(3.64)	39-1176-80C
$C_{20}H_{14}ClN$			
3H-Indole, 3-chloro-2,3-diphenyl-	CH_2Cl_2	225(4.22),328(3.88)	142-0867-80
$C_{20}H_{14}Cl_3NO$			
Ethanone, 1,2-bis(2-chlorophenyl)-2-[(4-chlorophenyl)amino]-	MeOH	252(4.36),295s(3.44)	73-3593-80
$C_{20}H_{14}FeO_2$			
Ferrocene, 1,1'-[1,3-dioxo-2-(phenylmethylene)-1,3-propanediyl]-	dioxan MeOH	312(4.11) 312(--)	73-1290-80 73-1290-80
$C_{20}H_{14}FeO_4$			
Iron, tetracarbonyl[(1,2-η)-2a,2b,3,8-8a,8b-hexahydro-3,8-ethenocyclobuta[3,4]cyclobuta[1,2-b]naphthalene]-	hexane	230s(4.44),275(3.81), 400(1.90)(end abs.)	89-0307-80
$C_{20}H_{14}N_2$			
Benzenamine, N-(2-phenyl-3H-indol-3-ylidene)-	EtOH	428(3.61)	7-0009-80
Isoquinoline, 4,4'-(1,2-ethenediyl)bis-, cis	C_6H_{12}	283(3.87),331(3.93)	44-1557-80
trans	C_6H_{12}	230(4.62),340(4.27)	44-1557-80
1,7-Phenanthroline, 2-(2-phenylethenyl)-	MeOH	328(4.52)	56-2365-80
1,7-Phenanthroline, 4-(2-phenylethenyl)-	MeOH	326(4.45)	56-2365-80
1,8-Phenanthroline, 2-(2-phenylethenyl)-	MeOH	320(4.53)	56-2365-80
1,8-Phenanthroline, 4-(2-phenylethenyl)-	MeOH	326(4.41)	56-2365-80
Quinoline, 2,2'-(1,2-ethenediyl)bis-	CH_2Cl_2	273(4.66),342(4.52), 357(4.57)	5-0291-80
Quinoline, 4,4'-(1,2-ethenediyl)bis-	CH_2Cl_2	237(4.40),244(4.36), 330(4.27)	5-0291-80
Quinoline, 2-[2-(4-quinolinyl)ethenyl]-	CH_2Cl_2	259(4.40),343(4.41)	5-0291-80
$C_{20}H_{14}N_2O$			
Benzoxazole, 2-[4-[2-(3-pyridinyl)ethenyl]phenyl]-	DMF	348(4.75)	33-1311-80
Methanone, phenyl[1-(2-pyridinyl)-3-indolizinyl]-	$CHCl_3$	241(4.25),274(4.23), 302(4.16),354(4.08), 391(4.18)	103-0506-80

Compound	Solvent	$\lambda_{max}(\log \epsilon)$	Ref.
Methanone, phenyl[1-(4-pyridinyl)-3-indolizinyl]-	CHCl$_3$	236(4.40),268(4.26), 309(4.20),353(4.18), 384(4.26)	103-0506-80
$C_{20}H_{14}N_2OS_3$			
2(5H)-Isothiazolecarboxamide, 3-mercapto-N-1-naphthalenyl-4-phenyl-5-thioxo-	EtOH	317(4.41),406(4.39)	142-0785-80
$C_{20}H_{14}N_2O_2$			
9,10-Anthracenedione, 1-amino-4-(phenylamino)-	gas	539(4.01)	135-0344-80
	hexane	564(--)	135-0344-80
	DMF	577(4.10)	135-0344-80
Methanone, (2-hydroxyphenyl)(3-phenylimidazo[1,2-a]pyridin-2-yl)-	EtOH	234(4.53),248(4.40), 352(3.91)	39-0354-80C
	EtOH-pH 1	212s(4.46),269s(3.96), 313(3.82)	39-0354-80C
2-Propenoic acid, 2-methyl-, 4-(2,2-dicyano-1-phenylethenyl)phenyl ester	EtOH	230(3.96),305(4.05)	116-0244-80
$C_{20}H_{14}N_2O_3$			
Ethanone, 2-(1H-indeno[2,1-b]pyridin-1-yl)-1-(4-nitrophenyl)-	EtOH	252(4.55),300s(4.00), 480(3.04),580(3.16)	103-1149-80
Ethanone, 2-(7-nitro-1H-indeno[2,1-b]pyridin-1-yl)-1-phenyl-	DMF	524(3.20)	103-1149-80
$C_{20}H_{14}N_2O_4$			
Furo[2,3-c]pyridin-2(6H)-one, 3-(4-nitrophenyl)-6-(phenylmethyl)- (mixt. with isomer)	EtOH	225(4.18),356(4.05), 432(4.53)	39-1176-80C
$C_{20}H_{14}N_2S$			
Naphtho[2',1':5,6]thiopyrano[4,3-c]-pyrazole, 3,11-dihydro-3-phenyl-	EtOH	216(4.51),277(4.32)	4-0121-80
$C_{20}H_{14}N_4O_2$			
1H-Benz[de]isoquinoline-1,3(2H)-dione, 2-[2-(1H-benzotriazol-1-yl)ethyl]-	dioxan	240(4.32),291(3.79), 335(4.16),350(4.10)	56-0107-80
1H-Benz[de]isoquinoline-1,3(2H)-dione, 2-[2-(2H-benzotriazol-2-yl)ethyl]-	dioxan	246(4.33),281(4.14), 334(4.01),378(3.89)	56-0107-80
$C_{20}H_{14}N_4O_2S$			
2H-1,4-Benzothiazin-2-one, 3-phenyl-, (4-nitrophenyl)hydrazone	EtOH	225(4.41),250(4.31), 282(4.28),346s(4.03), 430(4.38)	39-2923-80C
$C_{20}H_{14}N_4O_4$			
1,3,4,6-Hexanetetrone, 2,5-bis(diazo)-1,6-bis(4-methylphenyl)-	CH$_2$Cl$_2$	264(4.62)	39-2670-80C
$C_{20}H_{14}N_4O_4S$			
4H-1,3-Benzothiazine, 2-[(4-nitrophenyl)azo]-3-phenyl-, 1,1-dioxide	EtOH	233(4.36),274s(4.14), 308s(3.99),412(4.43)	39-2923-80C
$C_{20}H_{14}N_4O_6$			
2,2'-Bibenzoxazole, 2,2',3,3'-tetrahydro-6,6'-dinitro-2-phenyl-	0.5M NaOH	275(4.16),384(4.40), 460s(--)	4-1629-80
	MeOH	235s(--),258(4.14), 315s(--),365(4.36)	4-1629-80
1,3,4,6-Hexanetetrone, 2,5-bis(diazo)-1,6-bis(4-methoxyphenyl)-	CH$_2$Cl$_2$	275(4.43)	39-2670-80C

Compound	Solvent	$\lambda_{max}(\log \epsilon)$	Ref.
$C_{20}H_{14}N_6$ 7,18,23,24,25,26-Hexaazapentacyclo-[17.3.1.1^{2,6}.1^{8,12}.1^{13,17}]hexacosa-1(23),2,4,6(26),8,10,12(25),13,15-17(24),19,21-dodecaene	CHCl$_3$	<u>280(4.3),302(4.3),</u> <u>310(4.3),335(4.3),</u> <u>430f(3.9),505(3.4)</u>	39-2527-80C
$C_{20}H_{14}N_6O_8$ 1-Piperidineacetonitrile, α-(2,4,5,7-tetranitro-9H-fluoren-9-ylidene)-	MeCN	356(4.28),447(4.15), 538(4.11)	104-0740-80
$C_{20}H_{14}O_2$ 1,3-Azulenedicarboxaldehyde, 2-(2-phen-ylethenyl)-	CH$_2$Cl$_2$	317(4.59),340(4.59), 500(2.80)	18-3696-80
1(7aH)-Isobenzofuranone, 3,7a-diphenyl-	C$_6$H$_{12}$	235(3.94),246(3.94), 266(3.74),325(3.04)	44-3782-80
Methanone, 1,2-phenylenebis[phenyl-	EtOH	211(4.27),255(4.39)	12-2653-80
Naphth[2,1-a]azulene-12-carboxylic acid, methyl ester	MeOH	270(4.20),278(4.21), 319(4.20),355(4.24), 396(3.91),618(2.57)	138-0167-80
$C_{20}H_{14}O_2S$ 1H-Phenalen-1-one, 4-methoxy-3-(phenyl-thio)-	EtOH	342(4.26),387(4.15)	44-4611-80
$C_{20}H_{14}O_2S_2$ 1H-2-Benzothiopyran-4(3H)-one, 3,3'-(1,2-ethanediylidene)bis-	EtOH CHCl$_3$	476(4.31) 481(4.32)	24-1708-80 24-1708-80
$C_{20}H_{14}O_3$ 3,8[1',2']-Benzenoanthra[2,3-b]oxirene-2,9-dione, 1a,2a,3,8,8a,9a-hexahydro-, (1aα,2aβ,3β,8β,8aβ,9aα)-	MeCN	251(3.01),265(3.11), 272(3.14),299s(1.70)	78-1183-80
$C_{20}H_{14}O_4$ 4a,9a-[2]Buteno-1,4-ethanoanthracene-9,10,11,14-tetrone, 1,4-dihydro-	EtOH	208s(4.30),227(4.68), 302(3.46)	39-1007-80C
1,4-Ethanonaphthacene-6,11-dione, 1,4-dihydro-5,12-dihydroxy-	EtOH	206(4.15),253s(4.36), 258(4.40),287(3.58), 468s(4.16),492(3.71), 529(3.52)	39-1007-80C
1,4-Ethanonaphthacene-5,6,11,12-tetrone, 1,4,4a,12a-tetrahydro-, (1α,4α,4aα-12aα)-	EtOH	209(4.31),230(4.21), 262(4.16),270(4.05), 284s(3.91),356(3.58)	39-1007-80C
1H,4H-Furo[3,4-c]furan-1,4-dione, 3,6-bis(4-methylphenyl)-	CH$_2$Cl$_2$	243(4.51),263(4.03), 293(3.90),385s(3.97), 408(4.42),433(4.72), 463(4.78)	39-2670-80C
5,12-Naphthacenedione, 7,10-dimethoxy-	MeCN	259(4.94),300(3.98), 458(3.85)	23-1161-80
$C_{20}H_{14}O_5$ 5a,11a-Epoxy-1,4-ethanonaphthacene-5,6,11,12-tetrone, 1,4,4a,12a-tetra-hydro-, (1α4α,4aα,5aα,11aα,12aα)-	EtOH	206(3.69),236(3.92), 266(3.42),312(3.00)	39-1007-80C
5,12-Naphthacenedione, 8-ethyl-1,6,11-trihydroxy-	MeOH	267(4.64),459(4.02), 491(4.28),526(4.29)	24-2976-80
5,12-Naphthacenedione, 9-ethyl-1,6,11-trihydroxy-	MeOH	267(4.62),461(3.98), 490(4.26),525(4.26), 555(3.60)	24-2976-80

Compound	Solvent	$\lambda_{max}(\log \epsilon)$	Ref.
$C_{20}H_{14}O_6$			
1H,4H-Furo[3,4-c]furan-1,4-dione, 3,6-bis(4-methoxyphenyl)-	CH_2Cl_2	253(4.49),302(4.06), 425s(4.48),452(4.83), 483(4.95)	39-2670-80C
5,12-Naphthacenedione, 1,4-dihydroxy-7,10-dimethoxy-	CH_2Cl_2	267(4.61),285s(--), 498(3.84),505s(3.84)	23-1161-80
$C_{20}H_{14}O_{12}$			
[1,1'-Biisobenzofuran]-5,7'-dicarboxylic acid, 1,1',3,3'-tetrahydro-1,1'-dihydroxy-4',7-dimethoxy-3,3'-dioxo-	pH 1	221(4.76),311(3.87)	94-3601-80
	pH 13	278s(--),333(3.59)	94-3601-80
$C_{20}H_{14}S$			
Benzene, 1,1'-(thiodi-2,1-ethenediyl)-bis[2-ethynyl-, cis-cis	THF	227(4.44),248s(4.29), 326(4.33)	18-1127-80
cis-trans	THF	226(4.57),250(4.42), 322(4.50)	18-1127-80
trans-trans	THF	225(4.55),252(4.41), 337(4.44)	18-1127-80
$C_{20}H_{14}S_2$			
1,3-Dithiepin, 2-(5H-dibenzo[a,d]cyclohepten-5-ylidene)-	CH_2Cl_2	287(4.56)	138-1427-80
$C_{20}H_{15}ClN_4O$			
2H-Benzotriazole, 2-(4-chlorophenyl)-5-methoxy-6-[2-(3-pyridinyl)ethenyl]-	DMF	364(4.54)	33-1311-80
$C_{20}H_{15}ClO$			
Phenol, 4-(2-chloro-1,2-diphenylethenyl)-, (E)-	EtOH	302(3.85)	12-0461-80
(Z)-	EtOH	291(4.04)	12-0461-80
$C_{20}H_{15}ClO_4S$			
3-Thiophenecarboxylic acid, 4-(benzoyloxy)-5-[(4-chlorophenyl)methyl]-, methyl ester	EtOH	227(4.51),278s(--)	33-1542-80
3-Thiophenecarboxylic acid, 4-(benzoyloxy)-5-[(4-chlorophenyl)methylene]-2,5-dihydro-, methyl ester, (Z)-	EtOH	237(4.32),265(4.26), 362(4.34),378s(--)	33-1542-80
$C_{20}H_{15}N$			
1H-Benz[g]indole, 3-(2-phenylethenyl)-(isomeric mixture)	EtOH	205(4.58),225(4.66), 274(4.59),325(4.51)	103-1048-80
trans	EtOH	206(4.49),225(4.60), 278(4.50),322(4.52)	103-1048-80
3H-Benz[e]indole, 1-(2-phenylethenyl)-(isomeric mixture)	EtOH	204(4.59),228(4.68), 319(4.38)	103-1048-80
trans	EtOH	206(4.60),227(4.91), 317(4.41)	103-1048-80
7,8:9,10-Dibenzotricyclo[4.2.2.1^{2,5}]-undeca-3,7,9-triene-1-carbonitrile	MeCN	263(2.88),271(3.06), 279(3.25)	24-1458-80
8,9:10,11-Dibenzotricyclo[5.2.2.0^{2,6}]-undeca-3,8,10-triene-1-carbonitrile	MeCN	250s(2.63),258(2.75), 264(2.90),271(2.97)	24-1458-80
1H-Indole, 2,3-diphenyl-	EtOH	212(4.41),225(4.40), 250(4.36),309(4.24)	39-0339-80B
$C_{20}H_{15}NO$			
Ethanone, 2-(1H-indeno[2,1-b]pyridin-1-yl)-1-phenyl-	EtOH	300(4.28),346s(3.46), 460(3.01),520(3.09)	103-1149-80

Compound	Solvent	λ_{max}(log ϵ)	Ref.
1H-Indole, 1-hydroxy-2,3-diphenyl-	EtOH	228(4.36),252(4.33), 308(4.12)	39-0339-80B
C$_{20}$H$_{15}$NO$_2$			
Furo[2,3-c]pyridin-2(6H)-one, 3-phenyl-6-(phenylmethyl)-	EtOH	273(3.92),380(4.39)	39-1176-80C
Furo[3,2-b]pyridin-2(4H)-one, 3-phenyl-4-(phenylmethyl)-	EtOH	212(4.32),293(3.99), 374(4.10)	39-1176-80C
Pyrrolo[2,1-a]isoquinoline-1-carboxylic acid, 2-phenyl-, methyl ester	EtOH	253s(4.42),274s(4.62), 281(4.68),329(4.08)	18-0297-80
C$_{20}$H$_{15}$NO$_2$S			
Ethene, 1-nitro-1,2-diphenyl-2-(phenylthio)-, (Z)-	MeOH-pH 10.6	350(3.89)	28-0021-80A
C$_{20}$H$_{15}$NO$_3$			
Furo[2,3-c]pyridin-2(6H)-one, 3-(4-methoxyphenyl)-6-phenyl-	EtOH	212(4.34),268(3.98), 398(4.40)	39-1176-80C
Furo[3,2-b]pyridin-2(4H)-one, 3-(4-methoxyphenyl)-4-phenyl-	EtOH	210(4.24),250(4.03), 294(3.89),388(3.94)	39-1176-80C
C$_{20}$H$_{15}$NO$_3$S			
1H-Pyrido[2,1-b]benzothiazole-4-carboxylic acid, 1-oxo-2-phenyl-, ethyl ester	MeOH	229(4.33),3.0[sic](4.14), 371(4.23)	44-2474-80
C$_{20}$H$_{15}$NO$_3$S$_2$			
1,4-Naphthalenedione, 3-[(2-benzothiazolylthio)methylene]-2,3-dihydro-2-methoxy-2-methyl-	EtOH	247(4.33),260(4.21), 294s(3.96),358(4.24)	77-0777-80
C$_{20}$H$_{15}$NO$_4$			
4,9-Methano-1H-benz[f]isoindole-4(2H)-carboxylic acid, 3,3a,9,9a-tetrahydro-1,3-dioxo-2-phenyl-, (3aα,4β-9α,9aα)-	EtOH	255(2.86),261(2.82), 269(2.64)	44-3456-80
Spiro[5aH-cyclopenta[d]pyrido[2,1-b]-[1,3]oxazine-4(3H),2'-[2H]indene]-1',3,3'-trione, 1,2-dihydro-6-methyl-	MeCN	229(4.75),252(4.42), 331(4.10)	4-1577-80
Spiro[5aH-cyclopenta[d]pyrido[2,1-b]-[1,3]oxazine-4(3H),2'-[2H]indene]-1',3,3'-trione, 1,2-dihydro-7-methyl-	MeCN	229(4.73),251(4.43), 342(4.09)	4-1577-80
Spiro[2H-indene-2,6'-[4aH,6H]pyrido-[1,2-a][3,1]benzoxazine]-1,3,7'(8'H)-trione, 9',10'-dihydro-	MeCN	227(4.67),243s(4.28), 258s(4.18),349(4.05)	4-1577-80
C$_{20}$H$_{15}$NO$_5$			
[1,3]Dioxolo[4,5-h]-1,3-dioxolo[4,5]-indeno[2,1-a][3]benzazepin-14(6H)-one, 7,8-dihydro-6-methyl-	EtOH	223s(4.41),304s(4.39), 324(4.52),493(3.34)	4-0417-80
C$_{20}$H$_{15}$NO$_6$			
5H-Benzo[g]-1,3-benzodioxolo[6,5,4-de]-quinoline-5,6(7H)-dione, 9,10-dimethoxy-7-methyl-	EtOH	220(4.54),245(4.62), 308(4.21),321(4.25), 435(4.21)	102-2735-80
Nantenine, 4,5-dioxodehydro-	MeOH	223s(4.48),241(4.59), 246(4.59),286s(4.04), 301(4.14),315(4.30), 327(4.42),466(4.04)	95-0337-80

Compound	Solvent	$\lambda_{max}(\log \epsilon)$	Ref.
$C_{20}H_{15}N_3O$			
8H-1,2,4-Oxadiazino[4,5-a]perimidine, 11-(4-methylphenyl)-	MeOH	232(4.47),328(4.01)	118-0155-80
4H-1,3,4,5-Oxatriazine, 2,4,6-triphenyl-	EtOH	240(4.39),315(4.10), 401(3.53)	12-2447-80
2H-1,2,3-Triazole, 2,4,5-triphenyl-, 1-oxide	isooctane	260(4.50),292s(4.19)	12-2447-80
$C_{20}H_{15}N_3O_4$			
4,8-Iminocyclohepta[c]pyrrole-1,3,5-(2H)-trione, 3a,4,8,8a-tetrahydro-2-phenyl-9-(4-pyridinyl)-, N-oxide, (3aα,4α,8α,8aα)-	EtOH	213(4.60),301(4.64)	150-3337-80
$C_{20}H_{15}N_3O_5S$			
4H-1,3,5-Oxadiazine-4-thione, 3-(2-furanylmethyl)-2,3-dihydro-2-(4-hydroxyphenyl)-6-(4-nitrophenyl)-	dioxan	237(4.44),287(4.44)	73-2254-80
$C_{20}H_{15}N_3S$			
2H-1,4-Benzothiazin-2-one, 3-phenyl-, phenylhydrazone	MeOH	249(4.22),282(4.29), 318(4.26),426(4.09)	39-2923-80C
$C_{20}H_{15}N_5$			
2H-1,2,3-Triazole, 2,4-diphenyl-5-(phenylazo)-	EtOH	285(4.37),364(4.08), 450s(3.30)	24-1226-80
$C_{20}H_{15}N_7$			
2H-1,2,3-Triazole, 2-phenyl-4,5-bis-(phenylazo)-	EtOH	228(4.26),315(4.49), 345s(4.43),440s(3.39)	24-1226-80
$C_{20}H_{15}OP$			
5H-Dibenzo[b,f]phosphepin, 5-phenyl-, 5-oxide	EtOH	220(4.64),272(3.82), 302(4.06)	139-0243-80A
$C_{20}H_{15}P$			
1H-Dibenzo[b,f]phosphepin, 5-phenyl-	EtOH	215(4.59),232(4.49), 250(4.24),302(4.03)	139-0243-80A
$C_{20}H_{15}PS$			
5H-Dibenzo[b,f]phosphepin, 5-phenyl-, 5-sulfide	EtOH	219(4.67),259(3.96), 304(4.03)	139-0243-80A
$C_{20}H_{15}S_2$			
1-Benzothiopyrylium, 4-[(4-methyl-2H-1-benzothiopyran-2-ylidene)methyl]-, perchlorate	acetone	614(4.92)	18-2415-80
$C_{20}H_{16}$			
Cycloocta[c]octalene (or isomer)	C_6H_{12}	229(4.58),300s(4.03)	88-0107-80
$C_{20}H_{16}BrOP$			
5H-Dibenzo[b,f]phosphepin, 10-bromo-10,11-dihydro-5-phenyl-, 5-oxide	EtOH	231(4.25),262(3.38), 267(3.44),269(3.42), 285(3.24)	139-0243-80A
$C_{20}H_{16}Br_2O_2$			
Ethanone, 1-(4-bromophenyl)-2-[5-(4-bromophenyl)-2,2-dimethyl-3(2H)-furanylidene]-	EtOH	419(4.57)	5-1744-80

Compound	Solvent	$\lambda_{max}(\log \epsilon)$	Ref.
$C_{20}H_{16}ClNO_2$ Cyclohepta[b]pyrrole-3-carboxylic acid, 2-chloro-8-(2-phenylethenyl)-, ethyl ester	EtOH	225(4.51),295(4.50), 322s(4.43),392(4.47), 445s(3.59)	18-1406-80
$C_{20}H_{16}ClNO_5$ Cyclopenta[b]pyrano[2,3-d]pyridine-3-carboxylic acid, 6-(4-chlorophenyl)-2,5,6,7,8,9-hexahydro-2,5-dioxo-, ethyl ester	EtOH	274(4.05),380(4.22)	49-0093-80
$C_{20}H_{16}ClNO_6$ 8-Azabicyclo[3.2.1]octa-2,6-diene-6,7-dicarboxylic acid, 8-[3-(4-chlorophenyl)-3-oxo-1-propenyl]-4-oxo-, dimethyl ester, (E)-	CHCl$_3$	265(4.28),325(4.47)	39-0362-80C
$C_{20}H_{16}Cl_2N_4O_3$ Benzoic acid, 2-chloro-, [(2-chlorophenyl)(1,2,3,4-tetrahydro-1,3-dimethyl-2,4-dioxo-5-pyrimidinyl)methylene]hydrazide	MeOH	275(4.26),294s(4.21)	24-2566-80
Benzoic acid, 4-chloro-, [(4-chlorophenyl)(1,2,3,4-tetrahydro-1,3-dimethyl-2,4-dioxo-5-pyrimidinyl)methylene]hydrazide	MeOH	285s(4.38),306(4.40)	24-2566-80
$C_{20}H_{16}Cl_2O_2$ Ethanone, 1-(4-chlorophenyl)-2-[5-(4-chlorophenyl)-2,2-dimethyl-3(2H)-furanylidene]-	EtOH	415(4.55)	5-1744-80
$C_{20}H_{16}Cl_2O_4$ 2-Propenal, 3,3'-(3,3'-dimethoxy[1,1'-biphenyl]-4,4'-diyl)bis[2-chloro-	film	305(3.97)	104-2207-80
$C_{20}H_{16}Cl_2O_6$ 2-Propenoic acid, 3,3'-(3,3'-dimethoxy-[1,1'-biphenyl]-4,4'-diyl)bis[2-chloro-	film	304(3.89)	104-2207-80
$C_{20}H_{16}Fe_2Si$ Ferrocene, 1,1',1'',1'''-silanetetrayl-bis-	C$_6$H$_{12}$	483(2.73)	101-0345-80J
$C_{20}H_{16}NO_4$ Pyridinium, 1-[2-(2,3-dihydro-2-hydroxy-1,3-dioxo-1H-inden-2-yl)-3-oxo-1-cyclohexen-1-yl]-, chloride	MeOH-HCl	228(4.43),242s(4.17)	4-1577-80
Pyridinium, 1-[2-(2,3-dihydro-2-hydroxy-1,3-dioxo-1H-inden-2-yl)-3-oxo-1-cyclopenten-1-yl]-3-methyl-, chloride	MeOH-HCl	233(4.68),252s(4.22)	4-1577-80
Pyridinium, 1-[2-(2,3-dihydro-2-hydroxy-1,3-dioxo-1H-inden-2-yl)-3-oxo-1-cyclopenten-1-yl]-4-methyl-, chloride	MeOH-HCl	233(4.70),251s(4.34)	4-1577-80
$C_{20}H_{16}N_2$ 3H-Indole, 3-(1-methyl-2(1H)-pyridinylidene)-2-phenyl-	n.s.g.	253(4.5),310(4.4), 430(4.2)	103-0743-80

Compound	Solvent	$\lambda_{max}(\log \epsilon)$	Ref.
3H-Indole, 3-(1-methyl-4(1H)-pyridin-ylidene)-2-phenyl-	n.s.g.	426(4.35)	103-0743-80
Pyridine, 3,3'-(1,4-phenylenedi-2,1-ethenediyl)bis-	DMF	356(4.78)	33-1311-80
$C_{20}H_{16}N_2O_2$			
Benzoic acid, 2-benzoyl-1-phenylhydra-zide	EtOH	228(4.30),236s(3.90)	70-1159-80
2-Propynamide, N,N'-1,2-ethanediylbis-[3-phenyl-	EtOH	248(4.7),258(4.8), 280(4.5)	114-0235-80C
1H,5H-Pyrazolo[1,2-a]pyrazole-1,5-di-one, 2,6-dimethyl-3,7-diphenyl-	dioxan	248(4.34),344(4.27)	35-4983-80
1H,7H-Pyrazolo[1,2-a]pyrazole-1,7-di-one, 2,6-dimethyl-3,5-diphenyl-	dioxan	220(3.88),262(4.01), 395(3.90)	35-4983-80
2,4(1H,3H)-Pyrimidinedione, 1,3-dimeth-yl-5-(9-phenanthrenyl)-	MeOH	220(4.58),258(4.70), 297(4.45)	88-2813-80
$C_{20}H_{16}N_2O_3S$			
4H-1,3,5-Oxadiazine-4-thione, 3-(2-fur-anylmethyl)-2,3-dihydro-2-(4-hydroxy-phenyl)-6-phenyl-	dioxan	242(4.44),277(4.44)	73-2254-80
$C_{20}H_{16}N_2O_5S_2$			
4-Thia-1-azabicyclo[3.2.0]hept-2-ene-2-carboxylic acid, 7-oxo-3-[(phenyl-methyl)thio]-, (4-nitrophenyl)methyl ester	EtOH	262(4.21),340(4.02)	94-3232-80
$C_{20}H_{16}N_2O_6S$			
4H-[1]Benzothieno[3,2-b]pyran-2-carbox-ylic acid, 4-(tetrahydro-1,3-dimeth-yl-2,4,6-trioxo-5(2H)-pyrimidinyli-dene)-, ethyl ester	dioxan	290(4.12),318(4.12), 462(4.46)	83-0557-80
$C_{20}H_{16}N_2O_7$			
4H-Pyrano[3,2-b]benzofuran-2-carbox-ylic acid, 4-(tetrahydro-1,3-dimeth-yl-2,4,6-trioxo-5(2H)-pyrimidinyli-dene)-, ethyl ester	dioxan	321(4.24),448(4.48)	83-0557-80
$C_{20}H_{16}N_3O$			
1,2,4-Benzotriazinyl, 1,4-dihydro-7-methoxy-1,3-diphenyl-	MeOH	274(4.57),317(3.84), 335s(3.62),373(3.83), 410(3.66),424s(3.63), 493s(3.03),555s(2.78)	24-1205-80
$C_{20}H_{16}N_4O$			
2H-Benztriazole, 5-methoxy-2-phenyl-6-[2-(3-pyridinyl)ethenyl]-	DMF	363(4.53)	33-1311-80
2H-Benztriazole, 5-methoxy-2-[4-[2-(3-pyridinyl)ethenyl]phenyl]-	DMF	359(4.73)	33-1311-80
$C_{20}H_{16}N_4O_2$			
2,4(1H,3H)-Pteridinedione, 1,3-dimeth-yl-6,7-diphenyl-	pH -5.5	240s(4.27),252(4.33), 290s(4.04),415(4.15)	142-0437-80B
	pH 10.0	227(4.43),275(4.21), 364(4.19)	142-0437-80B
$C_{20}H_{16}N_4O_2S_2$			
Indeno[1,2-e]thieno[3,4-b][1,4]diaze-pine-3-carbonitrile, 4,9-dihydro-	EtOH	214(4.31),247(4.27), 283(4.58),314(4.59),	95-0699-80

Compound	Solvent	$\lambda_{max}(\log \epsilon)$	Ref.
1-(methylthio)-10-morpholino-9-oxo-		454(3.64)	95-0699-80
$C_{20}H_{16}N_4O_3$			
3H,8H-Imidazo[1,2,3-ij]pteridine-8,10(9H)-dione, 5,6-dihydro-3-hydroxy-2,3-diphenyl-	pH -1.0	250s(4.15),284(4.15), 415(4.06)	142-0437-80B
	pH 6.0	231(4.23),276(4.20), 337(4.09)	142-0437-80B
	pH 13.0	243(4.18),280(4.07), 347(4.06)	142-0437-80B
7(1H)-Pteridinone, 2,4-bis(phenylmethoxy)-	pH 2.0	238(3.94),246(3.93), 270s(3.69),317s(4.17), 326(4.18)	24-1535-80
	pH 8.0	248(4.06),265s(3.70), 319(4.15),328(4.19), 342(4.08)	24-1535-80
$C_{20}H_{16}N_4O_4$			
Indolo[7,6-g]indole, 3,8-dihydro-1,6-bis(2-nitro-1-propenyl)-	EtOH	205(3.45),262s(3.56), 272(3.64),295(3.27), 351(3.20),420(3.43)	103-1139-80
$C_{20}H_{16}N_6$			
Dipyrazolo[3,4-c:4',3'-e]pyridazine, 3,6-dihydro-1,8-dimethyl-3,6-diphenyl-	CHCl₃	420(3.70)	103-1160-80
$C_{20}H_{16}N_6O_2S_2$			
1,4-Butanedione, 1,4-bis[5-(phenylamino)-1,2,3-thiadiazol-4-yl]-	MeOH	207(4.25),228(4.01), 326(4.27)	103-0151-80
$C_{20}H_{16}N_6O_4$			
1,1-Ethenediamine, 2-nitro-2-[(4-nitrophenyl)azo]-N,N'-diphenyl-	MeCN	273(4.25),389(4.41)	48-0087-80
$C_{20}H_{16}O$			
Naphthalene, 1,2-dihydro-4-(2-naphthalenyloxy)-	hexane	263(4.09),271(4.08), 297s(--),314(3.08), 320(3.03),329(3.09)	118-0847-80
Naphtho[2,1-b]furan, 2-ethyl-1-phenyl-	MeOH	216(4.53),226(4.49), 247(4.34),300(3.96), 306(3.90),313(3.91), 320(3.78),327(3.88)	142-0777-80B
Naphtho[2,1-b]furan, 1-methyl-2-(phenylmethyl)-	MeOH	217(4.60),239(4.49), 247(4.56),299(4.05), 306(3.96),312(4.01), 319(3.86),325(4.08)	142-0777-80B
$C_{20}H_{16}O_2$			
1-Azulenecarboxylic acid, 2-(2-phenylethenyl)-, methyl ester	MeOH	335(4.50),402(4.05), 424(3.90),575(2.86)	18-3276-80
$C_{20}H_{16}O_2S_2$			
3-Benzothiepin-1(2H)-one, 2-(4,5-dihydro-1-oxo-3-benzothiepin-2(1H)-ylidene)-4,5-dihydro-	EtOH CHCl₃	336(3.98) 338(3.97)	24-1708-80 24-1708-80
4H-1-Benzothiopyran-4-one, 2,3-dihydro-6-methyl-3-(6-methyl-4-oxo-2H-1-benzothiopyran-3(4H)-ylidene)-	dioxan	241(4.7),275(4.0), 296(3.5),383(3.1)	83-0311-80
$C_{20}H_{16}O_3$			
2,5-Furandione, 3-(diphenylmethylene)-dihydro-4-(1-methylethylidene)-	n.s.g.	354(3.98)	97-0188-80

Compound	Solvent	λ_{max}(log ϵ)	Ref.
photoisomer B (cont.)	n.s.g.	490(3.89)	97-0188-80
Methanone, 7-oxabicyclo[2.2.1]hept-2-ene-2,3-diylbis[phenyl-	MeOH	260(4.07)	44-3187-80
5,12-Naphthacenedione, 2-acetyl-1,2,3,4-tetrahydro-	EtOH	210(4.26),231(4.69), 275s(4.36),284(4.41), 296(4.36),404(3.69)	33-0232-80
C$_{20}$H$_{16}$O$_4$			
9,10-Anthracenedione, 6-(1-hexynyl)-1,4-dihydroxy-	MeOH	227(4.45),272(4.54), 297s(4.13),367(3.56), 484(3.98),516(3.72)	24-2976-80
4H-1-Benzopyran-4-one, 3-(2-benzofuran-yl)-6-ethyl-7-methoxy-	EtOH	285(4.57),296(4.53)	103-0685-80
1,4-Ethanonaphthacene-5,12-dione, 1,4,4a,12a-tetrahydro-6,11-di-hydroxy-, (1α,4α,4aα,12aα)-	EtOH	208(3.91),245s(4.30), 255(4.32),270s(4.26), 282(4.13),290(4.12), 390s(3.38),404(4.03), 424(4.03)	39-1007-80C
C$_{20}$H$_{16}$O$_4$S			
3-Thiophenecarboxylic acid, 4-(benzoyl-oxy)-2,5-dihydro-5-(phenylmethylene)-, methyl ester, (Z)-	EtOH	238(4.32),263(4.20), 362(4.29),374s(--)	33-1542-80
3-Thiophenecarboxylic acid, 4-(benzoyl-oxy)-5-(phenylmethyl)-, methyl ester	EtOH	232(4.36),275s(--)	33-1542-80
C$_{20}$H$_{16}$O$_6$			
1,4-Anthracenedione, 5,8-diacetoxy-2,3-dimethyl-	CH$_2$Cl$_2$	273(5.11),284(5.06), 297(4.93),310s(3.75), 405(3.67)	23-1161-80
5,12-Naphthacenedione, 8-acetyl-7,8,9,10-tetrahydro-1,6,11-tri-hydroxy-	CHCl$_3$	255(4.76),448(4.24), 536(4.09)	35-5881-80
C$_{20}$H$_{16}$O$_9$			
7H-Isobenzofuro[4,5-b][1,4]benzodioxe-pin-11-carboxaldehyde, 1,3-dihydro-4-hydroxy-1,10-dimethoxy-5,8-dimeth-yl-3,7-dioxo-	EtOH	238(4.62),312(3.77)	102-0328-80
C$_{20}$H$_{16}$S			
Naphtho[2,1-b]thiophene, 2,5-dimethyl-4-phenyl-	n.s.g.	243(4.58),285(3.92), 315(3.28),329(3.41)	18-1763-80
C$_{20}$H$_{17}$BrN$_4$O$_3$			
Benzoic acid, [(6-bromo-1,2,3,4-tetra-hydro-1,3-dimethyl-2,4-dioxo-5-pyri-midinyl)phenylmethylene]hydrazide	MeOH	285(4.46)	24-2566-80
C$_{20}$H$_{17}$ClN$_2$O$_2$			
6H-Anthra[1,9-cd]isoxazol-6-one, 3-chloro-5-(cyclohexylamino)-	dioxan	260(4.55),500(4.20), 535(4.27)	103-0704-80
C$_{20}$H$_{17}$ClN$_2$O$_3$			
1H-Pyrido[3,4-b]indole-3-carboxylic acid, 4-(2-chlorophenyl)-2,3,4,9-tetrahydro-1-oxo-, ethyl ester	EtOH	298(4.21)	103-0048-80
C$_{20}$H$_{17}$ClN$_4$O$_2$			
4H-[1,2,4]Triazolo[4,3-a][1,4]benzodi-azepine-4-carboxylic acid, 8-chloro-	EtOH	223(4.58),247s(4.16), 260s(3.86),290s(3.56)	87-0643-80

Compound	Solvent	$\lambda_{max}(\log \epsilon)$	Ref.
1-methyl-6-phenyl-, ethyl ester (cont.)			87-0643-80
$C_{20}H_{17}ClN_4O_3$			
Benzoic acid, [(6-chloro-1,2,3,4-tetra-hydro-1,3-dimethyl-2,4-dioxo-5-pyrim-idinyl)phenylmethylene]hydrazide	MeOH	282(4.42)	24-2566-80
$C_{20}H_{17}Cl_2NO_2$			
Methanone, [1-[(2,6-dichlorophenyl)-methyl]-1,6-dihydro-6-methoxy-3-pyridinyl]phenyl-	CH_2Cl_2	290s(4.3),327(4.4)	5-1350-80
$C_{20}H_{17}N$			
7,8:9,10-Dibenzotricyclo[4.2.2.1^{2,5}]un-deca-7,9-diene-1-carbonitrile	MeCN	256s(2.72),260(2.76), 267(2.88),275(2.94)	24-1458-80
$C_{20}H_{17}NO$			
2(1H)-Naphthalenone, 1-[3-[(phenylmeth-yl)amino]-2-propenylidene]-, (?,E)-	PhCN	315(3.75),353(3.58)	103-0799-80
3H-Naphtho[2,1-b]pyran-3-amine, N-(4-methylphenyl)-	MeOH	310(3.94),348(3.78), 380(3.58),547(2.85)	103-0799-80
	MeCN	337(4.06),355(4.03), 385(3.87)	103-0799-80
	PhCN	315(3.92),353(3.85), 490(4.00)	103-0799-80
	DMSO	355(3.76),380(3.58), 506(2.30)	103-0799-80
$C_{20}H_{17}NO_2$			
3,5-Hexadienoic acid, 3-cyano-6,6-di-phenyl-, methyl ester, cis	EtOH	236(4.15),252s(4.00), 323(4.50)	44-4864-80
trans	EtOH	235(4.17),251s(4.00), 320(4.44)	44-4864-80
3H-Naphtho[2,1-b]pyran-3-amine, N-(3-methoxyphenyl)-	MeOH	310(3.95),345(3.72)	103-0799-80
	PhCN	310(3.76),350(3.61), 495(3.92)	103-0799-80
	DMSO	295(4.06),350(3.73), 480(3.20)	103-0799-80
	CCl_4	300(4.10),354(3.73)	103-0799-80
3H-Naphtho[2,1-b]pyran-3-amine, N-(4-methoxyphenyl)-	MeOH	310(3.97),346(3.73), 386(3.20)	103-0799-80
	DMSO	310(4.05),357(3.95), 384(3.91),498(3.89)	103-0799-80
$C_{20}H_{17}NO_3$			
1-Azabicyclo[3.2.0]hept-2-ene-2-carbox-ylic acid, 7-oxo-3-phenyl-, phenyl-methyl ester	EtOH	295(3.95)	94-3494-80
$C_{20}H_{17}NO_4$			
[1,3]Dioxolo[4,5-h]-1,3-dioxolo[4,5]-indeno[2,1-a][3]benzazepine, 6,7,8,14-tetrahydro-6-methyl-	EtOH	272(3.89),344(4.27)	4-0417-80
	EtOH-HCl	247(4.10),316(4.03), 342(4.10)	4-0417-80
Phenol, 2-[4-(2-benzofuranyl)-3-isoxa-zolyl]-4-ethyl-5-methoxy-	EtOH	288(4.35),300(4.31)	103-0685-80
Phenol, 2-[4-(2-benzofuranyl)-5-isoxa-zolyl]-4-ethyl-5-methoxy-	EtOH	285(4.16),315(4.28), 330(4.16)	103-0685-80
$C_{20}H_{17}NO_5$			
Fumariline	EtOH	203(4.60),237(4.31), 263(4.05),294(3.66),	100-0305-80

Compound	Solvent	λ_{max} (log ϵ)	Ref.
(cont.)		355(3.51)	100-0305-80
	EtOH	236(4.38),262(4.07),	100-0305-80
		293(3.68),352(3.51)	
Thalicmidine, 7-hydroxy-	EtOH	246(4.98),294(4.11),	142-1135-80
		304(3.94),382(4.06),	
		486(4.00)	
$C_{20}H_{17}NO_6$			
Corydaine	EtOH	236(4.49),290(4.04),	100-0305-80
		314(4.03)	
Methanone, 1,3-dioxolo[4,5-g]isoquino-	MeOH	236(4.97),290(4.45),	100-0151-80
lin-5-yl(2,3,4-trimethoxyphenyl)-		328(4.25)	
Sibiricine	n.s.g.	205(4.80),240(3.94),	100-0305-80
		291(3.91),313s(3.99)	
$C_{20}H_{17}NO_7$			
6H-Benzo[g]-1,3-benzodioxolo[5,6-a]-	CH_2Cl_2	238(4.35),267(3.90),	39-0919-80C
quinolizine-8,13-dione, 5,13a-dihydro-		291(3.86),323(3.83)	
13a-hydroxy-9,10-dimethoxy-			
Benzoic acid, 6-[(7,8-dihydro-1,3-diox-	MeOH	220(4.41),286(4.11),	39-0919-80C
olo[4,5-g]isoquinolin-5-yl)carbonyl]-		304(4.01)	
2,3-dimethoxy-			
1,3-Dioxolo[4,5-g]isoquinolin-5(6H)-	MeOH	264(4.21),312(3.89)	39-0911-80C
one, 6-(2-formyl-3,4-dimethoxy-			
benzoyl)-7,8-dihydro-			
8,13a-Epidioxy-13aH-benzo[g]-1,3-benzo-	EtOH	226(4.49),269(4.04),	39-0911-80C
dioxolo[5,6-a]quinolizin-13(8H)-one,		309(3.93)	
5,6-dihydro-4,10-dimethoxy-			
$C_{20}H_{17}N_3$			
1,2,4-Benzotriazine, 1,4-dihydro-	EtOH	216s(4.28),243(4.26),	24-1205-80
4-methyl-1,3-diphenyl-		308(3.93)	
$C_{20}H_{17}N_3O$			
Pyrimido[4,5-b]quinolin-4(10H)-one,	EtOH	233(4.27),260(4.19),	94-3514-80
2-phenyl-10-propyl-		271(4.22),299(4.26),	
		341(3.92),404s(3.59),	
		430(3.83),451(3.87)	
$C_{20}H_{17}N_3O_2$			
Pyrimido[4,5-b]quinoline-2,4(1H,3H)-	EtOH	247(4.31),260(4.40),	94-3049-80
dione, 3,7,8-trimethyl-5-phenyl-		318(3.69),365(3.50),	
		381(3.36)	
Pyrimido[4,5-b]quinoline-2,4(3H,10H)-	EtOH	264(4.38),320(3.76),	94-3049-80
dione, 10-(3,4-dimethylphenyl)-3-		389s(3.70),401(3.79),	
methyl-		417s(3.69)	
Pyrimido[4,5-b]quinoline-2,4(3H,10H)-	EtOH	225(4.34),268(4.38),	94-3514-80
dione, 3-phenyl-10-propyl-		313s(3.68),323(3.74),	
		378s(3.65),400(3.82),	
		418s(3.74)	
$C_{20}H_{17}N_5O_5$			
Benzenamine, 4-[(2,4-dinitro-5-phenoxy-	$CHCl_3$	540(4.34)	49-0529-80
phenyl)azo]-N,N-dimethyl-			
$C_{20}H_{17}N_7O_5$			
2,5-Pyrrolidinedione, 1-[3-[[4-[(4-azi-	$CHCl_3$	360(4.23)	69-4423-80
dophenyl)azo]benzoyl]amino]-1-oxo-			
propoxy]-			

Compound	Solvent	$\lambda_{max}(\log \epsilon)$	Ref.
$C_{20}H_{17}OP$			
5H-Dibenzo[b,f]phosphepin, 10,11-dihydro-5-phenyl-, 5-oxide	EtOH	230(4.32),271(3.04)	139-0243-80A
$C_{20}H_{17}PS$			
5H-Dibenzo[b,f]phosphepin, 10,11-dihydro-5-phenyl-, 5-sulfide	EtOH	220(4.31),258(3.69)	139-0243-80A
$C_{20}H_{18}$			
Bicyclo[2.2.1]hept-2-ene, 5-(diphenylmethylene)-	EtOH	252(4.12)	78-0397-80
$C_{20}H_{18}BNO$			
Borinic acid, diphenyl-, 2-[(methylimino)methyl]phenyl ester	benzene	285(3.94),385(3.54)	101-0001-80I
	DMSO	283(3.95),375(3.53)	101-0001-80I
Boron, [2-[(methylimino)methyl]phenolato-N,O]diphenyl-, (T-4)-	CHCl$_3$	283(4.01),383(3.43)	49-0863-80
$C_{20}H_{18}BrNO_2S$			
3-Thiophenecarboxamide, N-(4-bromophenyl)-2,5-dihydro-4-methoxy-2-methyl-5-(phenylmethylene)-, (Z)-	EtOH	235(4.25),268(4.21), 340(4.36),358s(--)	33-1542-80
3-Thiophenecarboxamide, N-(4-bromophenyl)-4-methoxy-2-methyl-5-(phenylmethyl)-	EtOH	278(4.38)	33-1542-80
$C_{20}H_{18}BrNO_3$			
7H-Pyrano[2,3-c]acridin-7-one, 9-bromo-3,12-dihydro-6-methoxy-3,3,12-trimethyl-	MeOH	250(4.32),281(4.66), 294(4.58),315(4.21), 395(3.81)	5-0503-80
$C_{20}H_{18}BrN_7$			
1H-Pyrazol-5-amine, 4-[(4-bromo-3-methyl-1-phenyl-1H-pyrazol-5-yl)azo]-3-methyl-1-phenyl-, (E)-	MeOH	390(4.52),420(4.53)	103-1166-80
$C_{20}H_{18}ClNO_2$			
2H-Pyran-2-one, 3-chloro-4-(diphenylamino)-6-(1-methylethyl)-	EtOH	251(4.14),273(4.15), 348(4.07)	4-0507-80
$C_{20}H_{18}ClN_5O$			
1H-Indole-2,3-dione, 1-(2-methylpropyl)-, 3-[(3-chloro-2(1H)-quinoxalinylidene)hydrazone], (E,Z)-	EtOH	332(3.92),430s(4.16), 453s(4.26),472(4.25), 490s(4.22),525s(3.83)	103-1073-80
	EtOH-NaOH	335(3.74),385(3.97), 516(4.54)	103-1073-80
(Z,Z)-	EtOH	328(3.97),409(4.47)	103-1073-80
	EtOH-NaOH	330s(3.83),386(4.09), 515(4.53)	103-1073-80
$C_{20}H_{18}NO$			
Benz[cd]indolium, 5-ethoxy-1-methyl-2-phenyl-, tetrafluoroborate	CH$_2$Cl$_2$	246(4.33),333(4.08), 420(4.50)	83-0977-80
$C_{20}H_{18}N_2$			
1-Naphthalenepropanenitrile, α-methyl-α-(phenylamino)-	dioxan	274(3.92),284(4.00), 295s(3.86),314(2.81)	24-2462-80
3H-Pyrrolo[1,2-d][1,4]diazepine, 4,5-dihydro-1,8-diphenyl-	EtOH	258(4.17),284(4.03), 312(4.03)	39-1441-80B
	EtOH-acid	321(3.93),401(4.00)	39-1441-80B

Compound	Solvent	$\lambda_{max}(\log \epsilon)$	Ref.
$C_{20}H_{18}N_2O$			
Ethanone, 1-[4-[2-(4-methylphenyl)-2-phenylethenyl]-1H-pyrazol-3-yl]-	EtOH	239(4.17),318(4.01)	78-1331-80
3H-Pyrazol-3-one, 2,4-dihydro-5-methyl-4-[3-(4-methylphenyl)-2-propenylidene]-2-phenyl-	n.s.g.	252(4.48),375(4.69),485(3.29)	124-0642-80
$C_{20}H_{18}N_2O_2$			
Ethanone, 1-[4-[2-(4-methoxyphenyl)-2-phenylethenyl]-1H-pyrazol-3-yl]-	EtOH	237(3.76),324(3.88)	78-1331-80
3H-Pyrazol-3-one, 2,4-dihydro-4-[3-(4-methoxyphenyl)-2-propenylidene]-5-methyl-2-phenyl-	n.s.g.	255(4.56),393(4.72),485(3.48)	124-0642-80
$C_{20}H_{18}N_2O_3$			
Acetamide, N-[2-[(1,4-dihydro-1,4-dioxo-3-phenyl-2-naphthalenyl)amino]-ethyl]-	EtOH	272(4.40),460(3.53)	83-0603-80
$C_{20}H_{18}N_2O_4$			
Oxazolium, 4-[(benzoylmethylamino)acetyl]-5-hydroxy-3-methyl-2-phenyl-, hydroxide, inner salt	MeCN	228(4.15),264(4.10),340(4.26)	5-1836-80
$C_{20}H_{18}N_2O_4S$			
2,6-Pyridinediol, 3-(1-isoquinolinyl)-4-methyl-5-(methylthio)-, diacetate	EtOH	220(4.78),277(3.94),287(3.93),313(3.64),325(3.69)	95-1261-80
2,6-Pyridinediol, 4-methyl-3-(methylthio)-5-(2-quinolinyl)-, diacetate	EtOH	235(4.63),280(3.92),318(3.68)	94-2892-80
$C_{20}H_{18}N_2O_6$			
4-Hexen-2-yn-1-ol, 1,-bis(4-nitrophenyl)-5-ethoxy-	EtOH	281(4.32)	78-1331-80
$C_{20}H_{18}N_4O_4$			
Benzoic acid, [phenyl(1,2,3,4-tetrahydro-1,3-dimethyl-2,4-dioxo-5-pyrimidinyl)methylene]hydrazide	MeOH	282(4.40),298s(4.38)	24-2566-80
$C_{20}H_{18}N_4O_5$			
1,5,7-Triazabicyclo[4.1.0]hept-3-ene-6-carboxylic acid, 7-(4-nitrophenyl)-2-oxo-5-(phenylmethyl)-, ethyl ester	EtOH	255(4.10),330(4.05)	142-0843-80B
$C_{20}H_{18}N_5O$			
7H-Purinium, 6-(benzoylamino)-7-methyl-9-(phenylmethyl)-, iodide	pH 1 H2O	283(4.33) 280(4.16),320s(3.48)	142-0895-80B 142-0895-80B
$C_{20}H_{18}N_6O_5$			
Acetamide, N-(4-nitrophenyl)-N-[4,5,6-7-tetrahydro-2-(4-nitrophenyl)-2H-benzotriazol-4-yl]-	n.s.g.	322(2.79)	39-0744-80C
$C_{20}H_{18}N_6O_8$			
Indolo[7,6-g]indole, 3,8-dihydro-1,6-bis[2-nitro-1-(nitromethyl)ethyl]-	EtOH	209(4.56),256s(4.78),266(4.97),288s(4.45),296(4.41),309s(4.26),337(4.11),351(4.03)	103-1139-80

Compound	Solvent	$\lambda_{max}(\log \epsilon)$	Ref.
$C_{20}H_{18}O$			
2,4,6,12,14,16-Cycloheptadecahexaene-8,10-diyn-1-one, 2,7,12-trimethyl-	THF	280s(4.63),298(4.84), 307(4.85),356s(3.90)	39-0473-80C
	CF_3COOH	316(--),334(--), 393(--)	39-0473-80C
Naphthalene, 2-[(1-phenyl-1-butenyl)-oxy]-	hexane	252s(--),284s(--), 314(3.15),321(3.07), 328(3.29)	118-0847-80
3-Oxatricyclo[4.2.1.0^{2,5}]non-7-ene, 4,4-diphenyl-, (1α,2β,5β,6α)-	EtOH	255(2.76)	78-0397-80
$C_{20}H_{18}O_2$			
Butanedial, bis[(4-methylphenyl)meth-ylene]-	$CHCl_3$	302(4.65)	118-0898-80
Cyclobuta[b]naphthalene-3,8-dione, 2a-ethyl-1,2,2a,8a-tetrahydro-1-phenyl-	$CHCl_3$	242(4.19),253(4.22), 300(3.37),308(3.34), 335(2.43)	18-0757-80
Cyclobuta[b]naphthalene-3,8-dione, 1,2,2a,8a-tetrahydro-1,2a-dimethyl-1-phenyl-, anti	$CHCl_3$	256(4.11),298(3.27), 307(3.25),335(2.30)	18-0757-80
Cyclobuta[b]naphthalene-3,8-dione, 1,2,2a,8a-tetrahydro-1,8a-dimethyl-1-phenyl-, anti	$CHCl_3$	242(4.05),254(4.11), 298(3.28),307(3.23), 330(2.30)	18-0757-80
Cyclobuta[b]naphthalene-3,8-dione, 1,2,2a,8a-tetrahydro-2a,8a-dimethyl-1-phenyl-, anti	$CHCl_3$	258(4.12),297(3.31), 306(3.28),332(2.45)	18-0757-80
syn	$CHCl_3$	250(4.04),295(3.20), 305(3.16),337(2.30)	18-0757-80
Ethanone, 2-(2,2-dimethyl-5-phenyl-3(2H)-furanylidene)-1-phenyl-	EtOH	410(4.47)	5-1744-80
Ethanone, 1-(1,2,3,4,5,12-hexahydro-5,12-epoxynaphthalen-2-yl)-	EtOH	235(4.53),260s(4.03), 269(3.96),278s(3.65), 297(2.60),304(2.54), 310(2.78),324(2.81)	33-0232-80
9a,1,10-Ethanylylidene-6,9-methano-9aH-benzo[4,5]cycloocta[1,2,3-cd]pental-ene-2,13(1H)-dione, 5a,6,9,9b,10,11-11a,11b-octahydro-	MeOH	240(c.3.7),283(c.3.3)	88-1369-80
2-Oxabicyclo[4.1.0]hept-3-en-5-one, 1,3-dimethyl-4,6-diphenyl-	MeOH	<u>272(4.0)</u>	18-0469-80
$C_{20}H_{18}O_2S_2$			
2,4-Hexadiene-1,6-dione, 2,5-bis(meth-ylthio)-1,6-diphenyl-	EtOH	388(4.14)	24-1708-80
	$CHCl_3$	398(4.11)	24-1708-80
$C_{20}H_{18}O_3$			
4H-1-Benzopyran-4-one, 8-(1,2-dimethyl-2-propenyl)-7-hydroxy-2-phenyl-	MeOH	260(4.20),315(4.16)	2-0866-80
	MeOH-NaOAc	275(--),316(--)	2-0866-80
4H-Furo[2,3-h]-1-benzopyran-4-one, 8,9-dihydro-8,8,9-trimethyl-2-phenyl-	MeOH	259(4.35),314(4.29)	2-0866-80
3,4,5-Hexatrien-2-one, 6,6-bis(4-meth-oxyphenyl)-	EtOH	258(4.26),420(4.48)	78-1331-80
$C_{20}H_{18}O_4$			
4H-1-Benzopyran-4-one, 7-hydroxy-2-(4-hydroxyphenyl)-6-(3-methyl-2-buten-yl)- (licoflavone A)	MeOH	250s(4.00),320s(4.44), 331(4.47)	102-2179-80
	MeOH-NaOMe	255(4.25),265(4.24), 330(4.24),392(4.57)	102-2179-80
4H-1-Benzopyran-4-one, 7-hydroxy-2-(4-hydroxyphenyl)-8-(3-methyl-2-buten-yl)-	MeOH	250(4.21),258(4.22), 313s(4.36),329(4.41)	102-2179-80
	MeOH-NaOMe	272(4.40),337(4.18), 390(4.49)	102-2179-80

Compound	Solvent	$\lambda_{max}(\log \epsilon)$	Ref.
[3,6'-Bi-4H-1-benzopyran]-4-one, 2',3'-dihydro-7-hydroxy-2',2'-dimethyl-	MeOH	275(4.10),310(3.88)	142-1163-80B
	MeOH-NaOH	335(4.32)	142-1163-80B
Butanedial, bis[(4-methoxyphenyl)methylene]-, (E,E)-	CHCl₃	324(4.7)	118-0898-80
Indeno[1,2-b]pyran-5(2H)-one, 3,4-dihydro-2,2-dimethoxy-4-phenyl-	CHCl₃	249(4.53),313(2.7), 397(2.9)	24-1020-80
C₂₀H₁₈O₅			
5,12-Naphthacenedione, 9-ethyl-7,8,9-10-tetrahydro-6,9,11-trihydroxy-	MeOH	254(4.55),289(3.83), 459(3.88),481(3.96), 514(3.81)	24-2976-80
C₂₀H₁₈O₆			
9,10-Anthracenedione, 1,4-dihydroxy-8-methoxy-2-(3-oxopentyl)-	MeOH	231(4.56),249(4.33), 287(3.94),385s(--), 450s(--),476(4.03), 493(4.03),526(3.78)	24-2994-80
1,3-Benzodioxole, 5,5'-(tetrahydro-1H,3H-furo[3,4-c]furan-1,4-diyl)bis-(sesamin)	EtOH	204(5.01),238(4.10), 287(4.00)	78-3551-80
2H-1-Benzopyran-7-ol, 3-(4-acetoxy-2-methoxyphenyl)-, acetate	MeOH	238s(4.25),287s(4.09), 320(4.25)	94-1172-80
4H-1-Benzopyran-4-one, 3-(1,3-benzodioxol-5-ylmethyl)-5,7-dimethoxy-8-methyl-	EtOH	230(4.47),251(4.49), 259(4.53),292(4.09), 315s(3.86)	94-2487-80
4H-1-Benzopyran-4-one, 3-(1,3-benzodioxol-5-ylmethyl)-5-hydroxy-7-methoxy-6,8-dimethyl-	EtOH	230(4.53),245(4.53), 265(4.55),341(3.60)	94-1477-80
	EtOH	230(4.43),245(4.45), 265(4.50),341(3.66)	94-2487-80
	EtOH-AlCl₃	276(--),380(--)	94-2487-80
3,12-Dioxatricyclo[12.2.2.2⁶,⁹]eicosa-1(16),6,8,14,17,19-hexaene-15-carboxylic acid, 4,11-dioxo-, methyl ester	MeOH	271(4.13)	44-4496-80
6H-Furo[2,3-c]xanthen-6-one, 1,2-dihydro-5,10-dimethoxy-2-(2-methyl-oxiranyl)-	EtOH	240s(4.62),246(4.68), 309(4.29),339(3.80)	100-0296-80
2(5H)-Furanone, 5-acetoxy-4,5-bis(2-methoxyphenyl)-	MeOH	281(4.21),330(3.89)	18-0179-80
5H-Furo[3,2-g][1]benzopyran-5-one, 6,7-dihydro-6-(2,4,5-trimethoxyphenyl)- (ambonone)	MeOH	234(4.62),275(4.11), 333(3.81)	39-1804-80C
5,12-Naphthacenedione, 8-ethyl-7,8,9-10-tetrahydro-1,6,7,11-tetrahydroxy-	MeOH	234(4.42),254(4.48), 293(3.86),440s(--), 465(4.02),490(4.15), 512(3.99),524(4.02)	24-2994-80
5,12-Naphthacenedione, 9c-ethyl-7,8,9-10-tetrahydro-6,7r,9t,11-tetrahydroxy-	MeOH	227(4.32),250(4.56), 284(3.94),457s(3.93), 479(4.01),512(3.87)	24-2976-80
5,12-Naphthacenedione, 9t-ethyl-7,8,9-10-tetrahydro-6,7r,9c,11-tetrahydroxy-	MeOH	227(4.23),250(4.58), 285(3.91),458s(3.96), 481(4.00),512(3.82)	24-2976-80
Pyrano[3,2-a]xanthen-12(3H)-one, 11-hydroxy-5,9-dimethoxy-3,3-dimethyl-	MeOH	242(4.47),264(4.51), 319(4.35),376(3.81)	39-2353-80C
9H-Xanthen-9-one, 7-[(1,1-dimethyl-2-propynyl)oxy]-1-hydroxy-3,6-dimethoxy-	MeOH	240(4.47),255(4.59), 308(4.29),350(4.01)	39-2353-80C
C₂₀H₁₈O₇			
1,3-Benzodioxol-5-ol, 6-[4-(1,3-benzodioxol-5-yl)tetrahydro-1H,3H-furo-	MeOH	228(4.32),282(3.78)	102-0332-80
	MeOH-NaOMe	245s(--),298(--)	102-0332-80

Compound	Solvent	$\lambda_{max}(\log \epsilon)$	Ref.
[3,4-c]furan-1-yl]- (cont.)			102-0332-80
4H-1-Benzopyran-4-one, 7-acetoxy-3-(1,3- benzodioxol-5-ylmethyl)-2,3-dihydro-5-hydroxy-6-methyl-	EtOH	225(4.18),282(4.04)	94-2039-80
5,12-Naphthacenedione, 9t-ethyl-7,8,9-10-tetrahydro-1,6,7r,9c,11-penta-hydroxy-	MeOH	233(4.42),252(4.25), 292(3.73),490(3.99), 524(3.82)	24-2976-80
5,12-Naphthacenedione, 9t-ethyl-7,8,9-10-tetrahydro-4,6,7r,9c,11-penta-	MeOH	234(4.47),253(4.36), 293(3.78),491(4.09), 515s(--),526(3.95)	24-2976-80
β-Rhodomycinone, 10-deoxy-	CHCl₃	391(3.48),412(3.60), 467(4.13),496(4.25), 519(4.12),531(4.10), 564(3.24)	73-1991-80
γ-Rhodomycinone, (±)-	MeOH	235(4.15),253(4.20), 292(3.70),410(3.40), 466(3.96),478(3.99), 492(4.08),510(3.91), 526(3.93)	24-2994-80
$C_{20}H_{18}O_8$			
5,12-Naphthacenedione, 9t-ethyl-7,8,9-10-tetrahydro-1,6,7r,9c,10c,11-hexa-hydroxy-	MeOH	233(4.42),252(4.16), 293(3.59),491(4.00), 528(3.83)	24-2976-80
β-Rhodomycinone, 10-epi-	MeOH	233(4.46),251(4.24), 290(3.79),491(3.98), 526(3.80)	24-2976-80
$C_{20}H_{18}O_{10}$			
4H-1-Benzopyran-4-one, 3-(L-arabino-syl)-2-(3,4-dihydroxyphenyl)-5,7-dihydroxy- (avicularin)	MeOH	215(4.36),258(4.31), 296s(3.88),357(4.27)	36-0360-80
$C_{20}H_{18}O_{11}$			
4H-1-Benzopyran-4-one, 3-(arabinosyl-oxy)-2-(3,4-dihydroxyphenyl)-5,7-di-hydroxy- (guaijaverin)	MeOH	256(4.36),266s(4.30), 295s(3.97),358(4.25)	100-0739-80
	MeOH-NaOMe	270(--),328(--), 406(--)	100-0739-80
	MeOH-AlCl₃	274(--),304s(--), 364(--),437(--)	100-0739-80
$C_{20}H_{18}S_2Sn$			
Stannanecarbodithioic acid, triphenyl-, methyl ester	CHCl₃	313(3.71),532(2.10)	89-0220B-80
$C_{20}H_{19}BrN_4O$			
Morpholine, 4-[(4-bromophenyl)(2-quino-linylhydrazono)methyl]-	MeOH	260(4.21),380(4.04)	56-0661-80
monohydriodide	MeOH	260(4.31),380(4.17)	56-0661-80
$C_{20}H_{19}BrO_2$			
Benzenemethanol, 4-bromo-α-(4-ethoxy-3-penten-1-ynyl)-α-phenyl-	EtOH	232(4.36),245s(4.35)	78-1331-80
$C_{20}H_{19}ClN_2O_2$			
9,10-Anthracenedione, 1-amino-2-chloro-4-(cyclohexylamino)-	n.s.g.	583(4.11),629(4.13)	93-1963-80
$C_{20}H_{19}ClN_2O_2S$			
Benzenesulfonamide, 4-chloro-N-(1,2,3-3a,4,5-hexahydro-11H-cyclopenta[2,3]-	EtOH	228(4.40),242s(4.35), 281(4.00),420(3.80)	39-2870-80C

Compound	Solvent	$\lambda_{max}(\log \epsilon)$	Ref.
pyrrolo[1,2-a]indol-11-ylidene)- (cont.)			39-2870-80C
$C_{20}H_{19}ClN_2O_3S$			
Benzenesulfonamide, 4-chloro-N-(6,7,8-9,10,11-hexahydro-8-oxoazocino[1,2-a]indol-12-yl)-	EtOH	224(4.61),282(3.96)	39-2870-80C
Benzenesulfonamide, 4-chloro-N-(1,2,4-5-tetrahydro-12-oxo-2a,6-methano-2aH-azeto[1,2-a][1]benzazocin-6(3H)-yl-	EtOH	225(4.32),260(4.00)	39-2870-80C
$C_{20}H_{19}ClN_2O_4$			
7-Azabicyclo[4.3.1]deca-3,8-dien-10-one, 7-[3-(2-chloro-5-nitrophenyl)-3-oxo-1-propenyl]-3,4-dimethyl-, (E)-	$CHCl_3$	265(4.30),340(4.08)	39-0362-80C
$C_{20}H_{19}ClN_2O_4S$			
Benzenesulfonamide, 4-chloro-N-(2,3,4-5,6,7-hexahydro-4,13-dioxo-8H-1,8-methano-1-benzazecin-8-yl)-	EtOH	235(4.23),265(3.76)	39-2870-80C
$C_{20}H_{19}ClN_2O_9$			
Benzamide, N-[3-[6-acetoxy-5-(acetoxy-methyl)tetrahydro-2-oxofuro[2,3-d]-oxazol-3(2H)-yl]-1-oxo-2-propenyl]-3-chloro-, [3aR-[3(E),3α,5β,6α,6aα]]-	MeOH	271(4.48)	44-1577-80
$C_{20}H_{19}ClN_4O$			
Morpholine, 4-[(3-chlorophenyl)(2-quin-olinylhydrazono)methyl]-monohydriodide	MeOH	265(4.18),380(3.99)	56-0661-80
	MeOH	265(4.30),380(4.16)	56-0661-80
$C_{20}H_{19}ClO_6$			
6H-Furo[2,3-c]xanthen-9-one, 2-(2-chloro-1-hydroxy-1-methylethyl)-1,2-dihydro-5,10-dimethoxy-	EtOH	239(4.57),246(4.65), 300s(--),310(4.27)	100-0296-80
$C_{20}H_{19}FO_2$			
5(6H)-Benzocyclooctenone, 9-(4-fluoro-phenoxy)-7,8-dihydro-7,7-dimethyl-	EtOH	242(4.41),272(4.02), 330(3.73)	44-0240-80
Cyclobuta[a]naphthalen-8b(1H)-ol, 3-(4-fluorophenoxy)-2,2a-dihydro-2,2-dimethyl-	EtOH	224(4.33),230s(4.26), 273(4.17),280s(4.13), 299s(3.65),310s(3.46)	44-0240-80
$C_{20}H_{19}N$			
Benzenamine, 4-[2-(2-azulenyl)ethenyl]-N,N-dimethyl-	MeOH	262(4.30),294(4.68), 340(4.56)	18-3276-80
4a,9-Methano-4aH-dibenzo[3,4:6,7]cyclo-hepta[1,2-c]pyridine, 2,3,4,9-tetra-hydro-2-methyl-	C_6H_{12}	322(4.08)	44-1505-80
$C_{20}H_{19}NO_2$			
1H-Pyrrole-2,5-dione, 1-butyl-3,4-di-phenyl-	MeCN	359(3.57)	40-0837-80
	60% dioxan	366(3.59)	40-0837-80
1H-Pyrrole-2,5-dione, 1-(1,1-dimethyl-ethyl)-3,4-diphenyl-	60% dioxan	360(3.58)	40-0837-80
1H-Pyrrole-2,5-dione, 1-(1-methylprop-yl)-3,4-diphenyl-	60% dioxan	365(3.59)	40-0837-80
1H-Pyrrole-2,5-dione, 1-(2-methylprop-yl)-3,4-diphenyl-	60% dioxan	365(3.60)	40-0837-80

Compound	Solvent	$\lambda_{max}(\log \epsilon)$	Ref.
$C_{20}H_{19}NO_2S$			
3-Thiophenecarboxamide, 2,5-dihydro-4-methoxy-N-(4-methylphenyl)-5-(phenylmethylene)-, (Z)-	EtOH	232(4.19),261(4.15), 340s(--),355(4.35)	33-1542-80
3-Thiophenecarboxamide, 4-methyl-N-(4-methylphenyl)-5-(phenylmethyl)-	EtOH	274(4.27)	33-1542-80
$C_{20}H_{19}NO_3$			
5H-[1]Benzopyrano[3,4-c]pyridin-5-one, 1,2,3,4-tetrahydro-10-hydroxy-8-methyl-3-(phenylmethyl)-	EtOH	256(4.02),306(4.12)	2-0495-80
Methanone, phenyl(2,3,3a,6a-tetrahydro-3a,5-dimethyl-2-phenylfuro[2,3-d]isoxazol-3-yl)-	MeOH	244(4.41)	73-3546-80
$C_{20}H_{19}NO_4$			
Benzenemethanol, α-(4-ethoxy-3-penten-1-ynyl)-4-nitro-α-phenyl-	EtOH	244(4.30)	78-1331-80
Dehydrocrebanine	EtOH	248s(4.36),272(4.77), 296s(4.17),337(4.15), 385(3.49)	102-2735-80
12H-Naphtho[1,2-b]pyrrolo [1,2-d][1,4]-oxazin-12-one, 6-acetoxy-1,2,3,12a-tetrahydro-5-(2-propenyl)-, (S)-	MeOH	240(4.49),255(4.32), 297(3.86),330(3.40)	44-1260-80
$C_{20}H_{19}NO_5$			
Benzo[4,5]cyclohepta[1,2-b]pyrrolizine-1,12-dicarboxylic acid, 1,2,3,5,10,11-hexahydro-5-oxo-, dimethyl ester	MeOH	216(4.18),232(4.22), 242(4.21),320(4.18)	4-1081-80
Perfumine	EtOH	235(4.42),260(4.10), 290s(--),358(3.42)	100-0305-80
Protopine	EtOH-acid	240(3.9),285(3.9)	142-1159-80
$C_{20}H_{19}NO_6$			
Corpaine	EtOH	242(3.4),298(3.3), 315(3.4)	100-0305-80
1,3-Dioxolo[4,5-g]isoquinoline-5-methanol, α-(2,3,4-trimethoxyphenyl)-	MeOH	237(4.95),278(4.08), 290(3.96),313(3.98), 327(4.04)	100-0151-80
Ledeborine	MeOH	238(4.38),293(3.98), 316(3.90)	100-0305-80
Ochrobirine	MeOH	205(4.80),240(3.94), 291(3.91)	100-0305-80
	EtOH	201(4.21),239(3.91), 291(3.87)	100-0305-80
	EtOH	205(4.81),240(3.94), 250(3.91)	100-0305-80
Severzinine	EtOH	290(4.04)	100-0305-80
$C_{20}H_{19}N_3O_2$			
2H-1,3-Benzoxazin-2-one, 4-(2,4-dimethyl-3H-1,5-benzodiazepin-3-yl)-3,4-dihydro-3-methyl-	EtOH	213(4.42),236s(4.18), 273(3.82),310s(3.48)	4-0519-80
2H-1,3-Benzoxazin-2-one, 4-(3,5-dimethyl-1-phenyl-1H-pyrazol-4-yl)-3,4-dihydro-3-methyl-	EtOH	245(4.14)	4-0519-80
$C_{20}H_{19}N_3O_4$			
2H-1,3-Benzoxazin-2-one, 4-(2,5-dihydro-3-methyl-5-oxo-1-phenyl-1H-pyrazol-4-yl)-3,4-dihydro-8-methoxy-3-methyl-	EtOH	246(4.15),271(4.08)	4-0519-80

Compound	Solvent	$\lambda_{max}(\log \epsilon)$	Ref.
$C_{20}H_{19}N_5O_2$			
2,3-Quinoxalinedione, 1,4-dihydro-, mono(1-butyl-1,2-dihydro-2-oxo-3H-indol-3-ylidene)hydrazone], (Z,?)-	EtOH	296s(3.84),415(4.46)	103-1073-80
$C_{20}H_{19}N_5O_3$			
Morpholine, 4-[(4-nitrophenyl)(2-quinolinylhydrazono)methyl]-	MeOH	270(4.48),380(3.98)	56-0661-80
monohydriodide salt	MeOH	275(4.48),380(4.11)	56-0661-80
$C_{20}H_{19}OS$			
Sulfonium, (2'-hydroxy[1,1':3',1"-terphenyl]-5'-yl)dimethyl-, hexafluoroarsenate	n.s.g.	243(4.53),300(3.95), 335(3.62)	47-1021-80
$C_{20}H_{20}$			
Bicyclo[3.1.0]hex-2-ene, 3,4-dimethyl-1,2-diphenyl-, exo	EtOH	257(4.00)	35-5648-80
Bicyclo[3.1.0]hex-2-ene, 3,5-dimethyl-1,2-diphenyl-	EtOH	256(3.97)	35-5648-80
Bicyclo[3.1.0]hex-2-ene, 3,6-dimethyl-1,2-diphenyl-, endo	EtOH	256(3.99)	44-2181-80
exo	EtOH	252(3.81)	44-2181-80
1,2'-Binaphthalene, 1,2,3,3',4,4'-hexahydro-, (±)-	EtOH	265(4.26)	44-4769-80
1-Butene, 3-(1-methyl-2,3-diphenyl-2-cyclopropen-1-yl)-	EtOH	228(4.25),322(4.43), 338(4.29)	35-2797-80
	EtOH	228(4.25),332(4.43), 338(4.29)	35-5648-80
1-Butene, 3-(2-methyl-1,3-diphenyl-2-cyclopropen-1-yl)-	EtOH	267(4.19)	35-2797-80 +35-5648-80
2-Butene, 1-(1-methyl-2,3-diphenyl-2-cyclopropen-1-yl)-, (E)-	EtOH	229(4.24),237(4.13), 322(4.43),338(4.30)	35-2797-80
(Z)-	EtOH	228(4.25),327(4.43), 338(4.31)	35-2797-80
2-Butene, 1-(2-methyl-1,3-diphenyl-2-cyclopropen-1-yl)-, (E)-	EtOH	264(4.20)	35-2797-80
(Z)-	EtOH	264(4.19)	35-2797-80
1,5-Hexadiene, 4-methyl-3-methylene-1,2-diphenyl-, (E)-	EtOH	226(4.16),285(4.20)	35-5648-80
(Z)-	EtOH	223(4.19),288(4.15)	35-5648-80
1H-Indene, 1-(3-butenyl)-2-methyl-3-phenyl)-	EtOH	223(4.29),259(3.96)	44-4555-80
1H-Indene, 3-(3-butenyl)-2-methyl-1-phenyl-	EtOH	262(4.04)	44-4555-80
1-Propene, 2-methyl-3-(1-methyl-2,3-diphenyl-2-cyclopropen-1-yl)-	EtOH	229(4.28),321(4.43), 337(4.29)	35-5648-80
1-Propene, 2-methyl-3-(2-methyl-1,3-diphenyl-2-cyclopropen-1-yl)-	EtOH	263(4.25)	35-5648-80
Tricyclo[2.2.0.0^{2,6}]hexane, 3,6-dimethyl-1,2-diphenyl-, endo	EtOH	246(4.15)	35-2797-80
exo	EtOH	245(4.15)	35-2797-80
Tricyclo[2.2.0.0^{2,6}]hexane, 5,6-dimethyl-1,2-diphenyl-, endo	EtOH	244(4.22)	35-2797-80
exo	EtOH	246(4.10)	35-2797-80
$C_{20}H_{20}Br_2$			
1H-Indene, 3-(bromomethylene)-2-(bromophenylmethyl)-2,3-dihydro-1,1,2-trimethyl-, (E)-	CCl₄	288(3.85),297(3.78)	5-1207-80

Compound	Solvent	$\lambda_{max}(\log \epsilon)$	Ref.
$C_{20}H_{20}ClNO_2$ 7-Azabicyclo[4.3.1]deca-3,8-dien-10-one, 7-[3-(4-chlorophenyl)-3-oxo-1-propen- yl]-3,4-dimethyl-, (E)-	$CHCl_3$	263(4.39),360(4.60)	39-0362-80C
$C_{20}H_{20}ClNO_3$ 1H-Indole, 1-(4-chlorobenzoyl)-5-meth- oxy-3-(2-methoxyethyl)-2-methyl-	EtOH	230(4.63),270(4.50), 320(4.00)	80-0245-80
$C_{20}H_{20}ClNO_4$ 2H-Naphth[2,1-e]-1,3-oxazin-2-one, 4-(5-chloro-2-hydroxyphenyl)-3,4,4a- 5,6,10b-hexahydro-9-methoxy-3-methyl-	EtOH	227(4.33),282(3.65)	4-0277-80
$C_{20}H_{20}ClN_2$ 3H-Indolium, 1-[(4-chlorophenyl)meth- yl]-3-(1-pyrrolidinylmethylene)-, chloride	MeOH	250s(4.06),258(4.07), 269s(3.79),276(3.82), 348(4.33)	94-1711-80
$C_{20}H_{20}ClN_3O_8$ Benzamide, 3-chloro-N-[1-(3,5-di-O-acet- yl-β-D-arabinofuranosyl)-1,2-dihydro- 2-oxo-4-pyrimidinyl]-	MeOH	259(4.37),307(4.04)	44-1577-80
$C_{20}H_{20}N$ 1H-Benz[f]isoindolium, 2,3-dihydro- 2,2-dimethyl-4-phenyl-, bromide	EtOH	230(4.90),288(3.95)	39-1477-80C
$C_{20}H_{20}NOS$ Thiazolium, 3-ethyl-2-[2-(4-methoxy- phenyl)ethenyl]-4-phenyl-, iodide	EtOH	220(4.52),255s(--), 390(4.16)	49-1213-80
	DMF	393(4.45)	49-1213-80
	DMSO	394(4.33)	49-1213-80
	$CHCl_3$	292(4.06),400(4.36)	49-1213-80
$C_{20}H_{20}NO_2S$ Thiazolium, 3-ethyl-2-[2-(4-hydroxy-3- methoxyphenyl)ethenyl]-4-phenyl-, iodide	EtOH	210(3.99),417(3.90), 554(3.99)	49-1213-80
	DMF	414(4.23),577(4.51)	49-1213-80
	DMSO	415(3.78),580(4.37)	49-1213-80
	$CHCl_3$	423(4.11),580(3.00)	49-1213-80
$C_{20}H_{20}NO_4$ Dibenzo[a,g]quinolizinium, 5,6-dihydro- 3-hydroxy-2,10,11-trimethoxy-, chloride	MeOH	243(4.24),265(4.21), 289(4.48),310s(4.36), 341(4.19),379s(3.82)	36-1061-80
	MeOH-NaOH	254(4.42),310(4.24), 378(4.37)	36-1061-80
$C_{20}H_{20}N_2$ Pyrrolo[3,2-b]pyrrole, 3,3a,6,6a-tetra- hydro-3a,6a-dimethyl-2,5-diphenyl-, cis	EtOH	248(4.05)	44-0168-80
$C_{20}H_{20}N_2O_3$ Naucleidinal	EtOH	226(4.47),282s(3.85), 290(3.80)	102-1884-80
$C_{20}H_{20}N_2O_4$ Dibenz[de,gh]pyrazino[1,2,3,4-lmn]- [1,10]phenanthroline-7,8,9,10-	EtOH	274(4.13),305(3.79)	33-0938-80

Compound	Solvent	$\lambda_{max}(\log \epsilon)$	Ref.
tetrol, 1,2,4,5,12,13,14a,14b-octa-hydro-, dihydrobromide, trans-(±)-			33-0938-80
Spiro[2H-1-benzopyran-2,2'-[2H]indole], 1',3'-dihydro-8-methoxy-1',3',3'-tri-methyl-6-nitro-	EtOH	560(4.43)	103-0041-80
$C_{20}H_{20}N_2O_4S_2$			
3,8-Diazatricyclo[5.1.0.0²,⁴]oct-5-ene, 3,8-bis[(4-methylphenyl)sulfonyl]-, (1α,2α,4α,7α)-	MeCN	233(4.44),246(2.98), 253s(3.08),258(3.14), 264(3.07)	24-3161-80
1,4-Diazocine, 1,4-dihydro-1,4-bis-[(4-methylphenyl)sulfonyl]-	MeCN	250s(4.07)	24-3161-80
$C_{20}H_{20}N_2O_5S$			
Acetic acid, (3-acetyl-3,6-dihydro-1,3-thiazin-2-ylidene)phthalimido-, 1,1-dimethylethyl ester	MeOH	214(4.51),235s(4.32), 342(4.48)	4-0767-80
$C_{20}H_{20}N_2O_6S$			
Acetic acid, [3-(methoxycarbonyl)-3,6-dihydro-1,3-thiazin-2-ylidene)phthal-imido-, 1,1-dimethylethyl ester	MeOH	214(4.59),230s(4.34), 337(4.52)	4-0767-80
$C_{20}H_{20}N_2O_7S$			
6-Thiatetracycline	EtOH	252(4.43),354(4.08)	88-0247-80
	MeOH-borate	250(4.36),376(4.14)	88-0247-80
hydrochloride	H₂O	249(4.33),275(4.12), 351(4.13)	88-0247-80
5a-epi-	EtOH	252(4.32),353(4.00)	35-7021-80
	MeOH-borate	251(4.36),374(4.15)	35-7021-80
6-Thiatetracycline, 11a-hydroxy-12a-de-hydroxy-	EtOH	252(4.33),315(4.16), 377s(3.84)	35-7021-80
	MeOH-borate	244(4.34),337(4.30)	35-7021-80
$C_{20}H_{20}N_3$			
1H-Benzimidazolium, 1,3-diethyl-2-(2-quinolinyl)-, iodide	EtOH	205(4.62),233(4.44), 285(3.95)	103-1261-80
$C_{20}H_{20}N_4O$			
1H-Imidazo[1,5-b]pyrazole-3-carboni-trile, hexahydro-4,4-dimethyl-6-oxo-1,3a-diphenyl-	EtOH	198(4.6),241(4.1), 284(3.3)	5-1016-80
Methanimidamide, N'-[4-formyl-1-(4-methylphenyl)-3-phenyl-1H-pyrazol-5-yl]-N,N-dimethyl-	EtOH	254(4.46),335(3.76)	114-0127-80C
Morpholine, 4-[phenyl(2-quinolinyl-hydrazono)methyl]-	MeOH	260(4.32),370(3.95)	56-0661-80
hydriodide	MeOH	260(4.31),370(4.02)	56-0661-80
$C_{20}H_{20}N_4O_2$			
Methanimidamide, N'-[4-formyl-1-(4-methoxyphenyl)-3-phenyl-1H-pyrazol-5-yl]-N,N-dimethyl-	EtOH	252(4.43),340(3.82)	114-0127-80C
Morpholine, 4-[(4-hydroxyphenyl)(2-quinolinylhydrazono)methyl]-	MeOH	260(4.36),300(4.33), 370(4.03)	56-0661-80
hydriodide	MeOH	260(4.31),290(4.33), 380(4.14)	56-0661-80
2-Pyrimidinamine, N,N-diethyl-5-nitro-4,6-diphenyl-	EtOH	256(4.46),352(3.68)	103-0970-80

Compound	Solvent	$\lambda_{max}(\log \epsilon)$	Ref.
$C_{20}H_{20}N_4O_5$			
2,3-Pyrazinedicarbonitrile, 5-(2,3,5,6-8,9,11,12-octahydro-1,4,7,10,13-benzopentaoxacyclopentadecin-15-yl)-	MeCN	370(4.27)	138-0921-80
sodium complex	MeCN	356(4.27)	138-0921-80
$C_{20}H_{20}N_4O_5S$			
Benzenesulfonamide, N-(1,1'-dimethyl-2'-oxospiro[3H-indole-3,3'-piperidin]-2(1H)-ylidene)-4-nitro-	EtOH	218s(4.44),270(4.27), 300s(4.16)	39-1512-80C
$C_{20}H_{20}N_6O_6S$			
L-Glutamic acid, N-[4-[[(2,4-diamino-1,5-dihydro-5-oxopyrido[2,3-d]pyrimidin-6-yl)methyl]thio]benzoyl]-	pH 1	258(4.54),281(4.26)	44-3746-80
	pH 7	256(4.49),281(4.25)	44-3746-80
	pH 11	257(4.42),289(4.26)	44-3746-80
$C_{20}H_{20}N_6O_7$			
11-Oxahomofolic acid	pH 13	253(4.57),362(3.84)	87-0059-80
$C_{20}H_{20}O$			
Cyclobuta[a]naphthalen-8b(1H)-ol, 2,2a-dihydro-2,2-dimethyl-3-phenyl-	EtOH	207(4.26),300s(4.23), 318(4.22),335s(3.95)	44-0240-80
2-Cyclohexen-1-one, 4-methyl-2-(4-methylphenyl)-4-phenyl-	EtOH	220(4.21)	22-0295-80
3,5,7,10,12,14-Heptadecahexaene-1,16-diyn-9-one, 3,8,15-trimethyl-	THF	230(3.95),270s(4.26), 284(4.41),295(4.43), 308(4.42),325(4.44), 359s(4.61),378(4.67), 396s(4.60)	39-0473-80C
Pyrene, 10b,10c-dihydro-10b-(2-methoxyethyl)-10c-methyl-, trans	C_6H_{12}	275(2.89),324(4.49), 337(4.83),346(4.99), 357(4.40),380(4.58), 430(3.61),481(3.76), 533(2.79),569(2.51), 583(2.38),635(2.84), 651(2.76)	44-2746-80
$C_{20}H_{20}OS$			
5(6H)-Benzocyclooctenone, 7,8-dihydro-7,7-dimethyl-9-(phenylthio)-	EtOH	257(4.29),280(3.92), 345(3.91)	44-0240-80
5(6H)-Benzocyclooctenone, 7,10-dihydro-7,7-dimethyl-9-(phenylthio)-	EtOH	249(4.22)	44-0240-80
Cyclobuta[a]naphthalen-8b(1H)-ol, 2,2a-dihydro-2,2-dimethyl-3-(phenylthio)-	EtOH	232(4.21),237s(4.19), 290s(4.08),297(4.11), 304s(4.10),309s(4.09), 320s(4.03)	44-0240-80
$C_{20}H_{20}O_2$			
Benzenemethanol, α-(4-ethoxy-3-penten-1-ynyl)-α-phenyl-	EtOH	220s(4.27),240(4.28)	78-1331-80
5(6H)-Benzocyclooctenone, 7,8-dihydro-7,7-dimethyl-9-phenoxy-	EtOH	242(4.37),272(3.98), 332(3.70)	44-0240-80
5(6H)-Benzocyclooctenone, 7,10-dihydro-7,7-dimethyl-9-phenoxy-	EtOH	241(4.13)	44-0240-80
Cyclobuta[a]naphthalen-8b(1H)-ol, 2,2a-dihydro-2,2-dimethyl-3-phenoxy-	EtOH	224(4.30),230(4.24), 273(4.12),280s(4.09), 298s(3.64),310s(3.47)	44-0240-80
Dibenzo[a,g]biphenylene-3,9-diol, 5,6,6a,6b,11,12,12a,12b-octahydro-, (6aα,6bβ,12aβ,12bα)-	EtOH	280(3.64)	87-1410-80
	EtOH-base	300(3.78)	87-1410-80

Compound	Solvent	$\lambda_{max}(\log \epsilon)$	Ref.
Ethanone, 1-(1,2,3,4,6,11-hexahydro-5-hydroxy-2-naphthacenyl)-	EtOH	212(4.45),234s(3.98), 266(3.20),272(3.27), 283(3.18),296s(2.70), 405(1.95)	33-0232-80
Ethanone, 1-(1,2,3,4,6,11-hexahydro-12-hydroxy-2-naphthacenyl)-	EtOH	213(4.39),234s(3.93), 265(3.11),271(3.16), 282(3.04),310s(2.10), 360s(1.48)	33-0232-80
$C_{20}H_{20}O_3$			
Gona-1,3,5,7,9-pentaene-11,17-dione, 12-methyl-, cyclic 17-(1,2-ethanediyl acetal), (13)-(±)-	MeOH	216(4.61),309(3.95)	56-2247-80
$C_{20}H_{20}O_4$			
4H-1-Benzopyran-4-one, 2,3-dihydro-7-hydroxy-2-[4-hydroxy-3-(3-methyl-2-butenyl)phenyl]-	MeOH	276(4.11),310(3.81)	142-1163-80B
	MeOH-NaOH	335(4.34)	142-1163-80B
$C_{20}H_{20}O_5$			
Benzo[a]heptalen-9(5H)-one, 1,2,3,10-tetramethoxy-	EtOH	246(4.65),355(4.18)	33-0050-80
Benzo[a]heptalen-10(5H)-one, 1,2,3,9-tetramethoxy-	EtOH	237(4.58),285s(4.03), 350(4.29)	33-0050-80
4H-1-Benzopyran-4-one, 5,7-dimethoxy-3-[(4-methoxyphenyl)methyl]-8-methyl-	EtOH	230(4.76),249(4.64), 255(4.66),279s(4.20), 285(4.21),310s(4.01)	94-2487-80
4H-1-Benzopyran-4-one, 5-hydroxy-7-methoxy-3-[(4-methoxyphenyl)methyl]-6,8-dimethyl-	EtOH	230(4.63),245(4.54), 265(4.60),341(3.79)	94-2487-80
	EtOH-AlCl$_3$	277(--),405(--)	94-2487-80
2-Propen-1-one, 1-(3,4-dihydro-3,5-dihydroxy-2,2-dimethyl-2H-1-benzopyran-8-yl)-3-(4-hydroxyphenyl)-	MeOH	242(4.06),308s(4.11), 350(4.39)	102-0336-80
	MeOH-NaOMe	263(4.08),318(3.98), 422(4.55)	102-0336-80
2-Propen-1-one, 1-(2,4-dihydroxy-3-(3-methyl-2-butenyl)phenyl]-3-(2,4-dihydroxyphenyl)-, (E)-	EtOH	250s(3.81),317(3.87), 388(4.39)	102-0336-80
Spiro[benz[b]indeno[5,4-d]pyran-1(4H)-2'-[1,3]dioxolan]-4-one, 2,10,11,11a-tetrahydro-7-methoxy-11a-methyl-, (S)-	EtOH	221(4.35),250(4.14), 350(4.41)	23-1427-80
$C_{20}H_{20}O_6$			
4H-1-Benzopyran-4-one, 3-(1,3-benzodioxol-5-ylmethyl)-2,3-dihydro-5-hydroxy-7-methoxy-6,8-dimethyl-	EtOH	216(4.34),287(4.24)	94-1477-80
	EtOH-AlCl$_3$	220(--),310(--)	94-1477-80
3,5-Cyclohexadiene-1,2-dione, 4-methoxy-5-(6-methoxyspiro[1,3-benzodioxole-2,1'-cyclohexan]-5-yl)-	EtOH	209(--),243(3.99), 299(4.09),340(3.34), 420(3.46),511(3.26)	12-0527-80
1,4-Ethanoanthracene-9,10-dione, 5-ethoxy-1,4-dihydro-8-hydroxy-7-(hydroxymethyl)-1-methoxy-	MeOH	219(4.47),280(3.84), 492(3.73)	24-1575-80
1,4-Ethanoanthracene-9,10-dione, 8-ethoxy-1,4-dihydro-5-hydroxy-6-(hydroxymethyl)-1-methoxy-	MeOH	218(4.51),278(3.92), 488(3.75)	24-1575-80
2-Propen-1-one, 3-(1,3-benzodioxol-5-yl)-1-(2-hydroxy-4,6-dimethoxy-3,5-dimethylphenyl)-	EtOH	265(4.09),303(4.21), 358(4.60)	94-2487-80
	EtOH-AlCl$_3$	331(--),370(--)	94-2487-80
$C_{20}H_{20}O_7$			
4H-1-Benzopyran-4-one, 5,7-dimethoxy-3-(2,4,5-trimethoxyphenyl)-	EtOH	255(4.42),291(4.15)	18-0831-80

Compound	Solvent	$\lambda_{max}(\log \epsilon)$	Ref.
4H-1-Benzopyran-4-one, 3,5,6,7,8-penta-methoxy-2-phenyl-	MeOH	267(4.43),309(4.23)	102-2795-80
$C_{20}H_{20}O_8$ 4H-1-Benzopyran-4-one, 2,3-dihydro-5,6,7-trimethoxy-2-(7-methoxy-1,3-benzodioxol-5-yl)- (agecorynin A)	EtOH	276(4.31),323(3.74)	102-2439-80
$C_{20}H_{20}O_9$ 4H-1-Benzopyran-4-one, 5,6-dihydroxy-3,7-dimethoxy-2-(2,4,5-trimethoxy-phenyl)-	MeOH	263(4.11),310s(3.83), 340(3.89)	102-2731-80
4H-1-Benzopyran-4-one, 5-hydroxy-2-(4-hydroxy-3,5-dimethoxyphenyl)-3,6,7-trimethoxy- (murrayanol)	EtOH	255(4.28),267(4.26), 344s(4.29),360(4.30)	102-2227-80
	EtOH-NaOMe	257(--),338(--), 413(--)	102-2227-80
	EtOH-NaOAc	255(--),270s(--), 335s(--),376(--), 410(--)	102-2227-80
$C_{20}H_{21}ClN_2O_2$ 1H-Pyrazole, 5-(4-chlorophenyl)-4,5-di-hydro-3-(4-methoxyphenyl)-1-(2-meth-yl-1-oxopropyl)-	MeOH	295(3.94)	2-0364-80
$C_{20}H_{21}ClN_2O_3S$ Benzenesulfonamide, 4-chloro-N-(6,7,8-9,10,11-octahydro-8-hydroxyazocino-[1,2-a]indol-12-yl)-	CHCl$_3$	235(4.20),285(3.93)	39-2870-80C
Benzenesulfonamide, 4-chloro-N-(2,3,3a-4,5,10c-hexahydro-10c-hydroxypyrrolo-[3,2,1-jk]carbazol-10b(1H)-yl)-	EtOH	238(4.19),300(3.49)	39-2870-80C
$C_{20}H_{21}ClN_4O_4$ Acetamide, N,N'-[5-(4-chlorophenyl)-6-ethyl-2,4-pyrimidinediyl]bis[N-acetyl-	EtOH	210(4.35),250s(3.97), 285s(3.37)	142-0471-80
$C_{20}H_{21}N$ 2-Naphthalenemethanamine, N,N,3-tri-methyl-1-phenyl-	EtOH	229(4.83),273(3.70), 283(3.75),293(3.66), 325(2.70)	39-1477-80C
2-Naphthalenemethanamine, N,N,3-tri-methyl-4-phenyl-	EtOH	229(4.90),275(3.76), 284(3.85),293(3.81), 325(2.85)	39-1477-80C
$C_{20}H_{21}NO$ 2-Cyclohexen-1-one, 3-(4-methylphenyl)-2-[(phenylmethyl)amino]-	ether	210(4.42),336(3.64)	78-1585-80
3-Penten-2-one, 4-[[bis(4-methylphen-yl)methylene]amino]-, (Z)-	n.s.g.	273(4.17)	39-1866-80C
$C_{20}H_{21}NO_2$ 9,10-(Methaniminomethano)anthracen-9(10H)-ol, 12-ethyl-, acetate	EtOH	211(4.27),259s(2.09), 265(3.03),272(3.05)	95-1127-80
$C_{20}H_{21}NO_3$ Benzo[4,5]cyclohepta[1,2-b]pyrrolizine-1-carboxylic acid, 1,2,3,5,10,11-hexa-hydro-5-oxo-, 1-methylethyl ester	MeOH	215(3.93),222(3.92), 257(3.84),331(4.26)	4-1081-80

Compound	Solvent	$\lambda_{max}(\log \epsilon)$	Ref.
Benzoic acid, 4-[[3-(4-methoxyphenyl)-2-propenylidene]amino]-, propyl ester, bis(trichloroacetate)	benzene	300(2.04),380(3.18)	65-1870-80
1H-Indole-2,3-dione, 7-methoxy-4-(5-phenylpentyl)-	EtOH	325(3.7),435(3.3)	78-2441-80
$C_{20}H_{21}NO_3S$			
7-Azabicyclo[4.2.0]octan-5-one, 7-[(4-methylphenyl)sulfonyl]-8-phenyl-, (1α,6α,8β)-	CHCl₃	250(3.75),272s(3.10), 310(2.20)	78-1585-80
Benzenesulfonamide, 4-methyl-N-(6-oxo-1-cyclohexen-1-yl)-N-(phenylmethyl)-	EtOH	220(4.23),323(2.15)	78-1585-80
$C_{20}H_{21}NO_4$			
Dehydrocorydine	EtOH	220(4.33),310(4.27), 340(4.10)	105-0177-80
	EtOH	225(4.43),281(4.17), 327(4.32),566(3.57)	142-1135-80
Indolo[7,1-ab][3]benzazepine-7,8-dicarboxylic acid, 4,5,10,11,12,12a-hexahydro-, dimethyl ester	MeOH and MeOH-HClO₄	233(4.15),307(3.73), 355(4.25)	39-0535-80C
Noraporphine, N-acetyl-9-hydroxy-1,2-dimethoxy-	EtOH	214(4.02),233s(3.71), 283(3.63)	88-0723-80
$C_{20}H_{21}NO_5$			
Benzo[e][1,3]dioxolo[4,5-k][3]benzazecin-7(6H)-one, 5,8,14,15-tetrahydro-3,4-dimethoxy-	EtOH	285(3.28)	78-1515-80
6H-1,3-Benzodioxolo[5,6-d][2]benzazonine-6-carboxaldehyde, 5,7,12,13-tetrahydro-8,9-dimethoxy-	EtOH	288(3.47)	78-1515-80
Canadine N-oxide	EtOH	283(3.81)	78-1515-80
Fumaritine	EtOH	287(3.83)	100-0305-80
$C_{20}H_{21}NO_5S$			
1H-Indole-3-carboxylic acid, 7-(benzoylthio)-5,6,7,7a-tetrahydro-7a-hydroxy-1,2-dimethyl-5-oxo-, ethyl ester, trans-(±)-	MeOH	239(4.37),278(4.38), 405(4.30)	24-3405-80
$C_{20}H_{21}N_3$			
Mostueine	EtOH	229(4.47),268(3.80), 281(3.82),287(3.85), 293(3.81)	28-0191-80B
Pyrrolo[3,2-e]benzimidazole, 3-butyl-3,6-dihydro-8-methyl-7-phenyl-	EtOH	252s(4.08),319(4.48)	103-0062-80
$C_{20}H_{21}N_3O$			
3H-Pyrazol-3-one, 1,2-dihydro-1,2-diphenyl-5-piperidino-	EtOH	222.2(4.54)	56-2217-80
$C_{20}H_{21}N_3OS$			
2(1H)-Pyridinone, 4-methyl-3-(methylthio)-6-pyrrolidino-5-(2-quinolinyl)-	EtOH	231(4.68),259(4.18), 306s(3.85),321(3.96)	94-2892-80
$C_{20}H_{21}N_3O_2S$			
Thiourea, N-[7-(dimethylamino)-4-methyl-2-oxo-2H-1-benzopyran-3-yl]-N'-(phenylmethyl)-	EtOH	246(4.45),379(4.41)	95-0289-80

Compound	Solvent	$\lambda_{max}(\log \epsilon)$	Ref.
$C_{20}H_{21}N_3O_3$			
2-Propenoic acid, 2-cyano-3-[5-[4-(phen-ylmethyl)-1-piperazinyl]-2-furanyl]-, methyl ester	MeOH	211(4.02),234(4.23), 463(4.67)	73-1831-80
$C_{20}H_{21}N_3O_4$			
1H-Pyrazole, 4,5-dihydro-3-(4-methoxy-phenyl)-1-(2-methyl-1-oxopropyl)-5-(4-nitrophenyl)-	MeOH	293(3.97)	2-0364-80
1H-Pyrazole, 4,5-dihydro-3-(4-methoxy-phenyl)-5-(4-nitrophenyl)-1-(1-oxo-butyl)-	MeOH	295(4.43)	2-0364-80
$C_{20}H_{21}N_4O_3P$			
Phosphonic acid, ethenyl-, bis[2-(1H-benzimidazol-1-yl)ethyl] ester	EtOH	206(4.11),249(3.50), 275(3.36),282(3.34)	65-0052-80
$C_{20}H_{21}N_5O$			
3,4,8,10,11b-Pentaazacyclohepta[jk]-fluoren-11(10H)-one, 1,2,3,5,6,7-hexahydro-3-methyl-10-(phenylmethyl)-	EtOH	260(4.34),299(4.13)	103-0853-80
$C_{20}H_{21}N_5O_2$			
[1,2,5]Oxadiazolo[3,4-d]pyrimidine, 3,7-dihydro-7-[2-(4-morpholinyl)-2-cyclohexen-1-ylidene]-5-phenyl-	MeOH	237(4.25),262(4.32), 383(4.12)	44-3827-80
$C_{20}H_{21}N_7O_2$			
Methanimidamide, N,N-dimethyl-N'-[3-methyl-1-(4-nitrophenyl)-4-[(phen-ylhydrazono)methyl]-1H-pyrazol-5-yl]-	EtOH	225(4.25),284(4.27), 301(4.29),342(4.41)	114-0127-80C
$C_{20}H_{21}N_7O_5$			
L-Glutamic acid, N-[4-[2-(2,4-diamino-6-pteridinyl)ethyl]benzoyl]-	pH 1	242(4.48),337(4.01), 352s(3.99)	87-0320-80
	pH 7	254(4.48),372(3.86)	87-0320-80
	pH 13	256(4.49),372(3.86)	87-0320-80
$C_{20}H_{21}N_7O_5S$			
L-Glutamic acid, N-[4-[[2-(2,4-diamino-6-pteridinyl)ethyl]thio]benzoyl]-	pH 1	248(4.43),337(3.99)	87-0899-80
	pH 13	258(4.51),372(3.85)	87-0899-80
$C_{20}H_{21}N_7O_6$			
L-Glutamic acid, N-[4-[[(2,4-diamino-1,5-dihydro-5-oxopyrido[2,3-d]pyri-midin-6-yl)methyl]amino]benzoyl]-	pH 1	257(4.60),295(4.04)	44-3746-80
	pH 7	255(4.29),293(4.32)	44-3746-80
	pH 11	258(4.34),291(4.36)	44-3746-80
$C_{20}H_{21}N_7S$			
Hydrazinecarbothioamide, 2-[[5-[[(di-methylamino)methylene]amino]-1,3-diphenyl-1H-pyrazol-4-yl]methylene]-	EtOH	280(4.36),320(4.11)	114-0127-80C
$C_{20}H_{22}$			
1,3-Butadiene, 3-(1,1-dimethylethyl)-1,2-diphenyl-, (E)-	EtOH	228(4.29),277(4.06)	35-5648-80
(Z)-	EtOH	218(4.14),282(4.24)	35-5648-80
1-Cyclopentene, 2,3,3-trimethyl-1,5-di-phenyl-	EtOH	248(4.06)	35-5648-80
Cyclopropene, 2-(1,1-dimethylethyl)-3-methyl-1,3-diphenyl-	EtOH	264(4.24)	35-5648-80

Compound	Solvent	$\lambda_{max}(\log \epsilon)$	Ref.
Cyclopropene, 3-(1,1-dimethylethyl)-3-methyl-1,2-diphenyl-	EtOH	230(4.22),239(4.11), 315(4.37),323(4.43), 341s(4.28)	35-5648-80
1H-Indene, 2,3-dihydro-1,1,3,3-tetramethyl-2-(phenylmethylene)-	C_6H_{12}	271(3.40),289(2.20), 308s(2.02)	5-1207-80
1H-Indene, 2,3-dihydro-1,1,2-trimethyl-3-methylene-2-(phenylmethyl)-	C_6H_{12}	250(3.80),286(3.15), 294(3.07)	5-1207-80
$C_{20}H_{22}BrN_5O_7S$ Guanosine, 8-bromo-2',3'-O-(1-methylethylidene)-, 5'-(4-methylbenzenesulfonate)	MeOH	225(4.15),261(4.25)	78-3509-80
$C_{20}H_{22}ClN_3O_2S$ Benzenesulfonamide, 4-chloro-N-(1,1'-dimethylspiro[3H-indole-3,3'-piperidin]-2(1H)-ylidene)-	EtOH	225(4.38),282(4.20)	39-1512-80C
$C_{20}H_{22}N$ 1H-Benz[f]isoindolium, 2,3,3a,4-tetrahydro-2,2-dimethyl-4-phenyl-, bromide	EtOH	215s(4.38),218(4.41), 253s(3.94),268(3.97), 272s(3.96),328(1.94)	39-1477-80C
$C_{20}H_{22}NS_2Tl$ Thallium, diethyl[2-[[(phenylmethyl)imino]methyl]benzo[b]thiophene-3(2H)-thionato-N^2,S^3]-, (T-4)-	benzene	285(4.32),328(4.04), 440(3.82),500s(--)	104-2004-80
	BuOH	278(4.15),330(4.01), 390(3.60),490(3.40)	104-2004-80
	$C_2H_4Cl_2$	287(4.22),330(4.05), 442(3.64),500s(--)	104-2004-80
$C_{20}H_{22}N_2$ 1-Aziridinamine, N-5-hexenylidene-2,3-diphenyl-, trans	MeOH	298(3.90)	44-3756-80
$C_{20}H_{22}N_2O$ Anhydroakagerine	MeOH	225(4.43),256(4.42), 296(3.83),305(3.88)	32-0097-80
$C_{20}H_{22}N_2O_2$ Anhydroakagerine, 10-hydroxy-	MeOH	225(4.45),261(4.38), 282s(3.92),310(3.84)	32-0097-80
Condylocarpine	MeOH	230(4.03),288(4.00), 328(4.16)	73-1419-80
	n.s.g.	227(4.02),295(3.99), 328(4.08)	64-0885-80B
3,14-Dehydrodeoxoperivine	EtOH	227(4.29),296(3.97)	23-1829-80
Pleiocarpamine	MeOH	227(4.4),285(3.9)	102-0307-80
Strychnopivotine	MeOH	209(4.00),252(3.71), 282(3.02),290(2.98), 313s(2.51)	102-1531-80
$C_{20}H_{22}N_2O_3$ Akagerinelactone	EtOH	222(4.33),276(3.90), 283(3.91),293(3.80)	100-0595-80
Condylocarpine N_b-oxide	n.s.g.	225(4.16),294(4.00), 328(4.03)	64-0885-80B
$C_{20}H_{22}N_2O_3S$ Acetamide, N-[4-[[3-methyl-4-(phenylimino)-2-pentenyl]sulfonyl]phenyl]-	EtOH	240(4.52)	104-0849-80

Compound	Solvent	$\lambda_{max}(\log \epsilon)$	Ref.
$C_{20}H_{22}N_2O_4$ Dibenzo[de,gh][1,10]phenanthroline- 5,6,7,8-tetrol, 1,2,3,10,11,12,12a- 12b-octahydro-1,12-dimethyl-, dihy- drobromide, trans-(±)-	EtOH	280(3.98),305(3.81)	33-0938-80
$C_{20}H_{22}N_2O_4S$ Carbamic acid, [4-[[3-methyl-4-(phenyl- imino)-2-pentenyl]sulfonyl]phenyl]-, methyl ester	EtOH	236(4.59)	104-0849-80
$C_{20}H_{22}N_2O_5$ 1H-Indolizino[8,7-b]indole-2-propanoic acid, 2-carboxy-α-ethyl-2,3,5,6,11- 11b-hexahydro-3-oxo-	EtOH	223(4.52),272(3.80), 290(3.75)	78-1063-80
$C_{20}H_{22}N_2O_6$ Pyrimido[1,2-a]indole-4,10-dicarboxylic acid, 3-acetyl-1,4-dihydro-4-meth- oxy-, diethyl ester	EtOH	255(3.78),358(4.15)	94-2972-80
$C_{20}H_{22}N_2O_7$ Butanedioic acid, [[[3-(ethoxycarbo- nyl)-1H-indol-2-yl]amino]methylene]- oxo-, diethyl ester	EtOH	260(4.00),365(4.33)	94-2972-80
$C_{20}H_{22}N_2O_8$ Carbamic acid, (1-acetoxy-9-formyl- 2,3,5,8-tetrahydro-7-methoxy-6-meth- yl-5,8-dioxo-1H-pyrrolo[1,2-a]indol- 2-yl)methyl-, ethyl ester, trans-(±)-	MeOH	213(4.27),241(4.11), 270(4.16),326(3.71), 415(2.92)	142-0799-80
$C_{20}H_{22}N_3O$ 1H-Pyrazolium, 4-[[4-(dimethylamino)- phenyl]methylene]-4,5-dihydro-2,3- dimethyl-5-oxo-1-phenyl-, perchlorate	MeOH	245s(4.19),261(4.27), 351(2.77),484s(3.77), 514(4.06)	83-0301-80
$C_{20}H_{22}N_4$ 1H-Pyrazole, 4,4'-(1,4-phenylenedi-2,1- ethenediyl)bis[1,3-dimethyl-	dioxan	360(4.69)	65-1922-80
1H-Pyrazole, 4,4'-(1,4-phenylenedi-2,1- ethenediyl)bis[1,5-dimethyl-	dioxan	360(4.69)	65-1922-80
2,5-Pyrimidinediamine, N^2,N^2-diethyl- 4,6-diphenyl-	EtOH	229(4.31),246(4.43), 400(3.70)	103-0970-80
$C_{20}H_{22}N_4O$ 4H-Imidazol-4-one, 1,5-dihydro-2-(4- methyl-1-piperazinyl)-5,5-diphenyl-	EtOH	220.0(4.46)	56-2217-80
$C_{20}H_{22}N_4O_5$ L-Tryptophan, N-acetyl-2-(1,2,3,4- tetrahydro-1,3-dimethyl-2,4-dioxo- 5-pyrimidinyl)-, methyl ester	MeCN	264(4.08),288(4.02), 337(3.73)	35-7535-80
$C_{20}H_{22}O$ Bicyclo[2.2.2]octane, 1-acetyl-4-(1- naphthalenyl)-	C_6H_{11}Me-iso- pentane (4:1)	260s(3.61),269(3.81), 279(3.91),287(3.73), 291(3.74),311(2.60)	44-3933-80
Bicyclo[2.2.2]octane, 1-acetyl-4-(2- naphthalenyl)-	C_6H_{11}Me-iso- pentane (4:1)	255s(3.51),265(3.65), 274(3.67),285s(3.51), 303(2.59),317(2.42)	44-3933-80

Compound	Solvent	$\lambda_{max}(\log \epsilon)$	Ref.
1,5-Hexadiene, 3-methoxy-3-methyl-1,2-diphenyl-, (E)-	EtOH	256(4.15)	44-2181-80
$C_{20}H_{22}O_3$			
Gona-1,3,5(10),7-tetraene-11,17-dione, 9-methyl-, cyclic 17-(1,2-ethanediyl acetal), (13α)-(±)-	MeOH	208(4.01),226(2.36)	56-2247-80
$C_{20}H_{22}O_4$			
Dehydrodiisoeugenol	MeOH	220(4.54),272(4.43)	100-0353-80
Phenol, 4-[2-(1,3-benzodioxol-5-yl)-1-methylethyl]-5-methoxy-2-(2-propenyl)-, (R)-	MeOH	230s(4.30),287(4.08)	102-0285-80
Phenol, 2-methoxy-6-[2-methoxy-4-(2-propenyl)phenoxy]-4-(2-propenyl)-	MeOH	275s(3.96),285(3.96), 325s(3.70)	102-0681-80
Tricyclo[11.3.1.1^{5,9}]octadeca-1(17),5-8,13,15-pentaene-7,18-dione, 15,17-dimethoxy-, anti	dioxan CHCl$_3$	387(3.53) 402(3.51)	24-0241-80 24-0241-80
syn	dioxan CHCl$_3$	388(3.40) 402(3.43)	24-0241-80 24-0241-80
$C_{20}H_{22}O_5$			
Angelin	EtOH	208(4.47),222(4.19), 250(4.30),321(4.28)	94-1782-80
Benzeneacetic acid, α-acetyl-4-methoxy-α-(4-methoxyphenyl)-, ethyl ester	EtOH	215(4.34),234(4.34), 275(3.85),281(3.81)	12-0113-80
4H-1-Benzopyran-4-one, 2,3-dihydro-5-hydroxy-7-methoxy-3-[(4-methoxyphenyl)methyl]-6,8-dimethyl-	EtOH EtOH-AlCl$_3$	220(4.24),285(4.06) 313(--)	94-1477-80 94-1477-80
Dibenzo[b,e][1,4]dioxin-2,3-dione, 7-hydroxy-1,9-dimethyl-4,6-bis(1-methylethyl)-	EtOH	288s(3.60),444(3.93)	33-0225-80
2-Propen-1-one, 1-(2-hydroxy-4,6-dimethoxy-3,5-dimethylphenyl)-3-(4-methoxyphenyl)-	EtOH EtOH-AlCl$_3$	225(4.36),282(3.88), 358(4.32) 320(--),384(--)	94-2487-80 94-2487-80
2H,5H-Pyrano[3,2-c][1]benzopyran-5-one, 4-ethenyl-3,4-dihydro-2-hydroxy-2-(1-hydroxy-2-methyl-2-propenyl)-4,10-dimethyl-	ether	275(4.08),288(4.08), 308(3.83),323(3.67)	102-1519-80
Spiro[oxetane-2,2'-[2H,5H]pyrano[3,2-c][1]benzopyran]-5'-one, 4'-ethenyl-3',4'-dihydro-3-hydroxy-4,4,4',10'-tetramethyl-	ether	275(4.08),288(4.07), 308(3.83),323(3.68)	102-1519-80
$C_{20}H_{22}O_6$			
1-Propanone, 3-(1,3-benzodioxol-5-yl)-1-(2-hydroxy-4,6-dimethoxy-3,5-dimethylphenyl)-	EtOH EtOH-AlCl$_3$	219(4.34),279(4.22) 310(--)	94-2487-80 94-2487-80
$C_{20}H_{22}O_7$			
2-Propenal, 3-[4-[2-hydroxy-2-(4-hydroxy-3-methoxyphenyl)-1-(hydroxymethyl)ethoxy]-3-methoxyphenyl]-	EtOH	230(4.02),288(3.84), 336(4.04)	102-0445-80
erythro	EtOH	230(4.27),288(4.07), 336(4.26)	102-0445-80
threo	EtOH	230(4.28),288(4.11), 336(4.30)	102-0449-80
$C_{20}H_{23}ClN_2O_6$			
Phenol, 2-chloro-4-[(2,3,5,6,8,9,11,12-octahydro-1,4,7,10,13-benzopentaoxa-	CHCl$_3$	370(4.24)	18-1550-80

Compound	Solvent	$\lambda_{max}(\log \epsilon)$	Ref.
cyclopentadecin-15-yl)azo]- (cont.)			18-1550-80
$C_{20}H_{23}NO_3$			
2-Pentenamide, 4-hydroxy-N-(4-methoxy-phenyl)-4-(2,5-dimethylphenyl)-	EtOH	282(4.28)	115-0401-80
$C_{20}H_{23}NO_3S$			
Benzenamine, N-[1,2-dimethyl-4-[(4-methylphenyl)sulfonyl]-2-butenyl-idene]-4-methoxy-	EtOH	238(4.51)	104-0849-80
Benzenesulfonamide, 4-methyl-N-(2-oxo-cyclohexyl)-N-(phenylmethyl)-	ether	224(4.07),264s(2.88)	78-1585-80
$C_{20}H_{23}NO_4$			
6H-Dibenzo[de,g]quinoline-6-ethanol, 4,5,6a,7-tetrahydro-11-hydroxy-2,10-dimethoxy-, (R)-	EtOH	269(4.15),279(4.17), 300(3.92)	44-2275-80
4H-Dibenzo[de,g]quinolin-10-ol, 5,6,6a,7-tetrahydro-1,2,11-trimeth-oxy-6-methyl- (N-methylhernagine)	EtOH	221(4.39),269(4.04), 307(3.73)	102-0161-80
Discretine	MeOH	225s(4.18),287(3.87)	36-1061-80
	MeOH-NaOH	245(4.08),291(3.96), 300s(3.83)	36-1061-80
Isoquinoline, 3-(3,4-dimethoxyphenyl)-3,4-dihydro-6,7-dimethoxy-1-methyl-	MeOH	275(4.12),305(4.05)	2-0556-80
1H-Pyrrole-3,4-dicarboxylic acid, 1-cyclohexyl-2-phenyl-, dimethyl ester	CCl_4	302.5(3.81)	22-0552-80
$C_{20}H_{23}NO_5$			
Benzo[a]heptalen-10(5H)-one, 7-amino-6,7-dihydro-1,2,3,9-tetramethoxy-, (S)- (N-deacetylisocolchicine)	EtOH	243(4.47),340(4.27)	33-0050-80
Corydine N-oxide	EtOH	225(4.43),270(3.89), 313(3.70)	105-0177-80
L-Proline, 1-[1,4-dimethoxy-3-(2-oxo-ethyl)-2-naphthalenyl]-, methyl ester	MeOH	263(4.12),296(3.78), 327s(3.14)	44-1260-80
$C_{20}H_{23}N_3O$			
Lysergic acid ethylvinylamide	EtOH	243(4.29),313(3.94)	39-0902-80C
2H,10H-1,9-Methano-1,5,9-benzotriaza-cyclododecen-15-one, 3,4,5,6,7,8-hexahydro-10-phenyl-	pH 1	259(3.86)	94-2587-80
	pH 13	259(3.95)	94-2587-80
	EtOH	267(3.95)	94-2587-80
	$CHCl_3$	271(3.91),295s(3.37)	94-2587-80
2H-Pyrimido[2,1-b]quinazoline, 6-eth-oxy-1,3,4,6-tetrahydro-1-methyl-6-phenyl-	pH 1	251(4.42)	94-2024-80
	pH 13	280(4.27)	94-2024-80
	EtOH	284(4.20)	94-2024-80
$C_{20}H_{23}N_3OS$			
2(1H)-Pyridinone, 6-(butylamino)-4-methyl-3-(methylthio)-5-(2-quinolin-yl)-	EtOH	229(4.65),278s(4.02), 348(4.22),380s(4.05)	94-2892-80
2(1H)-Pyridinone, 6-(diethylamino)-4-methyl-3-(methylthio)-5-(2-quinolin-yl)-	EtOH	228(4.67),320s(4.01), 350(4.24)	94-2892-80
$C_{20}H_{23}N_3O_2$			
10(9H)-Acridineacetamide, N-[3-(di-methylamino)propyl]-9-oxo-	MeOH	255(4.83),264s(4.50), 290(3.43),386(3.93), 399(3.96)	73-3593-80

Compound	Solvent	λ_{max} (log ϵ)	Ref.
C$_{20}$H$_{23}$N$_3$O$_6$ Benzamide, N-[1,4-dihydro-5-methyl-1-[2,3-O-(1-methylethylidene)-β-D-ribofuranosyl]-4-oxo-2-pyrimidinyl]-	EtOH	250(4.15),274s(4.22), 301(4.36)	33-2179-80
C$_{20}$H$_{23}$N$_5$O$_3$S$_2$ Benzenesulfonamide, N-[imino[[3-(5-oxo-1-phenyl-2-thioxo-4-imidazolidinyl)-propyl]amino]methyl]-4-methyl-, monohydrochloride, (S)-	EtOH	269.5(4.18)	18-0201-80
C$_{20}$H$_{23}$N$_5$O$_4$ Benzamide, N-[(3a,4,5,6,11,11a-hexahydro-2,2-dimethyl-4,11-epoxy-1,3-dioxolo[4,5-f]imidazo[1,5-a][1,3]diazocin-7-yl]iminomethyl]-4-methyl-, [3aR-(3aα,4α,11α,11aα)]-	MeOH	250s(--),272(4.27), 336(4.23)	18-3670-80
C$_{20}$H$_{23}$N$_5$O$_7$S Adenosine, 2',3'-O-(1-methylethylidene)-, 5'-(4-methylbenzenesulfonate), 1-oxide	MeOH	229(4.58),261(3.91), 297(3.40)	44-0788-80
	MeOH-HCl	258(4.06)	44-0788-80
	MeOH-NaOH	226(4.48),266(3.91), 310(3.56)	44-0788-80
C$_{20}$H$_{23}$N$_7$O$_3$ Adenosine, 5'-[[2-amino-3-(4-methoxyphenyl)-1-oxopropyl]amino]-2',3'-didehydro-2',3',5'-trideoxy-, (S)-	H$_2$O	261.5(4.16)	136-0067-80A
C$_{20}$H$_{24}$ Bicyclo[4.1.0]heptane, 7,7'-[2,4-bis-(methylene)-1,3-cyclobutanediylidene]bis-	heptane	202(4.06),256(3.24)	35-6813-80
C$_{20}$H$_{24}$ClNO 2,5-Cyclohexadien-1-one, 4-[(4-chlorophenyl)imino]-2,6-bis(1,1-dimethylethyl)-	hexane	442(3.60)	104-2020-80
	+ CF$_3$COOH	399(4.12)	104-2020-80
	benzene	443(3.58)	104-2020-80
	+ CF$_3$COOH	410(4.10)	104-2020-80
	CH$_2$Cl$_2$	436(3.59)	104-2020-80
	+ CF$_3$COOH	407(4.11)	104-2020-80
	CHCl$_3$	438(3.60)	104-2020-80
	+ CF$_3$COOH	407(4.08)	104-2020-80
perchlorate	CH$_2$Cl$_2$	411(4.11)	104-2020-80
C$_{20}$H$_{24}$ClNO$_5$ 2H-1,3-Benzoxazine-4-acetic acid, 6-chloro-3-cyclohexyl-3,4-dihydro-α-(1-hydroxyethylidene)-2-oxo-, ethyl ester	EtOH	228s(4.04),252s(3.88), 290(3.37)	4-0519-80
C$_{20}$H$_{24}$NO$_3$ Isothebaine methiodide	MeOH	223(4.65),273(4.13), 300(3.98)	73-0914-80
C$_{20}$H$_{24}$NO$_4$ Cyclanoline iodide	MeOH	286(3.82)	73-0914-80
Oxazolium, 5-(2-acetoxy-1,1-dimethylethyl)-4,5-dihydro-3-methyl-4-oxo-2-(4-phenyl-1,3-butadienyl)-, perchlorate	HOAc	412(4.49)	103-0023-80
	HOAc-HClO$_4$	412(4.56)	103-0023-80

Compound	Solvent	$\lambda_{max}(\log \epsilon)$	Ref.
$C_{20}H_{24}N_2$			
Benzenepropanenitrile, α,2,3,5,6-penta-methyl-α-(phenylamino)-	dioxan	274s(3.23),282(3.22)	24-2462-80
$C_{20}H_{24}N_2O$			
Aristoserratine	n.s.g.	228(4.42),275s(3.79), 282(3.82),290(3.75)	33-2130-80
Rosibiline (same spectrum in acid and base)	MeOH	210(4.32),252(3.90), 303(3.4)	102-1531-80
$C_{20}H_{24}N_2O_2$			
Akagerine	EtOH	229(4.41),278(3.78), 283(3.78),296(3.72)	100-0097-80
2-Azabicyclo[2.2.2]oct-7-ene-6-carbox-ylic acid, 2-methyl-6-(1-methyl-1H-indol-2-yl)-, ethyl ester, (1α,4α,6α)-	MeOH	226(5.06),287(4.52)	44-1657-80
Condylocarpine, 19,20-dihydro-, (+)-	MeOH	228(4.21),298(3.91), 329(4.04)	102-1213-80
20-Epiibophyllidine	EtOH	226(4.28),298(4.33), 320(4.46)	88-0055-80
Ibophyllidine	EtOH	226(4.01),302(3.92), 333(3.72)	64-1465-80B
	EtOH	228(4.33),298(4.39), 330(4.54)	88-0055-80
3H-Indol-3-one, 2-[(1,3,4,5,6,7-hexa-hydro-1-methyl-3-oxo-2H-indol-2-yl-idene)ethylidene]-1,2,4,5,6,7-hexa-hydro-1-methyl-	CHCl$_3$	346(4.19),558(4.08)	5-0564-80
1H-Pyrido[3,2-c]carbazole-6-carboxylic acid, 2,4a,5,6,7,11c-hexahydro-1,7-dimethyl-, ethyl ester	MeOH	225(4.07),275(3.59)	44-1657-80
Tubotaiwine	MeOH	218(4.10),292(3.98), 325(4.00)	73-1419-80
	n.s.g.	225(4.01),294(3.97), 328(4.10)	64-0885-80B
$C_{20}H_{24}N_2O_2S$			
Carbamothioic acid, [ethoxy[(phenyl-methyl)imino]methyl](phenylmethyl)-, O-ethyl ester	EtOH	252(4.19)	39-0665-80C
1H-Indolizino[8,7-b]indole-2-propanoic acid, α-ethyl-2,3,5,6,11,11b-hexahy-dro-3-thioxo-, methyl ester	EtOH	223(4.57),274(4.43)	78-1057-80
$C_{20}H_{24}N_2O_2S_2$			
Thioperoxydicarbonimidic acid, bis-(phenylmethyl)-, diethyl ester	EtOH	243(4.39)	39-0665-80C
$C_{20}H_{24}N_2O_3$			
Akagerine, 10-hydroxy-	MeOH	225(4.33),279(3.83), 302s(3.60),310s(3.45)	32-0097-80
	MeOH-HCl	272(3.81),305(3.39)	32-0097-80
	MeOH-NaOH	320(3.29)	32-0097-80
	EtOH	231(4.38),280(3.93), 308s(3.60),312(3.52)	100-0595-80
	EtOH-KOH	232(4.74),279(3.89), 322(3.54)	100-0595-80
Δ^{20}-Cleavamine, 15,20-dihydro-16-(meth-oxycarbonyl)-5-oxo-, (16S)-	MeOH	224(--),286(3.89), 294(3.87),346(3.98)	142-0245-80B
(16R)-	MeOH	224(--),286(--), 294(--),344(--)	142-0245-80B

Compound	Solvent	$\lambda_{max}(\log \epsilon)$	Ref.
20-Epiibophyllidine, 18-hydroxy-	EtOH	229(4.04),300(4.09), 329(4.21)	88-3363-80
20-Epiibophyllidine, 19R-hydroxy-	EtOH	229(3.98),298(4.04), 331(4.22)	88-3363-80
20-Epiibophyllidine, 19S-hydroxy-	EtOH	229(3.99),299(4.01), 330(4.04)	88-3363-80
Ibophyllidine, 19-hydroxy-	EtOH	229(3.99),299(3.99), 330(4.14)	88-3363-80
Ibophyllidine N_b-oxide	EtOH	226(4.04),302(3.95), 332(3.69)	64-1465-80B
1H-Indolizino[8,7-b]indole-2-propanoic acid, α-ethyl-2,3,5,6,11,11b-hexahydro-3-oxo-, methyl ester	EtOH	222(4.59),273(3.86), 281(3.88),290(3.79)	78-1063-80
Indolo[2,3-a]quinolizine-3-carboxylic acid, 3-ethyl-1,2,3,4,6,7,12,12b-octahydro-4-oxo-, ethyl ester	EtOH	224(4.52),274s(3.82), 280(3.83),290(3.73)	94-2527-80
$C_{20}H_{24}N_2O_4$			
Gelsemicine	EtOH	261(3.69),280(3.58), 295(3.46)	28-0191-80B
$C_{20}H_{24}N_2O_6$			
Phenol, 4-[(2,3,5,6,8,9,11,12-octahydro-1,4,7,10,13-benzopentaoxacyclopentadecin-15-yl)azo]-	CHCl$_3$	363(4.36)	18-1550-80
$C_{20}H_{24}N_2S_2$			
Piperazine, 1-[10,11-dihydro-8-(methylthio)dibenzo[b,f]thiepin-10-yl]-3-methyl-	MeOH	274.5(4.25)	73-0504-80
$C_{20}H_{24}N_4$			
1H-Benzimidazole, 1-ethyl-5,6-dimethyl-2-[(2,4,6-trimethylphenyl)azo]-	MeOH	390(3.41)	104-2008-80
$C_{20}H_{24}N_4O$			
4(1H)-Pyridinone, 3-hexyl-5-[5-(methylthio)-4-phenyl-4H-1,2,4-triazol-3-yl]-	EtOH	260(4.02)	4-0175-80
$C_{20}H_{24}N_5O_6PS$			
Adenosine, 8-[(phenylmethyl)thio]-N-propyl-, cyclic 3',5'-(hydrogen phosphate)	pH 1 pH 7	287(4.28) 292(4.20)	87-0242-80 87-0242-80
$C_{20}H_{24}O_2$			
Naphtho[2,3-b]furan-2(3H)-one, 3,4-dimethyl-7-(1-methylethyl)-3-propyl-, (R)-	EtOH	236(4.80),282(3.76), 293s(3.63),312(3.07), 320s(2.90),327(3.08)	138-0425-80
[2.2]Paracyclophane, 4,7-dimethoxy-5,8-dimethyl-	THF	229(4.25),254s(3.63), 291(2.62),313(2.82)	18-2943-80
$C_{20}H_{24}O_2S_2$			
2,11-Dithia[3.3]paracyclophane, 5,8-dimethoxy-6,9-dimethyl-	THF	224(4.23),261(3.60), 279s(3.14),303(3.00)	18-2943-80
$C_{20}H_{24}O_3$			
1,3-Benzenediol, 4-[3-[4-hydroxy-3-(3-methyl-2-butenyl)phenyl]propyl]-	EtOH	225s(4.19),281(3.75), 287s(3.65)	138-1459-80
Spiro[1,3-benzodioxole-2,3'-tricyclo[3.1.0.0^{2,6}]hexan]-4'-one, 1',2',4,5-5',6,6',7-octamethyl-	EtOH	207(4.64),290(3.49), 336(1.96)	44-4337-80

Compound	Solvent	$\lambda_{max}(\log \epsilon)$	Ref.
$C_{20}H_{24}O_4$			
1,4-Benzocyclodecenediol, 5,8,9,12-tetrahydro-6,10-dimethyl-, diacetate, (E,E)- (wigandol acetate)	MeOH	212(4.27)	102-2202-80
1,4-Naphthalenediol, 6-ethenyl-5,6,7,8-tetrahydro-6-methyl-7-(1-methylethenyl)-, diacetate, cis	EtOH	212(3.99)	102-2202-80
1-Phenanthrenepropanoic acid, 4b,5,6,7-9,10-hexahydro-4-methoxy-4b-methyl-7-oxo-, methyl ester, (±)-	EtOH	229(4.35),277(3.49), 284(3.48)	78-2513-80
$C_{20}H_{24}O_5$			
Bicyclo[3.2.1]octane-2,8-dione, 7-(4-hydroxy-3-methoxyphenyl)-3-methoxy-6-methyl-5-(2-propenyl)-, [1S-(6-endo,7-exo)]-	MeOH	228s(3.88),281(3.48)	102-0474-80
	MeOH-NaOH	236s(3.91),291(3.76)	102-0474-80
Bicyclo[3.2.1]octan-3-one, 7-(1,3-benzodioxol-5-yl)-8-hydroxy-2-methoxy-6-methyl-5-(2-propenyl)-, (2α)-(2β)-	MeOH	232(3.83),286(3.71)	102-0474-80
	MeOH	233(3.72),286(3.64)	102-0474-80
Nectandrin B	MeOH	230(4.00),278(3.60)	100-0353-80
	MeOH-NaOH	250(4.04),290(3.64)	100-0353-80
1-Propanone, 1-(2-hydroxy-4,6-dimethoxy-3,5-dimethylphenyl)-3-(4-methoxyphenyl)-	EtOH	223(4.76),277(4.49)	94-2487-80
	EtOH-AlCl$_3$	309(--)	94-2487-80
$C_{20}H_{24}O_6$			
2H-1-Benzopyran-3,7-diol, 3,4-dihydro-4,5-dimethoxy-2-(4-methoxyphenyl)-6,8-dimethyl-, [2R-(2α,3β,4β)]-	MeOH	227(3.65),275(2.62), 282(2.56)	94-1884-80
Dihydrochalcone, 2',3,4,4',6'-pentamethoxy-	EtOH	209(4.61),227(4.18), 280(3.63)	102-0476-80
2,3-Naphthalenedimethanol, 1,2,3,4-tetrahydro-7-hydroxy-1-(4-hydroxy-3-methoxyphenyl)-6-methoxy-, [1S-(1α,2β,3α)]-	CHCl$_3$	222(4.56),285(4.26), 290(4.16)	100-0482-80
$C_{20}H_{24}O_7$			
2-Butenoic acid, 2-methyl-, 2,3,3a,4,5-6,6a,7,9a,9b-decahydro-6,8-dihydroxy-6,9-dimethyl-3-methylene-2,7-dioxoazuleno[4,5-b]furan-4-yl ester	MeOH	215(4.24),265(3.91)	44-3163-80
1,3-Propanediol, 1-(4-hydroxy-3-methoxyphenyl)-2-[4-(3-hydroxy-1-propenyl)-2-methoxyphenoxy]-	EtOH	266(3.94)	102-0449-80
$C_{20}H_{24}O_8$			
Ethanone, 1,1',1'',1'''-(5-hydroxy-5,5',6'a-trimethylspiro[furan-2(5H),2'(3'H)-furo[2,3-b]furan]-3,3'a,4,4'(6'aH)-tetrayl)tetrakis-, [2'α(R*),3'aβ,6'aβ]-	MeOH	220(3.72),266(3.96)	23-1645-80
$C_{20}H_{25}FO_3$			
Androsta-1,4-diene-3,17-dione, 9-fluoro-11-hydroxy-16-methyl-, (11β,16β)-	MeOH	238(4.24)	95-0072-80
$C_{20}H_{25}NO_2$			
2,4(1H,3H)-Quinolinedione, 1-methyl-3,3-bis(3-methyl-2-butenyl)-	EtOH	235(3.53),258(2.65), 342(2.40)	102-0941-80

Compound	Solvent	$\lambda_{max}(\log \epsilon)$	Ref.
$C_{20}H_{25}NO_3$			
2,3-Benzoxazonine, 1,3,4,5,6,7-hexahydro-9,10-dimethoxy-3-methyl-1-phenyl-	MeOH	233s(3.99),269s(3.21), 280s(3.50),285s(3.54), 289s(3.0)	12-1323-80
1H-Dibenzo[a,f]quinolizin-1-one, 2,3,4,5,6,7,11b,12,13-octahydro-9,10-dimethoxy-3-methyl-	MeOH	227(4.01),318(4.49)	135-0956-80
$C_{20}H_{25}NO_4$			
1H-Benzo[f]pyrrolo[1,2-a]indole, 11-(dimethoxymethyl)-2,3,11,11a-tetrahydro-5,10-dimethoxy-, cis	MeOH	266(3.80),294(3.79), 304(3.77),347(3.34) (changing)	44-1260-80
Isoquinoline, 1-[(3,4-dimethoxyphenyl)-methyl]-1,2,3,4-tetrahydro-6,7-di-methoxy-	EtOH	283(3.94)	39-1696-80B
5-Isoquinolinol, 1,2,3,4-tetrahydro-6,7-dimethoxy-1-[(4-methoxyphenyl)-methyl]-2-methyl-, (S)-	n.s.g.	283(3.85)	100-0472-80
$C_{20}H_{25}NO_5$			
2,3-Benzoxazepine, 1,3,4,5-tetrahydro-7,8-dimethoxy-1-(3,4-dimethoxyphenyl)-3-methyl-	MeOH	235(3.96),281(3.59), 284s(3.58)	12-0833-80
$C_{20}H_{25}NO_7$			
1,1-Cyclohexanedicarboxylic acid, 3-(aminocarbonyl)-4-(benzoyloxy)-, diethyl ester, trans	EtOH	231(4.13)	23-1860-80
$C_{20}H_{25}NO_7S$			
1H-Pyrrole-2-acetic acid, 3-(methoxy-carbonyl)-1-[2-(methylsulfonyl)oxy]-ethyl]-4-(2-phenylethyl)-, methyl ester	MeOH	216(4.16),239(4.00), 260(3.82)	4-1081-80
$C_{20}H_{25}NO_8$			
3aH-Indole-2,3,3a,4-tetracarboxylic acid, 1-butyl-1,7a-dihydro-, tetramethyl ester	MeOH	277(4.26),300s(3.94)	44-4573-80
$C_{20}H_{25}N_3$			
Dihydrocleavamine, 16-cyano-	EtOH	226(4.57),278s(3.91), 284(3.95),293(3.89)	78-1063-80
1H,11H-4,5-Propanopyrimido[1,2-a]quin-azoline, 2,3,4,4a,5,6-hexahydro-6-phenyl- (isomer has same spectrum)	pH 1 pH 13 EtOH	243(3.98),289(3.30) 248(3.97),294(3.32) 253(4.03),298(3.40)	94-2587-80 94-2587-80 94-2587-80
$C_{20}H_{25}N_3O_2$			
Ergoline-8-carboxamide, 9,10-didehydro-N-ethyl-N-(2-hydroxyethyl)-6-methyl-	EtOH	243(4.32),312(3.96)	39-0902-80C
2-Imidazolidinone, 5-ethoxy-4,4-dimeth-yl-5-(4-methylphenyl)-1-(phenylamino)-	EtOH	208(4.2),218(4.2), 235(4.2),282(3.3)	5-1016-80
$C_{20}H_{25}N_3O_6$			
3,5-Pyridinedicarboxylic acid, 2-[2-(di-methylamino)ethyl]-1,4-dihydro-6-methyl-4-(4-nitrophenyl)-, dimethyl ester	EtOH	237(4.31),282(4.14)	94-3163-80
$C_{20}H_{25}N_5$			
2-Pyrimidinamine, N-(4-butylphenyl)-	EtOH	270(4.79)	103-0309-80

Compound	Solvent	$\lambda_{max}(\log \epsilon)$	Ref.
4-(3,5-dimethyl-1H-pyrazol-1-yl)- 6-methyl- (cont.)	EtOH-HCl	290(4.49)	103-0309-80
4-Pyrimidinamine, N-(4-butylphenyl)- 2-(3,5-dimethyl-1H-pyrazol-1-yl)- 6-methyl-	EtOH	<u>256(4.4)</u>,285s(4.3)	103-0868-80
$C_{20}H_{26}$ Azulene, 7-(1,5-dimethyl-4-hexenyl)- 1,4-dimethyl-	MeOH	215(4.05),243(4.27), 283(4.48),288(4.48), 303(3.96),340(3.30), 348(3.36),365(3.23), 605(2.47),655(2.30), 730(1.98)	24-3848-80
$C_{20}H_{26}NO_3$ Armepavine, N-methyl-, chloride	MeOH	281(3.23),287s(3.22)	100-0270-80
$C_{20}H_{26}N_2$ Diazene, bis(1,1-dimethyl-2-phenyl- ethyl)-	hexane	370(1.54)	78-1753-80
Diazene, bis(1-methyl-1-(4-methyl- phenyl)ethyl)-	C_6H_{12}	367(1.67)	44-4629-80
s-Indacene-4,8-diamine, 2-(1,1-dimeth- ylethyl)-N,N,N',N'-tetramethyl-	dioxan	284(4.63),410(4.28), 471(4.21),693(2.46)	89-0199-80
6-Isoquinolinamine, 1,2,3,4-tetrahydro- N,N,2,3,3-pentamethyl-4-phenyl-	EtOH	208(4.47),257(4.07), 308s(3.34)	4-1563-80
$C_{20}H_{26}N_2O$ Ibogaine	MeOH	228(4.40),300(3.92)	64-0219-80B
$C_{20}H_{26}N_2O_4$ Strychnofendlerine, N_a-deacetyl-	EtOH	244(3.86),300(3.42)	32-0081-80
$C_{20}H_{26}N_2O_4$ Propanedioic acid, [2-(2,3,4,9-tetra- hydro-1H-pyrido[3,4-b]indol-1-yl)- ethyl]-, diethyl ester	EtOH	225(4.52),277s(3.86), 281(3.87),290(3.79)	94-2527-80
3,5-Pyridinedicarboxylic acid, 2- [2-(dimethylamino)ethyl]-1,4-dihydro- 6-methyl-4-phenyl-, dimethyl ester	EtOH	241(4.28),356(3.86)	94-3163-80
$C_{20}H_{26}N_2O_6$ Benzenepropanoic acid, α-[2-(hydroxy- methyl)-4,5-dimethoxyphenyl]-3,4-di- methoxy-, hydrazide	EtOH	238(4.02),281(3.74)	39-2013-80C
1,1-Cyclohexanedicarboxylic acid, 3-(aminocarbonyl)-4-(benzoyl- amino)-, diethyl ester, cis	EtOH	228.5(3.80)	23-1860-80
trans	EtOH	228(4.01)	23-1860-80
$C_{20}H_{26}O_2$ B-Norestra-1,3,5(10),8-tetraen-17β-ol, 3-methoxy-6,6-dimethyl-, (±)-	EtOH	262(3.85),308(3.66), 324(3.56)	39-0448-80C
Retinal, 4-oxo-	EtOH	375(4.71)	33-1391-80
$C_{20}H_{26}O_3$ Benzeneacetic acid, α-[5-(5-oxo-1- cyclopenten-1-yl)pentyl]-, ethyl ester	MeOH	224(4.06)	44-4702-80
Kaura-9(11),16-dien-18-oic acid, 12- oxo-, (4α)-	MeOH	250(4.18)	39-1270-80C

Compound	Solvent	$\lambda_{max}(\log \epsilon)$	Ref.
Tricyclo[6.2.2.0^{2,7}]dodeca-2,4,6,9-tetraen-11-one, 1,8,9,10,12,12-hexamethyl-3,6-dimethoxy-	C_6H_{12}	292(3.56)	44-0034-80
$C_{20}H_{26}O_4$			
1-Phenanthrenepropanoic acid, 4b,5,6,7-8,8a,9,10-octahydro-4-methoxy-4b-methyl-7-oxo-, methyl ester, trans	EtOH	275(3.29),282(3.29)	78-2513-80
$C_{20}H_{26}O_5$			
Arturin	MeOH	210(3.67)	102-2765-80
Bicyclo[3.2.1]octane-6,8-dione, 2-(2,4-dimethoxyphenyl)-2-(2-methoxyethyl)-5-methyl-, endo-exo	n.s.g.	227(3.90),277(3.36), 284(3.30)	2-0433-80
exo-endo	n.s.g.	226(3.92),277(3.40), 283(3.37)	2-0433-80
5,7,17-Briaratrien-3-one, 11,12-epoxy-2,14-dihydroxy-, (1R*,2R*,5Z,10R*-11S*,12R*,14S*)-	MeOH	271(3.76)	12-2307-80
Deltoidin A	EtOH	213(4.21)	102-1975-80
$C_{20}H_{26}O_6$			
Deltoidin B	EtOH	214(4.32)	102-1975-80
1,4:5,8-Diepoxynaphthalene-2,3-dicarboxylic acid, 1,4,4a,5,8,8a-hexahydro-, bis(1,1-dimethylethyl) ester, exo-endo	EtOH	227s(3.76),242(3.74)	24-0531-80
exo-exo	EtOH	235(3.67)	24-0531-80
$C_{20}H_{27}FN_2O_{10}S$			
D-arabino-Hexitol, 2-deoxy-1-S-ethyl-1-C-(5-fluoro-3,4-dihydro-2,4-dioxo-1(2H)-pyrimidinyl)-1-thio-, 3,4,5,6-tetraacetate	MeOH	270(3.95)	136-0356-80C
$C_{20}H_{27}N$			
Retinonitrile, all-trans	EtOH	239(3.72),355(4.53)	87-1013-80
$C_{20}H_{27}NO_7$			
D-Arabinitol, 1-C-[4-(ethoxycarbonyl)-5-methyl-1-(phenylmethyl)-1H-pyrrol-3-yl]-, (S)-	EtOH	243(3.79),261s(--)	39-1199-80C
$C_{20}H_{27}N_5O_8$			
1,2-Hydrazinedicarboxylic acid, 1,1'-(4,5,6,7-tetramethyl-2H-isoindole-1,3-diyl)bis-, tetramethyl ester	CH$_2$Cl$_2$ at -20°	275(3.86),310s(3.30), 337(1.51)	88-3471-80
1,2-Hydrazinedicarboxylic acid, 1,1'-[2-(1,1-dimethylethyl)-2H-isoindole-1,3-diyl]bis-, tetramethyl ester	MeOH	268(3.24),273(3.25), 279(3.35),329(3.83)	88-3471-80
$C_{20}H_{28}$			
Abieta-6,8,11,13-tetraene, (-)-	isooctane	220(4.46),264(3.95)	102-1121-80
Benzene, 1-methyl-4-[1-methyl-2-[2-methyl-5-(1-methylethyl)-2-cyclo-hexen-1-yl]ethenyl]-	pentane	248(4.08)	83-0237-80
Benzene, 1-methyl-4-[1-methyl-2-[3-methyl-6-(1-methylethyl)-2-cyclo-hexen-1-yl]ethenyl]-	pentane	247(4.08)	83-0237-80
Benzene, 1-methyl-4-[1-methyl-2-[5-methyl-2-(1-methylethylidene)cyclo-	pentane	242(4.03),247(4.08), 252(4.07),259(3.99)	83-0237-80

Compound	Solvent	$\lambda_{max}(\log \epsilon)$	Ref.
hexyl]ethenyl]- (cont.)			83-0237-80
$C_{20}H_{28}N_2O$			
Deacetylaspidospermine	MeOH	246(3.88),289(3.41)	73-1419-80
$C_{20}H_{28}N_2O_2$			
3H-Pyrazol-3-one, 4-butyl-2-[(4-butyl-	CHCl$_3$	340(4.23),515(4.00)	5-0564-80
1,3-dihydro-5-methyl-3-oxo-2H-pyrrol-	tert-BuOH	344(--),521(--)	5-0564-80
2-ylidene)ethylidene]-1,2-dihydro-	+ base	585(--)	5-0564-80
5-methyl-	CF$_3$COOH	566(--)	5-0564-80
$C_{20}H_{28}N_2O_3$			
1-Cyclohexene-1-carboxylic acid, 3,5-	EtOH	400(4.30),505(4.79)	70-0980-80
bis[3-(dimethylamino)-2-propenyli-	CHCl$_3$	380(--),485(--)	70-0980-80
dene]-2-methyl-4-oxo-, ethyl ester,			
(all-E)-			
$C_{20}H_{28}N_4$			
2-Pyrimidinamine, N-(4-butylphenyl)-	EtOH	272(4.45),290s(4.21)	103-0309-80
4-methyl-6-(1-piperidinyl)-	EtOH-HCl	260(4.45)	103-0309-80
1H-Tetrazole, 5-[2,6-dimethyl-8-(2,6,6-	EtOH	341(4.74)	87-1013-80
trimethyl-1-cyclohexen-1-yl)-1,3,5,7-			
octatetraenyl]-, (all-E)-			
$C_{20}H_{28}N_4OS_2$			
2H-1,3,5-Thiadiazine-2-thione, 3-benz-	CH$_2$Cl$_2$	255(4.47),352(3.55)	24-0079-80
oyl-6-[bis(1-methylethyl)amino]-4-		(plus shoulders)	
[(1,1-dimethylethyl)imino]-3,4-dihydro-			
$C_{20}H_{28}N_4O_2S$			
2H-1,3,5-Thiadiazin-2-one, 3-benzoyl-	CH$_2$Cl$_2$	255(4.45),279(4.16)	24-0079-80
6-[bis(1-methylethyl)amino]-4-(1,1-			
dimethylethyl)imino]-3,4-dihydro-			
$C_{20}H_{28}O$			
8,11,13-Abietatrien-7-one, (+)-	EtOH	211(4.39),254(4.02),	102-1121-80
		303(3.38)	
	EtOH	209(4.36),255(4.00),	102-1121-80
		302(3.30)	
Retinal, all-trans	hexane	368(4.68)	46-0134-80
	hexane	368(4.68)	130-0406-80
	3-Mepentane	369(4.70)	35-2963-80
at 77°K	3-Mepentane	385(4.73)	35-2963-80
	CCl$_4$	381(4.68)	35-2963-80
Retinal, 7-cis	heptane	359(4.65)	46-0134-80
Retinal, 9-cis	hexane	363(4.60)	46-0134-80
			+130-0406-80
Retinal, 11-cis	hexane	363(4.42)	46-0134-80
	MeOH	375(4.30)	35-6370-80
Retinal, 13-cis	hexane	366(4.59)	46-0134-80
Retinal, 9,11-di-cis	hexane	352(4.49)	130-0406-80
$C_{20}H_{28}O_2$			
[1,1'-Bibicyclo[3.3.1]nonane]-3,3'-di-	n.s.g.	233(3.46),322(1.61)	44-3545-80
one, 2-methyl-2'-methylene-,			
[1α(1'S*,5'R*),2β,5β]-			
1H-Inden-1-one, octahydro-4-[(5-hydr-	EtOH	270(4.34)	44-2013-80
oxy-2-methylenecyclohexylidene)eth-			
ylidene]-3a,7a-dimethyl-			
B-Norestra-1,3,5(10)-trien-17β-ol,	EtOH	286(3.74)	39-0448-80C
3-methoxy-6,6-dimethyl-, (±)-			

Compound	Solvent	$\lambda_{max}(\log \epsilon)$	Ref.
Phenanthro[1,2-c]furan-6-carboxaldehyde, 3b,4,5,5a,6,7,8,9,9a,9b,10,11-dodeca-hydro-3b,6,9a-trimethyl-	n.s.g.	220(3.48)	20-0399-80
2H-Pyran-3(6H)-one, 4-methyl-6-[2-meth-yl-4-(2,6,6-trimethyl-1-cyclohexen-1-yl)-1,3-butadienyl]-, (±)-(E,E)-	EtOH	238(4.36),267(4.11)	78-1179-80
Retinal, 3-hydroxy-, (3R)-	CHCl₃	386(4.65)	33-1467-80
Retinoic acid, 11,12-dihydro-11-hy-droxy-, δ-lactone	MeOH	233(4.34),268s(4.08)	44-1181-80
13-cis	MeOH	225(4.27),269(4.08)	44-1181-80
$C_{20}H_{28}O_3$			
2,4,6,8-Hexadecatetraenal, 3,7,11,11-tetramethyl-10,15-dioxo-, (all-E)-	EtOH	370(4.77)	33-1391-80
15-Oxatricyclo[9.3.2.1⁴,⁸]heptadec-11-ene-2,16-dione, 1,7,8-trimethyl-17-methylene-, [1R-(1R*,4R*,7S*,8R*)]-	EtOH	218(3.77)	78-3489-80
Panamensin	MeOH	303(3.96)	78-1167-80
	MeOH-NaOH	360(--)	78-1167-80
Phenanthro[1,2-c]furan-6-carboxylic acid, 3b,4,5,5a,6,7,8,9,9a,10,11-dodecahydro-3b,6,9a-trimethyl-	n.s.g.	220(3.56)	20-0399-80
Retinoic acid, 3-hydroxy-, (3R)-	CHCl₃	362(4.66)	33-1467-80
$C_{20}H_{28}O_4$			
1H-Benz[e]indene-3,7(2H,3aH)-dione, 3a-ethyl-4,5,8,9,9a,9b-hexahydro-6-[(2-methyl-1,3-dioxolan-2-yl)-methyl]-	n.s.g.	248(4.11)	77-0472-80
[1,1'-Bicycloheptyl]-3,3',6,6'-tetrone, 2,5,5,5',5'-pentamethyl-2'-methylene-	MeOH	221(3.62)	33-1499-80
2-Oxaandrost-4-en-3-one, 17 -acetoxy-	n.s.g.	223(3.97),270(3.04)	33-0473-80
Oxidopanamensin	MeOH	288(4.18)	78-1167-80
	MeOH-NaOH	335(--)	78-1167-80
$C_{20}H_{28}O_5$			
Effusanin A	MeOH	240(3.99)	138-1635-80
B-Homo-A-nor-2-oxaandrostane-3,6-dione, 17β-acetoxy-	EtOH	202(3.45),262(3.80)	33-0473-80
ferric complex	EtOH-NaOH	202(3.82),290(4.11)	33-0473-80
	EtOH	540(2.30)	33-0473-80
Longikaurin A	MeOH	235(3.98)	77-0205-80
2-Oxaandrostan-3-one, 17β-acetoxy-4α,5α-epoxy-	n.s.g.	202(3.30),270(3.23)	33-0473-80
2-Oxaandrost-4-en-3-one, 17β-acetoxy-1ξ-hydroxy-	n.s.g.	227(4.08)	33-0473-80
$C_{20}H_{28}O_6$			
Effusanin E	MeOH	238.5(3.92)	138-1635-80
$C_{20}H_{28}O_7$			
Cyclodeca[b]furan-6-carboxylic acid, 2,3,3a,4,5,8,9,10,11,11a-decahydro-10-(hydroxymethyl)-3-methylene-4-(2-methyl-1-oxopropoxy)-2-oxo-, methyl ester, [3S-(3aR*,4S*,6E,10R*,11aS*)]-	MeOH	202(4.38)	44-4028-80
Melnerin A	MeOH	212(4.84)	44-4028-80
Viguilenin, dehydro-	EtOH	215(3.93)	102-1795-80
$C_{20}H_{28}O_8$			
Soulameanone	EtOH	239(4.02)	78-2983-80

Compound	Solvent	$\lambda_{max}(\log \epsilon)$	Ref.
$C_{20}H_{28}O_{10}$			
Setulosopteroside	MeOH	217(4.42),259(4.10), 306(3.33)	102-1743-80
$C_{20}H_{29}NO_5S$			
Latrunculin B	MeOH	212(4.24),269s(--)	88-3629-80
$C_{20}H_{29}N_2O_3$			
2-Furanmethanaminium, 5-(2-nitrophenyl)-N,N,N-tripropyl-, bromide	MeOH	250(4.30)	73-1715-80
2-Furanmethanaminium, 5-(3-nitrophenyl)-N,N,N-tripropyl-, bromide	MeOH	274(4.41)	73-1715-80
2-Furanmethanaminium, 5-(4-nitrophenyl)-N,N,N-tripropyl-, bromide	MeOH	336(4.30)	73-1715-80
$C_{20}H_{29}N_3O$			
Ethanamine, N,N-diethyl-2-[[4,5,6,7-tetrahydro-1-(phenylmethyl)-1H-indazol-3-yl]oxy]-	EtOH	232(3.94)	18-0825-80
$C_{20}H_{29}N_3O_4$			
1,5,7-Triazacyclotridecan-4-one, 9-aceoxy-1-acetyl-2-phenyl-, (S)-	EtOH	248(2.27),253(2.34), 258(2.40),265(2.29)	102-0163-80
$C_{20}H_{29}N_3O_5$			
Dodecanoic acid, 2-[(4-nitrophenyl)hydrazono]-3-oxo-, ethyl ester	MeOH	372(4.542)	2-0676-80
$C_{20}H_{29}N_7$			
4-Pyrimidinamine, 2-(4-ethyl-3,5-dipropyl-1H-pyrazol-1-yl)-6-methyl-N-(5-methyl-1H-pyrazol-3-yl)-	EtOH	230(4.10),277(4.31)	103-1271-80
$C_{20}H_{30}N_2$			
4,4'-Bipyridinium, 1,1'-dipentyl-, diiodide	n.s.g.	258(4.28)	98-1026-80
$C_{20}H_{30}N_2O$			
Acetonitrile, [3,5-bis(1,1-dimethylethyl)-4-oxo-2,5-cyclohexadien-1-ylidene](diethylamino)-	isooctane	424(4.47)	73-2675-80
$C_{20}H_{30}N_2O_9$			
D-galacto-Octonic acid, 2,3-dideoxy-3-(nitromethyl)-2-[1-[(phenylmethyl)amino]ethylidene]-, ethyl ester, [2(Z),3ξ]-	EtOH	297(4.22)	39-1199-80C
$C_{20}H_{30}N_8$			
2-Pyrimidinamine, 4-(3,5-dimethyl-1H-pyrazol-1-yl)-5-ethyl-N-(5-hexyl-1H-1,2,4-triazol-3-yl)-6-methyl-	EtOH	258(4.47),292(3.65)	103-1275-80
4-Pyrimidinamine, 2-(3,5-dimethyl-1H-pyrazol-1-yl)-5-ethyl-N-(5-hexyl-1H-1,2,4-triazol-3-yl)-6-methyl-	EtOH	229(4.15),266(4.41), 300(4.01)	103-1271-80
$C_{20}H_{30}O$			
Dibenz[b,f]oxepin, 1,2,3,4,4a,10,11-11a-octahydro-1,1,4a-trimethyl-8-(1-methylethyl)-, (4aR-cis)-	isooctane	215s(--),224s(--), 278(2.97),272(3.00)	102-1121-80

Compound	Solvent	λ_{max}(log ϵ)	Ref.
15-Oxabicyclo[12.1.0]pentadeca-4,6,10-triene, 4,10,14-trimethyl-7-(1-methylethenyl)-	EtOH	271s(4.24),281(4.35), 292s(4.24)	12-0879-80
Phenanthro[1,2-c]furan, 3b,4,5,5a,6,7-8,9,9a,9b,10,11-dodecahydro-3b,6,6-9a-tetramethyl-	n.s.g.	220(3.46)	20-0399-80
Vitamin A	C$_6$H$_{12}$	326.5(4.70)	5-2039-80
C$_{20}$H$_{30}$O$_2$			
Butanedial, [2-(decahydro-5,5,8a-trimethyl-2-methylene-1-naphthalenyl)-ethylidene]-, [1α(E),4aβ,8aα]-	EtOH	235(3.95),292s(2.53)	94-3452-80
D-Homoandrost-4-en-3-one, 17aβ-hydroxy-	MeOH	242(4.20)	24-0203-80
3-Menthyl 4-phenylbutanoate, (-)-	CHCl$_3$	262(2.44),265(2.35), 269(2.31)	126-0201-80
Retinol, 3-hydroxy-, (3R)-, all-trans	CHCl$_3$	329(4.68)	33-1467-80
C$_{20}$H$_{30}$O$_3$			
Cleomeolide	EtOH	214(3.68)	78-3489-80
D-Homo-17a-oxa-5α-androstan-17-one, 3β-hydroxy-16-methylene-	EtOH	214(3.58)	87-0090-80
Oxiranebutanoic acid, 3-(1,3,5,8-tetradecatetraenyl)-	hexane	260(4.43),280(4.55), 291(4.45)	35-5425-80
2H-Pyran-3-ol, 3,6-dihydro-4-methyl-6-[2-methyl-4-(2,2,6-trimethyl-7-oxabicyclo[4.1.0]hept-1-yl)-1,3-butadienyl]-, [1α[1E,1(3R*,6S*),3E],6α]-(±)-	EtOH	240(4.34)	78-1179-80
Rondeletin	MeOH	285(3.85)	78-1167-80
	MeOH-NaOH	333(--)	78-1167-80
C$_{20}$H$_{30}$O$_4$			
Cyclonona[c]pyran-1,9-diol, 1,3,4,4a,5-6,9,10,11,11a-decahydro-4-(4-hydroxy-4-methyl-2-pentenylidene)-7-methyl-11-methylene- (xenialactol)	MeOH	243(4.19)	44-3814-80
Prosta-5,8(12),13-trien-1-oic acid, 15-hydroxy-9-oxo- (1-prostaglandin B)	MeOH	278(4.42)	87-0903-80
C$_{20}$H$_{30}$O$_7$			
Viguilenin	EtOH	220(3.94)	102-1795-80
C$_{20}$H$_{30}$O$_{13}$			
β-D-Glucopyranoside, 1,4a,5,7a-tetrahydro-7-(hydroxymethyl)-5-(β-D-xylopyranosyloxy)cyclopenta[c]pyran-1-yl	MeOH	204(3.6)	100-0649-80 +102-0571-80
C$_{20}$H$_{32}$			
2,6,8,10,14-Hexadecapentaene, 2,6,11,15-tetramethyl-	hexane	287(4.63),298(4.56)	39-1045-80C
C$_{20}$H$_{32}$N$_2$O			
1H-Indole-3-ethanamine, N,N-dibutyl-5-methoxy-2-methyl-, monohydrochloride	EtOH	226(4.34),284(3.85), 296(3.83)	80-0245-80
C$_{20}$H$_{32}$O			
Benzo[a]cyclopropa[c]cyclohepten-8(1H)-one, 1a,2,3,4,4a,5,8a,8b-octahydro-1,4-dimethyl-1-(4-methylpentyl)-	MeOH	225(4.02)	24-3848-80
1,3,11-Cyclotetradeca-1,3,11-triene, 7,8-epoxy-1-(1-methylethyl)-4,8,12-	EtOH	243s(4.18),249(4.20), 256s(4.15)	12-0879-80

Compound	Solvent	$\lambda_{max}(\log \epsilon)$	Ref.
trimethyl-, (E,E,E)- (cont.)			12-0879-80
1-Naphthalenol, 2-(1,5-dimethyl-4-hex-enyl)-1,2,3,4,4a,8a-hexahydro-4a,8-dimethyl- ((-)-dictyolene)	EtOH	206(3.64),266(3.60)	35-5337-80
$C_{20}H_{32}O_2$			
2,6,10-Dodecatrienal, 12-hydroxy-6,10-dimethyl-2-(4-methyl-3-pentenyl)-, (E,E,E)-	EtOH	230(4.0)	102-2207-80
2,6,10,15-Hexadecatetraenal, 14-hydroxy-2,6,10,14-tetramethyl-	EtOH	227(4.03)	1-0391-80
2,6,10,15-Hexadecatetraen-8-one, 14-hydroxy-2,6,10,14-tetramethyl-, (E,E)-	EtOH	244(4.10)	1-0391-80
8,11a-Methano-11aH-cyclohepta[a]naphthalen-2(1H)-one, dodecahydro-9-hydroxy-4,4,9,11b-tetramethyl-, (4aα,6aβ,8α,9α,11aα,11bβ)-(±)-	MeOH	293(1.60)	94-1859-80
$C_{20}H_{32}O_4$			
6,8,10,14-Eicosatetraenoic acid, 5,12-dihydroxy-	MeOH	258(4.57),268(4.67), 278(4.54)	35-7986-80
$C_{20}H_{33}NO_4$			
1-Pyrrolidineheptanoic acid, 2-oxo-5-(3-oxo-1-octenyl)-, methyl ester, [R-(E)]-	MeOH	215(4.14)	94-1449-80
[S-(E)]-	MeOH	215(4.13)	94-1449-80
$C_{20}H_{34}N_2O_4$			
1-Imidazolidineheptanoic acid, 3-methyl-2-oxo-5-(3-oxo-1-octenyl)-, methyl ester, (E)-(±)-	MeOH	215(4.15)	94-1459-80
$C_{20}H_{34}O_3$			
1,2,3-Naphthalenetriol, decahydro-3,4a,8,8-tetramethyl-4-(3-methyl-2,4-pentadienyl)- (austroinulin)	EtOH	237(4.06)	102-0326-80
2H-Pyran-2-one, 4-hydroxy-6-pentadecyl-(conrauanalactone)	EtOH	286(3.94)	102-1187-80
	NaOH	303(--)	102-1187-80
$C_{20}H_{37}N_3O$			
1-Octadecanone, 1-(1H-1,2,4-triazol-3-yl)-	THF	240(3.72)	33-0588-80
1H-1,2,4-Triazole, 1-(1-oxooctadecyl)-	THF	227(3.88)	33-0588-80
$C_{20}H_{50}Si_5$			
Cyclopentasilane, decaethyl-	isooctane	210s(4.48),255s(4.04), 266s(3.04)	101-00C5-80K

Compound	Solvent	$\lambda_{max}(\log \epsilon)$	Ref.
$C_{21}H_5F_{14}N$ Benzenamine, N-[bis[2,3,5,6-tetra- fluoro-4-(trifluoromethyl)phenyl]- methylene]-	EtOH	222(4.04),284(3.81), 342(3.49)	70-1149-80
$C_{21}H_7Cl_8NO_7$ 2(1H)-Pyridinone, 1-[2-(2-acetoxy- 3,4,5,6-tetrachlorophenoxy)-5,6,7,8- tetrachloro-2,3-dihydro-3-oxo-1,4- benzodioxin-2-yl]-	MeCN	207(5.06),290s(3.74), 299(3.80),312s(3.73), 329s(3.43)	5-1836-80
$C_{21}H_{10}D_2O$ 15H-Dibenzo[a,g]cyclotridecen-15-one, 5,6,7,8-tetradehydro-α,α'-d_2	EtOH	224(4.55),282(4.62), 296(4.68),350s(3.34), 374s(3.29)	39-0466-80C
$C_{21}H_{12}BrN_3$ Benzo[b]pyrido[2,3-h][1,6]naphthyri- dine, 3-bromo-7-phenyl-	EtOH	211(4.58),260s(4.61), 267(4.62),296s(4.47), 305(4.58)	4-1225-80
$C_{21}H_{12}ClN_3$ Benzo[b]pyrido[2,3-h][1,6]naphthyri- dine, 3-chloro-7-phenyl-	EtOH	212(4.55),259s(4.56), 266(4.58),296s(4.40), 304(4.47)	4-1225-80
$C_{21}H_{12}D_2O$ 1,4-Pentadien-3-one, 1,5-bis(2-ethynyl- phenyl)-α,α'-d_2	EtOH	225(4.55),250(4.38), 332(4.41)	39-0466-80C
$C_{21}H_{12}O$ 15H-Dibenzo[a,g]cyclotridecen-15-one, 5,6,7,8-tetradehydro-	ether	224(4.61),266s(4.46), 279(4.62),293(4.66), 354s(3.53),364s(3.52)	39-0466-80C
$C_{21}H_{12}O_6$ [2,2'-Binaphthalene]-1,1',4,4'-tetrone, 8-hydroxy-8'-methoxy-	CHCl3	248(4.36),270s(4.29), 330s(3.47),417(3.87)	5-1321-80
$C_{21}H_{13}BrO$ 9(10H)-Anthracenone, 10-(bromophenyl- methylene)-	EtOH	228(4.58),285(4.19), 354(3.94)	35-3837-80
$C_{21}H_{13}ClN_2O_2$ 6H-Anthra[1,9-cd]isoxazol-6-one, 3-chloro-5-[(phenylmethyl)amino]-	dioxan	259(4.55),495(4.19), 530(4.20)	103-0704-80
$C_{21}H_{13}Cl_2NOS$ Thiazolium, 3-(3,4-dichlorophenyl)-4- hydroxy-2,5-diphenyl-, hydroxide, inner salt	EtOH	268(3.78),455(3.67)	44-2165-80
$C_{21}H_{13}FeNO_2$ Ferrocene, 1,1'-[2-[(4-cyanophenyl)- methylene]-1,3-dioxo-1,3-propanediyl]-	dioxan MeOH	304(4.10) 300(--)	73-1290-80 73-1290-80
$C_{21}H_{13}N$ Dibenz[a,c]acridine	MeOH	251s(3.75),257(3.78), 272(3.81),281(3.92), 305(4.29),324(3.96),	39-1233-80C

Compound	Solvent	$\lambda_{max}(\log \epsilon)$	Ref.
Dibenz[a,c]acridine (cont.)		340(4.08),357(4.27), 375(4.32)	39-1233-80C
	MeOH-acid	248s(3.72),256(3.84), 264(3.69),280(3.51), 290(3.49),304(4.41), 318(4.48),398(4.43)	39-1233-80C
$C_{21}H_{13}NO$ 4H-Benz[def]carbazole, 4-benzoyl-	EtOH	213(4.63),227(4.63), 256(4.49),303(4.19), 315s(4.14),338(3.45), 345(3.18),354(3.30)	18-0494-80
$C_{21}H_{13}NO_4$ 8H-Naphtho[2,3-a]phenoxazine-8,13(4H)- dione, 7-hydroxy-2-methyl-	THF	267(4.71),607(4.27), 670(4.08)	104-1884-80
$C_{21}H_{13}NO_5$ 5H,8H-Pyrano[2',3':4,5]pyrido[3,2,1- jk]carbazole-6-carboxylic acid, 5,8-dioxo-, ethyl ester	EtOH	249(4.35),341(4.23), 393(4.17)	49-0093-80
$C_{21}H_{13}NO_5S$ 3H,14H-Pyrano[2',3':4,5]pyrido[3,2,1- kl]phenothiazine-2-carboxylic acid, 3,14-dioxo-, ethyl ester	EtOH	280(4.11),321(4.29), 378(4.31)	49-0093-80
$C_{21}H_{13}N_3$ Propanedinitrile, (1-methyl-2-phenyl- benz[cd]indol-5(1H)-ylidene)-	CH_2Cl_2	242(4.03),310(3.70), 400(3.36),526(4.28), 560(4.26)	83-0977-80
$C_{21}H_{13}N_3O$ Benzo[b]pyrido[2,3-h][1,6]naphthyri- din-3(4H)-one, 7-phenyl-	EtOH	211(4.51),267(4.96), 312s(4.31),321(4.43)	4-1225-80
$C_{21}H_{13}N_3O_2$ 1H-Phenanthro[9,10-d]imidazole, 2-(4- nitrophenyl)-	MeOH	257(4.41),300(3.58), 392(2.97)	56-2365-80
$C_{21}H_{13}N_3O_4$ 9,10-Anthracenedione, 1-azido-4-hydr- oxy-2-(4-methylphenoxy)-	THF	250(4.58),445(3.81)	104-1884-80
Pyridinium, 1-[3,4-dihydro-1-hydroxy- 3-[(4-nitrophenyl)imino]-4-oxo-2- naphthalenyl]-, hydroxide, inner salt	dioxan	221s(4.16),278s(4.18), 334s(4.04),353s(4.04), 471(3.56)	44-5139-80
$C_{21}H_{14}ClNO$ Pyridine, 3-[2-[4-(5-chloro-2-benzofur- anyl)phenyl]ethenyl]-	DMF	356(4.80)	33-1311-80
$C_{21}H_{14}ClNOS$ Thiazolium, 3-(2-chlorophenyl)-4-hy- droxy-2,5-diphenyl-, hydroxide, inner salt	EtOH	263(3.92),455(3.85)	44-2165-80
Thiazolium, 3-(3-chlorophenyl)-4-hy- droxy-2,5-diphenyl-, hydroxide, inner salt	EtOH	262(3.40),450(3.23)	44-2165-80
Thiazolium, 3-(4-chlorophenyl)-4-hy- droxy-2,5-diphenyl-, hydroxide, inner salt	EtOH	268(3.89),452(3.83)	44-2165-80

Compound	Solvent	$\lambda_{max}(\log \epsilon)$	Ref.
Thiazolium, 5-(2-chlorophenyl)-4-hydroxy-2,3-diphenyl-, hydroxide, inner salt	EtOH	285s(3.77),445(3.97)	44-2165-80
$C_{21}H_{14}ClNS$ Pyridine, 3-[2-[4-(5-chlorobenzo[b]-thien-2-yl)phenyl]ethenyl]-	DMF	355(4.77)	33-1311-80
$C_{21}H_{14}ClN_3O$ Pyridine, 3-[2-[4-[3-(4-chlorophenyl)-1,2,4-oxadiazol-5-yl]phenyl]ethenyl]-	DMF	335(4.68)	33-1311-80
Pyridine, 3-[2-[4-[5-(4-chlorophenyl)-1,3,4-oxadiazol-2-yl]phenyl]ethenyl]-	DMF	343(4.75)	33-1311-80
$C_{21}H_{14}NO_3S$ Pyrylium, 4-(5-nitro-2-thienyl)-2,6-diphenyl-, perchlorate	$C_2H_4Cl_2$	280(4.40),375(4.40), 435s(4.15)	150-4041-80
$C_{21}H_{14}N_2$ 1H-Phenanthro[9,10-d]imidazole, 2-phenyl-	MeOH	258(4.37),308(3.93), 359(3.58)	56-2365-80
$C_{21}H_{14}N_2O$ Propanedinitrile, (3-methyl-4-oxo-2,5-diphenyl-2-cyclopenten-1-ylidene)-	MeCN	300(4.34)	24-0424-80
$C_{21}H_{14}N_2O_2$ 6H-Anthra[1,9-cd]isoxazol-6-one, 5-[(3-methylphenyl)amino]-	dioxan	262(4.39),496(4.26), 512(4.28)	103-0704-80
6H-Anthra[1,9-cd]isoxazol-6-one, 5-[(4-methylphenyl)amino]-	dioxan	265(4.40),504(4.19), 528(4.24)	103-0704-80
Methanone, pyrazolo[1,5-a]pyridine-2,3-diylbis[phenyl-	MeOH	217(4.57),253(4.43), 316(4.10)	44-0090-80
$C_{21}H_{14}N_2O_3$ 9,10-Anthracenedione, 1,4-diamino-2-benzoyl-	DMF	609(4.10)	135-0344-80
6H-Anthra[1,9-cd]isoxazol-6-one, 5-[(3-methoxyphenyl)amino]-	dioxan	265(4.35),491(4.20), 515(4.25)	103-0704-80
$C_{21}H_{14}N_2S$ Thiazolo[3,4-a]benzimidazole-2-S^{IV}, 1,3-diphenyl-	EtOH	261(4.21),314(4.33), 512(3.74)	138-1369-80
Thieno[3',4':3,4]pyrazolo[1,5-a]pyridine-2-S^{IV}, 1,3-diphenyl-	MeOH	221(4.41),256(4.59), 264s(4.15),326(4.33), 424s(3.71),481(4.05)	44-0090-80
$C_{21}H_{14}N_4$ Pyrido[1',2':1,5]pyrazolo[3,4-d]pyridazine, 1,4-diphenyl-	MeOH	231(4.43),268(4.27), 283s(4.34),316s(4.10), 368(4.11)	44-0090-80
$C_{21}H_{14}N_4O_3Se$ Benzamide, N-[3-(4-nitrophenyl)-5-phenyl-1,3,4-selenadiazol-2(3H)-ylidene]-	EtOH	256(4.48),347(4.59)	4-1185-80
$C_{21}H_{14}N_6O_4S$ 1,2,4-Triazine-3(2H)-thione, 4,5-dihydro-6-nitro-2-(4-nitrophenyl)-4-phenyl-5-(phenylimino)-	DMF	288s(4.30),342s(4.06)	48-0087-80

Compound	Solvent	$\lambda_{max}(\log \epsilon)$	Ref.
$C_{21}H_{14}N_6O_5$			
1,2,4-Triazin-3(2H)-one, 4,5-dihydro-6-nitro-2-(4-nitrophenyl)-4-phenyl-5-(phenylimino)-	DMF	321(4.23)	48-0087-80
$C_{21}H_{14}O_2$			
1,4-Anthracenedione, 9-(phenylmethyl)-	MeOH	234(5.02),267(4.16), 283(4.12),295(4.11), 371(3.52),406(3.66)	44-1817-80
Benzo[a]pyren-1-ol, 6-methoxy-	MeOH	257(4.64),266(4.61), 276(4.44),288(4.55), 300(4.61),386(4.34), 388(4.34),395(4.36), 407(4.39),423(3.87)	87-0919-80
Benzo[a]pyren-3-ol, 6-methoxy-	MeOH	227(4.66),257(4.63), 261(4.63),269(4.63), 297(4.43),311(4.50), 351(3.79),367(4.17), 387(4.41),407(4.17), 432(4.14)	87-0919-80
Benzo[a]pyren-12-ol, 6-methoxy-	MeOH	219(4.42),223(4.42), 256(4.53),291(4.57), 301(4.60),372(4.00), 390(4.27),412(4.27)	87-0919-80
Spiro[naphthalene-1(4H),2'(1'H)-naphtho[2,1-b]furan]-4-one	EtOH	243(4.22),269(3.89), 279(3.90),281(3.76), 329(3.64),341(3.64)	39-1986-80C
$C_{21}H_{14}O_2Se$			
Selenonium, diphenyl-, 1,3-dihydro-1,3-dioxo-2H-inden-2-ylide	EtOH	223(4.82),247(4.57), 278(4.38),315(3.78), 320(3.70),365(3.24)	104-0119-80
$C_{21}H_{14}O_3$			
4H-1-Benzopyran-4-one, 7-hydroxy-2,3-diphenyl-	pH 4.5 pH 10.5	246(4.10),308(3.94) 264(4.50),312(4.00), 349(4.14)	86-0977-80 86-0977-80
Benzo[a]pyrene-1,3-diol, 6-methoxy-	MeOH	235(4.59),279(4.22), 312(3.88),338(3.86), 354(3.98),382(4.14), 403(4.17),441(3.81)	87-0919-80
$C_{21}H_{14}O_4S_2$			
Pyrylium, 2,6-diphenyl-4-(5-sulfo-2-thienyl)-, betaine	$C_2H_4Cl_2$	280(3.64),440(4.09)	150-4041-80
$C_{21}H_{15}BrClNO$			
2-Propen-1-one, 3-[(4-bromophenyl)amino]-1-(4-chlorophenyl)-3-phenyl-	C_6H_{12} EtOH	263(4.41),381(4.51) 261(4.38),382(4.53)	34-0083-80 34-0083-80
$C_{21}H_{15}BrN_2O$			
2(1H)-Naphthalenone, 1-[[(6-bromo-1-methyl-2(1H)-quinolinylidene)methyl]imino]-	EtOH benzene acetone CHCl$_3$	648(4.23) 644(--) 652(--) 640(--)	104-0185-80 104-0185-80 104-0185-80 104-0185-80
$C_{21}H_{15}ClINO$			
2-Propen-1-one, 1-(4-chlorophenyl)-3-[(4-iodophenyl)amino]-3-phenyl-	C_6H_{12} EtOH	263(4.37),384(4.48) 261(4.33),384(4.48)	34-0083-80 34-0083-80

Compound	Solvent	λ$_{max}$(log ε)	Ref.
C$_{21}$H$_{15}$ClN$_2$			
Isoindolo[2,1-a]quinazoline, 3-chloro-5,11-dihydro-5-phenyl-	MeOH	206(4.48),240(4.26), 276(3.60),282(3.65), 312(3.69)	83-0729-80
1H-Pyrazole, 5-(2-chlorophenyl)-1,3-di-phenyl-	C$_6$H$_{12}$	259(4.42)	23-1880-80
C$_{21}$H$_{15}$ClN$_2$O$_2$			
9,10-Anthracenedione, 1-amino-2-chloro-4-[(4-methylphenyl)amino]-	n.s.g.	586(4.10),620(4.11)	93-1963-80
C$_{21}$H$_{15}$ClN$_2$O$_3$			
9,10-Anthracenedione, 1-amino-2-chloro-4-[(4-methoxyphenyl)amino]-	n.s.g.	587(4.06),616(4.09)	93-1963-80
C$_{21}$H$_{15}$Cl$_2$N			
Pyridine, 2,6-bis[2-(4-chlorophenyl)-ethenyl]-	DMF	296(4.66),345(4.48)	33-1311-80
C$_{21}$H$_{15}$Cl$_2$NO			
2-Propen-1-one, 1-(4-chlorophenyl)-3-[(4-chlorophenyl)amino]-3-phenyl-	C$_6$H$_{12}$ EtOH	262(4.24),381(4.36) 260(4.28),380(4.46)	34-0083-80 34-0083-80
C$_{21}$H$_{15}$Cl$_2$N$_5$O$_3$			
7H,13H-[1,2,4]Triazino[1',6':3,4]imid-azo[1,5-a][1,4]benzodiazepine-8,13-(9H)-dione, 3-chloro-5-(2-chloro-phenyl)-10-methoxy-9-methyl-	isoPrOH	215s(4.61),239(4.51), 306s(3.76),329(3.83)	4-1697-80
7H,13H-[1,2,4]Triazino[1',6':3,4]imid-azo[1,5-a][1,4]benzodiazepine-8,10,13(9H,11H)-trione, 3-chloro-5-(2-chlorophenyl)-9,11-dimethyl- ‘	isoPrOH	215(4.71),238s(4.42), 255s(4.20),312(4.00)	4-1697-80
C$_{21}$H$_{15}$N			
Pyridine, 3-[2-[4-(phenylethynyl)phen-yl]ethenyl]-	DMF	342(4.75)	33-1311-80
C$_{21}$H$_{15}$NO			
Benz[g]isoquinolinium 2-oxo-2-phenyl-ethylide	CHCl$_3$	258(4.62),290s(4.10)	103-0626-80
Benzoxazole, 2-(1,2-diphenylethenyl)-	MeCN	226(4.21),280s(4.13), 318(4.41)	88-3751-80
Pyridine, 3-[2-[4-(2-benzofuranyl)phen-yl]ethenyl]-	DMF	354(4.76)	33-1311-80
C$_{21}$H$_{15}$NO$_2$			
1-Azulenecarboxylic acid, 3-cyano-2-(2-phenylethenyl)-	MeOH	232(4.06),291(4.31), 342(4.77),410(4.35)	18-3276-80
Furo[2,3-c]pyridin-2(6H)-one, 3-phenyl-6-(2-phenylethenyl)-, (E)-	EtOH	214(4.08),275(3.98), 419(4.49)	39-1176-80C
Furo[3,2-b]pyridin-2(4H)-one, 3-phenyl-4-(2-phenylethenyl)-, (E)-	EtOH	217(4.20),278(4.41), 410(4.18)	39-1176-80C
C$_{21}$H$_{15}$NS			
Benzothiazole, 2-(1,2-diphenylethenyl)-, (E)-	MeCN	265(4.15),318(4.26)	88-3751-80
Pyridine, 3-[2-[4-(benzo[b]thien-2-yl-phenyl)ethenyl]-	DMF	354(4.74)	33-1311-80
C$_{21}$H$_{15}$N$_3$			
Benzenamine, N-[(3,8-dihydroindolo[7,6-	EtOH	205(4.51),266(4.92),	103-1139-80

Compound	Solvent	$\lambda_{max}(\log \epsilon)$	Ref.
g]indol-1-yl)methylene]- (cont.)		294(4.54),324(4.52)	103-1139-80
$C_{21}H_{15}N_3O$			
Pyridine, 3-[2-[4-(3-phenyl-1,2,4-oxa-diazol-5-yl)phenyl]ethenyl]-	DMF	335(4.68)	33-1311-80
Pyridine, 3-[2-[4-(5-phenyl-1,3,4-oxa-diazol-2-yl)phenyl]ethenyl]-	DMF	342(4.74)	33-1311-80
$C_{21}H_{15}N_3O_2$			
6H-Anthra[1,9-cd]isoxazol-6-one, 3-(methylamino)-5-(phenylamino)-	dioxan	252(4.48),479(4.29), 510(4.38)	103-0704-80
Phenanthro[9',10':3,4]cyclobuta[1,2-d]-pyrimidine-8c(9H)-carbonitrile, 10,11,12,12a-tetrahydro-9,11-di-methyl-10,12-dioxo-	MeCN	250(4.76),258(4.76), 282(4.02),292(4.00), 305(4.07)	88-2317-80
$C_{21}H_{15}N_3O_3$			
2(1H)-Naphthalenone, 1-[[(1-methyl-6-nitro-2(1H)-quinolinylidene)-methyl]imino]-	EtOH	672(4.17)	104-0185-80
	benzene	642(--)	104-0185-80
	acetone	656(--)	104-0185-80
	CHCl$_3$	645(--)	104-0185-80
$C_{21}H_{15}N_5O_2S$			
Acetamide, N-[1,5-dihydro-1-(2-methyl-phenyl)-5-oxo-2H-thiazolo[4',5':4,5]-pyrimido[1,6-a]quinazolin-2-ylidene]-	EtOH	240(4.15)	2-0037-80
$C_{21}H_{15}OS$			
Pyrylium, 2,4-diphenyl-6-(2-thienyl)-, perchlorate	$C_2H_4Cl_2$	320(3.88),370(4.49), 455(4.38)	150-4041-80
$C_{21}H_{15}S_3$			
Cyclopropenylium, tris(phenylthio)-, (OC-6-11)-, hexachloroantimonate(1-)	MeCN	285(4.40)	118-0225-80
$C_{21}H_{15}Se_3$			
Cyclopropenylium, tris(phenylseleno)-, (OC-6-11)-, hexachloroantimonate(1-)	MeCN	295(4.36)	118-0225-80
$C_{21}H_{16}$			
5,11[1',2']-Benzeno-5H-cyclohepta[b]-naphthalene, 5a,11-dihydro-	EtOH	276(3.5)	138-0349-80
$C_{21}H_{16}ClN$			
Pyridine, 2-[2-[4-[2-(4-chlorophenyl)-ethenyl]phenyl]ethenyl]-	DMF	361(4.83)	33-1311-80
Pyridine, 3-[2-[4-[2-(4-chlorophenyl)-ethenyl]phenyl]ethenyl]-	DMF	359(4.81)	33-1311-80
$C_{21}H_{16}ClNO$			
2-Propen-1-one, 1-(4-chlorophenyl)-3-phenyl-3-(phenylamino)-	C_6H_{12}	259(4.30),380(4.42)	34-0083-80
	EtOH	257(4.26),380(4.47)	34-0083-80
$C_{21}H_{16}ClN_3O_4S$			
Benzenesulfonamide, 5-[(4-amino-3-chlo-ro-9,10-dihydro-9,10-dioxo-1-anthra-cenyl)amino]-2-methyl-	n.s.g.	573(4.00),605(3.99)	93-1963-80
$C_{21}H_{16}Cl_2N_2O_4$			
Propanedioic acid, (4,6-dichloro-2-pyr-imidinyl)-, bis(phenylmethyl) ester	CHCl$_3$	263(3.74)	4-0589-80
	DMSO	334(3.87)	4-0589-80

Compound	Solvent	$\lambda_{max}(\log \epsilon)$	Ref.
$C_{21}H_{16}FeO_2$			
Ferrocene, 1,1'-[2-[(4-methylphenyl)-methylene]-1,3-dioxo-1,3-propane-diyl]-	dioxan MeOH	325(4.22) 330(--)	73-1290-80 73-1290-80
$C_{21}H_{16}FeO_3$			
Ferrocene, 1,1'-[2-[(4-methoxyphenyl)-methylene]-1,3-dioxo-1,3-propanediyl]-	dioxan MeOH	329(4.21) 335(--)	73-1290-80 73-1290-80
$C_{21}H_{16}N_2$			
Benzenamine, 4-methyl-N-(2-phenyl-3H-indol-3-ylidene)-	EtOH	435(3.65)	7-0009-80
1H-Benzimidazole, 2-(1,2-diphenyleth-enyl)-	MeCN	226(4.33),275(4.31), 305(4.22)	88-3751-80
1H-Pyrazole, 1,3,5-triphenyl-	C_6H_{12}	255(4.49)	23-1880-80
$C_{21}H_{16}N_2O$			
Anthracene, 10-diazo-9,10-dihydro-9-methoxy-9-phenyl-	ether	295(4.33)	28-0211-80B
Benzenamine, 4-methoxy-N-(2-phenyl-3H-indol-3-ylidene)-	MeOH	460(3.68)	7-0009-80
Benzo[a]furo[2,3-c]phenazine, 1,2-di-hydro-2-(1-methylethenyl)-	EtOH	225(4.51),239(4.62), 275(4.42),308(4.52), 335(3.53),350(3.59), 370(3.42),420(3.92)	2-0017-80
Benzoxazole, 5-methyl-2-[4-[2-(3-pyri-dinyl)ethenyl]phenyl]-	DMF	351(4.75)	33-1311-80
Benzoxazole, 6-methyl-2-[4-[2-(3-pyri-dinyl)ethenyl]phenyl]-	DMF	352(4.74)	33-1311-80
2(1H)-Naphthalenone, 1-[[(1-methyl-2(1H)-quinolinylidene)methyl]imino]-	EtOH benzene acetone CHCl_3	637(4.02) 639(--) 660(--) 665(--)	104-0185-80 104-0185-80 104-0185-80 104-0185-80
$C_{21}H_{16}N_2O_2$			
9,10-Anthracenedione, 1-amino-4-[(phen-ylmethyl)amino]-	MeOH	571(4.14),613(4.18)	18-3725-80
9,10-Anthracenedione, 1-(methylamino)-4-(phenylamino)-	C_6H_5Cl	<u>390(3.5),600(4.2), 645(4.2)</u>	104-2039-80
Benzoxazole, 5-methoxy-2-[4-[2-(3-pyri-dinyl)ethenyl]phenyl]-	DMF	356(4.73)	33-1311-80
4,8-Etheno-3H,8H-pyrazolo[1,5-c][1,3]-oxazepin-3-one, 3a,4-dihydro-2,3a-diphenyl-, (3aα,4α,8α)-	n.s.g.	402(3.58)	142-0373-80B
Methanone, (2-hydroxyphenyl)(7-methyl-3-phenylimidazo[1,2-a]pyridin-2-yl)-	EtOH	235(4.55),249(4.48), 352(3.93)	39-0354-80C
	EtOH-acid	225s(4.45),272(3.97), 315(3.85)	39-0354-80C
Methanone, (2-hydroxyphenyl)(8-methyl-3-phenylimidazo[1,2-a]pyridin-2-yl)-	EtOH	229s(4.47),247(4.38), 352(3.90)	39-0354-80C
	EtOH-acid	221s(4.42),272(3.97), 314(3.78)	39-0354-80C
$C_{21}H_{16}N_4O_3$			
1H-Benz[de]isoquinoline-1,3(2H)-dione, 2-[2-(1H-benzotriazol-1-yl)ethyl]-5-methoxy-	dioxan	246(3.46),288(3.76), 336(4.01),378(3.89)	56-0107-80
1H-Benz[de]isoquinoline-1,3(2H)-dione, 2-[2-(1H-benzotriazol-1-yl)ethyl]-6-methoxy-	dioxan	252(4.40),290(3.72), 363(4.13)	56-0107-80

Compound	Solvent	$\lambda_{max}(\log \epsilon)$	Ref.
1H-Benz[de]isoquinoline-1,3(2H)-dione, 2-[2-(2H-benzotriazol-2-yl)ethyl]-5-methoxy-	dioxan	240(4.25),282(4.10), 333(4.11),349(4.08)	56-0107-80
1H-Benz[de]isoquinoline-1,3(2H)-dione, 2-[2-(2H-benzotriazol-2-yl)ethyl]-6-methoxy-	dioxan	252(4.37),280(4.09), 362(4.14)	56-0107-80
$C_{21}H_{16}N_4O_3S$			
2H-1,4-Benzothiazin-2-one, 3-(4-methoxyphenyl)-, (4-nitrophenyl)hydrazone	CHCl_3	257(4.26),282(4.21), 353s(4.17),417(4.38)	39-2923-80C
$C_{21}H_{16}N_5O_4S_2$			
Thiazolo[3,2-a]pyridinium, 3-hydroxy-2-[[[(1-methylpyridinium-2-yl)thio]-[[(4-nitrophenyl)hydrazono]acetyl]-, hydroxide, inner salt, tetrafluoroborate	EtOH	420(4.27),480(4.20)	103-0227-80
$C_{21}H_{16}N_6O_3$			
1H-Benzimidazole, 2-[[(hydroxyimino)(4-nitrophenyl)methyl]azo]-1-(phenylmethyl)-	EtOH	388(4.00)	103-0857-80
$C_{21}H_{16}O_2$			
Tetracyclo[2.2.1.0^{2,6}.0^{3,5}]heptane, 2,3-dibenzoyl-	EtOH	243(4.39),280(3.64)	44-3782-80
$C_{21}H_{16}O_3$			
Azuleno[2,1-b]furan-9-carboxylic acid, 2-phenyl-, ethyl ester	MeOH	213(4.34),282(4.29), 320(4.78),335(4.76), 411(4.15),430(4.13), 550(2.89),572(2.90)	142-0835-80B
9,10-Epoxyanthracene-1,4-diol, 9,10-dihydro-9-(phenylmethyl)-	MeOH	301(3.65)	44-1817-80
9,10-Epoxyanthracene-1,4-dione, 4a,9,9a,10-tetrahydro-9-(phenylmethyl)-, (4aα,9α,9aα,10α)-	MeOH	227(4.01),257(3.23)	44-1817-80
$C_{21}H_{16}O_4$			
1,3-Azulenedicarboxylic acid, 2-(2-phenylethenyl)-, 3-methyl ester	MeOH	233(4.50),295(4.50), 338(4.71),404(4.20), 540(2.75)	18-3276-80
1,3-Benzodioxol-5-ol, 2,2-diphenyl-, acetate	EtOH	208(4.44),285(3.70)	12-0527-80
2H-Pyran-2-one, 3-(3-[1,1'-biphenyl]-4-y l-1-oxo-2-propenyl)-4-hydroxy-6-methyl-	MeOH	367(4.4)	83-0344-80
$C_{21}H_{16}O_5$			
5,12-Naphthacenedione, 8-ethyl-6,11-dihydroxy-1-methoxy-	MeOH	265(4.65),468(4.04), 496(4.24),531(4.21)	24-2976-80
5,12-Naphthacenedione, 9-ethyl-6,11-dihydroxy-1-methoxy-	MeOH	265(4.61),465(4.00), 495(4.21),531(5.31)	24-2976-80
$C_{21}H_{17}BrN_2$			
1H-1,5-Benzodiazepine, 2-(4-bromophenyl)-2,3-dihydro-4-phenyl-	EtOH	267(4.42),376(3.84)	103-0547-80
1H-1,5-Benzodiazepine, 4-(4-bromophenyl)-2,3-dihydro-2-phenyl-	EtOH	255(4.41),370(3.80)	103-0547-80

Compound	Solvent	$\lambda_{max}(\log \epsilon)$	Ref.
$C_{21}H_{17}BrN_2O$			
Benzo[a]furo[2,3-c]phenazine, 2-(1-bromo-1-methylethyl)-1,2-dihydro-	EtOH	225(4.49),237(4.58), 278(4.42),307(4.53), 350(3.68),370(3.56), 420(3.97)	2-0017-80
$C_{21}H_{17}ClN_2$			
1H-1,5-Benzodiazepine, 4-(4-chlorophenyl)-2,3-dihydro-2-phenyl-	EtOH	263(4.39),377(3.82)	103-0547-80
$C_{21}H_{17}ClO$			
1,4,6,8-Nonatetraen-3-one, 7-chloro-1,9-diphenyl-, (Z,?,E,?)-	EtOH	387(4.68)	40-1804-80
$C_{21}H_{17}N$			
1H-Benz[g]indole, 3-[2-(4-methylphenyl)-ethenyl]-, (E)-	EtOH	207(4.52),226(4.59), 277(4.50),323(4.47)	103-1048-80
1H-Indole, 2-phenyl-1-(phenylmethyl)-	EtOH	228(4.35),296(4.29), 306s(4.29)	104-0766-80
8H-Indolo[3,2,1-de]acridine, 8,8-dimethyl-	C_6H_{12}	212(4.63),250(4.72), 287s(4.41),294(4.48), 339(3.81),356(3.89)	24-0358-80
	EtOH	212(4.58),249(4.66), 286s(4.36),340(3.73), 352(3.76)	24-0358-80
Pyridine, 2,4-bis(2-phenylethenyl)-	DMF	299(4.65),311(4.65)	33-1311-80
Pyridine, 2,5-bis(2-phenylethenyl)-	DMF	361(4.74)	33-1311-80
Pyridine, 2,6-bis(2-phenylethenyl)-	DMF	293(4.60),345(4.40)	33-1311-80
Pyridine, 2-[2-[4-(2-phenylethenyl)-phenyl]ethenyl]-	DMF	359(4.78)	33-1311-80
Pyridine, 3-[2-[4-(2-phenylethenyl)-phenyl]ethenyl]-	DMF	357(4.79)	33-1311-80
Pyridine, 4-[2-[4-(2-phenylethenyl)-phenyl]ethenyl]-	DMF	357(4.78) 358(4.73)	33-1311-80 33-1311-80
$C_{21}H_{17}NO$			
2-Propen-1-one, 1,3-diphenyl-3-(phenylamino)-	EtOH	210(4.31),252(4.18), 380(4.37)	39-1870-80C
9H-Quino[3,2,1-kl]phenoxazine, 9,9-dimethyl-	C_6H_{12}	215(4.37),243s(4.35), 248(4.39),278(4.14), 310(4.08),337s(3.84)	24-0358-80
	EtOH	210(4.47),241s(4.30), 246(4.31),277(4.05), 309(4.00),334s(3.80)	24-0358-80
$C_{21}H_{17}NO_2$			
1H-Azuleno[2,1-b]pyrrole-9-carboxylic acid, 2-phenyl-, ethyl ester	MeOH	216(4.38),295(4.33), 345(4.83),451(4.03), 560(2.79)	142-0835-80B
$C_{21}H_{17}NO_2S$			
Benzene, 1-methyl-4-[(2-nitro-1,2-diphenylethenyl)thio]-, (Z)-	MeOH-pH 10.6	355(3.80)	28-0021-80A
Benzene, 1,1'-[1-nitro-2-[(phenylmethyl)thio]-1,2-ethenediyl]bis-, (Z)-	MeOH-pH 10.6	360(3.88)	28-0021-80A
$C_{21}H_{17}NO_3$			
Furo[2,3-c]pyridin-2(6H)-one, 3-(4-methoxyphenyl)-6-(phenylmethyl)-	EtOH	220(4.33),266(4.21), 400(4.53)	39-1176-80C
Furo[3,2-b]pyridin-2(4H)-one, 3-(4-methoxyphenyl)-4-(phenylmethyl)-	EtOH	212(4.16),264(4.40), 395(4.16)	39-1176-80C

Compound	Solvent	$\lambda_{max}(\log \epsilon)$	Ref.
$C_{21}H_{17}NO_3S$			
3H-Phenoxazin-3-one, 2-ethoxy-7-[(4-methylphenyl)thio]-	n.s.g.	467(4.45)	103-0032-80
$C_{21}H_{17}NO_4$			
Spiro[2H-indene-2,6'-[4aH,6H]pyrido-[1,2-a][3,1]benzoxazine]-1,3,7'(8'H)-trione, 9',10'-dihydro-3'-methyl-	MeCN	227(4.75),242s(4.37), 260s(4.29),348(4.14)	4-1577-80
Spiro[2H-indene-2,6'-[4aH,6H]pyrido-[1,2-a][3,1]benzoxazine]-1,3,7'(8'H)-trione, 9',10'-dihydro-4'-methyl-	MeCN	227(4.71),242s(4.33), 258s(4.22),352(4.14)	4-1577-80
$C_{21}H_{17}NO_6$			
Oxolirioferine acetate	EtOH	242(4.59),272(4.54), 286s(4.26),333(3.85), 376(3.79),430(3.77)	142-1131-80
$C_{21}H_{17}NS$			
9H-Quino[3,2,1-kl]phenothiazine, 9,9-dimethyl-	C_6H_{12}	212(4.47),240s(4.11), 255s(4.34),264(4.52), 294(4.21),310s(4.01)	24-0358-80
	EtOH	209(4.56),239s(4.15), 263(4.54),286(4.23)	24-0358-80
$C_{21}H_{17}N_2O$			
Pyridinium, 4-(1-benzoyl-1H-indol-2-yl)-1-methyl-, chloride	n.s.g.	215(3.85),238(3.02), 390(4.07)	103-0585-80
$C_{21}H_{17}N_3O$			
1-Naphthaleneacetic acid hydrazide, N -[(1H-indol-2-yl)methylene]-	C_6H_{12}	271(4.21),283(4.24), 309(4.38)	115-0151-80
	EtOH	271(4.29),283(4.29), 309(4.44)	115-0151-80
	50% EtOH	271(4.38),283(4.40), 313(4.59)	115-0151-80
4H-1,3,4,5-Oxatriazine, 4-(4-methylphenyl)-2,6-diphenyl-	EtOH	249(4.42),313(4.09), 402(3.51)	12-2447-80
2H-1,2,3-Triazole, 2-(4-methylphenyl)-4,5-diphenyl-, 1-oxide	MeCN	256(4.47),293s(4.15)	12-2447-80
$C_{21}H_{17}N_3OS$			
2H-1,4-Benzothiazin-2-one, 3-phenyl-, (4-methoxyphenyl)hydrazone	EtOH	235(4.24),280s(4.16), 308(4.18),335s(4.06), 438(4.02)	39-2923-80C
$C_{21}H_{17}N_3O_2$			
1H-1,5-Benzodiazepine, 2,3-dihydro-2-(4-nitrophenyl)-4-phenyl-	EtOH	264(4.43),364(3.75)	103-0547-80
1H-1,5-Benzodiazepine, 2,3-dihydro-4-(4-nitrophenyl)-2-phenyl-	EtOH	298(4.38),420(3.83)	103-0547-80
$C_{21}H_{17}N_3O_3$			
Acetamide, N-(11-cyano-4,7-dimethoxy-11H-indeno[1,2-c]isoquinolin-5-yl)-	EtOH	217(4.38),250(4.56), 279s(4.39),286(4.41), 325(4.18),384(4.23), 520(3.65)	18-2885-80
$C_{21}H_{17}N_3O_3S$			
4-Thiazolidinol, 4-(4-nitrophenyl)-3-phenyl-2-(phenylimino)-, mono-hydrobromide	MeOH	263(4.34)	78-2675-80

Compound	Solvent	$\lambda_{max}(\log \epsilon)$	Ref.
$C_{21}H_{17}N_3O_5S$ 4H-1,3,5-Oxadiazine-4-thione, 3-(2-fur- anylmethyl)-2,3-dihydro-2-(4-methoxy- phenyl)-6-(4-nitrophenyl)-	dioxan	238(4.44),288(4.43)	73-2254-80
$C_{21}H_{17}N_3S$ 4H-1,4-Benzothiazine, 4-methyl-3-phen- yl-2-(phenylazo)-	EtOH	232(4.21),276s(4.11), 315(4.24),505(4.17)	39-2923-80C
$C_{21}H_{17}N_5O$ 1H-Benzimidazole, 2-[[(hydroxyimino)- phenylmethyl]azo]-1-(phenylmethyl)-	50% EtOH	386(4.24)	103-0857-80
$C_{21}H_{17}N_5O_4$ 4,7-Etheno-1H-benzo[3,4]cyclobuta[1,2- c]pyrazole-5,6-dicarboxylic acid, 3a,3b,4,7,7a,7b-hexahydro-3-methyl- 1-(tricyanoethenyl)-, dimethyl ester, (3aα,3bβ,4aα,7α,7aβ,7bα)-	EtOH	370(4.34)	142-1115-80
$C_{21}H_{18}$ 1,6:8,17:10,15-Trismethano[18]annulene, syn-syn	C_6H_{12}	350(5.2),420(3.9), 620(2.3)	108-0215-80
$C_{21}H_{18}ClNO_2$ Cyclohepta[b]pyrrole-3-carboxylic acid, 2-chloro-8-[2-(4-methylphenyl)ethen- yl]-, ethyl ester	EtOH	226(4.41),236(4.41), 287s(4.40),297(4.41), 322s(4.31),403(4.43), 455s(3.78)	18-1406-80
$C_{21}H_{18}Cl_2$ Bicyclo[4.1.0]heptane, 7,7-dichloro- 3,4-bis(methylene)-2,5-diphenyl-, (1α,2α,5α,6α)-	pentane	243(3.92)	44-4183-80
$C_{21}H_{18}N_2$ 1-Azulenecarbonitrile, 2-[2-[4-(dimeth- ylamino)phenyl]ethenyl]-	MeOH	260(4.17),307(4.63), 357(4.45),490(4.57)	18-3276-80
1H-1,5-Benzodiazepine, 2,3-dihydro- 2,4-diphenyl-	EtOH	256(4.39),367(3.79)	103-0547-80
3H-Indole, 5-methyl-3-(1-methyl-4(1H)- pyridinylidene)-2-phenyl-	n.s.g.	426(4.65)	103-0743-80
$C_{21}H_{18}N_2O$ Phenanthridinium, 8-amino-5-ethyl-3-hy- droxy-6-phenyl-, hydroxide, inner salt	EtOH at -195°	299(4.6),340s(4.0), 540(3.7)	61-1129-80
	DMF	294(4.3),320(4.7), 378(4.1),400(3.4), 614(3.8)	61-1129-80
dication	EtOH	241(4.5),270(4.7), 325(3.8),340(3.8), 410(3.8),435(3.8)	61-1133-80
$C_{21}H_{18}N_2O_2$ 3,4-Diazatricyclo[4.2.1.0^{2,5}]non-7-ene, 3,4-dibenzoyl-	EtOH	275s(3.78)	23-1316-80
$C_{21}H_{18}N_2O_2S$ Thiazolo[3,2-a]pyridinium, 2-[(1-ethyl- 6-methyl-2(1H)-quinolinylidene)acet- yl]-3-hydroxy-, hydroxide, inner salt	EtOH	490(4.65),520(4.73)	103-0227-80

Compound	Solvent	$\lambda_{max}(\log \epsilon)$	Ref.
$C_{21}H_{18}N_2O_3S$			
4H-1,3,5-Oxadiazine-4-thione, 3-(2-fur-anylmethyl)-2,3-dihydro-2-(4-methoxy-phenyl)-6-phenyl-	dioxan	242(4.31),277(4.38)	73-2254-80
Thiazolo[3,2-a]pyridinium, 2-[1-ethyl-6-methoxy-2(1H)-quinolinylidene)-acetyl]-3-hydroxy-, hydroxide, inner salt	EtOH	500(4.62),530(4.70)	103-0227-80
$C_{21}H_{18}N_2O_5S$			
2(1H)-Pyrimidinone, 1-[2-(benzoyloxy)-1-[(benzoyloxy)methyl]ethyl]-3,4-di-hydro-4-thioxo-	pH 2	235(3.78),330(3.85)	103-0864-80
	pH 7	235(4.08),332(4.00)	103-0864-80
	pH 11	318(4.27)	103-0864-80
$C_{21}H_{18}N_2O_5S_2$			
4-Thia-1-azabicyclo[3.2.0]heptane-2-carboxylic acid, 7-oxo-3-[2-(phenyl-thio)ethylidene]-, (4-nitrophenyl)-methyl ester, (2α,3Z,5α)-(±)-	EtOH	253(4.28)	88-0561-80
$C_{21}H_{18}N_2O_6$			
Indeno[1,2-b]pyran-2-carboxylic acid, 4,5-dihydro-4-(tetrahydro-1,3-di-methyl-2,4,6-trioxo-5(2H)-pyrimi-dinylidene)-, ethyl ester	dioxan	330(4.24),463(4.47)	83-0557-80
$C_{21}H_{18}N_2O_8$			
Imidazo[1,2-a]pyridine-5,6,7,8-tetra-carboxylic acid, 3-phenyl-, tetra-methyl ester	EtOH	261(4.41),300s(3.69), 357(3.53)	18-3308-80
$C_{21}H_{18}N_3$			
Cyclopropenylium, tris(phenylamino)-, chloride	MeCN	270(4.41)	77-0223-80
$C_{21}H_{18}N_4$			
8(1H)-Cycloheptapyrazolone, 3-methyl-1-phenyl-, phenylhydrazone	MeOH	285s(4.06),384(4.32)	4-1293-80
8(2H)-Cycloheptapyrazolone, 3-methyl-2-phenyl-, phenylhydrazone	MeOH	236(4.45),298(4.29), 400(4.30)	4-1293-80
$C_{21}H_{18}N_4O_2$			
2H-Benzotriazole, 5,6-dimethoxy-2-[4-[2-(3-pyridinyl)ethenyl]phenyl]-	DMF	363(4.82)	33-1311-80
2H-Benzotriazole, 5-methoxy-2-(4-meth-oxyphenyl)-6-[2-(3-pyridinyl)ethenyl]-	DMF	367(4.57)	33-1311-80
4(1H)-Pyrimidinone, 5-ethyl-2-[(10-hy-droxy-9-phenanthrenyl)azo]-6-methyl-	EtOH	204(4.38),238(4.35), 290(4.10),467(4.09)	103-1279-80
$C_{21}H_{18}N_4O_3$			
4,8-Iminocyclohepta[c]pyrrole-1,3,5-(2H)-trione, 9-(4,6-dimethyl-2-pyri-midinyl)-3a,4,8,8a-tetrahydro-2-phenyl-	CHCl₃	242(4.32),280(3.70)	39-0331-80C
7(8H)-Pteridinone, 6-methyl-2,4-bis-(phenylmethoxy)-	pH 5.0	236(3.85),244s(3.81), 270s(3.75),313s(4.19), 321(4.20)	24-1535-80
	pH 10.0	246(4.05),266s(3.69), 315(4.20),325(4.25), 339(4.13)	24-1535-80

Compound	Solvent	$\lambda_{max}(\log \epsilon)$	Ref.
3H,5H,9H-Pyrimido[1,2,3-ij]pteridine-9,11(10H)-dione, 6,7-dihydro-3-hydroxy-2,3-diphenyl-	pH 0.0	260s(4.07),283(4.14), 400(4.08)	142-0437-80B
	pH 6.0	231(4.29),286(4.25), 350(4.09)	142-0437-80B
	pH 12.0	234s(4.20),287(4.17), 356(4.09)	142-0437-80B
$C_{21}H_{18}O$			
5H-Benzocycloheptene, 6,7-dihydro-9-(2-naphthalenyloxy)-	hexane	280s(--),292s(--), 314(3.16),320(3.11), 329(3.23)	118-0847-80
2,4,6,8,14,16,18-Cyclononadecaoctaene-10,12-diyn-1-one, 9,14-dimethyl-(E,E,Z,Z,E,E,E)-	THF	248(4.20),254(4.23), 260(4.23),278(4.25), 329(4.71),420s(3.79)	44-3564-80
	CF_3COOH	295s(--),302(--), 362s(--),410(--), 425(--),565s(--), 618(--),664(--)	44-3564-80
$C_{21}H_{18}O_2$			
Methanone, bicyclo[2.2.1]hept-2-ene-2,3-diylbis[phenyl-	MeOH	260(4.16)	44-3187-80
Spiro[2H-indene-2,3'(4'H)-[2H]naphtho-[2,3-b][1,4]dioxepin], 1,3-dihydro-	$CHCl_3$	243(4.49),275(3.92), 314(3.22),330(3.23)	49-0413-80
$C_{21}H_{18}O_4$			
2H,6H-Benzo[1,2-b:5m4-b']dipyran-6-one, 5-methoxy-2,2-dimethyl-8-phenyl-	n.s.g.	275(4.35),316(4.04)	102-0707-80
4H,8H-Benzo[1,2-b:3,4-b']dipyran-4-one, 5-methoxy-8,8-dimethyl-2-phenyl-	n.s.g.	269(4.07),335(3.10)	102-0707-80
4H-1-Benzopyran-4-one, 3-(2-benzofuranyl)-6-ethyl-7-methoxy-2-methyl-	EtOH	235(4.46),285(4.54)	103-0685-80
4H-1-Benzopyran-4-one, 7-[(1,1-dimethyl-2-propynyl)oxy]-5-hydroxy-3-methyl-2-phenyl-	MeOH	260(4.15),353(3.35)	2-0101-80
Pyrano[2",3":7,6]flavone, 5-hydroxy-3,6",6"-trimethyl-	MeOH	235(3.96),269(4.26), 358(3.39)	2-0101-80
Pyrano[2",3":7,8]flavone, 5-hydroxy-3,6",6"-trimethyl-	MeOH	235(4.20),272(4.31), 356(3.43)	2-0101-80
$C_{21}H_{18}O_5$			
5,12-Naphthacenedione, 2-acetyl-1,2,3-4-tetrahydro-11-hydroxy-7-methoxy-	$CHCl_3$	246(4.45),275s(--), 491(3.69)	35-5881-80
$C_{21}H_{18}O_7$			
Psorospermin acetate	EtOH	237(4.54),254(4.34), 287(3.95),307(4.17), 339(3.85)	100-0296-80
$C_{21}H_{18}O_8$			
Oruwacin	EtOH	205(4.05),241(4.08), 317s(3.84),348(4.13)	100-0649-80
$C_{21}H_{19}BrN_2O_3$			
Acetamide, N-(3-bromo-1,4-dihydro-1,4-dioxo-2-naphthalenyl)-N-[2-(methylphenylamino)ethyl]-	benzene	523(3.23)	104-0520-80
$C_{21}H_{19}ClN_4O_2$			
4H-[1,2,4]Triazolo[4,3-a][1,4]benzodi-	EtOH	223(4.58),250s(4.15),	87-0643-80

Compound	Solvent	$\lambda_{max}(\log \epsilon)$	Ref.
azepine-4-carboxylic acid, 8-chloro-1,4-dimethyl-6-phenyl-, ethyl ester		270(3.85),290(3.58)	87-0643-80
$C_{21}H_{19}Cl_2NO_2$ Methanone, [1-[(2,6-dichlorophenyl)-methyl]-6-ethoxy-1,6-dihydro-3-pyridinyl]phenyl-	CH_2Cl_2	290s(3.9),326(4.0)	5-1350-80
$C_{21}H_{19}Cl_2N_3O_2$ 3-Pyridinecarboxamide, 4-(benzoylamino)-1-[(2,6-dichlorophenyl)methyl]-1,4-dihydro-N-methyl-	CH_2Cl_2	335(4.0)	64-1431-80B
$C_{21}H_{19}Fe_2$ Methylium, diferrocenyl-, perchlorate	$CHCl_3$	358(5.09),618(5.04)	65-2039-80
$C_{21}H_{19}N$ Benzeneethanamine, α-phenyl-N-(phenylmethylene)-	EtOH	251(4.19)	104-0683-80
$C_{21}H_{19}NO$ Benzamide, N-(1,2-diphenylethyl)-, (-)-	EtOH	220(4.70),230(4.56), 294(3.10),308(3.04)	104-0683-80
$C_{21}H_{19}NO_4$ Phenol, 2-[4-(2-benzofuranyl)-3-methyl-5-isoxazolyl]-4-ethyl-5-methoxy-	EtOH	260(4.40),293(4.28)	103-0685-80
Phenol, 2-[4-(2-benzofuranyl)-5-methyl-3-isoxazolyl]-4-ethyl-5-methoxy-	EtOH	291(4.33),300(4.24)	103-0685-80
1H-Pyrrole-3,4-dicarboxylic acid, 2-phenyl-1-(phenylmethyl)-, dimethyl ester	CCl_4	266.5(3.95)	22-0552-80
$C_{21}H_{19}NO_5$ 1,3-Dioxolo[4,5-h]indeno[2,1-a][3]benz-azepin-12(5H)-one, 6,7-dihydro-10,11-dimethoxy-7-methyl-	EtOH	222s(4.46),311s(4.48), 322(4.58),497(3.36)	4-0417-80
1,3-Dioxolo[4,5-h]indeno[2,1-a][3]benz-azepin-13(6H)-one, 7,8-dihydro-10,11-dimethoxy-6-methyl-	EtOH	223(4.36),302s(4.44), 319(4.50),499(3.42)	4-0417-80
Methanone, [(5-acetoxymethyl)-2,3,3a,6a-tetrahydro-2-phenylfuro[2,3-d]isoxazol-3-yl]phenyl-, (3α,3aα,6aα)-	MeOH	245(4.42)	73-3546-80
13-Oxidonorcoralyne	EtOH	227(4.48),237s(4.45), 264(4.51),284(4.50), 296s(4.40),319(4.27), 408s(4.13),428(4.30), 453(4.38)	39-0919-80C
2H-Pyrano[3,2-c]quinoline-3-carboxylic acid, 5,6,7,8,9,10-hexahydro-2,5-dioxo-6-phenyl-, ethyl ester	EtOH	390(4.32)	49-0093-80
$C_{21}H_{19}NO_6$ 7H-Pyrano[2,3-c]acridin-7-one, 9(or 11)-acetoxy-3,12-dihydro-11(or 9)-hydroxy-6-methoxy-3,3-dimethyl-	MeOH	262(4.63),285s(--), 295s(--),320s(--), 390(3.74)	5-0503-80
$C_{21}H_{19}NO_7$ 6H-Benzo[g]-1,3-benzodioxolo[5,6-a]quinolizine-8,13-dione, 5,13a-dihydro-9,10,13a-trimethoxy-, (±)-	MeOH	236(4.38),262s(4.00), 290(3.99),324(3.85)	39-0919-80C

Compound	Solvent	$\lambda_{max}(\log \epsilon)$	Ref.
Benzoic acid, 2-[(6,7-dimethoxy-1-iso-quinolinyl)carbonyl]-4,5-dimethoxy-, hydrochloride	EtOH	234(4.34),262(4.07), 312(3.85),353(3.48)	39-0919-80C
$C_{21}H_{19}N_3O$ Pyrimido[4,5-b]quinolin-4(10H)-one, 10-butyl-2-phenyl-	EtOH	233(4.11),261(4.27), 271(4.27),288s(4.20), 300s(4.03),340(3.50), 404s(3.18),430(3.41), 451(3.44)	94-3514-80
$C_{21}H_{19}N_3O_2$ Pyrimido[4,5-b]quinoline-2,4(3H,10H)-dione, 10-butyl-3-phenyl-	EtOH	225(4.28),269(4.33), 313s(3.64),323(3.70), 378s(3.59),401(3.78), 418s(3.70)	94-3514-80
$C_{21}H_{19}N_3O_5S$ Naphtho[2',1':5,6]thiopyrano[4,3-c]-pyrazole-3(2H)-carboxamide, N,N,2-triacetyl-3a,11-dihydro-3a-hydroxy-	EtOH	· 227(4.46),264(4.29), 294(4.31)	4-0121-80
5-Thia-1,3-diazabicyclo[4.2.0]oct-2-ene-2-carboxylic acid, 8-oxo-7-[(phenoxyacetyl)amino]-, phenylmethyl ester	THF	242(3.65),332(2.70)	35-6171-80
$C_{21}H_{19}N_3O_6$ Pyrano[3,2-b]indole-2-carboxylic acid, 4,5-dihydro-5-methyl-4-(tetrahydro-1,3-dimethyl-2,4,6-trioxo-5(2H)-pyrimidinylidene)-, ethyl ester	dioxan	281(4.19),350(4.22), 514(4.47)	83-0557-80
$C_{21}H_{19}N_3O_8S$ 4-Thiazolidinecarboxylic acid, 2-[1-(1,3-dihydro-1,3-dioxo-2H-isoind-ol-2-yl)-2-[(1,3-dioxo-1-pyrrolidin-yl)oxy]-2-oxoethylidene]-5,5-dimethyl-	CHCl$_3$	291(4.42)	44-1481-80
$C_{21}H_{19}N_5O$ 1H-Imidazo[1,5-b]pyrazole-2,3-dicarbo-nitrile, hexahydro-4,4-dimethyl-6-oxo-1,3a-diphenyl-	EtOH	200(4.4),237(4.1), 276(3.7)	5-1016-80
$C_{21}H_{19}N_5O_3$ 1,3,7,8-Tetraazaspiro[4.5]deca-6,9-di-ene-10-carboxylic acid, 4-oxo-1-phenyl-2-(phenylimino)-, ethyl ester	DMSO	320(3.8)	39-1339-80B
$C_{21}H_{19}OS$ 5H-Cyclopenta[b]thiopyrylium, 6,7-di-hydro-2-(4-methoxyphenyl)-4-phenyl-, perchlorate	CH$_2$Cl$_2$	258(4.09),443(4.43)	104-0170-80
$C_{21}H_{20}$ Pyrene, 10b-(3-butenyl)-10b,10c-dihy-dro-10c-methyl-, trans	C$_6$H$_{12}$	237(3.76),275(2.83), 320(4.57),341(4.98), 345(4.02),358(4.52), 380(4.61),384(4.69), 415(3.62),439(3.58), 450(3.77),475(3.79),	44-2746-80

Compound	Solvent	$\lambda_{max}(\log \epsilon)$	Ref.
(cont.)		483(3.76),534(2.78), 574(2.76),590(2.79), 605(3.11),617(3.18), 634(3.27),651(3.30)	44-2746-80
$C_{21}H_{20}BNO$ Boron, [2-[(ethylimino)methyl]phenol- ato-N,O]diphenyl-, (T-4)-	CHCl₃	280(3.92),383(3.46)	49-0863-80
$C_{21}H_{20}BrN$ Benzenamine, 4-[4-(4-bromophenyl)- 1,3,6-cycloheptatrien-1-yl]-N,N- dimethyl-	heptane	206(--),253(--), 361(4.385)	97-0214-80
$C_{21}H_{20}ClN$ Benzenamine, 4-[4-(4-chlorophenyl)- 1,3,5-cycloheptatrien-1-yl]-N,N- dimethyl-	heptane	203(--),253(--), 358(4.423)	97-0214-80
$C_{21}H_{20}ClNO_2$ 2H-Pyran-2-one, 3-chloro-6-(1,1-dimeth- ylethyl)-4-(diphenylamino)-	EtOH	250(4.23),274(4.20), 347(4.14)	4-0507-80
$C_{21}H_{20}Cl_2N_2O_2$ Apovincamine, 14,15-dehydro-10,12-di- chloro-	EtOH	241(4.48),279(4.11), 316(3.85),327(3.97)	142-1915-80
$C_{21}H_{20}Cl_2N_4O_5$ 6H-1,2-Oxazin-5-amine, 3-(2,6-dichloro- phenyl)-N-(4-methoxy-3-nitrophenyl)- 6-(4-morpholinyl)-	MeOH	327(4.03),427(3.62)	150-0242-80S
$C_{21}H_{20}FN$ Benzenamine, 4-[4-(4-fluorophenyl)- 1,3,6-cycloheptatrien-1-yl]-N,N- dimethyl-	heptane	203(--),246(--), 354(4.371)	97-0214-80
$C_{21}H_{20}F_3N_2$ Quinolinium, 2-[2-[4-(dimethylamino)- phenyl]ethenyl]-1-methyl-4-(tri- fluoromethyl)-, perchlorate	MeCN	570(4.84)	124-0827-80
Quinolinium, 4-[2-[4-(dimethylamino)- phenyl]ethenyl]-1-methyl-2-(tri- fluoromethyl)-, perchlorate	MeCN	623(4.80)	124-0827-80
$C_{21}H_{20}NO$ Acridinium, 1,2,3,4-tetrahydro-3,3-di- methyl-1-oxo-10-phenyl-, perchlorate	n.s.g.	254(4.12),325(4.18)	104-1592-80
$C_{21}H_{20}N_2$ 3H-Pyrrolo[1,2-d][1,4]diazepine, 4,5- dihydro-3-methyl-1,8-diphenyl-	EtOH	256(4.33),287(4.17), 319(4.23)	39-1441-80B
	EtOH-acid	324(4.08),408(4.21)	39-1441-80B
$C_{21}H_{20}N_2O$ 1-Azulenecarboxamide, 2-[2-[4-(dimeth- ylamino)phenyl]ethenyl]-	MeOH	302(4.50),352(4.36), 468(4.44)	18-3276-80
1,4-Benzenediamine, N,N-dimethyl-N'- 3H-naphtho[2,1-b]pyran-3-yl-	MeOH	310(3.93),347(3.78), 410(3.80),547(3.04)	103-0799-80
	MeCN	312(3.97),340(3.86), 400(3.30)	103-0799-80

Compound	Solvent	$\lambda_{max}(\log \epsilon)$	Ref.
(cont.)	C_6H_5CN	313(3.93),350(3.79),	103-0799-80
	CCl_4	318(4.01),355(3.95)	103-0799-80
	DMSO	330(4.08),385(4.14), 498(4.36)	103-0799-80
	DMSO-NaOMe	370(4.14),495(4.49)	103-0799-80
$C_{21}H_{20}N_2OS$			
2(1H)-Quinazolinethione, 3-benzoyl-3,4,5,6,7,8-hexahydro-4-phenyl-	EtOH	237(4.08),280(4.01), 347(3.81)	114-0147-80B
$C_{21}H_{20}N_2O_3$			
Pyrazole, 3-acetyl-4-[2,2-bis(4-methoxyphenyl)ethenyl]-	EtOH	248(4.03),335(3.89)	78-1331-80
$C_{21}H_{20}N_3$			
Phenanthridinium, 3,8-diamino-5-ethyl-6-phenyl-, azide	pH 7	458(3.72)	69-3221-80
diazide	pH 7	432(3.77)	69-3221-80
bromide	pH 7	476(3.75)	69-3221-80
$C_{21}H_{20}N_3OS$			
Benzothiazolium, 2-[2-(2,3-dihydro-1,5-dimethyl-3-oxo-2-phenyl-1H-pyrazol-4-yl)ethenyl]-3-methyl-, perchlorate	HOAc	428(4.23)	48-0543-80
$C_{21}H_{20}N_3OSe$			
Benzoselenazolium, 2-[2-(2,3-dihydro-1,5-dimethyl-3-oxo-2-phenyl-1H-pyrazol-4-yl)ethenyl]-3-methyl-, perchlorate	HOAc	437(4.18)	48-0543-80
$C_{21}H_{20}N_3O_2$			
Benzoxazolium, 2-[2-(2,3-dihydro-1,5-dimethyl-3-oxo-2-phenyl-1H-pyrazol-4-yl)ethenyl]-3-methyl-, perchlorate	HOAc	408(4.63)	48-0543-80
$C_{21}H_{20}N_4O$			
2,4,6-Cycloheptatrien-1-one, 2-(2-phenylhydrazino)-7-[1-(phenylhydrazono)ethyl]-	MeOH	247(4.55),270s(4.33), 345(4.11),420(4.28)	4-1293-80
2-Naphthalenol, 1-[[2-methyl-1-(1-methylethyl)-1H-benzimidazol-7-yl]azo]-	EtOH	265(3.99),275(3.97), 287(3.85),333(3.60), 388s(3.43),428(3.59), 463s(3.53)	104-1458-80
$C_{21}H_{20}N_8$			
2,2a,4,5-Tetraazabenz[cd]azulene, 4,4'-methylenebis[3,4-dihydro-1-methyl-	MeOH	222(4.65),293(3.88), 370(4.29)	118-0331-80
$C_{21}H_{20}O$			
Isobenzofuran, 4,5,6,7-tetrahydro-4-methyl-1,3-diphenyl-	EtOH	240(2.23),330(2.54)	88-3717-80
Methanone, phenyl(3-phenylbicyclo[2.2.2]oct-2-en-2-yl)-	MeOH	230(3.91),247(4.11), 254(4.05),282(3.67)	44-3187-80
3,5,7,10,12,14,16-Nonadecaheptaene-1,8-diyn-9-one, 3,17-dimethyl-, (E,E,Z,Z,E,E,E)-	ether	232s(3.95),278s(4.18), 288s(4.25),390(4.66)	44-3564-80
$C_{21}H_{20}O_2$			
Bicyclo[3.1.0]hex-2-ene-6-carboxylic	EtOH	250(3.95)	35-5648-80

Compound	Solvent	$\lambda_{max}(\log \epsilon)$	Ref.
acid, 3-methyl-1,2-diphenyl-, methyl ester, (1α,5α,6α)- (cont.)			35-5648-80
2-Butenoic acid, 4-(1-methyl-2,3-di-phenyl-2-cyclopropen-1-yl)-, methyl ester	EtOH	223(4.37),318(4.44), 336(4.32)	35-5648-80
2-Butenoic acid, 4-(2-methyl-1,3-di-phenyl-2-cyclopropen-1-yl)-, methyl ester	EtOH	260(4.24)	35-5648-80
Cyclobuta[b]naphthalene-3,8-dione, 8a-ethyl-1,2,2a,8a-tetrahydro-1-methyl-1-phenyl-, (1α,2aβ,8aβ)-	CHCl$_3$	255(4.14),297(3.30), 308(3.25),340(2.43)	18-0757-80
Cyclobuta[b]naphthalene-3,8-dione, 1,2,2a,8a-tetrahydro-1,2a,8a-tri-methyl-1-phenyl-	CHCl$_3$	254(4.11),296(3.27), 330(2.36)	18-0757-80
Hydroperoxide, 1-methyl-1-[1,1':2',1"-terphenyl]-4'-ylethyl	EtOH	235(4.49),255(4.30)	18-3279-80
Methanone, bicyclo[2.2.1]heptane-2,3-diylbis[phenyl-, (2-endo,3-exo)	EtOH	210(3.76),248(4.39), 278(3.62)	44-3187-80
Tricyclo[2.2.0.0^{2,6}]hexane-3-carboxylic acid, 6-methyl-1,2-diphenyl-, methyl ester	EtOH	238(4.11)	35-5648-80
$C_{21}H_{20}O_3$			
Benzo[b]cyclopropa[d]pyrimidin-2(1H)-one, 1a-benzoyl-1-(1,1-dimethyleth-yl)-1a,7b-dihydro-, (1α,1aα,7bα)-	EtOH	250(4.17)	39-2937-80C
2H-Benzo[b]cycloprop[e]oxepin-2-one, 1a-benzoyl-1,1a,8,8a-tetrahydro-1,8,8-trimethyl-, (1R*,1aS*,8aR*)-	EtOH	247(4.18)	39-2937-80C
2H-1-Benzopyran-2-one, 7-methoxy-6-(3-methyl-4-phenyl-2-butenyl)-	EtOH	243(3.81),254(3.71), 300(3.85),330(4.14)	12-0395-80
4H-1-Benzopyran-4-one, 8-(1,1-dimethyl-2-propenyl)-7-hydroxy-3-methyl-2-phenyl-	MeOH	255(4.34),312(4.21)	2-0866-80
4H-1-Benzopyran-4-one, 8-(1,2-dimethyl-2-propenyl)-7-hydroxy-3-methyl-2-phenyl-	MeOH	255(4.32),311(4.20)	2-0866-80
1-Benzoxepin-2(5H)-one, 3-benzoyl-4-ethyl-5,5-dimethyl-	EtOH	245(4.07),255s(3.99), 283(3.80)	39-2937-80C
Bicyclo[2.2.1]heptane-1-carboxylic acid, 3-(phenoxyphenylmethylene)-, (1α,2α,3Z,4α)-	MeOH	229(4.06),260(4.13)	44-3782-80
4H-Furo[2,3-h]-1-benzopyran-4-one, 8,9-dihydro-2,8,9,9-tetramethyl-3-phenyl-	MeOH	244(4.44),304(4.03)	2-0866-80
4H-Furo[2,3-h]-1-benzopyran-4-one, 8,9-dihydro-3,8,8,9-tetramethyl-2-phenyl-	MeOH	260(4.38),315(4.23)	2-0866-80
4H-Furo[2,3-h]-1-benzopyran-4-one, 8,9-dihydro-3,8,9,9-tetramethyl-2-phenyl-	MeOH	260(4.41),315(4.23)	2-0866-80
Unknown compd., m. 184-6°	MeOH	258(4.36),315(4.19)	2-0866-80
$C_{21}H_{20}O_5$			
1,4-Anthracenediol, 5-methoxy-2,3-di-methyl-, diacetate	CH$_2$Cl$_2$	264(4.67),266(4.68), 357(3.71),364(3.69), 376(3.81),396(3.68)	23-1161-80
4H-1-Benzopyran-4-one, 2-(1,3-benzodi-oxol-5-yl)-2,3-dihydro-7-hydroxy-6-(3-methyl-2-butenyl)-	MeOH	235(4.01),285(3.82), 325(3.45)	102-1558-80

Compound	Solvent	$\lambda_{max}(\log \epsilon)$	Ref.
4H-1-Benzopyran-4-one, 2-(1,3-benzodi-oxol-5-yl)-2,3-dihydro-7-hydroxy-8-(3-methyl-2-butenyl)-	MeOH	240(3.80),285(3.76)	102-1558-80
4H-1-Benzopyran-4-one, 2-(1,3-benzodi-oxol-5-yl)-2,3-dihydro-7-[(3-methyl-2-butenyl)oxy]-	MeOH	235(4.24),280(4.25),310(3.94)	102-1558-80
Cyclohepta[de]naphthalene-8-carboxylic acid, 10-acetoxy-6-methoxy-7-methyl-, ethyl ester	CHCl₃	277(5.04),303(4.56)	120-0250-80
2-Propen-1-one, 3-hydroxy-1-(5-hydroxy-7-methoxy-2,2-dimethyl-2H-1-benzopyr-an-6-yl)-3-phenyl-, (Z)-	n.s.g.	272(4.20),295s(3.98),372(3.91)	102-0707-80
$C_{21}H_{20}O_6$			
9,10-Anthracenedione, 1-hydroxy-4,8-di-methoxy-2-(3-oxopentyl)-	MeOH	229(4.56),248(4.22),278(3.91),376(3.43),448(3.91),467(3.94),493(3.77)	24-2994-80
4H-1-Benzopyran-4-one, 3-(1,3-benzodi-oxol-5-ylmethyl)-5,7-dimethoxy-6,8-dimethyl-	EtOH	236(4.58),255s(4.38),285(4.06),308(3.91)	94-2487-80
Pyrano[3,2-a]xanthen-12(3H)-one, 5,9,11-trimethoxy-3,3-dimethyl-	MeOH	243(4.53),260(4.50),314(4.39),366(3.83)	39-2353-80C
$C_{21}H_{20}O_7$			
2H-1-Benzopyran-7-ol, 3-(3-acetoxy-2,4-dimethoxyphenyl)-, acetate (haginin A diacetate)	MeOH	237s(4.34),290(4.18),320(4.22)	94-1172-80
4H-1-Benzopyran-4-one, 7-acetoxy-3-(1,3-benzodioxol-5-ylmethyl)-2,3-dihydro-5-hydroxy-6,8-dimethyl-, (-)-	EtOH EtOH-AlCl₃	212(4.10),283(3.99) 319(--)	94-1477-80 94-1477-80
5,12-Naphthacenedione, 9t-ethyl-7,8,9,10-tetrahydro-6,7r,9c,11-tetrahydroxy-1-methoxy-	MeOH	232(4.46),247(4.32),287(3.82),477(3.98),493(4.00),527(3.77)	24-2976-80
5,12-Naphthacenedione, 9t-ethyl-7,8,9,10-tetrahydro-6,7r,9c,11-tetrahydroxy-4-methoxy-	MeOH	233(4.45),250(4.33),287(3.84),469(3.97),496(3.99),529s(3.74)	24-2976-80
$C_{21}H_{20}O_8$			
1-Propanone, 3-(4-acetoxyphenyl)-1-(2,4-diacetoxy-6-hydroxyphenyl)-	MeOH MeOH-AlCl₃	259(3.56),324s(3.03) 285(--)	100-0739-80 100-0739-80
$C_{21}H_{20}O_{10}$			
Isovitexin	EtOH	272(4.45),338(4.42)	36-0053-80
$C_{21}H_{20}O_{11}$			
Astragalin	EtOH MeOH-NaOMe	268(4.31),352(4.24) 276(4.45),327(4.19),401(4.44)	94-3137-80 94-3137-80
$C_{21}H_{20}O_{12}$			
Hyperin	MeOH	258(4.36),270s(4.30),300s(3.98),360(4.27)	100-0739-80
$C_{21}H_{20}S_2Sn$			
Stannanecarbodithioic acid, triphenyl-, ethyl ester	CHCl₃	314(3.70)	89-0220B-80
$C_{21}H_{21}IN_2O_3$			
Criocerine, 14-iodo-	MeOH	226(4.30),260(3.79),289(3.34)	78-0511-80

Compound	Solvent	λ_{max}(log ϵ)	Ref.
$C_{21}H_{21}N$			
Benzenamine, N,N-dimethyl-4-(4-phenyl-1,3,6-cycloheptatrien-1-yl)-	heptane	206(--),249(--), 351(4.367)	97-0214-80
Benz[f]isoquinoline, 1,2,3,4-tetrahydro-2,2-dimethyl-1-phenyl-	EtOH	228(4.83),280(3.81)	4-1563-80
$C_{21}H_{21}NO_2STe$			
Tellurilimine, Te,Te-bis(3-methylphenyl)-N-[(phenylmethyl)sulfonyl]-	MeOH	219(4.50),271(3.75)	104-2210-80
Tellurilimine, Te,Te-bis(4-methylphenyl)-N-[(phenylmethyl)sulfonyl]-	MeOH	244(4.23),267s(3.91)	104-2210-80
$C_{21}H_{21}NO_4$			
1,3-Dioxolo[4,5-h]indeno[2,1-a][3]benzazepine, 5,6,7,12-tetrahydro-10,11-dimethoxy-7-methyl-	EtOH EtOH-HCl	266(3.93),340(4.32) 239(4.15),316(4.10), 341(4.18)	4-0417-80 4-0417-80
1,3-Dioxolo[4,5]indeno[2,1-a][3]benzazepine, 6,7,8,13-tetrahydro-10,11-dimethoxy-6-methyl-	EtOH	263(4.00),344(4.34)	4-0417-80
Ochotensine	MeOH EtOH EtOH EtOH-dioxan	290(4.26) 226(4.49),285(4.18) 226(4.41),287(4.20) 284(4.04)	100-0305-80 100-0305-80 100-0305-80 100-0305-80
$C_{21}H_{21}NO_4STe$			
Tellurilimine, Te,Te-bis(4-methoxyphenyl)-N-[(phenylmethyl)sulfonyl]-	MeOH 75% H_2SO_4	250(4.24),273(4.32) 325(3.83),376(4.07)	104-2210-80 104-2210-80
$C_{21}H_{21}NO_5$			
Benzo[4,5]cyclohepta[1,2-b]pyrrolizine-1,12-dicarboxylic acid, 1,2,3,5,10-11-hexahydro-5-oxo-, 1-(1-methylethyl) ester	MeOH	217(4.16),232(4.19), 243(4.16),264(3.77), 324(4.18)	4-1081-80
Parfumidine	n.s.g.	235(4.46),263(4.14), 290s(--),360(3.40)	100-0305-80
$C_{21}H_{21}NO_6$			
Benzo[a]cyclopenta[g]quinolizine-9-carboxylic acid, 5,6,8,9,10,11-hexahydro-2,3-dimethoxy-8,11-dioxo-, ethyl ester, (±)-	EtOH	286(4.19),303s(4.14), 380(4.18)	142-1097-80B
Fumarofine, O-methyl-	EtOH	208(4.45),235(4.35), 259(3.96),286(3.37), 350(3.40)	100-0305-80
1H-Isoindol-1-one, 3-[(6-ethyl-4-methoxy-1,3-benzodioxol-5-yl)methylene]-2,3-dihydro-6,7-dimethoxy-, (Z)-	MeOH	220(4.48),269(4.17), 351(4.25)	73-2125-80
Raddeanone	EtOH	238(4.58),289(4.12), 313(4.06)	100-0305-80
Yenhusomidine, (-)-	EtOH	204(4.80),240(3.94), 291(3.91),313(3.99)	100-0305-80
Yenhusomidine, (±)-	EtOH	207(4.40),238(4.21), 290(3.74),314(3.72)	100-0305-80
$C_{21}H_{21}NO_7$			
Benzo[g]-1,3-benzodioxolo[5,6-a]quinolizin-8-one, 5,6,13,13a-tetrahydro-13-hydroxy-9,10,13a-trimethoxy-, cis-(±)-	MeOH	232s(4.28),290(3.82), 308s(3.36)	39-0919-80C
1H-Isoindol-1-one, 2,3-dihydro-3-	MeOH	218(4.83),296(3.90)	73-2125-80

Compound	Solvent	λ_{max}(log ϵ)	Ref.
[[6-(1-hydroxyethyl)-4-methoxy-1,3-benzodioxol-5-yl]methylene]-6,7-dimethoxy-, (E)- (cont.)			73-2125-80
C$_{21}$H$_{21}$NS$_2$			
2H-Thiopyran-2-thione, 6-(diethylamino)-3,5-diphenyl-	C$_6$H$_{12}$	232(4.16),265s(3.93), 349(3.84),499(3.73)	22-0530-80
	EtOH	230(4.36),347(3.97), 514(4.12)	22-0530-80
4H-Thiopyran-4-thione, 2-(diethylamino)-3,5-diphenyl-	C$_6$H$_{12}$	227(4.34),338(4.28), 456(3.79)	22-0530-80
	EtOH	224(4.36),329(4.18), 450(3.88)	22-0530-80
C$_{21}$H$_{21}$N$_2$OS$_2$			
Benzothiazolium, 2-[2-(methylthio)-2-[(1-oxo-3-phenyl-2-propenyl)imino]-ethyl]-, perchlorate	MeOH	233(4.84),279s(4.42), 455(4.54),525(4.16)	48-0434-80
C$_{21}$H$_{21}$N$_2$S$_2$			
Benzothiazolium, 3-ethyl-2-[3-(3-ethyl-2(3H)-benzothiazolylidene)-1-propenyl]-	60% EtOH	557(5.20)	104-2080-80
C$_{21}$H$_{21}$N$_3$			
1,3,5-Triazine, 1,3,5-triphenylhexahydro-	EtOH	280(3.25)	23-2477-80
C$_{21}$H$_{21}$N$_3$O$_2$			
1H-Isoindole-1,3(2H)-dione, 2-[4-(2-amino-1-methyl-1H-indol-3-yl)butyl]-, monohydrochloride	EtOH	219(4.72),261(3.87)	103-0368-80
C$_{21}$H$_{21}$N$_3$O$_3$			
2H-1,3-Benzoxazin-2-one, 4-[2,5-dihydro-3-methyl-5-oxo-1-(2-phenylethyl)-1H-pyrazol-4-yl]-3,4-dihydro-3-methyl-	EtOH	253(3.87)	4-0519-80
C$_{21}$H$_{22}$			
1-Butene, 3-methyl-3-(1-methyl-2,3-diphenyl-2-cyclopropen-1-yl)-	EtOH	230(4.26),323(4.41), 341(4.26)	35-5648-80
1-Butene, 3-methyl-3-(2-methyl-1,3-diphenyl-2-cyclopropen-1-yl)-	EtOH	263(4.13),268(4.15), 275(4.15)	35-5648-80
2-Butene, 3-methyl-1-(1-methyl-2,3-diphenyl-2-cyclopropen-1-yl)-	EtOH	230(4.23),238(4.15), 321(4.40),338(4.28), 238[sic](4.28)	35-5648-80
2-Butene, 3-methyl-1-(2-methyl-1,3-diphenyl-2-cyclopropen-1-yl)-	EtOH	264(4.18)	35-5648-80
C$_{21}$H$_{22}$BrNO$_2$			
7-Azabicyclo[4.3.1]deca-3,8-dien-10-one, 7-[3-(4-bromophenyl)-3-oxo-1-propenyl]-3,4,8-trimethyl-, (E)-	CHCl$_3$	265(4.39),360(4.60)	39-0362-80C
C$_{21}$H$_{22}$BrNO$_5$			
8H-Pyrano[2,3-h]quinoline-2-carboxylic acid, 3-(2-bromo-2-propenyl)-4,5-dimethoxy-8,8-dimethyl-, methyl ester	MeOH	265(4.67),385(3.57)	5-0503-80
C$_{21}$H$_{22}$NO$_3$P			
Phosphorin, 4-(acetylamino)-1,1-dihy-	C$_6$H$_{12}$	236(4.28),424(4.24)	24-3313-80

Compound	Solvent	$\lambda_{max}(\log \epsilon)$	Ref.
dro-1,1-dimethoxy-2,6-diphenyl-			24-3313-80
$C_{21}H_{22}N_2OS_2$			
Compd., m. 141°C.	EtOH	228(5.64),350(5.46)	1-0597-80
$C_{21}H_{22}N_2O_2$			
Strychnine	MeOH	253(4.08)	5-0895-80
$C_{21}H_{22}N_2O_3$			
Benzaldehyde, [6-(4-methoxyphenoxy)-3-	n.s.g.	227(4.26),338(4.66),	24-2579-80
oxo-1-cyclohexen-1-yl]methylhydrazone		354(4.67)	
Strychnine, 4-hydroxy-	MeOH	264(3.82),292(3.55)	5-0895-80
	MeOH-HCl	262(3.78),296(3.56)	5-0895-80
$C_{21}H_{22}N_2O_3S$			
Benzenesulfonamide, 4-methyl-N-(1,2,3a-	EtOH	205s(4.37),229(4.51),	39-2870-80C
4-tetrahydro-3a-methyl-5H,11H-furo-		247s(4.21),282(4.01),	
[2',3':2,3]pyrrolo[1,2-a]indol-11-		293s(3.86),380s(3.38),	
ylidene)-		420(3.70),450s(3.38)	
$C_{21}H_{22}N_2O_4$			
Strychnine, 4,16-dihydroxy-	MeOH	263(3.74),299(3.58)	5-0895-80
$C_{21}H_{22}N_2O_4S$			
4,5-Secoakuammilan-5,17-dioic acid,	EtOH	238(3.79),273(4.21)	22-0400-80
1,2-dihydro-2-hydroxy-4-(thioxo-			
methyl)-, 5,2-lactone, 17-methyl			
ester, (2α)-			
$C_{21}H_{22}N_2O_5$			
Glycine, N-[1-oxo-3-phenyl-2-[[(phenyl-	EtOH	272.5(4.20)	39-0858-80C
methoxy)carbonyl]amino]-2-propenyl]-,			
ethyl ester, (Z)-			
Indolizino[8,1-ef][1]benzazonine-7-car-	MeOH	221(4.10),277s(3.34)	78-0511-80
boxylic acid, 8a-ethyl-5,6,7,8,8a,9-			
10,11-octahydro-7-hydroxy-6-oxo-,			
methyl ester, 12-oxide			
4,5-Secoakuammilan-5,17-dioic acid,	EtOH	236(3.90),290(3.53)	22-0400-80
4-formyl-1,2-dihydro-2-hydroxy-,	EtOH-base	264(--)	22-0400-80
5,2-lactone, 17-methyl ester, (2α)-			
$C_{21}H_{22}N_2O_6$			
Fumschleicerine	EtOH	294(3.6),314(3.5)	102-2507-80
$C_{21}H_{22}N_3S_2$			
Benzothiazolium, 2-[2-amino-3-(3-ethyl-	60% EtOH	472(4.76)	104-2080-80
2(3H)-benzothiazolylidene)-1-propen-			
yl]-3-ethyl-, iodide			
$C_{21}H_{22}N_4$			
Piperidine, 1-[phenyl(2-quinolinylhy-	MeOH	260(4.27),370(3.94)	56-0661-80
drazono)methyl]-			
monohydriodide	MeOH	260(4.25),370(4.00)	56-0661-80
$C_{21}H_{22}N_4O$			
1H-Imidazo[1,5-b]pyrazole-3-carboni-	n.s.g.	198(4.6),217(4.1),	5-1016-80
trile, hexahydro-4,4-dimethyl-3a-(4-		241(4.1),270(3.6)	
methylphenyl)-6-oxo-1-phenyl-			
$C_{21}H_{22}N_8O_5$			
1H-Pyrrole-2-carboxamide, N-[5-[[(2-	DMF	298(4.18),348(4.11)	36-1334-80

Compound	Solvent	$\lambda_{max}(\log \epsilon)$	Ref.
cyanoethyl)amino]carbonyl]-1-methyl-1H-pyrrol-2-yl]-1-methyl-5-[[(1-methyl-5-nitro-1H-pyrrol-2-yl)-carbonyl]amino]- (cont.)			36-1334-80
C_{21}H_{22}O_2			
Benzenemethanol, α-(4-ethoxy-3-penten-1-ynyl)-4-methyl-α-phenyl-	EtOH	224(4.26),245(4.17)	78-1331-80
C_{21}H_{22}O_2S			
5(6H)-Benzocyclooctenone, 7,8-dihydro-9-[(4-methoxyphenyl)thio]-7,7-dimethyl-	EtOH	235(4.40),257(4.27),284(3.97),349(3.91)	44-0240-80
5(6H)-Benzocyclooctenone, 7,10-dihydro-9-[(4-methoxyphenyl)thio]-7,7-dimethyl-	EtOH	237(4.30)	44-0240-80
Cyclobuta[a]naphthalen-8b(1H)-ol, 2,2a-dihydro-3-[(4-methoxyphenyl)-thio]-2,2-dimethyl-	EtOH	232(4.42),288s(4.14),298(4.18),310s(4.12),320s(4.06)	44-0240-80
2-Propanone, 1-(dihydro-5-hydroxy-3,5-dimethyl-3-phenyl-2(3H)-thienylidene)-1-phenyl-	n.s.g.	297(3.47)	18-1763-80
C_{21}H_{22}O_3			
Benzenemethanol, α-(4-ethoxy-3-penten-1-ynyl)-4-methoxy-α-phenyl-	EtOH	232(4.34)	78-1331-80
5(6H)-Benzocyclooctenone, 7,8-dihydro-9-(4-methoxyphenoxy)-7,7-dimethyl-	EtOH	242(4.39),273(4.04),334(3.77)	44-0240-80
Cyclobuta[a]naphthalen-8b(1H)-ol, 2,2a-dihydro-3-(4-methoxyphenoxy)-2,2-dimethyl-	EtOH	224(4.37),229s(4.31),276(4.18),282s(4.17),300s(3.71),310s(3.52)	44-0240-80
1,4-Naphthalenedione, 3-[2,2-bis(2-methylcyclopropyl)ethenyl]-2-methoxy-	EtOH	256s(4.04),274(4.13),326(3.32),427(3.18)	18-0567-80
C_{21}H_{22}O_4			
1,3-Azulenedicarboxylic acid, 6-ethynyl-5-(1-methylethyl)-, diethyl ester	C_6H_{12}	240(4.66),275(4.40),318s(4.83),323(4.91),354(4.16),383(3.97),549(2.89),585(2.83),645(2.44)	18-1647-80
2H-1-Benzopyran-2-one, 8-[3-(4-hydroxyphenyl)-3-methylbutyl]-7-methoxy-	EtOH	209(4.47),258(3.95),324(4.17)	2-0341-80
	EtOH-NaOH	214(4.08),242(4.04),324(4.10)	2-0341-80
4H-1-Benzopyran-4-one, 2,3-dihydro-5-hydroxy-7-methoxy-8-(3-methyl-2-butenyl)-2-phenyl-	MeOH	240s(4.11),292(4.19),343(3.41)	102-1267-80
Bergaptin	EtOH	222(4.39),244s(4.20),251(4.25),260(4.20),269(4.19),310(4.14)	94-1847-80
7H-Furo[3,2-g][1]benzopyran-7-one, 4-[(3,7-dimethyl-2,6-octadienyl)oxy]-, (E)-	EtOH	218(4.48),245s(4.38),250(4.40),265s(4.17),301(4.11)	94-1847-80
C_{21}H_{22}O_5			
9(10H)-Anthracenone, 1,4,5-trimethoxy-2-methyl-10-(2-oxopropyl)-	CHCl_3	281(4.04),330(3.64)	44-0012-80
1,3-Benzenediol, 4-(3,4-dihydro-8,8-dimethyl-2H,8H-benzo[1,2-b:3,4-b']dipyran-3-yl)-2-methoxy-, (R)- (3'-methoxyglabridin)	MeOH	280(3.98),289s(3.89),311(3.36)	100-0259-80

$C_{21}H_{22}O_5-C_{21}H_{22}O_{10}$

Compound	Solvent	$\lambda_{max}(\log \epsilon)$	Ref.
6-Benzofuranol, 2-(2-hydroxy-4-methoxy-phenyl)-3-methoxy-5-(3-methyl-2-but-enyl)- (ambofuranol)	MeOH	220(3.96),274(4.10), 300(4.41),327(3.87)	88-4535-80
6H-Benzofuro[3,2-c][1]benzopyran-3,6a(1aH)-diol, 9-methoxy-10-(3-methyl-2-butenyl)-, (6aS-cis)-	MeOH	215(4.46),280(3.88), 286s(--)	142-1163-80B
4H-1-Benzopyran-4-one, 5,7-dimethoxy-3-[(4-methoxyphenyl)methyl]-6,8-di-methyl-	EtOH	230(4.55),235(4.55), 250s(3.93),284(3.89), 310(3.83)	94-2487-80

$C_{21}H_{22}O_6$

Compound	Solvent	$\lambda_{max}(\log \epsilon)$	Ref.
9,10-Anthracenedione, 3c-(1-hexynyl)-1,2,3,4-tetrahydro-3t,5,8-trihydroxy-1r-methoxy-	MeOH	215(4.15),277(3.86), 475(3.75),508(3.79), 548(3.55)	24-2976-80
9,10-Anthracenedione, 3t-(1-hexynyl)-1,2,3,4-tetrahydro-3c,5,8-trihydroxy-1r-methoxy-	MeOH	215(4.52),280(3.83), 480(3.78),509(3.82), 549(3.59)	24-2976-80
1,3-Benzodioxole, 5-[4-(3,4-dimethoxy-phenyl)tetrahydro-1H,3H-furo[3,4-c]-furan-1-yl]-	EtOH	203(4.98),232(4.18), 283(3.84)	78-3551-80
4H-1-Benzopyran-4-one, 7-acetoxy-2,3-dihydro-5-hydroxy-3-[(4-methoxyphen-yl)methyl]-6,8-dimethyl-	EtOH EtOH-AlCl$_3$	224(4.41),278(4.21) 318(--)	94-1477-80 94-1477-80
Croverin	MeOH	211(4.13),283(3.20)	77-0920-80
1,4-Ethanoanthracene-9,10-dione, 5-acetoxy-8-ethoxy-1,4,4a,9a-tetra-hydro-1-methoxy-	MeOH	233(3.98),335(3.31)	24-1575-80
Fargesin	EtOH	203(4.99),232(4.18), 282(3.90)	78-3551-80
4,6-Heptadien-3-one, 5-hydroxy-1,7-bis(4-hydroxy-3-methoxyphenyl)-	EtOH	250(4.10),260s(--), 280(3.84),305(3.73), 375(4.39)	102-2031-80
Naphtho[2,3-c]furan-1(3H)-one, 4-(3,4-dimethoxyphenyl)-3a,4,9,9a-tetra-hydro-6-hydroxy-7-methoxy-	EtOH	230s(4.21),263(3.74), 282(3.85)	94-0850-80

$C_{21}H_{22}O_7$

Compound	Solvent	$\lambda_{max}(\log \epsilon)$	Ref.
1,4-Benzodioxin-2-methanol, 3-(4-acet-oxy-3-methoxyphenyl)-2,3-dihydro-6-methyl-, acetate, trans	EtOH	275s(3.74),281(3.80), 287s(3.59)	39-0775-80C

$C_{21}H_{22}O_8$

Compound	Solvent	$\lambda_{max}(\log \epsilon)$	Ref.
4-Cyclohexene-1,3-dione, 4-acetyl-2-[(5-acetyl-2,4-dihydroxy-3,3-dimeth-yl-6-oxo-1,4-cyclohexadien-1-yl)meth-ylene]-5-hydroxy-6,6-dimethyl-	EtOH CHCl$_3$	300(4.17),490(4.85) 350(4.33)	18-0289-80 18-0289-80

$C_{21}H_{22}O_9$

Compound	Solvent	$\lambda_{max}(\log \epsilon)$	Ref.
4H-1-Benzopyran-4-one, 2,3-dihydro-5,6,7,8-tetramethoxy-2-(7-methoxy-1,3-benzodioxol-5-yl)-	EtOH	277(4.27),332(3.71)	102-2439-80
4H-1-Benzopyran-4-one, 2-(4-hydroxy-3,5-dimethoxyphenyl)-3,5,6,7-tetra-methoxy-	MeOH	262(4.06),268s(4.03), 323(4.27),345s(4.18)	102-2794-80

$C_{21}H_{22}O_{10}$

Compound	Solvent	$\lambda_{max}(\log \epsilon)$	Ref.
1,3-Benzodioxole-5-carboxylic acid, 7-methoxy-, 2-acetyl-3,4,5,6-tetra-methoxyphenyl ester	MeOH	277(4.128)	102-0669-80

Compound	Solvent	$\lambda_{max}(\log \epsilon)$	Ref.
$C_{21}H_{23}ClN_2O_3$			
Eburnamenine-14-carboxylic acid, 10-chloro-17,18-didehydro-14,15-dihydro-14-hydroxy-, methyl ester, (3α,14β-16α)-	EtOH	232(4.41),282(3.76), 289(3.75),300(3.58)	142-1915-80
$C_{21}H_{23}ClN_5O_6PS$			
9H-Purine, 8-[(4-chlorophenyl)thio]-9-(3,5-O-phosphinico-β-D-ribofurano-syl)-6-piperidino-	pH 1 pH 11	294(4.27) 305(4.20)	87-0242-80 87-0242-80
$C_{21}H_{23}ClO_7$			
Benzoic acid, 3-chloro-2-hydroxy-4-methoxy-6-propyl-, 4-carboxy-3-hy-droxy-5-propylphenyl ester	MeOH	220(4.70),275(4.35), 305(4.15)	102-0645-80
$C_{21}H_{23}NO_4$			
1H-Indole-2,3-dione, 6,7-dimethoxy-4-(5-phenylpentyl)-	EtOH	<u>253(4.1),345(3.9)</u>	78-2441-80
$C_{21}H_{23}NO_5$			
Benzenepropanoic acid, 4-methoxy-2-[3-(4-methoxyphenyl)-1-oxo-2-prop-enyl]amino]-, methyl ester, cis	MeOH	205(4.59),275(4.47)	102-2125-80
trans	MeOH	205(4.65),288(4.57)	102-2125-80
Fagarine isomer	EtOH	288(3.99)	142-0011-80
Fumaricine	EtOH	207(4.74),235(3.94), 288(3.74)	100-0305-80
	EtOH	286(3.81)	100-0305-80
Fumaritridine	CHCl	215(3.73),230(3.70), 285(3.48)	100-0305-80
3(2H)-Isoquinolinone, 4-[(3,4-dimeth-oxyphenyl)methyl]-6,7-dimethoxy-2-methyl-, hydrochloride	EtOH	256(4.73)	39-2013-80C
$C_{21}H_{23}NO_6$			
Benzo[a]cyclopenta[g]quinolizine-9-car-boxylic acid, 5,6,8,9,10,11-hexahy-dro-11-hydroxy-2,3-dimethoxy-8-oxo-, ethyl ester	EtOH	269(3.95),348(4.39)	142-1097-80B
Methanone, (3,4-dihydro-6,7-dimethoxy-1-isoquinolinyl)[2-(hydroxymethyl)-4,5-dimethoxyphenyl]-	EtOH	234(4.10),283(3.97), 316(3.78)	73-0956-80
Yenhusomine	EtOH	241(4.11),288(3.85)	100-0305-80
$C_{21}H_{23}NO_7$			
Clivacetine	n.s.g.	<u>205(4.3),225(4.4), 266(3.9),306(3.8)</u>	94-1827-80
$C_{21}H_{23}NS$			
2-Azetidinethione, 3-(1,1-dimethyl-2-propenyl)-4-phenyl-1-(phenylmethyl)-	isooctane	273(4.2),330(2.0)	24-3024-80
2H-Azeto[2,1-a]isoquinoline-2-thione, 1-(1,1-dimethylethyl)-1,4,5,9b-tetrahydro-1-phenyl-, trans	isooctane	283(3.1),355(1.7)	24-3010-80
$C_{21}H_{23}N_2O$			
7-Aza-6-azoniabicyclo[3.2.0]hept-2-ene, 3,5,6,6-tetramethyl-4-oxo-1,2-diphen-yl-, iodide	EtOH	300(3.91)	23-1316-80

Compound	Solvent	$\lambda_{max}(\log \epsilon)$	Ref.
$C_{21}H_{23}N_2S$			
Thiazolium, 2-[2-[4-(dimethylamino)-phenyl]ethenyl]-3-ethyl-4-phenyl-, iodide	EtOH	490(3.93)	49-0657-80
	EtOH	220(4.53),276s(--), 490(4.51)	49-1213-80
	DMF	275s(--),486(4.64)	49-1213-80
	DMSO	275(4.28),487(4.51)	49-1213-80
	CHCl₃	244(4.38),278s(--), 505(4.67)	49-1213-80
$C_{21}H_{23}N_3O_2$			
Benzoic acid, 4-[[2-(1,1-dimethyleth-yl)-2H-isoindol-1-yl]azo]-, ethyl ester	CH₂Cl₂	260(3.86),295(3.98), 492(4.59)	89-0320-80
$C_{21}H_{23}N_3O_4$			
2H-1,3-Benzoxazine-4-acetic acid, 3,4-dihydro-α-[1-[(2-aminophenyl)amino]-ethylidene]-3-methyl-2-oxo-, ethyl ester	EtOH	222s(4.39),290(4.12)	4-0519-80
2H-1,3-Benzoxazine-4-acetic acid, 3,4-dihydro-α-[1-[(2-aminophenyl)imino]-ethyl]-3-methyl-2-oxo-, ethyl ester	EtOH	220s(4.39),289(4.13)	4-0519-80
Eburnamenine-14-carboxylic acid, 10-nitro-, methyl ester	EtOH	262(4.23),292(4.24), 330(4.02)	142-1915-80
$C_{21}H_{23}N_5O$			
5H-Naphth[2',1':4,5]indeno[1,2-d]tetra-zolo[1,5-a]pyrimidine, 4b,6,6a,13-13a,13b,14,15-octahydro-2-methoxy-6a-methyl-, [4bS-(4bα,6aβ,13aα,13bβ)]-	MeOH	213(4.15),243(4.11), 311(4.06)	39-1019-80C
$C_{21}H_{23}N_7O_6$			
L-Glutamic acid, N-[4-[[(2,4-diamino-1,5-dihydro-5-oxopyrido[2,3-d]pyri-midin-6-yl)methyl]methylamino]benz-oyl]-	pH 1	257(4.60),298(3.87)	44-3746-80
	pH 7	253(4.37),304(4.46)	44-3746-80
	pH 11	257(4.38),307(4.45)	44-3746-80
$C_{21}H_{24}$			
Bicyclo[2.2.2]octane, 1-(1-naphthal-enyl)-4-(1-propenyl)-, cis	4:1 C₆H₁₁Me-isopentane	251s(3.34),261(3.63), 269(3.84),280(3.93), 286(3.75),291(3.76), 300s(2.97),311(2.60)	44-3933-80
trans	EtOH	252s(3.34),262s(3.63), 271(3.83),281(3.91), 288(3.74),292(3.74), 302s(2.97),312(2.61)	44-3933-80
$C_{21}H_{24}BrNO_5$			
4H-Pyrano[2,3-h]quinolin-4-one, 3-(2-bromo-2-propenyl)-2-(dimethoxymeth-yl)-1,8-dihydro-5-methoxy-8,8-di-methyl-	MeOH	282(4.47),342(3.75), 375(4.47)	5-0503-80
$C_{21}H_{24}ClNO_3$			
4H-Dibenzo[de,g]quinolin-11-ol, 6-[2-(2-chloroethoxy)ethyl]-5,6,6a,7-tetrahydro-10-methoxy-	EtOH	276(4.38),310(3.81)	87-1008-80
$C_{21}H_{24}N$			
2-Naphthalenemethanaminium, N,N,N,3-	EtOH	234(4.89),275s(3.71),	39-1477-80C

Compound	Solvent	$\lambda_{max}(\log \epsilon)$	Ref.
tetramethyl-1-phenyl-, iodide (cont.)		286(3.84),295(3.79), 320(3.29),334(3.37)	39-1477-80C
2-Naphthalenemethanaminium, N,N,N,3-tetramethyl-4-phenyl-, iodide	EtOH	233(4.91),252s(3.76), 275s(3.76),284(3.85), 294s(3.80),316(3.26), 331(3.35),353(2.38)	39-1477-80C
$C_{21}H_{24}NO_4$			
Eschscholtzidine, N-methyl-, chloride	MeOH	230s(3.91),257(3.46), 289(3.74)	100-0270-80
$C_{21}H_{24}N_2OS$			
Aspidospermidine-8-thione, 1-acetyl-2,3-didehydro-, (±)-	EtOH	223(4.19),272(4.37)	4-1133-80
$C_{21}H_{24}N_2O_2$			
Retulinal	MeOH	212(4.4),251(4.07), 282(3.46)	88-2439-80
$C_{21}H_{24}N_2O_2S$			
1-Naphthalenesulfonamide, 5-(dimethyl-amino)-N-(1-methyl-2-phenylethyl)-, (S)-(+)-	EtOH-HCl	278(3.77),288(3.84), 298(3.72),320(3.26)	87-0282-80
$C_{21}H_{24}N_2O_3$			
Akuammidine	n.s.g.	226(4.49),275s(3.80), 281(3.81),292(3.75)	64-0885-80B
Coronaridine, 19-hydroxy-	MeOH	228(4.41),285(3.90), 292(3.60)	102-2185-80
Coronaridine lactam	MeOH	225(4.50),285(3.90), 293(3.84)	102-2185-80
Criocerine, 3,14-dihydro-	MeOH	228(4.24),271(3.71), 283(3.62),295(3.34)	78-0511-80
14,15-Dehydrovincamine	EtOH	228(4.30),275(3.97), 282(3.80),290(3.70)	78-0511-80
Isoretulinal, 16-hydroxy- (same spectrum in acid or base)	MeOH	210(4.34),251(4.09), 283(3.59),292(3.51)	102-1531-80
Modestanine	EtOH	230(3.93),298(3.93), 329(4.09)	102-1473-80
Pleiocarpamine, 10-methoxy-	MeOH	230(4.4),283(3.8)	102-0307-80
Raucaffrinoline	n.s.g.	222(4.25),228(4.15), 260(3.66)	102-0989-80
Retulinal, 12-hydroxy-	MeOH	217(4.05),252(3.45), 288(3.08)	88-2439-80
	MeOH-base	221(3.96),306(3.24)	88-2439-80
Δ^{14}-Vincamine	MeOH	225(4.46),273(3.92), 284(3.90),290(3.72)	56-2397-80
$C_{21}H_{24}N_2O_3S$			
1-Naphthalenesulfonamide, 5-(dimethyl-amino)-N-[1-(hydroxymethyl)-2-phen-ylethyl]-, (R)-	EtOH-HCl	278(3.71),290(3.82), 302(3.71),322(3.22)	87-0282-80
$C_{21}H_{24}N_2O_4$			
Indolizino[8,1-ef][1]benzazonine-7-carboxylic acid, 8a-ethyl-5,6,7,8,8a,9,10,11-octahydro-7-hy-droxy-6-oxo-, methyl ester	MeOH	219(3.90),267s(3.20)	78-0511-80
$C_{21}H_{24}N_2O_4S$			
Benzenesulfonamide, N-(1,2,3a,4,5,10c-	EtOH	205(4.47),232(4.16),	39-2870-80C

Compound	Solvent	$\lambda_{max}(\log \epsilon)$	Ref.
hexahydro-10c-hydroxy-3a-methyl-10bH-benzo[b]pyrano[2,3,4-gh]pyrrolizin-10b-yl)-4-methyl- (cont.)		225s(3.87),302(3.46)	39-2870-80C
$C_{21}H_{24}N_2O_5S$ Carbamic acid, [4-[[4-[(4-methoxyphenyl)imino]-3-methyl-2-pentenyl]sulfonyl]phenyl]-, methyl ester	EtOH	234(4.81)	104-0849-80
$C_{21}H_{24}N_2O_5S_2$ 2-Pentenedioic acid, 3-[[4-amino-5-benzoyl-2-(methylthio)-3-thienyl]amino]-, diethyl ester	EtOH	279(4.39),368(4.32)	95-0699-80
$C_{21}H_{24}N_2O_6$ 2H-Isoindole-2-acetic acid, 1,3-dioxo-α-[4-(methoxycarbonyl)-5,5-dimethyl-2-thiazolidinylidene]-, 1,1-dimethylethyl ester	CHCl$_3$	284(4.09)	44-1481-80
$C_{21}H_{24}N_2O_7$ 1,1-Cyclohexanedicarboxylic acid, 3-(aminocarbonyl)-4-(1,3-dihydro-1,3-dioxo-2H-isoindol-2-yl)-, diethyl ester, trans	EtOH	222(4.64)	23-1860-80
$C_{21}H_{24}N_2O_9$ 1H-Pyrrolo[1,2-a]indole-9-carboxylic acid, 1-acetoxy-2-[(ethoxycarbonyl)-methylamino]-2,3,5,8-tetrahydro-7-methoxy-6-methyl-5,8-dioxo-, methyl ester, trans-(±)-	MeOH	211(4.28),244(4.28), 286(4.10),324s(3.73), 410(2.90)	39-1607-80C
$C_{21}H_{24}N_3O_2$ 1H-Isoindolium, 2-(1,1-dimethylethyl)-1-[[4-(ethoxycarbonyl)phenyl]hydrazono]-, tetrafluoroborate	MeOH-HClO$_4$	266(4.39),464(3.82)	89-0320-80
$C_{21}H_{24}N_4O_2$ 4H-Imidazol-4-one, 1,5-dihydro-2-[4-(2-hydroxyethyl)-1-piperazinyl]-5,5-diphenyl-	EtOH	221.4(4.47)	56-2217-80
$C_{21}H_{24}N_4O_3$ 6H-1,2-Oxazine-5,6-diamine, N^6,N^6-dimethyl-N^5-(4-nitrophenyl)-3-(2,4,6-trimethylphenyl)-	MeOH	244(3.98),286(3.89), 386(4.31)	150-0242-80S
$C_{21}H_{24}N_4O_6$ Vincadifformine, 1,2-dehydro-2,16-dihydro-10,16-dinitro-	EtOH	300(4.06)	142-1915-80
$C_{21}H_{24}N_4O_8$ L-Tryptophan, 2-(1,2,3,4-tetrahydro-2,4-dioxo-1-β-D-ribofuranosyl-5-pyrimidinyl)-, methyl ester	EtOH	268(3.66),292(3.55), 326s(3.32)	35-7535-80
$C_{21}H_{24}O_2$ 1,1'-Spirobi[1H-indene]-4,4'-diol, 2,2',3,3'-tetrahydro-5,5',7,7'-tetramethyl-	EtOH	207(4.93),231s(4.34), 277s(3.53),285(3.59)	138-0743-80

Compound	Solvent	$\lambda_{max}(\log \epsilon)$	Ref.
$C_{21}H_{24}O_4$ [1,1'-Biphenyl]-2-ol, 2',3,3'-trimeth- oxy-5,5'-di-2-propenyl-	MeOH	270s(3.62),283(3.81)	102-0681-80
$C_{21}H_{24}O_5$ Eusiderin D	MeOH	219(4.53),232s(4.39), 276(3.73)	102-1523-80
$C_{21}H_{24}O_6$ Bicyclo[3.2.1]octan-3-one, 2-acetoxy- 7-(1,3-benzodioxol-5-yl)-8-hydroxy- 6-methyl-5-(2-propenyl)-, [1S- (2-endo,6-endo,7-exo,8-anti)]-	MeOH	235(3.66),287(3.61)	102-0474-80
Tricyclo[12.3.1.1^{2,6}]nonadeca-1(18),2- 4,6(19),14,16-hexaen-7-one, 3,9,15- trihydroxy-16,17-dimethoxy-, (R)-	MeOH	224(4.23),262(4.24), 281s(4.01)	102-0705-80
$C_{21}H_{24}O_7$ 2(3H)-Furanone, 4-[(3,4-dimethoxyphen- yl)hydroxymethyl]dihydro-3-[(4-hy- droxy-3-methoxyphenyl)methyl]-, (5-hydroxyarctigenin)	EtOH	232(4.16),281(3.81)	94-0850-80
2-Propenoic acid, 5-acetoxy-6-formyl- 2,3,3a,4,5,8,9,11a-octahydro-10-meth- yl-3-methylene-2-oxocyclodeca[b]furan- 4-yl ester, [3aS-(3aR*,4R*,5R*,6E- 10E,11aS*)]-	n.s.g.	230(4.27) (end absorption)	102-0323-80
$C_{21}H_{24}O_8$ 2(3H)-Furanone, 4-[(3,4-dimethoxyphen- yl)hydroxymethyl]dihydro-3-hydroxy-3- [(4-hydroxy-3-methoxyphenyl)methyl]-, [3S-[3α,4a(R*)]]- (5-hydroxytrachelo- genin)	EtOH	231(4.13),281(3.75)	94-0850-80
$C_{21}H_{24}O_{10}$ Phloridzin	MeOH	223(4.37),285(4.27)	100-0739-80
$C_{21}H_{24}O_{11}$ Phloretin, 3-hydroxy-, 4'-β-D-glucoside	EtOH	207(4.54),224(4.41), 284(4.39)	102-0476-80
Phloridzin, 3-hydroxy-	MeOH	222(4.39),285(4.36)	100-0739-80
$C_{21}H_{25}BrN_2O_2$ Vincadifformine, 10-bromo-	MeOH	310(4.24),330(4.22)	142-1915-80
$C_{21}H_{25}BrN_2O_3$ Vincamine, 10-bromo-	MeOH	233(4.53),285(3.88), 290(3.89),300(3.76)	142-1915-80
$C_{21}H_{25}ClN_2O_4$ 4H-Furo[3,2-b]pyrrole-5-carboxylic acid, 2-(4-chlorophenyl)-4-[2-hydroxy-3- [(1-methylethyl)amino]propyl]-, hydrochloride	MeOH	343(4.71),358(4.71)	73-2949-80
$C_{21}H_{25}FN_2O_2$ 1-Butanone, 1-(4-fluorophenyl)-4-[4-hy- droxy-4-(4-aminophenyl)piperidinyl]-, hydrochloride	MeOH	241(4.38),280(4.26)	87-0075-80

Compound	Solvent	$\lambda_{max}(\log \epsilon)$	Ref.
$C_{21}H_{25}NO_2$			
Benzamide, N-[3,5-bis(1,1-dimethyleth-yl)-4-oxo-2,5-cyclohexadien-1-yli-dene]-	C_6H_{12}	234(4.07),280(4.43)	88-1265-80
$C_{21}H_{25}NO_3$			
Carbamic acid, [2-ethyl-2-hydroxy-1-(phenylmethylene)butyl]-, phenylmethyl ester, (Z)-	EtOH	257.5(4.04)	39-0858-80C
$C_{21}H_{25}NO_4$			
Triketolactam 14	EtOH	242(4.3)	23-1889-80
$C_{21}H_{25}NO_5$			
Benzenemethanol, 2-[(3,4-dihydro-6,7-dimethoxy-1-isoquinolinyl)methyl]-4,5-dimethoxy-	EtOH	235(4.40),283(4.12), 318(3.92)	73-0956-80
Dibenz[c,g]azecin-7(6H)-one, 5,8,13,14-tetrahydro-2,3,10,11-tetramethoxy-	EtOH	283(4.19)	78-1515-80
5H-Dibenzo[a,d]cycloheptene-10-carbox-amide, 10,11-dihydro-2,3,7,8-tetra-methoxy-N-methyl-	EtOH	237(3.77),287(3.72)	39-2013-80C
$C_{21}H_{25}NO_6$			
3(2H)-Isoquinolinone, 4-[(3,4-dimeth-oxyphenyl)hydroxymethyl]-1,4-dihydro-6,7-dimethoxy-2-methyl-	EtOH	232(3.74),278(3.65)	39-2013-80C
Papaverinol, 1,2,3,4-tetrahydro-2'-(hy-droxymethyl)-	EtOH	235(4.21),285(3.80)	73-0956-80
Tricyclo[3.3.1.0^{1,3}]honane-4-carboxylic acid, 3,6,6-trimethyl-9-[(4-nitro-benzoyl)oxy]-, methyl ester, (1α,3α,4β,5α,9R*)-	ether	257.5(4.32)	33-1856-80
$C_{21}H_{25}NO_7$			
Clivatine	MeOH	205(4.23),225(4.33), 266(3.76),306(3.75)	94-1827-80
$C_{21}H_{25}N_2$			
3H-Indolium, 2-[2-[4-(dimethylamino)-phenyl]ethenyl]-1,3,3-trimethyl-, iodide	H_2O	520(4.60)	140-1570-80
protonated	H_2O	375(4.43)	140-1570-80
hydroxide	H_2O	350(4.45)	140-1570-80
$C_{21}H_{25}N_3O_4$			
Vincadifformine, 1,2-dehydro-2,16-di-hydro-16-nitro-	EtOH	283(3.77)	142-1915-80
Vincadifformine, 10-nitro-	MeOH	263(3.87),289(3.79), 390(4.28)	142-1915-80
$C_{21}H_{25}N_9O_5$			
1H-Pyrrole-2-carboxamide, N-[5-[[(3-am-ino-3-iminopropyl)amino]carbonyl]-1-methyl-1H-pyrrol-2-yl]-1-methyl-5-[[(1-methyl-5-nitro-1H-pyrrol-2-yl)-carbonyl]amino]-, monohydrochloride	EtOH	261(3.94),295(4.00)	36-1334-80
$C_{21}H_{26}NO_2$			
Isoquinolinium, 1-ethyl-3,4-dihydro-6,7-dimethoxy-2-methyl-3-(phenyl-	MeOH	250(4.29),309(3.97), 366(3.97)	83-1033-80

Compound	Solvent	$\lambda_{max}(\log \epsilon)$	Ref.
methyl)-, perchlorate (cont.)			83-1033-80
$C_{21}H_{26}N_2O$			
Aspidospermidine, 1-acetyl-2,3-didehy-dro-, (±)-	EtOH	223(3.92),265(4.01), 280s(3.68)	4-1133-80
$C_{21}H_{26}N_2O_2$			
Akagerine, O-methyl- (5λ,4ε)	EtOH	229(4.47),278(3.78), 283(3.78),292(3.67), 306(?)	100-0097-80
Coronaridine	MeOH	228(4.52),285(3.90), 293(3.89)	64-0219-80B +102-2185-80
	MeOH	244(4.55),284(3.89), 292(3.83)	102-1213-80
Dispiro[tricyclo[3.1.0.0^{2,6}]hexane-3,3'-[3H]pyrazole-5'(4'H),3''-tri-cyclo[3.1.0.0^{2,6}]hexane]-4,4''-dione, 1,1'',2,2'',5,5'',6,6''-octamethyl-	EtOH	214(3.80),253(3.57), 318(3.00)	44-4337-80
Vincadifformine	MeOH	288(3.99),300(4.00), 326(4.19)	73-1419-80
$C_{21}H_{26}N_2O_3$			
Akagerine, 10-hydroxy-17-O-methyl-	EtOH	232(4.52),279(4.20), 301(3.86),305(3.70)	100-0097-80
	EtOH-KOH	239(4.68),275(4.18), 328(4.13)	100-0097-80
Cleavamine, dihydro-16-acetoxy-21-oxo-	EtOH	224(5.62),277(3.93), 285(3.95),294(3.86), 320s(2.67)	78-1057-80
Coronaridine, 10-hydroxy-	MeOH	218(4.33),282(3.80), 304(3.78)	102-1213-80
Coronaridine, hydroxyindolenine	MeOH	225(4.28),259(3.73), 292s(3.61)	64-0219-80B
Heyneanine	MeOH	225(4.50),286(3.91), 292(3.85)	64-0219-80B
(-)-(19S)-	MeOH	224(4.71),284(4.33), 292(4.27)	102-1213-80
Kribine, 10-hydroxy-21-O-methyl-	EtOH	215(4.51),269(4.62), 312(4.08),322s(4.03)	100-0097-80
	EtOH-KOH	234(4.50),284(4.52), 330(4.15)	100-0097-80
epimer	EtOH	216(4.56),270(4.60), 312(4.08),322s(4.01)	100-0097-80
	EtOH-KOH	229(4.39),286(4.21), 329(4.13)	100-0097-80
Pleiocarpamine, 2,7-dihydro-10-methoxy-	MeOH	210(4.47),249(4.06), 297(3.48)	102-0307-80
Strychnosplendine, N_a-acetyl-	EtOH	250(4.08),278(3.41), 286s(3.31)	32-0081-80
$C_{21}H_{26}N_2O_4$			
Vallesamine, O-acetyl-	MeOH	222(4.62),283(3.91), 292(3.86)	102-1213-80
Vincadifformine, 14,15-dihydroxy-	EtOH	226(4.07),294(3.80), 329(4.09)	102-1473-80
$C_{21}H_{26}N_4$			
1H-Benzimidazole, 1-ethyl-5,6-dimethyl-2-[(2,3,5,6-tetramethylphenyl)azo]-	MeOH	374(3.36)	104-2008-80

Compound	Solvent	$\lambda_{max}(\log \epsilon)$	Ref.
$C_{21}H_{26}N_4O_7$			
Riboflavin 5'-butanoate	EtOH	223(4.45),270(4.50), 352(3.94),445(4.09)	94-0181-80
$C_{21}H_{26}N_4O_{11}$			
D-Ribitol, 1-deoxy-1-(2,4-dimethoxy-7-oxo-8(7H)-pteridinyl)-, 2,3,4,5-tetraacetate	MeOH	240(3.98),248(4.00), 270s(3.55),316(4.06), 326(4.05),340s(3.88)	24-1535-80
$C_{21}H_{26}N_5O_6PS$			
Adenosine, N-butyl-8-[(phenylmethyl)-thio]-, cyclic 3',5'-(hydrogen phosphate)	pH 1 pH 11	288(4.35) 291(4.26)	87-0242-80 87-0242-80
$C_{21}H_{26}N_6O_{10}$			
β-D-Glucopyranoside, (2,4-diamino-6-pteridinyl)methyl, 2,3,4,6-tetraacetate	pH 2.0 pH 7.0	243(4.21),285(3.74), 335(4.02) 258(4.35),370(3.86)	24-1514-80 24-1514-80
$C_{21}H_{26}OS$			
2(3H)-Naphthalenone, 4,4a,5,6,7,8-hexa-hydro-4a,5-dimethyl-3-(1-methyleth-ylidene)-1-(phenylthio)-, cis-(±)-	EtOH	202(4.37),248(4.27), 276s(3.86)	39-0963-80C
$C_{21}H_{26}OSi$			
Benzenemethanol, α-phenyl-α-[5-(tri-methylsilyl)-2,4-pentadienyl]-, (E,E)-	MeOH	204(4.44),242(4.56)	33-0555-80
$C_{21}H_{26}O_2$			
Dispiro[tricyclo[3.1.0.$0^{2,6}$]hexane-3,1'-cyclopropane-2',3"-tricyclo-[3.1.0.$0^{2,6}$]hexane]-4,4"-dione, 1,1",2,2",5,5",6,6"-octamethyl-	EtOH	216(3.62),240(3.48), 295(2.46)	44-4337-80
D-Homo-C,18-dinorandrosta-5,13,15,17-tetraen-3-one, 17a-methyl-, cyclic ethanediyl acetal	EtOH	205(3.95),215s(3.80), 273(2.48)	18-0243-80
Methanone, [2-hydroxy-5-(1,1,3,3-tetra-methylbutyl)phenyl]phenyl-	EtOH	259(4.08),350(3.57)	90-0431-80
19-Norpregna-1,3,5(10)-trien-20-one, 16,17-epoxy-4-methyl-, (16α)-	EtOH	285(2.69)	39-0556-80C
$C_{21}H_{26}O_3$			
Methanone, [2-hydroxy-4-(octyloxy)phen-yl]phenyl-	hexane	<u>244(4.0),286(4.0), 323(4.0)</u>	135-0160-80
Pregna-1,4-diene-3,6,20-trione	EtOH	248(4.09)	39-2700-80C
$C_{21}H_{26}O_3S$			
D-Homo-16-thiaestra-1,3,5(10),8-tetra-en-17a-ol, 3-methoxy-, acetate, (14α,17aα)-	EtOH	275(4.28)	88-2549-80
(14α,17aβ)-	EtOH	276(4.27)	88-2549-80
(14β,17aα)-	EtOH	277(4.31)	88-2549-80
(14β,17aβ)-	EtOH	277(4.29)	88-2549-80
16-Thiaestra-1,3,5(10),8-tetraene-17-methanol, 3-methoxy-, acetate, (14β,17α)-	EtOH	277(4.23)	88-2549-80
(14β,17β)-	EtOH	276(4.15)	88-2549-80
(17α)-	EtOH	278(4.20)	88-2549-80
(17β)-	EtOH	276(4.16)	88-2549-80

Compound	Solvent	$\lambda_{max}(\log \epsilon)$	Ref.
$C_{21}H_{26}O_4$			
Bicyclo[3.2.1]octane-6,8-dione, 2-exo-(2,4-dimethoxyphenyl)-5-methyl-2-endo-(2-methyl-1-propenyl)-	EtOH	228(3.95),282(3.44), 288(3.43)	2-0433-80
17-Epipregna-3,11-diene-3,12,20-trione, 17-hydroxy-	EtOH	284(3.85)	18-0254-80
Phenol, 4-[2-(3,4-dimethoxyphenyl)-1-methylethyl]-5-methoxy-2-(2-propenyl)-, (R)-	MeOH	225s(4.23),282(3.80)	102-0285-80
$C_{21}H_{26}O_5$			
2,5-Cyclohexadien-1-one, 4-[2-(4-hydroxy-3-methoxyphenyl)-1-methylethyl]-4,5-dimethoxy-2-(2-propenyl)-, (8R,3'R)- (lancifolin B)	MeOH	231(4.10),283(3.69)	102-0285-80
	MeOH-NaOH	241(4.10),293(3.69)	102-0285-80
(8R,3'S)-	MeOH	235(4.10),285(3.69)	102-0285-80
	MeOH-NaOH	243(4.09),294(3.65)	102-0285-80
Phenol, 4-[5-(3,4-dimethoxyphenyl)-tetrahydro-3,4-dimethyl-2-furanyl]-2-methoxy- (nectandrin A)	MeOH	231(4.23),278(3.75)	100-0353-80
	MeOH-NaOH	294(4.26)	100-0353-80
$C_{21}H_{26}O_6$			
Δ^2-Picrasin B	EtOH	256(4.00)	78-2983-80
$C_{21}H_{26}O_7$			
Cyclodeca[b]furan-6-carboxylic acid, 2,3,3a,4,5,8,9,11a-octahydro-5-hydroxy-10-methyl-3-methylene-4-[(2-methyl-1-oxo-2-butenyl)oxy]-2-oxo-, methyl ester (sphaerocephalin)	EtOH	214(4.13)	102-1549-80
Linearilobin D	MeOH	205(4.26)	102-0849-80
Linearilobin E	MeOH	204(4.26)	102-0849-80
Linearilobin H	MeOH	202(4.32)	102-0849-80
$C_{21}H_{26}O_8$			
9(1H)-Phenanthrenone, 3-(formyloxy)-2,3,4,4a-tetrahydro-5,6,8,10-tetrahydroxy-7-(2-hydroxy-1-methylethyl)-1,1,4a-trimethyl-, [3S-[3α,4aβ,7(S*)]]-(2α-formoxycoleon C)	EtOH	268(4.07),285s(3.83), 329(3.67),397(3.90)	33-0095-80
$C_{21}H_{26}O_9$			
Cyclopenta[g]-2-benzopyran-1,6-dione, 8-(β-D-glucopyranosyloxy)-3,4,7,8-tetrahydro-5,7,7-trimethyl-, (R)-	MeOH	260(4.17),323(3.45)	94-1869-80
$C_{21}H_{26}O_{10}$			
Agnuside	H_2O	258(4.15)	100-0649-80
	base	299(--)	100-0649-80
$C_{21}H_{26}O_{12}$			
Plumieride	EtOH	216(4.2)	100-0649-80
$C_{21}H_{27}ClN_2O_{11}$			
1H-Pyrazole-5-carboxylic acid, 3-(chloromethyl)-1-(2,3,4,6-tetra-O-acetyl-α-D-glucopyranosyl)-, ethyl ester	EtOH	230(3.89),240s(3.76)	87-0657-80
β-	EtOH	230(4.03),240s(3.92)	87-0657-80
$C_{21}H_{27}ClN_4O_8S$			
D-arabino-Hexitol, 1-C-(6-chloro-9H-	MeOH	266(3.6)	136-0356-80C

Compound	Solvent	$\lambda_{max}(\log \epsilon)$	Ref.
purin-9-yl)-2-deoxy-1-S-ethyl-1-thio-, 3,4,5,6-tetraacetate (cont.)			136-0356-80C
$C_{21}H_{27}FO_4$ D(17a)-Homo-C,18-dinorpregn-4-ene-3,11,20-trione, 17a-fluoro-13-hydroxy-17a-methyl-, (17α,17aα)-	EtOH	235(4.00)	18-0254-80
$C_{21}H_{27}IN_2O_{11}$ 1H-Pyrazole-5-carboxylic acid, 3-(iodomethyl)-1-(2,3,4,6-tetra-0-acetyl-α-D-glucopyranosyl)-, ethyl ester	EtOH	228(4.27),240s(4.08)	87-0657-80
$C_{21}H_{27}NO$ 2,5-Cyclohexadien-1-one, 2,6-bis(1,1-dimethylethyl)-4-[(4-methylphenyl)-imino]-	hexane	453(3.61)	104-2020-80
	+CF₃COOH	414(4.10)	104-2020-80
	benzene	456(3.63)	104-2020-80
	+CF₃COOH	430(4.10)	104-2020-80
	CH₂Cl₂	453(3.73)	104-2020-80
	+CF₃COOH	428(4.14)	104-2020-80
	CHCl₃	451(3.67)	104-2020-80
	+CF₃COOH	427(4.11)	104-2020-80
perchlorate	CH₂Cl₂	431(4.12)	104-2020-80
$C_{21}H_{27}NO_2$ Methanone, [2-hydroxy-5-(1,1,3,3-tetramethylbutyl)phenyl]phenyl-, oxime, anti	EtOH	261(3.93),315(3.56)	90-0431-80
$C_{21}H_{27}NO_3$ 1H-Dibenzo[a,f]quinolizin-1-one, 2,3,4,6,7,11b,12,13-octahydro-9,10-dimethoxy-3,3-dimethyl-	MeOH	228(3.95),293(4.02), 320(4.52)	135-0956-80
Spiro[estra-4,6-dien-17,5'-oxazolidine]-2',3-dione, 3'-methyl-, (17β)-	EtOH	281(4.42)	13-0361-80A
Spiro[estra-4,9-dien-17,5'-oxazolidine]-2',3-dione, 3'-methyl-, (17β)-	EtOH	301(4.30)	13-0361-80A
$C_{21}H_{27}NO_4$ Isoquinoline, 1-[2-(3,4-dimethoxyphenyl)ethyl]-1,2,3,4-tetrahydro-6,7-dimethoxy-	EtOH	283(3.81)	39-1696-80B
Phenol, 4-[(5-ethoxy-1,2,3,4-tetrahydro-6,7-dimethoxy-2-methyl-1-isoquinolinyl)methyl]-, (S)-	n.s.g.	282(3.54)	100-0472-80
3,5-Pyridinedicarboxylic acid, 1,4-dihydro-2,4,6-trimethyl-1-(phenylmethyl)-, diethyl ester	EtOH	207(4.19),234(4.21), 275s(4.06),348(3.79)	103-0377-80
$C_{21}H_{27}NO_5$ Benzeneethanamine, 2-[2-(3,4-dimethoxyphenyl)ethenyl]-N-hydroxy-4,5-dimethoxy-N-methyl-, (E)-	MeOH	220s(4.30),295s(4.20), 336(4.38),350s(4.20)	12-0379-80
$C_{21}H_{27}NO_5S$ Spiro[1,5-benzothiazepine-2(3H),6'(5'H)-furo[2,3-d][1,3]dioxole, 5'-(2,2-dimethyl-1,3-dioxolan-4-yl)-3'a,6'a-dihydro-2',2',4-trimethyl-, [3'aR-[3'aα,5'α(R),6'α,6'aα]]-	EtOH	220(3.95),259(3.77)	33-1779-80

Compound	Solvent	$\lambda_{max}(\log \epsilon)$	Ref.
$C_{21}H_{27}NO_6$			
Benzenepropanamide, α-[2-(hydroxymethyl)-4,5-dimethoxyphenyl]-3,4-dimethoxy-N-methyl-	EtOH	285(3.58)	39-2013-80C
Spiro[1,5-benzoxazepine-2(3H,6'(5'H)-furo[2,3-d][1,3]dioxole], 5'-(2,2-dimethyl-1,3-dioxolan-4-yl)-3'a,6'a-dihydro-2',2',4-trimethyl-, [3aR-[3'aα,5'α(R*),6'α,6'aα]]-	EtOH	213(4.13),277(3.42), 287(3.42)	33-1779-80
$C_{21}H_{28}IN_3O_2$			
Acorenone B, (4-iodo-2-nitrophenyl)hydrazone	MeOH	314(4.49),465(3.83)	100-0598-80
$C_{21}H_{28}N_2O$			
Eburnamenine, 14-ethoxy-14,15-dihydro-, (14α)-	MeOH	228(4.04),282(3.63), 293(3.54)	102-1959-80
$C_{21}H_{28}N_2O_2$			
Alkaloid OR4	MeOH	214(4.23),249(4.00), 284(3.67)	102-2741-80
Aspidospermine, demethyl-	MeOH	225(4.40),260(3.53), 291(3.21)	73-1419-80
Vallesine	MeOH	214(4.47),255(3.94)	73-1419-80
$C_{21}H_{28}N_2O_3$			
Velbanamine, 16α-(methoxycarbonyl)-	EtOH	228(4.40),286(3.85), 291(3.82)	44-3259-80
20-epi-	EtOH	230(4.36),286(3.86), 291(3.83)	44-3259-80
Velbanamine, 16β-(methoxycarbonyl)-	EtOH-HClO₄	228(4.44),276(4.05), 286(4.05),296(3.85)	44-3259-80
20-epi-	EtOH-HCl	228(4.44),285(4.0), 293(3.97)	44-3259-80
$C_{21}H_{28}N_2O_4S$			
Cyclohexanecarboxylic acid, 4-[[[[5-(dimethylamino)-1-naphthalenyl]sulfonyl]amino]methyl]-, methyl ester, trans	MeOH	330(3.62)	35-3214-80
$C_{21}H_{28}N_2O_5$			
Spiro[2H-1,5-benzodiazepine-2,6'(5'H)-furo[2,3-d][1,3]dioxole, 5'-(2,2-dimethyl-1,3-dioxolan-4-yl)-1,3,3'a-6'a-tetrahydro-2',2',4-trimethyl-, [3'aR-(3'aα,5'α,6'α,6'aα)]-	EtOH	217(4.25),241(3.88), 318(3.42)	33-1779-80
$C_{21}H_{28}N_4O_3$			
Octanamide, N-[5-[[4-(dimethylamino)-phenyl]imino]-1,2,5,6-tetrahydro-2,6-dioxo-3-pyridinyl]-	EtOH	260(4.42),350(3.95), 580(4.35)	39-1788-80C
$C_{21}H_{28}N_6O_4$			
Adenosine, 2'-O-(2-amino-3-phenyl-propyl)-N,N-dimethyl-	EtOH	275(4.23)	44-4006-80
Adenosine, 3'-O-(2-amino-3-phenyl-propyl)-N,N-dimethyl-	EtOH	275(4.23)	44-4006-80
$C_{21}H_{28}N_6O_{11}P_2$			
Adenosine, 5'-(trihydrogen phosphate),	pH 7	260(4.18),334(4.33)	5-1259-80

Compound	Solvent	λ_{max}(log ϵ)	Ref.
mono[3-[(4-acetylphenyl)amino]propyl] ester (cont.)			5-1259-80
$C_{21}H_{28}N_7O_{17}P_3$			
Nicotinamide adenine dinucleotide	pH 7.3	<u>336(3.8)</u>	35-1713-80
free radical	pH 7.3	393(3.31)	35-1713-80
free radical dimer	pH 7.3	345(3.72)	35-1713-80
$C_{21}H_{28}O_2$			
3,19-Cyclo-3,4-secopregn-4-en-20-yn-1-one, 17α-hydroxy-	EtOH	303(1.72)	44-5088-80
A-Homo-19-norpregn-5(10)-en-20α-yn-4-one, 17β-hydroxy-	EtOH	294(2.36)	44-5088-80
Pregna-1,5-diene-3,20-dione	EtOH	234(4.05)	39-2700-80C
Pregna-4,6-dien-3,20-dione	EtOH	283(4.41)	12-1537-80
$C_{21}H_{28}O_3$			
B-Norestra-1,3,5(10),8-tetraen-17β-ol, 1,4-dimethoxy-6,6-dimethyl-, (±)-	EtOH	270(3.85),278(3.71), 313(3.68),325(3.58)	39-0448-80C
B-Norestra-1,3,5(10),8-tetraen-17β-ol, 2,3-dimethoxy-6,6-dimethyl-, (±)-	EtOH	282(3.99),305(3.95)	39-0448-80C
19-Norpregna-1,3,5(10)-trien-20-one, 2,11α-dihydroxy-4-methyl-	MeOH MeOH-base	277(3.30),282(3.30) 285(3.38),294s(3.28)	44-2324-80 44-2324-80
19-Norpregna-1,3,5(10)-trien-20-one, 21-hydroxy-3-methoxy-	MeOH	278(3.32),286(3.30)	44-4404-80
Oxiranebutanoic acid, 3-(1,3-tetradeca-diene-5,8-diynyl)-, methyl ester, [2α,3α(1E,3E)]-	EtOH	260(4.43),272(4.55), 285(4.47)	35-5425-80
Pregna-1,4-diene-3,20-dione, 11α-hy-droxy- (lumi)	EtOH	223(3.61),272s(3.23)	44-2324-80
Pregn-4-ene-3,11,20-trione	EtOH	238(4.17)	23-2703-80
$C_{21}H_{28}O_4$			
Bicyclo[3.2.1]octane-6,8-dione, 2-(2,4-dimethoxyphenyl)-5-methyl-2-(2-methyl-phenyl)- (same spectra for both iso-mers)	EtOH	226(3.95),279(4.46), 284(3.42)	2-0433-80
D-Homo-C,18-dinorandrosta-4,8(14)-dien-3-one, 17-acetoxy-17a-hydroxy-17a-methyl-	EtOH	210(4.08),232(4.08)	18-0243-80
Pregn-4-ene-3,12,20-trione, 11-hydroxy-, (11β,17α)-	EtOH	239(4.11)	18-0254-80
$C_{21}H_{28}O_5$			
Androst-2-ene-1,17-dione, 4-acetoxy-5-hydroxy-	EtOH	210(3.6)	105-0167-80
D(17a)-Homo-C,18-dinorpregn-4-ene-3,11,20-trione, 13,17a-dihydroxy-17a-methyl-	EtOH	245(4.23)	18-0254-80
Lumiprednisolone	MeOH	234(3.62),262s(3.36)	44-2324-80
17-Norkaur-9(11)-en-18-oic acid, 16,16-[1,2-ethanediylbis(oxo)]-12-oxo-, (4α)-	MeOH	248(4.01)	39-1270-80C
10α-Pregn-4-ene-3,20-dione, 1β,11β-ep-oxy-17α,21-dihydroxy-	MeOH	285.7(2.58)	44-2324-80
$C_{21}H_{28}O_6$			
α-D-Glucofuranose, 3-O-[(ethenylphen-yl)methyl]-1,2:5,6-bis-O-(1-methyl-ethylidene)-	hexane	284(2.88),294(2.72)	116-0234-80

Compound	Solvent	$\lambda_{max}(\log \epsilon)$	Ref.

$C_{21}H_{28}O_{13}$
    Haploperoside A
     ($5\lambda,4\epsilon$)
	EtOH	230(4.16),252s(3.56),
		 260s(3.64),281(3.80),
		 344(?)
			105-0125-80

$C_{21}H_{29}BrN_2$
    Pyrrolo[2,3-b]indole, 6-bromo-3a-(1,1-
     dimethyl-2-propenyl)-1,2,3,3a,8,8a-
     hexahydro-1-methyl-8-(3-methyl-2-
     butenyl)-, cis
	EtOH
	
	 EtOH-HCl
		218(4.30),263(3.93),
		 319(3.53)
		 218(4.30),255(3.88),
		 307(3.54)
			44-1586-80
			
			 44-1586-80

Pyrrolo[2,3-b]indole, 6-bromo-1,2,3,3a-
     8,8a-hexahydro-1-methyl-3a,8-bis(3-
     methyl-2-butenyl)-, cis
	EtOH
	
	 EtOH-HCl
		218(4.30),262(3.96),
		 317(3.54)
		 219(4.32),253(3.89),
		 305(3.54)
			44-1586-80
			
			 44-1586-80

$C_{21}H_{29}FO_2$ Pregn-4-ene-3,20-dione, 14α-fluoro-	EtOH	239(4.08)	152-0239-80

$C_{21}H_{29}FO_4$
    D(17a)-Homo-C,18-dinorpregn-4-ene-
     3,20-dione, 17a-fluoro-11,13-di-
     hydroxy-17a-methyl-, (11β,17α,17aα)-
	EtOH	239(4.04)	18-0254-80

$C_{21}H_{29}N_2O_2$
    1H-Indolizino[8,7-b]indol-4-ium,
     2,3,5,6,11,11b-hexahydro-2-[2-(meth-
     oxycarbonyl)butyl]-4-methyl-, iodide
	EtOH	224(4.76),274(3.89),
		 279(3.86),290(3.76)
			78-1057-80

$C_{21}H_{29}N_3O_4$
    Cyclopent[c]azepine-4,5-dicarboxylic
     acid, 1,3-bis(dimethylamino)-7-(1,3-
     dimethylethyl)-, dimethyl ester
	hexane	207s(4.17),237s(4.08),
		 252s(4.13),279(4.23),
		 340(4.44),381s(3.96),
		 456(4.06)
			88-0041-80

$C_{21}H_{29}N_5$
    1H-Cyclopenta[5,6]naphtho[1,2-g]tetra-
     zolo[1,5-a]quinazoline, 2,3,3a,3b-
     4,5,5a,6,13,13a,13b,14,15,15a-tetra-
     decahydro-13a,15a-dimethyl-, [3aS-
     (3aα,3bβ,5aα,13aβ,13bα,15aβ)]-
	MeOH	215(4.26),248(3.73),
		 280(3.63)
			39-1019-80C

$C_{21}H_{29}N_5O$
    1H-Cyclopenta[5,6]naphtho[1,2-g]tetra-
     zolo[1,5-a]quinazolin-1-ol, 2,3,3a-
     3b,4,5,5a,6,13,13a,13b,14,15,15a-
     tetradecahydro-13a,15c-dimethyl-,
     [1S-(1α,3aβ,3bα,5aβ,13aα,13bβ,15aα)]-
	MeOH	215(4.29),279(3.73)	39-1019-80C

$C_{21}H_{30}NO_4$
    Benzo[a]quinolizinium, 2-(2-ethoxy-2-
     oxoethyl)-3-ethyl-1,2,3,4,6,7-hexa-
     hydro-9,10-dimethoxy-, iodide, (2R,3R)-
	EtOH	246(4.21),304(3.96),
		 354(3.96)
			78-1539-80

perchlorate	EtOH	246(4.22),304(3.97), 354(3.96)	78-1539-80
perchlorate, (2S,3R)-	EtOH	246(4.21),304(3.96), 354(3.96)	78-1539-80
Scopolammonium, N-butyl-, bromide, iodine complex	CHCl$_3$ C$_2$H$_4$Cl$_2$	280(4.56) 282(4.68)	106-0030-80 106-0030-80
$C_{21}H_{30}N_2O$ 1-Piperidineacetonitrile, α-[3,5-bis-	isooctane	416(4.31)	73-2675-80

Compound	Solvent	$\lambda_{max}(\log \epsilon)$	Ref.
(1,1-dimethylethyl)-4-oxo-2,5-cyclo-dien-1-ylidene]- (cont.)			73-2675-80
$C_{21}H_{30}O$			
Pregna-1,4-dien-3-one	n.s.g.	245(4.15)	35-0807-80
Retinal, 14-methyl-, all-trans	hexane	373(4.66)	46-0134-80
9-cis	hexane	365(4.54)	46-0134-80
11-cis	hexane	338(4.26)	46-0134-80
13-cis	hexane	358(4.54)	46-0134-80
$C_{21}H_{30}O_2$			
1,4-Benzenediol, 2-[(1,2,3,4,5,6,7,8-octahydro-1,2,5,5-tetramethyl-1-naphthalenyl)methyl]-	MeOH	220(3.70),299(3.70)	44-1435-80
1,4-Benzenediol, 2-[(3,4,4a,5,6,7,8,8a-octahydro-2,5,5,8a-tetramethyl-1-naphthalenyl)methyl]-, (4aR-trans)-	MeOH	210(4.32),295(3.56)	44-1435-80
1,4-Benzenediol, 2-(3,7,11-trimethyl-2,6,10-dodecatrienyl)-, (E,E)-	MeOH	293(3.58)	102-2202-80
Benzo[d]xanthen-10-ol, 1,2,3,4,4a,5,6-7,7a,8-decahydro-4,4,7,7a-tetramethyl-(aureol)	MeOH MeOH-base	216(3.66),299(3.49) 227(3.70),302(3.43)	44-1435-80 44-1435-80
2H-Benzo[a]xanthen-10-ol, 1,3,4,4a,5,6-6a,12,12a,12b-decahydro-4,4,6a,12b-tetramethyl-	MeOH MeOH-base	210(4.21),300(3.49) 305(3.51)	44-1435-80 44-1435-80
2,4,6,8-Nonatetraenoic acid, 9-(2-eth-yl-6,6-dimethyl-1-cyclohexen-1-yl)-3,7-dimethyl-, (E)-	EtOH	244(3.68),342(4.65)	87-1013-80
5β-Pregn-1-ene-3,20-dione	MeOH	230(3.95)	35-0352-80
$C_{21}H_{30}O_3$			
5α,10α-Estr-1-en-3-one, 17β-acetoxy-5-methyl-	n.s.g.	237(3.99)	119-0045-80
5β-Estr-1-en-3-one, 17β-acetoxy-5-methyl-	n.s.g.	234(3.96)	119-0045-80
B-Norestra-1,3,5(10)-trien-17β-ol, 1,4-dimethoxy-6,6-dimethyl-, (±)-	EtOH	287(3.28)	39-0448-80C
B-Nor-9β-estra-1,3,5(10)-trien-17β-ol, 1,4-dimethoxy-6,6-dimethyl-, (±)-	EtOH	284(3.24)	39-0448-80C
B-Nor-9β-estra-1,3,5(10)-trien-17β-ol, 2,3-dimethoxy-6,6-dimethyl-, (±)-	EtOH	284(3.74)	39-0448-80C
19-Norpregn-4-ene-3,20-dione, 17-hy-droxy-9-methyl-, (9β,10α)-	n.s.g.	242(4.20)	119-0127-80
19-Norpregn-4-ene-3,20-dione, 18-(hy-droxymethyl)-, 18a,20-hemiketal	MeOH	241(4.21)	24-1106-80
Phenanthro[1,2-c]furan-6-carboxylic acid, 3b,4,5,5a,6,7,8,9,9a,9b,10,11-dodecahydro-3b,6,9a-trimethyl-, methyl ester	n.s.g.	219(3.58)	20-0399-80
Retinoic acid, 3-hydroxy-, methyl ester, (3R)-	CHCl₃	360(4.65)	33-1467-80
$C_{21}H_{30}O_4$			
1,5-Cyclo-1,10-secopregn-3-ene-2,20-di-one, 10,11-dihydroxy-	MeOH	229.5(3.80)	44-2324-80
12α,13-Epietiojerva-5,8(14)-dien-3-one, 13β,17α-dihydroxy-, 3,3-ethylene acetal	EtOH	207(3.95)	18-0243-80
13β,17β-	EtOH	208(4.00)	18-0243-80
B(9a)-Homo-A,19-dinorpregn-3(5)-ene-	MeOH	236(4.32),280(2.71)	44-2324-80

Compound	Solvent	$\lambda_{max}(\log \epsilon)$	Ref.
2,20-dione, 9a,11-dihydroxy-9a-methyl-, (9aα,10α,11α)- (cont.)			44-2324-80
19-Norpregn-4-ene-3,20-dione, 21-hydroxy-18-(hydroxymethyl)-, 18a,20-hemiketal	MeOH	241(4.22)	24-1106-80
$C_{21}H_{30}O_5$			
Androst-4-en-3-one, 17β-acetoxy-1ξ,2ξ-dihydroxy-	n.s.g.	242(4.09)	33-0473-80
13-Epietiojerv-4-en-3-one, 12α,13β,17β-trihydroxy-, 17-acetate	EtOH	239(3.99)	18-0243-80
D(17a)-Homo-C,18-dinorpregn-4-ene-3,20-dione, 11,13,17a-trihydroxy-17a-methyl-	EtOH	239(4.11)	18-0254-80
$C_{21}H_{30}O_6$			
1,3-Benzodioxole-5,6-diol, 2-methyl-2-nonyl-, diacetate	EtOH	245(3.62),300(3.79)	12-0527-80
1,5-Cyclo-1,10-secopregn-3-ene-2,20-dione, 10,11,17,21-tetrahydroxy-, (5α,10α,11β)-	MeOH	229(3.96),296(2.24)	44-2324-80
B(9a)-Homo-A,19-dinorpregn-3(5)-ene-2,20-dione, 9a,11,17,21-tetrahydroxy-9a-methyl-, (9aα,10α,11β)-	MeOH	236(4.13)	44-2324-80
$C_{21}H_{30}O_7$			
Cyclodeca[b]furan-6-carboxylic acid, 2,3,3a,4,5,8,9,10,11,11a-decahydro-10-(hydroxymethyl)-3-methylene-4-(2-methyl-1-oxobutoxy)-2-oxo-, methyl ester (melnerin B)	n.s.g.	212(4.40)	44-4028-80
$C_{21}H_{30}O_8$			
Onitin 2'-O-β-D-alloside	MeOH	231(4.45),271(4.21), 324(3.67)	102-1743-80
Onitin 2'-O-β-D-glucoside	MeOH	232(4.45),271(4.21), 324(3.71)	102-1743-80
$C_{21}H_{30}O_{10}$			
Penstemide	n.s.g.	214(4.33)	100-0649-80
$C_{21}H_{31}NO_5$			
Butanedioic acid, [[2,4-bis(1,1-dimethylethyl)-6-methylphenyl]imino]-, dimethyl ester, N-oxide	hexane	281(4.18)	39-1365-80C
$C_{21}H_{31}N_3O_9S$			
D-Xylitol, 1-C-(4-amino-2-oxo-1(2H)-pyrimidinyl)-1-S-(2-methylpropyl)-1-thio-, 2,3,4,5-tetraacetate, (R)-	MeOH	278(3.92)	136-0364-80C
(S)-	MeOH	277(4.02)	136-0364-80C
$C_{21}H_{32}N_2O$			
2,5-Heptadien-4-one, 1-(1-cyclohexen-1-yl)-2,6-dipyrrolidino-	EtOH	378(4.01)	94-2460-80
$C_{21}H_{32}N_4OS$			
2,4-Pyrimidinediamine, 5-[[3,5-bis(1,1-dimethylethyl)-4-methoxyphenyl]methyl]-6-(methylthio)-, monohydrochlor-	pH 2	222(4.33),241s(4.16), 308(4.08)	87-0535-80
	pH 12	232s(4.31),248s(3.98), 296(4.00)	87-0535-80

Compound	Solvent	$\lambda_{max}(\log \epsilon)$	Ref.
$C_{21}H_{32}O_2$			
A-Norestr-3(5)-en-2-one, 17β-(1,1-di-methylethoxy)-	MeOH	233(4.19)	24-2249-80
$C_{21}H_{32}O_3$			
7H-Benz[e]inden-7-one, 3-(1,1-dimethyl-ethoxy)-1,2,3,3a,4,5,8,9,9a,9b-deca-hydro-3a-methyl-6-(2-oxopropyl)-	MeOH	249(4.14)	24-2249-80
Cannabinol, hexahydro-2α-hydroxy-equatorial	EtOH	282(3.17),286(3.19)	87-1068-80
	EtOH	279(3.04),285(3.05)	87-1068-80
Cannabinol, hexahydro-7-hydroxy-, axial equatorial	EtOH	276(3.29),282(3.25)	87-1068-80
	EtOH	275(3.08),282(3.07)	87-1068-80
4-Oxatricyclo[10.3.1.0³,⁵]hexadec-8-ene-9-carboxylic acid, 5,12,13-tri-methyl-16-methylene-, methyl ester, [1R-(1R*,3R*,5R*,8Z,12R*,13S*)]-	EtOH	218(3.77)	78-3489-80
Oxiranebutanoic acid, 3-(1,3,5,8-tetra-decatetraenyl)-, methyl ester	MeOH	269(--),278(4.60), 289(--)	35-1436-80
(6R-leukotriene A)	MeOH	269(--),278(4.60)	88-3463-80
cis	MeOH	269(4.52),278(4.60), 290(4.48)	88-1485-80
trans		269(4.49),278(4.58), 290(4.48)	88-1485-80
Pregna-5,7-diene-3β,17,20-triol	MeOH	272(3.96),282(3.98), 294(3.73)	39-0556-80C
$C_{21}H_{32}O_4$			
1,3-Benzodioxol-5-ol, 2-methyl-2-undec-yl-, acetate	EtOH	235(3.52),286(3.65)	12-0527-80
Bicyclo[9.3.1]pentadec-4-ene-4-carbox-ylic acid, 8-hydroxy-1,8,14-trimeth-yl-15-methylene-9-oxo-, methyl ester, [1R-(1R*,4Z,8R*,11R*,14S*)]-	EtOH	224(3.72)	78-3489-80
Prosta-5,8(12),13-trien-1-oic acid, 15-hydroxy-9-oxo-, methyl ester (1-prostaglandin B_2 methyl ester)	MeOH	278(4.38)	87-0903-80
$C_{21}H_{32}O_{12}$			
Montinioside	MeOH	251(4.0)	100-0649-80
$C_{21}H_{32}O_{13}$			
Tecoside	MeOH	225(4.6),262(4.4), 293(4.1),330(3.3)	100-0649-80
$C_{21}H_{32}O_{14}$			
Ulmoside	EtOH	204(3.6)	100-0649-80
$C_{21}H_{32}O_{15}$			
β-D-Glucopyranoside, 1b,2,6,6a-tetrahy-dro-6-hydroxy-1a-methyloxirano[4,5]-cyclopenta[1,2-c]pyran-2,5a(1aH)-diyl-bis-, [1aS-(1aα,1bβ,2β,5aβ,6β,6aα)]-	n.s.g.	208(3.5)	100-0649-80
Melittoside	EtOH	209(3.57)	100-0649-80
$C_{21}H_{33}NO_2$			
2-Dodecenamide, N-[2-(4-hydroxyphenyl)-ethyl]-3-methyl-, (E)-	MeOH	278(--),284s(3.53)	12-1799-80
(Z)-	MeOH	278(3.46)	12-1799-80
$C_{21}H_{33}NO_3$			
3-Pyridinecarboxaldehyde, 1-cyclohexyl-	C_6H_{12}	396(3.35)	88-4097-80

Compound	Solvent	$\lambda_{max}(\log \epsilon)$	Ref.
5-(1,1-dimethylethyl)-6-(2,2-dimeth-yl-1-oxopropyl)-1,6-dihydro-6-hydr-oxy- (cont.)			88-4097-80
$C_{21}H_{34}O_5$			
3-Furancarboxylic acid, 2,5-dihydro-4-methyl-5-oxo-2-(14-oxopentadecyl)-(isomuronic acid)	EtOH	227(4.1)	102-1117-80
Prosta-8,13-dien-1-oic acid, 9,15-di-hydroxy-10-oxo-, methyl ester, (13E,15S)-(±)-	EtOH EtOH-NaOH	262(4.09) 301(c. 4.00)	88-1685-80 88-1685-80
$C_{21}H_{35}NO_4$			
1-Pyrrolidineheptanoic acid, 2-oxo-5-(3-oxo-1-noneyl)-, methyl ester, [R-(E)]-	MeOH	215(4.16)	94-1449-80
$C_{21}H_{36}O_2$			
2,11,14-Eicosatrienoic acid, methyl ester, (E,Z,Z)-	n.s.g.	206(4.24)	54-0132-80
$C_{21}H_{36}O_3$			
Benzene, 1,3,5-tris(2-methylbutoxy)-	MeCN	225(3.96),267(2.72)	108-0142-80
1,3,5-Benzenetrimethanol, α,α',α''-triethyl-α,α',α''-trimethyl-	MeCN	202(4.19),215s(3.90), 264(2.51),269s(2.42), 273s(2.30)	108-0142-80
$C_{21}H_{38}N$			
Pyridinium, 1-hexadecyl-, chloride, iodine complex	CHCl$_3$ C$_2$H$_4$Cl$_2$	263(4.49),368(3.68) 262(4.58),370(4.03)	106-0030-80 106-0030-80
Pyridinium, 1-hexadecyl-, iodide, iodine complex	CHCl$_3$ C$_2$H$_4$Cl$_2$	295(4.56),365(4.40) 295(4.64),365(4.45)	106-0030-80 106-0030-80
$C_{21}H_{38}N_2O_4$			
Propanedioic acid, bis(2,2,6,6-tetra-methyl-4-piperidinyl) ester	C$_6$H$_{12}$	254(4.24),323(1.94)	22-0147-80
$C_{21}H_{39}N_3O$			
1H-1,2,4-Triazole, 1-(4-methyl-1-oxo-octadecyl)-	THF	225(3.88)	33-0588-80

Compound	Solvent	$\lambda_{max}(\log \epsilon)$	Ref.
$C_{22}H_{10}N_4$ 2,7-Pyrenediacetonitrile, α,α'-dicyano-	MeCN	260(3.97),272(4.05), 305(3.95),323(4.00), 338(4.08)	77-0947-80
$C_{22}H_{10}N_8O$ 9,10-Epoxyanthracene-2,2,3,3,6,6,7,7- (1H,4H)-octacarbonitrile, 5,8,9,10- tetrahydro-	EtOH	210(3.85),240s(3.59)	33-1149-80
$C_{22}H_{11}ClO_2S$ Anthra[1,2-b]thiophene-6,11-dione, 4-(4-chlorophenyl)-	CHCl$_3$	258(4.51),292(4.51), 353(3.78),432(3.48)	4-0695-80
$C_{22}H_{11}Cl_8NO_8$ 1(2H)-Pyridineacetic acid, α-(2-acet- oxy-3,4,5,6-tetrachlorophenoxy)-2- oxo-α-(2,3,4,5-tetrachloro-6-hy- droxyphenoxy)-, methyl ester	MeCN	211(5.014),301(3.889), 317s(3.568),330s(3.254)	5-1836-80
$C_{22}H_{12}Br_2O_2S_6$ Ethanone, 2,2'-dithiobis[1-(4-bromo- phenyl)-2-(1,3-dithiol-2-ylidene)-	EtOH	225s(4.26),270(3.98), 340(3.78),425(4.37)	18-2281-80
$C_{22}H_{12}Cl_4N_2O_6$ 2,5-Epoxy-1,6,3-benzodioxazocin-4(5H)- one, 7,8,9,10-tetrachloro-2,3-dihy- dro-3-methyl-5-(4-nitrophenyl)-2- phenyl-	MeCN	215(4.90),240s(4.311), 252(4.291)	5-1850-80
$C_{22}H_{12}N_2$ 9,14-Diazabiphenyleno[2,3-1]phenanthr- ene	EtOH	253(5.04),276(4.68), 286(4.66),298(4.55), 343s(3.99),354(4.16), 401(4.41),424(4.59)	150-2941-80
Dipyrido[4,5-b:12,13-b'][2.2]para- cyclophane	EtOH	207(4.57),213(4.60), 231(4.44),234(4.44), 249(4.25),303(3.67), 306(3.67),316(3.60), 320(3.60)	19-0529-80
Dipyrido[4,5-b:13,12-b'][2.2]para- cyclophane	EtOH	207(4.48),213(4.54), 229(4.29),233(4.30), 247(4.19),306(3.43), 311(3.54),317(3.52), 319(3.52),347(2.93)	19-0529-80
$C_{22}H_{12}N_2O_4$ Benzo[1,2-c:4,5-c']dipyrrole-1,3,5,7- (2H,6H)-tetrone, 2,6-diphenyl-	Me$_3$PO$_4$	308(<u>3.7</u>)	116-0826-80
$C_{22}H_{12}N_4$ Propanedinitrile, 2,2'-(4,5,9,10-tetra- hydro-2,7-pyrenediylidene)bis- bis(tetrabutylammonium) compd.	C$_3$H$_7$CN C$_3$H$_7$CN	243(4.60),340(3.31), 557(4.12) 292(3.91),312(4.08), 327(4.52),341(4.26), 371(4.36)	77-0947-80 77-0947-80
$C_{22}H_{12}N_4O_6$ 2H,7H-Dipyrimido[6,1-b:5',4'-e][1,3]- oxazine-10-carboxaldehyde, 3,4,8,9- tetrahydro-2,4,7,9-tetraoxo-3,8-diphenyl-	MeOH MeOH-acid	495(3.90),575(4.90) 363(2.8),495(<u>4.3</u>), <u>580s(4.2)</u>	103-0773-80 103-0773-80

Compound	Solvent	$\lambda_{max}(\log \epsilon)$	Ref.
$C_{22}H_{12}O_2S$			
Anthra[1,2-b]thiophene-6,11-dione, 4-phenyl-	CHCl$_3$	250(4.51),305(4.54), 375(3.54),410(3.65)	4-0695-80
Anthra[2,1-b]thiophene-6,11-dione, 4-phenyl-	CHCl$_3$	252(4.42),292(4.61), 303s(4.58),378s(3.58), 412(3.67)	4-0695-80
Benz[a]anthracene-7,12-dione, 5-(2-thienyl)-	CHCl$_3$	248(4.00),292(4.54), 345s(3.79),429(3.72)	4-0695-80
Benz[a]anthracene-7,12-dione, 5-(3-thienyl)-	CHCl$_3$	250(4.52),285(4.45), 340(3.75),425(3.60)	4-0695-80
$C_{22}H_{12}O_3$			
Anthra[2,1-b]furan-6,11-dione, 4-phenyl-	CHCl$_3$	244(4.43),282s(4.54), 291(4.54),341s(3.70), 393(3.90)	4-0695-80
$C_{22}H_{12}O_4$			
5,8,13,14-Pentaphenetetrone, 6,7-dihydro-	CHCl$_3$	251(4.38),270s(4.24), 295s(4.11),333(3.76)	39-0282-80C
$C_{22}H_{12}O_5$			
Dinaphtho[1,2-b:2',1'-d]furan-5,6-dione, 8-acetoxy-	CHCl$_3$	255s(4.61),266(4.68), 276(4.73),290s(4.30), 299s(4.26),319s(3.91), 336(3.76),380s(3.26), 476(3.48)	39-0090-80C
$C_{22}H_{13}BrClNO_3$			
2H-Anthra[1,2-d][1,3]oxazine-7,12-dione, 6-bromo-2-(2-chlorophenyl)-1,4-dihydro-	EtOH	486(3.81)	18-3007-80
2H-Anthra[1,2-d][1,3]oxazine-7,12-dione, 6-bromo-2-(4-chlorophenyl)-1,4-dihydro-	EtOH	478(3.95)	18-3007-80 +146-0513-80
$C_{22}H_{13}BrN_2O_5$			
2H-Anthra[1,2-d][1,3]oxazine-7,12-dione, 6-bromo-1,4-dihydro-2-(2-nitrophenyl)-	EtOH	478(3.96)	18-3007-80 +146-0513-80
2H-Anthra[1,2-d][1,3]oxazine-7,12-dione, 6-bromo-1,4-dihydro-2-(3-nitrophenyl)-	EtOH	482(3.91)	18-3007-80 +146-0513-80
2H-Anthra[1,2-d][1,3]oxazine-7,12-dione, 6-bromo-1,4-dihydro-2-(4-nitrophenyl)-	EtOH	486(4.77)	18-3007-80 +146-0513-80
$C_{22}H_{13}ClN_2O_5$			
Furo[3,2-b]pyridin-2(4H)-one, 4-[3-(4-chlorophenyl)-3-oxo-1-propenyl]-3-(4-nitrophenyl)-, (E)-	CHCl$_3$	280(4.19),450(4.03)	39-1176-80C
$C_{22}H_{13}NO_4$			
6H,16H-[1]Benzopyrano[4,3-d][1]benzoxocino[4,3-b]pyridine-6,16-dione, 7-methyl-	MeOH	244(3.47),278(3.43), 317(3.21)	4-1737-80
$C_{22}H_{13}N_3O_3S$			
3-Furancarbonitrile, 2-[[(5-nitro-2-thienyl)methylene]amino]-4,5-diphenyl-	MeOH	448(3.83)	73-1581-80

Compound	Solvent	λ_{max}(log ϵ)	Ref.
$C_{22}H_{13}N_3O_4$ 3-Furancarbonitrile, 2-[[(5-nitro-2-furanyl)methylene]amino]-4,5-diphenyl-	MeOH	455(4.13)	73-1581-80
$C_{22}H_{14}BrNO_3$ 2H-Anthra[1,2-d][1,3]oxazine-7,12-dione, 6-bromo-1,4-dihydro-2-phenyl-	EtOH	488(3.86)	18-3007-80 +146-0513-80
$C_{22}H_{14}BrNO_4$ 2H-Anthra[1,2-d][1,3]oxazine-7,12-dione, 6-bromo-1,4-dihydro-2-(2-hydroxyphenyl)-	EtOH	482(3.91)	18-3007-80 +146-0513-80
2H-Anthra[1,2-d][1,3]oxazine-7,12-dione, 6-bromo-1,4-dihydro-2-(3-hydroxyphenyl)-	EtOH	488(3.93)	18-3007-80 +146-0513-80
2H-Anthra[1,2-d][1,3]oxazine-7,12-dione, 6-bromo-1,4-dihydro-2-(4-hydroxyphenyl)-	EtOH	478(3.95)	18-3007-80 +146-0513-80
$C_{22}H_{14}ClNO_3$ Furo[3,2-b]pyridin-2(4H)-one, 4-[3-(4-chlorophenyl)-3-oxo-1-propenyl]-3-phenyl-, (E)-	CHCl₃	283(4.52),450(4.20)	39-1176-80C
$C_{22}H_{14}Cl_2O$ 1-Naphthaleneacetyl chloride, α-chloro-α-1-naphthalenyl-	hexane	223(4.91),288(4.13)	78-2291-80
2-Naphthaleneacetyl chloride, α-chloro-α-2-naphthalenyl-	hexane	218(4.95),232(4.94)	78-2291-80
$C_{22}H_{14}N_2OS$ 3-Furancarbonitrile, 4,5-diphenyl-2-[(2-thienylmethylene)amino]-	MeOH	431(4.34)	73-1581-80
$C_{22}H_{14}N_2O_2$ 3-Furancarbonitrile, 2-[(2-furanylmethylene)amino]-4,5-diphenyl-	MeOH	422(3.60)	73-1581-80
$C_{22}H_{14}N_2O_2S$ Methanone, (2-hydroxyphenyl)(3-phenylpyrazolo[5,1-b]benzothiazol-2-yl)-	EtOH	218(4.41),250s(--), 290(4.11),340s(--)	39-0354-80C
$C_{22}H_{14}N_2O_3S$ 12H-[1]Benzothiopyrano[2,3-b]indolizine-6-carboxamide, 12-oxo-N-phenyl-, 5-oxide	CHCl₃	314(4.04),331s(4.09), 345(4.22),396(4.12)	150-0139-80
$C_{22}H_{14}N_2O_4S$ 12H-[1]Benzothiopyrano[2,3-b]indolizine-6-carboxamide, 12-oxo-N-phenyl-, 5,5-dioxide	CHCl₃	300s(3.96),331s(4.10), 341(4.22),394(4.15)	150-0139-80
12H-[1]Benzothiopyrano[3,2-b]indolizine-11-carboxamide, 12-oxo-N-phenyl-, 5,5-dioxide	CHCl₃	291(4.10),301s(3.98), 328(4.02),340(3.97), 417(4.13)	150-0139-80
$C_{22}H_{14}N_4$ Pyrazino[2,3-c]cinnoline, 2,3-diphenyl-	dioxan	225(4.39),286(4.24) 392(4.06)	150-2941-80
$C_{22}H_{14}N_6$ Quinoxaline, 2,3-bis(1H-benzimidazol-2-yl)-	CHCl₃	257(4.52),276(4.36), 316(4.57),346s(4.33),	150-2941-80

Compound	Solvent	λ_{max}(log ϵ)	Ref.
(cont.)		362s(4.27),390s(4.12)	150-2941-80
$C_{22}H_{14}N_6O_6$			
4,5-Imidazolidinedione, 2-[nitro-[(4-nitrophenyl)azo]methylene]-1,3-diphenyl-	MeCN	280(3.93),402(4.53)	48-0087-80
$C_{22}H_{14}O$			
15H-Dibenzo[a,g]cyclotridecen-15-one, 5,6,7,8-tetradehydro-14-methyl-	ether	222(4.54),268s(4.39), 280(4.55),295(4.59), 352(3.57),370s(3.48)	39-0466-80C
	CF₃COOH	289s(--),300(--), 348s(--),410s(--)	39-0466-80C
Methanone, 4H-cyclopenta[def]phenanthren-1-ylphenyl-	EtOH	210(4.53),225(4.47), 252(4.71),321(3.98)	18-0494-80
$C_{22}H_{14}O_2$			
6,13-Epidioxypentacene, 6,13-dihydro-	THF	250(4.89),270(4.63), 308(3.12),312(3.12), 317(3.07),327(3.03)	78-2225-80
7,14-Epoxydinaphth[2,3-b:2',3'-e]oxepin, 7,14-dihydro-	THF	243(4.76),248(4.81), 268(4.18),279(4.11), 308(3.30),322(3.49), 337(3.55)	78-2225-80
Ethanedione, di-1-naphthalenyl-	EtOH	330(4.2),410s(--)	46-2623-80
	CCl₄	326(4.2),420s(--)	46-2623-80
$C_{22}H_{14}O_6$			
[2,2'-Binaphthalene]-1,1',4,4'-tetrone, 5,5'-dihydroxy-7,7'-dimethyl-	CHCl₃	249(4.17),255(4.18), 261(4.16),278(4.11), 350s(3.43),445(3.88)	5-1321-80
[2,2'-Binaphthalene]-1,1',4,4'-tetrone, 5,8'-dihydroxy-6',7-dimethyl-	CHCl₃	253(4.29),277(4.24), 443(3.95)	5-1321-80
[2,2'-Binaphthalene]-1,1',4,4'-tetrone, 8,8'-dihydroxy-6,6'-dimethyl-(mamegakinone)	CHCl₃	252(4.26),276(4.19), 350(3.54),440(3.92)	5-1321-80
[2,2'-Binaphthalene]-1,4,5',8'-tetrone, 1',5-dihydroxy-3',7-dimethyl-(diospyrin)	pH 1 pH 13	438(3.99) 560(4.18)	120-0180-80 120-0180-80
[2,2'-Binaphthalene]-1,1',4,4'-tetrone, 5,5'-dimethoxy-	CHCl₃	246(4.40),271(4.30), 405(3.91)	5-1321-80
[2,2'-Binaphthalene]-1,1',4,4'-tetrone, 5,8'-dimethoxy-	CHCl₃	246(4.39),270s(4.26), 320s(3.45),405(3.89)	5-1321-80
[2,2'-Binaphthalene]-1,1',4,4'-tetrone, 8,8'-dimethoxy-	CHCl₃	247(4.39),320s(3.53), 404(3.86)	5-1321-80
5,12-Naphthacenedione, 7,10-diacetoxy-	CH₂Cl₂	265(4.53),272(4.54), 283(4.55),295(4.53), 316s(3.84),398(3.70)	23-1161-80
$C_{22}H_{14}O_7$			
Batocanone	MeOH	258(4.39),306s(3.64), 324(3.82),444s(3.32)	88-2459-80
[2,2'-Binaphthalene]-1,4,5',8'-tetrone, 1',5,6'-trihydroxy-3',7-dimethyl-	MeOH	249s(4.22),292(3.92), 437(3.58)	39-1161-80C
[2,2'-Binaphthalene]-1,4,5',8'-tetrone, 1',5,7'-trihydroxy-3',7-dimethyl-	MeOH	232s(4.48),263s(4.34), 430(3.81)	39-1161-80C
Naphth[2,3-b]oxirene-2,7-dione, 4-(1,4-dihydro-5-hydroxy-7-methyl-1,4-dioxo-2-naphthalenyl)-1a,7a-dihydro-3-hydroxy-5-methyl-	MeOH	248(4.40),289s(3.86), 375(3.81),422s(3.74)	39-1161-80C

Compound	Solvent	$\lambda_{max}(\log \epsilon)$	Ref.
$C_{22}H_{14}O_8$ 5,12-Naphthacenedione, 7,10-diacetoxy-1,4-dihydroxy-	CH_2Cl_2	265s(4.47),280(4.58), 290(4.53),301(4.46), 470(4.25),480s(4.24), 498s(4.14),512s(3.98)	23-1161-80
$C_{22}H_{14}O_9$ Benzoic acid, 5-[(3-carboxy-4-hydroxyphenyl)(3-carboxy-4-oxo-2,5-cyclohexadien-1-ylidene)methyl]-2-hydroxy-	EtOH	530(3.23)	147-0409-80A
$C_{22}H_{14}S$ Anthra[2,1-b]thiophene, 4-phenyl-	$CHCl_3$	248s(4.58),256s(4.62), 271(4.74),284s(4.77), 293(4.84),337s(3.74), 350(3.94),368(4.08), 388(3.94)	4-0695-80
Dibenzo[d,j]thiacyclopentadecin, 16,17,18,19-tetradehydro-	THF	222(4.61),283s(4.57), 300s(4.66),313(4.70), 375s(3.61)	18-1127-80
$C_{22}H_{15}BrO$ 9(10H)-Anthracenone, 10-[bromo(4-bromophenyl)methylene]-	EtOH	238(4.67),283(4.26), 356(4.02)	35-3837-80
$C_{22}H_{15}BrO_2$ 9(10H)-Anthracenone, 10-[bromo(2-methoxyphenyl)methylene]-	EtOH	230(4.54),285(4.18), 353(3.90)	35-3837-80
9(10H)-Anthracenone, 10-[(5-bromo-2-methoxyphenyl)methylene]-	EtOH	237(4.62),282(4.15), 375(4.03)	35-3837-80
4H-1-Benzopyran-4-one, 3-[(4-bromophenyl)methylene]-2,3-dihydro-2-phenyl-, (E)-	EtOH	240s(--),311(4.17), 350s(--)	114-0369-80B
	H_2SO_4	406(4.36),470(4.12)	114-0369-80B
$C_{22}H_{15}ClN_4O$ 2-Naphthalenol, 1-[[4-[(4-chlorophenyl)azo]phenyl]azo]-	acetone	504(4.48)	7-0173-80
$C_{22}H_{15}ClO_2$ 4H-1-Benzopyran-4-one, 3-[(4-chlorophenyl)methylene]-2,3-dihydro-2-phenyl-, (E)-	EtOH	220s(--),309(4.22), 350s(--)	114-0369-80B
	H_2SO_4	400(4.36),470(4.08)	114-0369-80B
$C_{22}H_{15}Cl_3N_2O$ Benzenepropanenitrile, 2-chloro-β-[3-chloro-6-(methoxyimino)-2,4-cyclohexadien-1-ylidene]-α-(2-chlorophenyl)-	MeOH	267(3.88),290s(3.71)	73-3593-80
$C_{22}H_{15}Cl_4N_3O$ 2-Propenamide, N-[bis[(3,4-dichlorophenyl)amino]methylene]-3-phenyl-	$CHCl_3$	297(4.70)	48-0434-80
$C_{22}H_{15}NO_2$ 5(4H)-Oxazolone, 2-[1,1'-biphenyl]-4-yl-4-(phenylmethylene)-	$CHCl_3$	380(4.75)	103-0701-80
1H-Pyrrole-2,5-dione, 1,3,4-triphenyl-	MeCN	360(3.59)	40-0837-80
$C_{22}H_{15}NO_3$ 2H-Anthra[1,2-d][1,3]oxazine-7,12-dione, 1,4-dihydro-2-phenyl-	EtOH	498(4.12)	18-3007-80 +146-0513-80

Compound	Solvent	$\lambda_{max}(\log \epsilon)$	Ref.
$C_{22}H_{15}NO_4$			
4H-1-Benzopyran-4-one, 2,3-dihydro-3-[(4-nitrophenyl)methylene]-2-phenyl-, (E)-	EtOH	215(4.48),305(4.33), 350s(--)	114-0369-80B
	H_2SO_4	380(4.33),465(4.04)	114-0369-80B
$C_{22}H_{15}NO_4S$			
Benzoic acid, 2-[(1,4-dihydro-1,4-dioxopyrido[1,2-a]indol-10-yl)thioxomethyl]-, ethyl ester	$CHCl_3$	240(4.35),262(4.13), 312(3.87),338(3.80), 403(3.83),535(3.83)	39-1070-80C
$C_{22}H_{15}N_2OS$			
Pyrylium, 2-(2-benzimidazolyl)-4-phenyl-6-(2-thienyl)-, perchlorate	$C_2H_4Cl_2$	343(4.24),395(4.14), 512(4.03)	150-4041-80
$C_{22}H_{15}N_3$			
Benzo[b]pyrido[2,3-h][1,6]naphthyridine, 3-methyl-7-phenyl-	EtOH	213(4.58),256s(4.50), 272(4.51),293s(4.46), 301(4.52)	4-1225-80
$C_{22}H_{15}N_5O_3$			
2-Naphthalenol, 1-[[4-[(4-nitrophenyl)azo]phenyl]azo]-	acetone	515(4.55)	7-0173-80
$C_{22}H_{16}$			
Bicyclo[6.2.0]deca-1,3,5,7,9-pentaene, 9,10-diphenyl-	C_6H_{12}	235(4.2),325(4.8), 420s(2.9)	88-0107-80
Phenanthrene, 1-(2-phenylethenyl)-, cis	hexane	300(4.14)	70-0563-80
trans	hexane	320(4.36)	70-0563-80
Phenanthrene, 2-(2-phenylethenyl)-, cis	hexane	310(4.29)	70-0563-80
trans	hexane	280(4.6),292(4.6), 325(4.61)	70-0563-80
Phenanthrene, 3-(2-phenylethenyl)-, cis	hexane	275f(4.7),310(4.24)	70-0563-80
trans	hexane	275f(4.6),330(4.66)	70-0563-80
Phenanthrene, 9-(2-phenylethenyl)-, cis	hexane	301(4.08)	70-0563-80
trans	hexane	315(4.41)	70-0563-80
$C_{22}H_{16}BrNO$			
2(1H)-Naphthalenone, 1-[(6-bromo-1-methyl-2(1H)-quinolinylidene)ethylidene]-	EtOH	611(4.27)	104-0185-80
	benzene	605(--)	104-0185-80
	acetone	604(--)	104-0185-80
	$CHCl_3$	608(--)	104-0185-80
$C_{22}H_{16}BrNO_3$			
Benzamide, N-[2-[[3-(4-bromophenyl)-3-oxo-1-propenyl]oxy]phenyl]-, (E)-	dioxan	270(4.47)	48-0099-80
2-Propen-1-one, 3-[[2-(benzoyloxy)phenyl]amino]-1-(4-bromophenyl)-, (Z)-	dioxan	237(4.35),261(4.24), 377(4.47)	48-0099-80
$C_{22}H_{16}Br_2O_2$			
9(10H)-Anthracenone, 10-bromo-10-[bromo[(2-methoxyphenyl)methyl]-	EtOH	230s(4.30),265s(4.11), 285s(4.04)	35-3837-80
$C_{22}H_{16}ClNO_3$			
Benzamide, N-[2-[[3-(4-chlorophenyl)-3-oxo-1-propenyl]oxy]phenyl]-, (E)-	dioxan	266(4.46)	48-0099-80
2-Propen-1-one, 3-[[2-(benzoyloxy)phenyl]amino]-1-(4-chlorophenyl)-, (Z)-	dioxan	236(4.36),256(4.22), 376(4.46)	48-0099-80
$C_{22}H_{16}ClN_5O$			
1,2,4-Triazin-5(2H)-one, 6-[(4-chlorophenyl)methyl]-2-phenyl-3-(phenylazo)-	EtOH	220(4.19),300(4.00), 330(4.51),358s(4.48)	12-0619-80

Compound	Solvent	$\lambda_{max}(\log \epsilon)$	Ref.
$C_{22}H_{16}Cl_4O_2$			
1-Oxaspiro[3.5]nona-5,8-dien-7-one, 5,6,8,9-tetrachloro-2,3-bis(4-methylphenyl)-, trans	THF	260(4.11),307(3.80)	18-0726-80
$C_{22}H_{16}FNO_3$			
Benzamide, N-[2-[[3-(4-fluorophenyl)-3-oxo-1-propenyl]oxy]phenyl]-, (E)-	dioxan	262(4.37)	48-0099-80
2-Propen-1-one, 3-[[2-(benzoyloxy)phenyl]amino]-1-(4-fluorophenyl)-, (Z)-	dioxan	236(4.39),253s(4.18), 371(4.45)	48-0099-80
$C_{22}H_{16}INO_3$			
Benzamide, N-[2-[[3-(4-iodophenyl)-3-oxo-1-propenyl]oxy]phenyl]-, (E)-	dioxan	285(4.48)	48-0099-80
2-Propen-1-one, 3-[[2-(benzoyloxy)phenyl]amino]-1-(4-iodophenyl)-, (Z)-	dioxan	233(4.35),272(4.18), 378(4.49)	48-0099-80
$C_{22}H_{16}N_2$			
Acridine, 9,10-dihydro-9-(3H-indol-3-ylidene)-10-methyl-	n.s.g.	550(4.39)	103-0743-80
Benz[f]quinoline, 3,4-dihydro-3-(3H-indol-3-ylidene)-4-methyl-	n.s.g.	521(4.38)	103-0743-80
Quinoline, 2,2'-(1,3-butadiene-1,4-diyl)bis-	CH_2Cl_2	219(4.59),285(4.51), 362s(4.69),371(4.72), 375(4.72),387s(4.58)	5-0291-80
Quinoline, 4,4'-(1,3-butadiene-1,4-diyl)bis-	CH_2Cl_2	221(4.65),233s(4.59), 360(4.55)	5-0291-80
Quinoline, 2-[4-(4-quinolinyl)-1,3-butadienyl]-	CH_2Cl_2	262(4.31),274(4.33), 363(4.58)	5-0291-80
$C_{22}H_{16}N_2O$			
Pyridine, 3-[2-[4-(5-phenyl-2-oxazolyl)phenyl]ethenyl]-	DMF	356(4.73)	33-1311-80
$C_{22}H_{16}N_2O_2$			
Methanone, (5-methylpyrazolo[1,5-a]pyridine-2,3-diyl)bis[phenyl-	MeOH	223(4.52),254(4.42), 322(4.07)	44-0090-80
Methanone, (7-methylpyrazolo[1,5-a]pyridine-2,3-diyl)bis[phenyl-	MeOH	223(4.52),254(4.42), 322(4.07)	44-0090-80
2,4(1H,3H)-Pyrimidinedione, 1,3-dimethyl-5-(pyrenyl)-	MeCN	242(4.62),267(4.31), 277(4.47),327(4.36), 342(4.40)	88-2813-80
minor isomer	MeCN	242(4.73),267(4.42), 276(4.58),326(4.36), 341(4.50)	88-2813-80
$C_{22}H_{16}N_2O_3$			
6H-Anthra[1,9-cd]isoxazol-6-one, 5-[(4-ethoxyphenyl)amino]-	dioxan	261(4.45),500(4.16), 512(4.24)	103-0704-80
2(1H)-Naphthalenone, 1-[(1-methyl-6-nitro-2(1H)-quinolinylidene)-ethylidene]-	EtOH	637(3.56)	104-0185-80
	benzene	606(--)	104-0185-80
	acetone	618(--)	104-0185-80
	$CHCl_3$	607(--)	104-0185-80
$C_{22}H_{16}N_2O_5$			
Benzamide, N-[2-[[3-(4-nitrophenyl)-3-oxo-1-propenyl]oxy]phenyl]-, (E)-	dioxan	269(4.41)	48-0099-80
2-Propen-1-one, 3-[[2-(benzoyloxy)phenyl]amino]-1-(4-nitrophenyl)-, (Z)-	dioxan	233(4.35),272(4.21), 398(4.34)	48-0099-80

Compound	Solvent	$\lambda_{max}(\log \epsilon)$	Ref.
$C_{22}H_{16}N_2O_7$			
1(2H)-Quinolineacetic acid, 4-hydroxy-3-[(4-hydroxy-2-oxo-1(2H)-quinolinyl)acetyl]-2-oxo-	H_2O	282(4.08),333(4.28)	78-1385-80
$C_{22}H_{16}N_2S$			
Thieno[3',4':3,4]pyrazolo[1,5-a]pyridine-2-S^{IV}, 6-methyl-1,3-diphenyl-	MeOH	208(4.30),244(4.11), 266s(3.95),318(4.18), 380(3.39),477(3.84)	44-0090-80
Thieno[3',4':3,4]pyrazolo[1,5-a]pyridine-2-S^{IV}, 8-methyl-1,3-diphenyl-	MeOH	221(4.47),259(4.21), 274(4.21),327(4.48), 402(3.93),488(4.28)	44-0090-80
$C_{22}H_{16}N_4$			
Pyrido[1',2':1,5]pyrazolo[3,4-d]pyridazine, 7-methyl-1,4-diphenyl-	MeOH	212(4.42),233(4.23), 245(4.19),270(4.32), 284(4.29),315s(4.04), 360s(3.97),376(4.05)	44-0090-80
Pyrido[1',2':1,5]pyrazolo[3,4-d]pyridazine, 9-methyl-1,4-diphenyl-	MeOH	233s(4.30),269(4.32), 315s(4.04),374(4.04)	44-0090-80
$C_{22}H_{16}N_4O$			
2-Naphthalenol, 1-[[4-(phenylazo)phenyl]azo]-	acetone	502(4.44)	7-0173-80
$C_{22}H_{16}N_4O_5S$			
4H-1,3,5-Oxadiazine-4-thione, 2,3-dihydro-2,6-bis(4-nitrophenyl)-3-(phenylmethyl)-	dioxan	240s(--),291(4.59)	73-2254-80
$C_{22}H_{16}N_4O_7S_2$			
1,3-Naphthalenedisulfonic acid, 7-hydroxy-8-[[4-(phenylazo)phenyl]azo]-	dianion	218(4.28),245(4.30), 330s(4.04),346(4.08), 513(4.42)	59-0279-80
	trianion	226(4.23),252(4.20), 330s(4.20),349(4.20), 445s(3.95),545(3.85)	59-0279-80
$C_{22}H_{16}O$			
9(10H)-Anthracenone, 10-[(4-methylphenyl)methylene]-	EtOH	237(4.62),300(4.07), 382(4.03)	35-3837-80
9H-Benzocycloheptadecen-9-one, 16,17,18,19-tetradehydro-15-methyl-	THF	298(4.71),315s(4.67), 400s(3.67)	39-0473-80C
	CF_3COOH	288(--),332(--), 341(--),404s(--), 655(--)	39-0473-80C
1,4-Pentadien-3-one, 1,5-bis(2-ethynylphenyl)-2-methyl-	ether	224(4.57),245(4.53), 252s(4.47),305(4.39)	39-0466-80C
$C_{22}H_{16}O_2$			
9,10-Anthracenedione, 1-ethyl-3-phenyl-	$CHCl_3$	263(4.59),315(3.52), 435s(1.86)	4-0695-80
9(10H)-Anthracenone, 10-[(2-methoxyphenyl)methylene]-	EtOH	239(4.56),275s(4.12), 385(3.97)	35-3837-80
4H-1-Benzopyran-4-one, 2,3-dihydro-2-phenyl-3-(phenylmethylene)-, (E)-	EtOH	220s(--),304(4.24), 350s(--)	114-0369-80B
	H_2SO_4	400(4.25),460(4.18)	114-0369-80B
[1,1'-Binaphthalene]-8-carboxaldehyde, 8'-(hydroxymethyl)-	EtOH	257(4.12),286(4.12), 298(3.97),323(3.55)	65-2104-80
Dibenz[a,h]anthracene-3,4-diol, 3,4-dihydro-	EtOH	280(4.73),289(4.86), 299(3.79),338(3.68)	39-1920-80C

Compound	Solvent	$\lambda_{max}(\log \epsilon)$	Ref.
(cont.)		353(3.82),361(3.89), 388(3.74),395(3.72)	39-1920-80C
Dinaphtho[1,8a,8-ab:1',8'a,8'-de]cyclo-octene-10,11-diol, 10,11-dihydro-	EtOH	307(3.62),313(3.58), 327(3.46)	65-2104-80
6,13-Pentacenediol, 6,13-dihydro-, cis	THF	238(5.02),260(3.86), 269(3.89),278(3.85), 290(3.59),305(2.91), 314(2.59),319(2.84)	78-2225-80
1,4-Phenanthrenedione, 2,3-dimethyl-9-phenyl-	CHCl$_3$	241(4.26),286(4.38), 373(3.32),427(3.30)	44-1424-80
$C_{22}H_{16}O_3$			
4H-1-Benzopyran-4-one, 2,3-dihydro-3-[(4-hydroxyphenyl)methylene]-2-phen-yl-, (E)-	EtOH H$_2$SO$_4$	220s(--),351(4.25) 412(4.20),502(4.35)	114-0369-80B 114-0369-80B
$C_{22}H_{16}O_4$			
2H-Pyran-2-one, 3-[3-(9H-fluoren-2-yl)-1-oxo-2-propenyl]-4-hydroxy-6-methyl-	MeOH	387(4.4)	83-0344-80
$C_{22}H_{16}O_6$			
1H-Benz[f]indene-4,9-dione, 3-(3-acet-yl-4-hydroxy-2-oxo-2H-pyran-6-yl)-1,1-dimethyl-	MeOH	337(4.2)	83-0509-80
1(2H)-Naphthalenone, 5-hydroxy-2-(5-hy-droxy-4-methoxy-1-oxo-2(1H)-naphthyl-idene)-4-methoxy-	CHCl$_3$	287(4.27),330s(4.02), 665(4.36)	5-1321-80
1(2H)-Naphthalenone, 8-hydroxy-2-(8-hy-droxy-4-methoxy-1-oxo-2(1H)-naphthyl-idene)-4-methoxy-	CHCl$_3$	243(4.38),284(4.29), 327s(3.87),490(3.57), 693(4.43)	5-1321-80
$C_{22}H_{16}O_7$			
Benzo[kl]xanthene-1,2,3-tricarboxylic acid, trimethyl ester	dioxan	225(4.55),266s(4.42), 272(4.43),298(3.75), 360(3.92),390(3.96)	5-0867-80
$C_{22}H_{16}S$			
Benzene, 1-ethynyl-2-[2-[[4-(2-ethyn-ylphenyl)-1,3-butadienyl]thio]ethen-yl]-, (E,E,E)-	THF	227(4.53),237s(4.47), 255(4.40),290(4.15), 349(4.52)	18-1127-80
$C_{22}H_{16}S_2$			
1,3-Dithiole, 4,5-diphenyl-2-(phenyl-methylene)-	MeCN	237(4.37),339(4.32)	116-0240-80
$C_{22}H_{16}S_3$			
1-Propanethione, 2-(6b,9a-dihydroace-naphtho[1,2-d][1,3]dithiol-8-yli-dene)-1-phenyl-	MeOH	226(4.88),284s(4.22), 297(4.27),305(4.26), 310s(4.24),427(4.28), 580(2.37)	104-0395-80
$C_{22}H_{17}ClN_2O$			
3(2H)-Pyridazinone, 6-(4-chlorophenyl)-1,6-dihydro-2,6-diphenyl-	EtOH	238(4.45)	118-0457-80
$C_{22}H_{17}ClN_2O_3$			
9,10-Anthracenedione, 1-amino-2-chloro-4-[[4-(2-hydroxyethyl)phenyl]amino]-	n.s.g.	584(4.08),622(4.08)	93-1963-80

Compound	Solvent	$\lambda_{max}(\log \epsilon)$	Ref.
$C_{22}H_{17}ClN_2O_4$			
9,10-Anthracenedione, 1-amino-2-chloro-4-[(2,5-dimethoxyphenyl)amino]-	n.s.g.	576(4.09),611(--)	93-1963-80
8-Azabicyclo[3.2.1]oct-3-en-2-one, 8-[3-(2-chloro-5-nitrophenyl)-3-oxo-1-propenyl]-6-phenyl-, [1α,5α,6β,8(E)]-	CHCl$_3$	250(4.36),305(4.08)	39-0362-80C
$C_{22}H_{17}ClN_6O$			
3H-Pyrazol-3-one, 4-[[4-[(4-chlorophenyl)azo]phenyl]azo]-2,4-dihydro-5-methyl-2-phenyl-	acetone	420(4.35)	7-0173-80
$C_{22}H_{17}NO$			
Benz[g]isoquinolinium, 8-methyl-, 2-oxo-2-phenylethylide	CHCl$_3$	257(4.70),320s(4.00)	103-0626-80
2(1H)-Naphthalenone, 1-[(1-methyl-2(1H)-quinolinylidene)ethylidene]-	EtOH	602(4.21)	104-0185-80
	benzene	603(--)	104-0185-80
	acetone	624(--)	104-0185-80
	CHCl$_3$	622(--)	104-0185-80
6H-1,3-Oxazine, 2,6,6-triphenyl-	n.s.g.	239(4.20),338(3.79)	39-1866-80C
Pyridine, 3-[2-[4-[(4-methoxyphenyl)-ethynyl]phenyl]ethenyl]-	DMF	346(4.75)	33-1311-80
Pyridine, 3-[2-[4-(5-methyl-2-benzofuranyl)phenyl]ethenyl]-	DMF	356(4.76)	33-1311-80
Pyridine, 3-[2-[4-(6-methyl-2-benzofuranyl)phenyl]ethenyl]-	DMF	359(4.76)	33-1311-80
5H,9H-Quino[3,2,1-de]acridin-5-one, 9,9-dimethyl-	C$_6$H$_{12}$	201(4.57),229(4.23), 256(4.54),293s(3.99), 303(3.96),377s(3.97), 398(4.04)	24-0358-80
	EtOH	210(4.16),231(4.33), 261(4.67),405(4.06)	24-0358-80
	H$_2$SO$_4$	200(4.47),232s(4.19), 272(4.69),348(3.98), 454(3.93)	24-0358-80
$C_{22}H_{17}NOS$			
Thiazolium, 4-hydroxy-2-(4-methylphenyl)-3,5-diphenyl-, hydroxide, inner salt	EtOH	265(3.85),450(3.83)	44-2165-80
Thiazolium, 4-hydroxy-3-(2-methylphenyl)-2,5-diphenyl-, hydroxide, inner salt	EtOH	262(3.92),450(3.81)	44-2165-80
$C_{22}H_{17}NO_2$			
4H-1-Benzopyran-4-one, 3-[(diphenylamino)methylene]-2,3-dihydro-, (E)-	EtOH	218s(4.15),242(3.97), 265(4.07),330s(3.77), 387(4.21)	4-0061-80
1,3-Dioxolo[4,5-g]isoquinoline, 7,8-dihydro-5,7-diphenyl-	MeOH	285(3.93),316(3.96)	2-0556-80
Pyridine, 3-[2-[4-(5-methoxy-2-benzofuranyl)phenyl]ethenyl]-	DMF	357(4.78)	33-1311-80
$C_{22}H_{17}NO_2S$			
Thiazolium, 4-hydroxy-3-(4-methoxyphenyl)-2,5-diphenyl-, hydroxide, inner salt	EtOH	271(4.50),450(4.45)	44-2165-80
$C_{22}H_{17}NO_3$			
Benzamide, N-[2-[3-oxo-3-phenyl-1-propenyl)oxy]phenyl]-, (E)-	dioxan	260(4.39)	48-0099-80

Compound	Solvent	$\lambda_{max}(\log \epsilon)$	Ref.
2-Cyclopenten-1-one, 4-[cyano(methoxy-carbonyl)methylene]-2-methyl-3,5-di-phenyl-	MeCN	301(4.21)	24-0424-80
2-Propen-1-one, 3-[[2-(benzoyloxy)phen-yl]amino]-1-phenyl-, (Z)-	dioxan	238(4.39),253s(4.21), 373(4.43)	48-0099-80
Pyrrolo[2,1-a]isoquinoline-1-carboxylic acid, 3-benzoyl-2-methyl-, methyl ester	EtOH	216s(4.40),273(4.60), 320(4.13),368s(4.12), 382(4.18)	18-0297-80
$C_{22}H_{17}NO_4S_2$			
Benzenesulfonamide, N-[2-[(3-hydroxy-benzo[b]thien-2-yl)carbonyl]phenyl]-4-methyl-	MeOH	267(4.06),324(3.96), 391(3.71)	83-0027-80
$C_{22}H_{17}NO_5S_3$			
1,3-Dithiole-4,5-dicarboxylic acid, 2-[2-(benzoylamino)-1-phenyl-2-thi-oxoethylidene]-, dimethyl ester	CHCl$_3$	321(4.25),440(4.43)	39-2693-80C
$C_{22}H_{17}NS$			
Pyridine, 3-[2-[4-(5-methylbenzo[b]thi-en-2-yl)phenyl]ethenyl]-	DMF	356(4.75)	33-1311-80
Pyridine, 3-[2-[4-(6-methylbenzo[b]thi-en-2-yl)phenyl]ethenyl]-	DMF	357(4.74)	33-1311-80
5H,9H-Quino[3,2,1-de]acridine-5-thione, 9,9-dimethyl-	C$_6$H$_{12}$	209(4.37),249(4.38), 293(4.23),306s(4.16), 340s(3.44),470s(4.11), 486(4.19)	24-0358-80
	EtOH	208(4.45),232(4.19), 252(4.41),262s(4.32), 293(4.19),420s(3.54), 492(4.08)	24-0358-80
$C_{22}H_{17}N_2S$			
Thiopyrylium, 2-(6-amino-3-pyridinyl)-4,6-diphenyl-, perchlorate	n.s.g.	302(3.54),425(3.38)	39-1345-80C
$C_{22}H_{17}N_3O$			
Pyridine, 3-[2-[4-[3-(4-methylphenyl)-1,2,4-oxadiazol-5-yl]phenyl]ethenyl]-	DMF	335(4.66)	33-1311-80
$C_{22}H_{17}N_3O_2$			
6H-Anthra[1,9-cd]isoxazol-6-one, 3-(di-methylamino)-5-(phenylamino)-	dioxan	254(4.46),489(4.33), 519(4.42)	103-0704-80
6H-Anthra[1,9-cd]isoxazol-6-one, 3-(eth-ylamino)-5-(phenylamino)-	dioxan	253(4.39),486(4.24), 515(4.33)	103-0704-80
6H-Anthra[1,9-cd]isoxazol-6-one, 3-(methylamino)-5-[(4-methylphenyl)-amino]-	dioxan	256(4.55),494(4.31), 510(4.39)	103-0704-80
Pyridine, 3-[2-[4-[5-(4-methoxyphenyl)-1,3,4-oxadiazol-2-yl]phenyl]ethenyl]-	DMF	344(4.74)	33-1311-80
$C_{22}H_{17}N_3O_3S$			
4H-1,3,5-Oxadiazine-4-thione, 2,3-di-hydro-6-(4-nitrophenyl)-2-phenyl-3-(phenylmethyl)-	dioxan	245s(--),293(4.37)	73-2254-80
$C_{22}H_{17}N_3O_4S$			
Benzoic acid, 4-[(3-phenyl-4H-1,4-benzothiazin-2-yl)azo]-, methyl ester, S,S-dioxide	EtOH	228(4.32),266s(4.19), 301s(4.02),397(4.43)	39-2923-80C

Compound	Solvent	$\lambda_{max}(\log \epsilon)$	Ref.
$C_{22}H_{17}N_5O$ 1,2,4-Triazin-5(2H)-one, 2-phenyl-3-(phenylazo)-6-(phenylmethyl)-	EtOH	218(4.14),295(3.95), 328(4.45),355(4.49)	12-0619-80
$C_{22}H_{17}N_5O_3$ Acetamide, N-[2-[2-(1H-benzotriazol-1-yl)ethyl]-2,3-dihydro-1,3-dioxo-1H-benz[de]isoquinolin-5-yl]-	dioxan	256(4.61),341(4.04), 375(3.76)	56-0107-80
Acetamide, N-[2-[2-(1H-benzotriazol-1-yl)ethyl]-2,3-dihydro-1,3-dioxo-1H-benz[de]isoquinolin-6-yl]-	dioxan	247(4.41),370(4.13)	56-0107-80
Acetamide, N-[2-[2-(2H-benzotriazol-2-yl)ethyl]-2,3-dihydro-1,3-dioxo-1H-benz[de]isoquinolin-5-yl]-	dioxan	247(4.41),281(4.21), 369(4.18)	56-0107-80
$C_{22}H_{17}N_7O_3$ 3H-Pyrazol-3-one, 2,4-dihydro-5-methyl-4-[[4-[(4-nitrophenyl)azo]phenyl]azo]-2-phenyl-	acetone	430(4.41)	7-0173-80
$C_{22}H_{17}OP$ 7H-Dibenzo[d,f]phosphonin, 7-phenyl-, 7-oxide	EtOH	202(4.66),259s(3.88)	35-4838-80
$C_{22}H_{17}O_2P$ 4H-1,4-Oxaphosphorin, 2,4,6-triphenyl-, 4-oxide	MeOH	<u>248(4.6)</u>	97-0261-80
$C_{22}H_{17}P$ 7H-Dibenzo[d,f]phosphonin, 7-phenyl-	EtOH	202(4.64),255s(3.82)	35-4838-80
$C_{22}H_{18}$ Cyclopropene, 2-methyl-1,3,3-triphenyl-	EtOH	262(4.26)	44-4555-80
1H-Indene, 1-methyl-2,3-diphenyl-	EtOH	238(4.35),303(4.23)	44-4555-80
1H-Indene, 2-methyl-1,3-diphenyl-	EtOH	227(4.47),263(4.03)	44-4555-80
1H-Indene, 3-methyl-1,2-diphenyl-	EtOH	230(4.20),295(4.22)	44-4555-80
$C_{22}H_{18}ClNO$ 2-Propen-1-one, 1-(4-chlorophenyl)-3-[(3-methylphenyl)amino]-	C_6H_{12}	256(4.20),382(4.37)	34-0083-80
	EtOH	256(4.27),381(4.45)	34-0083-80
2-Propen-1-one, 1-(4-chlorophenyl)-3-[(4-methylphenyl)amino]-	C_6H_{12}	256(4.30),382(4.42)	34-0083-80
	EtOH	254(4.25),382(4.44)	34-0083-80
$C_{22}H_{18}ClNO_2$ 8-Azabicyclo[3.2.1]oct-3-en-2-one, 8-[3-(4-chlorophenyl)-3-oxo-1-propenyl]-6-phenyl-, [1α,5α,6β,8(E)]-	$CHCl_3$	258(4.32),336(4.72)	39-0362-80C
2-Propen-1-one, 1-(4-chlorophenyl)-3-[(4-methoxyphenyl)amino]-3-phenyl-	C_6H_{12}	256(4.28),385(4.40)	34-0083-80
	EtOH	252(4.26),385(4.41)	34-0083-80
$C_{22}H_{18}ClN_3O_4S$ Benzenesulfonamide, 5-[(4-amino-3-chloro-9,10-dihydro-9,10-dioxo-1-anthracenyl)amino]-N,2-dimethyl-	n.s.g.	573(4.00),605(3.96)	93-1963-80
$C_{22}H_{18}Cl_2N_4O_5$ 1H-Imidazolo[1,5-a][1,4]benzodiazepine-3-carboxylic acid, 8-chloro-6-(2-chlorophenyl)-2-[(ethoxycarbonyl)amino]-2,4-dihydro-1-oxo-, methyl ester	isoPrOH	210s(4.66),277(4.36)	4-1697-80

Compound	Solvent	$\lambda_{max}(\log \epsilon)$	Ref.
$C_{22}H_{18}Cl_2O_2$ Ethanone, 1-(4-chlorophenyl)-2-[2-(4-chlorophenyl)-1-oxaspiro[4.4]non-2-en-4-ylidene]-	EtOH	425(4.47)	5-1744-80
$C_{22}H_{18}Cl_2O_6$ 7H-Benzo[c]fluoren-7-one, 5,6-dichloro-2,3,8,9,10-pentamethoxy-	MeOH	390(3.56)	2-0552-80
$C_{22}H_{18}F_3N_3O_{11}$ β-D-Ribofuranoside, methyl 3-deoxy-3-[(trifluoroacetyl)amino]-, 2,5-bis(4-nitrobenzoate)	EtOH	207(3.93),258(4.32)	33-2258-80
$C_{22}H_{18}FeGe$ Ferrocene, 1,1'-(diphenylgermylene)-	C_6H_{12}	486(2.36)	101-0345-80J
$C_{22}H_{18}FeSi$ Ferrocene, 1,1'-(diphenylsilylene)-	C_6H_{12}	483(2.43)	101-0345-80J
$C_{22}H_{18}N_2$ Dibenzo[a,c]phenazine, 9,14-dihydro-9,14-dimethyl-	benzene	360(3.6)	46-1841-80
Dibenzo[b,i]phenazine, 6,13-dihydro-6,13-dimethyl-	benzene benzene	296(4.63),397(4.06) 393(4.1)	35-0306-80 46-1841-80
2,9-Ethano-1,4-ethenodibenzo[a,e]cyclooctene-15,16-dicarbonitrile, 1,4,5,6,11,12-hexahydro-	EtOH	212(4.36),237(4.06), 284(3.11),355(2.60)	24-2358-80
$C_{22}H_{18}N_2O$ Benzoxazole, 5,6-dimethyl-2-[4-[2-(3-pyridinyl)ethenyl]phenyl]-	DMF	354(4.77)	33-1311-80
Ethanone, 1-(1-methyl-1H-benzimidazol-2-yl)-2,2-diphenyl-	EtOH	243(4.09),258(4.06), 280(4.03),287(4.02), 309(3.95)	44-2518-80
2(1H)-Naphthalenone, 1-[[(1,6-dimethyl-2(1H)-quinolinylidene)methyl]imino]-	EtOH benzene acetone CHCl$_3$	632(3.78) 646(--) 662(--) 663(--)	104-0185-80 104-0185-80 104-0185-80 104-0185-80
3(2H)-Pyridazinone, 1,6-dihydro-2,6,6-triphenyl-	EtOH	238(4.39)	118-0457-80
$C_{22}H_{18}N_2OS$ 4H-1,3,5-Oxadiazine-4-thione, 2,3-dihydro-2,6-diphenyl-3-(phenylmethyl)-	dioxan	245(4.22),280(4.07)	73-2254-80
$C_{22}H_{18}N_2O_2$ 2(1H)-Naphthalenone, 1-[[6-methoxy-1-methyl-2(1H)-quinolinylidene)methyl]-imino]-	EtOH benzene acetone CHCl$_3$	627(4.06) 650(--) 664(--) 664(--)	104-0185-80 104-0185-80 104-0185-80 104-0185-80
$C_{22}H_{18}N_2O_2S$ 2,6(1H,3H)-Pyridinedione, 4-methyl-5-(methylthio)-1-phenyl-3(2H)-quinolinylidene)-	EtOH	299(4.93),343(4.86), 463(4.32)	94-2892-80
$C_{22}H_{18}N_2O_3$ Pyrrolo[2,1-a]isoquinoline-1-carboxylic acid, 2-amino-3-benzoyl-, ethyl ester	EtOH	214s(4.46),228s(4.40), 287(4.62),362(4.30)	18-0297-80

Compound	Solvent	λ_{max}(log ϵ)	Ref.
C$_{22}$H$_{18}$N$_2$O$_4$			
Benzo[e]pyrrolo[3,4-g]isoindole- 1,3,4,6(2H,5H)-tetrone, 3a,3b,6a,10b- tetrahydro-2,5-dimethyl-6a-phenyl-, (3aα,3bα,6aα,10bα)-	MeCN	252s(--),256s(--), 262(2.96),269(2.83), 274s(--)	40-0846-80
Cyclobuta[1,2-c:3,4-c']dipyrrole- 1,3,4,6(2H,5H)-tetrone, 2,5-dimethyl- 3a,3b-diphenyltetrahydro-, cis	MeCN	254(3.19),259(3.25), 265(3.21),269s(--)	40-0846-80
trans	MeCN	260(3.37),266(3.33), 270(3.29)	40-0846-80
Cyclobuta[1,2-c:3,4-c']dipyrrole- 1,3,4,6(2H,5H)-tetrone, 2,5-dimethyl- 3a,6a-diphenyltetrahydro-	MeCN	253s(3.29),260(3.25), 267(3.17),272s(--)	40-0846-80
3H-1,2a-Diazacyclopenta[ef]heptalene- 4,5-dicarboxylic acid, 3-phenyl-, dimethyl ester	EtOH	293(3.98),455(3.64)	18-1406-80
3H-1,2a-Diazacyclopent[cd]azulene-3,4- dicarboxylic acid, 3-(2-phenylethen- yl)-, dimethyl ester, (E)-	EtOH	233(4.54),291(4.46), 354(3.95),370s(3.94), 415(3.84),441(3.96), 466(3.92),497(3.67)	18-1406-80
C$_{22}$H$_{18}$N$_2$O$_5$S$_3$			
1,3-Dithiole-4,5-dicarboxylic acid, 2-[1-phenyl-2-[[(phenylamino)carbo- nyl]amino]-2-thioxoethylidene]-, dimethyl ester	EtOH	310(3.93),421(4.36)	142-0785-80
C$_{22}$H$_{18}$N$_2$O$_7$			
5-Oxa-1-azabicyclo[4.2.0]oct-2-ene-2- carboxylic acid, 4,8-dioxo-7-[(phen- oxyacetyl)amino]-, phenylmethyl ester	dioxan	270(3.70),278(3.72), 298(3.76)	44-3682-80
C$_{22}$H$_{18}$N$_2$O$_9$			
1,2,6-Indolizinetricarboxylic acid, 3-(4-nitrobenzoyl)-, 6-ethyl 1,2- dimethyl ester	CHCl$_3$	252(4.64),381(4.17)	103-0506-80
1,2,8-Indolizinetricarboxylic acid, 3-(4-nitrobenzoyl)-, 8-ethyl 1,2- dimethyl ester	CHCl$_3$	265(4.54),373(4.12)	103-0506-80
C$_{22}$H$_{18}$N$_4$O$_2$S			
Acetamide, 2-[(1,2-dihydro-2-oxo-4- pyrimidinyl)thio]-N-[4-(phenyl- amino)-1-naphthalenyl]-	EtOH	217(4.78),256(4.39), 295(4.16),348(4.05)	94-1722-80
Acetamide, 2-[(1,4-dihydro-4-oxo-2- pyrimidinyl)thio]-N-[4-(phenyl- amino)-1-naphthalenyl]-	EtOH	218(4.78),253(4.34), 350(4.03)	94-1722-80
C$_{22}$H$_{18}$N$_6$O			
3H-Pyrazol-3-one, 2,4-dihydro-5-methyl- 2-phenyl-4-[[4-(phenylazo)phenyl]- azo]-	acetone	418(4.56)	7-0173-80
C$_{22}$H$_{18}$N$_6$O$_4$			
2-Naphthalenecarboxamide, 4-[(1,3-di- methyl-1H-pyrazol-4-yl)azo]-3-hy- droxy-N-(3-nitrophenyl)-	EtOH	247(3.81),445(4.55)	65-1705-80
C$_{22}$H$_{18}$N$_6$O$_6$			
1,2,4-Triazolidine-3,5-dione, 1,1'- (2,6-dioxocyclohexylidene)bis[4-phenyl-	MeCN	226(4.066),270(2.861)	44-1232-80

Compound	Solvent	$\lambda_{max}(\log \epsilon)$	Ref.
$C_{22}H_{18}O$			
6,13-Epoxypentacene, 5,6,7,12,13,14-hexahydro-	EtOH	210(4.25),230s(3.88), 261(3.38),267s(3.37), 274(3.34)	33-0232-80
1,3,6,8,10-Tridecapentaen-12-yn-5-one, 1-(2-ethynylphenyl)-11-methyl-	THF	262s(4.21),271(4.27), 288s(4.20),378(4.64)	39-0473-80C
$C_{22}H_{18}OS$			
Benzo[b]thiophen-3(2H)-one, 2,2-bis(phenylmethyl)-	EtOH	239(4.19),260(3.52), 370(3.09)	94-3430-80
$C_{22}H_{18}O_2$			
Anthracene, 1,4-dimethoxy-9-phenyl-	CH_2Cl_2	272(4.63),350(3.58), 368(3.86),394(3.80)	23-1161-80
[1,1'-Binaphthalene]-8,8'-dimethanol	EtOH	300(4.02)	65-2104-80
3H-Cyclopenta[1,3]cyclopropa[1,2-a]-naphthalen-3-one, 1-ethoxy-3a,3b-dihydro-3a-phenyl-	EtOH	266(4.14)	78-2291-80
7H-Dibenz[a,kl]anthracene-13-methanol, 1,13b-dihydro-7-hydroxy-	EtOH	228(4.82),268(3.93), 277(3.98),288(3.93), 300(3.73)	65-2104-80
7H-Dibenz[a,kl]anthracene-13-methanol, 7a,13a-dihydro-7-hydroxy-	EtOH	228(4.85),268(3.96), 277(4.00),288(3.98), 300(3.78)	65-2104-80
4,7-Ethanoisobenzofuran-1(4H)-one, 7,7a-dihydro-3,7a-diphenyl-	EtOH	224(3.74),240(3.64), 260(3.40)	44-3782-80
$C_{22}H_{18}O_2S$			
Benzo[c]thiophene, 4,7-dimethoxy-1,3-diphenyl-	CH_2Cl_2	257(4.36),335(3.50), 397(4.11)	23-1161-80
$C_{22}H_{18}O_2S_2$			
1-Benzothiepin-3(2H)-one, 2,2'-(1,2-ethanediylidene)bis[4,5-dihydro-	$CHCl_3$	357(4.23)	24-1708-80
3-Benzothiepin-1(2H)-one, 2,2'-(1,2-ethanediylidene)bis[4,5-dihydro-	EtOH	419(3.76)	24-1708-80
	$CHCl_3$	419(3.78)	24-1708-80
$C_{22}H_{18}O_3$			
Cyclobut[f]isobenzofuran-1,3-dione, 3a,4,5,6,7,7a-hexahydro-4,7-diphenyl-	ether	252(2.65),256(2.72), 262(2.76),268(2.67)	44-4183-80
$C_{22}H_{18}O_4$			
1,3-Azulenedicarboxylic acid, 2-(2-phenylethenyl)-, dimethyl ester	MeOH	233(4.59),294(4.58), 338(4.80),404(4.31), 540(2.81)	18-3276-80
4H-1-Benzopyran-4-one, 2,3-dihydro-5-hydroxy-3-phenyl-7-(phenylmethoxy)-	MeOH	290(3.99)	42-0208-80
$C_{22}H_{18}O_7$			
4,13:7,10-Diethenocyclododeca[c]furan-8,9-dicarboxylic acid, 1,3,5,6,11,12-hexahydro-1,3-dioxo-, dimethyl ester	EtOH	250s(4.15),308(3.64)	24-0531-80
$C_{22}H_{18}O_8$			
4H-1-Benzopyran-4-one, 5,7-diacetoxy-3-(1,3-benzodioxol-5-ylmethyl)-6-methyl-	EtOH	228(4.82),252s(4.55), 291(4.25),340(3.93)	94-2039-80
4H-1-Benzopyran-4-one, 5,7-diacetoxy-3-(1,3-benzodioxol-5-ylmethyl)-8-methyl-	EtOH	227(4.24),295(3.68), 308s(3.57)	94-2039-80

Compound	Solvent	$\lambda_{max}(\log \epsilon)$	Ref.
$C_{22}H_{18}Si$			
Silacyclopenta-2,4-diene, 1,2,5-tri-phenyl-	dioxan	382(4.26)	61-1122-80
$C_{22}H_{19}ClN_2O$			
1H-Pyrazole, 5-(4-chlorophenyl)-4,5-di-hydro-3-(4-methoxyphenyl)-1-phenyl-	MeOH	347(3.82)	2-0364-80
3(2H)-Pyridazinone, 6-(4-chlorophenyl)-tetrahydro-2,6-diphenyl-	EtOH	233(4.04),268(4.11)	48-0617-80
3(2H)-Pyridazinone, 6-(4-chlorophenyl)-tetrahydro-4,6-diphenyl-	EtOH	284(4.29)	48-0617-80
$C_{22}H_{19}ClN_2O_3S$			
1H-Pyrazole, 5-(4-chlorophenyl)-4,5-di-hydro-3-(4-methoxyphenyl)-1-(phenyl-sulfonyl)-	MeOH	296(3.49)	2-0364-80
$C_{22}H_{19}ClN_2O_8$			
8-Azabicyclo[3.2.1]octa-2,6-diene-6,7-dicarboxylic acid, 8-[3-(2-chloro-5-nitrophenyl)-3-oxo-1-propenyl]-4-oxo-, diethyl ester, trans	CHCl₃	275(4.20),345(4.00)	39-0362-80C
$C_{22}H_{19}FeNO_2$			
Ferrocene, 1,1'-[2-[[4-(dimethylamino)-phenyl]methylene]-1,3-dioxo-1,3-pro-panediyl]-	dioxan	427(4.21)	73-1290-80
	MeOH	443(--)	73-1290-80
$C_{22}H_{19}N$			
9-Anthracenamine, N,N-dimethyl-10-phen-yl-	ether	253s(4.87),257(4.91), 353(3.62),373(3.83), 393(3.86)	78-2453-80
$C_{22}H_{19}NO$			
2-Propen-1-one, 3-(diphenylamino)-2-methyl-1-phenyl-	EtOH	241(4.14),280(4.02), 343(4.41)	4-1201-80
2-Propen-1-one, 1,3-diphenyl-3-[(phen-ylmethyl)amino]-	EtOH	210(4.32),248(4.14), 358(4.39)	39-1870-80C
2-Propen-1-one, 3-(methylphenylamino)-1,2-diphenyl-	EtOH	236(4.16),335(4.27)	4-1201-80
Pyridine, 2-[2-[4-[2-(3-methoxyphenyl)-ethenyl]phenyl]ethenyl]-	DMF	360(4.79)	33-1311-80
Pyridine, 2-[2-[4-[2-(4-methoxyphenyl)-ethenyl]phenyl]ethenyl]-	DMF	368(4.79)	33-1311-80
Pyridine, 3-[2-[4-[2-(2-methoxyphenyl)-ethenyl]phenyl]ethenyl]-	DMF	364(4.75)	33-1311-80
Pyridine, 3-[2-[4-[2-(3-methoxyphenyl)-ethenyl]phenyl]ethenyl]-	DMF	358(4.79)	33-1311-80
Pyridine, 3-[2-[4-[2-(4-methoxyphenyl)-ethenyl]phenyl]ethenyl]-	DMF	365(4.78)	33-1311-80
Pyridine, 4-[2-[4-[2-(4-methoxyphenyl)-ethenyl]phenyl]ethenyl]-	DMF	369(4.74)	33-1311-80
$C_{22}H_{19}NO_5S$			
2H-Naphtho[2,3-b]-1,4-thiazine-5,10-di-one, 2-acetoxy-3-ethoxy-3,4-dihydro-3-phenyl-	CHCl₃	295(4.31),353s(3.22), 494(3.36)	39-2923-80C
$C_{22}H_{19}NO_7$			
1,2,6-Indolizinetricarboxylic acid, 3-benzoyl-, 6-ethyl 1,2-dimethyl ester	n.s.g.	248(4.69),293(4.21), 358(4.11),374(4.18)	103-0506-80

Compound	Solvent	$\lambda_{max}(\log \epsilon)$	Ref.
1,2,8-Indolizinetricarboxylic acid, 3-benzoyl-, 8-ethyl 1,2-dimethyl ester	$CHCl_3$	248(4.52),365(4.18)	103-0506-80
$C_{22}H_{19}NO_8$ Spiro[3H-2-benzopyran-3,5'(6'H)-[1,3]-dioxolo[4,5-g]isoquinoline]-1,4-dione, 6'-acetyl-7',8'-dihydro-7,8-dimethoxy-, (±)-	CH_2Cl_2	240(4.43),283s(4.13), 289(4.18),322(3.98)	39-0919-80C
$C_{22}H_{19}NS$ Pyridine, 2-[2-[4-[2-[4-(methylthio)-phenyl]ethenyl]phenyl]ethenyl]-	DMF	370(4.82)	33-1311-80
Pyridine, 3-[4-[2-[4-(methylthio)-phenyl]ethenyl]phenyl]ethenyl]-	DMF	370(4.83)	33-1311-80
Pyridine, 4-[2-[4-[2-[4-(methylthio)-phenyl]ethenyl]phenyl]ethenyl]-	DMF	373(4.80)	33-1311-80
$C_{22}H_{19}N_3$ 1,4-Benzenediamine, N,N-dimethyl-N'-(2-phenyl-3H-indol-3-ylidene)-	benzene-ligroin	579(3.85)	7-0009-80
1-Triazene, 3,3-dimethyl-1-(10-phenyl-9-anthracenyl)-	ether	262(5.02),407(4.08)	28-0211-80B
$C_{22}H_{19}N_3O$ 2-Propenamide, N-[bis(phenylamino)meth-ylene]-3-phenyl-	MeOH	258(4.51)	48-0434-80
$C_{22}H_{19}N_3OS$ 4H-1,4-Benzothiazine, 2-[(4-methoxy-phenyl)azo]-4-methyl-3-phenyl-	EtOH	233(4.29),273(4.14), 333(4.28),506(4.25)	39-2923-80C
2(1H)-Pyridinone, 4-methyl-3-(methyl-thio)-6-(phenylamino)-5-(2-quinolin-yl)-	EtOH	229(4.67),320s(4.12), 360(4.30)	94-2892-80
$C_{22}H_{19}N_3O_3$ 1H-Pyrazole, 4,5-dihydro-3-(4-methoxy-phenyl)-5-(4-nitrophenyl)-1-phenyl-	MeOH	345(3.72)	2-0364-80
$C_{22}H_{19}N_3O_3S$ Acetamide, N-[4-[3-(2-furanylmethyl)-3,4-dihydro-6-phenyl-4-thioxo-2H-1,3,5-oxadiazin-2-yl]phenyl]-	dioxan	240s(--),276(4.66)	73-2254-80
$C_{22}H_{19}N_3O_4$ 2-Butenoic acid, 2-[[1-(phenylazo)-2-naphthalenyl]amino]-, dimethyl ester, (Z,E)-	MeOH	232(4.40),252(4.53), 298(4.28),362(4.19), 430(4.06)	44-3182-80
$C_{22}H_{19}N_3O_5S$ 1H-Pyrazole, 4,5-dihydro-3-(4-methoxy-phenyl)-5-(4-nitrophenyl)-1-(phenyl-sulfonyl)-	MeOH	290(3.60)	2-0364-80
$C_{22}H_{19}N_5O$ 1,2,4-Triazine-3,5(2H,4H)-dione, 3-(2-phenylhydrazone)	EtOH	217(4.23),300(4.07), 327(4.48),350(4.38)	12-0619-80
$C_{22}H_{19}N_5O_3S$ Benzoic acid, 2-[[[[2-(acetylimino)-5-cyano-2,3-dihydro-3-(2-methylphenyl)-4-thiazolyl]imino]methyl]amino]-,	EtOH	320(4.44)	2-0037-80

Compound	Solvent	$\lambda_{max}(\log \epsilon)$	Ref.
methyl ester (cont.)			2-0037-80
$C_{22}H_{19}O_2S_2$			
1-Benzothiopyrylium, 7-methoxy-4-[(7-methoxy-4-methyl-2H-1-benzothiopyran-2-ylidene)methyl-, perchlorate	acetone	625(4.79)	18-2415-80
$C_{22}H_{19}S_2$			
1-Benzothiopyrylium, 4-[(4,6-dimethyl-2H-1-benzothiopyran-2-ylidene)methyl]-6-methyl-, perchlorate	acetone	624(4.63)	18-2415-80
$C_{22}H_{20}$			
Naphth[2,1-a]azulene, 2-(1,1-dimethylethyl)-	MeOH	270(3.90),315(4.51), 327(4.56),375(3.90), 396(3.93),580(2.46), 640(2.55)	138-0167-80
$C_{22}H_{20}BrN_3O_3$			
1H-1,2,4-Triazolium, 1-(phenylmethyl)-, 4-[1-(4-bromobenzoyl)-4-ethoxy-4-oxo-2-butenylide]	n.s.g.	349(4.24)	80-0407-80
$C_{22}H_{20}ClNO_2$			
Cyclohepta[b]pyrrole-3-carboxylic acid, 2-chloro-8-[1-(phenylmethylene)propyl]-, ethyl ester	EtOH	236(4.55),288(4.66), 323(4.10),366s(3.46), 442(3.17)	18-1406-80
$C_{22}H_{20}ClN_5O_2$			
Hydrazinecarboxamide, N-[3-(4-chlorophenyl)-1-oxo-2-(phenylhydrazono)-propyl]-2-phenyl-	EtOH	238(4.11),272(4.06), 348(4.22)	12-0619-80
$C_{22}H_{20}Cl_2N_2O_3$			
Carbamic acid, [3-benzoyl-1-[(2,6-dichlorophenyl)methyl]-1,4-dihydro-4-pyridinyl]-, ethyl ester	CH_2Cl_2	290s(3.6),332(3.8)	64-1431-80B
$C_{22}H_{20}Cl_2N_5O_7P$			
Adenosine, N-[bis(2-chlorophenoxy)phosphinyl]-	pH 4.0	263(4.22),271s(4.16), 284s(3.83)	142-0761-80B
	pH 10.0	211s(4.23),274(4.35)	142-0761-80B
	MeOH	262(4.28),270s(4.22), 285s(3.77)	142-0761-80B
$C_{22}H_{20}FN_3O_5$			
1(2H)-Pyrimidinebutanoic acid, γ-(benzoylamino)-5-fluoro-3,4-dihydro-2,4-dioxo-, phenylmethyl ester	MeOH	269(3.94)	94-1137-80
$C_{22}H_{20}N_2$			
1H-1,5-Benzdiazepine, 2,3-dihydro-4-(4-methylphenyl)-2-phenyl-	EtOH	267(4.41),364(3.84)	103-0547-80
[1,1'-Biphenyl]-4-propanenitrile, α-methyl-α-(phenylamino)-	dioxan	248(4.47)	24-2462-80
$C_{22}H_{20}N_2O$			
1H-Benzimidazole-2-methanol, α-(diphenylmethyl)-1-methyl-	EtOH	257(4.00),270(3.99), 277(4.01),284(3.99)	44-2518-80
1H-1,5-Benzodiazepine, 2,3-dihydro-2-(4-methoxyphenyl)-4-phenyl-	EtOH	274(4.31),362(3.91)	103-0547-80

Compound	Solvent	$\lambda_{max}(\log \epsilon)$	Ref.
1H-1,5-Benzodiazepine, 2,3-dihydro-4-(4-methoxyphenyl)-2-phenyl-	EtOH	274(4.31),360(3.93)	103-0547-80
3(2H)-Pyridazinone, tetrahydro-2,6,6-triphenyl-	EtOH	228(--),270(4.10)	48-0617-80
3(2H)-Pyridazinone, tetrahydro-4,6,6-triphenyl-	EtOH	287(4.28)	48-0617-80
$C_{22}H_{20}N_2O_3S$ 4H-1,3-Oxazin-4-one, 2,3-dihydro-2-hydroxy-6-methyl-5-(methylthio)-2-(phenyl-2(1H)-quinolinylidenemethyl)-	EtOH	280(4.10),293(4.08), 307(4.10),310(4.10), 319(4.12),328(4.05), 418(4.02),437(4.25), 462(4.04)	94-0795-80
$C_{22}H_{20}N_2O_4$ 2-Propynamide, N,N'-1,2-ethanediylbis-[3-(4-methoxyphenyl)-	EtOH	278(4.9),291(4.85)	114-0235-80C
$C_{22}H_{20}N_2O_6S$ 1H-Indole-2-carboxylic acid, 5,5'-sulfonylbis-, diethyl ester	mineral oil	204(4.3),227(4.1), 321(4.5),347(4.7)	103-1146-80
$C_{22}H_{20}N_3O_3$ Pyrido[2,1-b]benzoxazolium, 9-[2-[4-(dimethylamino)phenyl]ethenyl]-7-methyl-6-nitro-, chloride	n.s.g.	584(4.79)	124-1306-80
$C_{22}H_{20}N_4$ 1H-Pyrrolo[1,2-a]indole, 9,9'-azobis-[2,3-dihydro-	$CHCl_3$	282(4.12),380(4.25), 410s(4.37),426(4.41)	39-2870-80C
$C_{22}H_{20}N_4O_3$ 3-Pyridinecarboxylic acid, 4-[[[bis-(phenylamino)methylene]amino]carbonyl]-, ethyl ester	MeOH	284(4.28)	39-1667-80C
4-Pyridinecarboxylic acid, 3-[[[bis-(phenylamino)methylene]amino]carbonyl]-, ethyl ester	MeOH	272(4.26)	39-1667-80C
$C_{22}H_{20}N_6$ 2H-Benzimidazol-2-one, 1,3-dihydro-1-phenyl-, [1-[(4-methylphenyl)-azo]ethylidene]hydrazone]	EtOH	452(4.46)	103-0637-80
$C_{22}H_{20}N_6O_4$ 1,1-Ethenediamine, N,N'-bis(4-methylphenyl)-2-nitro-2-[(4-nitrophenyl)-azo]-	MeCN	280(4.30),297s(4.27), 389(4.42)	48-0087-80
$C_{22}H_{20}N_6O_6$ 1,1-Ethenediamine, N,N'-bis(4-methoxyphenyl)-2-nitro-2-[(4-nitrophenyl)-azo]-	MeCN	226(4.33),292(4.27), 390(4.39)	48-0087-80
$C_{22}H_{20}N_6O_8$ Pyrrolidine, 1,1'-[(2,4,5,7-tetranitro-9H-fluoren-9-ylidene)methylene]bis-	MeCN	385(4.46),650(3.70)	104-0740-80
$C_{22}H_{20}N_6O_{10}$ Morpholine, 4,4'-[(2,4,5,7-tetranitro-9H-fluoren-9-ylidene)methylene]bis-	MeCN	363(4.59),610(3.63)	104-0740-80

Compound	Solvent	$\lambda_{max}(\log \epsilon)$	Ref.
$C_{22}H_{20}O$			
2,4,6,8,14,16,18-Cyclononadecaheptaene-10,12-diyn-1-one, 9,14,19-trimethyl-, (E,E,Z,Z,E,E,E)-	THF	<u>250s(4.2),342(4.7),</u> <u>415s(4.2)</u>	138-0225-80
$C_{22}H_{20}O_2$			
4,7-Ethanoisobenzofuran-1(4H)-one, 5,6,7,7a-tetrahydro-3,7a-diphenyl-	MeOH	236(4.33),242s(4.00), 280(3.85),290(3.81)	44-3782-80
Ethanone, 1-phenyl-2-(2-phenyl-1-oxa-spiro[4.4]non-2-en-4-ylidene)-	EtOH	423(4.46)	5-1744-80
3H-Fluoren-4-ol, 4,4a-dihydro-4a,9-di-methyl-, benzoate	EtOH	289s(4.18),301(4.27), 315s(4.12)	39-1909-80C
Methanone, bicyclo[2.2.2]oct-2-ene-2,3-diylbis[phenyl-	MeOH	260(4.21) *	44-3187-80
$C_{22}H_{20}O_2S$			
Naphtho[1,2-c]thiophene-1-carboxylic acid, 4,5-dihydro-3-(4-methylphen-yl)-, ethyl ester	CHCl$_3$	264(4.39),322(4.34)	54-0049-80
$C_{22}H_{20}O_2S_2$			
2H-1-Benzothiopyran-3(4H)-one, 2-(3,4-dihydro-4,4-dimethyl-3-oxo-2H-1-benzothiopyran-2-ylidene)-4,4-dimethyl-	C$_6$H$_{12}$	265(4.17),300s(3.42), 340s(3.28),447(4.02)	24-1708-80
	EtOH	262(4.15),350s(3.28), 447(3.98)	24-1708-80
	CHCl$_3$	266(4.20),353(3.21), 454(3.96)	24-1708-80
$C_{22}H_{20}O_3$			
Bicyclo[2.2.2]oct-5-ene-2-carboxylic acid, 3-(phenoxyphenylmethylene)-, endo	EtOH	226(4.12),260(4.04)	44-3782-80
exo	EtOH	229(4.08),260(4.16)	44-3782-80
13,4,8-[1]Butene[1,2,4]triylbenzo[5,6]-cycloocta[1,2-f]isobenzofuran-1,3-di-one, 3a,4,5,6,11,12,13,13a-octahydro-	EtOH	200(4.20),278(2.85)	24-2358-80
Ethanone, 1-(5-acetoxy-1,2,3,4-tetra-hydro-2-naphthacenyl)-	EtOH	224(4.02),252s(4.81), 260(5.10),288s(3.64), 302s(3.73),316(3.78), 350(3.60),368(3.69), 388(3.60)	33-0232-80
Ethanone, 1-(12-acetoxy-1,2,3,4-tetra-hydro-2-naphthacenyl)-	EtOH	226(4.13),252(4.97), 260(4.25),288s(3.82), 292(3.83),318s(3.46), 332(3.53),349(3.65), 367(3.76),388(3.69), 410s(2.60),465(2.30), 496(2.26)	33-0232-80
$C_{22}H_{20}O_3S$			
Naphtho[1,2-c]thiophene-1-carboxylic acid, 4,5-dihydro-3-(4-methylphenyl)-, ethyl ester, 2-oxide	CHCl$_3$	266(3.96),330(3.35)	54-0049-80
$C_{22}H_{20}O_4S$			
Naphtho[1,2-c]thiophene-1-carboxylic acid, 4,5-dihydro-3-(4-methylphenyl)-, ethyl ester, 2,2-dioxide	CHCl$_3$	252(4.05),344(3.96)	54-0049-80
$C_{22}H_{20}O_5$			
6,11-Naphthacenedione, 8-acetyl-	CHCl$_3$	248s(--),265(4.50),	35-5881-80

Compound	Solvent	$\lambda_{max}(\log \epsilon)$	Ref.
7,8,9,10-tetrahydro-1,5-dimethoxy-		387(3.52),442(3.51)	35-5881-80
$C_{22}H_{20}O_7$			
5,12-Naphthacenedione, 9t-acetyl- 7,8,9,10-tetrahydro-6,7c,9c,11- tetrahydroxy-2,3-dimethyl-	MeOH	225(4.28),264(4.55), 289(3.99),457s(3.93), 479(3.99),509(3.80)	24-2976-80
$C_{22}H_{20}O_8$			
4H-1-Benzopyran-4-one, 5,7-diacetoxy- 3-(1,3-benzodioxol-5-ylmethyl)-2,3- dihydro-6-methyl-, (-)-	EtOH	218(4.48),260(4.04), 288(3.83)	94-2039-80
1,4-Methanoanthra[2,3-c]oxepin-7,12-di- one, 1,3,4,5-tetrahydro-4,6,13-trihy- droxy-3,11-dimethoxy-3-methyl-	MeOH	219(4.18),235(4.33), 252(4.21),289(3.69), 477(4.90),495(4.89), 530(3.63)	24-2976-80
isomer 11	MeOH	219(4.18),235(4.33), 252(4.21),289(3.69), 477(4.90),495(4.89), 530(3.63)	24-2976-80
$C_{22}H_{20}O_9$			
4H-1-Benzopyran-4-one, 5,7-diacetoxy- 3-(2,4,5-trimethoxyphenyl)-	EtOH	294.5(4.11)	18-0831-80
10-Epi-ε-rhodomycinone	EtOH	234(4.67),251(4.58), 295(4.05),495(4.03), 531(4.19),577(4.00)	23-1869-80
5,12-Naphthacenedione, 8-acetyl- 7,8,9,10-tetrahydro-6,8,10,11-tetra- hydroxy-1,3-dimethoxy-, cis-(±)-	MeOH	231(4.52),273(4.26), 300s(3.96),470(4.04), 494(4.03),529(3.75)	24-2976-80
5,12-Naphthacenedione, 9-acetyl- 7,8,9,10-tetrahydro-6,7,9,11-tetra- hydroxy-1,3-dimethoxy-, cis-(±)-	MeOH	233(4.55),275(4.27), 305s(--),477(4.06), 529(3.76)	24-2976-80
$C_{22}H_{21}NO$			
3H-Naphtho[2,1-b]pyran-3-amine, N-(2,4,6-trimethylphenyl)-	o-$C_6H_4Cl_2$ C_6H_5Cl DMSO	315(3.92),355(3.74) 317(4.02),350(3.84) 317(3.89),370(4.01), 535(2.90)	103-0799-80 103-0799-80 103-0799-80
$C_{22}H_{21}NO_2S$			
Benzenamine, N-[1,2-dimethyl-4-(2-naph- thalenylsulfonyl)-2-butenylidene]-	EtOH	240(4.96)	104-0849-80
2-Naphthalenamine, N-[1,2-dimethyl- 4-(phenylsulfonyl)-2-butenylidene]-	EtOH	236(5.17)	104-0849-80
$C_{22}H_{21}NO_5$			
Dibenzo[a,g]quinolizinium, 13-hydroxy- 2,3,10,11-tetramethoxy-8-methyl-, hydroxide, inner salt	MeOH	230s(4.54),236(4.55), 264(4.43),288(4.37), 323(4.24),411(4.00), 439(4.09),466(4.15)	39-0911-80C
hydrochloride	EtOH	215(4.07),224(4.06), 236s(3.90),260s(3.89), 270s(4.02),280s(4.18), 314(4.22),330(4.16), 367(3.45),394s(3.61), 419(3.88),442(4.01), 470s(3.39)	39-0911-80C
$C_{22}H_{21}NO_6$			
10H-[1,3]Dioxolo[6,7]phenanthro[4,5- bcd]pyran-10-one, 3-[2-(dimethyl-	MeOH	295(4.14),382(3.91), 394(3.92)	100-0567-80

Compound	Solvent	$\lambda_{max}(\log \epsilon)$	Ref.
amino)ethyl]-1,2-dimethoxy-(thalflavidine) (cont.)			100-0567-80
Ethanone, 1-[2-[(6,7-dimethoxy-1-iso-quinolinyl)carbonyl]-4,5-dimethoxy-phenyl]-	EtOH	237(4.41),314(3.66), 326(3.66)	39-0911-80C
Nornantenine, N-acetyl-3-methoxy-, (±)-	EtOH	206(4.31),263(4.63), 284(4.26),324(3.89)	35-6513-80
$C_{22}H_{21}NO_7$			
2-Propene-1,1,3-tricarboxylic acid, 3-[2-(benzoylamino)phenyl]-, trimethyl ester	MeOH	222s(4.23),260(3.99)	142-0047-80
$C_{22}H_{21}N_3O$			
1(2H)-Phthalazinone, 4-[4-(dimethyl-amino)phenyl]-3,4-dihydro-4-phenyl-	EtOH	263(4.30)	94-3561-80
$C_{22}H_{21}N_3O_5$			
1,2,5-Triazabicyclo[4.2.0]oct-7-ene-6,7-dicarboxylic acid, 2-methyl-3-oxo-4,8-diphenyl-, dimethyl ester, trans	MeOH	219(4.39)	44-4587-80
$C_{22}H_{21}N_3O_5S_2$			
4-Thia-1-azabicyclo[3.2.0]heptane-2-carboxylic acid, 3,3-dimethyl-6-[[(4-methylphenyl)thio]imino]-7-oxo-, (4-nitrophenyl)methyl ester, (2S-cis)-	CHCl₃	267(4.23),354(3.92)	35-1690-80
$C_{22}H_{21}N_3S$			
1-Pyrazolidinecarbothioamide, N,2,3-triphenyl-	EtOH	257(4.32)	103-0169-80
$C_{22}H_{21}N_5O$			
1H-Imidazo[1,5-b]pyrazole-2,3-dicarbo-nitrile, hexahydro-4,4-dimethyl-3a-(4-methylphenyl)-6-oxo-1-phenyl-	EtOH	217(4.2),231(4.1), 272(3.6)	5-1016-80
$C_{22}H_{21}N_5O_3$			
1,3,6,8-Tetraazaspiro[4.5]deca-2,6,9-triene-10-carboxylic acid, 7-methyl-4-oxo-1-phenyl-2-(phenylamino)-, ethyl ester	MeOH	250(4.35),300s(3.76)	39-1667-80C
$C_{22}H_{21}OS$			
1-Benzothiopyrylium, 5,6,7,8-tetrahy-dro-2-(4-methoxyphenyl)-4-phenyl-, perchlorate	CH₂Cl₂	262(4.11),445(4.38)	104-0170-80
$C_{22}H_{22}$			
Benzene, 1,1'-[3-(tetramethylcycloprop-ylidene)-1,2-propadien-1-ylidene]bis-	heptane	247(2.65),254(2.64), 324(2.88)	35-6813-80
3,3'-Bi-1H-indene, 4,4',7,7'-tetra-methyl-	EtOH	214(4.53),230(4.26), 254(4.22),288(3.26), 299(3.26)	24-3112-80
$C_{22}H_{22}BrN_3O_5$			
16,19-Secostrychnidine-10,16-dione, 2-bromo-19-methyl-4-nitro-	MeOH	240s(4.06),268s(3.84), 333(3.58)	5-0895-80

Compound	Solvent	$\lambda_{max}(\log \epsilon)$	Ref.
$C_{22}H_{22}Br_2N_2O_{10}$			
Glycine, N,N'-[1,2-ethanediylbis[oxy(4-bromo-2,1-phenylene)]]bis[N-(carboxymethyl)-	tetraanion	263(4.30)	69-2396-80
calcium chelate	n.s.g.	240(4.20),282(3.72)	69-2396-80
$C_{22}H_{22}ClNO_6$			
8-Azabicyclo[3.2.1]oct-2-ene-6,7-dicarboxylic acid, 8-[3-(4-chlorophenyl)-3-oxo-1-propenyl]-4-oxo-, diethyl ester, [1α,5α,6β,7α,8(E)]-	CHCl$_3$	263(4.14),327(4.43)	39-0362-80C
$C_{22}H_{22}N_2$			
3H-Pyrrolo[1,2-d][1,4]diazepine, 4,5-dihydro-2,7-dimethyl-1,8-diphenyl-	EtOH EtOH-acid	252(4.19),309(4.10) 318(4.03),392(4.19)	39-1441-80B 39-1441-80B
$C_{22}H_{22}N_2O$			
Indolo[4,5-c]quinolizin-4(1H)-one, 5,5a,6,7,8,9-hexahydro-1-methyl-2-phenyl-	EtOH	229(4.42),372(4.18)	4-0403-80
$C_{22}H_{22}N_2O_3$			
Spiro[2H-1-benzopyran-2,2'-[2H]indole], 1',3'-dihydro-1',3',3'-trimethyl-6-nitro-8-(2-propenyl)-	EtOH	540(4.53)	103-0041-80
$C_{22}H_{22}N_2O_6$			
Benzoic acid, 3,3'-[1,2-cyclohexanediylbis(nitrilomethylidyne)]bis[2-hydroxy-, (R)-	DMSO	<u>405(4.2)</u>	1-0469-80A
4,5-Secoakuammilan-5,17-dioic acid, 1,4-diformyl-1,2-dihydro-2-hydroxy-, 5,2-lactone, 17-methyl ester, (2α)-	EtOH	244(3.89),285(3.30)	22-0400-80
$C_{22}H_{22}N_2O_7$			
Anhydrotetracycline	aq H$_2$SO$_4$	272(4.59),435(3.95)	106-0024-80
Epianhydrotetracycline	aq H$_2$SO$_4$	272(4.53),435(3.95)	106-0024-80
$C_{22}H_{22}N_2S$			
Quinazoline, 1,4,5,6,7,8-hexahydro-2-(methylthio)-4-phenyl-8-(phenylmethylene)-	EtOH	234(4.39),275(4.64), 326(4.17)	114-0147-80B
monohydriodide	EtOH	274(4.51),322(4.62)	114-0147-80B
2(1H)-Quinazolinethione, 3,4,5,6,7,8-hexahydro-3-methyl-4-phenyl-8-(phenylmethylene)-	EtOH	267(4.41),319(4.07)	114-0147-80B
$C_{22}H_{22}N_4$			
1H-Pyrazole, 1,1'-([1,1'-biphenyl]-2,2'-diyl)bis[3,5-dimethyl-	MeOH	216s(4.393),231(4.444), 250(4.198)	39-0982-80C
$C_{22}H_{22}N_4O_3$			
Benzo[g]pteridine-2,4(3H,10H)-dione, 10-[2-(3-methoxyphenyl)ethyl]-3,7,8-trimethyl-	pH 5.0	269(4.61),372(4.03), 449(4.08),472(3.98)	35-5036-80
	MeOH	269(4.61),352(3.96), 444(4.10),472s(3.97)	35-5036-80
Benzoic acid, 4-methyl-, [(4-methylphenyl)(1,2,3,4-tetrahydro-1,3-dimethyl-2,4-dioxo-5-pyrimidinyl)methylene]hydrazide	MeOH	285s(4.37),307(4.40)	24-2566-80
Morpholine, 4-[(4-acetoxyphenyl)(2-	MeOH	263(4.27),380(4.18)	56-0661-80

Compound	Solvent	$\lambda_{max}(\log \epsilon)$	Ref.
quinolinylhydrazono)methyl]-, mono- hydriodide (cont.)			56-0661-80

$C_{22}H_{22}N_4O_5S$
  1H-Pyrrole-3-propanoic acid, 5-[(3-eth-
  enyl-1,5-dihydro-4-methyl-5-oxo-2H-
  pyrrol-2-ylidene)methyl]-4-methyl-
  2-[(tetrahydro-4,6-dioxo-2-thioxo-
  5(2H)-pyrimidinylidene)methyl]-,
  methyl ester

	Solvent	$\lambda_{max}(\log \epsilon)$	Ref.
	MeOH	325(4.24),520s(--), 553(4.49)	77-0178-80
	MeOH- NaOH	520s(--),568(4.48), 605(4.50)	77-0178-80

$C_{22}H_{22}N_5O_6P$

	Solvent	$\lambda_{max}(\log \epsilon)$	Ref.
3'-Adenylic acid, 2'-deoxy-, diphenyl ester	MeOH	258(4.21)	142-0761-80B
5'-Adenylic acid, 2'-deoxy-, diphenyl ester	MeOH	258(4.27)	142-0761-80B
Phosphoramidic acid, N-[9-(2-deoxy-β-D- erythro-pentofuranosyl)-9H-purin-6- yl]-, diphenyl ester	pH 4.0	261(4.24),269s(4.18), 285s(3.68)	142-0761-80B
	pH 10.0	214s(4.42),276(4.45)	142-0761-80B
	MeOH	260(4.27),268s(4.13), 285s(3.40)	142-0761-80B

$C_{22}H_{25}N_5O_7P$

	Solvent	$\lambda_{max}(\log \epsilon)$	Ref.
Adenosine, N-(diphenoxyphosphinyl)-	pH 4.0	261(4.20),269s(4.14), 285s(3.57)	142-0761-80B
	pH 10.0	215s(4.38),276(4.39)	142-0761-80B
	MeOH	259(4.25),267s(4.14), 285s(3.29)	142-0761-80B
5'-Adenylic acid, diphenyl ester	MeOH	259(4.18)	142-0761-80B

$C_{22}H_{22}O$

	Solvent	$\lambda_{max}(\log \epsilon)$	Ref.
Isobenzofuran, 4,5,6,7-tetrahydro-5,6- dimethyl-1,3-diphenyl-	EtOH	240(2.25),330(2.56)	88-3717-80

$C_{22}H_{22}O_2$

	Solvent	$\lambda_{max}(\log \epsilon)$	Ref.
Benzene, 1,4-dimethoxy-2,3-bis(phenyl- methyl)-	CH_2Cl_2	269(--),291(3.68), 296s(--)	23-1161-80
1H-Fluoren-4-ol, 2,3,4,4a-tetrahydro- 4a,9-dimethyl-, benzoate	EtOH	262(4.08),285s(3.41), 294(2.93)	39-1909-80C

$C_{22}H_{22}O_3$

	Solvent	$\lambda_{max}(\log \epsilon)$	Ref.
Bicyclo[2.2.1]heptane-2-carboxylic acid, 3-(phenoxyphenylmethylene)-, methyl ester, (1α,2α,3Z,4α)-	MeOH	233(4.10),260(4.29), 274(3.96)	44-3782-80
Bicyclo[2.2.2]octane-2-carboxylic acid, 3-(phenoxyphenylmethylene)-, (Z)-	MeOH	222(4.08),260(4.09)	44-3782-80

$C_{22}H_{22}O_4$

	Solvent	$\lambda_{max}(\log \epsilon)$	Ref.
5H-Benzo[c]fluorene-5,8,11-trione, 7,7a,11a,11b-tetrahydro-11b-hydroxy- 6,7,9,10,11a-pentamethyl-, (7α,7aα,11aβ,11bα)-	EtOH	251(4.20),282(3.78)	39-1994-80C
(7α,7aβ,11aβ,11bα)-	EtOH	249(5.10),289(4.00), 312(3.60),322(3.48), 330(3.30)	39-1994-80C
7H-Benzo[c]xanthene-8,11-dione, 7a,11a- dihydro-5-hydroxy-6,7,9,10,11a-penta- methyl-	EtOH	243(4.89),310(3.99), 320(4.03),334(3.94)	39-1994-80C
4a,9a-Epoxy-1,4-ethanoanthracene- 9,10,12-trione, 1,4-dihydro-1,2,3,4- 13,13-hexamethyl-, (1α,4α,4aα,9aα)-	MeOH	302(3.22),350(2.49)	44-0034-80

Compound	Solvent	$\lambda_{max}(\log \epsilon)$	Ref.
$C_{22}H_{22}O_5$			
2-Propen-1-one, 1-(5,7-dimethoxy-2,2-dimethyl-2H-1-benzopyran-6-yl)-3-hydroxy-3-phenyl-	n.s.g.	270(4.44),311(4.31), 327s(--)	102-0707-80
$C_{22}H_{22}O_6$			
1,4-Anthracenediol, 5,8-dimethoxy-2,3-dimethyl-, diacetate	MeCN	248(4.81),264(4.71), 369(3.68),394(3.65)	23-1161-80
Butanedial, bis[(2,5-dimethoxyphenyl)-methylene]-	CHCl₃	290(4.5),377(4.1)	118-0898-80
2-Naphthalenecarboxylic acid, 4-hydroxy-1,5-dimethoxy-3-(2-methoxy-5-methylphenyl)-, methyl ester	EtOH	230(4.40),291(3.17), 317(3.19),330(3.24), 345(4.34)	44-4071-80
$C_{22}H_{22}O_7$			
2H-2,4a-Epoxynaphthalene-3,4-dicarboxylic acid, 7-(benzoyloxy)-5,6,7,8-tetrahydro-2-methyl-, dimethyl ester	MeCN	228(4.20),272(3.19), 280(3.14),292(2.82)	24-3249-80
$C_{22}H_{22}O_9$			
Benzoic acid, 2-(2,6-diacetoxy-4-methylbenzoyl)-3,5-dimethoxy-, methyl ester	EtOH	251(4.06),315(3.74)	32-0629-80
$C_{22}H_{22}O_{10}$			
4H-1-Benzopyran-4-one, 6-β-D-glucopyranosyl-5,7-dihydroxy-2-(4-methoxyphenyl)- (swertisin)	EtOH	272(4.28),334(4.38)	36-0053-80
Isoswertisin	EtOH	272(4.17),335(4.30)	36-0053-80
$C_{22}H_{23}BrN_2O_3$			
16,19-Secostrychnidine-10,16-dione, 2-bromo-19-methyl-	MeOH	258(4.21),288s(3.60)	5-0895-80
	MeOH-HCl	260(4.18),297s(3.26)	5-0895-80
$C_{22}H_{23}BrN_4O_4$			
Spiro[imidazolidine-4,2'(3'H)-quinoxaline]-2,3',5-trione, 7'-bromo-4'-ethyl-1',4'-dihydro-1'-[2-(3-methoxyphenyl)ethyl]-1-methyl-	EtOH	228(4.61),263(3.86), 272s(3.82),280(3.76), 309(3.82)	35-5036-80
	EtOH-NaOH	233(4.61),272(4.26), 280(3.87),314(3.83)	35-5036-80
$C_{22}H_{23}BrO_8$			
α-D-galacto-Octopyranuronic acid, 6,6,7,7-tetradehydro-6,7-dideoxy-1,2:3m4-bis-O-(1-methylethylidene)-, 2-(4-bromophenyl)-2-oxoethyl ester	MeCN	273(3.70)	33-1181-80
$C_{22}H_{23}ClN_2O_5$			
2H-Naphth[2,1-e]-1,3-oxazin-2-one, 4-[5-chloro-2-[(methylamino)carbonyl]-oxy]phenyl]-3,4,4a,5,6,10b-hexahydro-9-methoxy-3-methyl-	EtOH	227(4.31),281(3.59), 293s(3.38)	4-0277-80
$C_{22}H_{23}ClO_5$			
Propanedioic acid, [1-(4-chlorophenyl)-3-oxo-3-phenylpropyl]-, diethyl ester	EtOH	244(4.27)	34-0085-80
$C_{22}H_{23}N$			
Benzenamine, N,N-dimethyl-4-[4-(4-methylphenyl)-1,3,6-cycloheptatrien-1-yl]-	heptane	204(--),251(--), 352(4.430)	97-0214-80
Benz[f]isoquinoline, 1,2,3,4-tetrahy-	EtOH	223(4.79),280(3.88)	4-1563-80

Compound	Solvent	$\lambda_{max}(\log \epsilon)$	Ref.
dro-2,2,3-trimethyl-1-phenyl- (cont.) Benz[h]isoquinoline, 1,2,3,4-tetrahy- dro-2,3,3-trimethyl-4-phenyl-	EtOH	230(4.91)	4-1563-80 4-1563-80
$C_{22}H_{23}NO$ Benzenamine, 4-[4-(4-methoxyphenyl)- 1,3,6-cycloheptatrien-1-yl]-N,N- dimethyl-	heptane	204(--),254(--), 354(4.428)	97-0214-80
$C_{22}H_{23}NO_2$ 2-Cyclohexen-1-one, 6-acetyl-5-[4-(di- methylamino)phenyl]-3-phenyl-	n.s.g.	287(3.97),363(4.00)	80-1335-80
$C_{22}H_{23}NO_3$ Benzenepropanoic acid, α-[3-(dimethyl- amino)-2-phenyl-2-propenylidene]-β- oxo-, ethyl ester	hexane	234(4.29),260(4.12), 350(4.14)	70-1643-80
	MeOH	250s(4.03),360(4.25), 400(4.15)	70-1643-80
	EtOH	240(4.09),360(4.31), 410(4.11)	70-1643-80
	CHCl$_3$	356(4.17),410s(3.53)	70-1643-80
	67% MeOH	250(3.95),368(4.19), 405(4.21)	70-1643-80
	50% MeOH	290(3.91),368(4.06), 405(4.36)	70-1643-80
6,10-Etheno-5H-cyclohepta[b]naphthalen- 5,11-imine-12-carboxylic acid, 5a,6- 7,10,10a,11-hexahydro-7-oxo-, 1,1-di- methylethyl ester, (5α,5aβ,6α,10α- 10aβ,11α)-	EtOH	238(3.85),264(3.39), 271(3.19),327(1.75)	44-0476-80
$C_{22}H_{23}NO_4$ 6,10-Etheno-5H-cyclohepta[b]naphthalen- 5,11-imine-12-carboxylic acid, 5a,6- 7,10,10a,11-hexahydro-6-hydroxy-7- oxo-, 1,1-dimethylethyl ester, (5α,5aβ,6β,10α,10aβ,11α)-	EtOH	241(3.83),272(3.16), 327(1.93)	44-0476-80
Ochotensimine	MeOH	226(4.41),287(4.12)	100-0305-80
$C_{22}H_{23}NO_5$ Benz[d]indeno[1,2-b]azepin-12(5H)-one, 6,7-dihydro-2,3,10,11-tetramethoxy- 7-methyl-	EtOH	225s(4.30),242s(4.26), 305s(4.43),317(4.51), 500(3.34)	4-0417-80
$C_{22}H_{23}NO_6$ Fumarophycine	n.s.g.	290(3.88)	100-0305-80
$C_{22}H_{23}NO_7$ Benzoic acid, 2,3-dimethoxy-6-[(5,6,7- 8-tetrahydro-6-methyl-1,3-dioxolo- [4,5-g]isoquinolin-5-yl)carbonyl]-, methyl ester, (±)-	CH$_2$Cl$_2$	230(4.21),278(4.07), 295(4.06)	39-0919-80C
$C_{22}H_{23}NS_2$ 4H-Thiopyran-4-thione, 2-(diethylami- no)-5-(4-methylphenyl)-3-phenyl-	C$_6$H$_{12}$	227(4.29),340(4.27), 455(3.78)	22-0530-80
	EtOH	227s(4.19),322(4.06), 382(3.75),447(3.85)	22-0530-80
2H-Thiopyran-2-thione, 6-(diethylami- no)-3-(4-methylphenyl)-5-phenyl-	C$_6$H$_{12}$	233(4.41),262s(4.28), 349(4.12),500(4.03)	22-0530-80

Compound	Solvent	$\lambda_{max}(\log \epsilon)$	Ref.
(cont.)	EtOH	230(4.36),258s(4.25), 342(4.04),511(4.14)	22-0530-80
$C_{22}H_{23}N_3O_2$			
1H-Isoindole-1,3(2H)-dione, 2-[5-(2-amino-1-methyl-1H-indol-3-yl)pentyl]-, monohydrochloride	EtOH	219(4.78),263(3.88)	103-0368-80
5(4H)-Isoxazolone, 4-[[4-(dimethylamino)phenyl]-1-pyrrolidinylmethylene]-3-phenyl-	MeOH	385(4.36)	97-0020-80
$C_{22}H_{23}N_3O_3$			
5(4H)-Isoxazolone, 4-[[4-(dimethylamino)phenyl]-4-morpholinylmethylene]-3-phenyl-	MeOH	396(4.38)	97-0020-80
$C_{22}H_{23}N_3O_4$			
9,10-Anthracenedione, 1-amino-2,4-dimorpholino-	MeOH	565(3.92)	18-3725-80
$C_{22}H_{23}N_3O_5$			
16,19-Secostrychnidine-10,16-dione, 19-methyl-2-nitro-	MeOH MeOH-HCl	234(4.180),336(4.13) 228(4.06),324(4.14)	5-0895-80 5-0895-80
$C_{22}H_{23}N_4O$			
1H-Benzimidazolium, 2-[2-(2,3-dihydro-1,5-dimethyl-3-oxo-2-phenyl-1H-pyrazol-4-yl)ethenyl]-1,3-dimethyl-, perchlorate	HOAc	331(4.13)	48-0543-80
$C_{22}H_{24}$			
1H-Indene, 1-(2,3-dihydro-2,2-dimethyl-1H-inden-1-ylidene)-2,3-dihydro-2,2-dimethyl-, trans	EtOH	208(4.16),240(3.90), 247(3.85),258(3.42), 326(4.31)	24-3112-80
$C_{22}H_{24}BrN_4$			
Pyridinium, 1-[(4-bromophenyl)methyl]-4-[[4-(diethylamino)phenyl]azo]-, bromide	H_2O	576(4.84)	96-0768-80
$C_{22}H_{24}ClN_5O$			
1H-[1,2,4]Triazolo[4,3-a][1,4]benzodiazepin-1-one, 8-chloro-2-[2-(diethylamino)ethyl]-2,4-dihydro-6-phenyl-	EtOH	215(4.63),249s(4.26), 280s(3.69),303s(3.30)	87-0402-80
$C_{22}H_{24}ClN_5O_7$			
9H-Purine, 6-chloro-9-[2,3-O-[1-ethoxy-2-[[(phenylmethoxy)carbonyl]amino]-ethylidene]-β-D-ribofuranosyl]-	EtOH	264(3.84)	87-0781-80
$C_{22}H_{24}NO_5$			
Glabrine dimethyl ether	EtOH	242(4.20),289(4.53), 312s(4.26),343s(4.14), 390(4.87)	2-0561-80
$C_{22}H_{24}N_2O$			
1H-Pyrido[3,4-b]indol-1-one, 2-butyl-2,3,4,9-tetrahydro-9-(phenylmethyl)-	isoPrOH	226s(4.37),232(4.37), 304(4.22),331s(3.78)	103-0244-80

Compound	Solvent	$\lambda_{max}(\log \epsilon)$	Ref.
$C_{22}H_{24}N_2O_2$ 1-Naphthalenecarboxamide, 5-(dimethyl-amino)-N-[1-(hydroxymethyl)-2-phenyl-ethyl]-, (R)-	EtOH-HCl	275(3.89),283(3.93), 293(3.83),317(3.04)	87-0282-80
$C_{22}H_{24}N_2O_3$ 6,10-Etheno-5H-cyclohepta[b]naphthalen-5,11-imine-12-carboxylic acid, 6-ami-no-5a,6,7,10,10a,11-hexahydro-7-oxo-, 1,1-dimethylethyl ester, (5α,5aβ,6β-10α,10aβ,11α)-	EtOH	240(3.72),271(3.15), 326(1.91)	78-2119-80
16,19-Secostrychnidine-10,16-dione, 19-methyl- (icajine)	MeOH	251(4.16)	5-0895-80
	MeOH-HCl	253(4.06)	5-0895-80
$C_{22}H_{24}N_2O_4$ Benzo[1,2-c:4,5-c']dipyrrole-1,3,5,7-(2H,6H)-tetrone, 2,6-dicyclohexyl-	n.s.g.	310s(<u>3.4</u>),320(<u>3.4</u>)	116-0826-80
Vomicine	MeOH	221(4.31),243(4.08), 262s(3.94),296s(3.52)	5-0895-80
	MeOH-HCl	220(4.35),262(3.72), 296(3.59)	5-0895-80
$C_{22}H_{24}N_2O_8$ Tetracycline	aq H_2SO_4	267(4.26),357(4.15)	106-0024-80
epitetracycline	aq H_2SO_4	254(4.19),357(4.13)	106-0024-80
$C_{22}H_{24}N_2O_{10}$ Glycine, N,N'-[1,2-ethanediylbis(oxy-2,1-phenylene)]bis[N-(carboxymethyl)-calcium chelate	tetraanion	254(4.20),287(3.75)	69-2396-80
	n.s.g.	274(3.62)	69-2396-80
$C_{22}H_{24}N_4OSe$ Benzenamine, 4,4'-[1,4-oxaselenin-3,5-diylbis(methylidynenitrilo)]bis[N,N-dimethyl-	n.s.g.	240(4.26),320(4.03), 425(4.78),550(3.49)	124-0640-80
$C_{22}H_{24}N_4O_2$ 1H-Indole-2-ethanol, 3,3'-azobis[1-methyl-	CHCl$_3$	255s(4.20),280(4.11), 300s(4.00),383(4.38), 402(4.39),425(4.39)	39-1688-80C
$C_{22}H_{24}N_4O_3$ 1-Piperazinecarboxylic acid, 4-(4,5-di-hydro-5-oxo-4,4-diphenyl-1H-imidazol-2-yl)-, ethyl ester	EtOH	221.2(4.55)	56-2217-80
$C_{22}H_{24}N_4O_{11}$ 2,4,7(1H,3H,8H)-Pteridinetrione, 6-phenyl-1,3-di-β-D-ribofuranosyl-	pH 1.0	279(4.11),342(4.20)	24-1524-80
	pH 6.0	217(4.62),236s(4.19), 293(4.10),346(4.28)	24-1524-80
$C_{22}H_{24}N_4SSe$ Benzenamine, 4,4'-[1,4-thiaselenin-3,5-diylbis(methylidynenitrilo)]bis[N,N-dimethyl-	n.s.g.	240(4.30),340(3.95), 415(4.94),665(3.15)	124-0640-80
$C_{22}H_{24}N_5O_2$ Pyridinium, 4-[[4-(diethylamino)phen-yl]azo]-1-[(4-nitrophenyl)methyl]-, bromide	H_2O	578(4.87)	96-0768-80

Compound	Solvent	$\lambda_{max}(\log \epsilon)$	Ref.
$C_{22}H_{24}N_8O_2$			
Bis(tetramethylammonium) salt of 1,2,3-tris(dicyanomethylene)-4-cyclopentene-4,5-diol	H_2O	282(4.15),316(4.16), 378(4.15),398(4.15), 512s(4.26),599(4.81)	44-1338-80
$C_{22}H_{24}O$			
2-Cyclohexen-1-one, 4-methyl-4-phenyl-2-(3-phenylpropyl)-	EtOH	236(4.0)	22-0304-80
$C_{22}H_{24}O_2$			
2-Cyclopropene-1-acetic acid, 1-methyl-2,3-diphenyl-, 1,1-dimethylethyl ester	EtOH	227(4.23),236(4.10), 316(4.43),333(4.32)	35-2797-80
2-Cyclopropene-1-acetic acid, 2-methyl-1,3-diphenyl-, 1,1-dimethylethyl ester	EtOH	203(4.38),262(4.15)	35-2797-80
Dibenzo[a,g]biphenylene, 5,6,6aα,6bβ-11,12,12aβ,12bα-octahydro-3,9-dimethoxy-	EtOH	232(4.31),280(3.54)	87-1410-80
$C_{22}H_{24}O_2S_5$			
α-D-Altrofuranoside, methyl 2,3-bis-S-(phenylmethyl)-2,3,5,6-tetrathio-, cyclic carbonotrithioate	dioxan	318(4.09),455(1.79)	94-0110-80
β-L-Galactofuranoside, methyl 2,3-bis-S-(phenylmethyl)-2,3,5,6-tetrathio-, cyclic carbonotrithioate	dioxan	319(4.20),455(1.94)	94-0110-80
$C_{22}H_{24}O_3$			
Cyclopropa[3,4]pentaleno[1,2-b]naphthalene-2,3,8(1H)-trione, 2a,2b,2c,8a-8b,8c-hexahydro-1,1,2a,2b,8b,8c-hexamethyl-	MeOH	240(3.96),291(3.20), 345(2.62)	44-0034-80
$C_{22}H_{24}O_4$			
2H-1-Benzopyran-2-one, 7-methoxy-8-[3-(4-methoxyphenyl)-3-methylbutyl]-	EtOH	206(4.59),258(3.77), 280(3.80),283(3.81), 322(4.16)	2-0341-80
4H-1-Benzopyran-4-one, 2,3-dihydro-5,7-dimethoxy-8-(3-methyl-2-butenyl)-2-phenyl-	MeOH	240s(4.21),285(4.20), 338s(3.40)	102-1267-80
$C_{22}H_{24}O_4U$			
Uranium, bis[(1,2,3,4,5,6,7,8-η)-ethyl 1,3,5,7-cyclooctatetraene-1-carboxylate]	THF	600(3.31),626(2.76), 643(2.52)	125-1863-80
$C_{22}H_{24}O_5$			
Isolouisfieserone	EtOH	213(4.46),285(4.39), 330(3.00)	102-1262-80
Lancifolin F	MeOH	236(4.06),286(3.77)	102-0285-80
Propanedioic acid, (3-oxo-1,3-diphenylpropyl)-, diethyl ester	EtOH	243(4.16)	34-0085-80
$C_{22}H_{24}O_6$			
Naphtho[2,3-c]furan-1(3H)-one, 4-(3,4-dimethoxyphenyl)-3a,4,9,9a-tetrahydro-6,7-dimethoxy-	EtOH	231(4.20),282(3.84)	94-0850-80
$C_{22}H_{24}O_7$			
Ashantin	EtOH	204(5.00),230s(4.17),	78-3551-80

Compound	Solvent	λ_{max}(log ϵ)	Ref.
Ashantin (cont.)		283(3.73)	78-3551-80
4H-1-Benzopyran-4-one, 2,3-dihydro-3,5-	MeOH	292(4.08),345(3.70)	102-0478-80
dihydroxy-2-(3-hydroxy-4-methoxyphen-	MeOH-NaOAc	291(--),345(--)	102-0478-80
yl)-7-methoxy-8-(3-methyl-2-butenyl)-,	MeOH-AlCl$_3$	272(--),316(--)	102-0478-80
(2R-trans)- (tirumalin)			
Epiashantin	EtOH	205(4.97),231s(4.16),	78-3551-80
		283(3.72)	
Naphtho[2,3-c]furan-1(3H)-one, 9-(3,4-	EtOH	230s(4.19),284(3.84)	94-0850-80
dimethoxyphenyl)-3a,4,9,9a-tetrahydro-			
9a-hydroxy-6,7-dimethoxy-, [3aS-			
(3aα,9α,9aα)]-			
2H-Pyran-2-one, 3-[[5-acetyl-2,3-dihy-	CHCl$_3$	293(4.31)	102-0639-80
dro-4,6-dihydroxy-2-(1-methylethenyl)-			
7-benzofuranyl]methyl]-6-ethyl-4-hy-			
droxy-5-methyl- (italipyrone)			
C$_{22}$H$_{24}$O$_8$			
9,10-Anthracenedione, 2-[3-(dimethoxy-	MeOH	232(4.53),250(4.30),	24-2994-80
methyl)-3-hydroxypentyl]-1,4,8-tri-		292(3.84),410(3.43),	
hydroxy-, (±)-		464(3.99),478(4.04),	
		490(4.10),506(3.96),	
		523(3.43)	
C$_{22}$H$_{24}$O$_9$			
4H-1-Benzopyran-4-one, 5,6,7,8-tetra-	EtOH	256(4.29),267(4.27),	102-2439-80
methoxy-2-(2,4,5-trimethoxyphenyl)-		361(4.27)	
C$_{22}$H$_{24}$O$_{11}$			
4H-1-Benzopyran-4-one, 2-[4-(β-D-gluco-	EtOH	231(4.27),249(4.31),	88-1227-80
pyranosyloxy)-1-hydroxy-2,5-cyclohex-		257s(4.27),293(3.92),	
adien-1-yl]-5-hydroxy-7-methoxy-		324s(3.62)	
C$_{22}$H$_{24}$O$_{13}$			
4H-1-Benzopyran-4-one, 2-[3-(β-D-gluco-	MeOH	231(5.32),296(5.29),	102-0893-80
pyranosyloxy)-4,5-dihydroxyphenyl]-		333(4.69)	
2,3-dihydro-3,5,7-trihydroxy-6-	MeOH-AlCl$_3$	231(5.69),319(5.63)	102-0893-80
methyl-, (2R-trans)-	MeOH-HCl-	231(5.72),319(5.72)	102-0893-80
	AlCl$_3$		
C$_{22}$H$_{25}$NO$_6$			
L-Alanine, N-(4-methoxy-cis-cinnamoyl)-	MeOH	207(4.57),284(4.41)	102-2125-80
3-(3,4-dimethoxyphenyl)-, methyl ester			
trans	MeOH	205(4.47),225(4.44),	102-2125-80
		285(4.40),305(4.38)	
2-Naphthalenecarboxamide, 1,2-dihydro-	MeOH	300(3.84)	2-0552-80
6,7-dimethoxy-1-(3,4,5-trimethoxy-			
phenyl)-			
Spiro[3H-2-benzopyran-3,1'(2'H)-iso-	EtOH	238(4.35),285(4.14),	73-0956-80
quinolin]-4(1H)-one, 3',4'-dihydro-		312(3.85)	
6,6',7,7'-tetramethoxy-2'-methyl-			
C$_{22}$H$_{25}$NO$_7$			
Acetamide, N-(7a,8,11,12-tetrahydro-	EtOH	211(4.75),231s(4.32)	33-0406-80
2,3,4,7a-tetramethoxy-8-oxo-10H-benz-			
[7,8]azuleno[1,8a-b]furan-10-yl)-,			
[7aR-(4bR*,7aα,10β)]-			
2-Naphthalenecarboxamide, 1,2,3,4-tet-	MeOH	315(3.62)	2-0552-80
rahydro-6,7-dimethoxy-4-oxo-1-(3,4,5-			
trimethoxyphenyl)-, trans			

Compound	Solvent	$\lambda_{max}(\log \epsilon)$	Ref.
$C_{22}H_{25}N_3OS$ 2(1H)-Pyridinone, 6-(cyclohexylamino)-4-methyl-3-(methylthio)-5-(2-quinolinyl)-	EtOH	228(4.65),282(4.01), 349(4.20),380s(4.10)	94-2892-80
$C_{22}H_{25}N_3O_2$ 5(4H)-Isoxazolone, 4-[(diethylamino)-[4-(dimethylamino)phenyl]methylene]-3-phenyl-	MeOH	394(4.36)	97-0020-80
$C_{22}H_{25}N_3O_3$ 16,19-Secostrychnidine-10,16-dione, 4-amino-19-methyl-	MeOH MeOH-HCl	229(4.34),270s(3.81), 300s(3.45) 253(4.02),285s(3.38)	5-0895-80 5-0895-80
$C_{22}H_{25}N_3O_6S$ Urea, N-methyl-N-nitroso-N-[5,6,7,9-tetrahydro-1,2,3-trimethoxy-10-(methylthio)-9-oxobenzo[a]heptalen-7-yl]-, (S)-	EtOH	253(4.41),285(4.09), 380(4.29)	87-1440-80
$C_{22}H_{25}N_4$ Pyridinium, 4-[[4-(diethylamino)phenyl]azo]-1-(phenylmethyl)-, bromide	H_2O	576(4.82)	96-0768-80
$C_{22}H_{25}N_5O$ Benzaldehyde, 2-hydroxy-, [2-[(4-butylphenyl)amino]-6-methyl-4-pyrimidinyl]hydrazone]	EtOH	208(4.42),242(4.22), 289(4.46),343(4.39)	103-1279-80
$C_{22}H_{25}N_5O_{14}$ 1,4,7,10,13,16-Benzohexaoxacyclooctadecin-18-amine, 2,3,5,6,8,9,11,12-14,16-decahydro-19-nitro-N-(2,4,6-trinitrophenyl)- K salt	10% dioxan CHCl$_3$ CHCl$_3$ CHCl$_3$	345(4.17),420(4.16) 340(4.13),424(4.16) 425(4.16) 457(4.33)	3-1668-80 3-1668-80 18-1550-80 3-1668-80
$C_{22}H_{26}BrNO_5$ 8H-Pyrano[2,3-h]quinoline, 3-(2-bromo-2-propenyl)-2-(dimethoxymethyl)-4,5-dimethoxy-8,8-dimethyl- 4H-Pyrano[2,3-h]quinolin-4-one, 3-(2-bromo-2-propenyl)-2-(dimethoxymethyl)-1,8-dihydro-5-methoxy-1,8,8-trimethyl-	MeOH MeOH	265(4.65),370(3.59) 255(4.23),285(4.30), 348(3.70)	5-0503-80 5-0503-80
$C_{22}H_{26}Cl_2N_2O_4$ Aspidospermidine-3-carboxylic acid, 15,17-dichloro-6,7-didehydro-3-hydroxy-2-methoxy-, methyl ester, (2β,3β,5α,12β,19α)-	EtOH	254(3.81),317(3.36)	142-1915-80
$C_{22}H_{26}N_2O$ 1H-Imidazole, 4-(2,2-diphenylethenyl)-2,5-dihydro-1,2,2,5,5-pentamethyl-, 3-oxide	EtOH	234(4.20),317(3.85)	70-0956-80
$C_{22}H_{26}N_2O_2$ 9,10-Anthracenedione, 1-amino-2-(octylamino)- 9,10-Anthracenedione, 1-amino-4-(octylamino)-	MeOH MeOH	539(4.03) 573(4.16),617(4.23)	18-3725-80 18-3725-80

Compound	Solvent	λ_{max} (log ϵ)	Ref.
$C_{22}H_{26}N_2O_2S_2$			
Diazene, bis[2-[(tetrahydro-2H-pyran-2-yl)thio]phenyl]-	CHCl$_3$	250(3.94),324(3.91), 410(3.79)	86-1001-80
$C_{22}H_{26}N_2O_4$			
Dibenzo[de,gh][1,10]phenanthroline, 1,2,3,10,11,12,12a,12b-octahydro-5,6,7,8-tetramethoxy-, trans-(±)-	EtOH	270(4.17),295s(3.76)	33-0938-80
Heyneatine	MeOH	220(4.50),280(4.02), 300(3.93)	102-1213-80
Voacangine lactam	MeOH	225(4.45),286(3.96), 298(3.92)	64-0219-80B
Voacryptine	MeOH	224(4.44),282(3.97), 300s(3.94)	102-1213-80
$C_{22}H_{26}N_2O_5$			
Eglandine, 10-methoxy-, N-oxide	MeOH	224(4.46),282(3.98), 300s(3.96),312s(3.65)	102-1213-80
Vulkensine	MeOH	213(4.3),244(4.0), 303(3.9)	102-0307-80
$C_{22}H_{26}N_2O_5S$			
3-Thietaneacetic acid, 2,2-dimethyl-4-oxo-3-[7-oxo-3-(phenylmethyl)-4-oxa-2,6-diazabicyclo[3.2.0]hept-2-en-6-yl]-, 1,1-dimethylethyl ester	EtOH	214(4.12)	39-0388-80C
Urea, N-methyl-N'-[5,6,7,9-tetrahydro-1,2,3-trimethoxy-10-(methylthio)-9-oxobenzo[a]heptalen-7-yl]-, (S)-	EtOH	255(4.33),290(4.08), 380(4.28)	87-1440-80
$C_{22}H_{26}N_4O_4$			
6H-1,2-Oxazine-5,6-diamine, N^5-(4-methoxy-2-nitrophenyl)-N^6,N^6-dimethyl-3-(2,4,6-trimethylphenyl)-	MeOH	321(4.15),435(3.67)	150-0242-80S
$C_{22}H_{26}N_4O_6S$			
Propanoic acid, 2,2'-[sulfonylbis(4,1-phenylene-2-hydrazinyl-1-ylidene)]-bis-, diethyl ester	mineral oil	228(4.3),321s(4.7), 345(4.8)	103-1146-80
$C_{22}H_{26}N_4O_{12}$			
1,4,7,10,13,16-Benzohexaoxacyclooctadecin-18-amine, 2,3,5,6,8,9,11,12-14,15-decahydro-N-(2,4,6-trinitrophenyl)-	10% dioxan CHCl$_3$	392(4.13) 400(4.06)	3-1668-80 3-1668-80 +18-1550-80
K salt	anion n.s.g.	450(4.32) 445(4.39)	3-1668-80 3-1668-80
$C_{22}H_{26}O_2$			
2-Cyclohexen-1-one, 4,4'-phenylenebis[4,6-dimethyl-	EtOH	234(4.43)	22-0267-80
$C_{22}H_{26}O_3$			
D-Homopregna-1,4,6,16-tetraene-3,20-dione, 17a-hydroxy-	EtOH	222(4.10),258(3.97), 301(4.11)	33-1867-80
1H-3a,7-Methanoazulen-9-one, 5-(benzoyloxy)-2,3,4,7,8,8a-hexahydro-3,6,8,8-tetramethyl-, [3R-(3α,3aα,7α,8aβ)]-	EtOH	232(4.26)	78-0731-80
[3R-(3α,3aβ,7β,8aα)]-	EtOH	232(4.26)	78-0731-80

Compound	Solvent	$\lambda_{max}(\log \epsilon)$	Ref.
$C_{22}H_{26}O_4$			
D-Homopregna-1,4-diene-3,6,11,20-tetr-one	MeOH	243(4.09)	24-0203-80
D-Homopregna-1,4-diene-3,11,15,20-tetr-one	MeOH	239(4.16)	24-0203-80
D-Homopregna-1,4-diene-3,11,17,20-tetr-one	MeOH	238(4.16)	24-0203-80
D-Homopregna-1,4-diene-3,12,15,20-tetr-one	MeOH	244(4.15)	24-0203-80
$C_{22}H_{26}O_6$			
1,4-Benzodioxin, 2,3-dihydro-5-methoxy-3-methyl-7-(2-propenyl)-2-(3,4,5-tri-methoxyphenyl)-, (eusiderin C)	MeOH	219(4.47),270(3.23)	102-1523-80
Epieudesmin	EtOH	204(5.01),232(4.29), 279(3.83)	78-3551-80
2(3H)-Furanone, 3,4-bis[(3,4-dimethoxy-phenyl)methyl]dihydro-, (3R-trans)-	EtOH	230(3.93),285(3.73)	2-0241-80
$C_{22}H_{26}O_7$			
2(3H)-Furanone, 4-[(3,4-dimethoxyphen-yl)hydroxymethyl]-3-[(3,4-dimethoxy-phenyl)methyl]dihydro-	EtOH	233(4.24),280(3.80)	94-0850-80
isomer	EtOH	231(4.16),280(3.72)	94-0850-80
Linearilobin H	MeOH	202(4.32)	102-0849-80
$C_{22}H_{26}O_8$			
2(3H)-Furanone, 3-[(3,4-dimethoxyphen-yl)hydroxymethyl]-4-[(3,4-dimethoxy-phenyl)methyl]dihydro-3-hydroxy-	EtOH	232(4.21),279(3.72)	94-0850-80
Plicatipyrone	$CHCl_3$	296(4.30)	102-0639-80
$C_{22}H_{26}O_{10}$			
Auriculoside	MeOH	221(5.67),278(4.53), 286s(4.42)	102-1560-80
Phloridzin, 4-O-methyl-	MeOH	224(4.45),285(4.34), 325s(3.75)	100-0739-80
$C_{22}H_{26}C_{11}$			
Globularifolin	MeOH	229(4.1),274(2.9)	33-0117-80 +100-0649-80
Symplocoside	MeCN	204(4.91),227(4.26), 278(3.66)	102-1825-80
Veronicoside	MeOH	205(4.09),232(4.18), 275(3.02)	100-0649-80
$C_{22}H_{26}O_{12}$			
Catalposide	MeOH	260(4.2)	100-0524-80
	EtOH	260(4.27)	100-0649-80
	EtOH-base	303(--)	100-0649-80
$C_{22}H_{26}O_{13}$			
Verproside	MeOH	216(4.09),224(4.07), 263(4.09),295(3.87)	33-1905-80
$C_{22}H_{27}ClN_2O_4$			
4H-Furo[3,2-b]pyrrole-5-carboxylic acid, 2-(4-chlorophenyl)-4-[3-[(1,1-dimethylethyl)amino]-2-hydroxyprop-yl]-, ethyl ester, monohydrochloride	MeOH	343(4.75),359(4.66)	73-2949-80

Compound	Solvent	$\lambda_{max}(\log \epsilon)$	Ref.
$C_{22}H_{27}ClN_4O_{10}S$ D-Glucitol, 1-C-(6-chloro-9H-purin-9-yl)-1-S-methyl-1-thio-, 2,3,4,5,6-pentaacetate	MeOH	266(4.53)	136-0241-80C
$C_{22}H_{27}FN_2O_4$ Pregna-1,4-diene-3,20-dione, 21-diazo-9-fluoro-11,17-dihydroxy-16-methyl-, (11β,16α)-	MeOH	246(4.42)	63-0953-80
$C_{22}H_{27}FO_4$ Pregna-1,4,17(20)-trien-21-al, 9α-fluoro-11β,20-dihydroxy-16β-methyl-3-oxo-	MeOH	240(4.22),273(4.17)	95-0072-80
Pregna-1,4,16-triene-3,20-dione, 9α-fluoro-11β,21-dihydroxy-16-methyl-	MeOH	245(4.36)	95-0072-80
$C_{22}H_{27}NO_3$ Spiro[androsta-1,4,6-triene-17,5'-oxazolidine]-2',3-dione, 3'-methyl-, (17β)-	EtOH	221(4.05),255(3.96), 298(4.08)	13-0361-80A
Spiro[gona-4,9,11-triene-17,5'-oxazolidine]-2',3-dione, 13-ethyl-3'-methyl-, (17β)-	EtOH	235(3.76),335(4.46)	13-0361-80A
$C_{22}H_{27}NO_5$ Benzo[a]heptalen-10(5H)-one, 7-(dimethylamino)-6,7-dihydro-1,2,3,9-tetramethoxy-, (S)-	EtOH	246(4.47),340(4.23)	33-0050-80
Dibenz[c,g]azecin-13(6H)-one, 5,7,8,14-tetrahydro-2,3,10,11-tetramethoxy-6-methyl-	EtOH	282(3.98)	142-0011-80
Spiro[3H-2-benzopyran-3,1'(2'H)-isoquinoline], 1,3',4,4'-tetrahydro-6,6',7,7'-tetramethoxy-2'-methyl-	EtOH	286(3.92)	73-0956-80
$C_{22}H_{27}NO_6$ Benzenepropanamide, α-(2-formyl-4,5-dimethoxyphenyl)-3,4-dimethoxy-N,N-dimethyl-	EtOH	243(4.06),283(4.00), 310(3.76)	39-2013-80C
$C_{22}H_{27}NO_7$ 2-Naphthalenecarboxamide, 1,2,3,4-tetrahydro-3-hydroxy-6,7-dimethoxy-1-(3,4,5-trimethoxyphenyl)-, (1α,2β,3β)-	MeOH	279(3.60)	2-0552-80
2-Naphthalenecarboxamide, 1,2,3,4-tetrahydro-4-hydroxy-6,7-dimethoxy-1-(3,4,5-trimethoxyphenyl)-, (1α,2β,4α)-	MeOH	279(3.86)	2-0552-80
(1α,2β,4β)-	MeOH	279(3.90)	2-0552-80
$C_{22}H_{27}NO_7S$ 4H-Indol-4-one, 1,5,6,7-tetrahydro-6,6-dimethyl-2-[5-O-[(4-methylphenyl)sulfonyl]-α-D-arabinofuranosyl]-	EtOH	242(4.17),285(4.10)	136-0037-80C
$C_{22}H_{27}N_3O$ Benzonitrile, 4-[[4-(nonyloxy)phenyl]azo]-	n.s.g.	<u>250f(4.1)</u>,360f(4.5), 440(3.20)	56-1233-80
$C_{22}H_{27}N_3O_2$ Benzonitrile, 4-[[4-(nonyloxy)phenyl]-NNO-azoxy]-	n.s.g.	<u>250(4.2)</u>,374f(<u>4.3</u>)	56-1233-80

Compound	Solvent	$\lambda_{max}(\log \epsilon)$	Ref.
Benzonitrile, 4-[[4-(nonyloxy)phenyl]-ONN-azoxy]-	n.s.g.	240(<u>3.9</u>),340(<u>4.3</u>)	56-1233-80
$C_{22}H_{27}N_9O_4$			
1H-Pyrrole-2-carboxamide, N-[5-[[(3-amino-3-iminopropyl)amino]carbonyl]-1-methyl-1H-pyrrol-2-yl]-5-[[[5-(formylamino)-1-methyl-1H-pyrrol-2-yl]-carbonyl]amino]-1-methyl-, monohydrochloride	EtOH	324(4.39)	36-1334-80
$C_{22}H_{28}NO_4$			
Largemonine, N-methyl-, chloride	MeOH	286(3.86)	100-0270-80
$C_{22}H_{28}N_2O_2$			
9-Azabicyclo[3.3.1]nonan-3-one, 9,9'-(1,4-phenylene)bis-	MeCN	273(4.2),320s(3.3)	35-5482-80
1H-Imidazole-4-ethanol, 2,5-dihydro-1,2,2,5,5-pentamethyl-α,α-diphenyl-, 3-oxide	EtOH	212(4.00),250(3.96)	70-0956-80
$C_{22}H_{28}N_2O_3$			
Strychnofendlerine	EtOH	248(4.16),278(3.53), 286s(3.45)	32-0081-80
Voacangine	MeOH	226(4.41),286(3.95), 299(3.92)	64-0219-80B
$C_{22}H_{28}N_2O_4$			
Strychnorubigine	EtOH	227(4.68),274s(3.91), 284s(3.84),293(3.84)	102-0992-80
Voacangarine, (19S)-	MeOH	222(4.45),282(3.98), 302(3.90),314s(3.64)	102-1213-80
Voacangine hydroxyindolenine	MeOH	225(4.45),271(3.79), 285(3.95),293(3.92), 314s(3.48)	64-0219-80B
Voacristine	n.s.g.	225(4.48),286(3.97), 301(3.92)	64-0885-80B
$C_{22}H_{28}N_2O_4S_2$			
1-Piperazinepropanol, 4-[10,11-dihydro-8-(methylsulfonyl)dibenzo[b,f]thiepin-10-yl]-, S-oxide	MeOH	235(4.19),270s(3.58)	73-0529-80
1-Piperazinepropanol, 4-[10,11-dihydro-8-(methylsulfonyl)dibenzo[b,f]thiepin-10-yl]-, 1-oxide	MeOH	227(4.11),288(4.00)	73-0529-80
$C_{22}H_{28}N_2O_5$			
2,5-Cyclohexadien-1-one, 4-[[4-(1,4,7-10-tetraoxa-13-azacyclopentadec-13-yl)phenyl]imino]-	MeCN	583(4.77)	24-0457-80
Propanedioic acid, [2-(2-acetyl-2,3,4,9-tetrahydro-1H-pyrido[3,4-b]-indol-1-yl)ethyl]-, diethyl ester	EtOH	225(4.62),274s(3.89), 279(3.90),290(3.80)	94-2527-80
1H-Pyrrole-3-propanoic acid, 2-[(1,1-dimethylethoxy)carbonyl]-5-[(4-ethenyl-1,5-dihydro-3-methyl-5-oxo-2H-pyrrol-2-ylidene)methyl]-4-methyl-, methyl ester	MeOH	265(4.26),400(4.54), 415s(--)	24-1603-80
	+ Zn(OAc)₂	274(4.26),280s(--), 454(4.55)	24-1603-80
Strychnosplendine, N_a-acetyl-12-hydroxy-11-methoxy-	EtOH	226(4.42),254(3.87), 296s(3.30)	32-0081-80
	EtOH-base	306(3.74)	32-0081-80

Compound	Solvent	$\lambda_{max}(\log \epsilon)$	Ref.
$C_{22}H_{28}N_4O_{10}S_2$			
D-Glucitol, 1-C-(1,6-dihydro-6-thioxo-9H-purin-9-yl)-1-S-methyl-1-thio-, 2,3,4,5,6-pentaacetate, (S)-	MeOH	225(4.34),324(4.56)	136-0241-80C
$C_{22}H_{28}O$			
Phenol, 3-[4-methyl-6-(2,6,6-trimethyl-1-cyclohexen-1-yl)-1,3,5-hexatrien-yl]-, (E,E,E)-	EtOH	340(4.45)	87-1013-80
(E,Z,E)-	EtOH	330(4.34)	87-1013-80
$C_{22}H_{28}O_2$			
1H-3a,7-Methanoazulen-5-ol, 2,3,4,7,8-8a-hexahydro-3,6,8,8-tetramethyl-, benzoate, [3R-(3α,3aβ,7β,8aα)]-	EtOH	231(4.22)	78-0731-80
2,4,6-Octatrienoic acid, 7-(2,3-dihydro-3,3-dimethyl-1H-inden-5-yl)-3-methyl-, ethyl ester, (E,E,E)-	EtOH	342(4.50)	33-1604-80
$C_{22}H_{28}O_3$			
D-Homopregna-1,4-diene-3,11,20-trione	MeOH	238(4.17)	24-0203-80
D-Homopregna-1,4-diene-3,15,20-trione	MeOH	244(4.19)	24-0203-80
D-Homopregna-4,6,16-triene-3,20-dione, 17a-hydroxy-	EtOH	285(4.42)	33-1867-80
$C_{22}H_{28}O_4$			
D-Homopregn-4-ene-3,6,11,20-tetrone	MeOH	244(3.99),310(3.27)	24-0203-80
D-Homopregn-4-ene-3,11,15,20-tetrone	MeOH	238(4.18)	24-0203-80
D-Homopregn-4-ene-3,11,17,20-tetrone	MeOH	238(4.18)	24-0203-80
D-Homopregn-4-ene-3,12,15,20-tetrone	MeOH	239(4.22)	24-0203-80
$C_{22}H_{28}O_5$			
2,5-Cyclohexadien-1-one, 4-[2-(3,4-dimethoxyphenyl)-1-methylethyl]-4,5-dimethoxy-2-(2-propenyl)- (lancifolin C)	MeOH	280(3.83),285s(3.82)	102-0285-80
2H-Cyclopenta[b]furan-2-one, 4-[3-(benzoyloxy)-1-octenyl]hexahydro-5-hydroxy-, (R)-	MeOH	228(4.14),266s(2.89), 273(2.95),280(2.85)	44-1528-80
(S)-	MeOH	228(4.14),266s(2.94), 273(2.97),279(2.88)	44-1528-80
Furan, 2,5-bis(3,4-dimethoxyphenyl)-tetrahydro-3,4-dimethyl- (galgravin)	MeOH	232(3.65),278(4.18)	100-0353-80
Lancifolin D	MeOH	281(3.84),286(3.82)	102-0285-80
Pregna-1,4,6-triene-3,20-dione, 11β,17α,21-trihydroxy-16α-methyl-16β-	MeOH	220(4.11),252(4.00), 300(4.08)	87-0430-80
	MeOH	220(4.05),250(3.95), 299(4.03)	87-0430-80
$C_{22}H_{28}O_6$			
Arturin acetate	MeOH	213(3.58)	102-2765-80
2-Cyclohexen-1-one, 4-[4,5-dimethoxy-2-(2-propenyl)phenoxy]-3,4-dimethoxy-6-(2-propenyl)-	MeOH	242(4.49),286(3.96)	102-0285-80
Effusin	EtOH	234(3.97)	77-1206-80
$C_{22}H_{28}O_7$			
Deltoidin B acetate	EtOH	218(4.00)	102-1975-80
Linearilobin I	MeOH	202(4.32)	102-0849-80

Compound	Solvent	$\lambda_{max}(\log \epsilon)$	Ref.
$C_{22}H_{28}O_8$			
1,2-Benzenedicarboxylic acid, 4-(3-ethoxy-3-oxo-1-propenyl)-5-(3-ethoxy-3-oxopropyl)-, diethyl ester, (E)-	EtOH	228(4.33),279(4.39)	118-0950-80
2-Butenoic acid, 2-methyl-, 8-acetoxy-2,3,3a,4,5,6,7,8,9,11a-decahydro-9-hydroxy-6,10-dimethyl-3-methylene-2-oxo-6,9-epoxycyclodeca[b]furan-4-yl ester	MeOH	214(4.28)	44-3163-80
Coleon C, 2α-formoxy-12-O-methyl-	EtOH	265(4.08),273s(3.92), 321(3.74),397(3.86)	33-0095-80
Linearilobin C (as acetate)	MeOH	208(4.34)	102-0849-80
2,3-Naphthalenedimethanol, 1,2,3,4-tetrahydro-7-hydroxy-1-(4-hydroxy-3,5-dimethoxyphenyl)-6,8-dimethoxy-(pygeoresinol)	MeOH	218(4.738),281(3.481)	2-0279-80
2,4,6-Octatrienedioic acid, 4,5-bis(3-ethoxy-3-oxo-1-propenyl)-, diethyl ester, (all-E)-	ether	255(4.32),330(4.46)	118-0950-80
$C_{22}H_{28}O_9$			
2H-Cycloundeca[b]furan-6-carboxylic acid, 5-acetoxy-3,3a,4,5,8,9,10,11-12,12a-decahydro-3-methylene-4-(2-methyl-1-oxopropoxy)-2,11-dioxo-, methyl ester	MeOH	205(4.23)	44-4028-80
$C_{22}H_{29}ClO_5$			
Pregna-1,4-diene-3,20-dione, 7-chloro-11,17,23-trihydroxy-16-methyl-, (7α,11β,16α)-	MeOH	242(4.19)	145-1618-80
$C_{22}H_{29}FO_5$			
1,5-Cyclopregn-3-ene-2,20-dione, 9-fluoro-11,17,21-trihydroxy-16-methyl-, (1α,5β,11β,16β)-	MeOH	270(3.23)	95-0072-80
$C_{22}H_{29}NO_2S$			
2-Azaspiro[3.5]nonan-1-one, 5,5,9,9-tetramethyl-3-thioxo-2-(2,4,6-trimethylbenzoyl)-	isooctane	263(4.2),325s(--), 460(1.5)	88-4247-80
$C_{22}H_{29}NO_3$			
3-Pyridinecarboxaldehyde, 5-(1,1-dimethylethyl)-6-(2,2-dimethyl-1-oxopropyl)-1,6-dihydro-6-hydroxy-1-(phenylmethyl)-	C_6H_{12}	387(3.39)	88-4097-80
Spiro[androsta-1,4-diene-17,5'-oxazolidine]-2',3-dione, 3'-methyl-, (17β)-	EtOH	243(4.20)	13-0361-80A
Spiro[androsta-4,6-diene-17,5'-oxazolidine]-2',3-dione, 3'-methyl-, (17β)-	EtOH	282(4.39)	13-0361-80A
Spiro[gona-4,6-diene-17,5'-oxazolidine]-2',3-dione, 13-ethyl-3'-methyl-, (17β)-	EtOH	281(4.38)	13-0361-80A
Spiro[gona-4,9-diene-17,5'-oxazolidine]-2',3-dione, 13-ethyl-3'-methyl-, (17β)-	EtOH	301(4.31)	13-0361-80A
Spiro[gona-5(10),9(11)-diene-17,5'-oxazolidine]-2',3-dione, 13-ethyl-3'-methyl-, (17β)-	EtOH	239(4.19)	13-0361-80A

Compound	Solvent	$\lambda_{max}(\log \epsilon)$	Ref.
$C_{22}H_{29}NO_6$ Benzenepropanamide, α-[2-(hydroxymethyl)-4,5-dimethoxyphenyl]-3,4-dimethoxy-N,N-dimethyl-	EtOH	242(3.93),281(3.77)	39-2013-80C
$C_{22}H_{29}NO_7$ Acetamide, N-(6,7,7a,8,9,10,11,12-octahydro-1,2,3,10-tetramethoxy-9-oxo-5H-10,12a-epoxybenzo[a]heptalen-7-yl)-	EtOH	208(4.70),228s(4.12)	33-0406-80
$C_{22}H_{29}NO_8S$ D-Arabinitol, 1-C-(4,5,6,7-tetrahydro-6,6-dimethyl-4-oxo-1H-indol-2-yl)-, 5-(4-methylbenzenesulfonate), (S)-	EtOH	245(4.16),287(4.06)	136-0037-80C
$C_{22}H_{29}N_3$ Benzenamine, 4-[2-[1-(1-methylethyl)-3-phenyl-2-imidazolidinyl]ethenyl]-N,N-dimethyl-	MeCN MeCN-H₂O MeCN-HCl	300(4.42) 480(4.43) 512(4.74)	35-3062-80 35-3062-80 35-3062-80
$C_{22}H_{29}N_3O$ Benzamide, N-[2-[[(1-methylpropyl)amino][(1-methylpropyl)imino]methyl]-phenyl]-	EtOH	215(4.37),230s(4.31), 260s(4.05)	1-0637-80
$C_{22}H_{29}N_3O_6$ Aspidospermidine-3-carboxylic acid, 3-hydroxy-2-methoxy-15-nitro-, methyl ester, (2β,5α,12β,19α)-	EtOH	230(3.74),245(3.65), 258(3.60),372(4.13)	142-1915-80
$C_{22}H_{29}N_3O_{11}$ Aconitan-3-one, 1,2-didehydro-8,13,14-15-tetrahydroxy-6,16-dimethoxy-4-(methoxymethyl)-2-nitro-20-nitroso-, (6α,14α,15α,16β)-	EtOH	230(4.1),343(3.1)	18-1381-80
$C_{22}H_{29}N_3O_{12}P_2$ Pyridinium, 1-[5-O-[7-[(4-acetylphenyl)amino]-1,3-dihydroxy-2,4-dioxa-1,3-diphosphahept-1-yl]-β-D-ribofuranosyl]-3-(aminocarbonyl)-, hydroxide, inner salt, P,P'-dioxide	pH 1 pH 11	262(3.78) 331(4.32)	5-1259-80 5-1259-80
$C_{22}H_{29}N_5$ 4-Pyrimidinamine, N-(4-butylphenyl)-2-(3,5-dimethyl-1H-pyrazol-1-yl)-5-ethyl-6-methyl-	EtOH	<u>253(4.5),285s(4.4)</u>	103-0868-80
$C_{22}H_{30}N_2O_2$ Aspidospermidine, 1-acetyl-17-methoxy-	MeOH	223(4.56),255(4.09), 286s(--)	73-1419-80
$C_{22}H_{30}N_2O_3S$ 1H-Perimidine-6-sulfonic acid, 2-undecyl-	pH 13 MeOH	342(3.49) 324(3.88)	103-0429-80 103-0429-80
$C_{22}H_{30}N_4O_4$ Benzo[1,2-b:3,4-b']dipyrrole-2,7-dicarboxylic acid, 3,8-bis[(dimethylamino)methyl]-1,6-dihydro-, diethyl ester	EtOH	209(4.38),293(4.56), 331s(4.05),348s(3.82)	103-0495-80

Compound	Solvent	$\lambda_{max}(\log \epsilon)$	Ref.
$C_{22}H_{30}N_4O_5S$			
3-Pyridinecarboxylic acid, 5-butyl-1,4-dihydro-4-oxo-, 2-[[[2-(3,4,5-trimethoxyphenyl)ethyl]amino]thioxomethyl]hydrazide	EtOH	250(4.25),281(3.97)	4-0175-80
$C_{22}H_{30}N_4O_{12}$			
D-Glucitol, 1-[(6-amino-1,2,3,4-tetrahydro-1,3-dimethyl-2,4-dioxo-5-pyrimidinyl)imino]-1-deoxy-, 2,3,4,5,6-pentaacetate	EtOH	284(4.27)	94-2835-80
$C_{22}H_{30}O$			
Acetaldehyde, [4-[1-methyl-3-(2,6,6-trimethyl-1-cyclohexen-1-yl)-2-propenylidene]-2-cyclohepten-1-ylidene]-, "11-cis"	MeOH	230(3.90),265(3.95), 295(4.08),376(4.40)	35-6370-80
"9,11-di-cis"	MeOH	230(3.95),295(4.04), 371(4.30)	35-6370-80
"11,13-di-cis"	MeOH	225(4.00),295(4.08), 371(4.34)	35-6370-80
"9,11,13-tri-cis"	MeOH	225(4.00),285(4.08), 366(4.20)	35-6370-80
$C_{22}H_{30}O_2$			
D-Homo-1,4-pregnadiene-3,20-dione	MeOH	245(4.18)	24-0203-80
$C_{22}H_{30}O_2S$			
5(1H)-Azulenone, 3-(1,1-dimethylethoxy)-2,3,3a,4,8,8a-hexahydro-3a,8-dimethyl-6-(phenylthio)-	EtOH	258(3.83)	78-2701-80
isomer	EtOH	257(3.87)	78-2701-80
$C_{22}H_{30}O_3$			
2-Butenoic acid, 3-(2-acetyl-1a,2,3,5-6,7-hexahydro-2,5,5-trimethyl-1,3-methano-1H-cycloprop[d]inden-8-yl)-, ethyl ester, (1α,1aβ,2α,3α,7aS*-8S*(E)]-	EtOH	218(4.18)	33-1604-80
D-Homoandrosta-4,6-diene-3,17-dione, 17aα-hydroxy-6,17aβ-dimethyl-(17aβ)-	EtOH	289(4.39)	13-0511-80A
	EtOH	288(4.40)	13-0511-80A
D-Homoandrosta-4,6-diene-3,17a-dione, 17α-hydroxy-6,17β-dimethyl-	EtOH	288(4.38)	13-0511-80A
D-Homopregna-1,4-diene-3,20-dione, 11α-hydroxy-	MeOH	248(4.24)	24-0203-80
D-Homopregna-4,16-diene-3,20-dione, 17a-hydroxy-	EtOH	240(4.23)	33-1867-80
D-Homopregn-4-ene-3,11,20-trione	MeOH	238(4.19)	24-0203-80
D-Homopregn-4-ene-3,15,20-trione	MeOH	240(4.23)	24-0203-80
2,4,6-Octatrienoic acid, 7-(2,3,4,5,6-7-hexahydro-3,3-dimethyl-7-oxo-1H-inden-5-yl)-3-methyl-, ethyl ester, (E,E,E)-	EtOH	253(4.20),309(4.63)	33-1604-80
2,4-Pentadienoic acid, 5-(3a-acetyl-2,3,3a,4-tetrahydro-1,1,5-trimethyl-1H-inden-4-yl)-3-methyl-, ethyl ester	EtOH	263(4.57)	33-1604-80
2,4-Pentadienoic acid, 5-(5-acetyl-2,3,3a,4-tetrahydro-1,1,5-trimethyl-1H-inden-4-yl)-3-methyl-, ethyl ester	EtOH	264(4.45)	33-1604-80

Compound	Solvent	$\lambda_{max}(\log \epsilon)$	Ref.
$C_{22}H_{30}O_4$			
D-Homopregna-1,4-diene-3,20-dione, 11α,15α-dihydroxy-	MeOH	249(4.24)	24-0203-80
D-Homopregna-1,4-diene-3,20-dione, 11β,17α-dihydroxy-	MeOH	244(4.16)	24-0203-80
D-Homopregna-1,4-diene-3,20-dione, 12β,15α-dihydroxy-	MeOH	245(4.16)	24-0203-80
D-Homopregn-4-ene-3,11,20-trione, 14α-hydroxy-	MeOH	238(4.18)	24-0203-80
D-Homopregn-4-ene-3,11,20-trione, 17α-hydroxy-	MeOH	238(4.17)	24-0203-80
$C_{22}H_{30}O_5$			
D-Homopregn-4-ene-3,11,20-trione, 7α,14α-dihydroxy-	MeOH	238(4.17)	24-0203-80
$C_{22}H_{30}O_6$			
Effusanin B	MeOH	240(3.98)	138-1635-80
$C_{22}H_{30}O_7$			
Effusanin C	MeOH	240(3.98)	138-1635-80
Longikaurin B	MeOH	234.5(3.98)	77-0205-80
$C_{22}H_{30}O_8$			
Butanoic acid, 2-methyl-, 4-(acetoxy-methyl)-6,7a-dihydrospiro[cyclopenta-[c]pyran-7(1H),2'-oxirane]-1,6-diyl ester (valtrate)	MeOH	204(3.0),256(4.2)	100-0649-80
$C_{22}H_{30}O_9$			
Melnerin A, 9α-acetoxy-	MeOH	213(4.18)	44-4028-80
$C_{22}H_{31}NO_5S$			
Latrunculin A	MeOH	218(4.37),268s(--)	88-3629-80
$C_{22}H_{31}NO_9$			
D-Arabinitol, 1-C-[1-[((3,4-dimethoxy-phenyl)methyl]-4-(ethoxycarbonyl)-5-methyl-1H-pyrrol-3-yl]-, (S)-	EtOH	239(4.14),265(--)	39-1199-80C
D-Arabinitol, 5-C-[1-[((3,4-dimethoxy-phenyl)methyl]-4-(ethoxycarbonyl)-5-methyl-1H-pyrrol-3-yl]-, (S)-	EtOH	236(4.21),262(--)	39-1199-80C
$C_{22}H_{31}N_3O_{12}P_2$			
3-Pyridinecarboxamide, 1-[5-O-[7-[(4-acetylphenyl)amino]-1,3-dihydroxy-2,4-dioxa-1,3-diphosphahept-1-yl]-β-D-ribofuranosyl]-1,4-dihydro-, P,P'-dioxide	pH 9.5	327(4.41)	5-1259-80
$C_{22}H_{31}N_5O$			
1H-Cyclopenta[5,6]naphtho[1,2-g]tetra-zolo[1,5-a]quinazolin-1-ol, 2,3,3a-3b,4,5,5c,6,13,13a,13b,14,15,15a-tetradecahydro-1,13a,15a-trimethyl-, [1S-(1α,3aβ,3bα,5aβ,13aα,13bβ,15aα)]-	MeOH	216(4.31),280(3.72)	39-1019-80C
$C_{22}H_{31}N_5O_8$			
Guanosine, N-(2-methyl-1-oxopropyl)-, 2',5'-bis(2-methylpropanoate)	EtOH	280(4.08)	39-0563-80C

Compound	Solvent	$\lambda_{max}(\log \epsilon)$	Ref.
1,2-Hydrazinedicarboxylic acid, 1,1'-(2-ethyl-2H-isoindole-1,3-diyl)bis-, tetraethyl ester	MeOH	269(3.17),273(3.20), 279(3.33),327(3.93)	88-3471-80
$C_{22}H_{32}NO_5$			
Benzo[a]quinolizinium, 2-(2-ethoxy-2-oxoethyl)-3-ethyl-1,2,3,4,6,7-hexahydro-9,10,11-trimethoxy-, iodide, trans-(±)-	EtOH	246s(4.11),318(4.28)	78-0965-80
perchlorate	EtOH	247(4.03),319(4.22)	78-0965-80
$C_{22}H_{32}N_2$			
9-Azabicyclo[3.3.1]nonane, 9,9'-(1,4-phenylene)bis-	MeCN	279(4.1),340(3.1)	35-5482-80
$C_{22}H_{32}N_2S_4$			
Cyclopentanamine, N,N'-[dithiobis(carbonothioyl-2-cyclopentyl-1-ylidene)]-bis-	CHCl_3	312(4.02),415(4.70)	118-0566-80
$C_{22}H_{32}N_4O_4$			
Distigmine bromide, iodine complex	CHCl_3	280(4.85)	106-0030-80
$C_{22}H_{32}O$			
14'-Apo-β,ψ-carotenol, all-trans	3-Mepentane	262(3.78),356(4.77)	149-0739-80B
at 77ºK	3-Mepentane	262(4.02),343(4.68)	149-0739-80B
$C_{22}H_{32}O_2$			
2H-Benzo[a]xanthene, 1,3,4,4a,5,6,6a-12,12a,12b-decahydro-10-methoxy-4,4,6a,12b-tetramethyl-	n.s.g.	210(4.28),300(3.59)	44-1435-80
D-Homopregna-5,17(17a)-dien-20-one, 3β-hydroxy-	EtOH	231(3.97)	33-1867-80
D-Homopregn-4-ene-3,20-dione	MeOH	241(4.23)	24-0203-80
$C_{22}H_{32}O_3$			
D-Homopregna-5,17-dien-21-one, 3β,16α-dihydroxy-	EtOH	227(3.91)	33-1867-80
D-Homopregna-5,17-dien-21-one, 3β,16β-dihydroxy-	EtOH	233(3.90)	33-1867-80
D-Homopregn-4-ene-3,20-dione, 11α-hydroxy-	MeOH	241(4.19)	24-0203-80
D-Homopregn-4-ene-3,20-dione, 15α-hydroxy-	MeOH	243(4.20)	24-0203-80
D-Homopregn-4-ene-3,20-dione, 17a-hydroxy-	EtOH	241(4.20)	33-1867-80
2,4,6-Octatrienoic acid, 7-(2,3,4,5,6-7-hexahydro-7-hydroxy-3,3-dimethyl-1H-inden-5-yl)-3-methyl-, ethyl ester, [5α(2E,4E,6E),7α]-	EtOH	313(4.60)	33-1604-80
Pregn-4-ene-3,20-dione, 18-(hydroxymethyl)-, 18a,20-hemiketal	MeOH	240(4.21)	24-1106-80
2H-Pyran-3-ol, 3,6-dihydro-4-methyl-6-[2-methyl-4-(2,6,6-trimethyl-1-cyclohexen-1-yl)-1,3-butadienyl]-, acetate, [3α,6α(1E,3E)]-(±)-	EtOH	245(4.00),270(4.00)	78-1179-80
$C_{22}H_{32}O_4$			
Cleomeolide acetate	EtOH	216(3.68)	78-3489-80
3-Cyclohexene-1,3-dicarboxylic acid,	EtOH	275(4.23)	44-2080-80

Compound	Solvent	$\lambda_{max}(\log \epsilon)$	Ref.
1-(4-methyl-1,2-pentadienyl)-5-(2-methylpropylidene)-, diethyl ester			44-2080-80
13-Epietiojerv-4-en-3-one, 12α,13β,17β-trihydroxy-, 13,17-acetonide	EtOH	239(4.08)	18-0243-80
D-Homopregn-4-ene-3,20-dione, 6β,11α-dihydroxy-	MeOH	236(4.12)	24-0203-80
D-Homopregn-4-ene-3,20-dione, 7β,11α-dihydroxy-	MeOH	244(4.20)	24-0203-80
D-Homopregn-4-ene-3,20-dione, 7β,17α-dihydroxy-	MeOH	243(4.19)	24-0203-80
D-Homopregn-4-ene-3,20-dione, 11α,15α-dihydroxy-	MeOH	244(4.20)	24-0203-80
D-Homopregn-4-ene-3,20-dione, 11β,17α-dihydroxy-	MeOH	242(4.20)	24-0203-80
D-Homopregn-4-ene-3,20-dione, 12β,15α-dihydroxy-	MeOH	243(4.22)	24-0203-80
D-Homopregn-4-ene-3,20-dione, 15α,16α-dihydroxy-	MeOH	243(4.23)	24-0203-80
Pregn-4-ene-3,20-dione, 21-hydroxy-18-(hydroxymethyl)-, 18a,20-hemiketal	MeOH	241(4.21)	24-1106-80
$C_{22}H_{32}O_5$			
Diisophor-2(7)-en-3-one, 1,4-diacetoxy-	n.s.g.	246(3.98)	39-0733-80C
Galeopsin	EtOH	288.5(1.91)	102-1805-80
Pregaleopsin	EtOH	288(1.88)	102-1805-80
$C_{22}H_{32}O_8$			
Butanoic acid, 2-methyl-, 4-(acetoxymethyl)-4a,5,6,7a-tetrahydrospiro[cyclopenta[c]pyran-7(1H),2'-oxirane]-1,6-diyl ester, [1S-(1α,4aα,6α,7β,7aα)]-	MeOH	206(3.0)	100-0649-80
Viguilenin acetate	EtOH	222(3.84)	102-1795-80
$C_{22}H_{34}N_2$			
4,4'-Bipyridinium, 1,1'-dihexyl-, diiodide	H_2O	259(4.32)	98-1026-80
$C_{22}H_{34}N_6O_{16}S$			
Deseryladenomycin	H_2O	260(4.15)	88-3203-80
$C_{22}H_{34}O_3$			
2,6,10-Dodecatrienal, 12-acetoxy-6,10-dimethyl-2-(4-methyl-3-pentenyl)-, (E,E,E)-	EtOH	230(4.0)	102-2207-80
2,6,10,14-Hexadecatetraen-4-one, 16-acetoxy-2,6,10,14-tetramethyl-, (E,E,E)- (eleganolone acetate)	EtOH	242(4.05)	102-2759-80
9(10H)-Phenanthrenone, 2,3,4,4a,4b,5-6,7,8,8a-decahydro-2-hydroxy-8-(3-hydroxypropyl)-1,1,4a,8a-tetramethyl-7-methylene-	n.s.g.	244(4.12)	33-1554-80
$C_{22}H_{34}O_4S$			
2-Hexadecenethioic acid, 4,5,15-trihydroxy-, S-phenyl ester, [4S-(2E,4R*,5R*,15S*)]-	MeOH	228(4.25),265(3.82)	88-1479-80
$C_{22}H_{36}OS$			
23-Thiabicyclo[18.2.1]tricosa-20,22-	MeCN	294(4.04)	44-1906-80

Compound	Solvent	$\lambda_{max}(\log \epsilon)$	Ref.
dien-2-one (cont.)			44-1906-80
$C_{22}H_{36}O_2$			
1-Octanone, 1-(2-hydroxy-5-octylphenyl)-	EtOH	255(3.99),338(3.58)	90-0431-80
$C_{22}H_{36}O_4$			
Andalusol, 6-acetyl-	EtOH	225(4.04)	102-2405-80
Austroinulin, 6-O-acetyl-	EtOH	237(4.21)	102-0326-80
Isoandalusol, 6-acetyl-	EtOH	225.5(4.05)	102-2405-80
$C_{22}H_{36}O_8$			
2-Furanbutanoic acid, tetrahydro-β-hydroxy-3-(9-hydroxy-2-methyl-3-oxo-4,6-decadienyl)-γ,5-dimethoxy-, methyl ester	MeOH	279(4.19)	88-2837-80
$C_{22}H_{37}BrO_2$			
Phenol, 4-[(16-bromohexadecyl)oxy]-	n.s.g.	297(3.48)	44-3923-80
$C_{22}H_{37}NO_2$			
1-Octanone, 1-(2-hydroxy-5-octylphenyl)-, oxime	EtOH	257(3.94),313(3.59)	90-0431-80
$C_{22}H_{37}NO_3$			
2-Aza-1,10-secoandrost-5(10)-en-3-one, 1-(1,1-dimethylethoxy)-17β-hydroxy-	n.s.g.	217(3.83)	33-2380-80
$C_{22}H_{37}NO_4$			
1-Pyrrolidineheptanoic acid, 2-oxo-5-(3-oxo-1-decenyl)-, methyl ester, [R-(E)]-	MeOH	215(4.14)	94-1449-80
$C_{22}H_{37}N_3O_3$			
3,5-Isoxazoledicarboxamide, N,N'-dibutyl-4-(2,6-dimethyl-5-heptenyl)-	MeOH	246(4.00)	94-0479-80
$C_{22}H_{37}N_5OS_2$			
2H-1,3,5-Thiadiazine-3(4H)-carboxamide, 6-(dicyclohexylamino)-4-[(1,1-dimethylethyl)imino]-N,N-dimethyl-2-thioxo-	CH_2Cl_2	262(4.27),284(4.23), 345(3.42)	24-0079-80
$C_{22}H_{37}N_7O$			
1H-Pyrrole-2-carboxamide, N-(3-amino-3-iminopropyl)-4-[[bis(cyclohexylamino)methylene]amino]-1-methyl-, monohydrochloride	EtOH	266(3.83)	4-1797-80
$C_{22}H_{38}N_2O_3$			
1-Octanamine, N-[2-(5-nitro-2-furanyl)-ethenyl]-N-octyl-, (E)-	MeOH	282(3.90),523(4.00)	73-0155-80
$C_{22}H_{38}O_8$			
2-Furanbutanoic acid, 3-(3,9-dihydroxy-2-methyl-4,6-decadienyl)tetrahydro-β-hydroxy-γ,5-dimethoxy-, methyl ester	MeOH	232(4.37)	88-2837-80
$C_{22}H_{39}NO$			
Cycloheptadecanone, 2-[3-(dimethylamino)-2-propenylidene]-	EtOH	378(4.56)	70-0987-80

Compound	Solvent	$\lambda_{max}(\log \epsilon)$	Ref.
$C_{22}H_{39}NS_2$			
2-Propanesulfenamide, N-[3,5-bis(1,1-dimethylethyl)phenyl]-N-[(1,1-dimethylethyl)thio]-2-methyl-	hexane	253(4.02)	18-0720-80
$C_{22}H_{40}Si_4$			
Silane, 2,3,6,7-naphthalenetetrayl-tetrakis[trimethyl-	EtOH	244(5.15),256s(4.14), 273(4.84),284s(3.75), 292s(3.54),311s(2.79), 320(2.91),326(2.92), 334(3.16)	35-5245-80
$C_{22}H_{44}N_5O_9P$			
5-Pyrimidinecarboxaldehyde, 1-(2-deoxy-β-D-ribofuranosyl)-1,2,3,4-tetrahydro-2,4-dioxo-, oxime, 5'-phosphate, bis(triethylamine) salt	pH 1 H₂O pH 13	288(4.05) 288(4.05) 250(4.06),282s(--)	87-0661-80 87-0661-80 87-0661-80

Compound	Solvent	$\lambda_{max}(\log \epsilon)$	Ref.
$C_{23}H_{12}N_2O_3S_2$ 3-Furancarbonitrile, 2-[[(4-oxo-4H-1-benzopyran-3-yl)methylene]amino]-4,5-di-2-thienyl-	MeOH	418(4.07)	73-1581-80
$C_{23}H_{12}N_2O_5$ [2,2':3',2"-Terfuran]-4'-carbonitrile, 5'-[[(4-oxo-4H-1-benzopyran-3-yl)methylene]amino]-	MeOH	420(4.10)	73-1581-80
$C_{23}H_{14}Cl_2N_2O_4$ 2H-Isoindole-2-acetamide, N-[4-chloro-2-(3-chlorobenzoyl)phenyl]-1,3-dihydro-1,3-dioxo-	MeOH	238(4.62),265(4.18), 272s(4.23),346(3.75)	73-3593-80
$C_{23}H_{14}Cl_4N_2O_5$ 1,4-Benzodioxin-2-carboxamide, 2-(benzoylmethylamino)-5,6,7,8-tetrachloro-2,3-dihydro-3-oxo-N-phenyl-	MeCN	209(5.15),296s(3.49)	5-1836-80
$C_{23}H_{14}F_2O_2$ 4-Cyclopentene-1,3-dione, 2,4-bis(4-fluorophenyl)-5-phenyl-	MeCN	255(4.49),310(3.82), 335s(--),355s(--)	24-0408-80
4-Cyclopentene-1,3-dione, 4,5-bis(4-fluorophenyl)-2-phenyl-	MeCN	225(4.31),285s(--), 325s(--)	24-0408-80
$C_{23}H_{14}N_2O_3$ Benzamide, 2-(6,11-dihydro-6,11-dioxobenzo[f]pyrido[1,2-a]indol-12-yl)-	EtOH	207(4.50),260(4.55), 333(4.03),506(3.65)	2-0836-80
Benzo[f]pyrido[1,2-a]indole-12-carboxamide, 6,11-dihydro-6,11-dioxo-N-phenyl-	CHCl₃	276(4.61),330s(4.21), 336(4.23),357(4.04), 510(3.86)	150-0139-80
$C_{23}H_{14}O_2S$ Anthra[1,2-b]thiophene-6,11-dione, 4-(4-methylphenyl)-	CHCl₃	255(4.54),288(4.53), 351(3.70),429(3.45)	4-0695-80
Anthra[2,1-b]thiophene-6,11-dione, 4-(4-methylphenyl)-	CHCl₃	294(4.60),306(4.59), 381(3.58),413(3.67)	4-0695-80
Benz[a]anthracene-7,12-dione, 2-methyl-5-(2-thienyl)-	CHCl₃	250(4.46),292(4.54), 347(3.78),430(3.72)	4-0695-80
Benz[a]anthracene-7,12-dione, 2-methyl-5-(3-thienyl)-	CHCl₃	253(4.40),295(4.51), 345(3.70),435(3.48)	4-0695-80
$C_{23}H_{14}O_4$ 3-Furancarboxaldehyde, 4-[(5-oxo-2-phenyl-5H-naphtho[1,8-bc]furan-4-yl)methyl]-	CHCl₃	267(4.35),401(4.49)	39-0643-80C
$C_{23}H_{15}BrO$ 2,4-Cyclopentadien-1-one, 2-bromo-3,4,5-triphenyl-	MeCN	260(4.14),328(3.84), 443(2.87),505(2.90)	24-0408-80
$C_{23}H_{15}Cl_3O_2$ 1,10-Anthracenedione, 2,3,4-trichloro-9-(2,4,6-trimethylphenyl)-	benzene	485(4.08)	104-0159-80
$C_{23}H_{15}NO_2$ Benzonitrile, 4-[(4-oxo-2-phenyl-2H-1-benzopyran-3(4H)-ylidene)methyl]-, (E)-	EtOH	240s(--),290(4.23), 350s(--)	114-0369-80B
	H₂SO₄	385(4.33),470(3.88)	114-0369-80B

Compound	Solvent	$\lambda_{max}(\log \epsilon)$	Ref.
3H-Naphth[2,3-e]indole-6,11-dione, 3-methyl-4-phenyl-	CHCl$_3$	247s(4.46),250(4.48), 291(4.51),306s(4.43), 392(3.70),420s(3.64), 440s(3.61)	4-0695-80
$C_{23}H_{15}N_3O_2$ Phenol, 4-[1,2,4]triazolo[4,3-a]quinolin-1-yl-, benzoate	MeOH	285(4.05)	56-0661-80
$C_{23}H_{16}BrNO_3$ 2H-Anthra[1,2-d][1,3]oxazine-7,12-dione, 6-bromo-1,4-dihydro-2-methyl-2-phenyl-	EtOH	477(3.89)	18-3007-80 +146-0513-80
2H-Anthra[1,2-d][1,3]oxazine-7,12-dione, 6-bromo-1,4-dihydro-2-(4-methylphenyl)-	EtOH	478(3.89)	18-3007-80 +146-0513-80
$C_{23}H_{16}BrNO_4$ 2H-Anthra[1,2-d][1,3]oxazine-7,12-dione, 6-bromo-1,4-dihydro-2-(4-methoxyphenyl)-	EtOH	488(3.93)	18-3007-80 +146-0513-80
$C_{23}H_{16}ClNO_4$ Furo[3,2-b]pyridin-2(4H)-one, 4-[3-(4-chlorophenyl)-3-oxo-1-propenyl]-3-(4-methoxyphenyl)-, (E)-	CHCl$_3$	285(4.20),460(3.86)	39-1176-80C
$C_{23}H_{16}ClN_3$ 2-Naphthalenamine, N-[(4-chlorophenyl)-methylene]-1-(phenylazo)-	MeOH	232s(4.43),244(4.55), 252s(4.40),306(4.15), 365s(3.42),388(3.54), 396(3.54),492(4.03)	44-3182-80
1H-Naphth[1,2-d]imidazol-1-amine, 2-(4-chlorophenyl)-	MeOH	236(4.61),270s(4.52), 276(4.53),289s(4.26), 335s(4.08),337(4.11)	44-3182-80
$C_{23}H_{16}Cl_2O_2$ 1,10-Anthracenedione, 2,4-dichloro-9-(2,4,6-trimethylphenyl)-	benzene EtOH	485(4.13) 297(--),310(--), 325(--),477(3.6), 496s(--)	104-0159-80 110-0200-80
$C_{23}H_{16}Cl_2O_6$ Benzoic acid, 5-[(3-carboxy-5-methyl-4-oxo-2,5-cyclohexadien-1-ylidene)-(2,6-dichlorophenyl)methyl]-2-hydroxy-3-methyl-	n.s.g.	582(3.98)	147-0409-80A
$C_{23}H_{16}Cl_2O_9S$ Benzoic acid, 5-[(3-carboxy-5-methyl-4-oxo-2,5-cyclohexadien-1-ylidene)-(2,6-dichloro-3-sulfophenyl)methyl]-2-hydroxy-3-methyl-	n.s.g.	585(4.74)	147-0409-80A
Chromazurol S, H$_3$L form	n.s.g.	470(4.27)	73-1525-80
H$_2$L form	n.s.g.	498(4.29)	73-1525-80
HL form	n.s.g.	426(4.28),429(4.28)	73-1525-80
$C_{23}H_{16}Cl_4N_2O_3$ 2,5-Imino-1,6,3-benzodioxazocin-4(5H)-one, 7,8,9,10-tetrachloro-2,3-dihydro-3,11-dimethyl-2,5-diphenyl-	MeCN	217(4.789),293(3.194)	5-1850-80

Compound	Solvent	$\lambda_{max}(\log \epsilon)$	Ref.
$C_{23}H_{16}N_2O_2S$ 5H-Thiazolo[3,2-a]quinolizinium, 1-hy- droxy-4-(4-methylphenyl)-5-oxo-2- phenyl-, hydroxide, inner salt	MeCN	273(4.19),310(4.17), 444(3.98)	2-0638-80
$C_{23}H_{16}N_2O_3$ 3H-Dibenz[f,ij]isoquinoline-2,7-dione, 1-hydroxy-3-methyl-6-(phenylamino)-	n.s.g.	345(3.98),382(3.98), 505(4.18)	124-0755-80
$C_{23}H_{16}N_2O_3S$ 5H-Thiazolo[3,2-a]quinazolinium, 1-hy- droxy-4-(4-methoxyphenyl)-5-oxo-2- phenyl-, hydroxide, inner salt	MeCN	272(4.23),308(4.18), 446(4.00)	2-0638-80
$C_{23}H_{16}N_4$ 2H-Naphtho[1,2-d]triazole, 2-[4-[2-(3- pyridinyl)ethenyl]phenyl]-	DMF	316(4.37),365(4.77)	33-1311-80
$C_{23}H_{16}N_4O_2$ 2-Naphthalenamine, N-[(4-nitrophenyl)- methylene]-1-(phenylazo)-	MeOH	232s(4.39),242(4.50), 258s(4.35),298(4.14), 377s(3.53),385(3.54), 394s(3.54),492(--)	44-3182-80
1H-Naphth[1,2-d]imidazol-1-amine, 2-(4- nitrophenyl)-N-phenyl-	MeOH	234(4.69),244s(4.62), 272s(4.22),328s(4.02), 364(4.23)	44-3182-80
$C_{23}H_{16}O_3$ Benzo[a]pyren-1-ol, 6-methoxy-, acetate	MeOH	225(4.63),255(4.65), 267(4.67),279(4.39), 290(4.61),302(4.71), 360(4.07),376(4.33), 384(4.32),389(4.30), 397(4.34),412(3.94), 432(3.42)	87-0919-80
Benzo[a]pyren-3-ol, 6-methoxy-, acetate	MeOH	225(4.63),255(4.65), 267(4.67),279(4.39), 290(4.61),302(4.71), 360(4.07),376(4.33), 384(4.32),389(4.30), 397(4.34),412(3.94), 432(3.42)	87-0919-80
Benzo[a]pyren-12-ol, 6-methoxy-, acetate	MeOH	227(4.57),254(4.63), 266(4.66),285(4.64), 297(4.76),358(4.09), 360(4.09),376(4.37), 384(4.27),397(4.41), 411(3.88)	87-0919-80
Methanone, (10-acetoxy-9-anthracenyl)- phenyl-	EtOH	246(4.68),336(3.59), 352(3.83),370(4.00), 391(3.96)	35-3837-80
$C_{23}H_{16}O_4$ 2H-Pyran-2-one, 3-[3-(9-anthracenyl)- 1-oxo-2-propenyl]-4-hydroxy-6-methyl-	MeOH	385(3.9)	83-0344-80
$C_{23}H_{16}O_4S$ 8H-Dibenzo[b,h]xanthene-8,13(13aH)-di- one, 5-hydroxy-13a-methyl-6-(methyl- thio)-	EtOH	248(4.37),265s(4.23), 312s(4.10),319(4.12), 350s(3.74),478(3.82)	39-0282-80C

Compound	Solvent	$\lambda_{max}(\log \epsilon)$	Ref.
$C_{23}H_{17}BrN_2O_2$ 4(3H)-Quinazolinone, 6-bromo-2-[2-(4-methoxyphenyl)ethenyl]-3-phenyl-	n.s.g.	282(3.95),350(4.00)	18-2389-80
$C_{23}H_{17}BrO_3$ 9(10H)-Anthracenone, 10-[(5-bromo-2,4-dimethoxyphenyl)methylene]-	EtOH	241(4.69),280s(4.18), 397(4.08)	35-3837-80
$C_{23}H_{17}ClNS$ Thiopyrylium, 2-(4-amino-2-chlorophenyl)-4,6-diphenyl-, perchlorate	n.s.g.	367(4.52),588(4.06)	39-1345-80C
$C_{23}H_{17}ClO_3$ 1,4-Anthracenedione, 2-chloro-10-hydroxy-9-(2,4,6-trimethylphenyl)-	benzene	455s(3.83),481(3.88), 502s(3.79)	104-0159-80
$C_{23}H_{17}Cl_2NO_2$ 1,10-Anthracenedione, 4-amino-2,3-dichloro-9-(2,4,6-trimethylphenyl)-	benzene	520s(4.03),560(4.03), 603(3.96)	104-0159-80
1H-Indene-1,3(2H)-dione, 2-[(2,6-dichlorophenyl)methyl]-2-(2,6-dimethyl-4-pyridinyl)-	M HCl	210(4.46),218s(4.43), 236(4.32),261(4.23), 280s(4.00),320(3.88)	4-0997-80
$C_{23}H_{17}N$ 3H-Naphth[2,3-e]indole, 3-methyl-4-phenyl-	EtOH	207(4.46),223s(4.51), 237(4.63),271(4.75), 288(4.69),302s(4.48), 360s(3.79),376(3.91), 396(3.80)	4-0695-80
$C_{23}H_{17}NO_2$ 1H-Pyrrole-2,5-dione, 3,4-diphenyl-1-(phenylmethyl)-	60% dioxan	366(3.58)	40-0837-80
1H-Pyrrole-2,5-dione, 1-(2-methylphenyl)-3,4-diphenyl-	MeCN	360(3.57)	40-0837-80
$C_{23}H_{17}NO_5$ Carbonic acid, phenyl (2,3,5,10-tetrahydro-5,10-dioxo-1H-benzo[f]pyrrolo-[1,2-a]indol-11-yl)methyl ester	MeOH	244s(4.27),259(4.49), 267(4.43),280s(4.20), 330(3.74),409(3.51)	44-1260-80
$C_{23}H_{17}N_2$ Benzo[c]pyrido[1,2-a][1,8]naphthyridin-13-ium, 12-methyl-10-phenyl-, perchlorate	EtOH	215(4.30),233(4.33), 250(4.30),272(4.30), 322(4.14),374(4.23), 392(4.0)	39-1879-80C
$C_{23}H_{17}N_2O$ Acridinium, 9-(8-hydroxy-5-quinolinyl)-10-methyl-, iodide	EtOH	256(4.80),365(3.83), 427(3.44)	104-0192-80
perchlorate	EtOH	262(4.55),362(3.47), 429(2.95)	104-0192-80
$C_{23}H_{17}N_3$ 2-Naphthalenamine, 1-(phenylazo)-N-(phenylmethylene)-	MeOH	232(4.37),242(4.51), 308(4.1),388(3.52), 396s(3.51),492(4.00)	44-3182-80
1H-Naphth[1,2-d]imidazol-1-amine, N,2-diphenyl-	MeOH	234(4.5),269(4.50), 287s(4.20),332s(3.94), 339(3 97)	44-3182-80

Compound	Solvent	λ_{max}(log ϵ)	Ref.
$C_{23}H_{17}N_3O$			
Benzo[b]pyrido[2,3-h][1,6]naphthyri-dine, 3-ethoxy-7-phenyl-	EtOH	210(4.55),264(4.77), 271s(4.69),295(4.51), 306(4.63)	4-1225-80
$C_{23}H_{17}N_3O_2Se$			
Benzamide, N-[5-benzoyl-3-(4-methyl-phenyl)-1,3,4-selenadiazol-2(3H)-ylidene]-	EtOH	279(4.23),345(4.21)	4-1185-80
Benzamide, N-[5-(4-methylbenzoyl)-3-phenyl-1,3,4-selenadiazol-2(3H)-ylidene]-	EtOH	277(4.21),338(4.11)	4-1185-80
$C_{23}H_{17}N_3O_4$			
1,2,4-Triazolidine-3,5-dione, 1-(1-ben-zoyl-2-oxo-2-phenylethyl)-4-phenyl-	MeCN	235(3.916),260(4.188)	44-1232-80
$C_{23}H_{17}N_3O_5$			
6-Indolizinecarboxylic acid, 3-(4-ni-trobenzoyl)-1-(2-pyridinyl)-, ethyl ester	CHCl$_3$	255(4.56),310(4.38), 414(4.20)	103-0506-80
6-Indolizinecarboxylic acid, 3-(4-ni-trobenzoyl)-1-(4-pyridinyl)-, ethyl ester	CHCl$_3$	260(4.59),305(4.38), 407(4.19)	103-0506-80
$C_{23}H_{17}O$			
Pyrylium, 2,4,6-triphenyl-, tetraflu-oroborate	MeCN	355(4.60),405(4.48)	35-0299-80
	CH$_2$Cl$_2$	368(4.59),417(4.43)	35-0299-80
$C_{23}H_{17}S$			
Thiopyrylium, 2,4,6-triphenyl-, tetrafluoroborate	MeCN	368(4.23),405s(4.34)	35-0299-80
	CH$_2$Cl$_2$	382(4.49),420s(4.36)	35-0299-80
$C_{23}H_{18}$			
Naphthalene, 2-methyl-1,3-diphenyl-	EtOH	234(4.72),286(3.90)	44-4555-80
Naphthalene, 3-methyl-1,2-diphenyl-	EtOH	228(4.77),282(3.94)	44-4555-80
$C_{23}H_{18}ClNO_2$			
1,10-Anthracenedione, 4-amino-2-chloro-9-(2,4,6-trimethylphenyl)-	benzene	523s(3.90),560(4.04), 607(3.98)	104-0159-80
	isoPrOH	527s(3.92),563(4.05), 607(3.94)	104-0159-80
$C_{23}H_{18}ClNO_4$			
3H-2a-Azacyclopenta[ef]heptalene-4,5-dicarboxylic acid, 2-chloro-3-phen-yl-, dimethyl ester	EtOH	215(4.58),250s(4.34), 285s(4.15),440(4.34), 456(4.34),488s(4.13), 527(3.97),565(3.69), 618(3.13)	18-1406-80
4H-Azuleno[7,8,1-gha]pyrrolizine-5,6-dicarboxylic acid, 2-chloro-4a,5-dihydro-4-phenyl-, dimethyl ester, (4α,4aα,5β)-	EtOH	268(4.10),337(3.85), 415(3.60)	18-1406-80
2H-Cyclohepta[gh]pyrrolizine-1,2-di-carboxylic acid, 4-chloro-2-(2-phen-ylethenyl)-, dimethyl ester, (E)-	EtOH	242(4.71),282s(4.24), 292s(4.14),375(4.14), 395(4.13),438(3.80), 466(3.79),498(3.63), 535(3.20)	18-1406-80
$C_{23}H_{18}Cl_4O_4$			
Compound m. 198°	CHCl$_3$	247(3.47),263s(2.94),	78-0267-80

Compound	Solvent	$\lambda_{max}(\log \epsilon)$	Ref.
(cont.)		270(2.61),325(2.33)	78-0267-80
$C_{23}H_{18}F_3N_3O_{12}$ β-D-Ribofuranose, 3-deoxy-3-[(trifluoroacetyl)amino]-, 1-acetate 2,5-bis(4-nitrobenzoate)	EtOH	207(3.98),258(4.38)	33-2258-80
$C_{23}H_{18}NO$ Benz[a]acridinium, 8,9,10,11-tetrahydro-11-oxo-7-phenyl-, bromide	n.s.g.	225(4.70),290(4.51)	104-1592-80
perchlorate	n.s.g.	232(4.84),288(4.44), 349(4.11)	104-1592-80
$C_{23}H_{18}NS$ Thiopyrylium, 2-(4-aminophenyl)-4,6-diphenyl-, perchlorate	n.s.g.	367(4.27),584(4.21)	39-1345-80C
$C_{23}H_{18}N_2O$ 3,4-Diazabicyclo[4.1.0]hept-4-en-2-one, 3,5,7-triphenyl-	MeOH	246(3.16),303(2.99)	4-0541-80
3H-Pyrazol-3-one, 4-([1,1'-biphenyl]-4-ylmethylene)-2,4-dihydro-5-methyl-2-phenyl-	n.s.g.	250(4.47),355(4.65), 450(3.19)	124-0642-80
5-Quinolinol, 8-(9,10-dihydro-10-methyl-9-acridinyl)-	EtOH	288(4.12)	104-0192-80
$C_{23}H_{18}N_2O_2$ Acetic acid, cyano(1-methyl-2-phenylbenz[cd]indol-5(1H)-ylidene)-, ethyl ester, (E)-	CH_2Cl_2	242(4.28),316(3.92), 400(3.76),526(4.47), 578(4.45)	83-0977-80
$C_{23}H_{18}N_2O_3$ 6-Indolizinecarboxylic acid, 3-benzoyl-1-(2-pyridinyl)-, ethyl ester	$CHCl_3$	258(4.55),320(4.38), 405(4.25)	103-0506-80
6-Indolizinecarboxylic acid, 3-benzoyl-1-(4-pyridinyl)-, ethyl ester	$CHCl_3$	257(4.56),315(4.34), 398(4.25)	103-0506-80
$C_{23}H_{18}N_4O$ 2-Naphthalenol, 1-[[4-[(4-methylphenyl)azo]phenyl]azo]-	acetone	503(4.43)	7-0173-80
$C_{23}H_{18}N_4O_2$ 2-Naphthalenol, 1-[[4-[(4-methoxyphenyl)azo]phenyl]azo]-	acetone	500(4.55)	7-0173-80
$C_{23}H_{18}N_4O_6S$ 2,4,6(1H,3H,5H)-Pyrimidinetrione, 1,3-dimethyl-5H-[1]benzothieno[2',3'-5,6]pyrano[2,3-d]pyrimidin-5-ylidene)ethylidene]-, (Z)-	dioxan	224(4.27),266(4.06), 329(3.89),481(4.41)	83-0557-80
$C_{23}H_{18}N_4O_7$ 2,4,6(1H,3H,5H)-Pyrimidinetrione, 1,3-dimethyl-5-[(1,2,3,4-tetrahydro-1,3-dimethyl-2,4-dioxo-5H-benzofuro[2,3'-5,6]pyrano[2,3-d]pyrimidin-5-ylidene)ethylidene]-, (Z)-	dioxan	220(3.89),254(3.85), 336(3.69),471(4.20)	83-0557-80
$C_{23}H_{18}N_4S$ Imidazo[1',5':1,6]pyrido[3,2-d]pyrimidine, 9-(ethylthio)-1,3-diphenyl-	EtOH	223s(4.44),265(4.51), 278s(4.44),400(4.05)	88-4193-80

Compound	Solvent	$\lambda_{max}(\log \epsilon)$	Ref.
$C_{23}H_{18}N_6O_4S$ 1,2,4-Triazine-3(2H)-thione, 4,5-dihydro-4-(4-methylphenyl)-5-[(4-methylphenyl)imino]-6-nitro-2-(4-nitrophenyl)-	DMF	339s(4.10)	48-0087-80
$C_{23}H_{18}N_6O_5$ 1,2,4-Triazin-3(2H)-one, 4,5-dihydro-4-(4-methylphenyl)-5-[(4-methylphenyl)imino]-6-nitro-2-(4-nitrophenyl)-	DMF	324(4.24),417s(3.54)	48-0087-80
$C_{23}H_{18}N_6O_6S$ 1,2,4-Triazine-3(2H)-thione, 4,5-dihydro-4-(4-methoxyphenyl)-5-[(4-methoxyphenyl)imino]-6-nitro-2-(4-nitrophenyl)-	DMF	338(4.13),442(3.38)	48-0087-80
$C_{23}H_{18}N_6O_7$ 1,2,4-Triazin-3(2H)-one, 4,5-dihydro-4-(4-methoxyphenyl)-5-[(4-methoxyphenyl)imino]-6-nitro-2-(4-nitrophenyl)-	DMF	319(4.22),422s(3.45)	48-0087-80
$C_{23}H_{18}O$ 9H-Benzocycloheptadecen-9-one, 16,17,18,19-tetradehydro-8,15-dimethyl-, (E,E,E,Z,E)-	THF CF₃COOH	280s(4.52),297(4.63), 320(4.59),405s(3.54) 290(--),334(--), 340(--),420(--), 630(--)	39-0473-80C 39-0473-80C
9H-Benzocycloheptadecen-9-one, 16,17,18,19-tetradehydro-10,15-dimethyl-, (E,E,E,Z,E)-	THF CF₃COOH	286s(4.58),301(4.66), 312(4.58),402s(3.61) 286(--),335(--), 393s(--),661(--)	39-0473-80C 39-0473-80C
$C_{23}H_{18}O_2$ 4H-1-Benzopyran-4-one, 2,3-dihydro-3-[(4-methylphenyl)methylene]-2-phenyl-, (E)-	EtOH H₂SO₄	240s(--),320(4.00) 400(4.30),475(4.19)	114-0369-80B 114-0369-80B
1-Naphthalenemethanol, 2-hydroxy-α,α-diphenyl-	ether	267(3.68),278(3.76), 290(3.70),321(3.50), 331(3.53),335(3.59)	35-4659-80
$C_{23}H_{18}O_3$ 9(10H)-Anthracenone, 10-[(2,4-dimethoxyphenyl)methylene]-	EtOH	242(4.64),275s(4.08), 404(4.07)	35-3837-80
4H-1-Benzopyran-4-one, 2,3-dihydro-3-[(4-methoxyphenyl)methylene]-2-phenyl-	EtOH 80% H₂SO₄	242s(--),340(4.23) 415(4.15),510(4.41)	114-0369-80B 114-0369-80B
$C_{23}H_{18}O_3S_3$ 4H-1-Benzothiopyran-4-one, 2,3-bis-[(4-methylphenyl)thio]-, 1,1-dioxide	EtOH	248s(4.25),263s(4.17), 390(3.53)	150-0139-80
$C_{23}H_{18}O_5$ 4H-Anthra[1,2-b]pyran-4,7,12-trione, 11-methoxy-5-methyl-2-(1-methyl-1-propenyl)-, (E)-	EtOH	216(4.43),237(4.53), 268(4.45),320(3.77), 384(3.88)	44-3061-80
$C_{23}H_{18}O_9S$ Benzoic acid, 5-[(3-carboxy-5-methyl-4-oxo-2,5-cyclohexadien-1-ylidene)-	n.s.g.	520(2.90)	147-0409-80A

Compound	Solvent	$\lambda_{max}(\log \epsilon)$	Ref.
(2-sulfophenyl)methyl]-2-hydroxy-3-methyl- (cont.)			147-0409-80A
C$_{23}$H$_{19}$ClN$_2$O$_2$			
9,10-Anthracenedione, 1-amino-2-chloro-4-[(2,4,6-trimethylphenyl)amino]-	n.s.g.	573(4.05),613(4.05)	93-1963-80
1H-Pyrazole, 1-benzoyl-5-(4-chlorophenyl)-4,5-dihydro-3-(4-methoxyphenyl)-	MeOH	307(3.83)	2-0364-80
C$_{23}$H$_{19}$ClO$_3$			
Propanoic acid, 3-[4-(2-chloro-1,2-diphenylethenyl)phenoxy]-, (E)-	EtOH	302(4.03)	12-0461-80
(Z)-	EtOH	299(4.06)	12-0461-80
C$_{23}$H$_{19}$IO$_3$			
4H-1-Benzopyran-4-one, 2,3-dihydro-3-(iodomethyl)-3-phenyl-7-(phenylmethoxy)-	MeOH	280(4.18),315(3.92)	42-0208-80
C$_{23}$H$_{19}$N			
1H-Pyrrole, 2,3-diphenyl-1-(phenylmethyl)-	EtOH	205(4.62),246(4.18), 285(3.98)	44-2741-80
C$_{23}$H$_{19}$NO			
Benz[g]isoquinolinium, 7,8-dimethyl-, 2-oxo-2-phenylethylide	CHCl$_3$	258(4.72),290s(4.16), 396(3.44),430(3.16), 466(3.06)	103-0626-80
2-Buten-1-one, 3-[(diphenylmethylene)-amino]-1-phenyl-, (Z)-	n.s.g.	209(4.34),323(3.92)	39-1866-80C
2(1H)-Naphthalenone, 1-[(1,6-dimethyl-2(1H)-quinolinylidene)ethylidene]-	EtOH	596(3.94)	104-0185-80
	benzene	610(--)	104-0185-80
	acetone	628(--)	104-0185-80
	CHCl$_3$	622(--)	104-0185-80
Pyridine, 3-[2-[4-(5,6-dimethyl-2-benzofuranyl)phenyl]ethenyl]-	DMF	362(4.76)	33-1311-80
Pyridine, 3-[2-[4-(5,7-dimethyl-2-benzofuranyl)phenyl]ethenyl]-	DMF	358(4.77)	33-1311-80
C$_{23}$H$_{19}$NO$_2$			
Benzamide, N-methyl-N-(3-oxo-1,3-diphenyl-1-propenyl)-	EtOH	212(4.13),252(4.01), 315(3.83)	39-1870-80C
2(1H)-Naphthalenone, 1-[(6-methoxy-1-methyl-2(1H)-quinolinylidene)ethylidene]-	EtOH	592(4.29)	104-0185-80
	benzene	620(--)	104-0185-80
	acetone	632(--)	104-0185-80
	CHCl$_3$	631(--)	104-0185-80
Pyridine, 3-[2-[4-[(3,4-dimethoxyphenyl)ethynyl]phenyl]ethenyl]-	DMF	348(4.75)	33-1311-80
C$_{23}$H$_{19}$NO$_3$			
Benzamide, N-[2-[[3-(4-methylphenyl)-3-oxo-1-propenyl]oxy]phenyl]-, (E)-	dioxan	274(4.46)	48-0099-80
2-Propen-1-one, 3-[[2-(benzoyloxy)phenyl]amino]-1-(4-methylphenyl)-, (Z)-	dioxan	236(4.37),258(4.15), 372(4.47)	48-0099-80
C$_{23}$H$_{19}$NO$_4$			
Benzamide, N-[2-[[3-(4-methoxyphenyl)-3-oxo-1-propenyl]oxy]phenyl]-, (E)-	dioxan	295(4.50)	48-0099-80
2-Propen-1-one, 3-[[2-(benzoyloxy)phenyl]amino]-1-(4-methoxyphenyl)-, (Z)-	dioxan	231(4.38),281(4.03), 372(4.53)	48-0099-80

Compound	Solvent	$\lambda_{max}(\log \epsilon)$	Ref.
$C_{23}H_{19}NO_4S_2$ Benzenesulfonamide, N-[2-[(3-hydroxy-benzo[b]thien-2-yl)carbonyl]phenyl]-N,4-dimethyl-	MeOH	265(4.29),317(4.15), 376(3.87)	83-0027-80
$C_{23}H_{19}NS$ 2H-Azeto[2,1-a]isoquinoline-2-thione, 1,4,5,9b-tetrahydro-1,1-diphenyl-	isooctane	275(3.8),355s(--)	24-3010-80
$C_{23}H_{19}N_2S$ Thiopyrylium, 2-(6-amino-4-methyl-3-pyridinyl)-4,6-diphenyl-, perchlorate	n.s.g.	298(3.48),424(3.36)	39-1345-80C
$C_{23}H_{19}N_3$ Pyrrolo[3,2-e]benzimidazole, 3,6-di-hydro-2-methyl-7-phenyl-3-(phenyl-methyl)-	EtOH	253(4.24),328(4.54)	103-0062-80
Pyrrolo[3,2-e]benzimidazole, 3,6-di-hydro-8-methyl-7-phenyl-3-(phenyl-methyl)-	EtOH	253s(4.11),320(4.51)	103-0062-80
$C_{23}H_{19}N_3O_2$ Acetamide, N-[1,2-dihydro-1-methyl-2-[[(2-oxo-1(2H)-naphthalenylidene)-amino]methylene]-6-quinolinyl]-	EtOH acetone	639(4.26) 634(--)	104-0185-80 104-0185-80
6H-Anthra[1,9-cd]isoxazol-6-one, 3-(di-methylamino)-5-[(4-methylphenyl)ami-no]-	dioxan	254(4.54),480(4.36), 510(4.43)	103-0704-80
6H-Anthra[1,9-cd]isoxazol-6-one, 3-(ethylamino)-5-[(4-methylphenyl)-amino]-	dioxan	254(4.51),480(4.33), 510(4.40)	103-0704-80
1(2H)-Quinolineacetamide, 2-oxo-N-phen-yl-4-(phenylamino)-	EtOH	306(4.42)	78-1385-80
$C_{23}H_{19}N_3O_3$ 2H-Naphth[2,3-e][1,3]oxazin-2-one, 4-(2,5-dihydro-3-methyl-5-oxo-1-phen-yl-1H-pyrazol-4-yl)-3,4-dihydro-3-methyl-	EtOH	228(4.83),323(3.30)	4-0519-80
$C_{23}H_{19}N_3O_3S$ Benzoic acid, 4-[[3-(4-methoxyphenyl)-2H-1,4-benzothiazin-2-ylidene]hydra-zino]-, methyl ester	EtOH	257(4.22),285(4.25), 329(4.37),408(4.19)	39-2923-80C
$C_{23}H_{19}N_3O_4$ 1H-Pyrazole, 1-benzoyl-4,5-dihydro-3-(4-methoxyphenyl)-5-(4-nitrophenyl)-	MeOH	299(4.29)	2-0364-80
$C_{23}H_{19}N_3O_4S$ 4H-1,3,5-Oxadiazine-4-thione, 2,3-di-hydro-2-(4-methoxyphenyl)-6-(4-nitro-phenyl)-3-(phenylmethyl)-	dioxan	239(4.39),289(4.37)	73-2254-80
4H-1,3-Oxazin-4-one, 6-methyl-5-(meth-ylthio)-2-[2-(4-nitrophenyl)-1-(2(1H)-quinolinylidene)ethyl]-	EtOH	266(4.11),303(4.01), 317(4.00),330(3.99), 424s(4.07),446(4.28), 472(4.25)	94-0795-80
$C_{23}H_{20}$ 1H-Indene, 2-methyl-1-phenyl-3-(phenyl-methyl)-	EtOH	265(3.97)	44-4555-80

Compound	Solvent	$\lambda_{max}(\log \epsilon)$	Ref.
$C_{23}H_{20}ClNO_6$ 3H-Pyrano[2,3-c]acridine-9,11-diol, 7-chloro-6-methoxy-3,3-dimethyl-, diacetate	MeOH	250(4.48),290(4.87), 470(--)	5-0503-80
$C_{23}H_{20}ClN_3OS$ 1H-Pyrazole-1-carbothioamide, 5-(4-chlorophenyl)-4,5-dihydro-3-(4-methoxyphenyl)-N-phenyl-	MeOH	324(3.96)	2-0364-80
$C_{23}H_{20}ClN_3O_2$ 1H-Pyrazole-1-carboxamide, 5-(4-chlorophenyl)-4,5-dihydro-3-(4-methoxyphenyl)-N-phenyl-	MeOH	305(3.50)	2-0364-80
$C_{23}H_{20}Cl_2O_2$ Ethanone, 1-(4-chlorophenyl)-2-[2-(4-chlorophenyl)-1-oxaspiro[4.5]dec-2-en-4-ylidene]-	EtOH	422(4.49)	5-1744-80
$C_{23}H_{20}NO$ Benz[g]isoquinolinium, 7,8-dimethyl-2-(2-oxo-2-phenylethyl)-, bromide	CHCl₃	288(5.02),380(3.76)[sic], 360(3.90),382(4.22), 460(3.72)	103-0626-80
$C_{23}H_{20}N_2$ 1H-1,5-Benzodiazepine, 2,3-dihydro-2-phenyl-4-(2-phenylethenyl)-	EtOH	300(4.46),392(4.01)	103-0547-80
$C_{23}H_{20}N_2O$ 3(2H)-Pyridazinone, 1,6-dihydro-6-(4-methylphenyl)-2,6-diphenyl-	EtOH	241(4.45)	118-0457-80
$C_{23}H_{20}N_2O_2$ 9-Anthracenecarbonitrile, 9-(dimethylamino)-9,10-dihydro-10-hydroperoxy-10-phenyl-	ether	259(3.51),275(3.13), 270s(3.23)	78-2453-80
2(1H)-Naphthalenone, 1-[[(6-ethoxy-1-methyl-2(1H)-quinolinylidene)methyl]imino]-	EtOH benzene acetone CHCl₃	629(3.86) 648(--) 661(--) 668(--)	104-0185-80 104-0185-80 104-0185-80 104-0185-80
$C_{23}H_{20}N_2O_2S$ 4H-1,3,5-Oxadiazine-4-thione, 2,3-dihydro-2-(4-methoxyphenyl)-6-phenyl-3-(phenylmethyl)-	dioxan	243(4.48),278(4.53)	73-2254-80
$C_{23}H_{20}N_2O_3S$ 3H-Phenoxazin-3-one, 7-[(4-methylphenyl)thio]-2-morpholino-	n.s.g.	485(4.24)	103-0032-80
$C_{23}H_{20}N_4O_3S_2$ 5-Thia-1-azabicyclo[4.2.0]oct-2-ene-2-carboxylic acid, 7-amino-3-(5-methyl-1,3,4-thiadiazol-2-yl)-8-oxo-, diphenylmethyl ester, (6R-trans)-	EtOH	307(4.02)	94-2116-80
$C_{23}H_{20}N_4O_4$ 1H-Pyrazole-1-carboxamide, 4,5-dihydro-3-(4-methoxyphenyl)-5-(4-nitrophenyl)-N-phenyl-	MeOH	300(4.19)	2-0364-80

Compound	Solvent	$\lambda_{max}(\log \epsilon)$	Ref.
$C_{23}H_{20}N_4O_9S_2$ 4-Thia-1-azabicyclo[3.2.0]hept-2-ene-2-carboxylic acid, 3-[[2-[[[(4-nitrophenyl)methoxy]carbonyl]amino]ethyl]thio]-7-oxo-, (4-nitrophenyl)methyl ester	THF	264(4.41),338(4.03)	94-3232-80
$C_{23}H_{20}N_6O$ 3H-Pyrazol-3-one, 2,4-dihydro-5-methyl-4-[[4-[(4-methylphenyl)azo]phenyl]azo]-2-phenyl-	acetone	418(4.50)	7-0173-80
$C_{23}H_{20}N_6O_2$ 3H-Pyrazol-3-one, 2,4-dihydro-4-[[4-[(4-methoxyphenyl)azo]phenyl]azo]-5-methyl-2-phenyl-	acetone	426(4.45)	7-0173-80
$C_{23}H_{20}O$ 2,4,6,8,14,16,18,20-Cycloheneicosaoctaene-10,12-diyn-1-one, 9,14-dimethyl-, (E,E,Z,Z,E,E,E)-	THF	245(4.17),255s(4.15), 307s(4.72),327(4.93), 340(4.97),415s(3.85)	44-3564-80
	THF	250(4.2),340(5.0)	138-1299-80
Trideca-1,3,6,8,10-pentaen-12-yn-5-one, 1-(2-ethynylphenyl)-4,11-dimethyl-	THF	260s(4.21),268(4.26), 288(4.25),317s(4.30)	39-0473-80C
Trideca-1,3,6,8,10-pentaen-12-yn-5-one, 1-(2-ethynylphenyl)-6,11-dimethyl-, (E,E,E,Z,E)-	THF	236(4.29),268s(4.29), 268(4.34),290s(4.40), 302(4.44),315(4.44), 359s(4.60),374(4.64), 392s(4.56)	39-0473-80C
$C_{23}H_{20}O_2$ Spiro[6H-dibenzo[f,h][1,5]dioxonin-7(8H),2'-[2H]indene], 1',3'-dihydro-	CHCl₃	248(4.00),275(3.83)	49-0413-80
$C_{23}H_{20}O_3$ 2,4-Cyclopentadien-1-one, 3-(1-acetyl-2-hydroxy-1-propenyl)-5-methyl-	MeCN	264(4.31),290s(--), 320s(--),425(2.95)	24-0424-80
2,4-Pentanedione, 3-(3-methyl-4-oxo-2,5-diphenyl-2-cyclopenten-1-ylidene)-	MeCN	212(4.26),269(4.06), 299(4.12)	24-0424-80
$C_{23}H_{20}O_4$ 9(10H)-Anthracenone, 1-hydroxy-5-methoxy-2-methyl-4-(phenylmethoxy)-	CHCl₃	268(4.15),326(3.42), 390(3.40)	44-0012-80
$C_{23}H_{20}O_8$ 4H-1-Benzopyran-4-one, 5,7-diacetoxy-3-[(4-acetoxyphenyl)methyl]-2-methyl-	MeOH	230(4.44),296(3.91)	100-0739-80
$C_{23}H_{20}O_9$ 2H-1-Benzopyran-2-one, 6,6'-[(2-hydroxy-1,3-propanediyl)bis(oxy)]bis[7-methoxy-	EtOH	293(3.05),341(3.34)	2-0495-80
$C_{23}H_{20}O_{10}$ Eriodictyol tetraacetate	MeOH	261(3.88),315(3.59)	100-0739-80
$C_{23}H_{20}P$ 7H-Dibenzo[d,f]phosphoninium, 7-methyl-7-phenyl-, iodide, (E,Z)-	EtOH	202(4.68),259s(4.02)	35-4838-80

Compound	Solvent	$\lambda_{max}(\log \epsilon)$	Ref.
$C_{23}H_{21}ClN_2O_3S$ 1H-Pyrazole, 5-(4-chlorophenyl)-4,5-di- hydro-3-(4-methoxyphenyl)-1-[(4-meth- ylphenyl)sulfonyl]-	MeOH	291(3.90)	2-0364-80
$C_{23}H_{21}Cl_2N_3O_5$ Pyrrolo[3,4-c]pyrazole-3a,4(1H)-dicarb- oxylic acid, 3,6-bis(4-chlorophenyl)- 6,6a-dihydro-6a-methoxy-1-methyl-, dimethyl ester, (3aα,6α,6aα)-	EtOH	221(4.38),300(4.18)	44-4587-80 +88-1529-80
$C_{23}H_{21}N$ 5,12[1',2']-Benzenodibenzo[a,e]cyclo- octene-5(6H)-carbonitrile, 6a,7,10- 10a,11,12-hexahydro-	MeCN	251s(2.56),257(2.73), 263(2.88),266s(2.72), 270(2.87)	24-1458-80
$C_{23}H_{21}NO$ 2-Propen-1-one, 3-[[(4-methylphenyl)- methyl]amino]-1,3-diphenyl-	EtOH	210(4.29),246(4.16), 356(4.34)	39-1870-80C
Pyridine, 2-[2-[4-[2-(4-ethoxyphenyl)- ethenyl]phenyl]ethenyl]-	DMF	369(4.79)	33-1311-80
Pyridine, 3-[2-[4-[2-(4-ethoxyphenyl)- ethenyl]phenyl]ethenyl]-	DMF	365(4.79)	33-1311-80
Pyridine, 4-[2-[4-[2-(4-ethoxyphenyl)- ethenyl]phenyl]ethenyl]-	DMF	370(4.76)	33-1311-80
Spiro[2H-indole-2,2'-[2H]naphtho[2,3- b]pyran], 1,3-dihydro-1,3,3-tri- methyl-	20% MeOH	300(4.01),350s(3.65), 480(3.40)	32-0613-80
protonated	20% MeOH	360s(3.88),479(4.54)	32-0613-80
$C_{23}H_{21}NO_2$ Benzoic acid, 2-(9,9-dimethyl-10(9H)- acridinyl)-, methyl ester	C_6H_{12}	205(4.77),282(4.29)	24-0358-80
Isoquinoline, 3,4-dihydro-6,7-dimeth- oxy-1,3-diphenyl-	MeOH	285(3.91),312(3.90), 316(4.0)	2-0556-80
Pyridine, 2,4-bis[2-(4-methoxyphenyl)- ethenyl]-	DMF	338(4.66)	33-1311-80
Pyridine, 2,5-bis[2-(2-methoxyphenyl)- ethenyl]-	DMF	374(4.71)	33-1311-80
Pyridine, 2,5-bis[2-(3-methoxyphenyl)- ethenyl]-	DMF	363(4.75)	33-1311-80
Pyridine, 2,5-bis[2-(4-methoxyphenyl)- ethenyl]-	DMF	375(4.77)	33-1311-80
Pyridine, 2-[2-[4-[2-(3,4-dimethoxy- phenyl)ethenyl]phenyl]ethenyl]-	DMF	372(4.77)	33-1311-80
Pyridine, 3-[2-[4-[2-(3,4-dimethoxy- phenyl)ethenyl]phenyl]ethenyl]-	DMF	368(4.77)	33-1311-80
$C_{23}H_{21}NO_5$ Benzoic acid, 2,2'-[(4-methoxyphenyl)- imino]bis-, dimethyl ester	C_6H_{12}	211(4.56),297(4.26), 363(3.58)	24-0358-80
$C_{23}H_{21}NO_5S$ 1,3-Dioxane, 4-[[(4-nitrophenyl)sulfin- yl]methyl]-2,6-diphenyl-	MeOH	251(3.83),294(3.85)	12-2635-80
$C_{23}H_{21}NO_7$ 6H-Benzo[g]-1,3-benzodioxolo[5,6-a]- quinolizine-8,13-dione, 5,13a-dihy- dro-9,10-dimethoxy-13a-(2-oxopropyl)-, (±)-	MeOH	237(4.45),279s(4.10), 290(4.11),319(3.97)	39-0919-80C

Compound	Solvent	$\lambda_{max}(\log \epsilon)$	Ref.
$C_{23}H_{21}NO_8$ 1H-Indole-2,4,6,7-tetracarboxylic acid, 1-(phenylmethyl)-, tetramethyl ester	MeCN	355s(3.93)	88-1145-80
$C_{23}H_{21}NS_2$ Pyridine, 2,4-bis[2-[4-(methylthio)-phenyl]ethenyl]-	DMF	347(4.76)	33-1311-80
Pyridine, 2,5-bis[2-[4-(methylthio)-phenyl]ethenyl]-	DMF	384(4.85)	33-1311-80
Pyridine, 2,6-bis[2-[4-(methylthio)-phenyl]ethenyl]-	DMF	332(4.68),360(4.63)	33-1311-80
$C_{23}H_{21}N_3O_3$ 1H-Pyrazole, 4,5-dihydro-3-(4-methoxy-phenyl)-5-(4-nitrophenyl)-1-(phenyl-methyl)-	MeOH	293(4.21)	2-0364-80
$C_{23}H_{21}N_3O_4$ Indolizino[1,2-b]quinoline-8-carboxylic acid, 9,11-dihydro-9-oxo-7-[2-oxo-2-(1-pyrrolidinyl)ethyl]-, methyl ester	EtOH	215(4.59),256(4.43), 289(3.71),372(4.26)	78-0321-80
$C_{23}H_{21}N_3O_5S$ 1H-Pyrazole, 4,5-dihydro-3-(4-methoxy-phenyl)-1-[(4-methylphenyl)sulfonyl]-5-(4-nitrophenyl)-	MeOH	284(3.72)	2-0364-80
$C_{23}H_{21}N_5O_2$ 2-Naphthalenecarboxamide, 4-[(1,3-di-methyl-1H-pyrazol-4-yl)azo]-3-hy-droxy-N-(2-methylphenyl)-	EtOH	264(3.91),435(4.25)	65-1705-80
$C_{23}H_{21}N_7O_2S$ 1,2,4-Triazin-6(1H)-one, 6-hydrazone, tetrahydro-4-(4-methylphenyl)-5-[(4-methylphenyl)imino]-2-(4-nitrophen-yl)-3-thioxo-	MeCN	282(4.29),328s(4.07)	48-0087-80
$C_{23}H_{21}N_7O_3$ 1,2,4-Triazine-3,6-dione, tetrahydro-4-(4-methylphenyl)-5-[(4-methylphen-yl)imino]-2-(4-nitrophenyl)-, 6-hy-drazone	EtOH	234(4.31),354(4.23)	48-0087-80
$C_{23}H_{22}BrNO_3S$ 6H-Thieno[2',3':5,6][1,3]oxazepino-[2,3-a]isoquinoline, 10-bromo-5,8,12,13a-tetrahydro-3-methoxy-2-(phenylmethoxy)-	MeOH	238(2.80),312(2.35), 370(2.31)	118-1021-80
$C_{23}H_{22}Cl_2N_5O_7P$ Phosphoramidic acid, N-methyl-N-(9-β-D-ribofuranosyl-9H-purin-6-yl)-, bis(2-chlorophenyl) ester	pH 7.0 MeOH	266(4.17),276s(4.03) 265(4.23),273s(4.14)	142-0761-80B 142-0761-80B
$C_{23}H_{22}FN_3O_6$ 1(2H)-Pyrimidinebutanoic acid, 5-flu-oro-3,4-dihydro-2,4-dioxo-γ-[[(phen-ylmethoxy)carbonyl]amino]-, phenyl-methyl ester	MeOH	266(3.81)	94-1137-80

Compound	Solvent	$\lambda_{max}(\log \epsilon)$	Ref.
$C_{23}H_{22}N_2$			
1,3-Imidazolidine, 1,3-diphenyl-2-(2-phenylethenyl)-	MeCN	253(4.68)	35-3062-80
1H-Pyrrolo[1,2-a]indole, 9,9'-methylenebis[2,3-dihydro-	EtOH	232(4.86),286(4.11), 295s(4.06)	39-0097-80C
5H,9H-Quino[3,2,1-de]phenazine, 5-ethyl-9,9-dimethyl-	C_6H_{12}	212(4.42),235(4.07), 260(5.67),291(4.06), 336(4.06)	24-0358-80
	EtOH	212(4.46),259(4.67), 283(4.08),336(4.08)	24-0358-80
$C_{23}H_{22}N_2O$			
3(2H)-Pyridazinone, tetrahydro-6-(4-methylphenyl)-2,6-diphenyl-	EtOH	273(4.14),283(3.98)	48-0617-80
3(2H)-Pyridazinone, tetrahydro-6-(4-methylphenyl)-4,6-diphenyl-	EtOH	296(4.30)	48-0617-80
$C_{23}H_{22}N_2OS$			
2(1H)-Quinazolinethione, 3-acetyl-3,4,5,6,7,8-hexahydro-4-phenyl-8-(phenylmethylene)-	EtOH	269(4.32),293(4.28), 339(3.9)	114-0147-80B
$C_{23}H_{22}N_2O_2$			
3(2H)-Pyridazinone, tetrahydro-6-(4-methoxyphenyl)-4,6-diphenyl-	EtOH	297(4.33)	48-0617-80
2(1H)-Quinazolinone, 3-acetyl-3,4,5,6-7,8-hexahydro-4-phenyl-8-(phenylmethylene)-	EtOH	262(4.38),296(4.37)	114-0147-80B
$C_{23}H_{22}N_2O_3$			
Cyclopent[e][1,3,4]oxadiazin-7(1H)-one, 1-acetyl-4a,7a-dihydro-3,6,7a-trimethyl-4a,5-diphenyl-	EtOH	242(4.19)	23-1316-80
$C_{23}H_{22}N_2O_4$			
1,3-Azulenedicarboxylic acid, 2-[[[4-(dimethylamino)phenyl]imino]methyl]-, monoethyl ester	MeOH	239(4.51),308(4.49), 540(4.25)	18-3696-80
$C_{23}H_{22}N_3O$			
Quinolinium, 4-[2-(2,3-dihydro-1,5-dimethyl-3-oxo-2-phenyl-1H-pyrazol-4-yl)ethenyl]-1-methyl-, perchlorate	HOAc	456(4.41)	48-0543-80
$C_{23}H_{22}N_4O_4$			
Benzo[g]pteridine-2,4(3H,10H)-dione, 10-[2-(3-acetoxyphenyl)ethyl]-3,7,8-trimethyl-	MeOH	269(4.53),350(3.91), 420s(3.91),444(4.03), 472s(3.92)	35-5036-80
$C_{23}H_{22}N_6O$			
2H-Benzimidazol-2-one, 1,3-dihydro-1-(2-methoxyphenyl)-, [1-[(4-methylphenyl)azo]ethylidene]hydrazone	EtOH	460(4.38)	103-0637-80
2H-Benzimidazol-2-one, 1,3-dihydro-1-(4-methoxyphenyl)-, [1-[(4-methylphenyl)azo]ethylidene]hydrazone	EtOH	455(4.32)	103-0637-80
$C_{23}H_{22}O$			
3,5,7,9,12,14,16,18-Heneicosaoctaene-1,20-diyn-11-one, 3,19-dimethyl-, (E,E,Z,Z,E,E,E,E)-	THF	227(3.98),268(4.06), 282s(4.20),304s(4.34), 323(4.36),403(4.75)	44-3564-80

Compound	Solvent	$\lambda_{max}(\log \epsilon)$	Ref.
Naphthalene, 2-(cyclohexylidenephenyl-methoxy)-	hexane	260s(--),272s(--), 301(3.15),314(3.34), 321(3.27),329(3.46)	118-0847-80
$C_{23}H_{22}O_2$			
2,5-Cyclohexadien-1-one, 4-[(2-hydroxy-3,5-dimethylphenyl)phenylmethylene]-2,6-dimethyl-	EtOH	218(5.10),256(4.84), 279(4.78),361(4.97)	39-1986-80C
	EtOH-NaOH	245s(5.06),305(4.79), 401(4.80),600(4.56)	39-1986-80C
Ethanone, 1-phenyl-2-(2-phenyl-1-oxaspiro[4.5]dec-2-en-4-ylidene)-	EtOH	420(4.49)	5-1744-80
Spiro[benzofuran-2(3H),1'-cyclohexadien]-4'-one, 3',5,5',7-tetramethyl-3-phenyl-	EtOH	235(5.34),284(4.67), 293s(4.60)	39-1986-80C
$C_{23}H_{22}O_3$			
3,6-Methano-2H-cyclopenta[b]furan-5-carboxylic acid, 3,3a,6,6a-tetrahydro-2,2-diphenyl-, ethyl ester	EtOH	223(3.85)	78-0397-80
$C_{23}H_{22}O_6$			
4H,8H-Benzo[1,2-b:3,4-b']dipyran-4-one, 8,8-dimethyl-3-(2,4,5-trimethoxyphenyl)- (barbigerone)	MeOH	236(4.35),263(4.47), 294(4.08),323s(3.86)	102-0988-80
Pyrano[3,2-a]xanthen-12(3H)-one, 5,9,11-trihydroxy-3,3-dimethyl-10-(3-methyl-2-butenyl)- (garcinone B)	EtOH	246(4.44),266(4.37), 339(4.12),380s(4.24)	2-1008-80
	EtOH-NaOAc	247(4.37),266(4.37), 363(4.20),389s(4.15)	2-1008-80
$C_{23}H_{22}O_7$			
2-Anthracenepropanoic acid, 9,10-dihydro-1-hydroxy-4-methoxy-9,10-dioxo-α-(1-oxopropyl)-, ethyl ester	MeOH	250(4.45),278(4.09), 330(3.42),445(3.88), 460(3.91),489(3.76)	24-2994-80
Naphthaceno[1,2-d]-1,3-dioxole-7,12-dione, 3a-ethyl-3a,4,5,13b-tetrahydro-6,8,13-trihydroxy-2,2-dimethyl-, cis-(±)-	MeOH	234(4.45),251(4.25), 294(3.88),410s(--), 460(3.89),490(3.96), 508(3.85),525(3.83)	24-2994-80
$C_{23}H_{22}O_8$			
4H-1-Benzopyran-4-one, 5,7-diacetoxy-3-(1,3-benzodioxol-5-ylmethyl)-2,3-dihydro-6,8-dimethyl-, (-)-	EtOH	219(4.47),263(4.02)	94-1477-80
$C_{23}H_{22}O_9$			
1-Propanone, 3-(4-acetoxyphenyl)-1-(2,4,6-triacetoxyphenyl)-	MeOH	246s(3.77),313s(2.92)	100-0739-80
$C_{23}H_{22}O_{12}$			
β-D-Glucopyranosiduronic acid, 2-(3,4-dimethoxyphenyl)-5-hydroxy-4-oxo-4H-1-benzopyran-7-yl	MeOH	250(5.13),270(5.08), ?(5.19)	102-0480-80
	MeOH-NaOMe	280(--),305s(--), 395(--)	102-0480-80
	MeOH-NaOAc	250(--),270(--), 340(--)	102-0480-80
	MeOH-AlCl$_3$	263(--),275(--), 290(--),355(--), 382(--)	102-0480-80
$C_{23}H_{23}NO_2S$			
2-Naphthalenamine, N-[1,2-dimethyl-4-[(4-methylphenyl)sulfonyl]-2-buten-	EtOH	240(4.94)	104-0849-80

Compound	Solvent	$\lambda_{max}(\log \epsilon)$	Ref.
ylidene]- (cont.)			104-0849-80
$C_{23}H_{23}NO_3$			
Hydroperoxide, 10-(dimethylamino)-9,10-dihydro-10-methoxy-9-phenyl-9-anthracenyl	ether	259(3.38),263(3.37), 296s(2.58)	78-2453-80
$C_{23}H_{23}NO_8$			
Cyclopenta[3,4]cyclobuta[1,2-b]pyrrole-3,3a,6,6a-tetracarboxylic acid, 1,3b,4,6b-tetrahydro-1-phenyl-, tetramethyl ester, cis-anti-cis	MeOH	204(4.26),297(3.85), 345(4.34)	39-0081-80C
1H-Indole-4,5,6,7-tetracarboxylic acid, 3a,6-dihydro-1-(2-methylphenyl)-, tetramethyl ester	MeOH	290(3.78),341(3.99)	44-4582-80
1H-Isoindol-1-one, 3-[6-[(1-acetoxyethyl)-4-methoxy-1,3-benzodioxol-5-yl]-methylene]-2,3-dihydro-6,7-dimethoxy-	MeOH	218(4.81),296(3.88)	73-2125-80
$C_{23}H_{23}N_2OS$			
Benzothiazolium, 2-[[2-[2-(dimethylamino)ethenyl]-4H-1-benzopyran-4-ylidene]methyl]-3-ethyl-, iodide	MeCN	416(4.37),558(5.01)	124-0965-80
Benzothiazolium, 2-[[4-[2-(dimethylamino)ethenyl]-2H-1-benzopyran-2-ylidene]methyl]-3-ethyl-, perchlorate	MeCN	396(4.36),571(5.00)	124-0965-80
$C_{23}H_{23}N_2S_2$			
Benzothiazolium, 3-ethyl-2-[5-(3-ethyl-2(3H)-benzothiazolylidene)-1,3-pentadienyl]-, iodide	60% EtOH	652(5.34)	104-2080-80
$C_{23}H_{23}N_3O_4S$			
Pyrrolo[3,4-c]pyrazole-3a,4(1H)-dicarboxylic acid, 6,6a-dihydro-1-methyl-6a-(methylthio)-3,6-diphenyl-, dimethyl ester	MeOH	225s(4.08),303(4.08)	44-4587-80 +88-1529-80
$C_{23}H_{23}N_3O_5$			
Pyrrolo[3,4-c]pyrazole-3a,4(1H)-dicarboxylic acid, 6,6a-dihydro-6a-methoxy-1-methyl-3,6-diphenyl-, dimethyl ester, (3aα,6α,6aα)-	MeOH	215s(4.17),296(4.02)	44-4587-80 +88-1529-80
$C_{23}H_{23}N_5O_3$			
Hydrazinecarboxamide, N-[3-(4-methoxyphenyl)-1-oxo-2-(phenylhydrazono)-propyl]-2-phenyl-	EtOH	240(4.13),276(4.08), c.349(4.16)	12-0619-80
1,3,6,8-Tetraazaspiro[4.5]deca-6,9-diene-10-carboxylic acid, 3,7-dimethyl-4-oxo-1-phenyl-2-(phenylimino)-, ethyl ester	MeOH	250(4.05),277(4.04)	39-1667-80C
$C_{23}H_{23}N_7O_5$			
Benzamide, 4-[(4-azidophenyl)azo]-N-[6-[(2,5-dioxo-1-pyrrolidinyl)oxy]-6-oxohexyl]-	CHCl$_3$	357(4.45)	69-4423-80
$C_{23}H_{23}O_2S$			
1-Benzothiopyrylium, 5,6,7,8-tetrahydro-2,4-bis(4-methoxyphenyl)-	CH$_2$Cl$_2$	266(4.50),434(4.69)	104-0170-80

Compound	Solvent	λ_{max}(log ϵ)	Ref.
C$_{23}$H$_{24}$BNO Boron, [2-[(butylimino)methyl]phenolato-N,O]diphenyl-, (T-4)-	CHCl$_3$	285(3.92),383(3.49)	49-0863-80
C$_{23}$H$_{24}$F$_3$NO$_6$ Isoquinolinium, 4-[(3,4-dimethoxyphenyl)methylene]-6,7-dimethoxy-2-methyl-3,4-dihydro-, trifluoroacetate	EtOH	259(4.16),313(4.09)	39-2013-80C
C$_{23}$H$_{24}$NO$_5$ Dibenzo[a,g]quinolizinium, 2,3,10,11,13-pentamethoxy-8-methyl-, iodide	EtOH	221(4.24),235s(4.09), 244s(3.96),288(4.28), 305(4.34),316(4.37), 331(4.28),367(3.54), 390s(3.51),414(3.83), 436(3.98)	39-0911-80C
C$_{23}$H$_{24}$N$_2$ Quinolinium, 1,1'-(1,3-propanediyl)-bis[4-methyl-, dibromide	H$_2$O	312(4.1)	104-2044-80
C$_{23}$H$_{24}$N$_2$S 6H,8H-Pyrimido[2,1-a:4,3-a']diisoquinoline-6-thione, 4b,5,9,13b,15,16-hexahydro-5-(2-propenyl)-	CHCl$_3$	286(4.1),348s(2.2)	24-3024-80
Quinazoline, 2-(ethylthio)-1,4,5,6,7,8-hexahydro-4-phenyl-8-(phenylmethylene)-, monohydrobromide	EtOH	236(4.38),276(4.61), 323(4.18)	114-0147-80B
Quinazoline, 3,4,5,6,7,8-hexahydro-3-methyl-2-(methylthio)-4-phenyl-8-(phenylmethylene)- monohydriodide	EtOH EtOH	235(4.15),279(4.45), 334(3.86) 280(4.43),340(3.84)	114-0147-80B 114-0147-80B
C$_{23}$H$_{24}$N$_4$S$_2$ 3H-Pyrazole-3-thione, 4,4'-methylenebis[1,2-dihydro-1,5-dimethyl-2-phenyl-	benzene H$_2$O	278(4.07),344(4.05) 256(4.28),288(4.28)	140-0560-80 140-0560-80
C$_{23}$H$_{24}$N$_5$O$_7$P Phosphoramidic acid, N-methyl-N-(9-β-D-ribofuranosyl)-9H-purin-6-yl)-, diphenyl ester	pH 7.0 MeOH	266(4.24),276s(4.09) 264(4.31),274s(4.17)	142-0761-80B 142-0761-80B
C$_{23}$H$_{24}$N$_6$O 1H-Indole-2,3-dione, 3-[[2-[(4-butylphenyl)amino]-6-methyl-4-pyrimidinyl]hydrazone]	EtOH	206(4.48),260(4.37), 266s(4.34),281s(4.23), 357(4.32)	103-1279-80
C$_{23}$H$_{24}$N$_8$ 2,2a,4,5-Tetraazabenz[cd]azulene, 4,4'-methylenebis[3,4-dihydro-1,3-dimethyl-	MeOH	221(4.58),292(3.97), 350(4.30)	118-0331-80
C$_{23}$H$_{24}$O$_2$ Cyclobuta[b]naphthalene-3,8-dione, 2a,8a-diethyl-1,2,2a,8a-tetrahydro-1-methyl-1-phenyl-, anti	CHCl$_3$	250(4.06),295(3.21), 330(2.38)	18-0757-80
C$_{23}$H$_{24}$O$_4$ Tricyclo[8.5.1.1^{3,8}]heptadeca-1,3,5,7-9,11,14-heptaene-12,14-dicarboxylic acid, diethyl ester	dioxan	317(4.91),339s(4.84), 397(3.75)	89-0041-80

Compound	Solvent	$\lambda_{max}(\log \epsilon)$	Ref.
$C_{23}H_{24}O_5$			
Acetic acid, phenoxy-, 3,5,5-trimethyl-4-(3-methyl-5-oxo-3-penten-1-ynyl)-2-oxo-3-cyclohexen-1-yl ester, [S-(E)]-	EtOH	315(4.31)	33-1473-80
4H-1-Benzopyran-4-one, 5-acetoxy-2,3-dihydro-7-methoxy-8-(3-methyl-2-butenyl)-2-phenyl-	MeOH	240s(4.24),285(4.23), 338s(3.36)	102-1267-80
2-Propen-1-one, 1-(5,7-dimethoxy-2,2-dimethyl-2H-1-benzopyran-6-yl)-3-methoxy-3-phenyl-, (Z)-	n.s.g.	284(4.18)	102-0707-80
9H-Xanthen-9-one, 1,3,6-trihydroxy-2,4-bis(3-methyl-2-butenyl)- (garcinone A)	EtOH	245(4.47),260(4.02), 289(4.0),323(4.1), 372(3.47)	2-1008-80
$C_{23}H_{24}O_7$			
4H-1-Benzopyran-4-one, 5,7-diacetoxy-2,3-dihydro-3-[(4-methoxyphenyl)-methyl]-6,8-dimethyl-	EtOH	222(4.60),263(4.13)	94-1477-80
Naphtho[2,3-c]furan-1(3H)-one, 6-acet-oxy-4-(3,4-dimethoxyphenyl)-3a,4,9-9a-tetrahydro-7-methoxy-	EtOH	225(4.20),279(3.73)	94-0850-80
$C_{23}H_{24}O_7S_2$			
9,10-Anthracenedione, 2-[3-(1,3-dithi-an-2-yl)-3-hydroxypentyl]-1,4,8-tri-hydroxy-, S-oxide	MeOH	233(4.24),250(4.08), 291(3.60),408(3.17), 464(3.83),479(3.88), 491(3.94),509(3.79), 524(3.74)	24-2994-80
$C_{23}H_{24}O_{10}$			
Vitexin 4',7-di-O-methyl ether	EtOH	270(4.27),324(4.22)	36-0053-80
$C_{23}H_{25}NO_3$			
Acetoxyocoxylonine, (±)-	EtOH	225(4.49),285(4.22), 303(4.1),311(4.05)	35-6513-80
$C_{23}H_{25}NO_4$			
6,10-Etheno-5H-cyclohepta[b]naphthalen-5,11-imine-12-carboxylic acid, 5a,6-7,10,10a,11-hexahydro-6-methoxy-7-oxo-, 1,1-dimethylethyl ester, (5α,5aβ,6β,10α,10aβ,11α)-	EtOH	263(3.36),271(3.18), 326(2.00)	78-2119-80
6,10-Etheno-5H-cyclohepta[b]naphthalen-5,11-imine-12-carboxylic acid, 5a,6-7,10,10a,11-hexahydro-8-methoxy-7-oxo-, 1,1-dimethylethyl ester, (5α,5aβ,6α,10α,10aβ,11α)-	EtOH	264(3.61),271(3.61), 282(3.55),327(2.18)	78-2119-80
$C_{23}H_{25}NO_6$			
Norlirioferine, N,O-diacetyl-	EtOH	216(4.71),282(4.29), 294s(4.22),302s(4.11)	142-1131-80
$C_{23}H_{25}NO_8$			
1H-Azepine-2,5-dicarboxylic acid, 2,3-dihydro-6-[3-methoxy-1-(methoxycarb-onyl)-3-oxo-1-propenyl]-1-(phenyl-methyl)-, dimethyl ester, (E)-	MeCN	335(3.96)	88-1145-80
1H-Azonine-2,5,7,8-tetracarboxylic acid, 2,3-dihydro-1-(phenylmethyl)-, tetramethyl ester	MeCN	274(4.13)	88-1145-80

Compound	Solvent	$\lambda_{max}(\log \epsilon)$	Ref.
1H-Indole-2,4,6,7-tetracarboxylic acid, 2,3,3a,7-tetrahydro-1-(phenylmethyl)-, tetramethyl ester	MeCN	296(3.67)	88-1145-80
$C_{23}H_{25}NS$ "Blue compd."	EtOH	610(c.4.0)	150-3523-80
$C_{23}H_{25}N_3O_2$ 5(4H)-Isoxazolone, 4-[[4-(dimethylamino)phenyl]-1-piperidinylmethylene]-3-phenyl-	MeOH	389(4.37)	97-0020-80
$C_{23}H_{25}N_5O_2$ 1H-Indole-2,3-dione, 1-butyl-, 3-[[3-(1-methylethoxy)-2-quinoxalinyl]hydrazone], (Z)-	EtOH	306s(3.76),409(4.51)	103-1073-80
$C_{23}H_{25}N_5O_4$ Neoxaline	MeOH	237(4.25),330(4.47)	94-2987-80
$C_{23}H_{26}ClN_3O_6S$ Urea, N-(2-chloroethyl)-N-nitroso-N'-[5,6,7,9-tetrahydro-1,2,3-trimethoxy-10-(methylthio)-9-oxobenzo[a]heptalen-7-yl]-, (S)-	EtOH	255(4.43),285(4.24), 380(4.31)	87-1440-80
$C_{23}H_{26}Cl_2N_2O_4$ 4H-Dibenzo[de,g]quinoline-2,11-diol, 6-[[bis(2-chloroethyl)amino]acetyl]-5,6,6a,7-tetrahydro-10-methoxy-	EtOH	270(4.08),279(4.09), 305(3.87)	87-1008-80
$C_{23}H_{26}F_3NO_5$ Isoquinolinium, 4-[(3,4-dimethoxyphenyl)methyl]-6,7-dimethoxy-2-methyl-, trifluoroacetate	EtOH	247(4.11),295(3.71), 312(3.73),355(3.76)	39-2013-80C
$C_{23}H_{26}N_2O_4$ 10H-Benz[f]isoquino[8,1,2-hij]pyrrolo-[1,2,3-de]quinoxalin-10-one, 1,2,4-5,13,14,15a,15b-octahydro-7,8,11-trimethoxy-, (12aS,15aα,15bα)-(±)-	EtOH	288(4.11),317s(3.85)	33-0938-80
$C_{23}H_{26}N_2O_6$ 1H-Isoindol-1-one, 3-[[6-[2-(dimethylamino)ethyl]-4-methoxy-1,3-benzodioxol-5-yl]methylene]-2,3-dihydro-6,7-dimethoxy-, (E)-	MeOH	261(4.25),345(4.04)	73-2125-80
$C_{23}H_{26}N_2O_7$ 1H-Isoindol-1-one, 3-[[6-[2-(dimethylamino)ethyl]-4-methoxy-1,3-benzodioxol-5-yl]methylene]-2,3-dihydro-6,7-dimethoxy-, N-oxide, (Z)-	MeOH	214(4.40),264(4.06), 350(4.13)	73-2125-80
2(1H)-Pyridinone, 6-amino-3,5-bis[(4-hydroxy-3,5-dimethoxyphenyl)methyl]-	6M HCl	232(4.35),281s(3.42), 324(4.01)	87-0384-80
	pH 7	237s(4.26),281s(3.40), 338(4.09)	87-0384-80
	M NaOH	246(4.31),297(3.97), 316(3.99)	87-0384-80

Compound	Solvent	$\lambda_{max}(\log \epsilon)$	Ref.
$C_{23}H_{26}N_3S_2$			
Benzothiazolium, 3-ethyl-2-[2-(ethyl-amino)-3-(3-ethyl-2(3H)-benzothia-zolylidene)-1-propenyl]-, iodide	60% EtOH	472(4.44)	104-2080-80
$C_{23}H_{26}N_4O$			
3H-Pyrazol-3-one, 4-[[4-(dimethylami-no)phenyl]-1-pyrrolidinylmethylene]-2,4-dihydro-5-methyl-2-phenyl-	MeOH	367(4.68)	97-0020-80
$C_{23}H_{26}N_4O_2$			
3H-Pyrazol-3-one, 4-[[4-(dimethylami-no)phenyl]-4-morpholinylmethylene]-2,4-dihydro-5-methyl-2-phenyl-	MeOH	373(4.77)	97-0020-80
$C_{23}H_{26}N_4O_4$			
Spiro[imidazolidine-4,2'(3'H)-quinoxa-line]-2,3',5-trione, 4'-ethyl-1',4'-dihydro-1'-[2-(3-hydroxyphenyl)eth-yl]-1,6',7'-trimethyl-	EtOH	264s(3.83),273s(3.81), 281s(3.73),307(3.81)	35-5036-80
$C_{23}H_{26}N_4O_6S$			
Acetamide, 2-[(1,2-dihydro-2-oxo-1-β-D-ribofuranosyl-4-pyrimidinyl)thio]-N-[4-(dimethylamino)-1-naphthalenyl]-	EtOH	215(4.66),247(4.18), 306(4.21)	94-1722-80
Acetamide, 2-[(1,4-dihydro-4-oxo-1-β-D-ribofuranosyl-2-pyrimidinyl)thio]-N-[4-(dimethylamino)-1-naphthalenyl]-	EtOH	217(4.74),318(3.89)	94-1722-80
$C_{23}H_{26}N_4O_9$			
L-Tryptophan, N-acetyl-2-(1,2,3,4-tet-rahydro-2,4-dioxo-1-β-D-ribofurano-syl-5-pyrimidinyl)-, methyl ester	EtOH	267(4.03),292(3.91), 329(3.61)	35-7535-80
$C_{23}H_{26}O_5$			
2H,8H-Benzo[1,2-b:3,4-b']dipyran, 3,4-dihydro-8,8-dimethyl-3-(2,3,4-tri-methoxyphenyl)-, (R)-	MeOH	278(3.99),289s(3.61), 311(3.10)	100-0259-80
Propanedioic acid, [1-(4-methylphenyl)-3-oxo-3-phenylpropyl]-, diethyl ester	EtOH	242(4.20)	34-0085-80
Spiro[5.5]undecane-1,5,9-trione, 7,11-bis(5-methyl-2-furanyl)-3,3-dimethyl-	dioxan	249(3.62)	44-2925-80
$C_{23}H_{26}O_7$			
2(3H)-Furanone, 3-[(4-acetoxy-3-meth-oxyphenyl)methyl]-4-[(3,4-dimethoxy-phenyl)methyl]dihydro- (arctigenin monoacetate)	EtOH	224(4.02),281(3.61)	94-0850-80
Isoarctigenin monoacetate	EtOH	225(4.15),282(3.73)	94-0850-80
Spiro[cyclopropane-1,2'(1'H)-phenan-threne]-1',4'(3'H)-dione, 3'-acetoxy-10'-(formyloxy)-4'b,5',6',7',8',8'a-9',10'-octahydro-9'-hydroxy-2,4'b-dimethyl-7',8'-bis(methylene)-	EtOH	231(4.10)	33-0095-80
9H-Xanthen-9-one, 1,3,6,7-tetrahydroxy-8-(3-hydroxy-3-methylbutyl)-2-(3-methyl-2-butenyl)- (garcinone C)	EtOH	242(4.52),259(4.40), 370(4.32)	2-1008-80
$C_{23}H_{26}O_8$			
1,3-Benzodioxole, 4-methoxy-6-(tetra-	EtOH	207(4.98),235s(4.13),	78-3551-80

Compound	Solvent	$\lambda_{max}(\log \epsilon)$	Ref.
hydro-4-(3,4,5-trimethoxyphenyl)-1H,3H-furo[3,4-c]furan-1-yl]-, (1R,3aR,4R,6aR)- (diasesartemin)		273(3.34)	78-3551-80
Episesartemin A	EtOH	209(4.02),236s(4.12), 273(3.34)	78-3551-80
Episesartemin B	EtOH	208(4.99),235s(4.12), 273(3.36)	78-3551-80
Sesartemin	EtOH	207(4.99),236s(4.15), 273(3.40)	78-3551-80
$C_{23}H_{26}O_{10}$			
Aurapin	MeOH	228(4.16),292(4.03)	142-1979-80
	MeOH-AlCl$_3$	228(4.10),329(4.20)	142-1979-80
$C_{23}H_{26}O_{11}$			
Isovitexin 4',7-di-O-methyl ether	EtOH	268(4.28),324(4.36)	36-0053-80
1-Propanone, 1-[2-[(2-O-acetyl-β-D-glucopyranosyl)oxy]-4,6-dihydroxyphenyl]-3-(4-hydroxyphenyl)-	MeOH	223(4.37),284(4.28)	100-0739-80
$C_{23}H_{26}O_{12}$			
1-Propanone, 1-[2-[(2-O-acetyl-β-D-glucopyranosyl)oxy]4,6-dihydroxyphenyl]-3-(3,4-dihydroxyphenyl)-	MeOH	220(4.36),284(4.26)	100-0739-80
$C_{23}H_{27}ClN_2O_2$			
1H-Indole-3-ethanamine, 1-(4-chlorobenzoyl)-N,N-diethyl-5-methoxy-2-methyl-, monohydrochloride	EtOH	226(4.29),250(4.25), 320(3.79)	80-0245-80
$C_{23}H_{27}ClN_2O_3$			
1H-Indole-3-ethanamine, 1-(4-chlorobenzoyl)-N-ethyl-N-(2-hydroxyethyl)-5-methoxy-2-methyl-, hydrochloride	EtOH	226(4.29),250(4.24), 320(3.78)	80-0245-80
$C_{23}H_{27}ClN_2O_5S$			
Urea, N-(2-chloroethyl)-N'-[5,6,7,9-tetrahydro-1,2,3-trimethoxy-10-(methylthio)-9-oxobenzo[a]heptalen-7-yl]-, (S)-	EtOH	255(4.33),290(4.07), 380(4.28)	87-1440-80
$C_{23}H_{27}NO$			
9H-Carbazol-2-ol, 1-(3,7-dimethyl-2,6-octadienyl)-3-methyl-, (E)-	EtOH	244(4.26),260(4.14), 296(3.98),325(3.40), 339(3.38)	25-0697-80
$C_{23}H_{27}NO_6$			
Acetamide, N-methyl-N-(5,6,7,9-tetrahydro-1,2,3,10-tetramethoxy-9-oxobenzo[a]heptalen-7-yl)-, (S)-	EtOH	242(4.49),350(4.29)	33-0050-80
Acetamide, N-methyl-N-(5,6,7,10-tetrahydro-1,2,3,9-tetramethoxy-10-oxobenzo[a]heptalen-7-yl)-, (S)-	EtOH	244(4.49),343(4.28)	33-0050-80
$C_{23}H_{27}NO_7$			
L-Tyrosine, N-[3-(3,4-dimethoxyphenyl)-1-oxo-2-propenyl]-3-methoxy-O-methyl-, methyl ester, cis	MeOH	205(4.61),230(4.52), 283(4.39),312(4.35)	102-2125-80
trans	MeOH	205(4.33),230(4.31), 285(4.25),315(4.25)	102-2125-80

Compound	Solvent	$\lambda_{max}(\log \epsilon)$	Ref.
$C_{23}H_{27}NO_8$			
9,9(10H)-Acridinedicarboxylic acid, 2,4,5,7-tetramethoxy-, diethyl ester	MeCN	219(4.24),271(4.16), 330(3.91)	152-0389-80
Clivatine, O-acetyl-	MeOH	205(4.35),225(4.45), 266(3.88),306(3.88)	94-1827-80
$C_{23}H_{27}NS$			
2-Azetidinethione, 3-(1,1-dimethylethyl)-1-methyl-4,4-diphenyl-3-(2-propenyl)-	isooctane	267(4.1),341(1.7)	24-3010-80
2-Azetidinethione, 3-(1,1-dimethylethyl)-4-phenyl-1-(phenylmethyl)-3-(2-propenyl)-, trans	isooctane	268s(4.1),272(4.1), 335s(2.0)	24-3010-80
$C_{23}H_{27}N_3O_2$			
1H-[1,2,4]Triazolo[1,2-a]pyridazine-1,3(2H)-dione, 5-(3,7-dimethyl-1,4,6-octatrienyl)-5,8-dihydro-6-methyl-2-phenyl-	EtOH	234(4.38)	44-2523-80
$C_{23}H_{27}N_3O_2STe$			
Tellurilimine, Te,Te-bis[4-(dimethylamino)phenyl]-N-[(phenylmethyl)sulfonyl]-	MeOH	317(4.05)	104-2210-80
$C_{23}H_{27}N_3O_6$			
Phenol, 4,4'-[(2,4-diamino-3,5-pyridinediyl)bis(methylene)]bis[2,6-dimethoxy-	pH 1	221s(4.70),273(4.00), 281s(3.97)	87-0384-80
	pH 13	245(4.35),282(4.06)	87-0384-80
Phenol, 4,4'-[(2,6-diamino-3,5-pyridinediyl)bis(methylene)]bis[2,6-dimethoxy-	pH 2	236(4.37),280s(3.48), 342(4.19)	87-0384-80
	pH 8.4	232s(4.35),313(3.99)	87-0384-80
	pH 13	242s(4.37),308(4.14)	87-0384-80
$C_{23}H_{27}N_4$			
Pyridinium, 4-[[4-(diethylamino)phenyl]azo]-1-(4-methylphenyl)methyl]-, bromide	H_2O	574(4.81)	96-0768-80
$C_{23}H_{27}N_5O_6S$			
2,1-Benzisothiazole, 5-nitro-3-[[4-(1-4,7,10-tetraoxa-13-azacyclopentadec-13-yl)phenyl]azo]-	MeCN	585(5.03)	24-0457-80
$C_{23}H_{28}Cl_2N_2O_4$			
Aspidospermidine-3-carboxylic acid, 15,17-dichloro-6,7-didehydro-2-ethoxy-3-hydroxy-, methyl ester, (2β,3β,5α,12β,19α)-	EtOH	254(4.00),317(3.50)	142-1915-80
$C_{23}H_{28}N_2OS$			
13,16-Epithiocyclopentadecapyrazol-3(2H)-one, 1,4,5,6,7,8,9,10,11,12-decahydro-1-methyl-2-phenyl-	$CHCl_3$	270(3.85),350(3.79)	103-0711-80
$C_{23}H_{28}N_2O_3$			
Deacetylakuammiline	MeOH	222(4.25),267(3.76)	102-2741-80
$C_{23}H_{28}N_2O_4$			
7,11a-(Iminoethano)-11aH-dibenzo[de,g]-	EtOH	237(4.34),280(3.85)	33-0938-80

Compound	Solvent	$\lambda_{max}(\log \epsilon)$	Ref.
quinolin-9(4H)-one, 5,6,6a,7-tetra-hydro-1,2,10-trimethoxy-6,14-dimethyl-, (6aα,7α,11aα)-(±)- (cont.)			33-0938-80
(6aα,7β,11aβ)-(±)-	EtOH	237(4.33),275(3.79)	33-0938-80
$C_{23}H_{28}N_2O_5$			
1H-Indolizino[8,7-b]indole-2-propanoic acid, 2-(ethoxycarbonyl)-α-ethyl-2,3,5,6,11,11b-hexahydro-3-oxo-, methyl ester	EtOH	220(4.57),264(3.83), 290(3.71)	78-1063-80
Quaternine	MeOH	210(4.70),243(4.10), 305(3.90)	102-0307-80
$C_{23}H_{28}N_4O$			
3H-Pyrazol-3-one, 4-[(diethylamino)-[4-(dimethylamino)phenyl]methylene]-2,4-dihydro-5-methyl-2-phenyl-	MeOH	375(4.51)	97-0020-80
$C_{23}H_{28}O_2$			
D-Homo-18-norandrosta-8,11,13,15,17-pentaen-3-ol, acetate, (3β,5α)-	EtOH	284(3.66),313(3.16), 327(3.13)	39-0556-80C
$C_{23}H_{28}O_3$			
3'H-Cyclopropa[1,2]-D-homopregna-1,4,6,16-tetraene-3,20-dione, 1,2-dihydro-17a-hydroxy-, (1β,2β)-	EtOH	283(4.30)	33-1867-80
2H-Pyran-2-one, 4-methoxy-5-methyl-6-(7,9,11-trimethyl-1,3,5,7,9,11-tridecahexaenyl)-, (all-E)-(citreomontanine)	EtOH	208(4.25),232(4.15), 268(4.13),315(4.17), 415(4.75)	102-0427-80
$C_{23}H_{28}O_4$			
7,13c-Epoxy-13aH-benzo[c]furo[3',2'-6,7]cyclohepta[1,2,3-ij][2]benzopyran-13(1H)-one, 2,3,3a,7,8,8a,10,11-12,13b-decahydro-5,7,11,11-tetra-methyl-	MeOH	267(4.04)	44-2925-80
isomer	MeOH	268(4.32)	44-2925-80
Spiro[5.5]undecane-1,5-dione, 3,3-di-methyl-7,11-bis(5-methyl-2-furanyl)-, cis	dioxan	249(3.45)	44-2925-80
	dioxan	248(3.48)	44-2925-80
$C_{23}H_{28}O_5$			
Pregna-4,9(11)-diene-3,12,20-trione, 11-acetoxy-, (17α)-	EtOH	243(4.30)	18-0254-80
$C_{23}H_{28}O_5S$			
α-D-Glucofuranose, 3-O-methyl-1,2-O-(1-methylethylidene)-5-C-phenyl-6-S-(phenylmethyl)-6-thio-	EtOH	212(4.08)	33-0016-80
$C_{23}H_{28}O_7$			
Spiro[5H-benzocycloheptene-5,1'-[2,5]-cyclohexadiene]-4',9(6H)-dione, 7,8-dihydro-2,3,3',4,5'-pentamethoxy-7,8-dimethyl-, (7R-trans)-	EtOH	223(4.37),278(4.12)	12-1823-80
$C_{23}H_{28}O_8$			
Gomisin P	EtOH	220(4.59),254s(4.02), 283s(3.49),294s(3.37)	94-3357-80

Compound	Solvent	$\lambda_{max}(\log \epsilon)$	Ref.
$C_{23}H_{29}ClN_4O_{10}S$ D-Glucitol, 1-C-(6-chloro-9H-purin-9-yl)-1-S-ethyl-1-thio-, 2,3,4,5,6-pentaacetate, (S)-	MeOH	264(4.53)	136-0241-80C
$C_{23}H_{29}ClO_4$ Pregna-1,4-diene-3,20-dione, 17-acetoxy-7-chloro-, (7α)-	MeOH	242(4.21)	87-0430-80
$C_{23}H_{29}NO$ 2H-Benz[e]indolo[1,2-a]indol-3(4H)-one, 1,4a,5,6,6a,13,13a,13b-octahydro-4,4,13a,13b-tetramethyl- (polyavolensinone)	MeOH	237(3.21),279(3.77), 285(3.78),294(3.65)	78-2005-80
$C_{23}H_{29}NO_5$ Kreysigine, O-methyl-, (±)-	MeOH	220(4.54),260(4.01), 296(3.54)	35-6513-80
$C_{23}H_{29}NO_{11}$ D-Galactopentitol, 1-C-(4,5,6,7-tetrahydro-4-oxo-1H-indol-2-yl)-, 1,2,3,4,5-pentaacetate	EtOH	237(4.24),273(4.25)	136-0017-80A
D-Glucopentitol, 1-C-(4,5,6,7-tetrahydro-4-oxo-1H-indol-2-yl)-, 1,2,3,4,5-pentaacetate	EtOH	236(4.28),274(4.29)	136-0017-80A
D-Mannopentitol, 1-C-(4,5,6,7-tetrahydro-4-oxo-1H-indol-2-yl)-, 1,2,3,4,5-pentaacetate	EtOH	237(4.26),274(4.28)	136-0017-80A
$C_{23}H_{29}N_3O$ Androsta-5,16-dieno[16,17-g]pyrazolo-[1,5-a]pyrimidin-3β-ol	MeOH	206(3.99),234(4.58), 330(3.53)	39-0481-80C
Androsta-2,4-dieno[2,3-g]pyrazolo[1,5-a]pyrimidin-17β-ol	MeOH	209(3.89),235s(4.48), 242(4.57),370(3.98)	39-0481-80C
$C_{23}H_{29}N_3O_3$ Vincamine, 10-(acetylamino)-	EtOH	246(4.10)	142-1915-80
$C_{23}H_{29}N_5O_2$ Androst-4-eno[3,2-f](tetrazolo[1,5-a]pyrimidine, 17β-acetoxy-	MeOH	213(4.18),243(4.22), 311(4.19)	39-1019-80C
$C_{23}H_{29}N_5O_3$ 5ξ-Androst-2-eno[2,3-g](tetrazolo[1,5-a]pyrimidine, 17β-acetoxy-4-oxo-	MeOH	214(4.13),249(3.98), 287(3.81)	39-1019-80C
$C_{23}H_{30}N_2O_3$ Deacetylakuammiline, 1,2β-dihydro-	MeOH	210(4.04),244(3.58), 302(3.23)	102-2741-80
19-Ethoxycoronaridine	n.s.g.	225(4.51),286(3.92), 292(3.88)	102-0716-80
1,3-Propanediol, 2-(2,5-dihydro-1,2,2-5,5-pentamethyl-1H-imidazol-4-yl)-1,3-diphenyl-, N-oxide	EtOH	235(3.92)	70-0956-80
$C_{23}H_{30}N_2O_4$ Strychnofendlerine, 11-methoxy-	EtOH	251(4.03),290(3.72), 296s(3.69)	32-0081-80

Compound	Solvent	$\lambda_{max}(\log \epsilon)$	Ref.
$C_{23}H_{30}N_2O_5$			
Strychnofendlerine, 12-hydroxy-11-methoxy-	EtOH	226(4.41),254(3.90), 290s(3.28)	32-0081-80
	EtOH-base	308(3.77)	32-0081-80
$C_{23}H_{30}N_4O_{10}S_2$			
D-Glucitol, 1-S-methyl-C-[6-(methylthio)-9H-purin-9-yl)-1-thio-, 2,3,4,5,6-pentaacetate, (S)-	MeOH	230(4.33),283(4.58), 291(4.57)	136-0241-80C
$C_{23}H_{30}N_5O_6PS$			
Adenosine, N-hexyl-8-[(phenylmethyl)-thio]-, cyclic 3',5'-(hydrogen phosphate)	pH 1	288(4.26)	87-0242-80
	pH 11	292(4.18)	87-0242-80
$C_{23}H_{30}N_{12}O_4$			
1H-Pyrrole-2-carboxamide, N-[5-[[(2-amino-2-iminoethyl)amino]carbonyl]-1-methyl-1H-pyrrol-3-yl]-4-[[[4-[[[(aminoiminomethyl)amino]acetyl]amino]-1-methyl-1H-pyrrol-2-yl]carbonyl]-amino]-1-methyl-, dihydrochloride	EtOH	240(4.37),308(4.39)	87-1144-80
$C_{23}H_{30}O_4$			
Pregna-3,5-diene-11,20-dione, 3-acetoxy-	EtOH	233(4.28)	23-2703-80
Pregna-4,6-dien-20-one, 3β-acetoxy-16α,17α-epoxy-	MeOH	232(4.16),239(4.20), 247(4.01)	39-0556-80C
Pregna-5,7-dien-20-one, 3β-acetoxy-16α,17α-epoxy-	EtOH	271(3.97),282(4.02), 294(3.76)	39-0556-80C
$C_{23}H_{30}O_5$			
Dibenzo[a,c]cyclooctene, 5,6,7,8-tetrahydro-1,2,3,10,11-pentamethoxy-6,7-dimethyl-	EtOH	215(4.89),253(4.40), 280(4.05)	94-2422-80
Pregn-4-ene-3,6,20-trione, 1α-acetoxy-	EtOH	249(4.04)	39-2700-80C
Trichodermadiene	EtOH	264(4.41)	88-0787-80
Unnamed compd. 18, m. 158°	MeOH	266(4.15)	44-2925-80
$C_{23}H_{30}O_6$			
Dibenzo[a,c]cycloocten-3-ol, 5,6,7,8-tetrahydro-1,2,10,11,12-pentamethoxy-6,7-dimethyl- (gomisin K_1)	EtOH	217(4.74),250(4.21), 276s(3.57),285s(3.48)	94-2422-80
Gomisin K_2, (+)-	EtOH	216(4.74),250(4.21), 276s(3.55),285s(3.46)	94-2422-80
Gomisin K_3	EtOH	219(4.71),251s(4.21), 277(3.58),283s(3.56)	94-2422-80
Lumiprednisolone acetate	EtOH	265s(3.40),233(3.67)	44-2324-80
Spiro[5H-benzocycloheptene-5,1'-[2,5]-cyclohexadien]-4'-one, 6,7,8,9-tetrahydro-2,3,3',4,5'-pentamethoxy-7,8-dimethyl-, (7R-trans)-	EtOH	216(4.63),235s(4.15), 278(4.09)	12-1823-80
$C_{23}H_{30}O_7$			
1,5-Cyclo-1,10-secopregn-3-ene-3,11,20-trione, 21-acetoxy-10,17-dihydroxy-, (5α,10α)-	MeOH	217.5(3.82)	44-2334-80
Spiro[5H-benzocycloheptene-5,1'-[2,5]-cyclohexadien]-4'-one, 6,7,8,9-tetrahydro-9-hydroxy-2,3,3',4,5'-pentamethoxy-7,8-dimethyl-, [7R-(7α,8β,9α)]-	EtOH	218(4.62),235s(4.15), 279(4.10)	12-1823-80

Compound	Solvent	$\lambda_{max}(\log \epsilon)$	Ref.
$C_{23}H_{31}BrO_3$ Benzo[d]xanthen-10-ol, 9-bromo-1,2,3,4-4a,5,6,7,7a,8-decahydro-4,4,7,7a-tetramethyl-, acetate, [4aS-(4aα-7β,7aα,13aR*)]-	MeOH	231(4.00),310(3.85)	44-1435-80
$C_{23}H_{31}FO_7S$ Pregna-1,4-diene-3,20-dione, 9-fluoro-11,17-dihydroxy-16-methyl-21-[(methylsulfonyl)oxy]-, (11β,16α)-	EtOH	239(4.22)	44-3084-80
$C_{23}H_{31}NO$ 5-Acephenanthrylenecarbonitrile, 1,2,3,3a,4,7,8,9,10,10a,10b,10c-dodecahydro-8-methoxy-7,7,10a,10c-tetramethyl-3-methylene-, (3aα,8β-10aβ,10bα,10cα)-	n.s.g.	280(4.30)	33-1554-80
$C_{23}H_{31}NO_3$ 1-Phenanthrenepropanenitrile, 7-acetoxy-1,4a,4b,5,6,7,8,10,10a-decahydro-2,4b,8,8-tetramethyl-10-oxo-, [1S-(1α,4aβ,4bα,7α,10aα)]-	n.s.g.	241(4.10)	33-1554-80
$C_{23}H_{31}N_3O$ 5α-Androst-16-eno[16,17-g]pyrazolo[1,5-a]pyrimidin-3β-ol	MeOH	236(4.51),327(3.38)	39-0481-80C
$C_{23}H_{32}ClNO_3$ 1-Phenanthrenepropanenitrile, 7-acetoxy-2-chloro-1,2,3,4,4a,4b,5,6,7,8-10,10a-dodecahydro-2,4b,8,8-tetramethyl-10-oxo-	n.s.g.	240(4.14)	33-1554-80
$C_{23}H_{32}FNO_3$ Acetamide, N-[(16α)-17-fluoro-3,20-dioxopregn-4-en-16-yl]-	EtOH	242(4.26),288(3.12)	70-1181-80
$C_{23}H_{32}N_2O_8S$ 1H-Pyrrole-3-propanoic acid, 5-[[1,5-dihydro-3-methyl-4-[2-[(methylsulfonyl)oxy]ethyl]-5-oxo-2H-pyrrol-2-ylidene]methyl]-2-[(1,1-dimethylethoxy)carbonyl]-4-methyl-, methyl ester	MeOH + Zn(OAc)₂	253s(--),259(4.28), 386(4.46),404s(--) 265(4.24),272s(--), 425s(--),442(4.48)	24-1603-80 24-1603-80
$C_{23}H_{32}N_4O_8S_2$ D-arabino-Hexitol, 2-deoxy-1-S-ethyl-1-C-[6-(ethylthio)-9H-purin-9-yl]-1-thio-, 3,4,5,6-tetraacetate	MeOH	283(4.2)	136-0356-80C
$C_{23}H_{32}O_3$ Benzo[d]xanthen-10-ol, 1,2,3,4,4a,5,6-7,7a,8-decahydro-4,4,7,7a-tetramethyl-, acetate, [4aS-(4aα,7β,7aα,13aR*)]-	MeOH	202(4.10),225(3.85), 279(3.48)	44-1435-80
2H-Benzo[a]xanthen-10-ol, 1,3,4,4a,5,6-6a,12,12a,12b-decahydro-4,4,6a,12b-tetramethyl-, acetate	MeOH	212(4.25),287(3.64)	44-1435-80
5H-Inden-5-one, 1-(1,1-dimethylethoxy)-1,2,3,6,7,7a-hexahydro-4-[2-(3-methoxyphenyl)ethyl]-7a-methyl-, (1S-cis)-	CHCl₃	255(4.08),280(3.42), 320(2.84)	24-0385-80

Compound	Solvent	$\lambda_{max}(\log \epsilon)$	Ref.
$C_{23}H_{32}O_4$			
Androst-5-ene-7,17-dione, 3β-acetoxy-4,4-dimethyl-	n.s.g.	239(4.09)	33-1554-80
19-Nor-9β,10α-pregn-4-ene-3,20-dione, 17α-acetoxy-9-methyl-	n.s.g.	241(4.20)	119-0127-80
A-Norpregn-4-ene-3,20-dione, 18-(acetoxymethyl)-	MeOH	240(4.25)	24-1106-80
$C_{23}H_{32}O_5$			
Dodecanoic acid, (7-methoxy-2-oxo-2H-1-benzopyran-4-yl)methyl ester	EtOH	323(4.13)	95-0744-80
D-Homo-C,18-dinorandrosta-5,13-dien-3-one, 17-acetoxy-17a-hydroxy-17a-methyl-, cyclic 3-(1,2-ethanediyl acetal)	EtOH	205(3.78)	18-0243-80
19-Norpregn-4-ene-3,20-dione, 21-acetoxy-18-(hydroxymethyl)-, 18a,20-hemiketal	MeOH	241(4.22)	24-1106-80
2-Oxabicyclo[2.2.1]heptane-1-carboxylic acid, 4,7,7-trimethyl-3-oxo-, 2,4,4-trimethyl-3-(3-oxo-1-butenyl)-2-cyclohexen-1-yl ester	EtOH	216(3.96),275(3.91)	33-0010-80
Praecansone A, octahydro-	n.s.g.	256(4.05)	102-0707-80
$C_{23}H_{32}O_6$			
Emblide	EtOH	220(3.94),284(4.19)	78-1307-80
Phenol, 4-[2,3-dimethyl-4-(3,4,5-trimethoxyphenyl)butyl]-2,6-dimethoxy-, [R-(R*,R*)]-	EtOH	228s(4.08),273(3.15)	12-1823-80
$C_{23}H_{32}O_7$			
1,5-Cyclo-1,10-secopregn-3-ene-2,20-dione, 21-acetoxy-10,11,17-trihydroxy-, (5α,10α,11β)-	EtOH	228(4.00)	44-2334-80
B(9a)-Homo-C,19-dinorpregn-3(5)-ene-2,20-dione, 21-acetoxy-9a,11,17-trihydroxy-9a-methyl-, (9aα,10α,11β)-	EtOH	235(4.15)	44-2334-80
$C_{23}H_{32}O_9$			
Melnerin B, 9α-acetoxy-	EtOH	213(4.53)	44-4028-80
$C_{23}H_{33}NO$			
5-Acephenanthrylenecarbonitrile, 1,2,3,3a,4,7,8,9,10,10a,10b,10c-dodecahydro-8-methoxy-3,7,7,10a,10c-pentamethyl-	n.s.g.	279(4.30)	33-1554-80
$C_{23}H_{33}NO_2$			
1-Phenanthrenepropanenitrile, 1,2,3,4-4a,4b,5,6,7,8,10,10a-dodecahydro-7-methoxy-4b,8,8,10a-tetramethyl-2-methylene-10-oxo-, [1R-(1α,4aα,4bβ-7α,10aβ)]-	n.s.g.	245(4.08)	33-1554-80
$C_{23}H_{33}NO_4$			
Acetic acid, [[(3-oxopregn-4-en-20-ylidene)amino]oxy]-	buffer	249(4.20)	65-0156-80
Androst-5-ene-7,17-dione, 3β-acetoxy-4,4-dimethyl-, 17-oxime	n.s.g.	240(4.09)	33-1554-80
Daphgraciline	MeOH	298(3.95)	138-0393-80

Compound	Solvent	$\lambda_{max}(\log \epsilon)$	Ref.
$C_{23}H_{33}NO_5$			
Daphgraciline, hydroxy-	MeOH	294(3.85)	138-0393-80
$C_{23}H_{33}NO_5S$			
Methylated latrunculin A	MeOH	218(4.41),269s(--)	88-3629-80
$C_{23}H_{33}N_3O_4$			
3,5-Pyridinedicarboxylic acid, 2,6-bis-[2-(dimethylamino)ethyl]-1,4-dihydro-4-phenyl-, dimethyl ester, dihydrochloride	EtOH	242(4.28),356(3.84)	94-3163-80
$C_{23}H_{34}NO_9P$			
Phosphonic acid, [[bis(2,4,6-trimethoxyphenyl)amino]methyl]-, diethyl ester	MeCN	222(4.34),280(4.04)	152-0389-80
$C_{23}H_{34}N_2O$			
3(2H)-Cyclopentadecapyrazolone, 1,4,5-6,7,8,9,10,11,12,13,14,15,16-tetradecahydro-1-methyl-2-phenyl-	CHCl₃	245(3.84),280(3.70)	103-0711-80
$C_{23}H_{34}N_2O_3$			
Acetic acid, [(3β)-3-acetoxyandrost-5-en-17-ylidene]hydrazide	MeOH dioxan	231(3.87) 235(4.09)	39-1356-80C 39-1356-80C
$C_{23}H_{34}N_6$			
Pyrimidine, 4-(3,5-dimethyl-1H-pyrazol-1-yl)-5-ethyl-2-(4-ethyl-3,5-dipropyl-1H-pyrazol-1-yl)-6-methyl-	EtOH	272(4.42)	103-1279-80
$C_{23}H_{34}O_2$			
Naphthalene, 1-[(2,5-dimethoxyphenyl)-methyl]-1,2,3,4,5,6,7,8-octahydro-1,2,5,5-tetramethyl-, (1R-trans)-	MeOH	222(3.74),301(3.65)	44-1435-80
2,4,6,8-Nonatetraenoic acid, 9-(2-ethyl-6,6-dimethyl-1-cyclohexen-1-yl)-3,7-dimethyl-, ethyl ester, (all-E)-	EtOH	242(3.93),351(4.53)	87-1013-80
$C_{23}H_{34}O_3$			
Phenol, 2,4-dimethoxy-6-[3-methyl-5-(1,2,6-trimethyl-2-cyclohexen-1-yl)-2-pentenyl]-	MeOH MeOH-base	212(4.18),293(3.46) 309(3.48)	44-1435-80 44-1435-80
$C_{23}H_{34}O_4$			
21-Norchol-22-en-24-oic acid, 2,14,20-trihydroxy-, γ-lactone, (3β,5β,14β-20S)-	MeOH	214(3.94)	48-1003-80
Uzarigenin	MeOH	217(4.29)	94-0401-80
$C_{23}H_{34}O_7$			
Nodusmicin	n.s.g.	end absorption	88-3659-80
$C_{23}H_{34}O_8$			
Homodidrovaltrate	n.s.g.	206(3)	100-0649-80
$C_{23}H_{34}O_9$			
2(3H)-Benzofuranone, 5-[4-[(6-O-acetyl-β-D-glucopyranosyl)oxy]-1-methylbutyl]-3a,4,7,7a-tetrahydro-6-methyl-3-methylene-, [3aR-[3aα,5(S*),7aα]]-	MeOH	211(3.95)	44-3163-80

Compound	Solvent	$\lambda_{max}(\log \epsilon)$	Ref.
$C_{23}H_{34}O_{11}$			
2H-Cyclopenta[b]furan-2-one, 4-[5-[(6-O-acetyl-β-D-glucopyranosyl)oxy]-2-methyl-1-oxopentyl]hexahydro-5-hydroxy-5-methyl-3-methylene-	n.s.g.	210(3.88)	44-3163-80
2(3H)-Furanone, 4-[6-[(6-O-acetyl-β-D-glucopyranosyl)oxy]-3-methyl-2-oxohexyl]dihydro-3-methylene-5-(2-oxopropyl)-	n.s.g.	210(3.90)	44-3163-80
$C_{23}H_{34}O_{15}$			
Genipin 1-O-β-gentiobioside	EtOH	238(4.11)	100-0649-80
$C_{23}H_{35}IN_2O_4$			
Pregn-5-en-3-ol, 18-iodo-20-(nitroamino)-, acetate, (3β,20R)-	EtOH	224(4.01)	77-0958-80
$C_{23}H_{36}N_2O_3$			
Acetic acid, [(3α,5α)-3-acetoxyandrostan-17-ylidene]hydrazide	MeOH	231(3.79)	39-1356-80C
2,5-Cyclohexadien-1-one, 2,6-bis(1,1-dimethylethyl)-4-(di-4-morpholinylmethylene)-	isooctane	425(4.49)	73-2675-80
$C_{23}H_{38}OSi_2$			
Silane, [6-(2-ethenylphenyl)-6-[(triethylsilyl)oxy]-1,3-hexadienyl]trimethyl-, (E,E)-	hexane	207(4.39),238(4.60)	33-0555-80
$C_{23}H_{39}NO_4$			
1-Pyrrolidineheptanoic acid, 2-oxo-5-(3-oxo-1-undecenyl)-, methyl ester, [R-(E)]-	MeOH	215(4.12)	94-1449-80
$C_{23}H_{40}N_2O_2$			
Benzenamine, 3,5-dimethyl-2-nitro-N-pentadecyl-	EtOH	242(3.89),295(3.23), 420(3.23)	103-0962-80
Benzenamine, 3,5-dimethyl-4-nitro-N-pentadecyl-	EtOH	250(3.20),310(2.68), 400(3.18)	103-0962-80
$C_{23}H_{40}O_2$			
4H-Pyran-4-one, 3,5-dibutyl-2,6-dipentyl-	EtOH	258(3.89)	44-3268-80
$C_{23}H_{44}N_2O_2$			
2-Pentadecanone, 1-(2,5-dihydro-1,2,2,5,5-pentamethyl-1H-imidazol-4-yl)-, N-oxide	EtOH	239(3.56),317(3.84)	70-0956-80

Compound	Solvent	$\lambda_{max}(\log \epsilon)$	Ref.
$C_{24}H_8O_6$ Perylo[3,4-cd:9,10-c'd']dipyran-1,3,8-10-tetrone	1% KOH	265(4.48),440(4.53), 465(4.61)	104-0762-80
$C_{24}H_{10}N_2O_{12}$ 3,4,9,10-Perylenetetracarboxylic acid, 1,7-dinitro-	1% KOH	265(4.36),345(4.05), 500(4.11)	104-0762-80
$C_{24}H_{12}N_2O_8$ 1H-Phenanthro[1,10,9,8-cdefg]carbazole-3,4,9,10-tetracarboxylic acid, 6-amino-	1% KOH	250(4.32),300(4.24), 427(3.77),500(4.01)	104-0762-80
$C_{24}H_{12}N_8O$ 9,10-Oxiranoanthracene-2,2,3,3,6,6,7,7-(1H,4H)-octacarbonitrile, 5,8,9,10-tetrahydro-, endo	EtOH	210(3.60)	78-0149-80
$C_{24}H_{12}O_2$ Naphtho[2,3-b]fluoranthene-8,13-dione	CHCl₃	241(4.30),254s(4.28), 286s(4.69),330s(3.95), 350s(3.67),374(3.68), 418(3.76)	44-1424-80
$C_{24}H_{12}O_3$ Anthra[1,2,3-kl]xanthene-10,15-dione	CHCl₃	242(4.34),305s(4.34), 319s(4.45),327(4.48), 373(3.78),391(3.99), 530(3.82)	4-0695-80
$C_{24}H_{13}ClO_3$ 5,11-Naphthacenedione, 6-chloro-12-phenoxy-	toluene	444(4.20),472(4.21)	104-1651-80
5,12-Naphthacenedione, 6-chloro-11-phenoxy-	toluene	398(3.74)	104-1651-80
$C_{24}H_{13}NO_4$ Benzo[f]pyrido[1,2-a]indole-6,11-dione, 12-(1,3-dihydro-3-oxo-1-isobenzofuranyl)-	CHCl₃	259(4.58),286(4.22), 328(4.07),493(3.78)	2-0836-80
$C_{24}H_{13}NO_5$ Benzoic acid, [(6,11-dihydro-6,11-dioxobenzo[f]pyrido[1,2-a]indol-12-yl)carbonyl]-	EtOH	206(4.42),263(4.45), 330(3.99),358(3.86), 481(3.74)	2-0836-80
5,11-Naphthacenedione, 6-nitro-12-phenoxy-	toluene	453(4.15),479(4.13)	104-1651-80
5,12-Naphthacenedione, 6-nitro-11-phenoxy-	toluene	394(3.70)	104-1651-80
$C_{24}H_{14}$ Benz[5,6]indeno[2,1-a]phenalene (10λ,9ε)	benzene	283(4.65),306(4.38), 333(3.96),360(4.10), 381(4.05),400(4.00), 450(4.18),485(4.18), 518(3.90),558(?)	39-2812-80C
$C_{24}H_{14}BrClN_4O_3$ 1H-Isoindole-1,3(2H)-dione, 2-[[4-(2-benzoyl-4-chlorophenyl)-5-bromo-4H-1,2,4-triazol-3-yl]methyl]-	EtOH	218(4.84),237s(4.24), 257(4.16),287(3.73)	4-0575-80

Compound	Solvent	$\lambda_{max}(\log \epsilon)$	Ref.
$C_{24}H_{14}Cl_4N_2O_6$ 1,4-Benzodioxin-2-carboxamide, N-benz- oyl-2-(benzoylmethylamino)-5,6,7,8- tetrachloro-2,3-dihydro-3-oxo-	MeCN	211(4.78),225s(4.69), 295s(3.15)	5-1836-80
$C_{24}H_{14}N_2O_8$ 3,4,9,10-Perylenetetracarboxylic acid, 1,7-diamino-	1% KOH	275(4.38),485(4.10)	104-0762-80
$C_{24}H_{14}O_2$ 1H-Indene-1,3(2H)-dione, 2-(9-anthra- cenylmethylene)-	$CHCl_3$	494(4.03)	18-1703-80
$C_{24}H_{14}O_3$ Benz[a]anthracene-7,12-dione, 11-hydr- oxy-5-phenyl-	$CHCl_3$	298(4.41),379(3.49), 441(3.78),460(3.77)	138-0827-80
$C_{24}H_{14}O_4$ 5,12-Naphthacenedione, 6-hydroxy- 11-phenoxy-	toluene	443(4.00)	104-1651-80
$C_{24}H_{15}ClN_4O_3$ 1H-Isoindole-1,3(2H)-dione, 2-[[4-(2- benzoyl-4-chlorophenyl)-4H-1,2,4-	EtOH	218(4.83),238s(4.24), 256(4.17),285(3.72)	4-0575-80
$C_{24}H_{15}NO_2$ Benz[cd]indol-5-ol, 2-phenyl-, benzoate	CH_2Cl_2	253(4.27),267(4.24), 467(4.42),540(3.39)	5-0971-80
$C_{24}H_{15}NO_3$ 5,11-Naphthacenedione, 6-amino-12-phen- oxy-	toluene	474(4.05),503(4.24), 538(4.17)	104-1651-80
5,12-Naphthacenedione, 6-amino-11-phen- oxy-	toluene	389(3.55),468(3.99)	104-1651-80
$C_{24}H_{15}N_3O_3$ 3-Furancarbonitrile, 2-[[(4-nitrophen- yl)methylene]amino]-4,5-diphenyl-	MeOH	430(4.03)	73-1581-80
$C_{24}H_{15}N_5O_7$ 1,2,4-Oxadiazole, 5-[5-(4-methoxyphen- yl)-3-(4-nitrophenyl)isoxazol-4-yl]- 3-(4-nitrophenyl)-	EtOH	278(4.40)	39-1635-80C
$C_{24}H_{16}$ Naphtho[2,3-k]fluoranthene, 6b,7-di- hydro-	EtOH	227(4.40),256(4.32), 265(4.29),287(4.17), 300(4.02),319(4.25), 333(4.51),359(4.12), 377(4.09),412(3.44), 437(3.44)	39-2812-80C
$C_{24}H_{16}ClNO_3$ 2H,5H-Pyrano[3,2-c][1]benzopyran-2-one, 3-chloro-4-(diphenylamino)-	EtOH	247s(4.13),277(4.26), 378(4.30)	4-0061-80
$C_{24}H_{16}F_6N_4O_2Pd$ Palladium, (1,1,1,5,5,5-hexafluoro- 2,4-pentanedionato-O,O')[1,1'-(phen- ylmethylene)bis[2-phenyldiazonato]]-	C_6H_{12}	253(4.62),312(4.32), 605(3.93)	125-2052-80

Compound	Solvent	$\lambda_{max}(\log \epsilon)$	Ref.
(1-)-N^2,N$^{2'}$]-, (SP-4-2)- (cont.)			125-2052-80
$C_{24}H_{16}I_2N_4O_2$ [1,1'-Biphenyl]-4,4'-dicarboxamide, 2,2'-diiodo-N,N'-di-2-pyridinyl-	EtOH	218(4.56)	126-0333-80
$C_{24}H_{16}NOS$ Pyrylium, 2-(2-benzothiazolyl)-4,6-diphenyl-, perchlorate	$C_2H_4Cl_2$	312(4.10),392(4.25), 460(4.13)	150-4041-80
$C_{24}H_{16}N_2O$ 3-Furancarbonitrile, 4,5-diphenyl-2-[(phenylmethylene)amino]-	MeOH	437(3.47)	73-1581-80
Naphtho[1,2-d]oxazole, 2-[4-[2-(3-pyridinyl)ethenyl]phenyl]-	DMF	318(4.40),367(4.74)	33-1311-80
$C_{24}H_{16}N_2O_2$ Benzoxazole, 2,2'-(1,4-phenylenedi-2,1-ethenediyl)bis-	CHCl$_3$	366(4.72),382(4.78), 401s(4.49)	103-0464-80
3-Furancarbonitrile, 2-[[(2-hydroxyphenyl)methylene]amino]-4,5-diphenyl-	MeOH	458(4.00)	73-1581-80
Methanone, (2-hydroxyphenyl)(3-phenylimidazo[2,1-a]isoquinolin-2-yl)-	EtOH	252(4.73),352(3.98)	39-0354-80C
	EtOH-acid	250(4.61),305(3.98)	39-0354-80C
Methanone, (2-hydroxyphenyl)(3-phenylimidazo[1,2-a]quinolin-2-yl)-	EtOH	252(4.72),351(3.99)	39-0354-80C
	EtOH-acid	250(4.60),302(3.97)	39-0354-80C
$C_{24}H_{16}N_2O_3$ Benzamide, 2-(6,11-dihydro-6,11-dioxobenzo[f]pyrido[1,2-a]indol-12-yl)-N-methyl-	EtOH	205(4.38),260(4.30), 307(3.43),333(3.67), 508(3.57)	2-0836-80
$C_{24}H_{16}N_2S_2$ Benzothiazole, 2,2'-(1,4-phenylenedi-2,1-ethenediyl)bis-	CHCl$_3$	373(4.62),391(4.61), 409s(4.37)	103-0464-80
$C_{24}H_{16}O_2S$ Anthra[2,1-b]thiophene-6,11-dione, 2-ethyl-4-phenyl-	CHCl$_3$	252(4.48),304(4.62), 390s(3.72),421(3.76)	4-0695-80
1H-Phenalen-1-one, 4-methoxy-3-(1-naphthalenylthio)-	n.s.g.	390(4.15)	44-4611-80
$C_{24}H_{16}S$ Dibenzo[f,l]thiacycloheptadecin, 18,19,20,21-tetradehydro-, (Z,Z,E,E)-	THF	226(4.58),272(4.62), 286(4.67),332(4.65), 348(4.60),375s(4.21), 404s(3.99)	18-1127-80
$C_{24}H_{17}ClN_2O_4$ 4,8-Iminocyclohepta[c]pyrrole-1,3,5(2H)-trione, 9-[3-(4-chlorophenyl)-3-oxo-1-propenyl]-3a,4,8,8a-tetrahydro-2-phenyl-, [3aα,4β,8β,8aα,9(E)]-	CHCl$_3$	265(3.49),319(3.66)	39-0362-80C
$C_{24}H_{17}Cl_2NO_3$ 2H,5H-Pyrano[3,2-c][1]benzopyran-2-one, 3,3-dichloro-4-(diphenylamino)-3,4-dihydro-	EtOH	237(4.34),278(4.08), 320s(3.69)	4-0061-80
$C_{24}H_{17}F_3O_2$ 9(10H)-Anthracenone, 10-[(4-methylphenyl)(2,2,2-trifluoroethoxy)methylene]-	EtOH	236(4.62),288(4.30), 373(4.04)	35-3837-80

Compound	Solvent	$\lambda_{max}(\log \epsilon)$	Ref.
$C_{24}H_{17}F_3O_3$			
9(10H)-Anthracenone, 10-[(2-methoxy-phenyl)(2,2,2-trifluoroethoxy)-methylene]-	EtOH	231(4.61),287(4.32), 363(3.99)	35-3837-80
9(10H)-Anthracenone, 10-[(4-methoxy-phenyl)(2,2,2-trifluoroethoxy)-methylene]-	EtOH	240(4.60),290(4.25), 372(4.15)	35-3837-80
$C_{24}H_{17}NO_3$			
Ethanone, 1-phenyl-2-(5-phenyl-2-furan-yl)-2-(phenylimino)-, N-oxide	MeOH	349(4.50),366(4.83)	73-3546-80
1H-Pyrrole-2,5-dione, 1-(2-oxo-2-phen-ylethyl)-3,4-diphenyl-	60% dioxan	365(3.64)	40-0837-80
$C_{24}H_{17}NO_3S$			
1,4-Naphthalenedione, 2-[(2-oxo-2-phen-ylethyl)thio]-3-(phenylamino)-	$CHCl_3$	253(4.24),285(4.33), 351(3.55),506(3.48)	39-2923-80C
$C_{24}H_{17}NO_4$			
3-Furancarboxamide, 4-benzoyl-2,5(or 4,5)-dihydro-5-oxo-N,2-diphenyl-	MeOH	294(4.15),397(4.57)	39-2670-80C
Methanone, [7-(benzoyloxy)-5-methoxy-8-isoquinolinyl]phenyl-	EtOH	240(4.28),299(3.53), 335(3.49)	39-0072-80C
	EtOH-HCl	245(4.29),310(2.49), 361(3.50)	39-0072-80C
1H-Pyrrole-2,3-dione, 4-benzoyl-1-(4-methoxyphenyl)-5-phenyl-	MeCN	238(4.30),278(4.18), 340s(3.64),426(3.51), 490s(3.18)	5-1801-80
$C_{24}H_{17}N_2O$			
Pyrylium, 2-(1H-benzimidazol-2-yl)-4,6-diphenyl-, perchlorate	$C_2H_4Cl_2$	337(4.32),382(4.51), 493(4.40)	150-4041-80
$C_{24}H_{17}N_3O$			
Benzo[b][1,8]naphthyridin-5(1H)-one, 2-amino-3,4-diphenyl-	EtOH	247(4.70),285(4.23), 325(3.85),360(3.80), 376(3.83)	142-0461-80
$C_{24}H_{17}N_3O_7$			
2H-Pyran, 2-methyl-2,4,6-tris(4-nitro-phenyl)-	CH_2Cl_2	274(4.40),370(4.15)	118-0041-80
$C_{24}H_{18}$			
7,14-Ethanodibenz[a,h]anthracene, 7,14-dihydro-, (7R)-	EtOH	232(4.99),284(4.05)	35-0506-80
1,1'-Spirobi[2H-indene], 3-methyl-3'-phenyl-	EtOH	245(4.53)	104-1298-80
$C_{24}H_{18}ClNO_2$			
2H-Pyran-2-one, 3-chloro-4-(diphenyl-amino)-5-methyl-6-phenyl-	EtOH	241(4.18),275(4.29), 336(4.14)	4-1201-80
$C_{24}H_{18}Fe_2N_2$			
Ferrocene, 1,1''-(dicyanoethenylidene)-bis-	neutral	<u>590(3.5)</u>	125-1125-80
	cation	<u>605(3.3)</u>	125-1125-80
	dication	<u>630(3.2)</u>	125-1125-80
$C_{24}H_{18}N$			
Pyrido[1,2-f]phenanthridinium, 4-meth-yl-2-phenyl-, perchlorate	EtOH	213(4.28),230(4.36), 259(4.57),281(4.57),	39-1879-80C

Compound	Solvent	$\lambda_{max}(\log \epsilon)$	Ref.
(cont.)		332(4.39),360(4.27), 396(4.25)	39-1879-80C
$C_{24}H_{18}NO$			
Acridinium, 9-(1-hydroxy-2-naphthalen-yl)-10-methyl-, chloride	EtOH	262(5.04),362(4.33), 429(3.84)	104-0192-80
iodide	EtOH	262(5.11),361(4.47), 423(3.87)	104-0192-80
$C_{24}H_{18}N_2$			
Phenanthro[4,5-abc]phenazine, 9,14-di-hydro-9,14-dimethyl-	benzene	314(4.53),328(4.52), 398(3.75)	46-1841-80
1H-Pyrrole-3-carbonitrile, 2,4-diphen-yl-1-(phenylmethyl)-	CCl₄	286(4.18)	22-0552-80
Quinoline, 2,2'-(1,3,5-hexatriene-1,6-diyl)bis-	CH_2Cl_2	296(4.30),387(4.87)	5-0291-80
Quinoline, 4,4'-(1,3,5-hexatriene-1,6-diyl)bis-	CH_2Cl_2	218(4.61),239(4.43), 278(4.06),381(4.70)	5-0291-80
$C_{24}H_{18}N_2O_3$			
Methanone, [5-(benzoyloxy)-3-methyl-1-phenyl-1H-pyrazol-4-yl]phenyl-	MeOH	235(4.53),275(4.33)	64-1019-80B
$C_{24}H_{18}N_4$			
1H-Pyrazole, 3,3'-(1,4-phenylene)bis-[1-phenyl-	dioxan	318(4.78)	103-0066-80
3-Pyridinecarbonitrile, 2-amino-1,6-di-hydro-6-imino-1,4,5-triphenyl-	EtOH	276(4.21),352(4.00)	142-0461-80
3-Pyridinecarbonitrile, 6-amino-4,5-di-phenyl-2-(phenylamino)-	EtOH	247(4.34),300(4.34), 337s(4.08)	142-0461-80
5-Pyrimidinecarbonitrile, 4-phenyl-6-(phenylamino)-2-(phenylmethyl)-	EtOH	278(4.18)	142-0461-80
$C_{24}H_{18}N_4O$			
2H-Naphtho[1,2-d]triazole, 2-[3-meth-oxy-4-[2-(3-pyridinyl)ethenyl]phenyl]-	DMF	293(4.29),372(4.71)	33-1311-80
$C_{24}H_{18}N_6O_6$			
4,5-Imidazolidinedione, 1,3-bis(4-meth-ylphenyl)-2-[nitro[(4-nitrophenyl)-azo]methylene]-	MeCN	279(4.50),407(3.96)	48-0087-80
2,8-Imino-3,7-methano-4-benzazecine-1,14(2H)-dione, 3,4,7,8,8a,9-hexa-hydro-4,13-bis(5-nitro-2-pyridinyl)-, (2α,3β,7β,8α,8aβ)-	EtOH	215s(3.13),228(4.16), 247s(4.04),366(4.34)	39-0331-80C
$C_{24}H_{18}N_6O_7$			
Benzenecarboximidamide, N-hydroxy-N'-[1-(4-methoxyphenyl)-2-[3-(4-nitro-phenyl)-1,2,4-oxadiazol-5-yl]ethen-yl]-4-nitro-	EtOH	285(4.51),360(4.57)	39-1635-80C
$C_{24}H_{18}N_6O_8$			
4,5-Imidazolidinedione, 1,3-bis(4-meth-oxyphenyl)-2-[nitro[(4-nitrophenyl)-azo]methylene]-	MeCN	228(4.47),277(4.06), 406(4.50)	48-00871-80
$C_{24}H_{18}N_8$			
5,5'-Bi-1H-pyrazole, 1,1'-bis[4-(1H-pyrazol-1-yl)phenyl]-	EtOH	213(4.44),273(4.67)	24-2749-80
1H-Pyrazole, 1,1',1'',1'''-[1,1'-biphen-	EtOH	215(4.42),258(4.48),	24-2749-80

Compound	Solvent	$\lambda_{max}(\log \epsilon)$	Ref.
yl]-2,2',5,5'-tetrayltetrakis- (cont.)		273(4.57)	24-2749-80
$C_{24}H_{18}O$ Naphthalene, 2-[(1,2-diphenylethenyl)-oxy]-	hexane	290(4.51)	118-0847-80
$C_{24}H_{18}OSn$ 10H-Phenoxastannin, 10,10-diphenyl-	pentane	250(4.05),285(3.78), 295(3.67)	65-1104-80
$C_{24}H_{18}O_2$ 2,4-Cyclopentadien-1-one, 3-methoxy-2,4,5-triphenyl-	MeCN	260(4.38),305s(--), 469(2.88)	24-0408-80
4-Cyclopentene-1,3-dione, 2-(4-methylphenyl)-4,5-diphenyl-	MeCN	241(4.39),327(3.96)	24-0408-80
4-Cyclopentene-1,3-dione, 4-(4-methylphenyl)-2,5-diphenyl-	MeCN	232(4.29),329(3.97)	24-0408-80
$C_{24}H_{18}O_2S_2$ 1,4-Naphthalenedione, 2,3-bis[(phenylmethyl)thio]-	EtOH	252(4.38),271s(4.27), 352s(3.61),460(3.54)	150-0139-80
$C_{24}H_{18}O_3$ 5H-Dibenzo[b,g]fluorene-5,8,13-trione, 7,7a-dihydro-6,7,7a-trimethyl-	EtOH	236(4.16),262(3.90), 288(3.90),333(3.92), 350(3.92),393(4.08)	39-1994-80C
Methanone, (10-acetoxy-9-anthracenyl)-(4-methylphenyl)-	n.s.g.	254(4.94),336(3.34), 352(3.72),371(3.94), 391(3.94)	35-3837-80
$C_{24}H_{18}O_4$ Methanone, (10-acetoxy-9-anthracenyl)-(2-methoxyphenyl)-	EtOH	256(5.03),325s(3.75), 335(3.78),354(3.83), 372(3.97),393(3.95)	35-3837-80
1,4-Naphthalenedione, 6,7-dibenzoyl-5,6,7,8-tetrahydro-	CH_2Cl_2	259(4.05),330(--)	23-1161-80
$C_{24}H_{18}O_6$ [2,2'-Binaphthalene]-1,1',4,4'-tetrone, 5,5'-dimethoxy-7,7'-dimethyl-	$CHCl_3$	248(4.39),274s(4.22), 412(3.94)	5-1321-80
[2,2'-Binaphthalene]-1,1',4,4'-tetrone, 5,8'-dimethoxy-6',7-dimethyl-	$CHCl_3$	248(4.40),273s(4.26), 330(3.45),411(3.89)	5-1321-80
[2,2'-Binaphthalene]-1,1',4,4'-tetrone, 8,8'-dimethoxy-6,6'-dimethyl-	$CHCl_3$	251(4.41),260s(4.39), 323(3.62),410(3.88)	5-1321-80
$C_{24}H_{18}O_7$ 6H,11H-[2]Benzopyrano[4,3-c][1]benzopyran-6-one, 7,10-dihydroxy-8-methoxy-11-(4-methoxyphenyl)-	EtOH	298(4.17),348(4.35)	12-0137-80
$C_{24}H_{18}O_9$ Benzoic acid, 5-[(3-carboxy-4-hydroxyphenyl)(3-carboxy-5-methyl-4-oxo-2,5-cyclohexadien-1-ylidene)methyl]-2-hydroxy-3-methyl-	n.s.g.	535(2.00)	147-0409-80A
$C_{24}H_{18}S$ Benzene, 1,1'-(thiodi-1,3-butadiene-4,1-diyl)bis[2-ethynyl-, (E,E,E,Z)-	THF	233(4.44),258s(4.31), 267(4.33),283(4.29), 365(4.49)	18-1127-80

Compound	Solvent	$\lambda_{max}(\log \epsilon)$	Ref.
$C_{24}H_{18}S_3$ [1,2]Dithiolo[1,5-b][1,2]dithiole-7-S^{IV}, 3-methyl-2,4,5-triphenyl-	dioxan	228s(4.52),276(4.37), 330(4.01),481(4.56), 587(2.82)	104-1775-80
1-Propanethione, 2-(4,5-diphenyl-1,3-dithiol-2-ylidene)-1-phenyl-	dioxan	250(4.68),273(4.67), 504(4.19)	104-0775-80
$C_{24}H_{19}BN_2O$ Boron, diphenyl[2-[(2-pyridinylimino)-methyl]phenolato]-, (T-4)-	$CHCl_3$	270(4.09),305(4.13), 350(4.08)	49-0863-80
Boron, diphenyl[2-[(3-pyridinylimino)-methyl]phenolato]-, (T-4)-	$CHCl_3$	275(4.18),340(4.00)	49-0863-80
$C_{24}H_{19}BrN_2O_3$ 2H-Anthra[1,2-d][1,3]oxazine-7,12-di-one, 6-bromo-2-[4-(dimethylamino)-phenyl]-1,4-dihydro-	EtOH	480(3.56)	18-3007-80 +146-0513-80
4(3H)-Quinazolinone, 6-bromo-2-[2-(4-methoxyphenyl)ethenyl]-3-(phenyl-methoxy)-	n.s.g.	287(4.43),350(4.61)	18-2389-80
$C_{24}H_{19}ClN_2O_3$ 2H-Anthra[1,2-d][1,3]oxazine-7,12-di-one, 6-[(2-chlorophenyl)amino]-1,4-dihydro-2,2-dimethyl-	EtOH	578(3.96)	18-3007-80 +146-0513-80
$C_{24}H_{19}ClN_2O_4$ Benzoic acid, 2-[[5-(4-chlorophenyl)-4,5-dihydro-3-(4-methoxyphenyl)-1H-pyrazol-1-yl]carbonyl]-	MeOH	301(3.72)	2-0364-80
$C_{24}H_{19}ClN_3$ Pyridinium, 1-[[(4-chlorophenyl)azo]-diphenylmethyl]-, bromide	CH_2Cl_2	289(4.21),402(2.54)	118-0694-80
$C_{24}H_{19}ClO_3$ 1,4-Anthracenedione, 2-chloro-10-meth-oxy-9-(2,4,6-trimethylphenyl)-	MeOH	238(4.34),293(3.80), 318(3.71),424(3.74)	104-0159-80
$C_{24}H_{19}NO$ 1-Naphthalenol, 2-(9,10-dihydro-10-methyl-9-acridinyl)-	EtOH	291(4.28)	104-0192-80
$C_{24}H_{19}NO_2$ 1H-Pyrrole-2,5-dione, 1-(2,6-dimethyl-phenyl)-3,4-diphenyl-	MeCN	360.5(3.50)	40-0837-80
1H-Pyrrole-2,5-dione, 3,4-diphenyl-1-(1-phenylethyl)-	60% dioxan	368(3.63)	40-0837-80
$C_{24}H_{19}NO_3$ Methanone, phenyl(2,3,3a,6a-tetrahydro-2,5-diphenylfuro[2,3-d]isoxazol-3-yl)-, (3α,3aα,6aα)-	MeOH	246(4.30)	73-3546-80
$C_{24}H_{19}NO_4$ 8H-Naphtho[2,3-a]phenoxazine-8,13(14H)-dione, 2-(1,1-dimethylethyl)-7-hy-droxy-	THF	267(4.66),607(4.19), 670(4.09)	104-1884-80
$C_{24}H_{19}NO_5S$ Benzoic acid, 2-[(1-acetoxy-4-hydroxy-	$CHCl_3$	253(4.53),285(3.97),	39-1070-80C

Compound	Solvent	$\lambda_{max}(\log \epsilon)$	Ref.
pyrido[1,2-a]indol-10-yl)thioxomethyl]-, ethyl ester (cont.)		302(3.88),325(3.88), 368(3.86),475(4.15), 522(4.33)	39-1070-80C
$C_{24}H_{19}N_3$			
2-Naphthalenamine, 1-[(4-methylphenyl)-azo]-N-(phenylmethylene)-	MeOH	230s(4.40),242(4.57), 252s(4.38),306(4.13), 382(3.56),394(3.55), 402s(3.51),492(4.04)	44-3182-80
1H-Naphth[1,2-d]imidazol-1-amine, N-(4-methylphenyl)-2-phenyl-	MeOH	232(4.70),265(4.57), 282s(4.30),330s(4.03), 335(4.06)	44-3182-80
$C_{24}H_{19}N_3O$			
2-Naphthalenamine, N-[(4-methoxyphenyl)methylene]-1-(phenylazo)-	MeOH	240(4.60),256s(4.34), 305(4.18),360(3.54), 382(3.60),392(3.59), 492(4.02)	44-3182-80
1H-Naphth[1,2-d]imidazol-1-amine, 2-(4-methoxyphenyl)-N-phenyl-	MeOH	228(4.88),274(4.58), 292s(4.26),332s(4.08), 338(4.09)	44-3182-80
5-Pyrimidinamine, 2-methoxy-4,6-diphenyl-N-(phenylmethylene)-	EtOH	256(4.47),338(4.18)	103-0970-80
$C_{24}H_{19}N_3O_2$			
1H-Isoindole-1,3(2H)-dione, 2-[2-(2-amino-1-phenyl-1H-indol-3-yl)ethyl]-, monohydrochloride	EtOH	220(4.63),267(3.96)	103-0368-80
1H-Pyridazino[4,5-b]indol-1-one, 3-benzoyl-2,3,4,5-tetrahydro-5-methyl-4-phenyl-	EtOH	211(4.62),248(4.35), 290(4.33),318(4.30)	4-0249-80
$C_{24}H_{19}N_3O_3$			
6H-Anthra[1,9-cd]isoxazol-6-one, 3-morpholino-5-(phenylamino)-	dioxan	256(4.50),488(4.33), 520(4.42)	103-0704-80
$C_{24}H_{19}N_3O_3S$			
4-Isoquinolinecarbonitrile, 1,2-dihydro-2-[(4-methylphenyl)sulfonyl]-1-oxo-3-[(phenylmethyl)amino]-	EtOH	317(4.42)	95-0456-80
$C_{24}H_{19}N_3O_4$			
9,10-Anthracenedione, 1-azido-2-[4-(1,1-dimethylethyl)phenoxy]-4-hydroxy-	THF	250(4.58),445(3.79)	104-1884-80
$C_{24}H_{19}N_3O_6$			
Benzoic acid, 2-[[4,5-dihydro-3-(4-methoxyphenyl)-5-(4-nitrophenyl)-1H-pyrazol-1-yl]carbonyl]-	MeOH	295(4.04)	2-0364-80
$C_{24}H_{19}N_3O_8$			
2-Hexen-1-one, 5-hydroxy-1,3,5-tris(4-nitrophenyl)-	CHCl₃	275(4.49)	118-0041-80
$C_{24}H_{19}OS_2$			
Sulfonium, diphenyl[4-(phenylsulfinyl)-phenyl]-, hexafluoroarsenate	n.s.g.	230(4.35),300(4.29)	47-2697-80
$C_{24}H_{19}O_2S_2$			
Sulfonium, diphenyl[4-(phenylsulfonyl)-phenyl]-, hexafluoroarsenate	n.s.g.	243(4.40)	47-2697-80

Compound	Solvent	$\lambda_{max}(\log \epsilon)$	Ref.
$C_{24}H_{19}S_2$			
Sulfonium, diphenyl[2-(phenylthio)phenyl]-, hexafluoroarsenate	n.s.g.	230(4.40)	47-2697-80
Sulfonium, diphenyl[3-(phenylthio)phenyl]-, hexafluoroarsenate	n.s.g.	230(4.39)	47-2697-80
Sulfonium, diphenyl[4-(phenylthio)phenyl]-, hexafluoroarsenate	n.s.g.	225(4.37),300(4.29)	47-2697-80
hexafluorophosphate	n.s.g.	227(4.35),300(4.26)	47-2697-80
$C_{24}H_{20}$			
Benzene, 1,1',1''-[3-(2-propenyl)-1-cyclopropene-1,2,3-triyl]tris-	EtOH	228(4.46),316(4.43), 333(4.34)	35-2797-80
Benzo[a]cyclopropa[cd]pentalene, 1,2,2a,2b,6b,6c-hexahydro-2b,6b-diphenyl-	C_6H_{12}	230s(4.29),259(3.00), 262(3.01),264(3.01), 269(2.97),280(2.87)	23-0210-80
Tricyclo[2.2.0.0^{2,6}]hexane, 1,2,6-triphenyl-	EtOH	300(end abs.)	35-2797-80
$C_{24}H_{20}BNO$			
Boron, [1-[(methylimino)methyl]-2-naphthalenolato-N,O]diphenyl-, (T-4)-	benzene	335(3.92),397(3.68)	101-0001-80I
	DMSO	328(3.92),397(3.68)	101-0001-80I
$C_{24}H_{20}Br_3N$			
5H-9H-Quino[3,2,1-de]acridine, 3,7,11-tribromo-5,5,9,9-tetramethyl-	EtOH	221(4.35),239s(4.10), 289s(4.53),310(4.62)	24-0358-80
	CHCl$_3$	288s(4.32),310(4.45)	24-0358-80
$C_{24}H_{20}Cl_4O_6$			
Spiro[1,4-ethano-5,8-methanonaphthalen-10,4'-[3]oxatricyclo[4.2.1.0^{2,5}]non-[7]en]-11-one, 9,9'-diacetoxy-1,2,3,4-tetrachloro-1,4,4a,5,8,8a-hexahydro-	MeCN	245s(3.14),320(2.21)	78-0155-80
$C_{24}H_{20}N$			
7H-Indolo[1,2-a]quinolinium, 7,7-dimethyl-5-phenyl-, perchlorate	MeCN	246(4.45),252s(4.31), 257s(4.23),310s(3.88), 323s(4.00),352(4.11), 368(4.21)	88-4631-80
$C_{24}H_{20}NOS$			
Thiopyrylium, 2-(4-amino-2-methoxyphenyl)-4,6-diphenyl-, perchlorate	n.s.g.	356(4.17),566(4.16)	39-1345-80C
Thiopyrylium, 2-(4-amino-3-methoxyphenyl)-4,6-diphenyl-, perchlorate	n.s.g.	366(4.23),588(4.19)	39-1345-80C
$C_{24}H_{20}NS$			
Thiopyrylium, 2-(4-amino-2-methylphenyl)-4,6-diphenyl-, perchlorate	n.s.g.	356(4.17),566(4.16)	39-1345-80C
Thiopyrylium, 2-(4-amino-3-methylphenyl)-4,6-diphenyl-, perchlorate	n.s.g.	366(4.28),588(4.19)	39-1345-80C
Thiopyrylium, 2-[4-(methylamino)phenyl]-4,6-diphenyl-, perchlorate	n.s.g.	368(4.38),596(4.32)	39-1345-80C
$C_{24}H_{20}N_2O$			
6H-Cyclopent[3,4]azeto[1,2-b][1,2]-diazepin-6-one, 5b,8a-dihydro-5b,7-dimethyl-8,8a-diphenyl-	EtOH	293(4.04)	138-0621-80
2(1H)-Pyridinone, 3-[(4-methylphenyl)amino]-4,6-diphenyl-	CHCl$_3$	347(4.10)	39-2743-80C
2(1H)-Pyridinone, 5-[(4-methylphenyl)amino]-4,6-diphenyl-	CHCl$_3$	318(3.95)	39-2743-80C

Compound	Solvent	λ_{max}(log ϵ)	Ref.
$C_{24}H_{20}N_2O_2$			
Acetamide, N-[1,2-dihydro-1-methyl-2-[(2-oxo-1(2H)-naphthalenylidene)-ethylidene]-6-quinolinyl]-	EtOH	600(4.09)	104-0185-80
	benzene	612(--)	104-0185-80
	acetone	617(--)	104-0185-80
	$CHCl_3$	614(--)	104-0185-80
$C_{24}H_{20}N_2O_3$			
2H-Anthra[1,2-d][1,3]oxazine-7,12-dione, 1,4-dihydro-2,2-dimethyl-6-(phenylamino)-	EtOH	620(4.02)	18-3007-80 +146-0513-80
$C_{24}H_{20}N_2O_3S$			
[2,3'-Bipyridin]-5'-ol, 2'-methyl-6'-phenyl-, 4-methylbenzenesulfonate	MeOH	230(4.9),292(4.6)	103-0951-80
$C_{24}H_{20}N_2O_4$			
5H-Oxazolo[3,2-a]quinazoline-1,5(2H)-dione, 3a-ethoxy-3a,4-dihydro-2,4-diphenyl-	MeOH	205(4.55),224(4.70), 249s(--),256s(--), 265s(--),310(3.63), 323(3.48)	2-0638-80
$C_{24}H_{20}N_2O_8S$			
Imidazo[1,5-a]pyridine-5,6,7,8-tetracarboxylic acid, 1-phenyl-3-(1-propynylthio)-, tetramethyl ester	EtOH	255(4.14),297s(3.74), 373(3.59)	18-3308-80
$C_{24}H_{20}N_3$			
Pyridinium, 1-[diphenyl(phenylazo)methyl]-, bromide	CH_2Cl_2	274(4.17),393(2.47)	118-0694-80
$C_{24}H_{20}N_4O_4S$			
Acetamide, N-[4-[3,4-dihydro-6-(4-nitrophenyl)-3-(phenylmethyl)-4-thioxo-2H-1,3,5-oxadiazin-2-yl]phenyl]-	dioxan	242s(--),284(4.59)	73-2254-80
$C_{24}H_{20}N_4O_6$			
2,4,6(1H,3H,5H)-Pyrimidinetrione, 1,3-dimethyl-5-[(1,2,3,4-tetrahydro-1,3-indeno[2',1':5,6]pyrano[2,3-d]pyrimidin-5(6H)-ylidene)ethylidene]-, (E)-	dioxan	214(4.37),259(4.28), 307(4.01),490(4.59)	83-0557-80
5H,9H-Quino[3,2,1-de]acridine, 5,5,9,9-tetramethyl-3,7,11-trinitro-	EtOH	207(4.67),232(4.20), 252(4.20),305s(3.52), 317s(3.59),388(4.43)	24-0358-80
	$CHCl_3$	256(4.29),320(3.62), 400(4.54)	24-0358-80
$C_{24}H_{20}OS_2$			
1(2H)-Naphthalenone, 3,4-dihydro-2-[(4-methylphenyl)(phenyldithio)methylene]-	$CHCl_3$	266(3.97),342(4.12)	54-0049-80
$C_{24}H_{20}O_2$			
Benzo[a]pyrene, 1,6-diethoxy-	MeOH	225(4.42),257(4.62), 267(4.58),289(4.50), 301(4.58),384(4.43), 393(4.42),405(4.49), 419(3.89)	87-0919-80
Tetracyclo[9.8.1.1^{3,9}.1^{13,18}]docosa-2,4,7,9,11,13,15,17,19-nonaene-5,7-dicarboxaldehyde	dioxan	251(4.45),363(5.08), 463s(3.94)	89-0041-80

Compound	Solvent	$\lambda_{max}(\log \epsilon)$	Ref.
$C_{24}H_{20}O_3$			
9(10H)-Anthracenone, 10-[ethoxy(4-methoxyphenyl)methylene]-	EtOH	236(4.68),286(4.29)	35-3837-80
Benzo[a]pyren-3-ol, 1,6-diethoxy-	MeOH	256(4.52),262(4.51), 271(4.49),297(4.25), 311(4.37),378(4.18), 397(4.37),417(4.18), 443(4.13)	87-0919-80
$C_{24}H_{20}O_4$			
1,3-Azulenedicarboxylic acid, 4-(phenylethynyl)-, diethyl ester	C_6H_{12}	255(4.53),300(4.51), 365(4.36),570(3.02), 590(3.00)	18-1647-80
1,3-Azulenedicarboxylic acid, 6-(phenylethynyl)-, diethyl ester	MeOH	235(4.54),270(4.14), 310s(4.43),348(4.70), 530(2.99)	18-1647-80
$C_{24}H_{20}O_5$			
Dinaphtho[2,1-b:1',2'-d]furan, 4,5,9,10-tetramethoxy-	$CHCl_3$	257(4.46),263(4.45), 304(3.84),316(3.91), 334(3.92),350(4.17), 368(4.39),387(4.47)	12-2531-80
5,12-Naphthacenedione, 6,11-dihydroxy-8-(2-oxohexyl)-	MeOH	217(4.11),263(4.79), 449(4.04),479(4.23), 514(4.18)	24-2976-80
5,12-Naphthacenedione, 9-(1-hexynyl)-7,8-dihydro-6,7,11-trihydroxy-	MeOH	205(4.27),284(4.35), 483s(3.99),510(4.06), 545(3.86)	24-2976-80
$C_{24}H_{20}O_6$			
2,5-Cyclohexadien-1-one, 2-benzoyl-3,5-dihydroxy-6-[3-(4-hydroxyphenyl)-1-oxo-2-propenyl]-4,4-dimethyl-	EtOH	405(4.5)	138-1095-80
6,11-Naphthacenediol, 1,4-dimethoxy-, diacetate	CH_2Cl_2	272(4.90),285(4.89), 295(5.04),368(3.34), 379(3.36),401(3.90), 430s(--),460s(3.52), 480(3.70),510(3.64)	23-1161-80
1(2H)-Naphthalenone, 2-(4,5-dimethoxy-1-oxo-2(1H)-naphthalenylidene)-4,5-dimethoxy-	$CHCl_3$	243(4.47),283(4.29), 335s(4.01),686(4.33)	5-1321-80
1(2H)-Naphthalenone, 2-(4,8-dimethoxy-1-oxo-2(1H)-naphthalenylidene)-4,8-dimethoxy-	$CHCl_3$	243(4.36),278(4.23), 307s(4.12),395(3.49), 594(4.25)	5-1321-80
1(2H)-Naphthalenone, 5-hydroxy-2-(5-hydroxy-4-methoxy-7-methyl-1-oxo-2(1H)-naphthalenylidene)-4-methoxy-7-methyl-	$CHCl_3$	294(4.16),682(4.18)	5-1321-80
1(2H)-Naphthalenone, 5-hydroxy-2-(8-hydroxy-4-methoxy-6-methyl-1-oxo-2(1H)-naphthalenylidene)-4-methoxy-7-methyl-	$CHCl_3$	292(4.22),683(4.30)	5-1321-80
1(2H)-Naphthalenone, 8-hydroxy-2-(8-hydroxy-4-methoxy-6-methyl-1-oxo-2(1H)-naphthalenylidene)-4-methoxy-6-methyl-	$CHCl_3$	291(4.33),635s(4.30), 685(4.42)	5-1321-80
$C_{24}H_{20}O_7$			
6,11-Naphthacenedione, 2-acetyl-5,12-diacetoxy-1,2,3,4-tetrahydro-	EtOH	211(4.49),236s(4.27), 261(4.65),280s(4.17), 296s(3.61),344(3.65), 410s(2.90)	33-0232-80

Compound	Solvent	$\lambda_{max}(\log \epsilon)$	Ref.
$C_{24}H_{20}O_8$ 6H-Benzofuro[3,2-c][1]benzopyran-6-one, 3,9-diacetoxy-2-[(3,3-dimethyloxiran-yl)methyl]-	MeOH	233s(4.45),260s(4.04), 288s(4.05),299(4.21), 329(4.43),336s(4.36), 344(4.36)	102–2232–80
$C_{24}H_{21}N$ 7H,11H-Benz[1,8]indolizino[2,3,4,5,6-defg]acridine, 7,7,11,11-tetramethyl-	C_6H_{12}	215(4.57),251(4.59), 271(4.19),294(4.31), 306s(3.9),357(3.76), 376(3.67)	24–0358–80
	EtOH	215(4.57),230s(4.45), 245s(4.47),251(4.58), 273(4.23),286s(4.17), 295(4.31),308s(3.96), 359(3.72)	24–0358–80
radical cation	CF_3COOH	262(4.23),272(4.24), 280s(4.21),358(3.90), 610s(3.70),680(3.79)	24–0358–80
$C_{24}H_{21}NO_2$ 4H-1-Benzopyran-4-one, 3-[[4-(dimethyl-amino)phenyl]methylene]-2,3-dihydro-2-phenyl-, (E)-	EtOH H_2SO_4	275(4.18),422(4.40) 380(4.35),470(3.78)	114–0369–80B 114–0369–80B
2(1H)-Naphthalenone, 1-[(6-ethoxy-1-methyl-2(1H)-quinolinylidene)ethyl-idene]-	EtOH benzene acetone $CHCl_3$	594(3.81) 617(--) 630(--) 630(--)	104–0185–80 104–0185–80 104–0185–80 104–0185–80
$C_{24}H_{21}NO_4S_2$ Benzenesulfonamide, N-ethyl-N-[2-[(3-hydroxybenzo[b]thien-2-yl)carbonyl]-phenyl]-4-methyl-	MeOH	264(4.29),317(4.14), 375(3.83)	83–0027–80
$C_{24}H_{21}N_3$ Pyrrolo[3,2-e]benzimidazole, 3,6-di-hydro-2,8-dimethyl-7-phenyl-3-(phen-ylmethyl)-	EtOH	253s(4.20),318(4.52)	103–0062–80
$C_{24}H_{21}N_3O$ Propanedinitrile, [3-(diethylamino)-4-oxo-2,5-diphenyl-2-cyclopenten-1-ylidene]-	MeCN	301(4.03),424(4.47)	24–0424–80
$C_{24}H_{21}N_3O_2S$ Acetamide, N-[4-[3,4-dihydro-6-phenyl-3-(phenylmethyl)-4-thioxo-2H-1,3,5-oxadiazin-2-yl]phenyl]-	dioxan	245s(--),278(4.64)	73–2254–80
$C_{24}H_{21}N_3O_3$ 4,8-Etheno-3H-pyrazolo[1,5-c][1,3]di-azepine-7(8H)-carboxylic acid, 3a,4-dihydro-3-oxo-2,3a-diphenyl-, ethyl ester, (3aα,4β,8β)-	benzene	340(3.81),400(3.60)	44–4455–80
$C_{24}H_{21}N_3O_4$ 5H,9H-Quino[3,2,1-de]acridine, 5,5,9,9-tetramethyl-3,7-dinitro-	C_6H_{12}	207(4.66),255(4.25), 285s(3.50),321s(3.79), 352(4.21),390(4.37)	24–0358–80
	EtOH	219(4.46),258(4.28),	24–0358–80

Compound	Solvent	$\lambda_{max}(\log \epsilon)$	Ref.
(cont.)		323s(3.62),368(4.16), 410(4.31)	24-0358-80
5H,9H-Quino[3,2,1-de]acridine, 5,5,9,9-tetramethyl-3,11-dinitro-	C_6H_{12}	207(4.70),245(4.24), 320s(3.82),349(4.07), 390s(4.43),407(4.49)	24-0358-80
	EtOH	220(4.30),249(4.26), 355s(4.04),417(4.33)	24-0358-80
$C_{24}H_{21}N_3O_9$			
α-D-Glucopyranose, 1,3,6-tri-3-pyridine-carboxylate	EtOH	222(4.41),260s(3.90), 265(3.92),272s(3.84)	102-1278-80
$C_{24}H_{21}N_5O_4S_2$			
5-Thia-1-azabicyclo[4.2.0]oct-2-ene-2-carboxylic acid, 3-[5-(acetylamino)-1,3,4-thiadiazol-2-yl]-7-amino-8-oxo-, diphenylmethyl ester, (6R-trans)-	EtOH	257(3.83),317(4.09)	94-2116-80
$C_{24}H_{22}$			
Cyclopropene, 3-methyl-3-(2-phenylethyl)-1,2-diphenyl-	EtOH	230(4.31),323(4.38), 341(4.23)	35-5648-80
1:1 diastereomeric mixture	EtOH	268(4.10)	35-5648-80
1H-Indene, 1-ethyl-3-methyl-1,2-diphenyl-	EtOH	222(3.71),290(3.35)	44-4555-80
1H-Indene, 4-ethyl-3-methyl-1,2-diphenyl-	EtOH	288(4.01)	44-4555-80
1H-Indene, 7-ethyl-1-methyl-2,3-diphenyl-	EtOH	238(4.36),303(4.24)	44-4555-80
$C_{24}H_{22}Cl_4O_6$			
Spiro[1,5,2,4-ethanediylidene-6H-cyclopent[cd]indene-6,4'-[3]oxatricyclo-[4.2.1.0²,⁵]nonan]-7(1H)-one, 3,9'-diacetoxy-1,5,7a,8-tetrachloroocta-hydro-, [1α,2β,2aα,3α,4β,4aα,5α-6α(1'R*,2'R*,5'S*,6'S*,9'S*),7aα-7bβ,8S*,9S*]-	MeCN	230(3.37)	78-0267-80
$C_{24}H_{22}N_2$			
1-Aziridinamine, 2,3-diphenyl-N-[[2-(2-propenyl)phenyl]methylene]-, trans	MeOH	293(4.15)	44-3756-80
4,4'-Bipyridinium, 1,1'-bis(phenylmethyl)-, dichloride	H_2O	257(4.32)	98-1026-80
$C_{24}H_{22}N_2O$			
Benzoxazole, 5-(1,1-dimethylethyl)-2-[4-[2-(3-pyridinyl)ethenyl]phenyl]-	DMF	351(4.78)	33-1311-80
$C_{24}H_{22}N_2OS$			
Benzenamine, 4-[[3-(4-methoxyphenyl)-2H-1,4-benzothiazin-2-ylidene]methyl]-N,N-dimethyl-	$CHCl_3$	264(4.25),344(4.32), 425(3.94)	39-2923-80C
monoperchlorate	$CHCl_3$	262(4.32),293s(4.06), 359(4.44),427(4.28), 580(4.47)	39-2923-80C
$C_{24}H_{22}N_2O_2$			
Benzamide, N-[2-phenyl-1-[[(1-phenylethyl)amino]carbonyl]ethenyl]-, [S-(E)]-	dioxan	274(4.18),282(4.19)	70-0789-80

Compound	Solvent	λ_{max}(log ϵ)	Ref.
5H,9H-Quino[3,2,1-de]acridine, 5,5,9,9-tetramethyl-3-nitro-	C$_6$H$_{12}$	206(4.63),262(4.14), 283s(4.04),321s(3.45), 396(4.23),414s(4.10)	24-0358-80
	EtOH	215(4.63),268(4.28), 410(4.20)	24-0358-80
5H,9H-Quino[3,2,1-de]acridine, 5,5,9,9-tetramethyl-7-nitro-	C$_6$H$_{12}$	207(4.63),285(4.12), 394(4.19),415s(4.04)	24-0358-80
	EtOH	222(4.28),278(4.22), 410(4.02)	24-0358-80
C$_{24}$H$_{22}$N$_2$O$_4$			
Benzoic acid, 2-[methyl[2-oxo-2-(phenylamino)ethyl]amino]-, 2-oxo-2-phenylethyl ester	MeOH	240(4.55),327(3.44)	83-0405-80
C$_{24}$H$_{22}$N$_2$O$_6$			
2,4(1H,3H)-Pyrimidinedione, 1-[3-(benzoyloxy)-4-[(benzoyloxy)methyl]cyclopentyl]-	pH 1 or 7	232(4.40),267(4.13)	4-0353-80
	pH 13	224(4.42),266(3.98)	4-0353-80
C$_{24}$H$_{22}$N$_4$			
2,2'-(2,4-Dimethyl-1,5-xylylene)bis-benzimidazole	n.s.g.	266(4.27),274(4.28), 330(3.90)	47-3265-80
2,2'-(2,5-Dimethyl-1,4-xylylene)bis-benzimidazole	n.s.g.	287(4.15),294(4.15), 335(3.53)	47-3265-80
1H-Pyrazole, 3,3'-(1,4-phenylene)bis-[4,5-dihydro-1-phenyl-	dioxan	310(4.08),419(4.81)	103-0066-80
C$_{24}$H$_{22}$N$_4$O$_3$S			
4H-1,3,5-Oxadiazine-4-thione, 2-[4-(dimethylamino)phenyl]-2,3-dihydro-6-(4-nitrophenyl)-3-(phenylmethyl)-	dioxan	241s(--),298(4.56)	73-2254-80
C$_{24}$H$_{22}$N$_5$			
1,2,4-Triazolo[1,5-a]pyridinium, 8-cyano-5-[2-[4-(dimethylamino)phenyl]-ethenyl]-7-methyl-1-phenyl-, perchlorate	n.s.g.	540(4.63)	124-1306-80
C$_{24}$H$_{22}$N$_6$O$_3$S$_3$			
5-Thia-1-azabicyclo[4.2.0]oct-2-ene-2-carboxylic acid, 3-[[(1-methyl-1H-tetrazol-5-yl)thio]methyl]-7-[(methylthio)imino]-8-oxo-, diphenylmethyl ester, (R)-	CHCl$_3$	263(3.84),333(4.08)	35-1690-80
C$_{24}$H$_{22}$N$_6$O$_6$			
1,2,4-Triazolidine-3,5-dione, 1,1'-(4,4-dimethyl-2,6-dioxocyclohexylidene)-bis[4-phenyl-	MeCN	359(4.187)	44-1232-80
C$_{24}$H$_{22}$N$_8$O$_6$			
2,8-Imino-3,7-methano-4-benzazecine-1,10(2H)-dione, 4,9-bis(4,6-dimethoxy-1,3,5-triazin-2-yl)-3,4,7,8-tetrahydro-, (2α,3β,7β,8α)-	EtOH	213(3.84),250(3.81), 265s(3.64)	39-0331-80C
C$_{24}$H$_{22}$O			
2,4,6,8,14,16,18,20-Cycloheneicosaoctaene-10,12-diyn-1-one, (E,E,Z,Z,E,E,E,E)-	THF	<u>250(4.2),345(5.0),</u> <u>400s(4.0)</u>	138-1299-80

Compound	Solvent	$\lambda_{max}(\log \epsilon)$	Ref.
$C_{24}H_{22}O_2S_2$			
2H-1-Benzothiopyran-3(4H)-one, 2,2'-(1,2-ethanediylidene)bis-[4,4-dimethyl-	C_6H_{12}	270(4.21),290s(4.13), 444(4.35)	24-1708-80
	EtOH	264(4.18),286(4.10), 452(4.32),458s(4.31)	24-1708-80
	$CHCl_3$	269(4.22),289s(4.12), 456(4.34)	24-1708-80
$C_{24}H_{22}O_5$			
1(2H)-Anthracenone, 3-(benzoyloxy)-3,4-dihydro-8,9-dimethoxy-6-methyl-	MeOH	224(4.63),262(4.80), 310(3.72),320(3.59), 373(3.89)	78-2449-80
Benzeneacetic acid, 2-methoxy-5-[(2-methoxyphenyl)acetyl]-, phenyl ester	EtOH	220(4.37),274(4.21)	49-0081-80
Ethanone, 1-(5,12-diacetoxy-1,2,3,4-tetrahydro-2-naphthacenyl)-	EtOH	226(4.03),253s(4.96), 260(5.12),320s(3.18), 334(3.46),350(3.72), 369(3.77)	33-0232-80
5,12-Naphthacenedione, 8-(1-hexynyl)-7,8,9,10-tetrahydro-6,8,11-trihydroxy-	MeOH	228(4.25),250(4.56), 255s(4.55),287(3.88), 454s(3.91),482(4.00), 501s(3.86),512(3.84)	24-2976-80
$C_{24}H_{22}O_6$			
5,12-Naphthacenedione, 8-(1-hexynyl)-7,8,9,10-tetrahydro-6,8,10,11-tetra-hydroxy-, cis-(±)-	MeOH	229s(--),251(4.59), 285(3.94),458s(3.93), 481(3.98),512(3.78)	24-2976-80
trans-(±)-	MeOH	226s(--),250(4.59), 285(3.92),458s(3.93), 482(3.98),510(3.77)	24-2976-80
$C_{24}H_{22}O_8$			
1,4,5,8-Anthracenetetrol, 2,3-dimethyl-, tetraacetate	CH_2Cl_2	262(4.72),325s(--), 339(3.48),357(3.72), 375(3.86),396(3.76)	23-1161-80
$C_{24}H_{23}Br_2NO_8$			
1H-Indole-4,5,6,7-tetracarboxylic acid, 2,3-dibromo-1-(2,6-dimethylphenyl)-2,3-dihydro-, tetramethyl ester	MeOH	226s(4.20),272s(3.75), 279s(3.79),298(3.89), 343(3.88)	44-4582-80
$C_{24}H_{23}Cl_2N_3O$			
Benzamide, N-[3-cyano-1-[(2,6-dichloro-phenyl)methyl]-1,4-dihydro-4-pyridin-yl]-4-(1,1-dimethylethyl)-	CH_2Cl_2	239(4.4),326(3.7)	64-1431-80B
$C_{24}H_{23}N$			
Pyridine, 2-[2-[4-[2-[4-(1-methyleth-yl)phenyl]ethenyl]phenyl]ethenyl]-	DMF	362(4.80)	33-1311-80
Pyridine, 3-[2-[4-[2-[4-(1-methyleth-yl)phenyl]ethenyl]phenyl]ethenyl]-	DMF	360(4.80)	33-1311-80
Pyridine, 4-[2-[4-[2-[4-(1-methyleth-yl)phenyl]ethenyl]phenyl]ethenyl]-	DMF	361(4.74)	33-1311-80
$C_{24}H_{23}N_3OS$			
4H-1,3,5-Oxadiazine-4-thione, 2-[4-(di-methylamino)phenyl]-2,3-dihydro-6-phenyl-3-(phenylmethyl)-	dioxan	240s(--),288(4.48)	73-2254-80
$C_{24}H_{23}N_5O_5$			
Adenosine, 5'-(α-phenylbenzeneacetate)	MeOH	260(4.10)	18-3670-80

Compound	Solvent	$\lambda_{max}(\log \epsilon)$	Ref.
$C_{24}H_{23}N_7O_6$ Adenosine, N-[(phenylamino)carbonyl]-, 5'-(phenylcarbamate)	MeOH	235(--),280(4.48)	18-3670-80
$C_{24}H_{24}ClN_3O_3$ 2H-1,3-Benzoxazin-2-one, 6-chloro-3-cy- clohexyl-4-(2,5-dihydro-3-methyl-5- oxo-1-phenyl-1H-pyrazol-4-yl)-3,4- dihydro-	EtOH	224(4.29),245s(4.14)	4-0519-80
$C_{24}H_{24}Cl_2N_4O_6$ 1,2-Hydrazinedicarboxylic acid, 1-[1- [7-chloro-5-(2-chlorophenyl)-1,3-di- hydro-2H-1,4-benzodiazepin-2-ylidene]- 2-methoxy-2-oxoethyl-, diethyl ester	isoPrOH	215s(4.48),272(3.94), 312(4.53),335s(3.60)	4-1697-80
$C_{24}H_{24}Cl_4O_6$ 1,5,2,4-Ethanediylidene-6H-cyclopent- [cd]inden-6-one, 3-acetoxy-7-(7-acet- oxy-3-hydroxybicyclo[2.2.1]hept-2-yl)- 1,5,7a,8-tetrachlorodecahydro-	MeCN	233s(2.34)	78-0155-80
$C_{24}H_{24}CuN_8S_8$ Copper, [2,3,7,8,12,13,17,18-octa- kis(methylthio)-21H,23H-porphyr- azinato-N^{21},N^{22},N^{23},N^{24}]-, (SP-4-1)-	CHCl$_3$	363(4.56),497(4.17), 610(4.30),667(4.68)	125-0383-80
$C_{24}H_{24}MgN_8S_8$ Magnesium, [2,3,7,8,12,13,17,18-octa- kis(methylthio)-21H,23H-porphyrazin- ato-N^{21},N^{22},N^{23},N^{24}]-, (SP-4-1)-	CHCl$_3$	375(4.84),500(4.11), 620(4.42),672(4.88)	125-0383-80
$C_{24}H_{24}N_2$ 5H,9H-Quino[3,2,1-de]acridin-3-amine, 5,5,9,9-tetramethyl-	C_6H_{12}	206(4.81),236s(3.86), 300(4.36)	24-0358-80
$C_{24}H_{24}N_2O$ 9(10H)-Anthracenone, 3-(dimethylamino)- 10-[4-(dimethylamino)phenyl]- Benz[a]azulen-10(4bH)-one, 7-(dimethyl- amino)-4b-[4-(dimethylamino)phenyl]-	EtOH EtOH	250(4.54),367(4.36) 263(4.42),461(4.41)	88-1043-80 88-1043-80
$C_{24}H_{24}N_2OS$ Quinazoline, 3-acetyl-3,4,5,6,7,8-hexa- hydro-2-(methylthio)-4-phenyl-8- (phenylmethylene)- 2(1H)-Quinazolinethione, 3,4,5,6,7,8- hexahydro-3-(1-oxopropyl)-4-phenyl- 8-(phenylmethylene)-	EtOH EtOH	230(4.31),284(4.66) 269(4.51),298(4.42), 339(4.12)	114-0147-80B 114-0147-80B
$C_{24}H_{24}N_2O_2$ 2(1H)-Quinazolinone, 3,4,5,6,7,8-hexa- hydro-3-(1-oxopropyl)-4-phenyl- 8-(phenylmethylene)-	EtOH	262(4.24),298(4.23)	114-0147-80B
$C_{24}H_{24}N_2O_4S$ Carbamic acid, [4-[[3-methyl-4-(2-naph- thalenylimino)-2-pentenyl]sulfonyl]- phenyl]-, methyl ester	EtOH	236(5.03)	104-0849-80

Compound	Solvent	$\lambda_{max}(\log \epsilon)$	Ref.
$C_{24}H_{24}N_2O_5$ 2H-1,3-Benzoxazin-2-one, 4,4'-(2-oxo-1,3-cyclohexanediyl)bis[3,4-dihydro-3-methyl-	EtOH	267(3.34),273(3.32)	4-0277-80
$C_{24}H_{24}N_2S$ Quinazoline, 1,4,5,6,7,8-hexahydro-4-phenyl-8-(phenylmethylene)-2-(2-pro-penylthio)-, monohydrobromide	EtOH	234(4.13),277(4.41), 324(3.95)	114-0147-80B
$C_{24}H_{24}N_4$ 2,2,3,3-Naphthalenetetracarbonitrile, 5,6,7,8-tetraethylidene-1,4-dimethyl-1,2,3,4,5,6,7,8-octahydro-	CH_2Cl_2	250s(4.05),285(4.18)	24-1663-80
$C_{24}H_{24}N_4O_2$ Spiro[1H-isoindole-1,9'-[9H]xanthen]-3(2H)-one, 2-amino-3',6'-bis(dimeth-ylamino)-	EtOH	238(4.79),268(4.51), 306(4.09)	94-3561-80
$C_{24}H_{24}N_5O_6PS$ Adenosine, N-(phenylmethyl)-8-[(phenyl-methyl)thio]-, cyclic 3',5'-(hydrogen phosphate)	pH 1 pH 11	289(4.31) 290(4.26)	87-0242-80 87-0242-80
$C_{24}H_{24}N_6O_8$ Piperidine, 1,1'-[(2,4,5,7-tetranitro-9H-fluoren-9-ylidene)methylene]bis-	MeCN	364(4.51),620(3.59)	104-0740-80
$C_{24}H_{24}N_8NiS_8$ Nickel, [2,3,7,8,12,13,17,18-octa-kis(methylthio)-21H,23H-porphyrazin-ato(2-)-$N^{21},N^{22},N^{23},N^{24}$]-, (SP-4-1)-	$CHCl_3$	347(4.60),482(4.27), 660(4.63)	125-0383-80
$C_{24}H_{24}N_8O_6$ 2,8-Imino-3,7-methano-4-benzazecine-1,14(2H)-dione, 4,13-bis(4,6-dimeth-oxy-1,3,5-triazin-2-yl)-3,4,7,8,8a,9-hexahydro-	EtOH	215s(4.00),232(4.11), 269(4.11)	39-0331-80C
$C_{24}H_{24}O_2$ 4H-1,3-Benzodioxin, 2,4-bis(1-phenyl-ethyl)-	EtOH	243(3.6),308(3.2)	118-0724-80
$C_{24}H_{24}O_4$ 1,1'-Biphenyl, 2-[2-(3,4-dimethoxy-phenyl)ethenyl]-3',4'-dimethoxy-, (E)-	EtOH	207(4.64),291(4.26), 317(4.74)	94-2948-80
2,9-Ethano-1,4-ethenodibenzo[a,e]cyclo-octene-15,16-dicarboxylic acid, 1,4,5,6,11,12-hexahydro-, dimethyl ester	EtOH	220(4.30),284(3.08), 291(3.05),323(2.86)	44-3974-80
$C_{24}H_{24}O_6$ Kuwanon B	MeOH	234(4.49),260(4.38), 280s(4.10),330s(4.00)	142-1531-80B
	MeOH-AlCl$_3$	214(4.52),269(4.44), 376(3.94)	142-1531-80B
5,12-Naphthacenedione, 1,2,3,4-tetra-hydro-7,11-dimethoxy-2-(2-methyl-1,3-dioxolan-2-yl)-, (S)-	$CHCl_3$	247(4.48),266(4.54), 374(3.65)	35-5881-80

Compound	Solvent	$\lambda_{max}(\log \epsilon)$	Ref.
$C_{24}H_{24}O_8$ 2-Anthracenepropanoic acid, 9,10-dihy- dro-1-hydroxy-4,8-dimethoxy-9,10-di- oxo-α-(1-oxopropyl)-, ethyl ester	MeOH	229(4.58),250(4.18), 275(3.93),389(3.47), 446(3.90),464(3.91), 491(3.72)	24-2994-80
$C_{24}H_{24}O_{12}$ 1,4-Naphthalenedione, 2-[(2,3,4,6-tet- ra-O-acetyl-β-D-glucopyranosyl)oxy]-	MeOH	242(4.2),247(4.2), 269s(4.2),273(4.2), 331(3.4)	73-2684-80
1,4-Naphthalenedione, 5-[(2,3,4,6-tet- ra-O-acetyl-β-D-glucopyranosyl)oxy]-	MeOH	238(4.2),365(3.5)	73-2684-80
$C_{24}H_{25}NO_2$ 1H-Pyrrole-3-carboxylic acid, 1-cyclo- hexyl-2,4-diphenyl-, methyl ester	CCl₄	283(4.38)	22-0552-80
$C_{24}H_{25}NO_5$ 6,10-Etheno-5H-cyclohepta[b]naphthalen- 5,11-imine-12-carboxylic acid, 6-(ac- etyloxy)-5a,6,7,10,10a,11-hexahydro- 7-oxo-, 1,1-dimethylethyl ester, (5α,5aβ,6β,10α,10aβ,11α)-	EtOH	240(3.76),264(3.31), 271(3.11),326(1.99)	78-2119-80
6,10-Etheno-5H-cyclohepta[b]naphthalen- 5,11-imine-12-carboxylic acid, 8-(ac- etyloxy)-5a,6,7,10,10a,11-hexahydro- 7-oxo-, 1,1-dimethylethyl ester, (5α,5aβ,6α,10α,10aβ,11α)-	EtOH	245(3.80),272(3.38), 326(2.08)	78-2119-80
$C_{24}H_{25}NO_8$ 1H-Indole-4,5,6,7-tetracarboxylic acid, 1-(2,6-dimethylphenyl)-3a,6-dihydro-, tetramethyl ester	MeOH	278s(3.73),290(3.82), 343(3.99)	44-4582-80
$C_{24}H_{25}NO_9$ Cyclopenta[3,4]cyclobuta[1,2-b]pyrrole- 3,3a,6,6a-tetracarboxylic acid, 1-(4- methoxyphenyl-1,3a,3b,4,6a,6b-hexahy- dro-, tetramethyl ester, cis-syn-cis	MeOH	206(4.36),234(4.11), 309(3.81),354(4.04)	39-0081-80C
$C_{24}H_{25}NO_{10}S$ Sulfamic acid, [2-[3,5-dihydroxy-4- [3-(3-hydroxy-4-methoxyphenyl)-1- oxopropyl]phenoxy]ethyl]-, 2-hy- droxyphenyl ester	EtOH	283(4.34)	44-5371-80
$C_{24}H_{25}N_2O_2S$ Benzothiazolium, 2-[[2-[2-(dimethylami- no)ethenyl]-4H-1-benzopyran-4-yli- dene]methyl]-3-ethyl-6-methoxy-	MeCN	419(4.42),565(4.88)	124-0965-80
Benzothiazolium, 2-[[4-[2-(dimethylami- no)ethenyl]-2H-1-benzopyran-2-yli- dene]methyl]-3-ethyl-6-methoxy-	MeCN	400(4.35),582(4.98)	124-0965-80
$C_{24}H_{25}N_3$ 1,2,4-Benzotriazine, 3-(1,1-dimethyl- ethyl)-1,4-dihydro-1-phenyl-4-(phen- ylmethyl)-	EtOH	237(4.19),291(3.97)	24-1205-80
$C_{24}H_{25}N_3O_5$ 1,2,5-Triazabicyclo[4.2.0]oct-7-ene-	EtOH	222(4.50)	44-4587-80

Compound	Solvent	$\lambda_{max}(\log \epsilon)$	Ref.
6,7-dicarboxylic acid, 2-methyl-4,8-bis(4-methylphenyl)-3-oxo-, dimethyl ester, trans			44-4587-80
$C_{24}H_{25}N_3O_7$			
1,2,5-Triazabicyclo[4.2.0]oct-7-ene-6,7-dicarboxylic acid, 4,8-bis(4-methoxyphenyl)-2-methyl-3-oxo-, dimethyl ester, trans	EtOH	228(4.52),270s(4.19)	44-4587-80
$C_{24}H_{25}N_5O_4$			
Oxaline	MeOH	228(4.33),345(4.40)	94-2987-80
$C_{24}H_{26}Cl_2O_2Pd_2$			
Palladium, di-μ-chlorobis[(1,5,6-η)-2-oxo-5-phenyl-5-hexenyl]di-	CH_2Cl_2	235(3.93),281(4.08)	12-1537-80
$C_{24}H_{26}N_2OSe$			
Benzenamine, 4,4'-(1,4-oxaselenin-3,5-diyldi-2,1-ethenediyl)bis[N,N-dimethyl-	n.s.g.	242(2.25),342(4.32), 595(2.90),635(2.95)	124-0640-80
$C_{24}H_{26}N_2O_2$			
3H-Indol-3-one, 6-(1,1-dimethylethyl)-2-[6-(1,1-dimethylethyl)-1,3-dihydro-3-oxo-2H-indol-2-ylidene]-1,2-dihydro-	C_6H_{12}	280(4.44),582(4.40)	5-2039-80
	benzene	598(4.36)	5-2039-80
	EtOH	610(4.30)	5-2039-80
	HCOOH	409(4.19),625(4.16)	5-2039-80
	$CHCl_3$	601(4.31)	5-2039-80
	DMSO	619(4.30)	5-2039-80
$C_{24}H_{26}N_2O_4$			
6,10-Etheno-5H-cyclohepta[b]naphthalen-5,11-imine-12-carboxylic acid, 6-(acetylamino)-5a,6,7,10,10a,11-hexahydro-7-oxo-, 1,1-dimethylethyl ester, (5α,5aβ,6α,10β,10aβ,11α)-	EtOH	259(3.65),265(3.69), 272(3.71),285(3.67), 326(2.97)	78-2119-80
6,10-Etheno-5H-cyclohepta[b]naphthalen-5,11-imine-12-carboxylic acid, 8-(acetylamino)-5a,6,7,10,10a,11-hexahydro-7-oxo-, 1,1-dimethylethyl ester, (5α,5aβ,6α,10α,10aβ,11α)-	EtOH	259(3.47),264(3.41), 271(3.33),326(1.93)	78-2119-80
$C_{24}H_{26}N_2O_5$			
2H-1,3-Benzoxazin-2-one, 4,4'-(2-hydroxy-1,3-cyclohexanediyl)bis[3,4-dihydro-3-methyl-	EtOH	267(3.34),273(3.32)	4-0277-80
$C_{24}H_{26}N_2O_6$			
2-Naphthalenol, 1-[(2,3,5,6,8,9,11,12-octahydro-1,4,7,10,13-benzopentaoxacyclopentadecin-15-yl)azo]-	CHCl	473(4.12)	18-1550-80
Pyrazino[2,1-a:3,4-a']diisoquinoline-4,5-dione, 1,2,7,8,12b,12c-hexahydro-10,11,14,15-tetramethoxy-, cis	EtOH	232(4.34),284(3.88)	33-0938-80
trans-(±)-	EtOH	228s(4.39),285(3.81)	33-0938-80
$C_{24}H_{26}N_2O_7$			
Acetamide, N-[2-[6-[(2,3-dihydro-4,5-dimethoxy-3-oxo-1H-isoindol-1-ylidene)methyl]-7-methoxy-1,3-benzodioxol-5-yl]ethyl]-N-methyl-, (Z)-	MeOH	210(4.66),269(4.17), 350(4.27)	73-2125-80

Compound	Solvent	$\lambda_{max}(\log \epsilon)$	Ref.
$C_{24}H_{26}N_2S$			
Quinazoline, 1,4,5,6,7,8-hexahydro-2-[(1-methylethyl)thio]-4-phenyl-8-(phenylmethylene)-	EtOH	237(4.20),276(4.44), 322(4.04)	114-0147-80B
hydriodide	EtOH	276(4.40),325(4.00)	114-0147-80B
$C_{24}H_{26}N_2SSe$			
Benzenamine, 4,4'-(1,4-thiaselenin-3,5-diyldi-2,1-ethenediyl)bis[N,N-dimethyl-	n.s.g.	240(3.99),330(4.40), 587(3.80),642(3.86)	124-0640-80
$C_{24}H_{26}N_3S_2$			
Benzothiazolium, 3-ethyl-2-[5-(3-ethyl-2(3H)-benzothiazolylidene)-2-(methyl-amino)-1,3-pentadienyl]-, iodide	60% EtOH	540(4.82)	104-2080-80
$C_{24}H_{26}N_4O$			
1(2H)-Phthalazinone, 4,4-bis[4-(dimeth-ylamino)phenyl]-3,4-dihydro-	EtOH	254(4.66)	94-3561-80
$C_{24}H_{26}N_4S_2$			
3H-Pyrazole-3-thione, 4,4'-ethylidene-bis[1,2-dihydro-1,5-dimethyl-2-phen-yl-	benzene H_2O	278(4.12),344(4.33) 267(4.30),288(4.29)	140-0560-80 140-0560-80
$C_{24}H_{26}N_8S_8$			
21H,23H-Porphyrazine, 2,3,7,8,12,13-17,18-octakis(methylthio)-	C_6H_5Cl	367(4.63),515(4.30), 637(4.41),709(4.54)	125-0383-80
$C_{24}H_{26}O_4$			
[4.2.2](1,3,4)-Cyclophane-2,3-dicarbox-ylic acid, dimethyl ester, trans	EtOH	206(4.69),273(2.57), 283(2.48)	24-2358-80
$C_{24}H_{26}O_7$			
2H-1-Benzopyran-3,4,4a(5H)-triol, hexahydro-8a-methoxy-, 3,4-di-benzoate, [3R-(3α,4α,4aα,8aβ)]-	MeOH	236(4.32)	39-1262-80C
$C_{24}H_{26}O_8$			
Oxysiphulin	EtOH	233s(4.46),290(4.18)	102-0467-80
$C_{24}H_{27}ClO_4$			
D-Homopregna-1,4,6,16-tetraene-3,20-di-one, 17a-acetoxy-6-chloro-	EtOH	229(4.05),258(4.03), 298(4.06)	33-1867-80
$C_{24}H_{27}N_3O_2$			
9,10-Anthracenedione, 1-amino-2,4-di-piperidino-	MeOH	580(3.91)	18-3725-80
$C_{24}H_{27}N_7O_5$			
L-Glutamic acid, N-[4-[2-(2,4-diamino-6-pteridinyl)ethenyl]benzoyl]-, diethyl ester	pH 1 pH 7 pH 13	314(4.48),385(4.26) 318(4.45),407(4.25) 319(4.48),407(4.26)	87-0320-80 87-0320-80 87-0320-80
$C_{24}H_{28}N_2O$			
Estra-1,3,5(10)-trien-17-ol, 3-(phen-ylazo)-, cis	benzene	440(3.09)	149-0305-80B
trans	benzene MeOH	445(2.85) 330(4.36)	149-0305-80B 149-0305-80B

Compound	Solvent	$\lambda_{max}(\log \epsilon)$	Ref.
$C_{24}H_{28}N_2O_4$ Dibenzo[de,gh]pyrazino[1,2,3,4-1mn]- [1,10]phenanthroline, 1,2,4,5,12,13- 14a,14b-octahydro-7,8,9,10-tetra- methoxy-, trans-(±)-	EtOH	271(4.19),297s(3.77)	33-0938-80
$C_{24}H_{28}N_2O_{10}$ Glycine, N,N'-(1,2-ethanediylbis[oxy- (4-methyl-2,1-phenylene)]bis[N- (carboxymethyl)-	tetraanion	251(4.11),282(3.66)	69-2396-80
calcium chelate	n.s.g.	279(3.69)	69-2396-80
$C_{24}H_{28}N_2P$ 3H-Indolium, 2-[[[(1,3-dihydro-1,3,3- trimethyl-2H-indol-2-ylidene)methyl]- phosphinidene]methyl]-1,3,3-tri- methyl-, tetrafluoroborate	CDCl$_3$	327(c.3.95),586(c.4.81)	5-2072-80
$C_{24}H_{28}N_3$ 3H-Indolium, 2-[[[(1,3-dihydro-1,3,3- trimethyl-2H-indol-2-ylidene)methyl]- imino]methyl]-1,3,3-trimethyl-, tetrafluoroborate	CHCl$_3$	288(3.98),530s(4.34), 563(4.81),602(5.06)	5-2072-80
$C_{24}H_{28}N_4O$ 1H-Cyclopenta[5,6]naphtho[1,2-g]pyrazo- lo[1,5-a]quinazoline-10-carbonitrile, 2,3,3a,3b,4,5,13,13a,13b,14,15,15a- dodecahydro-1-hydroxy-13a,15a-dimeth- yl-, [1S-(1α,3aβ,3bα,13aα,13bα,15aα)]-	MeOH	209(4.18),239(4.50), 251(4.25),313(3.59), 364(3.94)	39-0481-80C
1H-Naphth[2',1':4,5]indeno[2,1-e]pyra- zolo[1,5-a]pyrimidine-10-carbonitrile, 2,3,4,4a,4b,5,6,6a,13,13a,13b,14-do- decahydro-2-hydroxy-4a,6a-dimethyl-, [2S-(2α,4aα,4bβ,13aβ,13bα)]-	MeOH	207(4.12),233(4.54), 322(3.82)	39-0481-80C
3H-Pyrazol-3-one, 4-[[4-(dimethylami- no)phenyl]-1-piperidinylmethylene]- 2,4-dihydro-5-methyl-2-phenyl-	MeOH	377(4.65)	97-0020-80
$C_{24}H_{28}N_4O_4$ Spiro[imidazolidine-4,2'(3'H)-quinoxa- line]-2,3',5-trione, 4'-ethyl-1',4'- dihydro-1'-[2-(3-methoxyphenyl)eth- yl]-1,6',7'-trimethyl-	EtOH	271s(3.81),278(3.75), 307(3.80)	35-5036-80
$C_{24}H_{28}N_4O_5$ 6H-1,2-Oxazine, 5-[(4-methoxy-3-nitro- phenyl)amino]-6-morpholino-3-(2,4,6- trimethylphenyl)-	MeOH	322(4.12),436(3.67)	150-0242-80S
$C_{24}H_{28}N_6O_6S$ L-Glutamic acid, N-[4-[[(2,4-diamino- 1,5-dihydro-5-oxopyrido[2,3-d]pyri- midin-6-yl)methyl]thio]benzoyl]-, diethyl ester	pH 1 pH 7 pH 11	258(4.49),284(4.16) 255(4.32),289(4.30) 259(4.44),289(4.27)	44-3746-80 44-3746-80 44-3746-80
$C_{24}H_{28}O_3S_2$ Spiro[1,3-dithiolane-2,4'-[4H-3a,7]- methanoazulen]-9'-one, 5'-(benzoyl- oxy)-1',2',3',7',8',8'a-hexahydro- 3',6',8',8'-tetramethyl- (both forms)	EtOH	231(4.23)	78-0731-80

Compound	Solvent	$\lambda_{max}(\log \epsilon)$	Ref.
$C_{24}H_{28}O_4$			
Benzene, 4-[2-[2-(3,4-dimethoxyphenyl)-3-cyclohexen-1-yl)ethenyl]-1,2-dimethoxy-, cis	EtOH	262(4.28),268(4.27), 286s(3.99),300s(3.79), 312s(3.49)	94-2948-80
	CDCl$_3$	240(4.13),267(4.23), 273(4.25),289(4.02), 303(3.83),316(3.53)	64-0156-80C
trans	EtOH	262(4.27),268(4.27), 286s(3.99),299s(3.77), 312s(3.49)	94-2948-80
$C_{24}H_{28}O_7$			
4H-1-Benzopyran-4-one, 2,3-dihydro-5-hydroxy-7-methoxy-8-(3-methyl-2-butenyl)-2-(3,4,5-trimethoxyphenyl)-	MeOH	290(4.10),335(3.30)	42-1238-80
	MeOH-NaOMe	290(--),360(--)	42-1238-80
	MeOH-AlCl$_3$	315(--),365(--)	42-1238-80
Coleon Z, 12β-O-acetyl-	EtOH	231(4.20)	33-0095-80
$C_{24}H_{28}O_8$			
2(3H)-Furanone, 4-[acetoxy(3,4-dimethoxyphenyl)methyl]-3-[(3,4-dimethoxyphenyl)methyl]dihydro-, [3R-[3α,4β-(R*)]]-	EtOH	234(4.25),282(3.88)	94-0850-80
[3R-[3α,4β(S*)]]-	EtOH	233(4.12),280(3.68)	94-0850-80
Protosiphulin	EtOH	230(4.41),278(4.41)	102-0467-80
$C_{24}H_{28}O_{10}$			
β-D-Glucopyranoside, 1,4a,5,7a-tetrahydro-5-hydroxy-7-(hydroxymethyl)-cyclopenta[c]pyran-1-yl, 6-(3-phenyl-2-propenoate) (scrophularioside)	MeOH	204(4.26),216(4.19), 222(4.11),277(4.29)	100-0649-80
$C_{24}H_{28}O_{11}$			
Globularin	n.s.g.	278(4.30)	100-0649-80
$C_{24}H_{28}O_{12}$			
Odontoside	n.s.g.	232(3.66),273(2.61), 282(2.56)	100-0649-80
Specioside	MeOH	230(3.82),300s(4.06), 315(4.15)	100-0524-80
	MeOH	230(3.82),315(4.15)	100-0649-80
$C_{24}H_{29}ClO_4$			
D-Homopregna-4,6,16-triene-3,20-dione, 17a- acetoxy-6-chloro-	EtOH	285(4.31)	33-1867-80
$C_{24}H_{29}FO_4$			
D-Homopregna-4,6,16-triene-3,20-dione, 17a-acetoxy-6-fluoro-	EtOH	283(4.39)	33-1867-80
$C_{24}H_{29}N_3O_4$			
1H-Pyrazole, 4,5-dihydro-3-(4-methoxyphenyl)-5-(4-nitrophenyl)-1-(1-oxooctyl)-	MeOH	294(3.86)	2-0364-80
$C_{24}H_{29}N_3O_5$			
3H-Phenoxazine-1,9-dicarboxamide, N,N,N',N'-tetraethyl-7-hydroxy-4,5-dimethyl-3-oxo-	CHCl$_3$	260(4.20),289s(4.00), 335(3.96),430s(3.79), 484(3.79)	4-0017-80
$C_{24}H_{29}N_3O_8$			
1,4,7,10-Tetraoxa-13-azacyclopentadec-	MeCN	475.5(4.88)	24-0457-80

Compound	Solvent	$\lambda_{max}(\log \epsilon)$	Ref.
ane, 13-[4-[2-(2,4-dinitrophenyl)eth-enyl]phenyl]- (cont.)			24-0457-80
$C_{24}H_{29}N_5O_4S$ 1,4,7,10-Tetraoxa-13-azacyclopentadec-ane, 13-[4-[(3-phenyl-1,2,4-thiadia-zol-5-yl)azo]phenyl]-	MeCN	511(5.05)	24-0457-80
$C_{24}H_{29}N_5O_7$ 3H-Phenoxazine-1,9-dicarboxamide, N,N,N',N'-tetraethyl-7-hydroxy-4,6-dimethyl-8-nitro-3-oxo-	CHCl₃	258(4.19),373(4.23), 446(4.37)	4-0017-80
$C_{24}H_{29}N_7O_6$ L-Glutamic acid, N-[4-[[(2,4-diamino-1,5-dihydro-5-oxopyrido[2,3-d]pyri-midin-6-yl)methyl]amino]benzoyl]-, diethyl ester	pH 1 pH 7 pH 11	255(4.63),292(4.10) 252(4.45),293(4.47) 252(4.46),293(4.45)	44-3746-80 44-3746-80 44-3746-80
$C_{24}H_{29}N_{11}O_4$ 1H-Pyrrole-2-carboxamide, 4-[[[4-[[[(aminoiminomethyl)amino]acetyl]-amino]-1-methyl-1H-pyrrol-2-yl]carbo-nyl]amino]-N-[5-[[(2-cyanoethyl)ami-no]carbonyl]-1-methyl-1H-pyrrol-3-yl]-1-methyl-, monohydrochloride	EtOH	244(4.30),305(4.33)	87-1144-80
$C_{24}H_{30}ClNO_2Pd$ Palladium, chloro[(4,5,6-η)-3,17-dioxo-androst-5-en-4-yl](pyridine)-	CHCl₃	265(4.16),271(4.16)	12-2761-80
$C_{24}H_{30}Cl_2O_4$ D-Homopregna-4,6-diene-3,20-dione, 17a-acetoxy-4,6-dichloro-	EtOH	298(4.19)	33-1867-80
$C_{24}H_{30}N_2O_4$ Dibenzo[de,gh][1,10]phenanthroline, 1,2,3,10,11,12,12a,12b-octahydro-5,6,7,8-tetramethoxy-1,12-dimethyl-, trans-(±)-	EtOH	265(4.10),297(3.83)	33-0938-80
Pyrazino[2,1-a:3,4-a']diisoquinoline, 1,2,4,5,7,8,12b,12c-octahydro-10,11,14,15-tetramethoxy-, cis trans-(±)-	EtOH EtOH	230s(4.10),285(3.79) 230s(4.06),287(3.65)	33-0938-80 33-0938-80
$C_{24}H_{30}N_2O_6S_2$ Benzenesulfonic acid, 4-methyl-, hydra-zide, hydrazone with 3-O-methyl-1,2-O-(1-methylethylidene)-6-S-(phenyl-methyl)-6-thio-α-D-xylo-hexofuranos-5-ulose	EtOH	212(4.08),230s(--)	33-0016-80
$C_{24}H_{30}N_2S$ 6H,8H-Pyrimido[2,1-a:4,3-a']diisoquino-line-6-thione, 5c-(1,1-dimethyleth-yl)-4br,5,9,13b,15,16-hexahydro-5-methyl-	isooctane	234s(--),241s(--), 279(3.9),337s(--), 368s(--)	24-3010-80
$C_{24}H_{30}N_4O_5$ 3H-Phenoxazine-1,9-dicarboxamide, 2-am-	CHCl₃	291s(3.68),460(4.29)	4-0017-80

Compound	Solvent	$\lambda_{max}(\log \epsilon)$	Ref.
ino-N,N,N',N'-tetraethyl-7-hydroxy- 4,6-dimethyl-3-oxo- (cont.)			4-0017-80
$C_{24}H_{30}O_2$			
Phenol, 3-[4-methyl-6-(2,6,6-trimethyl- 1-cyclohexen-1-yl)-1,3,5-hexatrien- yl]-, acetate, (E,E,E)-	CCl_4	348(4.53)	87-1013-80
(E,E,Z)-	CCl_4	333(4.43)	87-1013-80
(E,Z,E)-	CCl_4	335.5(4.48)	87-1013-80
$C_{24}H_{30}O_2S_2$			
Spiro[1,3-dithiolane-2,9'-[1H-3a,7]- methanoazulen]5'-ol, 2',3',4',7',8'- 8'a-hexahydro-3',6',8',8'-tetrameth- yl-, benzoate, [3'R-(3'α,3'aα,7'α,8'aβ)]-	EtOH	289(3.52)	78-0731-80
[3'R-(3'α,3'aβ,7'β,8'aα)]-	EtOH	289(3.56)	78-0731-80
$C_{24}H_{30}O_4$			
D-Homopregna-1,4,6-triene-3,20-dione, 17a-acetoxy-	EtOH	223(4.06),252(3.99), 300(4.03)	33-1867-80
D-Homopregna-4,6,16-triene-3,20-dione, 17a-acetoxy-	EtOH	282(4.43)	33-1867-80
$C_{24}H_{30}O_5$			
D-Homopregna-4,6-diene-3,20-dione, 17a-acetoxy-16α,17α-epoxy-	EtOH	283(4.40)	33-1867-80
D-Homopregna-4,16-diene-3,20-dione, 17a-acetoxy-6α,7α-epoxy-	EtOH	240(4.16)	33-1867-80
6β,7β-	EtOH	245(4.22)	33-1867-80
$C_{24}H_{30}O_6$			
Benzo[4,5]cyclodeca[1,2-b]furan-7(6H)- one, 8,9-diacetoxy-8,8a,9,10,12a,13- hexahydro-1,5,8a,12-tetramethyl-, (5Z,8R*,8aR*,9S*,12aS*)-	MeOH	270(3.88)	12-2307-80
D-Homopregn-4-ene-3,20-dione, 17a-acet- oxy-6α,7α:16α,17α-diepoxy-	EtOH	241(4.17)	33-1867-80
$C_{24}H_{30}O_7$			
Oxireno[5',6']benzo[1',2':4,5]cyclo- deca[1,2-b]furan-5(1aH)-one, 3,4-di- acetoxy-2,3,3a,4,6,12,12a,12b-octa- hydro-3a,7,11,12b-tetramethyl-, (1aα,3β,3aα,4α,12aβ,12bα)-	MeOH	271(3.89)	12-2307-80
$C_{24}H_{30}O_8$			
1H,3H-Furo[3,4-c]furan, tetrahydro-1,4- bis(3,4,5-trimethoxyphenyl)- (dieyan- gambin)	EtOH	207(4.97),231s(4.16), 270(3.15)	78-3551-80
Epiyangambin	EtOH	207(5.00),232s(4.22), 270(3.28)	78-3551-80
Yangambin (lirioresinol B)	EtOH	207(4.93),232s(4.03), 270(3.08)	78-3551-80
$C_{24}H_{30}O_{10}$			
Laterioside	EtOH	207(4.06),218(4.13), 224(4.06),279(4.31)	100-0649-80
$C_{24}H_{30}O_{11}$			
Globularidin	MeOH	216(4.02),221s(--), 278(4.46)	100-0649-80

Compound	Solvent	$\lambda_{max}(\log \epsilon)$	Ref.
Harpagoside	n.s.g.	216(4.19),222(4.12), 276(4.36)	100-0649-80
$C_{24}H_{30}O_{12}$			
Globularimin	MeOH	217(4.08),223s(--), 278(4.38)	100-0649-80
Globularinin	MeOH	217(4.08),223s(--), 278(4.38)	100-0649-80
$C_{24}H_{31}BrO_4$			
D-Homopregna-4,6-diene-3,20-dione, 17a-acetoxy-6-bromo-	EtOH	288(4.30)	33-1867-80
$C_{24}H_{31}BrO_6$			
Pregna-1,4-diene-3,20-dione, 21-acetoxy-7α-bromo-11β,17α-dihydroxy-16α-methyl-	MeOH	242(4.18)	87-0430-80
16β-	MeOH	242(4.19)	87-0430-80
$C_{24}H_{31}ClO_4$			
D-Homopregna-4,6-diene-3,20-dione, 17a-acetoxy-6-chloro-	EtOH	285(4.35)	33-1867-80
D-Homopregna-4,16-diene-3,20-dione, 17a-acetoxy-6β-chloro-	EtOH	241(4.17)	33-1867-80
$C_{24}H_{31}ClO_6$			
Pregna-1,4-diene-3,20-dione, 21-acetoxy-7α-chloro-11β,17α-dihydroxy-16α-methyl-	MeOH	242(4.16)	87-0430-80
16β-	MeOH	241(4.19)	87-0430-80
$C_{24}H_{31}FO_4$			
D-Homopregna-4,6-diene-3,20-dione, 17a-acetoxy-6-fluoro-	EtOH	283(4.38)	33-1867-80
$C_{24}H_{31}FO_5$			
D-Homopregna-4,16-diene-3,20-dione, 17a-acetoxy-6β-fluoro-7α-hydroxy-	EtOH	232(4.07)	33-1867-80
$C_{24}H_{31}FO_6$			
Pregna-1,4-diene-3,20-dione, 21-acetoxy-7α-fluoro-11β,17α-dihydroxy-16α-methyl-	MeOH	241(4.11)	87-0430-80
$C_{24}H_{31}IO_6$			
Pregna-1,4-diene-3,20-dione, 21-acetoxy-11β,17α-dihydroxy-7α-iodo-16α-methyl-	MeOH	242(4.19)	87-0430-80
$C_{24}H_{31}N_3O_6$			
5H,14H-Pyrrolo[1",2":4',5']pyrazino-[1",2":1,6]pyrido[3,4-b]indole-5,14-dione, 1,2,3,5a,6,11,12,14a-octahydro-12-(2-hydroxy-2-methylpropyl)-5a,6,9-trimethoxy-, [5aS-(5aα,6β,12α,14aβ)]-	EtOH	223(4.62),265(3.66), 296(3.79),302s(3.72)	94-0245-80
$C_{24}H_{31}N_3O_6S_2$			
5,10-Dithia-1,8-diazatricyclo[7.3.0⁴,⁸]-dodecane-7,12-dicarboxylic acid, 2-oxo-3-phenylacetamido-6,6,11,11-tetramethyl-, dimethyl ester,	EtOH	212(4.05)	39-2001-80C

Compound	Solvent	$\lambda_{max}(\log \epsilon)$	Ref.
(3R,4R,7S,12S)- (cont.)			39-2001-80C
(3R,4S,7S,12S)-	EtOH	225(3.92)	39-2001-80C
(3S,4R,7S,12S)-	EtOH	213(3.94)	39-2001-80C
$C_{24}H_{31}N_7O_7$			
Adenosine, 2',3'-O-[[[N-(benzyloxycarbonyl)amino]methyl]ethoxymethylene]-N^6-(2-aminoethyl)-	EtOH	273(4.24)	87-0781-80
$C_{24}H_{32}$			
Bicyclo[4.1.0]heptane, 7,7'-[2,4-bis(1-methylethylidene)-1,3-cyclobutanediylidene]bis-	heptane	207(4.28),245(3.60), 264(3.60)	35-6813-80
[2.2]Paracyclophane, 4,5,7,8,12,13,15-16-octamethyl-	isooctane	236(4.01),266s(3.29), 310(2.64)	88-4901-80
$C_{24}H_{32}N_2O_3$			
1H-Indole, 1,1'-[oxybis(2,1-ethanediyloxy-2,1-ethanediyl)]bis[2,3-dihydro-	EtOH	257(4.27),306(3.62)	121-0379-80
$C_{24}H_{32}N_2O_6$			
Phenol, 2-(1,1-dimethylethyl)-4-[(2,3,5,6,8,9,11,12-octahydro-1,4,7,10,13-benzopentaoxacyclopentadecin-15-yl)azo]-	CHCl$_3$	368(4.35)	18-1550-80
$C_{24}H_{32}N_2O_6S$			
N-Methyl-2-(N-pyridinium)-4-aza-1,3-indanedione betaine decyl sulfate	50% EtOH	208(4.507),236(3.924), 270(3.482),375(4.129)	103-1239-80
N-Methyl-2-(N-pyridinium)-5-aza-1,3-indanedione betaine decyl sulfate	50% EtOH	205(4.478),228(4.305), 278(4.068),290s(3.90), 303s(3.78),360(4.072), 405-626(3.31)	103-1239-80
$C_{24}H_{32}N_4O_7$			
1,4,7,10,13-Pentaoxa-16-azacyclooctadecane, 16-[4-[(4-nitrophenyl)azo]phenyl]-	MeCN	477(4.77)	24-0457-80
$C_{24}H_{32}N_4O_{10}S_2$			
D-Glucitol, 1-S-ethyl-1-C-[6-(methylthio)-9H-purin-9-yl]-1-thio-, 2,3,4,5,6-pentaacetate, (S)-	MeOH	228(4.22),284(4.36), 292(4.36)	136-0241-80C
$C_{24}H_{32}N_6O_7$			
Dehydrochlorinated islanditoxinic amide	n.s.g.	268(4.23)	4-1809-80
$C_{24}H_{32}N_{12}O_4$			
1H-Pyrrole-2-carboxamide, 4-[[[4-[[[(aminoimino)methyl]amino]acetyl]amino]-1-methyl-1H-pyrrol-2-yl]carbonyl]amino]-N-[5-[[(3-amino-3-iminopropyl)amino]carbonyl]-1-methyl-1H-pyrrol-3-yl]-1-methyl-, dihydrochloride	EtOH	237(4.30),306(4.40)	87-1144-80
$C_{24}H_{32}O_4$			
Benzene, 4-[2-[2-(3,4-dimethoxyphenyl)-cyclohexyl]ethyl]-1,2-dimethoxy-, cis-(±)-	EtOH	229(4.17),279(3.72), 287s(3.62)	94-2948-80

Compound	Solvent	$\lambda_{max}(\log \epsilon)$	Ref.
Benzene, 4-[2-[2-(3,4-dimethoxyphenyl)-cyclohexyl]ethyl]-1,2-dimethoxy-, trans-(±)-	EtOH	230(4.22),279(3.77), 287s(3.66)	94-2948-80
D-Homoandrosta-4,6-diene-3,17-dione, 17a-acetoxy-6,17a-dimethyl-, (17aα)-	EtOH	288(4.40)	13-0511-80A
(17aβ)-	EtOH	288(4.40)	13-0511-80A
D-Homoandrosta-4,6-diene-3,17a-dione, 17-acetoxy-6,17-dimethyl-, (17α)-	EtOH	288(4.39)	13-0511-80A
D-Homopregna-1,4-diene-3,20-dione, 17a-acetoxy-	EtOH	244(4.21)	33-1867-80
D-Homopregna-4,6-diene-3,20-dione, 17a-acetoxy-	EtOH	285(4.43)	33-1867-80
D-Homopregna-4,16-diene-3,20-dione, 17a-acetoxy-	EtOH	240(4.23)	33-1867-80
$C_{24}H_{32}O_5$			
D-Homopregn-4-ene-3,20-dione, 17a-acetoxy-6α,7α-epoxy-	EtOH	240(4.18)	33-1867-80
$C_{24}H_{32}O_8$			
Pregna-1,4-diene-3,20-dione, 6β,7β,11β-17α,21-pentahydroxy-16α-methyl-, 21-acetate	MeOH	243(4.15)	87-0430-80
$C_{24}H_{32}O_9$			
β-D-Glucopyranosiduronic acid, 2,3-di-hydroxyestra-1,3,5(10)-trien-17β-yl, potassium salt	H_2O	287(3.62)	95-0867-80
$C_{24}H_{32}O_{10}$			
Acevaltrate	MeOH	204(3.0),256(4.23)	100-0649-80
$C_{24}H_{32}O_{12}$			
Boschnaloside tetraacetate	EtOH	247(4.30)	94-1730-80
2,9,16,23,29,30,31,32-Octaoxapentacy-clo[23.3.1.1^{4,8}.1^{11,15}.1^{18,22}]dotri-acontane-3,10,17,24-tetrone	MeCN	215(2.45)	126-0197-80B
$C_{24}H_{33}N_2O_4$			
Pyridinium, 1-methyl-4-[2-[4-(1,4,7,10-tetraoxa-13-azacyclopentadec-13-yl)-phenyl]ethenyl]-, iodide	MeCN	470(4.92)	24-0457-80
$C_{24}H_{33}N_3O$			
5α-Androstano[3,2-f]pyrazolo[1,5-a]-pyrimidine, 17β-hydroxy-17α-methyl-	MeOH	209(4.41),235(4.66), 238(4.66),287(3.27)	39-0481-80C
5α-Androst-2-eno[2,3-g]pyrazolo[1,5-a]-pyrimidine, 17β-hydroxy-17α-methyl-	MeOH	232(4.60),317(3.40)	39-0481-80C
$C_{24}H_{34}N_2$			
s-Indacene-4,8-diamine, 2,6-bis(1,1-di-methylethyl)-N,N,N',N'-tetramethyl-	dioxan	288(4.34),412(4.00), 476(3.91),720(2.12)	89-0199-80
$C_{24}H_{34}N_2O_{10}$			
3-Pyridinecarboxamide, N,N-diethyl-1,4-dihydro-1-(2,3,4,6-tetra-O-acetyl-β-D-glucopyranosyl]-	MeOH	307(3.45)	23-0387-80
$C_{24}H_{34}O$			
2,4,6,8,10,12-Tridecahexaen-1-ol, 7,11-	n.s.g.	270(4.08),387(4.96)	149-0739-80B

Compound	Solvent	$\lambda_{max}(\log \epsilon)$	Ref.
dimethyl-13-(2,6,6-trimethyl-1-cyclo-hexen-1-yl)-, (all-E)- (cont.)	at 77°K	366.0(4.83)	149-0739-80B
$C_{24}H_{34}O_2$			
1H,4H-Dicyclopenta[a,h]pentalene-2,4(3H)-dione, 10-(1,5-dimethyl-4-hexenyl)-6a,7,7a,8,9,10-hexahydro-6,7a-dimethyl-	EtOH	236(4.04)	94-1043-80
25-Norophiobola-2,6,19-triene-5,8-dione	EtOH	220(4.10),314(3.94)	94-1043-80
25-Norophiobola-3,6,19-triene-5,8-dione	EtOH	255.5(4.19)	94-1043-80
$C_{24}H_{34}O_4$			
D-Homopregn-4-ene-3,20-dione, 17a-acet-oxy-	EtOH	239(4.18)	33-1867-80
5H-Inden-5-one, 4-[2-(3,5-dimethoxy-phenyl)ethyl]-1-(1,1-dimethylethoxy)-1,2,3,6,7,7a-hexahydro-7a-methyl-, (1S-cis)-	CHCl$_3$	255(4.01),280(3.35),320(2.81)	24-0385-80
1-Phenanthrenemethanol, 2-acetoxy-7-ethenyl-1,2,3,4,4a,6,7,8,10,10a-decahydro-1,4a,7-trimethyl-, acetate	n.s.g.	242(4.14)	32-0621-80
Pregn-4-ene-3,20-dione, 18-(acetoxy-methyl)-	MeOH	241(4.25)	24-1106-80
Retinol, 3-acetoxy-, acetate, (3R)-	CHCl	331(4.68)	33-1467-80
$C_{24}H_{34}O_5$			
6H-Dibenzo[b,d]pyran-9-carboxylic acid, 1-acetoxy-6a,7,8,9,10,10a-hexahydro-6,6-dimethyl-3-pentyl-, methyl ester, axial	EtOH	277(3.20),284(3.24)	87-1068-80
equatorial	EtOH	277(3.22),284(3.25)	87-1068-80
Pregn-4-ene-3,20-dione, 21-acetoxy-18-(hydroxymethyl)-, 18a,20-hemi-ketal	MeOH	241(4.24)	24-1106-80
$C_{24}H_{34}O_6$			
Benzene, 1,1'-(2,3-dimethyl-1,4-butane-diyl)bis[3,4,5-trimethoxy-	EtOH	270(3.11)	12-1823-80
$C_{24}H_{35}NO$			
Cyclotetradecanone, 2-[3-(methylphenyl-amino)-2-propenylidene]-	EtOH	255(4.01),384(4.80)	70-0987-80
$C_{24}H_{35}NO_4$			
Daphgracine	MeOH	298(3.85)	138-0393-80
$C_{24}H_{35}N_3O_4$			
3,5-Pyridinedicarboxylic acid, 2,6-bis-[2-(dimethylamino)ethyl]-1,4-dihydro-1-methyl-4-phenyl-, dimethyl ester	EtOH	248(4.23),342(3.84)	94-3163-80
3,5-Pyridinedicarboxylic acid, 2,6-bis-[2-(dimethylamino)ethyl]-1,4-dihydro-4-(2-methylphenyl)-, dimethyl ester	EtOH	245(4.28),359(3.88)	94-3163-80
$C_{24}H_{35}N_3O_5$			
3,5-Pyridinedicarboxylic acid, 2,6-bis-[2-(dimethylamino)ethyl]-1,4-dihydro-4-(4-methoxyphenyl)-, dimethyl ester, dihydrochloride	EtOH	242s(4.22),278s(3.72),359(3.84)	94-3163-80

Compound	Solvent	$\lambda_{max}(\log \epsilon)$	Ref.
$C_{24}H_{35}N_5O_8$			
1,2-Hydrazinedicarboxylic acid, 1,1'-[2-(1,1-dimethylethyl)-2H-isoindole-1,3-diyl]bis-, tetraethyl ester	MeOH	268(3.45),272(3.43), 279(3.45),330(3.79)	88-3471-80
$C_{24}H_{36}N_2O_2S$			
5α-Androst-2-eno[2,3-b]azirin-17-one, 1'-(2-thiazolin-2-yl)-2α,3α-dihydro-, ethylene acetal	n.s.g.	212(4.02)	39-0766-80C
(2β,3β)-	n.s.g.	210(4.25)	39-0766-80C
5α-Androst-2-eno[3,2-e](imidazo[2,1-b]-thiazol)-17-one, 2α,2',3α,3'-tetrahydro-, ethylene acetal	n.s.g.	277(3.22)	39-0766-80C
$C_{24}H_{36}O_3$			
2H-Pyran-2-one, 5,6-dihydro-6-[2-methyl-4-(2,6,6-trimethyl-1-cyclohexen-1-yl)-1,3-butadienyl]-4-(pentyloxy)-, (E,E)-	MeOH	236(4.51),270s(4.20)	44-1181-80
$C_{24}H_{36}O_4$			
5β,14β-Card-20(22)-enolide, 3β,14-dihydroxy-21-methyl-, (21S)-	EtOH	221(4.16)	48-0991-80
5β,14β-Card-20(22)-enolide, 3β,14-dihydroxy-22-methyl-	EtOH	222.5(4.27)	48-0991-80
$C_{24}H_{36}O_5$			
21-Nor-5β,14β-chol-22-en-24-oic acid, 3β,14-dihydroxy-20-oxo-, methyl ester, (E)-	MeOH	227(4.10)	48-1003-80
$C_{24}H_{37}ClN_2O_2S$			
5α-Androstan-17-one, 2β-chloro-3α-[(4,5-dihydro-2-thiazolyl)amino]-, cyclic 1,2-ethanediyl acetal	n.s.g.	214(4.42),225(4.34)	39-0766-80C
$C_{24}H_{37}Cl_3O_2$			
3,5-Cyclohexadiene-1,2-dione, 3,4,6-trichloro-5-octadecyl-	CCl_4	455(3.23)	104-0129-80
$C_{24}H_{38}N_8$			
2-Pyrimidinamine, 4-(4-ethyl-3,5-dipropyl-1H-pyrazol-1-yl)-N-(5-hexyl-1H-1,2,4-triazol-3-yl)-6-methyl-	EtOH	261(4.49),302(4.16)	103-1275-80
4-Pyrimidinamine, 2-(4-ethyl-3,5-dipropyl-1H-pyrazol-1-yl)-N-(5-hexyl-1H-1,2,4-triazol-3-yl)-6-methyl-	EtOH	229(4.13),266(4.38), 300(4.00)	103-1271-80
$C_{24}H_{38}O_4$			
24-Nor-5β,14β-chol-20(22)-en-23-oic acid, 3β,14-dihydroxy-, methyl ester	MeOH	229(4.22)	48-1012-80
$C_{24}H_{39}CoN_4O_9S_3$			
Cobalt, tris[ethyl (4-morpholinylthioxomethyl)carbamato]-	$CHCl_3$	256(4.69),302s(4.35), 473(2.53),625(2.57)	97-0268-80
$C_{24}H_{40}N_2O$			
2,5-Cyclohexadien-1-one, 4-[(diethylamino)-1-piperidinylmethylene]-2,6-bis(1,1-dimethylethyl)-	isooctane	425(4.54)	73-2675-80

Compound	Solvent	$\lambda_{max}(\log \epsilon)$	Ref.
$C_{24}H_{40}N_4OS_3$ 2H-1,3,5-Thiadiazine-3(4H)-carbothioic acid, 6-(dicyclohexylamino)-4-[(1,1-dimethylethyl)imino]-2-thioxo-, S-butyl ester	CH_2Cl_2	258(4.18),293(4.11), 335s(3.79)	24-0079-80
$C_{24}H_{40}N_4O_5$ Tetradecanamide, N-[[[2,3,3a,9a-tetra-hydro-3-hydroxy-2-(hydroxymethyl)-6H-furo[2',3':4,5]oxazolo[3,2-a]-pyrimidin-6-ylidene]amino]methyl-, tetrafluoroborate	MeOH	240(4.08),269(4.20)	44-1577-80
$C_{24}H_{40}O_3$ 2H-Pyran-2-one, 3,5-dibutyl-6-(1-butyl-1-heptenyl)-4-hydroxy-	EtOH	220(4.15),300(3.97)	88-1281-80
$C_{24}H_{40}O_4$ 2H-Pyran-2-one, 3,5-dibutyl-6-(1-butyl-2-oxoheptyl)-4-hydroxy- (elasnin)	EtOH EtOH	291(3.89) 293(3.89)	44-3268-80 88-1281-80
$C_{24}H_{40}O_6$ 1-Octadecanone, 12,14-dihydroxy-1-(2,4,6-trihydroxyphenyl)-	MeOH	227(4.15),286(4.23), 330s(3.43)	102-1183-80
$C_{24}H_{41}BN_4$ Guanidine, N,N'-dicyclohexyl-N-(dipro-pylboryl)-N''-2-pyridinyl-	heptane	213(4.15),294(4.15), 370(3.79)	70-0481-80
$C_{24}H_{41}NO_4$ 1-Pyrrolidineheptanoic acid, 2-oxo-5-(3-oxo-1-dodecenyl)-, methyl ester, [R-(E)]-	EtOH	215(4.13)	94-1449-80
$C_{24}H_{42}N_4O_6$ Tetradecanamide, N-[[(1-β-D-arabino-furanosyl-1,2-dihydro-2-oxo-4-pyr-imidinyl)amino]methyl]-	MeOH	238(4.04),276(4.11)	44-1577-80
$C_{24}H_{42}O_2$ 1,2-Benzenediol, 4-octadecyl-	EtOH	283(3.70)	104-0129-80
$C_{24}H_{42}O_4$ 2H-Pyran-2-one, 3,5-dibutyl-6-(1-butyl-2-hydroxyheptyl)-4-hydroxy- (dihydro-elasnin)	EtOH	292(3.81)	44-3268-80
$C_{24}H_{43}NO$ 1H-Pyrrole-2-carboxaldehyde, 5-nona-decyl-	MeCN	297(4.20)	44-4980-80
$C_{24}H_{44}$ [11.11]Betweenanene	heptane	202s(3.76),208(3.83), 212(3.83)	88-3527-80
Tridecalene, docosahydro-	heptane	200(4.00)	88-3527-80
$C_{24}H_{46}N_2O$ Cycloheptadecanone, 2-[1,3-bis(dimeth-ylamino)-2-propenyl]-	EtOH	378(4.43)	70-0987-80

Compound	Solvent	$\lambda_{max}(\log \epsilon)$	Ref.
$C_{24}H_{46}O_3$			
2,4-Eicosanedione, 7-hydroxy-7,11,15,19- tetramethyl-	isoPrOH	274(3.72)	44-0803-80
$C_{24}H_{60}Si_5$			
Cyclohexasilane, dodecaethyl-	isooctane	205s(5.20),237(3.76), 259s(3.28)	101-00C5-80K

Compound	Solvent	$\lambda_{max}(\log \epsilon)$	Ref.
$C_{25}H_{13}F_3O_2$ Benz[a]anthracene-7,12-dione, 5-[3-(tri- fluoromethyl)phenyl]- (16% isomer)	CHCl$_3$	249(4.46),255s(4.43), 288(4.64),334(4.61), 363s(3.51),409(3.62)	44-1424-80
$C_{25}H_{14}N_4$ Pyrido[1,2-b]indazole-2,3-dicarbo- nitrile, 1,4-diphenyl-	MeOH	266(4.65),345(4.19), 385(3.91),404(3.88)	44-0090-80
$C_{25}H_{15}NO_5$ 1-Azulenecarbonitrile, 3,3-bis(benzoyl- oxy)-2,3-dihydro-2-oxo-	CHCl$_3$	388(4.40),408s(4.14)	138-0197-80
$C_{25}H_{16}ClNO_2S_3$ Benzeneethanethioamide, 4-chloro- α-(4,5-dibenzoyl-1,3-dithiol-2- ylidene)-	CHCl$_3$	308(4.20),384(4.22)	39-2693-80C
$C_{25}H_{16}ClNO_4S$ Benzenesulfonamide, N-(12-chloro-6,11- dihydro-6,11-dioxo-5-naphthacenyl)- 4-methyl-	toluene	422(3.87)	104-1651-80
$C_{25}H_{16}N_2O$ Benzo[h]phenanthro[9,10-b][1,6]naph- thyridin-10(11H)-one, 11-methyl-	MeOH	240(3.99),266(4.05), 273(3.41),305(3.86), 348(3.36),365(3.26), 382(3.11)	39-0512-80C
	MeOH-acid	232(4.13),265(4.04), 273(4.04),304(3.83), 365(3.26),382(3.07)	39-0512-80C
$C_{25}H_{16}N_2O_2$ Methanone, pyrazolo[5,1-a]isoquinoline- 1,2-diylbis[phenyl-	DMSO	280(4.41),325s(3.88), 340s(3.80),435(3.08)	44-0090-80
Methanone, pyrazolo[1,5-a]quinoline- 2,3-diylbis[phenyl-	MeOH	253(4.53),324s(4.13), 335(4.18),350(4.11)	44-0090-80
$C_{25}H_{16}N_2O_3$ 3-Furancarbonitrile, 2-[(1,3-benzodi- oxol-5-ylmethylene)amino]-4,5-diphen- yl-	MeOH	421(4.38)	73-1581-80
$C_{25}H_{16}N_2S$ Thieno[3',4':3,4]pyrazolo[5,1-a]iso- quinoline-10-S^{IV}, 9,11-diphenyl-	MeOH	233(4.55),262(4.32), 333(4.40),386(3.75), 495(4.36)	44-0090-80
Thieno[3',4':3,4]pyrazolo[1,5-a]quino- line-8-S^{IV}, 7,9-diphenyl-	MeOH	253(4.50),285(4.34), 325(4.17),336(4.22), 352(4.20)	44-0090-80
$C_{25}H_{16}N_4$ Pyridazino[4',5':3,4]pyrazolo[5,1-a]- isoquinoline, 9,12-diphenyl-	CHCl$_3$	273s(4.58),295(4,75), 377(4.46)	44-0090-80
$C_{25}H_{16}O_2$ 5,12-Naphthacenedione, 6-(phenylmeth- yl)-	MeOH	237(4.93),242(4.92), 273s(4.71),282(4.74), 293(4.78),391(3.77)	44-1817-80

Compound	Solvent	$\lambda_{max}(\log \epsilon)$	Ref.
$C_{25}H_{16}O_3$			
Benz[a]anthracene-7,12-dione, 8-methoxy-5-phenyl-	CHCl₃	289(4.56),298(4.50), 392(3.99)	138-0827-80
Benz[a]anthracene-7,12-dione, 9-methoxy-5-phenyl-	CHCl₃	299(4.33),346(3.93), 383(3.56),425(3.66), 440s(3.63)	138-0827-80
Benz[a]anthracene-7,12-dione, 10-methoxy-5-phenyl-	CHCl₃	292(4.67),344(3.90), 380(3.87),425s(3.44)	138-0827-80
Benz[a]anthracene-7,12-dione, 11-methoxy-5-phenyl-	CHCl₃	292(4.01),338(2.99), 362(3.16),403(3.23)	138-0827-80
6H-Naphthaceno[1,12-bc]furan-6,12(7H)-dione, 6a,12a-dihydro-1-phenyl-	CHCl₃	260(4.63),275s(4.47), 280s(4.42),295(4.38), 305s(4.31),360(4.25)	39-1654-80C
$C_{25}H_{16}O_4$			
5,11-Naphthacenedione, 6-methoxy-12-phenoxy-	toluene	447(4.16),469(4.16)	104-1651-80
5,12-Naphthacenedione, 6-methoxy-11-phenoxy-	toluene	400(3.82)	104-1651-80
2H-Pyran-2-one, 4-hydroxy-6-methyl-3-[1-oxo-3-(1-pyrenyl)-2-propenyl]-	MeOH	431(4.1)	83-0344-80
$C_{25}H_{17}ClN_4O_3$			
1H-Isoindole-1,3(2H)-dione, 2-[[4-(2-benzoyl-4-chlorophenyl)-5-methyl-4H-1,2,4-triazol-3-yl]methyl]-	EtOH	219(4.81),238s(4.22), 256(4.17),285(3.72)	4-0575-80
$C_{25}H_{17}ClN_4O_4$			
1H-Isoindole-1,3(2H)-dione, 2-[[4-(2-benzoyl-4-chlorophenyl)-5-(hydroxymethyl)-4H-1,2,4-triazol-3-yl]methyl]-	EtOH	218(4.83),238s(4.22), 255(4.17),285(3.76)	4-0575-80
$C_{25}H_{17}ClO$			
2,4-Pentadien-1-one, 5-chloro-1,5-di-1-naphthalenyl-, (Z,E)-	EtOH	218(4.85),355(4.53)	40-1804-80
$C_{25}H_{17}NO$			
Pyridine, 3-[2-(4-naphth[2,1-b]furan-2-ylphenyl)ethenyl]-	DMF	324(4.33),372(4.81)	33-1311-80
$C_{25}H_{17}NO_2S_3$			
Benzeneethanethioamide, α-(4,5-dibenzoyl-1,3-dithiol-2-ylidene)-	CHCl₃	305(4.18),383(4.26)	39-2693-80C
$C_{25}H_{17}NO_3$			
5,11-Naphthacenedione, 6-(methylamino)-12-phenoxy-	toluene	524(4.15),559(4.07)	104-1651-80
5,12-Naphthacenedione, 6-(methylamino)-11-phenoxy-	toluene	402(3.73),502(4.09)	104-1651-80
$C_{25}H_{17}NS$			
Pyridine, 3-[2-(4-naphtho[2,1-b]thien-2-ylphenyl)ethenyl]-	DMF	289(4.15),370(4.76)	33-1311-80
$C_{25}H_{17}N_3S_3$			
Benzeneethanethioamide, α-(4,7-diphenyl-1,3-dithiolo[4,5-d]pyridazin-2-ylidene)-	CHCl₃	275(4.55),382(4.35)	39-2693-80C
$C_{25}H_{17}N_7$			
Benzo[1,2-d:3,4-d']bistriazole, 2,7-di-	DMF	348(4.75)	33-1311-80

Compound	Solvent	$\lambda_{max}(\log \epsilon)$	Ref.
hydro-2-phenyl-7-[4-[2-(3-pyridinyl)-ethenyl]phenyl]- (cont.)			33-1311-80
$C_{25}H_{18}Cl_2N_4O_2$ Benzenamine, 4-[3-(4-chlorophenyl)-4-[3-(4-chlorophenyl)-1,2,4-oxadiazol-5-yl]-5-isoxazolyl]-N,N-dimethyl-	EtOH	277(4.40)	39-1635-80C
$C_{25}H_{18}N_2O$ 1H-Indol-3-amine, 1-methyl-N-(4-oxo-1(4H)-naphthalenylidene)-	ligroin	590(4.12)	7-0009-80
$C_{25}H_{18}N_2O_2$ Methanone, (5,6-dihydropyrazolo[5,1-a]-isoquinoline-1,2-diyl)bis[phenyl-	MeOH	257(4.40),427(4.18)	44-0090-80
$C_{25}H_{18}N_2O_2S$ 3H-Phenoxazin-3-one, 7-[(4-methylphen-yl)thio]-2-(phenylamino)-	n.s.g.	485(4.50)	103-0032-80
$C_{25}H_{18}N_2O_4$ 3H-Dibenz[f,ij]isoquinoline-2,7-dione, 1-acetoxy-3-methyl-6-(phenylamino)-	n.s.g.	345(3.98),514(4.16)	124-0755-80
$C_{25}H_{18}N_6O_6$ Benzenamine, N,N-dimethyl-4-[3-(4-ni-trophenyl)-4-[3-(4-nitrophenyl)-1,2,4-oxadiazol-5-yl]-5-isoxazolyl]-	EtOH	277(4.34)	39-1635-80C
$C_{25}H_{18}O_3$ 5,12-Epoxynaphthacene-6,11-dione, 5.5a.11a,12-tetrahydro-5-(phen-ylmethyl)-, (5α,5aα,11aα,12α)-	MeOH	227(4.47),251(3.99),308(3.08)	44-1817-80
$C_{25}H_{18}O_3S_2$ Naphtho[1,8-bc]furan-5-one, 4-[[4-(1,3-dithiolan-2-yl)-3-furanyl]methyl]-2-phenyl-	CHCl₃	267(4.25),401(4.16)	39-0643-80C
Spiro[6H-anthra[1,9-bc:6,7-c']difuran-11(7H),2'-[1,3]dithiolan]-6-one, 6a,11a-dihydro-1-phenyl-	CHCl₃	279(4.36),353(4.18)	39-0643-80C
$C_{25}H_{18}O_5$ Benzo[a]pyrene-1,3-diol, 6-methoxy-, diacetate	MeOH	256(4.60),260(4.60),267(4.64),289(4.55),301(4.63),368(4.19),380(4.34),387(4.39),391(4.35),393(4.34),399(--),413(4.01),433(3.52)	87-0919-80
$C_{25}H_{19}BClNO$ Boron, [2-[[(2-chlorophenyl)imino]-methyl]phenolato-N,O]diphenyl-, (T-4)-	CHCl₃	270(4.11),345(4.00)	49-0863-80
$C_{25}H_{19}BN_2O_3$ Boron, [2-[[(3-nitrophenyl)imino]meth-yl]phenolato]diphenyl-, (T-4)-	CHCl₃	263(4.24),343(3.95)	49-0863-80
Boron, [2-[[(4-nitrophenyl)imino]meth-yl]phenolato]diphenyl-, (T-4)-	CHCl₃	345(4.21)	49-0863-80

Compound	Solvent	$\lambda_{max}(\log \epsilon)$	Ref.
$C_{25}H_{19}ClO_2$			
Spiro[benzofuran-2(3H),1'(4'H)-naphthalen]-4'-one, 3'-chloro-5,7-dimethyl-3-phenyl-, trans-(±)-	EtOH	245s(5.14),285(4.95), 294s(4.90)	39-1986-80C
$C_{25}H_{19}F_6N_2$			
Quinolinium, 1-methyl-2-[3-[1-methyl-4-(trifluoromethyl)-2(1H)-quinolinylidene]-1-propenyl]-4-(trifluoromethyl)-, perchlorate	EtOH	588(--),637(5.14)	124-0827-80
	MeCN	588(--),632(--)	124-0827-80
Quinolinium, 1-methyl-4-[3-[1-methyl-2-(trifluoromethyl)-4(1H)-quinolinylidene]-1-propenyl]-2-(trifluoromethyl)-, fluorosulfate	EtOH	670(--),731(5.29)	124-0827-80
	MeCN	667(--),729(--)	124-0827-80
$C_{25}H_{19}N$			
Pyridine, 2-[2-[4-[2-(2-naphthalenyl)-ethenyl]phenyl]ethenyl]-	DMF	369(4.85)	33-1311-80
Pyridine, 3-[2-[4-[2-(1-naphthalenyl)-ethenyl]phenyl]ethenyl]-	DMF	366(4.72)	33-1311-80
Pyridine, 3-[2-[4-[2-(2-naphthalenyl)-ethenyl]phenyl]ethenyl]-	DMF	301(4.16),366(4.84)	33-1311-80
Pyridine, 4-[2-[4-[2-(2-naphthalenyl)-ethenyl]phenyl]ethenyl]-	DMF	368(4.83)	33-1311-80
$C_{25}H_{19}NO_3$			
Benzoic acid, 4-methyl-, 1,2-dihydro-2-oxo-4,6-diphenyl-3-pyridinyl ester	EtOH	333(4.15)	39-2743-80C
	CHCl₃	335(4.20)	39-2743-80C
$C_{25}H_{19}N_3O_2S$			
4H-1,3-Oxazin-4-one, 6-methyl-5-(methylthio)-2-(2-quinolinyl)-2(1H)-quinolinylidenemethyl)-	EtOH	229(4.94),303(4.32), 317(4.31),360s(--), 439(4.50),464(4.48)	94-0795-80
$C_{25}H_{19}N_3O_4$			
1H-Pyridazino[4,5-b]indol-1-one, 4-(1,3-benzodioxol-5-yl)-3-benzoyl-2,3,4,5-tetrahydro-5-methyl-	EtOH	211(4.65),240s(4.38), 324(4.24)	4-0249-80
$C_{25}H_{20}BNO$			
Boron, diphenyl[2-[(phenylimino)methyl]-phenolato-N,O]-, (T-4)-	CHCl₃	265(4.08),338(3.99)	49-0863-80
$C_{25}H_{20}N$			
Pyrido[1,2-f]phenanthridinium, 2,6-dimethyl-8-phenyl-, perchlorate	EtOH	213(4.36),260(4.48), 283(4.56),300(4.38), 335(4.31),380(4.19), 396(4.25)	39-1879-80C
$C_{25}H_{20}N_2O$			
3H-Pyrazol-3-one, 4-(3-[1,1'-biphenyl]-4-yl-2-propenylidene)-2,4-dihydro-5-methyl-2-phenyl-	n.s.g.	250(4.42),385(4.69), 485(3.35)	124-0642-80
$C_{25}H_{20}N_2O_6$			
Uridine, 5-(pyrenyl)-	MeOH	241(4.65),265(4.40), 276(4.55),324(4.28), 338(4.43)	88-2813-80
$C_{25}H_{20}N_2O_6S_2$			
10H-Benzo[b]thioxanthene-9-carboxamide,	MeOH-borax	471(4.54)	88-0247-80

Compound	Solvent	$\lambda_{max}(\log \epsilon)$	Ref.
5a,6,6a,7,10a,12-hexahydro-1,8,11-trihydroxy-10,12-dioxo-7-[(phenyl-thioxomethyl)amino]-, anti (cont.)			88-0247-80
syn	MeOH-borax	454s(--),478(4.59), 508s(--)	88-0247-80
$(C_{25}H_{20}N_4Ni)_n$			
Poly[methylene(5,10,15,20-tetramethyl-21H,23H-porphine-2,12-diyl) nickel complex (absorbances given)	CHCl$_3$	302(0.11),336(0.1), 427(1.04),537(0.14)	5-1082-80
$C_{25}H_{20}N_4O_3$			
4,10-Iminobenzo[4,5]cyclohepta[1,2-c]-pyrrole-1,3,9(2H)-trione, 11-(4,6-dimethyl-2-pyrimidinyl)-3a,4,10,10a-tetrahydro-2-phenyl-, (3aα,4β,10β-10aα)-	EtOH	215(4.08),240(4.04)	39-0331-80C
$C_{25}H_{20}N_4O_3S$			
4-Isothiazolecarboxylic acid, 5-[[[bis-(phenylamino)methylene]amino]carbo-nyl]-3-phenyl-, methyl ester	MeOH	240(4.53),282(4.44)	39-1667-80C
$C_{25}H_{20}O_2$			
Cyclobuta[b]naphthalene-3,8-dione, 1,2,2a,8a-tetrahydro-2a-methyl-1,1-diphenyl-, cis	CHCl$_3$	242(4.12),252(4.11), 302(3.32),310(3.30)	18-0757-80
Cyclobuta[b]naphthalene-3,8-dione, 1,2,2a,8a-tetrahydro-8a-methyl-1,1-diphenyl-, cis	CHCl$_3$	243(4.14),252(4.13), 302(3.31)	18-0757-80
4-Cyclopentene-1,3-dione, 2,4-bis(4-methylphenyl)-5-phenyl-	MeCN	227(4.40),280s(--), 352(3.99)	24-0408-80
4-Cyclopentene-1,3-dione, 4,5-bis(4-methylphenyl)-2-phenyl-	MeCN	236(4.31),286s(--), 339(4.03)	24-0408-80
$C_{25}H_{20}O_4$			
4-Cyclopentene-1,3-dione, 2,4-bis(4-methoxyphenyl)-5-phenyl-	MeCN	232(4.36),280s(--), 352(3.99)	24-0408-80
4-Cyclopentene-1,3-dione, 4,5-bis(4-methoxyphenyl)-2-phenyl-	MeCN	247(4.34),365(4.07)	24-0408-80
Spiro[4H-dinaphtho[2,1-f:1',2'-h][1,5]-dioxonin-5(6H),2'-[1,3]dioxolane]	CHCl$_3$	244(4.59),299(4.04), 331(3.86)	49-0413-80
$C_{25}H_{20}O_7$			
6H,11H-[2]Benzopyrano[4,3-c][1]benzo-pyran-11-one, 10-hydroxy-7,9-di-methoxy-6-(4-methoxyphenyl)-	EtOH	253(4.10),295(3.87), 345(4.13)	12-0137-80
$C_{25}H_{20}O_9$			
Benzoic acid, 5-[(3-carboxy-4-hydroxy-5-methylphenyl)(3-carboxy-5-methyl-4-oxo-2,5-cyclohexadien-1-ylidene)meth-yl]-2-hydroxy-3-methyl-	n.s.g.	535(2.00)	147-0409-80A
$C_{25}H_{20}O_{10}$			
Benzo[h][1]benzopyrano[5,4,3-cde][1]-benzopyran-5,12-dione, 10-[(6-deoxy-β-D-galactopyranosyl)oxy]-6-hydroxy-1-methyl-	EtOH	236(4.51),263(4.42)	87-0549-80

Compound	Solvent	$\lambda_{max}(\log \epsilon)$	Ref.
$C_{25}H_{20}O_{11}$ Benzo[h][1]benzopyrano[5,4,3-cde][1]-benzopyran-5,12-dione, 10-(β-D-glucopyranosyloxy)-6-hydroxy-1-methyl-	EtOH	237(4.61),264(4.53)	87-0549-80
$C_{25}H_{21}BN_2O$ Boron, diphenyl[2-[[(2-pyridinylmethyl)imino]methyl]phenolato]-, (T-4)-	CHCl$_3$	285(4.00),390(3.54)	49-0863-80
Boron, diphenyl[2-[[(3-pyridinylmethyl)imino]methyl]phenolato]-, (T-4)-	CHCl$_3$	290(3.96),390(3.46)	49-0863-80
Boron, diphenyl[2-[[(4-pyridinylmethyl)imino]methyl]phenolato]-, (T-4)-	CHCl$_3$	290(3.94),400(3.45)	49-0863-80
Boron, (2-hydroxybenzaldehyde phenylhydrazonato)diphenyl-, (T-4)-	CHCl$_3$	300(4.06),345(4.34)	49-0863-80
$C_{25}H_{21}ClN_2O_4$ 2H-1,4-Benzodiazepin-2-one, 7-chloro-1-[2-(2,5-dimethoxyphenyl)-2-oxo-ethyl]-1,3-dihydro-6-phenyl-	MeOH	227(4.64),250s(4.36), 330(3.75)	73-3593-80
$C_{25}H_{21}ClO_9$ Benzoic acid, 3-[2-chloro-4-(methoxycarbonyl)phenoxy]-4-methoxy-5-[4-(methoxycarbonyl)phenoxy]-, methyl ester	MeOH	253(3.62)	35-1671-80
$C_{25}H_{21}NO_4$ 8H-Naphtho[2,3-a]phenoxazine-8,13(14H)-dione, 2-(1,1-dimethylpropyl)-7-hydroxy-	THF	267(4.71),607(4.29), 670(4.20)	104-1884-80
3H-Pyrano[2,3-c]acridin-9-ol, 6-methoxy-3,3-dimethyl-7-phenoxy-(9-hydroxy-7-phenoxynoracronycin)	MeOH	252(4.42),280(4.79), 350(--),392(--), 455(--)	5-0503-80
$C_{25}H_{21}N_3O_2$ 6H-Anthra[1,9-cd]isoxazol-6-one, 5-(phenylamino)-3-piperidino-	dioxan	255(4.52),490(4.33), 520(4.43)	103-0704-80
$C_{25}H_{21}N_3O_3$ 6H-Anthra[1,9-cd]isoxazol-6-one, 5-[(4-methylphenyl)amino]-3-morpholino-	dioxan	262(4.58),485(4.40), 518(4.49)	103-0704-80
$C_{25}H_{21}N_3O_4$ 9,10-Anthracenedione, 1-azido-2-[4-(1,1-dimethylpropyl)phenoxy]-4-hydroxy-	THF	250(4.57),445(3.80)	104-1884-80
$C_{25}H_{21}N_7O_6$ Benzenecarboximidamide, N-[1-[4-(dimethylamino)phenyl]-2-[3-(4-nitrophenyl)-1,2,4-oxadiazol-5-yl]ethenyl]-N'-hydroxy-4-nitro-	EtOH	274(4.62),340(4.57)	39-1635-80C
$C_{25}H_{22}ClNO_2$ 1,10-Anthracenedione, 2-chloro-4-(ethylamino)-9-(2,4,6-trimethylphenyl)-	hexane	546(3.90),590(4.03), 641(3.94)	104-0159-80
	benzene	551s(3.91),590(4.07), 641(3.98)	104-0159-80
	isoPrOH	541s(3.90),584(4.03), 632(3.92)	104-0159-80

Compound	Solvent	$\lambda_{max}(\log \epsilon)$	Ref.
$C_{25}H_{22}ClNO_5S_3$ 1,3-Dithiole-4,5-dicarboxylic acid, 2-[2-[(4-chlorobenzoyl)amino]-1-(4-methylphenyl)-2-thioxoethylidene]-, diethyl ester	CHCl$_3$	323(4.14),442(4.32)	39-2693-80C
$C_{25}H_{22}NO$ Benz[a]acridinium, 8,9,10,11-tetrahydro-9,9-dimethyl-11-oxo-7-phenyl-, bromide	n.s.g.	232(4.55),291(4.34), 348(3.85)	104-1592-80
chloride	n.s.g.	231(4.55),289(4.23), 350(3.75)	104-1592-80
perchlorate	n.s.g.	234(4.84),284(4.40), 358(4.00)	104-1592-80
$C_{25}H_{22}NS$ 2-Benzothiopyrylium, 1-[2-[4-(dimethylamino)phenyl]ethenyl]-3-phenyl-, perchlorate	CH$_2$Cl$_2$	740(5.03)	103-0599-80
Thiopyrylium, 2-[4-(dimethylamino)phenyl]-4,6-diphenyl-	n.s.g.	378(4.41),610(4.49)	39-1345-80C
$C_{25}H_{22}N_2O_4$ 4,4'-Diacetyl-2,2'-isopropylidenedi-8-quinolinol	C$_6$H$_{12}$	269(4.68),330(3.67), 342(3.69),370s(3.46)	18-0809-80
	6M HCl	275(4.70),324s(3.86), 337s(3.94),395s(3.40)	18-0809-80
	pH 13	283(4.59),330s(3.66), 342s(3.61),396(3.55)	18-0809-80
	MeOH	266(4.67),324s(3.75), 335(3.76),365s(3.50)	18-0809-80
$C_{25}H_{22}N_2O_7$ 1(2H)-Quinolineacetic acid, 4-methoxy-3-[(4-methoxy-2-oxo-1(2H)-quinolinyl)acetyl]-2-oxo-, methyl ester	EtOH	214(4.48),260(4.14), 291(4.10)	78-1385-80
$C_{25}H_{22}O_4$ 1,3-Azulenedicarboxylic acid, 6-(1H-inden-3-yl)-, diethyl ester	CHCl$_3$	247(4.48),268(4.44), 309(4.63),348(4.39), 372(4.29),516(2.91), 552s(2.80),605s(2.42)	18-1647-80
$C_{25}H_{22}O_6$ Cyclomorusin	MeOH	223(4.45),255(4.38), 283(4.43),383(4.19)	142-1531-80B
	MeOH-AlCl$_3$	229(4.51),265(4.35), 285(4.41),379(4.24), 429(3.84)	142-1531-80B
$C_{25}H_{22}O_7$ 4H,8H-Benzo[1,2-b:3,4-b']dipyran-4-one, 2-(2,4-dihydroxyphenyl)-5-hydroxy-8,8-dimethyl-3-[3-(1-methylethenyl)-oxiranyl]-	EtOH	213(4.50),273(4.44), 305s(3.87),310s(3.84), 350s(3.71)	4-0641-80
	EtOH-NaOEt	277(4.38),300s(4.14), 320s(4.05),393(3.98)	4-0641-80
	EtOH-AlCl$_3$	213(4.45),226(4.44), 281(4.46),345(3.85), 405(3.59)	4-0641-80

Compound	Solvent	$\lambda_{max}(\log \epsilon)$	Ref.
$C_{25}H_{22}O_{10}$			
Isosilybin	EtOH	288(4.30),325(4.06)	39-0775-80C
Ovoic acid	MeOH	214(4.63),272(4.19), 302(3.75)	102-0885-80
$C_{25}H_{23}BrO_7$			
α-D-xylo-Heptofuranuronic acid, 5,5,6,6-tetradehydro-5,6-dideoxy-1,2-0-(1-methylethylidene)-3-0-(phenylmethyl)-, 2-(4-bromophenyl)-2-oxoethyl ester	MeCN	206(4.26),255(4.20)	33-1181-80
$C_{25}H_{23}F_3O_4S$			
Benzothiopyrylium, 2,4-bis(4-methoxy-phenyl)-5,6,7,8-tetrahydro-, tri-fluoroacetate	CH_2Cl_2	296(4.17),450(3.62)	104-0170-80
$C_{25}H_{23}N$			
Benzenamine, N,N-dimethyl-4-[4-(2-naph-thalenyl)-1,3,6-cycloheptatrien-1-yl]-	heptane	216(--),240(--), 364(4.491)	97-0214-80
Benz[f]isoquinoline, 1,2,3,4-tetrahy-dro-2,2-dimethyl-1-(2-naphthalenyl)-	EtOH	224(5.06),276s(4.08)	4-1563-80
$C_{25}H_{23}NO_5S_3$			
1,3-Dithiole-4,5-dicarboxylic acid, 2-[2-(benzoylamino)-1-(4-methyl-phenyl)-2-thioxoethylidene]-, diethyl ester	$CHCl_3$	323(4.19),441(4.30)	39-2693-80C
$C_{25}H_{23}NO_6$			
Benzoic acid, 5-[(3-carboxy-5-methyl-4-oxo-2,5-cyclohexadien-1-ylidene)-[4-(dimethylamino)phenyl]methyl]-2-hydroxy-3-methyl-	n.s.g.	568(4.45)	147-0409-80A
$C_{25}H_{23}N_2O_2P$			
Phosphorin, 1,1-dihydro-1,1-dimethoxy-2,6-diphenyl-4-(phenylazo)-	MeOH	255(4.20),395(4.50), 453(4.42)	24-3313-80
$C_{25}H_{23}N_2S$			
Thiazolium, 2-[2-[4-(dimethylamino)-phenyl]ethenyl]-3,5-diphenyl-	H_2O	550(4.67)	140-1570-80
protonated	H_2O	382(4.42)	140-1570-80
neutral	H_2O	290(4.28)	140-1570-80
$C_{25}H_{23}N_3$			
Propanedinitrile, [3-(diethylamino)-4-methyl-2,5-diphenyl-2,4-cyclopenta-dien-1-ylidene]-	MeCN	303(3.99),369(4.13), 615(3.66)	24-0424-80
$C_{25}H_{23}N_3O_4$			
Cyclopropanecarboxylic acid, 2-[[(4-ni-trophenyl)hydrazono]phenylmethyl]-3-phenyl-, ethyl ester	MeOH	222(3.42),287(2.88), 395(3.49)	4-0541-80
$C_{25}H_{24}$			
Tetracyclo[3.3.1.0^{2,8}.0^{4,6}]nonane, 1,4-dimethyl-3,9-bis(phenylmethylene)-, (E,E)-	MeCN	225s(4.20),295(4.44)	24-3932-80

Compound	Solvent	$\lambda_{max}(\log \epsilon)$	Ref.
$C_{25}H_{24}ClN_3O_5S$			
Benzenesulfonamide, 5-[(4-amino-3-chloro-9,10-dihydro-9,10-dioxo-1-anthracenyl)amino]-N-(3-methoxypropyl)-2-methyl-	n.s.g.	573(4.09),606(4.06)	93-1963-80
$C_{25}H_{24}N_2$			
1-Aziridinamine, N-[[2-(2-butenyl)phenyl]methylene]-2,3-diphenyl-, [1(2E),2α,3β]-	MeOH	295(4.01)	44-3756-80
[1(2Z),2α,3β]-	MeOH	293(3.99)	44-3756-80
1-Aziridinamine, N-[[2-(3-butenyl)phenyl]methylene]-2,3-diphenyl-	MeOH	290(4.02)	44-3756-80
$C_{25}H_{24}N_2O_2$			
Cyclopropanecarboxylic acid, 2-phenyl-3-[phenyl(phenylhydrazono)methyl]-, ethyl ester	MeOH	223(3.26),237s(3.18), 328(3.26)	4-0541-80
$C_{25}H_{24}O$			
Methanone, [4-(2-naphthalenyl)bicyclo[2.2.2]oct-1-yl]phenyl-	4:1 C_6H_{11}Me-isopentane	265(3.74),274(3.74), 285s(2.72),303(2.72), 350s(1.78)	44-3933-80
$C_{25}H_{24}O_4$			
Hispaglabridin B	MeOH	280(4.17),290s(4.11), 309(3.67)	100-0259-80
$C_{25}H_{24}O_5$			
4H-Anthra[1,2-b]pyran-4-one, 7,11,12-trimethoxy-5-methyl-2-(1-methyl-1-propenyl)-, (E)-	EtOH	245(4.52),264(4.89), 295(4.23),390(3.99)	44-3061-80
Benzeneacetic acid, 2-methoxy-5-[(2-methoxyphenyl)acetyl]-, 4-methylphenyl ester	EtOH	220(4.46),274(4.27)	49-0081-80
Phenanthrene, 2,3-dimethoxy-9-(2,4,5-trimethoxyphenyl)-	EtOH	203(4.80),255(4.86), 279(4.57),294s(4.40), 335(3.77),352(3.46)	94-2948-80
Phenanthrene, 2,3-dimethoxy-10-(2,4,5-trimethoxyphenyl)-	EtOH	203(4.74),257(4.86), 279(4.58),307s(4.20), 336(3.61),354(3.34)	94-2948-80
$C_{25}H_{24}O_6$			
1(2H)-Anthracenone, 3-(benzoyloxy)-3,4-dihydro-6,8,9-trimethoxy-3-methyl-, (S)-	MeOH	225(4.57),266(4.78), 320(3.70),332(3.72), 366(3.88)	78-2449-80
Kuwanon A	EtOH	208(4.49),261(4.26), 283s(4.11),325s(3.93)	142-1531-80B
	EtOH-AlCl₃	208(4.54),269(4.33), 373(3.81)	142-1531-80B
Morusin	EtOH	206(4.49),220s(4.43), 270(4.60),300s(4.00), 320s(3.90),350(3.81)	142-1531-80B
	EtOH-AlCl₃	279(4.63),338(3.89), 415(3.79)	142-1531-80B
$C_{25}H_{24}O_7$			
4H,8H-Benzo[1,2-b:3,4-b']dipyran-4-one, 2-(2,4-dihydroxyphenyl)-5-hydroxy-3-(2-hydroxy-3-methyl-3-butenyl)-8,8-dimethyl-	MeOH	206(4.61),271(4.60), 300s(4.09),320s(3.95), 350s(3.88)	4-0641-80

Compound	Solvent	$\lambda_{max}(\log \epsilon)$	Ref.
(cont.)	MeOH-NaOMe	273(4.59),315s(4.17), 380(4.11)	4-0641-80
	MeOH-AlCl$_3$	206(4.62),227(4.49), 279(4.63),341(3.99), 410s(3.86)	4-0641-80
2H,6H-Benzofuro[3,2-b]pyrano[3,2-g][1]-benzopyran-6-one, 6a,11b-dihydro-5,9,11b-trihydroxy-2,2-dimethyl-6a-(3-methyl-2-butenyl)-(sanggenon A)	MeOH	208(4.41),228(4.19), 235s(4.16),270s(4.46), 279(4.50),315(4.08), 377(3.37)	142-1785-80
	MeOH-NaOMe	248(4.28),287(4.41), 395(3.67)	142-1785-80
	MeOH-AlCl$_3$	209(4.51),225s(4.29), 279(4.49),332(4.10), 380s(3.44)	142-1785-80
3H,7H-Pyrano[2',3':7,8][1]benzopyrano-[3,2-d][1]benzoxepin-7-one, 8,9-di-hydro-6,12-dihydroxy-9-(1-hydroxy-1-methylethyl)-3,3-dimethyl-	MeOH	218(4.49),234(4.49), 278(4.51),334(4.24)	142-1531-80B
	MeOH-AlCl$_3$	224(4.53),261(4.41), 284(4.54),360(4.33), 417(4.02)	142-1531-80B
$C_{25}H_{24}O_9$			
Naphthaceno[1,12-de]-1,3-dioxin-6-carb-oxylic acid, 5-ethyl-3a,4,5,6,8,13-hexahydro-5,7,12-trihydroxy-2,2-di-methyl-8,13-dioxo-, methyl ester, [3aS-(3aα,5β,6α)]-	EtOH	234(4.65),251s(4.34), 291(4.03),476(4.18)	23-1869-80
[3aS-(3aα,5β,6β)]-	EtOH	234(4.49),250(4.15), 293(3.78),475(4.02)	23-1869-80
$C_{25}H_{24}O_{10}$			
1,3,5-Benzenetriol, 2-[1-acetoxy-3-(4-acetoxyphenyl)-1-propenyl]-, triace-tate	MeOH	236s(4.14),312(2.5)	100-0739-80
$C_{25}H_{24}O_{12}$			
Agecorynin D triacetate	EtOH	243(4.38),265(4.35), 314(4.20)	102-2439-80
4H-1-Benzopyran-4-one, 3-[(3,4-di-0-acetyl-6-deoxy-α-L-mannopyranosyl)-oxy]-5,7-dihydroxy-2-(4-hydroxy-phenyl)-	EtOH	266(4.38),318s(4.17), 345(4.21)	102-2643-80
	EtOH-NaOH	276(4.45),327(4.18), 396(4.42)	102-2643-80
	EtOH-NaOAc	274(4.43),300s(4.16), 352(4.16)	102-2643-80
	EtOH-AlCl$_3$	276(4.36),303(4.12), 344(4.20),397(4.10)	102-2643-80
$C_{25}H_{25}BrClNO_4$			
3,5-Pyridinedicarboxylic acid, 4-(4-bromophenyl)-1-(3-chlorophenyl)-1,4-dihydro-2,6-dimethyl-, diethyl ester	EtOH	202(4.58),215s(4.46), 241(4.43),350(3.72)	103-0377-80
$C_{25}H_{25}BrN_2O_6$			
3,5-Pyridinedicarboxylic acid, 1-(4-bromophenyl)-1,4-dihydro-2,6-di-methyl-4-(3-nitrophenyl)-, diethyl ester	EtOH	205(4.38),241(4.39), 350(3.68)	103-0377-80
3,5-Pyridinedicarboxylic acid, 1-(4-bromophenyl)-1,4-dihydro-2,6-di-methyl-4-(4-nitrophenyl)-, diethyl ester	EtOH	204(4.64),240(4.58), 282(4.33),360s(3.60)	103-0377-80

Compound	Solvent	$\lambda_{max}(\log \epsilon)$	Ref.
$C_{25}H_{25}Br_2NO_4$ 3,5-Pyridinedicarboxylic acid, 1,4-bis(4-bromophenyl)-1,4-dihydro-2,6-dimethyl-, diethyl ester	EtOH	203(4.63),240(4.61), 273s(4.18),342(3.86)	103-0377-80
$C_{25}H_{25}ClN_2O_6$ 3,5-Pyridinedicarboxylic acid, 1-(3-chlorophenyl)-1,4-dihydro-2,6-dimethyl-4-(4-nitrophenyl)-	EtOH	207(4.38),239(4.30), 281(4.18),366s(3.56)	103-0377-80
$C_{25}H_{25}NO$ 5H,9H-Quino[3,2,1-de]acridine, 3-methoxy-5,5,9,9-tetramethyl-	C_6H_{12}	205(4.70),236s(3.88), 285s(4.33),300(4.38)	24-0358-80
	EtOH	218(4.30),227s(4.02), 279s(4.38),301(4.42)	24-0358-80
$C_{25}H_{25}NO_2$ Pyridine, 2,4-bis[2-(4-ethoxyphenyl)-ethenyl]-	DMF	342(4.66)	33-1311-80
Pyridine, 2,5-bis[2-(4-ethoxyphenyl)-ethenyl]-	DMF	376(4.73)	33-1311-80
Pyridine, 2,6-bis[2-(4-ethoxyphenyl)-ethenyl]-	DMF	309(4.61),323(4.61), 350(4.51)	33-1311-80
$C_{25}H_{25}N_2S_2$ Benzothiazolium, 3-ethyl-2-[7-(3-ethyl-2(3H)-benzothiazolylidene)-1,3,5-heptatrienyl]-, iodide	60% EtOH	765(5.33)	104-2080-80
$C_{25}H_{25}N_3OS$ 4H-Imidazol-4-one, 1,5-dihydro-1-(3-mercaptopropyl)-5,5-diphenyl-2-[(phenylmethyl)amino]-	EtOH	218(4.48),246(3.94)	78-1079-80
$C_{25}H_{25}N_3O_2$ Propanedinitrile, [[1-[2-(benzoyloxy)-ethyl]-1,2,3,4-tetrahydro-2,2,4-tri-methyl-6-quinolinyl]methylene]-	benzene	444(4.71)	46-2803-80
	MeOH	447(4.72)	46-2803-80
	EtOAc	442(4.72)	46-2803-80
	BuOAc	442(4.72)	46-2803-80
	THF	445(4.71)	46-2803-80
	2-MeTHF	443(4.69)	46-2803-80
	MeCN	447(4.72)	46-2803-80
$C_{25}H_{25}N_3O_4S$ Cyclopropanecarboxylic acid, 2-[[[4-(aminosulfonyl)phenyl]hydrazono]-phenylmethyl]-3-phenyl-, ethyl ester	MeOH	239(3.42),261(3.40), 305(3.13)	4-0541-80
$C_{25}H_{25}N_3O_9$ Glycine, N-[2-[[2-[bis(carboxymethyl)-amino]-5-methylphenoxy]methyl]-8-quinolinyl]-N-(carboxymethyl)-, tetraanion	n.s.g.	262(4.53),350(3.61)	69-2396-80
calcium chelate	n.s.g.	233(4.56),279(3.79), 316(3.58)	69-2396-80
$C_{25}H_{26}BrNO_4$ 3,5-Pyridinedicarboxylic acid, 4-(4-bromophenyl)-1,4-dihydro-2,6-dimethyl-1-phenyl-, diethyl ester	EtOH	206(4.34),242(4.37), 352(3.76)	103-0377-80

Compound	Solvent	$\lambda_{max}(\log \epsilon)$	Ref.
$C_{25}H_{26}ClN_6O_{10}P$ Phosphoramidic acid, N-[9-(2,3,5-tri- O-acetyl-β-D-ribofuranosyl)-9H- purin-6-yl]-, 2-chlorophenyl 2- cyanoethyl ester	MeOH	258(4.23),265s(4.18), 285s(3.53)	142-0761-80B
$C_{25}H_{26}N_2$ 1H-Pyrrolo[1,2-a]indole, 2,3-dihydro- 1-(1H-indol-3-yl)-1,3,3-trimethyl- 9-(1-methylethenyl)-	EtOH EtOH-HClO₄	228(4.48),282(3.85) 265(4.03)	39-0553-80C 39-0553-80C
3,3'(2H,2'H)-Spirobi[cyclopent[b]ind- ole], 1,1',4,4'-tetrahydro-1,1,1',1'- tetramethyl-	EtOH EtOH-HClO₄	232(4.79),283(4.28) 210(4.33),260(4.35), 356(4.61)	142-0325-80B 142-0325-80B
$C_{25}H_{26}N_2OS$ Quinazoline, 3-acetyl-2-(ethylthio)- 3,4,5,6,7,8-hexahydro-4-phenyl- 8-(phenylmethylene)-	EtOH	230(4.46),284(4.83)	114-0147-80B
$C_{25}H_{26}N_2O_6$ 3,5-Pyridinedicarboxylic acid, 1,4-di- hydro-2,6-dimethyl-4-(2-nitrophenyl)- 1-phenyl-, diethyl ester	EtOH	207(4.35),241(4.28), 294(4.05),332-64(3.72)	103-0377-80
3,5-Pyridinedicarboxylic acid, 1,4-di- hydro-2,6-dimethyl-4-(3-nitrophenyl)- 1-phenyl-, diethyl ester	EtOH	204(4.27),248(4.24), 347(3.46)	103-0377-80
3,5-Pyridinedicarboxylic acid, 1,4-di- hydro-2,6-dimethyl-4-(4-nitrophenyl)- 1-phenyl-, diethyl ester	EtOH	204(4.30),239(4.18), 277(4.02),360s(3.60)	103-0377-80
$C_{25}H_{26}N_2S$ 4(1H)-Pyrimidinethione, tetrahydro- 1,3,5-trimethyl-2,5,6-triphenyl-	isooctane	286(4.0),378(1.4)	24-3010-80
$C_{25}H_{26}N_4O_7$ 1-Phenanthrenepropanoic acid, 7-[(2,4- dinitrophenyl)hydrazono]-4b,5,6,7,9- 10-hexahydro-4-methoxy-, methyl ester	CHCl₃	392(4.51)	78-2513-80
$C_{25}H_{26}N_5O_7P$ 5'-Adenylic acid, 2',3'-O-(1-methyl- ethylidene)-, diphenyl ester	MeOH	258(4.11)	142-0761-80B
$C_{25}H_{26}O_4$ [2,6'-Bi-2H-1-benzopyran]-4(3H)-one, 7-hydroxy-2',2'-dimethyl-8'-(3- methyl-2-butenyl)-, (S)-	MeOH MeOH-NaOH	276(4.10),312(3.83) 333(4.22)	142-1163-80B 142-1163-80B
2-Propen-1-one, 1-[5-hydroxy-2-methyl- 2-(4-methyl-3-pentenyl)-2H-1-benzo- pyran-6-yl]-3-(4-hydroxyphenyl)-, (E)- (lespeol)	MeOH	229(4.28),280(4.07), 371(4.53)	94-1172-80
$C_{25}H_{26}O_5$ 2,4-Hexadien-1-one, 1-(1-hydroxy- 8,9,10-trimethoxy-3-methyl-2-anthra- cenyl)-4-methyl-, (E,E)-	EtOH	228(4.15),262(4.91), 293(3.51),387(4.03), 418(3.78)	44-3061-80
Pyrano[2",3":7,6]flavone, 4',5-dihydr- oxy-6",6"-dimethyl-5"-C-prenyl-4",5"- dihydro-	EtOH EtOH-NaOH	235(5.64),275(5.42), 325(5.49) 250(5.25),270(5.33), 345(5.24)	2-0583-80 2-0583-80

Compound	Solvent	$\lambda_{max}(\log \epsilon)$	Ref.
(cont.)	EtOH-AlCl$_3$	270(5.37),305(5.31), 340(5.52)	2-0583-80
$C_{25}H_{26}O_6$			
Kuwanon G	EtOH	210(4.63),265(4.49), 315(4.06)	142-1531-80B
	EtOH-AlCl$_3$	275(4.55),335(4.02), 387(3.93)	142-1531-80B
Kuwanon D	EtOH	213(4.59),227s(4.07), 290(4.30),320s(3.86)	142-1531-80B
	EtOH-AlCl$_3$	213(4.58),220s(4.53), 308(4.39),373(3.67)	142-1531-80B
Kuwanon F	MeOH	225(4.49),288(4.19), 325s(3.39)	142-1531-80B
	MeOH-AlCl$_3$	223(4.56),310(4.33), 375(3.54)	142-1531-80B
$C_{25}H_{26}O_7$ 5,12-Naphthacenedione, 1,2,3,4-tetra- hydro-6,7,11-trimethoxy-2-(2-methyl- 1,3-dioxolan-2-yl)-	CHCl$_3$	247(4.82),395(3.94), 442(3.94)	35-5881-80
Oxydihydromorusin	MeOH	206(4.38),225(4.26), 242(4.26),270(4.44), 300s(3.82),350s(3.64)	142-1531-80B
	MeOH-AlCl$_3$	206(4.42),227(4.34), 279(4.47),336(3.76), 409(3.61)	142-1531-80B
$C_{25}H_{27}Cl_2N_3O_2$ 3-Pyridinecarboxamide, 1-[(2,6-dichlo- rophenyl)methyl]-4-[[4-(1,1-dimethyl- ethyl)benzoyl]amino]-1,4-dihydro-N- methyl-	CH$_2$Cl$_2$	335(4.0)	64-1431-80B
$C_{25}H_{27}NO_4$ 3,5-Pyridinedicarboxylic acid, 1,4-di- hydro-2,6-dimethyl-1,4-diphenyl-, diethyl ester	EtOH	206(4.34),242(4.33), 349(3.79)	103-0377-80
$C_{25}H_{27}N_3$ Benzenamine, 4-[2-(1,3-diphenyl-2-imid- azolidinyl)ethenyl]-N,N-dimethyl-	MeCN MeCN-acid	255(4.57),303(4.37) 512(4.76)	35-3062-80 35-3062-80
$C_{25}H_{27}N_3O_4S$ Pyrrolo[3,4-c]pyrazole-3a,4(1H)-dicarb- oxylic acid, 6,6a-dihydro-1-methyl- 3,6-bis(4-methylphenyl)-6a-(methyl- thio)-, dimethyl ester, (3aα,6α,6aα)-	EtOH	220s(4.28),304(4.14)	44-4587-80 +88-1529-80
$C_{25}H_{27}N_3O_5$ Pyrrolo[3,4-c]pyrazole-3a,4(1H)-dicarb- oxylic acid, 6,6a-dihydro-6a-methoxy- 1-methyl-3,6-bis(4-methylphenyl)-, dimethyl ester, (3aα,6α,6aα)-	EtOH	217s(4.32),296(4.25)	44-4587-80 +88-1529-80
$C_{25}H_{27}N_3O_6S$ Pyrrolo[3,4-c]pyrazole-3a,4(1H)-dicarb- oxylic acid, 6,6a-dihydro-3,6-bis(4- methoxyphenyl)-1-methyl-6a-(methyl- thio)-, dimethyl ester, (3aα,6α,6aα)-	EtOH	226(4.31),303(4.16)	44-4587-80 +88-1529-80

Compound	Solvent	$\lambda_{max}(\log \epsilon)$	Ref.
$C_{25}H_{27}N_3O_7$ Pyrrolo[3,4-c]pyrazole-3a,4(1H)-dicarb- oxylic acid, 6,6a-dihydro-6a-methoxy- 3,6-bis(4-methoxyphenyl)-1-methyl-, dimethyl ester, (3aα,6α,6aα)-	EtOH	225(4.31),296(4.15)	44-4587-80 +88-1529-80
$C_{25}H_{27}N_6O_{10}P$ Phosphoramidic acid, N-[9-(2,3,5-tri-O- acetyl-β-D-ribofuranosyl)-9H-purin-6- yl]-, 2-cyanoethyl phenyl ester	MeOH	259(4.24),268s(4.10)	142-0761-80B
$C_{25}H_{28}$ 1,1'-Spirobi[1H-indene], 3,3'-bis(1,1- dimethylethyl)-, (S)-	isooctane	<u>205(4.6),236f(4.6), 270f(3.9)</u>	88-3997-80
$C_{25}H_{28}BrNO_5$ 1,3-Cyclohexanedicarboxylic acid, 6- [(4-bromophenyl)imino]-4-hydroxy- 4-methyl-2-phenyl-, diethyl ester	EtOH	205(4.43),320(4.41)	103-0377-80
$C_{25}H_{28}ClNO_5$ 1,3-Cyclohexanedicarboxylic acid, 6- [(4-chlorophenyl)imino]-4-hydroxy- 4-methyl-2-phenyl-, diethyl ester	EtOH	204(4.44),317(4.39)	103-0377-80
$C_{25}H_{28}N_2O$ 1,3,6,8-Nonatetraen-5-one, 1,9-bis(di- methylamino)-2,8-diphenyl-	EtOH	205(4.46),235s(--), 275(4.17)	70-0771-80
$C_{25}H_{28}N_2S$ Quinazoline, 2-(butylthio)-1,4,5,6,7,8- hexahydro-4-phenyl-8-(phenylmethyl- ene)-	EtOH	237(4.13),276(4.38), 325(3.93)	114-0147-80B
monohydrobromide	EtOH	237(4.15),277(4.40), 324(3.95)	114-0147-80B
$C_{25}H_{28}N_2Se$ 6H,8H-Pyrimido[2,1-a:4,3-a']diisoquino- line-6-selone, 5-(1,1-dimethyl-2-pro- penyl)-4b,5,9,13b,15,16-hexahydro-	MeCN	305(4.1),408(2.3)	88-4251-80
$C_{25}H_{28}N_8$ 2,2a,4,5-Tetraazabenz[cd]azulene, 4,4'- methylenebis[3,4-dihydro-1,3,3-tri- methyl-	MeOH	222(4.60),292(3.97), 351(4.31)	118-0331-80
$C_{25}H_{28}O_4$ 4H-1-Benzopyran-4-one, 2,3-dihydro-7- hydroxy-2-[4-hydroxy-3,5-bis(3-meth- yl-2-butenyl)phenyl]- (abyssinone IV)	MeOH	275(4.00),312(4.78)	142-1163-80B
Erythrabyssin II	MeOH	220(4.27),287(3.91)	142-1163-80B
Hispaglabridin A	MeOH	281(4.05),290s(3.95), 312(3.41)	100-0259-80
2-Propen-1-one, 1-(2,4-dihydroxyphen- yl)-3-[4-hydroxy-3,5-bis(3-methyl- 2-butenyl)phenyl]- (abyssinone VI)	MeOH MeOH-NaOH	375(4.27) 462(4.34)	142-1163-80B 142-1163-80B
$C_{25}H_{28}O_5$ 4H-1-Benzopyran-4-one, 2,3-dihydro- 3,7-dihydroxy-2-[4-hydroxy-3-(3-meth- yl-2-butenyl)phenyl]-8-(3-methyl-2-	MeOH MeOH-NaOMe	282(4.22),312s(3.92) 247(4.30),284(4.05), 338(4.20)	100-0259-80 100-0259-80

Compound	Solvent	λ_{max} (log ϵ)	Ref.
butenyl)- (3-hydroxyglabrol) (cont.)	MeOH-AlCl$_3$	283(4.07),317(4.17)	100-0259-80
	MeOH-AlCl$_3$-HCl	283(4.20),315(3.90)	100-0259-80
4H-1-Benzopyran-4-one, 2,3-dihydro-5,7-dihydroxy-2-[4-hydroxy-3,5-bis-(3-methyl-2-butenyl)phenyl]-	MeOH	286(4.22),325s(3.75)	142-1163-80B
	MeOH-NaOH	326(4.53)	142-1163-80B
18-Norpregna-4,6,8,11,13-pentaen-20-one, 3β,16α-diacetoxy-17β-methyl-	EtOH	304(4.21),316(4.27), 332(4.07)	39-0556-80C
$C_{25}H_{28}O_6$			
4H-1-Benzopyran-4-one, 2-(3,4-dihydr-oxyphenyl)-6-(3,7-dimethyl-2,6-octa-dienyl)-2,3-dihydro-5,7-dihydroxy-	EtOH	207(4.69),230s(4.43), 294(4.29),340s(3.63)	142-0397-80
	EtOH-NaOMe	249(4.32),334(4.47)	142-0397-80
4H-1-Benzopyran-4-one, 2-[2-(3,7-di-methyl-2,6-octadienyl)-3,4-dihydroxy-phenyl]-2,3-dihydro-5,7-dihydroxy-	EtOH	215(4.51),230(4.32), 290(4.22)	142-0397-80
	EtOH-NaOMe	217(4.55),250(4.06), 328(4.44)	142-0397-80
$C_{25}H_{28}O_7$			
Kuwanon E	EtOH	212(4.56),289(4.26), 320s(3.73)	142-1531-80B
	EtOH-AlCl$_3$	212(4.55),220s(4.19), 308(4.33),374(3.57)	142-1531-80B
$C_{25}H_{28}O_9$			
2(3H)-Furanone, 3-acetoxy-3-[(4-acet-oxy-3-methoxyphenyl)methyl]-4-[(3,4-dimethoxyphenyl)methyl]dihydro- (trachelogenin diacetate)	EtOH	224(4.04),280(3.60)	94-0850-80
2(3H)-Furanone, 4-[(acetyloxy)(3,4-di-methoxyphenyl)methyl]-3-[(4-acetoxy-3-methoxyphenyl)methyl]dihydro- (5-acetoxyarctigenin monoacetate)	EtOH	228(4.18),282(3.83)	94-0850-80
Isoarctigenin, 5-acetoxy-, monoacetate	EtOH	228(4.24),282(3.84)	94-0850-80
$C_{25}H_{28}O_{12}$			
Centapicrin	MeOH	237(4.32),303(3.55)	100-0649-80
$C_{25}H_{28}O_{13}$			
Isocavuinin 7-O-glucoside	MeOH	265(4.67),330(3.99)	2-0429-80
	MeOH-AlCl$_3$	275(--),345(--)	2-0429-80
$C_{25}H_{29}ClO_4$			
3'H-Cyclopropa[1,2]-D-homopregna-1,4,6,16-tetraene-3,20-dione, 17a-acetoxy-6-chloro-1,2-dihydro-, (1β,2β)-	EtOH	283(4.24)	33-1867-80
$C_{25}H_{29}Cl_2N_3O_5$			
Carbamic acid, (2-chloroethyl)-, 6-[2-[[[(2-chloroethyl)amino]carbonyl]-oxy]ethyl]-5,6,6a,7-tetrahydro-10-methoxy-4H-dibenzo[de,g]quinolin-11-yl ester	EtOH	268(4.15),300(3.46)	87-1008-80
$C_{25}H_{29}NO_3$			
Benzenemethanol, 2,2'-[(4-methoxyphen-yl)imino]bis[α,α-dimethyl-	C$_6$H$_{12}$	204(4.70),237s(4.00), 289(4.11)	24-0358-80
$C_{25}H_{29}NO_5$			
6H-Dibenz[b,e]azepin-6-one, 5,11-dihy-dro-1,10,11-trihydroxy-8-methyl-4-(3-	MeOH	290(3.64),310(3.72)	142-0889-80B

Compound	Solvent	$\lambda_{max}(\log \epsilon)$	Ref.
methyl-2-butenyl)-7-[(3-methyl-2-butenyl)oxy]- (cont.)			142-0889-80B
$C_{25}H_{29}N_2$			
3H-Indolium, 2-[3-(1,3-dihydro-1,3,3-trimethyl-2H-indol-2-ylidene)-1-propenyl]-1,3,3-trimethyl-tetrafluoroborate	CH_2Cl_2	550(5.15)	88-2977-80
	$CHCl_3$	283(4.04),490s(4.38), 520(4.87),553(5.14)	5-2072-80
$C_{25}H_{30}N_3$			
Crystal Violet (chloride)	H_2O	592(4.96)	18-1922-80
$C_{25}H_{30}N_4O_8$			
Uridine, 5-[3-[2-(acetylamino)ethyl]-5-methoxy-1H-indol-2-yl]-2',3'-0-(1-methylethylidene)-	MeCN	219(4.33),274(3.91), 307(3.86),330(3.82)	35-7535-80
$C_{25}H_{30}O$			
Methanone, cyclohexyl[4-(1-naphthalen-yl)bicyclo[2.2.2]oct-1-yl]-	4:1 C_6H_{11}Me-isopentane	262s(3.66),271(3.85), 281(3.91),288(3.77), 292(3.77),312(2.71)	44-3933-80
Methanone, cyclohexyl[4-(2-naphthalen-yl)bicyclo[2.2.2]oct-1-yl]-	4:1 C_6H_{11}Me-isopentane	257s(3.59),265(3.68) 274(3.70),285s(3.55), 304(2.62),317(2.45)	44-3933-80
$C_{25}H_{30}O_2$			
4-Cyclopentene-1,3-dione, 2-[3,7-di-methyl-9-(2,6,6-trimethyl-1-cyclo-hexen-1-yl)-2,4,6,8-nonatetraenyl-idene]-, (all-E)-	EtOH	275(4.06),465(4.69)	87-0805-80
$C_{25}H_{30}O_3$			
12'-Apo-β,ψ-carotenal, 7,8-didehydro-3-hydroxy-4-oxo-, (3S)-	benzene	325s(4.05),337(4.19), 412s(4.81),432(4.95), 458(4.89)	33-1473-80
	$CHCl_3$	271(4.03),340(4.23), 417s(4.84),438(4.98), 463(4.92)	33-1473-80
(3S,9-cis)-	benzene	325(4.24),338(4.34), 406s(4.73),426(4.85), 451(4.78)	33-1473-80
$C_{25}H_{30}O_4$			
3'H-Cyclopropa[1,2]-D-homopregna-1,4,6,16-tetraene-3,20-dione, 17a-acetoxy-1,2-dihydro-, (1β,2β)-	EtOH	282(4.31)	33-1867-80
D-Homopregna-1,4,6,16-tetraene-3,20-di-one, 17a-acetoxy-6-methyl-	EtOH	227(4.14),254(3.97), 302(4.07)	33-1867-80
$C_{25}H_{30}O_5$			
Benzene, 1-[2-[2-(3,4-dimethoxyphenyl)-3-cyclohexen-1-yl]ethenyl]-2,4,5-tri-methoxy-, cis	EtOH	262(4.28),270(4.20), 287(3.76),315(3.72)	94-2948-80
trans	EtOH	262(4.24),269s(4.19), 287(3.93)	94-2948-80
Benzene, 1-[6-[2-(3,4-dimethoxyphenyl)-ethenyl]-2-cyclohexen-1-yl]-2,4,5-trimethoxy-, [1α,6α(E)]-(±)-	EtOH	205(4.83),262(4.29), 269s(4.28),287(4.08), 300s(3.98),313s(3.56)	94-2948-80
3'H-Cyclopropa[1,2]-D-homopregna-	EtOH	236(4.08)	33-1867-80

Compound	Solvent	$\lambda_{max}(\log \epsilon)$	Ref.
1,4,16-triene-3,20-dione, 17a-acetoxy-6,7-epoxy-1,2-dihydro-, (1β,2β,6α,7α)- (cont.)			33-1867-80
$C_{25}H_{30}O_6$			
Butanoic acid, 3-methyl-, 7,8-dihydro-4,6-dimethyl-1,9-bis(1-methylethyl)-7,8-dioxodibenzo[b,e][1,4]dioxin-2-yl ester (ecklonoquinone A)	EtOH	233(4.42),270s(3.57), 278s(3.43),403(3.96)	33-0225-80
Butanoic acid, 3-methyl-, 7,8-dihydro-4,9-dimethyl-1,6-bis(1-methylethyl)-7,8-dioxodibenzo[b,e][1,4]dioxin-2-yl ester	EtOH	234(4.43),268s(3.56), 277s(3.41),401(3.92)	33-0225-80
3'H-Cyclopropa[1,2]-D-homopregna-1,4-diene-3,20-dione, 17a-acetoxy-6,7-16,17-diepoxy-1,2-dihydro-, (1β,2β,6α,7α,16α,17α)-	EtOH	235(4.05)	33-1867-80
$C_{25}H_{30}O_{11}$			
Minecoside	MeOH	204(4.15),244(3.98), 298(4.09),328(4.18)	100-0649-80
$C_{25}H_{30}O_{13}$			
Grandifloroside	MeOH	219(4.2),230s(4.1), 300s(4.0),330(4.1)	100-0649-80
$C_{25}H_{31}ClO_4$			
3'H-Cyclopropa[1,2]-D-homopregna-1,4,6-triene-3,20-dione, 17a-acetoxy-6-chloro-1,2-dihydro-, (1β,2β)-	EtOH	283(4.23)	33-1867-80
$C_{25}H_{31}N_3O_2$			
Androsta-2,4-dieno[2,3-g]pyrazolo[1,5-a]pyrimidine, 17β-acetoxy-	MeOH	206(4.08),242(4.54), 374(3.77)	39-0481-80C
Androsta-5,16-dieno[16,17-g]pyrazolo-[1,5-a]pyrimidine, 3β-acetoxy-	MeOH	206(3.84),234(4.57), 284(3.16),331(3.33)	39-0481-80C
$C_{25}H_{31}N_7O_6$			
L-Glutamic acid, N-[4-[[(2,4-diamino-1,5-dihydro-5-oxopyrido[2,3-d]pyrimidin-6-yl)methyl]methylamino]benzoyl]-, diethyl ester	pH 1 pH 7 pH 11	258(4.60),301(3.92) 253(4.44),308(4.53) 253(4.46),311(4.53)	44-3746-80 44-3746-80 44-3746-80
$C_{25}H_{31}N_{11}O_4$			
1H-Pyrrole-2-carboxamide, 4-[[[4-[[[(aminoiminomethyl)amino]acetyl]-amino]-1-methyl-1H-pyrrol-2-yl]carbonyl]amino]-N-[5-[[(2-cyano-1-methyl-ethyl)amino]carbonyl]-1-methyl-1H-pyrrol-3-yl]-1-methyl-, monohydrochloride	EtOH	242(4.38),305(4.41)	87-1144-80
$C_{25}H_{32}Br_2O_4$			
D-Homopregn-4-ene-3,20-dione, 17a-acetoxy-6-(dibromomethylene)-	EtOH	249(4.02),280(3.78)	33-1867-80
$C_{25}H_{32}N_2O_4$			
Akuammiline, 1,2β-dihydro-	MeOH	213(4.19),244(3.89), 303(3.52)	102-2741-80

Compound	Solvent	λ_{max}(log ϵ)	Ref.
$C_{25}H_{32}N_4$			
2,4-Pyrimidinediamine, N,N'-bis(4-but-	EtOH	275(4.53),305s(4.25)	103-0309-80
ylphenyl)-6-methyl-	EtOH-HCl	270(4.28),305(4.27)	103-0309-80
$C_{25}H_{32}N_4O$			
5α-Androstano[3,2-f]pyrazolo[1,5-a]-	MeOH	207(4.05),235(4.66),	39-0481-80C
pyrimidine, 3'-cyano-17β-hydroxy-		240(4.66),315(3.33)	
17α-methyl-			
5α-Androst-2-eno[2,3-g]pyrazolo[1,5-a]-	MeOH	206(3.91),226(4.55),	39-0481-80C
pyrimidine, 3'-cyano-17β-hydroxy-		315(3.66)	
17α-methyl-			
$C_{25}H_{32}O_2$			
1,3-Cyclopentanedione, 2-[3,7-dimethyl-	hexane	280(4.06),484(4.74)	87-0805-80
9-(2,6,6-trimethyl-1-cyclohexen-1-yl)-	EtOH	265(3.96),520(4.55)	87-0805-80
2,4,6,8-nonatetraenylidene)-, (all-E)-	MeCN	275(3.96),500(4.63)	87-0805-80
$C_{25}H_{32}O_3$			
12'-Apo-β,ψ-carotenal, 3-hydroxy-4-	benzene	336(4.06),434(4.86)	33-1473-80
oxo-, (3S)-	CHCl$_3$	340(4.12),439(4.92)	33-1473-80
$C_{25}H_{32}O_4$			
D-Homopregna-4,16-diene-3,20-dione,	EtOH	261(4.03)	33-1867-80
17a-acetoxy-6-methylene-			
D-Homopregna-4,6,16-triene-3,20-dione,	EtOH	289(4.33)	33-1867-80
17a-acetoxy-6-methyl-			
4α,5-Methano-5α,14β-bufa-20,22-dieno-	MeOH	298(3.75)	5-0886-80
lide, 14-hydroxy-3-oxo-			
4β,5-Methano-5β,14β-bufa-20,22-dieno-	MeOH	298(3.74)	5-0886-80
lide, 14-hydroxy-3-oxo-			
$C_{25}H_{32}O_5$			
3'H-Cyclopropa[1,2]-D-homopregna-1,4-	EtOH	237(4.10)	33-1867-80
diene-3,20-dione, 17a-acetoxy-6,7-			
epoxy-1,2-dihydro-, (1β,2β,6α,7α)-			
18-Norpregna-5,7,13-trien-20-one,	EtOH	304(4.23),319(4.33),	39-0556-80C
3β,16α-diacetoxy-17β-methyl-		335(4.26)	
$C_{25}H_{32}O_8$			
Spiro[5H-benzocycloheptene-5,1'-[2,5]-	EtOH	218(4.63),237s(4.17),	12-1823-80
cyclohexadien]-4'-one, 9-acetoxy-		278(4.09)	
6,7,8,9-tetrahydro-2,3,3',4,5'-			
pentamethoxy-7,8-dimethyl-			
$C_{25}H_{32}O_9$			
Chaparrinone, 6α-tigloyl-	MeOH	225(4.40)	100-0503-80
$C_{25}H_{32}O_{11}$			
Tetrahelin D	MeOH	205(4.15)	102-0583-80
$C_{25}H_{32}O_{13}$			
Oleuropein	MeOH	234(4.20),284(3.48)	100-0649-80
$C_{25}H_{33}ClO_6$			
Pregna-1,4-diene-3,20-dione, 7-chloro-	MeOH	242(4.21)	145-1618-80
11,21-dihydroxy-16-methyl-17-(1-oxo-			
propoxy)-, (7α,11β,16α)-			
$C_{25}H_{33}NO_2$			
Polyavolensin	MeOH	238(3.25),278(3.88),	78-2005-80
		285(3.89),295(3.78)	

Compound	Solvent	$\lambda_{max}(\log \epsilon)$	Ref.
$C_{25}H_{33}NO_{11}$			
Indol-4-one, 4,5,6,7-tetrahydro-6,6-di-methyl-2-(penta-O-acetyl-D-galacto-pentitol-1-yl)-	EtOH	238(4.26),273(4.27)	136-0017-80A
Indol-4-one, 4,5,6,7-tetrahydro-6,6-di-methyl-2-(penta-O-acetyl-D-gluco-pentitol-1-yl)-	EtOH	238(4.25),274(4.27)	136-0017-80A
$C_{25}H_{33}N_3O_2$			
1H-Naphth[2',1':4,5]indeno[2,1-e]pyra-zolo[1,5-a]pyrimidin-2-ol, 2,3,4,4a-4b,5,6,6a,13,13a,13b,14,15,15a-tetra-decahydro-4a,6a-dimethyl-, acetate	MeOH	235(4.58),330(3.56)	39-0481-80C
$C_{25}H_{33}N_3O_3S_2$			
2,5-Piperazinedione, 3-[[2-(1,1-dimeth-yl-2-propenyl)-1-(methoxymethyl)-1H-indol-3-yl]methylene]-6-methyl-1,4-bis[(methylthio)methyl]-, (E)-(±)-	MeOH	226(4.59),267(4.14), 330(3.82)	88-2817-80
(Z)-(±)-	MeOH	223(4.52),283s(--), 293s(--),322(4.12)	88-2817-80
$C_{25}H_{34}N_6O$			
Benzaldehyde, 2-hydroxy-, [5-ethyl-2-(4-ethyl-3,5-dipropyl-1H-pyrazol-1-yl)-6-methyl-4-pyrimidinyl]hydra-zone	EtOH	206(4.36),247(4.31), 270(4.25),288(4.17), 300(4.18),312(4.24), 339(4.39),352(4.36)	103-1279-80
$C_{25}H_{34}N_{12}O_4$			
1H-Pyrrole-2-carboxamide, 4-[[[4-[[[(aminoiminomethyl)amino]acetyl]-amino]-1-methyl-1H-pyrrol-2-yl]carbo-nyl]amino]-N-[5-[[[2-(aminoiminometh-yl)-1-methylethyl]amino]carbonyl]-1-methyl-1H-pyrrol-3-yl]-1-methyl-, di-hydrochloride	EtOH	239(4.30),305(4.47)	87-1144-80
$C_{25}H_{34}O$			
2,4,6,8,10,12-Tridecahexaenal, 2,6,11-trimethyl-13-(2,6,6-trimethyl-1-cyclohexen-1-yl)-, (all-E)-	hexane	410(3.40),421(3.40)	33-0716-80
(E,E,E,Z,E,E)-	hexane	290(2.73),407(3.20), 425(3.17)	33-0716-80
$C_{25}H_{34}O_2$			
12'-Apo-β,ψ-carotenal, 3-hydroxy-, (3R)-	hexane	412(3.32),435s(--)	33-1451-80
	pet ether	413(--)	33-1377-80
	EtOH	427(3.23)	33-1377-80
2,4-Pentanedione, 3-[3,7-dimethyl-9-(2,6,6-trimethyl-1-cyclohexen-1-yl)-	hexane	275(3.89),414(4.78)	87-0805-80
	EtOH	270(3.89),423(4.67)	87-0805-80
2,4,6,8-nonatetraenylidene]-, (all-E)-	MeCN	275(3.95),414(4.74)	87-0805-80
$C_{25}H_{34}O_4$			
1,4-Benzenediol, 2-[(1,2,3,4,5,6,7,8-octahydro-1,2,5,5-tetramethyl-1-naphthalenyl)methyl]-, diacetate, (1R-trans)-	MeOH	257(3.11),265(3.04)	44-1435-80
1,4-Benzenediol, 2-(3,7,11-trimethyl-2,6,10-dodecatrienyl)-, diacetate, (E,E)-	EtOH	211(4.19),263(2.89)	102-2202-80

Compound	Solvent	$\lambda_{max}(\log \epsilon)$	Ref.
5α,14β-Cyclopropa[4,5]bufa-20,22-dienolide, 3α,14-dihydroxy-	MeOH	298(3.76)	5-0886-80
5α,14β-Cyclopropa[4,5]bufa-20,22-dienolide, 3β,14-dihydroxy-	MeOH	298(3.75)	5-0886-80
5β,14β-Cyclopropa[4,5]bufa-20,22-dienolide, 3α,14-dihydroxy-	MeOH	298(3.74)	5-0886-80
3β-	MeOH	299(3.75)	5-0886-80
D-Homopregna-4,6-diene-3,20-dione, 17a-acetoxy-6-methyl-	EtOH	289(4.40)	33-1867-80
D-Homopregna-4,16-diene-3,20-dione, 17a-acetoxy-6α-methyl-	EtOH	241(4.17)	33-1867-80
D-Homopregna-3,5,16-trien-20-one, 17a-acetoxy-3-methoxy-	EtOH	240(4.27)	33-1867-80
D-Homopregn-4-ene-3,20-dione, 17a-acetoxy-6-methylene-	EtOH	262(4.06)	33-1867-80
Ophiobola-3,6,19-trien-25-oic acid, 5,8-dioxo-	EtOH	258.5(4.20)	94-1043-80
$C_{25}H_{34}O_5$			
Benzene, 1-[2-[2-(3,4-dimethoxyphenyl)-cyclohexyl]ethyl]-2,4,5-trimethoxy-	EtOH	205(4.81),229(4.29), 286(3.86)	94-2948-80
isomer 28	EtOH	206(4.38),229(4.04), 282(3.64),286(3.65)	94-2948-80
16,17-Dehydrodigitoxigenin 3-acetate	EtOH	270(4.27)	94-2799-80
2(5H)-Furanone, 3-[13-(1,3-benzodioxol-5-yl)tridecyl]-4-hydroxy-5-methylene-	EtOH	237(4.21),281(4.03), 337s(3.10)	102-0455-80
	EtOH-NaOH	235s(4.34),291(4.05), 317(4.04)	102-0455-80
D-Homopregna-4,16-diene-3,20-dione, 17a-acetoxy-6β-(hydroxymethyl)-	EtOH	242(4.20)	33-1867-80
$C_{25}H_{34}O_6$			
Butanoic acid, 3-methyl-, 11,12-epoxy-14-hydroxy-3-oxobriara-5,7,17-trien-2-yl ester, (1R*,2R*,5Z,10R*,11S*-12R*,14S*)-	MeOH	271(3.76)	12-2307-80
$C_{25}H_{34}O_8$			
2-Butenoic acid, 4-hydroxy-2-(hydroxymethyl)-, 2,3,3a,4,5,8,9,11a-octahydro-6,10-dimethyl-3-methylene-9-(3-methyl-1-oxobutoxy)-2-oxocyclodeca-[b]furan-4-yl ester	MeOH	211(4.24)	102-1234-80
$C_{25}H_{34}O_9$			
1-Phenanthreneacetic acid, 5,6,7-tri-acetoxy-1,2,4a,4b,5,6,7,8,8a,9,10,10a-dodecahydro-4b,8-dimethyl-2-oxo-, methyl ester, [1S-(1α,4aβ,4bα,5β-6α,7α,8β,8aβ,10aβ)]-	n.s.g.	228(3.91)	33-1562-80
1-Phenanthreneacetic acid, 5,6,7-tri-acetoxy-2,3,4,4a,4b,5,6,7,8,8a,9,10-dodecahydro-4b,8-dimethyl-2-oxo-, methyl ester	n.s.g.	246(4.14)	33-1562-80
$C_{25}H_{35}N_3O_{12}P_2$			
Pyridinium, 1-[5-O-[10-[(4-acetylphenyl)amino]-1,3-dihydroxy-2,4-dioxa-1,3-diphosphadec-1-yl]-β-D-ribofuranosyl]-3-(aminocarbonyl)-, hydroxide, inner salt, P,P'-dioxide	pH 1 pH 11	238(4.13) 336(4.23)	5-1259-80 5-1259-80

Compound	Solvent	$\lambda_{max}(\log \epsilon)$	Ref.
cyanide adduct (cont.)	pH 11	334(4.34)	5-1259-80
$C_{25}H_{36}O_4$			
D-Homopregna-3,5-dien-20-one, 17a-acet- oxy-3-methoxy-	EtOH	238(4.32)	33-1867-80
$C_{25}H_{36}O_5$			
6H-Dibenzo[b,d]pyran-9-methanol, 1- acetoxy-6a,7,8,9,10,10a-hexahydro- 6,6-dimethyl-3-pentyl-, acetate, axial	EtOH	276(2.77),281(2.79)	87-1068-80
equatorial	EtOH	276(2.67),282(2.70)	87-1068-80
2(5H)-Furanone, 4-[3,6-dihydro-6-hy-	MeOH	227(3.70)	88-1611-80
droxy-5-[4-methyl-6-(2,6,6-trimethyl- 1-cyclohexen-1-yl)-3-hexenyl]-2H- pyran-2-yl]-5-hydroxy- (manoalide)	MeOH-base	246(3.89)	88-1611-80
D-Homopregn-4-ene-3,20-dione, 17a-acet- oxy-6β-(hydroxymethyl)-	EtOH	243(4.19)	33-1867-80
Pregna-5,7-diene-3,17,20-triol, 3,20- diacetate, (3β)-	MeOH	272(3.97),282(4.00), 294(3.75)	39-0556-80C
5β-Pregn-17(20)-en-21-al, 3α,11β-di- acetoxy-	pentane	243(4.25)	33-2328-80
5α-Pregn-16-en-20-one, 3β,12β-diacet- oxy-	EtOH	233(4.10)	102-0299-80
Tetradecanoic acid, (7-methoxy-2-oxo- 2H-1-benzopyran-4-yl)methyl ester	EtOH	324(4.16)	95-0744-80
Vibsanine E	EtOH	230(4.30)	39-1701-80B
$C_{25}H_{38}O_2$			
2H-Pyran-2-one, 4-hexyl-5,6-dihydro- 6-[2-methyl-4-(2,6,6-trimethyl-1- cyclohexen-1-yl)-1,3-butadienyl]-, (E,E)-	MeOH	227(4.38),263(4.13)	44-1181-80
Stellatic acid	EtOH	223(3.93)	88-1961-80
$C_{25}H_{38}O_3$			
5,13-Heptadecadiene-4,12-dione, 17-(3- furanyl)-2,6,10,14-tetramethyl-, (E,E)-	MeOH	243(4.22)	44-4976-80
6,14-Heptadecadiene-4,12-dione, 17-(3- furanyl)-2,6,10,14-tetramethyl-, (E,E)- (idiadione)	MeOH	211(4.44)	44-4976-80
D-Homoandrost-16-ene-17,17a-dicarbox- aldehyde, 12-hydroxy-4,4,8-trimeth- yl-, (5α,12β,17aα)-	MeOH	230(4.10)	44-4976-80
Scalarolide	MeOH	219(4.39)	44-4976-80
$C_{25}H_{38}O_4$			
5β,14β-Card-20-enolide, 3β,14-dihydroxy- 22,22-dimethyl-	EtOH	229(3.58)	48-0991-80
5β,14β-Card-20(22)-enolide, 3β,14-di- hydroxy-21,22-dimethyl-	EtOH	224(4.22)	48-0991-80
5β,14β-Card-20(22)-enolide, 14-hydroxy- 3β-methoxy-22-methyl-	EtOH	222.5(4.26)	48-0991-80
Retinoic acid, 2-(2-methoxyethoxy)ethyl ester	EtOH	353(4.42)	87-1013-80
$C_{25}H_{39}N_7O_{18}S$			
Adenomycin	H_2O	260(4.06)	88-3203-80

Compound	Solvent	$\lambda_{max}(\log \epsilon)$	Ref.
$C_{25}H_{40}N_2O$			
2,5-Cyclohexadien-1-one, 2,6-bis(1,1-dimethylethyl)-4-(di-1-piperidinyl-methylene)- (also other solvents)	isooctane acetone DMF	425(4.55) 415(--) 411(--)	73-2675-80 73-2675-80 73-2675-80
$C_{25}H_{40}O_2$			
5H-Inden-5-one, 1-(1,1-dimethylethoxy)-4-(4,8-dimethyl-3,7-nonadienyl)-1,2,3,6,7,7a-hexahydro-7a-methyl-, [1R-[1α(R*),3aβ,5α(R*),7aα]]-	CHCl₃	255(4.03),320(2.86)	24-0385-80
$C_{25}H_{41}NO_5S$			
7,9,11,14-Eicosatetraenoic acid, 6-[(2-amino-3-methoxy-3-oxopropyl)thio]-5-hydroxy-, methyl ester	EtOH	269(4.45),280(4.55), 291(4.46)	35-5425-80
$C_{25}H_{42}O_4$			
4H-Pyran-4-one, 3,5-dibutyl-2-(1-butyl-2-oxoheptyl)-6-methoxy-	EtOH	252(3.90)	44-3268-80
$C_{25}H_{43}NO_3$			
3-Pyridinecarboxylic acid, 1-decyl-1,4-dihydro-5-nonyl-4-oxo-	EtOH	261(4.01),284s(3.66)	4-0359-80
$C_{25}H_{43}NO_4$			
1-Pyrrolidineheptanoic acid, 2-oxo-5-(3-oxo-1-tridecenyl)-, methyl ester, [R-(E)]-	MeOH	215(4.11)	94-1449-80
$C_{25}H_{44}O_4$			
6-Dodecenoic acid, 2,4,6-tributyl-3,5-dioxo-, methyl ester	EtOH	238(4.0)	88-1281-80

Compound	Solvent	$\lambda_{max}(\log \epsilon)$	Ref.
$C_{26}Cl_{14}$ Benz[c]indeno[1,2,3-hi]acephenanthryl- ene, tetradecachloro-	CCl$_4$	263(4.74),309(4.58), 356(4.24),419(4.36)	88-0193-80
$C_{26}Cl_{14}O_2$ [9,9'-Bi-3H-fluorene]-3,3'-dione, 1,1',2,2',4,4',5,5',6,6',7,7',8,8'- tetradecachloro-	C$_6$H$_{12}$	219(4.72),252(4.48), 301(4.75),428(4.24), 449(4.25)	88-0193-80
1H-Fluoren-1-one, 2,3,4,5,6,7,8-hepta- chloro-9-(1,2,4,5,6,7,8-heptachloro- 3-oxo-3H-fluoren-9-yl)-	C$_6$H$_{12}$	222(4.71),253(4.57), 293(4.65),450(4.14), 499(4.06)	88-0193-80
$C_{26}Cl_{16}$ 9H-Fluorene, 1,2,3,4,5,6,7,8-octachlo- ro-9-(1,2,3,4,5,6,7,8-octachloro-9H- fluoren-9-ylidene)-	C$_6$H$_{12}$	209(4.55),242(4.66), 292(4.76),449(3.78), 591(4.23)	88-0193-80
$C_{26}H_2Cl_{14}O_2$ 9H-Fluoren-3-ol, 1,2,4,5,6,7,8-hepta- chloro-9-(1,2,3,4,5,7,8-heptachloro- 6-hydroxy-9H-fluoren-9-ylidene)-	C$_6$H$_{12}$	240(4.77),290(4.84), 450(3.85),591(4.32)	88-0193-80
$C_{26}H_2Cl_{16}$ 9,9'-Bi-9H-fluorene, 1,1',2,2',3,3',4- 4',5,5',6,6',7,7',8,8'-hexadeca- chloro-	CHCl$_3$	309(4.56)	88-0193-80
$C_{26}H_9Cl_8NO_7$ 2(1H)-Pyridinone, 1-[2-[2-(benzoyloxy)- 3,4,5,6-tetrachlorophenoxy]-5,6,7,8- tetrachloro-2,3-dihydro-3-oxo-1,4- benzodioxin-2-yl]-	MeCN	206(4.96),225s(4.73), 287(3.71),299(3.72), 314s(3.64),330s(3.34)	5-1836-80
$C_{26}H_{12}N_4$ Propanedinitrile, 2,2'-(9,10-dihydro- 9,10[1',2']-benzenoanthracene-1,4- diylidene)bis-	CH$_2$Cl$_2$ MeCN	409(4.66),535(3.40) 505(--)	89-0543B-80 89-0543B-80
$C_{26}H_{14}F_2N_2O$ Propanedinitrile, [2,5-bis(4-fluoro- phenyl)-4-oxo-3-phenyl-2-cyclopen- ten-1-ylidene]-	MeCN	265(4.09),353(4.18)	24-0424-80
$C_{26}H_{14}N_2$ 5,12[1',2']-Benzenonaphthacene-1,15-di- carbonitrile, 5,12-dihydro-, (5S)-	EtOH EtOH	241(4.86),282(4.12), 324(2.89) 241.0(4.86)	35-0501-80 35-0506-80
$C_{26}H_{14}O_2$ 1H-Indene-1,3(2H)-dione, 2-(3-pyrenyl- methylene)-	CHCl$_3$	487(4.64)	18-1703-80
Phenanthro[3,4-c]phenanthrene-1,2-dione	CH$_2$Cl$_2$	230(4.66),278(4.49), 285(4.47),297(4.46), 337(4.03),358(3.85), 423(3.65)	54-0391-80
$C_{26}H_{14}O_2S$ Anthra[2,1-b]benzo[d]thiophene-8,13-di- one, 6-phenyl-	CHCl$_3$	252(4.30),325(4.26), 336(4.20),410(3.42)	4-0695-80
Benz[a]anthracene-7,12-dione, 5-(benzo- [b]thien-2-yl)-	CHCl$_3$	254(4.32),285(4.20), 321(4.15),368(3.65)	4-0695-80

Compound	Solvent	$\lambda_{max}(\log \epsilon)$	Ref.
$C_{26}H_{14}O_3$ Benz[a]anthracene-7,12-dione, 5-(2-ben-zofuranyl)- (plus isomer)	$CHCl_3$	244(4.45),254(4.48), 294(4.52),313(4.49), 365s(3.86),448(3.99)	4-0695-80
$C_{26}H_{15}NO_3$ Naphthaceno[5,6-bc]pyran-2,8-dione, 9-(phenylamino)-	n.s.g.	<u>400(3.4)</u>,<u>520(4.1)</u>, <u>540s(4.0)</u>	104-1646-80
$C_{26}H_{16}Cl_2I_2N_2O_2$ [1,1'-Biphenyl]-4,4'-dicarboxamide, N,N'-bis(4-chlorophenyl)-2,2'-diiodo-	EtOH	279(4.60)	126-0333-80
$C_{26}H_{16}Cl_2N_4$ 1,1'-Bi-1H-pyrrolo[3,2-c]pyridine, 2,2'-bis(4-chlorophenyl)-	EtOH	244(4.55),251(4.56), 309(4.55)	142-0783-80
$C_{26}H_{14}Cl_4N_2$ Benzenamine, N,N'-[1,2-bis(2-chloro-phenyl)-1,2-ethanediylidene]bis[4-chloro-	MeOH	232(4.51),360(3.72)	73-3593-80
$(C_{26}H_{16}I_2N_2O_2)_n$ Poly[oxy-1,4-phenyleneiminocarbonyl-(2,2'-diiodo[1,1'-biphenyl]-4,4'-di-yl)carbonylimino-1,4-phenylene]	DMSO	352(4.32)	126-0333-80
$(C_{26}H_{16}I_2N_2O_4S)_n$ Poly[sulfonyl-1,4-phenyleneiminocarbo-nyl(2,2'-diiodo[1,1'-biphenyl]-4,4'-diyl)carbonylimino-1,4-phenylene]	DMSO	302(4.71)	126-0333-80
$C_{26}H_{16}N_2O$ Propanedinitrile, (4-oxo-2,3,5-triphen-yl-2-cyclopenten-1-ylidene)-	MeCN	265(4.02),355(4.24)	24-0424-80
$C_{26}H_{16}N_4O$ 1H-Perimidine, 2,2'-(2,5-furandiyl)bis-	MeOH	210(4.60),238(4.78), 340(4.59),490(3.38)	103-0081-80
$C_{26}H_{16}N_6O_8S_2$ Benzenamine, 4,4'-dithiobis[N-[(2,4-di-nitrophenyl)-1,2-ethanediyl]bis-	DMF-base	713(4.02)	3-1851-80
$C_{26}H_{16}O$ Benzo[j]fluoranthen-5-ol, 6-phenyl-	MeOH	224(4.67),236(4.70), 318(4.48),333(4.44), 366(3.69),385(3.81), 432(3.48)	23-1059-80
	MeOH-KOH	513(3.70)	23-1059-80
$C_{26}H_{16}O_2$ 5,12[1',2']-Benzenonaphthacene-1,15-di-carboxaldehyde, 5,12-dihydro-	EtOH	236(4.77),282(3.15)	35-0501-80
$C_{26}H_{16}O_5$ 5,12-Naphthacenedione, 6-acetoxy-11-phenoxy-	toluene	396(3.89)	104-1651-80
$C_{26}H_{16}O_6$ Benzo[h][1]benzopyrano[5,4,3-cde][1]-	EtOH	237(4.61),263(4.58)	87-0549-80

Compound	Solvent	$\lambda_{max}(\log \epsilon)$	Ref.
benzopyran-5,12-dione, 10-hydroxy-1-methyl-6-(phenylmethoxy)- (cont.)			87-0549-80
$C_{26}H_{17}Br$ Anthracene, 10-bromo-1,8-diphenyl-	EtOH	254s(4.80),262(5.05), 368s(3.87),387(4.06), 407(3.97)	44-1807-80
$C_{26}H_{17}Cl$ Anthracene, 10-chloro-1,8-diphenyl-	EtOH	253s(4.79),261(5.07), 347s(3.53),367(3.83), 384(4.02),408(3.94)	44-1807-80
$C_{26}H_{17}Cl_3N_2$ Benzenamine, N-[1,2-bis(2-chlorophenyl)-2-(phenylimino)ethylidene]-4-chloro-	MeOH	226(4.51),358(3.68)	73-3593-80
$C_{26}H_{17}NO_2$ Benzo[c]phenanthrene, 2-[2-(4-nitrophenyl)ethenyl]-, cis	CHCl₃	289(4.65),316s(4.29), 368(4.12)	54-0160-80
trans	CHCl₃	246(4.47),254s(4.45), 286s(4.52),294(4.54), 318s(4.34),332s(4.26), 384(4.41)	54-0160-80
$C_{26}H_{17}NO_3$ Acetamide, N-(6,11-dihydro-6,11-dioxo-5-naphthacenyl)-N-phenyl-	EtOH	399(3.66)	104-1646-80
$C_{26}H_{17}NO_4$ 5,11-Naphthacenedione, 6-(acetylamino)-12-phenoxy-	toluene	504(4.20)	104-1651-80
5,12-Naphthacenedione, 6-(acetylamino)-11-phenoxy-	toluene	429(3.87)	104-1651-80
$C_{26}H_{17}NO_4S$ Benzoic acid, 2-[(6,11-dihydro-6,11-dioxobenzo[f]pyrido[1,2-a]indol-12-yl)-thioxomethyl]-, ethyl ester	CHCl₃	245(4.50),285s(4.30), 330(4.12),400(3.84), 505(4.08)	39-1070-80C
$C_{26}H_{17}NO_5$ Benzoic acid, 2-[(6,11-dihydro-6,11-dioxobenzo[f]pyrido[1,2-a]indol-12-yl)-carbonyl]-, ethyl ester	CHCl₃	262(4.59),280(4.43), 325(4.18),333(4.17), 358(4.10),470(3.89)	39-1070-80C
Benzo[f]pyrido[1,2-a]indole-6,11-dione, 12-(1-ethoxy-1,3-dihydro-3-oxo-1-isobenzofuranyl)-	CHCl₃	258(4.59),288(4.14), 323(4.08),332s(3.98), 355(3.75),475(3.92)	39-1070-80C
$C_{26}H_{18}$ Phenanthrene, 9-[2-(1-naphthalenyl)ethenyl]-, cis	hexane	255s(4.3),300(4.15)	70-0563-80
trans	hexane	338(4.35)	70-0563-80
$C_{26}H_{18}Br_2N_2O_4$ Benzene, 1,1'-[1,2-bis[(4-bromophenyl)-aci-nitro]-1,2-ethanediyl]bis-	MeOH	357(4.57)	104-2059-80
$C_{26}H_{18}Cl_2N_2$ Benzenamine, N,N'-[1,2-bis(2-chlorophenyl)-1,2-ethanediylidene]bis-	MeOH	354(3.60)	73-3593-80

Compound	Solvent	$\lambda_{max}(\log \epsilon)$	Ref.
$C_{26}H_{18}Cl_2Pd_2$ Palladium, di-µ-chlorobis[(1,2,3-n)-1H-phenalen-1-yl]di-	CHCl$_3$	208(4.07),246(4.03), 277(3.62),323(3.53), 354(3.65)	101-0C11-80D
$C_{26}H_{18}F_2N_2S_2$ Benzenamine, 4,4'-dithiobis[N-[(4-fluorophenyl)methylene]-, anion	DMF-base	420s(2.30)	3-1851-80
$C_{26}H_{18}I_2N_2O_2$ [1,1'-Biphenyl]-4,4'-dicarboxamide, 2,2'-diiodo-N,N'-diphenyl-	DMSO	275(4.77)	126-0333-80
$C_{26}H_{18}N_2$ Tetrabenzo[b,d,h,j][1,6]diazacyclo-dodecine	EtOH	234(4.60),250s(4.55), 310s(3.76)	39-0107-80C
$C_{26}H_{18}N_2O$ Benzoxazole, 5-phenyl-2-[4-[2-(3-pyridinyl)eqhenyl]phenyl]-	DMF	354(4.81)	33-1311-80
Benzoxazole, 6-phenyl-2-[4-[2-(3-pyridinyl)ethenyl]phenyl]-	DMF	357(4.81)	33-1311-80
Pyridine, 3,3'-(3,7-dibenzofurandiyldi-2,1-ethenediyl)bis-	DMF	368(4.90),383(4.84)	33-1311-80
$C_{26}H_{18}N_2O_5$ Carbamic acid, [2-(6,11-dihydro-6,11-dioxobenzo[f]pyrido[1,2-a]indol-12-yl)benzoyl]-, ethyl ester	EtOH	207(4.51),261(4.50), 290(4.08),333(3.86), 508(3.80)	2-0836-80
$C_{26}H_{18}N_2S$ Pyridine, 3,3'-(3,7-dibenzothiophene-diyldi-2,1-ethenediyl)bis-	DMF	366(4.91),383(4.84)	33-1311-80
$C_{26}H_{18}N_4$ 1,1'-Bi-1H-pyrrolo[3,2-c]pyridine, 2,2'-diphenyl-	EtOH	242(4.48),248(4.49), 304(4.42)	142-0783-80
$C_{26}H_{18}N_4O_4S_2$ Benzenamine, 4,4'-dithiobis[N-(2-nitrophenyl)methylene]-	DMF-base	538(3.60)	3-1851-80
Benzenamine, 4,4'-dithiobis[N-(3-nitrophenyl)methylene]-	DMF-base	538(3.56)	3-1851-80
Benzenamine, 4,4'-dithiobis[N-(4-nitrophenyl)methylene]-	DMF-base	605(3.91)	3-1851-80
$C_{26}H_{18}N_4O_8$ Benzene, 1,1'-[1,2-bis[(4-nitrophenyl)-aci-nitro]-1,2-ethanediyl]bis-	CHCl$_3$	260(--),310(4.28), 360(4.39)	104-2059-80
$C_{26}H_{18}O$ Dibenzo[a,g]cycloheptadecen-9-one, 18,19,20,21-tetradehydro-8-methyl-	THF	298s(4.65),314(4.70), 373s(3.67)	39-0473-80C
	CF$_3$COOH	275s(--),293(--), 311(--),329(--), 364s(--),402(--), 581(--)	39-0473-80C
Dibenz[b,d]oxepin, 6,7-diphenyl-	CH$_2$Cl$_2$	307(4.19)	4-1349-80
Phenanthro[9,10-b]oxirene, 1a,9b-di-hydro-1a,9b-diphenyl-	CH$_2$Cl$_2$	236(4.22),269s(4.07), 279(4.19),288s(4.02), 303(3.54)	4-1349-80

Compound	Solvent	$\lambda_{max}(\log \epsilon)$	Ref.
$C_{26}H_{18}O_2$			
9(10H)-Anthracenone, 10-hydroxy-1,8-di-phenyl-	EtOH	236(4.54),288(4.02)	44-1807-80
9,10-Epidioxyanthracene, 9,10-dihydro-1,8-diphenyl-	EtOH	232(4.58)	44-1807-80
Methanone, (1,2-dihydro-1,2-acenaphth-ylenediyl)bis[phenyl-, cis	EtOH	225(4.78),238(4.43), 283(3.89),342(3.57)	44-2033-80
trans	EtOH	224(4.87),242(4.50), 283(3.96),325s(3.23)	44-2033-80
$C_{26}H_{18}O_4$			
Benz[a]anthracene-7,12-dione, 8,10-di-methoxy-	CHCl₃	293(4.69),318s(4.06), 392(4.06),446s(3.38)	138-0827-80
$C_{26}H_{18}O_4S$			
Anthra[2,1-b]thiophene, 6,11-diacetoxy-4-phenyl-	CHCl₃	246s(4.54),275s(4.60), 297(4.83),345s(3.85), 262(4.04),380(4.15), 402(4.08)	4-0695-80
$C_{26}H_{18}O_7$			
Dinaphtho[1,2-b:2',1'-d]furan-5,6,8-triol, triacetate	CHCl₃	263(4.83),271(4.80), 281(4.76),299s(4.20), 304s(4.13),318(4.12), 331(4.26),344(4.05), 352s(3.30)	39-0090-80C
$C_{26}H_{18}O_9$			
7H-8,15b-Methano-1H,3H,12H-benzo[de]-cyclohepta[1,2-g:3,4,5-d'e']bis[2]-benzopyran-3,7,12-trione, 8,14-di-hydro-4,11,15,16-tetrahydroxy-6,9-dimethyl-, [8R-(8α,15bα,16S*)]- (bacillosporin B)	MeOH	233(4.64),242s(4.61), 258s(4.52),275s(4.26), 324(3.96),353s(3.86), 373s(3.62),410s(3.08)	94-3649-80
$C_{26}H_{18}O_{10}$			
Bacillosporin C	MeOH	221s(4.63),233s(4.69), 241(4.70),270s(4.48), 275(4.49),317s(3.92), 345(3.81),361s(3.76)	94-3649-80
$C_{26}H_{19}Cl_4N_5O$			
Pyrido[3,4-a]indolizine-4,8-dicarbo-nitrile, 2-(2,6-dichlorophenyl)-5-[(2,6-dichlorophenyl)methyl]-1,2,4a-5,10a,10b-hexahydro-1-(hydroxyamino)-	CH₂Cl₂	274(4.2),327(3.7)	64-0896-80B
$C_{26}H_{19}NO_2S_3$			
Benzeneethanethioamide, α-(4,5-dibenz-oyl-1,3-dithiol-2-ylidene)-4-methyl-	CHCl₃	304(4.09),385(4.17)	39-2693-80C
$C_{26}H_{19}NO_3$			
5,12-Naphthacenedione, 6-(dimethyl-amino)-11-phenoxy-	toluene	408(3.78),465(3.60)	104-1651-80
$C_{26}H_{19}NO_3S_2$			
3H-Phenoxazin-3-one, 2-hydroxy-7,9-bis-[(4-methylphenyl)thio]-	n.s.g.	485(4.45)	103-0032-80
$C_{26}H_{19}NS$			
9H-Quino[3,2,1-kl]phenothiazine,	CHCl₃	244s(4.18),264(4.29),	24-0358-80

Compound	Solvent	$\lambda_{max}(\log \epsilon)$	Ref.
6-methyl-9-phenyl-, axial (cont.)		296(4.14)	24-0358-80
equatorial	CHCl$_3$	245s(4.25),265(4.39), 302(4.17)	24-0358-80
$C_{26}H_{19}N_3O_2$			
Acetamide, N-[4-[[(3-cyano-4,5-diphenyl-2-furanyl)imino]methyl]phenyl]-	MeOH	426(4.42)	73-1581-80
$C_{26}H_{19}N_3S_3$			
Benzeneethanethioamide, α-(4,7-diphenyl-1,3-dithiolo[4,5-d]pyridazin-2-ylidene)-4-methyl-	CHCl$_3$	260(4.42),280(4.41), 381(4.23)	39-2693-80C
$C_{26}H_{19}N_7O$			
Benzo[1,2-d:3,4-d']bistriazole, 2,7-dihydro-2-(2-methoxyphenyl)-7-[4-[2-(3-pyridinyl)ethenyl]phenyl]-	DMF	350(4.75)	33-1311-80
$C_{26}H_{19}N_7S$			
Benzo[1,2-d:3,4-d']bistriazole, 2,7-dihydro-2-[3-(methylthio)phenyl]-7-[4-[2-(3-pyridinyl)ethenyl]phenyl]-	DMF	347(4.80)	33-1311-80
$C_{26}H_{20}$			
1,1'-Biphenyl, 4,4'-(1,2-ethenediyl)-bis-, cis	THF	270(4.7)	35-3100-80
trans	THF	335(4.8)	35-3100-80
sodium derivative	THF	350(4.0),550(4.6), 600(4.8)	35-3100-80
disodium derivative	THF	780(5.1)	35-3100-80
$C_{26}H_{20}ClNO_7$			
10H-1,9-[1]Propen[1]yl[3]ylidenepyrrolo[1,2-a]azocine-2,7,8-tricarboxylic acid, 3-chloro-10-oxo-5-phenyl-, 2-ethyl 7,8-dimethyl ester	CHCl$_3$	267(4.54),301(4.23), 313(4.24),349(4.63), 391(3.88),665(3.30)	18-1406-80
$C_{26}H_{20}Cl_2N_2O_2$			
Benzamide, N-[3-benzoyl-1-[(2,6-dichlorophenyl)methyl]-1,4-dihydro-4-pyridinyl]-	CH$_2$Cl$_2$	305s(3.9),334(3.9)	64-1431-80B
$C_{26}H_{20}NOS$			
Benzothiazolium, 3-methyl-2-[3-(3-phenyl-1H-2-benzopyran-1-ylidene)-1-propenyl]-, perchlorate	CH$_2$Cl$_2$	574(4.72),616(4.74)	103-0137-80
$C_{26}H_{20}NS_2$			
Benzothiazolium, 3-methyl-2-[3-(3-phenyl-1H-2-benzothiopyran-1-ylidene)-1-propenyl]-, perchlorate	CH$_2$Cl$_2$	617(4.60)	103-0599-80
$C_{26}H_{20}N_2$			
Methanone, diphenyl-, (diphenylmethylene)hydrazone	CH$_2$Cl$_2$	235(4.42),282(4.33), 314(4.28)	88-2313-80
$C_{26}H_{20}N_2O$			
1(4H)-Naphthalenone, 4-[(1-ethyl-2-phenyl-1H-indol-3-yl)imino]-	ligroin	587(4.09)	7-0009-80

Compound	Solvent	$\lambda_{max}(\log \epsilon)$	Ref.
$C_{26}H_{20}N_2S$ Benzenecarboximidothioic acid, N-phenyl-, anhydrosulfide	EtOH	230(4.30)	39-0665-80C
$C_{26}H_{20}N_2S_2$ Disulfide, bis[phenyl(phenylimino)-methyl]	EtOH	235(4.50)	39-0665-80C
$C_{26}H_{20}N_8$ 1H-Tetrazolium, 5-[bis(phenylazo)methylene]-2,5-dihydro-2,3-diphenyl-, hydroxide, inner salt	EtOH-K_2CO_3	266(4.27),385s(4.04), 477(4.67)	24-1226-80
$C_{26}H_{20}O$ 1,3,6,8-Nonatetraen-5-one, 1,9-bis(2-ethynylphenyl)-4-methyl-	THF	265(4.11),367(4.37)	39-0473-80C
$C_{26}H_{20}OS$ Methanone, [4,5-dihydro-3-(4-methylphenyl)naphtho[1,2-c]thien-1-yl]-phenyl-	$CHCl_3$	257(4.43),345(3.88)	54-0049-80
$C_{26}H_{20}O_2$ 9,10-Anthracenediol, 9,10-dihydro-1,8-diphenyl-	C_6H_{12}	229(4.48)	44-1807-80
1H-Cyclopenta[2,3]cyclopropa[1,2-a]-naphthalen-1-one, 3-ethoxy-9b,9c-dihydro-9c-(2-naphthalenyl)-	EtOH	222(4.91),257(4.42)	78-2291-80
3H-Cyclopenta[1,3]cyclopropa[1,2-a]-naphthalen-3-one, 1-ethoxy-3a,3b-dihydro-3a-(1-naphthalenyl)-	hexane	219(4.84),271(4.23)	78-2291-80
1-Isobenzofuranol, 1,3-dihydro-1,3,3-triphenyl-	hexane	213(4.41),221s(4.32), 254(2.95),259(3.01), 265(2.95),270s(2.70)	104-1316-80
1-Phenanthrenol, 3-ethoxy-4-(2-naphthalenyl)-	EtOH	226(4.94),248(4.60), 282(4.26),311(4.09), 349(3.57),367(3.56)	78-2291-80
3-Phenanthrenol, 1-ethoxy-4-(2-naphthalenyl)-	EtOH	223(4.96),252(4.51), 276s(4.34),297s(4.06), 363(3.59)	78-2291-80
$C_{26}H_{20}O_2S$ Methanone, [4,5-dihydro-3-(4-methylphenyl)naphtho[1,2-c]thien-1-yl]-phenyl-, S-oxide	$CHCl_3$	255(4.30),345(2.90)	54-0049-80
Naphtho[2,3-c]thiophene, 5,8-dimethoxy-1,3-diphenyl-	MeCN	265(4.52),278s(--), 290(4.46),352(3.75), 510s(3.85),522(3.86)	23-1161-80
$C_{26}H_{20}O_3$ 6H-Naphthaceno[1,12-bc]furan-12(7H)-one, 6a,12a-dihydro-6-hydroxy-6-methyl-1-phenyl-	n.s.g.	245(4.37),298s(4.41), 311(4.45),325s(4.21)	39-1654-80C
$C_{26}H_{20}O_3S$ Methanone, [4,5-dihydro-3-(4-methylphenyl)naphtho[1,2-c]thien-1-yl]-phenyl-, S,S-dioxide	$CHCl_3$	252(4.38),330(3.64)	54-0049-80
$C_{26}H_{20}O_4$ Dibenz[a,h]anthracne-3,4-diol, 3,4-di-	EtOH	249(4.51),278(4.90),	39-1920-80C

Compound	Solvent	λ_{max}(log ϵ)	Ref.
hydro-, diacetate, trans (cont.)		287(4.99),298(5.05), 335(3.94),352(3.98), 372(3.92),400(3.72)	39-1920-80C
C$_{26}$H$_{20}$O$_9$ Bacillosporin C hydrogenation product	MeOH	219(4.67),254s(4.31), 276(4.25),327(3.96), 364s(3.73)	94-3649-80
Dinaphtho[2,1-b:1',2'-d]furan-2,12-di- carboxylic acid, 4,5,9,10-tetrameth- oxy-	CHCl$_3$	275(4.43),281(4.44), 305(3.99),318(3.91), 395s(4.03),413(4.22), 432(4.24)	12-2531-80
C$_{26}$H$_{21}$Br$_2$NSn Phenazastannine, 2,8-dibromo-5-ethyl- 5,10-dihydro-10,10-diphenyl-	pentane	282(3.82)	65-1104-80
C$_{26}$H$_{21}$Cl$_2$N$_5$O Pyrido[3,4-a]indolizine-4,8-dicarbo- nitrile, 2-(4-chlorophenyl)-5-[(4- chlorophenyl)methyl-1,2,4a,5,10a,10b- hexahydro-1-(hydroxyamino)-	CH$_2$Cl$_2$	274(4.2),326(3.7)	64-0896-80B
C$_{26}$H$_{21}$Cl$_2$N$_5$O$_6$ α-D-Ribofuranuronamide, 1-deoxy-1-(2,6- dichloro-9H-purin-9-yl)-N-ethyl-	MeOH	210s(--),217(4.43), 232(4.40),275(3.99), 282s(--)	24-2891-80
	MeOH	210s(--),217(4.43), 230(4.43),274(4.00), 282s(--)	24-2891-80
C$_{26}$H$_{21}$NO$_2$ 2,5-Pyrrolidinedione, 3-(diphenylmeth- ylene)-4-(1-methylethylidene)-1- phenyl-	n.s.g.	346(3.96)	97-0188-80
photoisomer B	n.s.g.	494(3.86)	97-0188-80
C$_{26}$H$_{21}$N$_2$O$_2$ Xanthylium, 9-[2-(2,3-dihydro-1,5-di- methyl-3-oxo-2-phenyl-1H-pyrazol-4- yl)ethenyl]-, perchlorate	HOAc	580(4.70)	48-0543-80
C$_{26}$H$_{21}$N$_3$ 1,2,4-Benzotriazine, 1,2-dihydro-1,3- diphenyl-2-(phenylmethyl)-	EtOH	237(4.31),252s(4.26), 317(3.86)	24-1205-80
1,2,4-Benzotriazine, 1,4-dihydro-1,3- diphenyl-4-(phenylmethyl)-	EtOH	242(4.19),308(3.89)	24-1205-80
C$_{26}$H$_{21}$N$_3$O 3-Furancarbonitrile, 2-[[[4-(dimethyl- amino)phenyl]methylene]amino]-4,5- diphenyl-	MeOH	446(4.69)	73-1581-80
C$_{26}$H$_{21}$N$_3$O$_2$ 1H-Cyclobuta[d][1,3,4]triazolo[1,2-a]- pyridazine-1,3(2H)-dione, 5,6,7,8- tetrahydro-2,5,8-triphenyl-, cis	ether	261(3.98),270(4.06), 282(3.93)	44-4183-80
C$_{26}$H$_{21}$N$_8$ 2H-Tetrazolium, 5-(1,5-diphenylformaz- anyl)-2,3-diphenyl-, chloride	EtOH	257(4.28),265(4.25), 303(4.51),458(4.31)	24-1226-80

Compound	Solvent	$\lambda_{max}(\log \epsilon)$	Ref.
$C_{26}H_{22}BNO$			
Boron, diphenyl[2-[[(phenylmethyl)imino]methyl]phenolato-N,O]-	$CHCl_3$	285(3.86),383(3.42)	49-0863-80
Boron, [2-[[(2-methylphenyl)imino]methyl]phenolato-N,O]diphenyl-	$CHCl_3$	268(4.11),340(4.03)	49-0863-80
Boron, [2-[[(3-methylphenyl)imino]methyl]phenolato-N,O]diphenyl-	$CHCl_3$	270(4.09),340(4.05)	49-0863-80
Boron, [2-[[(4-methylphenyl)imino]methyl]phenolato-N,O]diphenyl-	$CHCl_3$	270(4.09),340(4.11)	49-0863-80
$C_{26}H_{22}ClNO_6$			
3H-2a-Azacyclopenta[ef]heptalene-1,4,5-tricarboxylic acid, 2-chloro-3-phenyl-, 1-ethyl 4,5-dimethyl ester	EtOH	228(4.54),260(4.28), 434(4.38),492s(3.95), 530(3.74),570(3.43)	18-1406-80
4H-Azuleno[7,8,1-gha]pyrrolizine-1,5,6-tricarboxylic acid, 2-chloro-4a,5-dihydro-4-phenyl-, 1-ethyl 5,6-dimethyl ester, (4α,4aα,5β)-	EtOH	263(4.07),323(3.95), 394(3.58)	18-1406-80
Cyclobuta[a]cyclohepta[gh]pyrrolizine-1,5,6-tricarboxylic acid, 2-chloro-4,4a-dihydro-4-phenyl-, 1-ethyl 5,6-dimethyl ester	EtOH	226s(4.51),290(3.83)	18-1406-80
2H-Cyclohepta[gh]pyrrolizine-1,2,5-tricarboxylic acid, 4-chloro-2-(2-phenylethenyl)-, 5-ethyl 1,2-dimethyl ester	EtOH	252(4.72),375(4.17), 393(4.13),440(3.78), 468(3.71),502(3.51), 537(3.06)	18-1406-80
$C_{26}H_{22}N_2O_2$			
2,5-Pyrrolidinedione, 3-(diphenylmethylene)-4-(1-methylethylidene)-1-(phenylamino)-	n.s.g.	344(3.86)	97-0188-80
photoisomer B	n.s.g.	504(3.72)	97-0188-80
$C_{26}H_{22}N_4$			
Benzenecarbohydazonic acid, N-phenyl-, phenyl(phenylmethylene)hydrazide	MeCN	242(4.49),297(4.26), 339(4.55)	70-1159-80
	$CHCl_3$	300(4.29),348(4.54)	70-1159-80
5-Pyridinecarbonitrile, 4-amino-3,6-dihydro-2-(ethylphenylamino)-3,6-diphenyl-, cis	EtOH	247(4.30),337(3.94)	88-2097-80
trans	EtOH	247(4.31),330(3.96)	88-2097-80
$C_{26}H_{22}N_6$			
Methanone, (1,5-diphenylformazanyl)phenyl-, phenylhydrazone	EtOH	255(4.42),291(4.25), 345(4.46),407(4.41)	24-1226-80
$C_{26}H_{22}N_6O_2$			
Urea, N,N''-(azodi-4,1-phenylene)bis[N-phenyl-	DMF	398(4.70)	126-0287-80B
$C_{26}H_{22}N_8$			
Formazan, 3-(1,5-diphenylformazanyl)-1,5-diphenyl-	benzene	296(4.29),409(4.55)	24-1226-80
	dioxan	266(4.47),287s(4.36), 425(4.44)	24-1226-80
after irradiation	benzene	296(4.28),407(4.57)	24-1226-80
after irradiation	dioxan	257(4.39),287s(4.28), 406(4.68)	24-1226-80
$C_{26}H_{22}O_2$			
Cyclobuta[b]naphthalene-3,8-dione, 2a-ethyl-1,2,2a,8a-tetrahydro-1,1-diphenyl-	$CHCl_3$	242(4.10),250(4.08), 302(3.28),310(3.26)	18-0757-80

Compound	Solvent	$\lambda_{max}(\log \epsilon)$	Ref.
Cyclobuta[b]naphthalene-3,8-dione, 8a-ethyl-1,2,2a,8a-tetrahydro-1,1-diphenyl-	CHCl$_3$	242(4.15),250(4.14), 300(3.26)	18-0757-80
Cyclobuta[b]naphthalene-3,8-dione, 1,2,2a,8a-tetrahydro-2a,8a-dimethyl-1,1-diphenyl-	CHCl$_3$	243(4.13),254(4.15), 302(3.34)	18-0757-80
$C_{26}H_{22}O_2S_2$			
1,4-Naphthalenedione, 2,3-bis[[(4-methylphenyl)thio]methyl]-	EtOH	254(4.40),268s(4.29), 335(3.62)	39-0282-80C
1,4-Naphthalenedione, 2,3-bis[[(phenylmethyl)thio]methyl]-	EtOH	247s(4.28),253(4.29), 264(4.19),336(3.58)	39-0282-80C
$C_{26}H_{22}O_3$			
1-Naphthalenecarboxylic acid, 3,4-dihydro-4-ethoxy-1H-phenalen-6-yl ester	hexane	244(4.52),312(3.88), 325(3.89),343(3.81), 361(3.89),381(3.72)	78-2291-80
Naphtho[2,3-c]furan, 4,9-dihydro-5,8-dimethoxy-1,3-diphenyl-	MeCN	297(4.24),318s(--), 332(4.51),350s(--)	23-1161-80
$C_{26}H_{22}O_4$			
Benzo[a]pyren-3-ol, 1,6-diethoxy-, acetate	MeOH	225(4.33),258(4.49), 269(4.47),292(4.30), 303(4.37),384(4.28), 394(4.32),405(4.34), 421(3.86)	87-0919-80
1H-Indene-1,3(2H)-dione, 2-[2-(1,3-dihydro-1,3-dioxo-2H-inden-2-ylidene)-1,1-dimethylethyl]-2-(2-methyl-1-propenyl)-	CH$_2$Cl$_2$	256(4.69),302(3.84), 313(3.68),375(2.31)	49-0309-80
1,4-Naphthalenedione, 2,2'-(1,2-dimethyl-1,2-ethanediyl)bis[3-methyl-	EtOH	248(4.57),258(4.33), 270(4.30),330(3.75)	39-1994-80C
$C_{26}H_{22}O_7$			
6H,11H-[2]Benzopyrano[4,3-c][1]benzopyrano[4,3-c][1]benzopyran-11-one, 7,9,10-trimethoxy-6-(4-methoxyphenyl)-	EtOH	274(4.13),280(4.10), 332(4.55),340(4.58)	12-0137-80
$C_{26}H_{22}P$			
Phosphonium, (2,4,6-cycloheptatrien-1-ylidenemethyl)triphenyl-	EtOH	365(4.58)	88-2333-80
$C_{26}H_{23}BN_2O$			
Boron, [2-[[[(6-methyl-2-pyridinyl)-methyl]imino]methyl]phenolato]diphenyl-, (T-4)-	CHCl$_3$	280(4.01),385(3.52)	49-0863-80
$C_{26}H_{23}Cl_2N_3O_4S_2$			
Azocino[1,2-a]indole, 12-[(4-chlorophenyl)sulfonamido]-8-[(4-chlorophenyl)sulfonimido]hexahydro-	EtOH	225(4.73),282(3.96)	39-2870-80C
11H-Cyclopenta[2,3]pyrrolo[1,2-a]indole, 3a-[(4-chlorophenyl)sulfonamido]-11-[(4-chlorophenyl)sulfonimido]-1,2,3,3a,4,5-hexahydro-	CHCl$_3$	288(4.05),432(3.79)	39-2870-80C
2a,6-Methano-1H-azeto[1,2-a][1]benzazocine, 6-[(4-chlorophenyl)sulfonamido]-12-[(4-chlorophenyl)sulfonimido]-2,2a,3,4,5,6-hexahydro-	EtOH	228(4.46),250(3.79)	39-2870-80C
13-Oxa-14-thia-1,15-diazapentacyclo-	EtOH	235(4.54)	39-2870-80C

Compound	Solvent	$\lambda_{max}(\log \epsilon)$	Ref.
[10.4.2.0^{2,7}.0^8,^{16}.0^{12,16}]octadeca- 2,4,6,14-tetraene, 14-(4-chlorophen- yl)-8-[(4-chlorophenyl)sulfonamido]-, S-oxide (cont.)			39-2870-80C

$C_{26}H_{23}Fe_2P$
  Ferrocene, 1,1″-(phenylphosphinidene)-
  bis-
	C_6H_{12}	442(2.47)	101-0345-80J

$C_{26}H_{23}NO_6$
  1,3-Dioxolo[4,5-g]isoquinoline-5-meth-
  anol, α-[3,4-dimethoxy-2-(phenyl-
  methoxy)phenyl]-
	MeOH	236(4.89),276(3.92),
		290(3.79),315(3.75),
		328(3.86)
			100-0151-80

$C_{26}H_{23}NSn$
  Phenazastannine, 5-ethyl-5,10-dihydro-
  10,10-diphenyl-
	pentane	272(4.53),315(3.89),
		320(3.20)
			65-1104-80

$C_{26}H_{23}N_3O_2$
  6H-Anthra[1,9-cd]isoxazol-6-one, 5-[(4-
  methylphenyl)amino]-3-piperidino-
	dioxan	258(4.50),484(4.36),
		520(4.45)
			103-0704-80

$C_{26}H_{23}N_3O_9$
  1,3-Dioxolo[4,5-h][2]benzoxepin-5,8-im-
  ine-9-methanol, 5,7,8,9-tetrahydro-4-
  methoxy-11-methyl-α,7-bis(2-nitro-
  phenyl)-
	CHCl$_3$-HClO$_4$	255(4.40),345(4.15)	83-0715-80

$C_{26}H_{23}N_5O$
  Pyrido[3,4-a]indolizine-4,8-dicarbo-
  nitrile, 1,2,4a,5,10a,10b-hexahydro-
  1-(hydroxyamino)-2-phenyl-5-(phenyl-
  methyl)-
	CH$_2$Cl$_2$	275(4.6),329(4.0)	64-0896-80B

$C_{26}H_{23}S_2$
  Sulfonium, (3,4-dimethylphenyl)[4-
  (phenylthio)phenyl-, hexafluoroarsen-
  ate
	n.s.g.	235(4.33),300(4.29)	47-2697-80

$C_{26}H_{24}$
  1-Butene, 3-methyl-3-(1,2,3-triphenyl-
  2-cyclopropen-1-yl)-
	EtOH	226(4.36),323(4.37)	35-2797-80

2-Butene, 2-methyl-4-(1,2,3-triphenyl- 2-cyclopropen-1-yl)-	EtOH	228(4.46),318(4.41), 333(4.34)	35-2797-80

$C_{26}H_{24}NO$
  Benz[a]acridinium, 8,9,10,11-tetrahy-
  dro-9,9-dimethyl-7-(4-methylphenyl)-
  11-oxo-, bromide
	n.s.g.	230(4.83),285(4.65),
		354(4.20)
			104-1592-80

perchlorate	n.s.g.	232(4.72),284(4.32), 354(4.18)	104-1592-80

$C_{26}H_{24}NO_2$
  Benz[a]acridinium, 8,9,10,11-tetrahy-
  dro-7-(4-methoxyphenyl)-9,9-dimethyl-
  11-oxo-, bromide
	n.s.g.	230(4.55),290(4.37),
		352(3.88)
			104-1592-80

perchlorate	n.s.g.	228(4.56),284(4.35), 350(3.52)	104-1592-80
$C_{26}H_{24}N_2OS$ 2H-1,4-Benzothiazine, 2-[4-(dimethyl-	CHCl$_3$	256s(4.29),273(4.31),	39-2923-80C

Compound	Solvent	$\lambda_{max}(\log \epsilon)$	Ref.
amino)cinnamylidene]-3-(4-methoxy-phenyl)- (cont.)		374(4.35),455(4.25)	39-2923-80C
$C_{26}H_{24}N_2O_4$			
Benzamide, N-[2-(4-acetoxyphenyl)-[[(1-phenylethyl)amino]carbonyl]-ethenyl]-, (S)-	dioxan	285(4.29)	70-0789-80
Benzoic acid, 4-[[[2-(ethoxycarbonyl)-3-phenylcyclopropyl]phenylmethylene]-hydrazino]-	MeOH	229(3.35),272(2.83), 342(3.58)	4-0541-80
2-Propenoic acid, 3,3'-(1,4-phenylene)-bis[3-(phenylamino)-, dimethyl ester, (Z,Z)-	MeOH	275(4.34),331(4.35)	47-3029-80
$C_{26}H_{24}N_3O_9$			
1,3-Dioxolo[4,5-g]isoquinolinium, 7,8-dihydro-7,8-bis[hydroxy(2-nitrophen-yl)methyl]-4-methoxy-6-methyl-, perchlorate	MeOH	253(4.45),345(4.16)	83-0715-80
$C_{26}H_{24}N_6O_2$			
3,13-Diazatricyclo[5.3.1.1^{2,6}]dodec-4-ene-8,14-dione, 3,13-bis(4,6-di-methyl-2-pyrimidinyl)-(8a,12a-benzo)-	EtOH	212(4.28),240s(4.30), 258(4.57),265s(4.45), 290(3.99)	39-0331-80C
3,13-Diazatricyclo[5.3.1.1^{2,6}]dodec-4-ene-12,14-dione, 3,13-bis(4,6-di-methyl-2-pyrimidinyl)-(7a,11a-benzo)-	EtOH	211(4.26),240s(4.36), 253(4.48),260s(4.35), 300s(3.85)	39-0331-80C
$C_{26}H_{24}OP_2$			
Phosphine oxide, [2-(diphenylphosph-ino)ethyl]diphenyl-	CHCl$_3$	258(3.5)	140-0065-80
$C_{26}H_{24}O_2$			
4H-1-Benzopyran-4-one, 3-[[4-(1,1-di-methylethyl)phenyl]methylene]-2,3-dihydro-2-phenyl-, (E)-	EtOH H$_2$SO$_4$	240s(--),320(4.11) 407(4.28),480(4.19)	114-0369-80B 114-0369-80B
Pentacyclo[18.2.2.2^{9,12}.0^{4,15}.0^{6,17}]-hexacosa-4,6(17),9(26),11,15,20,22-23-octaene-10,25-dione	CH$_2$Cl$_2$	280(3.9),310s(3.3), 405(3.4)	18-2943-80
Pentacyclo[18.2.2.2^{9,12}.0^{4,15}.0^{6,17}]-hexacosa-4(15),6(17),9,11,20,22,23-25-octaene-5,16-dione	CH$_2$Cl$_2$	285(3.8),440(2.5)	18-2943-80
$C_{26}H_{24}O_3$			
2-Naphthaleneacetic acid, α-hydroxy-α-2-naphthalenyl-, 1,1-dimethylethyl ester	EtOH	218(6.00),231(5.03), 264(4.16),273(4.15)	78-2291-80
$C_{26}H_{24}O_4$			
Cyclopentanone, 2,2'-[1,2-ethenediyl-bis(2,1-phenylenecarbonyl)]bis-	EtOH	288(4.48)	44-1847-80
Dispiro[isobenzofuran-1(3H),1'-cyclo-butane-3',1"(3"H)-isobenzofuran]-3,3"-dione, 2',4'-bis(2-methyl-2-propenyl)-	hexane	201(4.82),228s(4.29), 268s(3.39),276(3.57), 283(3.61)	49-0309-80
Methanone, (1,2,3,4-tetrahydro-5,8-di-methoxy-2,3-naphthalenediyl)bis-[phenyl-	CH$_2$Cl$_2$	244(4.56),285(3.83)	23-1161-80
Spiro[cyclobutan-1,2'-[2H]indene]-1',3'-dione, 2-(2,3-dihydro-1,3-di-oxo-1H-inden-2-yl)-3,3-dimethyl-4-(1-	CHCl$_3$	290(3.18),303(3.04)	49-0309-80

Compound	Solvent	$\lambda_{max}(\log \epsilon)$	Ref.
methylethyl)- (cont.)			49-0309-80
$C_{26}H_{24}O_4P_2$			
Phosphinic acid, (1,2-ethanediyldi-2,1-phenylene)bis[phenyl-	EtOH	227(4.65),265(3.92), 271(3.99),278(3.90)	139-0243-80A
$C_{26}H_{24}O_6$			
1(2H)-Naphthalenone, 2-(4,5-dimethoxy-7-methyl-1-oxo-2(1H)-naphthalenyli-dene)-4,5-dimethoxy-7-methyl-	$CHCl_3$	244(3.86),290(4.28), 350s(3.97),708(4.35)	5-1321-80
1(2H)-Naphthalenone, 2-(4,8-dimethoxy-6-methyl-1-oxo-2(1H)-naphthalenyli-dene)-4,8-dimethoxy-6-methyl-	$CHCl_3$	243(4.43),281(4.24), 314(4.13),397(3.55), 592(4.18)	5-1321-80
$C_{26}H_{24}O_{10}$			
Benzoic acid, 4-[(2,4-dihydroxy-6-meth-ylbenzoyl)oxy]-2-methoxy-6-methyl-, 3-hydroxy-4-(methoxycarbonyl)-5-methylphenyl ester	MeOH	214(4.42),271(4.01), 302(3.71)	102-0885-80
$C_{26}H_{25}Br$			
Pentacyclo[18.2.2.2^{9,12}.0^{4,15}.0^{6,17}]-hexacosa-4,6(17),9,11,15,20,22,23,25-nonaene, 5-bromo-	THF	<u>280s(3.2),315(3.0), 360(2.4)</u>	18-1677-80
$C_{26}H_{25}BrN_6O_2$			
1,7-Imino-2,6-methano-3-benzazecine-8,14(1H)-dione, 5-bromo-3,13-bis(4,6-dimethyl-2-pyrimidinyl)-2,3,6,7,12-12a-hexahydro-, (1α,2β,6β,7α,12aβ)-	EtOH	211s(4.26),245(4.58), 279(4.64),300s(4.28)	39-0331-80C
$C_{26}H_{25}Cl_2N_3O_5S_2$			
Benzenesulfonamide, N,N'-(2,3,4,5-tet-rahydro-10c-hydroxypyrrolo[3,2,1-jk]-carbazole-3a,10b(1H,10cH)-diyl)bis-[4-chloro-	EtOH	226(4.45),255s(3.91), 292(3.18)	39-2870-80C
$C_{26}H_{26}$			
Triple-layered [2.2](2,2)Paracyclophane	THF	<u>280(3.3),350(2.3)</u>	18-0512-80
$C_{26}H_{26}HgSi_2$			
Mercury, bis(methyldiphenylsilyl)-	C_6H_{12}	274(4.15),325(3.23), 379.5(2.08)	101-0169-80N
$C_{26}H_{26}NO$			
Methanaminium, N-[3-(6,7-dihydro-3-phenyl-5H-1-benzopyran-8-yl)-2-phenyl-2-propenylidene]-N-methyl-, tetra-fluoroborate	$CHCl_3$	525(4.52),570(4.62), 610(4.39)	70-0771-80
$C_{26}H_{26}N_2OS$			
Quinazoline, 3-acetyl-3,4,5,6,7,8-hexa-hydro-4-phenyl-8-(phenylmethylene)-2-(2-propenylthio)-	EtOH	230(4.07),285(4.45)	114-0147-80B
$C_{26}H_{26}N_2O_2$			
Acetic acid, cyano[3-(diethylamino)-4-methyl-2,5-diphenyl-2,4-cyclopenta-dien-1-ylidene]-, methyl ester	MeCN	282(4.14),364(4.13), 590(3.48)	24-0424-80
perchlorate	MeCN	249(4.20),295(4.21), 457(4.09)	24-0424-80

Compound	Solvent	$\lambda_{max}(\log \epsilon)$	Ref.
$C_{26}H_{26}N_2O_4$ 2-Butenedioic acid, 2,3-bis(1,3-dimethyl-1H-indol-2-yl)-, dimethyl ester, (Z)-	EtOH	303(3.71),359(3.73)	44-0462-80
$C_{26}H_{26}N_4O$ 4H-Imidazol-4-one, 1,5-dihydro-5,5-diphenyl-2-[4-(phenylmethyl)-1-piperazinyl]-	EtOH	221.0(4.52)	56-2217-80
$C_{26}H_{26}N_4O_6$ [3,3'-Bi-1H-pyrrole]-4,4'-dicarboxylic acid, 2,2',5,5'-tetrahydro-1,1'-bis(6-methyl-2-pyridinyl)-2,2'-dioxo-, diethyl ester	EtOH	225(4.45),281(4.14), 314(4.04)	39-0227-80C
$C_{26}H_{26}N_5O_8P$ Phosphoramidic acid, N-[9-(3,5-di-O-acetyl-2-deoxy-β-D-erythro-pentofuranosyl)-9H-purin-6-yl]-, diphenyl ester	MeOH	259(4.29),268s(4.18), 280s(3.59)	142-0761-80B
$C_{26}H_{26}N_6O_2$ 1,7-Imino-2,6-methano-3-benzazecine-8,14(1H)-dione, 3,13-bis(4,6-dimethyl-2-pyrimidinyl)-2,3,6,7,12,12a-hexahydro-, (1α,2β,6β,7α,12aβ)-	EtOH	213s(4.09),250s(4.35), 270(4.44),295s(4.05)	39-0331-80C
1,7-Imino-2,6-methano-3-benzazecin-8(1H)-one, 3,13-bis(4,6-dimethyl-2-pyrimidinyl)-2,3,6,7-tetrahydro-14-hydroxy-, (1α,2β,6β,7α,14R*)-(14S*)-	EtOH	212(4.26),254(4.54), 264s(4.43),303(3.63)	39-0331-80C
	EtOH	215(4.11),256(4.46), 265(4.36),304(3.88)	39-0331-80C
$C_{26}H_{26}N_6O_3$ Compound, m. 210-211°	EtOH	215(4.26),241(4.61), 280s(4.08)	39-0331-80C
$C_{26}H_{26}O_6$ [1,1'-Binaphthalene], 2,2',4,4',5,5'-hexamethoxy-	CHCl₃	301(3.98),313(4.04), 340(3.96),348(3.96)	12-2531-80
$C_{26}H_{26}Si_2$ Disilane, 1,2-dimethyl-1,1,2,2-tetraphenyl-	isooctane	240.0(4.41)	101-0261-80Q
$C_{26}H_{27}N_3O_{10}$ Glycine, N-[2-[[8-[bis(carboxymethyl)-amino]-6-methoxy-2-quinolinyl]methoxy]-4-methylphenyl]-N-(carboxymethyl)-, tetraanion	n.s.g.	261(4.57),354(3.70)	69-2396-80
calcium chelate	n.s.g.	240(4.56),332(3.70)	69-2396-80
$C_{26}H_{27}N_5O_2$ 2,4-Pentanedione, 3-(3,4-dihydro-3-methyl-2-oxo-2H-1,3-benzoxazin-4-yl)-, bis(phenylhydrazone)	EtOH	283(4.56),300s(4.42)	4-0519-80
$C_{26}H_{28}BrNO_4$ 3,5-Pyridinedicarboxylic acid, 4-(4-bromophenyl)-1,4-dihydro-2,6-di-	EtOH	202(4.33),245(4.11), 349(3.56)	103-0377-80

Compound	Solvent	$\lambda_{max}(\log \epsilon)$	Ref.
methyl-1-(phenylmethyl)-, diethyl ester (cont.)			103-0377-80
$C_{26}H_{28}BrNO_5$			
3,5-Pyridinedicarboxylic acid, 1-(4-bromophenyl)-1,4-dihydro-4-(4-methoxyphenyl)-2,6-dimethyl-, diethyl ester	EtOH	202(4.52),227(4.46), 279s(4.02),349(3.81)	103-0377-80
3,5-Pyridinedicarboxylic acid, 4-(4-bromophenyl)-1,4-dihydro-1-(4-methoxyphenyl)-2,6-dimethyl-, diethyl ester	EtOH	204(4.52),244(4.44), 350(3.97)	103-0377-80
$C_{26}H_{28}ClNO_5$			
3,5-Pyridinedicarboxylic acid, 1-(3-chlorophenyl)-1,4-dihydro-4-(4-methoxyphenyl)-2,6-dimethyl-, diethyl ester	EtOH	202(4.59),221(4.46), 276s(3.95),348(3.75)	103-0377-80
$C_{26}H_{28}N_2O_4$			
2-Butenedioic acid, 2-(2,3-dihydro-1,3-dimethyl-1H-indol-2-yl)-3-(trans-1,3-dimethyl-1-H-inden-2-yl)-, dimethyl ester	EtOH	309(3.66),350s(3.23)	44-0462-80
$C_{26}H_{28}N_2O_7$			
3,5-Pyridinedicarboxylic acid, 1,4-di-hydro-1-(3-methoxyphenyl)-2,6-dimethyl-4-(3-nitrophenyl)-, diethyl ester	EtOH	205(4.27),223s(4.18), 242(4.22),269s(3.92), 354(3.64)	103-0377-80
3,5-Pyridinedicarboxylic acid, 1,4-di-hydro-1-(3-methoxyphenyl)-2,6-dimeth-yl-4-(4-nitrophenyl)-, diethyl ester	EtOH	202(4.55),222(4.40), 235(4.39),279(4.25), 356s(3.88)	103-0377-80
3,5-Pyridinedicarboxylic acid, 1,4-di-hydro-1-(4-methoxyphenyl)-2,6-dimeth-yl-4-(2-nitrophenyl)-, diethyl ester	EtOH	203(4.59),229(4.46), 290s(4.11),324-72(3.79)	103-0377-80
3,5-Pyridinedicarboxylic acid, 1,4-di-hydro-1-(4-methoxyphenyl)-2,6-dimeth-yl-4-(3-nitrophenyl)-, diethyl ester	EtOH	203(4.42),242(4.43), 350(3.72)	103-0377-80
3,5-Pyridinedicarboxylic acid, 1,4-di-hydro-1-(4-methoxyphenyl)-2,6-dimeth-yl-4-(4-nitrophenyl)-, diethyl ester	EtOH	203(4.35),243(4.26), 351(3.64)	103-0377-80
$C_{26}H_{28}O_2$			
1,8-Dodecanophenanthrene-16,17-dione	MeCN	253(4.62),261(4.72), 282(4.04),293(4.04), 306(4.12),337(2.46), 354(2.33),448(1.40)	44-1847-80
	2-MeTHF at 77°K	450(--)	44-1847-80
$C_{26}H_{28}O_5$			
4H-1-Benzopyran-4-one, 2-(1,3-benzodi-oxol-5-yl)-2,3-dihydro-7-hydroxy-6,8-bis(3-methyl-2-butenyl)-	MeOH	240(4.40),285(4.39)	102-1558-80
$C_{26}H_{28}O_6$			
Benzenehexanoic acid, 2,2'-(1,2-ethene-diyl)bis[ε-oxo-	EtOH	290(4.15),315s(4.08)	44-1847-80
$C_{26}H_{29}NO_4$			
3,5-Pyridinedicarboxylic acid, 1,4-di-	EtOH	206(4.33),243(4.32),	103-0377-80

Compound	Solvent	$\lambda_{max}(\log \epsilon)$	Ref.
hydro-2,6-dimethyl-1-(4-methylphen- yl)-4-phenyl-, diethyl ester (cont.)		348(3.75)	103-0377-80
3,5-Pyridinedicarboxylic acid, 1,4-di- hydro-2,6-dimethyl-4-phenyl-1-(phen- ylmethyl)-, diethyl ester	EtOH	207(4.38),246(4.29), 345(3.79)	103-0377-80
$C_{26}H_{29}NO_5$			
3,5-Pyridinedicarboxylic acid, 1,4-di- hydro-1-(4-methoxyphenyl)-2,6-di- methyl-4-phenyl-, diethyl ester	EtOH	203(4.35),243(4.26), 351(3.64)	103-0377-80
$C_{26}H_{29}NO_9$			
Indolo[7,1-ab]benzazepine-7,8-dicarbox- ylic acid, 4,5,8a,9,10,11,12,12a- octahydro-8a-hydroxy-12-[3-methoxy- 1-(methoxycarbonyl)-3-oxo-1-propen- yl]-, dimethyl ester	MeOH and MeOH-HClO4	250s(4.03),303(3.96), 346(4.06)	39-0535-80C
$C_{26}H_{29}NO_{10}$			
Parviflorine	MeOH	233(4.50),260(4.18), 288s(3.70),352(3.66)	88-1909-80
$C_{26}H_{30}Br_4O_4$			
D-Homopregn-4-ene-3,20-dione, 17a-acet- oxy-2,6-bis(dibromomethylene)-	EtOH	262(3.96),298(4.06)	33-1867-80
$C_{26}H_{30}N_2O_5$			
1(4H)-Naphthalenone, 4-[[4-(1,4,7,10- tetraoxa-13-azacyclopentadec-13-yl)- phenyl]imino]-	MeCN	577(4.41)	24-0457-80
$C_{26}H_{30}N_2O_7$			
4,5-Secoakuammilan-17-oic acid, 5-acet- oxy-1,4-diacetyl-2,5-epoxy-1,2-dihy- dro-, methyl ester	EtOH	248(4.02),280(3.63), 287(3.56)	22-0400-80
isomer	EtOH	248(3.99),280(3.52), 287(3.47)	22-0400-80
$C_{26}H_{30}N_2O_{10}$			
3,6,9,17,20,23-Hexaoxa-13,27-diazatri- cyclo[23.3.1.1^{11,15}]triaconta-1(29)- 11,13,15(30),25,27-hexaene-2,10,16- 24-tetrone, 12,14,26,28-tetramethyl-	MeCN	234(4.16),274(3.83), 282(3.79)	44-2854-80
$C_{26}H_{30}N_4O_2$			
1H-Cyclopenta[5,6]naphtho[1,2-g]pyrazo- lo[1,5-a]quinazoline-10-carbonitrile, 1-acetoxy-2,3,3a,3b,5a,6,13,13a,13b- 14,15,15a-dodecahydro-13a,15a-dimeth- yl-, [1S-(1α,3aβ,3bα,5aβ,13aα,13bβ- 15aα)]-	MeOH	208(4.07),239(4.49), 324(3.75)	39-0481-80C
$C_{26}H_{30}N_4O_9$			
L-Tryptophan, N-acetyl-2-[1,2,3,4-tet- rahydro-1-[2,3-0-(1-methylethylid- ene)-β-D-ribofuranosyl]-2,4-dioxo- 5-pyrimidinyl]-, methyl ester	MeCN	260(4.07),328(3.72)	35-7535-80
$C_{26}H_{30}N_4S_2$			
3H-Pyrazole-3-thione, 4,4'-butylidene- bis[1,2-dihydro-1,5-dimethyl-2-phenyl-	benzene H2O	278(4.10),336(4.35) 256(4.32),288(4.29)	140-0560-80 140-0560-80

Compound	Solvent	$\lambda_{max}(\log \epsilon)$	Ref.
$C_{26}H_{30}O_2$			
1,8-Dodecanophenanthren-16-one, 17-hydroxy-	MeOH	253(4.51),260(4.62), 282(3.90),293(3.94), 305(4.05)	44-1847-80
	2-MeTHF	331(2.45),337(2.55), 346(2.37),355(2.40)	44-1847-80
$C_{26}H_{30}O_3$			
2H-Benzo[b]cycloprop[e]oxepin-2-one, 1a-benzoyl-1,8-bis(1,1-dimethylethyl)-1,1a,8,8a-tetrahydro-, (1α,1aα,8α,8aα)-	EtOH	250(4.20)	39-2937-80C
$C_{26}H_{30}O_4$			
2,9-Butanodibenzo[a,e]cyclooctene-14,15-dicarboxylic acid, 5,6,11,12-tetrahydro-, diethyl ester	EtOH	215(3.04),273(2.84), 287(2.76)	44-3974-80
1,8-Phenanthrenedihexanoic acid	MeOH	253(4.34),260(4.36), 267s(4.04),281(3.74), 292(3.80),305(3.86)	44-1847-80
$C_{26}H_{30}O_6$			
Butanedioic acid, 2,3-dibenzoyl-,	MeOH	252(4.45),289s(3.42)	39-2670-80C
dibutyl ester, meso	MeOH-KOH	282(4.08)	39-2670-80C
racemic	MeOH	252(4.39),280s(3.46)	39-2670-80C
	MeOH-KOH	281(3.98)	39-2670-80C
$C_{26}H_{30}O_9$			
Coleon Z, 17-acetoxy-12β-O-acetyl-	EtOH	235(3.43)	33-0095-80
$C_{26}H_{30}O_{11}$			
Simplexoside	MeOH	228(4.26),279(3.65)	102-0332-80
$C_{26}H_{31}I$			
1,1'-Bibicyclo[2.2.2]octane, 4-iodo-4'-(1-naphthalenyl)-	$C_6H_{11}Me$-isopentane	223(4.84),227(5.03), 251(3.38),259(3.55), 265(3.63),274(3.64), 285(3.43),304s(2.53), 309s(2.26),318(2.36)	44-3933-80
$C_{26}H_{31}NO_{10}$			
Dihydroparviflorine	MeOH	260(3.94),278s(3.66), 290s(3.53)	88-1909-80
$C_{26}H_{31}N_5O$			
1(2H)-Phthalazinone, 7-(dimethylamino)-4,4-bis[4-(dimethylamino)phenyl]-3,4-dihydro-	EtOH	266(4.76)	94-3561-80
$C_{26}H_{31}N_5O_5$			
8H-Oxazolo[4,5-b]phenoxazine-4,6-dicarboxamide, 7-amino-N,N,N',N'-tetraethyl-2,9,11-trimethyl-8-oxo-	CHCl$_3$	247(4.56),430(4.49), 450(4.53)	4-0017-80
$C_{26}H_{31}N_5O_6$			
5H-Oxazolo[4,5-b]phenoxazine-4,6-dicarboxamide, N,N,N',N'-tetraethyl-2,9,11-trimethyl-8-nitro-	CHCl$_3$	305(4.08),442(3.95)	4-0017-80
$C_{26}H_{31}N_5O_7$			
5H-Oxazolo[4,5-b]phenoxazine-4,6-di-	CHCl$_3$	310(4.16),350(3.97),	4-0017-80

Compound	Solvent	$\lambda_{max}(\log \epsilon)$	Ref.
carboxamide, N,N,N',N'-tetraethyl-8-hydroxy-2,9,11-trimethyl-7-nitro-		520(3.80)	4-0017-80
$C_{26}H_{31}N_9O_6$ 2,8-Imino-3,7-methano-4-benzazecine-1,14(2H)-dione, 4,13-bis(4,6-dimethoxy-1,3,5-triazin-2-yl)-12-(dimethylamino)-3,4,7,8,8a,9,12,12a-octahydro-	$CHCl_3$	252s(4.18),270(4.23)	39-0331-80C
$C_{26}H_{32}N_4O_2$ 1H-Naphtho[2',1':4,5]indeno[2,1-e]pyrazolo[1,5-a]pyrimidine-10-carbonitrile, 2-acetoxy-2,3,4,4a,4b,5,6-6a,13,13a,13b,14,15,15a-tetradecahydro-4a,6a-dimethyl-, [2S-(2α,4aα,4bβ-6aα,13aβ,13bα,15aβ)]-	MeOH	207(4.11),234(4.50), 323(3.81)	39-0481-80C
$C_{26}H_{32}O$ [1,1'-Bibicyclo[2.2.2]octan]-4-ol, 4'-(1-naphthalenyl)-	$C_6H_{11}Me$-isopentane	210s(4.43),221s(4.77), 226(4.89),254s(3.33), 263s(3.61),272(3.82), 282(3.92),289(3.75), 292(3.74),294(3.76), 303s(3.03),308s(2.69), 313(2.68)	44-3933-80
[1,1'-Bibicyclo[2.2.2]octan]-4-ol, 4'-(2-naphthalenyl)-	$C_6H_{11}Me$-isopentane	251s(3.46),260s(3.62), 267(3.70),275(3.72), 284(3.57),304s(2.67), 310s(2.44),318(2.56)	44-3933-80
$C_{26}H_{32}OSe$ 1-Phenanthrenecarboselenoic acid, 1,2,3,4,4a,9,10,10a-octahydro-1,4a-dimethyl-7-(1-methylethyl)-, Se-phenyl ester, [1R-(1α,4aβ,10aα)]-	pentane	221(4.45),259(3.66), 275s(--)	33-2328-80
$C_{26}H_{32}O_3Se$ Androst-5-en-17-one, 3-[[(phenylseleno)carbonyl]oxy]-, (3β)-	pentane	213s(--),229s(--), 259(3.72),302(2.95)	33-2328-80
$C_{26}H_{32}O_4$ Benzenehexanoic acid, 2,2'-(1,2-ethenediyl)bis-	MeOH	288(4.34)	44-1847-80
$C_{26}H_{32}O_6$ Benzene, 1,2,4-trimethoxy-5-[2-[2-(2,4-5-trimethoxyphenyl)-3-cyclohexen-1-yl]ethenyl]-, [1α(E),2α]-(±)-	EtOH $CDCl_3$	205(4.53),261(4.03), 298(3.75),314(3.72) 261(4.29),298(3.96), 315(3.94)	94-2948-80 64-0156-80C
$C_{26}H_{32}O_7$ Pregna-1,4,6-triene-3,20-dione, 21-acetoxy-11-hydroxy-16,17-[(1-methylethylidene)bis(oxy)]-, (11β,16α)-	MeOH	222(4.07),254(3.98), 300(4.09)	87-0430-80
$C_{26}H_{32}O_{13}$ Durantoside I Ladroside	H_2O MeOH	224(4.24),282(4.29) 221(4.07),236(4.09), 328(3.99)	100-0649-80 100-0649-80
Methyl grandifloroside	MeOH	219(4.2),234(4.1), 300s(3.9),327(4.1)	100-0649-80

Compound	Solvent	λ_{max}(log ϵ)	Ref.
$C_{26}H_{32}O_{14}$ Lamiidoside	MeOH	212s(--),227(4.22), 311(4.18)	100-0649-80
$C_{26}H_{32}O_{16}$ Griselinoside tetraacetate	MeOH	233(3.97)	102-2685-80
$C_{26}H_{32}O_{17}$ Cyclopenta[c]pyran-4,7-dicarboxylic acid, 1,4a,5,6,7,7a-hexahydro-4a-hydroxy-5-oxo-1-[(2,3,4,6-tetra-O-acetyl-β-D-glucopyranosyl)oxy]-, dimethyl ester, [1S-(1α,4aα,7α,7aα)]- (aralidioside tetraacetate)	MeOH	228(3.91)	102-2685-80
$C_{26}H_{33}BrO_6$ Benzoic acid, 4-bromo-, 2-(2,6-diacetoxy-1,2,3,4,6,7,8,8a-octahydro-8,8a-dimethyl-1-naphthalenyl)propyl ester, [1R-[1α(R*),2α,6β,8β,8aβ]]-	EtOH	249(4.26)	12-2737-80
$C_{26}H_{33}BrO_7$ Pregna-1,4-diene-3,20-dione, 21-acetoxy-7-bromo-11-hydroxy-16,17-[(1-methylethylidene)bis(oxy)]-, (7α,11β,16α)-	MeOH	242(4.18)	87-0430-80
$C_{26}H_{33}ClO_7$ Pregna-1,4-diene-3,20-dione, 21-acetoxy-7-chloro-11-hydroxy-16,17-[(1-methylethylidene)bis(oxy)]-, (7α,11β,16α)-	MeOH	241(4.21)	87-0430-80
$C_{26}H_{33}N_3O_9$ 1,4,7,10,13-Pentaoxa-16-azacyclooctadecane, 16-[4-[2-(2,4-dinitrophenyl)-ethenyl]phenyl]-	MeCN	477(4.73)	24-0457-80
$C_{26}H_{33}N_7O$ 1H-Indole-2,3-dione, 3-[[5-ethyl-2-(4-ethyl-3,5-dipropyl-1H-pyrazol-1-yl)-6-methyl-4-pyrimidinyl]hydrazone]	EtOH	204(4.36),259(4.38), 272s(4.29),373(4.24), 455s(3.85),476s(3.68)	103-1279-80
$C_{26}H_{34}O_2$ 1,3-Cyclohexanedione, 2-[3,7-dimethyl-9-(2,6,6-trimethyl-1-cyclohexen-1-yl)-2,4,6,8-nonatetraenylidene]-, (all-E)-	hexane EtOH MeCN	275(4.16),465(4.74) 260(4.11),489(4.65) 280(4.19),475(4.70)	87-0805-80 87-0805-80 87-0805-80
$C_{26}H_{34}O_4$ Benzenehexanoic acid, 2,2'-(1,2-ethanediyl)bis-	MeOH	262(3.95),271(3.84), 291(3.23),303(3.20)	44-1847-80
$C_{26}H_{34}O_{13}$ 2H-1-Benzopyran-2-one, 7-[(6-O-β-D-glucopyranosyl-β-D-glucopyranosyl)-oxy]-8-(3-methyl-2-butenyl)-	EtOH	246s(3.83),256(3.87), 313(4.24)	94-1847-80
$C_{26}H_{35}ClO_6$ Pregna-1,4-diene-3,20-dione, 7-chloro-	MeOH	241(4.19)	145-1618-80

Compound	Solvent	$\lambda_{max}(\log \epsilon)$	Ref.
11,21-dihydroxy-16-methyl-17-(1-oxo-butoxy)-, (7α,11β,16α)- (cont.)			145-1618-80
$C_{26}H_{35}NO_{10}$ Propanedioic acid, [[bis(2,4,6-trimeth-oxyphenyl)amino]methyl]-, diethyl ester	MeCN	216(4.026),238(4.09)	152-0389-80
$C_{26}H_{35}N_5O_3S_2$ 2H-1,3,5-Thiadiazine-2-thione, 6-(di-cyclohexylamino)-4-[(1,1-dimethyl-ethyl)imino]-3,4-dihydro-3-(4-nitro-benzoyl)-	CH_2Cl_2	272(4.49),346(4.01)	24-0079-80
$C_{26}H_{36}N_4O_6$ Octanamide, N-[5-[1,6-dihydro-2,6-di-oxo-5-[(1-oxooctyl)amino]-3(2H)-py-ridinylidene]-1,2,5,6-tetrahydro-2,6-dioxo-3-pyridinyl]-	HOAc pyridine CH_2Cl_2	510(4.39) 520(4.39) 520(4.39)	39-1782-80C 39-1782-80C 39-1782-80C
$C_{26}H_{36}O_2$ D-Homoandrost-15-eno[17,17a-c]furan-12-one, 2',4,4,8-tetramethyl-, (5α)-	MeOH	223(3.92),230(3.98), 242(4.03)	12-1783-80
$C_{26}H_{36}O_3$ D-Homoandrost-15-eno[17,17a-c]furan-12-one, 19-hydroxy-2',4,4,8-tetra-methyl-, (5α)-	MeOH	241(4.14)	12-1783-80
$C_{26}H_{36}O_4$ Ophiobola-3,6,19-trien-25-oic acid, 5,8-dioxo-, methyl ester	EtOH	258(4.20)	94-1043-80
$C_{26}H_{36}O_5$ Card-20(22)-enolide, 3-acetoxy-14,21-epoxy-22-methyl-, (3β,5β)-	EtOH	219(4.16)	48-0991-80
D-Homopregna-5,17-dien-20-one, 3β,16α-diacetoxy-	EtOH	224(3.97)	33-1867-80
16β-	EtOH	226(3.96)	33-1867-80
$C_{26}H_{36}O_8$ Trillenogenin	EtOH	248.5(4.11)	94-1437-80
$C_{26}H_{36}O_{12}$ Foliamenthin	n.s.g.	228(4.24),245s(--)	100-0649-80
$C_{26}H_{37}N_2O_5$ Pyridinium, 1-methyl-4-[2-[4-(1,4,7-10,13-pentaoxa-16-azacyclooctadec-16-yl)phenyl]ethenyl]-, iodide	MeCN	471(4.97)	24-0457-80
$C_{26}H_{37}N_5$ 2-Pyrimidinamine, N-(4-butylphenyl)-4-(4-ethyl-3,5-dipropyl-1H-pyrazol-1-yl)-6-methyl-	EtOH EtOH-HCl	278(3.84) 297(3.92)	103-0309-80 103-0309-80
$C_{26}H_{37}N_5O_6$ Lemonnierin	pyridine	625(4.75)	39-1782-80C
Octanamide, N-[5-[[1,6-dihydro-2,6-di-oxo-5-[(1-oxooctyl)amino]-3(2H)-pyr-	pyridine or HOAc	640(4.75)	39-1782-80C

Compound	Solvent	$\lambda_{max}(\log \epsilon)$	Ref.
idinylidene]amino]-1,2,5,6-tetrahydro-2,6-dioxo-3-pyridinyl]- (cont.)			39-1788-80C
$C_{26}H_{38}D_4$			
Benzene, 1,2-bis(3,3-dimethyl-1-butenyl-1,2-d)-4,5-bis(1,1-dimethylethyl)-	hexane	241(4.48),264s(--)	88-0897-80
$C_{26}H_{38}N_4O_2S_3$			
2H-1,3,5-Thiadiazine-2-thione, 6-(dicyclohexylamino)-4-[(1,1-dimethylethyl)imino]-3,4-dihydro-3-[(4-methylphenyl)sulfonyl]-	CH_2Cl_2	243(4.28),284(4.02) (plus shoulder)	24-0079-80
$C_{26}H_{38}O_2$			
D-Homoandrost-15-eno[17,17a-c]furan-12-ol, 2',4,4,8-tetramethyl-, (5α,12α)-	MeOH	223(3.93),231(4.03), 244(4.10)	12-1783-80
(5α,12β)-	MeOH	223(3.92),230(3.98), 240(4.03)	12-1783-80
Methanone, 1,4-phenylenebis[(1,2,2,3-tetramethylcyclopentyl)-, [1R-[1α(1R*,3S*),3α]]-	MeCN	202(4.14),248(4.12), 280s(3.00),328(2.67)	108-0142-80
24-Norcholesta-1,4,22-trien-3-one, 12β-hydroxy-	MeOH	244(4.08)	88-4295-80
$C_{26}H_{38}O_4$			
24-Norchola-14,20(22)-dien-23-oic acid, 3-acetoxy-, methyl ester, (3β,5β)-	EtOH	223(3.95)	48-1012-80
Scalar-16-en-25-al, 22-hydroxy-24-methyl-12,24-dioxo-	MeOH	231(3.93)	12-1783-80
$C_{26}H_{38}O_5$			
5β,14β-Card-20(22)-enolide, 3β-acetoxy-14-hydroxy-21-methyl-, (21R)-	EtOH	219(4.18)	48-0991-80
(21S)-	EtOH	221(4.16)	48-0991-80
5β,14β-Card-20(22)-enolide, 3β-acetoxy-14-hydroxy-22-methyl-	EtOH	222.5(4.27)	48-0991-80
24-Nor-5β,14β-chol-20(22)-en-23-oic acid, 3β-acetoxy-14,15β-epoxy-, methyl ester	EtOH	226(3.90)	48-1012-80
$C_{26}H_{38}O_7$			
Retinoic acid, β-D-glucopyranosyl ester	EtOH	361(4.66)	33-0277-80
$C_{26}H_{39}ClN_3PS$			
2H-1,2,4-Benzothiadiazine, 3-amino-7-chloro-1,1-dihydro-2-(phenylmethyl)-1-(tributylphosphoranylidene)-	MeOH	250(4.36),286(4.09), 324(3.61)	44-3416-80
	MeOH-acid	272(4.12),294(4.03), 304(4.02)	44-3416-80
	MeOH-base	232(4.49),284(4.27)	44-3416-80
$C_{26}H_{40}$			
Naphthalene, 2,3,6,7-tetrakis(1,1-dimethylethyl)-	hexane	232s(4.95),237(5.10), 270(3.66)	88-0897-80
$C_{26}H_{40}O_4$			
5β,14β-Card-20-enolide, 3β,14-dihydroxy-21,22,22-trimethyl-	EtOH	230(3.55)	48-0991-80

Compound	Solvent	$\lambda_{max}(\log \epsilon)$	Ref.
$C_{26}H_{40}Si_3$ Silacycloprop-2-ene, 1,1-bis(2,4,6-tri-methylphenyl)-2,3-bis(trimethylsilyl)-	C_6H_{12}	238(4.29),260(4.12), 345(2.51)	101-0147-80K
$C_{26}H_{42}$ Benzene, 1,4-bis[(1,2,2,3-tetramethyl-cyclopentyl)methyl]-, [1R-[1α-(1R*,3S*),3α]]-	MeCN	260(2.43),265(2.53), 268s(2.46),274(2.45)	108-0142-80
$C_{26}H_{42}N_2$ 4,4'-Bipyridinium, 1,1'-dioctyl-, dibromide	H_2O	258(4.33)	98-1026-80
$C_{26}H_{42}N_8$ 4-Pyrimidinamine, 5-ethyl-2-(4-ethyl-3,5-dipropyl-1H-pyrazol-1-yl)-N-(5-hexyl-1H-1,2,4-triazol-3-yl)-6-methyl-	EtOH	229(4.29),265(4.38), 291(4.10)	103-1271-80
$C_{26}H_{42}O_2$ 1,4-Benzenedimethanol, α,α'-bis(1,2,2,3-tetramethylcyclopentyl)-	MeCN	222(4.06),256(2.40), 262(2.45),264s(2.40), 265s(2.30),268(2.28), 271s(2.08)	108-0142-80
isomer	MeCN	256(2.32),263(2.42), 268(2.28),272s(2.08)	108-0142-80
$C_{26}H_{42}O_4$ 2H-Pyran-2-one, 4-acetoxy-3,5-dibutyl-6-(1-butyl-1-heptenyl)-	EtOH	234(3.1),311(3.4)	88-1281-80
$C_{26}H_{42}O_5$ 2H-Pyran-2-one, 4-acetoxy-3,5-dibutyl-6-(1-butyl-2-oxoheptyl)-	EtOH	306(3.92)	88-1281-80
(-)-,	EtOH	306.5(3.86)	44-3268-80
2H-Pyran-2-one, 4-acetoxy-3,5-dibutyl-6-(2-butyl-3-pentyloxiranyl)-	EtOH	220(3.5),299(3.95)	88-1281-80
$C_{26}H_{43}NO$ Chola-5,7-dien-3-ol, 24-(dimethylamino)-	EtOH	262(4.05),281(4.06), 291(3.81)	130-0187-80
9,10-Secochola-5,7,10(19)-trien-3-ol, 24-(dimethylamino)-, (3β,5Z,7E)-	EtOH	265(4.24)	130-0187-80
$C_{26}H_{44}O_5$ 2H-Pyran-2-one, 3,5-dibutyl-4-hydroxy-6-[1-(2-pentyl-1,3-dioxolan-2-yl)-pentyl]- (elasnin ketal)	EtOH	284(3.60)	44-3268-80
$C_{26}H_{45}BN_4$ Guanidine, N,N'-dicyclohexyl-N-(dibut-ylboryl)-N''-2-pyridinyl-	heptane	213(4.05),294(4.17), 368(3.81)	70-0481-80

Compound	Solvent	$\lambda_{max}(\log \epsilon)$	Ref.
$C_{27}H_{14}N_4O$ Propanedinitrile, 2,2'-(9,10-dihydro-6-methoxy-9,10[1',2']benzenoanthracene-1,4-diylidene)bis-	CH_2Cl_2 MeCN	411(4.66),584(3.02) 544(--)	89-0543B-80 89-0543B-80
$(C_{27}H_{16}I_2N_2O_3)_n$ Poly[imino-1,3-phenylenecarbonyl-1,3-phenyleneiminocarbonyl(2,2'-diiodo-[1,1'-biphenyl]-4,4'-diyl)carbonyl]	DMSO	265(4.62)	126-0333-80
$C_{27}H_{16}N_2O_3$ 3-Furancarbonitrile, 2-[[(4-oxo-4H-1-benzopyran-3-yl)methylene]amino]-4,5-diphenyl-	MeOH	411(4.34)	73-1581-80
$C_{27}H_{17}NO_2$ 5H-Naphtho[2,3-c]carbazole-8,13-dione, 5-methyl-6-phenyl-	$CHCl_3$	246(4.60),268(4.51), 303(4.23),332s(4.38), 344(4.43),417(3.81), 440(3.76)	4-0695-80
$C_{27}H_{18}$ Dibenzo[c,g]triphenylene, 3-methyl-	MeOH	229(4.48),254(4.81), 262(4.79),279(4.52), 294(4.45),304(4.46), 330(4.09),347(3.94), 393(2.85)	54-0160-80
$(C_{27}H_{18}I_2N_2O_2)_n$ Poly[imino-1,4-phenylenemethylene-1,4-phenyleneiminocarbonyl(2,2'-diiodo-[1,1'-biphenyl]-4,4'-diyl)carbonyl]	DMSO	260(4.87)	126-0333-80
$C_{27}H_{18}N_2O$ Propanedinitrile, (3-methoxy-2,4,5-triphenyl-2,4-cyclopentadien-1-ylidene)-	MeCN	261(4.10),342(4.23), 525(2.54)	24-0424-80
Propanedinitrile, [3-(4-methylphenyl)-4-oxo-2,5-diphenyl-2-cyclopenten-1-ylidene]-	MeCN	265(4.08),373(4.34)	24-0424-80
$C_{27}H_{18}N_6O_6$ 9,10-Anthracenedione, 1-[[4-[(2,4-dinitrophenyl)azo]phenyl]amino]-4-(methylamino)-	C_6H_5Cl	360(4.2),540s(4.3), 615(4.4),650(4.4)	104-2039-80
$C_{27}H_{18}OS$ Spiro[2H-thiete-2,9'-[9H]xanthene], 3,4-diphenyl-	dioxan	240(4.56),310(4.06), 344(3.95)	5-0873-80
$C_{27}H_{18}O_2$ Spiro[naphthalene-1(4H),2'(1'H)-naphtho[2,1-b]furan]-4-one, 1'-phenyl-	EtOH	244(4.23),268(4.04), 279(4.04),291(3.92), 327(3.56),342(3.60)	39-1986-80C
$C_{27}H_{19}ClN_2O_5S$ Benzenesulfonic acid, 5-[(4-amino-3-chloro-9,10-dihydro-9,10-dioxo-1-anthracenyl)amino]-2-methyl-, phenyl ester	n.s.g.	564(4.09),595(4.05)	93-1963-80

Compound	Solvent	$\lambda_{max}(\log \epsilon)$	Ref.
$C_{27}H_{19}N$			
5H-Naphtho[2,3-c]carbazole, 5-methyl-6-phenyl-	EtOH	205(4.71),219(4.67), 232(4.54),251s(4.62), 260s(4.67),265(4.68), 290(4.72),310(4.52), 341(4.69),358(3.92), 377(4.08),403(3.72), 427(3.64)	4-0695-80
Pyridine, 3-[2-[4-([1,1'-biphenyl]-4-ylethynyl)phenyl]ethenyl]-	DMF	347(4.84)	33-1311-80
$C_{27}H_{19}NO$			
[1]Benzopyrano[4,3-b]indole, 6,11-di-hydro-6,6-diphenyl- (in 64% MeOH)	pH -4.5	370s(3.89),457(4.07)	33-1264-80
Pyridine, 3-[2-[4-(5-phenyl-2-benzo-furanyl)phenyl]ethenyl]-	DMF	358(4.83)	33-1311-80
$C_{27}H_{19}NO_2$			
Benzenepropanenitrile, α-(3-methyl-4-oxo-2,5-diphenyl-2-cyclopenten-1-ylidene)-β-oxo-	MeCN	291(4.31)	24-0424-80
$C_{27}H_{19}NO_4$			
5,11-Naphthacenedione, 6-(acetylmethyl-amino)-12-phenoxy-	toluene	448(4.19),476(4.20)	104-1651-80
5,12-Naphthacenedione, 6-(acetylmethyl-amino)-11-phenoxy-	toluene	396(3.85)	104-1651-80
$C_{27}H_{19}NO_5$			
Benzo[g]pyrrolo[2,1-a]isoquinoline-1,2-dicarboxylic acid, 3-benzoyl-, dimethyl ester	CHCl₃	260(4.90),300(5.00), 330(4.60),385(4.48), 405(4.44)	103-0626-80
Methanone, (6,11-diacetoxybenzo[f]pyri-do[1,2-a]indol-12-yl)phenyl-	CHCl₃	280s(4.42),325(4.20), 333(4.16),358(4.01), 470(3.91)	39-1070-80C
$C_{27}H_{19}N_3O$			
Pyridine, 3-[2-[4-(5-[1,1'-biphenyl]-4-yl-1,3,4-oxadiazol-2-yl)phenyl]-ethenyl]-	DMF	348(4.80)	33-1311-80
$C_{27}H_{19}N_3O_2$			
6H-Anthra[1,9-cd]isoxazol-6-one, 5-(phenylamino)-3-[(phenylmethyl)-amino]-	dioxan	258(4.52),490(4.23), 519(4.31)	103-0704-80
$C_{27}H_{20}$			
Anthracene, 10-methyl-1,8-diphenyl-	EtOH	261(5.04),345s(3.51), 363(3.82),382(3.99), 408(3.89)	44-1807-80
Chrysene, 6-[2-(4-methylphenyl)ethen-yl]-, cis	MeOH	220(4.58),259(4.83), 270(4.83),316s(4.09), 327(4.11)	54-0160-80
trans	MeOH	224(4.63),260(4.78), 275(4.73),348(4.44)	54-0160-80
15H-9,14[1',2']-endo-Cyclopentabenzo-[b]triphenylene, 9,14,16,17-tetra-hydro-, (9α,14α,15R*,16S*)-	MeCN	228(4.45),248(4.52), 257(4.59),262s(4.45), 271(4.31),285(3.83), 298(3.89),310(3.93), 325s(2.87),334(2.67), 342(2.93),350(2.67),	24-1626-80

Compound	Solvent	$\lambda_{max}(\log \epsilon)$	Ref.
(cont.) 15H-9,14[1',3']-endo-Cyclopentabenzo-[b]triphenylene, 9,14,16,17-tetra-hydro-	MeCN	359(3.00) 230(4.46),249(4.56), 256s(4.53),264s(4.40), 273(4.32),278s(4.18), 295s(3.69),307(3.84), 317(3.87),347(2.95), 356(2.70),365(2.99)	24-1626-80 24-1626-80
15H-7,14[1',2']-endo-Cyclopentadibenzo-[a,h]anthracene, 7,14,16,17-tetrahydro-	MeCN	235(4.87),262s(3.74), 274s(3.94),284(4.03), 299s(3.71),308(3.52), 315s(3.38),325(3.49)	24-1626-80
1,4-Methanonaphtho[1,2-b]triphenylene, 1,4,4a,16b-tetrahydro-, (1α,4α,4aβ-16β)-endo-	MeCN	233(4.33),278(4.78), 282(4.79),295s(4.43), 301(4.44),304s(4.42), 321(4.49),335(3.31), 343(2.86),351(3.37), 361(2.76),369(3.37)	24-1626-80
14,9,8b,15-[1,2]Propanediyl[3]ylidene-8bH-benzo[b]cyclobuta[d]triphenyl-ene, 9,13b,14,15-tetrahydro-	MeCN	237(4.77),244(4.79), 252(4.68),268s(4.09), 275s(4.16),282(4.19), 288s(4.16),293s(4.12), 306s(3.95),320(3.86)	24-1626-80
$C_{27}H_{20}ClN_3O_4S$ Benzenesulfonamide, 5-[(4-amino-3-chloro-9,10-dihydro-9,10-dioxo-1-anthracenyl)amino]-2-methyl-N-phenyl-	n.s.g.	573(4.08),605(4.01)	93-1963-80
$C_{27}H_{20}Cl_4N_4O$ Pyrido[3,2-a]indolizine-3,7-dicarbo-nitrile, 10-(2,6-dichlorophenyl)-1-[(2,6-dichlorophenyl)methyl]-1,4,4a,4b,10,10a-hexahydro-4-methoxy-	CH_2Cl_2	263(4.1),359(3.5)	64-0490-80B
$C_{27}H_{20}O$ 5,11-Epoxy-5H-cyclohepta[b]naphthalene, 5a,11-dihydro-5,11-diphenyl-, (5α,5aα,11α)-	EtOH	278(3.7)	138-0349-80
(5α,5aβ,11α)-	EtOH	278(3.4)	138-0349-80
Methanone, [2-(2,4,6-cycloheptatrien-1-ylidenephenylmethyl)phenyl]phenyl-	EtOH	248(4.3),332(4.0)	138-0349-80
$C_{27}H_{20}O_2$ Benzo[a]anthracene-7,12-dione, 2,3,4-trimethyl-5-phenyl-	$CHCl_3$	242(4.48),257(4.48), 386(3.59),442s(3.52), 447(3.48)	44-1424-80
Benzo[a]anthracene-7,12-dione, 5-(3,4,5-trimethylphenyl)-	$CHCl_3$	249(4.51),293(4.58), 335(4.72),365s(3.51), 426(3.69),445(3.63)	44-1424-80
$C_{27}H_{20}O_3S$ 1,2-Oxathiolan-5-one, 3,3,4,4-tetra-phenyl-, 2-oxide	MeCN	190(5.05)	44-4359-80
$C_{27}H_{20}O_7$ 1-Azulenecarboxylic acid, 3,3-bis(benz-oyloxy)-2,3-dihydro-2-oxo-, ethyl ester	$CHCl_3$	260s(4.27),394(4.24), 406(4.21)	138-0197-80
$C_{27}H_{20}S_4$ 1,3-Benzodithiole, 2,2'-bicyclo[4.4.1]-	CH_2Cl_2	234(4.64),271s(4.33),	89-0204-80

Compound	Solvent	$\lambda_{max}(\log \epsilon)$	Ref.
undeca-3,5,8,10-tetraene-2,7-diyli- denebis[methyl- (cont.)		316s(3.97),494(4.25)	89-0204-80
$C_{27}H_{21}N$			
Pyridine, 2-[2-[4-(2-[1,1'-biphenyl]- 4-ylethenyl)phenyl]ethenyl]-	DMF	370(4.88)	33-1311-80
Pyridine, 3-[2-[4-(2-[1,1'-biphenyl]- 4-ylethenyl)phenyl]ethenyl]-	DMF	369(4.88)	33-1311-80
Pyridine, 4-[2-[4-(2-[1,1'-biphenyl]- 4-ylethenyl)phenyl]ethenyl]-	DMF	370(4.86)	33-1311-80
$C_{27}H_{21}NO$			
2-Propen-1-one, 3-(diphenylamino)-1,2- diphenyl-	EtOH	230(3.94),274(3.91), 353(4.00)	4-1201-80
Pyridine, 4-[2-[4-[2-(4-phenoxyphenyl)- ethenyl]phenyl]ethenyl]-	DMF	364(4.77)	33-1311-80
$C_{27}H_{21}NO_3$			
Benzoic acid, 2-[(2-benzoylphenyl)phen- ylamino]-, methyl ester	C_6H_{12}	209(3.94),240(3.65), 293(3.57)	24-0358-80
$C_{27}H_{21}N_3O_3$			
1H-1,4,7-Triazonine, 1,4,7-tribenzoyl- 4,7-dihydro-, (Z,Z,Z)-	MeCN	267(4.21)	24-3127-80
$C_{27}H_{21}N_3O_4$			
1H-Pyrrolo[3,4-f]quinoline-1,3(2H)-di- one, 5-(2,5-dioxo-1-phenyl-3-pyrrol- idinyl)-3a,4,5,9b-tetrahydro-2-phenyl-	MeOH	260(2.80)	103-0833-80
$C_{27}H_{21}S_4$			
1,3-Benzodithiol-1-ium, 5-methyl-2- [7-(methyl-1,3-benzodithiol-2-yl)- bicyclo[4.4.1]undeca-1,3,5,7,9- pentaen-2-yl]-, tetrafluoroborate	CH_2Cl_2	233(4.59),250s(4.53), 320s(3.88),340s(3.82), 453s(3.87),521(3.99)	89-0204-80
	MeCN	207(4.56),237(4.47), 264s(4.32),324(3.85), 430s(3.88)	89-0204-80
$C_{27}H_{22}ClNO_7$			
10H-1,9-[1]Propen[1]yl[3]ylidenepyrro- lo[1,2-a]azocine-2,7,8-tricarboxylic acid, 3-chloro-5-(4-methylphenyl)- 10-oxo-, 2-ethyl 7,8-dimethyl ester	$CHCl_3$	269(4.54),301(4.17), 313(4.19),351(4.65), 390(3.98),665(3.18)	18-1406-80
$C_{27}H_{22}ClN_5O_3$			
1H-Isoindole-1,3(2H)-dione, 2-[[4-(2- benzoyl-4-chlorophenyl)-5-[(dimeth- ylamino)methyl]-4H-1,2,4-triazol-3- yl]methyl]-	EtOH	217(4.83),256(4.19), 239s(4.27),287(3.73)	4-0575-80
$C_{27}H_{22}Cl_2N_2O_3$			
Benzamide, N-[3-benzoyl-1-[(2,6-di- chlorophenyl)methyl]-1,4-dihydro- 4-pyridinyl]-4-methoxy-	CH_2Cl_2	305s(3.9),335(4.0)	64-1431-80B
$C_{27}H_{22}N_2$			
1H-1,5-Benzodiazepine, 4-[1,1'-biphen- yl]-4-yl-2,3-dihydro-2-phenyl-	EtOH	287(4.45),374(3.96)	103-0547-80
$C_{27}H_{22}N_2O$			
Urea, N-(1,2-diphenylethenyl)-N,N'-di-	MeOH	230(4.09),264(4.26),	39-0385-80C

Compound	Solvent	$\lambda_{max}(\log \epsilon)$	Ref.
phenyl- (cont.)		312(3.92)	39-0385-80C
$C_{27}H_{22}N_2O_2$			
2-Imidazolidinone, 4-hydroxy-1,3,4,5-tetraphenyl-	EtOH	255(4.38)	39-0385-80C
	CHCl$_3$	256(4.35)	39-0385-80C
Urea, N-(2-oxo-1,2-diphenylethyl)-N,N'-diphenyl-	EtOH	250(4.27)	39-0385-80C
	CH$_2$Cl$_2$	248(4.28)	39-0385-80C
$C_{27}H_{22}N_2O_5S_2$			
5-Thia-1-azabicyclo[4.2.0]oct-2-ene-2-carboxylic acid, 3-formyl-8-oxo-7-[(2-thienylacetyl)amino]-, diphenylmethyl ester, (6R-trans)-	EtOH	285(4.29)	94-2116-80
$C_{27}H_{22}O_2$			
Isobenzofuran, 1,3-dihydro-1-methoxy-1,3,3-triphenyl-	hexane	218(4.39),254(2.96), 260(3.02),265(2.96), 270s(2.75)	104-1316-80
1-Isobenzofuranol, 1,3-dihydro-1-(2-methylphenyl)-3,3-diphenyl-	hexane	219(4.17),255(3.14), 260(3.14),265(3.00), 270s(2.92)	104-1316-80
1-Isobenzofuranol, 1,3-dihydro-1-(3-methylphenyl)-3,3-diphenyl-	hexane	214(4.20),254(2.95), 260(3.02),266(3.01), 272s(2.84)	104-1316-80
1-Isobenzofuranol, 1,3-dihydro-1-(4-methylphenyl)-3,3-diphenyl-	hexane	217(4.50),254(2.94), 260(3.00),263(2.99), 271s(2.81)	104-1316-80
$C_{27}H_{22}S_4$			
1,3-Benzodithiole, 2,2'-bicyclo[4.4.1]-undeca-1,3,5,7,9-pentaene-2,7-diyl-bis[methyl-	CH$_2$Cl$_2$	234(4.63),268(4.77), 318(4.16),330s(4.14)	89-0204-80
	MeCN	231(4.65),265(4.79), 315(4.16),327s(4.14)	89-0204-80
$C_{27}H_{23}BN_2O_2$			
Boron, [N-[4-[[(2-hydroxyphenyl)methylene]amino]phenyl]acetamidato-N^N,O^N]-diphenyl-, (T-4)-	CHCl$_3$	270(4.11),350(4.20)	49-0863-80
$C_{27}H_{23}BrO_4$			
Propanedioic acid, (bromomethyl)methyl-, bis(2-naphthalenylmethyl) ester	CHCl$_3$	280(4.07)	24-0650-80
$C_{27}H_{23}F_2NO$			
2,4-Cyclopentadien-1-one, 3-(diethylamino)-4,5-bis(4-fluorophenyl)-2-phenyl-	MeCN	280(4.28),330s(--), 515(3.10)	24-0408-80
$C_{27}H_{23}IO_4$			
Propanedioic acid, (iodomethyl)methyl-, bis(2-naphthalenylmethyl) ester	CHCl$_3$	275(4.06)	24-0650-80
$C_{27}H_{23}NO$			
2,4-Cyclopentadien-1-one, 2,3,5-triphenyl-4-pyrrolidino-	MeCN	280(4.29),525(3.17)	24-0408-80
$C_{27}H_{23}NO_2$			
2,4-Cyclopentadien-1-one, 3-morpholino-2,4,5-triphenyl-	MeCN	279(4.33),330s(--), 520(3.05)	24-0408-80

Compound	Solvent	$\lambda_{max}(\log \epsilon)$	Ref.
$C_{27}H_{23}NO_6$ 3H-Pyrano[2,3-c]acridine-9,11-diol, 6-methoxy-3,3-dimethyl-7-phenoxy-, 11-acetate (or isomer)	MeOH	284(4.90),350(--), 370(--),455(--)	5-0503-80
$C_{27}H_{23}N_3O_4$ 2-Propenoic acid, 3-(4-hydroxyphenyl)- 2-[[5-(4-hydroxyphenyl)-3-(phenyl- methyl)pyrazinyl]amino]-, methyl ester	MeOH MeOH-NaOH	287(4.52),355s(4.30) 307(4.47),368(4.43)	138-0299-80 138-0299-80
$C_{27}H_{24}$ 2,2'-Spirobi[2H-benz[e]indene], 1',1',3,3'-tetrahydro-5,5'- dimethyl-, (R)-	heptane	233(5.30),258(4.43), 285(4.37),292(4.38), 297(4.34),312(3.95), 319(3.72),327(4.03)	89-0308-80
$C_{27}H_{24}ClNO_6$ 3H-2a-Azacyclopenta[ef]heptalene-1,4,5- tricarboxylic acid, 2-chloro-3-(4- methylphenyl)-, 1-ethyl 4,5-dimethyl ester	EtOH	260s(4.20),447(3.92), 487s(3.75),530(3.02), 575(2.97)	18-1406-80
4H-Azuleno[7,8,1-gha]pyrrolizine-1,5,6- tricarboxylic acid, 2-chloro-4a,5-di- hydro-4-(4-methylphenyl)-, 1-ethyl 5,6-dimethyl ester, (4α,4aα,5β)-	EtOH	238(4.13),264s(4.05), 324(3.90),395(3.59)	18-1406-80
Cyclobuta[a]cyclohepta[gh]pyrrolizine- 1,5,6-tricarboxylic acid, 2-chloro- 4,4a-dihydro-4-(4-methylphenyl)-, 1-ethyl 5,6-dimethyl ester	EtOH	240(4.17),293(3.82)	18-1406-80
2H-Cyclohepta[gh]pyrrolizine-1,2,5-tri- carboxylic acid, 4-chloro-2-[2-(4- methylphenyl)ethenyl]-, 5-ethyl 1,2-dimethyl ester	EtOH	253(4.73),375(4.14), 394(4.11),441(3.71), 470(3.66),503(3.45), 542(3.00)	18-1406-80
$C_{27}H_{24}ClN_5$ Pyrido[4,3-d]pyrimidin-4-amine, 8-(4- chlorophenyl)-7-(ethylphenylamino)- 5-phenyl-, trans	EtOH	249(4.28),276(4.09), 312(4.16)	88-2097-80
$C_{27}H_{24}N_2O$ Urea, N-(1,2-diphenylethyl)-N,N'-di- phenyl-	MeOH	239(4.31)	39-0385-80C
$C_{27}H_{24}N_2O_2$ 2,5-Pyrrolidinedione, 3-(diphenylmeth- ylene)-4-(1-methylethylidene)-1- (methylphenylamino)- photoisomer B	n.s.g. n.s.g.	354(4.11) 494(3.98)	97-0188-80 97-0188-80
$C_{27}H_{24}N_3O$ Acridinium, 9-[2-(2,3-dihydro-1,5-di- methyl-3-oxo-2-phenyl-1H-Pyrazol-4- yl)ethenyl]-10-methyl-, perchlorate	HOAc	531(4.49)	48-0543-80
$C_{27}H_{24}N_4O_4$ 1-Oxa-2,6,8-triazaspiro[4.4]nona-3,8- diene-4-carboxylic acid, 9-methoxy- 2-methyl-3,6-diphenyl-7-(phenylimi- no)-, methyl ester	MeOH	233(4.75),270s(4.29)	39-1667-80C

Compound	Solvent	λ_{max}(log ϵ)	Ref.
1-Oxa-2,6,8-triazaspiro[4.4]non-3-ene-4-carboxylic acid, 2,8-dimethyl-9-oxo-3,6-diphenyl-7-(phenylimino)-, methyl ester	MeOH	215(4.36),277(4.25)	39-1667-80C
$C_{27}H_{24}O$			
1H-Inden-1-one, 2,3,4,5,6,7-hexahydro-2,2,3-triphenyl-	EtOH	220(4.41),258(3.98)	44-4359-80
$C_{27}H_{24}O_2$			
Spiro[cyclopentane-1,5'(6'H)-[4H]dinaphtho[2,1-f:1',2'-h][1,5]dioxonin]	CHCl$_3$	244(4.71),286(4.06), 330(3.90)	49-0413-80
$C_{27}H_{24}O_4$			
Butanedioic acid, methyl-, bis(2-naphthalenylmethyl) ester	EtOH	280(4.06)	24-0650-80
Propanedioic acid, dimethyl-, bis(2-naphthalenylmethyl) ester	CHCl	275(4.05)	24-0650-80
$C_{27}H_{24}O_6$			
1,9-Anthracenediol, 5-methoxy-2-methyl-4-(phenylmethoxy)-, diacetate	CHCl$_3$	370(3.76),390(3.72), 410(3.53)	44-0012-80
$C_{27}H_{25}F_3N_2$			
1H-Pyrido[4,3-b]indole, 8-fluoro-5-(4-fluorophenyl)-2-[4-(4-fluorophenyl)-3-butenyl]-2,3,4,4a,5,9b-hexahydro-, monohydrochloride	MeOH	248(4.383)	87-0949-80
$C_{27}H_{25}NO$			
2,4-Cyclopentadien-1-one, 3-(diethylamino)-2,4,5-triphenyl-	MeCN	279(4.33),325s(--), 517(3.07)	24-0408-80
$C_{27}H_{25}N_3O_2$			
6H-Anthra[1,9-cd]isoxazol-6-one, 3-(cyclohexylamino)-5-[(4-methylphenyl)-amino]-	dioxan	254(4.57),475(4.36), 510(4.43)	103-0704-80
$C_{27}H_{26}ClNO_2$			
1,10-Anthracenedione, 4-(butylamino)-2-chloro-9-(2,4,6-trimethylphenyl)-	hexane	556(3.85),595(3.99), 649)3.90)	104-0159-80
	benzene	556s(3.91),595(4.05), 648(3.98)	104-0159-80
	isoPrOH	541s(3.92),588(4.03), 632(3.97)	104-0159-80
$C_{27}H_{26}NO$			
Pyrylium, 4-[4-(diethylamino)phenyl]-2,6-diphenyl-, tetrafluoroborate	MeCN	366(4.36),542(4.89)	35-0299-80
	CH$_2$Cl$_2$	381(4.31),558(4.91)	35-0299-80
$C_{27}H_{26}NS$			
Thiopyrylium, 4-[4-(diethylamino)phenyl]-2,6-diphenyl-, tetrafluoroborate	MeCN	368(4.19),583(4.82)	35-0299-80
	CH$_2$Cl$_2$	384(4.11),598(4.83)	35-0299-80
$C_{27}H_{26}N_2O_5$			
Benzamide, N-[2-(4-acetoxy-3-methoxyphenyl)-1-[[(1-phenylethyl)amino]-carbonyl]ethenyl]-, (S-(E)]-	dioxan	280(4.35),305(4.32)	70-0789-80
$C_{27}H_{26}N_2S$			
6H,8H-Pyrimido[2,1-a:4,3-a']diisoquino-	isooctane	247(4.0),256(3.1),	24-3010-80

Compound	Solvent	$\lambda_{max}(\log \epsilon)$	Ref.
line-6-thione, 4br,5,9,13b,15,16-hexahydro-5t-methyl-5-phenyl- (cont.)		275s(--),292(3.9), 296s(--),383(1.4)	24-3010-80
$C_{27}H_{26}N_4O_6S$			
Acetamide, 2-[(1,2-dihydro-2-oxo-1-β-D-ribofuranosyl-4-pyrimidinyl)thio]-N-[4-(phenylamino)-1-naphthalenyl]-	EtOH	217(4.69),256(4.31), 300(4.18),350(3.97)	94-1722-80
Acetamide, 2-[(1,4-dihydro-4-oxo-1-β-D-ribofuranosyl-2-pyrimidinyl)thio]-N-[4-(phenylamino)-1-naphthalenyl]-	EtOH	219(4.76),250(4.43), 350(4.00)	94-1722-80
$C_{27}H_{26}O_5$			
Spiro[cyclopentan-1,2'-[2H]indene]-1',3'-dione, 2-(2,3-dihydro-1,3-dioxo-1H-inden-2-yl)-5-methoxy-3,3,4,4-tetramethyl-	CHCl₃	292s(3.12),302(3.03)	49-0309-80
$C_{27}H_{26}O_8$			
Sanggenon A monoacetate	MeOH	279(4.54),318(4.31), 374(3.32)	142-1785-80
	MeOH-AlCl₃	279(4.53),337(4.30), 442(4.31)	142-1785-80
$C_{27}H_{27}F_3N_2O$			
2H-Pyrido[4,3-b]indole-2-butanol, 8-fluoro-α,5-bis(4-fluorophenyl)-1,3,4,4a,5,9b-hexahydro-, hydrochloride	MeOH	243(5.980),264(8.484), 270(8.016),298s(3.500) [sic]	87-0949-80
$C_{27}H_{27}NO_6S$			
β-D-Glucopyranoside, 4-(2,3-dihydro-2-phenyl-1,5-benzothiazepin-4-yl)phenyl	n.s.g.	231(4.30),265(4.17), 318(3.60)	114-0027-80A
β-D-Glucopyranoside, 4-(2,3-dihydro-4-phenyl-1,5-benzothiazepin-2-yl)phenyl	n.s.g.	222s(4.29),278(4.28), 342s(3.75)	114-0027-80A
$C_{27}H_{27}N_3O_6S_3$			
1H-1,4,7-Triazonine, 4,7-dihydro-1,4,7-tris[(4-methylphenyl)sulfonyl]-, (Z,Z,Z)-	MeCN	226(4.50),274s(3.82)	24-3127-80
$C_{27}H_{27}N_3O_7$			
Benzamide, N-[1-[5-O-benzoyl-2,3-O-(1-methylethylidene)-β-D-ribofuranosyl]-1,4-dihydro-5-methyl-4-oxo-2-pyrimidinyl]- (5λ,4ε)	EtOH	232(4.26),252s(4.14), 276s(4.22),284s(4.34), 301(?)	33-2179-80
$C_{27}H_{28}N_4O_2$			
Spiro[1H-isoindole-1,9'-[9H]xanthen]-3(2H)-one, 3',6'-bis(dimethylamino)-2-[(1-methylethylidene)amino]-	EtOH	239(4.75),270(4.65), 313(4.09)	94-3561-80
$C_{27}H_{28}O$			
Methanone, [2-(cycloheptylphenylmethyl)-phenyl]phenyl-	EtOH	250(4.3)	138-0349-80
$C_{27}H_{28}O_8$			
Leptolepisol C	EtOH	280(3.78)	102-0449-80
$C_{27}H_{29}BrO_5$			
Gibbane-1,10-dicarboxylic acid, 4a-hydroxy-1-methyl-8-methylene-, 1,4a-	EtOH	256(4.29)	105-0181-80

Compound	Solvent	$\lambda_{max}(\log \epsilon)$	Ref.
lactone, 10-[2-(4-bromophenyl)-1-oxo-ethyl] ester, (1α,4aα,4bβ,10β)- (cont.)			105-0181-80
$C_{27}H_{29}CoN_4$ Cobalt(1+), (octadehydro-1,3,7,8,12-13,17,19-octamethylcorrinato-$N^{21},N^{22},N^{23},N^{24}$)-, (SP-4-3)-, perchlorate	CHCl$_3$	276(4.27),350(4.07), 492(3.84)	135-1219-80
$C_{27}H_{29}N$ Pyridine, 2,4-bis[2-[4-(1-methylethyl)-phenyl]ethenyl]-	DMF	303(4.66),318(4.67)	33-1311-80
Pyridine, 2,5-bis[2-[4-(1-methylethyl)-phenyl]ethenyl]-	DMF	366(4.77)	33-1311-80
Pyridine, 2,6-bis[2-[4-(1-methylethyl)-phenyl]ethenyl]-	DMF	302(4.65),345(4.48)	33-1311-80
$C_{27}H_{29}NO_2$ Ethanone, 1,1'-[5'-(diethylamino)-6'-methyl[1,1':2',1"-terphenyl]-3',4'-diyl]bis-	MeCN	232(4.41),290s(--)	24-0424-80
$C_{27}H_{29}N_3$ 5-Phthalazinamine, N,N-diethyl-1,4,6-trimethyl-7,8-diphenyl-	MeCN	232(4.66),270s(--), 344(3.52)	24-0424-80
$C_{27}H_{29}N_3O_{12}$ D-Ribitol, 1-(8-acetoxy-3,4-dihydro-7-methyl-2,4-dioxopyrimido[4,5-b]quin-olin-10(2H)-yl)-1-deoxy-, 2,3,4,5-tetraacetate	MeOH	262(4.47),323(3.92), 397(4.14)	4-1709-80
$C_{27}H_{29}N_4Ni$ Nickel, (octadehydro-1,3,7,8,12,13,17-19-octamethylcorrinato-N^{21},N^{22},N^{23}-N^{24})-, (SP-4-4)-, perchlorate	CHCl$_3$	275(4.40),350(4.39), 470(3.78),552(4.09)	135-1219-80
$C_{27}H_{30}BrNO_5$ 3,5-Pyridinedicarboxylic acid, 4-(4-bromophenyl)-1-(4-ethoxyphenyl)-1,4-dihydro-2,6-dimethyl-, diethyl ester	EtOH	204(4.44),246(4.35), 354(3.67)	103-0377-80
$C_{27}H_{30}N_2OS$ Quinazoline, 3-acetyl-2-(butylthio)-3,4,5,6,7,8-hexahydro-4-phenyl-8-(phenylmethylene)-	EtOH	229(4.13),285(4.47)	114-0147-80B
$C_{27}H_{30}N_2O_7$ 3,5-Pyridinedicarboxylic acid, 1-(4-ethoxyphenyl)-1,4-dihydro-2,6-di-methyl-4-(2-nitrophenyl)-, diethyl ester	EtOH	202(4.64),234(4.52), 291s(4.12),329-65(3.8)	103-0377-80
3,5-Pyridinedicarboxylic acid, 1-(4-ethoxyphenyl)-1,4-dihydro-2,6-di-methyl-4-(3-nitrophenyl)-, diethyl ester	EtOH	202(4.53),241(4.53), 350(3.79)	103-0377-80
3,5-Pyridinedicarboxylic acid, 1-(4-ethoxyphenyl)-1,4-dihydro-2,6-di-methyl-4-(4-nitrophenyl)-, diethyl ester	EtOH	202(4.49),236(4.38), 268s(4.20),361(3.48)	103-0377-80

Compound	Solvent	$\lambda_{max}(\log \epsilon)$	Ref.
$C_{27}H_{30}N_4O$ 1H-Isoindol-1-one, 3,3-bis[4-(dimethyl-amino)phenyl]-2,3-dihydro-2-[(1-meth-ylethylidene)amino]-	EtOH	269(4.46)	94-3561-80
$C_{27}H_{30}O_{11}$ 2(3H)-Furanone, 3-acetoxy-4-[acetoxy-(3,4-dimethoxyphenyl)methyl]-3-[(4-acetoxy-3-methoxyphenyl)methyl]di-hydro-, [3S-[3α,4α(S)]-	EtOH	228(4.09),277(3.67), 280(3.68)	94-0850-80
$C_{27}H_{30}O_{15}$ Acacetin, 6-C-cellobiosyl-	MeOH	270(4.37),305s(--), 326(4.35)	102-1755-80
	MeOH-NaOH	277(--),293s(--), 370(--)	102-1755-80
	MeOH-NaOAc	278(--),293s(--), 367(--)	102-1755-80
$C_{27}H_{31}BrN_2O_4$ 3,5-Pyridinedicarboxylic acid, 4-(4-bromophenyl)-1-[4-(dimethylamino)-phenyl]-1,4-dihydro-2,6-dimethyl-, diethyl ester	EtOH	203(4.66),268(4.62), 382(4.16)	103-0377-80
$C_{27}H_{31}ClN_2O_4$ 3,5-Pyridinedicarboxylic acid, 4-(4-chlorophenyl)-1-[4-(dimethylamino)-phenyl]-1,4-dihydro-2,6-dimethyl-, diethyl ester	EtOH	204(4.66),268(4.68), 375(4.15)	103-0377-80
$C_{27}H_{31}NO_5$ 3,5-Pyridinedicarboxylic acid, 1,4-di-hydro-4-(4-methoxyphenyl)-2,6-dimeth-yl-1-(phenylmethyl)-, diethyl ester	EtOH	206(4.42),254(4.30), 350(3.76)	103-0377-80
$C_{27}H_{31}NO_6$ 3,5-Pyridinedicarboxylic acid, 1,4-di-hydro-1,4-bis(4-methoxyphenyl)-2,6-dimethyl-, diethyl ester	EtOH	202(4.68),226(4.48), 252s(4.33),347(4.06)	103-0377-80
$C_{27}H_{31}N_3O_6$ 3,5-Pyridinedicarboxylic acid, 1-[4-(dimethylamino)phenyl]-1,4-di-hydro-2,6-dimethyl-4-(3-nitrophenyl)-, diethyl ester	EtOH	203(4.51),210s(4.11), 268(4.60),365(3.90)	103-0377-80
3,5-Pyridinedicarboxylic acid, 1-[4-(dimethylamino)phenyl]-1,4-di-hydro-2,6-dimethyl-4-(4-nitrophenyl)-, diethyl ester	EtOH	203(4.46),272(4.50), 352(3.67)	103-0377-80
$C_{27}H_{32}N_2O_4$ 3,5-Pyridinedicarboxylic acid, 1-[4-(dimethylamino)phenyl]-1,4-di-hydro-2,6-dimethyl-4-phenyl-, diethyl ester	EtOH	203(4.60),241s(4.31), 268(4.62),352(3.90)	103-0377-80
3,5-Pyridinedicarboxylic acid, 4-[4-(dimethylamino)phenyl]-1,4-di-hydro-2,6-dimethyl-1-phenyl-, diethyl ester	EtOH	205(4.56),248(4.13), 317(3.88)	103-0377-80

Compound	Solvent	$\lambda_{max}(\log \epsilon)$	Ref.
$C_{27}H_{32}N_2O_8$ 4H-Dibenzo[de,g]quinoline-2,11-diol, 6-[[bis(2-hydroxyethyl)amino]acetyl]- 5,6,6a,7-tetrahydro-10-methoxy-, 2,11-diacetate, monohydrochloride	EtOH	269(4.19),302(3.83)	87-1008-80
$C_{27}H_{32}N_4O_2$ 2H-Imidazol-2-one, 4,4'-methylenebis[1- butyl-1,3-dihydro-5-phenyl-	EtOH	275(4.01)	94-1853-80
2H-Imidazol-2-one, 4,4'-methylenebis[3- butyl-1,3-dihydro-5-phenyl-	EtOH	291(4.34)	94-1853-80
$C_{27}H_{32}N_4S_2$ 3H-Pyrazole-3-thione, 4,4'-(3-methyl- butylidene)bis[1,2-dihydro-1,5-di- methyl-2-phenyl-	benzene H_2O	280(4.02),342(4.37) 256(4.33),288(4.30)	140-0560-80 140-0560-80
$C_{27}H_{32}O_4$ Hispaglabridin A dimethyl ether	MeOH	279(4.12),289s(3.77), 310(3.21)	100-0259-80
$C_{27}H_{32}O_6$ Benzeneacetic acid, α-ethyl-, 4-acet- oxy-2,3,3a,4,7,8,9,11a-octahydro- 6,10-dimethyl-3-methylene-2-oxo- cyclodeca[b]furan-9-yl ester, [3aS- [3aR*,4S*,5E,9R*(S*),10Z,11aR*]]-	n.s.g.	206(4.39),251s(--), 254s(--),258(2.47), 264(2.35)	44-1441-80
$C_{27}H_{32}O_7$ Italipyrone, 20-(3,3-dimethylallyl)-	$CHCl_3$	293(4.26)	102-0639-80
$C_{27}H_{32}O_9$ Toromycin, hexahydro-	MeOH	229(4.74),287(3.97), 322(4.02),339(4.05), 354(4.09)	94-3601-80
$C_{27}H_{33}N_2$ Ethanaminium, N-[4-[[4-(diethylamino)- phenyl]phenylmethylene]-2,5-cyclo- hexadien-1-ylidene]-N-ethyl-, per- chlorate	98% HOAc	430(4.26),630(5.08)	146-0317-80
$C_{27}H_{33}N_2O$ Methanaminium, N-[9-(dimethylamino)-5- ethoxy-2,8-diphenyl-2,4,6,8-nonatet- raenylidene]-N-methyl-, tetrafluoro- borate	CH_2Cl_2	620(4.98)	70-0771-80
$C_{27}H_{33}N_3O_2$ Pseudotubulosine	EtOH	226(4.68),282(3.99), 290(3.96)	33-1335-80
$C_{27}H_{33}N_3O_5$ Fumitremorgin B	EtOH	226(4.50),278(3.86), 295(3.90)	94-0861-80
$C_{27}H_{33}N_3O_7$ 5H,12H-3,4-Dioxa-5a,11a,15a-triaza- cyclooct[1m]indeno[5,6-b]fluorene- 11,15(2H,13H)-dione, 1,10,10a,14,14a- 15b-hexahydro-10,10a-dihydroxy-7-	EtOH	227(4.50),274(3.72), 296(3.69)	94-0245-80

Compound	Solvent	$\lambda_{max}(\log \epsilon)$	Ref.
methoxy-2,2-dimethyl-5-(2-methyl-1-propenyl)- (cont.)			94-0245-80
$C_{27}H_{33}N_5O$			
1H-Cyclopenta[5,6]naphtho[1,2-g]pyra-zolo[1,5-a]quinazoline-9-acetonitr-ile, 10-cyano-2,3,3a,3b,4,5,5a,6-13,13a,13b,14,15,15a-tetradecahydro-1-hydroxy-1,13a,15a-trimethyl-, [1S-(1α,3aβ,3bα,5aβ,13aα,13bβ,15aα)]-	MeOH	207(4.07),232(4.65), 313(3.76)	39-0481-80C
1(2H)-Phthalazinone, 7-(dimethylamino)-4,4-bis[4-(dimethylamino)phenyl]-3,4-dihydro-2-methyl-	EtOH	267(4.44)	94-3561-80
$C_{27}H_{34}N_2O_8$			
Deacetylvindoline 4-hemisuccinate	MeOH	250(3.77),303(3.60)	102-2083-80
$C_{27}H_{34}N_6$			
3,5-Pyridinedicarbonitrile, 1,1'-(1,5-pentanediyl)bis[1,4-dihydro-2,4,4,6-tetramethyl-	MeOH	225(4.62),346(4.13)	73-3370-80
$C_{27}H_{34}O_{12}$			
Cyclodeca[b]furan-6-carboxylic acid, 5-acetoxy-4-(2,3-diacetoxy-2-methyl-1-oxobutoxy)-2,3,3a,4,5,8,9,11a-octa-hydro-10-methyl-3-methylene-2-oxo-, methyl ester (tetrahelin A)	MeOH	205(4.04)	102-0583-80
$C_{27}H_{34}O_{13}$			
Tetrahelin B	MeOH	205(4.00)	102-0583-80
$C_{27}H_{34}O_{14}$			
Durantoside II	H_2O	189(4.29),228(4.29), 310(4.30)	100-0649-80
$C_{27}H_{34}O_{15}$			
Cornin-5,6-enol pentaacetate	MeOH	214(4.01),269(4.02)	102-2685-80
Cyclopenta[c]pyran-4-carboxylic acid, 7-(acetoxymethyl)-1,4a,7,7a-tetrahy-dro-1-[(2,3,4,6-tetra-0-acetyl-β-D-glucopyranosyl)oxy]-, methyl ester	n.s.g.	233(4.01)	102-2763-80
Oleuropein, 10-acetoxy-	MeOH	236(4.2),284(3.47)	100-0649-80
$C_{27}H_{34}O_{16}$			
Hastatoside	MeOH	229(3.8)	102-2685-80
$C_{27}H_{35}BrO_7$			
Pregna-1,4-diene-3,20-dione, 21-acet-oxy-7-bromo-11-hydroxy-16-methyl-17-(1-oxopropoxy)-, (7α,11β,16α)-	MeOH	242(4.19)	145-1618-80
$C_{27}H_{35}ClO_7$			
Pregna-1,4-diene-3,20-dione, 21-acet-oxy-7-chloro-11-hydroxy-16-methyl-17-(1-oxopropoxy)-, (7α,11β,16α)-	MeOH	241(4.20)	145-1618-80
$C_{27}H_{35}NO_{12}$			
2H-Pyran-5-carboxylic acid, 4-[(2-acet-yl-1,2,3,4-tetrahydro-6,7-dihydroxy-1-isoquinolinyl)methyl]-3-ethenyl-	EtOH	227(4.14),287(3.58)	24-0566-80

Compound	Solvent	λ_{max}(log ϵ)	Ref.
2-(β-D-glucopyranosyloxy)-3,4-dihy-dro-, methyl ester (ipecoside) (cont.)			24-0566-80
$C_{27}H_{35}N_3O_2$ Phenol, 4,4'-[(2,6-diamino-3,5-pyridine-diyl)bis(methylene)]bis[2,6-diethyl-	pH 2	242(4.20),278(3.54), 343(4.20)	87-0384-80
	pH 13	242(4.38),306(4.23)	87-0384-80
$C_{27}H_{35}N_3O_5$ Fumitremorgin B, dihydro-	EtOH	227(4.45),280(3.76), 298(3.89)	94-0861-80
$C_{27}H_{36}O_2$ 1,3-Cycloheptanedione, 2-[3,7-dimethyl-9-(2,6,6-trimethyl-1-cyclohexen-1-yl)-2,4,6,8-nonatetraenylidene]-, (all-E)-	EtOH	275(4.08),450(4.67)	87-0805-80
1,3-Cyclohexanedione, 2-[3,7-dimethyl-9-(2,6,6-trimethyl-1-cyclohexen-1-yl)-2,4,6,8-nonatetraenylidene]-5-methyl-, (all-E)-	EtOH	270(4.02),492(4.68)	87-0805-80
$C_{27}H_{36}O_6$ Manoalide monoacetate δ-lactone	MeOH	211(4.04)	88-1611-80
$C_{27}H_{36}O_7$ Butanoic acid, 3-methyl-, 1,4-diacet-oxy-11,12-epoxy-3-oxobriara-5,7,17-trien-2-yl ester, (1R*,2R*,5Z,10R*-11S*,12R*,14S*)-	MeOH	271(3.74)	12-2307-80
$C_{27}H_{36}O_9$ Pregna-1,4-diene-3,20-dione, 21-acet-oxy-7,11,17-trihydroxy-16-methyl-6-(1-oxopropoxy)-, (6β,7β,11β,16α)-	MeOH	244(4.13)	87-0430-80
$C_{27}H_{36}O_{12}$ β-D-Xylopyranoside, [1,2,3,4-tetrahydro-7-hydroxy-1-(4-hydroxy-3,5-dimethoxy-phenyl)-3-(hydroxymethyl)-6,8-dimeth-oxy-2-naphthalenyl]methyl (pygeoside)	MeOH MeOH-NaOH	218(4.694),281(3.496) 223(--),252(--), 293(--)	2-0279-80 2-0279-80
$C_{27}H_{36}O_{14}$ Sylvestroside III	MeOH	237(4.25)	100-0649-80
Sylvestroside IV	MeOH	233(3.97)	100-0649-80
$C_{27}H_{37}N_3O_5$ Fumitremorgin B, tetrahydro-	EtOH	227(4.57),278(3.80), 296(3.82)	94-0861-80
$C_{27}H_{37}N_3O_6$ 3,5-Pyridinedicarboxylic acid, 1,4-di-hydro-2,6-bis[2-(4-morpholinyl)eth-yl]-4-phenyl-, dimethyl ester	EtOH	242(4.26),356(3.81)	94-3163-80
$C_{27}H_{38}F_6O_2$ 9,10-Secocholesta-5,7,10(19)-triene-3,25-diol, 26,26,26,27,27,27-hexa-fluoro-, (3β,5Z,7E)-	EtOH	264(4.26)	77-0459-80

Compound	Solvent	$\lambda_{max}(\log \epsilon)$	Ref.
$C_{27}H_{38}N_2O_6$ 1-Imidazolidineheptanoic acid, 2-oxo-5-(3-oxo-1-octenyl)-3-[(phenylmethoxy)carbonyl]-, methyl ester, (E)-(±)-	MeOH	211(4.46)	94-1459-80
$C_{27}H_{38}N_4O_2S_2$ 2H-1,3,5-Thiadiazine-2-thione, 6-(dicyclohexylamino)-4-[(1,1-dimethylethyl)imino]-3,4-dihydro-3-(4-methoxybenzoyl)-	CH_2Cl_2	235(4.05),285(4.36), 347(3.75)	24-0079-80
$C_{27}H_{38}O_2$ 3,5-Heptanedione, 4-retinylidene-	EtOH	270(3.90),420(4.66)	87-0805-80
$C_{27}H_{38}O_4$ Spirost-4-ene-3,6-dione, (25R)-	EtOH	250(4.04)	64-0102-80B
$C_{27}H_{38}O_5$ 4-Hexen-2-one, 6-(2,5-dihydroxy-3-methylphenyl)-1-[2-(4-hydroxy-4-methyl-1-oxo-2-pentenyl]-1,2-dimethylcyclopentyl]-4-methyl-, [1α(Z),2α(E)]-(-)-(bifurcarenone)	n.s.g.	215(4.19),225(4.21), 292(3.53)	88-3123-80
$C_{27}H_{38}O_7$ Butanoic acid, 3-methyl-, 14-acetoxy-5-hydroxy-18-oxobriara-6,8(17),11-trien-2-yl ester, (1R*,2S*,6E,10S*-11Z,14S*)-	MeOH	205(4.21),220(3.11)	12-2307-80
$C_{27}H_{39}NO_{12}$ D-Arabinitol, 1-C-[1-butyl-4-(ethoxycarbonyl)-5-methyl-1H-pyrrol-3-yl]-,1,2,3,4,5-pentaacetate, (S)-	EtOH	243(3.94),254s(--)	39-1199-80C
D-Arabinitol, 5-C-[1-butyl-4-(ethoxycarbonyl)-5-methyl-1H-pyrrol-3-yl]-,1,2,3,4,5-pentaacetate, (S)-	EtOH	239(4.20),258s(--)	39-1199-80C
$C_{27}H_{40}O$ Cholesta-1,4,9(11)-trien-3-one	EtOH	243(4.14)	39-0892-80C
$C_{27}H_{40}O_2$ 9α,11α-Epoxycholesta-1,4-dien-3-one	EtOH	239(4.10)	39-0892-80C
$C_{27}H_{40}O_3$ Δ^4-Diosgenone	EtOH	242(4.32)	150-0064-80S
$C_{27}H_{40}O_{10}$ Valtrate isovaleroxyhydrin	MeOH	256(4.23)	100-0649-80
$C_{27}H_{41}FO_2$ 5α-Cholest-8(14)-ene-3,15-dione,9α-fluoro-	EtOH	248(4.14)	44-4034-80
$C_{27}H_{41}NO_2$ 6-Aza-B-homocholesta-1,4-diene-3,7-dione	MeOH	243(4.18),286(3.85)	23-2666-80
$C_{27}H_{42}F_2O$ Previtamin D_3, 19,19-difluoro-	ether	256(4.00)	44-2201-80

Compound	Solvent	$\lambda_{max}(\log \epsilon)$	Ref.
Tachysterol, 19,19-difluoro-	ether	270s(4.24),278(4.26), 288s(4.23)	44-2201-80
$C_{27}H_{42}FeN_9O_{12}$			
Ferrichrome	n.s.g.	<u>450(4.5)</u>	35-4224-80
$C_{27}H_{42}N_2O_{14}$			
D-gluco-Octonic acid, 2-[1-(butylamino)ethylidene]-2,3-dideoxy-3-(nitromethyl)-, ethyl ester, 4,5,6,7,8-pentaacetate, [2(Z),3ξ]-	EtOH	295(4.37)	39-1199-80C
D-glycero-L-gluco-Octonic acid, 2-[1-(butylamino)ethylidene]-2,3-dideoxy-3-(nitromethyl)-, ethyl ester, 4,5,6,7,8-pentaacetate, (2Z)-	EtOH	294(4.18)	39-1199-80C
$C_{27}H_{42}O$			
Cholesta-1,4-dien-3-one	EtOH	242(4.16)	39-2209-80C
	n.s.g.	241(4.16)	39-1212-80C
Cholesta-4,9(11)-dien-3-one	EtOH	250(4.10)	39-0892-80C
$C_{27}H_{42}O_2$			
Cholest-4-ene-3,6-dione	EtOH	250(4.25)	64-0102-80B
$C_{27}H_{43}FO_2$			
5α-Cholest-8(14)-en-15-one, 9 -fluoro-3β-hydroxy-	EtOH	248(4.13)	44-4034-80
$C_{27}H_{43}NO$			
B-Norcholest-5-ene-6-carbonitrile, 3β-hydroxy-	n.s.g.	231(2.22)	2-0510-80
5,6-Secocholest-2-ene-6-nitrile, 1-oxo-, (10α)-	n.s.g.	325(2.00)	2-0510-80
$C_{27}H_{43}NO_2$			
6-Aza-B-homocholest-1-ene-3,7-dione, (5α)-	MeOH	225(4.11)	23-2666-80
6-Aza-B-homocholest-4-ene-3,7-dione	MeOH	275(4.08)	23-2666-80
$C_{27}H_{44}$			
Cholesta-2,4-diene	heptane	265.5(3.81)	77-0346-80
$C_{27}H_{44}N_2O_2$			
3,6-Diaza-A-homo-B-homocholest-1-ene-3,7-dione, (5α)-	MeOH	226(3.92)	23-2666-80
3,6-Diaza-A-homo-B-homocholest-4a-ene-4,7-dione	MeOH	240(4.07)	23-2666-80
4,6-Diaza-A-homo-B-homocholest-1-ene-3,7-dione, (5α)-	MeOH	205(4.18)(end abs.)	23-2666-80
4,6-Diaza-A-homo-B-homocholest-4a-ene-3,7-dione	MeOH	254(4.11)	23-2666-80
$C_{27}H_{44}O$			
Cholesta-2,4-dien-6-ol, (6β)-	heptane	264(3.81)	77-0346-80
$C_{27}H_{44}O_2$			
4-Oxacholestan-3-one, 2-methylene-	EtOH	213(3.86)	87-0090-80
Vitamin D₃, 1α-hydroxy-	ether	264(4.25)	39-1405-80C
5,6-trans	EtOH	273(4.36)	44-3253-80

Compound	Solvent	$\lambda_{max}(\log \epsilon)$	Ref.
$C_{27}H_{44}O_3$			
5α-Cholest-8(14)-en-15-one, 3β,9α-di-hydroxy-	EtOH	254(4.13)	44-4034-80
$C_{27}H_{44}O_5$			
24-Nor-5β,14β-chol-20(22)-ene-22-carb-oxylic acid, 3β,14-dihydroxy-21-meth-oxy-22-methyl-, methyl ester	EtOH	210(3.95)	48-0991-80
$C_{27}H_{45}NO$			
4-Aza-A-homocholest-1-en-3-one, (5α)-	MeOH	213(4.11)	23-2666-80
4-Aza-A-homocholest-1-en-3-one, (5β)-	MeOH	213(4.11)	23-2666-80
4-Aza-A-homocholest-4a-en-3-one	MeOH	244(4.07)	23-2666-80
$C_{27}H_{45}NO_2$			
Cholestane-2,3-dione, 2-oxime	4:1 ether-MeOH	252(2.74)	24-0650-80
$C_{27}H_{46}N_2O_2$			
Cholestane-2,3-dione, dioxime	4:1 ether-MeOH	252(2.75)	24-0650-80
5α-Cholestan-2-one	EPA	285(1.48)	13-0189-80A
Cholestan-3-one	EPA	285(1.24)	13-0189-80A
$C_{27}H_{46}O_5$			
4H-Pyran-4-one, 3,5-dibutyl-2-methoxy-6-[1-(2-pentyl-1,3-dioxolan-2-yl)-pentyl]- (methylelasnin ketal)	EtOH	254.5(3.87)	44-3268-80
$C_{27}H_{46}O_8$			
Nonanoic acid, 9-[[3-methyl-1-oxo-4-[tetrahydro-3,4-dihydroxy-5-(5-hy-droxy-4-methyl-2-hexenyl)-2H-pyran-2-yl]-2-butenyl]oxy]-, methyl ester (methyl pseudomonate C)	n.s.g.	222(4.17)	88-0881-80

Compound	Solvent	$\lambda_{max}(\log \epsilon)$	Ref.
$C_{28}Cl_{18}$ Indeno[2,1-a]indene, 1,2,3,4,6,7,8,9- octachloro-5,10-bis(pentachloro- phenyl)-	C_6H_{12}	217(5.16),244(4.73), 300(4.77),312(4.89), 397(3.49),423(3.90), 448(4.21),480(4.30)	88-2845-80
$C_{28}Cl_{20}$ 1H-Indene, 4,5,6,7-tetrachloro-1- [chloro(pentachlorophenyl)methyl- ene]-2,3-bis(pentachlorophenyl)-	$CHCl_3$	275(4.59),360(3.88)	88-2845-80
Naphthalene, 1,2,3,4,5-pentachloro- 6,7,8-tris(pentachlorophenyl)-	$CHCl_3$	271(4.73),322s(4.00), 335(4.03)	88-2845-80
$C_{28}H_6Cl_{14}O_2$ 9H-Fluorene, 1,2,3,4,5,7,8-heptachloro- 9-(1,2,3,4,5,7,8-heptachloro-6-meth- oxy-9H-fluoren-9-ylidene)-6-methoxy-	C_6H_{12}	241(4.77),292(4.84), 460(3.85),591(4.33)	88-0193-80
$(C_{28}H_{12}I_2N_2O_2)_n$ Polymer from 2,2'-diiodobiphenyl-4,4'- dicarbonyl dichloride and 1,4-diami- nobenzene	DMSO	318(4.63)	126-0333-80
$C_{28}H_{14}O_2$ Dibenzo[a,j]perylene-8,16-dione (photochromic)	toluene	<u>425(3.4)</u>,580f(4.4)	151-0293-80A
$C_{28}H_{15}F_9O_2S_3$ 2-Cyclopenten-1-one, 2,4,4,5,5-penta- fluoro-3-[[4,4,5,5-tetrafluoro-3,4,4- tris(phenylthio)-1-cyclopenten-1-yl]- oxy]-	isooctane	218(4.36)	44-4429-80
$C_{28}H_{16}$ 5,12[1',2']-Benzenonaphthacene, 1,15- diethynyl-5,12-dihydro-, (5R)-	EtOH	241(4.88),268(3.95), 278(4.01),308(3.15), 322(3.18)	35-0501-80
	EtOH	241(4.88),278(4.01)	35-0506-80
$C_{28}H_{16}Br_2Cl_4S_4$ 1,3-Butadiene, 1,2-dibromo-1,3,4,4- tetrakis[(4-chlorophenyl)thio]-	heptane	200(5.00),225s(4.75), 265(4.51)	24-3342-80
1,3-Butadiene, 2,3-dibromo-1,1,4,4- tetrakis[(4-chlorophenyl)thio]-	heptane	195(4.89),223s(4.65), 287(4.42)	24-3342-80
$C_{28}H_{16}Cl_4I_2S_4$ 1,3-Butadiene, 2,3-diiodo-1,1,4,4- tetrakis[(4-chlorophenyl)thio]-	heptane	194(4.55),230s(4.18), 265(4.03)	24-3342-80
$C_{28}H_{16}Cl_6S_4$ 1,3-Butadiene, 2,3-dichloro-1,1,4,4- tetrakis[(4-chlorophenyl)thio]-	heptane	199(4.79),223s(4.55), 275(4.40)	24-3342-80
$C_{28}H_{16}F_4O_2S_2$ Ethanone, 1-(1,4-difluoro-11-hydroxy- dibenzo[b,f]thiepin-10-yl)-2-[2-(2,5- difluorophenyl)thio]phenyl]-	MeOH	243(4.40),282(4.06), 325(4.10)	73-2688-80
$C_{28}H_{16}N_4O_4S_2$ 2H-1,4-Benzothiazine, 3-(4-nitrophen- yl)-2-[3-(4-nitrophenyl)-2H-1,4-	EtOH	216(4.36),269(4.22), 308s(4.05),362(3.91),	39-2923-80C

Compound	Solvent	$\lambda_{max}(\log \epsilon)$	Ref.
benzothiazin-2-ylidene]- (cont.)		500(3.37)	39-2923-80C
$C_{28}H_{16}O_2$			
Benz[a]anthracene-7,12-dione, 5-(2-naphthalenyl)-	$CHCl_3$	249(4.63),290(4.62), 423(3.77)	44-1424-80
Benzo[a]naphthacene-7,14-dione, 5-phenyl-	$CHCl_3$	243(4.71),312(4.67), 412(3.95)	44-1424-80
Dibenzo[b,d]phenanthrene-9,14-dione, 7-phenyl-	$CHCl_3$	246(4.60),254(4.59), 269(4.60),325s(4.28), 338(4.51),408(3.68)	44-1424-80
$C_{28}H_{17}BrCl_4S_4$			
1,3-Butadiene, 2-bromo-1,1,4,4-tetrakis[(4-chlorophenyl)thio]-	heptane	197(4.79),221(4.47), 266(4.24)	24-3342-80
$C_{28}H_{17}Cl_5S_4$			
1,3-Butadiene, 2-chloro-1,1,4,4-tetrakis[(4-chlorophenyl)thio]-	heptane	200(4.94),222(4.66), 351(4.24)	24-3342-80
$C_{28}H_{17}NO_2$			
4H-Benzo[def]carbazole, 1,7-dibenzoyl-	EtOH	210(4.49),237(4.62), 258(4.64),296(4.36), 397(4.53)	18-0494-80
$C_{28}H_{17}NO_4$			
Acetamide, N-(2,8-dihydro-2,8-dioxonaphthaceno[5,6-bc]pyran-9-yl)-N-phenyl-	EtOH	<u>418(3.8)</u>	104-1646-80
$C_{28}H_{17}N_2$			
Benzo[c]benzo[1,2]quinolizino[3,4,5,6-ija][1,6]naphthyridin-15-ium, 9-phenyl-, perchlorate	MeOH	215(4.40),235(4.62), 275(4.28),300(4.39), 310(4.36),350(4.04), 406(3.6),428(3.65)	39-1879-80C
$C_{28}H_{18}$			
Dibenzo[b,d]phenanthrene, 7-phenyl-	benzene	344(3.61),361(3.73), 378(3.76),398(3.57)	44-1424-80
	EtOH	204(4.97),227(4.8), 250(4.71),288(4.54), 300(4.76),312(4.86)	44-1424-80
$C_{28}H_{18}BrNO_3$			
2H-Anthra[1,2-d][1,3]oxazine-7,12-dione, 6-bromo-1,4-dihydro-2,2-diphenyl-	EtOH	488(3.74)	18-3007-80 +146-0513-80
$C_{28}H_{18}Cl_2N_4O_8$			
3,11-Diazatricyclo[5.3.1.1^{2,6}]dodeca-4,8-diene-10,12-dione, 3,11-bis[trans-3-(2-chloro-5-nitrophenyl)-3-oxo-1-propenyl]-	MeCN	220(4.61),292(4.74), 343(4.46)	39-0362-80C
$C_{28}H_{18}Cl_4N_2O_3$			
2,5-Imino-1,6,3-benzodioxazocin-4(5H)-one, 7,8,9,10-tetrachloro-2,3-dihydro-3-methyl-2,5,11-triphenyl-	MeCN	216(4.853),291(3.142), 300(3.164)	5-1850-80
$C_{28}H_{18}Cl_4N_2O_3S$			
2,5-Imino-1,6,3-benzodioxazocin-4(5H)-one, 7,8,9,10-tetrachloro-2,3-dihydro-2-(methylthio)-3,5,11-triphenyl-	MeCN	216(4.819),291(3.136), 300(3.147)	5-1850-80

Compound	Solvent	$\lambda_{max}(\log \epsilon)$	Ref.
$C_{20}H_{18}N_2O_2$			
Benzoxazole, 2,2'-(1,5-naphthalenediyl-di-2,1-ethenediyl)bis-	CHCl$_3$	366(4.51)	103-0464-80
Benzoxazole, 2,2'-(2,6-naphthalenediyl-di-2,1-ethenediyl)bis-	CHCl$_3$	369s(4.81),384(4.88), 404(4.79)	103-0464-80
Benzoxazole, 2,2'-(2,7-naphthalenediyl-di-2,1-ethenediyl)bis-	CHCl$_3$	349(4.75)	103-0464-80
$C_{28}H_{18}N_2S_2$			
Benzothiazole, 2,2'-(2,6-naphthalenediyldi-2,1-ethenediyl)bis-	CHCl$_3$	376s(4.74),392(4.85), 414(4.71)	103-0464-80
$C_{28}H_{18}N_4$			
1H-Perimidine, 2,2'-(1,4-phenylene)bis-	MeOH	210(4.71),238(4.77), 335(4.55),360(4.35), 430(5.38)	103-0081-80
$C_{28}H_{18}N_4O_4S_2$			
2,2'-Bi-2H-1,4-benzothiazine, 3,3'-bis(4-nitrophenyl)-	CHCl	254(4.42),269s(4.38), 304(4.26),359(4.08)	39-2923-80C
$C_{28}H_{18}N_4S_2$			
Benzonitrile, 4,4'-[dithiobis(4,1-phen-ylenenitrilomethylidyne)]bis-	DMF-base	538(3.79)	3-1851-80
$C_{28}H_{18}N_6O_6$			
Methanone, [1,4-dihydro-1,4-bis(4-ni-trophenyl)-1,2,4,5-tetrazine-3,6-diyl]bis[phenyl-	CHCl$_3$	264(4.39),393(4.28)	39-2923-80C
$C_{28}H_{18}O_2$			
9(10H)-Anthracenone, 10-ethynyl-10-hy-droxy-1,8-diphenyl-	EtOH	222(4.43),286(3.99)	44-1807-80
5,8:11,14-Dietheno-1,18-methano-19H-dibenzo[a,d]cyclopentadecene-19,20-dione, 9,10-dihydro-	EtOH	256(4.55)	24-0676-80
$C_{28}H_{18}O_2S$			
5,8:12,15-Dietheno-1,19-methano-9H-dibenzo[g,j]thiacyclohexadecin-20,21(11H)-dione	CDCl$_3$	258(4.58)	24-0676-80
$C_{28}H_{18}O_4$			
[3,3'-Bibenzofuran]-2,2'(3H,3'H)-dione, 3,3'-diphenyl-	n.s.g.	231(4.29),282(3.62)	150-3901-80
$C_{28}H_{19}ClN_2O_2$			
Methanone, [1-(4-chlorophenyl)-2,5-di-phenyl-1H-imidazol-4-yl](2-hydroxy-phenyl)-	EtOH	213(4.40),263(4.30), 340s(--)	39-0354-80C
$C_{28}H_{19}NO_2$			
Benzo[g]isoquinolinium 1-benzoyl-2-oxo-2-phenylethylide	CHCl$_3$	256(4.68),340(3.88), 396(3.48),436s(3.42), 500(3.20)	103-0626-80
$C_{28}H_{19}N_2$			
Benzo[c]pyrido[1,2-a][1,8]naphthyridin-13-ium, 10,12-diphenyl-, perchlorate	EtOH	214(4.33),245(4.41), 277(4.42),301(4.26), 328(4.24),368(4.23), 404(4.14)	39-1879-80C

Compound	Solvent	$\lambda_{max}(\log \epsilon)$	Ref.
$C_{28}H_{19}N_3$ 1H-Indol-3-amine, 2-phenyl-N-(2-phenyl-3H-indol-3-ylidene)-	aq pyridine	575(4.01)	7-0009-80
$C_{28}H_{19}N_3O_2$ 4-Piperidinone, 1-benzoyl-3,6-bis[(4-cyanophenyl)methylene]-	dioxan	330(4.456)	106-0075-80
$C_{28}H_{20}$ Anthracene, 9-ethenyl-1,8-diphenyl-	EtOH	263(4.90),355s(3.68), 385(3.85),403(3.83)	44-1807-80
[2.2](3,3',4,4')Biphenylophane-1,15-dione	EtOH	211(4.67),237(4.57), 260(4.39),316(4.04)	12-0823-80
5,8:11,14-Dietheno-18,1-metheno-1H-dibenzo[a,d]cyclopentadecene, 9,10-dihydro-	CHCl	262(4.83),315(3.42), 331(3.68),348(3.89), 366(4.02),386(3.98)	24-0676-80
$C_{28}H_{20}BNO_2$ Boron, diphenyl[2-[(phenylimino)methyl]-1H-indene-1,3(2H)-dionato-N^2,O^1]-, (T-4)-	benzene	315(4.21),355(4.18), 440(3.72)	101-0001-80I
	MeCN	310(4.24),350(4.22), 440(3.70)	101-0001-80I
	DMSO	312(4.21),353(4.19), 440(3.67)	101-0001-80I
$C_{28}H_{20}Br_2N_2O_4$ Benzene, 1,1'-[1,2-bis[[(4-bromophenyl)-aci-nitro]methyl]-1,2-ethenediyl]bis-	MeOH	248(--),325(4.28)	104-2059-80
3,11-Diazatricyclo[5.3.1.1^{2,6}]dodeca-4,8-diene-10,12-dione, 3,11-bis-[trans-3-(4-bromophenyl)-3-oxo-1-propenyl]-	MeCN	215(4.41),259(4.38), 330(4.46)	39-0362-80C
$C_{28}H_{20}Br_2S_4$ 1,3-Butadiene, 2,3-dibromo-1,1,4,4-tetrakis(phenylthio)-	heptane	200(4.77),285(4.40)	24-3342-80
$C_{28}H_{20}Cl_2$ 1,1'-Biphenyl, 4,4'-bis(2-chloro-2-phenylethenyl)-	film	278(3.91)	104-2207-80
$C_{28}H_{20}Cl_2N_2O_4$ 3,11-Diazatricyclo[5.3.1.1^{2,6}]dodeca-4,8-diene-10,12-dione, 3,11-bis-[trans-3-(4-chlorophenyl)-3-oxo-1-propenyl]-	MeCN	215(4.50),254(4.43), 330(4.61)	39-0362-80C
$C_{28}H_{20}Cl_2N_{10}$ Quinoxaline, 2,3-bis[(5-chloro-3-methyl-1-phenyl-1H-pyrazol-4-yl)azo]-	CHCl₃	326(4.59),346s(4.56), 355s(4.55)	103-0653-80
$C_{28}H_{20}Cl_2O$ Benzene, 1,1'-oxybis[4-(2-chloro-2-phenylethenyl)-	film	287(3.86)	104-2207-80
$C_{28}H_{20}Cl_2O_2S$ Benzene, 1,1'-sulfonylbis[4-(2-chloro-2-phenylethenyl)-	film	293(3.89)	104-2207-80

Compound	Solvent	$\lambda_{max}(\log \epsilon)$	Ref.

$C_{28}H_{20}Cl_2S_4$
  1,3-Butadiene, 2,3-dichloro-1,1,4,4-
  tetrakis(phenylthio)-
	heptane	207(4.82),285(4.55)	24-3342-80

$C_{28}H_{20}F_3O_2P$
  Phosphonium, triphenyl-, 1-benzoyl-
  3,3,3-trifluoro-2-oxopropylide
	50% EtOH	255(4.22),303(3.75)	104-0729-80

$C_{28}H_{20}I_2S_4$
  1,3-Butadiene, 2,3-diiodo-1,1,4,4-
  tetrakis(phenylthio)-
	heptane	199(4.77),261(4.27),
		  289(4.25)
			24-3342-80

$C_{28}H_{20}N_2O$
  Propanedinitrile, (3-ethoxy-2,4,5-tri-
  phenyl-2,4-cyclopentadien-1-ylidene)-
	MeCN	261(4.17),344(4.27),
		  540(2.62)
			24-0424-80

Pyridine, 3-[2-[4-(4,5-diphenyl-2-oxaz- olyl)phenyl]ethenyl]-	DMF	355(4.70)	33-1311-80

$C_{28}H_{20}N_2O_2$
  Methanone, (2-hydroxyphenyl)(1,2,5-tri-
  phenyl-1H-imidazol-4-yl)-
	EtOH	214(4.40),263(4.30)	39-0354-80C

Oxazole, 2,2'-(1,4-phenylenedi-2,1-eth-
  enediyl)bis[5-phenyl-
	CHCl$_3$	382(4.74),397(4.75),
		  420s(4.58)
			103-0464-80

$C_{28}H_{20}N_2O_2S_2$
  Phenol, 2,2'-[2,2'-bi-2H-1,4-benzothi-
  azine]-3,3'-diylbis-
	CHCl$_3$	252s(4.20),268(4.32),
		  290s(3.98),347(3.99),
		  392(4.05)
			39-2923-80C

$C_{28}H_{20}N_4$
  Benzenamine, N,N',N'',N'''-1,2,3,4-cyclo-
  butanetetraylidenetetrakis-
	CH$_2$Cl$_2$	244(4.49),433(4.23)	89-0136B-80

Benzenamine, N,N'-[(3,8-dihydroindolo-
  [7,6-g]indole-1,6-diyl)dimethyli-
  dyne]bis-
	EtOH	205(3.65),267(3.72),
		  330(3.67)
			103-1139-80

$C_{28}H_{20}N_4O$
  Pyridine, 3,3'-[1,3,4-oxadiazole-2,5-
  diylbis(4,1-phenylene-2,1-ethene-
  diyl)]bis-
	DMF	357(4.91)	33-1311-80

$C_{28}H_{20}N_4O_8$
  Benzene, 1,1'-[1,2-bis[[(4-nitrophen-
  yl)-aci-nitro]methyl]-1,2-ethene-
  diyl]bis-
	MeOH	235(4.36),320(4.23),
		  400(4.45)
			104-2059-80

$C_{28}H_{20}N_{10}NiO_2$
  Nickel, [[4,4'-[2,3-quinoxalinediyl-
  bis(azo)]bis[2,4-dihydro-5-methyl-
  2-phenyl-3H-pyrazol-3-onato]](2-)]-
	CHCl$_3$	251(4.49),352(4.33),
		  456(4.37),518(4.34),
		  545s(4.26)
			103-0653-80

$C_{28}H_{20}O$
  9H-Dibenzo[a,g]cyclononadecen-9-one,
  20,21,22,23-tetradehydro-8-methyl-,
  (all-E)-
	THF	<u>225(3.8),335(4.6),</u>
		  <u>370(3.5)</u>
			138-0225-80

Furan, tetraphenyl-	EtOH	236(4.04),325(4.29)	12-2653-80

$C_{28}H_{20}O_2$
  9,10-Anthracenedione, 1,8-bis(4-methyl-
  phenyl)-
	EtOH	222(4.52),254(4.62),
		  349(3.67)
			24-0676-80

Dibenzoylstilbene, (Z)-	EtOH	216(4.36),257(4.38)	12-2653-80

Compound	Solvent	$\lambda_{max}(\log \epsilon)$	Ref.
$C_{28}H_{20}O_2P_2S$ 2,5-Thiophenedione, 3,4-bis(diphenyl- phosphino)-	CCl_4	420(3.5)	49-0177-80
$C_{28}H_{20}O_3Sb_2$ 2,5-Furandione, 3,4-bis(diphenylstib- ino)-	CCl_4	385(4.3),460(4.1)	49-0177-80
$C_{28}H_{20}O_4$ 5,12[1',2"]Benzenonaphthacene-1,15-di- carboxylic acid, 5,12-dihydro-, dimethyl ester, (5S)-	EtOH	210(4.74),233(4.92), 283(4.15),324(3.40)	35-0501-80
$C_{28}H_{20}O_{10}$ Bacillosporin A	MeOH	233(4.61),242s(4.59), 259s(4.48),278s(4.25), 322(3.95),354s(3.81), 376s(3.54),415(3.15)	94-3649-80
$C_{28}H_{21}NO$ 3H-Indole, 3-(diphenylmethylene)-2-(2- methoxyphenyl)- (in 64% MeOH) Phenol, 2-(2,4,5-triphenyl-1H-pyrrol- 1-yl)-	pH 0.06 pH 12.76 EtOH	364(3.86),455(4.03) 384(3.89) 217(4.46),258(4.34), 285(4.36)	33-1264-80 33-1264-80 39-1870-80C
$C_{28}H_{21}NO_2$ [1]Benzopyrano[4,3-b]indole, 6,11-di- hydro-6-(4-methoxyphenyl)-6-phenyl-	pH -3.5 (64% MeOH)	398(4.12),515(4.14)	33-1264-80
$C_{28}H_{21}NO_3$ Benzamide, N-(4-hydroxyphenyl)-N-(3- oxo-1,3-diphenyl-1-propenyl)-	EtOH	212(4.02),246(3.98), 285(3.88),366(3.86)	39-1870-80C
$C_{28}H_{21}NO_6$ 3-Pyridineacetic acid, 3,4-dihydro- 3-(methoxycarbonyl)- ,4-dioxo- 2,5,6-triphenyl-, methyl ester	EtOH	275(4.06),292s(3.48)	44-4898-80
$C_{28}H_{21}N_3$ Propanedinitrile, [3-(dimethylamino)- 2,4,5-triphenyl-2,4-cyclopentadien- 1-ylidene]-	MeCN	282(4.08),368(4.20), 610(3.72)	24-0424-80
$C_{28}H_{21}N_3O_2$ 6H-Anthra[1,9-cd]isoxazol-6-one, 5-[(4- methylphenyl)amino]-3-[(phenylmeth- yl)amino]-	dioxan	254(4.52),478(4.33), 506(4.40)	103-0704-80
$C_{28}H_{21}N_3O_3$ Benzamide, 4-[[1-benzoyl-5-[(4-cyano- phenyl)methylene]-4-oxo-3-piperi- dinylidene]methyl]-	dioxan	335(4.308)	106-0075-80
$C_{28}H_{21}N_7O_6S$ Benzenesulfonamide, N-[4,5-dihydro-6- nitro-2-(4-nitrophenyl)-4-phenyl- 5-(phenylimino)-1,2,4-triazin- 3(2H)-ylidene]-4-methyl-	DMF	299s(4.23),394s(3.62)	48-0087-80
$C_{28}H_{22}$ Anthracene, 1,8-bis(4-methylphenyl)-	EtOH	213s(4.49),259(5.09),	24-0676-80

Compound	Solvent	$\lambda_{max}(\log \epsilon)$	Ref.
(cont.)		354(3.91),373(4.02), 393(3.95)	24-0676-80
Anthracene, 9-ethyl-1,8-diphenyl-	EtOH	268(4.95),377(3.73), 395(3.89),417(3.81)	44-1807-80
Anthracene, 10-ethyl-1,8-diphenyl-	EtOH	263(5.00),345(3.47), 364(3.80),383(3.99), 402(3.92)	44-1807-80
$C_{28}H_{22}BrN_2$ Benzo[f]quinolinium, 3-(4-bromophenyl)- 4-methyl-1-[2-(phenylamino)ethenyl]-, iodide	EtOH	509(4.66)	103-0752-80
$C_{28}H_{22}ClN_2$ Benzo[f]quinolinium, 3-(4-chlorophenyl)- 4-methyl-1-[2-(phenylamino)ethenyl]-, iodide	EtOH	507(4.70)	103-0752-80
$C_{28}H_{22}FN_2$ Benzo[f]quinolinium, 3-(4-fluorophenyl)- 4-methyl-1-[2-(phenylamino)ethenyl]-, iodide	EtOH	507(4.66)	103-0752-80
$C_{28}H_{22}I_2N_2O_2$ [1,1'-Biphenyl]-4,4'-dicarboxamide, 2,2'-diiodo-N,N'-bis(4-methylphenyl)-	EtOH	285(4.57)	126-0333-80
$C_{28}H_{22}N_2OS$ Benzeneacetamide, N-[(diphenylamino)- thioxomethyl]-α-(phenylmethylene)-	MeOH	297(4.44)	142-1921-80
4H-1,3-Thiazin-4-one, 2-(diphenylami- no)-5,6-dihydro-5,6-diphenyl-	MeOH	270(4.21)	142-1921-80
$C_{28}H_{22}N_2OSe$ 4H-1,3-Selenazin-4-one, 2-(diphenyl- amino)-5,6-dihydro-5,6-diphenyl-	MeOH	273(4.25)	142-1921-80
$C_{28}H_{22}N_2O_2$ Tetrabenzo[b,d,h,j][1,6]diazacyclodo- decine, 3,6-dimethoxy-	EtOH	235s(4.64),255s(4.51), 300(3.99)	39-0107-80C
$C_{28}H_{22}N_4$ 1,1'-Bi-1H-pyrrolo[3,2-c]pyridine, 2,2'-bis(4-methylphenyl)-	EtOH	250(4.73),306(4.61)	142-0783-80
$C_{28}H_{22}N_4O_2$ 1,1'-Bi-1H-pyrrolo[3,2-c]pyridine, 2,2'-bis(4-methoxyphenyl)-	EtOH	253(4.44),260(4.43), 309(4.43)	142-0783-80
$C_{28}H_{22}N_4O_3S_2$ 5-Thia-1-azabicyclo[4.2.0]oct-2-ene- 2-carboxylic acid, 7-amino-8-oxo- 3-(5-phenyl-1,3,4-thiadiazol-2-yl)-, diphenylmethyl ester, (6R-trans)-	EtOH	280s(3.94),328(4.21)	94-2116-80
$C_{28}H_{22}N_8$ Formazan, 3-methyl-1,5-bis(1-phenyl- 2-benzimidazolyl)-	EtOH	539(4.61)	103-0637-80
$C_{28}H_{22}N_8O$ Diazene, 1,1',1'',1'''-(oxydi-2-ethenyl-	dioxan	253(4.49),384(4.69)	24-1226-80

Compound	Solvent	$\lambda_{max}(\log \epsilon)$	Ref.
1-ylidene)tetrakis[phenyl- (cont.)			24-1226-80
$C_{28}H_{22}N_{10}O_2$ 2,3-Quinoxalinedione, bis[(1,5-dihydro- 3-methyl-5-oxo-1-phenyl-4H-pyrazol-4- ylidene)hydrazone]	CHCl$_3$	250s(4.53),325s(4.20), 357(4.36),423(4.54)	103-0653-80
$C_{28}H_{22}O_3$ 2,4-Cyclopentadien-1-one, 3-(1-acetyl- 2-hydroxy-1-propenyl)-2,4,5-tri- phenyl-	MeCN	260(4.49),320s(--), 480(3.35)	24-0424-80
1,6-Heptadiene-3,5-dione, 4-(1-oxo-3- phenyl-2-propenyl)-1,7-diphenyl-	EtOH	305(4.46),397(4.63)	102-2643-80
	EtOH-NaOH	298(4.61),384(4.43)	102-2643-80
4H-Pyran-4-one, 2,3-dihydro-5-(1-oxo- 3-phenyl-2-propenyl)-2-phenyl-6-(2- phenylethenyl)-	EtOH	301(4.48),348(4.52)	102-2643-80
	EtOH-NaOH	299(4.63),384(4.47)	102-2643-80
	EtOH-HOAc	306(4.48),396(4.65)	102-2643-80
$C_{28}H_{22}Si$ Silacyclopenta-2,4-diene, 2,3,4,5- tetraphenyl-	dioxan	369(4.16)	61-1122-80
$C_{28}H_{23}BN_2O$ 2H-Indol-2-one, 3-[[(diphenylboryl)- phenylamino]methylene]-1,3-dihydro- 1-methyl-	benzene	284(4.22),380(4.43)	101-0001-80I
$C_{28}H_{23}BrN_4O_8$ Benzenamine, 4-[(3-bromophenyl)(4-meth- oxyphenyl)(2,4,6-trinitrophenoxy)- methyl]-N,N-dimethyl-	MeCN	508(4.48)	104-1436-80
	HOAc	516(4.48)	104-1436-80
Benzenamine, 4-[(4-bromophenyl)(4-meth- oxyphenyl)(2,4,6-trinitrophenoxy)- methyl]-N,N-dimethyl-	MeCN	512(4.57)	104-1436-80
	HOAc	520(4.56)	104-1436-80
$C_{28}H_{23}NO_3S_2$ 3H-Phenoxazin-3-one, 2-ethoxy-7,9-bis- [(4-methylphenyl)thio]-	n.s.g.	481(4.55)	103-0032-80
$C_{28}H_{23}N_2$ Benzo[f]quinolinium, 4-methyl-3-phenyl- 1-[2-(phenylamino)ethenyl]-, iodide	EtOH	511(4.69)	103-0752-80
$C_{28}H_{23}N_3O_2$ 4-Piperidinone, 1-benzoyl-3,5-bis[(4- cyanophenyl)methyl]-	MeOH	236(4.526)	106-0075-80
$C_{28}H_{23}N_3O_4$ 1H-Pyrrolo[3,4-f]quinoline-1,3(2H)-di- one, 5-(2,5-dioxo-1-phenyl-3-pyrrol- idinyl)-3a,4,5,6b-tetrahydro-8-meth- yl-2-phenyl-	MeOH	265(2.85)	103-0833-80
1H-Pyrrolo[3,4-f]quinoline-1,3(2H)-di- one, 5-(2,5-dioxo-1-phenyl-3-pyrrol- idinyl)-3a,4,5,9b-tetrahydro-7-meth- yl-2-phenyl-	MeOH	262(2.80)	103-0833-80
$C_{28}H_{23}N_3O_8$ Benzo[a]pyrrolo[1',2':3,4]pyrimido- [6,1,2-cd]pyrrolizine-8,9,10,11- tetracarboxylic acid, 4-(2-cyano-1- methylethenyl)-7b,11a-dihydro-,	EtOH	212(4.71),333(3.97)	24-0614-80

Compound	Solvent	$\lambda_{max}(\log \epsilon)$	Ref.
tetramethyl ester (cont.)			24-0614-80
$C_{28}H_{23}N_3O_{13}$ Methanone, (6-nitro-1,3-benzodioxol- 5-yl)[5,6,7,8-tetrahydro-9-[hydroxy- (6-nitro-1,3-dioxol-5-yl)methyl]-4- methoxy-6-methyl-1,3-dioxolo[4,5-g]- isoquinolin-5-yl]-, perchlorate	MeOH	255(4.45),348(4.15)	83-0715-80
$C_{28}H_{23}N_5$ 1,2,4,5-Tetrazine-3-acetonitrile, 1,2,3,4-tetrahydro- ,2,4,6-tetra- phenyl-	hexane	227(4.29),252(--), 333(4.15)	30-0224-80
$C_{28}H_{23}N_5O_{10}$ Benzenamine, 4-[(4-methoxyphenyl)(3-ni- trophenyl)(2,4,6-trinitrophenoxy)- methyl]-N,N-dimethyl-	MeCN HOAc	505(4.34) 513(4.34)	104-1436-80 104-1436-80
$C_{28}H_{24}$ [2.2](3,3',4,4')Biphenylophane	EtOH	211(4.61),253(4.24), 274s(4.08),284s(4.04)	12-0823-80
$C_{28}H_{24}ClN_5O_3$ 1H-Isoindole-1,3(2H)-dione, 2-[[4-(2- benzoyl-4-chlorophenyl)-5-[2-(di- methylamino)ethyl]-4H-1,2,4-triazol- 3-yl]methyl]-	EtOH	218(4.79),238s(4.21), 257(4.15),288s(3.71)	4-0575-80
$C_{28}H_{24}Cl_2N_4O$ Pyrido[3,2-a]indolizine-3,7-dicarbo- nitrile, 10-(4-chlorophenyl)-1-[(4- chlorophenyl)methyl]-4-ethoxy-1,4,4a- 4b,10,10a-hexahydro-	CH_2Cl_2	268(4.4),352(3.6)	64-0490-80B
$C_{28}H_{24}N_2O_3S$ 2(1H)-Quinazolinethione, 3-benzoyl- 3,4,5,6,7,8-hexahydro-4-phenyl- 8-(phenylmethylene)-	EtOH	233(4.53),277(4.61), 350(3.95)	114-0147-80B
$C_{28}H_{24}N_4O_8$ Benzenamine, 4-[(4-methoxyphenyl)phen- yl(2,4,6-trinitrophenoxy)methyl]- N,N-dimethyl-	MeCN	510(4.52)	104-1436-80
$C_{28}H_{24}N_5O_4P$ 8,12-Epoxy-3H,7H-[1,3,2]dioxaphospholo- [4',5':5,6][1,3]diazocino[1,2,3-cd]- purine, 5-amino-8,8a,10,10,11a,12- hexahydro-3-oxo-10,10,10-triphenyl-, [8R-(8α,8aβ,11aβ,12α)]-	MeCN	235(4.42),258(4.12)	18-3670-80
$C_{28}H_{24}N_6O_5$ Pyrido[3,2-a]indolizine-3,7-dicarbo- nitrile, 4-ethoxy-1,4,4a,4b,10,10a- hexahydro-10-(4-nitrophenyl)-1-[(4- nitrophenyl)methyl]-	CH_2Cl_2	269(4.5),340(3.6)	64-0490-80B
$C_{28}H_{24}N_8$ 3,3'-Bi-1,2,4,5-tetrazinium, 5,5',6,6'- tetrahydro-1,1',5,5'-tetraphenyl-,	DMF HCOOH	686(3.91) 347(4.60),535(4.43)	24-2049-80 24-2049-80

Compound	Solvent	$\lambda_{max}(\log \epsilon)$	Ref.
bis[(T-4)-tetrachloroferrate(1-)]-			24-2049-80
$C_{28}H_{24}O$			
1H-Acenaphth[5,6-kl]acephenanthrylene-11-methanol, 2,5,7,8-tetrahydro-α,5-dimethyl-	EtOH	234(4.62),278(4.10), 288(4.16),300(4.22), 308(4.10),314(4.08), 327(3.82)	65-2096-80
$C_{28}H_{24}O_2$			
1H-Acenaphth[5,6-kl]acephenanthrylene-11-methanol, 2,5,7,8-tetrahydro-5-hydroxy-α,5-dimethyl-	EtOH	215(4.34),233(4.52), 280(4.62),290(4.67), 302(4.73),312(4.65), 327(4.37)	65-2096-80
Isobenzofuran, 1,3-dihydro-1-methoxy-1-(2-methylphenyl)-3,3-diphenyl-	hexane	219(4.42),255(3.03), 261(3.07),265s(3.04), 271(2.92)	104-1316-80
Isobenzofuran, 1,3-dihydro-1-methoxy-1-(3-methylphenyl)-3,3-diphenyl-	hexane	217(4.33),254(2.93), 260(3.02),266(3.01), 273(2.79)	104-1316-80
Isobenzofuran, 1,3-dihydro-1-methoxy-1-(4-methylphenyl)-3,3-diphenyl-	hexane	213(4.50),221s(4.44), 254(2.95),260(3.02), 264(3.00),271s(2.83)	104-1316-80
$C_{28}H_{24}O_4$			
5,12[1',2']-Benzenonaphthacene-1,15-dicarboxylic acid, 5,5a,6,11,11a,12-hexahydro-, dimethyl ester. [5S-(5α,5aβ,11aβ,12α)]-	EtOH	235s(4.30),272s(3.38), 293(3.71)	35-0501-80
$C_{28}H_{24}O_9$			
Dinaphtho[2,1-b:1',2'-d]furan-2,12-dicarboxylic acid, 4,5,9,10-tetramethoxy-, dimethyl ester	CHCl$_3$	276(4.50),282(4.50), 306(4.02),319(3.93), 393s(4.01),415(4.25), 437(4.27)	12-2531-80
$C_{28}H_{24}O_{15}$			
Kaempferol 3-O-glucoside-2"-gallate	MeOH	269(4.44),295s(--), 345s(4.23)	102-1877-80
	MeOH-NaOAc	271(--),302(--), 370s(--)	102-1877-80
$C_{28}H_{24}O_{16}$			
Quercetin 3-(2"-galloylglucoside)	MeOH	258s(--),268(4.41), 365(4.25)	102-0482-80
$C_{28}H_{25}NO$			
2,4-Cyclopentadien-1-one, 2,3,5-triphenyl-4-piperidino-	MeCN	278(4.34),305s(--), 469(2.88)	24-0408-80
perchlorate	MeCN	254(4.21),291(3.87), 353(4.04)	24-0408-80
$C_{28}H_{25}NO_2$			
2,4-Cyclopentadien-1-one, 2-(4-methylphenyl)-3-morpholino-4,5-diphenyl-	MeCN	273(4.37),317s(--), 497(3.07)	24-0408-80
$C_{28}H_{25}N_2OS$			
Benzothiazolium, 3-ethyl-2-[[2-[2-(methylphenylamino)ethenyl]-4H-1-benzopyran-4-ylidene]methyl]-, perchlorate	MeCN	424(4.30),585(5.02)	124-0965-80
Benzothiazolium, 3-ethyl-2-[[4-	MeCN	412(4.24),585(4.88)	124-0965-80

Compound	Solvent	$\lambda_{max}(\log \epsilon)$	Ref.
[2-(methylphenylamino)ethenyl]-2H-1-benzopyran-2-ylidene]methyl-, iodide			124-0965-80
$C_{28}H_{25}N_5O_4S_3$			
5-Thia-1-azabicyclo[4.2.0]oct-2-ene-2-carboxylic acid, 3-[[(aminothioxomethyl)hydrazono]methyl]-8-oxo-7-[[(2-thienylacetyl)amino]-, diphenylmethyl ester, (6R-trans)-	EtOH	350(4.44)	94-2116-80
$C_{28}H_{26}$			
Bicyclo[2.2.2]octane, 1,4-di-2-naphthalenyl-	4:1 C_6H_{11}Me-isopentane	255s(3.87),263(3.97), 272(3.98),283s(3.80), 302(2.91),316(2.77)	44-3933-80
$C_{28}H_{26}ClNO_6$			
Cyclobuta[a]cyclohepta[gh]pyrrolizine-1,5,6-tricarboxylic acid, 2-chloro-4a-ethyl-4,4a-dihydro-4-phenyl-, 1-ethyl 5,6-dimethyl ester, (4α,4aβ,6aR*)-	EtOH	238(4.12),291(3.79)	18-1406-80
2H-Cyclohepta[gh]pyrrolizine-1,2,5-tricarboxylic acid, 4-chloro-2-[1-(phenylmethylene)propyl]-, 5-ethyl 1,2-dimethyl ester	EtOH	246(4.77),252s(4.77), 374(4.14),392(4.10), 439(3.72),467(3.69), 500(3.51),537(3.10)	18-1406-80
$C_{28}H_{26}Cl_2N_5O_{10}P$			
Phosphoramidic acid, N-[9-(2,3,5-tri-O-acetyl-β-D-ribofuranosyl)-9H-purin-6-yl]-, bis(2-chlorophenyl) ester	MeOH	259(4.29),266s(4.27), 280s(3.89)	142-0761-80B
$C_{28}H_{26}N_4O_2$			
Piperidine, 1-[[2-(benzoyloxy)phenyl]-(2-quinolinylhydrazono)methyl-, monohydriodide	MeOH	265(4.27),380(4.12)	56-0661-80
1H-Pyrazole, 3,3'-(1,4-phenylene)bis-[1-acetyl-4,5-dihydro-5-phenyl-	dioxan	332s(4.50),344(4.66), 358s(4.55)	103-0066-80
	MeCN	326s(4.66),341(4.72), 354(4.59)	103-0066-80
$C_{28}H_{26}N_5O_4P$			
Adenosine, 3',5'-O-(triphenylphosphoranylidene)-	MeCN	260(3.87)	18-3670-80
$C_{28}H_{26}OPS$			
Phosphonium, [2-methoxy-1-(methylthio)-2-phenylethenyl]triphenyl-, (E)-	n.s.g.	226s(3.83),267s(3.39), 273(3.41),278s(3.38)	104-0573-80
$C_{28}H_{26}OPSe$			
Phosphonium, [2-methoxy-1-(methylseleno)-2-phenylethenyl]triphenyl-, (E)-	n.s.g.	225s(4.71),270s(4.43), 275s(4.36),340(3.38)	104-0573-80
$C_{28}H_{26}O_2$			
1H-Acenaphth[5,6-kl]acephenanthrylene-11-methanol, 2,5,5a,7,8,11b-hexahydro-5-hydroxy-α,5-dimethyl-	EtOH	215(4.53),233(4.74), 280(4.91),290(4.97), 302(5.01),312(4.85), 327(4.46)	65-2096-80
1H-Acenaphth[5,6-kl]acephenanthrylene-11-methanol, 2,5,7,8,11c,12-hexahydro-5-hydroxy-α,5-dimethyl-	EtOH	215(4.55),233(4.79), 280(4.90),290(4.96), 302(5.03),312(4.89), 327(4.25)	65-2096-80

Compound	Solvent	$\lambda_{max}(\log \epsilon)$	Ref.
Cyclobuta[b]naphthalene-3,8-dione, 2a,8a-diethyl-1,2,2a,8a-tetrahydro-1,1-diphenyl-, cis	CHCl$_3$	243(4.15),252(4.15), 300(3.35)	18-0757-80
$C_{28}H_{26}O_6$ 1,2-Benzenedicarboxylic acid, 4-(1-acetyl-2-hydroxy-1-propenyl)-6-methyl-3,5-diphenyl-, dimethyl ester	MeCN	290(3.91)	24-0424-80
$C_{28}H_{26}O_7Se$ α-D-Glucopyranoside, methyl 4,6-O-(phenylmethylene)-, 3-benzenecarboselenoate 2-benzoate, (R)-	EtOH	228(4.02),256(3.63), 332(3.61)	39-2184-80C
$C_{28}H_{26}O_{10}$ [1,1'-Binaphthalene]-7,7'-dicarboxylic acid, 2,2',4,4',5,5'-hexamethoxy-	CHCl$_3$	291(4.03),302(4.01), 315(3.97),388(4.05)	12-2531-80
$C_{28}H_{27}N_3O_3$ 5-Pyrimidinecarboxylic acid, 1-(2,6-dimethylphenyl)-1,2,3,4-tetrahydro-6-methyl-2-oxo-3-phenyl-4-(phenylimino)-, ethyl ester	CH$_2$Cl$_2$	275(4.1),315(3.9)	24-2509-80
$C_{28}H_{27}S_2$ Sulfonium, [4-(1,1-dimethylethyl)phenyl]phenyl[4-(phenylthio)phenyl]-, hexafluoroarsenate	n.s.g.	230(4.37),300(4.29)	47-2697-80
$C_{28}H_{28}ClFN_2OS$ 1-Butanone, 4-[4-(8-chloro-10,11-dihydrodibenzo[b,f]thiepin-10-yl)-1-piperazinyl]-1-(4-fluorophenyl)-, dihydrochloride	MeOH	243(4.26),264s(4.01)	73-3182-80
$C_{28}H_{28}N_2O_4$ 2-Propenoic acid, 3,3'-(1,4-phenylenediimino)bis[3-phenyl-, diethyl ester, (Z,Z)-	H$_2$SO$_4$	242(4.37),262(4.26), 285(4.23)	47-3029-80
$C_{28}H_{28}N_4$ Pyrazolidine, 3-(1,2-diphenylhydrazino)-5-methyl-1,2-diphenyl-	MeOH	201(4.92),248(4.58), 284s(3.82)	73-2417-80
$C_{28}H_{28}N_5O_{10}P$ Phosphoramidic acid, N-[9-(2,3,5-tri-O-acetyl-β-D-ribofuranosyl)-9H-purin-6-yl]-, diphenyl ester	MeOH	259(4.31),268s(4.21), 280s(3.58)	142-0761-80B
$C_{28}H_{28}N_6O_3$ 1,7-Imino-2,6-methano-3-benzazecin-8(1H)-one, 10-acetoxy-3,9-bis(4,6-dimethyl-2-pyrimidinyl)-2,3,6,7-tetrahydro-, (1α,2β,6β,7α,10S*)-	EtOH	210(4.26),255(4.28), 270s(4.15),300s(3.64)	39-0331-80C
$C_{28}H_{28}OP$ Phosphonium, (2,7-dimethyl-8-oxo-2,4,6-octatrienyl)triphenyl-, chloride, (E,E,E)-	EtOH	330(4.66)	33-1473-80

Compound	Solvent	$\lambda_{max}(\log \epsilon)$	Ref.
$C_{28}H_{28}O_4$			
Pentacyclo[18.2.2.2^{9,12}.0^{4,15}.0^{6,17}]-hexacosa-4,6(17),9(26),11,15,20,22-23-octaene-10,25-dione, 21,23-di-methoxy-isomer	CH_2Cl_2	290(4.0),315(3.6), 445(3.3)	18-2943-80
isomer	CH_2Cl_2	290s(3.9),310s(3.4), 440(3.3)	18-2943-80
isomer	CH_2Cl_2	315(3.3),405(3.2)	18-2943-80
Tetracyclo[9.8.1.1^{3,9}.1^{13,18}]docosa-2,4,7,9,11,13,15,17,19-nonaene-5,7-dicarboxylic acid, diethyl ester	dioxan	247(4.43),356(5.06), 424(3.92)	89-0041-80
$C_{28}H_{28}O_9$			
Dehydrophysalin B	EtOH	328(4.70)	102-1175-80
Epidehydrophysalin B	EtOH	340(3.78)	102-1175-80
$C_{28}H_{29}Br$			
Pentacyclo[18.2.2.2^{9,12}.0^{4,15}.0^{6,17}]-hexacosa-4,6(17),9,11,15,20,22,23,25-nonaene, 5-bromo-10,25-dimethyl-	THF	295s(3.1),345s(2.1)	18-1677-80
Pentacyclo[18.2.2.2^{9,12}.0^{4,15}.0^{6,17}]-hexacosa-4,6(17),9,11,15,20,22,23,25-nonaene, 11-bromo-10,25-dimethyl-	THF	302(3.2),320s(3.0), 372(2.5)	18-1677-80
$C_{28}H_{30}$			
6,9:10,13-Dimethanodicyclohepta[a,c]-naphthalene, 4b,5,6,7,8,9,9a,10,11-12,13,14-dodecahydro-4b-phenyl-, (4bα,6β,9β,9aα,10α,13α)-(±)-	C_6H_{12}	221(4.32),227(4.32), 233(4.24),283(3.96)	23-1847-80
[2.2]]2.2]Paracyclophane, 4,7-dimethyl-	THF	290s(3.2),350(2.2)	18-1677-80
[2.2][3.3]Paracyclophane (triple layer)	THF	280s(3.1),330s(2.2)	18-0512-80
$C_{28}H_{30}N_2$			
Benzo[5',6']pyrrolizino[1',7':3,4,5]-cyclohept[1,2-b]indole, 1,2,8,9,10-14c-hexahydro-2,2,8,14c-tetramethyl-8-(1-methylethenyl)-	EtOH	230(4.41),382(3.87)	39-0553-80C
$C_{28}H_{30}N_4$			
Propanedinitrile, [3,4-bis(diethyl-amino)-2,5-diphenyl-2,4-cyclopenta-dien-1-ylidene]-	MeCN	283(3.77),422(4.42), 640(2.98)	24-0424-80
$C_{28}H_{30}N_6$			
Tetrapyrido[2,1,6-de:2',1',6'-gh-2'',1'',6''-kl:2''',1''',6'''-na][1,3,5,8-10,12]hexaazacyclotetradecene	CHCl	335(4.5),430(3.9), 500s(3.4)	39-2527-80C
$C_{28}H_{30}N_6O_2S$			
1,7-Imino-2,6-methano-3-benzazecin-8(1H)-one, 3,13-bis(4,6-dimethyl-2-pyrimidinyl)-2,3,6,7-tetrahydro-14-[(methylthio)methoxy]-, (1α,2β,6β,7α,14S*)-	EtOH	212(4.26),254(4.41), 265s(4.30),305s(3.74)	39-0331-80C
$C_{28}H_{30}O_2$			
Triple-layered [2.2]paracyclophane, 12,15-dimethoxy-	THF	226(4.24),295(3.23), 315s(3.11),375(2.99)	18-2943-80
$C_{28}H_{30}O_2S_2$			
8,15-Dithiapentacyclo[20.2.2.2^{10,13}-	THF	225(4.31),290s(3.31),	18-2943-80

Compound	Solvent	$\lambda_{max}(\log \epsilon)$	Ref.
$0^4,^{17}.0^6,^{19}$]octacosa-4,6(19),10,12-17,22,24,25,27-nonaene, 5,18-di-methoxy- (cont.)		311s(2.98),351(3.06)	18-2943-80
$C_{28}H_{30}O_{10}$ 16,24-Cyclo-13,14-secoergosta-2,4-di-ene-18,26-dioic acid, 14,17:14,27-diepoxy-6,13,20,22-tetrahydroxy-1,15-dioxo-, γ-lactone δ-lactone, (6β,14α,16β,22α,25S)-	EtOH	325(3.81)	102-1175-80
Physalin G	EtOH	312(3.60)	102-1175-80
$C_{28}H_{30}O_{11}$ 16,24-Cyclo-13,14-secoergost-2-ene-18,26-dioic acid, 14,17:14,27-di-epoxy-5,13,20,22-tetrahydroxy-1,6,15-trioxo- (physalin D-6-one)	EtOH	228(3.86)	102-1175-80
Physalin K	EtOH	228(3.81)	102-1175-80
$C_{28}H_{31}ClO_{10}$ Physalin B, 5α-chloro-5,6-dihydro-6β-hydroxy-	EtOH	226(3.85)	102-1175-80
$C_{28}H_{31}NO_5$ Spiro[7H-benzo[de]quinoline-7,1'-[2,5]-cyclohexadien]-4'-one, 1,2,3,8,9,9a-hexahydro-3',5,5'-trimethoxy-1-methyl-6-(phenylmethoxy)-, (±)-	MeOH	222(4.6),278(4.12)	35-6513-80
$C_{28}H_{31}NO_9$ 6H-Dibenz[b,e]azepin-6-one, 5-acetyl-1,10,11-triacetoxy-5,11-dihydro-7-hydroxy-8-methyl-4-(3-methylbutyl)-	MeOH	253(4.03),277s(3.32), 321(3.79)	142-0889-80B
$C_{28}H_{31}N_4$ Ethanaminium, N-[4-(dicyanomethylene)-2-(diethylamino)-3,5-diphenyl-2-cy-clopenten-1-ylidene]-N-ethyl-, per-chlorate	MeCN	240(3.88),313(4.21), 457(4.14)	24-0424-80
$C_{28}H_{32}$ Dispiro[bicyclo[4.1.0]heptane-7,1'-[3,5,9,11]cyclododecatetrayne-2',7''-bicyclo[4.1.0]heptane], 7',7',8',8'-tetramethyl-	EtOH	244(3.34),258(3.34), 273(3.19)	35-5406-80
$C_{28}H_{32}CuN_{10}$ Copper, [1,10,11,20-tetrahydro-3,8,13-14-tetramethyl-1,11-dipropyldibenzo-[c,j]dipyrazolo[3,4-f:3',4'-m][1,2,5-8,9,12]hexaazacyclotetradecinato(2-)-N^4,N^{10},N^{14},N^{20}]-, (SP-4-2)-	$CHCl_3$	470(4.20),580(3.28)	103-1166-80
$C_{28}H_{32}N_2O$ 2H-1-Benzopyran-2-amine, 8-[3-(dimeth-ylamino)-2-phenyl-2-propenylidene]-5,6,7,8-tetrahydro-N,N-dimethyl-3-phenyl-	CH_2Cl_2	335(4.19),420(4.30)	70-0771-80
$C_{28}H_{32}N_8O_6$ 2,8-Imino-3,7-methano-4-benzazecin-	EtOH	220s(4.30),235(4.30),	39-0331-80C

Compound	Solvent	$\lambda_{max}(\log \epsilon)$	Ref.
1(2H)-one, 4,13-bis(4,6-diethoxy-1,3,5-triazin-2-yl)-3,4,7,8-tetra-hydro-14-hydroxy- (cont.)		265s(4.28)	39-0331-80C
$C_{28}H_{32}O_{11}$ Physalin D	EtOH	227(3.81)	102-1174-80
$C_{28}H_{32}O_{15}$ Isoswertisin 5-O-β-D-glucoside	EtOH EtOH-NaOAc	270(4.23),336(4.26) 262s(--),268(--), 393(--)	36-0053-80 36-0053-80
Swertisin 5-O-β-D-glucoside	EtOH EtOH-NaOAc	271(4.26),335(4.30) 262s(--),268(--), 388(--)	36-0053-80 36-0053-80
$C_{28}H_{33}BrCuN_{10}$ Copper, [N-[2-[(5-amino-3-methyl-1-propyl-1H-pyrazol-4-yl)azo]-5-methyl-phenyl]-4-[(2-bromo-4-methylphenyl)-azo]-3-methyl-1-propyl-1H-pyrazol-5-aminato(2-)]-	CHCl$_3$	360(4.46),440(4.40), 600(3.18)	103-1166-80
$C_{28}H_{33}ClN_2O_5Se$ 1H-Pyrrole-3-propanoic acid, 5-[[4-[2-[(4-chlorophenyl)seleno]ethyl]-1,5-dihydro-3-methyl-5-oxo-2H-pyrrol-2-ylidene]methyl] 2-[(1,1-dimethyleth-oxy)carbonyl]-4-methyl-, methyl ester	MeOH + Zn(OAc)$_2$	255s(--),260(4.39), 388(4.52),406s(--) 266(4.41),424(4.51), 443(4.55)	24-1603-80 24-1603-80
$C_{28}H_{33}NO_6$ 3,5-Pyridinedicarboxylic acid, 1-(4-ethoxyphenyl)-1,4-dihydro-4-(4-meth-oxyphenyl)-2,6-dimethyl-, diethyl ester	EtOH	202(4.42),228(4.28), 257s(4.13),348(3.86)	103-0377-80
$C_{28}H_{33}N_7O_5$ Benzamide, 4-[(4-azidophenyl)azo]-N-[11-[(2,5-dioxo-1-pyrrolidinyl)oxy]-11-oxoundecyl]-	CHCl$_3$	358(4.54)	69-4423-80
$C_{28}H_{34}CuN_{10}$ Copper, [1,4,5,11,15,20-hexahydro-3,8,13,18-tetramethyl-1,11-dipropyl-dibenzo[c,j]dipyrazolo[3,4-f:3',4'-m][1,2,5,8,9,12]hexaazacyclotetra-decinato(2-)-N^4,N^{10},N^{14},N^{20}]-, (SP-4-2)-	CHCl$_3$	380(4.10),468(4.38), 585(3.70)	103-1166-80
$C_{28}H_{34}N_2O_4$ 3,5-Pyridinedicarboxylic acid, 4-[4-(dimethylamino)phenyl]-1,4-di-hydro-2,6-dimethyl-1-(phenylmethyl)-, diethyl ester	EtOH	205(4.36),225(4.30), 248s(4.20),348(3.81)	103-0377-80
$C_{28}H_{34}N_6O$ 1-Naphthalenol, 2-[[5-ethyl-2-(4-ethyl-3,5-dipropyl-1H-pyrazol-1-yl)-6-methyl-4-pyrimidinyl]azo]-	EtOH	237(4.47),258(4.51), 298(3.92),400s(4.42), 411(4.47),429(4.38)	103-1279-80
$C_{28}H_{34}O_4$ 1,8-Phenanthrenedihexanoic acid,	MeOH	253(4.69),260(4.80),	44-1847-80

Compound	Solvent	$\lambda_{max}(\log \epsilon)$	Ref.
dimethyl ester (cont.)		267s(4.45),287(4.08), 293(4.18),306(4.28)	44-1847-80
	2-MeTHF	330(2.41),338(2.51), 345(2.33),353(2.33)	44-1847-80
	MeCN	220(4.2),270(4.6), 320f(4.1),340f(2.3)	46-0768-80
$C_{28}H_{34}O_4Se$ Pregn-4-ene-3,20-dione, 11-[[(phenyl-seleno)carbonyl]oxy]-, (11β)-	pentane	215s(--),241(4.23), 262s(--)	33-2328-80
$C_{28}H_{34}O_7$ Ergost-2-en-26-oic acid, 5,6:24,25-di-epoxy-22-hydroxy-1,4,15-trioxo-, δ-lactone, (5β,6β,22R,24S,25S)-	EtOH	224(4.07)	150-2134-80
$C_{28}H_{34}O_9$ Tigloylgomisin P	EtOH	217(4.68),255s(3.99), 282(3.51)	94-3357-80
$C_{28}H_{34}O_{17}$ Cyclopenta[c]pyran-4,7-dicarboxylic acid, 5-acetoxy-1,6,7,7a-tetrahydro-1-[(2,3,4,6-tetra-O-acetyl-β-D-gluco-pyranosyl)oxy]-, dimethyl ester, [1S-(1α,7α,7aα)]-	MeOH	211(4.05),267(4.08)	102-2685-80
$C_{28}H_{34}O_{18}$ Cyclopenta[c]pyran-4,7-dicarboxylic acid, 4a-acetoxy-1,4a,5,6,7,7a-hexa-hydro-5-oxo-1-[(2,3,4,6-tetra-O-acet-yl-β-D-glucopyranosyl)oxy]-, dimethyl ester (aralidioside pentaacetate)	MeOH	231(3.96)	102-2685-80
$C_{28}H_{35}BrN_{10}$ 1H-Pyrazol-5-amine, N-[2-[(5-amino-3-methyl-1-propyl-1H-pyrazol-4-yl)azo]-5-methylphenyl]-4-[(2-bromo-4-methyl-phenyl)azo]-3-methyl-1-propyl-, (E,E)-	CHCl₃	385(4.33),420(4.24)	103-1166-80
$C_{28}H_{35}BrO_7$ Pregna-1,4-diene-3,11,20-trione, 7-bromo-16-methyl-17,21-bis(1-oxo-propoxy)-, (7α,16α)-	MeOH	242(4.19)	145-1618-80
$C_{28}H_{35}N_3O_2$ 7-Isoquinolinol, 1,2,3,4-tetrahydro-6-methoxy-1-(17-norcorynan-16-yl)-	EtOH	226(4.56),282(4.01), 290(3.97)	33-1335-80
$C_{28}H_{35}N_3O_4$ Marcfortine A	n.s.g.	226(4.48),268s(3.67)	77-0601-80
$C_{28}H_{35}N_3O_7S$ 5-Thia-1-azabicyclo[4.2.0]oct-2-ene-2-carboxylic acid, 7-[3-[(1,1-dimeth-ylethoxy)carbonyl]-2,2-dimethyl-5-oxo-4-phenyl-1-imidazolidinyl]-3-methyl-4,8-dioxo-, 1,1-dimethyethyl ester, [6R-[6α,7β(R*)]]-	EtOH	308(3.70)	33-0201-80

Compound	Solvent	$\lambda_{max}(\log \epsilon)$	Ref.
$C_{28}H_{36}N_2O$			
Benzenamine, 4,4'-(methoxyphenylmeth-ylene)bis[N,N-diethyl-	98% HOAc	430(4.26),629.5(5.08)	146-0317-80
$C_{28}H_{36}N_2O_2S$			
1'H-Androst-2-eno[2,3-b]azirin-17-one, 1'-(benzothiazol-2-yl)-2,3-dihydro-, cyclic 1,2-ethanediyl acetal, (2α,3α,5α)-	n.s.g.	225(4.69),268(4.35), 296(3.92)	39-0766-80C
Spiro[1H-cyclopenta[7',8']phenanthro-[3',2':4,5]imidazo[2,1-b]benzothia-zole-1,2'-[1,3]dioxolane], 2,3,3a,3b-4,5,5a,6,6a,13a,14,14a,14b,15,16,16a-hexadecahydro-1,4a,16a-trimethyl-, [3aS-(3aα,3bβ,5aα,6aα,13aα,14aβ-14bα,16aβ)]-	n.s.g.	226(4.81),267(4.25), 302(3.91)	39-0766-80C
$C_{28}H_{36}N_6$			
3,5-Pyridinedicarbonitrile, 1,1'-(1,6-hexanediyl)bis[1,4-dihydro-2,4,4,6-tetramethyl-	MeOH	225(4.48),347(3.93)	73-3370-80
$C_{28}H_{36}N_{10}O_{10}$			
Adenosine, N,N'-1,2-ethanediylbis-[2',3'-O-(ethoxymethylene)-	EtOH	272(4.50)	69-0163-80
$C_{28}H_{36}O_3$			
1,3-Cyclohexanedione, 2-[3,7-dimethyl-9-(2,6,6-trimethyl-3-oxo-1-cyclohex-en-1-yl)-2,4,6,8-nonatetraenylidene]-5,5-dimethyl-, (all-E)-	EtOH	470(4.72)	33-1391-80
$C_{28}H_{36}O_3Se$			
Androst-5-ene-17β-carboselenoic acid, 3β-acetoxy-, Se-phenyl ester	pentane	224(4.19),260(3.62)	33-2328-80
$C_{28}H_{36}O_4$			
Benzenehexanoic acid, 2,2'-(1,2-ethene-diyl)bis-, dimethyl ester	C_6H_{12}	288(4.29)	44-1847-80
$C_{28}H_{36}O_6$			
Ergosta-2,24-dien-26-oic acid, 5β,6β-epoxy-20,22-dihydroxy-1,4-dioxo-, δ-lactone, (22R)-	EtOH	224(4.31)	102-1503-80
$C_{28}H_{36}O_7$			
Pregna-1,4,6-triene-3,20-dione, 11-hy-droxy-16-methyl-17,21-bis(1-oxoprop-oxy)-, (11β,16α)-	MeOH	220(4.08),253(3.97), 298(3.97)	87-0430-80
(11β,16β)-	MeOH	220(4.02),250(3.90), 298(3.91)	87-0430-80
$C_{28}H_{36}O_{15}$			
Durantoside III	H_2O	191(4.34),226(4.31), 311(4.16)	100-0649-80
$C_{28}H_{37}BrO_7$			
Pregna-1,4-diene-3,20-dione, 7-bromo-11-hydroxy-16-methyl-17,21-bis(1-oxopropoxy)-, (7α,11β,16α)-	MeOH	242(4.19)	87-0430-80
16β-	MeOH	242(4.19)	87-0430-80

Compound	Solvent	$\lambda_{max}(\log \epsilon)$	Ref.
$C_{28}H_{37}ClN_2O_2S$			
5α-Androstan-17-one, 3α-(2-benzothiazolylamino)-2β-chloro-, cyclic 1,2-ethanediyl acetal	n.s.g.	227(4.76),273(4.35), 296(3.66)	39-0766-80C
$C_{28}H_{37}ClO_7$			
Pregna-1,4-diene-3,20-dione, 21-acetoxy-7-chloro-11-hydroxy-16-methyl-17-(1-oxobutoxy)-, (7α,11β,16α)-	MeOH	241(4.20)	145-1618-80
Pregna-1,4-diene-3,20-dione, 7-chloro-11-hydroxy-16-methyl-17,21-bis(1-oxopropoxy)-, (7α,11β,16α)-	MeOH	242(4.19)	87-0430-80
16β-	MeOH	241(4.18)	87-0430-80
$C_{28}H_{37}CrNO_6Si$			
Chromium, tricarbonyl[(1,2,3,4,11,12-η)-(5α,6α,10α)-7,8-didehydro-6-[[(1,1-dimethylethyl)dimethylsilyl]-oxy]-4,5-epoxy-3-methoxy-10,17-dimethylmorphinan]	n.s.g.	325(3.79)	152-0369-80
$C_{28}H_{37}FO_7$			
Pregna-1,4-diene-3,20-dione, 7-fluoro-11-hydroxy-16-methyl-17,21-bis(1-oxopropoxy)-, (7α,11β,16α)-	MeOH	240(4.20)	87-0430-80
16β-	MeOH	240(4.18)	87-0430-80
$C_{28}H_{37}IO_7$			
Pregna-1,4-diene-3,20-dione, 11-hydroxy-7-iodo-16-methyl-17,21-bis(1-oxopropoxy)-, (7α,11β,16α)-	MeOH	241(4.16)	87-0430-80
16β-	MeOH	241(4.17)	87-0430-80
$C_{28}H_{38}N_2O_2S$			
Androst-2-eno[2,3-d]thiazol-17-one, 2,2',3,3'-tetrahydro-2'-(phenylimino)-, cyclic 1,2-ethanediyl acetal, (2α,3α,5α)-	n.s.g.	225(4.59),267(4.32), 196(4.11)[sic]	39-0766-80C
Androst-2-eno[3,2-d]thiazol-17-one, 2,2',3,3'-tetrahydro-2'-(phenylimino)-, cyclic 1,2-ethanediyl acetal, (2β,3β,5α)-	n.s.g.	260(4.07)	39-0766-80C
$C_{28}H_{38}O_2$			
1,3-Cyclohexanedione, 5,5-dimethyl-2-retinylidene-	EtOH	270(4.10),490(4.70)	87-0805-80
9-cis	EtOH	255(4.09),483(4.62)	87-0805-80
1,3-Cyclohexanedione, 5-ethyl-2-retinylidene-	EtOH	280(4.11),495(4.38)	87-0805-80
1,3-Cyclooctanedione, 2-retinylidene-	EtOH	280(4.03),432(4.70)	87-0805-80
$C_{28}H_{38}O_3$			
1,3-Cyclohexanedione, 2-(5,6-epoxy-5,6-dihydroretinylidene)-5,5-dimethyl-	EtOH	290(4.08),470(4.70)	33-1391-80
1,3-Cyclohexanedione, 2-(5,8-epoxy-5,8-dihydroretinylidene)-5,5-dimethyl-	EtOH	435(4.64)	33-1391-80
1,3-Cyclohexanedione, 2-(4'-hydroxy-retinylidene)-5,5-dimethyl-	EtOH	480(4.68)	33-1391-80

Compound	Solvent	$\lambda_{max}(\log \epsilon)$	Ref.
$C_{28}H_{38}O_4$			
1,3-Cyclohexanedione, 5,5-dimethyl-2-(3,7,11,11-tetramethyl-10,15-dioxo-2,4,6,8-hexadecatetraenylidene)-, (all-E)-	EtOH	305(4.18),455(4.78)	33-1391-80
$C_{28}H_{38}O_5$			
5α-Androstane-16-carboxylic acid, 3β-hydroxy-16-(4-methoxyphenyl)-17-oxo-, methyl ester	EtOH	228(4.23),276(3.81), 281(3.79)	12-0113-80
Euglobal III	EtOH	278(4.51),345s(3.69)	94-2546-80
$C_{28}H_{38}O_6$			
20R,22R-Witha-2-enolide, 2,4-dioxo-5β,6β-epoxy-20α-hydroxy-	EtOH	224(4.11)	102-1503-80
$C_{28}H_{38}O_7$			
17-Isowithanolide E	n.s.g.	225(4.26)	150-4275-80
Pregna-1,4-diene-3,20-dione, 11-hydroxy-16-methyl-17,21-bis(1-oxopropoxy)-, (11β,16α)-	MeOH	243(4.18)	87-0430-80
Withaphysanolide	EtOH	212(4.11)	105-0167-80
$C_{28}H_{38}O_8$			
Pregna-1,4-diene-3,20-dione, 7,11-dihydroxy-16-methyl-17,21-bis(1-oxopropoxy)-, (7β,11β,16α)-	MeOH	243(4.13)	87-0430-80
$C_{28}H_{38}O_{11}$			
Tetrahelin C	MeOH	205(4.20)	102-0583-80
$C_{28}H_{38}O_{12}$			
Tetrahelin E	MeOH	205(4.28)	102-0583-80
$C_{28}H_{39}NO$			
Aflavinine	EtOH	226(4.43),284(3.72), 292(3.65)	88-0243-80
$C_{28}H_{39}N_3O_6$			
3,5-Pyridinedicarboxylic acid, 1,4-dihydro-1-methyl-2,6-bis[2-(4-morpholinyl)ethyl]-4-phenyl-, dimethyl ester	EtOH	247(4.27),343(3.88)	94-3163-80
3,5-Pyridinedicarboxylic acid, 1,4-dihydro-4-(2-methylphenyl)-2,6-bis[2-(4-morpholinyl)ethyl]-, dimethyl ester	EtOH	245(4.28),359(3.88)	94-3163-80
$C_{28}H_{40}O_5$			
D(17a)-Homopregn-16-ene-17a-carboxaldehyde, 19-acetoxy-4,4,8-trimethyl-12,20-dioxo-, (5α,17aβ)-	MeOH	231(3.97)	12-1783-80
$C_{28}H_{40}O_6$			
Prosta-5,13-dien-1-oic acid, 9-(benzoyloxy)-11,15-dihydroxy-, methyl ester, (15S)-	MeOH	229(4.09),267s(2.88), 273(2.94),280(2.86)	44-1528-80
Prosta-5,13-dien-1-oic acid, 11-(benzoyloxy)-9,15-dihydroxy-, methyl ester, (15S)-	MeOH	228(4.11),267s(2.89), 273(2.92),280(2.90)	44-1528-80

Compound	Solvent	$\lambda_{max}(\log \epsilon)$	Ref.
Prosta-5,13-dien-1-oic acid, 15-(benz-oyloxy)-9,11-dihydroxy-, methyl ester, (15R)-	MeOH	229(4.13),267s(2.89), 272(2.95),279(2.86)	44-1528-80
(15S)-	MeOH	228(4.14),266s(2.89), 273(2.94),279(2.84)	44-1528-80
Witha-24-enolide, 5β,6β-epoxy-4β,20α-dihydroxy-1-oxo-, (20R,22R)-	EtOH	227(3.92)	102-1503-80
$C_{28}H_{41}NO_3$ D-Homopregna-3,5-dien-20-one, 17a-acetoxy-3-pyrrolidino-	EtOH	278(4.29)	33-1867-80
$C_{28}H_{41}NO_8$ Retinamide, N-[2-(β-D-glucopyranurono-syloxy)ethyl]-, monosodium salt	EtOH	345(4.54)	136-0121-80H
$C_{28}H_{41}N_3O_3$ 1H-1,2,4-Triazole, 1-(3β-acetoxy-24-oxochol-5-en-24-yl)-	THF	222(3.87)	33-0588-80
$C_{28}H_{41}N_5O_6$ Lemonnierin, N-methyl-	CH$_2$Cl$_2$ DMF	645(4.73) 635(4.80)	39-1782-80C 39-1782-80C
$C_{28}H_{42}O_4$ D(17a)-Homopregn-16-ene-17a-carbox-aldehyde, 12-acetoxy-4,4,8-tri-methyl-20-oxo-, (5α,12α,17aβ)-	MeOH	230(3.65)	12-1783-80
$C_{28}H_{44}$ Ergosta-2,4,6-triene	EtOH	290s(--),315(4.20), 340(4.01)	94-1747-80
	80% H$_2$SO$_4$	470s(--),502(--)	94-1747-80
$C_{28}H_{44}O_2$ 3,5-Cyclovitamin D$_3$, 1-oxo-	EtOH	248(3.54)	44-3253-80
Vitamin D$_2$, 1α-hydroxy-	EtOH	265(4.26)	44-3253-80
5,6-trans	EtOH	273(4.35)	44-3253-80
$C_{28}H_{46}$ Cholest-4-ene, 3-methylene-	heptane	239(4.40)	77-0346-80
$C_{28}H_{46}O$ Cholesta-1,5-diene, 3α-methoxy-	hexane	208(4.51)	23-1759-80
3β-	hexane	210(--)	23-1759-80
Ergosterol	EtOH	262(3.94),271(4.06), 281(4.07),292(3.84)	94-1747-80
$C_{28}H_{46}O_4$ Hexadecanoic acid, 4-(3,4-dimethoxy-phenyl)-3-butenyl ester, (E)-	EtOH	260(4.18),267s(4.17), 294(3.73),299s(3.69), 312s(3.43)	94-2948-80
$C_{28}H_{46}O_6$ Acetylelasnin ketal	EtOH	305(3.87)	44-3268-80
$C_{28}H_{47}NO_2$ 1H-Pyrrole-2-carboxaldehyde, 5-(23-oxo-6-tricosenyl)-, (Z)-	MeOH	297(4.15)	44-4980-80

Compound	Solvent	$\lambda_{max}(\log \epsilon)$	Ref.
$C_{28}H_{48}N_4O_6$			
L-Histidine, N^α,N^{im}-bis(tert-butoxy-carbonyloxy)-, dicyclohexylamine salt	MeOH	241(3.56)	105-0286-80
$C_{28}H_{48}O$			
Cholestan-6-ol, 3-methylene-	heptane	239.5(4.42)	77-0346-80
Cholestan-2-one, 3-methyl-, (3α)-	EPA	288(1.48)	13-0189-80A
Cholestan-2-one, 3-methyl-, (3β)-	EPA	285(1.49)	13-0189-80A
5α-Cholestan-3-one, 2α-methyl-	EPA	285(1.36)	13-0189-80A
5α-Cholestan-3-one, 2β-methyl-	EPA	284(1.44)	13-0189-80A
$C_{28}H_{50}O_2$			
5α-Cholestan-2β-ol, 3α-methoxy-	EPA	307(1.57)	13-0189-80A
$(C_{28}H_{54}NiP_2)_n$			
Nickel, 1,3-butadiyne-1,4-diylbis(tri-phenylphosphine)-, homopolymer	nujol	297(4.0),372(4.2), 414(4.1)	101-0237-80E
$C_{28}H_{70}Si_7$			
Cycloheptasilane, tetradecaethyl-	isooctane	200s(4.78),227s(4.26), 244(3.15),257s(3.64)	101-00C5-80K

Compound	Solvent	$\lambda_{max}(\log \epsilon)$	Ref.
$C_{29}H_{18}N$			
Benzo[1,2]quinolizino[3,4,5,6-def]phenanthridinium, 9-phenyl-, perchlorate	EtOH	228(4.58),240(4.54), 278(4.50),302(4.70), 326(4.27),349(4.32), 410(3.82),432(3.90)	39-1879-80C
$C_{29}H_{18}N_2O_3$			
5(4H)-Oxazolone, 2-(1-naphthalenyl)-4-[[4-(5-phenyl-2-oxazolyl)phenyl]methylene]-	toluene	345(4.52)	135-0930-80
$C_{29}H_{19}N_2$			
Benzo[c]benzo[1,2]quinolizino[3,4,5,6-ija][1,6]naphthyridin-15-ium, 9-(4-methylphenyl)-, perchlorate	EtOH	218(4.40),237(4.66), 268(4.38),302(4.39), 317(4.38),348(4.19), 366(4.17),406(3.76), 428(3.64)	39-1879-80C
$C_{29}H_{20}BrNO_4$			
2H-Anthra[1,2-d][1,3]oxazine-7,12-dione, 6-bromo-1,4-dihydro-2-(hydroxyphenylmethyl)-2-phenyl-	EtOH	488(3.64)	18-3007-80 +146-0513-80
$C_{29}H_{20}S$			
2H-Dibenzo[b,f]cyclopenta[d]thiepin, 1,3-diphenyl-	EtOH	<u>220(4.5),250(4.6),</u> <u>340(3.4)</u>	88-4287-80
$C_{29}H_{21}ClN_2O_3$			
2H-Anthra[1,2-d][1,3]oxazine-7,12-dione, 6-[(2-chlorophenyl)amino]-1,4-dihydro-2-methyl-2-phenyl-	EtOH	608(3.84)	18-3007-80 +146-0513-80
Methanone, [1-(4-chlorophenyl)-2-(4-methoxyphenyl)-5-phenyl-1H-imidazol-4-yl](2-hydroxyphenyl)-	EtOH	218(4.49),265(4.46), 346(3.97)	39-0354-80C
$C_{29}H_{21}ClN_2O_4$			
1,10-Anthracenedione, 2-chloro-4-[(4-nitrophenyl)amino]-9-(2,4,6-trimethylphenyl)-	hexane	500(4.00),625s(3.40)	104-0159-80
	benzene	508(3.98),576s(3.83), 625(3.52)	104-0159-80
	isoPrOH	510(3.96),580s(3.90), 625s(3.75)	104-0159-80
$C_{29}H_{21}N$			
Pyridine, 2,4-bis[2-(2-naphthalenyl)ethenyl]-	DMF	328(4.74)	33-1311-80
Pyridine, 2,5-bis[2-(2-naphthalenyl)ethenyl]-	DMF	378(4.83)	33-1311-80
Pyridine, 2,6-bis[2-(1-naphthalenyl)ethenyl]-	DMF	340(4.52)	33-1311-80
Pyridine, 2,6-bis[2-(2-naphthalenyl)ethenyl]-	DMF	318(4.72),352(4.58)	33-1311-80
$C_{29}H_{21}NO$			
Pyridinium, 1-(2-hydroxyphenyl)-2,4,6-triphenyl-, hydroxide, inner salt	EtOH	208(4.19),306(4.26)	39-1870-80C
$C_{29}H_{21}NO_2$			
Pyridinium, 3-hydroxy-1-(2-hydroxyphenyl)-2,4,6-triphenyl-, hydroxide, inner salt	EtOH	212(4.52),302(4.41), 318(3.90)	39-1870-80C

Compound	Solvent	λ_{max}(log ϵ)	Ref.
Pyridinium, 3-hydroxy-1-(4-hydroxyphen-yl)-2,4,6-triphenyl-, hydroxide, inner salt	EtOH	230(4.28),276(4.30), 390(3.91)	39-1870-80C
$C_{29}H_{21}N_2$ Benzo[c]pyrido[1,2-a][1,8]naphthyridin-13-ium, 10-(4-methylphenyl)-12-phen-yl-, perchlorate	EtOH	212(4.21),248(4.29), 279(4.26),300(4.11), 343(4.17),372(4.26), 402(4.16)	39-1879-80C
$C_{29}H_{21}N_3$ 1H-Indol-3-amine, 1-methyl-2-phenyl-N-(2-phenyl-3H-indol-3-ylidene)-	benzene-ligroin	560(4.10)	7-0009-80
$C_{29}H_{22}$ 5,8:11,14-Dietheno-18,1-metheno-1H-di-benzo[a,d]cyclopentadecene, 9,10-di-hydro-20-methyl-	CHCl$_3$	265(4.71),324(3.23), 340(3.48),357(3.75), 376(3.92),397(3.88)	24-0676-80
$C_{29}H_{22}BNO$ Boron, [2-[(1-naphthalenylimino)meth-yl]phenolato-N,O]diphenyl-, (T-4)-	CHCl$_3$	353(4.09)	49-0863-80
$C_{29}H_{22}ClNO_2$ 1,10-Anthracenedione, 2-chloro-4-(phen-ylamino)-9-(2,4,6-trimethylphenyl)-	hexane	500(3.92),573s(3.68), 625(3.48)	104-0159-80
	benzene	530(3.90),580(3.86), 625(3.73)	104-0159-80
	isoPrOH	539(3.89),581(3.90), 625(3.76)	104-0159-80
$C_{29}H_{22}Cl_2$ Benzene, 1,1'-methylenebis[4-(2-chloro-2-phenylethenyl)-	film	265(3.75)	104-2207-80
$C_{29}H_{22}N_2O_2$ Methanone, (2-hydroxyphenyl)[1-(4-meth-ylphenyl)-2,5-diphenyl-1H-imidazol-4-yl]-	EtOH	213(4.51),263(4.33), 340s(--)	39-0354-80C
$C_{29}H_{22}N_2O_3$ 2H-Anthra[1,2-d][1,3]oxazine-7,12-di-one, 1,4-dihydro-2-methyl-2-phenyl-6-(phenylamino)-	EtOH	609(3.85)	18-3007-80 +146-0513-80
Methanone, (2-hydroxyphenyl)[1-(4-meth-oxyphenyl)-2,5-diphenyl-1H-imidazol-4-yl]-	EtOH	213(4.47),263(4.35)	39-0354-80C
$C_{29}H_{22}N_3$ 1H-Indol-3-aminium, N-methyl-2-phenyl-N-(2-phenyl-3H-indol-3-ylidene)-, perchlorate	n.s.g.	675(4.27)	7-0009-80
$C_{29}H_{22}O$ Ethanone, 1-(9-methyl-4,5-diphenyl-1-anthracenyl)-	EtOH	215(4.49),266(4.67), 270(4.68),396s(3.86), 408(3.87)	44-1807-80
Ethanone, 1-(9-methyl-4,5-diphenyl-2-anthracenyl)-	EtOH	218(4.49),248(4.44), 263s(4.63),272(4.73), 297(4.51),340(3.43), 357(3.66),376(3.80),	44-1807-80

Compound	Solvent	$\lambda_{max}(\log \epsilon)$	Ref.
(cont.)		405(3.77),421(3.75)	44-1807-80
$C_{29}H_{22}O_2$ 2,3-Dioxabicyclo[2.2.1]hept-5-ene, 1,4,5,6-tetraphenyl-	EtOH	218(4.44)	12-2653-80
$C_{29}H_{22}O_{10}$ Methylbacillosporin A	MeOH	229(4.56),247(4.62), 255s(4.60),280s(4.29), 308(4.05),317(4.05), 350s(3.74),371s(3.59)	94-3649-80
$C_{29}H_{23}NO_2$ Benzamide, N-(2-methylphenyl)-N-(3-oxo- 1,3-diphenyl-1-propenyl)- Benzamide, N-(3-oxo-1,3-diphenyl-1- propenyl)-N-(phenylmethyl)- 3H-Indole, 2-(2-methoxyphenyl)-3-[(4- methoxyphenyl)phenylmethylene]- (in 64% methanol)	EtOH EtOH pH 2.25 pH 10.44	210(4.33),265s(4.15), 335s(3.88) 210(4.32),248(4.14), 354(4.39) 397(4.11),516(4.14) 334s(3.78),411(4.04)	39-1870-80C 39-1870-80C 33-1264-80 33-1264-80
$C_{29}H_{23}NO_3$ [1]Benzopyrano[4,3-b]indole, 6,11-di- hydro-6,6-bis(4-methoxyphenyl)-	pH -2.0 in 64% MeOH	435(4.44),527(4.22)	33-1264-80
$C_{29}H_{23}N_2O_2$ Benzo[f]quinolinium, 3-(1,3-benzodiox- ol-5-yl)-4-methyl-1-[2-(phenylamino)- ethenyl]-, iodide	EtOH	509(4.73)	103-0752-80
$C_{29}H_{23}N_3$ Pyrrolo[3,2-e]benzimidazole, 3,6-di- hydro-8-methyl-2,7-diphenyl- 3-(phenylmethyl)-	EtOH	291(4.34)	103-0062-80
$C_{29}H_{23}N_3O_4$ Butanedioic acid, [[1-(phenylazo)-2- naphthalenyl]imino](phenylmethyl- ene)-, dimethyl ester	MeOH	245(4.30),275s(4.28), 282(4.30),315s(3.76), 358s(3.59),402s(3.88), 466(4.45)	44-3182-80
$C_{29}H_{23}N_7O_6S$ Benzenesulfonamide, N-[4,5-dihydro- 4-(4-methylphenyl)-5-[(4-methylphen- yl)imino]-6-nitro-2-(4-nitrophenyl)- 1,2,4-triazin-3(2H)-ylidene]-	DMF	301s(4.20),389s(3.66)	48-0087-80
$C_{29}H_{23}N_7O_8S$ Benzenesulfonamide, N-[4,5-dihydro- 4-(4-methoxyphenyl)-5-[(4-methoxy- phenyl)imino]-6-nitro-2-(4-nitro- phenyl)-1,2,4-triazin-3(2H)-ylidene]-	DMF	300s(4.25),424s(3.49)	48-0087-80
$C_{29}H_{24}Br_2N_2O_6S_2$ Benzoic acid, 4-bromo-, [6-[(4-bromo- benzoyl)oxy]-1,2,3,4,10,10a-hexahy- dro-2-methyl-3,10a-bis(methylthio)- 1,4-dioxopyrazino[1,2-a]indol-3-yl]- methyl ester, (3R-cis)-	EtOH	246(3.84)	39-0119-80C

Compound	Solvent	$\lambda_{max}(\log \epsilon)$	Ref.
$C_{29}H_{24}Cl_4N_4O$ Pyrido[3,2-a]indolizine-3,7-dicarbo- nitrile, 10-(2,6-dichlorophenyl)-1- [(2,6-dichlorophenyl)methyl]-1,4,4a- 4b,10,10a-hexahydro-4-propoxy-	CH_2Cl_2	263(4.5),360(3.8)	64-0490-80B
$C_{29}H_{24}NOS$ Benzothiazolium, 2-[3-(2,6-diphenyl- 4H-pyran-4-ylidene)-1-propenyl]-3- ethyl-, perchlorate	CH_2Cl_2	588(4.91),625(5.00)	103-0696-80
Benzothiazolium, 2-[3-(4,6-diphenyl- 2H-pyran-2-ylidene)-1-propenyl]-3- ethyl-, perchlorate	CH_2Cl_2	658(4.73),708(4.53)	103-0696-80
$C_{29}H_{24}N_2O$ Benzenamine, 4-(6,11-dihydro-6-phenyl- [1]benzopyrano[4,3-b]indol-6-yl)- N,N-dimethyl-	pH 1.25 in 64% MeOH	415(3.07),597(3.63)	33-1264-80
$C_{29}H_{24}N_2OS$ Carbamimidothioic acid, N'-(1-oxo-2,3- diphenyl-2-propenyl)-N,N-diphenyl-, methyl ester	MeOH	222s(4.44),250s(4.29), 308(4.33)	142-1921-80
$C_{29}H_{24}N_3O_2$ Benzo[f]quinolinium, 2,4-dimethyl-3-(4- nitrophenyl)-1-[2-(phenylamino)ethen- yl]-, iodide	EtOH	519(4.46)	103-0752-80
$C_{29}H_{24}N_4O_4S_3$ 5-Thia-1-azabicyclo[4.2.0]oct-2-ene- 2-carboxylic acid, 3-(5-methyl-1,3,4- thiadiazol-2-yl)-8-oxo-7-[(2-thienyl- acetyl)amino]-, diphenylmethyl ester, (6R-trans)-	EtOH	307(4.08)	94-2116-80
$C_{29}H_{24}O_4$ 1,3-Azulenedicarboxylic acid, 6-(9H- fluoren-9-yl)-, diethyl ester	MeCN	233(4.71),270(4.66), 310(4.79),375(3.42), 500(2.88)	18-1647-80
Hydroperoxide, 2,5-dihydro-5-methoxy- 2,3,4,5-tetraphenyl-2-furanyl-	MeOH	224(4.28),257(3.65)	12-2653-80
$C_{29}H_{24}O_5$ [1,1':2',1"-Terphenyl]-3',4'-dicarbox- ylic acid, 6'-methoxy-5'-phenyl-, dimethyl ester	MeCN	237(4.53)	24-0408-80
$C_{29}H_{24}O_{10}$ Trimethylbacillosporin C	MeOH	218s(4.53),238(4.64), 267s(4.47),275(4.53), 312(3.86),360(3.69)	94-3649-80
$C_{29}H_{25}BN_2O_2$ Boron, diphenyl[2-(4,5,6,7-tetrahydro- 3-hydroxy-1-methyl-1H-indol-2-yl)- 3H-indol-3-onato-N^1,O^2]-, (T-4)-	$CHCl_3$	270(4.40),327(4.57), 670(4.12)	5-0564-80
$C_{29}H_{25}N_2O$ Benzo[f]quinolinium, 3-(4-methoxyphen- yl)-4-methyl-1-[2-(phenylamino)eth-	EtOH	508(4.72)	103-0752-80

Compound	Solvent	$\lambda_{max}(\log \epsilon)$	Ref.
enyl]-, iodide (cont.)			103-0752-80
$C_{29}H_{25}N_2O_2$ Benzo[f]quinolinium, 3-(2-hydroxy-3-methoxyphenyl)-4-methyl-1-[2-(phenyl-amino)ethenyl]-, iodide	EtOH	505(4.76)	103-0752-80
$C_{29}H_{25}N_3O_4$ 1H-Pyrrolo[3,4-f]quinoline-1,3(2H)-di-one, 5-(2,5-dioxo-1-phenyl-3-pyrrol-idinyl)-8-ethyl-3a,4,5,9b-tetrahydro-2-phenyl-	MeOH	265(2.90)	103-0833-80
$C_{29}H_{25}N_3O_6$ Cyclopent[e][1,3,4]oxadiazine-1(4aH)-carboxylic acid, 7,7a-dihydro-6,7a-dimethyl-3-(4-nitrophenyl)-7-oxo-4a,5-diphenyl-, ethyl ester	EtOH	287(4.32),338(4.00)	23-1316-80
$C_{29}H_{25}N_5O_4S_3$ 5-Thia-1-azabicyclo[4.2.0]oct-2-ene-2-carboxylic acid, 3-[5-(methylami-no)-1,3,4-thiadiazol-2-yl]-8-oxo-7-[(2-thienylacetyl)amino]-, diphenyl-methyl ester, (6R-trans)-	EtOH	333(4.06)	94-2116-80
$C_{29}H_{26}NO$ 3H-Indolium, 1,3,3-trimethyl-2-[3-(3-phenyl-1H-2-benzopyran-1-ylidene)-1-propenyl]-, perchlorate	CH_2Cl_2	582(4.76),625(4.83)	103-0137-80
$C_{29}H_{26}NS$ 3H-Indolium, 1,3,3-trimethyl-2-[3-(3-phenyl-1H-2-benzothiopyran-1-yli-dene)-1-propenyl]-, perchlorate	CH_2Cl_2	636(4.70),680(4.65)	103-0599-80
$C_{29}H_{26}N_4O_4S_2$ 5-Thia-1-azabicyclo[4.2.0]oct-2-ene-2-carboxylic acid, 8-oxo-7-[(2-thi-enylacetyl)amino]-3-[[(1-thioxoeth-yl)hydrazono]methyl]-, diphenylmethyl ester, (6R-trans)-	EtOH	363(4.52)	94-2116-80
$C_{29}H_{26}N_4O_8$ Benzenamine, 4-[(4-methoxyphenyl)(3-methylphenyl)(2,4,6-trinitrophen-oxy)methyl]-N,N-dimethyl-	MeCN HOAc	512(4.47) 520(4.47)	104-1436-80 104-1436-80
Benzenamine, 4-[(4-methoxyphenyl)(4-methylphenyl)(2,4,6-trinitrophen-oxy)methyl]-N,N-dimethyl-	MeCN	515(4.48)	104-1436-80
$C_{29}H_{26}N_4O_9$ Benzenamine, 4-[(3-methoxyphenyl)(4-methoxyphenyl)(2,4,6-trinitrophen-oxy)methyl]-N,N-dimethyl-	MeCN HOAc	513(4.24) 521(4.25)	104-1436-80 104-1436-80
$C_{29}H_{26}N_5O_7P$ 3'-Adenylic acid, N-benzoyl-2'-deoxy-, diphenyl ester	MeOH	227s(4.19),260s(4.19), 278(4.37)	142-0761-80B

Compound	Solvent	$\lambda_{max}(\log \epsilon)$	Ref.
$C_{29}H_{26}O_2$ Methanone, [2-(hydroxydiphenylmethyl)-phenyl](2,4,6-trimethylphenyl)-	hexane	216(4.66),255(4.26), 293(3.74),345(2.36)	104-1316-80
$C_{29}H_{27}N_2O_2S$ Benzothiazolium, 3-ethyl-6-methoxy-2-[[2-[2-(methylphenylamino)ethenyl]-4H-1-benzopyran-4-ylidene]methyl]-, perchlorate	MeCN	425(4.40),575(4.94)	124-0965-80
Benzothiazolium, 3-ethyl-6-methoxy-2-[[4-[2-(methylphenylamino)ethenyl]-2H-1-benzopyran-2-ylidene]methyl]-, perchlorate	MeCN	414(4.30),600(4.87)	124-0965-80
$C_{29}H_{27}N_5O_4S_3$ 5-Thia-1-azabicyclo[4.2.0]oct-2-ene-2-carboxylic acid, 3-[[[(methylamino)thioxomethyl]hydrazono]methyl]-8-oxo-7-[(2-thienylacetyl)amino]-, diphenylmethyl ester, (6R-trans)-	EtOH	350(4.49)	94-2116-80
$C_{29}H_{27}N_6Ni$ Nickel(1+), (2,3,7,8,12,13,17,18-octadehydro-1,3,7,8,12,13,17,19-octamethyl-2,18-corrindicarbonitrilato-N^{21}-N^{22},N^{23},N^{24})-, (SP-4-3)-, perchlorate	CHCl$_3$	292(4.27),380(4.10), 475(3.80),583(3.93)	135-1219-80
$C_{29}H_{28}Cl_2N_5O_{10}P$ Phosphoramidic acid, N-methyl-N-[9-(2,3,5-tri-O-acetyl-β-D-ribofuranosyl)-9H-purin-6-yl]-, bis(2-chlorophenyl) ester	MeOH	263(4.28),271s(4.16)	142-0761-80B
$C_{29}H_{28}N_4O$ Pyrido[3,2-a]indolizine-3,7-dicarbonitrile, 1,4,4a,4b,10,10a-hexahydro-10-phenyl-1-(phenylmethyl)-4-propoxy-	CH$_2$Cl$_2$	267(4.4),353(3.7)	64-0490-80B
$C_{29}H_{28}N_4S_2$ 3H-Pyrazole-3-thione, 4,4'-(phenylmethylene)bis[1,2-dihydro-1,5-dimethyl-2-phenyl-	benzene H$_2$O	278(4.22),342(4.36) 252(4.34),288(4.31)	140-0560-80 140-0560-80
$C_{29}H_{28}O_6$ 1,6:2,5-Dimethanonaphthalene-4,8,9,10-tetrone, 3-[1-(1,4-dihydro-3-methyl-1,4-dioxo-2-naphthalenyl)ethyl]octahydro-2,4a,6,8a-tetramethyl-	EtOH	247(4.24),266(4.14), 326(3.59)	39-1994-80C
$C_{29}H_{28}O_9$ Sanggenon A diacetate	MeOH	256(4.73),290s(3.94), 346(3.54)	142-1785-80
	MeOH-AlCl$_3$	256(4.73),290s(3.94), 346(3.60)	142-1785-80
$C_{29}H_{28}O_{10}$ [1,1'-Binaphthalene]-7,7'-dicarboxylic acid, 4-hydroxy-2,2',4',5,5'-pentamethoxy-, dimethyl ester	CHCl$_3$	293(4.08),302(4.06), 316(4.02),381s(4.07), 389(4.08)	12-2531-80

Compound	Solvent	$\lambda_{max}(\log \epsilon)$	Ref.
$C_{29}H_{29}BrO_8$ Gibb-3-ene-1,10-dioic acid, 2-acetoxy-4a,7-dihydroxy-1-methyl-8-methylene-, 1,4a-lactone, 10-[2-(4-bromophenyl)-2-oxoethyl] ester, $(1\alpha,2\beta,4a\alpha,4b\beta,10\beta)$-	EtOH	256(4.32)	105-0181-80
$C_{29}H_{29}CoN_4O_2$ Cobalt(1+), (octadehydro-1,3,7,8,12,13-17,19-octamethyl-2,18-corrindicarbox-aldehydato-$N^{21},N^{22},N^{23},N^{24}$)-, (SP-4-3)-, perchlorate	$CHCl_3$	278(4.30),352(4.05), 498(3.84),564(3.64)	135-1219-80
$C_{29}H_{29}NO$ 2,4-Cyclopentadien-1-one, 3-(diethylamino)-4,5-bis(4-methylphenyl)-2-phenyl-	MeCN	279(4.04),327s(--), 521(3.07)	24-0408-80
$C_{29}H_{29}NO_2$ Benzenemethanol, 2-[[2-(1-hydroxy-1-methylethyl)phenyl]phenylamino]-α-methyl-α-phenyl-	C_6H_{12}	210(4.65),239s(3.89), 284(4.23)	24-0358-80
$C_{29}H_{29}NO_3$ 2,4-Cyclopentadien-1-one, 3-(diethylamino)-4,5-bis(4-methoxyphenyl)-2-phenyl-	MeCN	274(4.33),342(4.03), 525(3.00)	24-0408-80
$C_{29}H_{29}N_3O_4S_2$ 2H-1,3-Thiazine-5-carboxylic acid, 3-(2,6-dimethylphenyl)-3,6-dihydro-4-methyl-2-[[(4-methylphenyl)sulfonyl]imino]-6-(phenylimino)-, ethyl ester	CH_2Cl_2	260(4.2),290(4.0), 310(3.9),333(3.7)	24-2509-80
$C_{29}H_{29}N_3O_8$ Adduct 15 from dimethyl acetylenedicarboxylate and 2,3-dimethyl-5,6-diphenyl-2,5-dihydro-1,2,4-triazine (1:2) (structure unknown)	EtOH	220s(4.13),234(3.66), 357(4.18)	44-4587-80
Adduct 16 (structure unknown)	EtOH	283(3.83),305s(3.82), 418(3.53)	44-4587-80
$C_{29}H_{29}N_4NiO_2$ Nickel(1+), (octadehydro-1,3,7,8,12,13-17,19-octamethyl-2,18-corrindicarbox-aldehydato-$N^{21},N^{22},N^{23},N^{24}$)-, (SP-4-3), perchlorate	$CHCl_3$	288(4.42),366(4.22), 458(3.74),569(4.05)	135-1219-80
$C_{29}H_{30}N_4O_8$ Saframycin A	MeOH	267(4.34),370s(--)	31-1025-80
$C_{29}H_{30}N_5O_{10}P$ Phosphoramidic acid, N-methyl-N-[9-(2,3,5-tri-O-acetyl-β-D-ribofuranosyl)-9H-purin-6-yl]-, diphenyl ester	MeOH	264(4.34),272s(4.26), 290s(3.71)	142-0761-80B
$C_{29}H_{30}O_{12}$ Amaropanin	MeOH	210(4.39),240s(--), 315(3.48)	100-0649-80

Compound	Solvent	$\lambda_{max}(\log \epsilon)$	Ref.
$C_{29}H_{30}O_{13}$ Amarogentin	n.s.g.	230(4.46),266(4.07), 306(3.68)	100-0649-80
$C_{29}H_{31}CoN_5$ Cobalt, [2,3,7,8-tetrahydro-2,2,8,8- 12,13,17,18-octamethyl-21H,23H-por- phine-5-carbonitrilato(2-)-N^{21},N^{22}- N^{23},N^{24}]-, (SP-4-2)-	CH_2Cl_2	345s(4.45),372(4.68), 405s(4.20),515(3.78), 550(4.12),587(4.71)	89-0143-80
$C_{29}H_{32}FeO_3$ Estra-1,3,5(10)-triene-3,17-diol, 17-ester with carboxyferrocene	ether	444(2.35)	5-1181-80
$C_{29}H_{32}O_2$ 1H-Indene-1,3(2H)-dione, 2-retinyli- dene-	EtOH	275(4.27),507(4.74)	87-0805-80
$C_{29}H_{32}O_6$ 2H-Cyclopenta[b]furan-2-one, 5-(benz- oyloxy)-4-[3-(benzoyloxy)-1-octen- yl]hexahydro-, (R)-	MeOH	229(4.40),267s(3.18), 273s(3.23),280(3.15)	44-1528-80
(S)-	MeOH	229(4.39),268s(3.19), 273(3.23),281(3.14)	44-1528-80
$C_{29}H_{32}O_7$ Uvafzelin	MeOH	215(4.19),283(4.29), 305s(4.05)	35-7365-80
$C_{29}H_{32}O_7S$ Gibbane-1,10-dicarboxylic acid, 7-acet- oxy-4a-hydroxy-1-methyl-8-methylene- 2-(phenylthioxomethoxy)-, 1,4a-lact- one, 10-methyl ester	EtOH	253(3.97),293(4.06)	39-0885-80C
$C_{29}H_{32}O_{11}$ Physalin I, 6-oxo-	EtOH	229(3.81)	102-1175-80
$C_{29}H_{32}O_{13}$ Amorphigenin, 8'-C-β-D-glucopyranosyl- 12a-hydroxy-, (-)-	MeOH	205(4.72),240(4.47), 292(4.45)	39-2463-80C
$C_{29}H_{33}N_3O_2$ Acetic acid, [3,4-bis(diethylamino)- 2,5-diphenyl-2,4-cyclopentadien-1- ylidene]cyano-, methyl ester	MeCN	285(3.89),397(4.33), 590(2.86)	24-0424-80
perchlorate	MeCN	244(4.36),255s(--), 327(4.28)	24-0424-80
$C_{29}H_{33}N_5$ 21H,23H-Porphine-5-carbonitrile, 2,3,7,8-tetrahydro-2,2,8,8,12,13,17- 18-octamethyl-	CH_2Cl_2	363s(4.90),369(4.95), 380(4.71),402(5.21), 483(4.03),508(4.09), 541(3.82),585(4.25), 629(4.63)	89-0143-80
$C_{29}H_{34}N_3S_2$ Benzothiazolium, 2-[2-(butylamino)- 7-(3-ethyl-2(3H)-benzothiazolyli- dene)-1,3,5-heptatrienyl]-, iodide	60% EtOH	310(4.2),410(4.6), 585(4.7)	104-2080-80
	60% EtOH- HCl	290(--),380(--)	104-2080-80

Compound	Solvent	$\lambda_{max}(\log \epsilon)$	Ref.
Benzothiazolium, 2-[4-(butylamino)-7-(3-ethyl-2(3H)-benzothiazolylidene)-1,3,5-heptatrienyl]-, iodide	60% EtOH	604(4.68)	104-2080-80
$C_{29}H_{34}O_{11}$ Physalin I	EtOH EtOH-NaOEt	227(3.86) 218(--)	102-1175-80 102-1175-80
$C_{29}H_{35}NO_{12}$ D-Arabinitol, 1-C-[4-(methoxycarbonyl)-5-methyl-1-(phenylmethyl)-1H-pyrrol-3-yl]-, 1,2,3,4,5-pentaacetate, (S)-	EtOH	240(3.86),254s(--)	39-1199-80C
$C_{29}H_{35}N_5$ 21H,23H-Porphine-5-carbonitrile, 2,3,7,8,9,10-hexahydro-2,2,8,8-12,13,17,18-octamethyl-	CH_2Cl_2	271(4.45),280s(4.41), 335s(4.45),354(4.59), 370s(4.35),402(3.88), 432(3.84),465(3.74), 523s(3.96),562(4.14), 588(4.13),618s(4.02)	89-0143-80
21H,23H-Porphine-5-carbonitrile, 2,3,7,8,15,22-hexahydro-2,2,8-8,12,13,17,18-octamethyl-	CH_2Cl_2	294(4.57),420(4.06)	89-0143-80
$C_{29}H_{35}N_5O$ 1H-Isoindol-1-one, 6-(dimethylamino)-3,3-bis[4-(dimethylamino)phenyl]-2,3-dihydro-2-[(1-methylethylidene)amino]-	EtOH	270(4.51)	94-3561-80
$C_{29}H_{36}N_4O_{10}$ L-Tryptophan, N-[(1,1-dimethylethoxy)-carbonyl]-2-[1,2,3,4-tetrahydro-1-[2,3-O-(1-methylethylidene)-β-D-ribofuranosyl]-2,4-dioxo-5-pyrimidinyl]-, methyl ester	MeCN	213(4.36),266(3.99), 291(3.85),332(3.61)	35-7535-80
$C_{29}H_{36}N_4S_2$ 3H-Pyrazole-3-thione, 4,4'-heptylidene-bis[1,2-dihydro-1,5-dimethyl-2-phenyl-	benzene H_2O	278(4.07),342(4.36) 254(4.35),288(4.31)	140-0560-80 140-0560-80
$C_{29}H_{36}O_4S$ Pregn-4-ene-3,20-dione, 17-acetoxy-1α-(phenylthio)-	EtOH	216(4.21),243(4.19)	13-0481-80A
$C_{29}H_{36}O_8$ Butanoic acid, 3-methyl-, 7,8-diacetoxy-4,6-dimethyl-1,9-bis(1-methylethyl)dibenzo[b,e][1,4]dioxin-2-yl ester	EtOH	235(4.54),290(3.15)	33-0225-80
Butanoic acid, 3-methyl-, 7,8-diacetoxy-4,9-dimethyl-1,6-bis(1-methylethyl)dibenzo[b,e][1,4]dioxin-2-yl ester	EtOH	238(4.61),293(3.49)	33-0225-80
$C_{29}H_{36}Si_2$ Silacycloprop-2-ene, 2-phenyl-1,1-bis(2,4,6-trimethylphenyl)-3-(trimethylsilyl)-	C_6H_{12}	238(4.40),258(4.29), 322(2.64)	101-0147-80K
$C_{29}H_{37}N_3O_2$ 17αH-Norcorynan, 16-(1,2,3,4-tetrahy-	EtOH	226(4.42),282(4.02),	33-1335-80

Compound	Solvent	$\lambda_{max}(\log \epsilon)$	Ref.
dro-6,7-dimethoxy-1-isoquinolinyl)- 17βH,20βH-	EtOH	290(4.01) 226(4.41),282(4.03), 290(4.01)	33-1335-80 33-1335-80
$C_{29}H_{37}N_3O_7$ Fumitremorgin A(1) degradation product	EtOH	227(4.41),275(3.64), 297(3.64),303s(3.59)	94-0245-80
$C_{29}H_{38}N_2O_{14}$ D-gluco-Octonic acid, 2,3-dideoxy- 3-(nitromethyl)-2-[1-(phenylmethyl)- amino]ethylidene]-, methyl ester, 4,5,6,7,8-pentaacetate	EtOH	294(4.17)	39-1199-80C
$C_{29}H_{38}N_6$ 3,5-Pyridinedicarbonitrile, 1,1'-(1,7- heptanediyl)bis[1,4-dihydro-2,4,4,6- tetramethyl-	MeOH	225(4.62),346(4.13)	73-3370-80
$C_{29}H_{38}O_4Se$ Androst-5-en-3-one, 17-[[[(phenylsel- eno)carbonyl]oxy]methyl]-, cyclic 3-(1,2-ethanediyl acetal)-, (17β)-	pentane	255(3.51)	33-2328-80
$C_{29}H_{39}BrO_7$ Pregna-1,4-diene-3,20-dione, 21-acet- oxy-7-bromo-11-hydroxy-16-methyl-17- [(1-oxopentyl)oxy]-, (7α,11β,16α)-	MeOH	242(4.20)	145-1618-80
Pregna-1,4-diene-3,20-dione, 7-bromo- 11-hydroxy-16-methyl-17-(1-oxobut- oxy)-21-(1-oxopropoxy)-, (7α,11β,16α)-	MeOH	243(4.19)	145-1618-80
Pregna-1,4-diene-3,20-dione, 7-bromo- 11-hydroxy-16-methyl-21-(1-oxobut- oxy)-17-(1-oxopropoxy)-, (7α,11β,16α)-	MeOH	241(4.20)	145-1618-80
$C_{29}H_{39}ClO_7$ Pregna-1,4-diene-3,20-dione, 21-acet- oxy-7-chloro-11-hydroxy-16-methyl- 17-[(1-oxopentyl)oxy]-, (7α,11β,16α)-	MeOH	240(4.22)	145-1618-80
Pregna-1,4-diene-3,20-dione, 7-chloro- 11-hydroxy-16-methyl-17-(1-oxobut- oxy)-21-(1-oxopropoxy)-, (7α,11β,16α)-	MeOH	242(4.18)	145-1618-80
Pregna-1,4-diene-3,20-dione, 7-chloro- 11-hydroxy-16-methyl-21-(1-oxobut- oxy)-17-(1-oxopropoxy)-, (7α,11β,16α)-	MeOH	242(4.21)	145-1618-80
$C_{29}H_{39}N_5O_3$ 5α-Spirost-2-eno[2,3-g](tetrazolo- [1,5-a]pyrimidine), 11-oxo-	MeOH	214(4.32),279(3.70)	39-1019-80C
$C_{29}H_{40}F_6O_3$ Cholesta-5,7-diene-3,25-diol, 26,26,26- 27,27,27-hexafluoro-, 3-acetate, (3β)-	EtOH	262s(3.90),271(4.04), 282(4.06),293(3.81)	77-0459-80
$C_{29}H_{40}O_2$ 1,3-Cyclohexanedione, 5-(1-methylethyl)- 2-retinylidene-	EtOH	270(4.07),492(4.66)	87-0805-80
1,3-Cyclononanedione, 2-retinylidene-	EtOH	277(4.02),428(4.67)	87-0805-80
$C_{29}H_{40}O_8$ Chol-7-ene-24-carboxylic acid, 2,3-di-	MeOH	239(4.08)	88-4323-80

Compound	Solvent	$\lambda_{max}(\log \epsilon)$	Ref.
acetoxy-14,22-dihydroxy-6-oxo-, γ-lactone, (2β,3β,5α,22R)- (cont.)			88-4323-80
$C_{29}H_{40}O_9$ Chol-7-ene-24-carboxylic acid, 2,3-diacetoxy-14-hydroperoxy-22-hydroxy-6-oxo-, γ-lactone, (2β,3β,5α,22R)-	MeOH	240(4.06)	88-4323-80
$C_{29}H_{42}O_2$ 4,6-Nonanedione, 5-retinylidene-	EtOH	275(4.02),418(4.68)	87-0805-80
$C_{29}H_{43}NO_5$ 7a-Aza-13-homospirost-5-en-7-one, 3β-acetoxy-, (25R)-	MeOH	242(4.05)	64-1575-80B
$C_{29}H_{44}O_3$ Cholesta-4,6-dien-3-one, 6-acetoxy-	MeOH	298(4.37)	78-2341-80
$C_{29}H_{44}O_9$ Deglucouzarin	MeOH	218(4.16)	94-0401-80
$C_{29}H_{45}FO_2$ Vitamin D_3, 25-fluoro-, acetate	EtOH	265(4.20)	130-0187-80
$C_{29}H_{45}FO_3$ 5α-Cholest-8(14)-en-15-one, 3β-acetoxy-9α-fluoro-	EtOH	248(4.14)	44-4034-80
$C_{29}H_{45}N_5$ 5α-Cholest-2-eno[2,3-g](tetrazolo-[1,5-a]pyrimidine)	MeOH	215(4.32),277(3.68)	39-1019-80C
$C_{29}H_{46}O$ Cholesta-1,5-dien-3-one, 4,4-dimethyl- Stigmasta-4,6-dien-3-one	EtOH EtOH	230(3.86) 284(4.42)	39-2209-80C 102-1121-80
$C_{29}H_{46}O_2$ 5α-Cholesta-8,14-dien-3β-ol, acetate Stigmast-4-ene-3,6-dione Triterpene B	EtOH EtOH MeOH	249(4.20) 250(4.18) 235(3.98),243(4.03), 252(3.88)	102-2777-80 64-0102-80B 24-1754-80
$C_{29}H_{46}O_3$ 9,10-Secocholesta-5,7,10(19)-triene-3,25-diol, 3-acetate	EtOH	265(4.18)	130-0187-80
$C_{29}H_{46}O_4$ 5α-Cholest-8(14)-en-15-one, 3β-acetoxy-9α-hydroxy-	EtOH	254(4.14)	44-4034-80
$C_{29}H_{47}NO$ Acetamide, N-[(6β)-cholesta-2,4-dien-6-yl]-	dioxan	267(3.83)	77-0346-80
$C_{29}H_{47}N_5O_4$ 3,5-Pyridinedicarboxylic acid, 2,6-bis-[2-(dimethylamino)-1-[(dimethylamino)methyl]ethyl]-1,4-dihydro-4-phenyl-, dimethyl ester	EtOH	243(4.27),358(3.83)	94-3163-80

Compound	Solvent	λ_{max} (log ϵ)	Ref.
$C_{29}H_{48}N_2O_2$ 18-Tetracosenenitrile, 24-(5-formyl- 1H-pyrrol-2-yl)-2-hydroxy-, (Z)-	MeCN	297(4.21)	44-4980-80
$C_{29}H_{48}N_2O_4$ 6,10-(Iminomethano)-10H-cyclopenta[a]- phenanthren-3-ol, 17-(1,5-dimethyl- hexyl)hexadecahydro-13-methyl-21- nitro-, acetate	EtOH	241(3.87)	77-0958-80
$C_{29}H_{48}O$ Stigmast-4-en-3-one	EtOH EtOH	241(4.28) 241(4.21)	2-0331-80 102-1121-80
$C_{29}H_{48}O_2$ 5α-Cholesta-8,14-dien-3β-ol, 15-ethoxy- A-Norlanostane-1,2-dione	EtOH EtOH	254(4.18) 488(1.88)	44-4034-80 39-2209-80C
$C_{29}H_{49}N$ Cholesta-2,4-dien-6-amine, N-ethyl-, (6β)-	dioxan	266(3.81)	77-0346-80
$C_{29}H_{50}N_2O$ Acetic acid, [(5α,6E)-cholestan-6-yli- dene]hydrazide Acetic acid, [(5α,6Z)-cholestan-6-yli- dene]hydrazide	MeOH dioxan MeOH dioxan	216(3.78),234(3.78) 236(4.11) 219(4.05),232(4.06) 235(4.12)	39-1356-80C 39-1356-80C 39-1356-80C 39-1356-80C
$C_{29}H_{50}O_2$ α-Tocophenol-[5-^{13}CH$_3$]	hexane	291(3.48),298(3.51)	94-1992-80
$C_{29}H_{50}O_3$ 2,5-Cyclohexadiene-1,4-dione, 2-(3-hy- droxy-3,7,11,15-tetramethylhexadec- yl)-3,5,6-trimethyl-	isoPrOH	268(4.19)	44-0803-80
$C_{29}H_{52}O_2$ Benzenepropanol, 3-hydroxy- ,2,4,5- tetramethyl-α-(4,8,12-trimethyl- tridecyl)-	isoPrOH	204(4.67),224(3.97)	44-0803-80

Compound	Solvent	$\lambda_{max}(\log \epsilon)$	Ref.
$C_{30}H_6Cl_{14}O_4$ 9H-Fluoren-1-ol, 9-(3-acetoxy-1,2,4,5-6,7,8-heptachloro-9H-fluoren-9-ylidene)-2,3,4,5,6,7,8-heptachloro-, acetate	CHCl$_3$	239(4.76),305(4.54), 448(2.74),592(3.11)	88-0193-80
9H-Fluoren-3-ol, 9-(3-acetoxy-1,2,4,5-6,7,8-heptachloro-9H-fluoren-9-ylidene)-1,2,4,5,6,7,8-heptachloro-, acetate	C_6H_{12}	239(4.75),286(4.83), 455(3.83),585(4.28)	88-0193-80
$C_{30}H_{16}O_2$ 9(10H)-Anthracenone, 10,10'-(1,2-ethenediylidene)bis-	CHCl$_3$	250(4.81),335(4.20), 510s(--),540(4.81)	35-5047-80
$C_{30}H_{17}BrN_2O_5$ 2H-Anthra[1,2-d][1,3]oxazine-7,12-dione, 2-(1-amino-9,10-dihydro-9,10-dioxo-2-anthracenyl)-6-bromo-1,4-dihydro-	EtOH	488(4.14)	18-3007-80 +146-0513-80
$C_{30}H_{17}NO_2$ Benzo[1,2]quinolizino[3,4,5,6-def]phenanthridinium, 2-carboxy-9-phenyl-, hydroxide, inner salt	EtOH	214(4.30),243(4.53), 280(4.39),304(4.68), 332(4.23),350(4.30), 364(4.23),416(3.75), 439(3.83)	39-1879-80C
$C_{30}H_{18}Br_2$ Azuleno[2,1-a]azulene, 6,12-bis(4-bromophenyl)-	C_6H_{12}	259(4.47),340(4.66), 364(5.10),410(3.74), 435(3.78),461(3.90), 580s(2.37),840s(2.26), 920(2.32),1055(2.35), 1242(2.22)	88-4001-80
$C_{30}H_{19}NO_3$ 5,11-Naphthacenedione, 12-phenoxy-6-(phenylamino)-	toluene	525(3.94),558(3.86)	104-1651-80
5,12-Naphthacenedione, 11-phenoxy-6-(phenylamino)-	toluene	404(3.84),496(3.95)	104-1651-80
$C_{30}H_{20}$ Azulene[2,1-a]azulene, 6,12-diphenyl-	C_6H_{12}	210(4.45),229(4.37), 254(4.44),344s(4.76), 357(5.11),409(3.75), 430(3.87),457(4.02), 486(4.05),570s(2.34), 915(2.41),1050(2.49), 1253(2.34)	88-4001-80
$C_{30}H_{20}Cl_2O_2$ Ethanone, 1-(4-chlorophenyl)-2-[5-(4-chlorophenyl)-2,2-diphenyl-3(2H)-furanylidene]-	EtOH	413(4.48)	5-1744-80
$C_{30}H_{20}Cl_4N_2O_5$ 2,5-Imino-1,6,3-benzodioxazocine-5(2H)-carboxylic acid, 7,8,9,10-tetrachloro-3,4-dihydro-4-oxo-2,3,11-triphenyl-, ethyl ester	MeCN	216(4.93),292(3.28), 300(3.32),325(2.69)	5-1850-80

Compound	Solvent	λ_{max}(log ϵ)	Ref.
$C_{30}H_{20}N$			
Benzo[1,2]quinolizino[3,4,5,6-def]phenanthridinium, 2-methyl-9-phenyl-, perchlorate	EtOH	231(4.62),241(4.59), 280(4.38),305(4.72), 330(4.3),349(4.32), 364(4.26),410(3.82), 432(3.90)	39-1879-80C
Benzo[1,2]quinolizino[3,4,5,6-def]phenanthridinium, 5-methyl-9-phenyl-, perchlorate	EtOH	228(4.51),243(4.53), 278(4.42),304(4.66), 327(4.25),349(4.28), 410(3.81),432(3.91)	39-1879-80C
Benzo[1,2]quinolizino[3,4,5,6-def]phenanthridinium, 9-(4-methylphenyl)-, perchlorate	EtOH	228(4.49),242(4.43), 279(4.35),300(4.42), 316(4.48),350(4.26), 366(4.48),408(3.75), 430(3.79)	39-1879-80C
$C_{30}H_{20}N_2O$			
1(4H)-Naphthalenone, 4-[(1,2-diphenyl-1H-indol-3-yl)imino]-	ligroin	583(4.02)	7-0009-80
$C_{30}H_{20}N_2O_2$			
1H,7H-Pyrazolo[1,2-a]pyrazole-1,7-dione, 2,3,5,6-tetraphenyl-	dioxan	255(4.35),350s(3.94), 409(4.00)	35-4983-80
$C_{30}H_{20}N_2O_3$			
1H-Furo[3,4-b]pyrrole-2,3-dione, 6,6a-dihydro-1,4,6a-triphenyl-6-(phenylimino)-, (Z)-	MeCN	239(4.29),260s(4.23), 352(4.18)	5-1801-80
$C_{30}H_{20}O_2$			
9,10[3',4']-Furanoanthracene, 9,10-dihydro-2',5'-diphenyl-	EtOH	222(3.71),278(3.38)	89-0907-80
$C_{30}H_{20}S_4$			
1,3-Dithiole, 2-(4,5-diphenyl-1,3-dithiol-2-ylidene)-4,5-diphenyl-	THF	296(4.31),405(3.56)	11-0196-80A
$C_{30}H_{21}BrO_3$			
9,10-Ethanoanthracene-11-carboxylic acid, 12-benzoyl-12-bromo-9,10-dihydro-11-phenyl-	EtOH	240(4.31),278(3.34)	89-0907-80
$C_{30}H_{21}ClN_2O_3$			
2-Pyrrolidinecarboxamide, 3-(chlorophenylmethylene)-4,5-dioxo-N,1,2-triphenyl-, radical cation	MeCN	243(4.29),326(3.95), 430s(2.48)	5-1801-80
$C_{30}H_{21}N_3O_2S$			
1,3-Oxazin-4-one, 6-phenyl-5-(phenylthio)-2-[2(1H)-quinolinylidene-2-quinolinyl]methyl-	EtOH	230(4.91),266s(4.34), 320(4.37),422s(4.26), 444(4.53),470(4.53)	94-0795-80
$C_{30}H_{22}$			
p-Quaterphenyl, 2-phenyl-	C_6H_{12}	205(4.90),237s(4.29), 264s(4.40),295(4.63)	18-2610-80
p-Quaterphenyl, 3-phenyl-	C_6H_{12}	207(4.88),253s(4.37), 296(4.68)	18-2610-80
m-Quinquephenyl	C_6H_{12}	196(4.77),205(4.78), 249(4.92)	18-2610-80
m-Terphenyl, 2,2"-diphenyl-	C_6H_{12}	192(4.87),204s(4.80), 234(4.76),250s(4.43)	18-2610-80

Compound	Solvent	λ_{max} (log ϵ)	Ref.
m-Terphenyl, 4,4"-diphenyl-	C$_6$H$_{12}$	205(4.91),280(4.82)	18-2610-80
o-Terphenyl, 4,4"-diphenyl-	C$_6$H$_{12}$	204(4.93),264(4.70), 284s(4.49)	18-2610-80
p-Terphenyl, 2,2"-diphenyl-	C$_6$H$_{12}$	198(4.93),242(4.64), 280(4.27)	18-2610-80
p-Terphenyl, 2,3"-diphenyl-	C$_6$H$_{12}$	197(4.91),250(4.66), 275s(4.47)	18-2610-80
p-Terphenyl, 3,3"-diphenyl-	C$_6$H$_{12}$	207(4.82),258(4.71), 280s(4.58)	18-2610-80
C$_{30}$H$_{22}$Br$_2$ Azuleno[2,1-a]azulene, 6,12-bis(4- bromophenyl)-6,6a,12,12a-tetrahydro- (6α,6aα,12β,12aα)-	C$_6$H$_{12}$	223(4.57),232(4.56), 246(4.51),305(3.75), 400(4.23)	88-4001-80
C$_{30}$H$_{22}$Cl$_2$N$_6$Ru Ruthenium(2+), bis(2,2'-bipyridine- N,N')(4,4'-dichloro-2,2'-bipyridine- N,N')-, (OC-6-22)-, bis(hexafluoro- phosphate)	MeCN	216(4.73),245(4.39), 253(4.38),287(4.99), 327(3.98),350(3.80), 357s(3.82),396s(3.83), 448(4.10)	33-1675-80
C$_{30}$H$_{22}$N$_2$ 1H-Isoindole, 1-[(2-methyl-3-phenyl-2H- isoindol-1-yl)methylene]-3-phenyl-	benzene	295(4.26),555(4.77)	40-1185-80
C$_{30}$H$_{22}$N$_2$O$_2$ Benzamide, N-(1,2-dihydro-2-oxo-4,6-di- phenyl-3-pyridinyl)-N-phenyl-	CHCl$_3$	354(4.30)	39-2743-80C
Benzamide, N-(1,6-dihydro-6-oxo-2,4-di- phenyl-3-pyridinyl)-N-phenyl-	CHCl$_3$	293(4.35),340s(--)	39-2743-80C
C$_{30}$H$_{22}$N$_2$O$_2$S$_2$ 2H-1,4-Benzothiazine, 3-(4-methoxyphen- yl)-2-[3-(4-methoxyphenyl)-2H-1,4- benzothiazin-2-ylidene]-	EtOH	217(4.27),266(4.23), 310s(3.89),368(3.82), 464(3.39)	39-2923-80C
	EtOH-HCl	217(4.24),266(4.15), 335(3.81),424(3.79), 584(3.27)	39-2923-80C
C$_{30}$H$_{22}$N$_2$O$_4$ 2-Pyrrolidinecarboxamide, 3-(hydroxy- phenylmethylene)-4,5-dioxo-N,1,2- triphenyl- (radical cation)	MeCN	252(4.40),310s(3.88)	5-1801-80
Tetrabenzo[b,d,h,j][1,6]diazacyclo- dodecine-2,7-dicarboxylic acid, dimethyl ester	EtOH	253(4.62)	39-0107-80C
Tetrabenzo[b,d,h,j][1,6]diazacyclo- dodecine-4,5-dicarboxylic acid, dimethyl ester	EtOH	227(4.70),256s(4.52), 300s(4.04)	39-0107-80C
C$_{30}$H$_{22}$N$_4$O$_4$S$_2$ Benzenamine, 4,4'-dithiobis[N-[3-(4-ni- trophenyl)-2-propenylidene]- (anion)	DMF-base	609(3.75)	3-1851-80
C$_{30}$H$_{22}$N$_6$O$_8$ Methanone, [1,4-dihydro-1,4-bis(4-ni- trophenyl)-1,2,4,5-tetrazine-3,6- diyl]bis[(4-methoxyphenyl)-	EtOH	254(4.34),316(4.55), 395(4.43)	39-2923-80C

Compound	Solvent	λ_{max}(log ϵ)	Ref.
$C_{30}H_{22}O$			
11H-Dibenzo[a,g]cycloheneicosen-11-one, 22,23,24,25-tetrahydro-10-methyl-, (all-E)-	THF	235(4.7),335(5.0)	138-1299-80
$C_{30}H_{22}O_2$			
5,8:13,16-Dietheno-1,20-methano-21H-dibenzo[a,d]cycloheptadecene-21,22-dione, 9,10,11,12-tetrahydro-	EtOH	255(4.54),350(3.46)	24-0676-80
Ethanone, 1-phenyl-2-(2,2,5-triphenyl-3(2H)-furanylidene)-	EtOH	408(4.42)	5-1744-80
$C_{30}H_{22}O_2S_2$			
5,8:15,18-Dietheno-1,22-methano-9H-dibenzo[j,m][1,4]dithiacyclononadecin-23,24(14H)-dione, 11,12-dihydro-	CDCl₃	256(4.70),350(3.76)	24-0676-80
$C_{30}H_{22}O_3$			
5H-Dibenzo[b,j]fluorene-5,8,13-trione, 7,7a-dihydro-7,7a-dimethyl-6-(phenylmethyl)-	EtOH	239(4.45),287(3.98), 333(3.97),348(3.97), 384(3.94)	39-1994-80C
9,10-Ethanoanthracene-11-carboxylic acid, 9,10-dihydro-12-(hydroxyphenylmethylene)-11-phenyl-	MeOH	250(3.88),278(3.57), 330(3.86)	89-0907-80
$C_{30}H_{22}O_4$			
Phenanthro[9,10-b][1,4]dioxin-2-methanol, 2,3-dihydro-3-phenyl-, benzoate, trans	C_6H_{12}-benzene	272(4.2),283(3.9), 296(4.0),309(4.1)	83-0476-80
$C_{30}H_{22}O_5$			
Benzoic acid, 2-[4-[[[1,3-dihydro-1-(4-methylphenyl)-3-oxo-1-isobenzofuranyl]methyl]benzoyl]-	n.s.g.	259(4.2)	40-1749-80
$C_{30}H_{22}S$			
3aH-Dibenzo[b,f]cyclopenta[d]thiepin, 2-methyl-1,3-diphenyl-	EtOH	225(4.7),268(4.5)	88-4287-80
3aH-Dibenzo[b,f]cyclopenta[d]thiepin, 3a-methyl-1,3-diphenyl-	EtOH	225(4.8),265(4.6)	88-4287-80
$C_{30}H_{23}F_2N_3$			
Propanedinitrile, [3-(diethylamino)-2,5-bis(4-fluorophenyl)-4-phenyl-2,4-cyclopentadien-1-ylidene]-	MeCN	283(4.06),375(4.20), 607(3.74)	24-0424-80
$C_{30}H_{23}N_3$			
1H-Indol-3-amine, 1-ethyl-2-phenyl-N-(2-phenyl-3H-indol-3-ylidene)-	benzene-ligroin	557(4.32)	7-0009-80
Propanedinitrile, [2,3,5-triphenyl-4-(1-pyrrolidinyl)-2,4-cyclopentadien-1-ylidene]-	MeCN	284(4.01),363(4.17), 620(3.79)	24-0424-80
$C_{30}H_{23}N_3O$			
Propanedinitrile, [3-(4-morpholinyl)-2,4,5-triphenyl-2,4-cyclopentadien-1-ylidene]-	MeCN	279(4.01),376(4.12), 610(3.46)	24-0424-80
perchlorate	MeCN	239(3.99),325(4.26)	24-0424-80
$C_{30}H_{24}$			
Azuleno[2,1-a]azulene, 6,6a,12,12a-	C_6H_{12}	246(4.53),303(3.78),	88-4001-80

Compound	Solvent	$\lambda_{max}(\log \epsilon)$	Ref.
tetrahydro-6,12-diphenyl-, (6α,6aα,12β,12aα)- (cont.)		403(4.35)	88-4001-80
$C_{30}H_{24}Br_2N_2O_4$ 3,11-Diazatricyclo[5.3.1.1^{2,6}]dodeca-4,8-diene-10,12-dione, 3,11-bis[3-(4-bromophenyl)-3-oxo-1-propenyl]-4,7-dimethyl-, [1α,2β,3(E),6β,7α,11(E)]-	CHCl$_3$	270(4.43),325(4.50)	39-0362-80C
$C_{30}H_{24}N_2O_2S_2$ 2,2'-Bi-2H-1,4-benzothiazine, 3,3'-bis(4-methoxyphenyl)-	CHCl$_3$	250(4.35),277(4.36), 303(4.27),340(4.14), 361(4.10)	39-2923-80C
$C_{30}H_{24}N_2O_3$ 6H-Anthra[1,9-cd]isoxazol-6-one, 3-[4-(1,1-dimethylethyl)phenoxy]-5-(phenylamino)-	THF	265(5.05),430(3.87), 614(4.36),666(4.38)	104-1884-80
6H-Anthra[1,9-cd]isoxazol-6-one, 3-(4-methylphenoxy)-5-[(2,4,6-trimethylphenyl)amino]-	THF	265(5.04),420(3.90), 612(4.33),664(4.34)	104-1884-80
$C_{30}H_{24}N_2O_4$ Butanediamide, 2,3-dibenzoyl-N,N'-diphenyl-	CH$_2$Cl$_2$	258(4.53)	39-2670-80C
$C_{30}H_{24}N_3$ 1H-Indol-3-aminium, N,1-dimethyl-2-phenyl-N-(2-phenyl-3H-indol-3-ylidene)-, perchlorate	CHCl$_3$-ether	660(4.29)	7-0009-80
3H-Indolium, 1-methyl-3-[(1-methyl-2-phenyl-1H-indol-3-yl)imino]-2-phenyl-, perchlorate	n.s.g.	630(4.48)	7-0009-80
$C_{30}H_{24}N_4O_3$ 9,10-Anthracenedione, 1-azido-2-[4-(1,1-dimethylethyl)phenoxy]-4-(phenylamino)-	THF	257(4.67),506(4.10)	104-1884-80
9,10-Anthracenedione, 1-azido-2-(4-methylphenoxy)-4-[(2,4,6-trimethylphenyl)amino]-	THF	257(4.65),506(4.08)	104-1884-80
$C_{30}H_{24}N_6Ru$ Ruthenium(II), tris(2,2'-bipyridine-N,N')-, perchlorate	n.s.g.	244(4.41),254(4.35), 287(4.90),314(4.07), 454(4.15)	39-0557-80B
Ruthenium(III), tris(2,2'-bipyridine-N,N')-, perchlorate	n.s.g.	287(4.35),304(4.64), 314(4.64),418(3.18), 454(2.40),678(2.60)	39-0557-80B
$C_{30}H_{24}O$ 2H-Pyran, 2,4,6-triphenyl-2-(phenylmethyl)-	EtOH	245(4.2),323(4.0)	97-0261-80
4H-Pyran, 2,4,6-triphenyl-4-(phenylmethyl)-	EtOH	250(4.3)	97-0261-80
$C_{30}H_{24}O_4$ 10H,11H-6a,7,9:11a,1,12-Diethanylylidene-6,11-etheno-2H-pentaleno[1"',6"'-2",3",4"]cyclobuta[1",2":4',5']benzo-[1',2':4,5]cyclooncta[1,2,3-cd]-	MeOH	241(3.62),276(3.42)	88-1369-80

Compound	Solvent	$\lambda_{max}(\log \epsilon)$	Ref.
pentalene-2,10,15,17-tetrone, 1,5a,6,6b,7,8,8a,9,10b,11b,12,13-13a,13b-tetradecahydro- (cont.)			88-1369-80
$C_{30}H_{24}O_5$			
9,10-Anthracenedione, 5-methoxy-2-methyl-1,4-bis(phenylmethoxy)-	CHCl$_3$	390(3.92)	44-0012-80
$C_{30}H_{24}O_{10}$			
Dimethylbacillosporin A	MeOH	231s(4.57),246(4.62), 253s(4.59),278(4.39), 305s(4.06),316s(4.02), 360s(3.66),373s(3.61)	94-3649-80
$C_{30}H_{25}NO_2$			
Benzamide, N-[(4-methylphenyl)methyl]-N-(3-oxo-1,3-diphenyl-1-propenyl)-	EtOH	208(4.27),250(4.01), 325s(3.78)	39-1870-80C
$C_{30}H_{25}NO_3$			
3H-Indole, 3-[bis(4-methoxyphenyl)methylene]-2-(2-methoxyphenyl)- (in 64% methanol)	pH 1.27 pH 8.53	437(4.44),526(4.22) 326s(3.98),353(4.02), 425(4.15)	33-1264-80 33-1264-80
$C_{30}H_{25}N_2OS$			
Thiopyrylium, 2-[2-(2,3-dihydro-1,5-dimethyl-3-oxo-2-phenyl-1H-pyrazol-4-yl)ethenyl]-4,6-diphenyl-, perchlorate	HOAc	551(4.47)	48-0543-80
$C_{30}H_{25}N_2O_2$			
Pyrylium, 2-[2-(2,3-dihydro-1,5-dimethyl-3-oxo-2-phenyl-1H-pyrazol-4-yl)-ethenyl]-4,6-diphenyl-, perchlorate	HOAc	416(4.45)	48-0543-80
$C_{30}H_{25}N_3$			
Propanedinitrile, [3-(diethylamino)-2,4,5-triphenyl-2,4-cyclopentadien-1-ylidene]-	MeCN	288(4.19),370(4.16), 615(3.57)	24-0424-80
perchlorate	MeCN	240(4.00),319(4.25), 360s(--)	24-0424-80
$C_{30}H_{25}N_3O_9$			
Cytosine, 5,6-dihydro-N -hydroxy-6-(hydroxyamino)-1-(2,3,5-tri-O-benzoyl-β-D-ribofuranosyl)-	EtOH	230(4.68)	39-0563-80C
$C_{30}H_{25}N_5O_5S_3$			
5-Thia-1-azabicyclo[4.2.0]oct-2-ene-2-carboxylic acid, 3-[5-(acetylamino)-1,3,4-thiadiazol-2-yl]-8-oxo-7-[(2-thienylacetyl)amino]-, diphenylmethyl ester, (6R-trans)-	EtOH	315(4.12)	94-2116-80
$C_{30}H_{26}$			
Anthracene, 10-butyl-1,8-diphenyl-	EtOH	261(5.01),347(3.51), 368(3.83),385(4.02), 398(3.95)	44-1807-80
$C_{30}H_{26}Cl_4N_4O$			
3,7-Dipyrido[1,2-a:3',2'-c]pyrroledicarbonitrile, 1-[(2,6-dichlorophen-	CH$_2$Cl$_2$	263(4.5),359(3.8)	64-0490-80B

Compound	Solvent	$\lambda_{max}(\log \epsilon)$	Ref.
yl)methyl]-9-(2,6-dichlorophenyl)- 4-(2-methyl-2-propoxy)-1,4,4a,4b,9- 9a-hexahydro- (cont.)			64-0490-80B
$C_{30}H_{26}N_2O$ Benzenamine, 4-[[2-(2-methoxyphenyl)- 3H-indol-3-ylidene]phenylmethyl]-N,N- dimethyl-, monoperchlorate (in 64% methanol)	pH 2.40 pH 10.45	418(4.03),595(4.58) 374(3.83),503(4.23)	33-1264-80 33-1264-80
$C_{30}H_{26}N_2O_2$ Benzenamine, 4-[6,11-dihydro-6-(4-meth- oxyphenyl)[1]benzopyrano[4,3-b]indol- 6-yl]-N,N-dimethyl-	pH 1.47 in 64% MeOH	459(3.94),585(4.33)	33-1264-80
$C_{30}H_{26}N_3$ Ethanaminium, N-[4-(dicyanomethylene)- 2,3,5-triphenyl-2-cyclopenten-1-yli- dene]-N-ethyl-, perchlorate	MeCN	240(4.00),319(4.25), 360s(--)	24-0424-80
$C_{30}H_{26}N_4O_5S$ Furo[2',3':4,5]thiazolo[3,2-e]purin- 4(3H)-one, 6a,7,8,9a-tetrahydro-7- hydroxy-8-[[(4-methoxyphenyl)diphen- ylmethoxy]methyl]-, [6aS-(6aα,7α,8β- 9aα)]-	n.s.g.	232(4.21),264(4.19)	94-3621-80
$C_{30}H_{26}N_6O_3S_3$ 5-Thia-1-azabicyclo[4.2.0]oct-2-ene- 2-carboxylic acid, 7-[[(4-methylphen- yl)thio]imino]-3-[[(1-methyl-1H- tetrazol-5-yl)thio]methyl]-8-oxo-, diphenylmethyl ester, (R)-	MeOH	261(4.00),355(4.05)	35-1690-80
$C_{30}H_{26}N_8O_2$ Formazan, 3-methyl-1,5-bis[1-(2-meth- oxyphenyl)-2-benzimidazolyl]- Formazan, 3-methyl-1,5-bis[1-(4-meth- oxyphenyl)-2-benzimidazolyl]-	EtOH EtOH	534(4.62) 543(4.60)	103-0637-80 103-0637-80
$C_{30}H_{26}O_4$ 9-Anthracenol, 5-methoxy-2-methyl- 1,4-bis(phenylmethoxy)-	$CHCl_3$	260(4.43),359(3.62), 378(3.75),388(3.70), 412(3.53)	44-0012-80
$C_{30}H_{26}O_{10}$ Tetramethylbacillosporin C	MeOH	227(4.62),240(4.66), 270s(4.61),275(4.62), 312(3.88),340(3.70), 366(3.75)	94-3649-80
$C_{30}H_{26}O_{16}$ Chaetochromin	EtOH	235(4.64),280(4.67), 292(4.73),328(4.18), 415(4.02)	94-2428-80
$C_{30}H_{26}Si$ Silacyclopenta-2,4-diene, 1,1-dimethyl- 2,3,4,5-tetraphenyl-	dioxan	358(4.01)	61-1122-80

Compound	Solvent	$\lambda_{max}(\log \epsilon)$	Ref.
$C_{30}H_{27}NO_7$			
11-Azatricyclo[4.4.1.1^{2,5}]dodeca-3,7,9-triene-2,5,11-tricarboxylic acid, 12-oxo-3,4-diphenyl-, 11-ethyl 2,5-dimethyl ester	EtOH	226(4.21),251(4.15)	44-4455-80
isomer	EtOH	254(4.07),296(4.07)	44-4455-80
6,9-Methano-3H-3-benzazepine-3,6,9-tricarboxylic acid, 5a,9a-dihydro-10-oxo-7,8-diphenyl-, 3-ethyl 6,9-dimethyl ester, (5α,6β,9β,9aα)-	EtOH	228(4.42)	44-4455-80
$C_{30}H_{27}N_2O_2$			
Benzo[f]quinolinium, 3-(2,4-dimethoxyphenyl)-4-methyl-1-[2-(phenylamino)-ethenyl]-, iodide	EtOH	505(4.67)	103-0752-80
Benzo[f]quinolinium, 3-(3,4-dimethoxyphenyl)-4-methyl-1-[2-(phenylamino)-ethenyl]-, iodide	EtOH	508(4.67)	103-0752-80
$C_{30}H_{27}N_2S$			
Benzothiazolium, 3-ethyl-2-[3-(1-methyl-2,6-diphenyl-4(1H)-pyridinylidene)-1-propenyl]-, perchlorate	CH_2Cl_2	585(5.10)	103-0696-80
Benzothiazolium, 3-ethyl-2-[3-(1-methyl-4,6-diphenyl-2(1H)-pyridinylidene)-1-propenyl]-, perchlorate	CH_2Cl_2	575(4.98)	103-0696-80
$C_{30}H_{27}N_3O_2$			
Benzeneacetonitrile, α-[3-(diethylamino)-4-methyl-2,5-diphenyl-2,4-cyclopentadien-1-ylidene]-4-nitro-	MeCN	272(4.22),373(4.17), 580(3.57)	24-0424-80
$C_{30}H_{27}N_5O_4S_3$			
5-Thia-1-azabicyclo[4.2.0]oct-2-ene-2-carboxylic acid, 3-[5-(dimethylamino)-1,3,4-thiadiazol-2-yl]-8-oxo-7-[(2-thienylacetyl)amino]-, diphenylmethyl ester, (6R-trans)-	EtOH	343(4.12)	94-2116-80
$C_{30}H_{28}Cl_2N_2O_2$			
Benzamide, N-[3-benzoyl-1-[(2,6-dichlorophenyl)methyl]-1,4-dihydro-4-pyridinyl]-4-(1,1-dimethylethyl)-	CH_2Cl_2	305s(3.9),335(4.0)	64-1431-80B
$C_{30}H_{28}N_3O_{11}$			
1,3-Dioxolo[4,5-g]isoquinolinium, 7,8-bis[(acetoxy)(2-nitrophenyl)methyl]-7,8-dihydro-4-methoxy-6-methyl-, perchlorate	$CHCl_3$	258(4.41),349(4.25)	83-0715-80
$C_{30}H_{28}N_6$			
Benzenamine, 4,4'-[1,1'-bi-1H-pyrrolo-[3,2-c]pyridine]-2,2'-diylbis[N,N-dimethyl-	EtOH	225(4.53),279(4.22), 334(4.74)	142-0783-80
$C_{30}H_{28}N_6O_3S_3$			
5-Thia-1-azabicyclo[4.2.0]oct-2-ene-2-carboxylic acid, 7-amino-7-[(4-methylphenyl)thio]-3-[[(1-methyl-1H-tetrazol-5-yl)thio]methyl]-8-oxo-, diphenylmethyl ester, (6R-cis)-	MeOH	257(4.01),288(3.89)	35-1690-80

Compound	Solvent	$\lambda_{max}(\log \epsilon)$	Ref.
$C_{30}H_{28}O_3$ Isobenzofuran, 1,3-dihydro-1-methoxy-3,3-diphenyl-1-(2,4,6-trimethyl-phenyl)-	hexane	213(4.35),221s(4.24), 254(2.80),260(2.90), 267(2.92),274(2.79), 281s(2.39)	104-1316-80
$C_{30}H_{28}O_6$ 2H-1-Benzopyran-2-one, 6,6'-[5-methyl-2-(1-methylethenyl)-4-cyclohexene-1,3-diyl]bis[7-methoxy-	EtOH	255(4.05),299(4.14), 333(4.38)	12-0395-80
$C_{30}H_{29}NO$ Benzenamine, 4-[4-[4-[2-(4-methoxyphenyl)ethenyl]phenyl]-1,3,6-cyclohepta-trien-1-yl]-N,N-dimethyl-	heptane	202(--),268(--), 385(4.725)	97-0214-80
$C_{30}H_{29}N_5O_4S_3$ 5-Thia-1-azabicyclo[4.2.0]oct-2-ene-2-carboxylic acid, 3-[[(dimethylam-ino)thioxomethyl]hydrazono]methyl]-8-oxo-7-[(2-thienylacetyl)amino]-, diphenylmethyl ester, (6R-trans)-	EtOH	343(4.37)	94-2116-80
$C_{30}H_{30}N_2O_{14}S$ Compd., m. 235-6° from dimethyl acetyl-enedicarboxylate and thiazoloimidazole	EtOH	298(4.20),420(4.06)	18-3308-80
$C_{30}H_{30}N_3O_9P$ Benzamide, N-[1-[5-O-[bis(phenylmeth-oxy)phosphinyl]-β-D-arabinofurano-syl]-1,2-dihydro-2-oxo-4-pyrimidinyl]-	EtOH	261(4.39),308(--)	18-3670-80
5'-Cytidylic acid, N-benzoyl-, bis(phen-ylmethyl) ester	MeOH	262(4.38)	18-3670-80
$C_{30}H_{30}N_4O_2$ 1H-Pyrazole, 3,3'-(1,4-phenylenebis-[4,5-dihydro-1-(1-oxopropyl)-5-phenyl-	dioxan	336s(4.61),347(4.72), 363s(4.61)	103-0066-80
	MeCN	329s(4.49),343(4.60), 356s(4.48)	103-0066-80
$C_{30}H_{30}N_4O_4$ 1H-Imidazole-4-carbonitrile, 5-amino-1-[2,3,5-tris-O-(phenylmethyl)-β-D-arabinofuranosyl]-	MeOH	254(4.07)	39-2304-80C
Porphine, 12,18-bis[(2-methoxycarbonyl)-ethyl]-13,17-dimethyl-	CHCl₃	398(5.26),495(4.16), 527(3.73),565(3.76), 618(3.34)	78-1833-80
	+ TFA	405(5.53),549(4.18), 590(3.56)	78-1833-80
Porphine, 13,17-bis[(2-methoxycarbonyl)-ethyl]-12,18-dimethyl-	CHCl₃	398(5.23),495(4.15), 527(3.71),565(3.73), 618(3.34)	78-1833-80
	+ TFA	405(5.50),549(4.16), 590(3.53)	78-1833-80
Porphine, 13,18-bis[(2-methoxycarbonyl)-ethyl]-12,17-dimethyl-	CHCl₃	398(5.26),495(4.17), 528(3.73),566(3.76), 619(3.34)	78-1833-80
	+ TFA	404(5.53),549(4.18), 590(3.54)	78-1833-80

Compound	Solvent	$\lambda_{max}(\log \epsilon)$	Ref.
$C_{30}H_{30}O_{10}$ [1,1'-Binaphthalene]-7,7'-dicarboxylic acid, 2,2',4,4',5,5'-hexamethoxy-, dimethyl ester	CHCl$_3$	292(4.29),302(4.27), 315(4.24),387(4.29)	12-2531-80
$C_{30}H_{31}NO_9$ Benzoic acid, 3,4-dimethoxy-, (2,3-dihydro-6,7-dimethoxy-2-methyl-3-oxo-4(1H)-isoquinolinylidene)(3,4-dimethoxyphenyl)methyl ester	EtOH	223(4.42),260(4.36), 300(4.29),330(4.07)	39-2013-80C
$C_{30}H_{32}N_2O_4S_2$ 1,4-Benzenediamine, N,N'-bis[1,2-dimethyl-4-(phenylsulfonyl)-2-butenylidene]-	EtOH	248(4.56)	104-0849-80
$C_{30}H_{32}O_{11}$ Physalin G acetate 2-Propenoic acid, 3-(4-hydroxyphenyl)-, 4'-ester with 8-(β-D-glucopyranosyloxy)-3,4,7,8-tetrahydro-5,7,7-trimethylcyclopenta[g]-2-benzopyran-1,6-dione, (R)-	EtOH MeOH	312(3.60) 260(4.19),267(4.20), 316(4.38)	102-1175-80 94-1869-80
$C_{30}H_{34}O_6$ 2H-Cyclopenta[b]furan-2-one, 5-(benzoyloxy)-4-[3-(benzoyloxy)-3-methyl-1-octenyl]hexahydro-, (R)- (S)-	MeOH MeOH	229(4.44),266s(3.23), 273(3.28),280(3.15) 229(4.43),266s(3.21), 273(3.27),280(3.16)	44-1528-80 44-1528-80
$C_{30}H_{34}O_7$ Dianhydroelaeodendroside B	EtOH	218(3.89),337(4.31)	2-0944-80
$C_{30}H_{34}O_8$ Dibenzo[a,c]cyclooctene-1,7-diol, 5,6,7,8-tetrahydro-2,3,10,11,12-pentamethoxy-6,7-dimethyl-, 1-benzoate	EtOH	215s(4.71),231s(4.47), 280(4.08)	12-1823-80
$C_{30}H_{34}O_{12}$ Physalin D acetate	EtOH	224(3.83)	102-1175-80
$C_{30}H_{35}FN_2O_{20}$ β-D-Glucopyranuronic acid, 1-deoxy-1-[5-fluoro-2-oxo-4-[(2,3,4-tri-O-acetyl-6-methyl-β-D-glucopyranuronosyl)-thio]-1(2H)-pyrimidinyl]-, methyl ester, 2,3,4-triacetate	pH 7 pH 14	266(3.98) 267(3.98)	106-0587-80 106-0587-80
$C_{30}H_{36}N_2O_{20}$ β-D-Glucopyranuronic acid, 1,1'-(2,4-dioxo-1,3(2H,4H)-pyrimidinediyl)-bis[1-deoxy-, dimethyl ester, 2,2',3,3',4,4'-hexaacetate	pH 7 pH 14	260(3.96) 260(3.96)	106-0587-80 106-0587-80
$C_{30}H_{36}N_4P$ Ethanaminium, N-[4-(diethylamino)-5-[(triphenylphosphoranylidene)methyl]-2H-imidazol-2-ylidene]-N-ethyl-, iodide	CHCl$_3$	340(4.20),365(3.95), 430(4.04)	88-2879-80

Compound	Solvent	λ_{max}(log ϵ)	Ref.
C$_{30}$H$_{36}$N$_6$O 4H-Imidazolium, 5-[[[2-[4-(dimethylami- no)phenyl]ethenyl]imino]methyl]-4- [[5-[4-(dimethylamino)phenyl]-1-meth- yl-3-oxo-1,4-pentadienyl]methylimi- nio]-1-methyl-, diperchlorate	H$_2$O MeOH 50% MeOH	712(4.6) 204(4.7),253(4.3), 300(4.2),381(4.2), 434(4.3),521(4.6), 721(4.8) 734(4.3)	83-0180-80 83-0180-80 83-0180-80
C$_{30}$H$_{36}$O$_5$ 1(4H)-Anthracenone, 3,8,9-trihydroxy- 4-(4-hydroxy-3-methyl-2-butenyl)-6- methyl-4,7-bis(3-methyl-2-butenyl)-, (+)- (γ-hydroxyferruginin A)	CHCl$_3$	245(4.55),261(4.31), 280(4.24),418(3.95)	100-0487-80
C$_{30}$H$_{36}$O$_6$ 1(4H)-Anthracenone, 3,8,9-trihydroxy- 4-[4-hydroxy-3-(hydroxymethyl)-2- butenyl]-6-methyl-4,7-bis(3-methyl- 2-butenyl)- Nymphaeol C 	CHCl$_3$ EtOH EtOH-NaOMe	245(4.54),261(4.32), 281(4.27),420(3.95) 209(4.66),233s(4.26), 294(4.12) 210(4.69),251(4.05), 334(4.32)	100-0487-80 142-0397-80 142-0397-80
C$_{30}$H$_{36}$O$_8$ Tricyclo[8.2.2.2^{4,7}]hexadeca-4,6,10,13- 15-hexaene-5,6,11,12-tetracarboxylic acid, 5,6-bis(1,1-dimethylethyl) 11,12-dimethyl ester	EtOH	227(4.68),300(3.38), 325s(2.78)	24-0531-80
C$_{30}$H$_{37}$NO$_{12}$ D-Arabinitol, 1-C-[4-(ethoxycarbonyl)- 5-methyl-1-(phenylmethyl)-1H-pyrrol- 3-yl]-, 1,2,3,4,5-pentaacetate, (S)- D-Arabinitol, 5-C-[4-(ethoxycarbonyl)- 5-methyl-1-(phenylmethyl)-1H-pyrrol- 3-yl]-, 1,2,3,4,5-pentaacetate	EtOH EtOH	239(3.82),254s(--) 238(4.20),260s(--)	39-1199-80C 39-1199-80C
C$_{30}$H$_{38}$N$_2$O$_2$S$_2$ [1,1':4',1''-Terphenyl]-4,4''-diethan- aminium, N,N'-bis(2-mercaptoethyl)- N,N,N',N'-tetramethyl-β,β'-dioxo-, dibromide	H$_2$O	326(4.45)	87-0541-80
C$_{30}$H$_{38}$N$_2$O$_4$ Morpholinium, 2,2'-[1,1':4',1''-terphen- yl]-4,4''-diylbis[2-hydroxy-4,4-di- methyl-, dibromide	H$_2$O	289(4.42)	87-0541-80
C$_{30}$H$_{38}$N$_2$O$_{12}$ 3,6,9,12,20,23,26,29-Octaoxa-16,33-di- azatricyclo[29.3.1.1^{14,18}]hexatria- conta-1(35),14,16,18(36),31,33-hexa- ene-2,13,19,30-tetrone, 15,17,32,34- tetramethyl-	MeCN	233(4.08),274(3.66), 282(3.59)	44-2854-80
C$_{30}$H$_{38}$O$_5$S Pregn-4-ene-3,20-dione, 17-acetoxy- 7α-[(4-methoxyphenyl)thio]-	EtOH	231(4.34)	13-0481-80A

Compound	Solvent	$\lambda_{max}(\log \epsilon)$	Ref.
$C_{30}H_{38}O_7$			
Zeylasterone	EtOH	211(4.19),226(4.05), 255(4.08),295(3.79), 340(3.70)	88-4749-80
$C_{30}H_{38}O_9$			
Carda-4,16,20(22)-trienolide, 2,3- [(dihydro-6-methyl-4H-1,3-dioxolo- [4,5-c]pyran-3a,4(6H)-diyl)bis(oxy)]- 11,14-dihydroxy- (elaeodendroside B)	EtOH	212(3.76),270(4.28)	2-0944-80
$C_{30}H_{39}N_3O_3$			
17-Norcorynan, 16-(1,2,3,4-tetrahydro- 6,7,8-trimethoxy-1-isoquinolinyl)-	EtOH	226(4.66),280(3.96), 290(3.87)	33-1335-80
$C_{30}H_{40}N_2O_{14}$			
D-galacto-Octonic acid, 2,3-dideoxy- 3-(nitromethyl)-2-[1-[(phenylmethyl)- amino]ethylidene]-, ethyl ester, 4,5,6,7,8-pentaacetate, (2Z,3ξ)-	EtOH	295(4.23)	39-1199-80C
D-gluco-Octonic acid, 2,3-dideoxy- 3-(nitromethyl)-2-[1-[(phenylmethyl)- amino]ethylidene]-, ethyl ester, 4,5,6,7,8-pentaacetate	EtOH	296(4.38)	39-1199-80C
$C_{30}H_{40}N_2P$			
3H-Indolium, 1,3,3-triethyl-2-[[[(1,3- 3-triethyl-1,3-dihydro-2H-indol-2- ylidene)methyl]phosphinidene]meth- yl]-, tetrafluoroborate	CHCl₃	302(3.95),332(3.95), 590(4.79)	5-2072-80
$C_{30}H_{40}N_3$			
3H-Indolium, 1,3,3-triethyl-2-[[[(1,3- 3-triethyl-1,3-dihydro-2H-indol-2- ylidene)methyl]imino]methyl]-, tetrafluoroborate	CDCl₃	292(4.04),530s(4.40), 564(4.87),605(5.14)	5-2072-80
$C_{30}H_{40}N_4O_5$			
4H-1,16-Etheno-5,15-(propaniminoeth- ano)furo[3,4-1][1,5,10]triazacyclo- hexadecine-4,21-dione, 3-(3,4-dimeth- oxyphenyl)-3,3a,6,7,8,9,10,11,12,13- 14,15-dodecahydro-, dihydrobromide, (ephedradine C)	MeOH	231(4.16),280(3.62)	142-0295-80
$C_{30}H_{40}N_{10}O_{10}$			
Adenosine, N,N'-1,4-butanediylbis- [2',3'-O-(ethoxymethylene)-	pH 2	265(4.55)	69-0163-80
$C_{30}H_{40}O$			
8'-Apo-β-caroten-8'-al, 13-demethyl- 14-methyl-, 11-cis	hexane	333(3.05),448(3.41), 474(3.30)	33-0716-80
2,4,6,8,10,12,14,16-Heptadecaoctaenal, 2,6,10,15-tetramethyl-17-(2,6,6-tri- methyl-1-cyclohexen-1-yl)-	hexane	452(3.43),481(3.33)	33-0716-80
$C_{30}H_{40}O_2$			
β-Citraurin	hexane	453(3.37),481(3.28)	33-1377-80

Compound	Solvent	$\lambda_{max}(\log \epsilon)$	Ref.
$C_{30}H_{40}O_4$ 1,3-Cyclohexanedione, 2-[9-(3-acetoxy-2,6,6-trimethyl-1-cyclohexen-1-yl]-3,7-dimethyl-2,4,6,8-nonatetraenyli-dene]-5,5-dimethyl-, (all-E)-	EtOH	265(4.11),285(4.09), 480(4.71)	33-1391-80
$C_{30}H_{40}O_4Se$ Pregn-5-ene-3,20-diol, 3-acetate. 20-(Se-phenyl carbonoselenoate), (3β)-	pentane	255(3.49)	33-2328-80
$C_{30}H_{40}O_8$ 26,27-Dinorfurosta-7,14-dien-25-oic acid, 2,3-diacetoxy-6-oxo-, methyl ester	MeOH	275(3.98)	88-4323-80
26,27-Dinorfurosta-8,14-dien-25-oic acid, 2,3-diacetoxy-6-oxo-, methyl ester	MeOH	245(4.24)	88-4323-80
5β-Ergost-2-en-26-oic acid, 15α-acet-oxy-5,6β:24,25-diepoxy-4β,22-di-hydroxy-1-oxo-, δ-lactone, (22R,24S-25S)-	EtOH	214(3.91)	150-2134-80
5β-Ergost-2-en-26,22-olide, 15α-acet-oxy-5,6β:24,25-diepoxy-1,4-dioxo-, (22S,22R,24S,25S)-	EtOH	224(4.10)	150-2134-80
$C_{30}H_{41}BrO_7$ Pregna-1,4-diene-3,20-dione, 7-bromo-11-hydroxy-16-methyl-17,21-bis(1-oxobutoxy)-, (7α,11β,16α)-	MeOH	243(4.19)	145-1618-80
$C_{30}H_{41}ClO_7$ Pregna-1,4-diene-3,20-dione, 7-chloro-11-hydroxy-16-methyl-17,21-bis(1-oxobutoxy)-, (7α,11β,16α)-	MeOH	240(4.22)	145-1618-80
Pregna-1,4-diene-3,20-dione, 7-chloro-11-hydroxy-16-methyl-17-(1-oxoprop-oxy)-21-[(1-oxopentyl)oxy]-, (7α,11β,16α)-	MeOH	240(4.22)	145-1618-80
$C_{30}H_{41}FN_3O_{12}P$ Pregn-4-ene-3,20-dione, 9-fluoro-11,17-dihydroxy-21-(phosphonooxy)-, (11β)-, 5'-ester with 4-amino-1-β-D-arabino-furanosyl-2(1H)-pyrimidinone, mono-ammonium salt	pH 1 H_2O pH 13	242(4.20),275(4.11) 238(4.32),265s(4.03) 238(4.32),265s(4.05)	87-1343-80 87-1343-80 87-1343-80
$C_{30}H_{42}FeN_2O_6$ 1-Piperidinyloxy, 4,4'-[1,1'-ferrocene-diylbis(carbonyloxy)]bis[2,2,6,6-tetramethyl-	C_6H_{12} benzene DMF	450(4.00) 450(3.60) 450(3.78)	88-2409-80 88-2409-80 88-2409-80
$C_{30}H_{42}N_2O_8$ Macbecin	MeOH	274(4.41),397(3.38)	88-0309-80
$C_{30}H_{42}N_3O_{10}P$ Pregn-4-ene-3,20-dione, 21-(phosphono-oxy)-, 5'-ester with 4-amino-1-β-D-arabinofuranosyl-2(1H)-pyrimidinone, monoammonium salt	pH 1 H_2O pH 13	244(4.31) 248(4.22),272s(4.13) 244(4.27)	87-1343-80 87-1343-80 87-1343-80

Compound	Solvent	$\lambda_{max}(\log \epsilon)$	Ref.
$C_{30}H_{42}N_3O_{11}P$			
Pregn-4-ene-3,20-dione, 11-hydroxy-21-(phosphonooxy)-, 5'-ester with 4-amino-1-β-D-arabinofuranosyl-2(1H)-pyrimidinone, monoammonium salt	pH 1 H₂O pH 13	247(4.24),272s(4.11) 242(4.31) 243(4.31)	87-1343-80 87-1343-80 87-1343-80
Pregn-4-ene-3,20-dione, 17-hydroxy-21-(phosphonooxy)-, 5'-ester with 4-amino-1-β-D-arabinofuranosyl-2(1H)-pyrimidinone, monoammonium salt	pH 1 H₂O pH 13	250(4.22),272s(4.14) 245(4.29) 243(4.29)	87-1343-80 87-1343-80 87-1343-80
$C_{30}H_{42}O$			
β-Citraurinine	hexane	404(3.27),425(3.42), 450(3.35)	33-1377-80
$C_{30}H_{42}O_2$			
β-Citraurol	hexane	403(3.27),426(3.45), 451(3.41)	33-1377-80
$C_{30}H_{42}O_7$			
Witha-24-enolide, 4β-acetoxy-20α-hydroxy-1-oxo-5β,6β-epoxy-, (20R,22R)-	EtOH	226(3.91)	102-1503-80
$C_{30}H_{42}O_8$			
26,27-Dinorfurost-4-en-25-oic acid, 2,3-diacetoxy-6-oxo-, methyl ester, (2β,3β,22β)-	MeOH	232(3.85)	88-4323-80
26,27-Dinorfurost-7-en-25-oic acid, 2,3-diacetoxy-6-oxo-, methyl ester, (2β,3β,5α,22β)-	MeOH	243(4.12)	88-4323-80
Physapubescin	EtOH	214.5(4.00)	150-2134-80
$C_{30}H_{42}O_9$			
26,27-Dinorfurost-7-en-25-oic acid, 2,3-diacetoxy-14-hydroxy-6-oxo-, methyl ester, (2β,3β,5α,22β)-	MeOH	239(4.08)	88-4323-80
$C_{30}H_{44}N_2O_8$			
Macbecin II	MeOH	255(4.23),308s(--)	88-0309-80
$C_{30}H_{44}O$			
α-Amyr-1-en-3-one	EtOH	229(3.94)	39-2209-80C
$C_{30}H_{44}O_2$			
2,5-Cyclohexadien-1-one, 4-[1-[3,5-bis(1,1-dimethylethyl)-4-hydroxyphenyl]ethylidene]-2,6-bis(1,1-dimethylethyl)-	C_6H_{12}	266(3.89),289(3.84), 366(4.24)	12-0351-80
$C_{30}H_{44}O_4$			
14,15-Dioxadispiro[5.1.5.2]pentadeca-1,4,9,12-tetraene-3,11-dione, 2,4,10,12-tetrakis(1,1-dimethylethyl)-7-methyl-	C_6H_{12}	252(4.36)	12-0351-80
D-Homoandrost-15-eno[17,17a-c]furan-12-ol, 2',4,4,8-tetramethyl-, 3-hydroxybutanoate, (5α,12β)-	MeOH	220(3.95),228(3.97), 242(4.00)	12-1783-80
Oleana-11,13(18)-dien-28-oic acid, 21α-hydroxy-3-oxo-	CHCl₃	243(--),251(4.26), 260(--)	39-0325-80C
Olean-11,13(18)-dien-28-oic acid, 3,21,22-trihydroxy-, β-lactone, (3α,21α,22β)-	CHCl₃	248(--),256(4.37), 264(--)	39-0325-80C

Compound	Solvent	$\lambda_{max}(\log \epsilon)$	Ref.
$C_{30}H_{45}FO_2$			
Ergosta-5,7,22-trien-3-ol, 6-fluoro-, (3β,22E)-	C_6H_{12}	265s(3.88),273(3.94), 283(3.90),295s(3.62)	39-0639-80C
$C_{30}H_{45}NO_2$			
2,5-Cyclohexadien-1-one, 4-[[4-(octadecyloxy)phenyl]imino]-	hexane	486(3.88)	104-2020-80
	+CF₃COOH	521(4.22)	104-2020-80
	benzene	500(3.87)	104-2020-80
	+CF₃COOH	530(4.23)	104-2020-80
	CH₂Cl₂	504(3.93)	104-2020-80
	+CF₃COOH	539(4.24)	104-2020-80
	CHCl₃	506(3.92)	104-2020-80
	+CF₃COOH	532(4.22)	104-2020-80
perchlorate	CH₂Cl₂	541(4.26)	104-2020-80
$C_{30}H_{46}N_2$			
Diazene, bis[2,4-bis(1,1-dimethylethyl)-6-methylphenyl]-	hexane	238(3.96),247s(3.93), 312(4.19),486(3.24)	18-0205-80
$C_{30}H_{46}O_2$			
D-Homo-30-nordammara-13,15,17-trien-3-ol, 17,23-epoxy-, (3β,20ξ,23S)-	EtOH	244(4.34),260(3.43)	12-2071-80
Olean-12-ene-3,11-dione	MeOH	252(4.05)	102-0255-80
Urs-12-ene-3,11-dione	MeOH	252(4.02)	102-0255-80
$C_{30}H_{46}O_3$			
Multiflora-7,9(11)-dien-19α-oic acid, 3α-hydroxy-	EtOH	232(4.04),241(4.10), 248(4.04)	39-2933-80C
Oleanolic acid, 3-oxo-	H₂SO₄	310(4)	105-0464-80
Ursolic acid, 3-oxo-	H₂SO₄	310(3.97)	105-0464-80
$C_{30}H_{46}O_4$			
Oleana-11,13(18)-dien-28-oic acid, 3α,21α-dihydroxy- (papyriogenin E)	CHCl₃	242(--),249(4.38)	39-0325-80C
$C_{30}H_{46}O_5$			
D(17a)-Homopregn-16-ene-17a-carboxaldehyde, 12-(3-hydroxy-1-oxobutoxy)-4,4,8-trimethyl-20-oxo-, (5α,12β,17aβ)-	MeOH	232(3.95)	12-1783-80
$C_{30}H_{46}O_6$			
Acacic acid, 2β,23-dihydroxy-, lactone	MeOH	260s(2.60),269(2.62), 278s(2.57)	102-0273-80
Acinosolic acid	EtOH	205(3.70)	100-0510-80
$C_{30}H_{47}N_3O_9S$			
Glycine, N-[S-[1-(4-carboxy-1-hydroxybutyl)-2,4,6,9-pentadecatetraenyl]-N-L-γ-glutamyl-L-cysteinyl]amino]methyl]-	n.s.g.	278(4.60)	88-3143-80
$C_{30}H_{48}N_4O_7$			
Tetradecanamide, N-[[[2,3,3a,9a-tetrahydro-3-(1-oxopropoxy)-2-[(1-oxopropoxy)methyl]-6H-furo[2',3':4,5]oxazolo[3,2-a]pyrimidin-6-ylidene]amino]methyl]-, [2R-(2α,3β,3aβ,9aβ)]-, tetrafluoroborate	MeOH	239s(4.10),268(4.26)	44-1577-80
$C_{30}H_{48}O_2$			
Cholest-4-en-6-ol, 3-methylene-, acetate, (6β)-	heptane	241(4.41)	77-0346-80

Compound	Solvent	$\lambda_{max}(\log \epsilon)$	Ref.
Locereol acetate	EtOH	249(4.32)	102-2777-80
Olean-12-en-11-one, 3β-hydroxy-	MeOH	252(4.03)	102-0255-80
Urs-12-en-11-one, 3β-hydroxy-	MeOH	252(4.03)	102-0255-80
$C_{30}H_{48}O_3$			
5α-Cholesta-8,14-diene-3β,11α,12β-tri-ol, 4,4-dimethyl-24-methylene-	EtOH	249(4.35)	39-2914-80C
Ebelin, 24,25-dihydro-, lactone	EtOH	232(4.46),238(4.47), 246(4.28)	12-2071-80
Oleana-11,13(18)-diene-3α,21β,28-triol	CHCl₃	242(--),251(4.18), 260(--)	39-0325-80C
Oleanolic acid	H₂SO₄	310(4.08)	105-0464-80
Triterpene A	MeOH	244(4.46),252(4.51), 262(4.36)	24-1754-80
Ursolic acid	H₂SO₄	310(4.11)	105-0464-80
$C_{30}H_{48}O_5$			
Aescigenin	MeOH	202(3.59)	20-1001-80
$C_{30}H_{49}NO$			
Acetamide, N-[(6β)-3-methylenecholest-4-en-6-yl]-	dioxan	242(4.37)	77-0346-80
$C_{30}H_{50}Cl_2O_4Pd_2$			
Palladium(II), di-μ-chlorobis[α-4-6-η-(17β-hydroxy-3-oxo-19-norandrost-enyl]-	CHCl₃	249(3.85),281(3.94)	12-1537-80
$C_{30}H_{50}O$			
D-Friedoolean-14-en-3β-ol (taraxerol)	H₂SO₄	310(4.39)	105-0464-80
Lupeol	H₂SO₄	310(4.07)	105-0464-80
Olean-12-en-3β-ol (β-amyrin)	H₂SO₄	310(4.10)	105-0464-80
$C_{30}H_{50}O_2$			
Betulinol	H₂SO₄	310(4.31)	105-0464-80
$C_{30}H_{52}O$			
Friedelanol	H₂SO₄	310(4.26)	105-0464-80
$C_{30}H_{52}O_2$			
2H-1-Benzopyran-6(5H)-one, 3,4-dihydro-2,5,5,7,8-pentamethyl-2-(4,8,12-tri-methyltridecyl)-	hexane	334(3.72)	94-1992-80

Compound	Solvent	λ_{max}(log ϵ)	Ref.
C$_{31}$H$_{16}$O$_3$ 9(10H)-Anthracenone, 10,10'-(3-oxo-1,2-cyclopropanediylidene)bis-	CHCl$_3$	258(4.40),627(4.20)	35-5047-80
C$_{31}$H$_{18}$O$_3$ 2-Cyclopropen-1-one, 2,3-bis(10-hydroxy-9-anthracenyl)-	MeOH	260(4.75),320(3.29), 350(3.19),368(3.30), 390(3.41),412(3.54), 440(3.50),485(3.86), 510(3.83)	35-5047-80
C$_{31}$H$_{19}$NO$_2$ Benzo[1,2]quinolizino[3,4,5,6-def]phenanthridinium, 2-carboxy-5-methyl-9-phenyl-, hydroxide, inner salt	EtOH	216(4.50),245(4.53), 282(4.39),305(4.67), 334(4.23),350(4.28), 418(3.78),441(3.87)	39-1879-80C
C$_{31}$H$_{19}$NO$_3$ Benzamide, N-(6,12-dihydro-6,12-dioxo-5-naphthacenyl)-N-phenyl-	EtOH decane	$\underline{382(3.7)}$ $\underline{380(3.7)}$	104-1646-80 104-1646-80
C$_{31}$H$_{19}$N$_3$O$_2$ 1H-Pyrido[1,2-b]pyrrolo[3,4-f]indazole-1,3(2H)-dione, 2,4,11-triphenyl-	MeOH	276(4.57),365(4.22)	44-0090-80
C$_{31}$H$_{20}$N Benzo[kl]benzo[1,2]quinolizino[3,4,5,6-7-defg]acridinium, 1,2-dihydro-14-phenyl-, tetrafluoroborate	EtOH	228(4.50),242(4.43), 278(4.39),302(4.59), 333(4.13),345(4.07), 410(3.78),432(3.88)	39-1879-80C
C$_{31}$H$_{20}$N$_2$O$_3$ Benzeneacetonitrile, 4-nitro-α-(4-oxo-2,3,5-triphenyl-2-cyclopenten-1-ylidene)-	MeCN	337(4.33)	24-0424-80
5(4H)-Oxazolone, 2-[1,1'-biphenyl]-4-yl-4-[[4-(5-phenyl-2-oxazolyl)phenyl]methylene]-	toluene	345(4.55)	135-0930-80
C$_{31}$H$_{21}$NO$_5$S Benzenesulfonamide, N-(6,11-dihydro-6,11-dioxo-12-phenoxy-5-naphthacenyl)-4-methyl-	toluene	422(3.77)	104-1651-80
C$_{31}$H$_{21}$NO$_6$ Naphthaceno[5,6-bc]pyran-3-carboxylic acid, 9-(acetylphenylamino)-2,8-dihydro-2,8-dioxo-, ethyl ester	EtOH	423(3.94)	104-1646-80
C$_{31}$H$_{21}$OS 2-Benzopyrylium, 3-phenyl-1-[(3-phenyl-1H-2-benzothiopyran-1-ylidene)methyl]-, perchlorate	CH$_2$Cl$_2$	604(4.70)	103-0599-80
C$_{31}$H$_{21}$O$_2$ 2-Benzopyrylium, 3-phenyl-1-[(2-phenyl-4H-1-benzopyran-4-ylidene)methyl]-, perchlorate	CH$_2$Cl$_2$	588(4.70)	103-0137-80
2-Benzopyrylium, 3-phenyl-1-[(3-phenyl-1H-2-benzopyran-1-ylidene)methyl]-, perchlorate	CH$_2$Cl$_2$	596(4.57)	103-0137-80

Compound	Solvent	$\lambda_{max}(\log \epsilon)$	Ref.
$C_{31}H_{21}S_2$			
2-Benzothiopyrylium, 3-phenyl-1-[(2-phenyl-4H-1-benzothiopyran-4-ylidene)methyl]-	CH_2Cl_2	676(4.70)	103-0599-80
2-Benzothiopyrylium, 3-phenyl-1-[(3-phenyl-1H-2-benzothiopyran-1-ylidene)methyl]-, perchlorate	CH_2Cl_2 CF_3COOH- $HClO_4$	615(4.75) 286(4.89),322(4.10), 450(4.14)	103-0599-80 103-0599-80
$C_{31}H_{22}N_2O_4$			
1H-Furo[3,4-b]pyrrole-2,3-dione, 6,6a-dihydro-1-(4-methoxyphenyl)-4,6a-diphenyl-6-(phenylimino)-, (Z)-(±)-	MeCN	225s(4.49),260s(4.34), 351(4.23)	5-1801-80
Indazolo[2,3-a]quinoline-8,9-dicarboxylic acid, 7,10-diphenyl-, dimethyl ester	MeOH	275(4.55),295(4.23), 310(4.17),359(3.97), 378(4.10),397(4.11)	44-0090-80
$C_{31}H_{22}N_6O_6$			
1,2,4-Triazolidine-3,5-dione, 1,1'-(1-benzoyl-2-oxo-2-phenylethylidene)bis-[4-phenyl-	MeCN	263(4.395)	44-1232-80
$C_{31}H_{23}N_2$			
Benzo[c]benzo[1,2]quinolizino[3,4,5,6-ija][1,6]naphthyridin-15-ium, 5,13-dimethyl-9-(4-methylphenyl)-, perchlorate	EtOH	217(4.05),232(4.35), 249(4.35),279s(4.20), 302(4.39),317(4.39), 350(4.14),362(4.14), 408(3.68),433(3.78)	39-1879-80C
$C_{31}H_{23}N_2P$			
9H-Fluoren-9-one, (triphenylphosphoranylidene)hydrazone	CH_2Cl_2	247(4.44),257(4.15), 294(3.84),387(4.03)	88-2313-80
$C_{31}H_{23}N_9O_2$			
Ethenetricarbonitrile, [3,13-bis(4,6-dimethyl-2-pyrimidinyl)-1,2,3,6,7,8-hexahydro-8,14-dioxo-1,7-imino-2,6-methano-3-benzazecin-5-yl]-	EtOH	213(4.20),247(4.18), 290s(3.80),460(4.35)	39-0331-80C
$C_{31}H_{24}N_2O_2$			
Benzamide, N-(1,2-dihydro-2-oxo-4,6-diphenyl-3-pyridinyl)-N-(4-methylphenyl)-	$CHCl_3$	351(4.18)	39-2743-80C
Benzamide, N-(1,6-dihydro-6-oxo-2,4-diphenyl-3-pyridinyl)-N-(4-methylphenyl)-	$CHCl_3$	332(3.95)	39-2743-80C
$C_{31}H_{24}O$			
7H-Benzocycloheptene, 7-(diphenylmethylene)-5-methoxy-9-phenyl-	$CHCl_3$	245(4.39),298(4.38), 332(4.31)	88-4869-80
Dibenz[a,de]anthracen-13-one, 8-butyl-12-phenyl-	EtOH	247(4.71),281(4.67), 385(3.51),475(4.06)	44-1807-80
$C_{31}H_{24}O_2$			
Spiro[4H-dinaphtho[2,1-f:1',2'-h][1,5]-dioxonin-5(6H),2'-[2H]indene], 1',3'-dihydro-	$CHCl_3$	243(4.73),269(4.09), 302(4.02),331(3.86)	49-0413-80
$C_{31}H_{24}O_{10}$			
[10,10'-Bi-4H-naphtho[2,3-b]pyran]-4,4'-dione, 5,5',6-trihydroxy-6',8,8'-trimethoxy-2,2'-dimethyl-, (S)-	MeOH	226(4.60),278(4.80), 408(4.00)	39-2474-80C

Compound	Solvent	$\lambda_{max}(\log \epsilon)$	Ref.
$C_{31}H_{24}S$			
3aH-Dibenzo[b,f]cyclopenta[d]thiepin, 2,3a-dimethyl-1,3-diphenyl-	EtOH	220(4.7),260(4.4), 340(3.8)	88-4287-80
7aH-Dibenzo[b,f]cyclopenta[d]thiepin, 7a-ethyl-1,3-diphenyl-	EtOH	220(4.7),240(4.6), 270s(4.4)	88-4287-80
$C_{31}H_{25}N_2$			
3H-Indolium, 1-methyl-3-[(1-methyl-2-phenyl-1H-indol-3-yl)methylene]-2-phenyl-, perchlorate	n.s.g.	515(4.36)	7-0009-80
$C_{31}H_{25}N_2P$			
Methanone, diphenyl-, (triphenylphos-phoranylidene)hydrazone	CH_2Cl_2	231(4.31),323(4.00)	88-2313-80
$C_{31}H_{25}N_3O$			
Propanedinitrile, [3-(4-methylphenyl)-4-(4-morpholinyl)-2,5-diphenyl-2,4-cyclopentadien-1-ylidene]-	MeCN	277(4.13),381(4.19), 603(3.64)	24-0424-80
perchlorate	MeCN	240(3.88),313(4.21), 457(4.14)	24-0424-80
$C_{31}H_{26}Br_2S_3$			
1,3-Butadiene, 2,3-dibromo-1-phenyl-1,4,4-tris[(4-methylphenyl)thio]-	heptane	200(4.91),269(4.40)	24-3342-80
$C_{31}H_{26}NOS$			
Benzothiazolium, 2-[5-(2,6-diphenyl-4H-pyran-4-ylidene)-1,3-pentadienyl]-3-ethyl-, perchlorate	CH_2Cl_2	676(4.88),735(4.97)	103-0696-80
Benzothiazolium, 2-[5-(4,6-diphenyl-2H-pyran-2-ylidene)-1,3-pentadienyl]-3-ethyl-, perchlorate	CH_2Cl_2	748(4.91),815(4.74)	103-0696-80
$C_{31}H_{26}N_2O_8$			
2,4(1H,3H)-Pyrimidinedione, 4-[2,3-bis(benzoyloxy)-4-[(benzoyloxy)-methyl]cyclopentyl]-	pH 7 pH 13	235(4.50),268(4.33) 225(4.53),267(3.98)	4-0353-80 4-0353-80
$C_{31}H_{26}N_3$			
1H-Indol-3-aminium, 1-ethyl-N-methyl-2-phenyl-N-(2-phenyl-3H-indol-3-ylidene)-, perchlorate	CHCl$_3$-ether	657(4.19)	7-0009-80
3H-Indolium, 3-[(1-ethyl-2-phenyl-1H-indol-3-yl)imino]-1-methyl-2-phenyl-, perchlorate	n.s.g.	630(4.48)	7-0009-80
$C_{31}H_{26}N_4Ni$			
Nickel, [5,10,15,20-tetramethyl-2-(phenylmethyl)-21H,23H-porphinato-(2-)-$N^{21},N^{22},N^{23},N^{24}$]-, (SP-4-2)-	CHCl$_3$	302(4.07),333(4.03), 422(5.27),543(4.09)	5-1082-80
$C_{31}H_{26}O_2$			
9-Anthracenecarboxylic acid, 10-butyli-dene-9,10-dihydro-1,8-diphenyl-	EtOH	236(4.62)	44-1807-80
2,4-Pentadien-1-one, 5-ethoxy-1,2,4,5-tetraphenyl-	EtOH	215(4.22),238(4.22), 266s(4.06),354(4.10)	39-2554-80C
$C_{31}H_{27}NO$			
Phenol, 2-[2,3,5-tris(4-methylphenyl)-1H-pyrrol-1-yl]-	EtOH	210(4.40),258(4.16), 278(4.14)	39-1870-80C

Compound	Solvent	$\lambda_{max}(\log \epsilon)$	Ref.
$C_{31}H_{27}N_2OS_2$			
Benzothiazolium, 3-ethyl-2-[[2-[3-(3-ethyl-2(3H)-benzothiazolylidene)-1-propenyl]-4H-1-benzopyran-4-ylidene]-methyl]-, iodide	MeCN	445(4.34),472(4.47), 713(5.10)	124-0965-80
Benzothiazolium, 3-ethyl-2-[[4-[3-(3-ethyl-2(3H)-benzothiazolylidene)-1-propenyl]-2H-1-benzopyran-2-ylidene]-methyl]-, iodide	MeCN	454(4.28),472(4.47), 731(5.18)	124-0965-80
$C_{31}H_{27}N_3O$			
Spiro[[1]benzopyrano[4,3-b]indole-6(11H),9'-[9H]fluorene]-3',6'-di-amine, N,N,N',N'-tetramethyl-	pH 3.18 in 64% MeOH	446s(3.70),475(3.81), 619(4.23),812s(3.92), 879(3.98)	33-1264-80
$C_{31}H_{27}N_5O_5S_3$			
5-Thia-1-azabicyclo[4.2.0]oct-2-ene-2-carboxylic acid, 3-[5-(acetylmeth-ylamino)-1,3,4-thiadiazol-2-yl]-8-oxo-7-[(2-thienylacetyl)amino]-, diphenylmethyl ester, (6R-trans)-	EtOH	315(4.10)	94-2116-80
$C_{31}H_{27}N_5O_6$			
Adenosine, N-(phenylmethyl)-, 2',5'-di-benzoate	EtOH	230(4.41),270(4.28)	39-0563-80C
Adenosine, N-(phenylmethyl)-, 3',5'-di-benzoate	EtOH	230(4.41),269(4.26)	39-0563-80C
$C_{31}H_{27}N_6$			
[1,2,4]Triazolo[1,5-a:4,3-a']dipyrimi-din-5-ium, 4-[2-[4-(dimethylamino)-phenyl]ethenyl]-2-methyl-8,10-di-phenyl-, perchlorate	EtOH mixt.	532(4.83)	124-0835-80
[1,2,4]Triazolo[1,5-a:4,3-a']dipyrimi-din-5-ium, 10-[2-[4-(dimethylamino)-phenyl]ethenyl]-8-methyl-2,4-di-phenyl-, perchlorate	EtOH mixt.	556(4.63)	124-0835-80
$C_{31}H_{28}NO$			
3H-Indolium, 2-[3-(2,6-diphenyl-4H-pyran-4-ylidene)-1-propenyl]-1,3,3-trimethyl-, perchlorate	CH_2Cl_2	595(4.87),632(4.95)	103-0696-80
3H-Indolium, 2-[3-(4,6-diphenyl-2H-pyran-2-ylidene)-1-propenyl]-1,3,3-trimethyl-, perchlorate	CH_2Cl_2	654(4.71),682(4.63)	103-0696-80
$C_{31}H_{28}N_2O$			
Benzenepropanenitrile, α-[3-(diethyl-amino)-4-methyl-2,5-diphenyl-2,4-cyclopentadien-1-ylidene]-β-oxo-	MeCN	270(4.20),362(4.05), 595(3.40)	24-0424-80
$C_{31}H_{28}N_2O_2$			
Acetic acid, cyano[3-(diethylamino)-2,4,5-triphenyl-2,4-cyclopentadien-1-ylidene]-, methyl ester	MeCN	284(4.19),367(4.14), 582(3.56)	24-0424-80
perchlorate	MeCN	238(4.06),318(4.26)	24-0424-80
Benzenamine, 4-[(4-methoxyphenyl)[2-(2-methoxyphenyl)-3H-indol-3-ylidene]-methyl]-N,N-dimethyl-, perchlorate	pH 6.29 in 64% MeOH	461(4.25),585(4.62)	33-1264-80
	pH 12.77 in 64% MeOH	395(4.09),498(4.27)	33-1264-80

Compound	Solvent	$\lambda_{max}(\log \epsilon)$	Ref.
$C_{31}H_{28}N_3O$ Pyridinium, 2-[2-(2,3-dihydro-1,5-di-methyl-3-oxo-2-phenyl-1H-pyrazol-4-yl)ethenyl]-1-methyl-4,6-diphenyl-, perchlorate	HOAc	412(4.36)	48-0543-80
$C_{31}H_{28}N_4O_2$ Pyrimido[4',5':4,5]pyrrolo[2,3-c]azep-ine-4,6-dione, 3,5,7,8,9,10-hexahy-dro-3,5,7-tris(phenylmethyl)-	EtOH	253s(4.50),285(4.17)	103-0853-80
$C_{31}H_{28}O_2$ 9-Anthracenecarboxylic acid, 10-butyl-9,10-dihydro-1,8-diphenyl-	EtOH	212(4.71),240s(4.17)	44-1807-80
$C_{31}H_{28}O_9$ 1,6-Heptadiene-3,5-dione, 1,7-bis(4-hy-droxy-3-methoxyphenyl)-4-[3-(4-hy-droxy-3-methoxyphenyl)-1-oxo-2-propenyl]-	EtOH EtOH-NaOH	365s(--),434(4.79), 450s(--) 250(--),424(4.86)	102-2643-80 102-2643-80
$C_{31}H_{28}P$ Phosphonium, [6,8-dimethyl-4-azulenyl)-methyl]triphenyl-, tetrafluoroborate	MeOH	227(4.57),251(4.49), 279s(4.43),290(4.58), 309s(4.00),341(3.52), 356(3.58),566(2.71), 600s(2.65),657s(2.23)	89-0621-80
$C_{31}H_{29}NO_2$ [1,1':2',1"-Terphenyl]-3'-carboxalde-hyde, 4'-benzoyl-5'-(diethylamino)-6'-methyl-	MeCN	216(4.51),265s(--), 300s(--)	24-0424-80
$C_{31}H_{29}N_2O_2$ Ethanaminium, N-[4-(1-cyano-2-methoxy-2-oxoethylidene)-2,3,5-triphenyl-2-cyclopenten-1-ylidene]-N-ethyl-, perchlorate	MeCN	238(4.06),318(4.26)	24-0424-80
$C_{31}H_{29}N_3O$ Benzenamine, 4,4'-([1]benzopyrano[4,3-b]indol-6(11H)-ylidene)bis[N,N-di-methyl- Phenol, 2-[3-[bis[4-(dimethylamino)-phenyl]methylene]-3H-indol-2-yl]-, monoperchlorate	pH 3.74 in 64% MeOH pH 4.3 in 64% MeOH	551(4.62),590(4.65) 300(4.4),590(4.85)	33-1264-80 33-1284-80
$C_{31}H_{30}O_5$ Benzoic acid, 3-methoxy-2-[[4-methyl-2,5-bis(phenylmethoxy)phenyl]meth-yl]-, methyl ester	CHCl$_3$	294(3.81)	44-0012-80
$C_{31}H_{30}O_{10}$ 2H,6H-Benzofuro[3,2-b]pyrano[3,2-g]-[1]benzopyran-6-one, 5,9,11b-triacet-oxy-6a,11b-dihydro-2,2-dimethyl-6a-(3-methyl-2-butenyl)-	MeOH	258(4.27),270s(4.24), 300s(3.87),343(3.51)	142-1785-80
$C_{31}H_{30}O_{16}$ Benzo[h][1]benzopyrano[5,4,3-cde][1]-benzopyran-5,12-dione, 10-[(4-O-α-D-	EtOH	236(4.57),264(4.48)	87-0549-80

Compound	Solvent	$\lambda_{max}(\log \epsilon)$	Ref.
glucopyranosyl-β-D-glucopyranosyl)-oxy]-6-hdroxy-1-methyl- (cont.)			87-0549-80
$C_{31}H_{31}BrO_9$ 20-Norgibberella-1,16-diene-7,17-dioic acid, 3β,13-diacetoxy-10-hydroxy-, 7-(4-bromophenacyl) ester, 19,10-lactone	EtOH	256(4.29)	105-0181-80
$C_{31}H_{32}N_4O_2$ 3α-Cinchophylline, 4',5',6',17-tetra-dehydro-	EtOH	218(4.52),231(4.6), 248s(4.3),259s(4.15), 290(4.14),298(4.25)	102-2451-80
	EtOH-HClO₄	214(4.5),223(4.47), 271(4.25),298(4.07), 301(4.16)	102-2451-80
$C_{31}H_{33}NO_5$ 9(10H)-Anthracenone, 10-[[4-(1,4,7,10-tetraoxa-13-azacyclopentadec-13-yl)-phenyl]methylene]-	MeCN	451(4.41)	24-0457-80
$C_{31}H_{33}NO_7$ Staudine	MeOH	230(4.25),274s(4.04), 279(4.08),418s(4.53), 427(4.55)	100-0103-80
$C_{31}H_{33}N_5O_5$ 8H-Oxazolo[4,5-b]phenoxazine-4,6-dicarb-oxamide, 7-amino-N,N,N',N'-tetraeth-yl-9,11-dimethyl-8-oxo-2-phenyl-	CHCl₃	248(4.50),294(4.38), 440(4.52),458(4.60)	4-0017-80
$C_{31}H_{33}N_5O_6$ 5H-Oxazolo[4,5-b]phenoxazine-4,6-di-carboxamide, N,N,N',N'-tetraethyl-9,11-dimethyl-8-nitro-2-phenyl-	CHCl₃	287(4.33),382(4.20), 440(4.11)	4-0017-80
$C_{31}H_{33}N_5O_7$ 5H-Oxazolo[4,5-b]phenoxazine-4,6-di-carboxamide, N,N,N',N'-tetraethyl-8-hydroxy-9,11-dimethyl-7-nitro-2-phenyl-	CHCl₃	289(4.36),301(4.36), 320(4.40),392(4.17), 535(4.18)	4-0017-80
$C_{31}H_{33}N_5O_8$ Benzenecarboximidic acid, N-[[[2,3,3a-9a-tetrahydro-3-(1-oxopropoxy)-2-[(1-oxopropoxy)methyl]-6H-furo-[2',3':4,5]oxazolo[3,2-a]pyrimidin-6-ylidene]amino]methyl]-, (benzoyl-amino)methyl ester, monohydrochloride	MeOH	232(4.17),268(4.05)	44-1577-80
$C_{31}H_{34}N_2O_4$ Butanoic acid, 3-methyl-, 4,6-dimethyl-1,13-bis(1-methylethyl)[1,4]benzodi-oxino[2,3-b]phenazin-2-yl ester	CHCl₃	266(4.63),299s(3.65) 310s(3.41),409(4.04), 417(4.05)	33-0225-80
Butanoic acid, 3-methyl-, 4,13-dimeth-yl-1,6-bis(1-methylethyl)[1,4]benzo-dioxino[2,3-b]phenazin-2-yl ester	CHCl₃	267(4.82),303s(3.85), 316s(3.58),405(4.26), 419(4.27)	33-0225-80
$C_{31}H_{34}N_4O_2$ 3α-Cinchophylline, 4',17-dehydro-	EtOH	216(4.63),297(4.07),	102-2451-80

Compound	Solvent	$\lambda_{max}(\log \epsilon)$	Ref.
(cont.)	EtOH-HClO$_4$	309(4.05),328(4.03) 218(4.68),272(4.01), 297(3.82),308(3.67)	102-2451-80 102-2451-80
$C_{31}H_{34}N_4O_4$ Bonellin	CHCl$_3$	394(5.17),488s(3.90), 494(3.92),523(3.28), 542(3.11),590(3.40), 620s(3.43),641(4.20) (anom.)	39-1080-80C
	6% HCl	402(5.13),526(3.42), 540(2.78),548(2.70), 586s(3.43),636(4.18)	39-1080-80C
$C_{31}H_{35}ClO_7$ Pregna-1,4-diene-3,20-dione, 21-acet-oxy-17-(benzoyloxy)-7-chloro-11-hy-droxy-16-methyl-, (7α,11β,16α)-	MeOH	242(4.20)	145-1618-80
$C_{31}H_{35}NO_7$ Staudine, dihydro-	MeOH MeOH-NaOH	226(4.33),286(3.94) 235(--),294(--)	100-0103-80 100-0103-80
$C_{31}H_{35}NO_8$ Silvaticamide triacetate	MeOH	276s(3.43),296(3.66)	142-0889-80B
$C_{31}H_{35}N_3O_{13}$ Aconitan-3-one, 8-acetoxy-14-(benzoyl-oxy)-1,2-didehydro-13,15-dihydroxy-6,16-dimethoxy-4-(methoxymethyl)-2-nitro-20-nitroso-, (6α,14α,15α,16β)-	EtOH	230(4.2),343(3.4)	18-1381-80
$C_{31}H_{36}N_2O_2$ 1,10-Anthracenedione, 2,4-bis(butyl-amino)-9-(2,4,6-trimethylphenyl)-	hexane	385(3.66),411(3.61), 551s(3.84),593(4.03), 644(3.96)	104-0159-80
	benzene	387(3.63),425(3.60), 546s(3.83),592(4.04), 638(3.99)	104-0159-80
	isoPrOH	380s(3.59),430(3.67), 568(4.00),601s(3.92)	104-0159-80
1,10-Anthracenedione, 4-(butylamino)-2-(diethylamino)-9-(2,4,6-trimethyl-phenyl)-	hexane	387(3.69),417(3.63), 595(4.02),636s(3.92)	104-0159-80
	benzene	388(3.67),424(3.63), 590(4.00),625s(3.90)	104-0159-80
	isoPrOH	378(3.72),421(3.75), 558(4.03)	104-0159-80
$C_{31}H_{36}N_4O_2$ Cinchophyllamine	EtOH	228(4.72),283(4.25), 297(4.19),308(3.86)	102-2451-80
Cinchophylline, (3α,17α)- (isocincho-phyllamine)	EtOH	228(4.74),282(4.26), 296(4.20),308(3.96)	102-2451-80
(3α,17β)-	EtOH	228(4.71),282(4.23), 296(4.18),308(3.91)	102-2451-80
(3β,17α)-	EtOH	227(4.66),282(4.17), 296(4.11),308(3.81)	102-2451-80
$C_{31}H_{36}O_7$ 2,5-Cyclohexadien-1-one, 4-[(4-hydroxy-3,5-dimethylphenyl)(2,3,5,6,8,9,11,12-	dioxan	465(3.66)	18-1550-80

Compound	Solvent	$\lambda_{max}(\log \epsilon)$	Ref.
octahydro-1,4,7,10,13-benzopentaoxa-cyclopentadecin-15-yl)methylene]-2,6-dimethyl- (cont.)			18-1550-80
$C_{31}H_{38}O_{12}$			
6α-Tigloylchaparrinone triacetate	MeOH	225(4.41)	100-0503-80
$C_{31}H_{38}O_{17}$			
Caviunin 7-O-rhamnoglucoside	MeOH	264(4.66),291(4.42)	102-1563-80
	MeOH-NaOAc	265(--),291(--)	102-1563-80
	MeOH-AlCl$_3$	275(--),300s(--)	102-1563-80
$C_{31}H_{41}FN_3O_{12}P$			
Pregna-1,4-diene-3,20-dione, 9-fluoro-11,17-dihydroxy-16-methyl-21-(phos-phonooxy)-, 5'-ester with 4-amino-1-β-D-arabinofuranosyl-2(1H)-pyrimi-dinone, monoammonium salt, (11β,16α)-	pH 1	239(4.23),270(4.24)	87-1343-80
	H$_2$O	234(4.33),260s(4.26)	87-1343-80
	pH 13	234(4.34),260s(4.20)	87-1343-80
$C_{31}H_{41}N_2$			
3H-Indolium, 1,3,3-triethyl-2-[3-(1,3,3-triethyl-1,3-dihydro-2H-indol-2-yli-dene)-1-propenyl]-, tetrafluoroborate	CHCl$_3$	286(4.00),492s(4.40), 520(4.91),557(5.19)	5-2072-80
$C_{31}H_{41}N_3O_3$			
5α-Spirostano[3,2-f]pyrazolo[1,5-a]-pyrimidine, 11-oxo-	MeOH	208(4.22),231(4.70), 280(3.57),316(3.53)	39-0481-80C
5α-Spirost-2-eno[2,3-g]pyrazolo[1,5-a]-pyrimidine, 11-oxo-	MeOH	207(4.33),227(4.62), 314(3.96)	39-0481-80C
$C_{31}H_{42}N_3O_{12}P$			
Pregna-1,4-diene-3,20-dione, 11,17-di-hydroxy-6-methyl-21-(phosphonooxy)-, 5'-ester with 4-amino-1-β-D-arabino-furanosyl-2(1H)-pyrimidinone, mono-ammonium salt	pH 1	252s(4.25),268(4.28)	87-1343-80
	H$_2$O	240(4.31),258(4.27)	87-1343-80
	pH 13	240(4.32),258s(4.27)	87-1343-80
$C_{31}H_{42}O_7$			
Bifurcarenone diacetate	n.s.g.	271(4.11)	88-3123-80
$C_{31}H_{44}CuN_7O_6$			
Copper tetra-tert-butyl isocyanide 1-cyclopentadienyl-2,4,6-trinitro-cyclohexadienide	benzene	472(4.443),560(4.146)	1-0119-80
$C_{31}H_{44}O_7$			
Chola-5,17(20)-dien-24-oic acid, 3-acetoxy-22-(acetoxymethyl)-16ξ,23-epoxy-. ethyl ester	EtOH	252(2.50)	70-0140-80
$C_{31}H_{44}O_8$			
Cyclopropa[4,5]bufa-20,22-dienolide, 3-[(6-deoxy-α-L-nmannopyranosyl)-oxy]-3',4-dihydro-14-hydroxy-, (3β,4β,5S)-	MeOH	297(3.74)	5-0886-80
$C_{31}H_{44}O_{17}$			
Nuzhenide	EtOH	226(4.13),277(3.34)	100-0649-80
$C_{31}H_{46}N_2O_9$			
2,4,8-Pentadecatrienoic acid, 7-[(ami-	MeOH	270(4.47),485(3.29)	88-0309-80

Compound	Solvent	$\lambda_{max}(\log \epsilon)$	Ref.
nocarbonyl)oxy]-15-(5-amino-3,6-di-oxo-1,4-cyclohexadien-1-yl)-11,12,15-trimethoxy-2,6,8,10,14-pentamethyl-, methyl ester, [6S-(2E,4Z,6R*,7S*,8E-10S*,11R*,12S*,14R*,15S*)]-			88-0309-80
$C_{31}H_{46}O_2$			
2,5-Cyclohexadien-1-one, 4-[1-[3,5-bis(1,1-dimethylethyl)-4-hydroxy-phenyl]propylidene]-2,6-bis(1,1-dimethylethyl)-	C_6H_{12}	248s(--),266(3.86), 295(3.88),363(4.37)	12-0351-80
$C_{31}H_{46}O_3$			
Oleana-11,13(18)-dien-28-oic acid, 3-oxo-, methyl ester	$CHCl_3$	247(--),252(4.49), 262(--)	39-0325-80C
$C_{31}H_{46}O_4$			
4-Cyclohexene-1,3-diol, 5-[[1-(1,5-di-methylhexyl)-2,3,3a,6,7,7a-hexahydro-7a-methyl-1H-inden-4-yl]ethynyl]-4-methyl-, diacetate, [1R-[1α(R*),3aβ-4(1R*,3S*),7aα]]-	EtOH	267s(--),274(4.25), 288(4.14)	39-1405-80C
$C_{31}H_{46}O_5$			
Cholesta-4,6-dien-3-one, 6,7-diacetoxy-	MeOH	320(4.34)	78-2341-80
$C_{31}H_{47}N_3$			
5α-Cholestano[3,2-f]pyrazolo[1,5-a]-pyrimidine	MeOH	206(4.33),229(4.76), 233(4.74),280(3.56)	39-0481-80C
5α-Cholest-2-eno[2,3-g]pyrazolo[1,5-a]-pyrimidine	MeOH	283(4.59),317(3.19)	39-0481-80C
$C_{31}H_{48}O_3$			
Oleana-11,13(18)-dien-28-oic acid, 3 -hydroxy-, methyl ester	$CHCl_3$	247(--),252(4.61), 262(--)	39-0325-80C
$C_{31}H_{48}O_4$			
Vitamin D_3, 19β-acetoxy-, acetate	ether	219(4.43),267(4.26)	44-2201-80
$C_{31}H_{48}O_6$			
Pokeberrygenin	EtOH	205(3.80)	100-0510-80
$C_{31}H_{50}N_2O_3$			
18-Tetracosenenitrile, 2-acetoxy-24-(5-formyl-1H-pyrrol-2-yl)-, (Z)-	MeOH	298(4.16)	44-4980-80
$C_{31}H_{52}O_2$			
Dammaran-3-one, 20-hydroxy-24-methyl-ene-, (20R)- (vellozone)	EtOH	288(1.38)	102-2486-80
$C_{31}H_{52}O_6$			
1,3-Benzenedicarboxylic acid, 2-hydr-oxy-4-(3-hydroxy-3,7,11,15-tetra-methylhexadecyl)-6-methyl-, dimethyl ester	isoPrOH	214(4.38),251(4.00), 314(3.71)	44-0803-80

Compound	Solvent	$\lambda_{max}(\log \epsilon)$	Ref.
$C_{32}H_{16}O_2$ Dinaphtho[2,1-a:8',1',2'-cde]naphtha-cene-11,16-dione	$CHCl_3$	245(4.65),250s(4.63), 282(4.59),304(4.79), 335(4.45),349(4.45), 380s(4.08),494(4.04)	44-1424-80
$C_{32}H_{18}$ Dinaphtho[2,1-a:8',1',2'-cde]naphtha-cene	benzene	281(4.67),294(4.59), 317(4.93),329(5.04), 338s(4.81),366s(3.58), 388(3.65),410(4.00), 434(4.30),462(4.38)	44-1424-80
$C_{32}H_{18}O_2$ Benzo[b]chrysene-7,12-dione, 5-(1-naph-thalenyl)-	$CHCl_3$	254(4.64),277(4.51), 324(4.45),348s(4.28), 385(4.28),445s(3.83), 495s(3.71)	44-1424-80
Benzo[b]chrysene-7,12-dione, 5-(2-naph-thalenyl)-	$CHCl_3$	246s(4.64),265(4.62), 315s(4.48),327(4.52), 428(3.86)	44-1424-80
Dibenzo[b,d]phenanthrene-9,14-dione, 7-(2-naphthalenyl)-	$CHCl_3$	247(4.73),327s(4.73), 337(4.38),411(4.77)	44-1424-80
$C_{32}H_{20}$ Benzo[b]chrysene, 5-(2-naphthalenyl)-	$CHCl_3$	243(4.66),260(4.69), 293(4.85),297(4.85), 311(3.79),356(3.79), 373(3.79),390s(3.65), 400s(3.51)	44-1424-80
7,14[1',2']-Naphthalenobenzo[a]naph-thacene, 7,14-dihydro-, (7S)-	EtOH EtOH-0.2% dioxan	229(5.06),264.5(4.55) 214(4.98),229(5.06), 242(4.98),265(4.55), 331(3.90)	35-0506-80 35-0501-80
$C_{32}H_{20}N_2$ Dibenzo[b,j][1,10]phenanthroline, 5,8-diphenyl-	MeCN	257(4.78),296(4.53), 486(3.65)	33-1675-80
$C_{32}H_{20}N_2O_2$ Naphth[1,2-d]oxazole, 2,2'-(1,4-phenyl-enedi-2,1-ethenediyl)bis-, (E,E)-	$CHCl_3$	392(4.84),412(4.89), 434s(4.69)	103-0464-80
Naphth[2,1-d]oxazole, 2,2'-(1,4-phenyl-enedi-2,1-ethenediyl)bis-	$CHCl_3$	394(4.79),406(4.90), 426s(4.70)	103-0464-80
Naphth[2,3-d]oxazole, 2,2'-(1,4-phenyl-enedi-2,1-ethenediyl)bis-, (E,E)-	$CHCl_3$	390(4.48)	103-0464-80
$C_{32}H_{20}N_2S_2$ Naphtho[1,2-d]thiazole, 2,2'-(1,4-phen-ylenedi-2,1-ethenediyl)bis-	$CHCl_3$	400(4.65),418(4.72), 440s(4.55)	103-0464-80
$C_{32}H_{20}N_4$ 4,4''',6,6'''-Tetraaza-m-hexaphenylene	$CHCl_3$	252(5.01),292(4.55)	24-2739-80
$C_{32}H_{21}N_3O_2$ 1H-Pyrido[1,2-b]pyrrolo[3,4-f]indazole-1,3(2H)-dione, 7-methyl-2,4,11-tri-phenyl-	MeOH	273(4.25),367(3.98)	44-0090-80
1H-Pyrido[1,2-b]pyrrolo[3,4-f]indazole-1,3(2H)-dione, 9-methyl-2,4,11-tri-phenyl-	MeOH	206(4.25),215s(4.14), 279(4.36),373(4.04)	44-0090-80

Compound	Solvent	$\lambda_{max}(\log \epsilon)$	Ref.
$C_{32}H_{22}$ 6,15-Ethanonaphtho[2,3-c]pentaphene, 6,15-dihydro-, (6R)-	EtOH	267(5.43),371(4.05)	35-0506-80
$C_{32}H_{22}N_2O_2$ Oxazole, 2,2'-(2,6-naphthalenediyldi- 2,1-ethenediyl)bis[5-phenyl-	CHCl$_3$	377s(4.77),396(4.86), 415s(4.66)	103-0464-80
$C_{32}H_{22}N_4O_{18}S_4$ 2,7-Naphthalenedisulfonic acid, 3,3'- [(3,3'-dihydroxy[1,1'-biphenyl]- 4,4'-diyl)bis(azo)]bis[4,5-di- hydroxy-	dianion	222(4.11),270(3.85), 290(3.85),335(3.85), 625(4.00),670s(3.78)	59-0279-80
	tetraanion	220(4.26),260(3.90), 335(3.95),625(4.04), 670s(3.78)	59-0279-80
	hexaanion	224(4.18),255(3.90), 335(4.04),620(4.04), 670(3.90)	59-0279-80
$C_{32}H_{22}O$ Cyclobuta[b]naphthalen-1(2H)-one, 2-(diphenylmethylene)-8-methyl- 3-phenyl-	CHCl$_3$	253(4.59),285(4.40), 324(4.63),382(4.17), 430(4.13)	88-4869-80
$C_{32}H_{22}O_3$ Benzenepropanal, β-oxo-α-(4-oxo-2,3,5- triphenyl-2-cyclopenten-1-ylidene)-	MeCN	254(4.32),335(4.26)	24-0424-80
$C_{32}H_{23}NO$ 2-Naphthalenol, 1-(2,3,5-triphenyl- 1H-pyrrol-1-yl)-	EtOH	230(4.79),280(4.42), 290(4.42)	39-1870-80C
$C_{32}H_{23}N_5O_7$ 9H-Purine-6-carbonitrile, 9-(2,3,5- tri-O-benzoyl-β-D-ribofuranosyl)-	EtOH	230(4.60),275s(4.00), 282(4.04)	94-0150-80
$C_{32}H_{24}$ Benzene, 1,1',1'',1'''-[[3,4-bis(methyl- ene)-1,2-cyclobutanediylidene]di- methanetetrayl]tetrakis-	CHCl$_3$	262(4.51),320s(3.97), 405(3.76)	88-2713-80
$C_{32}H_{24}N$ Benzo[1,2]quinolizino[3,4,5,6-def]phen- anthridinium, 5,13-dimethyl-9-(4- methylphenyl)-, perchlorate	EtOH	237(4.57),245(4.59), 305(4.43),321(4.45), 364(4.14),412(3.89), 436(4.02)	39-1879-80C
$C_{32}H_{24}N_4O_{10}$ 2,4,7(1H,3H,8H)-Pteridinetrione, 1- (2,3,5-tri-O-benzoyl-β-D-ribo- furanosyl)-	MeOH	229(4.69),274(4.12), 281s(4.08),324(4.16), 338s(3.94)	24-1524-80
2,4,7(1H,3H,8H)-Pteridinetrione, 3- (2,3,5-tri-O-benzoyl-β-D-ribo- furanosyl)-	MeOH	228(4.66),276(4.13), 280s(4.13),328(4.20), 341s(4.09)	24-1524-80
2,4,7(1H,3H,8H)-Pteridinetrione, 8- (2,3,5-tri-O-benzoyl-β-D-ribo- furanosyl)-	MeOH	227(4.60),281(4.07), 356(4.07)	24-1535-80
$C_{32}H_{24}N_{10}O_4S_2$ Pyridine, 3,3'-[dithiobis[1-methyl-5-	MeOH	207(3.63),246s(3.54)	39-0326-80B

Compound	Solvent	$\lambda_{max}(\log \epsilon)$	Ref.
[(4-nitrophenyl)azo]-1H-pyrrole-4,2-diyl]]bis- (cont.)		297s(3.42),452(3.66)	39-0326-80B
$C_{32}H_{24}O_2$ 7,14[1',2']-Naphthalenobenzo[a]naphtha-cene-4,20(1H,17H)-dione, 2,3,7,14,18-19-hexahydro-, (7S)-	EtOH	220(4.77),239(4.87), 244(4.92),270(4.52), 324(3.20)	35-0501-80
$C_{32}H_{24}O_{10}$ Thermorubin	EtOH	252(4.38),298(4.75), 325(4.73),423s(4.29), 435(4.27)	35-5580-80
$C_{32}H_{26}BrNO_3$ Benzo[a]phenanthridine-3-carboxylic acid, 5-(4-bromophenyl)-1,2,5,6-tetrahydro-4-hydroxy-2-phenyl-, ethyl ester	EtOH	226(4.67),274(4.66), 328(4.62)	103-0758-80
$C_{32}H_{26}ClNO_3$ Benzo[a]phenanthridine-3-carboxylic acid, 5-(4-chlorophenyl)-1,2,5,6-tetrahydro-4-hydroxy-2-phenyl-, ethyl ester	EtOH	234(4.67),281(4.63), 293(4.64),342(4.59), 373(4.60)	103-0758-80
$C_{32}H_{26}Cl_2N_2O_2$ 2-Propen-1-one, 3,3'-(1,2-ethanediyldi-imino)bis[1-(4-chlorophenyl)-3-phen-yl-, (Z,Z)-	EtOH	250(4.4),350(4.6)	114-0235-80C
$C_{32}H_{26}N_2O_3$ 2(1H)-Pyridinone, 1-[[(4-methoxyphen-yl)imino](2-methylphenyl)methoxy]-4,6-diphenyl-	CHCl$_3$	327(3.89)	39-2743-80C
$C_{32}H_{26}N_2O_5$ Benzo[a]phenanthridine-3-carboxylic acid, 1,2,5,6-tetrahydro-4-hydroxy-5-(3-nitrophenyl)-2-phenyl-, ethyl ester	EtOH	232(4.67),281(4.63), 294(4.64)	103-0758-80
Benzo[a]phenanthridine-3-carboxylic acid, 1,2,5,6-tetrahydro-4-hydroxy-5-(4-nitrophenyl)-2-phenyl-, ethyl ester	EtOH	232(4.66),288(4.63), 370(4.58)	103-0758-80
Methanone, (octahydro-2,6-diphenyl-furo[2,3-d:4,5-d']diisoxazole-3,7-diyl)bis[phenyl-	MeOH	247(4.64)	49-0909-80
isomer	MeOH	248(4.63)	49-0909-80
$C_{32}H_{26}N_4O_9$ 2H-1,2,3-Triazole-4-carboxylic acid, 5-(cyanomethyl)-2-(2,3,5-tri-O-benz-oyl-β-D-ribofuranosyl)-, methyl ester	pH 1 pH 11 EtOH	235(4.09) 228(4.17),275s(3.74) 231(4.26),270s(3.96)	4-0159-80 4-0159-80 4-0159-80
$C_{32}H_{26}N_4O_9S$ 9H-Purine, 6-(methylsulfonyl)-9-(2,3,5-tri-O-benzoyl-β-D-ribofuranosyl)-	EtOH	230(4.59),275(4.06), 282s(4.00)	94-0150-80
$C_{32}H_{26}O_2$ Ethanone, 1-(4-methylphenyl)-2-[5-(4-	EtOH	415(4.51)	5-1744-80

Compound	Solvent	$\lambda_{max}(\log \epsilon)$	Ref.
methylphenyl)-2,2-diphenyl-3(2H)-furanylidene]- (cont.)			5-1744-80
$C_{32}H_{26}O_{10}$			
[10,10'-Bi-4H-naphtho[2,3-b]pyran]-4,4'-dione, 5,5'-dihydroxy-6,6',8,8'-tetramethoxy-2,2'-dimethyl-, (S)-(nigerone)	MeOH	226(4.71),278(4.92), 407(4.15)	39-2474-80C
4H-Naphtho[1,2-b]pyran-4-one, 5-hydroxy-6-(5-hydroxy-6,8-dimethoxy-2-methyl-4-oxo-4H-naphtho[2,3-b]pyran-10-yl)-8,10-dimethoxy-2-methyl-	MeOH	228(4.70),248(4.75), 279(4.82),390(3.98)	39-2474-80C
$C_{32}H_{26}S$			
7aH-Dibenzo[b,f]cyclopenta[d]thiepin, 1,3-diphenyl-7a-propyl-	EtOH	220(4.6),238(4.5), 270s(4.3)	88-4287-80
$C_{32}H_{27}NO$			
Pyridinium, 1-(2-hydroxyphenyl)-2,4,6-tris(4-methylphenyl)-, hydroxide, inner salt	EtOH	208(4.23),322(4.12)	39-1870-80C
$C_{32}H_{27}NO_2$			
Pyridinium, 3-hydroxy-1-(2-hydroxyphenyl)-2,4,6-tris(4-methylphenyl)-, hydroxide, inner salt	EtOH	209(4.15),325(4.12)	39-1870-80C
$C_{32}H_{27}NO_3$			
Benzo[a]phenanthridine-3-carboxylic acid, 1,2,5,6-tetrahydro-4-hydroxy-2,5-diphenyl-, ethyl ester	EtOH	233(4.67),271(4.61), 282(4.63),293(4.63), 343(4.51),373(4.60)	103-0758-80
$C_{32}H_{27}NO_4$			
Benzo[a]phenanthridine-3-carboxylic acid, 1,2,5,6-tetrahydro-5-(2-hydroxyphenyl)-4-hydroxy-2-phenyl-, ethyl ester	EtOH	233(4.67),271(4.63), 284(4.64),295(4.65), 377(4.61)	103-0758-80
$C_{32}H_{27}N_2$			
3H-Indolium, 3-[(1-ethyl-2-phenyl-1H-indol-3-yl)methylene]-1-methyl-2-phenyl-, perchlorate	n.s.g.	507(4.34)	7-0009-80
$C_{32}H_{28}$			
7,14[1',2']-Naphthalenobenzo[a]naphthacene, 1,2,3,4,7,14,17,18,19,20-decahydro-, (7S)-	EtOH	224(4.98),250(4.60), 310(3.20),324(3.30)	35-0501-80
$C_{32}H_{28}Br_2N_2O_2$			
3-Pyridinecarboxylic acid, 1-(4-bromophenyl)-4-[(4-bromophenyl)amino]-1,2,5,6-tetrahydro-2,6-diphenyl-, ethyl ester	EtOH	265(4.37),313(4.36)	103-0377-80
$C_{32}H_{28}Br_2S_4$			
1,3-Butadiene, 1,2-dibromo-1,3,4,4-tetrakis[(4-methylphenyl)thio]-	heptane	198(4.53),268(3.96)	24-3342-80
1,3-Butadiene, 2,3-dibromo-1,1,4,4-tetrakis[(4-methylphenyl)thio]-	heptane	199(4.89),223s(4.62), 285(4.37)	24-3342-80

Compound	Solvent	$\lambda_{max}(\log \epsilon)$	Ref.
$C_{32}H_{28}ClNO_{10}$ 3H-2a-Azadicyclopenta[ef,kl]heptalene- 1,5,5a,6,7(6H)-pentacarboxylic acid, 2-chloro-3-phenyl-, 1-ethyl 5,5a,6,7-tetramethyl ester	EtOH	238(4.28),288(3.84), 327(3.91),380(3.64)	18-1406-80
$C_{32}H_{28}Cl_2N_2O_2$ 3-Pyridinecarboxylic acid, 1-(4-chloro- phenyl)-4-[(4-chlorophenyl)amino]- 1,2,5,6-tetrahydro-2,6-diphenyl-, ethyl ester	EtOH	264(4.42),314(4.34)	103-0377-80
$C_{32}H_{28}Fe_2Ge$ Ferrocene, 1,1"-(diphenylgermylene)bis-	C_6H_{12}	451(2.37)	101-0345-80J
$C_{32}H_{28}Fe_2Si$ Ferrocene, 1,1"-(diphenylsilylene)bis-	C_6H_{12}	452(2.39)	101-0345-80J
$C_{32}H_{28}I_2S_4$ 1,3-Butadiene, 2,3-diiodo-1,1,4,4- tetrakis[(4-methylphenyl)thio]-	heptane	199(5.12),226s(4.80), 268(4.55)	24-3342-80
$C_{32}H_{28}N_2O_2$ 2-Propen-1-one, 3,3'-(1,2-ethanediyldi- imino)bis[1,3-diphenyl-, (Z,Z)-	EtOH	245(4.3),350(4.5)	114-0235-80C
$C_{32}H_{28}N_2O_3$ 6H-Anthra[1,9-cd]isoxazol-6-one, 3- [4-(1,1-dimethylethyl)phenoxy]-5- [(2,4-dimethylphenyl)amino]-	THF	265(5.05),430(3.87), 614(4.33),666(4.35)	104-1884-80
$C_{32}H_{28}N_2O_5$ 3H-Naphth[1,2-e][1,3]oxazin-3-one, 1,1'-(2-oxo-1,3-cyclohexanediyl)- bis[1,2-dihydro-2-methyl-	EtOH	267s(3.92),277(4.03), 284(3.97),289(3.97), 310(3.45),323(3.59)	4-0277-80
$C_{32}H_{28}N_3$ 3H-Indolium, 1-ethyl-3-[(1-ethyl-2- phenyl-1H-indol-3-yl)imino]-2- phenyl-, perchlorate	n.s.g.	630(4.46)	7-0009-80
$C_{32}H_{28}N_3O_{15}$ 1,3-Dioxolo[4,5-g]isoquinolinium, 7,8- bis[acetoxy(6-nitro-1,3-benzodioxol- 5-yl)methyl]-7,8-dihydro-4-methoxy- 6-methyl-, perchlorate	$CHCl_3$	255(4.50),351(4.37)	83-0715-80
$C_{32}H_{28}N_4O_3$ 9,10-Anthracenedione, 1-azido-2-[4-(1,1- dimethylethyl)phenoxy]-4-[(2,4-di- methylphenyl)amino]-	THF	257(4.69),506(4.00)	104-1884-80
$C_{32}H_{28}O_2$ 9-Anthracenecarboxylic acid, 10-butyli- dene-9,10-dihydro-1,8-diphenyl-, methyl ester	EtOH	232(4.60)	44-1807-80
$C_{32}H_{28}O_7$ 4H-1-Benzopyran-4-one, 5,7-bis(phenyl- methoxy)-3-(2,4,5-trimethoxyphenyl)-	EtOH	255(4.46),291(4.20)	18-0831-80

Compound	Solvent	λ_{max}(log ϵ)	Ref.
C$_{32}$H$_{29}$NO$_5$			
1,2-Benzenedicarboxylic acid, 3-morpholino-4,5,6-triphenyl-, dimethyl ester	MeCN	267(3.97),290s(--)	24-0408-80
1,2-Benzenedicarboxylic acid, 4-morpholino-3,5,6-triphenyl-, dimethyl ester	MeCN	314(3.64)	24-0408-80
C$_{32}$H$_{29}$N$_2$O$_2$S$_2$			
Benzothiazolium, 3-ethyl-2-[3-[2-[(3-ethyl-2(3H)-benzothiazolylidene)methyl]-4H-1-benzopyran-4-ylidene]-1-propenyl]-6-methoxy-, iodide	MeCN	446(4.19),472(4.33), 730(5.03)	124-0965-80
Benzothiazolium, 3-ethyl-2-[3-[4-[(3-ethyl-2(3H)-benzothiazolylidene)methyl]-2H-1-benzopyran-2-ylidene]-1-propenyl]-6-methoxy-, iodide	MeCN	455(4.21),487(4.38), 740(5.22)	124-0965-80
Benzothiazolium, 3-ethyl-2-[[2-[3-(3-ethyl-2(3H)-benzothiazolylidene)-1-propenyl]-4H-1-benzopyran-4-ylidene]-methyl]-6-methoxy-, iodide	MeCN	454(4.23),482(4.34), 712(4.10)	124-0965-80
Benzothiazolium, 3-ethyl-2-[[4-[3-(3-ethyl-2(3H)-benzothiazolylidene)-1-propenyl]-2H-1-benzopyran-2-ylidene]-methyl]-6-methoxy-, iodide	MeCN	460(4.24),492(4.48), 738(5.14)	124-0965-80
C$_{32}$H$_{29}$N$_2$S			
Benzothiazolium, 3-ethyl-2-[5-(1-methyl-2,6-diphenyl-4(1H)-pyridinylidene)-1,3-pentadienyl]-, perchlorate	CH$_2$Cl$_2$	676(5.07)	103-0696-80
Benzothiazolium, 3-ethyl-2-[5-(1-methyl-4,6-diphenyl-2(1H)-pyridinylidene)-1,3-pentadienyl]-, perchlorate	CH$_2$Cl$_2$	660(5.06)	103-0696-80
C$_{32}$H$_{29}$N$_3$			
Propanedinitrile, [3-(diethylamino)-2,5-bis(4-methylphenyl)-4-phenyl-2,4-cyclopentadien-1-ylidene]-	MeCN	282(4.12),377(4.21), 614(3.73)	24-0424-80
C$_{32}$H$_{29}$N$_3$O$_2$			
Propanedinitrile, [3-(diethylamino)-2,5-bis(4-methoxyphenyl)-4-phenyl-2,4-cyclopentadien-1-ylidene]-	MeCN	282(4.19),374(4.17), 608(3.69)	24-0424-80
C$_{32}$H$_{30}$N$_2$O$_2$			
3-Pyridinecarboxylic acid, 1,2,5,6-tetrahydro-4-(phenylamino)-1,2,6-triphenyl-, ethyl ester	EtOH	252(4.43),307(4.31)	103-0377-80
C$_{32}$H$_{30}$O$_2$			
9-Anthracenecarboxylic acid, 10-butyl-9,10-dihydro-1,8-diphenyl-, methyl ester	EtOH	235s(4.22)	44-1807-80
C$_{32}$H$_{31}$NO$_2$			
Ethanone, 1-[4'-benzoyl-5'-(diethylamino)-6'-methyl[1,1':2',1''-terphenyl]-3'-yl]-	MeCN	238(4.49),287s(--)	24-0424-80
Ethanone, 1,1'-[5'-(diethylamino)-6'-phenyl[1,1':2',1''-terphenyl]-3',4'-diyl]bis-	MeCN	230(4.40),265s(--), 290s(--)	24-0424-80
1H-Inden-1-one, 4-(diethylamino)-2,3-dihydro-3-hydroxy-5-methyl-3,6,7-	MeCN	221(4.66),303(3.54)	24-0424-80

Compound	Solvent	$\lambda_{max}(\log \epsilon)$	Ref.
triphenyl- (cont.)			24-0424-80
$C_{32}H_{31}NO_4$			
1,2-Benzenedicarboxylic acid, 3-(diethylamino)-4,5,6-triphenyl-, dimethyl ester	MeCN	268(3.95),274s(--), 293s(--)	24-0408-80
1,2-Benzenedicarboxylic acid, 4-(diethylamino)-3,5,6-triphenyl-, dimethyl ester	MeCN	315(3.66)	24-0408-80
$C_{32}H_{31}N_2$			
3H-Indolium, 1,3,3-trimethyl-2-[3-(1-methyl-2,6-diphenyl-4(1H)-pyridinylidene)-1-propenyl]-, perchlorate	CH_2Cl_2	562(4.84)	103-0696-80
3H-Indolium, 1,3,3-trimethyl-2-[3-(1-methyl-4,6-diphenyl-2(1H)-pyridinylidene)-1-propenyl]-, perchlorate	CH_2Cl_2	550(4.84)	103-0696-80
$C_{32}H_{31}N_2O_2$			
Benzenaminium, 4-[(4-methoxyphenyl)-[2-(2-methoxyphenyl)-3H-indol-3-indol-3-ylidene]methyl]-N,N,N-trimethyl-, perchlorate (in 64% MeOH)	pH 0.00 pH 12.28	384(4.01),513(4.15) 407(3.36)	33-1264-80 33-1264-80
$C_{32}H_{31}N_3$			
5-Phthalazinamine, N,N-diethyl-1,6-dimethyl-4,7,8-triphenyl-	MeCN	241(4.50),270s(--), 375(3.46)	24-0424-80
$C_{32}H_{31}N_3O$			
Benzenamine, 4-[[4-(dimethylamino)phenyl][2-(2-methoxyphenyl)-3H-indol-3-ylidene]methyl]-N,N-dimethyl- (in 64% MeOH)	pH -0.6	295(4.3),400(4.0), 620(4.6)	33-1284-80
	pH 4.2	300(4.4),590(4.9)	33-1284-80
	pH 12.2	475(4.4)	33-1284-80
	pH 12.2	478(4.45),512(4.43)	33-1264-80
Benzenamine, 4,4'-(11-methyl[1]benzopyrano[4,3-b]indol-6(11H)-ylidene)-bis[N,N-dimethyl-	pH 1.75 in 64% MeOH	589(4.92)	33-1264-80
$C_{32}H_{31}N_3O_5$			
4H-Pyrrolo[2,3-d]pyrimidin-4-one, 1,7-dihydro-7-[2,3,5-tris-O-(phenylmethyl)-β-D-ribofuranosyl]-	MeOH	259(4.00)	24-3389-80
$C_{32}H_{31}N_3S_3$			
Benzothiazolium, 2,2'-[3-(3-ethyl-2(3H)-benzothiazolylidene)-1,4-pentadiene-1,5-diyl]bis[3-ethyl-, diperchlorate	EtOH	603(5.03)	124-0389-80
$C_{32}H_{31}N_5O_5S_3$			
5-Thia-1-azabicyclo[4.2.0]oct-2-ene-2-carboxylic acid, 3-[[(4-morpholinylthioxomethyl)hydrazono]methyl]-8-oxo-7-[(2-thienylacetyl)amino]-, diphenylmethyl ester, (6R-trans)-	EtOH	347(3.40)	94-2116-80
$C_{32}H_{32}N_2$			
11,15,16,20-[1,3]Butadiene[1,4]diylidenecyclodocosa[b]quinoxaline, 6,7-8,9,10,21,22,23,24,25-decahydro-	MeOH	238(4.51),252(4.42), 260(4.46),268s(4.20), 292(3.34),305(4.00), 316(3.51)	44-1847-80

Compound	Solvent	$\lambda_{max}(\log \epsilon)$	Ref.
$C_{32}H_{32}N_2O_2$ Benzoxazole, 2,2'-(1,4-phenylenedi-2,1-ethenediyl)bis[5-(1,1-dimethyl-ethyl)-	$CHCl_3$	373(4.88),388(4.91), 406s(4.70)	103-0464-80
$C_{32}H_{32}N_3O$ Benzenaminium, 4-[6-[4-(dimethylamino)-phenyl]-6,11-dihydro[1]benzopyrano-[4,3-b]indol-6-yl]-N,N,N-trimethyl-, perchlorate	pH 5.15 in 64% MeOH	554(4.64),593(4.74)	33-1264-80
$C_{32}H_{32}N_3S_2$ Benzothiazolium, 3-ethyl-2-[7-(3-ethyl-2(3H)-benzothiazolylidene)-2-[(phen-ylmethyl)amino]-1,3,5-heptatrienyl]-, perchlorate	60% EtOH	595(4.66)	104-2080-80
$C_{32}H_{32}N_4$ [1,2,4,5]Tetrazino[6,1-a:3,4-a']diiso-quinoline, 5,6,8,8a,13,14,16,16a-octahydro-8,16-bis(4-methylphenyl)-	C_6H_{12}	210(4.76),243(4.26), 273s(--),279s(--)	88-4877-80
$C_{32}H_{32}N_4O_4$ 7H-Pyrrolo[2,3-d]pyrimidin-4-amine, 7-[2,3,5-tris-O-(phenylmethyl)-β-D-arabinofuranosyl]-	MeOH	269(4.08)	24-2069-80
$C_{32}H_{32}N_8O_2$ 2,3-Quinoxalinedione, 1,4-dihydro-, bis[[1,2-dihydro-1-(2-methylpropyl)-2-oxo-3H-indol-3-ylidene]hydrazone], (E,Z,?,Z)-	EtOH EtOH-NaOH	328(4.21),430(4.50), 490s(4.15),510s(3.94) 339(4.20),389(4.36), 521(4.45)	103-1073-80 103-1073-80
$C_{32}H_{32}O_4$ 1,4-Ethanobiphenylene-9,10-dicarboxylic acid, 1,4,4a,4b,8a,8b-hexahydro-5,8-dimethyl-6,7-diphenyl-, dimethyl ester, (1α,4α,4aα,4bβ,8aβ,8bα,9R*-10S*)-	EtOH	235(4.03),289(3.56)	78-3033-80
$C_{32}H_{32}O_8$ 2H-1-Benzopyran-2-one, 8-[2-[2-(5,7-di-methoxy-2-oxo-2H-1-benzopyran-8-yl)-1,4-dimethyl-3-cyclohexen-1-yl]eth-enyl]-5,7-dimethoxy- (toddasin) Mexolide	EtOH EtOH	228(4.91),263(4.85), 285(4.77),325(4.84) 248(4.70),254(4.80), 260(4.70),283(4.90)	102-1258-80 78-3563-80
$C_{32}H_{34}N_4O$ 20-Phorbinone, 3,4-didehydro-3,9,14-triethyl-4,8,13,18-tetramethyl-	$CHCl_3$	418(5.27),432s(4.98), 523(3.95),564(4.22), 586(4.09),638(3.43)	12-1095-80
$C_{32}H_{34}N_4O_2$ 1H-Pyrazole, 3,3'-(1,4-phenylene)bis-[4,5-dihydro-1-(2-methyl-1-oxoprop-yl)-5-phenyl- 1H-Pyrazole, 3,3'-(1,4-phenylene)bis-[4,5-dihydro-1-(1-oxobutyl)-5-phenyl-	dioxan MeCN dioxan	334s(4.43),348(4.53), 363s(4.42) 330s(4.72),343(4.81), 358s(4.61) 334s(4.68),347(4.75), 363s(4.62)	103-0066-80 103-0066-80 103-0066-80

Compound	Solvent	$\lambda_{max}(\log \epsilon)$	Ref.
(cont.)	MeCN	330s(4.63),343(3.70), 356s(4.57)	103-0066-80
$C_{32}H_{34}N_4O_3$ Anhydrobonellin methyl ester	CHCl$_3$	404(5.34),470s(3.53), 502(4.07),536(3.88), 572s(3.23),627(3.77), 676(5.57)(anom.)	39-1080-80C
$C_{32}H_{34}N_4O_4$ Deuteroporphyrin dimethyl ester	EtOH	494(4.116),525(2.864), 566(2.742),620(2.311)	110-1413-80
$C_{32}H_{34}O_8$ Mexolide, dihydro-	EtOH	248(5.20),254(4.80), 260(4.80),322(4.70)	78-3563-80
$C_{32}H_{35}N_3O_6$ 1H-Imidazole-4-carboxylic acid, 5-amino-1-[2,3,5-tris-O-(phenylmethyl)-β-D-arabinofuranosyl]-, ethyl ester	MeOH	268(4.03)	39-2304-80C
$C_{32}H_{36}N_2O_4S_2$ 1,4-Benzenediamine, N,N'-bis[1,2-dimethyl-4-[(4-methylphenyl)sulfonyl]-2-butenylidene]-	EtOH	250(4.72)	104-0849-80
$C_{32}H_{36}N_4$ Phorbine, 3,4-didehydro-3,9,14-triethyl-4,8,13,18-tetramethyl-	CHCl$_3$	400(5.36),500(4.20), 534(3.61),563(3.81), 616(3.79)	12-1095-80
$C_{32}H_{36}N_4O_6$ Benzaldehyde, 3,4-dimethoxy-, [3-[[2-[[(3.4-dimethoxyphenyl)methylene]-methylhydrazino]-4-oxo-2-cyclohexen-1-yl]oxy]phenyl]methylhydrazone	n.s.g.	352(4.76)	24-2579-80
$C_{32}H_{36}O_3$ Estra-1,3,5(10)-trien-17β-ol, 2,3-bis(phenylmethoxy)-	MeOH	286(3.63)	95-0867-80
$C_{32}H_{36}O_6S$ Estra-1,3,5(10)-trien-17β-ol, 2,3-bis(phenylmethoxy)-, hydrogen sulfate, potassium salt	MeOH	284(3.63)	95-0867-80
$C_{32}H_{36}O_7$ Methanone, (2,4-dimethoxyphenyl)-[6-(2,4-dimethoxyphenyl)-2-(2,6-dimethoxyphenyl)-4-methyl-3-cyclohexen-1-yl]-	EtOH	210(4.85),226s(4.60), 271(4.22),303(4.00)	138-1577-80
isomer	EtOH	208(4.87),225s(4.57), 269(4.21),300(4.00)	138-1577-80
$C_{32}H_{38}O_2$ 1,3-Cyclohexanedione, 5-phenyl-2-retinylidene-	EtOH	270(4.02),495(4.67)	87-0805-80
$C_{32}H_{38}O_4$ Androst-2-ene-3,17-diol, 17β-acetate,	hexane	238(4.78),271(3.83),	39-1659-80B

Compound	Solvent	$\lambda_{max}(\log \epsilon)$	Ref.
3-(2-naphthalenecarboxylate) (cont.)		280(3.89),291(3.73), 319(3.06),326(3.02), 334(3.22)	39-1659-80B
$C_{32}H_{38}O_9$ Anhydroelaeodendroside B	EtOH	218(4.06),333(4.30)	2-0944-80
$C_{32}H_{39}NO_4$ Aflatrem	EtOH	231(4.44),282(3.96), 292s(3.89)	88-0239-80
$C_{32}H_{40}N_2O_{15}$ Aconitan-3-one, 20-acetyl-8,13,14,15-tetraacetoxy-1,2-didehydro-6,16-dimethoxy-4-(methoxymethyl)-2-nitro-, (6α,14α,15α,16β)-	EtOH	228s(4.3),343(3.8)	18-1381-80
$C_{32}H_{40}N_4O_3$ 5α-Spirost-2-eno[2,3-g]pyrazolo[1,5-a]-pyrimidine, 11-oxo-3'-cyano-	MeOH	207(4.33),227(4.62), 314(3.96)	39-0481-80C
$C_{32}H_{40}N_4O_4$ 2-Butene-1,4-dione, 2,3-bis(2,5-dihydro-1,2,2,5,5-pentamethyl-1H-imidazol-4-yl)-1,4-diphenyl-, N^2,N^3-dioxide	EtOH	228(4.11),272(4.12)	70-0956-80
$C_{32}H_{40}O_5$ 1(4H)-Anthracenone, 8-hydroxy-4-(4-hydroxy-3-methyl-2-butenyl)-3,9-dimethoxy-6-methyl-4,7-bis(3-methyl-2-butenyl)-	EtOH	235(4.58),269(4.49), 390(3.85)	100-0487-80
2(1H)-Anthracenone, 5-hydroxy-1-(4-hydroxy-3-methyl-2-butenyl)-4,10-dimethoxy-7-methyl-1,6-bis(3-methyl-2-butenyl)-	EtOH	243(4.50),304(4.22), 387(3.81)	100-0487-80
$C_{32}H_{40}O_6$ Spiro[naphthalene-1(2H),1'-[1H]phenalene]-7,9'-diacetic acid, 2',3',4'-4a,5,6,6'a,7,7',8',9',9'a-dodecahydro-α,α',4a,6'a-tetramethyl-2,4'-dioxo-, dimethyl ester, [1'S-[1α-[4aR*,7S*(R*)],6'aβ,9'β(R),9'aβ]]-	EtOH	232(4.32),270(3.99)	94-3244-80
$C_{32}H_{40}O_8$ Ergosta-2,4,24-trien-26-oic acid, 6,17-diacetoxy-14,20-epoxy-22-hydroxy-1-oxo-, δ-lactone, (6β,17α,20ξ)-	EtOH	225(3.95),307(3.70)	39-0531-80C
$C_{32}H_{40}O_{10}$ Elaeodendroside B acetate	EtOH	217(3.87),272(4.27)	2-0944-80
$C_{32}H_{41}ClN_2O_8$ Normaytansine	EtOH	240(4.53),250(4.41), 281(3.61),288(3.59)	100-0637-80
$C_{32}H_{41}NO_{14}$ D-Arabinitol, 1-C-[1-[(3,4-dimethoxy-phenyl)methyl]-4-(ethoxycarbonyl)-5-methyl-1H-pyrrol-3-yl]-, 1,2,3,4,5-pentaacetate, (S)-	EtOH	236(4.14),260s(--)	39-1199-80C

Compound	Solvent	$\lambda_{max}(\log \epsilon)$	Ref.
D-Arabinitol, 5-C-[1-(3,4-dimethoxy-phenyl)methyl]-4-(ethoxycarbonyl)-5-methyl-1H-pyrrol-3-yl]-, 1,2,3,4,5-pentaacetate, (S)-	EtOH	236(4.14),260s(--)	39-1199-80C
$C_{32}H_{41}N_3O$			
1H-1,2,4-Triazole, 1-[2,6,11,15-tetra-methyl-1-oxo-17-(2,6,6-trimethyl-1-cyclohexen-1-yl)-2,4,6,8,10,12,14,16-heptadecaoctaenyl]-, (all-E)-	EtOH	476(4.57)	33-0277-80
$C_{32}H_{41}N_3O_7$			
5H,12H-3,4-Dioxa-5a,11a,15a-triazacy-clooct[1m]indeno[5,6-b]fluorene-11,15(2H,13H)-dione, 1,10,10a,14-14a,14b-hexahydro-10a-hydroxy-7-meth-oxy-2,2-dimethyl-10-[(3-methyl-2-but-enyl)oxy]-5-(2-methyl-1-propenyl)-	EtOH	229(4.63),277(3.91), 295(3.88)	94-0245-80
Fumitremorgin A	EtOH	226(4.50),278(3.72), 296(3.69)	94-0245-80
$C_{32}H_{42}N_8O_6S_4$			
Ulithiacyclamide	MeOH	247(3.85)	35-5688-80
$C_{32}H_{42}O_5Se$			
5β-Pregn-17(20)-ene-20-carboselenoic acid, 3α,11β-diacetoxy-, Se-phenyl ester	pentane	241(4.33),298(3.81)	33-2328-80
$C_{32}H_{44}N_2O_{16}$			
D-galacto-Octonic acid, 2,3-dideoxy-2-[1-[[(3,4-dimethoxyphenyl)methyl]-amino]ethylidene]-3-(nitromethyl)-, ethyl ester, 4,5,6,7,8-pentaacetate	EtOH	295(4.46)	39-1199-80C
D-gluco-	EtOH	293(4.14)	39-1199-80C
$C_{32}H_{44}O_2$			
β-Citraurinine acetate	hexane	403(3.23),424(3.33), 450(3.29)	33-1377-80
$C_{32}H_{44}O_5$			
6-Oxodimethylpristimerol	EtOH	210(4.13),225(4.00), 247(4.07),285(3.80), 300(3.93)	88-4749-80
$C_{32}H_{44}O_6Se$			
5β-Pregnane-20-carboselenoic acid, 3α,11α-diacetoxy-, Se-phenyl ester	pentane	225s(--),255(3.57)	33-2328-80
5β-Pregnane-20-carboselenoic acid, 3α,12α-diacetoxy-, Se-phenyl ester	pentane	233(4.23),257(3.68)	33-2328-80
$C_{32}H_{44}O_{14}$			
Crocetin di-β-D-galactopyranosyl ester	EtOH	433(5.02),459(4.97)	27-0020-80
$C_{32}H_{46}N_4$			
5α-Cholest-2-eno[2,3-g]pyrazolo[1,5-a]-pyrimidine, 3'-cyano-	MeOH	232(4.58),279(3.73), 314(3.77)	39-0481-80C
$C_{32}H_{46}O_2Si_2$			
Silane, [1,8-[6]dodecenophenanthrene-16,17-diylbis(oxy)]bis[trimethyl-	C_6H_{12}	255(4.54),262(4.64), 270s(4.38),293(4.02),	44-1847-80

Compound	Solvent	$\lambda_{max}(\log \epsilon)$	Ref.
(cont.)		307(4.08)	44-1847-80
$C_{32}H_{46}O_4$			
Ergosta-8,14,24(28)-triene-3,11-dione, 12-acetoxy-4,4-dimethyl-, (5α,12β)-	EtOH	292(4.10)	39-2914-80C
$C_{32}H_{46}O_8$			
Ergost-2-en-1-one, 15-acetoxy-5,6:22-26:24,25-triepoxy-26-ethoxy-4-hydroxy-, (4β,5β,6β,15α,22R,24S,25S-26R)-	EtOH	214(3.95)	150-2134-80
$C_{32}H_{48}O_2$			
D-Homo-28-noroleana-12,15,17-trien-3β-ol, acetate	EtOH	202(4.11),210(3.77), 230s(3.63)	12-2517-80
$C_{32}H_{48}O_3$			
D-Homo-30-nordammara-13,15,17-trien-3-ol, 17,23-epoxy-, acetate, (3β,20ξ,23S)-	EtOH	224(4.33),260(3.42)	12-2071-80
$C_{32}H_{48}O_4$			
14,15-Dioxadispiro[5.1.5.2]pentadeca-1,4,9,12-tetraene-3,11-dione, 2,4,10,12-tetrakis(1,1-dimethylethyl)-7-(1-methylethyl)-	C_6H_{12}	212s(--),254(4.28)	12-0351-80
Multiflora-7,9(11)-dien-29α-oic acid, 3α-acetoxy-	EtOH	234(4.04),241(4.08), 249(3.91)	39-2933-80C
$C_{32}H_{50}O_3$			
Olean-12-en-11-one, 3β-acetoxy-	MeOH	252(4.07)	102-0255-80
Urs-12-en-11-one, 3β-acetoxy-	MeOH	250(4.08)	2-0165-80
	MeOH	252(4.08)	102-0255-80
$C_{32}H_{50}O_3Te$			
5α-Spirost-9(11)-en-3β-ol, 2,2-dimethylpropanetelluroate	C_6H_{12}	243(3.57),265s(2.74), 346(3.83),590(2.38)	39-2191-80C
$C_{32}H_{50}O_4$			
Betulinic acid acetate	H_2SO_4	310(3.94)	105-0464-80
Ergosta-8,14,24(28)-triene-3,11,12-triol, 4,4-dimethyl-, 12-acetate, (3β,5α,11α,12β)-	EtOH	248(4.26)	39-2914-80C
16,17-Secodammara-17(20),22-dien-16-oic acid, 3β-acetoxy-30-hydroxy-, γ-lactone, (17E,22E)-	EtOH	232(4.46),237(4.47), 246(4.27)	12-2071-80
Ursolic acid acetate	H_2SO_4	310(4.17)	105-0464-80
$C_{32}H_{52}O_2$			
β-Amyrin acetate	H_2SO_4	310(4.29)	105-0464-80
$C_{32}H_{56}N_6S_2$			
Bis(tetrapropylaminium) 1,2,3,4-tetracyano-1,3-butadiene-1,4-dithiolate	CH_2Cl_2	280s(3.66),360(3.95), 447(4.17)	44-5113-80
$C_{32}H_{56}N_6S_3$			
Bis(2-mercapto-1,2-dicyanoethenyl) suldie, tetrapropylaminium salt	EtOH	220s(4.21),378(4.28)	44-5113-80

Compound	Solvent	$\lambda_{max}(\log \epsilon)$	Ref.
$C_{32}H_{56}OTe$			
5α-Cholestan-3β-ol, 2,2-dimethylprop-anetelloroate	C_6H_{12}	243(3.63),266s(2.92), 346(3.88),592(2.51)	39-2191-80C
$C_{32}H_{56}P_2Pt$			
Platinum, di-1,3-butadiynylbis(tribut-ylphosphine)-, (SP-4-1)-	CH_2Cl_2	241(4.45),251s(4.32), 268(4.01),287(3.95), 318(4.39)	47-0661-80
polymer	CH_2Cl_2	270(4.29),303(4.47), 328s(4.51),350(4.85), 368(4.80),397(4.52), 432(4.22),459s(3.30), 501(2.66)	47-0661-80
$C_{32}H_{72}Cr_2N_2O_7$			
Bis(tetrabutylaminium) dichromate	n.s.g.	275(3.67),345(3.50), 360(3.54)	107-0075-80
$C_{32}H_{80}Si_8$			
Cyclooctasilane, hexadecaethyl-	isooctane	196s(4.91),221s(4.38), 244(4.32),260s(3.79)	101-00C5-80K

Compound	Solvent	$\lambda_{max}(\log \epsilon)$	Ref.
$C_{33}H_{20}Cl_4N_2O_3$			
2,5-Imino-1,6,3-benzodioxazocin-4(5H)-one, 7,8,9,10-tetrachloro-2,3-dihydro-2,3,5,11-tetraphenyl-	MeCN	216(4.948),292(3.19), 301(3.228)	5-1850-80
$C_{33}H_{23}NO$			
Pyridinium, 1-(2-hydroxy-1-naphthalenyl)-2,4,6-triphenyl-, hydroxide, inner salt	EtOH	210(4.40),240(4.49), 303(4.31)	39-1870-80C
$C_{33}H_{23}NO_2$			
Benzo[1,2]quinolizino[3,4,5,6-def]phenanthridinium, 2-carboxy-5,13-dimethyl-9-(4-methylphenyl)-, hydroxide, inner salt	EtOH	220(4.32),234(4.43), 254(4.56),308(4.57), 318(4.55),354(4.32), 368(4.29),418(3.78), 440(3.96)	39-1879-80C
Pyridinium, 3-hydroxy-1-(2-hydroxy-1-naphthalenyl)-2,4,6-triphenyl-, hydroxide, inner salt	EtOH	230(4.34),312(4.12)	39-1870-80C
$C_{33}H_{23}O_2$			
2-Benzopyrylium, 3-phenyl-1-[3-(2-phenyl-4H-1-benzopyran-4-ylidene)-1-propenyl]-, perchlorate	CH_2Cl_2	712(5.20)	103-0137-80
2-Benzopyrylium, 3-phenyl-1-[3-(3-phenyl-1H-2-benzopyran-1-ylidene)-1-propenyl]-, perchlorate	CH_2Cl_2	707(5.02)	103-0137-80
$C_{33}H_{23}S_2$			
2-Benzothiopyrylium, 3-phenyl-1-[3-(2-phenyl-4H-1-benzothiopyran-4-ylidene)-1-propenyl]-, perchlorate	CH_2Cl_2	810(5.11)	103-0599-80
2-Benzothiopyrylium, 3-phenyl-1-[3-(3-phenyl-1H-2-benzothiopyran-1-ylidene)-1-propenyl]-, perchlorate	CH_2Cl_2	820(5.01)	103-0599-80
$C_{33}H_{25}Cl$			
4,5:10,11:13,14:15,16-Tetrabenzopentacyclo[6.4.2^{3,6}.2^{9,12}.1^{2,7}.0]heptadeca-4,10,13,15-tetraene, 3-chloro-	MeCN	267(3.24),273(3.30), 275s(3.24)	24-1458-80
4,5:10,11:13,14:15,16-Tetrabenzopentacyclo[6.4.2^{3,6}.2^{9,12}.1^{2,7}.0]heptadeca-4,10,13,15-tetraene, 9-chloro-	MeCN	259s(3.08),266(3.18), 272(3.29),277(3.23)	24-1458-80
$C_{33}H_{25}N$			
Pyridine, 2,4-bis(2-[1,1'-biphenyl]-4-ylethenyl)-	DMF	339(4.84)	33-1311-80
Pyridine, 2,5-bis(2-[1,1'-biphenyl]-4-ylethenyl)-	DMF	381(4.91)	33-1311-80
Pyridine, 2,6-bis(2-[1,1'-biphenyl]-4-ylethenyl)-	DMF	320(4.78),353(4.67)	33-1311-80
$C_{33}H_{25}NO_2S_3$			
3H-Phenoxazin-3-one, 2,7,9-tris[(4-methylphenyl)thio]-	n.s.g.	498(3.47)	103-0032-80
$C_{33}H_{26}$			
4,5:;0,11:13,14:15,16-Tetrabenzopentacyclo[6.4.2^{3,6}.2^{9,12}.1^{2,7}.0]heptadeca-4,10,13,15-tetraene	MeCN	260s(3.21),267(3.33), 273(3.42),276s(3.31)	24-1458-80

Compound	Solvent	$\lambda_{max}(\log \epsilon)$	Ref.
4,5:11,12:14,15:16,17-Tetrabenzopenta-cyclo[7.4.2^{3,6}.2^{10,13}.0.0^{2,7}]hepta-deca-4,11,14,16-tetraene	MeCN	251s(3.05),259s(3.19), 265(3.39),272(3.48)	24-1458-80
$C_{33}H_{26}N_4O_{10}$			
2,4,7(1H,3H,8H)-Pteridinetrione, 6-methyl-1-(2,3,5-tri-O-benzoyl-β-D-ribofuranosyl)-	MeOH	228(4.66),275(4.14), 281s(4.13),325(4.20), 338(4.05)	24-1524-80
2,4,7(1H,3H,8H)-Pteridinetrione, 6-methyl-3-(2,3,5-tri-O-benzoyl-β-D-ribofuranosyl)-	MeOH	229(4.68),276s(4.07), 281(4.09),327(4.22), 340s(4.10)	24-1524-80
2,4,7(1H,3H,8H)-Pteridinetrione, 6-methyl-8-(2,3,5-tri-O-benzoyl-β-D-ribofuranosyl)-	MeOH	229(4.64),283(4.02), 290(4.02),356(4.06)	24-1535-80
$C_{33}H_{27}NO_7$			
1,3-Dioxolo[4,5-g]isoquinoline-5-metha-nol, α-[3,4-dimethoxy-5-(phenylmeth-oxy)phenyl]-, benzoate	MeOH	238(4.82),282(3.83), 293(3.64),317(3.68), 331(3.78)	100-0151-80
$C_{33}H_{28}BrNO_4$			
Benzo[a]phenanthridine-3-carboxylic acid, 5-(4-bromophenyl)-1,2,5,6-tetrahydro-4-hydroxy-2-(4-methoxy-phenyl)-, ethyl ester	EtOH	232(4.68),282(4.64), 294(4.64),344(4.60), 374(4.61)	103-0758-80
$C_{33}H_{28}ClNO_4$			
Benzo[a]phenanthridine-3-carboxylic acid, 5-(4-chlorophenyl)-1,2,5,6-tetrahydro-4-hydroxy-2-(4-methoxy-phenyl)-, ethyl ester	EtOH	226(4.67),273(4.66), 281(4.65),294(4.64), 330(4.62),357(4.62)	103-0758-80
$C_{33}H_{28}FNO_4$			
Benzo[a]phenanthridine-3-carboxylic acid, 5-(4-fluorophenyl)-1,2,5,6-tetrahydro-4-hydroxy-2-(4-methoxy-phenyl)-, ethyl ester	EtOH	230(4.65),277(4.63), 291(4.63),344(4.54), 374(4.55)	103-0758-80
$C_{33}H_{28}N_2O_6$			
Benzo[a]phenanthridine-3-carboxylic acid, 1,2,5,6-tetrahydro-4-hydroxy-2-(4-methoxyphenyl)-5-(3-nitrophen-yl)-, ethyl ester	EtOH	233(4.67),271(4.63), 281(4.64),293(4.63), 341(4.60),373(4.60)	103-0758-80
Benzo[a]phenanthridine-3-carboxylic acid, 1,2,5,6-tetrahydro-4-hydroxy-2-(4-methoxyphenyl)-5-(4-nitrophen-yl)-, ethyl ester	EtOH	230(4.66),283(4.64), 294(4.64),370(4.59)	103-0758-80
Methanone, [octahydro-4a-(hydroxymeth-yl)-2,6-diphenylfuro[2,3-d:4,5-d']-diisoxazole-6,7-diyl]bis[phenyl-, (3α,3aα,4aβ,7β,7aβ,7bα)-	MeOH	246(4.45)	73-3546-80
$C_{33}H_{28}N_6O_8$			
β-D-Ribofuranoside, (2,4-diamino-6-pteridinyl)methyl 2,3,5-tribenzoate	pH 2.0	232(4.67),278(3.82), 335(3.96)	24-1514-80
	pH 7.0	231(4.83),260(4.54), 284s(4.06),373(3.99)	24-1514-80
	MeOH	230(4.71),261(4.44), 282s(3.99),372(3.88)	24-1514-80

Compound	Solvent	$\lambda_{max}(\log \epsilon)$	Ref.
$C_{33}H_{28}OPSe$ Phosphonium, [2-methoxy-2-phenyl- 1-(phenylseleno)ethenyl]triphenyl-, (E)-, tetrafluoroborate	n.s.g.	255s(4.91),270s(4.43), 275s(4.36),340(3.30)	104-0573-80
$C_{33}H_{28}O_6$ [1,1':2',1"-Terphenyl]-3',4'-dicarbox- ylic acid, 6'-(1-acetyl-2-hydroxy-1- propenyl)-5'-phenyl-, dimethyl ester	MeCN	216(4.61),290(3.90)	24-0424-80
$C_{33}H_{28}O_{10}$ [10,10'-Bi-4H-naphtho[2,3-b]pyran]- 4,4'-dione, 5-hydroxy-5',6,6',8,8'- pentamethoxy-2,2'-dimethyl-, (S)-	MeOH	225(4.77),275(4.97), 324(3.56),342(3.54), 392(4.16)	39-2474-80C
$C_{33}H_{29}NO_4$ Benzo[a]phenanthridine-3-carboxylic acid, 1,2,5,6-tetrahydro-4-hydroxy- 2-(4-methoxyphenyl)-5-phenyl-, ethyl ester	EtOH	232(4.67),271(4.61), 288(4.63),293(4.63), 342(4.61),373(4.61)	103-0758-80
Benzo[a]phenanthridine-3-carboxylic acid, 1,2,5,6-tetrahydro-4-hydroxy- 5-(4-methoxyphenyl)-2-phenyl-, ethyl ester	EtOH	230(4.67),283(4.63), 294(4.64),343(4.60), 373(4.61)	103-0758-80
$C_{33}H_{29}NO_5$ Benzo[a]phenanthridine-3-carboxylic acid, 1,2,5,6-tetrahydro-4-hydroxy- 5-(2-hydroxyphenyl)-2-(4-methoxy- phenyl)-, ethyl ester	EtOH	227(4.66),285(4.63)	103-0758-80
2,4,7-Cycloheptatriene-1,2-dicarboxylic acid, 6-oxo-4,5,7-triphenyl-3-pyrrol- idino-, dimethyl ester	MeCN	307(4.20),494(2.77)	24-0408-80
$C_{33}H_{29}NO_6$ 2,4,7-Cycloheptatriene-1,2-dicarboxylic acid, 3-morpholino-6-oxo-4,5,7-tri- phenyl-, dimethyl ester	MeCN	298(4.21),470(2.65)	24-0408-80
$C_{33}H_{29}N_2$ 3H-Indolium, 1-ethyl-3-[(1-ethyl-2- phenyl-1H-indol-3-yl)methylene]- 2-phenyl-, perchlorate	n.s.g.	508(4.32)	7-0009-80
$C_{33}H_{30}ClNO_{10}$ 3H-2a-Azadicyclopenta[ef,kl]heptalene- 1,5,5a,6,7(6H)-pentacarboxylic acid, 2-chloro-3-(4-methylphenyl)-, 1-ethyl 5,5a,6,7-tetramethyl ester	EtOH	262s(4.12),326(3.92), 385(3.65)	18-1406-80
$C_{33}H_{30}NO$ 3H-Indolium, 2-[5-(2,6-diphenyl-4H- pyran-4-ylidene)-1,3-pentadienyl]- 1,3,3-trimethyl-, perchlorate	CH_2Cl_2	685(4.97),740(5.15)	103-0696-80
3H-Indolium, 2-[5-(4,6-diphenyl-2H- pyran-2-ylidene)-1,3-pentadienyl]- 1,3,3-trimethyl-, perchlorate	CH_2Cl_2	750(4.97),796(4.87)	103-0696-80
$C_{33}H_{30}N_2O_3$ 6H-Anthra[1,9-cd]isoxazol-6-one, 3-	THF	265(5.04),415(3.87),	104-1884-80

Compound	Solvent	λ_{max}(log ϵ)	Ref.
[4-(1,1-dimethylethyl)phenoxy]-5- [(2,4,6-trimethylphenyl)amino]-		612(4.33),664(4.35)	104-1885-80
6H-Anthra[1,9-cd]isoxazol-6-one, 5- [(2,4-dimethylphenyl)amino]-3- [4-(1,1-dimethylpropyl)phenoxy]-	THF	265(5.06),430(3.88), 614(4.34),666(4.35)	104-1884-80
$C_{33}H_{30}N_4O_3$ 9,10-Anthracenedione, 1-azido-2-[4-(1,1- dimethylethyl)phenoxy]-4-[(2,4,6-tri- methylphenyl)amino]-	THF	257(4.70),506(3.96)	104-1884-80
9,10-Anthracenedione, 1-azido-4-[(2,4- dimethylphenyl)amino]-2-[4-(1,1-di- methylpropyl)phenoxy]-	THF	257(4.63),506(4.10)	104-1884-80
$C_{33}H_{30}O_5$ 9(10H)-Anthracenone, 5-methoxy-2-meth- yl-10-(2-oxopropyl)-1,4-bis(phenyl- methoxy)-	CHCl₃	332(3.53)	44-0012-80
$C_{33}H_{30}O_8$ 4H-1-Benzopyran-4-one, 2-[3,5-dimeth- oxy-4-(phenylmethoxy)phenyl]-5,6-di- methoxy-7-(phenylmethoxy)-	MeOH	240s(--),267(4.163), 320(4.453)	102-0669-80
$C_{33}H_{31}N_2O_3S_2$ Benzothiazolium, 3-ethyl-2-[[2-[3-(3- ethyl-6-methoxy-2(3H)-benzothiazol- ylidene)-1-propenyl]-4H-1-benzopyran- 4-ylidene]methyl]-6-methoxy, iodide	MeCN	460(4.26),482(4.35), 732(5.09)	124-0965-80
Benzothiazolium, 3-ethyl-2-[[4-[3-(3- ethyl-6-methoxy-2(3H)-benzothiazol- ylidene)-1-propenyl]-2H-1-benzopyran- 2-ylidene]methyl]-6-methoxy-, iodide	MeCN	462(4.24),496(4.40), 748(5.19)	124-0965-80
$C_{33}H_{32}ClN_3O_4S$ 7H-Pyrrolo[2,3-d]pyrimidine, 4-chloro- 2-(methylthio)-7-[2,3,5-tris-O-(phen- ylmethyl)-α-D-arabinofuranosyl]-	MeOH	252(4.32),275(3.83), 310(3.81)	24-2069-80
β-	MeOH	253(4.35),276(3.81), 310(3.81)	24-2069-80
$C_{33}H_{32}N_{10}O_9$ Urea, N,N'-bis[2-[(2,4-dinitrophenyl)- hydrazono]-1,1-dimethyl-2-phenyl- ethyl]-	EtOH	198(4.6),222(4.5), 254(4.4),357(4.6)	5-1016-80
$C_{33}H_{33}N_3O_5S$ 4H-Pyrrolo[2,3-d]pyrimidin-4-one, 1,7- dihydro-2-(methylthio)-7-[2,3,5-tris- O-(phenylmethyl)-α-D-ribofuranosyl]-	MeOH	269(4.06),286(4.04)	24-3389-80
β-	MeOH	268(4.11),288(4.08)	24-3389-80
$C_{33}H_{34}N_3O$ Benzenaminium, 4-[[4-(dimethylamino)- phenyl][2-(2-methoxyphenyl)-3H-indol- 3-ylidene]methyl]-N,N,N-trimethyl-, perchlorate (in 64% MeOH)	pH 5.25 pH 10.37	407(3.96),607(4.53) 367(3.63),508(4.03)	33-1264-80 33-1264-80
$C_{33}H_{34}N_4O_2$ Benzeneacetonitrile, α-[3,4-bis(dimeth- ylamino)-2,5-diphenyl-2,4-cyclopenta-	MeCN	245s(--),288(4.01), 405(4.18)	24-0424-80

Compound	Solvent	$\lambda_{max}(\log \epsilon)$	Ref.
dien-1-ylidene]-4-nitro- (cont.)			24-0424-80
$C_{33}H_{34}N_4O_3$ Pyropheophorbide a	acetone	409(5.08`,507(4.08), 535(3.J8),610(3.90), 667(4.74)	44-1969-80
$C_{33}H_{34}N_4O_4S$ 7H-Pyrrolo[2,3-d]pyrimidin-4-amine, 2-(methylthio)-7-[2,3,5-tris-O-(phen- ylmethyl)-β-D-arabinofuranosyl]-	MeOH	234(4.38),281(4.16)	24-2069-80
$C_{33}H_{36}$ 1,1'-Spirobi[benz[g]indan], 3,3'- bis(1,1-dimethylethyl)-	isooctane	226(4.2),285f(4.1), 305-320f(3.6)	88-4279-80
$C_{33}H_{36}FeO_2$ Ferrocene, 1,1'-[2-[3,7-dimethyl- 9-(2,6,6-trimethyl-1-cyclohexen-1- yl)-2,4,6,8-nonatetraenylidene]-1,3- dioxo-1,3-propanediyl]-, (all-E)-	EtOH	300(4.32),460(4.47)	87-0805-80
$C_{33}H_{36}N_4O_4Zn$ Zinc, [dimethyl 2,3-dihydro-3,3,7,12,17- pentamethyl-21H,23H-porphine-2,18-di- propanoato(2-)-$N^{21},N^{22},N^{23},N^{24}$]-	CHCl₃	402(5.08),504(3.34), 539(2.85),566(2.85), 583(2.45),612(4.39)	39-1080-80C
$C_{33}H_{37}CoN_4O_4$ Cobalt(1+), (diethyl octadehydro-1,3,7- 8,12,13,17,19-octamethyl-2,18-corrin- dicarboxylato-$N^{21},N^{22},N^{23},N^{24}$)-, (SP-4-3)-, perchlorate	CHCl₃	282(4.33),354(4.16), 420(3.88),498(3.89)	135-1219-80
$C_{33}H_{37}F_3O_2$ 1,3-Cyclohexanedione, 2-retinylidene- 5-[4-(trifluoromethyl)phenyl]-	EtOH	265(4.03),495(4.63)	87-0805-80
$C_{33}H_{37}NO_9$ Silvaticamide tetraacetate	MeOH	252(4.04),275s(3.45), 310(3.66)	142-0889-80B
$C_{33}H_{37}NO_{11}S$ β-D-Glucopyranoside, 4-(2,3-dihydro-2- phenyl-1,5-benzothiazepin-4-yl)phenyl 4-O-β-D-glucopyranosyl-	n.s.g.	226s(4.39),278(4.45), 326s(4.00)	114-0027-80A
β-D-Glucopyranoside, 4-(2,3-dihydro-4- phenyl-1,5-benzothiazepin-2-yl)phenyl 4-O-β-D-glucopyranosyl-	n.s.g.	224s(4.16),258(4.11), 318(3.46)	114-0027-80A
$C_{33}H_{37}N_4NiO_4$ Nickel(1+), (diethyl octadehydro-1,3,7- 8,12,13,17,19-octamethyl-2,18-corrin- dicarboxylato-$N^{21},N^{22},N^{23},N^{24}$)-, (SP-4-3)-, perchlorate	CHCl₃	288(4.42),365(4.23), 465(3.79),568(4.05)	135-1219-80
$C_{33}H_{38}N_4Ni$ Nickel, [2,7,12,17-tetraethyl-3,5,8,13- 18-pentamethyl-21H,23H-porphinato- (2-)-$N^{21},N^{22},N^{23},N^{24}$]-, (SP-4-2)-	CH₂Cl₂	404(5.21),529(3.85), 565(4.10)	130-0001-80
Nickel, [3,7,13,17-tetraethyl-2,5,8,12-	CHCl₃	393(5.20),520(4.01),	130-0063-80

Compound	Solvent	λ_{max}(log ϵ)	Ref.
18-pentamethyl-21H,23H-porphinato-(2-)-N^{21},N^{22},N^{23},N^{24}]-, (SP-4-2)-		554(4.40)	130-0063-80
$C_{33}H_{38}N_4O_2$ 21H,23H-Porphine-2-carboxylic acid, 7,12,18-triethyl-3,8,13,17-tetramethyl-, ethyl ester	CHCl$_3$	407(5.27),510(3.99), 548(4.18),573(3.94), 632(3.23)	12-1095-80
$C_{33}H_{38}N_4O_4$ 21H,23H-Porphine-2,18-dipropanoic acid, 2,3-dihydro-3,3,7,12,17-pentamethyl-, dimethyl ester	CHCl$_3$	394(5.29),488(4.16), 521(3.38),539(3.15), 590(3.52),620s(3.76), 641(4.59)	39-1080-80C
	6% HCl	402(5.08),523(3.53), 587s(3.66),631(4.39)	39-1080-80C
$C_{33}H_{38}N_4Zn$ Zinc, [2,7,12,17-tetraethyl-3,5,8,13-18-pentamethyl-21H,23H-porphinato-(2-)-N^{21},N^{22},N^{23},N^{24}]-, (SP-4-2)-	CH$_2$Cl$_2$	407(5.32),537(5.06), 570(4.04)	130-0001-80
$C_{33}H_{38}O_2$ 2-Cyclohexen-1-one, 4-[[3-(2-methoxy-5-methylphenyl)propyl]phenyl]-4-methyl-2-(3-phenylpropyl)-	EtOH	225(4.10)	22-0304-80
$C_{33}H_{39}N_7O_5S_2$ Ulicyclamide	MeOH	248(3.90)	35-5688-80
$C_{33}H_{40}BrNiP_4$ Nickel(1+), bromo(1,5,9,13-tetraphenyl-1,5,9,13-tetraphosphatridecane-P,P',P'',P''')-, bromide, (SP-5-13)-	MeOH CH$_2$Cl$_2$	295(3.78),425(2.71) 265(4.24),290s(--), 430(3.15)	24-1356-80 24-1356-80
$C_{33}H_{40}N_2O_9$ Reserpine (oxindole)	MeOH	218(4.54),248s(4.21), 287(3.68),294(3.65)	102-1833-80
$C_{33}H_{40}N_2O_{10}$ Yohimban-16-carboxylic acid, 1,2-didehydro-2,7-dihydro-7-hydroxy-11,17-dimethoxy-18-[(3,4,5-trimethoxybenzoyl)oxy]-, methyl ester	EtOH	233(4.3),267(4.1), 295(3.9)	35-6157-80
$C_{33}H_{40}N_4$ 21H,23H-Porphine, 2,7,12,17-tetraethyl-3,5,8,13,18-pentamethyl-	CH$_2$Cl$_2$	406(5.23),506(4.14), 539(3.75),576(3.76), 627(3.11)	130-0001-80
$C_{33}H_{40}N_4O$ 21H,23H-Porphine-5-methanol, 2,7,12,17-tetraethyl-3,8,13,18-tetramethyl-	CH$_2$Cl$_2$	404(5.04),504(4.08), 538(3.92),573(3.76), 624(3.60)	130-0001-80
$C_{33}H_{40}O_3$ 1,3-Cyclohexanedione, 5-(4-methoxyphenyl)-2-retinylidene-	EtOH	270(4.10),495(4.68)	87-0805-80
$C_{33}H_{42}N_2O$ 1H-Imidazole, 1-[2,6,11,15-tetramethyl-1-oxo-17-(2,6,6-trimethyl-1-cyclohex-	EtOH	464(4.66)	33-0277-80

Compound	Solvent	$\lambda_{max}(\log \epsilon)$	Ref.
en-1-yl)-2,4,6,8,10,12,14,16-hepta-decaoctaenyl]-, (all-E)-	EtOH	464(4.66)	33-0277-80
$C_{33}H_{42}N_4O_2$ 21H-Biline-1,19-dione, 3,8,12,17-tetra-ethyl-22,24-dihydro-2,7,13,18,21,24-hexamethyl-, (E,Z,E)-	CHCl$_3$	360(4.04),570(3.83)	64-0376-80B
(E,Z,Z)-	CHCl$_3$	360(4.05),575(3.92)	64-0376-80B
(Z,Z,Z)-	CHCl$_3$ + Zn(OAc)$_2$	360(4.10),585(3.73) 580(--)	64-0376-80B 64-0376-80B
$C_{33}H_{42}N_4O_{11}$ Riboflavin, α^8-oxo-, 2',3',4',5'-tetra-kis(2-methylpropanoate)	CHCl$_3$	340(4.08),444s(3.95), 464(4.04),488s(3.88)	35-7157-80
$C_{33}H_{44}N_2O_{10}$ 1,4,7,10,13-Benzopentaoxacyclopenta-decin-13-amine, 2,3,5,6,8,9,11,12-octahydro-N-[5-[(2,3,5,6,8,9,11,12-octahydro-1,4,7,10,13-benzopentaoxa-cyclopentadecin-15-yl)amino]-2,4-pentadienylidene]-, monohydrochloride	MeOH	505(5.25)	24-0457-80
$C_{33}H_{44}N_4O_{10}$ Riboflavin, 2',3',4',5'-tetrakis(2-methylpropanoate)	HCOOH	272(4.46),380(4.08), 442(3.97)	35-7157-80
$C_{33}H_{44}O_7$ Prostaglandin $F_{2\alpha}$, 9,11-dibenzoate methyl ester	MeOH	228(4.43),267s(3.22), 273(3.28),280(3.19)	44-1528-80
Zeylasterone, trimethyl-	EtOH	207(4.00),225(3.88), 245(3.99),287(3.72), 312(3.72)	88-4749-80
$C_{33}H_{46}O_{19}$ Cantleyoside	MeOH	235(4.31)	100-0649-80
$C_{33}H_{48}$ Cholesta-3,5-diene, 3-phenyl-	pentane	195(4.66),228(4.09), 235(4.06),282(4.45)	44-0715-80
$C_{33}H_{48}OSe$ Cholest-1-en-3-one, 2-(phenylseleno)-	n.s.g.	215(3.98),235s(3.61), 265(3.36),320(2.88)	39-1654-80C
$C_{33}H_{48}O_{19}$ Sylvestroside I	EtOH	236(4.32)	100-0649-80
$C_{33}H_{50}O_4$ 28-Noroleana-12,17-diene-2α,3β-diol, diacetate	MeOH	237(4.43),244(4.45), 252(4.31)	2-0315-80
28-Noroleana-12,18-diene-2,3-diol, diacetate	MeOH	237(3.98),244(4.00), 252(3.88)	2-0315-80
$C_{33}H_{51}I_2N_{11}O_9$ Luteinizing hormone-releasing factor (pig), 1-de(5-oxo-L-proline)-2-de-L-histidine-3-de-L-tryptophan-5-(3,5-di-1-L-tyrosine)-	H$_2$O base	286(3.35) 311(3.72)	69-2572-80 69-2572-80

Compound	Solvent	$\lambda_{max}(\log \epsilon)$	Ref.
$C_{33}H_{52}IN_{11}O_9$			
Luteinizing hormone-releasing factor (pig), 1-de(5-oxo-L-proline)-2-de-L-histidine-3-de-L-tryptophan-5-(3-iodo-L-tyrosine)-	H_2O base	282(3.36) 305(3.61)	69-2572-80 69-2572-80
$C_{33}H_{52}O_4$			
Heptanedioic acid, 4-phenyl-, bis[5-methyl-2-(1-methylethyl)cyclohexyl] ester, [1R-[1α(1'R*,2'S*,5'R*),2β,5α]]-	$CHCl_3$	260(2.38)	126-0201-80

Compound	Solvent	$\lambda_{max}(\log \epsilon)$	Ref.
$C_{34}H_{20}$			
Tetrapheno[4',3':3,4]tetraphene	1,2,4-$C_6H_3Cl_3$	<u>315(4.7)</u>,<u>325(4.7)</u>, <u>355(4.0)</u>,<u>375(4.0)</u>, <u>380(3.7)</u>,<u>410(3.2)</u>	35-3173-80
$C_{34}H_{20}Br_2O_2$			
Naphtho[2,3-b]naphtho[2',3':3,4]cyclobuta[1,2-e][1,4]dioxin, 7,12-dibromo-5b,13a-dihydro-5b,13a-diphenyl-	ether	228(5.03),278(4.11), 287(4.15),296(4.13), 308(3.99),322(3.68), 333(3.35)	78-2225-80
$C_{34}H_{20}N_2O_6$			
Benzo[1,2-c:4,5-c']dipyrrole-1,3,5,7-(2H,6H)-tetrone, 2,6-bis(4-phenoxyphenyl)-	Me_3PO_4	310s(<u>3.6</u>),328s(<u>3.4</u>), 371s(<u>2.9</u>)	116-0826-80
$C_{34}H_{21}BrO_2$			
Naphtho[2,3-b]naphtho[2',3':3,4]cyclobuta[1,2-e][1,4]dioxin, 7-bromo-5b,13a-dihydro-5b,13a-diphenyl-	THF	269(4.06),280(4.12), 290(4.13),301(3.97), 314(3.57),322(3.64), 330(3.51)	78-2225-80
$C_{34}H_{22}ClN_5O_7$			
2H-Isoindole-2-acetic acid, 1,3-dihydro-1,3-dioxo-, [[(2-benzoyl-4-chlorophenyl)[(1,3-dihydro-1,3-dioxo-2H-isoindol-2-yl]acetyl]amino]methylene]hydrazide	EtOH	218(5.00),239(4.60), 255(4.58),295s(3.90)	4-0575-80
$C_{34}H_{22}O_2$			
5,14-Epidioxypentacene, 5,14-dihydro-6,13-diphenyl-	THF	236(4.14),279(4.71), 316(2.91),332(3.22), 349(3.48),366(3.64), 386(3.54)	78-2225-80
6,13-Epidioxypentacene, 6,13-dihydro-6,13-diphenyl-	ether	244(4.89),272(4.23), 280(4.12),308(3.02), 312(2.96),317(2.76), 322(2.61),327(2.63)	78-2225-80
7,14-Epoxydinaphth[2,3-b:2',3'-e]oxepin, 7,14-dihydro-7,14-diphenyl-	ether	250(4.95),268(3.82), 280(3.73),305(3.31), 323(3.46),339(3.53)	78-2225-80
Naphtho[2,3-b]naphtho[2',3':3,4]cyclobuta[1,2-e][1,4]dioxin, 5b,13a-dihydro-5b,13a-diphenyl-	ether	275(4.03),295(3.87), 308(3.60),312(3.58), 322(3.62),327(3.59)	78-2225-80
Naphtho[2,3-b]naphtho[2',3':4,5]furo[2,3-d]furan, 5b,12b-dihydro-5b,12b-diphenyl-	ether	241(4.95),247(4.84), 268(4.21),279(4.16), 291(3.91),326(3.79), 340(3.87)	78-2225-80
$C_{34}H_{23}N_3$			
1H-Indol-3-amine, 1,2-diphenyl-N-(2-phenyl-3H-indol-3-ylidene)-	n.s.g.	557(4.22)	7-0009-80
$C_{34}H_{24}Cl_2S_5$			
1,3-Butadiene, 3-chloro-2-[(4-chlorophenyl)thio]-1,1,4,4-tetrakis(phenylthio)-	heptane	199(4.83),265(4.36)	24-3342-80
$C_{34}H_{24}N_2O_2S_6$			
Benzenecarbothioic acid, O,O'-[dithiobis[4-(4-methylphenyl)-5,3-isothia-	$CHCl_3$	267(4.56),320s(3.82), 403(4.65)	13-0401-80

Compound	Solvent	$\lambda_{max}(\log \epsilon)$	Ref.
zolediyl]] ester (cont.)			13-0401-80
$C_{34}H_{24}N_2O_3$ 2H-Anthra[1,2-d][1,3]oxazine-7,12-di-one, 1,4-dihydro-2,2-diphenyl-6-(phen-ylamino)-	EtOH	608(3.79)	18-3007-80 +146-0513-80
$C_{34}H_{24}N_6$ 2,2'-Biquinoline, 4,4'-bis(1-methyl-1H-benzimidazol-2-yl)-, diiodide	EtOH	217(4.64),272(4.57), 339(4.25)	103-1261-80
$C_{34}H_{24}N_{12}Ni$ Nickel, [3,4,9,10-tetrahydro-1,12-di-methyl-3,10-diphenyldipyrazolo[3,4-b:4',3'-j]quinoxalino[2,3-f][1,4,5-8,9,12]benzohexaazacyclotetradecin-ato(2-)-N^4,N^9,N^{14},N^{21}]-, (SP-4-2)-	CHCl$_3$	250(4.59),290(4.46), 312s(4.25),372(4.25), 408(4.25),453s(4.50), 485(4.41),525s(4.34), 618s(3.77)	103-0653-80
$C_{34}H_{24}N_{12}Pd$ Palladium, [3,4,9,10-tetrahydro-1,12-dimethyl-3,10-diphenyldipyrazolo[3,4-b:4',3'-j]quinoxalino[2,3-f][1,4,5-8,9,12]benzohexaazacyclotetradecin-ato(2-)-N^4,N^9,N^{14},N^{21}]-, (SP-4-2)-	CHCl$_3$	250(4.61),284(4.42), 395(4.37),412(4.43), 451(4.49),481(4.45), 512(4.53),542s(4.15), 610s(3.54),657s(3.26)	103-0653-80
$C_{34}H_{25}Br$ Anthracene, 10-bromo-1,8-bis(4-methyl-phenyl)-9-phenyl-	CHCl$_3$	275(4.77),378(3.94), 400(4.10),417(4.06)	24-0676-80
$C_{34}H_{25}ClSi$ Silacyclopentadiene, 1-chloro-1,2,3,4-5-pentaphenyl-	dioxan	356(3.86)	61-1122-80
$C_{34}H_{26}$ Anthracene, 1,8-bis(4-methylphenyl)-9-phenyl-	EtOH	224s(4.50),267(4.94), 361(3.88),379(4.03), 398(3.98)	24-0676-80
$C_{34}H_{26}N_2$ 1(4H),2'-Bipyridine, 2,3,5,6-tetraphen-yl-	EtOH	225(4.38),262(4.34), 310(4.13),345(3.89)	39-2554-80C
$C_{34}H_{26}N_2O$ Acridinium, 9,9'-(4-hydroxy-1,3-phenyl-ene)bis[10-methyl-, dinitrate	EtOH	256(4.85),364(4.30), 432(3.86)	104-0192-80
$C_{34}H_{26}N_4O_4S_3$ 5-Thia-1-azabicyclo[4.2.0]oct-2-ene-2-carboxylic acid, 8-oxo-3-(5-phenyl-1,3,4-thiadiazol-2-yl)-7-[(2-thienyl-acetyl)amino]-, diphenylmethyl ester, (6R-trans)-	EtOH	325(4.26)	94-2116-80
$C_{34}H_{26}Si$ Silacyclopenta-2,4-diene, 1,2,3,4,5-pentaphenyl-	dioxan	371(4.03)	61-1122-80
$C_{34}H_{28}ClN_3O_7S$ 7H-Pyrrolo[2,3-d]pyrimidine, 4-chloro-5-methyl-2-(methylthio)-7-(2,3,5-tri-O-benzoyl-β-D-ribofuranosyl)-	MeOH	227(4.57),255(4.30), 280(3.85),311(3.65)	24-2808-80

Compound	Solvent	$\lambda_{max}(\log \epsilon)$	Ref.
$C_{34}H_{28}FeP_2$ Ferrocene, 1,1'-bis(diphenylphosphino)-	C_6H_{12}	442(2.32)	101-0345-80J
$C_{34}H_{28}N_2O$ Phenol, 2,4-bis(9,10-dihydro-10-methyl-9-acridinyl)-	EtOH	289(3.65)	104-0192-80
$C_{34}H_{28}N_3O_5P$ 4,12-Epoxy-5H,8H-1,3,2-dioxaphospholo-[4,5-e]pyrimido[2,1-b][1,3]oxazocine, 2,2,3a,4,12,12a-hexahydro-8-(benzoyl-imino)-2,2,2-triphenyl-, [3aR- (3α,4β,12β,12aα)]-	MeCN	235s(--),318(4.16)	18-3670-80
$C_{34}H_{28}N_4O_2$ 3,7,9,11-Tetraazatricyclo[4.2.2.2^{2,5}]-dodeca-9,11-diene-4,8-dione, 3,7-di-methyl-2,6,10,12-tetraphenyl-	EtOH	261(3.56),351(2.65)	88-2529-80
$C_{34}H_{28}N_4O_4S_3$ 5-Thia-1-azabicyclo[4.2.0]oct-2-ene-2-carboxylic acid, 8-oxo-3-[[(phen-ylthioxomethyl)hydrazono]methyl]-7-[(2-thienylacetyl)amino]-, diphenyl-methyl ester, (6R-trans)-	EtOH	370(4.14)	94-2116-80
$C_{34}H_{28}N_4O_{10}$ 7(8H)-Pteridinone, 2,4-dimethoxy-8-(2,3,5-tri-O-benzoyl-β-D-ribo-furanosyl)-	MeOH	228(4.69),247s(4.23), 272(3.87),317(4.09)	24-1535-80
β-D-Ribofuranoside, 2,4-dimethoxy-7-pteridinyl, 2,3,5-tribenzoate	MeOH	229(4.67),280(3.72), 316(4.04)	24-1535-80
$C_{34}H_{28}N_6O_4$ 6,9-Ethano-5,19:10,16-dimetheno-1H,12H-bis[1,2,4]triazolo[1,2-a1',2'-a']-cyclodeca[1,2-c:6,5-c']dipyridazine-1,3,12,14(2H,13H)-tetrone, 5,7,8,10-15a,17,18,19a-octahydro-2,13-diphenyl-	EtOH	220(4.40),255(3.84)	24-2358-80
$C_{34}H_{28}O_{11}$ [10,10'-Bi-4H-naphtho[2,3-b]pyran]-4,4'-dione, 5-acetoxy-5'-hydroxy-6,6',8,8'-tetramethoxy-2,2'-dimethyl-	dioxan	267(4.78),278(4.80), 325(3.71),341(3.72), 370s(3.93),390(4.02)	39-2474-80C
$C_{34}H_{30}O_8$ [9,9'-Bianthracene]-10,10'(9H,9'H)-di-one, 4,4'-dihydroxy-5,5',7,7'-tetra-methoxy-2,2'-dimethyl-	EtOH	255s(4.18),277(4.24), 346(4.30)	32-0629-80
$C_{34}H_{31}NO_5$ 2,4,7-Cycloheptatriene-1,2-dicarboxylic acid, 6-oxo-4,5,7-triphenyl-3-piperi-dino-, dimethyl ester	MeCN	302(4.18),475(2.99)	24-0408-80
$C_{34}H_{31}N_4S$ Thiazolo[3,2-a]pyridinium, 8-cyano-5,7-bis[2-[4-(dimethylamino)phenyl]eth-enyl]-3-phenyl-, perchlorate	n.s.g.	358(4.76),560(4.34)	124-1306-80

Compound	Solvent	$\lambda_{max}(\log \epsilon)$	Ref.
$C_{34}H_{32}N_2O$ Propanedinitrile, [2,5-bis[4-(1,1-di-methylethyl)phenyl]-4-oxo-3-phenyl-2-cyclopenten-1-ylidene]-	MeCN	266(4.10),347(4.22)	24-0424-80
$C_{34}H_{32}N_2O_3$ 6H-Anthra[1,9-cd]isoxazol-6-one, 3-[4-(1,1-dimethylpropyl)phenoxy]-5-[(2,4,6-trimethylphenyl)amino]-	THF	265(5.06),420(3.86), 612(4.37),664(4.39)	104-1884-80
$C_{34}H_{32}N_2O_{16}S$ Compound m. 163-5°	EtOH	265(4.15),435(3.80)	18-3308-80
$C_{34}H_{32}N_4O_3$ 9,10-Anthracenedione, 1-azido-2-[4-(1,1-dimethylpropyl)phenoxy]-4-[(2,4,6-trimethylphenyl)amino]-	THF	257(4.69),506(3.94)	104-1884-80
$C_{34}H_{33}N_2$ 3H-Indolium, 1,3,3-trimethyl-2-[5-(1-methyl-2,6-diphenyl-4(1H)-pyridin-ylidene)-1,3-pentadienyl]-, perchlorate	CH_2Cl_2	646(4.81)	103-0696-80
3H-Indolium, 1,3,3-trimethyl-2-[5-(1-methyl-4,6-diphenyl-2(1H)-pyridin-ylidene)-1,3-pentadienyl]-, perchlorate	CH_2Cl_2	630(4.91)	103-0696-80
$C_{34}H_{33}OP_3$ Phosphine oxide, bis[2-(diphenylphos-phino)ethyl]phenyl-	$CHCl_3$	<u>266(3.5)</u>	140-0065-80
$C_{34}H_{33}O_2P_3$ Phosphine oxide, [(phenylphosphinid-ene)di-2,1-ethanediyl]bis[diphenyl-	$CHCl_3$	<u>266(3.8)</u>	140-0065-80
$C_{34}H_{34}O_{10}$ [1,9'-Bianthracene]-4',5(1'H,6H)-dione, 2',3',7,8-tetrahydro-2',4,5',7,10,10'-hexahydroxy-2,7'-dimethoxy-2',3,6',7-tetramethyl-, [S-(R*,R*)]-	MeOH	231(4.68),278(4.94), 317(4.15),331(4.04), 413(4.33)	78-2449-80
[9,9'-Bianthracene]-4,4'(1H,1'H)-dione, 2,2',3,3'-tetrahydro-2,2',5,5',10,10'-hexahydroxy-7,7'-dimethoxy-2,2',6,6'-tetramethyl-, [S-(R*,R*)]-	MeOH	233(4.85),278(5.06), 320(4.34),334(4.23), 417(4.45)	78-2449-80
$C_{34}H_{35}N_3O$ Benzenepropanenitrile, α-[3,4-bis(di-ethylamino)-2,5-diphenyl-2,4-cyclo-pentadien-1-ylidene]-β-oxo-	MeCN	280s(--),399(4.27), 590(3.02)	24-0424-80
$C_{34}H_{35}N_3O_5S$ 7H-Pyrrolo[2,3-d]pyrimidine, 4-methoxy-2-(methylthio)-7-[2,3,5-tris-O-(phen-ylmethyl)-α-D-ribofuranosyl]-	MeOH	238(4.20),282(4.14)	24-3389-80
β-	MeOH	238(4.20),282(4.15)	24-3389-80
4H-Pyrrolo[2,3-d]pyrimidine, 1,7-dihy-dro-5-methyl-2-(methylthio)-7-[2,3,5-tris-O-(phenylmethyl)-β-D-ribofurano-syl]-	MeOH	224(4.31),275s(3.98), 295(4.03)	24-2808-80

Compound	Solvent	$\lambda_{max}(\log \epsilon)$	Ref.
$C_{34}H_{36}N_2O_2$ Benzenepropanal, α-[3,4-bis(diethylamino)-2,5-diphenyl-2,4-cyclopentadien-1-ylidene]-β-oxo-	MeCN	245(4.25),408(4.35), 575(3.01)	24-0424-80
$C_{34}H_{36}N_3O$ Ethanaminium, N-[4-(1-cyano-2-oxo-2-phenylethylidene)-2-(diethylamino)-3,5-diphenyl-2-cyclopenten-1-ylidene]-N-ethyl-, perchlorate	MeCN	249(4.20),295(4.21), 457(4.09)	24-0424-80
$C_{34}H_{36}N_4O_3$ 21-Phorbinecarboxylic acid, 3,4-didehydro-3,9,14-triethyl-4,8,13,18-tetramethyl-20-oxo-, methyl ester	CHCl₃	422(5.26),523(3.92), 567(4.23),587(4.17), 636(3.32)	12-1095-80
$C_{34}H_{36}N_4O_4$ 2,4,7-Cycloheptatriene-1,2-dicarboxylic acid, 6-(dicyanomethylene)-3,4-bis(diethylamino)-5,7-diphenyl-, dimethyl ester	MeCN	268(4.44),405(4.25)	24-0424-80
$C_{34}H_{36}N_6O_2S$ Phenol, 4,4'-thiobis[2-(2H-benzotriazol-2-yl)-6-(1,1-dimethylethyl)-3-methyl-	EtOH	<u>287(4.5)</u>	109-0034-80
$C_{34}H_{38}N_4NiO_2$ Nickel, [methyl 3,7,13,17-tetraethyl-2,8,12,18-tetramethyl-21H,23H-porphine-5-carboxylato(2-)-N^{21},N^{22},N^{23}-N^{24}]-, (SP-4-2)-	CHCl₃	398(5.24),523(4.24), 560(4.59)	130-0063-80
$C_{34}H_{38}N_4O$ Spiro[cyclopentane-1,2'(3'H)-[21H,23H]-porphin]-2-one, 8',12',17'-triethyl-7',13',18'-trimethyl-3'-methylene-	CH₂Cl₂	399(5.32),496(4.15), 504(4.11),532(4.18), 596(3.57),655(4.69)	4-0481-80
$C_{34}H_{38}N_4O_3$ 21H,23H-Porphine-2-propanoic acid, 7,12,18-triethyl-3,8,13,17-tetramethyl-β-oxo-, methyl ester	CHCl₃	409(5.26),508(4.02), 547(4.20),571(3.99), 630(3.17)	12-1095-80
$C_{34}H_{38}N_4O_4$ 3-Phorbinepropanoic acid, 14-ethyl-9-(1-hydroxyethyl)-4,8,13,18-tetramethyl-20-oxo-, methyl ester	CH₂Cl₂	396(4.96),409(5.06), 504(4.02),535(4.02), 604(3.92),656(4.62)	44-2218-80
3-Phorbinepropanoic acid, 14-ethyl-9-(2-hydroxyethyl)-4,8,13,18-tetramethyl-20-oxo-, methyl ester, (3S-trans)-	CH₂Cl₂	395(4.97),408(5.08), 472(3.61),504(4.03), 533(4.02),601(3.95), 659(4.71)	44-2218-80
$C_{34}H_{38}N_4O_6$ 2,5-Cyclohexadien-1-one, 2,2'-[1,2-ethanediylbis(oxy-2,1-ethanediyloxy)]-bis[4-[[4-(dimethylamino)phenyl]imino]-	MeCN	572(4.73)	24-0457-80
$C_{34}H_{38}N_4O_6S_2$ Acetamide, N,N'-[1,4-phenylenebis[nitrilo(3,4-dimethyl-2-buten-1-yl-4-	EtOH	252(4.55)	104-0849-80

Compound	Solvent	$\lambda_{max}(\log \epsilon)$	Ref.
ylidene)sulfonyl-4,1-phenylene]]bis-		•	104-0849-80
$C_{34}H_{38}N_4O_8S_2$ Carbamic acid, [1,4-phenylenebis[nitrilo(3,4-dimethyl-2-buten-1-yl-4-ylidene)sulfonyl-4,1-phenylene]]-bis-, dimethyl ester	EtOH	250(4.05)	104-0849-80
$C_{34}H_{40}N_2O_5$ 10,11-Dinor[13]cytochalasa-13,17,21-triene-1,20,23-trione, 6,7-epoxy-5-ethyl-19-hydroxy-3-[1-(1H-indol-3-yl)ethyl]-16,18-dimethyl-, [3S(R)-5S,7S,13E,16S,17E,19R,21E]-	EtOH	219(4.65),274s(--), 282s(--),290s(--)	98-0139-80
$C_{34}H_{40}N_4O$ Spiro[cyclopentane-1,2'(3'H)-[21H,23H]-porphin]-2-one, 8',12',17'-triethyl-3',7',13',18'-tetramethyl-, trans	CH_2Cl_2	391(5.27),491(4.09), 516(3.57),602(3.57), 630(4.69)	4-0481-80
	+ 1% TFA	394(5.36),405(5.27), 518(3.72),622(4.41)	4-0481-80
$C_{34}H_{40}N_{12}$ Bis(tetraethylaminium) 1,1,2,3,4,5,6-7,8,9-decacyanooctatriene-1,8-diide	MeCN	298(4.66),348(3.93), 400(4.27),512(4.25)	44-5113-80
$C_{34}H_{41}NO_{14}$ 6H,8H-Benzo[a]pyrano[3,4-g]quinolizin-8-one, 12-ethenyl-5,11,12,12a,13,13a-hexahydro-2,3-dimethoxy-11-[(2,3,4,6-tetra-O-acetyl-β-D-glucopyranosyl)-oxy]-, [11S-(11α,12β,12aα,13aα)]-13aβ-	EtOH EtOH	234(4.39),289(3.66) 235(4.30),282(3.63)	24-0566-80 24-0566-80
$C_{34}H_{41}N_5$ Methanamine, N-[(2,7,12,17-tetraethyl-3,8,13,18-tetramethyl-21H,23H-porphin-5-yl)methylene]-	$CHCl_3$	405(4.57),525(4.15), 562(4.24)	103-0592-80
$C_{34}H_{41}N_5O_2$ 21H,23H-Porphine, 3,8,13,18-tetraethyl-2,7,12,17-tetramethyl-5-(2-nitroethyl)-	$CHCl_3$	409(4.21),508(4.12), 542(3.81),577(3.76), 628(3.38)	103-0730-80
$C_{34}H_{42}$ Pentacyclo[26.2.2.2^{13,16}.0^{6,21}.0^{8,23}]-tetratriaconta-6,8(23),13,15,21,28-30,31,33-nonaene	THF	<u>263f(3.0)</u>	18-0512-80
$C_{34}H_{42}N_2O_6$ [1,1':4',1"-Terphenyl]-4,4"-diethanaminium, N,N'-bis(2-acetoxyethyl)-N,N,N',N'-tetramethyl-β,β'-dioxo-, dibromide	H_2O	330(4.62)	87-0541-80
$C_{34}H_{44}O_{19}$ Myricoside	MeOH	216(4.30),246s(4.04), 288(4.14),300(4.16), 330(4.31)	35-7953-80
	MeOH-base	375(4.33)	35-7953-80
peracetate	MeOH	280(4.32)	35-7953-80

Compound	Solvent	λ_{max}(log ϵ)	Ref.
$C_{34}H_{46}N_2O_4$ [1,1':4',1"-Terphenyl]-4',4'-diethanam- inium, N,N'-bis(2-ethoxyethyl)-N,N- N',N'-tetramethyl-β,β'-dioxo-, di- bromide	H_2O	329(4.68)	87-0541-80
$C_{34}H_{46}N_2O_{14}$ 3,6,9,12,15,23,26,29,32,35-Decaoxa- 19,39-diazatricyclo[35.3.1.1^{17,21}]- dotetraconta-1(41),17,19,21(42),37- 39-hexaene-2,16,22,36-tetrone, 18,20,38,40-tetramethyl-	MeCN	232(4.16),274(3.79), 282(3.74)	44-2854-80
$C_{34}H_{46}O_{10}$ 5β-Ergost-2-en-1-one, 4β,15α,26-tri- acetoxy-5,6β:22,26:24,25-triepoxy-, (20S,22R,24S,25S)-	EtOH	216(3.98)	150-2134-80
$C_{34}H_{47}FO_3$ 5α-Cholest-8(14)-en-15-one, 3β-(benz- oyloxy)-9α-fluoro-	EtOH	232(4.23),248(4.15)	44-4034-80
$C_{34}H_{47}N_5$ 1H-Cyclopenta[5,6]naphtho[1,2-g]pyra- zolo[1,5-a]quinazoline-9-acetonitrile, 10-cyano-1-(1,5-dimethylhexyl)-2,3,3a- 3b,4,5,5a,6,13,13a,13b,14,15,15a- tetradecahydro-13a,15a-dimethyl-	MeOH	208(4.05),231(4.48), 311(3.69)	39-0481-80C
$C_{34}H_{48}ClNO_6S_2$ Spiro[2-azabicyclo[16.3.1]docosa-1(22)- 4,6,13,15,18,20-heptaene-11,2'-[1,3]- dithiacyclohexan]-3-one, 21-chloro- 12,20-dimethoxy-9-[(2-methoxyethoxy)- methoxy]-2,6,8,16-tetramethyl-, [9S- (4E,6E,9R*,12S*,13E,15E)]-	EtOH	234(4.63),247(4.71), 271(4.45),254(4.63)	35-1439-80
$C_{34}H_{48}O_4$ 5α-Cholest-8(14)-en-15-one, 3β-(benz- oyloxy)-9α-hydroxy-	EtOH	232(4.24),254(4.15)	44-4034-80
$C_{34}H_{48}O_5Se$ Cholane-24-selenoic acid, 3,12-diacet- oxy-, Se-phenyl ester, (3α,5β,12α)-	n.s.g.	221(4.20),256(3.68)	33-2328-80
$C_{34}H_{48}O_8$ Cyclopropa[4,5]bufa-20,22-dienolide, 3-[[6-deoxy-2,3-O-(1-methylethyli- dene)-α-L-mannopyranosyl]oxy]-3',4- dihydro-14-hydroxy-, (3β,4α,5S)-	MeOH	298(3.75)	5-0886-80
$C_{34}H_{48}O_9$ Cyclopropa[4,5]bufa-20,22-dienolide, 3-[[6-deoxy-2,3-O-(ethoxymethylene)- α-L-mannopyranosyl]oxy]-3',4-dihydro- 14-hydroxy-, (3β,4α,5S)-	MeOH	298(3.76)	5-0886-80
$C_{34}H_{49}N_3O_4$ 1H-Pyrazole, 4,5-dihydro-3-(4-methoxy- phenyl)-5-(4-nitrophenyl)-1-(1-oxo- octadecyl)-	MeOH	294(4.14)	2-0364-80

Compound	Solvent	$\lambda_{max}(\log \epsilon)$	Ref.
$C_{34}H_{49}N_{11}O_3$ 1H-Pyrrole-2-carboxamide, N-[5-[[(3-amino-3-iminopropyl)amino]carbonyl]-1-methyl-1H-pyrrol-3-yl]-4-[[[4-[[bis(cyclohexylamino)methylene]-amino]-1-methyl-1H-pyrrol-2-yl]carbo-nyl]amino]-1-methyl-, hydrochloride	EtOH	238(4.29),304(4.40)	4-1797-80
$C_{34}H_{50}$ Cholesta-3,5-diene, 3-(2-methylphenyl)-	pentane	195(4.28),218(4.19), 242(4.19),251(4.19)	44-0715-80
Cholesta-3,5-diene, 3-(3-methylphenyl)-	pentane	196(4.42),217s(4.28), 231s(4.17),238s(4.09)	44-0715-80
Cholesta-3,5-diene, 3-(4-methylphenyl)-	pentane	198(4.18),221(4.15), 230(4.09),237(4.03), 283(4.45)	44-0715-80
$C_{34}H_{50}N_6Pd$ Palladium(2+), 21,23-didehydro-2,3,7,8-12,13,17,18-octahydro-2,2,3,3,7,7,8-8,12,12,13,13,17,17,18,18-hexadeca-methyl-21H,23H-5,15-diazaporphine-$N^{21},N^{22},N^{23},N^{24}]$-, (SP-4-1)-, bis-(tetrafluoroborate	$CHCl_3$-Et_3O-BF_4	242(3.23),253(3.23), 294s(3.97),335(4.36), 427(4.01),452(4.05)	27-0279-80
$C_{34}H_{50}O$ Cholesta-3,5-diene, 3-(2-methoxyphen-yl)-	pentane	195(4.44),205(4.28), 225(4.14),268(4.17)	44-0715-80
Cholesta-3,5-diene, 3-(4-methoxyphen-yl)-	pentane	195(4.68),226(4.12), 235(3.97),315(4.51)	44-0715-80
$C_{34}H_{50}O_2$ 1,3-Cyclohexanedione, 4,6-bis(1,1-di-methylethyl)-2-retinylidene-	EtOH	283(4.37),467(4.72)	87-0805-80
1,3-Cyclotetradecanedione, 2-retinyli-dene-	EtOH	275(4.03),425(4.71)	87-0805-80
$C_{34}H_{50}O_8$ Aglycone of 22,23-dihydroavermectin B	MeOH	238(4.41),244(4.44), 252s(4.26)	87-1134-80
$C_{34}H_{51}Br_2CoN_6O$ Cobalt, dibromo(2,3,7,8,12,13,17,18-octahydro-2,2,3,3,7,7,8,8,12,12,13-13,17,17,18,18-hexadecamethyl-4H-21H-5,15-diazaporphin-4-olato-$N^{21},N^{22},N^{23},N^{24}$)-, (OC-6-13)-	$CHCl_3$	297(4.41),343s(4.23), 438(3.61),508s(3.42), 592s(3.25)	33-0733-80
$C_{34}H_{51}NO$ Cholest-5-en-3β-ol, benzenecarboximid-ate	C_6H_{12}	225(3.91),271(2.64), 279(2.49)	39-2184-80C
$C_{34}H_{52}O_4$ Multiflora-7,9(11)-dien-29α-oic acid, 3α-acetoxy-, ethyl ester	EtOH	233(3.84),240(3.88), 248(3.66)	39-2933-80C
$C_{34}H_{52}O_9$ 5β-Ergost-2-en-1-one, 15α-acetoxy-5,6β:22,26-diepoxy-24,26-diethoxy-4β,25-dihydroxy-, (20S,22R,26R)-	EtOH	214(3.96)	150-2134-80

Compound	Solvent	$\lambda_{max}(\log \epsilon)$	Ref.
$C_{34}H_{53}NO$ 5α-Cholestan-3β-ol, benzenecarboximidate	C_6H_{12}	225(3.88),271s(2.58), 279s(2.36)	39-2184-80C
$C_{34}H_{54}N_2O$ 5α-Cholestan-3β-ol, benzenecarboximidate	n.s.g.	267(3.86)	39-2184-80C
$C_{34}H_{54}O_5$ Lanost-8-en-21-oic acid, 3-acetoxy-16-hydroxy-24-methylene-, methyl ester, (3β,16α)-·(methyl pachymate)	n.s.g.	234(3.40),243(3.47), 251(3.30)	22-0473-80
$C_{34}H_{58}NiP_2$ Nickel, (1,4-phenylenedi-2,1-ethynediyl)bis(tributylphosphine)-, homopolymer	Nujol	287(4.3),368(4.4), 402(4.5)	101-0237-80E
$C_{34}H_{58}O_3$ Cholestan-3β-ol, 4,4-dimethyl-3-oxopentanoate	C_6H_{12}	245(4.20)	22-0147-80

Compound	Solvent	$\lambda_{max}(\log \epsilon)$	Ref.
C₃₅H₂₄			
Diindeno[2,1-a:1',2'-b]indene, 9,9a-di-hydro-9,14-diphenyl-	hexane	251(4.36),335(4.18)	44-2930-80
Phenanthro[3,4-c]phenanthrene, 11-[2-(4-methylphenyl)ethenyl]-, cis	MeOH	241(4.72),268(4.68), 282s(4.63),321(4.47), 350s(4.25),395s(3.14), 409s(2.80)	54-0160-80
trans	MeOH	227s(4.64),237(4.71), 277s(4.68),286(4.69), 300(4.66),311s(4.60), 324(4.52),349(4.33), 373s(4.08),398s(3.38), 416s(2.98)	54-0160-80
C₃₅H₂₅N₃			
2H-Isoindol-2-amine, N,1-diphenyl-3-[(3-phenyl-1H-isoindol-1-ylidene)-methyl]-	benzene	293(4.36),569(4.79)	40-1185-80
C₃₅H₂₅OS			
Pyrylium, 4-[(2,6-diphenyl-4H-thiopyr-an-4-ylidene)methyl]-2,6-diphenyl-, perchlorate	CH₂Cl₂ MeNO₂	590(5.11) 588(5.09)	124-1186-80 124-1186-80
C₃₅H₂₅OSe			
Pyrylium, 4-[(2,6-diphenyl-4H-selenin-4-ylidene)methyl]-2,6-diphenyl-, perchlorate	CH₂Cl₂ MeNO₂	611(5.14) 610(5.11)	124-1186-80 124-1186-80
C₃₅H₂₅O₂			
Pyrylium, 2-[(4,6-diphenyl-2H-pyran-2-ylidene)methyl]-4,6-diphenyl-, perchlorate	CH₂Cl₂	636(4.84)	103-0691-80
Pyrylium, 4-[(2,6-diphenyl-4H-pyran-4-ylidene)methyl]-2,6-diphenyl-, perchlorate	CH₂Cl₂	555(5.15)	103-0691-80
C₃₅H₂₅SSe			
Thiopyrylium, 4-[(2,6-diphenyl-4H-sel-enin-4-ylidene)methyl]-2,6-diphenyl-, perchlorate	CH₂Cl₂ MeNO₂	650(5.03) 647(5.01)	124-1186-80 124-1186-80
C₃₅H₂₅S₂			
Thiopyrylium, 2-[(4,6-diphenyl-2H-thio-pyran-2-ylidene)methyl]-4,6-diphenyl-, perchlorate	CH₂Cl₂	646(4.86)	103-0691-80
Thiopyrylium, 4-[(2,6-diphenyl-4H-thio-pyran-4-ylidene)methyl]-2,6-diphenyl-, perchlorate	CH₂Cl₂	630(5.12)	103-0691-80
C₃₅H₂₆			
Cyclopentadiene, 1,2,3,4,5-pentaphenyl-	dioxan	342(4.15)	61-1122-80
Diindeno[2,1-a:1',2'-b]indene, 9,9a,13b,14-tetrahydro-9,14-diphenyl-	hexane	264(3.40),271(3.51), 278(3.53)	44-2930-80
C₃₅H₂₆N₃			
1H-Indol-3-aminium, N-methyl-1,2-di-phenyl-N-(2-phenyl-3H-indol-3-yli-dene)-, perchlorate	n.s.g.	657(4.22)	7-0009-80

Compound	Solvent	$\lambda_{max}(\log \epsilon)$	Ref.
$C_{35}H_{27}N$			
Pyridine, 1,4-dihydro-1,2,3,5,6-penta- phenyl-	EtOH	227(4.43),266(4.35), 303(4.14),337(3.95)	39-2554-80C
$C_{35}H_{28}N_2O$			
Acridinium, 9,9'-(2-hydroxy-5-methyl- 1,3-phenylene)bis[10-methyl-, diperchlorate	EtOH	261(4.41),362(4.02), 432(3.40)	104-0192-80
Acridinium, 9,9'-(4-hydroxy-5-methyl- 1,3-phenylene)bis[10-methyl-, diiodide	EtOH	261(4.42),363(4.05), 430(3.44)	104-0192-80
dinitrate	EtOH	260(4.70),363(4.05), 432(3.62)	104-0192-80
$C_{35}H_{29}NO$			
2-Naphthalenol, 1-[2,3,5-tris(4-methyl- phenyl)-1H-pyrrol-1-yl]-	EtOH	232(4.64),281(4.28), 291(4.29)	39-1870-80C
$C_{35}H_{29}NO_4$			
[1,1':2',1''-Terphenyl]-3',4'-dicarbox- ylic acid, 5'-(methylphenylamino)- 6'-phenyl-, dimethyl ester	MeCN	245(4.56),317(3.78)	24-0408-80
$C_{35}H_{29}N_3O_2$			
Benzeneacetonitrile, α-[3-(diethylami- no)-2,4,5-triphenyl-2,4-cyclopenta- dien-1-ylidene]-4-nitro-	MeCN	281(4.25),376(4.13), 570(3.49)	24-0424-80
$C_{35}H_{30}N_2O$			
Phenol, 2,4-bis(9,10-dihydro-10-methyl- 9-acridinyl)-6-methyl-	EtOH	287(4.20)	104-0192-80
Phenol, 2,6-bis(9,10-dihydro-10-methyl- 9-acridinyl)-4-methyl-	EtOH	291(4.19)	104-0192-80
$C_{35}H_{30}N_2O_7$			
Methanone, [4a-(acetoxymethyl)octahy- dro-2,6-diphenylfuro[2,3-d:4,5-d']- diisoxazole-3,7-diyl]bis[phenyl-	MeOH	246(4.72)	73-3546-80
$C_{35}H_{30}N_3O_2$			
Ethanaminium, N-[4-[cyano(4-nitrophen- yl)methylene]-2,3,5-triphenyl-2-cy- clopenten-1-ylidene]-N-ethyl-, per- chlorate	MeCN	244(4.36),255s(--), 327(4.28)	24-0424-80
$C_{35}H_{30}N_4O_9$			
9H-Purine-6-acetic acid, 9-(2,3,5-tri- O-benzoyl-β-D-ribofuranosyl)-, ethyl ester	EtOH	232(4.49),266(3.85), 280s(3.45),323(3.00)	94-0150-80
$C_{35}H_{30}O_9$			
3-Benzofuranol, 2,2',2''-ethylidynetris- [6-methyl-, triacetate	EtOH	211(5.01),252(4.74), 260(4.77),280(4.42), 283(4.43),289(4.50)	1-0177-80
$C_{35}H_{30}O_{10}$			
4-Cyclohexene-1,3-dione, 2-[[2,4-di- hydroxy-5-[3-(4-hydroxyphenyl)-1-oxo- 2-propenyl]-3,3-dimethyl-6-oxo-1,4- cyclohexadien-1-yl]methylene]-5-hydr- oxy-4-[3-(4-hydroxyphenyl)-1-oxo-2-	EtOH	377(4.5),535(4.9)	138-1095-80

Compound	Solvent	$\lambda_{max}(\log \epsilon)$	Ref.
propenyl]-6,6-dimethyl- (cont.)			138-1095-80
$C_{35}H_{30}O_{12}$ Thermorubin, trimethyl-	EtOH	253(4.43),296(4.59), 325(4.71),403(3.81), 424(3.90)	35-5580-80
$C_{35}H_{34}N_2O_4$ Benzo[a]phenanthridine-3-carboxylic acid, 5-[4-(dimethylamino)phenyl]- 1,2,5,6-tetrahydro-4-hydroxy-2-(4- methoxyphenyl)-, ethyl ester	EtOH	232(4.67),282(4.63), 292(4.63),343(4.61), 371(4.62)	103-0758-80
$C_{35}H_{34}N_4O_6$ 3-Phorbinepropanoic acid, 9-ethenyl- 14-ethyl-13-formyl-21-(methoxycarbo- nyl)-4,8,18-trimethyl-20-oxo-, [3S- (3α,4β,21β)]-	acetone	439(5.19),530(4.09), 553(3.97),602(3.97), 653(4.60)	44-1969-80
$C_{35}H_{34}O_{13}$ 6H-Benzo[d]naphtho[1,2-b]pyran-6-one, 1-acetoxy-8-ethenyl-10,12-dimethoxy- 4-(tri-O-acetyl-6-deoxyhexosyl)-	MeOH	246(4.53),280(4.59), 323(4.15),335(4.11), 348(4.08),388(4.18)	94-3601-80
$C_{35}H_{35}NO_{10}S$ β-D-Glucopyranoside, 4-(2,3-dihydro- 2-phenyl-1,5-benzothiazepin-4-yl)- phenyl, 2,3,4,6-tetraacetate	n.s.g.	220s(4.29),278(4.28), 312(4.30)	114-0027-80A
β-D-Glucopyranoside, 4-(2,3-dihydro- 4-phenyl-1,5-benzothiazepin-2-yl)- phenyl, 2,3,4,6-tetraacetate	n.s.g.	224s(4.37),260(4.36), 322(3.70)	114-0027-80A
$C_{35}H_{36}N_4O_5$ Pheophorbide a	acetone	409(5.08),507(4.08), 535(3.98),610(3.90), 667(4.74)	44-1969-80
	THF	275(4.24),322(4.29), 411(5.02),471(3.63), 506(4.06),535(4.00), 558(3.50),609(3.91), 668(4.69)	118-0539-80
$C_{35}H_{36}N_{10}O_9$ Urea, N,N'-bis[2-[(2,4-dinitrophenyl)- hydrazono]-1,1-dimethyl-2-(4-methyl- phenyl)ethyl]-	EtOH	198(4.7),218(4.6), 249(4.4),358(4.6)	5-1016-80
$C_{35}H_{36}O_3P$ Phosphonium, [5-(4-acetoxy-2,6,6-tri- methyl-3-oxo-1-cyclohexen-1-yl)-3- methyl-2-penten-4-ynyl]triphenyl-, bromide	EtOH	268(4.10),276(4.17), 306(4.39),319s(4.34)	33-1473-80
$C_{35}H_{36}O_{13}$ 6H-Benzo[d]naphtho[1,2-b]pyran-6-one, 1-acetoxy-8-ethyl-10,12-dimethoxy- 4-(tri-O-acetyl-6-deoxyhexosyl)-	MeOH	245(4.57),268(4.40), 277(4.58),302(3.98), 325(4.02),337(4.09), 377(4.00)	94-3601-80
$C_{35}H_{37}N_3O_5S$ 7H-Pyrrolo[2,3-d]pyrimidine, 4-methoxy-	MeOH	244(4.26),285(4.06)	24-2808-80

Compound	Solvent	$\lambda_{max}(\log \epsilon)$	Ref.
5-methyl-2-(methylthio)-7-[2,3,5-tris-0-(phenylmethyl)-α-D-ribofuranosyl]- (cont.)			24-2808-80
β-	MeOH	244(4.31),285(4.12)	24-2808-80
$C_{35}H_{38}N_2O_2$ 1,3-Butanedione, 2-[3,4-bis(diethylamino)-2,5-diphenyl-2,4-cyclopentadien-1-ylidene]-1-phenyl-	MeCN	245s(--),360s(--), 395(3.95)	24-0424-80
$C_{35}H_{38}N_4O_3$ 3-Phorbinepropanoic acid, 9-ethenyl-14-ethyl-4,6,8,13,18-pentamethyl-20-oxo-, methyl ester, (3S-trans)-	CH_2Cl_2	416(5.05),486(3.61), 520(4.02),552(4.16), 614(3.86),672(4.69)	44-2218-80
$C_{35}H_{38}N_4O_4$ 3-Phorbinepropanoic acid, 9-ethenyl-14-ethyl-4,8,13,18-tetramethyl-20-oxo-, 2-hydroxyethyl ester, (3S-trans)-	acetone	409(5.08),507(4.08), 535(3.98),609(3.90), 667(4.74)	44-1969-80
$C_{35}H_{38}N_4O_6$ Bacteriopheophorbide a	acetone	357(4.91),384(4.65), 490s(3.59),524(4.29), 677(3.84),750(4.69)	44-1969-80
$C_{35}H_{38}O_{17}$ Phloridzin heptaacetate	MeOH	265(3.67)	100-0739-80
$C_{35}H_{39}ClN_4O_3$ 3-Phorbinepropanoic acid, 9-(2-chloroethyl)-14-ethyl-4,6,8,13,18-pentamethyl-20-oxo-, methyl ester, (3S-trans)-	CH_2Cl_2	414(5.11),484(3.64), 518(4.05),549(4.20), 612(3.89),669(4.74)	44-2218-80
$C_{35}H_{39}ClN_4O_4$ Porphyrin, 2-(2-chloroethyl)-4-ethyl-6-(methoxycarbonyl)-7-(3-methoxycarbonylpropyl)-1,3,5,8-tetramethyl-	CH_2Cl_2	404(5.38),508(4.03), 545(4.23),571(3.98), 628(3.28)	4-0481-80
$C_{35}H_{40}N_4O_3$ 3-Phorbinepropanoic acid, 9,14-diethyl-4,6,8,13,18-pentamethyl-20-oxo-, methyl ester, (3S-trans)-	CH_2Cl_2	412(5.06),514(3.97), 547(4.14),607(3.89), 665(4.69)	130-0001-80
$C_{35}H_{40}N_4O_6$ 22H-Biline-8,12-dipropanoic acid, 18-ethenyl-3-ethylidene-1,2,3,19,21,24-hexahydro-2,7,13,17-tetramethyl-1,19-dioxo-, dimethyl ester, (E)-	MeOH MeOH-HCl	372(4.76),610(4.25) 386(4.81),708(4.58)	24-1603-80 24-1603-80
(Z)-	MeOH MeOH-HCl	368(4.62),610(4.13) 382(4.58),702(4.39)	24-1603-80 24-1603-80
Bilirubin dimethyl ester	EtOH 2-BuOH CH_2Cl_2	408s(--),448(4.76) 417s(--),451(4.73) 396(4.88)	149-0017-80B 149-0017-80B 149-0017-80B
$C_{35}H_{41}NO$ 2,4-Cyclopentadien-1-one, 3-(diethylamino)-4,5-bis[4-(1,1-dimethylethyl)-phenyl]-2-phenyl-	MeCN	278(4.34),325s(--), 518(2.97)	24-0408-80

Compound	Solvent	$\lambda_{max}(\log \epsilon)$	Ref.
$C_{35}H_{42}CuN_4O_2$ Copper, [2-[(2,7,12,17-tetraethyl-3,8,13,18-tetramethyl-21H,23H-porphin-5-yl)methoxy]ethanolate(2-)-$N^{21},N^{22},N^{23},N^{24}$]-, (SP-4-2)-	CHCl$_3$	412(5.26),534(3.93), 572(4.20)	103-0730-80
$C_{35}H_{42}N_4Ni$ Nickel, [3,7,13,17-tetraethyl-2,8,12-18-tetramethyl-5-propyl-21H,23H-porphinato(2-)-$N^{21},N^{22},N^{23},N^{24}$]-, (SP-4-2)-	CHCl$_3$	392(5.20),520(4.05), 553(4.42)	130-0063-80
$C_{35}H_{42}N_4NiO_2$ Nickel, [2-[(2,7,12,17-tetraethyl-3,8,13,18-tetramethyl-21H,23H-porphin-5-yl)methoxy]ethanolato(2-)-$N^{21},N^{22},N^{23},N^{24}$]-, (SP-4-2)-	CHCl$_3$	406(4.26),534(3.93), 572(4.20)	103-0730-80
$C_{35}H_{42}N_4O_2$ 21H,23H-Porphine-2-butanoic acid, 8,12,17-triethyl-3,7,13,18-tetramethyl-, methyl ester	CH$_2$Cl$_2$ + 1% TFA	399(5.20),495(4.11), 528(3.96),561(3.77), 610(3.70) 402(5.63),542(4.23), 583(3.85)	4-0481-80 4-0481-80
$C_{35}H_{42}N_4O_6$ 22H-Biline-8,12-dipropanoic acid, 18-ethyl-3-ethylidene-1,2,3,19,21,24-hexahydro-2,7,13,17-tetramethyl-1,19-dioxo-, dimethyl ester, (3Z)-	MeOH MeOH-HCl	360(4.76),599(4.32) 368(4.67),685(4.57)	24-1603-80 24-1603-80
$C_{35}H_{42}O_{20}$ Trifloroside	MeOH	249(4.21),325(3.69)	100-0649-80
$C_{35}H_{43}N_5Ni$ Nickel, [2,7,12,17-tetraethyl-N,N,3,8-13,18-hexamethyl-21H,23H-porphine-5-methanaminato(2-)-$N^{21},N^{22},N^{23},N^{24}$]-, (SP-4-2)-	C$_2$H$_4$Cl$_2$ + 1%-CF$_3$COOH + excess CF$_3$COOH	411(5.18),539(3.95), 579(4.13) 411(5.16),542(3.90), 585(4.15) 410(5.06),552(3.81), 591(4.09)	103-0592-80 103-0592-80 103-0592-80
$C_{35}H_{44}O_7$ Prosta-5,13-dien-1-oic acid, 4,15-dibenzoyloxy-9-hydroxy-, methyl ester, (5Z,9α,11α,13E,15S)-	MeOH	229(4.43),266s(3.19), 272(3.26),279(3.15)	44-1528-80
$C_{35}H_{48}CuN_7O_6$ Copper tetra-tert-butyl isocyanide 1-indenyl-2,4,6-trinitrocyclohexadienide	benzene	470(4.477),542(4.176)	1-0119-80
$C_{35}H_{50}F_3NO_3S$ Cholest-5-en-3β-ol, N-[(trifluoromethyl)sulfonyl]benzenecarboximidate	C$_6$H$_{12}$	246(3.80)	39-2184-80C
$C_{35}H_{50}O$ Ergosta-5,7,22-triene, 3β-(phenylmethoxy)-	C$_6$H$_{12}$	252s(3.65),262s(3.91), 275(4.03),281(4.05), 293(3.80)	39-2184-80C

Compound	Solvent	$\lambda_{max}(\log \epsilon)$	Ref.
$C_{35}H_{50}O_{20}$			
Sylvestroside II	EtOH	238(4.38)	100-0649-80
$C_{35}H_{51}FO_3$			
5α-Cholestane-2β-carboxylic acid, 2α-(4-fluorophenyl)-3-oxo-, methyl ester	hexane	257(2.66),263(2.83), 269(2.81)	12-0113-80
$C_{35}H_{52}F_3N_3O_{10}S$			
7,9,11,14-Eicosatetraenoic acid, 5-hydroxy-6-[[2-[[5-methoxy-1,5-dioxo-4-[(trifluoroacetyl)amino]pentyl]amino]-3-[(2-methoxy-1-oxoethyl)amino]-3-oxopropyl]thio]-, methyl ester, [5R-[5R*,6S*(R*),7E,9E,11Z,14Z]]-	MeOH	266s(4.49),276(4.60), 286s(4.49)	88-3547-80
$C_{35}H_{52}O_7$			
Olean-12-ene-28,29-dioic acid, 2,3-[(1-methylethylidene)bis(oxy)]-23-oxo-, dimethyl ester, (2β,3β,4α,20β)-	EtOH	206(3.92),290(1.43)	100-0510-80
$C_{35}H_{54}O_{14}$			
Uzarigenin 3-O-β-D-glucopyranosyl-(1→4)-β-D-glucopyranoside	MeOH	217(4.16)	94-0401-80
$C_{35}H_{56}N_8S$			
Bis(tetrapropylaminium) 1,2,3,4,5,5-hexacyano-1-mercaptopentadienediide	n.s.g.	354(4.23),454(4.14)	44-5113-80
$C_{35}H_{60}O_3$			
2-Propenoic acid, 3-(4-hydroxyphenyl)-, hexacosyl ester	EtOH	212(3.96),228(4.00), 312(4.32)	2-0421-80
	EtOH-NaOH	207(3.75),242(3.86), 312(3.92),359(4.43)	2-0421-80

Compound	Solvent	$\lambda_{max}(\log \epsilon)$	Ref.
$C_{36}H_{16}CoN_8O_8$ 　Cobalt 4,4',4",4"'-tetracarboxylato- 　phthalocyanine	H_2O	295(4.77),620(4.72), 670(4.63)	126-0575-80
$C_{36}H_{16}CuN_8O_8$ 　Copper tetracarboxylatophthalocyanine	1% NH_3	330(4.57),604(4.55), 680s(4.08)	65-0907-80
$C_{36}H_{16}FeN_8O_8$ 　Iron(III) tetracarboxylatophthalocyan- 　ine	H_2O	330(4.62),638(4.62), 675(4.33)	126-0575-80
$C_{36}H_{18}N_2O_4S_2$ 　2H-Naphtho[2,3-b]-1,4-thiazine-5,10-di- 　one, 2-(5,10-dihydro-5,10-dioxo-3- 　phenyl-2H-naphtho[2,3-b]-1,4-thia- 　zin-2-ylidene)-3-phenyl-	dioxan dioxan + 12M HCl	275(4.53),353s(4.10), 562(3.59) 280(4.55),353s(4.25), 518(3.66)	39-2923-80C 39-2923-80C
$C_{36}H_{20}N_2O_4S_2$ 　[2,2'-Bi-4H-naphtho[2,3-b]-1,4-thiaz- 　ine]-5,5',10,10'-tetrone, 3,3'-di- 　phenyl-	$CHCl_3$	257(4.55),292(4.53), 372(4.26),570(3.04)	39-2923-80C
$C_{36}H_{22}N_2O_2$ 　Naphth[1,2-d]oxazole, 2,2'-(1,5-naph- 　thalenediyldi-2,1-ethenediyl)bis-	$CHCl_3$	389(4.66)	103-0464-80
Naphth[1,2-d]oxazole, 2,2'-(2,6-naph- 　thalenediyldi-2,1-ethenediyl)bis-	$CHCl_3$	388s(4.82),407(4.93), 430(4.80)	103-0464-80
Naphth[1,2-d]oxazole, 2,2'-(2,7-naph- 　thalenediyldi-2,1-ethenediyl)bis-	$CHCl_3$	363s(4.76),379(4.83), 398s(4.68)	103-0464-80
Naphth[2,1-d]oxazole, 2,2'-(2,6-naph- 　thalenediyldi-2,1-ethenediyl)bis-	$CHCl_3$	384(4.54),403(4.67), 426(4.55)	103-0464-80
Naphth[2,1-d]oxazole, 2,2'-(2,7-naph- 　thalenediyldi-2,1-ethenediyl)bis-	$CHCl_3$	356s(4.59),373(4.77), 390s(4.64)	103-0464-80
Naphth[2,3-d]oxazole, 2,2'-(1,5-naph- 　thalenediyldi-2,1-ethenediyl)bis-	$CHCl_3$	375(4.62)	103-0464-80
Naphth[2,3-d]oxazole, 2,2'-(2,6-naph- 　thalenediyldi-2,1-ethenediyl)bis-	$CHCl_3$	404(4.85)	103-0464-80
Naphth[2,3-d]oxazole, 2,2'-(2,7-naph- 　thalenediyldi-2,1-ethenediyl)bis-	$CHCl_3$	362(4.50)	103-0464-80
$C_{36}H_{24}$ 　6,15[1',2']:7,14[1",2"]-Dibenzenocyclo- 　octa[1,2-b:5,6-b']dinaphthalene, 　6,7,14,15-tetrahydro-, (6α,7α,14α- 　15α)- 　(6α,7β,14β,15α)-	ether ether	274(4.02),281(3.96), 293(3.72),312(2.93), 325(2.92) 271(4.09),281(4.03), 292(3.56),313(2.97), 327(2.96)	78-2311-80 78-2311-80
$C_{36}H_{24}O_4$ 　Benzo[b]chrysene-7,12-diol, 5-(2-naph- 　thalenyl)-, diacetate	$CHCl_3$	248(4.72),259(4.70), 301(4.94),314(4.89), 352(3.77),372(3.92), 392(4.04),415(3.89)	44-1424-80
$C_{36}H_{26}$ 　Biphenyl, 2,2'-bis(3-biphenylyl)- 　Biphenyl, 2,2'-bis(4-biphenylyl)-	C_6H_{12} C_6H_{12}	194(4.93),205(4.91), 236(4.80),245(4.80) 207(4.98),240(4.47), 272(4.72)	94-1468-80 94-1468-80

Compound	Solvent	$\lambda_{max}(\log \epsilon)$	Ref.
Biphenyl, 3,3'-bis(2-biphenylyl)-	C_6H_{12}	194(4.94),237(4.86), 252s(4.65)	94-1468-80
Biphenyl, 2,2',4,4'-tetraphenyl-	C_6H_{12}	205(4.96),254(4.76), 291(4.47)	94-1468-80
Biphenyl, 2,2',5,5'-tetraphenyl-	C_6H_{12}	206(4.89),250s(4.64), 271(4.71)	94-1468-80
Biphenyl, 3,3',4,4'-tetraphenyl-	C_6H_{12}	192(4.91),234(4.57), 250(4.68),286(4.57)	94-1468-80
o-Sexiphenyl-	C_6H_{12}	192(4.92),231(4.72)	94-1468-80
$C_{36}H_{26}N_2$ 1H-Isoindole, 3-phenyl-1-[[3-phenyl-2-(phenylmethyl)-2H-isoindol-1-yl]-methylene]-	benzene	297(4.13),554(4.72)	40-1154-80
$C_{36}H_{26}N_4$ 1H-Pyrazole, 3,3'-(1,4-phenylenebis)-[1,5-diphenyl-	dioxan	302(4.86)	103-0066-80
	MeCN	300(4.70)	103-0066-80
$C_{36}H_{26}O_2$ [2](1,3)Benzeno[2](1,4)benzeno(1,8)an-thraquinono(1,4)benzenophane	EtOH	255(4.50),349(3.61)	24-0676-80
[2](1,4)Benzeno[2](1,4)benzeno(1,8)an-thraquinono(1,4)benzenophane	EtOH	194(4.79),222(4.37), 254(4.35),350(3.48)	24-0676-80
$C_{36}H_{26}O_2S_2$ 2,11-Dithia[3](1,3)benzeno[3](1,4)benz-eno(1,8)anthraquinono(1,4)benzeno-phane	CDCl_3	255(4.75),351(3.80)	24-0676-80
2,11-Dithia[3](1,4)benzeno[3](1,4)benz-eno(1,8)anthraquinono(1,4)benzeno-phane	CDCl_3	255(4.58),350(3.67)	24-0676-80
$C_{36}H_{27}BrS_2$ 2,5-Dithia[6.0.0](1,4)benzeno(1,8)an-thraceno(1,4)benzenophane, 22- bromo-21-phenyl-	CHCl_3	275(4.75),407(4.09), 426(4.09)	24-0676-80
$C_{36}H_{27}N_3O_3$ 2-Pyrrolidinecarboxamide, 4,5-dioxo-N,1,2-triphenyl-3-[phenyl(phenyl-amino)methylene]-	MeCN	242(4.38),381(4.23)	5-1801-80
$C_{36}H_{28}Fe$ Ferrocene, 1,1'-[1,4-phenylenebis(2,1-ethenediyl-4,1-phenylene-2,1-ethene-diyl)]-, all-cis	EtOH	300(4.53)	1-0529-80
$C_{36}H_{28}NO$ Pyridinium, 4-[(2,6-diphenyl-4H-pyran-4-ylidene)methyl]-1-methyl-2,6-di-phenyl-, perchlorate	CH_2Cl_2	510(4.77)	124-1186-80
	MeNO_2	476(4.62)	124-1186-80
$C_{36}H_{28}NS$ Pyridinium, 4-[(2,6-diphenyl-4H-thio-pyran-4-ylidene)methyl]-1-methyl-2,6-diphenyl-, perchlorate	CH_2Cl_2	538(4.73)	124-1186-80
	MeNO_2	505(4.68)	124-1186-80
$C_{36}H_{28}NSe$ Pyridinium, 4-[(2,6-diphenyl-4H-sele-nin-4-ylidene)methyl]-1-methyl-2,6-	CH_2Cl_2	540(4.64)	124-1186-80
	MeNO_2	508(4.61)	124-1186-80

Compound	Solvent	$\lambda_{max}(\log \epsilon)$	Ref.
diphenyl-, perchlorate (cont.)			124-1186-80
$C_{36}H_{28}N_2O_2$ Benzeneacetic acid, α-phenyl-, 1-(1-methyl-1H-benzimidazol-2-yl)-2,2-diphenylethenyl ester	EtOH	262(4.15),303(4.27)	44-2518-80
$C_{36}H_{29}N$ Pyridine, 1,4-dihydro-2,3,5,6-tetra-phenyl-1-(phenylmethyl)-	EtOH	225(4.34),275(4.26), 315(3.95),350(3.79)	39-2554-80C
$C_{36}H_{29}NO$ Pyridinium, 1-(2-hydroxy-1-naphthalen-yl)-2,4,6-tris(4-methylphenyl)-, hydroxide, inner salt	EtOH	209(4.40),240(4.49), 303(4.31)	39-1870-80C
$C_{36}H_{29}NO_2$ Pyridinium, 3-hydroxy-1-(2-hydroxy-1-naphthalenyl)-2,4,6-tris(4-methyl-phenyl)-, hydroxide, inner salt	EtOH	210(4.48),231(4.53), 324(4.30)	39-1870-80C
$C_{36}H_{29}N_3O_5$ 2,4,7-Cycloheptatriene-1,2-dicarboxylic acid, 6-(dicyanomethylene)-3-morpho-lino-4,5,7-triphenyl-, dimethyl ester	MeCN	292(4.22),545(2.95)	24-0424-80
$C_{36}H_{30}ClN_3O_3$ Glycinamide, N-(triphenylmethyl)glycyl-N-(2-benzoyl-4-chlorophenyl)-	EtOH	238(4.51),274s(4.03), 343(3.53)	87-0764-80
$C_{36}H_{30}N_2O$ Benzenepropanenitrile, α-[3-(diethyl-amino)-2,4,5-triphenyl-2,4-cyclo-pentadien-1-ylidene]-β-oxo-	MeCN	279(4.28),365(4.07), 580(3.61)	24-0424-80
$C_{36}H_{30}N_4$ 1H-Pyrazole, 3,3'-(1,4-phenylene)bis-[4,5-dihydro-1,5-diphenyl-	dioxan MeCN	310(4.10),418(4.82) 310(3.91),416(4.52)	103-0066-80 103-0066-80
$C_{36}H_{30}N_4O_8S_2$ 2,5-Epoxy-1,3,6-benzotriazocin-4(1H)-one, 2,3,5,6-tetrahydro-3,8,9-tri-methyl-5-(4-nitrophenyl)-2-phenyl-1,6-bis(phenylsulfonyl)-	MeCN	263s(4.156),268(4.165), 273s(4.139)	5-1850-80
$C_{36}H_{30}O_{12}$ [10,10'-Bi-4H-naphtho[2,3-b]pyran-4,4'-dione, 5,5'-diacetoxy-6,6',8,8'-tetramethoxy-2,2'-dimethyl-, (S)-	MeOH	227(4.94),270(5.07), 334s(4.07),345(4.15), 384(4.32)	39-2474-80C
$C_{36}H_{30}Si$ Silacyclohexa-2,4-diene, 1-methyl-1,2,3,4,5-pentaphenyl-	dioxan	341(4.06)	61-1122-80
$C_{36}H_{31}NO_2$ Benzenepropanal, α-[3-(diethylamino)-2,4,5-triphenyl-2,4-cyclopentadien-1-ylidene]-β-oxo-	MeCN	284(4.25),368(4.12), 570(3.54)	24-0424-80
perchlorate	MeCN	237(4.23),312(4.21)	24-0424-80
[1,1':2',1''-Terphenyl]-3'-carboxalde-hyde, 4'-benzoyl-5'-(diethylamino)-	MeCN	239(4.51),280s(--)	24-0424-80

Compound	Solvent	$\lambda_{max}(\log \epsilon)$	Ref.
6'-phenyl- (cont.)			24-0424-80
$C_{36}H_{31}N_3OS$ 1,3,5-Triazine-2(1H)-thione, 1-benzoyl-tetrahydro-4,6-diphenyl-3,5-bis(phenylmethyl)-	dioxan	216(4.53),247(4.23), 273(4.32)	73-2254-80
$C_{36}H_{31}N_3O_4$ 2,4,7-Cycloheptatriene-1,2-dicarboxylic acid, 6-(dicyanomethylene)-3-(diethylamino)-4,5,7-triphenyl-, dimethyl ester	MeCN	291(4.29),320s(--)	24-0424-80
$C_{36}H_{32}$ 1,4-Cyclohexadiene, 2,5-di-2-propenyl-1,3,4,6-tetraphenyl-	EtOH	245(3.92)	44-2181-80
6,15[1',2']:7,14[1",2"]-Dibenzenocyclo-octa[1,2-b:5,6-b']dinaphthalene, 1,2-3,4,6,7,9,10,11,12,14,15-dodecahydro-, $(6\alpha,7\alpha,14\alpha,15\alpha)$-	C_6H_{12}	210(4.72),273(3.52), 281(3.58),289(3.41)	78-2311-80
$(6\alpha,7\beta,14\beta,15\alpha)$-	C_6H_{12}	210(4.92),271(3.32), 280(3.63),290(3.05)	78-2311-80
Tricyclo[3.1.0.0^{2,4}]hexane, 1,2,4,5-tetraphenyl-3,6-di-2-propenyl-, $(1\alpha,2\beta,3\beta,4\beta,5\alpha,6\alpha)$-	MeCN	230(4.45)	44-2181-80
$C_{36}H_{32}O_9$ [9,9'-Bianthracene]-4,4'(1H,1'H)-dione, 1,1'-diacetyl-2,3-dihydro-2,5,5'-tri-hydroxy-10,10'-dimethoxy-2,2'-dimethyl- (O-dimethylsetomimycin)	EtOH	226(4.65),264(4.65), 338(3.99)	35-7493-80
$C_{36}H_{33}N_7O_4$ 4,13a-Etheno-6,12-imino-7,11-methano-13aH-pyrrolo[3,4-j][3]benzazecine-1,3,13,17(2H)-tetrone, 8,16-bis(4,6-dimethyl-2-pyrimidinyl)-3a,4,5,5a,6-7,8,11,12,13b-decahydro-2-phenyl-	$CHCl_3$	252s(4.18),272(4.34)	39-0331-80C
$C_{36}H_{34}O_2$ Heptacyclo[28.2.2.2^{14,17}.0^{4,25}.0^{6,27}-0^{9,20}.0^{11,22}]hexatriaconta-4,6(27),9-11(22),14(36),16,20,25,30,32,33-unde-caeene-dione	CH_2Cl_2	<u>280(3.9),440(3.4)</u>	18-2943-80
$C_{36}H_{36}N_4O_6$ 3-Phorbinepropanoic acid, 9-ethenyl-14-ethyl-13-formyl-21-(methoxycarbo-nyl)-4,8,18-trimethyl-20-oxo-, methyl ester	THF	325(4.39),370(4.39), 414(4.79),436(5.18), 525(4.04),554(3.83), 599(3.87),655(4.49)	118-0539-80
$C_{36}H_{37}N_5O_6$ 21H,23H-Porphine-2,18-dipropanoic acid, 8-ethenyl-3,7,12,17-tetramethyl-13-(2-nitroethenyl)-, dimethyl ester	$CHCl_3$	380(4.91),438(4.88), 521(3.90),567(4.20), 586(4.15),648(3.46)	39-0490-80C
	+ CF_3COOH	426(--),526s(--), 561(--),611(--)	39-0490-80C
$C_{36}H_{38}MgN_4O_6$ Bacteriochlorophyllide a, methyl ester	$C_6H_{11}Me$	263(4.708(,306(4.502),	33-1048-80

Compound	Solvent	$\lambda_{max}(\log \epsilon)$	Ref.
(cont.)		360(4.732),392(4.555), 544(3.763),579(4.210), 705(3.968),774(4.683) (plus shoulders)	33-1048-80
$C_{36}H_{38}N_4O_4$			
Protoporphyrin dimethyl ester	EtOH	502(4.031),536(3.888), 575(3.705),628(3.501)	110-1413-80
Protoporphyrin IX dimethyl ester	n.s.g.	408(5.22),507(4.14), 542(4.07),575(3.82), 600(3.30),630(3.72)	35-6841-80
$C_{36}H_{38}N_4O_5$			
Methylpheophorbide a	THF	273(4.20),321(4.30), 411(5.03),470(3.64), 506(4.08),535(4.02), 559(--),609(3.49), 668(4.71)	118-0539-80
$C_{36}H_{38}N_4O_6$			
Deuteroporphyrin, 3,8-diformyl-, diethyl ester	CHCl₃	379(4.65),436(5.19), 525(4.16),561(3.92), 594(3.84),648(3.59)	12-0575-80
21H,23H-Porphine-2,12-dipropanoic acid, 3,8,13,18-tetramethyl-7,17-diformyl-, diethyl ester	CHCl₃	395s(4.72),418(5.38), 430(5.07),526(3.82), 573(4.36),595(4.20), 647(3.59)	12-0575-80
21H,23H-Porphine-2,12-dipropanoic acid, 3,8,13,17-tetramethyl-7,18-diformyl-, diethyl ester	CHCl₃	392s(4.70),419(5.29), 432(4.99),526(3.86), 571(4.41),597(4.19), 646(3.56)	12-0575-80
21H,23H-Porphine-2,18-dipropanoic acid, 3,8,12,17-tetramethyl-7,13-diformyl-, diethyl ester	CHCl₃	431(5.15),523(4.15), 560(3.89),590(3.85), 644(3.51)	12-0575-80
21H,23H-Porphine-2,18-dipropanoic acid, 3,7,13,17-tetramethyl-8,12-diformyl-, diethyl ester	CHCl₃	374(4.62),410s(4.83), 432(5.27),504s(3.84), 523(4.05),564(4.05), 595(3.80),651(3.86)	12-0575-80
$C_{36}H_{39}ClN_4O_4$			
21H,23H-Porphine-2,12-dipropanoic acid, 18-(2-chloroethyl)-7-ethenyl-3,8,13- 17-tetramethyl-, dimethyl ester	CHCl₃	403(5.24),502(4.13), 538(4.06),571(3.84), 625(3.62)	12-0557-80
21H,23H-Porphine-2,13-dipropanoic acid, 17-(2-chloroethyl)-7-ethenyl-3,8,12- 18-tetramethyl-, dimethyl ester	CHCl₃	403(5.23),502(4.13), 538(4.05),571(3.83), 625(3.60)	12-0557-80
21H,23H-Porphine-2,13-dipropanoic acid, 18-(2-chloroethyl)-7-ethenyl-3,8,12- 17-tetramethyl-, dimethyl ester	CHCl₃	403(5.24),502(4.13), 539(4.06),571(3.84), 625(3.60)	12-0557-80
$C_{36}H_{40}N_4O_6$			
Biliverdin dimethyl ester	toluene	381(4.72),654(4.19)	108-0196-80
	EtOH	377(4.72),665(4.15)	108-0196-80
	2-Me-1-BuOH	378(4.69),665(4.14)	108-0196-80
	2-octanol	378(4.67),658(4.15)	108-0196-80
	dioxan	376(4.72),656(4.15)	108-0196-80
	THF	376(4.72),644(4.20)	108-0196-80
	EtOAc	376(4.73),649(4.18)	108-0196-80
	MeCN	374(4.74),662(4.15)	108-0196-80
	CHCl₃	378(4.74),658(4.16)	108-0196-80

Compound	Solvent	$\lambda_{max}(\log \epsilon)$	Ref.
Biliverdin dimethyl ester, protonated	toluene	377(4.62),632(4.62), 714s(4.12)	108-0196-80
	EtOH	378(4.79),650s(4.35), 705(4.43)	108-0196-80
	2-Me-1-BuOH	383(4.73),657(4.42), 710s(4.35)	108-0196-80
	2-octanol	380(4.63),645(4.59)	108-0196-80
	dioxan	379(4.66),639(4.61)	108-0196-80
	THF	378(4.69),640(4.56)	108-0196-80
	EtOAc	376(4.73),647(4.59)	108-0196-80
	MeCN	362(4.79),660(4.51), 741s(4.19)	108-0196-80
	$CHCl_3$	381(4.74),668(4.58), 736s(4.29)	108-0196-80
Deuteroporphyrin, 3-acetyl-8-(1-hydroxyethyl)-, dimethyl ester	$CHCl_3$	411(5.26),510(4.05), 549(4.09),577(3.90), 635(3.27)	12-0585-80
Deuteroporphyrin, 8-acetyl-3-(1-hydroxyethyl)-, dimethyl ester	$CHCl_3$	411(5.26),510(4.05), 549(4.08),577(3.92), 635(3.31)	12-0585-80
21H,23H-Porphine-2,12-dipropanoic acid, 7-acetyl-18-(2-hydroxyethyl)-3,8,13-17-tetramethyl-, dimethyl ester	$CHCl_3$	410(5.26),510(4.03), 549(4.13),576(3.94), 634(3.24)	12-0557-80
21H,23H-Porphine-2,13-dipropanoic acid, 7-acetyl-17-(2-hydroxyethyl)-3,8,12-18-tetramethyl-, dimethyl ester	$CHCl_3$	409(5.26),510(4.03), 549(4.13),575(3.93), 634(3.19)	12-0557-80
21H,23H-Porphine-2,13-dipropanoic acid, 7-acetyl-18-(2-hydroxyethyl)-3,8,12-17-tetramethyl-, dimethyl ester	$CHCl_3$	410(5.27),510(4.03), 549(4.12),576(3.93), 634(3.22)	12-0557-80
$C_{36}H_{40}O_{18}$ Specioside hexaacetate	MeOH	281(4.1)	100-0524-80
$C_{36}H_{40}O_{20}$ Verproside heptaacetate	EtOH	205(4.39),236(4.15)	33-1905-80
$C_{36}H_{42}N_4O_4$ Mesoporphyrin dimethyl ester	EtOH	498(4.152),531(4.021), 569(3.834),622(2.832)	110-1413-80
$C_{36}H_{43}N_5O_2$ 21H,23H-Porphine, 2,3,7,8,12,13,17-heptaethyl-18-(2-nitroethenyl)-, (E)-	$CHCl_3$	378(4.90),431(4.84), 518(3.71),568(4.19), 586(4.20),646s(3.20)	39-0490-80C
	+ CF_3COOH	424(--),528s(--), 562(--),612(--)	39-0490-80C
$C_{36}H_{43}N_{11}O_{12}$ Glycine, N-[(phenylmethoxy)carbonyl]-, 2'(or 3')-ester with N-[4-[[9-[2(or 3)-O-acetyl-β-D-ribofuranosyl]-9H-purin-6-yl]amino]butyl]adenosine	pH 2	263(4.53)	87-0781-80
$C_{36}H_{44}CoN_4$ Cobalt(III), octaethylporphinato-, perchlorate	CH_2Cl_2	375(4.82),524(3.85), 556(3.86)	138-0521-80
$C_{36}H_{44}MgN_4$ Magnesium, octaethylporphinato-	$C_6H_{11}Me$	335(4.338),388(4.562), 409(5.611),504(3.382), 543(4.252),580(4.196)	33-1048-80

Compound	Solvent	$\lambda_{max}(\log \epsilon)$	Ref.

$C_{36}H_{44}N_4O$
  2-Butanone, 4-(2,7,12,17-tetraethyl-
  3,8,13,18-tetramethyl-21H,23H-por-
  phin-5-yl)-
	$CHCl_3$	409(4.31),508(4.14),
		543(3.77),577(3.77),
		628(3.20)
			103-0730-80

$C_{36}H_{44}N_4Tl_2$
  Porphine, octaethyl-, bis(thallium(I)
  complex
	CH_2Cl_2	370(4.76),478(5.12),
		604(3.90)
			88-0433-80

$C_{36}H_{45}NO_{14}$ Collinemycin	$CHCl_3$	257(4.35),288(3.97), 296(3.96),484(4.14), 494(4.17),514(4.05), 528(3.98)	100-0242-80
Musettamycin	MeOH	233(4.62),256(4.38), 284(4.02),466(4.01), 490(4.10),510(4.02), 524(3.97),570(3.37)	100-0242-80

$C_{36}H_{46}N_2O_2$
  Estra-1,3,5(10)-trien-17-ol, 3,3'-azo-
  bis-, cis
	benzene	440(3.29)	149-0305-80B

trans	benzene MeOH	445(2.98) 342(4.38)	149-0305-80B 149-0305-80B

$C_{36}H_{46}N_2O_4$
  [1,1':4',1"-Terphenyl]-4,4"-diethan-
  aminium, N,N,N',N'-tetramethyl-β,β'-
  dioxo-N,N'-bis(4-oxopentyl)-, dibrom-
  ide
	H_2O	333(4.60)	87-0541-80

$C_{36}H_{46}N_4O_2$
  21H,23H-Porphine, 2,7,12,17-tetraethyl-
  5-[(2-methoxyethoxy)methyl]-
  3,8,13,18-tetramethyl-
	$CHCl_3$	407(5.19),506(4.09),
		541(3.93),577(3.76),
		631(3.64)
			103-0730-80

$C_{36}H_{46}N_5$
  Ethanaminium, N-methyl-N-[(2,7,12,17-
  tetraethyl-3,8,13,18-tetramethyl-
  21H,23H-porphin-5-yl)methylene]-,
  iodide
	$CHCl_3$	383(4.90),442(4.74),
		517(3.80),550(3.69),
		540(3.75),642(3.70)
		[sic]
			103-0592-80

	+ 1% CF_3COOH	438(5.11),585(3.78), 645(3.90)	103-0592-80

$C_{36}H_{46}N_6O_{10}$
  Riboflavin, α⁸-1H-imidazol-1-yl-,
  2',3',4',5'-tetrakis(2-methyl-
  propanoate)
	$CHCl_3$	336(3.88),428s(3.92),
		448(4.00),472s(3.89)
			35-7157-80

$C_{36}H_{46}O_{13}$ Trillenogenin pentaacetate	EtOH	244.2(3.96)	94-1437-80

$C_{36}H_{47}NO_3S$
  3-Pyridinecarboxylic acid, 1,2-dihydro-
  2-oxo-6-[2-[4-(phenylthio)phenyl]-
  ethenyl]-, hexadecyl ester, (E)-
	C_6H_{12}	219(4.19),254(4.16),
		373(4.55)
			44-1354-80

$C_{36}H_{48}N_4O_5$
  4a,13b-Etheno-1H,9H-benzo[c]cyclopenta-
  [h][1,2,4]triazolo[1,2-a]cinnoline-
	EtOH	255(3.59)	130-0187-80

Compound	Solvent	$\lambda_{max}(\log \epsilon)$	Ref.
11-butanamide, 6-acetoxy-2,3,5,6,7,8-8a,8b,10,10a,11,12,13,13a-tetradeca-hydro-N,N, ,8a,10a-pentamethyl-1,3-dioxo-2-phenyl-, [4aS-[4aα,6α,8aα-8bβ,10aα,11α(S*),13aβ,13bα]]- (cont.)			130-0187-80
$C_{36}H_{48}N_4Zn$ Zinc, [2,3,7,8,12,13,17,18-octaethyl-2,3,7,8-tetrahydro-21H,23H-porphin-ato(2-)-$N^{21},N^{22},N^{23},N^{24}$]-, (SP-4-2)-	CHCl$_3$-10% MeOH	368(4.74),386(4.93), 400(4.96),490(3.59), 524(3.68),553(3.96), 597(4.64),642(3.08)	35-0364-80
$C_{36}H_{49}NO_3S$ 3-Pyridinecarboxylic acid, 1,2-dihydro-2-oxo-6-[2-[4-(phenylthio)phenyl]-ethyl]-, hexadecyl ester	C_6H_{12}	215(4.37),235(4.28), 254(4.21),300(4.21)	44-1354-80
$C_{36}H_{49}O_2$ [1,1':3',1"-Terphenyl]-2'-yloxy, 5'-(octadecyloxy)-	hexane	$\underline{415(4.3),470s(3.8),}$ $\underline{650(2.7)}$	70-0354-80
$C_{36}H_{50}N_2O_2$ [1,1':4',1"-Terphenyl]-4,4"-diethan-aminium, N,N,N',N'-tetramethyl-β,β'-dioxo-N,N'-dipentyl-, dibromide	H$_2$O	331(4.65)	87-0541-80
$C_{36}H_{50}N_4$ 21H,23H-Porphine, 2,3,7,8,12,13,17,18-octaethyl-2,3,7,8-tetrahydro-(octaethyl isobacteriochlorin)	benzene	355s(4.69),370(4.84), 380(4.89),402(4.65), 480(3.74),510(3.93), 545(4.18),586(4.44), 635(3.92)	35-0364-80
56-44 ttt-tct	CHCl$_2$	360s(4.75),373(4.96), 380s(4.90),403(4.64), 484(3.76),513(3.95), 548(4.21),590(4.46), 635(3.89)	89-0140-80
$C_{36}H_{50}O_7$ 8'-Apo-β,ψ-carotenoic acid, β-D-galac-topyranosyl ester	EtOH	450(4.99)	27-0020-80
8'-Apo-β,ψ-carotenoic acid, β-D-gluco-pyranosyl ester	EtOH	450(4.82)	33-0277-80
$C_{36}H_{51}BrN_2O_3$ Spiro[2H-1-benzopyran-2,2'-[2H]indole], 8-bromo-1',3'-dihydro-3',3'-dimethyl-6-nitro-1'-octadecyl-	EtOH	528(4.45)	103-0041-80
$C_{36}H_{51}CoN_8O$ Cobalt, bis(cyano-C)(2,3,7,8,12,13,17-18-octahydro-2,2,3,3,7,7,8,8,12,12-13,13,17,17,18,18-hexadecamethyl-4H,21H-5,15-diazaporphin-4-olato-$N^{21},N^{22},N^{23},N^{24}$)-, (OC-6-24)	CHCl$_3$	355(4.18),478(3.47), 520s(3.44)	33-0733-80
$C_{36}H_{52}N_2O_3$ Spiro[2H-1-benzopyran-2,2'-[2H]indole], 1',3'-dihydro-3',3'-dimethyl-6-nitro-1'-octadecyl-	EtOH	537(4.52)	103-0041-80

Compound	Solvent	λ_{max}(log ϵ)	Ref.
Spiro[2H-1-benzopyran-2,2'-[2H]indole, 1',3'-dihydro-3',3'-dimethyl-8-nitro-1'-octadecyl-	EtOH	550(4.42)	103-0041-80
C$_{36}$H$_{52}$O$_3$ 5α-Cholesta-8,14-dien-3β-ol, 15-ethoxy-, benzoate	EtOH	232(4.31),254(4.27)	44-4034-80
C$_{36}$H$_{54}$O$_3$ Methanone, 1,3,5-benzenetriyltris-[(1,2,2,3-tetramethylcyclopentyl)-	MeCN	223(4.44),285(2.65), 326(2.59)	108-0142-80
C$_{36}$H$_{54}$O$_4$ 5α-Cholestane-2β-carboxylic acid, 2α-(4-methoxyphenyl)-3-oxo-, methyl ester	hexane	227(4.03),268s(3.08), 273(3.18),280(3.15)	12-0113-80
C$_{36}$H$_{56}$N$_6$O$_2$Pd Palladium, [2,3,4,7,8,12,13,14,17,18-decahydro-4,14-dimethoxy-2,2,3,3,7,7-8,8,12,12,13,13,17,17,18,18-hexadeca-methyl-21H-23H-5,15-diazaporphinato-(2-)-N^{21},N^{22},N^{23},N^{24}]-, (SP-4-1)-	EtOH	245(4.09),258s(4.03), 303(4.00),390s(4.00), 408(4.09)	27-0279-80
C$_{36}$H$_{60}$ Benzene, 1,3,5-tris[(1,2,2,3-tetrameth-ylcyclopentyl)methyl]-	MeCN	222(4.12),249(2.53), 266(2.65),272(2.54), 275s(2.45)	108-0142-80
C$_{36}$H$_{60}$O$_3$ 1,3,5-Benzenetrimethanol, α,α',α''-tris(1,2,2,3-tetramethylcyclopentyl)-	MeCN	203(4.72),215s(4.20), 256(2.76),265(2.76)	108-0142-80
C$_{36}$H$_{62}$O$_3$ 2-Propenoic acid, 3-(4-methoxyphenyl)-, hexacosyl ester, (E)-	EtOH	212(4.10),227(4.22), 309(4.57)	2-0421-80

Compound	Solvent	$\lambda_{max}(\log \epsilon)$	Ref.
C$_{37}$H$_{25}$NO Cyclobuta[b]naphthalen-1(2H)-one, 2-(diphenylmethylene)-3-phenyl-8-(phenylamino)-	CHCl$_3$	248(4.54),282s(4.47), 344(4.34),413(4.24), 453s(4.01)	88-4869-80
C$_{37}$H$_{27}$OS Pyrylium, 4-[3-(2,6-diphenyl-4H-thiopyran-4-ylidene)-1-propenyl]-2,6-diphenyl-, perchlorate	CH$_2$Cl$_2$ MeNO$_2$	725(5.24) 715(5.19)	124-1186-80 124-1186-80
C$_{37}$H$_{27}$OSe Pyrylium, 4-[3-(2,6-diphenyl-4H-selenin-4-ylidene)-1-propenyl]-2,6-diphenyl-, perchlorate	CH$_2$Cl$_2$ MeNO$_2$	745(5.36) 734(5.31)	124-1186-80 124-1186-80
C$_{37}$H$_{27}$O$_2$ Pyrylium, 2-[3-(4,6-diphenyl-2H-pyran-2-ylidene)-1-propenyl]-4,6-diphenyl-, perchlorate	CH$_2$Cl$_2$	730(4.77),800(4.93)	103-0691-80
Pyrylium, 4-[3-(4,6-diphenyl-4H-pyran-4-ylidene)-1-propenyl]-2,6-diphenyl-, perchlorate	CH$_2$Cl$_2$	686(5.40)	103-0691-80
C$_{37}$H$_{27}$SSe Thiopyrylium, 4-[3-(2,6-diphenyl-4H-selenin-4-ylidene)-1-propenyl]-2,6-diphenyl-, perchlorate	CH$_2$Cl$_2$ MeNO$_2$	785(5.32) 780(5.26)	124-1186-80 124-1186-80
C$_{37}$H$_{27}$S$_2$ Thiopyrylium, 2-[3-(4,6-diphenyl-2H-thiopyran-2-ylidene)-1-propenyl]-4,6-diphenyl-, perchlorate	CH$_2$Cl$_2$	805(4.85)	103-0691-80
Thiopyrylium, 4-[3-(2,6-diphenyl-4H-thiopyran-4-ylidene)-1-propenyl]-2,6-diphenyl-, perchlorate	CH$_2$Cl$_2$	762(5.39)	103-0691-80
C$_{37}$H$_{28}$O$_4$ 2-Propenoic acid, 3-phenyl-, 3-oxo-2-(1-oxo-3-phenyl-2-propenyl)-5-phenyl-1-(2-phenylethenyl)-1,4-pentadienyl ester	CHCl$_3$	295(4.64),354(4.50)	102-2643-80
C$_{37}$H$_{30}$N$_4$Ni Nickel, [2-(diphenylmethyl)-5,10,15,20-tetramethyl-21H,23H-porphinato(2-)-N^{21},N^{22},N^{23},N^{24}]-, (SP-4-2)-	CHCl$_3$	304(4.07),332(4.03), 423(5.27),545(4.08)	5-1082-80
C$_{37}$H$_{31}$Cl$_2$N$_3$O Acetamide, N-[[5-chloro-3-(2-chlorophenyl)-1-methyl-1H-indol-2-yl]methyl]-2-[(triphenylmethyl)amino]-	EtOH	230(4.69),284(4.01)	87-0764-80
C$_{37}$H$_{31}$N$_2$ Pyridinium, 1-methyl-2-[(1-methyl-4,6-diphenyl-2(1H)-pyridinylidene)-methyl]-4,6-diphenyl-, perchlorate	CH$_2$Cl$_2$	540(4.51)	103-0691-80
Pyridinium, 1-methyl-4-[(1-methyl-2,6-diphenyl-4(1H)-pyridinylidene)-methyl]-2,6-diphenyl-, perchlorate	CH$_2$Cl$_2$	515(4.93)	103-0691-80

Compound	Solvent	$\lambda_{max}(\log \epsilon)$	Ref.
$C_{37}H_{33}NO_2$			
Ethanone, 1-[4'-benzoyl-5'-(diethyl-amino)-6'-phenyl[1,1':2',1"-ter-phenyl]-3'-yl]-	MeCN	240(4.50)	24-0424-80
Methanone, [5'-(diethylamino)-6'-meth-yl[1,1':2',1"-terphenyl]-3',4'-diyl]-bis[phenyl-	MeCN	242(4.53),280s(--)	24-0424-80
$C_{37}H_{33}N_3$			
5-Phthalazinamine, N,N-diethyl-6-meth-yl-1,4,7,8-tetraphenyl-	MeCN	244(4.60),300s(--), 384(3.65)	24-0424-80
$C_{37}H_{36}N_2O_9$			
Thalpindione (same in acid and base)	MeOH	275(3.78),283s(3.77)	100-0372-80
$C_{37}H_{38}N_2O_7$			
Berbaman-7-ol, 6,6'-dimethoxy-2,2'-di-methyl-12,13-[methylenebis(oxy)]-, (1β)-	EtOH	284(3.92)	39-1696-80B
$C_{37}H_{38}N_4O_7$			
3-Phorbinepropanoic acid, 9-ethenyl-14-ethyl-13-formyl-21-(methoxycarbonyl)-4,8,18-trimethyl-20-oxo-, 2-hydroxy-ethyl ester, [3S-(3α,4β,21β)]-	acetone	439(5.19),530(4.09), 553(3.97),603(3.97), 654(4.60)	44-1969-80
$C_{37}H_{39}N$			
Pyridine, 1,4-dihydro-1-octyl-2,3,5,6-tetraphenyl-	EtOH	230(4.55),273(4.55), 322(4.25),350(4.13)	39-2554-80C
$C_{37}H_{40}CuN_4O_6$			
Copper, [methyl 8-ethenyl-13-ethyl-2,3-dihydro-18-(methoxycarbonyl)-20-(2-methoxy-2-oxoethyl)-3,7,12,17-tetra-methyl-21H,23H-porphine-2-propano-ato(2-)-N^{21},N^{22},N^{23},N^{24}]-, [SP-4-2-(2S-trans)]-	CH_2Cl_2	396(4.90),412(5.03), 500(3.69),537(3.48), 587(4.00),627(4.66)	130-0001-80
$C_{37}H_{40}N_2O_6$			
Berbaman-7-ol, 6,6',12-trimethoxy-2,2'-dimethyl-	EtOH	283(3.97)	39-1696-80B
Berbaman-12-ol, 6,6',7-trimethoxy-2,2'-dimethyl-	EtOH	284(3.97)	39-1696-80B
Berbaman-12'-ol, 6,6',7-trimethoxy-2,2'-dimethyl-, (SR)-	EtOH	284(3.88)	39-1696-80B
(SS)-	EtOH	284(3.86)	39-1696-80B
Homoaromoline	EtOH	286(3.89)	12-0225-80
	EtOH-NaOH	289(--)	12-0225-80
Kalashine	MeOH	220(4.54),272(4.04), 290s(3.74),304(3.70)	88-3315-80
$C_{37}H_{40}N_2O_7$			
Thalrugosidine, N-demethyl-	MeOH	278(3.90),283(3.91)	100-0372-80
$C_{37}H_{40}N_4O_7$			
Rhodin g$_7$, trimethyl ester	CH_2Cl_2	408(4.79),429(5.24), 524(4.04),556(3.89), 592(3.78),650(4.36)	35-2437-80
	THF	313(4.39),359(4.34), 428(5.25),522(4.03), 558(3.86),597(3.76),	118-0541-80

Compound	Solvent	$\lambda_{max}(\log \epsilon)$	Ref.
Rhodin g₇, trimethyl ester (cont.)		652(4.41)	118-0541-80
$C_{37}H_{40}O_{19}$ 1-Propanone, 3-(3,4-diacetoxyphenyl)- 1-[2,4-diacetoxy-6-[(2,3,4,6-tetra- O-acetyl-β-D-glucopyranosyl)oxy]- phenyl]- (3-hydroxyphloridzin octaacetate)	MeOH	273(3.81)	100-0739-80
$C_{37}H_{41}ClN_4O_5$ 3-Phorbinepropanoic acid, 9-(2-chloro- ethyl)-14-ethyl-21-(methoxycarbonyl)- 4,6,8,13,18-pentamethyl-20-oxo-, methyl ester, [3S-(3α,4β,21β)]-	CH_2Cl_2	415(5.15),516(4.10), 549(4.24),613(3.96), 670(4.79)	44-2218-80
$C_{37}H_{42}N_4O_6$ 21H,23H-Porphine-2-propanoic acid, 8- ethenyl-13-ethyl-2,3-dihydro-18-(meth- oxycarbonyl)-20-(2-methoxy-2-oxoeth- yl)-3,7,12,17-tetramethyl-, methyl ester, (2S-trans)-	THF	303(3.98),402(5.09), 500(4.05),529(3.67), 558(3.24),608(3.66), 665(4.64)	118-0541-80
$C_{37}H_{42}N_4O_7$ 3-Phorbinepropanoic acid, 9-acetyl-14- ethyl-13,14-dihydro-21-(methoxycarb- onyl)-4,8,13,18-tetramethyl-20-oxo-, 2-hydroxyethyl ester	acetone	357(4.91),384(4.65), 492s(3.59),522(4.29), 676(3.84),750(4.69)	44-1969-80
$C_{37}H_{42}O_{18}$ β-D-Glucopyranose, 2-O-methyl-, cyclic 3,6-(4,4',5,5',6,6'-hexamethoxy[1,1'- biphenyl]-2,2'-dicarboxylate) 1-(3,4,5-trimethoxybenzoate)	MeOH	216(4.69),250(4.24), 290s(3.89)	142-1743-80
β-D-Glucopyranose, 4-O-methyl-, cyclic 3,6-(4,4',5,5',6,6'-hexamethoxy[1,1'- biphenyl]-2,2'-dicarboxylate) 1-(3,4,5-trimethoxybenzoate)	MeOH	216(4.69),250(4.28), 290s(3.89)	142-1743-80
$C_{37}H_{44}N_4O_3$ Bonafousine	EtOH	228(4.88),286(4.09), 294(4.06),300s(4.00)	22-0490-80
	EtOH-acid	224(4.88),286(4.46), 294(4.46),312(4.35)	22-0490-80
	EtOH	228(4.88),286(4.54), 294(4.54),322(4.49)	22-0490-80
Isobonafousine	EtOH	228(4.67),277(4.03), 294(4.00),302s(3.92)	22-0490-80
	EtOH-base	228(4.68),277(4.09), 294(4.00),320(3.92)	22-0490-80
$C_{37}H_{45}N_5O_4$ 21H,23H-Porphine-5-propanoic acid, 2,7,12,17-tetraethyl-3,8,13,18- tetramethyl-α-nitro-, ethyl ester	$CHCl_3$	411(4.21),510(4.09), 510(4.09),547(3.85), 582(3.73),634(3.45)	103-0730-80
$C_{37}H_{45}N_{11}O_{12}$ Adenosine, 2',3'-O-[1-ethoxy-2-[[(phen- ylmethoxy)carbonyl]amino]ethylidene]- N-[2-[[9-[2,3-O-(1-methoxyethyli- dene)-β-D-ribofuranosyl]-9H-purin- 6-yl]amino]ethyl]-	pH 2	263(4.40),274s(4.35)	87-0781-80

Compound	Solvent	$\lambda_{max}(\log \epsilon)$	Ref.
$C_{37}H_{46}CuN_4$ Copper, [2,3,7,8,12,13,17,18-octaethyl-5-methyl-21H,23H-porphinato(2-)-$N^{21},N^{22},N^{23},N^{24}$]-, (SP-4-2)-	CH_2Cl_2	406(5.37),533(4.04), 564(4.06)	130-0001-80
$C_{37}H_{46}CuN_4O$ Copper, [2,3,7,8,12,13,17,18-octaethyl-2,3-dihydro-21H,23H-porphin-5-carbox-aldehydato(2-)-$N^{21},N^{22},N^{23},N^{24}$]-, [SP-4-2-(trans)]-	CH_2Cl_2	391(4.79),410(5.06), 463(3.44),499(3.72), 537(3.46),605s(--), 648(4.45)	130-0001-80
$C_{37}H_{46}N_4OZn$ Zinc, [2,3,7,8,12,13,17,18-octaethyl-21H,23H-porphine-5-methanolato(2-)-$N^{21},N^{22},N^{23},N^{24}$]-, (SP-4-2)-	CH_2Cl_2	407(5.18),538(3.90), 579(3.95)	130-0001-80
$C_{37}H_{47}NO_{16}$ Ipecoside, dimethyltetraacetyl-	EtOH	230(4.22),282(3.61)	24-0566-80
$C_{37}H_{48}N_4$ 21H,23H-Porphine, 2,3,7,8,12,13,17,18-octaethyl-5-methyl-	CH_2Cl_2	408(5.15),507(4.06), 540(3.66),578(3.67), 629(3.04)	130-0001-80
$C_{37}H_{48}N_4O$ 21H,23H-Porphine, 5-(butoxymethyl)-2,7,12,17-tetraethyl-3,8,13,18-tetramethyl-	$CHCl_3$	406(5.22),508(4.12), 543(3.95),577(3.77), 630(3.62)	103-0730-80
21H,23H-Porphine, 5-[(1,1-dimethyleth-oxy)methyl]-2,7,12,17-tetraethyl-3,8,13,18-tetramethyl-	$CHCl_3$	408(5.21),509(4.08), 545(3.88),580(3.74), 631(3.53)	103-0730-80
$C_{37}H_{48}N_5$ Ethanaminium, N-ethyl-N-[(2,7,12,17-tetraethyl-3,8,13,18-tetramethyl-21H,23H-porphin-5-yl)methylene]-, iodide	$CHCl_3$	383(4.89),440(4.77), 516(3.79),550(3.70), 588(3.76),641(3.68)	103-0592-80
	+ 1% CF_3COOH	437(5.12),583(3.80), 642(3.91)	103-0592-80
$C_{37}H_{48}O$ 1H-Cyclopenta[7,8]phenanthro[2,1-b]-naphtho[1,2-d]furan, 3-(1,5-dimeth-ylhexyl)-2,3,3a,4,5,5a,5b,6,7,16-16a,16b-dodecahydro-3a,5b-dimethyl-	EtOH	216(4.75),227s(4.42), 245(4.28),309(3.95), 315(3.99),322(3.95), 329(3.97)	142-0777-80B
$C_{37}H_{50}N_4$ 21H,23H-Porphine, 2,3,7,8,12,13,17,18-octaethyl-2,3-dihydro-5-methyl-, trans	CH_2Cl_2	399(5.27),499(4.18), 574(3.32),546(3.32), 592(3.70),646(4.72)	130-0001-80
$C_{37}H_{51}NO_3S$ 3-Pyridinecarboxylic acid, 1,2-dihydro-1-methyl-2-oxo-6-[2-[4-(phenylthio)-phenyl]ethyl]-, hexadecyl ester	CH_2Cl_2	245(3.88),273(--), 345(3.80)	44-1354-80
3-Pyridinecarboxylic acid, 2-methoxy-6-[2-[4-(phenylthio)phenyl]ethyl]-, hexadecyl ester	CH_2Cl_2	229s(--),259(3.88), 289(3.91)	44-1354-80
$C_{37}H_{52}O_{13}$ Digitoxigenin glucoside acetate	MeOH	227(4.31)	102-0531-80

Compound	Solvent	$\lambda_{max}(\log \epsilon)$	Ref.
Epidigitoxigenin glucoside acetate	MeOH	225(4.31)	102-0531-80
$C_{37}H_{53}CoN_8O$ Cobalt, bis(cyano-C)(3,4,7,8,12,13,17-18-octahydro-4-methoxy-2,2,3,3,7,7,8-8,12,12,13,13,17,17,18,18-hexadeca-methyl-21H,23H-5,15-diazaporphinato-$N^{21},N^{22},N^{23},N^{24}$)-, (OC-6-24)-	CHCl₃	357(4.19),390s(3.74), 481(3.47),510s(3.45)	33-0733-80
$C_{37}H_{54}N_2O_4$ Spiro[2H-1-benzopyran-2,2'-[2H]indole], 1',3'-dihydro-8-methoxy-3',3'-dimeth-yl-6-nitro-1'-octadecyl-	EtOH	562(4.48)	103-0041-80
$C_{37}H_{54}N_4O_8$ Benzenamine, 4-(1,4,7,10-tetraoxa-13-azacyclopentadec-13-yl)-N-[5-[[4-(1,4,7,10-tetraoxa-13-azacyclopenta-dec-13-yl)phenyl]amino]-2,4-pentadi-enylidene]-, monohydrochloride	MeOH	554(5.12)	24-0457-80
$C_{37}H_{61}NO_{11}$ Mycinamycin IV	MeOH	215(4.32),281.5(4.33)	77-0119-80
$C_{37}H_{61}NO_{12}$ Mycinamycin I Mycinamycin V	MeOH MeOH	218(4.38),240s(4.11) 215(4.32),280(4.33)	77-0119-80 77-0119-80
$C_{37}H_{61}NO_{13}$ Mycinamycin I, 14-hydroxy-	MeOH	218(4.37),240s(4.09)	77-0119-80
$C_{37}H_{62}O_4$ 2-Propenoic acid, 3-(4-acetoxyphenyl)-, hexacosyl ester, (E)-	EtOH	207(4.44),218(4.46), 281(4.64)	2-0421-80
$C_{37}H_{69}N_6$ Cyclopropenylium, 1,1'-[1-(dimethylami-no)-3-(methyliminio)-1-propene-1,3-diyl]bis[2,3-bis[bis(1-methylethyl)-amino]-, triperchlorate	MeCN	396(4.54)	24-1746-80

Compound	Solvent	$\lambda_{max}(\log \epsilon)$	Ref.
$C_{38}H_{26}O_3$			
8,12-Ethenofluorantheno[8',9':3,4]cyclo-but[1,2-f]isobenzofuran-9,11-dione, 7a,7b,8,8a,11a,12,12a,12b-octahydro-7,13-diphenyl-, (7aα,7bβ,8α,8aβ,11β-12α,12aβ,12bα)-	EtOH	241(4.27),261(4.18), 368(3.95),381(3.95)	78-3033-80
1,3-Propanedione, 2-(4-oxo-2,3,5-tri-phenyl-2-cyclopenten-1-ylidene)-1,3-diphenyl-	MeCN	249(4.48),315s(--)	24-0424-80
$C_{38}H_{28}$			
Cyclobutane, 1,2-bis(diphenylmethyl-ene)-3-methylene-4-(phenylmethylene)-, (E)-	CHCl$_3$	280(4.39),310s(4.26), 350s(3.97),425(3.72)	88-2713-80
$C_{38}H_{28}N_4O_{10}$			
2,4,7(1H,3H,8H)-Pteridinetrione, 6-phenyl-1-(2,3,5-tri-O-benzoyl-β-D-ribofuranosyl)-	MeOH	229(4.75),276s(4.12), 282(4.17),294s(4.09), 346(4.23)	24-1524-80
2,4,7(1H,3H,8H)-Pteridinetrione, 6-phenyl-3-(2,3,5-tri-O-benzoyl-β-D-ribofuranosyl)-	MeOH	225(4.76),284s(4.03), 297(4.10),355(4.27)	24-1524-80
$C_{38}H_{29}NO_3$			
7,11-Etheno-6H-dibenz[4,5:6,7]indeno-[7a,1-c]azepine-10(11H)-carboxylic acid, 6a,7-dihydro 6-oxo-5,6a-di-phenyl-, ethyl ester, anti-endo	EtOH	255(4.39),323(3.92)	44-2368-80
9,15-Methano-12H-triphenyleno[2,3-d]-azepine-12-carboxylic acid, 9,9a-14,15-tetrahydro-16-oxo-9,15-di-phenyl-, ethyl ester, (9α,9aα,14aα-15α)-	EtOH	253(4.60),312(3.85)	44-2368-80
$C_{38}H_{30}NO$			
Pyridinium, 4-[3-(2,6-diphenyl-4H-pyran-4-ylidene)-1-propenyl]-1-meth-yl-2,6-diphenyl-, perchlorate	CH$_2$Cl$_2$ MeNO$_2$	578(4.81) 554(4.77)	124-1186-80 124-1186-80
$C_{38}H_{30}NS$			
Pyridinium, 4-[3-(2,6-diphenyl-4H-thio-pyran-4-ylidene)-1-propenyl]-1-meth-yl-2,6-diphenyl-, perchlorate	CH$_2$Cl$_2$ MeNO$_2$	602(4.81) 564(4.74)	124-1186-80 124-1186-80
$C_{38}H_{30}NSe$			
Pyridinium, 4-[3-(2,6-diphenyl-4H-sele-nin-4-ylidene)-1-propenyl]-1-methyl-2,6-diphenyl-, perchlorate	CH$_2$Cl$_2$ MeNO$_2$	610(4.72) 560(4.68)	124-1186-80 124-1186-80
$C_{38}H_{30}N_2O_5$			
Methanone, (octahydro-2,4a,6-triphenyl-furo[2,3-d:4,5-d']diisoxazole-3,7-di-yl)bis[phenyl-, (3α,3aα,4aβ,7β,7aβ,7bα)-	MeOH	246(4.66)	73-3546-80
$C_{38}H_{30}N_4$			
1H-Pyrazole, 3,3'-(1,4-phenylene)bis[5-phenyl-1-(phenylmethyl)-	dioxan MeCN	285(4.60) 284(4.69)	103-0066-80 103-0066-80
$C_{38}H_{30}N_4O_2$			
1H-Pyrazole, 3,3'-(1,4-phenylene)bis-	dioxan	300(4.73)	103-0066-80

Compound	Solvent	$\lambda_{max}(\log \epsilon)$	Ref.
[1-(4-methoxyphenyl)-5-phenyl- (cont.)	MeCN	300(4.56)	103-0066-80
$C_{38}H_{30}OPSe$ Phosphonium, [2-phenoxy-2-phenyl- 1-(phenylseleno)ethenyl]triphenyl-, tetrafluoroborate	n.s.g.	269s(4.46),276s(4.36), 350(3.25)	104-0573-80
$C_{38}H_{32}$ 5,6:13,14:18,19:20,21-Tetrabenzohepta- cyclo[8.6.2^4,^{7}.2^{12},^{15}.1^2,^{9}.1^{11},^{16}.0- 0^3,^{8}]docosa-5,13,18,20-tetraene	MeCN at 40°C	261s(3.19),268s(3.34), 271s(3.40),274(3.42), 278(3.37)	24-1458-80
$C_{38}H_{32}Cl_2S_5$ 1,3-Butadiene, 3-chloro-2-[(4-chloro- phenyl)thio]-1,1,4,4-tetrakis[(4- methylphenyl)thio]-	heptane	199(4.93),265(4.47)	24-3342-80
$C_{38}H_{32}N_4Ni$ Nickel, [5,10,15,20-tetramethyl-3,12- (or 13)-bis(phenylmethyl)-21H,23H- porphinato(2-)-N^{21},N^{22},N^{23},N^{24}]-	CHCl$_3$	302(4.04),335(4.00), 423(5.26),546(4.08)	5-1082-80
$C_{38}H_{32}O_2$ Pentacyclo[4.4.0.0^2,^{5}.0^3,^{9}.0^4,^{8}]decane- 7,10-dione, 1,6,8,9-tetramethyl- 2,3,4,5-tetraphenyl-	dioxan	220(4.37)	78-3443-80
$C_{38}H_{32}O_{13}$ Benzo[h][1]benzopyrano[5,4,3-cde][1]- benzopyran-5,12-dione, 1-methyl- 6-(phenylmethoxy)-10-[(2,3,4-tri-O- acetyl-6-deoxy-β-D-galactopyranosyl)- oxy]-	EtOH	236(4.58),266(4.62)	87-0549-80
$C_{38}H_{33}NO$ 1H-Inden-1-one, 4-(diethylamino)-5- methyl-2,3,6,7-tetraphenyl-	MeCN	267(4.60),475(3.23)	24-0424-80
$C_{38}H_{33}N_5O_6$ Adenosine, N-(diphenylacetyl)-, 5'-(α- phenylbenzeneacetate)-	MeOH	278(4.24)	18-3670-80
$C_{38}H_{34}N_4$ 1H-Pyrazole, 3,3'-(1,4-phenylene)bis- [4,5-dihydro-5-phenyl-1-(phenylmeth- yl)-	dioxan	320(4.52)	103-0066-80
$C_{38}H_{34}N_4O_2$ 1H-Pyrazole, 3,3'-(1,4-phenylene)bis- [4,5-dihydro-1-(4-methoxyphenyl)-5- phenyl-	dioxan MeCN	329(4.11),430(4.72) 330(4.02),425(4.57)	103-0066-80 103-0066-80
$C_{38}H_{34}O_{10}$ [9,9'-Bianthracene]-10,10'(9H,9'H)-di- one, 4,4'-diacetoxy-5,5',7,7'-tetra- methoxy-2,2'-dimethyl-, dl meso	EtOH EtOH	249s(4.60),267s(4.53), 306(4.56),328s(4.49) 249(4.61),266s(4.54), 294s(4.51),322(4.54)	32-0629-80 32-0629-80
$C_{38}H_{35}NO_2$ Ethanone, 1-[4'-benzoyl-5'-(diethyl-	MeCN	212(4.49),235s(--),	24-0424-80

Compound	Solvent	λ_{max}(log ϵ)	Ref.
amino)-6'-methyl[1,1':2',1"-terphen-yl]-3'-yl]-2-phenyl- (cont.)		290s(--)	24-0424-80
1H-Inden-1-one, 4-(diethylamino)-2,3-dihydro-3-hydroxy-5-methyl-2,3,6,7-tetraphenyl-	MeCN	218(4.71),305(3.56)	24-0424-80
$C_{38}H_{36}N_2O_4S_2$ 1,4-Benzenediamine, N,N'-bis[1,2-di-methyl-4-(2-naphthalenylsulfonyl)-2-butenylidene]-	EtOH	249(4.64)	104-0849-80
$C_{38}H_{36}N_2O_9$ Thalictrinine	MeOH	205s(4.79),236(4.62), 251s(4.50),285s(4.01), 301s(3.84),330(3.73)	44-0213-80
	MeOH-HCl	282s(4.13),340(3.64)	44-0213-80
$C_{38}H_{38}N_2O_9$ Thalibrunimine, oxo-	MeOH	240s(4.10),270s(3.86), 330s(3.40)	44-0213-80
	MeOH-HCl	250s(4.00),284(3.60), 346s(3.31)	44-0213-80
Thalictrinine, dihydro-	MeOH	238(4.81),249s(4.73), 285s(4.05),299s(3.95), 327(3.62)	44-0213-80
	MeOH-HCl	210s(4.96),240s(4.69), 252(4.75),303s(4.05), 340s(3.74)	44-0213-80
Thalrugosinone (same in acid or base)	MeOH	274(3.89),283s(3.86)	100-0143-80
$C_{38}H_{34}N_4S_4$ 3H-Pyrazole-3-thione, 5,5'-dithiobis-[4-butyl-1,2-dihydro-1,2-diphenyl-	EtOH	222(4.21),307(3.91)	1-0597-80
$C_{38}H_{38}O_4$ Heptacyclo[28.2.2.2^{14,17}.0^{4,25}.0^{6,27}.-0^{9,20}.0^{11,22}]hexatriaconta-4,6(27),9-11(22),14(36),16,20,25,30,32,33-unde-caene-15,35-dione, 31,33-dimethoxy-isomer	CH$_2$Cl$_2$	310s(3.6),440(3.3)	18-2943-80
	CH$_2$Cl$_2$	450(3.3)	18-2943-80
$C_{38}H_{39}N_5NiO_2$ Nickel, [3,7,13,17-tetraethyl-2,8,12-18-tetramethyl-5-(4-nitrophenyl)-21H,23H-porphinato(2-)-N^{21},N^{22},N^{23}-N^{24}]-, (SP-4-2)-	CHCl$_3$	402(5.34),526(4.05), 561(4.29)	130-0063-80
$C_{38}H_{40}N_2O_7$ Berbaman, 6,6',7-trimethoxy-2,2'-di-methyl-12,13-[methylenebis(oxy)]-	EtOH	283(3.88)	39-1696-80B
Calafutimine	MeOH and MeOH-NaOH	235s(4.85),280(4.40), 292s(3.93)	142-1137-80B
$C_{38}H_{40}N_2O_8$ Revolutinone	MeOH	205s(5.13),250(4.78), 258(4.76),272(4.69), 280s(4.66),301s(4.31)	100-0270-80
$C_{38}H_{40}N_4Ni$ Nickel, [3,7,13,17-tetraethyl-2,8,12-18-tetramethyl-5-phenyl-21H,23H-	CHCl$_3$	403(5.22),526(4.04), 561(4.30)	130-0063-80

Compound	Solvent	$\lambda_{max}(\log \epsilon)$	Ref.
porphinato(2-)-$N^{21},N^{22},N^{23},N^{24}$]-, (SP-4-2)- (cont.)			130-0063-80
$C_{38}H_{40}O_{18}$			
Spinosin, 6"-feruloyl-	EtOH	276(4.21),332(4.41)	102-2791-80
	EtOH-NaOEt	270(4.14),311(3.78), 396(4.52)	102-2791-80
	EtOH-NaOAc	275(4.16),334(4.35), 404(3.55)	102-2791-80
	EtOH-NaOAc-H_3BO_3	276(4.18),333(4.39)	102-2791-80
	EtOH-AlCl$_3$-HCl	234(4.27),287(4.23), 307(4.28),340(4.34)	102-2791-80
$C_{38}H_{41}ClCuN_4O_7$			
Copper, [methyl 8-(2-chloroethyl)-13-ethyl-5-formyl-2,3-dihydro-18-(methoxycarbonyl)-20-(2-methoxy-2-oxoethyl)-3,7,12,17-tetramethyl-21H,23H-porphine-2-propanoato(2-)-N^{21},N^{22}-N^{23},N^{24}]-, [SP-4-2-(2S-trans)]-	CH$_2$Cl$_2$	391(4.85),416(5.10), 507(3.68),546(3.72), 623(4.10),663(4.64)	44-2218-80
$C_{38}H_{41}N_3$			
Propanedinitrile, [3-(diethylamino)-2,5-bis[4-(1,1-dimethylethyl)phenyl]-4-phenyl-2,4-cyclopentadien-1-ylidene]-	MeCN	282(4.13),377(4.19), 612(3.69)	24-0424-80
$C_{38}H_{42}N_2O_6$			
Berbaman, 6,6',7,12-tetramethoxy-2,2'-dimethyl-, (R,R)-	EtOH	283(3.91)	39-1696-80B
(S,S)-	EtOH	283(3.92)	39-1696-80B
Berbaman, 6,6',7,12'-tetramethoxy-2,2'-dimethyl-, (S,R)-	EtOH	284(3.91)	39-1696-80B
(S,S)-	EtOH	283(3.88)	39-1696-80B
Funiferine dimethiodide	EtOH	229(4.82),286(4.10)	102-1882-80
Kalashine, 1-O-methyl-	MeOH	222(4.51),272(4.00), 302(3.68)	88-3315-80
Lumipakistanine	EtOH	220s(4.87),282(4.55)	88-0723-80
$C_{38}H_{42}N_4O_4$			
21H,23H-Porphine-2,8-dipropanoic acid, 12,18-diethenyl-3,7,13,17-tetramethyl-, diethyl ester	CHCl$_3$	407(5.22),505(4.15), 541(4.06),575(3.84), 629.5(3.75)	12-0557-80
21H,23H-Porphine-2,12-dipropanoic acid, 8,18-diethenyl-3,7,13,17-tetramethyl-, diethyl ester	CHCl$_3$	404(5.21),506(4.09), 544(4.12),574(3.87), 629(3.54)	12-0557-80
21H,23H-Porphine-2,18-dipropanoic acid, 7,13-diethenyl-3,8,12,17-tetramethyl-, diethyl ester	CHCl$_3$	407(5.22),505(4.15), 541(4.06),575(3.84), 630(3.74)	12-0557-80
21H,23H-Porphine-2,18-dipropanoic acid, 8,12-diethenyl-3,7,13,17-tetramethyl-, diethyl ester	CHCl$_3$	407(5.24),505(4.15), 541(4.06),575(3.84), 629.5(3.74)	12-0557-80
$C_{38}H_{42}N_4O_7$			
Deuteroporphyrin, 3-(1-acetoxyethyl)-8-acetyl-, dimethyl ester	CHCl$_3$	411(5.25),510(4.06), 549(4.05),577(3.90), 635(3.35)	12-0585-80
Deuteroporphyrin, 8-(1-acetoxyethyl)-3-acetyl-, dimethyl ester	CHCl$_3$	411(5.26),510(4.06), 549(4.07),577(3.89), 635(3.31)	12-0585-80

Compound	Solvent	$\lambda_{max}(\log \epsilon)$	Ref.
$C_{38}H_{43}ClCuN_4O_6$ Copper, [methyl 8-(2-chloroethyl)-13- ethyl-2,3-dihydro-18-(methoxycarbo- nyl)-20-(2-methoxy-2-oxoethyl)-3,5- 7,12,17-pentamethyl-21H,23H-porph- ine-2-propanoato(2-)-N^{21},N^{22},N^{23},N^{24}]-, [SP-4-2-(2S-trans)]-	CH_2Cl_2	414(5.12),508(3.63), 554(3.65),598(3.99), 639(4.63)	44-2218-80
$C_{38}H_{43}ClN_4O_4$ 21H,23H-Porphine-2,12-dipropanoic acid, 18-(2-chloroethyl)-8-ethenyl-3,7,13- 17-tetramethyl-, diethyl ester	$CHCl_3$	403(5.24),502(4.13), 539(4.07),571(3.84), 625(3.61)	12-0557-80
$C_{38}H_{43}NO_{19}$ β-D-Glucopyranose, cyclic 3,6-(4,4',5- 5',6,6'-hexamethoxy[1,1'-biphenyl]- 2,2'-dicarboxylate) 2-(methylcarb- amate) 1-(3,4,5-trimethoxybenzoate)	MeOH	218(4.68),250s(4.30), 292(3.90)	142-1753-80
β-D-Glucopyranose, cyclic 3,6-(4,4',5- 5',6,6'-hexamethoxy[1,1'-biphenyl]- 2,2'-dicarboxylate) 4-(methylcarb- amate 1-(3,4,5-trimethoxybenzoate)	MeOH	219(4.72),250s(4.36), 295s(3.95)	142-1743-80
$C_{38}H_{44}ClN_5O_3$ 21H,23H-Porphine-2-carboxylic acid, 12-(2-chloroethyl)-7-ethyl-3,8,13,17- tetramethyl-18-[4-oxo-4-(1-pyrroli- dinyl)butyl]-, methyl ester	CH_2Cl_2	404(5.15),508(3.84), 545(4.00),571(3.81), 626(3.20)	4-0481-80
$C_{38}H_{44}N_2O_6$ Neothalibrine	MeOH	284(4.10)	100-0270-80
	MeOH-base	285(4.10),310s(3.68)	100-0270-80
Phenol, 4-[(1,2,3,4-tetrahydro-6,7-di- methoxy-2-methyl-1-isoquinolinyl)- methyl]-2-[4-[(1,2,3,4-tetrahydro- 6,7-dimethoxy-2-methyl-1-isoquino- linyl)methyl]phenoxy]-, [R-(R*,R*)]-	EtOH	284(4.07)	39-1696-80B
$C_{38}H_{44}N_4O_6$ 21H,23H-Porphine-2,12-dipropanoic acid, 8-acetyl-18-(2-hydroxyethyl)-3,7,13- 17-tetramethyl-, diethyl ester	$CHCl_3$	410(5.28),510(4.03), 550(4.12),576(3.93), 634(3.21)	12-0557-80
$C_{38}H_{44}N_4O_7$ Deuteroporphyrin, 3-(1-acetoxyethyl)- 8-(1-hydroxyethyl)-, dimethyl ester	$CHCl_3$	402(5.28),499(4.16), 533(3.95),568(3.81), 622(3.63)	12-0585-80
Deuteroporphyrin, 8-(1-acetoxyethyl)- 3-(1-hydroxyethyl)-, dimethyl ester	$CHCl_3$	402(5.28),499(4.16), 533(3.95),568(3.81), 622(3.62)	12-0585-80
$C_{38}H_{44}O_9$ β-D-Glucopyranosiduronic acid, (17β)- 2,3-bis(phenylmethoxy)estra-1,3,5(10)- trien-17-yl, monopotassium salt	MeOH	287(3.61)	95-0867-80
$C_{38}H_{44}O_{18}$ Corilagin, udeca-O-methyl-	MeOH	218(4.78),254(4.43)	142-1743-80
$C_{38}H_{45}ClN_4O_6$ 21H,23H-Porphine-2-propanoic acid,	CH_2Cl_2	404(5.27),508(4.10),	44-2218-80

Compound	Solvent	$\lambda_{max}(\log \epsilon)$	Ref.
8-(2-chloroethyl)-13-ethyl-2,3-dihydro-18-(methoxycarbonyl)-20-(2-methoxy-2-oxoethyl)-3,5,7,12,17-pentamethyl-, dimethyl ester, (2S-trans)-		536(3.94),612(3.70), 666(4.69)	44-2218-80
$C_{38}H_{45}N_5O_2$ 21H,23H-Porphine-5-propanoic acid, α-cyano-2,7,12,17-tetraethyl-3,8,13,18-tetramethyl-, ethyl ester	$CHCl_3$	410(4.29),510(4.12), 546(3.88),581(3.76), 632(3.45)	103-0730-80
$C_{38}H_{46}CuN_4O_2$ Copper, [2,3,7,8,12,13,17,18-octaethyl-7,8-dihydro-21H,23H-porphine-5,10-dicarboxaldehydato(2-)-$N^{21},N^{22},N^{23},N^{24}$]-	CH_2Cl_2	390(4.92),415(4.82), 504(3.72),540(3.43), 615(3.99),662(4.57)	130-0001-80
$C_{38}H_{46}N_2O_{11}S$ Rifamycin P	pH 7.38	260(4.49),297(4.36), 405(4.15)	78-1415-80
$C_{38}H_{46}N_4O_2$ 2,4-Pentanedione, 3-[(2,7,12,17-tetraethyl-3,8,13,18-tetramethyl-21H,23H-porphin-5-yl)methyl]-	$CHCl_3$	411(4.26),511(4.11), 547(3.83),582(3.76), 633(3.26)	103-0730-80
$C_{38}H_{46}N_4O_3$ Bonafousine, O-methyl-	EtOH and EtOH-base	228(4.71),285(4.10), 295(4.08),313s(3.88)	22-0490-80
Isobonafousine, O-methyl-	EtOH and EtOH-base	228(4.52),284(4.02), 294(4.01),302s(3.94)	22-0490-80
$C_{38}H_{46}N_4O_6$ Deuteroporphyrin, N-(1-ethoxyethyl)-3-(1-hydroxyethyl)-, dimethyl ester	$CHCl_3$	402(5.29),499(4.16), 533(3.96),568(3.82), 622(3.64)	12-0585-80
Deuteroporphyrin, 3-(1-ethoxyethyl)-8-(1-hydroxyethyl)-, dimethyl ester	$CHCl_3$	402(5.26),499(4.14), 533(3.94),568(3.80), 622(3.62)	12-0585-80
Mesochlorin e_6, meso-methyl-, trimethyl ester	CH_2Cl_2	404(5.18),508(4.07), 537(3.88),608(3.64), 662(4.63)	130-0001-80
21H,23H-Porphine-2,18-dipropanoic acid, 7,12-bis(1-methoxyethyl)-3,8,13,17-tetramethyl-, dimethyl ester	EtOH	497(4.317),530(3.925), 569(3.777),623(3.585)	110-1413-80
$C_{38}H_{47}N_5O$ Pyrrolidine, 1-[1-oxo-4-(8,12,17-triethyl-3,7,13,18-tetramethyl-21H,23H-porphin-2-yl)butyl]-	CH_2Cl_2	398(5.28),494(4.10), 527(3.98),560(3.83), 609(3.67)	4-0481-80
	+1% TFA	403(5.64),542(4.23), 583(3.90)	4-0481-80
$C_{38}H_{49}N_4ORh$ Rhodium, (2-hydroxyethyl)[2,3,7,8,12-13,17,18-octaethyl-21H,23H-porphinato(2-)-$N^{21},N^{22},N^{23},N^{24}$]-, (SP-5-31)-	$CHCl_3$	399(5.11),516(4.07), 548(4.33)	101-0095-80B
$C_{38}H_{50}Cl_2O_4Pd_2$ Palladium, di-μ-chlorobis[(4,5,6-η)-3,17-dioxoandrost-5-en-4-yl]di-	$CHCl_3$	248(3.85),291(3.98)	12-2761-80

Compound	Solvent	$\lambda_{max}(\log \epsilon)$	Ref.
$C_{38}H_{50}N_4O$			
21H,23H-Porphine, 2,3,7,8,12,13,17,18- octaethyl-5-(methoxymethyl)-	CH_2Cl_2	405(5.16),506(4.08), 540(3.93),576(3.74), 627(3.61)	130-0001-80
$C_{38}H_{50}N_5Rh$			
Rhodium, (2-aminoethyl)[2,3,7,8,12,13- 17,18-octaethyl-21H,23H-porphinato- (2-)-N^{21},N^{22},N^{23},N^{24}]-, monohydro- chloride	$CHCl_3$	383(5.08),432(5.10), 510(4.12),543(4.62)	101-0095-80B
$C_{38}H_{50}O_6$			
Camboginol	n.s.g.	230(4.17),281(4.14)	88-1975-80
Isoxanthochymol	EtOH	232(4.22),275(4.28), 312(3.93)	2-0627-80
Xanthochymol	C_6H_{12}	264(4.09),364(3.99)	2-0627-80
	EtOH	230(4.20),276(4.3)	2-0627-80
$C_{38}H_{52}N_4$			
21H,23H-Porphine, 2,3,7,8,12,13,17,18- octaethyl-2,3-dihydro-5,20-dimethyl-, trans	CH_2Cl_2	407(5.23),510(4.10), 538(3.65),608(3.62), 663(4.66)	130-0001-80
$C_{38}H_{52}O$			
1H-Cyclopenta[7,8]phenanthro[2,1-b]- naphtho[1,2-d]furan, 3-(1,5-dimethyl- hexyl)-2,3,3a,4,5,5a,5b,6,7,14d,15- 16,16a,16b-tetradecahydro-3a,5b,7- trimethyl- epimer, m. 161-5°	C_6H_{12}	223(4.50),247(4.39), 254(4.44),305(3.98), 317(3.97),324(3.88), 331(4.03)	142-0777-80B
	C_6H_{12}	222(4.53),248(4.41), 255(4.47),305(4.05), 318(4.05),325(3.95), 332(4.06)	142-0777-80B
epimer	C_6H_{12}	222(4.51),247(4.38), 254(4.40),305(3.99), 317(3.97),324(3.88), 331(4.00)	142-0777-80B
$C_{38}H_{54}FeO_2$			
Cholest-5-en-3β-ol, ester with carboxy- ferrocene	MeOH	215(4.63),264(3.86), 310(3.16)	5-1181-80
$C_{38}H_{56}N_2O_5$			
Spiro[2H-1-benzopyran-2,2'-[2H]indole], 1',3'-dihydro-5,7-dimethoxy-3',3'-di- methyl-6-nitro-1'-octadecyl-	EtOH	510(4.49)	103-0041-80
$C_{38}H_{56}O_9$			
Sapogenol c	MeOH	198(3.8)	20-1001-80
$C_{38}H_{60}N_2O_2$			
Androstan-17-one, 3-hydroxy-, [(3α,5α)- androstan-17-ylidene]hydrazone, (3α,5α)-	MeOH	210(4.18),228(3.57)	39-1356-80C

Compound	Solvent	$\lambda_{max}(\log \epsilon)$	Ref.
$C_{39}H_{29}OS$			
Pyrylium, 4-[5-(2,6-diphenyl-4H-thio-pyran-4-ylidene)-1,3-pentadienyl]-2,6-diphenyl-, perchlorate	CH_2Cl_2 MeNO$_2$	846(5.43) 835(5.30)	124-1186-80 124-1186-80
$C_{39}H_{29}OSe$			
Pyrylium, 4-[5-(2,6-diphenyl-4H-sele-nin-4-ylidene)-1,3-pentadienyl]-2,6-diphenyl-, perchlorate	CH_2Cl_2 MeNO$_2$	864(5.38) 855(5.18)	124-1186-80 124-1186-80
$C_{39}H_{29}O_2$			
Pyrylium, 2-[5-(4,6-diphenyl-2H-pyran-2-ylidene)-1,3-pentadienyl]-4,6-di-phenyl-, perchlorate	CH_2Cl_2	820(4.91),910(5.08)	103-0691-80
Pyrylium, 4-[5-(2,6-diphenyl-4H-pyran-4-ylidene)-1,3-pentadienyl]-2,6-di-phenyl-, perchlorate	CH_2Cl_2	806(5.50)	103-0691-80
$C_{39}H_{29}SSe$			
Thiopyrylium, 4-[5-(2,6-diphenyl-4H-selenin-4-ylidene)-1,3-pentadien-yl]-2,6-diphenyl-, perchlorate	CH_2Cl_2 MeNO$_2$	910(5.41) 890(5.24)	124-1186-80 124-1186-80
$C_{39}H_{29}S_2$			
Thiopyrylium, 2-[5-(4,6-diphenyl-2H-thiopyran-2-ylidene)-1,3-pentadien-yl]-4,6-diphenyl-, perchlorate	CH_2Cl_2	905(4.85),1000(5.03)	103-0691-80
Thiopyrylium, 4-[5-(2,6-diphenyl-4H-thiopyran-4-ylidene)-1,3-pentadien-yl]-2,6-diphenyl-, perchlorate	CH_2Cl_2	889(5.45)	103-0691-80
$C_{39}H_{33}N_2$			
Pyridinium, 1-methyl-2-[3-(1-methyl-4,6-diphenyl-2(1H)-pyridinylidene)-1-propenyl]-4,6-diphenyl-, perchlor-ate	CH_2Cl_2	630(4.97)	103-0691-80
Pyridinium, 1-methyl-4-[3-(1-methyl-2,6-diphenyl-4(1H)-pyridinylidene)-1-propenyl]-2,6-diphenyl-, perchlor-ate	CH_2Cl_2	644(5.27)	103-0691-80
$C_{39}H_{36}O_9$			
Chalcomoracin	EtOH	218(4.77),294s(4.53), 329(4.70),334(4.62)	138-1573-80
$C_{39}H_{38}N_4O_4$			
7H-Pyrrolo[2,3-d]pyrimidin-4-amine, N-(phenylmethyl)-7-[2,3,5-tris-O-(phenylmethyl)-β-D-arabino-furanosyl]-	MeOH	277(4.25)	24-2069-80
$C_{39}H_{40}N_4NiO$			
Nickel, [4-(3,7,13,17-tetraethyl-2,8-12,18-tetramethyl-21H,23H-porphin-5-yl)benzaldehydato(2-)-$N^{21},N^{22},N^{23}-N^{24}$]-, (SP-4-2)-	CHCl$_3$	404(5.17),526(3.99), 562(4.25)	130-0063-80
$C_{39}H_{42}N_4Ni$			
Nickel, [3,7,13,17-tetraethyl-2,8,12-18-tetramethyl-5-(4-methylphenyl)-21H,23H-porphinato(2-)-$N^{21},N^{22},N^{23},N^{24}$]-	CHCl$_3$	400(5.21),524(3.99), 559(4.25)	130-0063-80

Compound	Solvent	$\lambda_{max}(\log \epsilon)$	Ref.
$C_{39}H_{42}N_4NiO$			
Nickel, 3,7,13,17-tetraethyl-5-(4-methoxyphenyl)-2,8,12,18-tetramethyl-21H,23H-porphinato(2-)-N^{21},N^{22},N^{23}-N^{24}]-, (SP-4-2)-	$CHCl_3$	402(5.26),525(4.18), 561(4.34)	130-0063-80
$C_{39}H_{42}O_{19}$			
Spinosin, 6''-sinapoyl-	EtOH	275(4.08),333(4.39)	102-2791-80
	EtOH-NaOEt	232(4.24),268(4.14), 318(3.61),395(4.50)	102-2791-80
	EtOH-NaOAc	273(4.10),335(4.29), 404(3.75)	102-2791-80
	EtOH-NaOAc-H_3BO_3	274(4.04),333(4.35)	102-2791-80
	EtOH-AlCl$_3$-HCl	238(4.30),287(4.09), 308(4.19),344(4.31)	102-2791-80
$C_{39}H_{44}N_2O_7$			
Berbaman, 5,6,6',7,12-pentamethoxy-2,2'-dimethyl-	EtOH	283(3.99)	39-1696-80B
$C_{39}H_{44}N_2O_8$			
Thalistine	n.s.g.	278(3.90)	100-0472-80
Thalmirabine	n.s.g.	280(3.95),314s(3.34)	100-0472-80
$C_{39}H_{44}N_4$			
21H,23H-Porphine, 3,7,13,17-tetraethyl-2,8,12,18-tetramethyl-5-(4-methylphenyl)-	$CHCl_3$	405(5.13),505(4.09), 536(3.74),572(3.70), 624(3.23)	130-0063-80
$C_{39}H_{44}N_4O$			
21H,23H-Porphine, 2,7,12,17-tetraethyl-3,8,13,18-tetramethyl-5-(phenoxymethyl)-	$CHCl_3$	406(5.24),507(4.12), 544(3.94),577(3.78), 630(3.69)	103-0730-80
$C_{39}H_{44}N_4O_6$			
21H,23H-Porphine-2-propanoic acid, 8-ethenyl-13-ethyl-2,3-dihydro-18-(methoxycarbonyl)-20-(2-methoxy-2-oxoethyl)-3,7,17-trimethyl-12-(1-propenyl)-, methyl ester	CH_2Cl_2	409(5.17),504(4.09), 534(3.51),558(3.30), 606(3.64),662(4.61)	35-2437-80
$C_{39}H_{45}NO_{19}$			
β-D-Glucopyranose, 2-O-methyl cyclic 3,6-(4,4',5,5',6,6'-hexamethoxy-[1,1'-biphenyl]-2,2'-dicarboxylate 4-methylcarbamate 1-(3,4,5-trimethoxybenzoate)	MeOH	215(4.72),250s(4.10), 294s(4.30)	142-1743-80
$C_{39}H_{46}N_2O_6$			
Thalibrine, O-methyl-	n.s.g.	280(4.02),285s(4.01)	100-0472-80
$C_{39}H_{46}N_2O_{12}S$			
Rifamycin verde	pH 7.38	223(4.52),328(4.06), 372(4.06),480(3.88), 720(3.84)	78-1415-80
$C_{39}H_{47}NO_{18}$			
Ipecoside, hexaacetyl-	EtOH	216(4.32),268s(3.28), 276(3.18)	24-0566-80

Compound	Solvent	$\lambda_{max}(\log \epsilon)$	Ref.
Ipecoside, hexaacetyl- (cont.)	EtOH	214(4.23),268(3.13), 276(3.10)	24-0566-80
Isoipecoside, hexaacetyl-	EtOH	219(4.26),265s(3.17), 275(3.13)	24-0566-80
$C_{39}H_{48}N_2O_{12}S$			
Rifamycin Q	pH 7.38	260(4.50),299(4.40), 410(4.14)	78-1415-80
$C_{39}H_{48}N_4O_6$			
21H,23H-Porphine-2-propanoic acid, 8,13-diethyl-2,3-dihydro-18-(methoxycarbonyl)-20-(2-methoxy-2-oxoethyl)-3,7,17-trimethyl-12-propyl-, methyl ester, (2S-trans)-	CH2Cl2	398(5.16),497(4.08), 523(3.48),548(3.30), 595(3.70),649(4.57)	35-2437-80
$C_{39}H_{49}NO_{11}$			
Retinamide, N-[4-[(2,3,4-tri-O-acetyl-6-methyl-β-D-glucopyranuronosyl)oxy]-phenyl]-	EtOH	362(4.72)	136-0121-80H
sodium salt	MeOH	233(4.16),360(4.68)	136-0121-80H
$C_{39}H_{49}N_{11}O_{12}$			
Adenosine, 2',3'-O-[1-ethoxy-2-[[(phenylmethoxy)carbonyl]amino]ethylidene]-N-[4-[[9-[2,3-O-(1-methoxyethylidene)-β-D-ribofuranosyl]-9H-purin-6-yl]amino]butyl]-	EtOH	267(4.51)	87-0781-80
$C_{39}H_{50}N_4O_2$			
21H,23H-Porphine-5-methanol, 2,3,7,8-12,13,17,18-octaethyl-, acetate	CH2Cl2	404(5.19),506(4.09), 540(3.95),575(3.76), 625(3.67)	130-0001-80
$C_{39}H_{52}$			
Cholesta-3,5-diene, 3-p-biphenylyl-	pentane	204(4.55),235(4.09), 242(4.05),302(4.41)	44-0715-80
$C_{39}H_{52}N_5$			
Methanaminium, N-methyl-N-[(2,3,7,8,12-13,17,18-octaethyl-21H,23H-porphin-5-yl)methylene]-, iodide	CHCl3	383(4.88),420(4.83), 514(3.79),549(3.72), 584(3.82),633(3.81), 660(3.76)	103-0592-80
	+ 1% CF3COOH	437(5.17),581(3.82), 659(3.96)	103-0592-80
$C_{39}H_{52}O_5$			
D:C-Friedooleana-7,9(11)-dien-29-oic acid, 3-[[3-(4-hydroxyphenyl)-1-oxo-2-propenyl]oxy]-, [3α(E),20α]-	EtOH	233(4.18),239(4.17), 249s(3.89),300(4.13), 315(4.19)	39-2933-80C
$C_{39}H_{56}N_2O_3$			
Spiro[2H-1-benzopyran-2,2'-[2H]indole], 1',3'-dihydro-3',3'-dimethyl-6-nitro-1'-octadecyl-8-(2-propenyl)-	EtOH	545(4.53)	103-0041-80

Compound	Solvent	$\lambda_{max}(\log \epsilon)$	Ref.
$C_{40}Cl_{28}$ Methyl, [1,2-ethynediylbis(2,3,5,6-tetrachloro-4,1-phenylene)]bis[bis-(pentachlorophenyl)-	C_6H_{12}	222(5.18),296s(4.23), 385(4.73),435(4.36), 460(4.45),637(4.62)	88-2435-80
$C_{40}Cl_{30}$ Methyl, [(1,2-dichloro-1,2-ethenediyl)-bis(2,3,5,6-tetrachloro-4,1-phenyl-ene)]bis[bis(pentachlorophenyl)-, (E)-	C_6H_{12}	222(5.22),290s(4.13), 340s(4.09),368s(4.55), 388(4.87),510(3.39), 563(3.37)	88-2435-80
$C_{40}H_{18}N_8O_{16}$ 29H,31H-Phthalocyanine-2,3,9,10,16,17-23,24-octacarboxylic acid, copper complex	H_2O 1% NH_3	340(4.52),628(4.74), 675s(4.23) 348(4.86),615(4.42), 655s(4.51),685(5.28)	65-0907-80 65-0907-80
$C_{40}H_{22}$ Spiro[benzo[ghi]perylene-5(6H),6'-[6H]-benzo[cd]pyrene]	hexane	216(4.96),232(4.82), 265s(4.61),279(4.66), 320(4.44),334(4.47), 390(3.91),413(3.92)	18-2036-80
$C_{40}H_{24}$ Spiro[benzo[ghi]perylene-5(6H),6'-[6H]-benzo[cd]pyrene], 7,7a-dihydro-	hexane	219(4.74),233(4.63), 249(4.19),256(4.24), 258s(4.22),262s(4.43), 282(4.67),293(4.63), 323(4.13),338(4.00)	18-2036-80
$C_{40}H_{24}Cl_2N_3O_4P_3$ Dispiro[dinaphtho[2,1-d:1',2'-f][1,3,2]-dioxaphosphepin-4,2'-[1,3,5,2,4,6]-triazatriphosphorine-4',4''-dinaphtho-[2,1-d:1',2'-f][1,3,2]dioxaphosphe-pin], 6',6'-dichloro-6',6'-dihydro-	C_6H_{12}	219(5.34),263(4.18), 305(4.45)	44-1672-80
$C_{40}H_{28}N_3$ 3H-Indolium, 3-[(1,2-diphenyl-1H-indol-3-yl)imino]-1,2-diphenyl-, perchlor-ate	n.s.g.	656(4.48)	7-0009-80
$C_{40}H_{28}N_{12}Ni$ Nickel, [9,10,25,26-tetrahydro-12,23-dimethyl-10,25-diphenylbenzo[10,11-12,13]dipyrazolo[4',3':7,8;3'',4''-15,16][1,2,5,6,9,14]hexaazacyclo-hexadecino[3,4-b]quinoxalinato(2-)-N^9,N^{14},N^{21},N^{26}]-, (SP-4-2)- corresponding palladium complex	$CHCl_3$ $CHCl_3$	266(4.59),395s(4.25), 422(4.28),499(4.49) 250s(4.62),268(4.57), 392s(4.30),424(4.34), 495(4.54)	103-0653-80 103-0653-80
$C_{40}H_{29}NS$ Benzenamine, N-(2,3-diphenyl-2-cyclo-propen-1-ylidene)-2-[(triphenyl-methyl)thio]-	MeCN	268s(4.91),300(4.86), 382s(4.03)	88-3751-80
$C_{40}H_{29}OS$ Pyrylium, 2,6-diphenyl-4-[5-(triphen-ylmethyl)-2-thienyl]-, perchlorate	$C_2H_4Cl_2$	280(4.16),415s(4.20), 450(4.43)	150-4041-80

Compound	Solvent	$\lambda_{max}(\log \epsilon)$	Ref.
$C_{40}H_{30}N_{10}O_6$ 2H-Tetrazolium, 2,2'-(2,2'-dimethoxy-[1,1'-biphenyl]-4,4'-diyl)bis[3-(4-nitrophenyl)-5-phenyl-, dichloride	H_2O	257(4.79)	46-0830-80
$C_{40}H_{31}ClN_2$ Pyridazine, 3-(4-chlorophenyl)-1,2,3,6-tetrahydro-1,3,5,6,6-pentaphenyl-	EtOH	247(4.60),277(4.51), 391(4.22)	118-0457-80
$C_{40}H_{31}N_{10}O_6$ 2H-Tetrazolium, 2-[2,2'-dimethoxy-4'-[5-(4-nitrophenyl)-3-phenyl-1-form-azano][1,1'-biphenyl]-4-yl]-3-(4-ni-trophenyl)-5-phenyl-, chloride	H_2O	530(4.41)	46-0830-80
$C_{40}H_{32}Fe_2$ [2](1,1')Ferroceno[2]para[2](1,1')-ferroceno[2]paracyclophanetetraene, cis,cis,cis,cis	EtOH	270(4.06),300(3.97)	1-0529-80
cis,cis,cis,trans	EtOH	305(4.09)	1-0529-80
$C_{40}H_{32}NO$ Pyridinium, 4-[5-(2,6-diphenyl-4H-pyran-4-ylidene)-1,3-pentadienyl]-1-methyl-2,6-diphenyl-, perchlorate	CH_2Cl_2 $MeNO_2$	640(4.85) 588(4.75)	124-1186-80 124-1186-80
$C_{40}H_{32}NS$ Pyridinium, 4-[5-(2,6-diphenyl-4H-thio-pyran-4-ylidene)-1,3-pentadienyl]-1-methyl-2,6-diphenyl-, perchlorate	CH_2Cl_2 $MeNO_2$	648(4.76) 585(4.65)	124-1186-80 124-1186-80
$C_{40}H_{32}NSe$ Pyridinium, 4-[5-(2,6-diphenyl-4H-sel-enin-4-ylidene)-1,3-pentadienyl]-1-methyl-2,6-diphenyl-, perchlorate	CH_2Cl_2 $MeNO_2$	643(4.76) 582(4.71)	124-1186-80 124-1186-80
$C_{40}H_{32}N_2$ Pyridazine, 1,2,3,6-tetrahydro-1,3,3,5,6,6-hexaphenyl-	EtOH	245(4.55),277(4.42), 392(4.15)	118-0457-80
$C_{40}H_{32}N_7$ 1H-Benzimidazolium, 5-cyano-2-[4-cyano-7-(5-cyano-3-ethyl-1,3-dihydro-1-phenyl-2H-benzimidazol-2-ylidene)-1,3,5-heptatrienyl]-3-ethyl-1-phen-yl-, perchlorate	DMSO	770(5.27)	103-0406-80
$C_{40}H_{34}O$ Tricyclo[3.2.1.0^{2,4}]oct-6-en-8-ol, 1,5-dimethyl-2,3,4,6,7-pentaphenyl-, endo	n.s.g.	275s(4.00)	44-0633-80
Tricyclo[3.2.1.0^{4,6}]oct-2-en-8-ol, 1,5-dimethyl-2,3,4,6,7-pentaphenyl-	n.s.g.	270s(3.61)	44-0633-80
$C_{40}H_{34}O_2$ Bicyclo[4.1.0]hept-4-ene-2-carboxylic acid, 2,5-dimethyl-1,3,4,6,7-penta-phenyl-	dioxan	217(3.96),254s(3.29)	44-0633-80
2,5-Cycloheptadiene-1-carboxylic acid, 1,5-dimethyl-2,3,4,6,7-pentaphenyl-	THF	273(4.17)	44-0633-89

Compound	Solvent	$\lambda_{max}(\log \epsilon)$	Ref.
$C_{40}H_{34}O_{15}$ Benzo[h][1]benzopyrano[5,4,3-cde][1]-benzopyran-5,12-dione, 1-methyl-6-(phenylmethoxy)-10-[(2,3,4,6-tetra-O-acetyl-β-D-glucopyranosyl)oxy]-	EtOH	236(4.59),267(4.62)	87-0549-80
$C_{40}H_{35}N_6$ 1H-Benzimidazolium, 5-cyano-2-[7-(5-cyano-3-ethyl-1,3-dihydro-1-phenyl-2H-benzimidazol-2-ylidene)-4-methyl-1,3,5-heptatrienyl]-3-ethyl-1-phenyl-, iodide	DMSO	749(5.25)	103-0406-80
$C_{40}H_{35}N_6O$ 1H-Benzimidazolium, 5-cyano-2-[7-(5-cyano-3-ethyl-1,3-dihydro-1-phenyl-2H-benzimidazol-2-ylidene)-4-methoxy-1,3,5-heptatrienyl]-3-ethyl-1-phenyl-, iodide	DMSO	692(4.88)	103-0406-80
$C_{40}H_{35}O_3$ 2-Furanylium, 4-[1-benzoyl-3-(2,2-dimethyl-5-phenyl-3(2H)-furanylidene)-2-phenyl-1-propenyl]-2,5-dihydro-5,5-dimethyl-2-phenyl-, perchlorate	EtOH-HClO$_4$	630(4.76)	5-1744-80
$C_{40}H_{36}O_2$ Pentacyclo[4.4.0.0^{2,5}.0^{3,9}.0^{4,8}]decane-7,10-dione, 1,6-diethyl-8,9-dimethyl-2,3,4,5-tetraphenyl-	dioxan	237(4.18)	78-3443-80
$C_{40}H_{36}O_{11}$ Albanin F	EtOH	208(4.81),227s(4.54), 265(4.47),279s(4.29), 319(4.16)	138-1577-80
Kuwanon G	MeOH	212(4.64),265(4.41), 280s(4.22),315(4.13)	94-2548-80 +142-1531-80B
	MeOH-NaOMe	275(4.45),336(4.39)	94-2548-80
	MeOH-AlCl$_3$	213(4.68),274(4.46), 307(4.22),360(3.89)	94-2548-80
Moracenin B	MeOH	209(4.80),264(4.49), 280s(4.31),320(4.18)	88-3381-80
$C_{40}H_{37}N_2O_{11}PS$ 1-Azetidineacetic acid, 2-[(3-methoxy-3-oxo-1-propenyl)thio]-3-[1-[[[(4-nitrophenyl)methoxy]carbonyl]oxy]ethyl]-4-oxo-α-(triphenylphosphoranylidene)-, 2-oxopropyl ester	n.s.g.	266(4.35)	35-2039-80
$C_{40}H_{38}O_{10}$ 1,4-Ethanoanthracene-9,10-dione, 6,6'-(1,2-ethanediyl)bis[8-ethoxy-1,4-dihydro-5-hydroxy-1-methoxy-	MeOH	222(4.75),282(4.09), 488(4.05)	24-1575-80
$C_{40}H_{40}Fe_2O_4$ Estra-1,3,5(10)-triene-3,17β-diol, diester with carboxyferrocene	ether	304(3.20),441(2.44)	5-1181-80
$C_{40}H_{40}N_2O_2$ 1,3-Propanedione, 2-[3,4-bis(diethyl-	MeCN	252(4.16),280s(--),	24-0424-80

Compound	Solvent	$\lambda_{max}(\log \epsilon)$	Ref.
amino)-2,5-diphenyl-2,4-cyclopenta-dien-1-ylidene]-1,3-diphenyl-, (cont.)		423(3.85)	24-0424-80
$C_{40}H_{40}N_4O_3$ 21-Phorbinecarboxylic acid, 3,4-didehy-dro-3,9,14-triethyl-4,8,13,18-tetra-methyl-20-oxo-, phenylmethyl ester	CHCl$_3$	422(5.27),525(3.92), 567(4.23),588(4.18), 636(3.31)	12-1095-80
$C_{40}H_{40}N_4O_4S$ 7H-Pyrrolo[2,3-d]pyrimidin-4-amine, 2-(methylthio)-N-(phenylmethyl)-7- [2,3,5-tris-O-(phenylmethyl)-β-D-arabinofuranosyl]-	MeOH	238(4.47),287(4.30)	24-2069-80
$C_{40}H_{42}$ 1H-Indene, 2-[[4-(1,3-dihydro-1,1,3,3-tetramethyl-2H-inden-2-ylidene)meth-ylene]-2,5-cyclohexadien-1-yl]phenyl-methylene]-2,3-dihydro-1,1,3,3-tetra-methyl-	CH$_2$Cl$_2$	245s(4.52),258(4.58), 265(4.60),271s(4.52)	5-1207-80
1H-Indene, 2-[[4-[(1,3-dihydro-1,1,3,3-tetramethyl-2H-inden-2-ylidene)meth-yl]phenyl]phenylmethylene]-2,3-dihy-dro-1,1,3,3-tetramethyl-	CH$_2$Cl$_2$	242(4.23),264(4.02), 272(3.96)	5-1207-80
$C_{40}H_{42}N_4O_6$ Deuteroporphyrin, 3,8-bis(1-ethoxyeth-yl)-, dimethyl ester	CHCl$_3$	402(5.27),499(4.16), 533(3.95),568(3.82), 622(3.63)	12-0585-80
$C_{40}H_{44}N_2O_5$ 1H-Indole, 5,5'-(2,5,8,11,14-pentaoxa-pentadecane-1,15-diyl)bis[1-(phenyl-methyl)-	EtOH	216(4.29),272(3.76)	121-0379-80
$C_{40}H_{44}O_4$ β,β-Carotene-4,4'-dione, 2,2',3,3',7-7',8,8'-octadehydro-3,3'-dihydroxy-, all-trans	benzene	300(4.29),347(4.19), 470s(4.93),496(5.03), 525(4.94)	33-1473-80
9-cis,9'-cis	benzene	300(4.25),350(4.24), 486(4.97),514s(4.87)	33-1473-80
$C_{40}H_{46}N_2O_8$ Northalicarpine (same in acid or base)	MeOH	282(4.21),303s(4.08), 314s(3.97)	100-0567-80
$C_{40}H_{46}N_4O_6$ 21H,23H-Porphine-2-propanoic acid, 8-ethenyl-13-ethyl-2,3-dihydro-18-(meth-oxycarbonyl)-20-(2-methoxy-2-oxoeth-yl)-3,7,17-trimethyl-12-(2-methyl-1-propenyl)-, methyl ester, (2S-trans)-	CH$_2$Cl$_2$	407(5.18),503(4.15), 532(3.63),557(3.40), 606(3.76),662(4.59)	35-2437-80
$C_{40}H_{46}N_4O_8$ Haematoporphyrin diacetate dimethyl ester	CHCl$_3$	402(5.28),499(4.17), 533(3.96),569(3.82), 623(3.64)	12-0585-80
$C_{40}H_{46}O_4$ β,β-Carotene-4,4'-dione, 7,7',8,8',15-15'-hexadehydro-3,3'-dihydroxy-, trans	benzene	320(4.12),460(4.90), 488(4.78)	33-1473-80

Compound	Solvent	$\lambda_{max}(\log \epsilon)$	Ref.
$C_{40}H_{48}N_2O_{10}$			
Bisaknadinine	EtOH	263(4.32),293s(4.00)	102-2735-80
$C_{40}H_{48}N_4O_7$			
Deuteroporphyrin, 8-(1-acetoxyethyl)-3-(1-ethoxyethyl)-, dimethyl ester	$CHCl_3$	402(5.27),499(4.16), 534(3.96),569(3.82), 622(3.63)	12-0585-80
$C_{40}H_{48}O_2$			
β,φ-Caroten-4-one, 2,3-didehydro-3-hydroxy-	benzene	483(5.27)	18-1629-80
$C_{40}H_{48}O_4$			
β,β-Carotene-4,4'-dione, 7,7',8,8'-tetradehydro-3,3'-dihydroxy-, (3S,3S')-all-trans	benzene	300(4.23),326(4.23), 466s(4.93),493(5.05), 524(4.95)	33-1473-80
(3S,3'S,9-cis,9'-cis)-	benzene	300(4.32),330(4.36), 456s(4.88),481(4.99), 510(4.90)	33-1473-80
	$CHCl_3$	300(4.34),335(4.39), 486(4.97),514s(4.88)	33-1473-80
$C_{40}H_{48}O_{20}$			
Osthenol-7-O-β-gentiobioside heptaacetate	dioxan	243(3.97),253(3.96), 298(4.18),320s(4.08)	94-1847-80
$C_{40}H_{50}D_6$			
β,β-Carotene-16,16,16,16',16',16'-d_6, (1R,1'R)-	hexane	450(5.13)	77-0527-80
$C_{40}H_{50}N_2O_{12}$			
2H-2,7-(Epoxypentadeca[1,11,13]trieno)-benzofuro[4,5-g]quinazoline-1,11,12-trione, 22-acetoxy-8,9-dihydro-5,6-18,20-tetrahydroxy-24-methoxy-2,4,9-13,17,19,21,23-octamethyl-	MeCN	226(4.55),280(4.26), 311(4.20),360(4.19), 602(3.99)	94-2309-80
$C_{40}H_{50}O$			
β,φ-Caroten-4-one	benzene	469(5.23)	18-1629-80
β,χ-Caroten-4-one	benzene	482(5.02)	18-1629-80
$C_{40}H_{50}O_2$			
[1,1'-Biphenyl]-2,2'-diol, 3,3'-bis-(1,1-dimethylethyl)-5,5'-bis[4-(1,1-dimethylethyl)phenyl]-	THF	217(4.80),263(4.76)	18-2695-80
$C_{40}H_{50}O_4$			
β,β-Carotene-4,4'-dione, 7,8-didehydro-3,3'-dihydroxy-, (3S,3'S)-(9-cis)-	benzene	390s(4.40),487(4.97), 515s(4.88)	33-1473-80
2,5-Cyclohexadien-1-one, 4,4'-[1,1'-biphenyl]-3,3'-diylbis[2,6-bis(1,1-dimethylethyl)-4-hydroxy-	THF	228(4.80)	18-2695-80
$C_{40}H_{52}$			
β,φ-Carotene	benzene	473(--),465(5.06), 494(--)	18-1629-80
β,χ-Carotene	benzene	474(5.12),506(--)	18-1629-80
$C_{40}H_{52}O$			
β,φ-Caroten-4-ol	benzene	436(--),463(5.11), 492(--)	18-1629-80

Compound	Solvent	$\lambda_{max}(\log \epsilon)$	Ref.
β,χ-Caroten-4-ol	benzene	449(--),474(5.11), 506(--)	18-1629-80
$C_{40}H_{52}O_4$			
β,β-Carotene-3,3',4,4'-tetrol, 7,7',8-8'-tetradehydro-, (3S,3'S,all-trans)-	acetone	431s(5.00),455(5.15), 485(5.11)	33-1473-80
(3S,3'S,9-cis,9'-cis)-	acetone	396s(4.56),421(4.81), 445(5.03),474(4.99)	33-1473-80
$C_{40}H_{54}O_4$			
β,β-Carotene-3,3',4,4'-tetrol, 7,8-didehydro-, (3S,3'S,all-trans)	acetone	343(4.02),432s(4.95), 454(5.11),482(5.05)	33-1473-80
(3S,3'S,9-cis)-	acetone	343(4.20),426s(4.89), 448(5.05),476(4.99)	33-1473-80
$C_{40}H_{56}O_2$			
Luteine, (3R,3'R,6'R,all-trans)-	dioxan	429(3.23),453(3.40), 482(3.35)	33-1451-80
Zeaxanthine, (3S,3'S,all-trans)-	hexane	275(2.61),407s(2.97), 432s(3.24),453(3.40), 481(3.34)	33-1456-80
(3R,3'S,meso)-	hexane	273(2.56),403(2.96), 430s(3.23),449(3.38), 477(3.33)	33-1456-80
$C_{40}H_{56}O_4$			
Violaxanthin, 13-cis	benzene	337(4.77),419(4.91), 445(5.06),475(5.00)	102-0623-80
Violaxanthin, 15-cis	benzene	337(4.77),423(4.83), 448(4.98),478(4.91)	102-0623-80
$C_{40}H_{58}O_{10}$			
Oleana-12,15-diene-3,21,22,23,28-pentol, pentaacetate (3β,4β,21α,22α)-	MeOH	204(3.66)	20-1001-80
$C_{40}H_{60}O_{11}$			
Protoascigenin 3,21,22,26,28-pentaacetate	MeOH	198(3.96)	102-0615-80
$C_{40}H_{75}N_3O_2$			
Juliprosopine	n.s.g.	none above 220 nm	33-2119-80
$C_{40}H_{90}Si_5$			
Cyclopentasilane, decakis(2-methylpropyl)-	C_6H_{12}	260s(3.30)	138-0735-80

Compound	Solvent	$\lambda_{max}(\log \epsilon)$	Ref.
$C_{41}H_{26}N_2O_2$ Methanone, (7,10-diphenylindazolo[2,3-a]quinoline-8,9-diyl)bis[phenyl-	MeOH	232(4.59),253(4.71), 294(4.61),365(4.11), 385(4.15),404(4.17)	44-0090-80
$C_{41}H_{26}N_2S$ Thieno[3',4':5,6]indazolo[2,3-a]quino-line-9-S^{IV}, 7,8,10,11-tetraphenyl-	DMSO	310(4.50),390(4.35), 632(4.16)	44-0090-80
$C_{41}H_{34}N_2$ Pyridazine, 1,2,3,6-tetrahydro-3-(4-methylphenyl)-1,3,5,6,6-pentaphenyl-	EtOH	245(4.63),281(4.48), 394(4.24)	118-0457-80
$C_{41}H_{46}N_4NiO_2$ Nickel, [5-[4-(dimethoxymethyl)phenyl]-3,7,13,17-tetraethyl-2,8,12,18-tetra-methyl-21H,23H-porphinato(2-)-$N^{21},N^{22},N^{23},N^{24}$]-, (SP-4-2)-	CHCl$_3$	404(5.31),526(4.09), 562(4.34)	130-0063-80
$C_{41}H_{46}N_4O_4$ Ibogamine-18-carboxylic acid, 3,4-dide-hydro-12-(4-demethyl-17-methoxy-17-oxovobasan-3-yl)-, methyl ester, (2α,5β,6α,18β)-	EtOH	228(4.53),284(4.20), 292(4.17)	23-1829-80
Ibogamine-18-carboxylic acid, 3,4-dide-hydro-13-(4-demethyl-17-methoxy-17-oxovobasan-3-yl)-, methyl ester, (2α,5β,6α,18β)-	EtOH	228(4.66),285(4.22), 293(4.22)	23-1829-80
$C_{41}H_{48}N_4O_5$ Deuteroporphyrin, 2-ethenyl-4-formyl-, bis(1,1-dimethylethyl) ester	CHCl$_3$	420(5.22),519(4.03), 560(4.18),584(3.97), 643(4.29)	44-5196-80
Deuteroporphyrin, 4-ethenyl-2-formyl-, bis(1,1-dimethylethyl) ester	CHCl$_3$	420(5.21),519(4.03), 560(4.15),584(3.98), 643(3.33)	44-5196-80
$C_{41}H_{51}N_5O_{11}$ L-Leucine, N-[N-[(1,1-dimethylethoxy)-carbonyl]-2-[1,2,3,4-tetrahydro-1-[2,3-O-(1-methylethylidene)-β-D-ribo-furanosyl]-2,4-dioxo-5-pyrimidinyl]-L-tryptophyl-, phenylmethyl ester	MeCN	260(4.49),285(4.41), 335s(4.15)	35-7535-80
$C_{41}H_{52}N_2O_{12}$ 2H-2,7-(Epoxypentadeca[1,11,13]trieno)-benzofuro[4,5-g]quinazoline, 22-acet-oxy-9-ethyl-1,8,9,11-tetrahydro-5,6,18,20-tetrahydroxy-24-methoxy-2,4,13,17,19,21,23-heptamethyl-1,11,12-trioxo-	MeOH	226(4.55),276(4.29), 311(4.18),360(4.20), 592(3.99)	94-2309-80
$C_{41}H_{52}N_4O_{11}S$ Rifamycin P, 2'-[(dimethylhydrazono)-methyl]-	pH 7.38	225(4.64),265(4.42), 322(4.39),394(4.37)	78-2009-80
$C_{41}H_{53}NO_{17}$ Alcindoromycin	CHCl$_3$	258(4.33),288(3.97), 484(4.15),495(4.18), 515(3.93)	100-0242-80

Compound	Solvent	$\lambda_{max}(\log \epsilon)$	Ref.
$C_{41}H_{53}N_4ORh$			
Rhodium, [2,3,7,8,12,13,17,18-octaethyl-21H,23H-porphinato(2-)-N^{21},N^{22}-N^{23},N^{24}](4-oxopentyl)-, (SP-5-31)-	$CHCl_3$	400(5.15),516(4.10), 548(4.39)	101-0095-80B
$C_{41}H_{53}N_4O_3Rh$			
Rhodium, (2-ethoxy-1-methoxy-2-oxoethyl)[2,3,7,8,12,13,17,18-octaethyl-21H,23H-porphinato(2-)-N^{21},N^{22},N^{23}-N^{24}]-, (SP-5-31)-	CH_2Cl_2	385(5.16),510(4.06), 545(5.59)	152-0311-80
$C_{41}H_{54}N_2O_{12}$			
11H-11,6-(Epoxypentadeca[1,11,13]trieno)-5H-benzofuro[4,5-g]oxazolo[3,2-c]quinazoline-12,29(13bH)-dione, 2,3-dihydro-7,8,13,19,21,23-hexahydroxy-17-methoxy-3,3,9,11,18,20,22,24,28-nonamethyl-	pH 4.02	234(4.46),272(4.30), 309(4.17),356(4.20), 568(4.00)	94-2309-80
	MeOH-NaHCO3	226(4.62),314(4.28), 450(4.12)	94-2309-80
$C_{41}H_{54}N_4O_2Rh$			
Rhodium(1+), (ethyl 2,3,7,8,12,13,17-18-octaethyl-21H,23H-porphine-21-acetato-N^{21},N^{22},N^{23},N^{24})methyl-, (SP-5-41)-, perchlorate	CH_2Cl_2	399(5.03),435s(4.35), 582(3.90)	152-0311-80
$C_{41}H_{54}O_6$			
D:C-Friedooleana-7,9(11)-dien-29-oic acid, 3-[[3-(4-acetoxyphenyl)-1-oxo-2-propenyl]oxy]-, [3α(E),20α]-	EtOH	241(4.50),248(4.41), 283(4.62)	39-2933-80C
$C_{41}H_{57}NO_3S$			
Cholest-5-en-3β-ol, N-[(4-methylphenyl)-sulfonyl]benzenecarboximidate	C_6H_{12}	234(3.90)	39-2184-80C
$C_{41}H_{58}N_8O_4$			
21H-Biline-8,12-dipropanamide, N,N'-bis(4-aminobutyl)-3,17-diethyl-1,19,22,24-tetrahydro-2,7,13,18-tetramethyl-1,19-dioxo-, (Z,Z,Z)-	$CHCl_3$	368(4.37),640(3.82)	49-0159-80
$C_{41}H_{62}O_{11}$			
Avermectin B, 22,23-dihydro-, monosaccharide	MeOH	238(4.43),245(4.48), 253s(4.28)	87-1134-80
$C_{41}H_{66}O_{16}S$			
Echinoside B (sodium salt)	MeOH	none above 210 nm	94-1651-80
$C_{41}H_{68}O_{13}$			
2,6,10,14,18,24,28,32-Hentetracontaneoctone, 8,16,26,34,36-pentahydroxy-	MeOH	280(2.19)	88-1537-80
$C_{41}H_{70}O_{13}$			
2,6,10,14,24,28,32-Hentetracontaneheptone, 8,16,18,26,34,36-hexahydroxy-	MeOH	280(2.19)	88-1537-80

Compound	Solvent	$\lambda_{max}(\log \epsilon)$	Ref.
$C_{42}H_{22}O_8$			
[6,6'-Bidinaphtho[1,2-b:2',3'-d]furan]-7,7',12,12'-tetrone, 5,5'-dimethoxy-	$CHCl_3$	263s(5.07),268(5.08), 298s(4.41),312s(4.16), 325s(3.96),338s(3.86), 446(4.03)	39-0090-80C
$C_{42}H_{30}$			
p-Quinquephenyl, 2,2''''-diphenyl-	C_6H_{12}	206(5.06),230s(4.66), 307(4.71)	18-2610-80
m-Septiphenyl	C_6H_{12}	192(4.86),204(4.82), 249(4.07)	94-3210-80
$C_{42}H_{30}N_4$			
1H-Imidazole, 2,4,5-triphenyl-1-(2,4,5-triphenyl-2H-imidazol-2-yl)-	MeOH	<u>263(4.5)</u>	138-0431-80
1H-Imidazole, 2,4,5-triphenyl-1-(2,4,5-triphenyl-4H-imidazol-4-yl)-	MeOH	<u>240(4.5),278(4.6)</u>	138-0431-80
2H-Imidazole, 2,4,5-triphenyl-2-(2,4,5-triphenyl-4H-imidazol-4-yl)-	MeOH	<u>232(4.6),276(4.5)</u>	138-0431-80
$C_{42}H_{31}BrS_2$			
17H,19H-5,8:20,23-Diethano-1,27:12,16-dimetheno-9H,11H-dibenzo[o,r][1,9]-dithiacyclotetracosin, 29-bromo-28-phenyl-	$CHCl_3$	274(4.80),396(4.13), 416(4.11)	24-0676-80
$C_{42}H_{32}O_9$			
Copalliferol A	EtOH	282(2.94)	77-0619-80
$C_{42}H_{33}NO_3$			
Methanone, [5'-(4-morpholinyl)-6'-phenyl-[1,1':2',1''-terphenyl]-3',4'-diyl]-bis[phenyl-	MeCN	243(4.60)	24-0408-80
$C_{42}H_{35}NO_2$			
Methanone, [5'-(diethylamino)-6'-phenyl-[1,1':2',1''-terphenyl]-3',4'-diyl]bis[phenyl-	MeCN	244(4.57)	24-0408-80 +24-0424-80
1,3-Propanedione, 2-[3-(diethylamino)-2,4,5-triphenyl-2,4-cyclopentadien-1-ylidene]-1,3-diphenyl-	MeCN	255(4.43),340(3.96), 550(3.27)	24-0424-80
$C_{42}H_{36}O_4$			
3,6-Ethanobenzo[a]cyclopropa[cd]penta-lene-7,8-dicarboxylic acid, 2a,2b-2c,3,6,6a,6b,6c-octahydro-1,2,2a,6a-tetraphenyl-, dimethyl ester, (2aα-2bα,2cβ,3α,6α,6aβ,6bα,6cα,7R*,8S*)-	EtOH	227(4.35),296(3.93)	78-3033-80
$C_{42}H_{38}N_5O_7P$			
Phosphoramidic acid, N-[9-[2-deoxy-5-O-[(4-methoxyphenyl)diphenylmethyl]-β-D-erythro-pentofuranosyl]-9H-purin-6-yl]-, diphenyl ester	MeOH	231(4.26),260(4.25)	142-0761-80B
$C_{42}H_{38}O_2$			
Peroxide, bis(1-methyl-1-[1,1':2',1''-terphenyl]-4'-ylethyl)	EtOH	236(4.78),255(4.43)	18-3279-80
$C_{42}H_{40}O_2$			
4,7-Methano-1H-indene-1,8-dione,	dioxan	218(4.46),265(4.27),	78-3443-80

Compound	Solvent	$\lambda_{max}(\log \epsilon)$	Ref.
3a,4,7,7a-tetrahydro-2,4,7,7a-tetra-methyl-3,3a,5,6-tetrakis(4-methyl-phenyl)-, (3aα,4α,7α,7aα)-		290(4.26)	78-3443-80
Pentacyclo[4.4.0.0²,⁵.0³,⁹.0⁴,⁸]decane-7,10-dione, 1,6,8,9-tetramethyl-2,3,4,5-tetrakis(4-methylphenyl)-	dioxan	227(4.33)	78-3443-80
$C_{42}H_{48}N_4O_{10}$			
21H,23H-Porphine-2,7,12,18-tetrapropan-oic acid, 3-(2-methoxy-2-oxoethyl)-8,13,17-trimethyl-, tetramethyl ester	CHCl₃	402(5.20),500(4.11),536(3.98),568(3.84),622(3.64)	130-0071-80
21H,23H-Porphine-2,7,12,18-tetrapropan-oic acid, 8-(2-methoxy-2-oxoethyl)-3,13,17-trimethyl-, tetramethyl ester	CHCl₃	402(5.19),500(4:11),536(3.98),568(3.83),622(3.66)	130-0071-80
21H,23H-Porphine-2,7,12,18-tetrapropan-oic acid, 13-(2-methoxy-2-oxoethyl)-3,8,17-trimethyl-, tetramethyl ester	CHCl₃	402(5.24),500(4.13),536(4.00),568(3.84),622(3.66)	130-0071-80
21H,23H-Porphine-2,7,12,18-tetrapropan-oic acid, 17-(2-methoxy-2-oxoethyl)-3,8,13-trimethyl-, tetramethyl ester	CHCl₃	402(5.28),500(4.15),536(3.97),568(3.82),622(3.62)	130-0071-80
$C_{42}H_{48}O_8$			
Prosta-5,13-dien-1-oic acid, 9,11,15-tris(benzoyloxy)-, methyl ester, (5Z,9α,11α,13E,15S)-	MeOH	229(4.59),273(3.43),280(3.35)	44-1528-80
$C_{42}H_{50}N_4O_4$			
21H,23H-Porphine-2,18-dipropanoic acid, 7,12-diethenyl-3,8,13,17-tetrameth-yl-, bis(1,1-dimethylethyl) ester	CHCl₃	407(5.22),506(4.15),541(4.06),576(3.84),630(3.74)	44-5196-80
$C_{42}H_{50}N_4O_5$			
Voacamidine, N-demethyl-	EtOH	228(4.40),284(4.04),292(4.02)	23-1829-80
Voacamine, N-demethyl-	EtOH	220(4.45),284(4.03),292(4.02)	23-1829-80
$C_{42}H_{52}N_2O_{16}$			
Rudolphomycin	MeOH	233(4.65),257(4.45),280(4.47),466s(--),480s(--),490(4.14),511s(--),523s(--)	100-0242-80
$C_{42}H_{55}NO_{17}$			
Marcellomycin	MeOH	233(4.60),256s(4.09),294s(3.95),490(4.13),510(4.03),524(3.95),580(2.97)	100-0242-80
Mimimycin	CHCl₃	258(4.37),296(3.97),495(4.19),515(4.07),529(4.00)	100-0242-80
$C_{42}H_{55}N_4O_2Rh$			
Rhodium, (4-ethoxy-4-oxobutyl)[2,3,7-8,12,13,17,18-octaethyl-21H,23H-porphinato(2-)-N²¹,N²²,N²³,N²⁴]-, (SP-5-31)-	CHCl₃	385(5.04),392(5.08),510(4.08),543(4.59)	101-0095-80I
$C_{42}H_{56}O_6$			
D:C-Friedooleana-7,9(11)-dien-29-oic acid, 3-[[3-(4-acetoxyphenyl)-1-oxo-	EtOH	226(4.17),231(4.12),240(4.13),249(4.05),	39-2933-80C

Compound	Solvent	$\lambda_{max}(\log \epsilon)$	Ref.
2-propenyl]oxy]-, methyl ester, [3α(E),20α]- (cont.)		282(4.23)	39-2933-80C
$C_{42}H_{58}Cl_2O_6Pd_2$ Palladium, bis[(4,5,6-η)-(17β)-17-acet-oxy-3-oxoandrost-5-en-4-yl]di-μ-chlorodi-	CHCl₃	251(3.85),281(3.97)	12-2761-80
$C_{42}H_{60}O_{12}$ 8'-Apo-β,ψ-carotenoic acid, 4-O-α-D-glucopyranosyl-β-D-glucopyranosyl ester	EtOH	449(5.00)	27-0020-80
$C_{42}H_{62}O_{20}$ 18-Norspirosta-5,13-dien-15-one, 1-[(O-6-deoxy-α-L-mannopyranosyl-(1→2)-O-[β-D-xylopyranosyl-(1→3)]-α-L-arabinopyranosyl)oxy]-3,21,23,24-tetrahydroxy-, (1β,3β,23S,24R,25S)-	EtOH	247(3.79)	94-1437-80
$C_{42}H_{66}O_{13}$ 5β,14β-Card-20(22)-enolide, 14-hydroxy-22-methyl-3β-tridigitoxosyloxy-	EtOH	222.5(4.26)	48-0991-80
$C_{42}H_{72}Cl_2O_2$ 3,5-Cyclohexadiene-1,2-dione, 3,5-di-chloro-4,6-dioctadecyl-	hexane	440(3.29)	104-0129-80
$C_{42}H_{78}O_2$ 1,2-Benzenediol, 3,5-dioctadecyl-	C_6H_{12}	283(3.76)	104-0129-80

Compound	Solvent	$\lambda_{max}(\log \epsilon)$	Ref.
$C_{43}H_{30}$ Benzo[a]cyclopropa[c]cycloheptene, 2-(diphenylmethylene)-1,2-dihydro-1,1,4-triphenyl-	CHCl₃	245(4.33),294(4.29), 328(4.25)	88-4869-80
$C_{43}H_{30}O$ Cyclobutanone, tris(diphenylmethylene)-	CHCl₃	402(4.30),548(3.68)	88-2713-80
$C_{43}H_{52}N_4O_5$ Voacangine	MeOH	224(4.41),285(3.95), 300(3.91)	102-1213-80
hydroxyindolenine	EtOH	226(4.26),272(3.80), 286(3.81),292(3.81), 314s(3.70)	102-1213-80
$C_{43}H_{52}O_7$ 4H,8H-Benzo[1,2-b:3,4-b']dipyran-4-one, 5-hydroxy-2-[2-hydroxy-4-[[1,3,5-tris(1,1-dimethylethyl)-4-oxo-2,5-cyclohexadien-1-yl]oxy]phenyl]-8,8-dimethyl-3-(3-methyl-2-butenyl)-	MeOH	209(4.75),242(4.68), 270(4.75),300s(4.19), 350s(3.94)	4-0641-80
	MeOH-NaOMe	211(4.95),245(4.72), 269(4.75),362(4.07)	4-0641-80
	MeOH-AlCl₃	209(4.75),228(4.70), 278(4.75),337(4.07), 415(3.90)	4-0641-80
$C_{43}H_{52}O_9$ 3H,7H-Pyrano[2',3':7,8][1]benzopyrano-[3,2-d][1]benzoxepin-7-one, 8,9-di-hydro-6,12-dihydroxy-3,3-dimethyl-9-[1-methyl-1-[[1,3,5-tris(1,1-di-methylethyl)-4-oxo-2,5-cyclohexa-dien-1-yl]dioxy]ethyl]-	MeOH	207(4.53),222(4.59), 237(4.64),279(4.55), 335(4.25)	4-0641-80
	MeOH-NaOMe	268(4.62),393(4.44)	4-0641-80
	MeOH-AlCl₃	209(4.56),229(4.63), 283(4.56),361(4.30), 418(4.04)	4-0641-80
$C_{43}H_{53}N_4ORh$ Rhodium, [2,3,7,8,12,13,17,18-octaeth-yl-21H,23H-porphinato(2-)-N²¹,N²²-N²³,N²⁴](5-oxobicyclo[2.2.1]hept-2-yl)-, [SP-5-31-(exo)]-	CHCl₃	386(5.18),511(4.12), 543(4.63)	101-0095-80B
$C_{43}H_{53}N_4Rh$ Rhodium, [2,3,7,8,12,13,17,18-octaeth-yl-21H,23H-porphinato(2-)-N²¹,N²²-N²³,N²⁴]tricyclo[2.2.1.0²,⁶]hept-3-yl-, (SP-5-31)-	CHCl₃	388(5.03),511(4.02), 544(4.41)	101-0095-80B
$C_{43}H_{54}N_4O_6$ Ibogamine-18-carboxylic acid, 14-[(3α,20β)-19,20-dihydro-17-methoxy-17-oxovobasan-3-yl]-20-hydroxy-13-methoxy-, methyl ester, (20R)-	EtOH	225(4.76),286(4.18), 294(4.15)	39-0601-80C
$C_{43}H_{55}N_4Rh$ Rhodium, bicyclo[3.1.1]hept-6-yl-[2,3,7,8,12,13,17,18-octaethyl-21H,23H-porphinato(2-)-N²¹,N²²-N²³,N²⁴]-	CHCl₃	387(5.10),395(5.16), 511(4.16),544(4.60)	101-0095-80E
$C_{43}H_{56}N_2O_{13}$ 2H-2,7-(Epoxypentadeca[1,11,13]trieno)-	pH 4.02	233(4.46),274(4.29),	94-2309-80

Compound	Solvent	$\lambda_{max}(\log \epsilon)$	Ref.
benzofuro[4,5-g]quinazoline, 22-acet-oxy-1,8,9,11-tetrahydro-5,6,18,20-tetrahydroxy-9-(2-hydroxy-1,1-dimeth-ylethyl)-24-methoxy-2,4,13,17,19,21-23-heptamethyl-1,11,12-trioxo-	MeOH-NaHCO$_3$	311(4.18),356(4.21), 571(4.02) 226(4.63),314(4.30), 449(4.14)	94-2309-80 94-2309-80
$C_{43}H_{59}O_7$			
Phenoxy, 4-[[3,5-bis(1,1-dimethyleth-yl)-4-oxo-2,5-cyclohexadien-1-yli-dene](2,3,5,6,8,9,11,12-octahydro-1,4,7,10,13-benzopentaoxacyclopenta-decin-15-yl)methyl]-2,6-bis(1,1-di-methylethyl)-	EtOH	434(4.48)	138-0613-80
$C_{44}H_{22}O_{10}$			
[6,6'-Bidinaphtho[1,2-b:2',3'-d]furan]-7,7',12,12'-tetrone, 5,5'-diacetoxy-	CHCl$_3$	260s(4.96),266(5.01), 283s(4.52),293s(4.38), 306s(4.15),334s(3.85), 425(4.01)	39-0090-80C
$C_{44}H_{28}FeN_4$			
Iron, [5,10,15,20-tetraphenyl-21H,23H-porphinato(2-)-N^{21},N^{22},N^{23},N^{24}]-	n.s.g.	419(5.03),442(4.90), 537(3.98)	35-4182-80
Iron(1+), [5,10,15,20-tetraphenyl-21H,23H-porphinato(2-)-N^{21},N^{22}-N^{23},N^{24}]-, (SP-4-1)-, sulfate (2:1)	CH$_2$Cl$_2$	347(4.63),372(4.71), 408(5.05),508(4.04), 576(5.54),680(3.46)	77-0455-80
$C_{44}H_{28}IN_4Rh$			
Rhodium, iodo[5,10,15,20-tetraphenyl-21H,23H-porphinato(2-)-N^{21},N^{22},N^{23}-N^{24}]-, (SP-5-12)-	CH$_2$Cl$_2$	422(5.18),535(4.20), 575(3.60)	152-0311-80
$C_{44}H_{28}N_4Tl$			
Thallium, [5,10,15,20-tetraphenyl-21H,23H-porphinato(2-)-N^{21},N^{22}-N^{23},N^{24}]-, (SP-4-1)-	CH$_2$Cl$_2$	358(4.67),478(5.28), 684(4.18)	88-0433-80
$C_{44}H_{32}$			
Cyclobutane, 1,2-bis(diphenylmethyl-ene)-3,4-bis(phenylmethylene)-, (E,E)-	CHCl$_3$	306(4.60),373(4.26), 450s(3.73)	88-2713-80
Cyclobutane, 1-methylene-2,3,4-tris(di-phenylmethylene)-	CHCl$_3$	284(4.45),310s(4.40), 340s(4.29),480s(3.45)	88-2713-80
$C_{44}H_{32}CuN_8O_8$			
Copper, [tetraethyl 29H,31H-phthalocya-nine-2,9,16,23-tetracarboxylato(2-)-N^{29},N^{30},N^{31},N^{32}]-, (SP-4-1)-	C$_6$H$_3$Cl$_3$	350(4.72),616(4.40), 687(5.02)	65-0907-80
$C_{44}H_{36}Cl_2N_4Ru$			
Ruthenium, dichlorobis(6,7-dihydro-5,8-dimethyldibenzo[b,j][1,10]phenanthro-line-N^{13},N^{14})-	MeCN	214(4.84),264(4.83), 297s(4.30),354(4.58), 434(3.77)	33-1675-80
$C_{44}H_{39}O_3$			
1-Oxaspiro[4.4]non-3-en-2-ylium, 4-[1-benzoyl-2-phenyl-3-(2-phenyl-1-oxa-spiro[4.4]non-2-en-4-ylidene)-1-propenyl]-2-phenyl-, perchlorate	EtOH-HClO$_4$	625(4.77)	5-1744-80
$C_{44}H_{42}N_8O_6Pd$			
Palladium, bis[[1,1'-[(4-methoxyphen-	CHCl$_3$	280(4.61),330s(--),	125-2052-80

Compound	Solvent	$\lambda_{max}(\log \epsilon)$	Ref.
yl)methylene]bis[2-(4-methoxyphenyl)-diazenato]](1-)-N^2,N^{21}]-, (SP-4-1)-		360s(--),500(4.81), 720(4.09)	125-2052-80
$C_{44}H_{46}N_4O_{16}$			
21H,23H-Porphine-2,3,7,8,12,13,17,18-octaacetic acid, octamethyl ester	CHCl₃	407(5.36),502(4.38), 535(4.06),573(3.95), 628(3.63)	5-0263-80
$C_{44}H_{50}N_4O_{12}$			
Porphyrin, δ-acetoxy-1,3,5-trimethyl-2,4,6,7-tetrakis(2-methoxycarbonyl-ethyl)-8-(methoxycarbonylmethyl)-	CHCl₃	405(5.33),502(4.20), 535(3.80),572(3.82), 628(3.22)	130-0071-80
Porphyrin, 1,3-dimethyl-2,4,6,7-tetra-kis(2-methoxycarbonylethyl)-5,8-bis-(methoxycarbonylmethyl)-	CHCl₃	403(5.25),501(4.17), 536(3.98),568(3.86), 623(3.71)	130-0071-80
Porphyrin, 1,5-dimethyl-2,4,6,7-tetra-kis(2-methoxycarbonylethyl)-3,8-bis-(methoxycarbonylmethyl)-	CHCl₃	404(5.33),501(4.18), 536(4.14),569(3.94), 623(3.58)	130-0071-80
Porphyrin, 1,8-dimethyl-2,4,6,7-tetra-kis(2-methoxycarbonylethyl)-3,5-bis-(methoxycarbonylmethyl)-	CHCl₃	403(5.25),501(4.17), 536(3.97),569(3.82), 623(3.49)	130-0071-80
Porphyrin, 3,5-dimethyl-2,4,6,7-tetra-kis(2-methoxycarbonylethyl)-1,8-bis-(methoxycarbonylmethyl)-	CHCl₃	403(5.26),501(4.16), 536(3.96),570(3.82), 623(3.64)	130-0071-80
Porphyrin, 3,8-dimethyl-2,4,6,7-tetra-kis(2-methoxycarbonylethyl)-1,5-bis-(methoxycarbonylmethyl)-	CHCl₃	403(5.27),501(4.18), 536(4.01),568(3.90), 623(3.61)	130-0071-80
Porphyrin, 5,8-dimethyl-2,4,6,7-tetra-kis(2-methoxycarbonylethyl)-1,3-bis-(methoxycarbonylmethyl)-	CHCl₃	403(5.23),501(4.24), 536(4.05),569(3.94), 623(3.78)	130-0071-80
$C_{44}H_{52}O_6$			
β,β-Carotene-4,4'-dione, 3,3'-diacet-oxy-7,7',8,8'-tetradehydro-, (3S,3'S)-	benzene	300(4.26),325(4.26), 465s(4.95),493(5.04), 525(4.96)	33-1473-80
9-cis	CHCl₃	470s(4.90),491(4.97), 520s(4.88)	33-1473-80
9,9'-di-cis	benzene	300(4.33),330(4.35), 456s(4.86),483(4.98), 512(4.89)	33-1473-80
	CHCl₃	300(4.34),333(4.39), 486(4.97),514s(4.88)	33-1473-80
$C_{44}H_{53}N_5O_5$			
Tabernaelegantinine C	EtOH	244(4.76),285(4.19), 293(4.15)	39-0601-80(
Tabernaelegantinine D	EtOH	226(4.74),287(4.18), 295(4.16)	39-0601-80(
$C_{44}H_{54}N_4O_7$			
Vincovalinine	EtOH	264(4.20),288(4.20), 294(4.20),306s(--)	33-0793-80
	EtOH-acid	258(4.20),302(4.20)	33-0793-80
$C_{44}H_{54}N_4O_{10}$			
Vincovalicine	EtOH	220(4.52),256(4.11), 300(4.00)	33-0793-80
$C_{44}H_{54}O_6$			
β,β-Carotene-4,4'-dione, 3,3'-diacet-oxy-7,8-didehydro-, (3S,3'S)-	benzene	300(4.24),320s(4.21), 460s(4.94),491(5.07),	33-1473-80

Compound	Solvent	$\lambda_{max}(\log \epsilon)$	Ref.
(cont.)		517s(4.98)	33-1473-80
	acetone	481(5.10)	33-1473-80
9-cis	benzene	386s(4.40),484(4.97), 512s(4.87)	33-1473-80
$C_{44}H_{60}CoN_4O_2$ Cobalt(1+), [2,3,7,8,12,13,17,18-octa-ethyl-21H,23H-porphinato(2-)-N^{21},N^{22}-N^{23},N^{24}]bis(tetrahydrofuran)-, (OC-6-12)-, perchlorate	CH_2Cl_2	373(4.82),524(3.85), 557(3.86)	138-0521-80
$C_{44}H_{61}N_4Rh$ Rhodium, butyl[5-butyl-2,3,7,8,12,13-17,18-octaethyl-21H,23H-porphinato-(2-)-N^{21},N^{22},N^{23},N^{24}]-, (SP-5-52)-	$CHCl_3$	404(5.04),519(4.07), 547(4.25)	39-1641-80C
$C_{44}H_{64}P_2Pd$ Palladium, bis[(4-ethynylphenyl)ethyn-yl]bis(tributylphosphine)-	CH_2Cl_2	320(4.91)	47-0661-80
polymer	CH_2Cl_2	351s(4.80),361(4.82), 410s(4.81)	47-0661-80
$C_{44}H_{64}P_2Pt$ Platinum, bis[(4-ethynylphenyl)ethyn-yl]bis(tributylphosphine)-, trans	CH_2Cl_2	279s(3.38),297(4.59), 338(4.73)	47-0661-80
polymer	CH_2Cl_2	268(4.26),305(4.35), 380s(4.93),403(5.09)	47-0661-80
$C_{45}H_{24}O_3$ 9(10H)-Anthracenone, 10,10',10"-(1,2,3-cyclopropanetriylidene)tris-	$CHCl_3$	260(4.76),310(3.88), 322(3.86),378(3.87), 505(3.74),638(3.93), 780s(4.04),850(4.18)	35-5047-80
$C_{45}H_{26}O_3$ 9(10H)-Anthracenone, 10-[2,3-bis(10-hy-droxy-9-anthracenyl)-2-cyclopropen-1-ylidene]-	MeOH	250(4.96),265(4.92), 285(4.69),335(3.91), 348(3.89),367(3.84), 387(3.88),415(3.69), 440s(4.02),452(4.16), 506(4.41),545s(--)	35-5047-80
	THF	450(--),505(--), 535(--)	35-5047-80
dianion	MeOH-NaOH	367(1.18),440(4.04), 460(4.03),542(4.42), 580(4.48)	35-5054-80
$C_{45}H_{28}N_4S$ 8,11-Epithiobis[5,6]indazolo[2,3-a]qui-noline-9,10-dicarbonitrile, 8,9,10,11-tetrahydro-7,8,11,12-tetraphenyl-	$CHCl_3$	261(4.51),285(4.61), 296(4.46),308(4.30), 357(4.12),373(4.24), 393(4.26)	44-0090-80
$C_{45}H_{30}IN_4Rh$ Rhodium, (iodomethyl)[5,10,15,20-tetra-phenyl-21H,23H-porphinato(2-)-N^{21},N^{22},N^{23},N^{24}]-, (SP-5-31)-	CH_2Cl_2	414(5.30),522(4.35)	152-0311-80
$C_{45}H_{32}N_{10}O_{21}S_6$ 2-Naphthalenesulfonic acid, 7,7'-(carb-onyldiimino)bis[4-hydroxy-3-[[2-sulfo-	hexaanion	220(4.08),235(4.11), 290(4.08),420(3.90),	59-0279-80

Compound	Solvent	$\lambda_{max}(\log \epsilon)$	Ref.
4-[(4-sulfophenyl)azo]phenyl]azo]-		520(4.40),545(4.42)	59-0279-80
$C_{45}H_{36}O_3$ 9(10H)-Anthracenone, 10,10'-[3-[3,5-bis(1,1-dimethylethyl)-4-oxo-2,5-cyclohexadien-1-ylidene]-1,2-cyclopropanediylidene]bis-	CHCl₃	310(3.94),368(3.84), 495(3.40),550(3.40), 700(3.80),795(3.42), 830(3.34)	35-5047-80
$C_{45}H_{38}O_3$ 9(10H)-Anthracenone, 10-[2-[3,5-bis-(1,1-dimethylethyl)-4-hydroxyphenyl]-3-(10-hydroxy-9-anthracenyl)-2-cyclopropen-1-ylidene]-	MeOH	240(4.75),265(4.81), 285s(4.60),360(3.98), 385(3.86),410(3.99), 500(4.34),535s(--)	35-5047-80
	THF	365(--),410(--), 475(--),525s(--)	35-5047-80
dianion	MeOH-NaOH	360(4.12),370(4.11), 505(4.36),537(4.48), 576(4.59)	35-5054-80
$C_{45}H_{44}O_{11}$ Kuwanon H	MeOH	224(4.57),263(4.45), 285(4.27),325s(4.12)	142-1921-80 +142-1531-80]
	MeOH-NaOMe	223(4.63),275(4.50), 343(4.48),380s(4.05)	142-1921-80
	MeOH-AlCl₃	224(4.59),274(4.54), 325(4.08),385(3.85)	142-1921-80
Moracenin C	MeOH	208(4.79),264(4.50), 280s(4.34),320s(4.20)	142-1461-80
$C_{45}H_{46}BrN_5O_{14}$ L-Tryptophanamide, N-acetyl-L-valyl-O-acetyl-3,5-diacetoxy-α,β-didehydro-tyrosyl-N-[2-(3,4-diacetoxyphenyl)-ethenyl]-6-bromo-, [3(E)]-	MeOH	227(4.90),289(4.78)	44-3687-80
$C_{45}H_{48}O_3$ 9(10H)-Anthracenone, 10-[bis[3,5-bis-(1,1-dimethylethyl)-4-oxo-2,5-cyclohexadien-1-ylidene]cyclopropylidene]-	CHCl₃	260(4.24),315(3.74), 395(4.13),480(3.19), 640s(4.01),710(4.18), 790(4.11)	35-5047-80
$C_{45}H_{50}O_3$ 9(10H)-Anthracenone, 10-[2,3-bis[3,5-bis(1,1-dimethylethyl)-4-hydroxyphenyl]-2-cyclopropen-1-ylidene]-	MeOH	247(4.58),270(4.42), 285(4.35),319(3.54), 357(3.80),487(4.24),	35-5047-80
	benzene	358(--),459(--)	35-5047-80
	THF	315(--),357(--), 462(--)	35-5047-80
dianion	MeOH-NaOH	360(4.14),393(4.29), 447(4.17),520(4.17), 550(4.14)	35-5054-80
	THF-DNB	320(4.30),348(4.08), 405(4.27),470(4.31), 510(4.30),570s(3.95)	35-5054-80
$C_{45}H_{52}O_{12}$ β-D-Glucopyranosiduronic acid, (17β)-2,3-bis(phenylmethoxy)estra-1,3,5(10)-trien-17-yl, methyl ester, triacetate	EtOH	286(3.61)	95-0867-80

Compound	Solvent	$\lambda_{max}(\log \epsilon)$	Ref.
$C_{45}H_{57}N_4O_2Rh$ Rhodium, [7-(methoxycarbonyl)bicyclo-[3.1.1]hept-6-yl][2,3,7,8,12,13,17-18-octaethyl-21H,23H-porphinato(2-)-$N^{21},N^{22},N^{23},N^{24}$]-	$CHCl_3$	387(5.12),393s(5.11), 512(4.11),544(4.64)	101-0095-80B
$C_{45}H_{58}N_2O_{12}$ 2H-2,7-(Epoxypentadeca[1,11,13]trieno)-benzofuro[4,5-g]quinazoline, 22-acet-oxy-9-cyclohexyl-1,8,9,11-tetrahydro-5,6,18,20-tetrahydroxy-24-methoxy-2,4,13,17,19,21,23-heptamethyl-1,11,12-trioxo-	MeOH	227(4.54),276(4.31), 312(4.20),361(4.27), 595(4.04)	94-2309-80
$C_{45}H_{64}N_4$ 21H,23H-Porphine, 2,5,7,12,17-penta-methyl-3,8,13,18-tetrapentyl-	CH_2Cl_2	409(5.25),508(4.15), 542(3.78),578(2.78), 628(3.15)	130-0001-80
$C_{45}H_{90}N_2O_9P$ 3-Oxazolidinyloxy, 2-[12-(hexadecyl-oxy)-15-hydroxy-20,20-dimethyl-9-oxo-10,14,16-trioxa-20-azonia-15-phospha-heneicos-1-yl]-2-hexyl-4,4-dimethyl-, hydroxide, inner salt, P-oxide	MeOH	228(3.20)	106-0010-80
$C_{46}H_{30}O_2$ 6,13-Epidioxypentacene, 6,13-dihydro-5,7,12,14-tetraphenyl-	THF	264(4.85),293(4.43)	78-2225-80
7,14-Epoxydinaphth[2,3-b:2',3'-e]oxepin, 7,14-dihydro-5,8,14,15-tetraphenyl-	THF	236(4.77),291(4.25), 332(3.74),349(3.75)	78-2225-80
Naphtho[2,3-b]naphtho[2',3':3,4]cyclo-buta[1,2-e][1,4]dioxin, 5b,13a-dihy-dro-5,7,12,14-tetraphenyl-	THF	248(4.88),253(4.90), 308(4.34),320(4.32), 333(4.29)	78-2225-80
$C_{46}H_{32}N_{14}O_2$ 1H-Pyrazol-5-amine, 4,4'-[1,4-phenyl-enebis(azo)]bis[N-phenyl-3-(3-pyri-dinyl)-1-(3-pyridinylcarbonyl)-	n.s.g.	460(4.02)	146-0078-80
$C_{46}H_{33}N_4ORh$ Rhodium, (methoxymethyl)[5,10,15,20-tetraphenyl-21H,23H-porphinato(2-)-$N^{21},N^{22},N^{23},N^{24}$]-, (SP-5-31)-	CH_2Cl_2	410(5.36),517(4.37)	152-0311-80
$C_{46}H_{36}N_2O_4$ 2,5-Pyrrolidinedione, 1,1'-(1,4-phenyl-ene)bis[3-(diphenylmethylene)-4-(1-methylethylidene)-	n.s.g.	350(3.86)	97-0188-80
photoproduct B	n.s.g.	500(3.62)	97-0188-80
$C_{46}H_{36}N_4O_{10}$ 7(8H)-Pteridinone, 2,4-bis(phenylmeth-oxy)-8-(2,3,5-tri-O-benzoyl-β-D-ribofuranosyl)-	MeOH	228(4.68),248s(4.29), 272(3.91),316(4.10), 340s(3.90)	24-1535-80
$C_{46}H_{38}FeSi_2$ Ferrocene, 1,1'-bis(triphenylsilyl)-	C_6H_{12}	447(2.22)	101-0345-80J

Compound	Solvent	$\lambda_{max}(\log \epsilon)$	Ref.
$C_{46}H_{43}O_3$ 1-Oxaspiro[4.5]dec-3-en-2-ylium, 4-[1-benzoyl-2-phenyl-3-(2-phenyl-1-oxaspiro[4.5]dec-2-en-4-ylidene)-1-propenyl]-2-phenyl-, perchlorate	EtOH-HClO$_4$	630(4.75)	5-1744-80
$C_{46}H_{48}BrN_5O_{14}$ L-Tryptophanamide, N-acetyl-L-leucyl-O-acetyl-3,5-diacetoxy-α,β-didehydro-tyrosyl-N-[2-(3,4-diacetoxyphenyl)-ethenyl]-6-bromo-, [3(E)]-	MeOH	227(4.86),289(4.71)	44-3687-80
$C_{46}H_{48}N_4O_9$ 21H,23H-Porphine-2,7,12,18-tetrapropanoic acid, 3,8,13,17-tetramethyl-β^{12}-oxo-, 2,7,18-trimethyl 12-(phenylmethyl) ester	CHCl$_3$	411(5.29),510(4.02), 550(4.15),576(3.97), 634(3.14)	12-1095-80
$C_{46}H_{50}N_4O_9$ 21H,23H-Porphine-2,7,12,18-tetrapropanoic acid, β^{12}-hydroxy-3,8,13,17-tetramethyl-, 2,7,18-trimethyl 12-(phenylmethyl) ester	CHCl$_3$	402(5.29),499(4.17), 534(3.99),568(3.84), 621(3.65)	12-1095-80
$C_{46}H_{52}N_4O_{14}$ Porphyrin, δ-acetoxy-1,5-dimethyl-2,4,6,7-tetrakis(2-methoxycarbonylethyl)-3,8-bis(methoxycarbonylmethyl)-	CHCl$_3$	407(5.35),503(4.23), 537(3.80),574(3.81), 630(3.20)	130-0071-80
Porphyrin, δ-acetoxy-3,8-dimethyl-2,4,6,7-tetrakis(2-methoxycarbonylethyl)-1,5-bis(methoxycarbonylmethyl)-	CHCl$_3$	407(5.35),503(4.24), 538(3.78),575(3.80), 630(3.20)	130-0071-80
Porphyrin, 1-methyl-2,4,6,7-tetrakis(2-methoxycarbonylethyl)-3,5,8-tris(methoxycarbonylmethyl)-	CHCl$_3$	404(5.33),501(4.18), 536(3.95),571(3.84), 622(3.56)	130-0071-80
Porphyrin, 3-methyl-2,4,6,7-tetrakis(2-methoxycarbonylethyl)-1,5,8-tris(methoxycarbonylmethyl)-	CHCl$_3$	404(5.27),501(4.13), 536(3.95),571(3.81), 624(3.42)	130-0071-80
Porphyrin, 5-methyl-2,4,6,7-tetrakis(2-methoxycarbonylethyl)-1,3,8-tris(methoxycarbonylmethyl)-	CHCl$_3$	404(5.28),501(4.14), 535(3.96),569(3.80), 624(3.37)	130-0071-80
Porphyrin, 8-methyl-2,4,6,7-tetrakis(2-methoxycarbonylethyl)-1,3,5-tris(methoxycarbonylmethyl)-	CHCl$_3$	404(5.26),500(4.08), 535(3.92),569(3.75), 623(3.31)	130-0071-80
$C_{46}H_{54}N_4O_{10}$ Leurosine, 21'-oxo-	EtOH	220(4.79),270(4.26), 290(4.22)	100-0157-80
$C_{46}H_{56}N_4O_9$ Vinblastine, 4'-deoxy-3'-oxo-	MeOH	215(4.17),260(3.66), 285(3.60)	33-0366-80
Isovincathicine	EtOH	215(4.55),260(4.11), 303(3.93)	33-0793-80
$C_{46}H_{56}N_4O_{10}$ Leurosidine, 3'-oxo-	MeOH	269(4.10),286(4.04), 295(4.01),312s(3.75)	33-0366-80
$C_{46}H_{58}N_4O_5$ 1H-Indole-3-methanamine, 5,5'-(2,5,8-11,14-pentaoxapentadecane-1,15-diyl)-	EtOH	221(4.59),277(3.82)	121-0379-80

Compound	Solvent	$\lambda_{max}(\log \epsilon)$	Ref.
bis[N,N-dimethyl-1-(phenylmethyl)-			121-0379-80
$C_{46}H_{58}N_4O_{10}$ Leurosidine, 3-hydroxy-, (3'S)-	MeOH	257(4.07),285(4.00), 294(3.96),305s(3.81)	33-0366-80
$C_{47}H_{32}N_2O_4$ Benz[5,6]indazolo[2,3-a]quinoline-9,10- dicarboxylic acid, 7,8,11,12-tetra- phenyl-, dimethyl ester	$CHCl_3$	249(4.55),299(4.66), 310s(4.64),342(4.45), 350s(4.44),422(3.77), 482(4.09),510(4.08)	44-0090-80
$C_{47}H_{33}N_4O_2Rh$ Rhodium, (ethoxycarbonyl)[5,10,15,20- tetraphenyl-21H,23H-porphinato(2-)- $N^{21},N^{22},N^{23},N^{24}$]-, (SP-5-31)-	CH_2Cl_2	414(5.26),522(4.28)	152-0311-80
$C_{47}H_{38}N_4O_{10}$ 7(8H)-Pteridinone, 6-methyl-2,4- bis(phenylmethoxy)-8-(2,3,5-tri- O-benzoyl-β-D-ribofuranosyl)-	MeOH	229(4.77),273(3.95), 281(3.95),313(4.12), 340s(3.89)	24-1535-80
$C_{47}H_{50}N_8O_5$ Deuteroporphyrin, 2-formyl-4-(2,2,3,3- tetracyanocyclobutyl)-, di-tert- butyl ester	acetone	413(5.20),511(4.08), 548(4.03),579(3.82), 637(3.52)	44-5196-80
Deuteroporphyrin, 2-formyl-4-vinyl-, di-tert-butyl ester, [4+2]TCNE adduct	$CHCl_3$	412(5.28),503(4.16), 537(3.66),562(3.28), 613(3.80),638(3.64), 669(4.73)	44-5196-80 44-5196-80
Deuteroporphyrin, 4-formyl-2-vinyl-, di-tert-butyl ester, [4+2]TCNE adduct	$CHCl_3$	413(5.11),508(4.09), 545(3.71),569(3.20), 621(3.70),648(3.57), 679(4.70)	44-5196-80
$C_{47}H_{51}NO_{18}S$ β-D-Glucopyranoside, 4-(2,3-dihydro-2- phenyl-1,5-benzothiazepin-4-yl)phenyl, 4-O-(2,3,4,5-tetra-O-acetyl-β-D- glucopyranosyl)-, 2,3,6-triacetate	n.s.g.	224s(4.28),276(4.28), 318(4.12)	114-0027-80A
β-D-Glucopyranoside, 4-(2,3-dihydro-4- phenyl-1,5-benzothiazepin-2-yl)phenyl, 4-O-(2,3,4,5-tetra-O-acetyl-β-D- glucopyranosyl)-, 2,3,6-triacetate	n.s.g.	224s(4.35),258(4.31), 322(3.87)	114-0027-80A
$C_{47}H_{56}N_4O_{10}S$ Vincaleukoblastine, 3',4'-(carbonothi- oylbis(oxy)]-4'-deoxy-	MeOH	260(4.23),286(4.14), 295(4.08),312s(3.68)	33-0366-80
$C_{47}H_{61}N_8O_{12}Rh$ Rhodibyrinic acid-ac-diamide dicyanide	H_2O	350(4.56),497(4.13), 528(4.20)	5-1699-80
$C_{47}H_{64}N_2O_{12}$ 2H-2,7-(Epoxypentadeca[1,11,13]trieno)- benzofuro[4,5-g]quinazoline-1,11,12- trione, 22-acetoxy-1,8,9,11-tetrahy- dro-5,6,18,20-tetrahydroxy-24-meth- oxy-2,4,13,17,19,21,23-heptamethyl- 9-octyl-	MeOH	227(4.54),277(4.29), 310(4.19),360(4.23), 595(4.00)	94-2309-80

Compound	Solvent	$\lambda_{max}(\log \epsilon)$	Ref.
2H-2,7-(Epoxypentadeca[1,11,13]trieno)-benzofuro[4,5-g]quinazoline-1,11,12-trione, 22-acetoxy-1,8,9,11-tetrahydro-5,6,18,20-tetrahydroxy-24-methoxy-2,4,13,17,19,21,23-heptamethyl-9-(1-methylheptyl)-	MeOH	226(4.54),276(4.32), 314s(4.17),361(4.26), 596(4.02)	94-2309-80
$C_{47}H_{70}O_{24}$ Trillenoside A	EtOH	249(3.93)	94-1437-80
$C_{48}H_{34}$ m-Octiphenyl	C_6H_{12}	192(4.91),204(4.87), 249(5.13)	94-3210-80
o-Octiphenyl	C_6H_{12}	225s(4.92)	94-3210-80
m-Quaterphenyl, 3,3'''-bis(2-biphenyl-yl)-	C_6H_{12}	192(5.00),203s(4.95), 238(5.03),249s(4.96)	94-3210-80
m-Quaterphenyl, 3,3'''-bis(4-biphenyl-yl)-	C_6H_{12}	205(5.00),262(4.96)	94-3210-80
o-Quaterphenyl, 2,2'''-bis(3-biphenyl-yl)-	C_6H_{12}	192(4.98),202s(4.96), 235(4.90),254s(4.77)	94-3210-80
o-Quaterphenyl, 2,2'''-bis(4-biphenyl-yl)-	C_6H_{12}	204(4.98),260(4.66), 276s(4.62)	94-3210-80
p-Sexiphenyl, 2,2''''''-diphenyl-	C_6H_{12}	203(5.11),234s(4.61), 315(4.80)	18-2610-80
$C_{48}H_{35}OP$ Phosphonium, [7-(diphenylmethylene)-5-hydroxy-9-phenyl-7H-benzocyclohepten-6-yl]triphenyl-, hydroxide, inner salt	CHCl₃	320(4.43),353(4.05), 385(4.06)	88-4869-80
$C_{48}H_{36}OP$ Phosphonium, [7-(diphenylmethylene)-5-hydroxy-9-phenyl-7H-benzocyclohepten-6-yl]triphenyl-, bromide	CHCl₃	253(4.60),294s(4.15), 365(3.79)	88-4869-80
$C_{48}H_{39}F_3N_2O_5$ Thymidine, α,α,α-trifluoro-3',5'-bis-O-(triphenylmethyl)-	MeOH MeOH-acid MeOH-base	262(4.04) 262(4.06) 260(3.95)	39-2755-80C 39-2755-80C 39-2755-80C
$C_{48}H_{39}F_3N_2O_6$ Uridine, 5-(trifluoromethyl)-2',5'-bis-O-(triphenylmethyl)-	MeOH MeOH-acid MeOH-base	262(3.92) 262(3.92) 260(3.86)	39-2755-80C 39-2755-80C 39-2755-80C
$C_{48}H_{40}FeMoP_2S_9$ $(Ph_4P)_2[(S_5)FeS_2MoS_2]$	DMF	305(4.17),410(4.00), 480(3.86),545s(--), 605(3.27)	35-1730-80
$C_{48}H_{40}FeP_2S_9W$ $(Ph_4P)_2[(S_5)FeS_2WS_2]$	DMF	366(3.97),398(3.89), 425(3.87),464s(--), 550(3.10)	35-1730-80
$C_{48}H_{46}N_8O_4$ Pyridinium, 4,4',4'',4'''-(21H,23H-porphine-5,10,15,20-tetrayl)tetrakis[1-(2-hydroxyethyl)-, tetrachloride, dihydrochloride	pH 0.0 pH 5.64	447(5.00),593(3.91), 642(4.00) 422(5.31),519(4.11), 557(3.85),583(3.84), 641(3.43)	18-2195-80 18-2195-80

Compound	Solvent	$\lambda_{max}(\log \epsilon)$	Ref.
(cont.)	pH 14.0	448(4.73),578(3.92), 622(3.80)	18-2195-80
$C_{48}H_{50}N_4O_6$ 21H,23H-Porphine-2,18-dipropanoic acid, 7,12-bis(1-hydroxyethyl)-3,8,13,17-tetramethyl-, bis(phenylmethyl) ester	$CHCl_3$	402(5.29),499(4.17), 533(3.97),569(3.82), 622(3.65)	12-0585-80
$C_{48}H_{50}N_8O_4$ 21H,23H-Porphine-2,18-dipropanoic acid, 8-ethenyl-3,7,12,17-tetramethyl-13-(2,2,3,3-tetracyanocyclobutyl)-, bis(1,1-dimethylethyl) ester	$CHCl_3$	410(5.29),508(4.12), 545(4.10),574(3.86), 629(3.37)	44-5196-80
Protoporphyrin, di-tert-butyl ester, [4+2]TCNE adduct	$CHCl_3$	404(5.26),501(4.14), 536(3.86),603(3.63), 631(3.55),660(4.69)	44-5196-80
isomer 2	$CHCl_3$	404(5.23),500(4.12), 535(3.82),602(3.62), 631(3.55),660(4.66)	44-5196-80
$C_{48}H_{53}N_4Rh$ Rhodium, [2,3,7,8,12,13,17,18-octaethyl-5-phenyl-21H,23H-porphinato(2-)-$N^{21},N^{22},N^{23},N^{24}$]phenyl-, (SP-5-52)-	$CHCl_3$	399(5.00),513(4.06), 546(4.57)	39-1641-80C
$C_{48}H_{54}ClFeN_8O_6$ Iron, chloro[methyl N-[N-[3-[7,12-diethenyl-18-(3-methoxy-3-oxopropyl)-3,8,13,17-tetramethyl-21H,23H-porphin-2-yl]-1-oxopropyl]-L-leucyl-L-histidinato(2-)]-, (OC-6-21)-	$CHCl_3$	407(4.85),536(3.88), 640(3.40)	65-0552-80
$C_{48}H_{54}N_4O_{16}$ 21H,23H-Porphine-2,7,12,18-tetrapropanoic acid, 15-acetoxy-3,8,13-tris(2-methoxy-2-oxoethyl)-17-methyl-, tetramethyl ester	$CHCl_3$	406(5.18),504(4.03), 536(3.58),577(3.58), 603(2.89)	130-0071-80
$C_{48}H_{60}N_4O_{10}$ Vincaleukoblastine, 3'-acetoxy-4'-deoxy-, (3'R)-	MeOH	260(4.12),286(4.02), 295(3.99),314(3.72)	33-0366-80
$C_{48}H_{74}O_{14}$ Avermectin A_{1a}, 5-O-demethyl-22,23-dihydro-	MeOH	238(4.43),245(4.48), 254s(4.29)	87-1134-80
C H O Avermectin A_{1a}, 5-O-demethyl-3,4,22,23-tetrahydro-	MeOH	238(4.41),244(4.47), 252s(4.28)	87-1134-80
$C_{49}H_{35}N_4O_2Rh$ Rhodium, [1-(ethoxycarbonyl)ethenyl]-[5,10,15,20-tetraphenyl-21H,23H-porphinato(2-)-$N^{21},N^{22},N^{23},N^{24}$]-, (SP-5-31)-	CH_2Cl_2	415(5.31),525(4.33)	152-0311-80
$C_{49}H_{37}N_4O_3Rh$ Rhodium, (2-ethoxy-1-methoxy-2-oxoethyl)[5,10,15,20-tetraphenyl-21H,23H-porphinato(2-)-$N^{21},N^{22},N^{23},N^{24}$]-, (SP-5-31)-	CH_2Cl_2	415(5.25),523(4.28)	152-0311-80

Compound	Solvent	$\lambda_{max}(\log \epsilon)$	Ref.
$C_{49}H_{38}OP$ Phosphonium, [7-(diphenylmethylene)-5-methoxy-9-phenyl-7H-benzocyclohepten-6-yl]triphenyl-, fluorosulfate	CHCl₃	250(4.31),290s(3.83), 360(3.45)	88-4869-80
$C_{49}H_{40}N_8Ni_2$ Nickel, [μ-[[2,2'-methylenebis[5,10,15-20-tetramethyl-21H,23H-porphinato]]-(4-)-N²¹,N²²,N²³,N²⁴:N²¹',N²²',N²³'-N²⁴']]di-	CHCl₃	426(5.41),544(4.42)	5-1082-80
$C_{49}H_{42}N_5O_8P$ 3'-Adenylic acid, N-benzoyl-2'-deoxy-5'-O-[(4-methoxyphenyl)diphenyl-methyl]-, diphenyl ester	MeOH	230(4.44),259s(4.17), 278(4.33)	142-0761-80B
$C_{49}H_{76}O_{14}$ Avermectin A₁ₐ, 22,23-dihydro-	MeOH	238(4.45),244(4.59), 252s(4.30)	87-1134-80
$C_{50}H_{35}N_4O_4Rh$ Rhodium, [3-methoxy-1-(methoxycarbo-nyl)-3-oxo-1-propenyl][5,10,15,20-tetraphenyl-21H,23H-porphinato(2-)-N²¹,N²²,N²³,N²⁴]-, (SP-5-31)-	CH₂Cl₂	414(5.30),525(4.33)	152-0311-80
$C_{50}H_{36}$ Cyclobutane, 1,2,3-tris(diphenylmethyl-ene)-4-(phenylmethylene)-	CHCl₃	298(4.50),320s(4.46), 400s(4.14),490(3.40)	88-2713-80
$C_{50}H_{37}N_4O_4Rh$ Rhodium, (1-acetoxy-2-ethoxy-2-oxoeth-yl)[5,10,15,20-tetraphenyl-21H,23H-porphinato(2-)-N²¹,N²²,N²³,N²⁴]-, (SP-5-31)-	CH₂Cl₂	412(5.23),520(4.31)	152-0311-80
$C_{50}H_{38}O_2$ Bicyclo[4.1.0]heptene-2-carboxylic acid, 1,2,3,4,5,6,7-heptaphenyl-	THF	245(4.31),275s(3.87)	44-0633-80
2,5-Cycloheptadiene-1-carboxylic acid, 1,2,3,4,5,6,7-heptaphenyl-	THF	270s(4.27)	44-0633-80
$C_{50}H_{40}N_4Ni$ Nickel, [2,12(or 13)-bis(diphenylmeth-yl)-5,10,15,20-tetraphenyl-21H,23H-porphinato(2-)-N²¹,N²²,N²³,N²⁴]-	CHCl₃	306(4.10),338(4.09), 428(5.26),550(4.10)	5-1082-80
$C_{50}H_{40}O_6$ Spiro[naphthalene-2(1H),2'-[2H]naphtho-[1,2-b]pyran]-2-one, 3',4'-dihydro-8,10'-dimethoxy-3',4'-diphenyl-4,6'-bis(phenylmethoxy)-	CHCl₃	250s(4.46),318(4.01), 333(4.09),347(4.11)	5-1321-80
$C_{50}H_{42}N_8Ni_2$ Nickel, [μ-[[2,2'-ethylidenebis-[5,10,15,20-tetramethyl-21H,23H-por-phinato]](4-)-N²¹,N²²,N²³,N²⁴:N²¹'-N²²',N²³',N²⁴']]di-	CHCl₃	303(4.32),335(4.29), 427(5.40),545(4.41)	5-1082-80
$C_{50}H_{50}Cl_3N_4O_{14}P$ Thymidine, P-deoxo-5'-O-(phenoxy-	EtOH	264(4.3?)	44-2715-80

Compound	Solvent	$\lambda_{max}(\log \epsilon)$	Ref.
acetyl)-P-(2,2,2-trichloroethyl)thy-midylyl)-(3'→5')-3'-O-[(4-methoxy-phenyl)diphenylmethyl]- (cont.)			44-2715-80
$C_{50}H_{54}N_4$ [1,4,10,13]Tetraazacyclooctadecino-[1,18-a:4,5-a':10,9-a":13,14-a"']-tetraindole-5,22-diium, 6,7,13,17-23,24,30,34-octahydro-13,13,17,17,30-30,34,34-octamethyl-	CH_2Cl_2	506(5.68),590(3.98)	88-2977-80
$C_{50}H_{56}N_4$ 3H-Indolium, 2-[3-[1,3-dihydro-1-[2-[2-[3-(1,3-dihydro-1,3,3-trimethyl-2H-indol-2-ylidene)-1-propenyl]-3,3-dimethyl-3H-indolium-1-yl]ethyl]-3,3-dimethyl-2H-indol-2-ylidene]-1-prop-enyl]-1,3,3-trimethyl-, diperchlorate	CH_2Cl_2	509(5.21),572(5.29)	88-2977-80
$C_{50}H_{68}O_{10}$ Digitoxigenin, 16,17-dehydro-, 3-acet-ate, dimer III	n.s.g.	217(4.20)	94-2799-80
dimer IV	n.s.g.	217(4.18)	94-2799-80
$C_{50}H_{71}BrCoN_{13}O_{10}$ 5,6-Secocobinamide, dicyano-10-bromo-5,6-dioxo-	MeOH	336(3.94),506(3.86)	5-0165-80
$C_{50}H_{80}O$ 2,6,10,14,18,22,26,30,34,38-Tetraconta-decaenal, 3,7,11,15,19,23,27,31,35-39-decamethyl-, (Z,Z,Z,Z,Z,Z,E,E,E)-	isooctane	243(4.15)	39-2098-80C
$C_{52}H_{34}O_{14}$ [6,6'-Bidinaphtho[1,2-b:2',3'-d]furan]-5,5',7,7',12,12'-hexol, hexaacetate	$CHCl_3$	269(5.27),302s(4.50), 323(4.39),337(4.43), 360(4.20),377(4.33)	39-0090-80C
$C_{52}H_{36}N_{14}O_2$ 1H-Pyrazol-5-amine, 4,4'-[[1,1'-bi-phenyl]-4,4'-diylbis(azo)]bis[N-phenyl-3-(3-pyridinyl)-1-(3-pyr-idinylcarbonyl)-	n.s.g.	470(4.25)	146-0078-80
$C_{52}H_{40}N_7O_2$ 1H-Benzimidazolium, 5-(2-benzoxazolyl)-2-[7-[5-(2-benzoxazolyl)-3-ethyl-1,3-dihydro-1-phenyl-2H-benzimidazol-2-ylidene]-4-cyano-1,3,5-heptatrien-yl]-3-ethyl-1-phenyl-, perchlorate	DMSO	785(5.30)	103-0406-80
$C_{52}H_{40}N_7S_2$ 1H-Benzimidazolium, 5-(2-benzothiazol-yl)-2-[7-[5-(2-benzothiazolyl)-3-ethyl-1,3-dihydro-1-phenyl-2H-benz-imidazol-2-ylidene]-4-cyano-1,3,5-heptatrienyl]-3-ethyl-1-phenyl-, tetrafluoroborate	DMSO	786(5.36)	103-0406-80
$C_{52}H_{43}N_6OS_2$ 1H-Benzimidazolium, 5-(2-benzothiazol-	DMSO	715(4.99)	103-0406-80

Compound	Solvent	$\lambda_{max}(\log \epsilon)$	Ref.
y1)-2-[7-[5-(2-benzothiazolyl)-3-eth-yl-1,3-dihydro-1-phenyl-2H-benzimida-zol-2-ylidene]-4-methoxy-1,3,5-hepta-trienyl]-3-ethyl-1-phenyl-, iodide			103-0406-80
$C_{52}H_{43}N_6O_2$ 1H-Benzimidazolium, 5-(2-benzoxazolyl)-2-[7-[5-(2-benzoxazolyl)-3-ethyl-1,3-dihydro-1-phenyl-2H-benzimidazol-2-ylidene]-4-methyl-1,3,5-heptatrien-yl]-3-ethyl-1-phenyl-, iodide	DMSO	762(5.34)	103-0406-80
$C_{52}H_{43}N_6O_3$ 1H-Benzimidazolium, 5-(2-benzoxazolyl)-2-[7-[5-(2-benzoxazolyl)-3-ethyl-1,3-dihydro-1-phenyl-2H-benzimidazol-2-ylidene]-4-methoxy-1,3,5-heptatrien-yl]-3-ethyl-1-phenyl-, iodide	DMSO	711(4.89)	103-0406-80
$C_{52}H_{43}N_6S_2$ 1H-Benzimidazolium, 5-(2-benzothiazol-yl)-2-[7-[5-(2-benzothiazolyl)-3-eth-yl-1,3-dihydro-1-phenyl-2H-benzimid-azol-2-ylidene]-4-methyl-1,3,5-hepta-trienyl]-3-ethyl-1-phenyl-, iodide	DMSO	765(5.35)	103-0406-80
$C_{52}H_{44}ClGaN_4O_8$ Gallium, chloro[5,10,15,20-tetrakis(3,5-dimethoxyphenyl)-21H,23H-porphinato-(2-)-$N^{21},N^{22},N^{23},N^{24}$]-, (SP-5-12)-	$CHCl_3$	403s(4.62),424(5.83), 510s(3.80),552(4.40), 589(3.40)	44-4296-80
$C_{52}H_{44}ClInN_4O_8$ Indium, chloro[5,10,15,20-tetrakis(3,5-dimethoxyphenyl)-21H,23H-porphinato-(2-)-$N^{21},N^{22},N^{23},N^{24}$]-, (SP-5-12)-	$CHCl_3$	410s(4.71),430(5.82), 518s(3.53),560(4.41), 599(3.76)	44-4296-80
$C_{52}H_{44}N_4O_9Ti$ Titanium, oxo[5,10,15,20-tetrakis(3,5-dimethoxyphenyl)-21H,23H-porphinato-(2-)-$N^{21},N^{22},N^{23},N^{24}$]-, (SP-5-12)-	$CHCl_3$	408s(4.73),427(5.70), 512s(3.50),552(4.44), 588(3.39)	44-4296-80
$C_{52}H_{46}N_4O_8$ 21H,23H-Porphine, 5,10,15,20-tetrakis-(3,5-dimethoxyphenyl)-	$CHCl_3$	421(5.72),516(4.36), 550(3.78),590(3.81), 646(3.56)	44-4296-80
$C_{52}H_{50}O_{23}$ Benzo[h][1]benzopyrano[5,4,3-cde][1]-benzopyran-5,12-dione, 1-methyl-6-(phenylmethoxy)-10-[[2,3,6-tri-O-acetyl-4-O-(2,3,4,6-tetra-O-acetyl-α-D-glucopyranosyl)-β-D-glucopyrano-syl]oxy]-	EtOH	236(4.59),266(4.62)	87-0549-80
$C_{52}H_{52}CuN_{12}O_4$ Copper, [N,N,N',N',N'',N'',N''',N'''-octa-ethyl-29H,31H-phthalocyanine-2,9,16-23-tetracarboxamidato(2-)-N^{29},N^{30}-N^{31},N^{32}]-, (SP-4-1)-	$CHCl_3$	341(4.95),607(4.68), 645(4.69),675(5.40)	65-0907-80

Compound	Solvent	$\lambda_{max}(\log \epsilon)$	Ref.
$C_{52}H_{54}N_4O_8$ 21H,23H-Porphine-2,18-dipropanoic acid, 7,12-bis[1-(acetyloxy)ethyl]-3,8,13-17-tetramethyl-, bis(phenylmethyl)-ester	CHCl$_3$	402(5.29),499(4.18), 533(3.97),569(3.82), 623(3.66)	12-0585-80
$C_{52}H_{62}N_4O_{16}$ 21H,23H-Porphine-2,3,7,8,12,13,17,18-octapropanoic acid, octamethyl ester	EtOH	406(5.31),502(4.18), 537(3.99),574(3.83), 627(3.62)	5-0263-80
	CHCl$_3$	406(5.29),502(4.19), 537(4.02),573(3.86), 627(3.62)	5-0263-80
$C_{52}H_{71}N_8O_{12}Rh$ Rhodibyrinic acid-a,c-diamide, dicyanide, pentamethyl ester	MeOH	350(4.56),489(4.13), 530(4.20)	5-1699-80
$C_{52}H_{72}BrCl_2N_4O_{16}Rh$ 5,6-Secorhodibyrinic acid, dichloro-10-bromo-5,6-dioxo-, heptamethyl ester	MeOH	285(3.96),343(3.93), 504(4.12)	5-0821-80
$C_{52}H_{73}Cl_2N_4O_{16}Rh$ 5,6-Secorhodibyrinic acid, dichloro-5,6-dioxo-, heptamethyl ester	MeOH	286(4.31),324(4.10), 479(4.38)	5-0821-80
$C_{53}H_{62}N_4O_{10}S$ Vincaleukoblastine, 3'-(phenylthioxomethoxy)-, (3'α,4'α)-	MeOH	259(4.11),288(4.05), 295(4.03),310s(3.83)	33-0366-80
(3'β,4'α)-	MeOH	262(4.23),285(4.17), 295(4.12),308(3.89)	33-0366-80
$C_{53}H_{66}$ Bicyclo[4.4.1]undeca-1,3,5,7,9-pentaene, 2,7-bis[4,8-dimethyl-10-(2,6,6-trimethyl-1-cyclohexen-1-yl)deca-1,3,5,7,9-pentaenyl]-	CH$_2$Cl$_2$	248(4.31),300(4.38), 347(4.57),410(4.54), 448s(4.62),470(4.65), 526(4.47)	83-0970-80
$C_{53}H_{72}Cl_2CoN_5O_{14}$ Cobyrinic acid, 10-chloro-, chloride cyanide, heptamethyl ester	MeCN-KCN	291(4.03),319(4.06), 356s(4.12),370(4.19), 562(3.76),605(3.72)	33-2320-80
$C_{53}H_{74}Cl_2CoN_5O_{19}$ Cobyrinic acid, 10-chloro-, aqua-cyanide, heptamethyl ester, perchlorate	MeCN-KCN	292(4.08),314(4.10), 372(4.22),434(3.58), 565(3.81),605(3.74)	33-2320-80
$C_{54}H_{50}N_{12}O_4$ 21H,23H-Porphine-2,18-dipropanoic acid, 3,7,12,17-tetramethyl-8,13-bis(2,2-3,3-tetracyanocyclobutyl)-, bis(1,1-dimethylethyl ester)	acetone	404(5.33),502(4.18), 534(3.96),571(3.84), 626(3.67)	44-5196-80
Protoporphyrin, di-tert-butyl ester, [2+2]/[4+2] TCNE adduct	CHCl$_3$	403(5.32),497(4.16), 531(3.47),553(3.20), 603(3.71),627(3.60), 658(4.76)	44-5196-80
isomer 2	CHCl$_3$	402(5.20),499(4.08), 533(3.60),556(3.07), 605(3.55),632(3.50), 663(4.70)	44-5196-80

Compound	Solvent	$\lambda_{max}(\log \epsilon)$	Ref.
Protoporphyrin, di-tert-butyl ester, [4+2]bis-TCNE adduct	CHCl$_3$	397(4.93),407(4.95), 430(5.09),515(3.86), 548(3.72),593(3.97), 640(4.42)	44-5196-80
$C_{54}H_{72}Cl_3CoN_6O_{15}$ Cobyrinic acid, 5α,10,13β-trichloro-5,6-dihydro-6α-hydroxy-, dicyanide, heptamethyl ester	MeOH-KCN	324(3.96),334s(3.59), 356s(3.54),472(3.96), 502(4.02)	5-1632-80
$C_{54}H_{88}O_{26}S$ Echinoside A, sodium salt	MeOH	none above 210 nm	94-1651-80
$C_{55}H_{41}N_4O_3Rh$ Rhodium, [2-ethoxy-2-oxo-1-(phenylmethoxy)ethyl][5,10,15,20-tetraphenyl-21H,23H-Porphinato(2-)-N^{21},N^{22},N^{23}-N^{24}]-, (SP-5-31)-	CH$_2$Cl$_2$	415(5.27),522(4.29)	152-0311-80
$C_{55}H_{44}N_8Ni_2$ Nickel, [μ-[[2,2'-(phenylmethylene)bis-[5,10,15,20-tetramethyl-21H,23H-porphinato]](4-)-$N^{21},N^{22},N^{23},N^{24}$-$N^{21'},N^{22'},N^{23'},N^{24'}$]]di-	CHCl$_3$	303(4.34),332(4.30), 424(5.39),431s(5.38), 545(4.42),580s(3.78)	5-1082-80
$C_{55}H_{72}MgN_4O_5$ Chlorophyll a	benzene	346(4.439),384(4.617), 434(4.879),536(3.477), 584(3.886),626(4.164), 668(4.719)	33-1048-80
	acetone	385(4.644),412(4.833), 431(4.972),505s(3.23), 535(3.519),580(3.806), 615(4.134),662(4.878)	33-1048-80
	ether	381(4.634),409(4.849), 428(5.045),495s(3.32), 528(3.568),574(3.833), 614(4.114),659(4.939)	33-1048-80
	dioxan	330(4.386),384(4.614), 410(4.820),433(5.082), 500(3.342),538(3.519), 587(3.869),623(4.152), 662(4.922)	33-1048-80
$C_{55}H_{74}N_4O_5$ Pheophytin a (shoulders not listed)	ether	273(4.025),320(4.283), 409(5.027),470(3.613), 505(4.068),533(4.004), 560(3.462),610(3.892), 668(4.772)	33-1048-80
	dioxan	274(4.201),324(4.314), 412(5.042),472(3.634), 506(4.072),537(3.996), 559(3.531),611(3.908), 669(4.718)	33-1048-80
$C_{55}H_{84}$ Ergosta-3,5,7,22-tetraene, 3-cholesta-3,5-dien-3-yl-, (22E)-	heptane	348(4.59),365(4.75), 386(4.68)	94-1747-80

Compound	Solvent	$\lambda_{max}(\log \epsilon)$	Ref.
$C_{56}H_{32}CoN_8O_4$			
Phthalocyanine, 3,3',3'',3'''-tetraphenoxy-, cobalt complex	C_6H_5Cl	312(4.73),615(4.46), 648s(4.57),686(5.10)	65-1874-80
Phthalocyanine, 4,4',4'',4'''-tetraphenoxy-, cobalt complex	C_6H_5Cl	326(4.79),370s(4.38), 604(4.47),640s(4.59), 671(5.11)	65-1874-80
$C_{56}H_{32}CoN_8S_4$			
Phthalocyanine, 3,3',3'',3'''-tetrakis-(phenylthio)-, cobalt complex	$C_6H_3Cl_3$	430(4.15),634(4.47), 710(5.04)	65-1874-80
Phthalocyanine, 4,4',4'',4'''-tetrakis-(phenylthio)-, cobalt complex	C_6H_5Cl	310(4.86),328s(4.83), 396s(4.35),612(4.53), 655(4.65),682(5.15)	65-1874-80
$C_{56}H_{32}CuN_8O_4$			
Phthalocyanine, 3,3',3'',3'''-tetraphenoxy-, copper complex	C_6H_5Cl	325(4.71),334s(4.51), 622(4.61),658s(4.43), 694(5.31)	65-1874-80
Phthalocyanine, 4,4',4'',4'''-tetraphenoxy-, copper complex	C_6H_5Cl	342(4.89),376s(4.64), 608(4.73),644s(4.70), 678(5.26)	65-1874-80
$C_{56}H_{32}CuN_8S_4$			
Phthalocyanine, 3,3',3'',3'''-tetrakis-(phenylthio)-, copper complex	$C_6H_3Cl_3$	332(4.88),430s(4.38), 640(4.56),680s(4.53), 718(5.25)	65-1874-80
Phthalocyanine, 4,4',4'',4'''-tetrakis-(phenylthio)-, copper complex	C_6H_5Cl	343(4.82),380s(4.50), 620(4.64),658s(4.62), 692(5.30)	65-1874-80
$C_{56}H_{32}N_8O_4Zn$			
Phthalocyanine, 3,3',3'',3'''-tetraphenoxy-, zinc complex	C_6H_5Cl + pyridine	318(4.63),360s(4.59), 624(4.49),660s(4.46), 694(5.31)	65-1874-80
Phthalocyanine, 4,4',4'',4'''-tetraphenoxy-, zinc complex	C_6H_5Cl	346(4.68),612(4.38), 648s(4.33),681(5.08)	65-1874-80
$C_{56}H_{32}N_8S_4Zn$			
Phthalocyanine, 3,3',3'',3'''-tetrakis-(phenylthio)-, zinc complex	$C_6H_3Cl_3$– pyridine	337(4.63),390s(4.32), 435(4.16),640(4.41), 688s(4.44),715(5.17)	65-1874-80
Phthalocyanine, 4,4',4'',4'''-tetrakis-(phenylthio)-, zinc complex	C_6H_5Cl	351(4.72),620(4.47), 660s(4.42),692(5.24)	65-1874-80
$C_{56}H_{34}N_8O_4$			
Phthalocyanine, 3,3',3'',3'''-tetraphenoxy-	C_6H_5Cl	324(4.67),346(4.64), 619(4.40),652(4.52), 685(5.04),716(5.10)	65-1874-80
Phthalocyanine, 4,4',4'',4'''-tetraphenoxy-	C_6H_5Cl	338(4.79),382s(4.55), 602(4.45),635(4.60), 665(5.09),701(5.10)	65-1874-80
$C_{56}H_{34}N_8S_4$			
Phthalocyanine, 3,3',3'',3'''-tetrakis-(phenylthio)-	$C_6H_3Cl_3$	336(4.85),400s(4.41), 435s(4.28),641(4.45), 674(4.50),712(5.04), 740(5.09)	65-1874-80
Phthalocyanine, 4,4',4'',4'''-tetrakis-(phenylthio)-	C_6H_5Cl	346(4.78),419(4.47), 616(4.47),649(4.59), 681(5.06),712(5.13)	65-1874-80

Compound	Solvent	$\lambda_{max}(\log \epsilon)$	Ref.
$C_{56}H_{34}O_8$ [3,6':3',3":6",3"'-Quaterbenzofuran]- 2,2',2",2"'(3H,3'H,3"H,3"'H)-tetrone, 3,3',3",3"'-tetraphenyl-	n.s.g.	230(5.00),279(4.28)	150-3901-80
$C_{56}H_{48}CuN_8O_{16}$ Copper, [octaethyl 29H,31H-phthalocya- nine-2,3,9,10,16,17,23,24-octacarb- oxylate(2-)-$N^{29},N^{30},N^{31},N^{32}$]-, (SP-4-1)-	$C_6H_3Cl_3$	350(4.80),618(4.46), 650s(4.27),690(5.15)	65-0907-80
$C_{56}H_{52}ClGaN_4O_{12}$ Gallium, chloro[5,10,15,20-tetrakis- (3,4,5-trimethoxyphenyl)-21H,23H- porphinato(2-)-$N^{21},N^{22},N^{23},N^{24}$]-, (SP-5-12)-	CHCl₃	407s(4.68),427(5.71), 515s(3.54),553(4.38), 592(3.61)	44-4296-80
$C_{56}H_{52}ClInN_4O_{12}$ Indium, chloro[5,10,15,20-tetrakis- (3,4,5-trimethoxyphenyl)-21H,23H- porphinato(2-)-$N^{21},N^{22},N^{23},N^{24}$]-, (SP-5-12)-	CHCl₃	412s(4.73),433(5.71), 523s(3.58),562(4.38), 602(3.95)	44-4296-80
$C_{56}H_{52}N_4O_{13}Ti$ Titanium, oxo[5,10,15,20-tetrakis- (3,4,5-trimethoxyphenyl)-21H,23H- porphinato(2-)-$N^{21},N^{22},N^{23},N^{24}$]-, (SP-5-12)-	CHCl₃	410s(4.65),430(5.55), 515s(3.53),553(4.35), 593(3.53)	44-4296-80
$C_{56}H_{54}N_4O_{12}$ 21H,23H-Porphine, 5,10,15,20-tetrakis- (3,4,5-trimethoxyphenyl)-	CHCl₃	407s(4.61),424(5.70), 517(4.33),554(3.92), 590(3.79),648(3.63)	44-4296-80
$C_{56}H_{57}BrMnN_8$ Manganese(1+), bromo[1-hexadecyl-4-(10- 15,20-tri-4-pyridinyl-21H,23H-porph- in-5-yl)pyridiniumato(2-)-N^{21},N^{22}- N^{23},N^{24}]-, (SP-5-13)-, perchlorate	MeOH	463(5.07),560(4.07), 590s(3.77),682(3.07), 773(3.07)	118-0537-80
$C_{56}H_{57}CuN_8$ Copper(1+), [1-hexadecyl-4-(10,15,20- tri-4-pyridinyl-21H,23H-porphin-5- yl)pyridiniumato(2-)-N^{21},N^{22},N^{23}- N^{24}]-, (SP-4-2)-, perchlorate	MeOH	414(5.37),543(4.23), 584(3.54)	118-0537-80
$C_{56}H_{57}N_8Zn$ Zinc(1+), [1-hexadecyl-4-(10,15,20-tri- 4-pyridinyl-21H,23H-porphin-5-yl)- pyridiniumato(2-)-$N^{21},N^{22},N^{23},N^{24}$]-, (SP-4-2)-, perchlorate	MeOH	423(5.37),559(4.26), 606(3.79)	118-0537-80
$C_{56}H_{59}N_8$ Pyridinium, 1-hexadecyl-4-(10,15,20- tri-4-pyridinyl-21H,23H-porphin-5- yl)-, bromide	MeOH	415(5.37),512(4.24), 548(3.81),591(3.76), 645(3.34)	118-0537-80
	EtOH-DMF	417(5.43),512(4.26), 548(3.80),588(3.77), 644(3.38)	118-0537-80

Compound	Solvent	λ_{max}(log ϵ)	Ref.
$C_{56}H_{82}$ 3,3'-Biergosta-3,5,7,22-tetraene, (22E)-(22'E)-	heptane	377(4.73),400(4.98), 426(4.98)	94-1747-80
$C_{56}H_{82}O_{17}$ Olean-12-ene-3,16,22,23,28-pentol, 21-[[2-O-acetyl-6-deoxy-3,4-bis-O-(2-methyl-1-oxo-2-butenyl)-β-D-galactopyranosyl]oxy]-, 3,22,23,28-tetraacetate	MeOH	215(4.26)	102-0615-80
Olean-12-ene-3,16,22,23,28-pentol, 21-[[2-O-acetyl-6-deoxy-3,4-bis-O-(2-methyl-1-oxo-2-butenyl)-β-D-glucopyranosyl]oxy]-, 3,22,23,28-tetraacetate	MeOH	216(4.26)	102-0615-80
$C_{56}H_{86}O_{17}$ Olean-12-ene-3,16,22,23,28-pentol, 21-[[2-O-acetyl-6-deoxy-3,4-bis-O-(2-methyl-1-oxobutyl)-β-D-glucopyranosyl]oxy]-, 3,16,23,28-tetraacetate, (3β,4β,16α,21β,22α)-	MeOH	198(3.98)	102-0615-80
$C_{57}H_{80}N_4O_{18}Pd$ 5,6-Secopalladibyrinic acid, acetylacetonato-5,6-dioxo-, heptamethyl ester	MeOH	273(4.08),347(3.73), 392(3.92)	5-0821-80
$C_{58}H_{44}N_4O_{17}$ 2,4,7(1H,3H,8H)-Pteridinetrione, 1,3-bis(2,3,5-tri-O-benzoyl-β-D-ribofuranosyl)-	MeOH	229(4.94),275(4.27), 281(4.27),325(4.26), 338s(4.12)	24-1524-80
$C_{58}H_{61}BrO_7$ Phenol, 2-[[2-[[2-[(3-bromo-2-hydroxy-5-methylphenyl)methyl]-2-hydroxy-5-methylphenyl]methyl]-2-hydroxy-5-methylphenyl]methyl]-6-[[3-[[3-[[5-(1,1-dimethylethyl)-2-hydroxyphenyl]-methyl]-2-hydroxy-5-methylphenyl]-methyl]-2-hydroxy-5-methylphenyl]-methyl]-4-methyl-	dioxan	280s(4.29),287(4.32)	126-2049-80
$C_{58}H_{83}BrO_{26}$ Olivomycin A, 5(or 7)-bromo-	MeOH	230(4.36),279(5.60), 340s(--),415(4.05)	87-0376-80
$C_{58}H_{83}NO_{28}$ Olivomycin A, 5(or 7)-nitro-	MeOH	223s(--),273(4.32), 402(3.80)	87-0376-80
$C_{58}H_{84}O_{18}$ Olean-12-ene-3,16,22,23,28-pentol, 21-[[2-O-acetyl-6-deoxy-3,4-bis(2-methyl-1-oxo-2-butenyl)-β-D-glucopyranosyl]oxy]-, pentaacetate, [3β,4β,16α,21β[3(Z),4(Z)]22α]-	MeOH	215(4.31)	102-0615-80
$C_{58}H_{86}O_{25}$ Olivomycin A, 1-deoxy-	MeOH	239(4.56),278(4.19), 342s(--),415(3.77)	87-0376-80

Compound	Solvent	$\lambda_{max}(\log \epsilon)$	Ref.
$C_{58}H_{86}O_{26}$			
Olivomycin A, 2'-dihydro-	MeOH	238(4.40),278(4.47), 316(3.77),335s(--), 413(3.83)	87-0376-80
$C_{59}H_{46}N_4O_{17}$			
2,4(1H,3H)-Pteridinedione, 6-methyl-1-(2,3,5-tri-O-benzoyl-β-D-ribofuranosyl)-7-[(2,3,5-tri-O-benzoyl-β-D-ribofuranosyl)oxy]-	MeOH	230(4.90),262s(4.12), 282(3.82),322(4.09)	24-1535-80
2,4,7(1H,3H,8H)-Pteridinetrione, 6-methyl-1,3-bis(2,3,5-tri-O-benzoyl-β-D-ribofuranosyl)-	MeOH	229(4.91),275s(4.20), 281(4.21),326(4.26), 338s(4.12)	24-1524-80
2(1H)-Pteridinone, 4-methoxy-1-(2,3,5-tri-O-benzoyl-β-D-ribofuranosyl)-7-[(2,3,5-tri-O-benzoyl-β-D-ribofuranosyl)oxy]-	MeOH	228(4.93),265s(4.01), 280s(3.91),327(4.19), 340s(4.12)	24-1535-80
$C_{59}H_{62}O_{17}$			
Octacyclo[37.3.1.1^{3,7}.1^{9,13}.1^{15,19}-1^{21,25}.1^{27,31}.1^{33,37}]nonatetraconta-1(43),3,5,7(49),9,11,13(48),15,17-19(47),21,23,25(46),27,29,31(45)-33,35,37(44)-39,41-heneicosaene-43-44,45,46,47,48,49-heptol, 5-(1,1-dimethylethyl)-11,17,28,29,33,41-hexamethyl-	dioxan	281s(4.30),288(4.32)	126-2049-80
$C_{59}H_{63}BrO_8$			
Benzenemethanol, 3-[[3-[[3-[[3-[[3-[[3-[(3-bromo-2-hydroxy-5-methylphenyl)-methyl]-2-hydroxy-5-methylphenyl]-methyl]-2-hydroxy-5-methylphenyl]-methyl]-2-hydroxy-5-methylphenyl]-methyl]-2-hydroxy-5-methylphenyl]-methyl]-2-hydroxy-5-methylphenyl]-methyl]-5-(1,1-dimethylethyl)-2-hydroxy-	dioxan	280s(4.30),287(4.31)	126-2049-80
$C_{59}H_{64}O_7$			
Phenol, 2-[[3-[[3-[[3-[[5-(1,1-dimethylethyl)-2-hydroxy-3-methylphenyl]-methyl]-2-hydroxy-3-methylphenyl]-methyl]-2-hydroxy-3-methylphenyl]-methyl]-6-[2-hydroxy-3-[[2-hydroxy-3-[(2-hydroxy-5-methylphenyl)methyl]-5-methylphenyl]methyl]-5-methylphenyl]methyl]-4-methyl-	dioxan	280s(4.29),287(4.32)	126-2049-80
$C_{59}H_{86}O_{26}$			
Olivomycin A, 8-O-methyl-	MeOH	224(3.94),278(4.31), 315s(--),410(3.71)	87-0376-80
$C_{59}H_{95}ClCoN_5O_4$			
Cobalt, chlorobis[[(5α)-cholestane-2,3-dionedioximato](1-)-N,N'](pyridine)-	CHCl$_3$	235(4.29)	24-0650-80
$C_{60}H_{72}O_{10}$			
β,β-Carotene-4,4'-dione, 7,7',8,8'-tetradehydro-3,3'-[bis[[(4,7,7-trimethyl-3-oxo-2-oxabicyclo[2.2.1]-	benzene	325(4.29),464s(4.97), 492(5.09),522(5.00)	33-1473-80

Compound	Solvent	$\lambda_{max}(\log \epsilon)$	Ref.
hept-1-yl)carbonyl]oxy]-, [3S(1S,4R)-3'S(1S,4R)]- (cont.)			33-1473-80
$C_{60}H_{84}O_4$			
2,5-Cyclohexadien-1-one, 4,4'-[1,4-bis-[3,5-bis(1,1-dimethylethyl)-4-hydroxyphenyl]but-2-ene-1,4-diylidene]-bis(1,1-dimethylethyl)-	C_6H_{12}	280(4.15),440(4.57), 458(4.89),502(5.02)	12-0351-80
$C_{60}H_{86}O_4$			
Spiro[2,5-cyclohexadiene-1,1'-[1H]indene]-4,4'(2'H)-dione, 7'-[1-[3,5-bis(1,1-dimethylethyl)-4-hydroxyphenyl]ethylidene]-2'-[3,5-bis(1,1-dimethylethyl)-4-oxo-2,5-cyclohexadien-1-ylidene]-3,3'a,5,5'-tetrakis(1,1-dimethylethyl)-3',3'a,7',7'a-tetrahydro-	C_6H_{12}	241(4.11),330(4.65)	12-0351-80
Spiro[2,5-cyclohexadiene-1,1'-[1H]indene]-4,4'(3'aH)-dione, 2'-[3,5-bis-(1,1-dimethylethyl)-4-hydroxyphenyl]-7'-[1-[3,5-bis(1,1-dimethylethyl)-4-hydroxyphenyl]ethylidene]-3,3'a,5,5'-tetrakis(1,1-dimethylethyl)-7,7'a-dihydro-	C_6H_{12}	258(4.23),327(4.51)	12-0351-80
$C_{60}H_{88}O_4$			
Spiro[2,5-cyclohexadiene-1,1'-[1H]indene]-4,4'(2'H)-dione, 2'-[3,5-bis-(1,1-dimethylethyl)-4-hydroxyphenyl]-7'-[1-[3,5-bis(1,1-dimethylethyl)-4-hydroxyphenyl]ethylidene]-3,3'a,5,5'-tetrakis(1,1-dimethylethyl)-3',3'a,7',7'a-tetrahydro-	C_6H_{12}	233(4.24),283(3.98), 320(4.00)	12-0351-80
$C_{60}H_{96}O_{24}$			
Trillenoside A permethyl ether	EtOH	247.4(3.86)	94-1437-80
$C_{60}H_{98}CoN_5O_4$			
Cobalt, bis[[(5α)-cholestane-2,3-dione dioximato](1-)-N,N']methyl(pyridine)-	EtOH	225(4.09),455(2.93)	24-0650-80
$C_{60}H_{104}N_2O_2S$			
Cholestan-3-ol, [[[(3β,5α)-cholestan-3-yl]oxy](ethylimino)methyl]ethylcarbamothioate, (3β,5α)-	dioxan	252(4.15)	39-0665-80C
$C_{61}H_{80}O_{10}$			
3H,7H-Pyrano[2',3':7,8][1]benzopyrano-[3,2-d][1]benzoxepin-7-one, 8,9-dihydro-6-hydroxy-3,3-dimethyl-9-[1-methyl-1-[[1,3,5-tris(1,1-dimethylethyl)-4-oxo-2,5-cyclohexadien-1-yl]dioxy]ethyl]-12-[[1,3,5-tris(1,1-dimethylethyl)-4-oxo-2,5-cyclohexadien-1-yl]oxy]-	MeOH MeOH-NaOMe MeOH-AlCl₃	206(4.77),238(4.69), 280(4.59),334(4.07) 237(4.69),284(4.50), 380s(3.90) 233(4.77),284(4.83), 358(4.61),420(4.07)	4-0641-80 4-0641-80 4-0641-80
$C_{62}H_{57}N_5O_9Ru$			
Ruthenium, carbonyl[4-(1,1-dimethylethyl)pyridine][5,10,15,20-tetrakis(3,5-	CHCl₃	415(5.45),533(4.34), 570(3.50)	44-4296-80

Compound	Solvent	$\lambda_{max}(\log \epsilon)$	Ref.
dimethoxyphenyl)-21H,23H-porphinato-(2-)-N^{21},N^{22},N^{23},N^{24}]-, (OC-6-14)-			44-4296-80
$C_{62}H_{80}N_{12}O_{16}$ Actinomycin D	MeOH	240(4.54),443(4.40)	4-1815-80
$C_{63}H_{45}O_9Os_3P_3$ Osmium, nonacarbonyltris(triphenylphosphine)tri-, triangulo-	toluene	347(3.97),422(3.86)	35-3022-80
$C_{63}H_{57}Cl_2N_{13}O_{19}P_2$ Guanosine, N-benzoyl-3'-0-[(4-chlorophenoxy)(phenylamino)phosphinyl]-P-(4-chlorophenyl)-2'-0-[(2-nitrophenyl)methyl]adenylyl-(5'→3')-N-(2-methyl-1-oxopropyl)-2'-0-[(2-nitrophenyl)methyl]-	EtOH	261.5(4.58),278(4.58)	94-0120-80
$C_{63}H_{88}CoN_{14}O_{14}P$ Vitamin B_{12}	H_2O	278(4.19),361(4.45), 551(3.94)	64-1335-80B
	KCN–pH 11	278(4.15),368(4.48), 543(3.93),584(3.99)	64-1335-80B
Vitamin B_{12r}	H_2O	310(4.45),405(3.89), 473(3.98)	35-1684-80
	M HCl	314(4.38),468(4.07)	35-1684-80
$C_{63}H_{91}CoN_{13}O_{14}P$ Methylcobalamine	pH 1	264(4.39),304(4.36), 375s(3.96),462(3.98)	22-0192-80
	pH 7	266(4.30),342(4.16), 375s(4.07),522(3.97)	22-0192-80
$C_{63}H_{92}CoFN_{13}O_{16}P_2$ Cobinamide-Co(II), hydroxide, monomethyl phosphorofluoridite, dihydrogen phosphate, inner salt, 3'-ester with 5,6-dimethyl-1-α-D-ribofuranosyl-1H-benzimidazole	H_2O	278(4.22),364(4.40), 548(3.93)	64-1335-80B
	KCN–pH 11	278(4.19),374(4.40), 555(3.91),595(3.94)	64-1335-80B
$C_{64}H_{48}N_4O_{17}$ 2,4,7(1H,3H,8H)-Pteridinetrione, 6-phenyl-1,3-bis(2,3,5-tri-0-benzoyl-β-D-ribofuranosyl)-	MeOH	229(5.00),276s(4.16), 282(4.22),296(4.23), 349(4.32)	24-1524-80
$C_{64}H_{62}N_4O_8$ Benzoic acid, 4,4',4",4"'-(21H,23H-porphine-5,10,15,20-tetrayl)tetrakis-, monohexadecyl ester	MeOH	416(5.65),513(4.26), 551(3.93),591(3.69), 646(3.55)	118-0537-80
	EtOH–DMF	418(5.57),513(4.18), 549(3.90),591(3.65), 648(3.60)	118-0537-80
$C_{64}H_{86}N_8O_8$ 21H,23H-Porphine-2,18-dipropanoic acid, 7,12-bis(1-acetoxyethyl)-3,8,13,17-tetramethyl-, dianhydride with N,N'-dicyclohexylcarbamimidic acid	$CHCl_3$	402(5.31),499(4.16), 534(3.95),569(3.82), 622(3.61)	12-0585-80

Compound	Solvent	λ_{max}(log ϵ)	Ref.
$C_{64}H_{95}CoN_{13}O_{17}P_2$ Dimethylphosphito-P-cobalamine	H_2O	278(4.27),364(4.32), 543(3.93)	64-1335-80B
	KCN–pH 11	278(4.26),374(4.28), 555(3.89),595(3.77)	64-1335-80B
$C_{64}H_{114}O_2Te$ Cholestane, 3,3'-tellurobis[(2,2-di- methylpropylidene)oxy]]bis-, (3β,5α)-(3'β,5'α)-	C_6H_{12}	263(3.89),302s(3.51), 358s(3.08)	39-2191-80C
$C_{65}H_{50}N_4O_{17}$ 2(1H)-Pteridinone, 4-(phenylmethoxy)- 1-(2,3,5-tri-O-benzoyl-β-D-ribo- furanosyl)-7-[(2,3,5-tri-O-benzoyl- β-D-ribofuranosyl)oxy]-	MeOH	229(4.97),280s(3.94), 330(4.26),342s(4.20)	24-1535-80
$C_{65}H_{57}ClN_{12}O_{18}P_2$ Adenosine, N-benzoyl-P-(4-chlorophen- yl)-2'-O-[(2-nitrophenyl)methyl]cy- tidylyl-(3'→5')-N-benzoyl-2'-O-[(2- nitrophenyl)methyl]-, 3'-(N,N-diphen- ylphosphorodiamidate)	EtOH	263.5(4.67)	94-0120-80
$C_{66}H_{52}N_4O_{17}$ 2(1H)-Pteridinone, 6-methyl-4-(phenyl- methoxy)-1-(2,3,5-tri-O-benzoyl-β-D- ribofuranosyl)-7-[(2,3,5-tri-O-benz- oyl-β-D-ribofuranosyl)oxy]-	MeOH	229(4.87),281s(3.80), 333(4.13),346s(4.04)	24-1535-80
$C_{66}H_{65}N_5O_{13}Ru$ Ruthenium, carbonyl[4-(1,1-dimethyleth- yl)pyridine][5,10,15,20-tetrakis- (3,4,5-trimethoxyphenyl)-21H,23H- porphinato(2-)-N^{21},N^{22},N^{23},N^{24}]-, (OC-6-14)-	$CHCl_3$	417(5.44),534(4.34), 568(3.68)	44-4296-80
$C_{66}H_{86}N_8O_{20}$ Riboflavin, 8,8"-(1,2-ethanediyl)bis- [8-demethyl-, 2',2"',3',3"',4',4"'- 5',5"'-octakis(2-methylpropanoate)	HCOOH	280s(4.56),262(4.81), 484s(4.75),500(4.78)	35-7157-80
isomer	HCOOH	274s(4.26),252(4.45), 372(3.74),444(3.83)	35-7157-80
$C_{66}H_{106}CoN_5O_8$ Cobalt, bis[[(5α)-cholestane-2,3-dione dioximato](1-)-N,N'][3-methoxy- 2-(methoxycarbonyl)-2-methyl-3- oxopropyl](pyridine)-	ether	250(4.32),445(2.70)	24-0650-80
$C_{68}H_{50}OSi_2$ Silacyclopenta-2,4-diene, 1,1'-oxybis- [1,2,3,4,5-pentaphenyl-	dioxan	383(4.23)	61-1122-80
$C_{68}H_{50}Si_2$ Bisilacyclopenta-2,4-dien-1-yl, 1,1',2,2',3,3',4,4',5,5'-decaphenyl-	dioxan	360(4.18)	61-1122-80
$C_{68}H_{70}N_8O_6$ 3-Phorbinepropanoic acid, 9-ethenyl-	acetone	409(5.08),505(4.08),	44-1969-80

Compound	Solvent	$\lambda_{max}(\log \epsilon)$	Ref.
14-ethyl-4,8,13,18-tetramethyl-20-oxo-, 1,2-ethanediyl ester, [3S-[3α(3'R*,4'R*),4β]]- (cont.)		534(3.98),611(3.90), 667(4.74)	44-1969-80
$C_{68}H_{84}CuN_{12}O_4$ Copper, [N,N,N',N',N'',N'',N''',N'''-octabutyl-29H,31H-phthalocyanine-2,9,16,23-tetracarboxamidato(2-)-N^{29},N^{30},N^{31},N^{32}]-, (SP-4-1)-	C_6H_5Cl	340(4.74),608(4.53), 644(4.49),678(5.28)	65-0907-80
$C_{69}H_{78}ClFeN_{10}O_9$ Iron, chloro[methyl N^2-[N-N-[3-(7,12-diethenyl)-18-(3-methoxy-3-oxopropyl)-3,8,13,17-tetramethyl-21H,23H-porphin-2-yl]-1-oxopropyl]-L-leucyl-1-(phenylmethyl)-L-histidyl]-N^6-[(phenylmethoxy)carbonyl]-L-lysinato(2-)]-, (OC-6-24)-	$CHCl_3$	390(4.95),511(4.45), 540(4.43),640(4.18)	65-0552-80
$C_{72}H_{70}N_8O_{12}$ 3-Phorbinepropanoic acid, 9-ethenyl-14-ethyl-13-formyl-21-(methoxycarbonyl)-4,8,18-trimethyl-20-oxo-, 1,2-ethanediyl ester, [3S-[3α(3'R*,4'R*-21'S*),4β,21β]]-	acetone	439(5.19),530(4.09), 551(3.97),602(3.97), 654(4.60)	44-1969-80
$C_{72}H_{74}N_8O_{10}$ 3-Phorbinepropanoic acid, 9-ethenyl-14-ethyl-21-(methoxycarbonyl)-4,8,13,18-tetramethyl-20-oxo-, 1,2-ethanediyl ester, [3S-[3α(3'R*,4'R*-21'S*),4β,21β]]-	acetone	409(5.08),505(4.08), 533(3.98),610(3.90), 668(4.74)	44-1969-80
$C_{72}H_{78}N_8O_{12}$ 3-Phorbinepropanoic acid, 9-acetyl-14-ethyl-13,14-dihydro-21-(methoxycarbonyl)-4,8,13,18-tetramethyl-20-oxo-, 1,2-ethanediyl ester, [3S-[3α(3'R*,4'R*,13'S*,14'S*,21R*),4β,13β,14α-21β]]-	acetone	355(4.91),384(4.65), 494s(3.59),522(4.29), 675(3.84),750(4.69)	44-1969-80
$C_{72}H_{86}N_8Ni_2O$ Nickel, [μ-[5,10,15,20-tetramethyl-12-(or 13)-[1-(5,10,15,20-tetramethyl-21H,23H-porphin-2-yl)dodecyl]-α-undecyl-21H,23H-porphine-2-methanolato(4-)-N^{21},N^{22},N^{23},N^{24}:$N^{21'}$,$N^{22'}$-$N^{23'}$,$N^{24'}$]]di-	$CHCl_3$	303(4.41),332(4.36), 421(5.41),545(4.38)	5-1082-80
$C_{72}H_{88}CuN_{16}O_8$ Copper, [N,N,N',N',N'',N'',N''',N''',N''''-N'''',N''''',N''''',N'''''',N'''''',N''''''',N'''''''-N'''''''',N''''''''-hexadecylethyl-29H,31H-phthalocyanine-2,3,9,10,16,17,23,24-octacarboxamidato(2-)-N^{29},N^{30},N^{31}-N^{32}]-, (SP-4-1)-	EtOH C_6H_5Cl	344(4.90),604(4.66), 640(4.62),671(5.41) 346(4.87),612(4.61), 645(4.54),681(5.35)	65-0907-80 65-0907-80
$C_{72}H_{92}N_8$ Pyridinium, 4,4'-(15,20-di-4-pyridinyl-21H,23H-porphine-5,10-diyl)bis[1-hexadecyl-, dibromide	EtOH-DMF	421(5.38),514(4.20), 551(3.84),589(3.76), 646(3.32)	118-0537-80

Compound	Solvent	$\lambda_{max}(\log \epsilon)$	Ref.
$C_{74}H_{60}N_{12}Ni_3$ Nickel, $[\mu_3-[5,10,15,20$-tetramethyl-2,12-bis[(5,10,15,20-tetramethyl-21H,23H-porphin-2-yl)methyl]-21H,23H-porphinato(6-)-$N^{21},N^{22},N^{23},N^{24}$:$N^{21'}$-$N^{22'},N^{23'},N^{24'}$]]tri-	$CHCl_3$	302(4.49),335(4.49), 422(5.55),430s(5.54), 547(4.63)	5-1082-80
$C_{74}H_{98}N_8$ 21H,23H-Porphine, 5,5'-(1,2-ethanediyl)bis[2,3,7,8,12,13,17,18-octaethyl-2,3-dihydro-	CH_2Cl_2	386(5.28),401(5.48), 499(4.48),525(3.68), 549(3.46),594(4.00), 644(4.93),652(4.73)	130-0001-80
$C_{76}H_{84}FeN_4O_{20}$ Iron, [5,10,15,20-tetrakis(2,3,5,6,8-9,11,12-octahydro-1,4,7,10,13-benzo-pentaoxacyclopentadecin-15-yl)-21H,23H-porphinato(2-)-N^{21},N^{22}-N^{23},N^{24}]-, (SP-4-1)-	$CHCl_3$	422(4.90),512(4.12), 652(3.59),693(3.60)	142-0675-80B
$C_{76}H_{92}ClGaN_4O_4$ Gallium, chloro[4,4',4'',4'''-(21H,23H-porphine-5,10,15,20-tetrayl)tetrakis[2,6-bis(1,1-dimethylethyl)phen-olato]](2-)-$N^{21},N^{22},N^{23},N^{24}$]-, (SP-5-12)-	$CHCl_3$	410s(4.55),430(5.66), 521s(3.55),556(4.26), 598(4.02)	44-4296-80
$C_{76}H_{92}N_4O_5Ti$ Titanium, oxo[[4,4',4'',4'''-(21H,23H-porphine-5,10,15,20-tetrayl)tetrakis[2,6-bis(1,1-dimethylethyl)phen-olato]](2-)-$N^{21},N^{22},N^{23},N^{24}$]-, (SP-5-12)-	$CHCl_3$	434(5.63),520s(3.63), 558(4.35),598(4.08)	44-4296-80
$C_{76}H_{94}N_4O_4$ Phenol, 4,4',4'',4'''-(21H,23H-porphine-5,10,15,20-tetrayl)tetrakis[2,6-bis(1,1-dimethylethyl)-	$CHCl_3$	409s(4.87),426(5.69), 523(4.22),561(4.17), 595(3.74),653(3.94)	44-4296-80
$C_{78}H_{114}CoN_5O_8$ Cobalt, bis[[(5α)-cholestane-2,3-dione dioximato](1-)-N,N'][2-methyl-3-oxo-3-(phenylmethoxy)-2-[(phenylmethoxy)-carbonyl]propyl](pyridine)-	$CHCl_3$	245(4.18),445(2.30)	24-0650-80
$C_{80}H_{100}ClGaN_4O_4$ Gallium, chloro[5,10,15,20-tetrakis-[3,5-bis(1,1-dimethylethyl)-4-meth-oxyphenyl]-21H,23H-porphinato(2-)-$N^{21},N^{22},N^{23},N^{24}$]-, (SP-5-12)-	$CHCl_3$	427(5.69),516s(3.44), 555(4.24),595(3.86)	44-4296-80
$C_{80}H_{100}N_4O_5Ti$ Titanium, oxo[5,10,15,20-tetrakis[3,5-bis(1,1-dimethylethyl)-4-methoxyphen-yl]-21H,23H-porphinato(2-)-$N^{21},N^{22},N^{23},N^{24}$]-, (SP-5-12)-	$CHCl_3$	407s(4.66),430(5.69), 519s(3.59),556(4.39), 595(3.97)	44-4296-80
$C_{80}H_{102}N_4O_4$ 21H,23H-Porphine, 5,10,15,20-tetrakis-[3,5-bis(1,1-dimethylethyl)-4-meth-	$CHCl_3$	406(4.95),424(5.77), 492s(3.70),521(4.30),	44-4296-80

Compound	Solvent	λ_{max}(log ϵ)	Ref.
oxyphenyl]- (cont.)		559(4.15),595(3.78), 651(3.92)	44-4296-80
$C_{83}H_{74}N_{16}O_{18}P_2$ 3'-Adenylic acid, N-benzoyl-P-(2-cyanoethyl)-2'-deoxy-5'-O-[(4-methoxyphenyl)diphenylmethyl]adenylyl-(3'→5')-N-benzoyl-2'-deoxy-, 5'-ester with 1-(2-deoxy-α-D-erythro-pentofuranosyl)-6,7-diphenyl-2,4(1H,3H)-pteridinedione	MeOH	228s(4.80),276(4.75), 358(4.11)	5-0065-80
β-	MeOH	225s(4.85),279(4.72), 361(4.11)	5-0065-80
$C_{85}H_{66}N_4O_{24}$ 2,4(1H,3H)-Pteridinedione, 6-methyl-1,3-bis(2,3,5-tri-O-benzoyl-β-D-ribofuranosyl)-7-[(2,3,5-tri-O-benzoyl-β-D-ribofuranosyl)oxy]-	MeOH	230(5.08),262s(4.17), 281(3.97),323(4.13)	24-1535-80
$C_{86}H_{118}CoN_5O_8$ Cobalt, [bis[[(5α)-cholestane-2,3-dione dioximato](1-)-N,N'][2-methyl-3-(2-naphthalenylmethoxy)-2-[(2-naphthalenylmethoxy)carbonyl]-3-oxopropyl]-(pyridine)-	EtOH	230(4.12),460(2.93)	24-0650-80
$C_{86}H_{118}N_5O_8Rh$ Rhodium, bis[[(5α)-cholestane-2,3-dione dioximato](1-)-N,N'][2-methyl-3-(2-naphthalenylmethoxy)-2-[(2-naphthalenylmethoxy)carbonyl]-3-oxopropyl]-(pyridine)-	EtOH	230(4.20),455(2.93)	24-0650-80
$C_{88}H_{125}N_8$ Pyridinium, 4,4',4"-[20-(4-pyridinyl)-21H,23H-porphine-5,10,15-triyl]tris-[1-hexadecyl-, tribromide	EtOH-DMF (1:1)	424(5.36),516(4.20), 553(3.85),590(3.78), 647(3.28)	118-0537-80
$C_{90}H_{113}N_5O_5Ru$ Ruthenium, carbonyl[4-(1,1-dimethylethyl)pyridine][5,10,15,20-tetrakis[3,5-bis(1,1-dimethylethyl)-4-methoxyphenyl]-21H,23H-porphinato(2-)-$N^{21},N^{22},N^{23},N^{24}$]-, (OC-6-14)-	CHCl₃	418(5.41),536(4.31), 574(3.88)	44-4296-80
$C_{94}H_{81}Cl_2N_{16}O_{28}P_3$ Adenosine, N-benzoyl-P-(4-chlorophenyl)-2'-O-[(2-nitrophenyl)methyl]cytidylyl-(3'→5')-N-benzoyl-P-(4-chlorophenyl)-2'-O-[(2-nitrophenyl)methyl]cytidylyl-(3'→5')-N-benzoyl-2'-O-[(2-nitrophenyl)methyl]-, 3'-(N,N'-diphenylphosphorodiamidate)	EtOH	263(4.88)	94-0120-80
$C_{104}H_{152}CuN_{16}O_8$ Copper, [N,N,N',N',N",N",N''',N''',N''''-N'''',N''''',N''''',N'''''',N'''''',N''''''',N'''''''-N'''''''',N''''''''-hexadecabutyl-29H,31H-phthalocyanine-2,3,9,10,16,17,23,24-	EtOH	347(4.94),605(4.63), 642(4.66),671(5.41)	65-0907-80

Compound	Solvent	$\lambda_{max}(\log \epsilon)$	Ref.
octacarboxamidato(2-)-N^{29},N^{30},N^{31}-N^{32}]-, (SP-4-1)- (cont.)			65-0907-80
$C_{104}H_{158}N_8$ Pyridinium, 4,4',4",4'''-(21H,23H-porphine-5,10,15,20-tetrayl)tetrakis[1-hexadecyl-, tetrabromide	MeOH	426(5.35),517(4.29), 557(4.06),593(3.99), 647(3.65)	118-0537-80
	EtOH-DMF (1:1)	425(5.36),516(4.23), 553(3.87),590(3.82), 646(3.26)	118-0537-80
$C_{112}H_{97}Cl_3N_{17}O_{30}P_3$ Adenosine, N-benzoyl-P-(4-chlorophenyl)-5'-O-[(4-methoxyphenyl)diphenylmethyl]-2'-O-[(2-nitrophenyl)methyl]-cytidylyl-(3'→5')-P-(4-chlorophenyl)-N-(2-methyl-1-oxopropyl)-2'-O-[(2-nitrophenyl)methyl]guanylyl-(3'→5')-N-benzoyl-2'-O-[(2-nitrophenyl)methyl]-, 3'-(4-chlorophenyl)phenylphosphoramidate	EtOH	262.5(4.84)	94-0120-80
$C_{115}H_{95}Cl_3N_{17}O_{29}P_3$ Adenosine, N-benzoyl-P-(4-chlorophenyl)-5'-O-[(4-methoxyphenyl)diphenylmethyl]-2'-O-[(2-nitrophenyl)methyl]-cytidylyl-(3'→5')-N-benzoyl-P-(4-chlorophenyl)-2'-O-[(2-nitrophenyl)methyl]adenylyl-(3'→5')-N-benzoyl-2'-O-[(2-nitrophenyl)methyl]-, 3'-(4-chlorophenyl)phenylphosphoramidate	EtOH	274(4.86)	94-0120-80

1-   -80, Acta Chem. Scand. B, 34 (1980)
0031   O. Buchardt et al.
0079   E.K. Pohjala
0119   A.-T. Hansson and M. Nilsson
0177   J. Bergman and B. Egestad
0289   A.S. Berg and P. Kolsaker
0295   K. Skinnemoen and K. Undheim
0391   I. Wallin et al.
0513   L. Finsen et al.
0529   D. Tanner and O. Wennerstrom
0597   A.A. El-Barbary et al.
0619   G.A. Ulsaker et al.
0637   K.E. Nielsen and E.B. Pedersen

1-   -80A, Acta Chem. Scand. A, 34 (1980)
0301   S. Wingefors
0469   H.P. Jensen

2-   -80, Indian J. Chem. B, 19 (1980)
0009   B.H. Bhide and K.K. Shah
0013   R.B. Gupta and R.N. Khanna
0017   R.B. Gupta and R.N. Khanna
0037   A. Singh et al.
0042   S.K. Agarwal et al.
0045   S.K. Agarwal et al.
0085   B.R. Sharma and P. Sharma
0093   P.S. Kalsi et al.
0097   G.S.R. Rao et al.
0101   A.C. Jain et al.
0146   M.S.A. Abd-El-Mottaleb
0156   H.H. Moussa and B. Haggag
0160   G.D. Pandey and K.P. Tiwari
0165   A. Dasgupta et al.
0240   C.B. Rao and E.K.S. Vijayakumar
0241   K.P. Tiwari et al.
0266   M.N. Basyouni et al.
0279   R.S. Chandel and R.P. Rastogi
0315   A. Goswami and H.N. Khastgir
0331   P.S. Subramanian and A.J. Laksh-
        manan
0341   J. Banerji et al.
0364   G.H. Sayed
0421   A. Chatterjee et al.
0429   M.R. Parthasarathy et al.
0433   T.R. Kasturi et al.
0463   W.M. Bandaranayake et al.
0492   A.C. Dash et al.
0495   B.S. Joshi et al.
0510   K.G. Pai and S.V. Sunthankar
0512   J. Roy and A.P. Bhaduri
0546   S.K. Talapatra et al.
0552   Y.A. Naik and A.B. Kulkarni
0556   N.S. Narasimhan et al.
0561   A. Patra et al.
0578   P.A. Reddy and G.S. Krishna Rao
0583   D. Roy and R.N. Khanna
0601   H.S. Prakash Rao and S.N. Balasubra-
        manyam
0615B   K.A. Kumar and G. Srimammarayana
0627   A.V. Rama Rao et al.
0638   P.B. Talukdar et al.
0676   R.J. Turel et al.
0753   P.A. Reddy and G.S. Krishna Rao
0815   W.M. Tadros et al.
0820   L.B. de Silva et al.
0836   N.R. Ayyangar et al.

0859   I.N. Kostova et al.
0866   K.V. Subba Raju et al.
0904   P.L. Kamat and A.M. Shaligram
0927   B. Talapatra et al.
0929   S.P. Dhoubhadel et al.
0944   A.S.R. Anjaneyulu and M.N. Rao
0955   A. Chatterjee et al.
0975   N. Latif and S.A. Meguid
0980   G.H. Sayed and H. Kjøsen
1008   A.K. Sen et al.
1028   S. Jeganathan and M. Srinivasan
1046   A.V. Rama Rao et al.
1078   N.K. Kapoor et al.

2-   -80A, Indian J. Chem. Section A, 19
        (1980)
0144   M.R. Mahmoud et al.
0789   M.A. Khattab and F.A. Amer

3-   -80, Anal. Chem., 52 (1980)
1668   H. Nakamura et al.
1851   T.J. Novak et al.

4-   -80, J. Heterocyclic Chem., 17 (1980)
0001   Y. Tamura et al.
0017   S.K. Sengupta and S.K. Tinter
0033   A. Bargagna et al.
0045   C. Barnascon et al.
0061   L. Mosti, P. Schenone and G.
        Menozzi
0113   M.T. Garcia Lopez et al.
0121   C. Brunelli et al.
0149   C.O. Okafor
0159   R.B. Meyer, Jr. et al.
0175   M. Balogh et al.
0181   I. Antonini et al.
0187   O. Subba Rao and W. Lwowski
0213   M.M. El-Abadelah et al.
0219   B.F. Powell et al.
0231   T. Kurihara, T. Uno and Y. Saka-
        moto
0249   A.M. Vega et al.
0277   G. Bobowski and J. Shavel, Jr.
0289   K. Ichikawa, S. Inoue and K. Sato
0299   G. Zvilichovsky et al.
0321   P. Meunier and J. Arrian
0353   Y.F. Shelay and C.A. O'Dell
0359   M. Balogh et al.
0373   W. Milkowski et al.
0393   H.J. Dou et al.
0403   H. Takahata et al.
0417   K. Orito et al.
0461   D.L. Kern, P.D. Cook and J.C.
        French
0481   K.M. Smith et al.
0507   A. Bargagna et al.
0519   G. Bobowski and J. Shavel, Jr.
0529   O. Migliara, S. Petruso and V.
        Sprio
0541   I. El-Sayed et al.
0575   J.B. Hester, Jr.
0583   J.A. Montgomery and H.J. Thomas
0589   G.F. Reynolds and M.B. Fenwick
0595   J.T. Lopez
0621   P. Sarti-Fantoni et al.
0641   T. Nomura et al.

0673	J. Perronnet and L. Taliani
0679	G. Lindgren et al.
0685	V. Jagodic et al.
0695	K. Maruyama et al.
0705	J.P. Chupp and K.L. Leschinsky
0767	G. Duguay et al.
0813	G.Y. Sarkis and H.T. Al-Badri
0897	C. Parkanyi and A.S. Shawali
0945	T. Kruihara et al.
0961	J. Ploquin et al.
0989	S.R. Caldwell and G.E. Martin
0997	J. Ploquin et al.
1053	H. Fujita and J. Yamauchi
1057	K. Imafuku et al.
1081	J. Ackrell et al.
1097	J.D. Woodyard, P.R. Morris and G.D. Hobbs
1101	A. Guzman et al.
1115	W.A. Feld, P.G. Seybold and M.P. Serve
1133	V.S. Giri, E. Ali and S.C. Pakrashi
1181	H.S. El Khadem et al.
1185	H.M. Hassaneen et al.
1201	A. Bargagna et al.
1225	A. Da Settimo et al.
1231	R. Madhav et al.
1259	M. Iwao, M.L. Lee and R.N. Castle
1293	K. Imafuku et al.
1305	V.J. Ram et al.
1313	R.J. Chorvat and B.N. Desai
1349	D. Avnir and J. Blum
1521	F.H. Al-Hajjar and A.A. Jarrar
1563	G. Bobowski, J.M. Gottlieb and B. West
1577	A. Carotti et al.
1587	C.O. Okafor
1617	R.E. van der Stoel et al.
1625	E. Belgodere et al.
1629	E. Belgodere et al.
1691	R. Milcent and C. Redeuilh
1697	A. Walser and T. Flynn
1709	W.T. Ashton and R.D. Brown
1713	N.F. Eweiss and A. Osman
1723	A.C. Veronese et al.
1737	K. Rajyalakshmi and V.R. Srinivasan
1797	M. Bialer et al.
1809	A.C. Ghosh and M. Ramgopal
1815	K. Okawa et al.

5-   -80, Ann. Chem. Liebigs (1980)

0065	R. Charubula et al.
0165	R.-P. Hinze et al.
0168	G. Bartels et al.
0241	I. Mester et al.
0263	B. Franck et al.
0291	P. Carsky et al.
0403	A. Roedig and H. Gopfert
0503	S. Blechert et al.
0557	J. Engels
0564	G. Pfeiffer and H. Bauer
0779	A. Mathey et al.
0798	G. Maier and U. Schafer
0821	R.-P. Hinze et al.
0867	H. Gotthardt and S. Nieberl
0873	H. Gotthardt et al.
0886	H.P. Albrecht

0895	P. Rosenmund et al.
0908	C. Rüchardt and V. Hassmann
0954	A. Mielert et al.
0971	R. Neidlein and F. Moller
1016	H. Gnichtel et al.
1082	B. von Maltzan
1181	K. Hoffmann et al.
1207	R. Knorr et al.
1259	H. Vutz et al.
1321	H. Lautsch
1350	W.H. Gündel
1409	G. Arndt et al.
1428	R. Jösel and G. Schröder
1623	K. Gewald et al.
1630	G. Kresze and W. Dittel
1632	E.M. Sauer et al.
1699	B. Dresow et al.
1744	A. Fabrycy and Z. Wichert
1786	L. Trabert and H. Hopf
1801	G. Kollenz et al.
1814	H. Quast et al.
1836	W. Friedrichsen et al.
1850	W. Friedrixhsen et al.
1960	A. Roedig and K. Fleischmann
2039	E. Wille and W. Luttke
2055	F. Feichtmayr and H. Pfitzner
2072	N. Gamon and C. Reichardt

7-   -80, Ann. chim.(Rome), 70 (1980)

0009	L. Pentimalli et al.
0167	G. Alberti et al.
0173	M.L. Longo and M. Torre

11-   -80A, Chemica Scripta, 15 (1980)

0023	S. Gronowitz and I. Ander
0135	S. Gronowitz and I. Ander
0145	S. Gronowitz and I. Ander
0196	M.L. Kaplan et al.

11-   -80B, Chemica Scripta, 16 (1980)

0102	S. Lidert and O. Gronowitz

12-   -80, Australian J. Chem., 33 (1980)

0091	N.J. Dickson and L.K. Dyall
0113	J.T. Pinhey and B.A. Rowe
0131	W.B. Cowden and N.W. Jacobsen
0137	L. Jurd and R.Y. Wong
0225	I.R.C. Bick et al.
0273	G.A. Lawrance and S. Suvachiffanont
0343	D. St.C. Black et al.
0351	S.M. Colegate and F.R. Hewgill
0379	J.B. Bremner and Le van Thuc
0395	J.R. Mock et al.
0461	D.W. Johnson et al.
0527	E.R. Cole et al.
0557	P.S. Clezy and C.J.R. Fookes
0575	P.S. Clezy and C.J.R. Fookes
0585	P.S. Clezy et al.
0619	M.T. Omar et al.
0823	D.N. Leach and J.A. Reiss
0833	J.B. Bremner et al.
0879	B.F. Bowden et al.
0885	B.F. Bowden et al.
0913	P. Tuntiwachwuttikul et al.
0927	B.F. Bowden et al.

1073	J.R. Cannon et al.		1045	A. Murai et al.
1095	I.A. Chaudhry et al.		1049	A. Murai et al.
1147	D.J. Brown and K. Shinozuka		1057	Y. Kawase et al.
1323	J.B. Bremner et al.		1127	J. Ojima et al.
1345	D.D. Ridley and M.A. Smal		1179	M. Yoshida et al.
1397	J.E. Rockley and L.A. Summers		1183	T. Tokumitsu and T. Hayashi
1537	R.K. Haynes et al.		1361	J. Sunamoto et al.
1553	E.R. Cole et al.		1381	T. Amiya et al.
1569	P.H. Ferber et al.		1406	N. Abe and T. Nishiwaki
1783	R. Kazlauskas et al.		1421	N. Suzuki et al.
1799	R. Kazlauskas et al.		1461	A. Yamane et al.
1805	D.W. Cameron et al.		1550	T. Yamashita et al.
1817	R.F.C. Brown and C.M. Jones		1629	M. Yasuhara et al.
1823	B.F. Bowden et al.		1647	T. Morita et al.
1833	B.F. Bowden et al.		1656	S. Kiyooka et al.
2071	G.V. Baddeley et al.		1661	J. Nakayama et al.
2299	R.C. Fernando and I.C. Calder		1677	T. Otsubo et al.
2307	B.N. Ravi et al.		1703	K. Chiba et al.
2447	G.J. Gainsford and A.D. Woolhouse		1739	M.N. Basyouni et al.
2517	O.D. Hensens et al.		1763	H. Yamaoka et al.
2531	D.W. Cameron et al.		1769	K. Kurosawa et al.
2635	D.J. Antonjuk et al.		1773	N. Abe and T. Nishiwaki
2653	R.K. Haynes et al.		1922	M. Takatsuki
2729	E. Dimitriadis and R.A. Massy-Westrop		1993	R. Akaba et al.
			2020	K. Kurata and T. Amiya
2737	B.F. Bowden et al.		2036	O. Hara et al.
2761	D.J. Collins et al.		2046	H. Nakazumi et al.
2781	K.A. Francesconi		2195	N. Kobayashi et al.
			2281	T. Nakayama et al.
13-	-80A, Steroids, 35 (1980)		2334	M. Sato et al.
0133	P.S. Jogdeo and G.V. Bhide		2340	Y. Yano et al.
0189	D.A. Lightner and F.P.C. Eng		2344	T. Sugimoto et al.
0361	S. Solyom et al.		2389	M.Z.A. Badr et al.
0481	B. Beyer et al.		2415	H. Nakazumi and T. Kitao
0511	J.C. Knight		2592	Y. Ozawa et al.
0599	P.S. Jogdeo and G.V. Bhide		2610	S. Ozasa et al.
			2666	S. Suzuki et al.
18-	-80, Bull. Chem. Soc. Japan, 53 (1980)		2695	K. Mukai and N. Inagaki
0179	K. Oishi and K. Kurosawa		2885	K. Ando et al.
0201	H. Aiba and Y. Shimonishi		2921	S. Sekiguchi et al.
0205	Y. Inagaki et al.		2933	A. Yabe
0243	A. Murai et al.		2938	R. Matsushima et al.
0254	A. Murai et al.		2943	H. Machida et al.
0259	A. Murai et al.		3007	S.A.M. Metwally et al.
0289	H. Obara et al.		3225	H. Suginome and T. Uchida
0291	F. Ogura et al.		3232	M. Kimura et al.
0297	M. Iwao and T. Kuraishi		3276	M. Saito et al.
0442	T. Kinoshita et al.		3279	A. Kawamoto et al.
0469	H. Yamaoka et al.		3308	N. Abe et al.
0494	T. Horaguchi et al.		3329	Y. Inouye et al.
0512	T. Otsubo et al.		3385	T. Sugimoto and S. Matsuura
0518	R. Matsushima and I. Hirao		3670	J. Kimura et al.
0561	M. Tamura and K. Harada		3696	M. Saito et al.
0567	K. Maruyama et al.		3725	K. Yoshida et al.
0709	T. Shibata et al.			
0717	M. Hirota et al.		19-	-80, Bull. Acad. Polon. Sci., Ser.
0720	Y. Miura et al.			Chim., 28 (1980)
0726	T. Oshima and T. Nagai		0001	J. Dmochowska-Gladysz
0745	K. Imafuku et al.		0009	J. Szychowski et al.
0757	K. Maruyama and N. Narita		0529	M.J. Maslankiewicz and L. Czucha-jowski
0775	S. Oae et al.			
0785	H. Hirota et al.			
0809	Y. Yamamoto et al.		20-	-80, Bull. soc. chim. Belges, 89 (1980)
0825	T. Soga et al.		0307	L. DeBuyck et al.
0831	M. Nakayama et al.		0353	P. Meunier and J. Arriau
1039	M. Ando et al.		0399	N. Capelle et al.

0773   N.V. Onyamboko et al.
1001   M. Kapundu et al.

22-   -80, **Bull. soc. chim. France, Pt. II**,
       (1979)
0133   P. LeBarny and M. Loucheux- Le-
       febvre
0147   R. Briere et al.
0192   D. Autissier et al.
0267   J.C. Jacquesy and M.P. Jouannetaud
0295   J.C. Jacquesy and M.P. Jouannetaud
0304   J.-P. Gesson et al.
0316   J. Bolte et al.
0400   G. Lewin and J. Poisson
0473   J. Valisolalao et al.
0490   M. Damak et al.
0530   A. Dibo et al.
0539   A. Dibo et al.
0552   B. Merah and F. Texier
0559   G. Tsatsaronis and D. Grekou-Lazano

23-   -80, **Can. J. Chem.**, 58 (1980)
0006   N.Y.M. Fung et al.
0051   P. Duperrouzel and E. Lee-Ruff
0201   D.C. Wigfield et al.
0210   S. Weigl and J. Warkentin
0369   I.W.J. Still and T.S. Leong
0387   N. Baba et al.
0786   P. Sarthou et al.
0794   M.E.M. Baggs and B. Gregory
0808   G.I. Dmitrienko et al.
1059   J.L. Charlton and G.N. Lypka
1106   J.S. Grossert et al.
1161   J. Laduranty et al.
1316   D.D. McIntyre et al.
1344   M.E. Isabelle et al.
1380   I. Kurobane et al.
1427   J.A. Findlay et al.
1609   E. Buncel et al.
1615   E. Buncel et al.
1645   G. Adembri et al.
1759   P.E. Georghiou and M.A. MacDiarmid
1810   A.F. Thomas et al.
1829   J.P. Kutney et al.
1847   A.R. Harris et al.
1860   V. Skaric et al.
1869   J.M. Essery et al.
1880   J. Grimshaw and A.P. de Silva
1889   S.P. Sethi et al.
2024   G. Just et al.
2061   P. Deslongchamps and M. Caron
2158   G.A. Poulton and T.D. Cyr
2460   J. LaFontaine et al.
2477   Y.L. Chow et al.
2537   W.J. Leigh et al.
2550   R.A. Earl and L.B. Townsend
2666   V. Dave et al.
2703   J.W. ApSimon et al.
2745   D.G. Garratt et al.
2765   G.M. Strunz et al.
2819   N. Kizilkilic et al.

24-   -80, **Chem. Ber.**, 113 (1980)
0024   A. Heesing and W. Müllen
0036   K. Wieghardt et al.
0079   J. Goerdeler and R. Losch

0183   H. Meier et al.
0203   K. Kieslich et al.
0241   H.A. Staab et al.
0358   D. Hellwinkel and W. Schmidt
0385   W. Weber et al.
0408   T. Eicher and M. Urban
0424   T. Eicher et al.
0457   J.P. Dix and F. Vögtle
0531   G. Weber et al.
0566   G. Höfle et al.
0577   W. Schmidt and E. Steckhan
0586   W.R. Roth et al.
0614   W. Flitsch and E.R. Gesing
0650   M. Fountoulakis and J. Retey
0669   K. Gubernator et al.
0676   R. Wingen and F. Vögtle
0699   M. Spiteller et al.
0806   A. Roedig and H. Göpfert
0811   A. Roedig et al.
0995   H. Wamhoff and C.H. Theis
1020   J. Bitter et al.
1033   P. Eilbracht et al.
1106   G. Neef et al.
1205   F.A. Neugebauer and I. Umminger
1226   F.A. Neugebauer and H. Fischer
1356   M. Baacke et al.
1420   P. Eilbracht et al.
1458   G. Kaupp and H.W. Grüter
1507   H. Gnichtel and U. Boehringer
1514   P.H. Boyle and W. Pfleiderer
1524   G. Ritzmann et al.
1535   G. Ritzmann et al.
1575   K. Tolkiehn and K. Krohn
1584   W. Tochtermann and P. Rösner
1603   J.P. Weller and A. Gossauer
1626   G. Kaupp and H.-W. Grüter
1663   C. Rücker et al.
1708   R. Hasenkamp et al.
1746   R. Weiss and H. Wolf
1754   R. Tschesche et al.
1818   W.R. Roth et al.
1855   W. Schoenfelder and G. Snatzke
1898   K. Hartke et al.
2028   W. Sucrow et al.
2040   H. Berneth and S. Hünig
2043   F. Seela and D. Hasselmann
2049   F.A. Neugebauer et al.
2069   H.D. Wikeler and F. Seela
2154   R. Askani et al.
2211   P. Eilbracht and U. Mayser
2221   W.A. König et al.
2227   G. Quinkert et al.
2249   U. Eder et al.
2255   C.-P. Klages and J. Voss
2358   A.E.E. Murad and H. Hopf
2462   R. Knorr et al.
2490   H. Boshagen and W. Geiger
2509   J. Goerdeler et al.
2530   W. Meyer and H. Follmann
2566   L. Farkas et al.
2579   S.R. Ramadas et al.
2739   B. Muke and T. Kauffmann
2749   H. Lexy and T. Kauffmann
2755   H. Lexy and T. Kauffmann
2779   T. Sayrac and G. Maier
2808   F. Seela et al.

2818	W. Ried et al.		0549	L. Abate et al.
2884	K.M. Wald et al.		0597	D. Pitea and G. Favini
2891	R.R. Schmidt et al.		0613	I.R. Bellobono et al.
2976	K. Krohn and T. Tolkiehn		0621	M. Curini et al.
2994	K. Krohn and B. Behnke		0629	G. Assante et al.
3010	E. Schaumann et al.			
3024	E. Schaumann and F.F. Grabley	33-	-80, Helv. Chim. Acta, 63 (1980)
3112	D. Lenoir and P. Lemmen		0001	R. Heckendorn and T. Winkler
3127	R. Schwesinger et al.		0010	A. Haag et al.
3161	M. Breuninger et al.		0016	J.M.J. Tronchet and H. Eder
3245	E.C. Miranda et al.		0050	C.D. Hufford et al.
3249	W. Tochtermann and H. Köhn		0063	M. Bui-Nguyen et al.
3313	K. Dimroth and M. Lückoff		0095	T. Miyase et al.
3342	A. Roedig and G. Zaby		0117	R.K. Chaudhuri and O. Sticher
3373	H. Gnichtel et al.		0121	T. Schmidlin and C. Tamm
3384	G. Ruban et al.		0154	J. Berger et al.
3389	F. Seela and D. Hasselmann		0201	I. Ernest
3405	U. Kuckländer et al.		0225	M. Uchida et al.
3848	D. Trautmann et al.		0232	Y. Bessiere and P. Vogel
3932	G. Kaupp and D. Schmitt		0277	H. Pfander et al.
			0293	B. Maurer et al.
25-	-80, Chem. and Ind.(London), (1980)	0366	J.P. Kutney et al.
0084	B.H. Bhide et al.		0406	A. Brossi et al.
0154	S.K. Talapatra et al.		0456	M. Julliard et al.
0198	J. Iqbal and W. Rahman		0473	M.J. Caus et al.
0466	J.R. Merchant and R.B. Upasani	0486	A. Canovas and J.J. Bonet
0572	R.G. Brown et al.		0555	W. Oppolzer et al.
0662	R.L. Khosa et al.		0571	M. Yoshioka et al.
0697	A.V. Rama Rao et al.		0588	K. Murato et al.
0791	J.R. Merchant and P.J. Shah	0697	E.W. Colvin et al.
			0716	H. Pfauder et al.
27-	-80, Chimia, 34 (1980)		0733	G. Rytz and R. Scheffold
0020	H. Pfander et al.		0738	M. von Buren et al.
0023	M. Tanner and A. Ludi		0793	M. Langlois et al.
0279	P. Geisser et al.		0938	M.-A. Siegfried et al.
			1016	J.M. Sonney et al.
28-	-80A, Compt. rend., 290 (1980)	1045	R.K. Chaudhuri et al.
0021	P. Dubois et al.		1048	E. Zass et al.
			1093	M. Lang et al.
28-	-80B, Compt. rend., 291 (1980)	1130	D. Ballus et al.
0161	F. Chanon et al.		1149	C. Mahaim et al.
0191	M. Onanga and F. Khuong-Huu	1158	A. Kumin et al.
0211	J. Rigaudy et al.		1176	L. Schwager and P. Vogel
0255	C. Metge and C. Bertrand	1181	J.M.J. Tronchet et al.
			1190	U. Burger and F. Dreier
30-	-80, Doklady Akad. Nauk S.S.S.R.,	1198	W. Oppolzer and R.D. Wylie
	250-255 (1980)		1204	R.W. Lang and H.-J. Hansen
0105	A.V. Bogatskii et al.		1264	S. Gunzenhauser and H. Balli
0224	E.I. Tomilenko et al.		1284	B. Hellrung and H. Balli
0456	V.V. Plemenkov et al.		1311	A.E. Siegrist et al.
			1335	E. Seguin et al.
31-	-80, Experientia, 36 (1980)	1377	H. Pfander et al.
0028	J.A. Hembree et al.		1391	N. Acton and A. Brassi
0891	Y. Kashman et al.		1400	H.-U. Naegeli and H. Zahner
1025	T. Arai et al.		1451	H. Mayer and A. Rüttimann
			1456	A. Rüttimann and H. Mayer
32-	-80, Gazz. chim. ital., 110 (1980)	1463	H. Mayer and J.-M. Santer
0037	M. Maltese et al.		1467	H. Mayer and J.M. Santer
0081	C. Galeffi et al.		1473	K. Bernhard et al.
0097	J.U. Oguakwa et al.		1499	H. Eichenberger et al.
0135	G.F. Bettinetti et al.		1520	K. Ishii et al.
0287	L. Klasine et al.		1542	R. Jaunin
0327	A. Balsamo et al.		1554	H.-R. Schlatter and W. Graf
0341	F. de Sarlo et al.		1562	J. Pfenninger and W. Graf
0519	A. Brandt et al.		1604	P. Loeliger and H. Mayer
0527	L. Abate et al.		1644	J.M.J. Tronchet and A.P. Bonentant

1665	M. Rosenberger et al.		2033	C.F. Bigge et al.
1675	P. Belser and A. von Zelewsky		2039	H.R. Pfaendler et al.
1779	J.M.J. Tronchet and B. Gentile		2437	K.M. Smith et al.
1805	K. Baumgartner and J.H. Bieri		2797	A. Padwa and T.J. Blacklock
1823	B. Scholl and H.-J. Hansen		2817	A.F. Lewis and L.B. Townsend
1833	A.P. Alder et al.		2963	K. Chihara and W.H. Waddell
1856	K. Murato et al.		3022	D.R. Tyler et al.
1867	M. Muller et al.		3056	T.F. Buckley, III and H. Rapoport
1905	F.U. Afifi-Yazar and O. Sticher		3062	T.H. Fife and A.M. Pellino
1915	H. Wehrli		3095	R.B. Gammill
2019	W. Ammann et al.		3100	C.K. Chien et al.
2119	R. Ott-Longoni et al.		3173	D. Biermann and W. Schmidt
2130	M.A. Hai et al.		3199	E.H. White et al.
2159	G. Schulte et al.		3214	H. Nakayama et al.
2179	V. Skaric and J. Matulic-Adamic		3507	G.A. Olah et al.
2212	K. Murato et al.		3837	Z. Rappoport et al.
2221	K. Murato et al.		3948	I. Saito et al.
2230	N. Nakamura et al.		4182	J.P. Collman et al.
2258	J.M.J. Tronchet et al.		4224	D. van der Helm et al.
2295	S. Huggenberg and M. Hesse		4278	E.J. Corey et al.
2320	E.M. Sauer et al.		4410	A. Meyer and O. Hofer
2328	J. Pfenninger et al.		4429	H. Bock and W. Kaim
2370	K. Tsutsumi and H.R. Wolf		4456	W.G. Dauben and M.S. Kellogg
2380	A. Canovas et al.		4472	S. Muto and T.C. Bruice
2488	P. Kohler et al.		4659	T.W. Lewis et al.
			4694	T.E. Wolff et al.
34-	-80, J. Chem. Eng. Data, 25 (1980)		4815	M. Caswell and G.L. Schmir
0083	F. Al-Hajjar et al.		4838	E.D. Middlemas and L.D. Quin
0085	F.H. Al-Hajjar et al.		4839	E.D. Sternberg and K.P.C. Voll-
0184	D.B. Knight et al.			hardt
			4848	G.G. Wubbels et al.
35-	-80, J. Am. Chem. Soc., 102 (1980)		4983	E.M. Kosower and B. Pazhenchevsky
0252	Y. Kobayashi et al.		5036	M. Iwata et al.
0259	J.E. Leffler and J.J. Zupancic		5047	J.L. Benham et al.
0299	F.D. Saeva and G.R. Olin		5054	J.L. Benham and R. West
0306	S.P. Schmidt and G.B. Schuster		5245	R.L. Funk and K.P.C. Vollhardt
0314	S. Ayral-Kaloustian and W.C. Agosta		5337	A.E. Greene
0331	P.M. Warner and S.-L. Lu		5370	J.L. Luche et al.
0352	W.S. Johnson et al.		5406	P.J. Stang and M. Ladika
0364	A.M. Stolzenberg et al.		5425	M. Rosenberger and C. Neukom
0409	D.I. Schuster and S. Hussain		5482	S.F. Nelsen et al.
0413	M.W. Grayston et al.		5580	F. Johnson et al.
0501	N. Harada et al.		5648	A. Padwa et al.
0506	N. Harada et al.		5688	C. Ireland and P.J. Scheuer
0643	L.A. Paquette et al.		5749	D.A. Lightner et al.
0711	F. Kataoka et al.		5881	K.A. Parker and J. Kallmerten
0735	E.P. Kyba and R.A. Abramovitch		6056	N.J. Turro and G.L. Farrington
0770	P.D. Sattsangi et al.		6114	M.P. Schneider and M. Goldbach
0807	F.J. Brown and C. Djerassi		6157	P.A. Wender et al.
0857	C. Colas et al.		6171	M. Aratani and M. Hashimoto
1058	T.J. Katz and W. Slusarek		6349	P. Radnia and J.S. McKennis
1064	D.S. Grierson et al.		6370	H. Akita et al.
1176	Y. Nishizawa et al.		6513	E.C. Taylor et al.
1390	W.R. Roush		6604	J.R. Scheffer and Y.-F. Wong
1436	E.J. Corey et al.		6633	E.D. Laganis and D.M. Lemal
1439	E.J. Corey et al.		6634	E.D. Laganis and D.M. Lemal
1577	J.A. Soderquist and A. Hassner		6780	J.W. Larsen et al.
1602	P.T. Lansbury et al.		6784	M.E. Grace et al.
1633	R.M. Wilson et al.		6813	P.J. Stang and T.E. Fisk
1671	W.J. McGahren et al.		6841	J.S. Seehra and P.M. Jordan
1684	H.-U. Blaset and J. Halpern		6859	P. Salvadori et al.
1690	E.M. Gordon et al.		6872	J. Studebaker et al.
1713	B.H.J. Bielski and P.C. Chan		6887	R.H. Magnuson et al.
1730	D. Coucouvanis et al.		6972	M. Levi et al.
1977	H.R. Bhattacharjee et al.		7021	R. Prewo et al.
1983	D.A. Lightner et al.		7059	H.F. Gilbert

7076	L.K. Bee et al.		0090	R. Buchan and O.C. Musgrave
7154	R. Fujimoto et al.		0097	A.S. Bailey et al.
7157	J.W. Frost and W.H. Rastetter		0107	B.A. Behnam and D.M. Hall
7365	C.D. Hufford et al.		0113	J.P. Ferezou et al.
7493	K. Kakinuma et al.		0119	G.W. Kirby et al.
7535	S. Ho, I. Saito and T. Matsuura		0176	F. Fringuelli et al.
7559	S. Muto and T.C. Bruice		0221	M. de Bernardi et al.
7591	E.J. Nanni, Jr. and D.T. Sawyer		0227	L. Vasvari-Debreezy et al.
7892	J.C. Luong et al.		0237	A.G.M. Barrett et al.
7939	W.G. Rohly and K.B. Mertes		0249	M.A. Ferreira et al.
7953	R. Cooper et al.		0282	R.H. Thomson and R.D. Worthington
7986	E.J. Corey et al.		0289	R.H. Thomson and R.D. Worthington
7987	D.T. Chou and B. Ganem		0311	T.L. Peppard et al.
			0325	M. Asada et al.

36- -80, J. Pharm. Sci., 69 (1980)

0049	J.-P. Rieu et al.		0331	A.R. Katritzky et al.
0053	S. Ghosal and D.K. Jaiswal		0354	A.R. Katritzky et al.
0164	C. Casalini et al.		0362	A.R. Katritzky et al.
0232	W.K. Anderson et al.		0385	F. De Sarlo
0360	M.M. El-Azizi et al.		0388	S.D. Carter et al.
0995	D.B. Garcia et al.		0419	C. Shin et al.
1019	H. Lee and R. Vince		0448	T.R. Kasturi and S. Parvathi
1061	C.-H. Chen et al.		0466	J. Ojima and M. Fujiyashi
1074	D.R. Hwang et al.		0473	J. Ojima et al.
1164	A. Osman and R. Abu-Eittah		0481	J.S. Bakwa and P.J. Sykes
1180	C.D. Hufford et al.		0490	R. Bonnett et al.
1334	M. Bialer et al.		0495	A.G. Caldwell et al.
1419	C.E. Cook et al.		0512	J.L. Asherson and D.W. Young
1446	A.D. Kinghorn		0522	J.L. Asherson et al.
			0531	I. Kirson et al.
			0535	R.M. Acheson et al.

39- -80B, J. Chem. Soc., Perkin Trans. II (1980)

0139	A.T. Hutton and H.M.N.H. Irving		0553	A. Chatterjee et al.
0146	D. Veltwisch et al.		0556	A.J. Bridgewater et al.
0291	T.J. Kemp et al.		0563	Y. Ishido et al.
0326	R.M. Acheson et al.		0579	R.M. Acheson et al.
0339	C. Berti et al.		0601	B. Danieli et al.
0453	B. Wladislaw et al.		0607	T. Nishio et al.
0557	A.J. Audsley et al.		0614	P. Hanley-Smith et al.
0592	A.J.A. van der Weerdt and H. Cerfontain		0639	A.G.M. Barrett et al.
0773	A. Blackhall et al.		0643	D.H.R. Barton et al.
0805	P.J. Baldry		0665	A.G.M. Barrett et al.
0838	A.A.M. Roof et al.		0712	D.H.R. Barton et al.
0849	D. Pitea and G. Favini		0714	D.J. Field and D.W. Jones
0931	Y.L. Chow and K. Iwai		0728	L.O. Ruzo and J.E. Casida
0937	E. Dubini-Paglia et al.		0733	A.A. Allen et al.
1051	J. Smolikova et al.		0744	R.N. Butler and M.G. Cunningham
1156	L. Forlani et al.		0766	M.M. Campbell and R.C. Craig
1159	A. Albini et al.		0775	L. Merlini et al.
1282	K. Maeda et al.		0804	S. Ghosh et al.
1339	S. Chimichi et al.		0858	J.H. Jones and M.J. Witty
1441	D. Lloyd et al.		0869	A. Gilbert et al.
1601	U. Nickel and W. Jaenicke		0885	M.H. Beale et al.
1659	D. Veicrov et al.		0892	B. Lythgoe and D.A. Roberts
1696	E.P. Gibson and J.H. Trunbull		0902	H. Ishii et al.
1701	K. Fukuyama et al.		0911	Y. Kondo et al.
1768	L. Carlsen and F. Duus		0919	Y. Kondo et al.
1792	N.S. Ooi and D.A. Wilson		0950	S. Hagishita and K. Kuriyama
			0959	E.E. Glover and C.W. Peck
			0963	S. Hagiwara et al.

39- -80C, J. Chem. Soc., Perkin Trans. I, (1980)

0007	T. Makino et al.		0978	F. Yoneda et al.
0020	C.V. Greco and J.R. Mehta		0982	J.M. Lindley et al.
0072	M.M. Baradarani and J.A. Joule		1007	M. Chandler and R.J. Stoodley
0081	R.M. Acheson et al.		1019	J.S. Bajwa and P.J. Sykes
			1045	P.J. Kocienski et al.
			1070	K. Buggle and J. Power
			1076	R.M. Adlington and A.G.M. Barrett
			1080	J.A. Ballantine et al.

1114	H. Molines and C. Wakselman		2184	A.G.M. Barrett et al.
1139	I. Charles et al.		2191	A.G.M. Barrett et al.
1161	T.J. Lillie and O.C. Musgrave		2205	E. Buncel et al.
1176	A.R. Katritzky et al.		2209	D.H.R. Barton et al.
1185	R.M. Acheson and M.W. Cooper		2222	P.H. Bentley and E. Hunt
1199	A. Gomez-Sancez et al.		2272	A.G.M. Barrett et al.
1212	D.H.R. Barton et al.		2278	Z. Czochanska et al.
1233	O. Bilgic and D.W. Young		2304	K. Kadir et al.
1262	S. David and M.-C. Lepine		2322	B.S. Orlek et al.
1270	N.J. Lewis and J. MacMillan		2353	P.J. Cotterill and F. Scheinmann
1319	M.A. Jessep and D. Leaver		2362	P.T. Gallagher et al.
1324	M.A. Jessep and D. Leaver		2405	A.K. Yagoub and G.M. Iskander
1345	B.J. Graphakos et al.		2463	F.R. van Heerden et al.
1347	J.P. Clayton et al.		2474	C.P. Gorst-Allman et al.
1352	J.P. Clayton et al.		2511	S.K. Maji et al.
1356	H. Suginome and T. Uchida		2527	S. Ogawa and S. Shiraishi
1365	R. Okazaki et al.		2535	T.A. Crabb et al.
1405	B. Lythgoe and I. Waterhouse		2554	A.R. Katritzky et al.
1407	W.R. Bowman and G.D. Richardson		2581	R.C. Cambie et al.
1414	K. Maruyama et al.		2637	P. Denniff et al.
1477	T. Laird et al.		2645	S.S. Al-Hassan et al.
1507	G.S. Phull et al.		2670	M.B. Rubin et al.
1512	A.S. Bailey and M.H. Vandrevala		2693	T. Nishiwaki et al.
1516	G. Gowda and T.B.H. McMurry		2700	H.E. Gottlieb et al.
1544	T.W. Hart et al.		2743	A.R. Katritzky et al.
1551	S. Bartlett et al.		2755	Y. Kobayashi et al.
1587	P. Horsewood and G.W. Kirby		2787	K. Yamauchi et al.
1607	T. Kametani et al.		2812	W. Kemp et al.
1614	P.J. Clarke et al.		2830	Y. Tamura et al.
1627	P.E. Hansen		2870	G.A. Bahadur et al.
1635	A. Corsaro et al.		2881	E.R. Ghatak et al.
1641	J. Setsune et al.		2904	A. Albini et al.
1654	N.J. Cussans et al.		2914	B. Yagen et al.
1667	R. Nesi et al.		2918	A. Albert
1688	G.A. Behadur et al.		2923	N.E. Mackenzie et al.
1726	J. Burdon et al.		2933	P.J. Hylands et al.
1752	A.R. Pinder		2937	F.M. Dean and B.K. Park
1756	M.J. Curry and I.D.R. Stevens			
1773	R.M. Acheson et al.		40-	-80, Nippon Kagaku Kaishi (1980)
1782	G. Ferguson et al.		0675	K. Hirano
1788	K.C. Jain and W.B. Whalley		0837	K. Ichimura et al.
1804	J.C. Breytenbach and G.J.H. Rall		0846	K. Ichimura et al.
1826	J.J. Hanson and P. Krogsgaard-		1154	O. Manabe et al.
	Larsen		1185	S. Nan'ya et al.
1834	K.J. Gould et al.		1397	T. Horie et al.
1841	O. Abou-Teim et al.		1749	M. Nishiyama et al.
1853	V.D. Patil et al.		1804	S. Morimura
1866	C. Kashima et al.		1862	T. Kasai et al.
1870	A.R. Katritzky et al.			
1879	A.R. Katritzky et al.		41-	-80, J. chim. phys., 77 (1980)
1909	D.J. Field and D.N. Jones		0161	P. Boule and J. Lemaire
1920	N.G. Kundu		0217	L.M. Coulangeon et al.
1986	F.M. Dean et al.		0497	L.M. Coulangeon et al.
1994	F.M. Dean et al.			
2001	R. Sharma and R.J. Stoodley		42-	-80, J. Indian Chem. Soc., 57 (1980)
2013	M.P. Carmody et al.		0208	M.L. Malik and S.K. Grover
2026	G. Lowe and B.V.L. Potter		0532	R.J. Patolia and K.N. Trivedi
2049	F.M. Dean and R.S. Johnson		1011	R.J. Patolia et al.
2065	J. Polonsky et al.		1238	S.K. Balani et al.
2070	A.E. Hauck and C.S. Giam			
2077	J. Iriarte et al.		44-	-80, J. Org. Chem., 45 (1980)
2081	P. Crabbe and J.-P. Depres		0012	B.J. Whitlock and H.W. Whitlock
2098	T. Suga and T. Shishibori		0020	J. Alexander et al.
2126	R.E. Bowman		0024	J. Alexander et al.
2134	D.C. Aldridge et al.		0034	H. Hart and K. Takagi
2174	J.C. Berridge et al.		0065	M. Poge et al.

0076 J.F. Hansen et al.
0090 K.T. Potts et al.
0158 H. Wynberg and B. Marsman
0168 R.B. Bates et al.
0174 P.M. Worster et al.
0177 Y. Fukuda et al.
0203 M.S. Poonian and E.F. Nowoswiat
0213 J. Wu et al.
0240 M. Essiz et al.
0357 K. Watanabe and T. Wakabayashi
0365 P.A. Wender and J.C. Hubbs
0367 P.A. Wender and L.J. Letendre
0456 P.D. Davis and D.C. Neckers
0462 P.D. Davis et al.
0476 T. Sasaki et al.
0501 W.K. Anderson and G.E. Lee
0527 J.E. Martinelli and M. Chaykovsky
0570 D. Becker and D. Birnbaum
0633 R.A. Brand and J.E. Mulvaney
0715 P. Seuron and G. Solladie
0724 S.D. Young and W.T. Borden
0735 P. Djura and D.J. Faulkner
0780 K.H. Park and G.D. Daves, Jr.
0788 M. MacCoss et al.
0803 G.L. Olson et al.
0856 M.S. Raasch
0870 Y. Gaoni and S. Sadeh
0906 E.A. Castro and M. Freudenberg
0920 N.R. Raulins et al.
0933 T.E. Young and A.R. Oyler
0936 Y. Hirai et al.
0958 R.T. Luibrand and E.M. Fujinari
0999 Y. Houminer
1081 U.R. Ghatak et al.
1117 J.E. Robbers et al.
1153 T.R. Demmin and M.M. Rogit
1181 R.W. Dugger and C.H. Heathcock
1232 A.G. Williams and G.B. Butler
1260 S.N. Falling and H. Rapoport
1286 R.R. Sauers and D.C. Lynch
1310 M.J. Haire
1312 A.G. Anderson, Jr. et al.
1334 T.G. Miller and R.C. Hollander
1338 A.J. Fatiadi
1354 P. Beak et al.
1421 K. Maruyama and N. Narita
1424 K. Maruyama et al.
1435 P. Djura et al.
1441 R.W. Doskotch et al.
1470 P.N. Confalone and D.L. Confalone
1473 S. Kubota et al.
1481 M.D. Bachi et al.
1505 E. Ciganek
1528 R.A. Johnson et al.
1540 E.G. Gibbons
1549 P. de Mayo et al.
1557 J. Vansant et al.
1577 K. Kondo and I. Inoue
1586 J.S. Carle and C. Christophersen
1628 I. Willner and M. Rabinovitz
1645 J.N. Jacob et al.
1657 B. Weinstein et al.
1662 G.H. Denny et al.
1672 K. Brandt and Z. Jedlinski
1695 A.G. Anderson, Jr. and T.Y. Tober
1713 A.S. Howard et al.
1715 E.D. Smith and V.S. Mayasandra
1753 R.S. Mariano et al.
1783 M. Yoshida et al.
1800 H.O. House et al.
1807 H.O. House et al.
1817 J.G. Smith et al.
1828 P. Canonne et al.
1847 M.B. Rubin and S. Welner
1889 T. Fujii and S. Yoshifugi
1901 J. Minamikawa et al.
1906 G. Catoni et al.
1918 J.A. Bristol and R.G. Lovey
1964 C. Ghosh and N. Tewari
1969 M.R. Wasielewski and W.A. Svec
2013 J.H. Shau and W. Reusch
2032 L. Bednarek and E.W. Neuse
2033 F.H. Greenberg and S. Schenendorf
2080 G. Saucy et al.
2091 H. Hart et al.
2096 H. Hart et al.
2099 T.H. Fife and J.E.C. Hutchins
2127 R.A. Scherrer and H.R. Beatty
2155 N.L. Agarwal and W. Schafer
2165 T. Sheradsky and D. Zbaida
2181 A. Padwa et al.
2189 H.-D. Becker and B. Ruge
2195 J.E. Herweh and C.E. Hoyle
2201 B. Sialom and Y. Mazur
2218 K.M. Smith et al.
2275 F.E. Granchelli et al.
2320 D.H. Bohn and J.S. Bradshaw
2324 J.R. Williams et al.
2331 M.A. Leoni et al.
2368 M. Yasuda et al.
2474 K.T. Potts et al.
2498 H. Pluim and H. Wynberg
2517 P. Beslin et al.
2518 M.J. Haddadin and H.H.N. Murad
2523 Y. Gopichand and F.J. Schmitz
2541 T.Y. Gu and W.P. Weber
2576 E.S. Stratford and R.W. Curley, Jr.
2632 M.V. Lakshmikantham and M.P. Cava
2666 F. Terrier et al.
2704 K. Stanley and J. Zemlicka
2715 B.P. Melnick et al.
2741 B.M. Trost and E. Keinan
2746 Y. Mao and V. Boekelheide
2813 R.R. Sauers et al.
2834 M.D. Corbett and B.R. Corbett
2854 R.M. Kellogg et al.
2874 H.H. Wasserman et al.
2883 W.J. Middleton and E.M. Bingham
2899 T.E. Young et al.
2903 N. Asai and D.C. Neckers
2925 W. Ten Hoeve and H. Wynberg
2930 W. Ten Hoeve and H. Wynberg
2959 N.F. Haley and M.W. Fichtner
3061 F.M. Hauser and R.P. Rhee
3072 R.H. Foster and N.J. Leonard
3084 S.S. Simons, Jr. et al.
3088 J.W. Huffman et al.
3149 W.H. Rastetter and L.J. Nummy
3163 W. Herz et al.
3182 A. Mitra et al.
3187 D.M. Chipman et al.
3211 F. Wudl et al.

3229	M. Nakazaki et al.		4611	D.H. Wadsworth and M.R. Detty
3253	H.E. Paaren et al.		4629	R.C. Neuman, Jr. and M.J. Amrich, Jr.
3259	M.E. Kuehne et al.		4702	K.F. Bernady et al.
3265	M. Sahai and A.B. Ray		4769	T.K. Dobbs et al.
3268	A. Nakagawa et al.		4810	R.L. Danheiser and H. Sard
3274	A. Matsuda et al.		4813	D. Goff et al.
3278	D. Caine and G. Hasenhuettl		4864	H.E. Zimmerman and R.J. Pasteris
3364	Y. Asscher and I. Agranat		4876	H.E. Zimmerman and R.J. Pasteris
3377	W.G. Dauben and E.G. Olsen		4898	J.P. Freeman and M.J. Haddadin
3396	D.B. Stierle and D.J. Faulkner		4976	R.P. Walker et al.
3401	V.J. Paul et al.		4980	D.B. Stierle and D.J. Faulkner
3416	N. Finch et al.		4999	R. Somanathan et al.
3422	D.R. Henton et al.		5088	J.R. Williams and G.M. Sarkisian
3456	W.E. Noland et al.		5095	T. Kiguchi et al.
3465	C.N. Filer et al.		5113	H.E. Simmons et al.
3518	D.A. Lightner et al.		5122	S.A. Vladuchick et al.
3545	H.O. House et al.		5139	N.L. Agarwal and W. Schäfer
3564	J. Ojima et al.		5144	N.L. Agarwal and W. Schäfer
3651	G. Roth et al.		5163	R.K. Hill et al.
3682	M. Aratani et al.		5196	R.K. DiNello and D. Dolphin
3687	R.J. Stonard and R.J. Andersen		5371	G.E. DuBois and R.A. Stephenson
3719	M. Kimura et al.		5383	Y. Gopichand and F.J. Schmitz
3731	H. Hart et al.			
3746	A. Srinivasan and A.D. Broom		46-	-80, J. Phys. Chem., 84 (1980)
3756	A. Padwa and H. Ku		0134	W.H. Waddell and J.L. West
3782	S. Lahiri et al.		0231	C.J. Hochanadel et al.
3790	D. Caine et al.		0768	D. Getz et al.
3814	Y. Kashman and A. Groweiss		0830	B.H.J. Bielski et al.
3827	L.E. Crane et al.		0847	G. Bartocci et al.
3865	K. Yamauchi et al.		1841	G.B. Schuster et al.
3918	C.N. Filer and D.G. Ahern		1909	V.S.F. Chew et al.
3919	W.R. Mallory and R.W. Morrison, Jr.		2623	R. Debnath and S.C. Bera
3923	A. Dalla Cort et al.		2803	R.O. Loutfy and K.Y. Law
3933	H.E. Zimmerman et al.			
3969	V. Nair and S.G. Richardson		47-	-80, J. Polymer Sci., Polymer Chem. Ed., 18 (1980)
3974	E.A. Truesdale and D.J. Cram			
3999	R.L. Cargill et al.		0427	Y. Kita et al.
4006	T. Kato and J. Zemlicka		0477	H.K. Hall, Jr. and S.C. Snider
4020	A.F. Cook et al.		0661	S. Takahashi et al.
4028	E.J. Olivier et al.		0949	T. Ishikawa et al.
4034	E.J. Parish and G.H. Schroepfer, Jr.		1021	J.V. Crivello and J.H.W. Lam
4071	F.M. Hauser and D.W. Combs		2697	J.V. Crivello and J.H.W. Lam
4073	G.R. Pettit et al.		2959	Y. Inaki et al.
4094	G. Snatzke et al.		3029	J.A. Moore et al.
4122	O. Lerman and S. Rozen		3265	A.M. Ibrahim et al.
4183	D. Davalian et al.			
4210	T.R. Demmin and M.M. Progic		48-	-80, J. prakt. Chem., 322 (1980)
4216	J. Cuomo et al.		0055	M. Augustin et al.
4219	K.E. Fahrenholtz et al.		0087	H. Schafer and K. Gewald
4233	M. Nakane and C.R. Hutchinson		0099	G.W. Fischer et al.
4296	A.L.W. Shroyer et al.		0336	J. Bodeker and K. Courault
4309	Z. Rappoport and N. Pross		0434	M. Richter et al.
4337	J. Elzinga et al.		0475	A.S. Radwan et al.
4359	P. Charumilind and H. Kohn		0517	H.J. Timpe et al.
4404	C.Y. Byon and M. Gut		0543	K. Kokkinos et al.
4429	P.J. Card and B.E. Smart		0554	A.M. Moiseenkov et al.
4455	K. Harano et al.		0559	H. Schick et al.
4462	C. Shih et al.		0617	A.K. Fateen et al.
4496	M. Hilbert and G. Solladie		0835	M.T. Omar and F.A. Sherif
4522	J.T. Gupton et al.		0909	J. Jamrozik
4555	A. Padwa et al.		0991	C. Lindig and K. Repke
4573	W.E. Noland and C.K. Lee		1003	F. Theil et al.
4582	W.E. Noland et al.		1012	F. Theil et al.
4587	T. Sasaki et al.		1021	K. Gewald et al.
4594	T. Sasaki et al.			
4597	M.A. Smith et al.			

49-   -80, Monatsh. Chem., 111 (1980)
0081   R. Martin et al.
0093   O.S. Wolfbeis et al.
0159   H. Falk et al.
0177   D. Fenske et al.
0309   H. Gorner et al.
0413   S. Smolinski and M. Paluchouska
0529   H. Berbalk and K. Eichinger
0563   E. Haslinger and P. Wolschann
0635   J. Svetlik et al.
0657   M.R. Mahmoud et al.
0749   H.-J. Becher et al.
0863   E. Hohaus
0909   L. Fisera et al.
1213   M.R. Mahmoud et al.

54-   -80, Rec. trav. chim., 99 (1980)
0049   M. van der Leij and B. Zwanenburg
0087   J.C.L. Armande and U.K. Pandit
0115   B. te Nijenhuis et al.
0132   R. Klok et al.
0160   J.B.M. Somers and W.H. Laarhoven
0246   C. Schenk et al.
0391   J.W. Dieveld et al.

56-   -80, Polish J. Chem., 54 (1980)
0033   A. Maslankiewicz and K. Pluta
0107   Z. Jankowski and R. Stolarski
0453   S. Mejer and R. Pacut
0661   M. Santus
0683   M.J. Korohoda
0901   M. Janczewski and E. Pawtowska
0925   J. Kruszenski et al.
1067   M. Santus
1177   R. Gawinecki and F. Muzalewski
1233   R. Dabrowski et al.
1281   M. Eckstein and H. Marona
1291   S. Skonieczny et al.
1319   G. Kuswik and G. Grynkiewicz
1557   L. Strekowski et al.
1585   L. Kaczmarek
2161   M. Janczewski and K. Kurys
2209   W. Zielinski
2217   K. Kiec-Kononowicz and A. Zeje
2247   S. Mejer et al.
2349   Z. Makarewicz and K. Oprzadek
2357   F. Kazmierczak and K. Golankiewicz
2365   L. Achremowicz et al.
2397   H. Tomczyk and W. Kisiel

59-   -80, Spectrochim. Acta, 36A (1980)
0103   P. Venuvanalingam et al.
0207   E.C. Okafor
0279   J.P. Hart and W.F. Smyth
0349   G. Alberghina et al.
0563   D. Sen and C.H.J. Wells

60-   -80, J. Chem. Soc., Faraday Trans.
          I, (1980)
0503   P.E. Watkins and E. Whittle

61-   -80, Ber. Bunsen Gesell. Phys. Chem.,
          84 (1980)
0056   E. Bastian et al.
1108   M. Melzig et al.
1115   O.S. Wolfbeis et al.

1122   H. Hennig et al.
1129   J.-H. Finkentey and H.W. Zimmer-
          mann
1133   J.-H. Finkentey and H.W. Zimmer-
          mann
1140   S. Kotowski et al.
1203   G. Winter and U. Steiner

62-   -80, Z. phys. Chem.(Leipzig),
          261 (1980)
0158   H. Mustroph and J. Epperlein

63-   -80, Z. physiol. Chem., 361 (1980)
0953   B. Manz and M.V. Govindan

64-   -80B, Z. Naturforsch., 35b (1980)
0102   A.M. Dawidar et al.
0219   H. Achenbach and B. Raffelsberger
0250   F.A. Neugebauer and H. Fischer
0376   H. Falk and K. Thirring
0401   R. Battaglia et al.
0458   S. Kato et al.
0490   W.H. Gundel
0715   E.C. Okafor
0885   H. Achenbach and B. Raffelsberger
0896   W.H. Gundel
1002   W. Friedrichsen
1019   E.C. Okafor
1335   R. Bieganowski and W. Friedrich
1431   W.H. Gundel
1459   H. Achenbach and J. Witzke
1465   H. Achenbach and B. Raffelsberger
1497   O. Soga and H. Iwamoto
1569   W. Neuenhaus et al.
1575   A.K. Singh and D.N. Dhar

64-   -80C, Z. Naturforsch., 35c (1980)
0030   Z. Kamiercznk et al.
0156   H. Dinter and R. Hansel
0363   G.G. Gross and K.J. Koelen
0824   H. Besl et al.
0878   J. Wierzchowski et al.

65-   -80, Zhur. Obshchei Khim., 50 (1980)
          (English translation pagination)
0052   G.L. Latevosyan et al.
0156   A.D. Zorina et al.
0162   P.F. Vlad et al.
0176   P.F. Vlad et al.
0180   P.F. Vlad et al.
0481   M.G. Voronkov et al.
0491   V.B. Kuyazhevskaya et al.
0552   V.A. Radyukhin et al.
0907   L.I. Solov'eva and E.A. Luk'yan-
          ets
0916   V.A. Krasnova et al.
0945   B.G. Sodnomov et al.
1104   I.E. Saratov et al.
1217   G.L. Matevosyan et al.
1280   E.A. Kirichenko et al.
1297   B.A. Suborov et al.
1339   O.M. Glozman et al.
1578   L.M. Sergienko et al.
1615   V.F. Traven' et al.
1621   V.F. Traven' et al.
1705   M.A. Andreeva et al.

1714   M.A. Andreeva et al.
1723   V.V. Alenin and V.D. Domkin
1739   L.A. Ganyushin et al.
1871   E.B. Agracheva et al.
1874   V.M. Derkacheva and E.A. Luk'yanets
1922   M.A. Andreeva et al.
2039   V.I. Boev and A.V. Dombrowskii
2072   G.V. Shandurenko et al.
2096   E.Y. Khmel'nitskaya et al.
2104   E.Y. Khmel'nitskaya et al.
2185   A.M. Panov et al.
2236   P.G. Sennikov et al.

69-   -80, Biochemistry, 19 (1980)
0163   J. Zemlicka
0731   S.C. Koerber et al.
2358   J.V. Schloss et al.
2396   R.Y. Tsien
2537   S. Ghisla et al.
2572   S. Terada et al.
3221   F. Garland et al.
3280   K. Muramoto and J. Ramachandran
3773   A.B. Kremer et al.
4423   C.L. Jaffe et al.
4539   C.D. Demoliou and R.M. Epand
4993   H.L. Levine et al.

70-   -80, Izvest. Akad. Nauk S.S.S.R.,
       29 (1980)
0039   L.I. Belen'kii et al.
0123   V.V. Semenov et al.
0140   A.V. Kamernitskii et al.
0263   U.M. Dzhemilev et al.
0354   Y.N. Malkin et al.
0418   B.P. Gusev et al.
0421   B.P. Gusev et al.
0425   O.M. Nefedov et al.
0468   I.V. Vasil'eva et al.
0481   V.A. Dorokhov et al.
0558   A.B. Teitel'baum et al.
0563   A. Abdukadirov et al.
0576   E.P. Prokof'ev et al.
0740   G.V. Kireev et al.
0754   L.P. Glushko et al.
0765   G.V. Shustov et al.
0771   Z.A. Krasnaya and V.F. Kucherov
0774   S.I. Zav'yalov and A.G. Zavozin
0789   E.I. Karpeiskaya et al.
0897   N.P. Gritsan and N.M. Bazhin
0956   V.V. Martin and L.B. Volodarskii
0980   Z.A. Krasnaya et al.
0987   Z.A. Krasnaya et al.
1087   P.P. Levin et al.
1149   N.I. Danilenko et al.
1159   B.I. Buzykin and N.G. Gazetdinova
1181   A.V. Kamernitskii et al.
1597   Y.P. Popov et al.
1643   Z.A. Krasnaya et al.
1655   G.G. Skvortsova et al.
1833   A.V. Semenovskii and N.M. Emel'ya-
       nov
1915   M.G. Voronkov et al.
1928   P.G. Sennikov et al.

73-   -80, Coll. Czech. Chem. Comm., 45
       (1980)

0092   V. Kral and Z. Arnold
0127   S. Kovac and V. Konecny
0135   J. Prousek et al.
0142   K. Spirkova et al.
0150   F. Povazanec et al.
0155   D. Vegh et al.
0423   V. Knoppova et al.
0491   K. Sindelar et al.
0504   J. Jilek et al.
0517   V. Valenta et al.
0529   V. Valenta et al.
0599   H. Hrebabecky et al.
0606   H. Pischel et al.
0746   A. Jurasek et al.
0906   V. Svak et al.
0910   V. Knoppova et al.
0914   J. Slavik et al.
0956   D. Walterova et al.
1072   L. Krasnec, Jr. et al.
1079   S. Stankovsky and M. Martvon
1086   K. Sindelar et al.
1290   M. Salisova et al.
1379   J. Slouka and V. Bekarek
1419   A. Laguna et al.
1502   A. Hrdlicka and M. Langova
1525   V. Kanicky et al.
1581   J. Prousek et al.
1704   J. Prousek et al.
1715   A. Krutosikova and J. Kovac
1826   I. Lukac et al.
1831   R. Kada et al.
1950   F. Santavy and I. Valka
1991   V. Prikrylova et al.
2049   J. Podlahova and J. Podlaha
2120   G. Cik et al.
2125   B. Proska and Z. Voticky
2247   V. Konecny et al.
2254   M. Uher et al.
2329   M. Marchalin and A. Martron
2334   J. Imrich et al.
2343   V. Konecny and S. Varkenda
2360   R. Kada et al.
2364   A. Holy and E. DeClerq
2417   V. Hanus et al.
2550   N.S. Padyukova and J. Smrt
2675   L. Pavlickova et al.
2684   M. Steinerova et al.
2688   I. Cenena et al.
2804   M. Uher et al.
2949   A. Krutosikova et al.
3166   K. Sindelar et al.
3182   V. Bartl et al.
3347   J. Prousek
3370   J. Palesek et al.
3546   E. Fisera et al.
3583   M. Semonsky et al.
3593   Z. Vejdelek et al.

77-   -80, J. Chem. Soc., Chem. Comm. (1980)
0022   R.M. Allen et al.
0070   M. Foglio et al.
0119   M. Hayashi et al.
0123   P. Mencarelli and F. Stegel
0178   P. Manitro and D. Monti
0205   T. Fujita et al.
0223   R. Weiss and M. Hertel

0243   K. Muthurama and V. Ramamurthy
0273   D.A. Lightner et al.
0285   M.V. Sargent
0346   J. Gawronski and K. Gawronska
0394   A. Treston et al.
0399   J. Amupitan et al.
0435   G.M. Sharma et al.
0444   T. Tsuchiya et al.
0454   T. Tsuchiya et al.
0455   M.A. Phillippi and H.M. Goff
0459   Y. Kobayashi et al.
0472   P. Crabbé et al.
0527   H.-P. Marki and C.H. Eugster
0601   J. Polonsky et al.
0619   M.U.S. Sultanbawa and S. Suren-
       drakumar
0621   M.F. Lappert et al.
0670   G.W. Klumpp and J. Stapersma
0691   T.L. Gilchrist et al.
0763   A.T. Hutton and H. Irving
0777   T.J. King et al.
0802   M.G.B. Drew et al.
0889   E.R. Talaty et al.
0920   E. Fujita et al.
0947   M. Maxfield et al.
0958   R. Hernandez et al.
0974   M. Kimura and S. Tai
0993   E. Guibe-Jampel et al.
1011   W.R. Baker et al.
1075   H.C. Charles et al.
1097   B.E. Cross and P. Filippone
1158   T. Itaya et al.
1197   C. Leuenberger et al.
1204   N. Burford et al.
1206   I. Kubo et al.
1220   A. Matsuo et al.

78-   -80, Tetrahedron, 36 (1980)
0149   R. Gabioud and P. Vogel
0155   E. Biala, A.S. Jones and R.T.
       and R.T. Walker
0267   E. Bueldt et al.
0321   H.G.M. Walraven and U.K. Pandit
0343   T. Bally and S. Masamune
0371   J. de-Pascual-Ti et al.
0397   A.J.G. Barwise et al.
0409   G. Bettoni et al.
0511   G. Hugel et al.
0515   W.D. Ollis et al.
0529   C.W. Bird and M. Latif
0631   L. Gorrichon-Guigon and S. Hammerer
0645   A. Baragliu et al.
0731   P. Joseph-Nathan et al.
0865   T. Sasaki et al.
0965   T. Fujii, S. Yoshifuji and K. Yam-
       ada
1057   J. Harley-Mason and Atta-Ur-Rahman
1063   Atta-Ur-Rahman et al.
1079   K. Kiec-Kononowicz et al.
1167   K. Koike et al.
1179   S.C. Welch et al.
1183   T. Kitamura et al.
1231   L.-F. Tietze et al.
1245   V. Bertini, F. Lucchesini and
       A. De Munno
1269   P.J. Barr et al.

1307   J.A. Toth et al.
1331   L. Vo-Quang et al.
1385   E. Tighineanu et al.
1415   R. Cricchio et al.
1451   F.A. Devillanova et al.
1455   K.M. Saplay et al.
1515   P. Chinnasamy et al.
1539   T. Fujii and S. Yoshifuji
1551   M. Suzuki, N. Kowata and E. Kuro-
       sawa
1579   J. Zylber et al.
1585   J.C. Arnould, J. Cossy and J.P.
       Pete
1613   A. Bianco et al.
1753   M.F. Dube and J.W. Timberlake
1791   W.-D. Rudorf
1801   M. Augustin et al.
1813   C.W. Bird and M. Latif
1833   C.L. Honeybourne et al.
1943   P. Beslin and J. Vialle
2005   D.A. Okorie
2009   R. Cricchio
2097   Y. Maki, T. Hiramitsu and M.
       Suzuki
2119   T. Sasaki et al.
2125   T.C.-G. Kazembe and D.A. Taylor
2133   C. Charles et al.
2225   D. Sparfel, F. Gobert and J. Ri-
       gaudy
2291   J.D. Wuest
2311   R. Lapouyade et al.
2337   R.N. Hunston et al.
2341   M.S. Ahmad, I.A. Khan and N.K.
       Pillai
2441   G.J. Kapadin et al.
2449   M. Endo and H. Naoki
2453   J. Santamaria and J. Rigaudy
2459   J. Gillaumel et al.
2513   A. Chatterjee and B.G. Hazra
2675   D. Lloyd and R.W. Millar
2681   G.W.H. Cheeseman and G. Rishman
2701   P.T. Lansbury et al.
2735   M. Shiozaki et al.
2955   P. Pollet and S. Gelin
2983   J. Polonsky et al.
2989   S. Moreau et al.
3033   I.A. Akhtar et al.
3087   S. Rajappa and R. Sreenivasan
3115   T. Sakai et al.
3177   J. Yamamoto et al.
3187   P. Courtot and J.-Y. Salaun
3361   W.J. Greenlee and R.B. Woodward
3367   W.J. Greenlee and R.B. Woodward
3443   B. Fuchs et al.
3489   B.A. Burke et al.
3509   T. Sasaki et al.
3551   H. Gregor and O. Hofer
3563   D.P. Chakraborty et al.

80-   -80, Revue Roumaine Chim., 25 (1980)
0245   C. Sarbu et al.
0407   H.J. Timpe et al.
0559   I.E. Khawad and G. Milskander
0651   V. Macovei
0701   F. Cornea et al.
1097   K. Takemoto et al.

1335	M. Abdalla et al.		0657	M.T. Garcia-Lopez et al.
			0661	J.S. Park et al.
83-	-80, Arch. Pharm., 313 (1980)		0702	J.-P. Kaplan et al.
0027	K. Görlitzer and J. Weber		0764	K. Hirai et al.
0048	G. Rücker and H.-W. Hembeck		0781	M. Murata et al.
0108	V.J. Ram		0805	N. Acton et al.
0180	K. Rehse and U. Stiemann		0852	A.F. Cook et al.
0237	G. Rücker and U. Molls		0873	J.B. Hester, Jr. et al.
0301	U. Pindur		0899	M.G. Nair et al.
0311	F. Eiden and L. Prielipp		0903	M.B. Floyd et al.
0315	H.J. Kallmayer and E. Wagner		0919	A.J. Alpert and E.L. Cavalieri
0344	K. Rehse et al.		0927	Y. Sato et al.
0385	K. Görlitzer and E. Engler		0949	W.M. Welch et al.
0405	K. Görlitzer and E. Engler		1008	J.L. Neumeyer et al.
0429	K. Görlitzer and E. Engler		1013	M.I. Dawson et al.
0476	P. Kertesz and J. Reisch		1068	R. Mecholam et al.
0509	K. Rehse et al.		1134	J.C. Chabala et al.
0557	K. Görlitzer and E. Engler		1144	M. Bialer et al.
0572	R. Neidlein and S. Throm		1153	C.R. Fernando et al.
0603	H.J. Kallmayer and K.-H. Seyfang		1178	B.K. Wasson et al.
0715	H. Möhrle et al.		1229	M.E. Phelps et al.
0729	J. Tröschutz		1235	T.-S. Lin et al.
0809	J. Knabe and R. Heckmann		1299	P. Bhuta et al.
0826	W. Dammertz and E. Reimann		1318	D.G. Musson et al.
0858	G. Dannhardt and R. Obergrusberger		1343	C.I. Hong et al.
0937	R.W. Grauert		1405	N. Finch et al.
0959	G. Seitz et al.		1410	P.H. Ruehle et al.
0970	R. Neidlein and H. Zeiner		1440	T.-S. Lin et al.
0977	R. Neidlein and F. Moller			
0990	H. Möhrle et al.		88-	-80, Tetrahedron Letters (1980)
1033	J. Knabe and R. Heckmann		0041	K. Hafner et al.
1048	J. Knabe and R. Heckmann		0055	C. Kan et al.
			0063	R. Besselievre
86-	-80, Talanta, 27 (1980)		0107	M. Oda and H. Oikawa
0349	A.T. Pilipenko et al.		0183	M.A.E. Sallam
0923	J.M.B. Rodriguez and J.M.C. Pavon		0193	M. Ballester et al.
0977	G.M. Huitink		0201	I. Bryson et al.
1001	R.V. Koch and D.L. Pringle		0239	R.T. Gallagher et al.
			0243	R.T. Gallagher et al.
87-	-80, J. Med. Chem., 23 (1980)		0247	R. Kirchlechner and W. Rogalski
0006	N.P. Jensen et al.		0293	M. Yokoyama and H. Monma
0039	A.J. Grant and L.M. Lerner		0301	M. Nukina et al.
0059	M.G. Nair et al.		0309	M. Muroi et al.
0075	S.H. Vincent et al.		0313	A.V. Bogatsky et al.
0090	S.S. Dehal et al.		0319	W.S. Murphy and K.P. Raman
0096	W.K. Anderson and G.E. Lee		0339	H. Lind, G. Rihs and G. Rist
0098	N.G. Anderson and J.R. Carson		0355	M. Hosomi et al.
0127	G.T. Shiau et al.		0433	K.M. Smith and J.J. Li
0242	J.P. Miller et al.		0471	M. Oda et al.
0252	C.L. Schmidt et al.		0479	H. Morisawa et al.
0282	H.G. Mautner et al.		0561	P.C. Cherry et al.
0320	J.R. Piper and J.A. Montgomery		0619	S. Oida et al.
0368	J.H. Wikel et al.		0671	M. Franck-Neumann and C. Dietrich-Buchecker
0376	V. Kumar et al.		0681	R.C. Ronald and S. Gurusiddaiah
0379	B. Roth et al.		0723	S.F. Hussain et al.
0384	B.S. Rauckman and B. Roth		0739	A. Wessiak et al.
0402	J.B. Hester, Jr. et al.		0759	H. Iida et al.
0430	H.-J. Shue et al.		0787	B.B. Jarvis et al.
0512	N.G. Kundu		0865	T.R. Kasturi and L. Krishnan
0535	B. Roth et al.		0881	J.P. Clayton et al.
0541	F.R. Domer et al.		0897	H. Hauptmann and M. Mader
0549	M. Takai et al.		0899	F.A. Neugebauer et al.
0569	F.J. Dinan and T.J. Bardos		0947	K. Komatsu et al.
0575	B.S. Huang et al.		1009	A. Padwa and H. Ku
0594	J.L. Neumeyer et al.		1027	S.L. Schreiber
0643	J.B. Hester, Jr. et al.			

1043	M. Kuzuya et al.		3167	M. Avenati et al.
1145	W. Eberbach and J.C. Carre		3203	T. Ogita et al.
1163	B.S. Joshi et al.		3241	C. Wilcox and R. Breslow
1165	S. Abramson and B. Fuchs		3293	J.F. Ayafor et al.
1221	R.A. Moss and R.C. Munjal		3307	S.V. Kessar et al.
1223	P. Gesche et al.		3315	S.F. Hussain and M. Shamma
1227	M. Hauteville et al.		3363	C. Kan et al.
1243	M. Sumiyoshi et al.		3375	M. Kato et al.
1265	A. Nishinaga et al.		3381	Y. Oshima et al.
1281	J.R. Pfister		3459	R.M. Wilson et al.
1369	G. Mehta et al.		3463	E.J. Corey and G. Goto
1471	A. Fukuzawa et al.		3471	R. Kreher et al.
1479	K. Tatsuda et al.		3527	A. Nickon and P. St.John Zurer
1485	J. Rokach et al.		3547	E.J. Corey and D.A. Clark
1529	T. Sasaki et al.		3583	T. Tsuji et al.
1537	Y. Kono et al.		3617	S. Braverman et al.
1577	N. Raju et al.		3629	Y. Kashman et al.
1599	F.L. Chung et al.		3659	H.A. Whaley et al.
1611	E.D. de Silva and P.J. Scheuer		3717	A. Sinha and S. Lahiri
1645	C. Kaneko et al.		3751	T. Eicher and D.F. Lerch
1685	M.P.L. Caton et al.		3759	J.P. Mayer and J.P. Fleury
1693	S.F. Hussain and M. Shamma		3771	K. Kohata et al.
1761	M. Mochizuki et al.		3783	A. Hosomi et al.
1765	M. Mochizuki et al.		3831	M.B. Stringer and D. Wege
1841	R. Askani and B. Pelech		3997	K. Shingu et al.
1861	T. Tahara et al.		4001	T. Toda et al.
1909	S.F. Hussain and M. Shamma		4009	M. Shibuya and S. Kubota
1961	I.H. Qureshi et al.		4027	S. Michel et al.
1971	T. Sato et al.		4043	P.T. Grant et al.
1975	A.V. Rama Rao et al.		4097	A. Nishinaga et al.
2011	M.S.R. Nair and S.T. Carey		4119	M. Ballester et al.
2097	S.A. Robev et al.		4193	P. Blatcher et al.
2101	S. Bruckner et al.		4241	W.M. Schubert and D.C. Green
2265	C.B. Reese and A. Ubasawa		4247	E. Schaumann et al.
2299	S. Caccamese et al.		4251	E. Schaumann and F. Grabley
2313	N. Suzuki et al.		4279	S. Imajo et al.
2317	I. Saito et al.		4287	M. Hori et al.
2333	G. Cavicchio et al.		4295	J.F. Kingston
2337	S. Bernasconi et al.		4323	Y.W. Lee et al.
2409	B. Nickel and A. Rassat		4481	M. Niwa et al.
2435	M. Ballester et al.		4507	P. Gesche et al.
2439	M. Tits et al.		4535	J.C. Breytenbach and G.J.H. Rall
2447	P.H. Ferber et al.		4561	J.E. Semple et al.
2459	A.C. Alves and M.A. Cruz Costa		4577	M.C. Pirrung
2529	T. Nishio et al.		4585	J.M. Muchowski and P.H. Nelson
2535	T. Sato and R. Noyori		4631	K.B. Soroka and J.A. Soroka
2549	T. Terasawa and T. Okada		4655	G.C. de Magalhaes et al.
2667	S.C. Pakrashi et al.		4749	G.B.K.B. Gunaherath et al.
2679	V.S. Ganu et al.		4869	F. Toda and K. Tanaka
2713	K. Tanaka and F. Toda		4877	G. Tomaschewski et al.
2799	O. Papies and W. Grimme		4901	S.H. Eltamany and H. Hopf
2813	I. Saito et al.		5001	G.D. Prestwich and M.S. Collins
2817	S. Nakatsuka et al.		5059	M. Poje and N. Begant
2837	K. Tatsuta et al.			
2845	M. Ballester et al.		89-	-90, Angew. Chem.(Intl. Ed.), 19
2879	R. Gompper and K. Bichlmayer			(1980)
2883	R. Gompper and M. Junius		0041	E. Vogel et al.
2887	W. Adolf and E. Hecker		0047	W. Eberbach et al.
2947	J. Cossy and J.P. Pete		0049	H. Quast et al.
2977	I.L. Mushkalo et al.		0052	G. Maier et al.
3025	J. Leitich		0136B	H.J. Bestmann et al.
3029	E. Cuny et al.		0140	C. Angst et al.
3077	H. Sakurai et al.		0143	P. Naath et al.
3123	H.H. Sun et al.		0199	K. Hafner and H.P. Krimmer
3131	J.R. Campbell		0204	R. Neidlein and H. Zeiner
3143	E.J. Corey et al.		0207	H. Röttele and G. Schröder

0220B	P.R. Bolz et al.		1131	K. Kubo et al.
0307	W. Grimme and H.G. Köser		1137	T. Nishitani et al.
0308	H. Neudeck and K. Schlögl		1157	C. Kaneko et al.
0320	R. Kreher and G. Use		1172	T. Miyase et al.
0400	H. Braun and M. Wiessler		1207	H. Yano et al.
0459	W. Steglich et al.		1437	T. Nohara et al.
0543B	K. Yamamura et al.		1449	S. Saijo et al.
0545	T. Nakazawa et al.		1459	S. Saijo et al.
0621	M. Müller et al.		1468	E. Ibuki et al.
0631	U.H. Brinker and J. Streu		1477	A. Tada et al.
0715	R. Gleiter and P. Schang		1509	A. Sato et al.
0724	F.A. Neugebauer and H. Fischer		1590	K. Takahashi et al.
0907	B. Pandey et al.		1622	K. Nozawa et al.
0919	E. Vogel et al.		1626	H. Takaku et al.
1003	O. Pilet and P. Vogel		1651	I. Kitagawa et al.
1015	E. Vogel et al.		1711	T. Moriya et al.
1018	J. Hartenstein et al.		1722	E. Sato et al.
1023	E.F.R. Gesing et al.		1730	F. Murai and M. Tagawa
1027	G. Quinkert et al.		1747	T. Niiya et al.
			1782	M. Kozawa et al.

90-   -80, J. Inorg. Nucl. Chem., 42 (1980)

0343	J.C. Fanning et al.		1810	K. Matoba et al.
0349	M.R. Mahmoud and M.T. El-Haty		1820	A. Sakai and A. Tanimura
0431	J.S. Preston and Z.B. Luklinska		1827	S. Kobayashi et al.
0441	J.S. Preston		1847	H. Sasaki et al.
0775	M.M. Jones et al.		1853	H. Yano et al.
0851	P.C. Kundu et al.		1859	T. Satake et al.
0977	N.S. Bhave and R.B. Kharst		1869	T. Murakami et al.
1029	N.C. Schroeder et al.		1884	N. Tanaka et al.
1123	W.R. Haag		1920	T. Itaya et al.
1155	E.C. Okafor		1932	C. Iwata et al.
			1954	K. Hayashi et al.
			1992	S. Urano et al.

93-   -80, J. Appl. Chem. U.S.S.R., 53 (1980)

1509	R.I. Federova		2024	F. Ishikawa et al.
1963	Y.B. Shteinberg and S.S. Tkachenko		2039	A. Tada et al.
			2116	T. Sugawara et al.
			2148	J. Matsumoto et al.

94-   -80, Chem. Pharm. Bull. Japan, 28
       (1980)

0049	S. Nakano et al.		2185	N. Tanaka et al.
0092	M. Uchida et al.		2309	G. Tsukamoto et al.
0110	T. Yamaguchi et al.		2356	S. Tamura et al.
0115	N. Yamaji et al.		2422	Y. Ikeya et al.
0120	E. Ohtsuka et al.		2428	S. Sekita et al.
0150	A. Yamane et al.		2460	N. Takeuchi et al.
0157	A. Yamane et al.		2487	A. Tada et al.
0181	J. Okuda and N. Horiguchi		2518	K. Nakashima and S. Akiyama
0189	M. Ikehara et al.		2522	T. Itaya et al.
0220	H. Takahata et al.		2527	E. Yamanaka et al.
0245	M. Yamazaki et al.		2531	J. Matsumoto et al.
0282	S. Inayama et al.		2546	T. Sadawa et al.
0401	K. Koike et al.		2548	T. Nomura and T. Fukai
0447	A. Takamizawa et al.		2587	F. Ishikawa
0479	E. Kaji and S. Zen		2602	T. Tsuchiya et al.
0500	N. Morisaki et al.		2720	M. Mano et al.
0529	S. Kamiya and M. Tanno		2734	M. Mano et al.
0567	Y. Okamoto et al.		2748	K. Tsuchida et al.
0657	M. Mori et al.		2753	H. Okabe et al.
0795	T. Kinoshita et al.		2770	M. Ishikawa et al.
0850	S. Nishibe et al.		2799	T. Hashimoto et al.
0861	M. Yamazaki et al.		2819	T. Itaya et al.
0876	A. Matsuda et al.		2835	S. Mineo et al.
0900	S. Naruto and O. Yonemitsu		2892	T. Kinoshita et al.
0939	S. Shibuya and T. Ueda		2924	S. Kobayashi et al.
1043	A. Itai and S. Nozoe		2948	M. Kuroyanagi et al.
1067	H. Matsumoto and M. Asakura		2972	T. Kurihara et al.
1071	M. Okamoto and S. Ohta		2987	Y. Konda et al.
			3049	F. Yoneda et al.
			3057	M. Mano et al.

3070   N. Tamaka et al.
3137   T. Murakami et al.
3150   T. Naito and C. Kaneko
3163   J. Aritomi et al.
3178   H. Mori et al.
3210   S. Ozasa et al.
3232   S. Oida et al.
3244   K. Yamakawa et al.
3258   S. Oida et al.
3265   K. Yamakawa et al.
3296   K. Harada et al.
3323   K. Kikugawa et al.
3357   Y. Ikeya et al.
3395   S. Tamura and R. Todoriki
3401   S. Tamura and R. Todoriki
3430   Y. Tamura et al.
3433   S. Kobayashi et al.
3443   T. Fujii et al.
3452   H. Itokawa et al.
3457   Y. Kurasawa and A. Takada
3494   S. Oida et al.
3514   F. Yoneda et al.
3537   Y. Kurasawa and A. Takada
3561   M. Kuzuya et al.
3601   S. HOrii et al.
3621   S. Uesugi et al.
3649   M. Yamazaki and E. Okuyama
3711   K. Kaneko et al.

95-   -80, J. Pharm. Soc. Japan, 100 (1980)
0072   T. Hidaka et al.
0289   S. Goya et al.
0337   J. Kunitomo et al.
0456   Y. Tominaga et al.
0466   S. Takagi et al.
0515   K. Nakashima and S. Akiyama
0571   T. Kato et al.
0615   S. Matsueda et al.
0657   M. Iinuma and S. Matsuura
0699   Y. Tominaga et al.
0718   I. Ibuki et al.
0744   S. Goya et al.
0819   S. Goya et al.
0826   S. Goya et al.
0867   I. Yoshizawa et al.
1127   S. Kimoto et al.
1187   J. Matsumoto et al.
1220   S. Takagi et al.
1261   T. Kinoshita et al.

96-   -80, The Analyst, 105 (1980)
0165   N.A. El-Rabbat et al.
0462   R.D. Jee
0470   A.K. Covington and A.J. Utting
0768   K. Higuchi et al.

97-   -80, Z. Chemie, 20 (1980)
0020B   R. Stolle
0053   M. Schulz and K. Likowski
0100   W. Müller-Litz and D. Thomzik
0188   M. Reichenbächer et al.
0214   W. Abraham et al.
0261   H.-G. Henning and R. Krüger
0268   L. Beyer
0342   J. Heinicke and A. Tzschach
0378   J. Bendig and D. Kreysig

0436   R. Mayer et al.

98-   -80, J. Agr. Food Chem., 28 (1980)
0071   N.B. Mandava et al.
0135   H.G. Cutler et al.
0139   H.G. Cutler et al.
0427   R.A. Andersen et al.
0989   H.G. Cutler et al.
1026   J.H. Ross and R.I. Krieger

100-   -80, J. Natural Products, 43 (1980)
0097   W.N.A. Rolfsen et al.
0103   A. Cave et al.
0143   W.-N. Wu et al.
0151   H.Y. Cheng and R.W. Doskotch
0157   A. El-Sayed et al.
0242   D.E. Nettleton, Jr. et al.
0259   L.A. Mitscher et al.
0270   J. Wu et al.
0285   S.P. Gunasekera et al.
0294   S. Michel et al.
0296   S.M. Kupchan et al.
0305   R.M. Preisner and M. Shamma
0319   R. Battaglia et al.
0353   P.W. LeQuesne et al.
0365   I.I. Mahmoud et al.
0372   W.N. Wu et al.
0407   F.S. El-Feraly and M.D. Hoffstetter
0411   R. Mata and J.L. McLaughlin
0472   W.-N. Wu et al.
0482   A.A. Olaniyi and J.W. Powell
0487   F.D. Monache et al.
0498   F. Tillequin et al.
0503   J. Polonsky et al.
0510   S.S. Kang and W.S. Woo
0524   S.F. El-Naggar and R.W. Doskotch
0527   F.S. El-Feraly and D.A. Benigni
0567   W.-N. Wu et al.
0571   P.D.L. Chao and G.H. Svoboda
0595   A.A. Olaniyi and W.N.A. Rolfsen
0598   L.H. Zalkow et al.
0637   A.T. Sneden and G.I. Beemstepboer
0649   L.J. El-Naggar and J.L. Beal
0739   S.F. El-Naggar et al.

101-   -80A, J. Organomet. Chem., 184 (1980)
0007   T. Yang Gu and W.P. Weber
0013   H. Sakurai et al.
0147   T. Veszpremi et al.

101-   -80B, J. Organomet. Chem., 185 (1980)
0095   H. Ogoshi et al.

101-   80C, J. Organomet. Chem., 186 (1980)
0039   J. Heinicke et al.
0247   E. Meier et al.

101-   -80D, J. Organomet. Chem., 187 (1980)
OC11   S. Lin and P. Boudjouk

101-   -80E, J. Organomet. Chem., 188 (1980)
0237   K. Sonogashira et al.

101-   -80I, J. Organomet. Chem., 192 (1980)
0001   Y. Kawada and W.M. Jones

0087   Y. Kawada and W.M. Jones

101-   -80J, J. Organomet. Chem., 193 (1980)
0345   A.G. Osborne et al.

101-   -80K, J. Organomet. Chem., 194 (1980)
0037   R. Mathiasch
0103   P. Narbel et al.
00C5   C.W. Carlson et al.
0147   M. Ishikawa et al.
0367   J.L. Roustan et al.

101-   -80L, J. Organomet. Chem., 195 (1980)
0029   T.Y. Gu and W.P. Weber

101-   -80N, J. Organomet. Chem., 197 (1980)
0159   T.H. Newman et al.
0169   T.F. Schaaf et al.

101-   -80P, J. Organomet. Chem., 199 (1980)
00C1   M. Wojnowska et al.

101-   -80Q, J. Organomet. Chem., 200 (1980)
0261   H. Sakura et al.

101-   -80R, J. Organomet. Chem., 201 (1980)
0233   A. Alvanipour et al.
0301   N.M. Loim et al.

102-   -80, Phytochemistry, 19 (1980)
0093   D. Andina et al.
0103   N. Ohno et al.
0141   K. Kurata and T. Amiya
0161   K. Yakushijin et al.
0162   H. Ripperger
0255   W.M. Bandaranayake
0273   R.M. Parkhurst et al.
0277   D.M.X. Donnelly and J. O'Reilly
0285   P.P. Diaz D. et al.
0299   K. Kaneko et al.
0307   B.A. Akinloye and W.E. Court
0313   A.M. Griesbrecht et al.
0323   R.N. Barua et al.
0326   M. Solichin et al.
0328   S. Shimada et al.
0332   S. Ghosal et al.
0336   J.L. Suri et al.
0427   S. Rebuffat et al.
0445   R.C. Carpenter et al.
0449   K. Miki et al.
0455   R. Braz Filho et al.
0467   S. Shimada et al.
0471   T. Murakami et al.
0474   J.C. Martinez V. et al.
0476   K. Ito et al.
0478   D. Adinarayana et al.
0480   D. Adinarayana et al.
0482   S. Dossaji and I. Kubo
0531   M. Hirotani and T. Furuya
0563   A.F. Rose et al.
0571   A. Bianco et al.
0583   F.C. Seaman and N.H. Fischer
0603   Y. Asakawa et al.
0615   M. Kapundu et al.
0623   P. Molnar and J. Szaboles
0639   R. Hänsel et al.

0645   S. Huneck et al.
0669   W. Herz et al.
0673   R. Mata and J.L. McLaughlin
0681   A.M.P. de Diaz et al.
0705   K.E. Malterud and T. Anthonsen
0707   G. Camele et al.
0716   H. Achenbach and B. Raffelsberger
0849   F.C. Seaman and N.H. Fischer
0885   S. Huneck et al.
0889   D.T. Coxon et al.
0893   P.K. Agrawal et al.
0921   M.D. Woodward
0935   D.L. Dreyer and R.C. Brenner
0941   D.L. Dreyer
0949   M. Lounasmaa et al.
0953   M. Lounasmaa et al.
0988   C. Vilain
0989   F. Libot et al.
0992   G.B. Marini-Bettolo et al.
0998   R.C. Rastogi and N. Borthakur
1117   B. Bodo and D. Molho
1121   A.H. Conner et al.
1175   L.R. Row et al.
1183   M.C. Lunel et al.
1187   P.G. Waterman and E.G. Crichton
1195   R. Braz Filho et al.
1199   S.K. Talapatra et al.
1213   S.P. Gunasekera et al.
1225   P. Forgacs et al.
1234   W. Herz and S.V. Govindan
1251   P. Forgacs et al.
1258   P.N. Sharma et al.
1260   P.K. Agrawal et al.
1262   X.A. Dominguez et al.
1267   I. Jayaraman et al.
1272   P. Pulla Rao and G. Srimanna-
         rayana
1278   S.K. Dutta et al.
1279   M.-F. Seguineau and N. Langlois
1282   F. Tillequin and M. Koch
1349   W. Hosel and R. Todenhagen
1473   A.-M. Bui, B.C. Das and P. Potier
1477   R. Schmitz et al.
1503   F.W. Eastwood et al.
1519   S.I. Balbaa et al.
1523   J.B. Fernandes et al.
1531   M. Tits et al.
1545   A. Ortega et al.
1554   R. Bhandari et al.
1556   B.R. Sharma et al.
1558   A. Islam et al.
1560   R. Sahai et al.
1563   K.G. Rajulu and J.R. Rao
1566   I.H. Bowen et al.
1735   R.D. Stipanovic et al.
1743   T. Murakami et al.
1755   M.L. Bouillant et al.
1795   A. Romo de Vivar et al.
1805   B. Rodriguez and G. Savona
1825   R. Tschesche et al.
1833   M.M. Amer and W.E. Court
1859   L.M.G. Aguiar et al.
1866   H. Thomas and H. Budzikiewicz
1877   T. Isobe et al.
1878   N.A. El-Emary et al.
1882   A.N. Tackie et al.

1884	F. Hotellier et al.		0303	I.I. Naumenko et al.
1959	J. Vercauteren et al.		0309	A.V. Ivashchenko et al.
1975	L. Quijano et al.		0316	V.V. Dovlatyan and A.V. Dovlatyan
2003	R.B. Filho et al.		0334	A.F. Oleinik et al.
2031	V. Ravindranath and M.N. Satyana-		0368	A.N. Kost et al.
	rayana		0377	A.E. Sausin' et al.
2034	B.K. Gupta et al.		0386	I.G. Il'ina et al.
2036	C.D. Hufford and B.O. Oguntimein		0406	V.M. Zubarovskii and Y.L. Briks
2083	J.P. Kutney et al.		0418	R.A. Paegle et al.
2125	F.R. van Heerden et al.		0429	A.F. Pozharskii et al.
2147	Y. Asakawa et al.		0464	E.P. Vernigor et al.
2179	S. Ayabe et al.		0488	B.A. Trofimov et al.
2185	H. Achenbach et al.		0495	S.A. Samsoniya et al.
2199	J.H. Cardellina, II and J. Meinwald		0501	V.I. Kelarev and G.H. Shvekhgei-
2202	F. Gomez et al.			mer
2207	A. Sato et al.		0506	P.B. Terent'ev et al.
2215	S.K. Garg et al.		0525	N.S. Prostakov et al.
2219	A. Chatterjee et al.		0529	N.S. Prostakov et al.
2227	T.-S. Wu et al.		0541	A.F. Pozharskii et al.
2229	C.C. Xaasan et al.		0547	V.D. Orlov et al.
2232	B.K. Gupta et al.		0578	A.N. Grinev and I.N. Mikhailova
2331	S. Ayabe et al.		0580	M.P. Nemeryuk et al.
2405	M.C. Garcia-Alvarez and B. Rodri-		0585	T.V. Stupnikova et al.
	guez		0592	L.B. Lazukova et al.
2439	L. Quijano et al.		0599	A.I. Tolmachev and L.M. Shulezhko
2451	M. Zeches et al.		0607	N.I. Traven and T.S. Safonova
2486	A.C. Pinto et al.		0626	I.V. Zuika et al.
2494	G.R. Nagarajan et al.		0628	V.A. Samsonov and L.B. Volodarskii
2507	H.G. Kiryakov et al.		0637	G.N. Tyurenkova et al.
2643	H.W.D. Matthes et al.		0645	G.V. Shishkin and A.A. Gall'
2651	Y. Asakawa et al.		0653	V.M. Dziomko et al.
2685	S.R. Jensen and B.J. Nielsen		0678	G.G. Melikyan et al.
2713	S. Huneck and G. Hofle		0685	V.P. Khilye et al.
2731	E. Malan and S. Naidoo		0691	M.A. Kudinova et al.
2735	J. Kunitomo et al.		0696	M.A. Kudinova et al.
2741	B.A. Akinlove and W.E. Court		0701	B.M. Krasovitskii et al.
2759	V. Amico et al.		0704	L.M. Gornostaev et al.
2763	F. Bailleul et al.		0711	Y.L. Gol'dfrab et al.
2765	M. Hoeneisen et al.		0718	S.Y. Solov'eva et al.
2777	C.E. Campbell and H.W. Kircher		0721	L.I. Skripnik et al.
2781	J. de Pacual-T. et al.		0730	G.V. Ponomarev
2791	W.S. Woo et al.		0741	A.B. Kamenskii et al.
2794	L.B. de Silva et al.		0743	T.V. Stupnikova et al.
2795	R.D. Torrenegra et al.		0752	N.S. Kozlov et al.
			0754	V.P. Semenov and A.N. Studenikov
103-	-80, Khim. Geterosikl. Soedin, 16 (1980)		0758	N.S. Kozlov et al.
0023	V.G. Kul'nevich et al.		0773	R.O. Kochkanyan and S.S. Lukanyuk
0028	I.Y. Kvitko et al.		0799	I.M. Andreeva et al.
0032	G.B. Afanas'eva et al.		0807	G.N. Dorofeenko et al.
0041	N.P. Samoilova et al.		0828	A.N. Grinev et al.
0045	V.S. Rozhkov et al.		0833	A.N. Kost et al.
0048	N.A. Kogan		0853	R.G. Glushkov and T.V. Stezhko
0062	V.P. Chetverikov et al.		0857	L.I. Medvedeva et al.
0066	G.P. Tokmakov et al.		0864	L.T. Kaulinya et al.
0071	A.F. Pozharskii et al.		0868	A.V. Ivashchenko et al.
0081	N.M. Starshikov and A.V. Pozharskii		0873	V.G. Granik et al.
0094	V.P. Shchipanov		0882	O.M. Polumbrik et al.
0137	A.I. Tolmachev and L.M. Shulezhko		0917	A.N. Kost et al.
0146	L.A. Kintsurashvili et al.		0921	A.N. Kost et al.
0151	V.G. Kartsev et al.		0926	P.A. Sharbatyan et al.
0169	N.Y. Deeva and A.N. Kost		0945	P.B. Terent'ev et al.
0182	Y.N. Bulychev et al.		0951	P.B. Terent'ev et al.
0227	E.D. Sych and L.T. Gorb		0962	A.N. Kost et al.
0244	G.P. Tokmakov and I.I. Grandberg		0965	A.N. Kost et al.
0247	G.A. Karlivan and R.E. Valter		0970	Z.D. Dubovenko and V.P. Mamaev
0260	V.G. Granik et al.		0974	V.L. Rusinov et al.

0991	A.V. Anisimov et al.
0993	V.K. Daukshas et al.
1000	V.G. Kartsev and A.M. Sipyagin
1003	V.G. Kartsev et al.
1031	T.V. Stupnikova et al.
1039	Y.I. Ostapovich et al.
1048	G.S. Grekova et al.
1073	V.M. Dziomko et al.
1115	I.K. Yurgevitsa and E.L. Kupche
1139	S.A. Samsoniya et al.
1146	I.S. Chikvaidze et al.
1149	N.S. Prostakov et al.
1153	N.S. Prostakov et al.
1160	V.M. Dziomko et al.
1166	V.M. Dziomko et al.
1171	V.S. Mokrushin et al.
1176	M.Y. Karpeiskii et al.
1239	O.Y. Neiland and A.A. Krauze
1248	B.G. Zaisev et al.
1261	I.V. Romanenko et al.
1271	A.V. Ivashchenko et al.
1275	A.V. Ivashchenko et al.
1279	A.V. Ivashchenko et al.
1286	V.A. Zyryanov et al.

104-   -80, Zhur. Organ. Khim., 16 (1980)

0037	V.F. Shner et al.
0119	N.N. Magdesieva et al.
0129	G.A. Karlivan et al.
0159	M.V. Grelik et al.
0170	T.V. Stolbova et al.
0185	E.P. Opanasenko et al.
0188	V.N. Drozd et al.
0192	V.I. Shilov et al.
0342	A.Y. Zheltov et al.
0347	A.V. Zibarev et al.
0375	T.P. Kofman et al.
0379	S.Y. Zherdeva et al.
0383	S.Y. Zherdeva et al.
0391	A. Barudi et al.
0395	V.N. Drozd et al.
0407	Y.V. Serov et al.
0520	L.G. Ignatovich et al.
0534	S.S. Mochalov et al.
0573	N.N. Magdesieva and V.A. Denilenko
0665	A.B. Kamenskii et al.
0683	V.M. Potapov et al.
0729	B.Y. Adamsone and O.Y. Neiland
0740	B.P. Bespalov andG.A. Tushbaev
0751	R.G. Dubenko et al.
0762	V.I. Rogovik et al.
0766	N.N. Suvorov et al.
0775	V.N. Drozd et al.
0822	K.N. Zelenin et al.
0849	A.D. Bulat et al.
0858	V.P. Ivshin et al.
0891	T.M. Ivanova and S.M. Shein
0905	N.A. Orlova et al.
0938	O.N. Chupakhin et al.
1006	V.P. Ivshin et al.
1092	I.B. Repinskaya et al.
1124	A.V. Bogatskii et al.
1143	M.V. Gorelik et al.
1150	A.B. Koshokov et al.
1200	P.I. Ogoiko et al.
1252	A.G. Ivanenko et al.

1292	N.V. Ignat'ev et al.
1298	I.B. Repinskaya and V.A. Koptyug
1316	D.A. Oparin et al.
1404	L.N. Chernova and V.D. Simonov
1436	A.V. Aleksandr et al.
1441	V.I. Krokhtyak and A.Y. Il'chenko
1458	L.B. Piotrovskii
1463	I.B. Repinskaya et al.
1536	R.G. Dubenko et al.
1592	B.M. Gutsylyak et al.
1612	B.P. Bespalov et al.
1646	Y.E. Gerasimenko et al.
1651	Y.E. Gerasimenko et al.
1780	S.S. Mochalov et al.
1794	B.A. Selivanov and V.T. Shteingarts
1813	B.A. Korolev et al.
1820	S.L. Solodar and V.A. Kochkin
1836	N.K. Genkina et al.
1856	A.V. El'tsov et al.
1879	M.B. Kolesova and N.V. Smirnova
1884	L.M. Gornostaev and V.A. Levdanskii
1890	A.F. Pozharskii et al.
1951	I.M. Yakovleva et al.
1963	A.N. Frolov et al.
1995	Y.S. Andreichikov et al.
2004	L.M. Sitkina et al.
2008	R.A. Sogomanova et al.
2020	E.Y. Markava et al.
2026	A.G. Gorshkov et al.
2039	N.V. Kazankov and L.G. Ginodman
2044	G.V. Kharitonov and L. Ch'in
2055	V.A. Buevich et al.
2059	E.S. Lipina et al.
2080	N.S. Spasokukotskii et al.
2099	A.N. Frolov et al.
2207	N.I. Gannshchak et al.
2210	V.I. Naddaka et al.
2236	N.N. Suvorov et al.

105-   -80, Khim. Prirodn. Soedin., 16 (1980)

0125	M.P. Yuldashev et al.
0167	V.A. Maslennikova et al.
0177	S.U. Karimova et al.
0181	A.G. Druganov et al.
0286	V.F. Pozdnev
0452	B.K. Abduazimov
0464	E.T. Oganesyan
0525	K.A. Kadyrov et al.
0558	E.K. Batirov et al.
0574	V.I. Akhmedzhanova et al.

106-   -80, Die Pharmazie, 35 (1980)

0010	P. Kertscher et al.
0024	A. Regosz and G. Zuk
0030	M. Atef Abdelkader et al.
0075	P. Richter and G. Wagner
0332	P. Pflegel et al.
0460	R. Mahrwald
0503	B.A.H. El-Tawil et al.
0587	R. Mahrwald and G. Wagner
0739	G. Wagner and V. Hantfield
0751	G. Dietz and F. Bahr
0798	A.M.M.E. Omar et al.

7-   -80, Synthetic Comm., 10 (1980)
0075   E. Santaniello and P. Ferraboschi
0267   K. Kondo et al.
0391   P.I. Svirskaya et al.
0523   G.D. Pandey and K.P. Tiwari
0581   G.A. Poulton and T.D. Cyr
0851   A. Banerji et al.
0929   E. Elfehail et al.

8-   -80, Israel J. Chem., 20 (1980)
0142   W. Schoenfelder and G. Snatzke
0196   S.E. Braslavsky et al.
0215   E. Vogel
0244   I. Murata and K. Nakasuji
0288   B. Neuschwander and V. Boekelheide
0291   H. Hopf et al.

9-   -80, Doklady Phys. Chem., 250-255 (1980)
0034   A.A. Efimov and V.S. Sivokhin
0158   M.G. Voronkov et al.

0-   -80, Russian J. Phys. Chem., 54 (1980)
0172   V.V. Zamkova et al.
0200   L.P. Brivina et al.
0294   S.N. Davydov et al.
0749   B.M. Yavorskii et al.
0843   N.O. Mchedlov-Petrosyan
1413   B.D. Berezin et al.

2-   -80, Spectroscopy Letters, 13 (1980)
0001   J. Kister et al.

4-   -80A, Acta Chim. Acad. Sci. Hung.,
            103 (1980)
0027   A. Levai et al.
0259   M. Lempert-Sreter et al.
0271   V. Szabo et al.
0329   Shafiullah and E.A. Khan

4-   -80B, Acta Chim. Acad. Sci. Hung.,
            104 (1980)
0147   T. Lorand et al.
0253   Barta-Szalai et al.
0369   David et al.
0389   Borda et al.

4-   -80C, Acta Chim. Acad. Sci. Hung.,
            105 (1980)
0127   Simay et al.
0235   M.N. Basyouni and F.A. Fouli

5-   -80, Egypt J. Chem., 23 (1980)
0013   M.A. Khattab et al.
0151   N.R. El-Rayyes and F.M. Al-Kharafi
0243   M.N. Basyouni et al.
0265   M.N. Basyouni et al.
0401   M.F. Ismail and N.C. Kandile
0423   V.B. Baghos et al.

6-   -80, Macromolecules, 13 (1980)
0234   K. Kobayashi and H. Sumitomo
0240   J.E. Mulvaney and D.M. Chang
0244   J.E. Mulvaney and R.A. Brand
0782   S.R. Turner
0826   H. Ishida et al.
1138   L.M. Aubrey et al.

117-   -80, Org. Preps. Procedures Intl.,
            12 (1980)
0219   S. Nakanishi and S.S. Massett
0275   Y. Inaki et al.

118-   -80, Synthesis (1980)
0030   M. Hankel and G. Jutz
0041   L.J. Mazza and A. Guarna
0070   W. Zielinski
0116   S.C. Shim and S.K. Lee
0155   B.R. Rao and K. Ahmed
0225   R. Weiss and P. Marolt
0236   W. Haefliger and D. Hauser
0238   K.B. Becker
0326   J.K. Ray et al.
0331   K. Imafuku et al.
0365   A. Kubo and T. Nakai
0405   M.C. Christensen et al.
0409   P.S. Manchand et al.
0457   A.K. Fateen et al.
0466   E. Vilsmaier and W. Troyer
0479   K. Senga et al.
0537   Y. Okuno et al.
0539   R.H. Hynninen and S. Lotjonen
0541   S. Lotjonen and P.H. Hynninen
0543   D. Butina and F. Sondheimer
0559   A.M. Ozols et al.
0566   N. Fukada et al.
0623   C. Deshayes and S. Gelin
0689   A. Mallouli and Y. LePage
0694   J. Schantl and H. Gstach
0698   G. Szilogyi et al.
0715   A. Chatterjee and R. Mallik
0721   M. Mizuta et al.
0724   F. Bigi et al.
0753   F. Fariña and T. Torres
0807   T. Veysoglu et al.
0815   M.P. Reddy and G.S. KrishnaRao
0847   T. Wolff and V. Reiffenruth
0874   A. Banerji and N.C. Goomer
0875   S. Gelin and M. Chabannet
0898   A.M. El Gendy et al.
0901   C. Cativiela and E. Melendez
0950   L. Lombardo and F. Sondheimer
1021   S. Jeganathan and M. Srinavasan
1022   W.-D. Rudorf and M. Augustin
1025   O. Kemal and C.B. Reese

119-   -80, S. African. J. Chem., 33 (1980)
0045   J.C.A. Boeyens et al.
0127   J.R. Bull, J. Floor and H. Tuin-
        man

120-   -80, Pakistan J. Sci. Ind. Research,
            23 (1980)
0016   I.H. Qureshi et al.
0180   M.R. Khan
0250   A. Essawy and A.Z.M. Heikal

121-   -80, J. Macromol. Sci., Pt. A,
            14 (1980)
0379   B.Z. Weiner and A. Zilkha
0853   T. Otsu et al.
1015   H. Ohnishi and T. Otsu

124-   -80, Ukrain. Khim. Zhur., 46 (1980)
0389   V.A. Chuiguk
0520   M.I. Shenlov et al.
0640   Y.V. Migalina et al.
0642   N.D. Trusevich et al.
0750   G.G. Dyadyasha et al.
0755   L.P. Gritsenko et al.
0823   S.A. Andronati
0827   R.V. Kovalchuk et al.
0835   V.A. Chujguk et al.
0957   V.D. Boiko
0965   A.I. Tolmachev et al.
1186   G.C. Dyadyusha et al.
1306   V. Achayguk et al.

125-   -80, Inorg. Chem., 19 (1980)
0383   C.J. Schramm and B.M. Hoffman
0458   G.D. Friesen et al.
0709   J.J. MacDougall et al.
1125   M.B. Freeman and L.G. Sneddon
1863   A. Streitwieser, Jr. et al.
2052   A.R. Siedle and L.H. Pignolet

126-   -80, Makromol. Chem., 181 (1980)
0031   M. Slongo et al.
0037   S. Schönholzer et al.
0201   R.N. Majumdar and C. Carlini
0333   A. Banihashemi and M.R. Oboodi
0575   H. Shirai et al.
0595   F.E. Karrer
1209   J. Pielichowski and J. Obrzut
1565   O. Nuyken et al.
2049   H. Kammerer and G. Happel

126-   -80B, Makromol. Chem. Rapid Comm.,
        1 (1980)
0197   I. Tajima et al.
0287   C.D. Eisenbach
0461   H. Kämmerer and G. Happel

128-   -80, Croatica Chem. Acta, 53 (1980)
0069   L. Fiser-Jakic et al.
0449   V. Skaric and V. Turjak-Zebic
0615   I. Murata et al.

130-   -80, Bioorg. Chem., 9 (1980)
0001   K.M. Smith et al.
0063   D. Harris et al.
0071   A.H. Jackson et al.
0187   B.L. Onisko et al.
0248   F. Kraicsovits et al.
0406   A. Kini et al.
0423   V. Nair and R.J. Wiechert

131-   -80C, J. Mol. Structure, 60 (1980)
0099   T. Veszpremi et al.

135-   -80, J. Appl. Spectroscopy S.S.S.R.,
        32 (1980)
0064   S.P. Molodnyakov et al.
0160   V.S. Sivokhin et al.
0344   G.N. Rodionova et al.
0860   P.A. Perov et al.
0930   B.M. Krasovitskii et al.
0956   N.I. Garbuz et al.
1219   T.M. Melent'eva et al.

136-   -80A, Carbohydrate Research, 78 (198
0017   F.G. Gonzalez et al.
0033   A. Rosenthal and R.H. Dodd
0067   T. Adachi et al.
0195   P. Angibeaud et al.

136-   -80B, Carbohydrate Research, 79 (198
0219   O.J. Varela et al.
0235   A. Rosenthal and S.M. Mikhailov

136-   -80C, Carbohydrate Research, 80 (198
0037   F.G. Gonzalez et al.
00C4   F.J. Lopez Aparicio and F.J.
        Lopez Herrera
0241   K.C. Blieszner et al.
0263   D. Horton and R.A. Markovs
0356   D. Horton and R.A. Markovs
0364   D. Horton and S.S. Kokrady

136-   -80H, Carbohydrate Research, 85 (198
0093   M.A.E. Sallam
0121   M.I. Dawson and P.D. Hobbs
0187   J.M.J. Tronchet and O.R. Martin

136-   -80I, Carbohydrate Research, 86 (198
0033   G. de Wit et al.

138-   -80, Chemistry Letters (1980)
0167   M. Yasunami et al.
0197   T. Morita et al.
0205   M. Yasunami et al.
0225   J. Ojima et al.
0299   S. Inoue et al.
0339   M. Takasugi et al.
0349   K. Saito et al.
0393   S. Yamamura et al.
0397   Y. Miyahara et al.
0401   T. Nishiwaki et al.
0425   T. Matsumoto et al.
0431   T. Goto et al.
0515   A. Susuki and M. Tada
0521   H. Sugimoto et al.
0559   T. Kondo et al.
0613   K. Mukai et al.
0619   S. Tamagaki et al.
0621   Y. Yamashita and M. Masumura
0631   Y. Fujise et al.
0659   E.M. Beccalli et al.
0679   T. Sato et al.
0735   H. Watanabe et al.
0739   T. Tanaka
0743   M. Matsuoka et al.
0749   Y. Yano et al.
0827   K. Maruyama et al.
0859   K. Maruyama et al.
0921   M. Tada et al.
0955   Y. Nomura et al.
1095   H. Obara et al.
1177   M. Suzuki and E. Kurosawa
1235   S. Shinkai et al.
1243   M. Nakayama et al.
1299   J. Ojima et al.
1369   O. Tsuge et al.
1389   K. Satake et al.
1391   H. Kasai et al.
1427   Y. Sugihara et al.

1453   H. Nozaki et al.
1459   M. Takasugi et al.
1485   K. Takahashi et al.
1521   Y. Inouye et al.
1555   Y. Yamamoto
1573   M. Takasugi et al.
1577   M. Takasugi et al.
1635   T. Fujita et al.

39-   -80A, P and S and Its Related Elements,
         8 (1980)
0079   D. Barillier
0171   V.C.J. Bhasu and D.N. Sathyanara-
        yana
0243   Y. Segall et al.

39-   -80B, P and S and Its Related Elements,
         9 (1980)
0127   R.L. Blakeley et al.

40-   -80, J. Anal. Chem. S.S.S.R., 35 (1980)
0065   L.N. Lomakina et al.
0314   N.M. Melakhova et al.
0560   A.V. Dolgorev et al.
0949   O.M. Petrukhin and N.V. Kolycheva
1105   V.A. Nazarenko et al.
1175   N.E. Karabut and L.P. Senetskaya
1561   E.A. Shpak and V.A. Satsyuk
1570   N.S. Balog and P.P. Kish

42-   -80, Heterocycles, 14 (1980)
0007   A. Yushirogochi et al.
0011   K. Orito et al.
0047   S. Kawai and C. Kaneko
0267   Y. Kurasawa and A. Takada
0295   C. Konno et al.
0397   K. Yakushijin et al.
0461   S.K. Robev
0471   N. Acton et al.
0585   N. Murugesan and M. Shamma
0635   K. Hirai et al.
0761   T. Sato et al.
0769   F.G. Contreras et al.
0783   T. Nishiwaki et al.
0785   T. Nishiwaki et al.
0799   T. Kametani et al.
0867   M. Ikeda and Y. Tamura
0943   M.D. Menachery and M.P. Cava
0955   M. Ogata et al.
1073   K. Yakushijin et al.
1115   A. Calatroni and R. Gandolfi
1125   H. Ogura et al.
1131   L. Castedo et al.
1135   L. Castedo et al.
1139   W.A. Romanchick and M.A. Joullie
1151   K. Kido and Y. Watanabe
1159   F. Santavy
1283   M. Tsukayama et al.
1319   Z. Witezak
1433   T. Watanabe et al.
1461   Y. Oshima et al.
1729   T. Fujii et al.
1739   J.J. Burger et al.
1743   T. Yoshida and T. Okuda
1785   T. Nomura et al.
1915   G. Lewin et al.

1921   M. Takahashi et al.
1943   T. Nomura et al.
1977   C.H. Phoebe, Jr. et al.
1979   P. Venturella et al.
1999   S. Oida et al.

142-   -80B, Heterocycles, 15 (1980)
0161   J. Rebek, Jr. and S. Shaber
0187   T. Hino et al.
0213   G.M. Sanders et al.
0245   R.Z. Andrianialisoa et al.
0285   K. Hirota et al.
0289   K. Hirota et al.
0321   T. Sato et al.
0325   J. Banerji et al.
0345   D.S. Wise, Jr. et al.
0369   H. Tachikawa et al.
0373   T. Ban and K. Kanematsu
0437   F. Uhlmann and W. Pfleiderer
0459   M. Peled et al.
0675   N. Koayashi and T. Osa
0679   Y. Tominaga et al.
0697   A.S. Shawali et al.
0761   R. Charubala and W. Pfleiderer
0777   E.W. Warnhoff and F.W. Yerhoff
0835   T. Morita et al.
0843   T. Momose et al.
0889   M. Yamazaki et al.
0895   Y. Maki et al.
0935   W. Benson and E. Winterfeldt
1049   H. Inoue et al.
1053   F.W. Lichtenthaler and E. Cuny
1083   M.M. Yousif et al.
1097   Y. Tsuda et al.
1119   H. Nakamura and T. Goto
1137   V. Fajardo et al.
1163   V.S. Kamat et al.
1195   C. Kaneko et al.
1227   J. Guillaume et al.
1531   T. Nomura and T. Fukai
1569   T. Mukai et al.

145-   -80, Arzneimittel. Forsch., 30 (1980)
0919   F. Schatz et al.
1051   E. Belgodere et al.
1135   S.H.S. Makoni and J.K. Sugden
1618   M.J. Green et al.
2087   E. Golovinsky et al.

146-   -80, J. Chem. Tech. Biotech., 30
          (1980)
0078   F.A. Amer et al.
0317   B.M. Fox et al.
0513   S.A.M. Metwally et al.

147-   -80A, J. Luminescence, 21 (1980)
0409   A. Janowski and J. Rzcszotavska

149-   -80A, Photochem. Photobiol.,
          31 (1980)
0195   S.N. Bose and R.J.H. Davies

149-   -80B, Photochem. Photobiol.,
          32 (1980)
0017   A.R. Holzwarth et al.
0143   O.S. Wolfbeis and K. Schaffner

0305   U. Kölle et al.
0327   N.J. Turro and P.C.C. Lee
0711   H. Morrison et al.
0739   P.K. Das and R.S. Becker

150-   -80, J. Chem. Research(M) (1980)
0113   J.M. Barker et al.
0127   D.M.X. Donnelly and J. O'Reilly
0139   R.M. Christie et al.
0549   R.J.A. Walsh and K.R.H. Wooldridge
0833   K. Clarke et al.
0908   J.M. Poirier and J. Verchere
1551   M. Bertrand et al.
1801   D. Bondon et al.
2134   I. Kirson et al.
2415   A. Clemson et al.
2601   M.Y. Jarrah and V. Thaller
2901   S. Kanoktanaporn and J.A.H. Mac-
        Bride
2911   S. Kanoktanaporn and J.A.H. Mac-
        Bride
2941   S. Kanoktanaporn and J.A.H. Mac-
        Bride
3079   R. Neidlein and G. Jeromin
3090   R. Neidlein and G. Jeromin
3172   S. Davidson et al.
3337   A.R. Katritzky et al.
3361   W. Ehmuser and J. Voss
3523   P.C. Hayes et al.
3630   S.S. Al-Hassan et al.
3650   G.M. Blackburn et al.
3853   J. Armand and R. Bassinet
3901   J.-P. Catteau et al.
3911   W.L.F. Armarego and P. Waring
4041   A.R. Katritzky and M.C. Rezende
4133   M. Muraoka et al.
4154   A. Taylor
4275   I. Kirson et al.
4432   P. Jardon et al.
4501   N.S. Ooi and D.A. Wilson
4601   J. Kossanyi et al.
4668   T. Shimidzu et al.
4726   N.S. Ooi and D.A. Wilson

150-   -80S, J. Chem. Research(S) (1980)
0064   S.B. Mahato et al.
0242   D. D'Oria et al.
0414   R. Hayes et al.

151-   -80A, J. Photochem., 12 (1980)
0293   H.-D. Brauef et al.
0305   J. Kossanyi et al.

151-   -80B, J. Photochem., 13 (1980)
0083   L.L. Costanzo et al.
0133   R.R. Düren et al.
0309   H.J. Griesser and U.P. Wild

152-   -80, Nouveau J. Chim., 4 (1980)
0239   D. Alker et al.
0311   H.J. Callot and E. Schaeffer
0369   H.B. Arzeno et al.
0389   G. Bidan and M. Genies
0615   D. Lopez et al.